PRENTICE HALL

Teacher's Edition

SCIENCE EXPLORER

Life Science

Prentice Hall

Needham, Massachusetts
Upper Saddle River, New Jersey
Glenview, Illinois

ISBN 0-13-062646-5
1 2 3 4 5 6 7 8 9 10   05 04 03 02 01

The exploration starts here.

Life, Earth, Physical Science

PRENTICE HALL SCIENCE EXPLORER

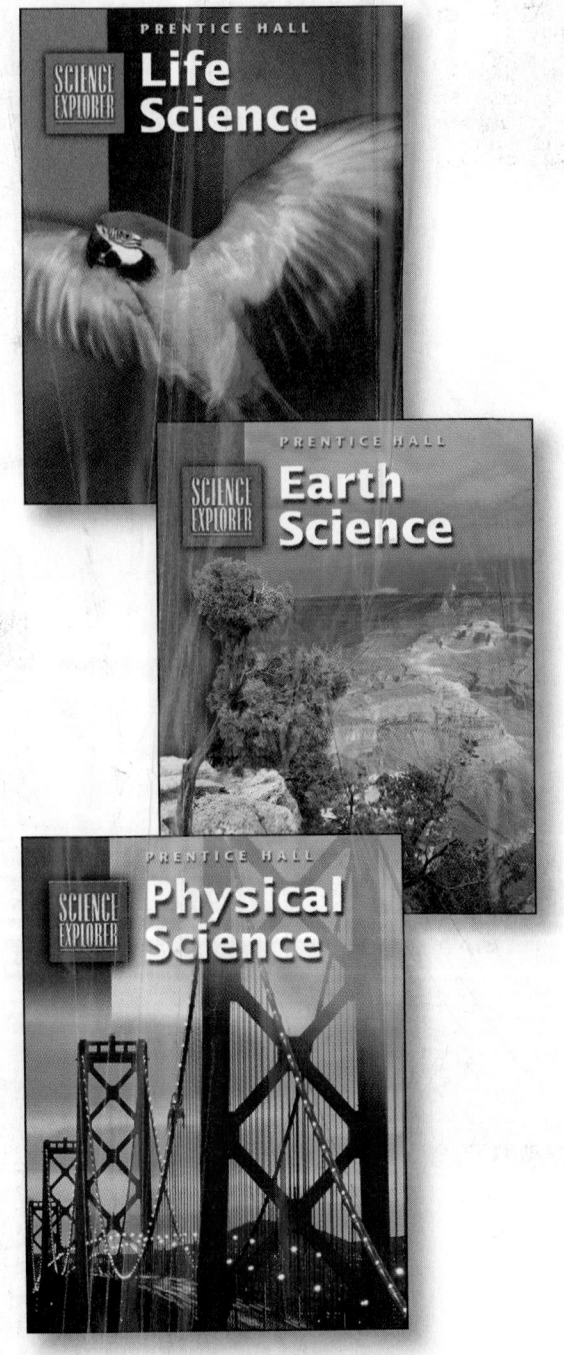

Now more than ever, middle-school students need a solid science education, and Prentice Hall *Science Explorer* helps you provide just that. Not only is *Science Explorer's* content comprehensive, but the three-book series contains a wealth of resources to help students access and better understand core science concepts.

Take a look at pages T3–T11 and explore for yourself the depth and breadth of science content found in every page of *Science Explorer Life Science, Science Explorer Earth Science,* and *Science Explorer Physical Science.*

Don't stop there. Continue exploring all of the activities...breathtaking visuals... reading support...multiple opportunities for ongoing, integrated assessment... and incredible supplementary resources that accompany this brand-new Life, Earth, and Physical Science program.

What will you see? Solid science content for today's students.

Solid science content

A comprehensive
science exploration,
just right for today's students.

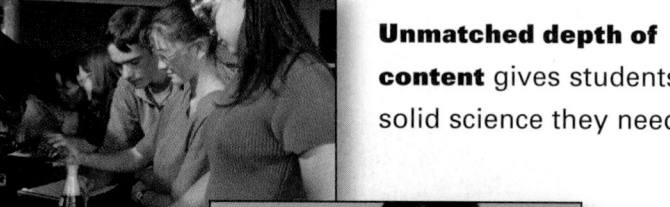

Unmatched depth of content gives students the solid science they need.

Hands-on activities reinforce concepts and engage all kinds of learners.

Built-in reading support enhances student comprehension.

GUIDE FOR READING

- ◆ How do stress forces affect rock?
- ◆ Why do faults form and where do they occur?
- ◆ How does movement along faults change Earth's surface?

Vivid graphics and dynamic photos bring science concepts to life.

SECTION 1

Flexible, self-contained sections give you more options for meeting your curriculum needs.

Wealth of assessment resources—both traditional and performance-based—make regular progress checks easy.

Life Science
Table of Contents

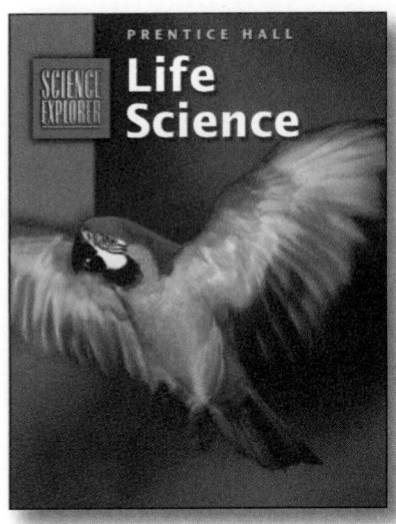

Introduction to Life Science

Unit 1 Cells and Heredity

Chapter 1 Cells: The Building Blocks of Life
1. What Is Life?
2. Discovering Cells
3. Looking Inside Cells
4. Integrating Earth Science: The Origin of Life

Chapter 2 Cell Processes and Energy
1. Integrating Chemistry: Chemical Compounds in Cells
2. The Cell in Its Environment
3. Photosynthesis
4. Respiration
5. Cell Division

Chapter 3 Genetics: The Science of Heredity
1. Mendel's Work
2. Integrating Mathematics: Probability and Genetics
3. The Cell and Inheritance
4. The DNA Connection

Chapter 4 Modern Genetics
1. Human Inheritance
2. Human Genetic Disorders
3. Integrating Technology: Advances in Genetics

Chapter 5 Changes Over Time
1. Darwin's Voyage
2. Integrating Earth Science: The Fossil Record
3. Other Evidence for Evolution

Interdisciplinary Exploration: Dogs—Loyal Companions

Unit 2 From Bacteria to Plants

Chapter 6 Bacteria and Viruses
1. Classifying Organisms
2. The Six Kingdoms
3. Bacteria
4. Integrating Health: Viruses

Chapter 7 Protists and Fungi
1. Protists
2. Integrating Environmental Science: Algal Blooms
3. Fungi

Chapter 8 Introduction to Plants
1. The Plant Kingdom
2. Mosses, Liverworts, and Hornworts
3. Ferns and Their Relatives
4. Integrating Technology: Feeding the World

Chapter 9 Seed Plants
1. The Characteristics of Seed Plants
2. Gymnosperms
3. Angiosperms
4. Integrating Chemistry: Plant Responses and Growth

Nature of Science: From Plants to Chemicals

Unit 3 Animals

Chapter 10 Sponges, Cnidarians, and Worms
1. What Is an Animal?
2. Integrating Mathematics: Symmetry
3. Sponges and Cnidarians
4. Worms

Chapter 11 Mollusks, Arthropods, and Echinoderms
1. Mollusks
2. Arthropods
3. Insects
4. Integrating Chemistry: The Chemistry of Communication
5. Echinoderms

Chapter 12 Fishes, Amphibians, and Reptiles
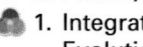 1. Integrating Earth Science:
   Evolution of Vertebrates
2. Fishes
3. Amphibians
4. Reptiles

Chapter 13 Birds and Mammals
1. Birds
 2. Integrating Physics:
   The Physics of Bird Flight
3. What Is a Mammal?
4. Diversity of Mammals

Chapter 14 Animal Behavior
 1. Integrating Psychology: Why Do
   Animals Behave As They Do?
2. Patterns of Behavior

**Interdisciplinary Exploration:
The Secret of Silk**

Unit 4 Human Biology and Health
Chapter 15 Bones, Muscles, and Skin
 1. Integrating Health: Body
   Organization and Homeostasis
2. The Skeletal System
3. The Muscular System
4. The Skin

Chapter 16 Food and Digestion
 1. Integrating Chemistry:
   Food and Energy
2. The Digestive Process Begins
3. Final Digestion and Absorption

Chapter 17 Circulation
1. The Body's Transportation System
2. A Closer Look at Blood Vessels
3. Blood and Lymph
 4. Integrating Health:
   Cardiovascular Health

Chapter 18 Respiration and Excretion
1. The Respiratory System
2. Integrating Health:
   Smoking and Your Health
3. The Excretory System

Chapter 19 Fighting Disease
1. Infectious Disease
2. The Body's Defenses
3. Integrating Health: Preventing
   Infectious Disease
4. Noninfectious Disease

Chapter 20 The Nervous System
1. How the Nervous System Works
2. Divisions of the Nervous System
3. The Senses
 4. Integrating Health:
   Alcohol and Other Drugs

**Chapter 21 The Endocrine System
and Reproduction**
1. The Endocrine System
2. The Male and Female
   Reproductive Systems
3. Integrating Health:
   The Human Life Cycle

Unit 5 Ecology
**Nature of Science:
Protecting Desert Wildlife**

Chapter 22 Populations and Communities
1. Living Things and the Environment
2. Integrating Mathematics:
   Studying Populations
3. Interactions Among Living Things

Chapter 23 Ecosystems and Biomes
1. Energy Flow in Ecosystems
2. Integrating Chemistry: Cycles of Matter
3. Biogeography
4. Earth's Biomes
5. Succession

Chapter 24 Living Resources
1. Integrating Environmental Science:
   Environmental Issues
2. Forests and Fisheries
3. Biodiversity

**Interdisciplinary Exploration:
African Rain Forests**

A rich assortment of optional activities promotes inquiry learning.

Science Explorer gives you more activities— and more types of activities—than any other middle school program available. This rich, flexible assortment of activities reinforces content, meets a variety of learning styles, fits your teaching style, and prepares students for today's standardized tests.

INTEGRATING CHEMISTRY

SECTION 2 The Properties of Water

DISCOVER

What Are Some Properties of Water?

1. Pour a small amount of water into a plastic cup. Pour an equal amount of vegetable oil into a second cup.
2. Cut two strips of paper towel. Hold the strips so that the bottom of one strip is in the water and the other is in the oil.
3. After one minute, measure how high each substance climbed up the paper towel.
4. Using a plastic dropper, place a big drop of water onto a piece of wax paper.

5. Using anoth[er] place a drop size as the w[ater] beside it on
6. Observe th[e] two drops
7. Follow you[r] instruction[s] the oil wh[ile] after this a[ctivity]

Think It Ov[er]
Observing

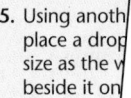

Discover Activities.
Quick exploration and inquiry before learning, at start of every lesson.

Chapter Projects.
Long-term inquiry opportunity, one per chapter.

TRY THIS ACTIVITY

How Do Your Algae Grow?

In this activity you will observe how fertilizers affect the growth of algae in pond water.

1. Label two jars A and B. Pour tap water into each jar until it is half full.
2. Add water from a pond or aquarium to each jar until it is three-quarters full.

3. Add 5 mL of liquid fertilizer to jar A only.
4. Cover both jars tightly and place them on a windowsill in the sunlight. Wash your hands with soap.
5. Observe the jars every day for a week.

Drawing Conclusions How did the fertilizer affect the growth of the algae in jar A? What was the purpose of jar B in this experiment?

Try This Activities.
Quick reinforcement of key concepts, two per chapter.

Sharpen Your Skills Activities.
Quick practice of a specific inquiry skill, two per chapter.

Skills Labs.
In-depth practice of an inquiry skill, one per chapter.

Real-World Lab

You, the Consumer

Testing the Waters

How does the bottled water sold in supermarkets differ from the water that comes out of your kitchen faucet? In this lab, you will discover some differences among various types of water.

Problem

How do distilled water, spring water, and mineral water differ from tap water?

Skills Focus

observing, inferring, drawing conclusions

Materials

hot plate
ruler
tap water, 200 mL
spring water, 200 mL
4 200-mL beakers
4 pieces of pH paper
25-mL graduated cylinder
4 paper cups per person

liquid soap
wax pencil
distilled water, 200 mL
mineral water, 200 mL
4 test tubes and stoppers
pH indicator chart

Procedure 🔒🧤🥼🔥

[ta]ble into your notebook.

2. Label the beakers A, B [...] 100 mL of tap water in[to ...] 100 mL of the other water samples into the [...] correct beaker (refer to the data table).
3. Heat each water sample on a hot plate until about 20 mL remains. Do not allow the water to boil completely away. **CAUTION:** *Do not touch the hot plate or beakers.*
4. After the water samples have cooled, look for solids that make the water cloudy. Rank the samples from 1 to 4, where 1 has the fewest visible solids and 4 has the most visible solids. Record your rankings in the data table.
5. Label the test tubes A, B, C, and D. Pour 10 mL of each water sample from the source bottle into the correct test tube.
6. Dip a pi[ece ...] tube A to measure its acid[ity ...] paper to a number on the pH indicator ch[art ...] Record the pH (1–14) in your data table.

Real-World Labs.
Everyday application of science concepts, one per chapter.

Solid science content

Ongoing assessment, right in the Student Edition, keeps students on track.

Science Explorer features a remarkable range of strategies for checking student progress—including both traditional and performance assessment. With this variety of assessment approaches, you'll always find the right strategies for your students.

- **Comprehensive Chapter Reviews** include a broad range of question types that students will encounter on state and local standardized tests: multiple choice, enhanced true/false, concept mastery, visual thinking, skill application, and critical thinking.

- **Chapter Projects** with two-part Wrap Ups (Present Your Project and Reflect and Record) and Getting Involved ideas present ample performance assessment opportunities in every Chapter Review.

- **Caption Questions** maximize the usefulness of the visuals, and help keep students on track by assessing critical thinking skills.

- **Checkpoint Questions** give students an immediate content check as new concepts are presented.

- **Section Reviews** provide "Check Your Progress" opportunities for the Chapter Project, Science at Home, and review questions for the section.

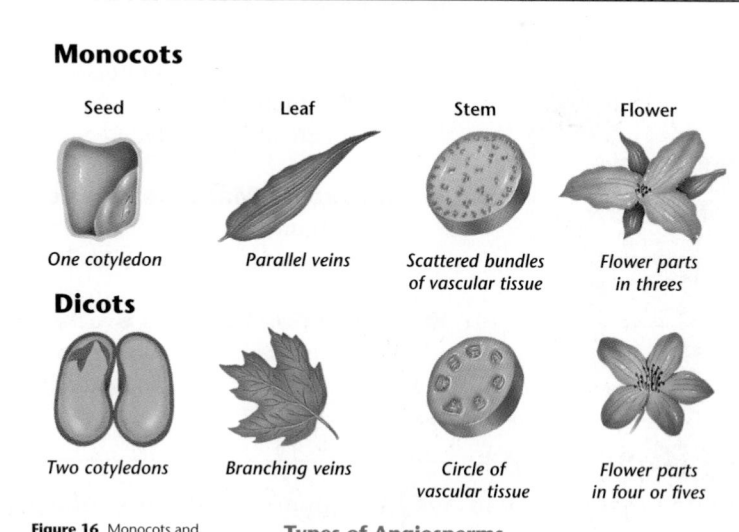

Monocots

Seed — *One cotyledon*

Leaf — *Parallel veins*

Stem — *Scattered bundles of vascular tissue*

Flower — *Flower parts in threes*

Dicots

Two cotyledons

Branching veins

Circle of vascular tissue

Flower parts in four or fives

Figure 16 Monocots and dicots are the two groups of angiosperms. The groups differ in the number of cotyledons, the arrangement of veins and vascular tissue, and the number of petals. *Classifying Would a plant whose flowers have 20 petals be a monocot or a dicot?*

Types of Angiosperms

Angiosperms are divided into two major groups: monocots and dicots. "Cot" is short for *cotyledon*. Recall from Section 1 that the cotyledon, or seed leaf, provides food for the embryo. *Mono* means "one" and *di* means "two". **Monocots** are angiosperms that have only one seed leaf. **Dicots,** on the other hand, produce seeds with two seed leaves. Look at Figure 16 to compare the characteristics of monocots and dicots.

Monocots Grasses, including corn, wheat, and rice, and plants such as lilies and tulips are monocots. The flowers of a monocot usually have either three petals or a multiple of three petals. Monocots usually have long, slender leaves with veins that run parallel to one another like train rails. The bundles of vascular tissue in monocot stems are usually scattered randomly throughout the stem.

Dicots Dicots include plants such as roses and violets, as well as dandelions. Both oak and maple trees are dicots, as are food plants such as beans and apples. The flowers of dicots often have either four or five petals or multiples of these numbers. The leaves are usually wide, with veins that branch off from one another. Dicot stems usually have bundles of vascular tissue arranged in a circle.

✓ *Checkpoint How do the petals of monocots and dicots differ in number?*

 **Section 3 Review**

1. What two characteristics do all angiosperms share? Explain the importance of those characteristics.
2. Give a brief description of how reproduction occurs in angiosperms.
3. List the parts of a typical flower. What is the function of each part?
4. **Thinking Critically** **Inferring** A certain plant has small, dull-colored flowers with no scent. Do you think the plant is pollinated by animals or by the wind? Explain.

Check Your Progress CHAPTER PROJECT
Your plants should now have, or will soon have, flowers. Make a diagram of the flower's structure. When the flowers open, you'll have to pollinate them. This work is usually done by insects or birds. After pollination, watch how the flower changes. (*Hint:* Discuss with your teacher and classmates how to pollinate the flowers.)

Innovative resources: unmatched in variety, content, and effectiveness.

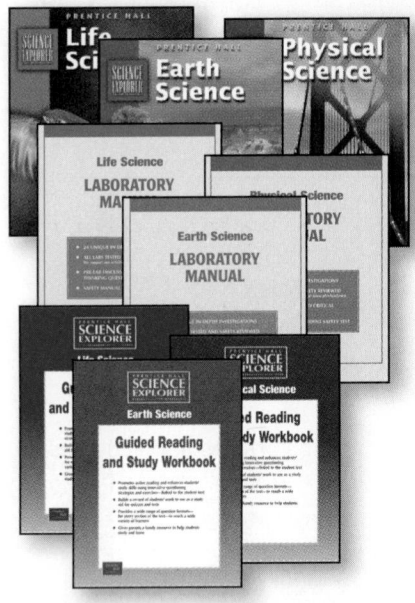

■ **Student Editions**—content-rich, vivid, and accessible. Solid science for today's classroom.

■ **Teacher's Editions**—comprehensive teacher support puts you in charge. Suggested answers, easy-to-manage lesson plans, and multiple assessment opportunities are located exactly where you need them. Plus, ideas for meeting the needs of diverse learners are also included.

■ **Laboratory Manuals (Student Consumable)**—classroom-proven inquiry opportunities bring the excitement of hands-on science to your students. Life, Earth, Physical versions available.

■ **Guided Reading and Study Workbooks**—promote active reading and enhance students' study skills using innovative questioning strategies and exercises—linked to the student text.

Teaching Resources

All the day-to-day resources you need to manage instruction effectively. Resources contain:

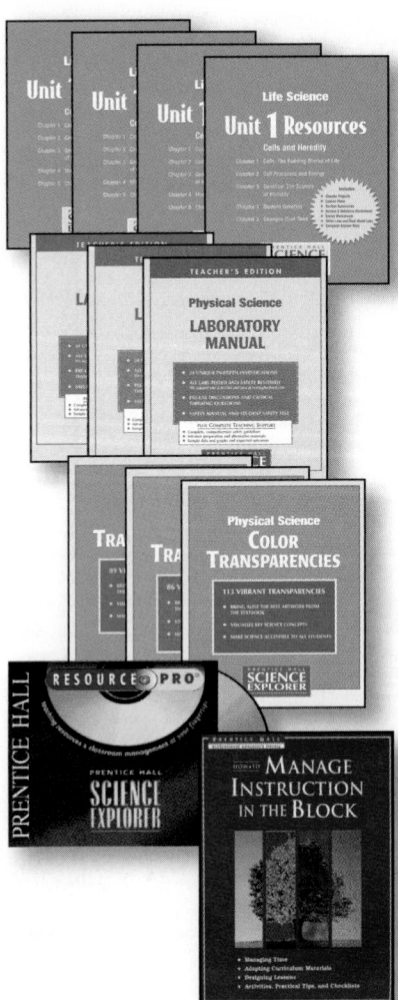

■ **Unit Resource Books**—organized by chapter, include Chapter Projects, Lesson Plans, Section Summaries, Review & Reinforce Worksheets, Enrich Worksheets, Skills Labs and Real-World Labs, complete Answer Keys. Life, Earth, Physical versions available.

■ **Laboratory Manual, Teacher's Edition**—in-depth labs with complete teaching support. Life, Earth, Physical versions available.

■ **Color Transparencies**—vibrant color transparencies bring difficult-to-understand concepts to life.

■ **Resource Pro® CD-ROM**—the ultimate lesson planning and scheduling tool, with electronic access to worksheets. Lets you plan by the day, week, month, or year!

■ **How to Manage Instruction in the Block**—comprehensive collection of block scheduling resources, from managing classroom routines to checklists for monitoring and assessing small-group learning.

■ **Correlation to National Science Education Standards**

Assessment Resources

Comprehensive assessment tools—all in one place!

- **Standardized Test Preparation Book**—provides students with hints, tips, strategies, and practice to help them prepare for state and local exams.

- **Chapter and Unit Tests**—provides complete tests for each chapter and each unit in the student text. Features a variety of question types, including multiple choice, modified true/false, essay, and interpreting diagrams.

- **Performance Assessment**—assess student problem-solving and process skills using easy-to-score rubrics.

- **Computer Test Bank Book with CD-ROM and Dial-A-Test®**—contains chapter tests featuring a variety of question types. Powerful Computer Test Bank software makes it easy to create customized tests.

- **How to Assess Student Work**—contains articles and activities on integrating assessments, using rubrics, and establishing a portfolio.

Student Performance Resources

Components to improve science comprehension and enhance process skills.

- **Section Summaries on Audio CD**—offers students summaries of important concepts from each section of every chapter. Also available in Spanish.

- **Interactive Student Tutorial CD-ROM (Life, Earth, or Physical)**—Explorations, re-teaching opportunities, helpful hints, and self-tests with instant scoring and complete explanations of answers.

- **Guided Reading and Study Workbook, Teacher's Edition**—contains complete answers to student worksheets designed for assessing, understanding, and developing study skills.

- **Reading in the Content Area with Literature Connections**—contains reading strategies to improve student comprehension.

- **Inquiry Skills Activity Book**—additional activities that introduce basic and advanced inquiry skills.

Additional Program-wide Resources

- **Consumable and non-consumable Materials Kits**

- **Order Assistant Plus CD-ROM**—generate a Master Materials List based on the activities you choose to teach.

- **Student-Centered Science Activities**—five activity books for the Northeast, Southeast, Midwest, Southwest, and West.

- **Teacher's ELL Handbook**—provides multiple strategies for reaching language learners. Select appropriate activities to meet the needs of individual students.

See next page for technology resources

for today's students.

Science Explorer connects your classroom to the power of interactivity.

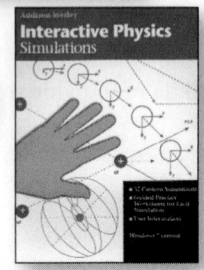

■ **iText**—an interactive text version of the Student Edition at *www.phschool.com* containing animations, simulations, and videos to enhance student understanding and retention of concepts.

■ **Lab Activity Videotape Library**—provides step-by-step instruction with students performing activities from every chapter. Promote and teach proper lab techniques, inquiry skills, and safety procedures.

■ **Section Summaries on Audio CD**—Available in English and Spanish.

■ **Science Explorer Videotapes and Videodiscs**—explore and visualize concepts through spectacular short documentaries and computer animations. Videotapes available in English and Spanish. Videodisc includes Spanish audio track.

■ **Presentation Pro® CD-ROM**—provides more than 150 slide show presentations organized by chapter. Each presentation includes guiding questions, color graphics, and concept organization slides.

■ **Probeware Lab Manual with CD-ROM**—provides detailed instruction for using Probeware to perform selected labs. Blackline masters of labs are included. Includes CD-ROM, workbook, and blackline masters.

■ **Interactive Student Tutorial CD-ROMs (Life, Earth, and Physical)**—explorations, helpful hints, and self-tests with instant scoring and complete explanations of answers.

■ **Computer Test Bank Book with CD-ROM and Dial-A-Test®**—contains chapter tests featuring a variety of question types. Computer Test Bank software makes it easy to create customized tests.

■ **Mindscape CD-ROMS**—bring science alive with compelling videoclips, 3-D animations, and interactive databases.

■ **Resource Pro® CD-ROM**—the ultimate lesson planning and scheduling tool, with electronic access to worksheets and lessons. Available in Life, Earth, and Physical Science.

■ **Interactive Physics**—explore physics concepts with computer simulations that encourage what-if questions.

Solid science content

On-line activities and teaching resources for every chapter of the text.

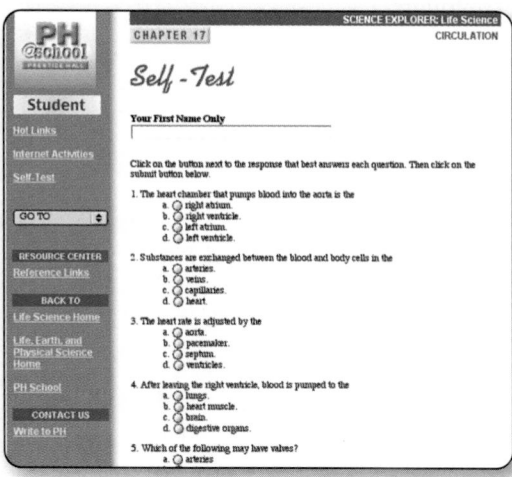

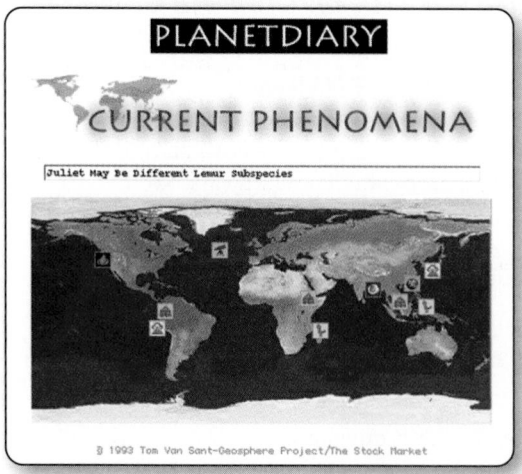

For Teachers

■ **What's New**—Create enthusiasm with our dynamic Internet activities—at least one per chapter.

■ **Further Exploration**—Links that enhance and reinforce Internet activity concepts.

■ **Teaching Links**—Web sites that relate to chapter content.

SCIENCE NEWS

■ **Science News®**—A weekly electronic and print newsletter providing the latest information on science news in earth science, biology, technology, and more.

For Students

■ **Hot Links to Web Sites**—Easy access to additional material extending chapter content.

■ **Internet Activities**—Enhance concepts with interactive, hands-on/minds-on activities.

■ **Self-Tests**—Help students to check how they are doing, and obtain scores instantly.

Plus! PlanetDiary

■ **PlanetDiary**—Get weekly reports on environmental news and natural phenomena.

■ **PlanetDiary**—Directly correlated to the *Science Explorer* series.

Options for Pacing *Life Science*

The Pacing Chart below suggests one way to schedule your instructional time. The ***Science Explorer*** program offers many other aids to help you plan your instructional time, whether regular class periods or **block scheduling**. Refer to the Chapter Planning Guide before each chapter to view all program resources with suggested times for Student Edition activities.

Pacing Chart

	Days	Blocks		Days	Blocks
Introduction to Life Science	2–3	1–$1\frac{1}{2}$	**Chapter 4 Modern Genetics**		
Chapter 1 Cells: The Building Blocks of Life			Chapter 4 Project A Family Portrait	Ongoing	Ongoing
Chapter 1 Project Mystery Object	Ongoing	Ongoing	1　Human Inheritance	1–2	$\frac{1}{2}$–1
1　What is Life?	2–3	1–$1\frac{1}{2}$	2　Human Genetic Disorders	$1\frac{1}{2}$–2	$\frac{3}{4}$–1
2　Discovering Cells	1–2	$\frac{1}{2}$–1	3　Integrating Technology: Advances in Genetics	$1\frac{1}{2}$–2	$\frac{3}{4}$–1
3　Looking Inside Cells	2–3	1–$1\frac{1}{2}$			
4　Integrating Earth Science: The Origin of Life	1	$\frac{1}{2}$	Chapter 4 Review and Assessment	1	$\frac{1}{2}$
Chapter 1 Review and Assessment	1	$\frac{1}{2}$	**Chapter 5 Changes Over Time**		
Chapter 2 Cell Processes and Energy			Chapter 5 Project Life's Long Calendar	Ongoing	Ongoing
Chapter 2 Project Egg-speriment With a Cell	Ongoing	Ongoing	1　Darwin's Voyage	2	1
1　Integrating Chemistry: Chemical Compounds in Cells	1–2	$\frac{1}{2}$–1	2　Integrating Earth Science: The Fossil Record	1–2	$\frac{1}{2}$–1
2　The Cell in Its Environment	1	$\frac{1}{2}$	3　Other Evidence for Evolution	1	$\frac{1}{2}$
3　Photosynthesis	1–2	$\frac{1}{2}$–1	Chapter 5 Review and Assessment	1	$\frac{1}{2}$
4　Respiration	$1\frac{1}{2}$–2	$\frac{3}{4}$–1	Interdisciplinary Exploration: Dogs—Loyal Companions	1–$1\frac{1}{2}$	$\frac{1}{2}$–$\frac{3}{4}$
5　Cell Division	2	1			
Chapter 2 Review and Assessment	1	$\frac{1}{2}$	**Chapter 6 Bacteria and Viruses**		
Chapter 3 Genetics: The Science of Heredity			Chapter 6 Project Be a Disease Detective	Ongoing	Ongoing
Chapter 3 Project All in the Family	Ongoing	Ongoing	1　Classifying Organisms	2–3	1–$1\frac{1}{2}$
1　Mendel's Work	$1\frac{1}{2}$–2	$\frac{3}{4}$–1	2　The Six Kingdoms	1	$\frac{1}{2}$
2　Integrating Mathematics: Probability and Genetics	1	$\frac{1}{2}$	3　Bacteria	2	1
3　The Cell and Inheritance	1–2	$\frac{1}{2}$–1	4　Integrating Heath: Viruses	2	1
4　The DNA Connection	1–2	$\frac{1}{2}$–1	Chapter 6 Review and Assessment	1	$\frac{1}{2}$
Chapter 3 Review and Assessment	1	$\frac{1}{2}$			

Pacing Chart

Chapter 7 Protists and Fungi	Days	Blocks
Chapter 7 Project A Mushroom Farm	Ongoing	Ongoing
1 Protists	$2\frac{1}{2}$	$1\frac{1}{4}$
2 Integrating Environmental Science: Algal Blooms	1	$\frac{1}{2}$
3 Fungi	2	1
Chapter 7 Review and Assessment	1	$\frac{1}{2}$
Chapter 8 Introduction to Plants		
Chapter 8 Project Become a Moss Expert	Ongoing	Ongoing
1 The Plant Kingdom	$2\frac{1}{2}$	$1\frac{1}{4}$
2 Mosses, Liverworts, and Hornworts	1	$\frac{1}{2}$
3 Ferns and Their Relatives	1	$\frac{1}{2}$
4 Integrating Technology: Feeding the World	1	$\frac{1}{2}$
Chapter 8 Review and Assessment	1	$\frac{1}{2}$
Chapter 9 Seed Plants		
Chapter 9 Project Cycle of a Lifetime	Ongoing	Ongoing
1 The Characteristics of Seed Plants	$2\frac{1}{2}$	$1\frac{1}{4}$
2 Gymnosperms	$1\frac{1}{2}$	$\frac{3}{4}$
3 Angiosperms	2	1
4 Integrating Chemistry: Plant Responses and Growth	1	$\frac{1}{2}$
Chapter 9 Review and Assessment	1	$\frac{1}{2}$
Nature of Science: From Plants to Chemicals	1	$\frac{1}{2}$

Chapter 10 Sponges, Cnidarians, and Worms	Days	Blocks
Chapter 10 Project Alive and Well	Ongoing	Ongoing
1 What Is an Animal?	2	1
2 Integrating Mathematics: Symmetry	$1-1\frac{1}{2}$	$\frac{1}{2}-\frac{3}{4}$
3 Sponges and Cnidarians	2	1
4 Worms	2	1
Chapter 10 Review and Assessment	1	$\frac{1}{2}$
Chapter 11 Mollusks, Arthropods, and Echinoderms		
Chapter 11 Project Going Through Changes	Ongoing	Ongoing
1 Mollusks	$1\frac{1}{2}$	$\frac{3}{4}$
2 Arthropods	2	1
3 Insects	2	1
4 Integrating Chemistry: The Chemistry of Communication	1	$\frac{1}{2}$
5 Echinoderms	$1-1\frac{1}{2}$	$\frac{1}{2}-\frac{3}{4}$
Chapter 11 Review and Assessment	1	$\frac{1}{2}$
Chapter 12 Fishes, Amphibians, and Reptiles		
Chapter 12 Project Animal Adaptations	Ongoing	Ongoing
1 Integrating Earth Science: Evolution of Vertebrates	$1\frac{1}{2}$	$\frac{3}{4}$
2 Fishes	2	1
3 Amphibians	$1\frac{1}{2}$	$\frac{3}{4}$
4 Reptiles	2	1
Chapter 12 Review and Assessment	1	$\frac{1}{2}$

Pacing Chart

	Days	Blocks		Days	Blocks
Chapter 13 Birds and Mammals			**Chapter 17 Circulation**		
Chapter 13 Project Bird Watch	Ongoing	Ongoing	Chapter 17 Project Travels of a Red Blood Cell	Ongoing	Ongoing
1 Birds	2	1	1 The Body's Transport System	2	1
2 Integrating Physics: The Physics of Bird Flight	1	$\frac{1}{2}$	2 A Closer Look at Blood Vessels	$1\frac{1}{2}$	$\frac{3}{4}$
3 What is a Mammal?	2	1	3 Blood and Lymph	2	1
4 Diversity of Mammals	2	1	4 Integrating Health: Cardiovascular Health	1	$\frac{1}{2}$
Chapter 13 Review and Assessment	1	$\frac{1}{2}$	Chapter 17 Review and Assessment	1	$\frac{1}{2}$
Chapter 14 Animal Behavior			**Chapter 18 Respiration and Excretion**		
Chapter 14 Project Learning New Tricks	Ongoing	Ongoing	Chapter 18 Project Get the Message Out	Ongoing	Ongoing
1 Integrating Psychology: Why Do Animals Behave As They Do?	2	1	1 The Respiratory System	$2\frac{1}{2}$	$1\frac{1}{4}$
2 Patterns of Behavior	2	1	2 Integrating Health: Smoking and Your Health	1	$\frac{1}{2}$
Chapter 14 Review and Assessment	1	$\frac{1}{2}$	3 The Excretory System	$1\frac{1}{2}$	$\frac{3}{4}$
Interdisciplinary Exploration: The Secret of Silk	$1-1\frac{1}{2}$	$\frac{1}{2}-\frac{3}{4}$	Chapter 18 Review and Assessment	1	$\frac{1}{2}$
Chapter 15 Bones, Muscles, and Skin			**Chapter 19 Fighting Disease**		
Chapter 15 Project On the Move	Ongoing	Ongoing	Chapter 19 Project Stop the Invasion	Ongoing	Ongoing
1 Integrating Health: Body Organization and Homeostasis	2	1	1 Infectious Disease	1	$\frac{1}{2}$
2 The Skeletal System	2	1	2 The Body's Defenses	3	$1\frac{1}{2}$
3 The Muscular System	2	1	3 Integrating Health: Preventing Infectious Disease	1	$\frac{1}{2}$
4 The Skin	2	1	4 Noninfectious Disease	2	1
Chapter 15 Review and Assessment	1	$\frac{1}{2}$	Chapter 19 Review and Assessment	1	$\frac{1}{2}$
Chapter 16 Food and Digestion			**Chapter 20 The Nervous System**		
Chapter 16 Project What's on Your Menu?	Ongoing	Ongoing	Chapter 20 Project Tricks and Illusions	Ongoing	Ongoing
1 Integrating Chemistry: Food and Energy	3	$1\frac{1}{2}$	1 How the Nervous System Works	$1\frac{1}{2}$	$\frac{3}{4}$
2 The Digestive Process Begins	2	1	2 Divisions of the Nervous System	2	1
3 Final Digestion and Absorption	1	$\frac{1}{2}$	3 The Senses	2	1
Chapter 16 Review and Assessment	1	$\frac{1}{2}$	4 Integrating Health: Alcohol and Other Drugs	3	$1\frac{1}{2}$
			Chapter 20 Review and Assessment	1	$\frac{1}{2}$

Pacing Chart

	Days	Blocks		Days	Blocks
Chapter 21 The Endocrine System and Reproduction			**Chapter 24 Living Resources**		
Chapter 21 Project A Precious Bundle	Ongoing	Ongoing	Chapter 24 Project Variety Show	Ongoing	Ongoing
1 The Endocrine System	1	$\frac{1}{2}$	**1** Integrating Environmental Science: Environmental Issues	1	$\frac{1}{2}$
2 The Male and Female Reproduction System	2	1	**2** Forests and Fisheries	1–2	$\frac{1}{2}$–1
3 Integrating Health: The Human Life Cycle	2	1	**3** Biodiversity	1–2	$\frac{1}{2}$–1
Chapter 21 Review and Assessment	1	$\frac{1}{2}$	Chapter 24 Review and Assessment	1	$\frac{1}{2}$
Nature of Science: Protecting Desert Wildlife	1	$\frac{1}{2}$	Interdisciplinary Exploration: African Rain Forests	1–1$\frac{1}{2}$	$\frac{1}{2}$–$\frac{3}{4}$
Chapter 22 Populations and Communities					
Chapter 22 Project What's a Crowd?	Ongoing	Ongoing			
1 Living Things and the Environment	2	1			
2 Integrating Mathematics: Studying Populations	2	1			
3 Interactions Among Living Things	2–3	1–1$\frac{1}{2}$			
Chapter 22 Review and Assessment	1	$\frac{1}{2}$			
Chapter 23 Ecosystems and Biomes					
Chapter 23 Project Breaking It Down	Ongoing	Ongoing			
1 Energy Flow in Ecosystems	2–3	1–1$\frac{1}{2}$			
2 Integrating Chemistry: Cycles of Matter	1–2	$\frac{1}{2}$–1			
3 Biogeography	1–2	$\frac{1}{2}$–1			
4 Earth's Biomes	3	1$\frac{1}{2}$			
5 Succession	1–2	$\frac{1}{2}$–1			
Chapter 23 Review and Assessment	1	$\frac{1}{2}$			

RESOURCE PRO

The Resource Pro® CD-ROM is the ultimate scheduling and lesson planning tool. Resource Pro® allows you to preview all the resources in the *Science Explorer* program, organize your chosen materials, and print out any teaching resource. You can follow the suggested lessons or create your own, using resources from anywhere in the program.

Project 2061 was established by the American Association for the Advancement of Science (AAAS) as a long-term project to improve science education nationwide. A primary goal of Project 2061 is to define a "common core of learning"—the knowledge and skills we want all students to achieve. Project 2061 published *Science for All Americans* in 1989 and followed this with *Benchmarks for Science Literacy* in 1993. *Benchmarks* recommends what students should know and be able to do by the end of grades 2, 5, 8, and 12. Project 2061 clearly states that *Benchmarks* is not a curriculum, but a tool for designing successful curricula.

The National Research Council (NRC) utilized *Science for All Americans* and *Benchmarks* to develop the National Science Education Standards (NSES), which were published in 1996. The NSES are organized into six categories (Content, Teaching, Assessment, Professional Development, Program, and System) to help schools establish the conditions necessary to achieve scientific literacy for all students.

Michael Padilla, the lead author of *Science Explorer*, guided one of six teams of teachers whose work led to the publication of *Benchmarks*. He also was a contributing writer of the National Science Education Standards. Under his guidance, *Science Explorer* has implemented these standards through its inquiry approach, a focus on student learning of important concepts and skills, and teacher support aligned with the NSES teaching standards.

Neither *Benchmarks* nor the NSES requires a single, uniform national curriculum, and in fact there is a great diversity nationwide in science curricula. The correlations that follow are designed to help you utilize the *Science Explorer* program to meet your particular curriculum needs.

National Science Education Standards Correlation

National Science Education Standards	*Life Science* Sections	*Earth Science* Sections	*Physical Science* Sections
CONTENT STANDARD A: SCIENCE AS INQUIRY			
A-1 Identify Questions that Can Be Answered Through Scientific Investigations.	1.1, 7.2, 7.3, 10.2, 10.4, 15.1, 15.3, 15.4, 16.1, 16.2, 17.1, 17.3, 18.1; Chapter Projects: 1, 10, 11, 14, 20	Chapter Projects: 15, 19	19.1; Chapter Projects: 1, 3, 7, 8, 14, 16, 18
A-2 Design and Conduct a Scientific Investigation.	2.4, 7.2, 8.1, 10.4, 12.2, 13.3, 20.1; Chapter Projects: 1, 7, 9, 10, 11, 14, 20, 22–24	3.6, 7.1, 10.2, 10.4, 13.3, 15.1, 18.1; Chapter Projects: 2, 7, 11–14, 18	6.2, 9.2, 13.4, 15.2–15.3, 16.1, 16.3, 18.2; Chapter Projects: 1, 3, 6, 8, 11, 12, 19, 20
A-3 Use Appropriate Tools and Techniques to Gather, Analyze, and Interpret Data.	1.3, 2.1, 2.5, 3.1, 6.3, 22.2; Chapter Projects: 1, 3, 6, 8, 10, 15, 16, 22, 23	2.1, 2.3, 3.5, 5.2, 11.2, 12.1, 14.1, 15.3, 16.3, 17.2, 17.4, 18.2; Chapter Projects: 1–3 , 7, 10, 15–19	8.1, 9.1, 14.1, 14.2; Chapter Projects: 1, 3, 5–9, 17, 21
A-4 Develop Descriptions, Explanations, Predictions, and Models Using Evidence.	3.1, 4.1, 5.1, 5.3, 19.2, 22.1, 23.4, 23.5, 24.1, 24.2; Chapter Projects: 1–5, 10–15, 17–20	1.2, 1.4, 4.4, 4.5, 6.1, 6.3, 7.2, 7.4, 8.1, 8.2, 9.2, 9.4, 13.4, 14.4, 20.4; Chapter Projects: 4, 7, 8, 11, 13–15, 19–21	1.2, 1.4, 3.1, 3.3, 3.4, 4.1–4.3, 11.1; Chapter Projects: 2, 4, 8, 15, 22
A-5 Think Critically and Logically to Make the Relationships between Evidence and Explanations.	4.1, 9.4, 14.2, 20.4; Chapter Projects: 1–4, 11, 15, 20	11.1, 11.3, 12.2, 16.1	1.4, 21.4; Chapter Projects: 6, 13, 14, 19, 21
A-6 Recognize and Analyze Alternative Explanations and Predictions.	Chapter Projects: 13, 16	Chapter Projects: 3, 16, 17	21.3
A-7 Communicate Scientific Procedures and Explanations.	4.1, 12.2; Chapter Projects: 1, 3–9, 13–19, 21–24	Chapter Projects: 1–21	5.1, 11.3, 19.3; Chapter Projects: 1–7, 9–22
A-8 Use Mathematics in All Aspects of Scientific Inquiry.	3.1, 3.2, 6.4, 7.2, 7.3, 19.3, 21.3; Chapter Projects: 3, 5, 6, 12, 13, 16	21.2; Chapter Projects: 16, 18	2.2, 2.3, 9.1–9.3, 11.1,11.3, 13.1, 13.4, 22.1, 22.3, Chapter Projects: 9, 17, 21

National Science Education Standards Correlation

National Science Education Standards	*Life Science* Sections	*Earth Science* Sections	*Physical Science* Sections
CONTENT STANDARD B: PHYSICAL SCIENCE			
B-1 Properties and Changes of Properties in Matter	2.2, 5.2, 5.3, 10.4, 11.1, 15.1, 16.1, 16.2, 17.2, 18.1, 19.2, 21.1, 23.2	2.1, 2.2, 4.1, 4.2, 4.4, 5.1, 6.1, 9.3, 13.3, 15.1–15.3, 21.1	1.1–1.4, 2.1–2.4, 3.1–3.5, 4.1–4.3, 5.1–5.4, 6.1–6.5, 7.1–7.3, 8.1–8.4, 9.1, 11.3, 13.1, 13.2, 14.1, 14.3, 17.3, 19.1, 19.3, 20.1, 21.4, 22.1
B-2 Motions and Forces	1.2, 11.1, 13.2, 17.1, 17.2, 18.1	8.3, 8.5, 8.6, 12.4, 13.1, 13.2, 13.4, 16.3, 20.1, 21.3	2.1, 3.1, 4.1, 4.2, 9.1–9.3, 10.1–10.5, 11.1–11.4, 15.1–15.4, 16.2, 17.1, 17.2, 19.1, 19.3, 19.4, 20.1, 20.2, 21.1–21.4
B-3 Transfer of Energy	13.1, 16.1, 19.4, 20.3, 23.1, 23.2	4.2, 4.5, 5.1, 5.2, 7.1, 8.3–8.6, 9.3, 9.4, 10.1, 10.3, 10.4, 11.1, 11.2, 12.4, 13.1, 13.2, 13.4, 14.1, 16.1, 16.2, 20.2, 21.1	2.4, 3.5, 4.1, 5.1, 5.3, 5.4, 6.4, 7.3, 8.3, 12.1–12.3, 13.1–13.4, 14.1–14.4, 15.1, 15.2, 15.4, 16.2, 17.1–17.4, 18.1–18.4, 19.3, 19.4, 20.1–20.3, 21.1–21.4, 22.1, 22.2
CONTENT STANDARD C: LIFE SCIENCE			
C-1 Structure and Function in Living Systems	1.1–1.4, 2.1–2.5, 3.1, 3.3, 3.4, 6.1–6.4, 7.1–7.3, 8.1–8.4, 9.1–9.4, 10.1–10.4, 11.1, 11.2, 12.1–12.4, 13.1–13.4, 15.1–15.4, 16.2, 16.3, 17.1–17.4, 18.1–18.3, 19.1–19.4, 20.1–20.4, 21.1–21.3	9.5, 11.4, 14.2, 14.3, 20.6	5.1, 6.5, 7.2, 7.3, 8.1, 11.1, 11.4, 12.4, 14.2, 16.4, 18.4, 20.4
C-2 Reproduction and Heredity	1.1, 3.1–3.4, 4.1–4.3, 6.3, 6.4, 7.3, 8.1–8.3, 9.1–9.3, 10.1, 10.3, 10.4, 11.2, 11.3, 11.5, 12.2–12.4, 21.2, 21.3		
C-3 Regulation and Behavior	1.1, 1.4, 2.2, 6.3, 6.4, 7.1–7.3, 8.1–8.3, 9.1–9.4, 11.4, 14.1, 14.2, 15.1, 15.3, 20.1–20.4, 21.1–21.3, 22.1–22.3, 23.1		16.5
C-4 Populations and Ecosystems	2.3, 2.4, 5.1, 6.3, 7.2, 10.3, 11.3, 12.3, 13.1, 14.1, 14.2, 22.1–22.3, 23.1–23.5	3.4, 7.2, 9.2, 11.2, 11.4, 13.4, 14.2, 14.3, 18.2	
C-5 Diversity and Adaptations of Organisms	5.1–5.3, 6.1, 6.3, 6.4, 7.1–7.3, 8.1–8.3, 10.1–10.4, 11.1–11.5, 12.1–12.4, 13.1–13.4, 14.1, 14.2, 22.3, 23.4, 24.3	9.1, 9.4, 9.5, 14.2, 14.3	7.2, 7.3, 10.4, 11.2
CONTENT STANDARD D: EARTH AND SPACE SCIENCE			
D-1 Structure of the Earth System	11.1, 23.2, 23.5	1.1, 1.2, 2.2, 3.1–3.6, 4.1, 4.2, 4.4, 4.5, 5.1–5.3, 6.1–6.3, 7.1–7.3, 8.1–8.6, 9.1–9.5, 11.1–11.4, 13.1–13.4, 14.1–14.3, 15.1, 15.3, 15.4, 16.1–16.5, 17.1–17.4, 18.1–18.4, 19.2, 20.3	1.4, 2.1, 2.4, 3.3, 3.4, 4.3, 5.2, 6.3, 7.1, 9.2, 14.2, 15.4, 19.2, 20.1

National Science Education Standards Correlation

National Science Education Standards	*Life Science* Sections	*Earth Science* Sections	*Physical Science* Sections
CONTENT STANDARD D: EARTH AND SPACE SCIENCE *(continued)*			
D-2 Earth's History	1.4, 5.1, 5.2, 12.1	4.3–4.5, 5.1, 8.1, 8.4, 9.1–9.5, 11.2, 18.3, 19.4, 21.4	8.4, 9.2, 13.3, 19.2
D-3 Earth in the Solar System	22.3	1.3, 3.6, 6.4, 9.3, 13.2, 16.1, 16.3, 16.4, 18.1, 19.1, 19.2, 19.4, 20.1–20.6, 21.5	3.5, 10.3, 10.5, 17.2, 18.5, 19.2
CONTENT STANDARD E: SCIENCE AND TECHNOLOGY			
E-1 Abilities of Technological Design		1.4, 5.3, 5.4, 7.4, 10.1–10.4, 15.1, 16.3, 19.3, 21.1; Chapter Projects: 1, 5, 7, 11, 13	1.3, 1.4, 3.3, 5.4, 6.4, 7.3, 8.1, 8.2, 10.3, 11.2, 11.3, 11.4, 12.1–12.3, 13.1, 13.2, 14.4, 17.3, 17.4, 19.1, 19.3, 19.4, 20.1–20.4, 21.1–21.4, 22.1–22.4; Chapter Projects: 6, 7, 10–14, 16, 18–20, 22
E-2 Understandings about Science and Technology	1.2, 4.2, 4.3, 5.3, 12.3, 14.1, 15.3, 17.1, 19.4, 24.1, 24.2	1.2–1.4, 2.3, 3.2, 3.3, 3.5, 3.6, 7.4, 10.1–10.4, 12.1, 12.2, 12.4, 14.1, 14.4, 15.2, 17.4, 19.3, 19.4, 21.1	3.3, 4.2, 5.4, 6.3, 7.1, 7.2, 8.1–8.4, 10.3, 10.5, 12.1, 13.2, 13.4, 14.2, 15.4, 16.5, 17.3, 17.4, 19.2, 21.3, 22.3, 22.4
CONTENT STANDARD F: SCIENCE IN PERSONAL AND SOCIAL PERSPECTIVES			
F-1 Personal Health	1.2, 2.4, 3.4, 4.2, 4.3, 6.4, 15.1–15.4, 16.1, 17.4, 18.2, 18.3, 19.1–19.4, 20.2–20.4, 21.3	7.4, 12.1, 12.3, 15.2, 17.2, 17.3	5.4, 6.5, 7.3, 8.4, 9.2, 14.2, 16.4, 16.5, 17.2, 18.5, 20.4
F-2 Populations, Resources, and Environments	2.3, 8.4, 10.3, 22.2, 24.1–24.3	2.3, 7.3, 7.4, 10.1–10.4, 12.1–12.3, 14.4, 18.2–18.4, 21.1	3.3, 5.2, 6.4, 8.4, 13.3, 21.2, 21.4
F-3 Natural Hazards	12.3, 15.4, 19.4	5.2, 5.3, 6.2, 6.3, 7.3, 8.1, 11.2, 11.3, 13.1, 16.5, 17.2, 17.3	7.2, 8.1, 15.4, 20.1, 20.4
F-4 Risks and Benefits	8.4, 12.3, 17.4, 20.2, 20.3, 20.4, 24.1, 24.3	2.3, 5.3, 6.3, 7.4, 8.2, 10.1–10.4, 11.2, 11.3, 12.2, 13.1, 15.2, 17.2, 20.6	5.4, 7.3, 8.4, 16.4, 17.2, 21.2, 22.4
F-5 Science and Technology in Society	4.3, 8.4, 22.2, 24.1, 24.2	1.3, 1.4, 2.3, 5.2–5.4, 7.3, 7.4, 10.1–10.4, 11.1–11.3, 12.2, 12.3, 13.1, 15.2, 16.5, 17.4, 18.4, 20.6, 21.1	1.3, 5.4, 8.4, 9.1, 12.3, 16.3, 16.5, 17.2–17.4, 18.2, 18.5, 22.1–22.4
CONTENT STANDARD G: HISTORY AND NATURE OF SCIENCE			
G-1 Science as a Human Endeavor	1.2, 3.3, 5.1, 14.1, 16.2, 17.3, 17.4, 19.1, 19.3, 24.1, 24.3	4.3, 7.3, 19.4	3.1, 3.2, 16.3, 17.4, 18.5
G-2 Nature of Science	1.2, 16.2, 19.1	4.3, 9.1–9.3, 9.5	3.1
G-3 History of Science	1.1, 1.2, 1.4, 3.1, 3.2, 5.1, 6.1, 13.1, 14.1, 16.2, 17.3, 17.4, 19.1, 19.3, 24.1	1.1, 1.2, 4.1, 4.3, 5.2, 15.4, 19.4 20.1, 20.3–20.5, 21.1	1.2, 1.3, 2.2, 3.1, 3.2, 8.1–8.3, 10.1–10.5, 11.2–11.4, 13.2, 13.4 16.2, 17.4, 18.5, 19.1–19.3, 20.2, 20.4, 21.3, 22.3, 22.4

Benchmarks Correlation			
Benchmarks for Science Literacy	***Life Science* Chapters**	***Earth Science* Chapters**	***Physical Science* Chapters**
1 THE NATURE OF SCIENCE			
1A The Scientific World View	8, 16, 19	4, 20	5, 17, 18, 21
1B Scientific Inquiry	1–8, 10, 11, 14, 17, 22, 23, 24	1–4, 6–18	1–3, 6–8, 13, 15, 20
1C The Scientific Enterprise	1, 3, 5, 19, 20, 24	1, 4, 21	11, 19, 22
2 THE NATURE OF MATHEMATICS			
2A Patterns and Relationships	10, 22	20, 21	3, 4, 15
2B Mathematics, Science, and Technology	22	12, 13	12, 21
2C Mathematical Inquiry	6, 17, 21	20, 21	16, 20
3 THE NATURE OF TECHNOLOGY			
3A Technology and Science	1, 4, 11, 24	1–5, 7, 9, 10, 12, 14–17, 19, 21	5, 8, 9, 18, 22
3B Design and Systems		5, 10, 12, 19	8, 10, 11, 13, 14, 20–22
3C Issues in Technology	4, 6–8, 13, 15, 17, 24	2, 7, 10–12, 14, 15, 18	1, 8, 12, 14, 16, 17, 21, 22
4 THE PHYSICAL SETTING			
4A The Universe		6, 20, 21	
4B The Earth	23, 24	1, 7, 8, 11–13, 15–20	13
4C Processes that Shape the Earth	5, 23	2–9, 11, 13, 14, 18, 19	15
4D Structure of Matter	18	2, 9, 11, 13, 15	1–8, 11, 14, 21
4E Energy Transformations		4, 5, 8, 13, 15, 16, 20, 21	2–5, 12–14, 17, 20–22
4F Motion	11	5, 16, 19	9, 10, 15, 16, 18
4G Forces of Nature		20	3, 19
5 THE LIVING ENVIRONMENT			
5A Diversity of Life	1, 5–13, 23, 24	3, 14	
5B Heredity	3, 4		
5C Cells	1, 2, 3, 8, 9, 15, 20		18
5D Interdependence of Life	2, 6, 7, 10–12, 22, 23	7, 11, 14, 18	
5E Flow of Matter and Energy	1, 2, 8, 16, 18, 23		6, 7, 13
5F Evolution of Life	1, 5, 12, 13, 14	9	
6 THE HUMAN ORGANISM			
6A Human Identity	14, 15	12	12, 16, 18
6B Human Development	15, 21		
6C Basic Functions	13, 15–18, 20		6, 7, 16
6D Learning	20		22
6E Physical Health	15–20	17	7
6F Mental Health	15		
7 HUMAN SOCIETY			
7A Cultural Effects on Behavior	18	12	22
7B Group Behavior	15	10	
7C Social Change	24	10, 17	
7D Social Trade-Offs	22, 24	5, 8, 12, 14, 15, 17	8

Benchmarks Correlation

Benchmarks for Science Literacy	*Life Science* Chapters	*Earth Science* Chapters	*Physical Science* Chapters
7 HUMAN SOCIETY *(continued)*			
7E Political and Economic Systems		12, 15	
7F Social Conflict		12, 14	
7G Global Interdependence	24	10, 11, 18	
8 THE DESIGNED WORLD			
8A Agriculture	8, 9	7, 11, 12	
8B Materials and Manufacturing	24	7	3, 8
8C Energy Sources and Use		10, 12, 13, 15	8, 12–14, 19–21
8D Communication		19	17, 18, 22
8E Information Processing		1	22
8F Health Technology	4, 15, 17–19, 24	12	8
9 THE MATHEMATICAL WORLD			
9A Numbers	3		9
9B Symbolic Relationships		14, 18	2, 9, 12, 13, 15
9C Shapes	10	1, 2	4, 7
9D Uncertainty	3	1	9
9E Reasoning	6, 14	3	3, 7, 10
10 HISTORICAL PERSPECTIVES			
10A Displacing the Earth from the Center of the Universe		19, 20	9
10B Uniting the Heavens and Earth		20	10
10C Relating Matter & Energy and Time & Space		21	
10D Extending Time	5	9, 21	
10E Moving the Continents		4	
10F Understanding Fire			1, 4
10G Splitting the Atom			8
10H Explaining the Diversity of Life	3, 5		
10I Discovering Germs	1, 19		
10J Harnessing Power			13, 14
11 COMMON THEMES			
11A Systems	17	21	12, 16, 20
11B Models	12	5, 6, 11, 13, 14, 20	1, 4, 11
11C Constancy and Change	9, 10, 15, 18	5, 19	5, 6, 15
11D Scale	7	9, 21	4
12 HABITS OF MIND			
12A Values and Attitudes	10; Chapter Projects (all)	Chapter Projects (all)	6, 21; Chapter Projects (all)
12B Computation and Estimation		1, 5, 15	2, 9
12C Manipulation and Observation		16	8, 10
12D Communication Skills	1, 4, 6, 11–13, 15, 16, 19	6, 9, 11, 18	1, 7, 10
12E Critical-Response Skills	6, 13, 20, 24	3, 12	6, 7, 8, 10, 17

Inquiry Skills Chart

The Prentice Hall *Science Explorer* program provides comprehensive teaching, practice, and assessment of science skills, with an emphasis on the process skills necessary for inquiry. The chart lists the skills covered in the program and cites the page numbers where each skill is covered.

	Basic Process SKILLS			
	Student Text: Projects and Labs	**Student Text: Activities**	**Student Text: Caption and Review Questions**	**Teacher's Edition: Extensions**
Observing	10, 17, 43, 80, 92, 140, 202–203, 217, 238, 247, 254, 260, 273, 294–295, 309, 318, 339, 345, 360, 353, 359, 368, 371, 373, 409, 415, 419, 422, 441, 458, 493, 498, 505, 517, 524–525, 575, 584, 585, 648, 687, 694, 715, 732, 746, 755, 761	27, 32, 54, 58, 61, 66, 86, 120, 132, 186, 197, 218, 233, 262, 266, 276, 310, 320, 324, 327, 332, 340, 354, 362, 381, 410, 417, 442, 480, 527, 549, 581, 612, 637, 663, 669, 690, 716, 718, 737	5, 11, 166, 196, 218, 276, 283, 316, 344, 358, 368, 404, 412, 520, 523, 532, 636, 704	5, 54, 57, 58, 60, 62, 63, 68, 75, 87, 89, 105, 132, 140, 148, 152, 166, 186–187, 190–191, 197, 200, 202, 203, 234, 236, 250, 252, 258, 274, 275, 276, 280, 281, 282, 284, 293, 311, 319, 322, 323, 328, 330, 343, 344, 350, 356, 362, 381, 384, 386, 398, 402, 410, 416, 426, 433, 445, 451, 454, 474, 484, 490, 495, 497, 527, 538, 550, 567, 573, 578, 583, 597, 597, 603, 606, 608, 615, 637, 638, 639, 674, 691, 705, 706, 719, 749, 765, 769, 770, 775
Inferring	85, 118, 202–203, 294–295, 318, 360, 458, 548, 555, 565, 678, 694, 775	44, 54, 58, 61, 63, 86, 102, 118, 125, 149, 151, 157, 159, 192, 204, 222, 248, 261, 262, 286, 297, 313, 340, 346, 374, 389, 395, 423, 425, 431, 447, 472, 490, 494, 536, 543, 566, 576, 589, 596, 622, 628, 637, 644, 658, 688, 723, 739, 762, 768	15, 34, 45, 46, 70, 82, 83, 90, 106, 115, 142, 173, 234, 245, 252, 271, 276, 286, 296, 303, 330, 359, 368, 377, 406, 426, 436, 447, 451, 461, 502, 503, 532, 588, 589, 616, 618, 662, 680, 697, 729, 752, 753, 774	5, 86, 102, 108, 122, 138, 149, 151, 157, 158, 167, 186–187, 192, 196, 202–203, 204, 206, 224, 226, 237, 263, 281, 286, 287, 290, 303, 297, 312, 340, 346, 349, 359, 363, 364, 374, 376, 383, 385, 389, 390, 395, 396, 424, 431, 432, 443, 447, 452, 455, 477, 483, 489, 496, 502, 503, 510, 546, 567, 586, 606, 608, 615, 634, 638, 646, 660, 664, 697, 706, 742, 744, 749, 771
Predicting	51, 71, 85, 100–101, 117, 170, 212, 231, 238, 336, 400–401, 498, 517, 621, 694, 701	55, 94, 109, 175, 182, 225, 228, 235, 256, 266, 365, 420, 442, 444, 488, 508, 518, 526, 557, 569, 571, 703, 728	48, 49, 54, 55, 57, 60, 78, 79, 82, 99, 114, 124, 143, 172, 183, 190–191, 237, 242, 244, 245, 253, 274, 284, 289, 293, 302, 311, 325, 341, 344, 369, 370, 385, 433, 438, 445, 448, 453, 460, 461, 487, 488, 489, 492, 502, 537, 562, 563, 586, 608, 626, 632, 641, 655, 719, 750, 753	89, 94, 95, 97, 109, 129, 152, 249, 252, 277, 298, 316, 329, 365, 420, 442, 444, 451, 502, 512, 559, 582, 585, 606, 717, 725, 770
Classifying	336, 360, 493, 611	20, 146, 165, 182, 253, 284, 310, 315, 324, 340, 342, 427, 484, 556, 560, 579, 709, 716	15, 48, 54, 70, 78, 86, 99, 106, 140, 174, 190, 191, 214, 229, 242, 274, 293, 302, 311, 325, 336, 341, 370, 383, 390, 433, 454, 488, 489, 533, 550, 556, 557, 566, 592, 615, 709, 719, 750, 753	146, 147, 165, 183, 184–185, 191, 214, 264, 278, 284, 293, 313, 316, 331, 333, 341, 342, 348, 359, 411, 417, 426, 434, 447, 451, 457, 482, 513, 697, 742

Basic Process SKILLS (continued)

	Student Text: Projects and Labs	Student Text: Activities	Student Text: Caption and Review Questions	Teacher's Edition: Extensions
Making Models	85, 100–101, 117, 140, 145, 152, 170, 212, 247, 260, 373, 388, 470–471, 535, 555, 575, 598, 599, 657, 694, 715, 732	40, 74, 122, 236, 315, 376, 392, 421, 473, 521, 552, 603, 671, 685, 699, 721	207	57, 59, 64, 75, 76, 77, 78, 104, 111, 122, 123, 135, 140, 152, 158, 223, 277, 285, 298, 316, 317, 324, 332, 348, 366, 375, 376, 378, 380, 385, 390, 392, 412, 422, 473, 491, 559, 567, 568, 578, 600, 601, 602, 608, 613, 624, 631, 641, 642, 659, 704, 725, 736, 738, 764, 773
Communicating	85, 117, 145, 170, 216–217, 232, 247, 273, 309, 339, 373, 409, 436, 439, 440, 441, 493, 535, 565, 591, 621, 687, 715	31, 36, 88, 127, 137, 154, 178, 179, 184, 215, 227, 241, 253, 258, 291, 322, 326, 331, 382, 456, 464, 467, 478, 486, 510, 540, 559, 572, 600, 607, 631, 635, 646, 654, 702, 774	15, 48, 82, 83, 114, 142, 143, 172, 173, 199, 214, 244, 270, 302, 336, 370, 379, 391, 406, 438, 460, 502, 532, 562, 588, 618, 654, 713	8, 12, 77, 87, 91, 95, 97, 103, 105, 106, 109, 111, 113, 121, 127, 133, 137, 138, 139, 149, 150, 151, 155, 159, 162, 163, 167, 169, 173, 311–314, 321, 322, 323, 325, 329, 331, 343, 347, 349, 351, 353, 363, 364, 367, 379, 382, 383, 384, 385, 391, 412, 419, 421, 425, 427, 429, 433, 435, 445, 446, 448, 451, 455, 460, 475, 478, 502, 519, 530, 532, 537, 542, 574, 577, 588, 594, 607, 614, 625, 635, 645, 651, 662, 671, 676, 680, 699, 700, 707, 710, 719, 735, 758, 770, 775
Measuring	51, 231, 238, 294–295, 345, 441, 505, 548, 627, 687, 715	146, 494, 640, 764	681	226, 650
Calculating	80, 145, 153, 212, 337, 611, 701	95, 160, 280, 453, 509, 544, 579, 592, 696, 698, 765	32, 95, 97, 115, 142, 173, 206, 280, 337, 515, 533, 681, 722, 757	74, 96, 120, 160, 280, 282, 377, 416, 427, 453, 507, 515, 544, 670, 697
Creating Data Tables	80, 92, 100, 153, 217, 231, 238, 345, 353, 360, 400, 458, 621, 775	350, 546	371	323, 404
Graphing	51, 400, 429, 436, 505, 524, 610, 621, 701	195, 356, 667	83, 371, 439, 619, 655, 681, 713, 779	256, 429, 553, 757

Advanced Process SKILLS

	Student Text: Projects and Labs	Student Text: Activities	Student Text: Caption and Review Questions	Teacher's Edition: Extensions
Posing Questions	181, 309, 388, 458, 565, 591	331, 506, 594, 748		329, 388, 445
Developing Hypotheses	92–93, 101, 217, 300, 334, 414–415, 449, 627, 648	56, 72, 463, 642, 724, 734	6, 49, 215, 332, 503, 713, 779	6, 221, 445, 451
Designing Experiments	10, 26, 93, 101, 117, 153, 181, 203, 217, 231, 238, 239, 254–255, 300, 334, 345, 361, 429, 441, 449, 458, 463, 525, 548, 599, 621, 687, 715, 761	24, 120	49, 215	6, 24, 93, 101, 120, 153, 154, 196, 231, 335, 345, 403, 426, 429, 444, 445, 629

Advanced Process SKILLS (continued)

	Student Text: Projects and Labs	Student Text: Activities	Student Text: Caption and Review Questions	Teacher's Edition: Extensions
Controlling Variables	71, 181, 217, 231, 309, 337, 429, 449, 598-599, 627, 687	630	49, 337, 407, 655	7, 412, 429, 445, 629
Forming Operational Definitions	627	18, 52, 107, 189, 289, 310, 450, 556, 695, 756		107, 189, 289, 411, 445, 450
Interpreting Data	26, 71, 80, 93, 101, 130, 153, 170, 181, 334, 400-401, 415, 421, 429, 458, 517, 584-585, 610-611, 627	75, 97, 179, 249, 350, 589, 619, 741	83, 143, 215, 245, 303, 332, 371, 407, 439, 461, 503, 533, 563, 589, 619, 681, 713, 779	8, 82, 90, 97, 130, 153, 168, 170, 350, 376, 391, 412, 429, 540
Drawing Conclusions	26, 51, 93, 101, 130, 140, 153, 202–203, 212, 231, 238, 255, 294–295, 300, 309, 318, 334, 337, 339, 345, 368, 400–401, 414, 440, 441, 498, 524–525, 548, 565, 584-585, 598–599, 613, 627, 690, 732, 746, 761, 767	166, 320, 324, 403, 482, 499, 589, 613, 619, 690, 767	115, 143, 173, 188, 271, 303, 337, 371, 407, 439, 563, 589, 619	103, 131, 140, 153, 166, 170, 198, 199, 200, 202, 203, 212, 264, 330, 378, 384, 390, 403, 412, 414, 418

Critical Thinking SKILLS

Comparing and Contrasting	51, 100–101, 153, 170, 202–203, 239, 318, 336, 339, 400–401, 429, 449, 505, 610, 678, 746	125, 132, 315, 320, 327	20, 28, 42, 48, 60, 62, 65, 67, 70, 73, 82, 113, 142, 148, 164, 172, 214, 219, 244, 259, 270, 271, 286, 288, 314, 323, 324, 336, 353, 370, 375, 384, 402, 405, 406, 416, 419, 424, 438, 463, 474, 481, 532, 542, 562, 588, 593, 618, 652, 668, 680, 689, 710, 712, 727, 738, 742, 745, 752, 760, 766	23, 29, 33, 36, 45, 135, 143, 150, 161, 164, 167, 170, 185, 193, 193, 205, 207, 234, 275, 276, 292, 293, 323, 341, 343, 347, 353, 354, 355, 357, 374, 391, 393, 398, 399, 400-403, 405, 411, 412, 424, 427, 429, 456, 477, 481, 484, 508, 514, 632, 666, 730, 743
Applying Concepts	117, 130, 140, 203, 309, 318, 361, 429, 458, 498, 505, 517, 555, 565, 585, 591, 599, 649, 701, 732, 761		7, 15, 24, 25, 33, 41, 48, 60, 62, 65, 67, 73, 91, 103, 114, 123, 134, 142, 156, 172, 188, 200, 201, 227, 264, 265, 267, 268, 270, 275, 299, 302, 312, 315, 317, 348, 353, 370, 391, 406, 443, 447, 457, 460, 476, 479, 500, 502, 508, 516, 527, 532, 538, 547, 567, 586, 588, 595, 601, 604, 609, 618, 624, 630, 638, 645, 654, 659, 673, 680, 693, 710, 749, 760, 769	20, 90, 184, 355, 375, 383, 384, 390, 391, 412, 429, 495, 546, 558, 602, 633, 639, 651

Inquiry Skills Chart

Critical Thinking SKILLS (continued)

	Student Text: Projects and Labs	Student Text: Activities	Student Text: Caption and Review Questions	Teacher's Edition: Extensions
Interpreting Diagrams, Graphs, Photographs, and Maps	318, 400–401, 505, 610–611, 649, 678	177, 313, 464	8, 59, 64, 69, 74, 89, 96, 104, 108, 119, 121, 155, 158, 160, 169, 187, 191, 194, 201, 210, 225, 253, 257, 281, 282, 290, 305, 332, 348, 355, 371, 377, 380, 382, 386, 407, 475, 482, 491, 496, 511, 512, 519, 522, 528, 541, 553, 571, 573, 615, 637, 647, 665, 666, 670, 690, 698, 717, 724, 726, 763, 768, 771	8, 147, 155, 161, 210, 313, 316, 321, 328, 355, 358, 367, 380, 383, 385, 386, 391, 397, 399, 413, 421, 425, 431, 432, 434–435, 485, 486, 491, 514, 519, 522, 528, 538, 552, 569, 571, 577, 582, 624, 625, 633, 639, 641, 659, 660, 666, 670, 708, 740
Relating Cause and Effect	334, 309, 415, 458		48, 87, 112, 126, 172, 223, 229, 244, 245, 270, 302, 333, 336, 370, 394, 396, 406, 421, 422, 478, 487, 495, 502, 529, 532, 554, 557, 560, 562, 574, 577, 580, 597, 603, 604, 614, 618, 634, 643, 654, 677, 680, 712, 740, 752, 778	126, 312, 376, 393, 412, 454, 580, 623
Making Generalizations	334		133, 150, 185, 240, 347, 380, 386, 399, 404, 420, 502, 546, 562, 618, 654, 712, 722, 736, 776, 778	352, 404, 515, 647
Making Judgements	309, 505, 555		15, 136, 138, 169, 211, 227, 270, 298, 370, 500, 588, 654, 662, 778	87, 267, 395, 560
Problem Solving	309	331	82, 99, 114, 129, 142, 214, 230, 244, 460, 595, 700, 712	159, 352, 455, 457

Information Organizing SKILLS

	Student Text: Projects and Labs	Student Text: Activities	Student Text: Caption and Review Questions	Teacher's Edition: Extensions
Concept Maps			47, 141, 301, 369, 459, 501, 653, 711	60, 387, 436, 501, 616, 689, 693
Compare/ Contrast Tables	334	256, 261	113, 269, 405, 437	405, 492, 521, 551, 737, 741
Venn Diagrams		249, 259, 265	213	23, 393
Flowcharts			171, 208, 243, 335, 531, 587, 617, 679	45, 230, 335, 413, 523, 541, 668
Cycle Diagrams			81, 751	394

The *Science Explorer* program provides additional teaching, reinforcement, and assessment of skills in the Inquiry Skills Activity Book and the Laboratory Manual.

Master Materials List

To make ordering supplies easier, the Master Materials List cross-references by chapter and section, the materials needed for activities. You can use the Materials List CD-ROM, which Science Kit and Boreal Laboratories developed to create an electronic list of the materials. Science Kit produces both Consumable Kits and Nonconsumable Kits for *Science Explorer* activities. For more information call 1-800-848-9500.

Consumable Materials

*	Description	Qty per class	Textbook Section(s)	*	Description	Qty per class	Textbook Section(s)
	Adrenaline Chloride, 0.01% Aqueous Solution, 25 mL		1 20-4 (Lab)	SS	Box, Shoe, with Lid	5	11-2 (TT)
SS	Advertisement from a teen magazine	5	8-4 (DIS)	SS	Bread Crumbs, pkg	1	14-2 (Lab)
SS	Air Freshener	1	2-2 (DIS)	SS	Bread without Preservatives, Slice	5	1-1 (Lab)
	Alcohol, Isopropyl (Rubbing), 500 mL	1	2-3 (SYS), 6-3 (Lab), 19-2 (Lab)	SS	Bread, Slice	10	7-3 (DIS), 23-1 (SYS)
	Aluminum Foil, roll 12" x 25'	1	6-4 (TT), 7-1 (SYS), 11-2 (TT), 11-4 (DIS)		Brine Shrimp Eggs, 6 Dram Vial	1	22-1 (TT)
SS	Animal	5	1-4 (DIS)		Bromothymol Blue, 100 mL	1	2-4 (Lab), 18-1 (TT)
SS	Apple	36	19-2 (Lab), 20-3 (SYS)		Bulb, Clear, 60 Watt	5	2-4 (Lab), 8-1 (Lab), 11-3 (Lab), 23-4 (Lab)
	Bag, Paper, 10 cm x 20 cm x 7.5 cm	30	3-2 (Lab), 4-1 (TT), 20-3 (DIS)	SS	Cacti, Live, set/5	1	23-4 (TT)
	Bag, Plastic Zip Lip, 6" x 8" (1 qt)	50	1-1 (Lab), 7-3 (DIS), 12-3 (TT), 15-4 (Lab), 16-1 (Lab), 19-2 (Lab), 23-1 (SYS)	SS	Candy, Piece	5	20-4 (DIS)
				SS	Cardboard	20	10-4 (Lab), 11-2 (DIS), 15-4 (TT)
	Baking Soda, 454 g	1	2-1 (DIS), 8-1 (Lab), 16-3 (TT)		Cards, Index, Blank, 3" x 5", pkg/100	1	4-2 (Lab), 22-2 (Lab), 23-4 (Lab)
	Balloons, Round, 13", pkg/10	1	18-1 (Lab)	SS	Celery Stalk	5	9-1 (SYS)
	Balloons, Round, 9", pkg/35	2	7-3 (TT), 7-3 (Lab), 18-1 (DIS), 18-1 (Lab)	SS	Cereal, Breakfast, 2 Varieties	1	16-1 (Lab)
					Chalk, White, pkg/12	1	2-1 (DIS)
	Batteries, Size D, pkg/6	2	10-4 (Lab)		Charcoal Pieces, 16 oz	1	22-1 (Lab)
SS	Beverages with and without Caffeine	5	20-4 (Lab)		Cheesecloth, 2 M Piece	1	11-3 (Lab), 17-3 (TT)
				SS	Chicken Wing, Uncooked	5	15-3 (Lab)
SS	Bird Seed	1	5-1 (TT)		Clay, Modeling (Cream) (water-resistant), lb	2	6-4 (TT), 7-3 (TT), 9-4 (Lab), 19-2 (TT)
	Biuret Reagent, 500 mL	1	18-3 (Lab)		Cone, Pine	5	9-2 (TT)
SS	Bone, Chicken Leg	10	15-2 (DIS), 15-2 (TT)		Cotton Balls, pkg/300	1	7-1 (TT), 7-3 (TT), 15-4 (TT)
SS	Bottle, Clear Plastic, 2L	5	11-3 (Lab), 22-1 (Lab)	SS	Cracker, Unsalted	35	2-1 (TT), 13-3 (DIS)

KEY: **DIS**: Discover; **SYS**: Sharpen Your Skills; **TT**: Try This; **Lab**: Lab; **INT**: Introduction Lab
* Items designated **SS** are School Supplied.
Quantities based on 5 lab groups per class.

T25

Master Materials List

Consumable Materials (continued)

*	Description	Qty per class	Textbook Section(s)	*	Description	Qty per class	Textbook Section(s)
	Cup, Plastic, Clear, 2 oz	5	17-1 (DIS)	SS	Fresh Fruit, Assortment	5	5-2 (TT), 9-3 (DIS)
	Cup, Plastic, Clear, Cocktail, 9 oz, pkg/50	1	(INT), 2-1 (DIS), 2-2 (TT), 2-3 (SYS), 5-1 (TT), 5-2 (TT), 13-3 (Lab), 17-3 (TT), 18-3 (DIS), 22-1 (TT), 24-3 (DIS)	SS	Fruit	5	7-3 (DIS)
					Gelatin, Box of 4 Packets	2	1-3 (TT)
					Glucose (d-Glucose) Anhydrous, Science Grade Granular, 500 g	1	18-3 (DIS), 18-3 (Lab)
					Glucose Test Strips, pk/40	1	18-3 (DIS), 18-3 (Lab)
	Cups, Medicine Type, Graduated, 30 mL, pkg/50	1	8-2 (DIS)	SS	Glue, School White, 4 oz	5	6-4 (TT), 13-2 (TT), 22-1 (DIS)
	Cups, Paper, 200 mL, pkg/100	1	6-3 (DIS), 11-4 (DIS), 12-3 (DIS), 17-3 (Lab)	SS	Goldfish, Live, Dozen	1	12-2 (DIS)
				SS	Grapefruit	5	12-4 (DIS)
SS	Disinfectant Products, Assortment	5	19-3 (DIS)	SS	Graph Paper, Metric Coordinates, 1-cm grid, pk/100	1	4-1 (DIS), 6-3 (SYS), 11-1 (Lab), 13-3 (Lab), 17-2 (Lab), 21-2 (SYS), 22-2 (Lab), 24-2 (DIS)
	Disinfectant, Lysol, 15 oz	1	6-3 (Lab)				
SS	Egg White, Boiled	5	16-2 (Lab)				
SS	Egg, Uncooked	5	13-1 (TT)	SS	Guppies, Live, Dozen	1	12-2 (Lab)
	Extract, Banana, 60 mL	1	11-4 (DIS)		Hydrochloric Acid, 1 M, 500 mL Solution	1	16-2 (Lab)
	Extract, Mint, 60 mL	1	11-4 (DIS)				
	Extract, Vanilla Imitation, 8 oz	1	11-4 (DIS)		Ink Pad, Washable (Black)	1	4-3 (DIS)
SS	Fern	5	8-3 (TT)	SS	Insect Collection	5	11-3 (DIS)
	Fertilizer, Granular, 8 oz	1	7-2 (Lab)		Iodine (Starch Test) Reagent Solution, 100 mL	1	16-1 (SYS)
	Filter Paper, 15 cm Diameter, pkg/100	1	18-3 (DIS)		Knives, Plastic, pkg/24	1	15-4 (Lab), 17-4 (TT)
	Filters, Coffee, box/100	1	2-3 (SYS)	SS	Labels, Pressure Sensitive, roll/100	1	2-1 (DIS)
SS	Fish Food	1	12-2 (Lab)	SS	Leaves, Average Rainfall Environment	5	8-1 (DIS)
	Fish, Perch, Preserved-Under 7", pkg/5	1	12-2 (SYS)				
				SS	Leaves, Desert Environment	5	8-1 (DIS)
SS	Flowers	15	(INT), 9-3 (Lab)	SS	Leaves, Set	5	2-3 (SYS), 9-2 (DIS)
	Food Coloring, Dark Red, 30 mL, In Dropper Bottle	1	2-2 (TT), 8-3 (DIS), 9-1 (SYS)	SS	Lemon, Slice	5	1-1 (TT)
					Lens Paper, pkg/50, 4" x 6"	1	9-3 (Lab)
	Food Coloring, pkg/4, 8 mL, Green, Yellow, Red, Blue	1	17-3 (Lab)		Lid, for 9 oz Cup	50	13-3 (Lab)
SS	Food Packages, Assortment	5	17-4 (DIS)		Litmus Test Paper, Blue, vial/100	1	16-2 (Lab)
SS	Food Samples	5	9-1 (DIS), 16-1 (SYS)		Live Coupon - Ants (about 100)	1	14-2 (Lab)

KEY: **DIS**: Discover; **SYS**: Sharpen Your Skills; **TT**: Try This; **Lab**: Lab; **INT**: Introduction Lab
* Items designated **SS** are School Supplied.

Consumable Materials (continued)

*	Description	Qty per class	Textbook Section(s)	*	Description	Qty per class	Textbook Section(s)
	Live Coupon - Blackworms (30 student quantity)	1	20-4 (Lab)	SS	Milk Carton, Cardboard	5	23-4 (Lab)
	Live Coupon - Chlorella (30 student quantity)	1	7-1 (TT)	SS	Moss Plants	5	22-1 (Lab)
	Live Coupon - Earthworms (12)	1	10-4 (SYS), 10-4 (Lab)		Moss, Sphagnum	1	8-2 (DIS)
	Live Coupon - Elodea (12 sprigs)	2	1-3 (Lab), 2-4 (Lab), 8-1 (Lab)	SS	Mushroom	5	6-2 (DIS), 7-3 (TT)
	Live Coupon - Euglena (30 student quantity)	1	7-1 (SYS)	SS	Newspapers	16	1-2 (DIS), 17-1 (DIS), 17-2 (DIS), 24-1 (Lab)
	Live Coupon - Hydra, Brown (30 student quantity)	1	10-3 (TT)	SS	Oatmeal, Instant	1	16-1 (Lab)
	Live Coupon - Mixed Pond Culture, 8 oz	2	1-2 (SYS), 7-1 (DIS)		Oil, Vegetable, 16 oz	1	16-3 (TT)
	Live Coupon - Moss Clump	1	8-2 (Lab)		Owl Pellets, pkg/6	1	13-1 (Lab)
	Live Coupon - Nutrient Agar Plates, pk/6	1	6-3 (Lab)		Paper Clips, box/100	1	6-4 (TT), 13-2 (TT), 17-3 (TT)
	Live Coupon - *Paramecium caudatum* (30 student quantity)	1	7-1 (TT)	SS	Paper Towel Roll	3	9-3 (Lab), 9-4 (Lab), 10-4 (Lab), 11-2 (TT), 15-3 (Lab), 16-1 (Lab), 18-3 (Lab), 19-2 (Lab)
	Live Coupon - Pill Bugs, 24	2	11-2 (TT)	SS	Paper, Construction, Asst, pkg/50	1	2-5 (TT), 5-1 (Lab), 14-2 (TT)
	Live Coupon - Planaria (30 student quantity)	1	10-4 (DIS)	SS	Paper, Construction, Black, pkg/15	1	14-2 (Lab)
	Live Coupon - Snail, Black Ramshorn, 15	1	11-1 (Lab), 12-2 (Lab)	SS	Paper, Construction, Green, pkg/50	1	6-4 (TT), 7-2 (DIS), 12-3 (DIS)
SS	Magazine Picture	5	22-1 (DIS)	SS	Paper, Construction, White, pkg/50	1	15-4 (Lab)
SS	Marker	5	4-2 (Lab), 5-1 (Lab)	SS	Paper, Long Strips (10 m length total)	5	6-4 (Lab)
	Marking Pencil, Black Wax	5	2-4 (Lab), 3-2 (Lab), 6-3 (Lab), 7-2 (Lab), 7-3 (Lab), 8-1 (Lab), 9-4 (Lab), 14-2 (Lab), 16-2 (Lab), 17-3 (Lab), 18-1 (TT), 18-3 (Lab), 19-2 (Lab), 22-1 (TT), 23-5 (Lab)	SS	Paper, Poster	5	10-4 (SYS)
SS	Materials that Resemble Cell Organelles, set	5	1-3 (TT)	SS	Paper, Sheet	105	1-3 (TT), 3-3 (DIS), 4-3 (DIS), 5-1 (SYS), 7-3 (TT), 9-2 (TT), 10-2 (DIS), 12-4 (Lab), 13-2 (DIS), 13-2 (TT), 14-1 (Lab), 17-3 (DIS), 17-3 (Lab), 19-1 (DIS), 19-2 (DIS), 20-1 (DIS), 22-1 (DIS), 22-1 (TT), 22-3 (DIS), 23-1 (DIS), 24-1 (DIS)
	Methylene Blue Chloride BIOstain, 1% Aqueous Solution, 100 mL	1	2-5 (DIS), 6-3 (TT)	SS	Peanut Butter	1	17-4 (TT)

KEY: **DIS**: Discover; **SYS**: Sharpen Your Skills; **TT**: Try This; **Lab**: Lab; **INT**: Introduction Lab
* Items designated **SS** are School Supplied.

Master Materials List

Consumable Materials (continued)

*	Description	Qty per class	Textbook Section(s)	*	Description	Qty per class	Textbook Section(s)
SS	Pear	5	20-3 (SYS)		Seeds, Grass, 30 g	1	23-4 (Lab)
	Pebbles, Gravel, 2.5 kg	1	22-1 (Lab)		Seeds, Impatiens, pkt/105 mg	1	23-4 (Lab)
SS	Pencil	5	6-4 (Lab), 12-4 (Lab), 14-1 (Lab), 15-4 (Lab)		Seeds, Lima Bean, 2 oz	1	9-1 (TT), 23-4 (Lab)
SS	Pencils, Colored, pkg/12	5	1-3 (Lab), 2-5 (Lab), 17-3 (DIS), 19-3 (Lab), 22-1 (DIS), 22-3 (DIS), 24-2 (Lab)		Seeds, Pea, Alaska (Smooth), 1 oz	1	9-1 (TT)
					Seeds, Split Pea, Green, 1 lb	1	12-3 (DIS)
					Seeds, Split Pea, Yellow, 1 lb	1	12-3 (DIS)
SS	Pens, Variety	40	5-3 (DIS)		Seeds, Sunflower, 30 g (Approx. 200 seeds)	1	5-1 (DIS)
	Pepsin Activity 1:3000 Powder, Science Grade, 30 g	1	16-2 (Lab), 18-3 (Lab)	SS	Shortening, Solid	1	13-3 (TT)
				SS	Soil & Leaf Litter, Fresh	5	11-3 (Lab)
	Pipe Cleaners, Asst Colors, 6", pkg/110	1	2-5 (TT)		Soil, Potting, 4 lb	3	10-4 (SYS), 22-1 (Lab), 23-4 (Lab)
	Pipe Cleaners, White, 12", pkg/30	1	6-4 (TT), 20-3 (TT)		Soil, Sandy, 2.5 kg	3	14-2 (Lab), 23-4 (Lab)
SS	Plant, Common House	5	1-4 (DIS), 6-2 (DIS), 9-4 (DIS), 22-1 (Lab)		Spoons, Plastic, pkg/24	1	(INT), 7-2 (DIS), 9-1 (SYS), 16-1 (Lab) 16-3 (TT), 22-1 (TT), 22-1 (Lab)
	Plastic Wrap Roll, 50 sq ft	1	22-1 (Lab), 23-4 (Lab), 24-1 (Lab)	SS	Stapler	5	13-2 (TT), 15-4 (Lab), 23-4 (Lab)
	Plates, Paper 9", pkg/50	1	1-1 (Lab), 5-1 (TT), 24-3 (DIS)		Steel Wool Pads, pkg/6	1	11-3 (Lab)
SS	Pond Water	1	23-5 (Lab)		Sticks, Craft, pkg/50	1	3-3 (DIS), 7-3 (TT)
SS	Potato	5	1-1 (SYS), 20-3 (SYS)		Stirrer Sticks, pkg/50	1	15-3 (TT), 16-2 (Lab)
	PTC Taste Paper, vial/100	1	3-1 (Lab)		Straws, Plastic, pkg/200	1	2-4 (DIS), 2-4 (Lab), 6-4 (TT), 7-3 (Lab), 16-2 (TT), 18-1 (TT), 19-4 (DIS), 20-3 (TT), 20-4 (Lab), 23-3 (DIS)
SS	Raisins, Box	1	5-1 (TT)				
	Rubber Bands, Assorted, 4 oz	1	6-4 (TT), 11-3 (Lab), 12-3 (TT), 12-4 (DIS), 13-2 (TT), 14-2 (Lab), 17-3 (TT), 22-1 (Lab)		String, Cotton, 200 ft	1	6-4 (TT), 12-1 (TT), 13-2 (TT), 16-3 (DIS)
					Sugar Cubes, 1 lb (pkg/96)	1	16-2 (DIS)
	Salt, Non-Iodized, 737 g	1	2-1 (DIS), 7-3 (Lab), 22-1 (TT)		Sugar, Granulated, 454 g	1	(INT), 2-4 (DIS), 7-3 (Lab), 14-2 (Lab)
	Sand, Fine, 1 kg	1	8-2 (DIS), 18-3 (DIS)	SS	Sunblock	1	2-1 (DIS)
	Seeds, Corn, 30 g	1	9-4 (Lab), 23-3 (DIS)				

KEY: **DIS**: Discover; **SYS**: Sharpen Your Skills; **TT**: Try This; **Lab**: Lab; **INT**: Introduction Lab
* Items designated **SS** are School Supplied.

Consumable Materials (continued)

*	Description	Qty per class	Textbook Section(s)	*	Description	Qty per class	Textbook Section(s)
	Sunprint Paper, 15 sheets	1	15-4 (Lab)		Timothy Hay, 4 oz	1	23-5 (Lab)
SS	Sunscreen, SPF 30	1	15-4 (Lab)		Toothpicks, Flat, box/750	1	8-2 (Lab), 10-3 (TT), 10-4 (DIS), 17-3 (Lab), 17-4 (TT), 19-2 (Lab), 20-4 (Lab)
SS	Sunscreen, SPF 4	1	15-4 (Lab)				
	Swab Applicators, Cotton, pkg/72	1	19-2 (Lab)				
	Tape, Adding Machine Roll, 2-1/4" Width (100 ft. length)	1	23-4 (DIS)	SS	Venus Fly Trap, Live	5	9-4 (DIS)
				SS	Vertebrate, Small, Live	5	14-1 (DIS)
	Tape, Brown Packing, 60 feet	1	1-1 (Lab), 7-3 (DIS)		Vinegar, 500 mL	2	15-2 (TT)
SS	Tape, Masking, 3/4" x 60 yd	5	3-2 (TT), 6-4 (TT), 6-4 (Lab), 7-3 (TT), 9-3 (Lab), 9-4 (Lab), 11-2 (DIS), 11-2 (TT), 13-4 (DIS), 14-2 (TT), 14-2 (Lab), 19-2 (TT), 22-2 (TT), 22-3 (DIS), 23-1 (SYS), 23-3 (DIS), 23-4 (Lab), 23-4 (DIS)	SS	Water Plants	5	12-2 (Lab)
				SS	Water, Aquarium	5	7-2 (Lab)
				SS	Water, Spring, gallon	2	10-4 (DIS), 11-1 (Lab), 20-4 (Lab), 22-1 (TT)
				SS	Water, Tap, Aged	5	7-2 (Lab)
				SS	Worm or Insect	5	6-2 (DIS)
					Yarn, Red, skein	1	23-1 (TT)
SS	Tape, Transparent Dispenser . Roll, 27.1 ft	1	6-3 (Lab), 13-2 (TT)	SS	Yeast, Dry Baking, 7 g pkg	6	2-4 (DIS), 2-5 (DIS), 7-3 (Lab)
				SS	Yogurt, Plain	1	6-3 (TT)

KEY: **DIS**: Discover; **SYS**: Sharpen Your Skills; **TT**: Try This; **Lab**: Lab; **INT**: Introduction Lab
* Items designated **SS** are School Supplied.

Master Materials List

Nonconsumable Materials

*	Description	Qty per class	Textbook Section(s)	*	Description	Qty per class	Textbook Section(s)
SS	Aquarium Dip Net	1	12-2 (Lab)		Cloth, Cotton, White, 18" x 22"	1	15-4 (Lab)
SS	Aquarium Filter Kit	1	12-2 (Lab)		Cloth, Flannel, White, 18" x 23"	1	15-4 (Lab)
SS	Aquarium Heater	1	12-2 (Lab)		Cloth, Polyester, 18" x 22"	1	15-4 (Lab)
SS	Aquarium Thermometer	1	12-2 (Lab)		Clothespin, Spring Type	5	5-1 (TT), 15-3 (DIS)
SS	Aquarium	1	12-2 (DIS), 12-2 (Lab), 14-1 (DIS)	SS	Coins	30	3-2 (DIS), 3-2 (TT), 17-3 (TT)
	Ball, Styrofoam, 1"	5	19-2 (TT)	SS	Cold Medication Packages, Empty	30	6-4 (DIS)
	Ball, Styrofoam, 2"	5	19-2 (TT)	SS	Compass with Pencil	5	19-3 (Lab)
SS	Bar Codes, set	5	4-3 (Lab)	SS	Container, Storage	5	10-4 (SYS), 10-4 (Lab)
	Beads, Plastic w/Hole, 13mm, pkg/125	1	12-1 (TT)		Coral Specimen	5	6-2 (DIS)
	Beads, Plastic, 3/8", pkg/144 (Assorted Colors)	1	3-2 (Lab), 4-1 (TT)		Cylinder, Graduated, Polypropylene, 10 mL	5	2-4 (DIS), 7-2 (Lab), 7-3 (Lab), 8-2 (DIS), 16-2 (Lab)
	Beaker, Pyrex, Low Form, Double Scale, 1000 mL	6	13-3 (Lab)		Cylinder, Graduated, Polypropylene, 100 mL	5	2-4 (Lab), 17-4 (TT), 18-1 (TT)
	Beaker, Pyrex, Low Form, 400 mL	5	7-3 (Lab), 8-1 (Lab)	SS	Dime	5	2-3 (SYS)
	Beaker, Pyrex, Low Form, 250 mL	5	22-2 (DIS)		Dowel, Wood, 8 x 1"	5	16-1 (Lab)
SS	Book	10	13-2 (DIS), 15-1 (DIS), 24-1 (Lab)		Droppers, Plastic, pkg/6	5	1-1 (Lab), 1-2 (SYS), 1-3 (Lab), 2-2 (TT), 2-5 (DIS), 6-3 (TT), 6-3 (Lab), 7-1 (DIS), 7-1 (TT), 8-2 (Lab), 8-3 (TT), 9-3 (Lab), 10-3 (TT), 10-4 (DIS), 10-4 (Lab), 11-5 (DIS), 16-1 (SYS), 17-3 (Lab), 18-1 (TT), 18-3 (Lab), 20-4 (Lab), 23-5 (Lab)
SS	Bottle, Plastic, Transparent, with Narrow Neck	5	18-1 (Lab)				
	Bottle, Spray Trigger, 16 oz	5	22-1 (Lab)				
SS	Bottle, Squeeze	5	17-2 (DIS)				
SS	Bottles, Narrow-necked, Small	25	7-3 (Lab)				
	Bowl, Opaque, 2 L	5	13-1 (TT), 24-1 (Lab)				
SS	Box	5	22-2 (Lab)	SS	Egg Beater	5	24-1 (Lab)
	Brush, Paint, 7"	5	10-4 (DIS)		Feather, White, 12–20 cm	5	13-1 (DIS)
	Capillary Tubes, Melting Point, vial/100	1	8-3 (DIS)		Flashlight, Plastic Size D	5	10-4 (Lab)
	Chips, Black, pkg/50	2	5-1 (SYS)		Flask, Erlenmeyer, Pyrex, 250 mL	15	2-4 (Lab)
	Chips, White, pkg/350	1	5-1 (SYS)		Forceps, Tweezers, Fine Tip, 115 mm	5	1-3 (Lab), 5-1 (TT), 13-1 (Lab), 14-2 (Lab)
SS	Clock	1	6-3 (Lab)				

KEY: **DIS**: Discover; **SYS**: Sharpen Your Skills; **TT**: Try This; **Lab**: Lab; **INT**: Introduction Lab
* Items designated **SS** are School Supplied.

Nonconsumable Materials (continued)

*	Description	Qty per class	Textbook Section(s)	*	Description	Qty per class	Textbook Section(s)
	Funnel, Plastic, 3.25"	5	17-4 (TT), 18-3 (DIS)	SS	Meter Stick, Wood	5	4-1 (DIS), 6-4 (Lab), 20-1 (Lab), 22-2 (TT), 23-4 (DIS)
SS	Glass	5	10-2 (DIS)		Mirrors, Plastic, 7.5 x 12.5 cm, pkg/6	1	1-1 (TT), 3-1 (Lab), 13-3 (DIS), 23-2 (DIS)
SS	Gravel, Aquarium, 10 lb	1	12-2 (Lab)				
SS	Hair Clips	5	5-1 (TT)	SS	Objects, Assortment	5	20-3 (DIS)
SS	Hair Dryer	5	1-1 (SYS)	SS	Pail, Plastic Utility	5	12-3 (TT), 13-3 (TT)
SS	Hole Punch	5	7-2 (DIS)		Pan, Aluminum Foil, 11 x 21 x 6 cm (bread pan)	5	1-3 (TT)
SS	Items, Desk, Assortment	5	6-1 (DIS)				
SS	Jar, Glass, Large	5	14-2 (Lab)		Pan, Aluminum Foil, 22.5 cm Diameter (pie pan)	5	1-3 (TT)
	Jar, Plastic, Wide-Mouth, 60 mL	5	11-3 (Lab), 23-5 (Lab)				
	Jar, Plastic, 16 oz, 89 mm Diameter	20	1-4 (DIS), 7-2 (Lab), 7-3 (TT), 9-1 (SYS), 11-3 (Lab), 15-2 (TT), 16-1 (Lab), 16-2 (DIS), 16-3 (TT), 17-4 (TT), 18-3 (DIS), 22-2 (DIS)		Pan, Aluminum Foil, 31 x 22 x 3 cm	5	10-4 (Lab), 14-2 (Lab), 15-3 (Lab), 23-3 (DIS)
					Pan, Aluminum Foil, 8" x 8" x 1-1/4"	5	24-1 (Lab)
				SS	Pan, Plastic Utility	10	17-1 (DIS), 17-2 (DIS)
	Lamp, Gooseneck	5	2-4 (Lab), 8-1 (Lab), 11-3 (Lab), 23-4 (Lab)		Paraffin Block	5	20-4 (Lab)
	Lid, Metal, 53 mm, Screw Type	5	23-5 (Lab)	SS	Penny	5	20-1 (DIS)
	Lid, Metal, 89 mm, Screw Type	20	1-4 (DIS), 7-2 (Lab), 15-2 (TT), 16-1 (Lab), 16-2 (DIS), 23-5 (Lab)		Petri Dish, Disposable Polystyrene, Sterile, 100 x 15 mm, pk/20	2	7-1 (SYS), 7-2 (DIS), 8-3 (DIS), 9-4 (Lab), 10-3 (TT), 10-4 (DIS), 11-1 (Lab), 17-3 (Lab)
	Magnet, Bar, Alnico w/Marked Poles, 3"	6	16-1 (Lab)				
	Magnifying Glasses, pkg/6	1	1-2 (DIS), 4-3 (Lab), 5-1 (DIS), 7-3 (DIS), 7-3 (TT), 8-1 (DIS), 8-2 (Lab), 8-3 (TT), 9-1 (TT), 9-2 (DIS), 9-2 (TT), 9-3 (DIS), 9-3 (Lab), 10-3 (DIS), 10-3 (TT), 10-4 (DIS), 11-3 (DIS), 11-3 (Lab), 12-2 (SYS), 13-1 (DIS), 13-1 (Lab), 13-1 (TT), 15-2 (DIS), 15-4 (DIS)		Pins, Bobby, card/60	1	5-1 (TT), 15-3 (TT)
					Pins, Straight, Steel, pkg/150	1	6-4 (Lab), 7-3 (TT)
				SS	Protractor	5	19-3 (Lab)
				SS	Puzzle, Jigsaw, Small	5	22-2 (TT)
				SS	Radio	1	7-2 (SYS)
				SS	Rock	5	15-2 (DIS)
				SS	Ruler	5	1-3 (DIS), 5-1 (DIS), 8-2 (Lab), 9-1 (SYS), 9-2 (DIS), 9-3 (DIS), 9-3 (Lab), 11-1 (Lab), 12-2 (Lab), 13-1 (Lab), 13-2 (DIS), 15-4 (Lab), 16-3 (DIS), 19-3 (Lab), 22-2 (DIS), 24-2 (Lab)

KEY: **DIS**: Discover; **SYS**: Sharpen Your Skills; **TT**: Try This; **Lab**: Lab; **INT**: Introduction Lab
* Items designated **SS** are School Supplied.

Master Materials List

Nonconsumable Materials (continued)

*	Description	Qty per class	Textbook Section(s)	*	Description	Qty per class	Textbook Section(s)
	Scalpel, Superior Grade, Forged Steel, 140 mm	5	9-3 (Lab)	SS	Socks Wool, Pair	5	13-3 (Lab)
SS	Scissors	5	1-2 (DIS), 2-3 (SYS), 4-2 (Lab), 5-1 (Lab), 6-4 (Lab). 9-4 (Lab), 10-2 (DIS), 10-3 (DIS), 11-3 (Lab), 13-2 (DIS), 13-3 (Lab), 14-2 (TT), 15-3 (Lab), 15-4 (Lab), 18-1 (Lab), 20-4 (Lab), 22-3 (DIS), 23-4 (Lab), 23-4 (TT)		Sponge 15 x 7.5 x 1.8 cm	5	10-3 (DIS), 14-2 (Lab)
					Sponge Natural 3 x 3", pkg/6	1	10-1 (DIS), 10-3 (DIS)
				SS	Staple Remover	5	15-4 (Lab)
					Starfish Shell, 4-6"	5	10-1 (DIS)
					Stopper, Rubber, Size 1, Solid, lb.	1	2-4 (DIS), 16-2 (Lab)
					Stopper, Rubber, Size 6, Solid, lb.	1	2-4 (Lab)
					Stopwatch, Electronic LED	5	5-1 (TT), 5-1 (SYS), 10-4 (Lab), 11-1 (Lab), 12-3 (DIS), 13-3 (Lab), 17-1 (DIS), 17-4 (TT), 22-2 (TT)
	Screen, Fiberglass, 12" x 26"	2	14-2 (Lab), 24-1 (Lab)				
	Seeds, Bean (White), 4 oz	1	24-3 (DIS)				
	Seeds, Bean, Kidney, lb	5	22-2 (DIS), 24-3 (DIS)	SS	Tags	30	8-4 (DIS)
	Seeds, Black Bean, lb	1	6-3 (DIS), 24-3 (DIS)		Tape Measure, 1.5 m, Dual Scale, pkg/6	1	18-1 (DIS), 20-3 (TT)
	Seeds, Soup Mix, 15 Bean, 20 oz Pkg	1	24-3 (DIS)		Teasing Needle, 145 mm with Wood Handle	5	13-1 (Lab)
	Shells, Assorted pkg/30	1	10-1 (DIS), 11-1 (DIS)		Test Tube Support, Wood, Holds 6–21 mm tubes, w/6 drying pins	5	2-4 (DIS), 16-2 (Lab), 18-3 (Lab)
	Slide - Allium (Onion) Root Tip, ls,	5	2-5 (Lab)				
	Slide - Animal Cell, General Type	5	1-3 (Lab)		Test Tube, 18 x 150 mm, 27 mL	30	2-4 (DIS), 8-1 (Lab), 16-2 (Lab), 18-1 (TT), 18-3 (Lab)
	Slide - Cork Section	5	1-2 (SYS)				
	Slide- Human Blood Smear	5	17-3 (DIS)		Thermometer, Red Liquid, -20°C to 110°C	15	11-1 (Lab), 13-3 (Lab), 15-4 (TT)
	Slide- Human Ovary, ls	3	21-2 (DIS)				
	Slide- Human Sperm Smear	3	21-2 (DIS)	SS	Timer	1	22-2 (DIS)
	Slide- Ovary cs, Mammal	2	21-2 (DIS)		Toy, Wind-Up	5	1-1 (DIS)
	Slide- Rat Sperm Smear	2	21-2 (DIS)		Tree Cross-Sections, 3 1/2-4 1/2" Diameter	5	24-2 (Lab)
	Slides, Plastic & Coverglass Set (Includes 72 plastic slides & 100 plastic coverglasses)	1	1-2 (SYS), 1-3 (Lab), 2-5 (DIS), 6-3 (TT), 7-1 (DIS), 7-1 (TT), 9-3 (Lab), 20-4 (Lab), 23-5 (Lab), 24-1 (Lab)	SS	Trowel	5	11-3 (Lab)
				SS	Umbrella	5	12-1 (DIS)
				SS	Watch or Clock with Second Hand	5	16-1 (Lab), 17-2 (Lab), 20-4 (Lab)
SS	Socks Cotton, pkg/2	3	12-4 (DIS)	SS	Watch, Ticking	5	20-3 (TT)

KEY: **DIS**: Discover; **SYS**: Sharpen Your Skills; **TT**: Try This; **Lab**: Lab; **INT**: Introduction Lab
* Items designated **SS** are School Supplied.

Equipment

*	Description	Qty per class	Textbook Section(s)	*	Description	Qty per class	Textbook Section(s)
SS	Apron, Vinyl	30	many activities	SS	Goggles, Chemical Splash - Class Set	1	many activities
SS	Balance, Triple Beam, Single Pan	5	1-1 (SYS), 16-1 (Lab), 21-3 (TT)	SS	Microscope	5	1-2 (DIS), 1-2 (SYS), 1-3 (Lab), 2-5 (DIS), 2-5 (Lab), 6-3 (TT), 7-1 (DIS), 7-1 (TT), 9-3 (Lab), 17-3 (DIS), 21-2 (DIS), 23-5 (Lab), 24-1 (Lab)
SS	Calculator	5	2-3 (DIS), 2-5 (Lab), 6-4 (Lab), 19-3 (Lab), 22-2 (Lab), 24-2 (Lab)				
SS	Gloves, Medium, Latex	1	13-3 (TT), 15-2 (TT). 15-3 (Lab), 15-4 (DIS)				
				SS	Stereomicroscope	5	20-4 (Lab)

KEY: **DIS**: Discover; **SYS**: Sharpen Your Skills; **TT**: Try This; **Lab**: Lab; **INT**: Introduction Lab
* Items designated **SS** are School Supplied.

PRENTICE HALL
SCIENCE EXPLORER

Life Science

Print Resources

Student Edition
Annotated Teacher's Edition
Unit Resource Books, including:
- Chapter Project Support
- Lesson Plans
- Section Summaries
- Review and Reinforce Worksheets
- Enrich Worksheets
- Student Edition Lab Worksheets
- Complete Answer Keys

Chapter and Unit Tests
Performance Assessment
Standardized Test Preparation Book
Laboratory Manual, Student Edition
Laboratory Manual, Teacher's Edition
Inquiry Skills Activity Book
Student-Centered Science Activity Books
Guided Reading and Study Workbook
Reading in the Content Area with Literature Connections
Science Explorer Interdisciplinary Explorations
Prentice Hall Interdisciplinary Explorations series
Product Testing Activities by Consumer Reports™
How to Manage Instruction in the Block
How to Assess Student Work
Teacher's ELL Handbook: Strategies for English Language
Learners

Media and Technology

Interactive Student Tutorial CD-ROM
Computer Test Bank Book with CD-ROM
Resource Pro® (Lesson Plans and Teaching
Resources on CD-ROM)
Internet Site at **www.phschool.com**
(includes www.PlanetDiary.com)
Color Transparencies
Section Summaries on Audio CD
Spanish Section Summaries on Audio CD
and Book
Probeware Lab Manual with CD-ROM
Lab Activity Video Library
Science Explorer Videotape Library
Science Explorer Spanish Videotape Library
Science Explorer Videodisc Library
Interactive Earth CD-ROM
Interactive Physics Software

Materials Kits

Consumable Materials Kit
Nonconsumable Materials Kit
Materials List CD-ROM

Acknowledgments

Excerpt on page 178 from *James Herriot's Dog Stories* by James Herriot. Copyright © 1986 by James Herriot. Reprinted by permission of St. Martin's Press, New York.

Excerpt on pages 466–467 from *Dragons and Dynasties: An Introduction to Chinese Mythology* by Yuan Ke. Selected and translated by Kim Echlin and Nie Zhixong and Penguin Books, 1993. First published in the People's Republic of China by Foreign Languages Press, Beijing, 1991–1993. Copyright © Foreign Languages Press, 1991, 1992, 1993.

Excerpt on page 784 from *The Amateur Naturalist* by Gerald Durrell. Copyright © 1982 by Gerald Durrell and Hermann Blume Ediciones, Madrid, Spain. Reprinted by permission of Alfred A. Knopf, Inc.

ISBN 0-13-062643-0
1 2 3 4 5 6 7 8 9 10   05 04 03 02 01

Prentice
Hall

Cover: A brilliantly colored macaw
flies gracefully through the sky.

Teacher's Edition ISBN 0-13-062646-5

Program Authors

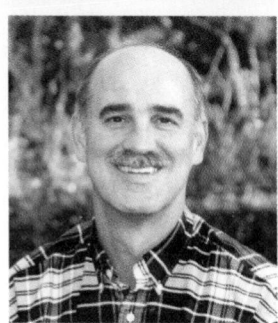

Michael J. Padilla, Ph.D.
Professor
Department of Science Education
University of Georgia
Athens, Georgia

Michael Padilla is a leader in middle school science education. He has served as an editor and elected officer for the National Science Teachers Association. He has been principal investigator of several National Science Foundation and Eisenhower grants and served as a writer of the National Science Education Standards.

As lead author of *Science Explorer,* Mike has inspired the team in developing a program that meets the needs of middle grades students, promotes science inquiry, and is aligned with the National Science Education Standards.

Ioannis Miaoulis, Ph.D.
Dean of Engineering
College of Engineering
Tufts University
Medford, Massachusetts

Martha Cyr, Ph.D.
Director, Engineering
  Educational Outreach
College of Engineering
Tufts University
Medford, Massachusetts

Science Explorer was created in collaboration with the College of Engineering at Tufts University. Tufts has an extensive engineering outreach program that uses engineering design and construction to excite and motivate students and teachers in science and technology education.

Faculty from Tufts University participated in the development of *Science Explorer* chapter projects, reviewed the student books for content accuracy, and helped coordinate field testing.

Book Authors

Elizabeth Coolidge-Stoltz, M.D.
Medical Writer
North Reading, Massachusetts

Donald Cronkite, Ph.D.
Professor of Biology
Hope College
Holland, Michigan

Dawn Graff-Haight, Ph.D., CHES
Associate Professor, Health
  Education
Linfield College
McMinnville, Oregon

Fred Holtzclaw
Science Teacher
Oak Ridge High School
Oak Ridge, Tennessee

Jan Jenner, Ph.D.
Science Writer
Talladega, Alabama

Linda Cronin Jones, Ph.D.
College of Education
University of Florida
Gainesville, Florida

Contributing Writers

Douglas E. Bowman
Health/Physical Education Teacher
Welches Middle School
Welches, Oregon

James Robert Kaczynski, Jr.
Science Teacher
Barrington Middle School
Barrington, Rhode Island

Evan P. Silberstein
Science Teacher
Spring Valley High School
Spring Valley, New York

Patricia M. Doran
Science Teacher
Rondout Valley Junior High School
Stone Ridge, New York

Susan Offner
Biology Teacher
Milton High School
Milton, Massachusetts

Joseph Stukey, Ph.D.
Department of Biology
Hope College
Holland, Michigan

Theresa Holtzclaw
Former Science Teacher
Clinton, Tennessee

Warren Phillips
Science Teacher
Plymouth Community
   Intermediate School
Plymouth, Massachusetts

Thomas R. Wellnitz
Science Teacher
The Paideia School
Atlanta, Georgia

Jorie Hunken
Science Consultant
Woodstock, Connecticut

Reading Consultant

Bonnie B. Armbruster, Ph.D.
Department of Curriculum
   and Instruction
University of Illinois
Champaign, Illinois

Interdisciplinary Consultant

Heidi Hayes Jacobs, Ed.D.
Teacher's College
Columbia University
New York, New York

Safety Consultants

W. H. Breazeale, Ph.D.
Department of Chemistry
College of Charleston
Charleston, South Carolina

Ruth Hathaway, Ph.D.
Hathaway Consulting
Cape Girardeau, Missouri

Content Reviewers

Jack W. Beal, Ph.D.
Department of Physics
Fairfield University
Fairfield, Connecticut

W. Russell Blake, Ph.D.
Planetarium Director
Plymouth Community
   Intermediate School
Plymouth, Massachusetts

Howard E. Buhse, Jr., Ph.D.
Department of Biological Sciences
University of Illinois
Chicago, Illinois

Dawn Smith Burgess, Ph.D.
Department of Geophysics
Stanford University
Palo Alto, California

A. Malcolm Campbell, Ph.D.
Assistant Professor
Davidson College
Davidson, North Carolina

Elizabeth A. De Stasio, Ph.D.
Associate Professor of Biology
Lawrence University
Appleton, Wisconsin

John M. Fowler, Ph.D.
Former Director of Special Projects
National Science Teachers
   Association
Arlington, Virginia

Jonathan Gitlin, M.D.
School of Medicine
Washington University
St. Louis, Missouri

Dawn Graff-Haight, Ph.D., CHES
Department of Health, Human
   Performance, and Athletics
Linfield College
McMinnville, Oregon

Deborah L. Gumucio, Ph.D.
Associate Professor
Department of Anatomy and
   Cell Biology
University of Michigan
Ann Arbor, Michigan

William S. Harwood, Ph.D.
Dean of University Division and
   Associate Professor of Education
Indiana University
Bloomington, Indiana

Cyndy Henzel, Ph.D.
Department of Geography
   and Regional Development
University of Arizona
Tucson, Arizona

Greg Hutton
Science and Health
   Curriculum Coordinator
School Board of Sarasota County
Sarasota, Florida

Susan K. Jacobson, Ph.D.
Department of Wildlife Ecology
   and Conservation
University of Florida
Gainesville, Florida

Judy Jernstedt, Ph.D.
Department of Agronomy and
   Range Science
University of California, Davis
Davis, California

John L. Kermond, Ph.D.
Office of Global Programs
National Oceanographic and
   Atmospheric Administration
Silver Spring, Maryland

David E. LaHart, Ph.D.
Institute of Science and
   Public Affairs
Florida State University
Tallahassee, Florida

Joe Leverich, Ph.D.
Department of Biology
St. Louis University
St. Louis, Missouri

Dennis K. Lieu, Ph.D.
Department of Mechanical
   Engineering
University of California
Berkeley, California

Cynthia J. Moore, Ph.D.
Science Outreach Coordinator
Washington University
St. Louis, Missouri

Joseph M. Moran, Ph.D.
Department of Earth Science
University of Wisconsin–Green Bay
Green Bay, Wisconsin

Joseph Stukey, Ph.D.
Department of Biology
Hope College
Holland, Michigan

Seetha Subramanian
Lexington Community College
University of Kentucky
Lexington, Kentucky

Carl L. Thurman, Ph.D.
Department of Biology
University of Northern Iowa
Cedar Falls, Iowa

Edward D. Walton, Ph.D.
Department of Chemistry
California State Polytechnic
   University
Pomona, California

Robert S. Young, Ph.D.
Department of Geosciences and
   Natural Resource Management
Western Carolina University
Cullowhee, North Carolina

Edward J. Zalisko, Ph.D.
Department of Biology
Blackburn College
Carlinville, Illinois

Activity Field Testers

Nicki Bibbo
Russell Street School
Littleton, Massachusetts

Connie Boone
Fletcher Middle School
Jacksonville Beach, Florida

Rose-Marie Botting
Broward County School District
Fort Lauderdale, Florida

Colleen Campos
Laredo Middle School
Aurora, Colorado

Elizabeth Chait
W. L. Chenery Middle School
Belmont, Massachusetts

Holly Estes
Hale Middle School
Stow, Massachusetts

Laura Hapgood
Plymouth Community
    Intermediate School
Plymouth, Massachusetts

Sandra M. Harris
Winman Junior High School
Warwick, Rhode Island

Jason Ho
Walter Reed Middle School
Los Angeles, California

Joanne Jackson
Winman Junior High School
Warwick, Rhode Island

Mary F. Lavin
Plymouth Community
    Intermediate School
Plymouth, Massachusetts

James MacNeil, Ph.D.
Concord Public Schools
Concord, Massachusetts

Lauren Magruder
St. Michael's Country
    Day School
Newport, Rhode Island

Jeanne Maurand
Glen Urquhart School
Beverly Farms, Massachusetts

Warren Phillips
Plymouth Community
    Intermediate School
Plymouth, Massachusetts

Carol Pirtle
Hale Middle School
Stow, Massachusetts

Kathleen M. Poe
Kirby-Smith Middle School
Jacksonville, Florida

Cynthia B. Pope
Ruffner Middle School
Norfolk, Virginia

Anne Scammell
Geneva Middle School
Geneva, New York

Karen Riley Sievers
Callanan Middle School
Des Moines, Iowa

David M. Smith
Howard A. Eyer Middle School
Macungie, Pennsylvania

Derek Strohschneider
Plymouth Community
    Intermediate School
Plymouth, Massachusetts

Sallie Teames
Rosemont Middle School
Fort Worth, Texas

Gene Vitale
Parkland Middle School
McHenry, Illinois

Zenovia Young
Meyer Levin Junior
    High School (IS 285)
Brooklyn, New York

Contents

Life Science

Introduction to Life Science ....**xxii**

Unit 1 Cells and Heredity

Chapter 1 **Cells: The Building Blocks of Life** **16**
  1 What Is Life? 18
  2 Discovering Cells 27
  3 Looking Inside Cells 34
  4 Integrating Earth Science: The Origin of Life 44

Chapter 2 **Cell Processes and Energy** **50**
  1 Integrating Chemistry: Chemical Compounds in Cells 52
  2 The Cell in Its Environment 56
  3 Photosynthesis 61
  4 Respiration 66
  5 Cell Division 72

Chapter 3 **Genetics: The Science of Heredity** **84**
  1 Mendel's Work 86
  2 Integrating Mathematics: Probability and Genetics 94
  3 The Cell and Inheritance 102
  4 The DNA Connection 107

Chapter 4 **Modern Genetics** **116**
  1 Human Inheritance 118
  2 Human Genetic Disorders 125
  3 Integrating Technology: Advances in Genetics 132

Chapter 5 **Changes Over Time** **144**
  1 Darwin's Voyage 146
  2 Integrating Earth Science: The Fossil Record 157
  3 Other Evidence for Evolution 165

**Interdisciplinary Exploration:
  Dogs—Loyal Companions** **174**

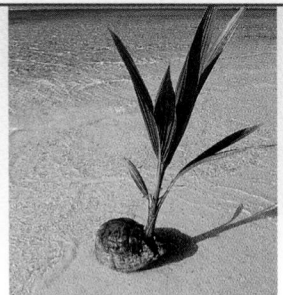

Unit 2   From Bacteria to Plants

Chapter 6   **Bacteria and Viruses** **180**
    1 Classifying Organisms 182
    2 The Six Kingdoms 189
    3 Bacteria 192
    4 Integrating Health: Viruses 204

Chapter 7   **Protists and Fungi** **216**
    1 Protists 218
    2 Integrating Environmental Science: Algal Blooms 228
    3 Fungi 233

Chapter 8   **Introduction to Plants** **246**
    1 The Plant Kingdom 248
    2 Mosses, Liverworts, and Hornworts 256
    3 Ferns and Their Relatives 261
    4 Integrating Technology: Feeding the World 266

Chapter 9   **Seed Plants** **272**
    1 The Characteristics of Seed Plants 274
    2 Gymnosperms 284
    3 Angiosperms 289
    4 Integrating Chemistry: Plant Responses and Growth 297

Nature of Science:
    From Plants to Chemicals **304**

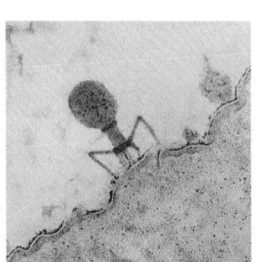

PRENTICE HALL
SCIENCE
EXPLORER
LIFE SCIENCE

Unit 3 Animals

Chapter 10 Sponges, Cnidarians, and Worms **308**
  1 What Is an Animal? 310
  2 Integrating Mathematics: Symmetry 315
  3 Sponges and Cnidarians 320
  4 Worms 327

Chapter 11 Mollusks, Arthropods, and Echinoderms ...**338**
  1 Mollusks 340
  2 Arthropods 346
  3 Insects 354
  4 Integrating Chemistry:
      The Chemistry of Communication 362
  5 Echinoderms 365

Chapter 12 Fishes, Amphibians, and Reptiles **372**
  1 Integrating Earth Science: Evolution of Vertebrates 374
  2 Fishes 381
  3 Amphibians 389
  4 Reptiles 395

Chapter 13 **Birds and Mammals** **408**
   1 Birds 410
   2 Integrating Physics: The Physics of Bird Flight 420
   3 What Is a Mammal? 423
   4 Diversity of Mammals 431

Chapter 14 **Animal Behavior** **440**
   1 Integrating Psychology:
       Why Do Animals Behave As They Do? 442
   2 Patterns of Behavior 450

Interdisciplinary Exploration: The Secret of Silk **462**

PRENTICE HALL
SCIENCE EXPLORER
LIFE SCIENCE

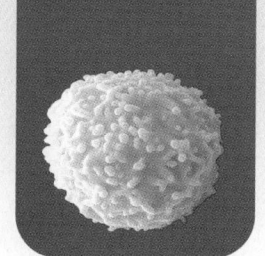

Unit 4 Human Biology and Health

Chapter 15 **Bones, Muscles, and Skin** **470**
  1 Integrating Health:
    Body Organization and Homeostasis 472
  2 The Skeletal System 480
  3 The Muscular System 488
  4 The Skin 494

Chapter 16 **Food and Digestion** **504**
  1 Integrating Chemistry: Food and Energy 506
  2 The Digestive Process Begins 518
  3 Final Digestion and Absorption 526

Chapter 17 **Circulation** **534**
  1 The Body's Transportation System 536
  2 A Closer Look at Blood Vessels 543
  3 Blood and Lymph 549
  4 Integrating Health: Cardiovascular Health 556

Chapter 18 **Respiration and Excretion** **564**
  1 The Respiratory System 566
  2 Integrating Health: Smoking and Your Health 576
  3 The Excretory System 581

Chapter 19 **Fighting Disease** **590**
   1 Infectious Disease 592
   2 The Body's Defenses 596
   3 Integrating Health: Preventing Infectious Disease 605
   4 Noninfectious Disease 612

Chapter 20 **The Nervous System** **620**
   1 How the Nervous System Works 622
   2 Divisions of the Nervous System 628
   3 The Senses 636
   4 Integrating Health: Alcohol and Other Drugs 644

Chapter 21 **The Endocrine System and Reproduction** ...**656**
   1 The Endocrine System 658
   2 The Male and Female Reproductive Systems 663
   3 Integrating Health: The Human Life Cycle 669

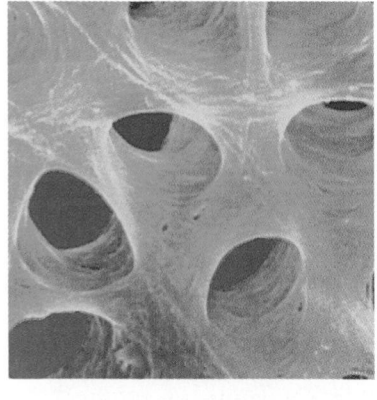

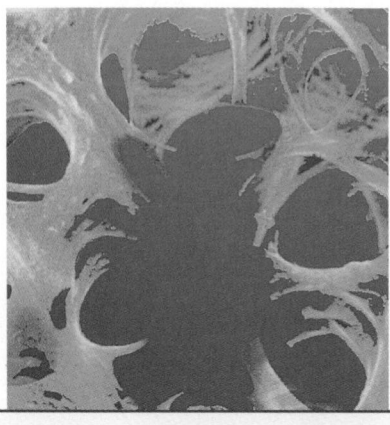

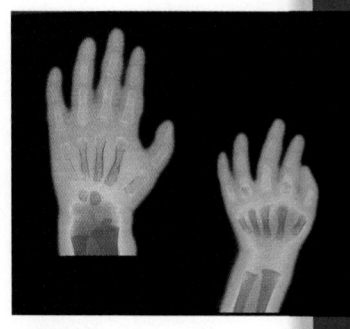

PRENTICE HALL
SCIENCE EXPLORER
LIFE SCIENCE

Unit 5   Ecology

Nature of Science: Protecting Desert Wildlife **682**

Chapter 22 **Populations and Communities** **686**

    1 Living Things and the Environment 688
    2 Integrating Mathematics: Studying Populations 695
    3 Interactions Among Living Things 703

Chapter 23 **Ecosystems and Biomes** **714**

    1 Energy Flow in Ecosystems 716
    2 Integrating Chemistry: Cycles of Matter 723
    3 Biogeography 728
    4 Earth's Biomes 734
    5 Succession 748

Chapter 24 **Living Resources** **754**

    1 Integrating Environmental Science: Environmental Issues ..756
    2 Forests and Fisheries 762
    3 Biodiversity 768

Interdisciplinary Exploration: African Rain Forests **780**

Reference Section

    Skills Handbook **786**
        Think Like a Scientist 786
        Making Measurements 788
        Conducting a Scientific Investigation 790
        Thinking Critically 792
        Organizing Information 794
        Creating Data Tables and Graphs 796
    Appendix A: Laboratory Safety **799**
    Appendix B: Using the Microscope **802**
    Glossary **804**
    Index **818**
    Acknowledgments **830**

Activities

Inquiry Activities

CHAPTER PROJECT

Opportunities for long-term inquiry

Chapter 1: Mystery Object 17
Chapter 2: Egg-speriment With a Cell 51
Chapter 3: All in the Family 85
Chapter 4: A Family Portrait 117
Chapter 5: Life's Long Calendar 145
Chapter 6: Be a Disease Detective 181
Chapter 7: A Mushroom Farm 217
Chapter 8: Become a Moss Expert 247
Chapter 9: Cycle of a Lifetime 273
Chapter 10: Alive and Well 309
Chapter 11: Going Through Changes 339
Chapter 12: Animal Adaptations 373
Chapter 13: Bird Watch 409
Chapter 14: Learning New Tricks 441
Chapter 15: On the Move 471
Chapter 16: What's on Your Menu? 505
Chapter 17: Travels of a Red Blood Cell ...535
Chapter 18: Get the Message Out 565
Chapter 19: Stop the Invasion 591
Chapter 20: Tricks and Illusions 621
Chapter 21: A Precious Bundle 657
Chapter 22: What's a Crowd? 687
Chapter 23: Breaking It Down 715
Chapter 24: Variety Show 755

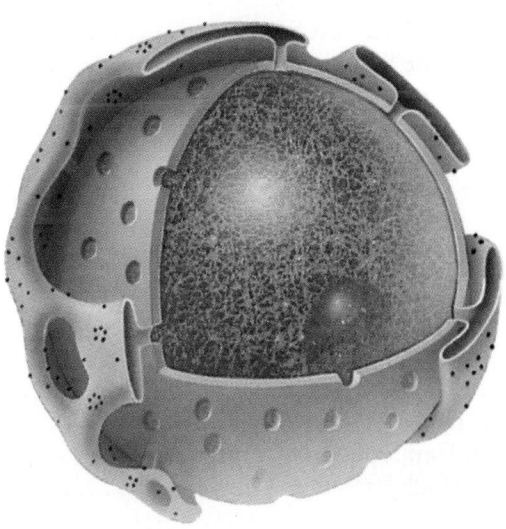

DISCOVER

Exploration and inquiry before reading

Is It Living or Nonliving? 17
Is Seeing Believing? 27
How Large Are Cells? 34
How Can the Composition of Air Change? ...44
What Is a Compound? 52
How Do Molecules Move? 56
Where Does the Energy Come From? 61
What Is a Product of Respiration? 66
What Are the Cells Doing? 72
What Does the Father Look Like? 86
What's the Chance? 94
Which Chromosome is Which? 102
Can You Crack the Code? 107
How Tall Is Tall? 118
How Many Chromosomes? 125
What Do Fingerprints Reveal? 132

DISCOVER
continued

How Do Living Things Vary? 146
What Can Fossils Tell You? 157
How Can You Classify Species? 165
Can You Organize a Junk Drawer? 182
Which Organism Goes Where? 189
How Fast Do Bacteria Multiply? 192
Can You Cure a Cold? 204
What Lives in a Drop of Water? 218
How Can Algal Growth Affect Pond Life? . . .228
Do All Molds Look Alike? 233
What Do Leaves Reveal About Plants? 248
Will Mosses Absorb Water? 256
How Quickly Can Water Move Upward? 261
Will There Be Enough to Eat? 266
Which Plant Part Is It? 274
Are All Leaves Alike? 284
What Is a Fruit? 289
Can a Plant Respond to Touch? 297
Is It an Animal? 310
How Many Ways Can You Fold It? 315
How Do Natural and Synthetic Sponges
    Compare? 320
What Can You See in a Worm? 327
How Can You Classify Shells? 340
Will It Bend and Move? 346
What Kinds of Appendages
    Do Insects Have? .354
Can You Match the Scents? 362
How Do Sea Stars Hold On? 365
How Is an Umbrella Like a Skeleton? 374
How Does Water Flow Over a Fish's Gills? . .381
What's the Advantage of Being Green? 389
How Do Snakes Feed? 395

What Are Feathers Like? 410
What Lifts Airplanes and Birds
    Into the Air? 420
What Are Mammals' Teeth Like? 423
How Is a Thumb Useful? 431
What Can You Observe About a
    Vertebrate's Behavior? 442
What Can You Express Without Words? 450
How Do You Lift Books? 472
Hard as a Rock? 480
How Do Muscles Work? 488
What Can You Observe About Skin? 494
Food Claims—Fact or Fiction? 506
How Can You Speed Up Digestion? 518
Which Surface Is Larger? 526
How Hard Does Your Heart Work? 536
How Does Pressure Affect the
    Flow of Blood? 543
What Kinds of Cells Are in Blood? 549
Which Foods Are "Heart Healthy"? 556
How Big Can You Blow Up a Balloon? 566
What Are the Dangers of Smoking? 576
How Does Filtering a Liquid Change
    What Is in It? 581
How Does a Disease Spread? 592
Which Pieces Fit Together? 596
What Substances Can Kill Pathogens? 605
What Happens When Airflow Is
    Restricted? 612
How Simple Is a Simple Task? 622
How Does Your Knee React? 628
What's in the Bag? 636
How Can You Best Say No? 644
What's the Signal? 658
What's the Big Difference? 663
How Many Ways Does a Child Grow? 669
What's in the Scene? .688
What's the Bean Population? 695
How Well Can You Hide a Butterfly? 703
Where Did Your Dinner Come From? 716
Are You Part of a Cycle? 723
How Can You Move a Seed? 728
How Much Rain Is That? 734
What Happened Here? 748
How Do You Decide? 756
What Happened to the Tuna? 762
How Much Variety Is There? 768

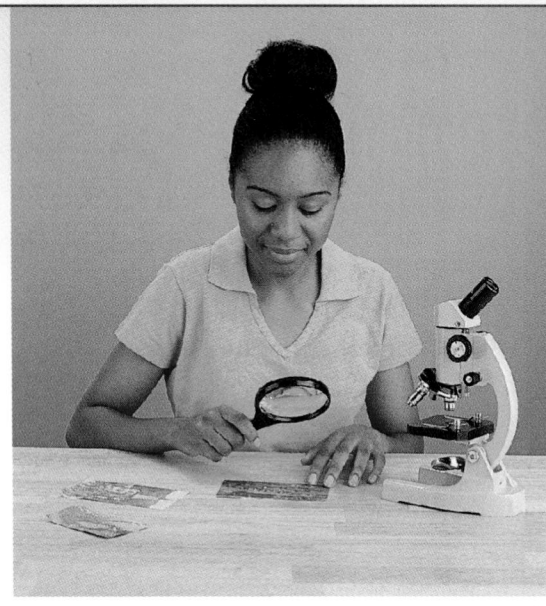

Sharpen your *Skills*

Practice of specific science inquiry skills

Designing an Experiment 24
Observing 32
Inferring 63
Interpreting Data 75
Predicting 109
Communicating 137
Inferring 151
Calculating 160
Drawing Conclusions 166
Observing 186
Graphing 195
Predicting 225
Interpreting Data 249
Calculating 280
Inferring 313
Communicating 331
Observing 332
Classifying 342
Graphing 356
Communicating 382
Drawing Conclusions 403
Classifying 427
Predicting 444
Classifying 484
Predicting 508

Creating Data Tables 546
Calculating 579
Posing Questions 594
Drawing Conclusions 613
Controlling Variables 630
Designing Experiments 642
Communicating 646
Graphing 667
Calculating 696
Classifying 709
Observing 718
Developing Hypotheses 724
Inferring 739
Interpreting Data 741
Communicating 760
Calculating 765
Communicating 774

TRY THIS

Reinforcement of key concepts

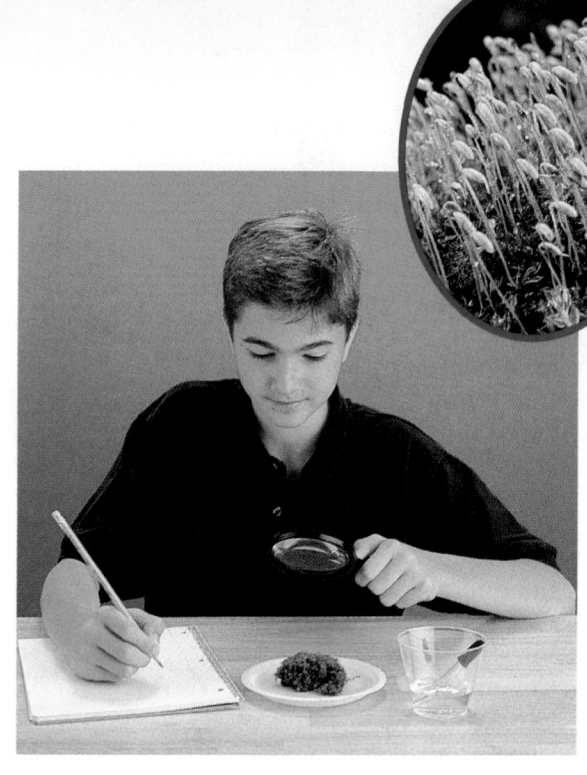

React 20
Gelatin Cell 40
What's That Taste? 54
Diffusion in Action 58
Modeling Mitosis 74
Coin Crosses 97
The Eyes Have It 120
Girl or Boy? 122
Bird Beak Adaptations 149
Preservation in Ice 159
Bacteria for Breakfast 197
Modeling a Virus 207
Feeding Paramecia 222
Making Spore Prints 235
Spreading Spores 236
Examining a Fern 262
The In-Seed Story 276
The Scoop on Cones 286
Hydra Doing? 324
Pill Bugs—Wet or Dry? 350
Bead-y Bones 376
Webbing Through Water 392
Eggs-amination 417
It's Plane to See 421
Insulated Mammals 425
Line Them Up 447
Worker Bees 453

How Is a Book Organized? 473
Soft Bones? 482
Get a Grip 490
Sweaty Skin 497
Modeling Peristalsis 521
Break Up! 527
Caught in the Web 552
Blocking the Flow 557
Do You Exhale Carbon Dioxide? 571
Stuck Together 603
Why Do You Need Two Eyes? 637
Tick! Tick! Tick! 640
Way to Grow! 671
With or Without Salt? 690
Elbow Room 699
Weaving a Food Web 721
Desert Survival 737

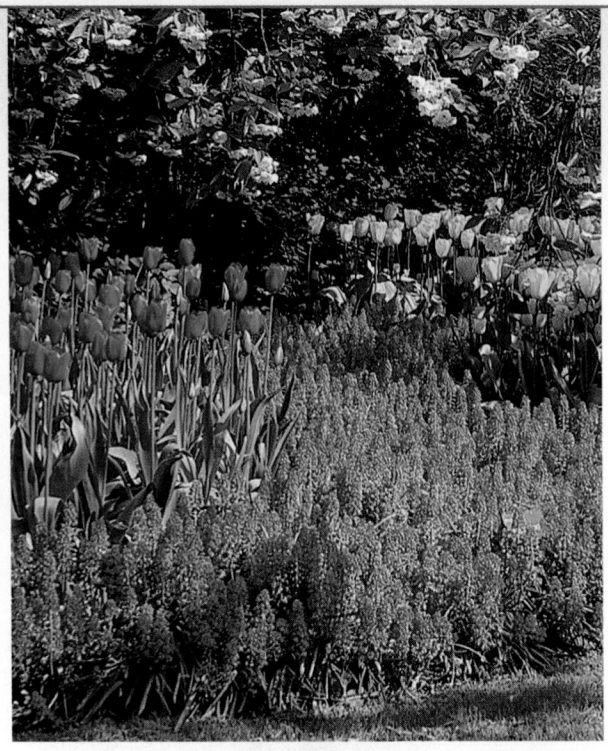

Skills Lab

In-depth practice of inquiry skills

Keeping Flowers Fresh 10
Please Pass the Bread! 26
A Magnified View of Life 43
Multiplying by Dividing 80
Take a Class Survey .92
Make the Right Call .100
Nature at Work 152
Telltale Molecules 170
How Many Viruses Fit on a Pin? 212
What's for Lunch? 238
Eye on Photosynthesis 254
Masses of Mosses 260
Which Way Is Up? 300
Earthworm Responses 334
A Snail's Pace 345
Soaking Up Those Rays 400
Looking at an Owl's Leftovers 414
Become a Learning Detective 449
A Look Beneath the Skin 493
As the Stomach Churns 524
Heart Beat, Health Beat 548
A Breath of Fresh Air 575
Causes of Death, Then and Now 610
Ready or Not 627
Growing Up 678
A World in a Bottle .694
Change in a Tiny Community 746
Tree Cookie Tales 767

Real-World Lab

Everyday application of science concepts

Gases in Balance 71
Family Puzzles 130
Guilty or Innocent? .140
Do Disinfectants Work? 202
An Explosion of Life 231
A Close Look at Flowers 294
A Tale Told By Tracks 318
What's Living in the Soil? 360
Home Sweet Home .388
Keeping Warm 429
One For All 458
Sun Safety 498
Iron for Breakfast 517
Do You Know Your A-B-O's? 555
Clues About Health .584
The Skin as a Barrier 598
With Caffeine or Without? 648
Counting Turtles 701
Biomes in Miniature 732
Is Paper a Renewable Resource? 761

Science at Home

Family involvement in science exploration

Building Blocks 42
Organic Compounds in Food 55
Fermentation in Bread .70
The Guessing Game 99
Grocery Genetics 138
Make Your Mark 164
Kitchen Classification 188
Helpful Bacteria 201
Kitchen Algae 227
State Flowers 253
Seed Germination 283
Front-End Advantages 317
Edible Mollusks 344
Chemicals and Insect Pests 364
Focus on Backbones .380
Mammals' Milk 428
Exercising Safely 487
Protection From the Sun 500
Healthy Hearts 560
Modeling Alveoli 574
Vaccination History 609
Stimulus and Response 626
Word Estimates 700
Sock Walk 731
Succession 750
Renewable Survey 766

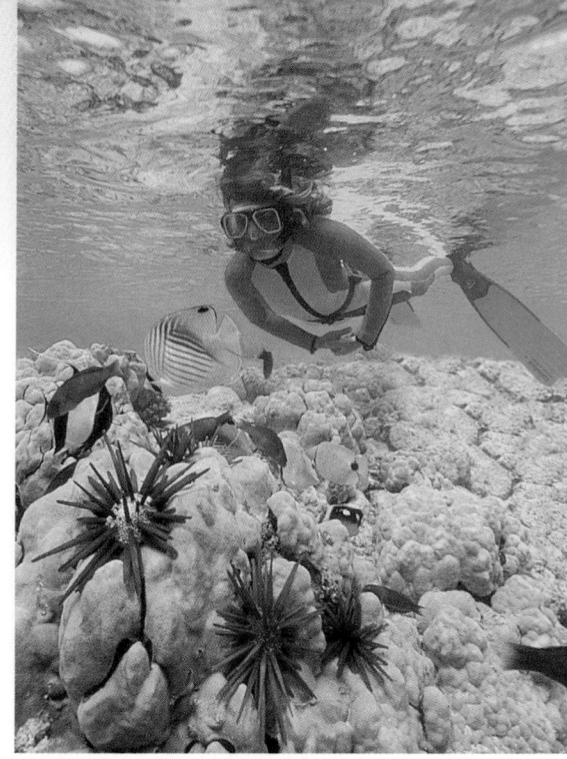

Interdisciplinary Activities

Science and History

The Microscope—Improvements Over Time . .30
Bacteria and Foods of the World 198
Discovering Vertebrate Fossils 378
Cardiovascular Advances in the
    Twentieth Century .558
Fighting Infectious Disease 606
Making a Difference .758

Science and Society

Who Should Have Access to Genetic
    Test Results? 139
Eutrophication—The Threat to Clear,
    Clean Water 232
Coral Reefs in Danger 326
Animals and Medical Research 430
Advertising and Nutrition 530
Should People Be Required to Wear
    Bicycle Helmets? 635
Animal Overpopulation: How Can
    People Help? 702

Math Toolbox

Calculating Probability 95
Calculating Percent .509
Pulse Rate 544
Inequalities 698

Connection

Language Arts 36
Social Studies 69
Language Arts 88
Social Studies 127
Social Studies 154
Language Arts 184
Language Arts 241
Social Studies 258
Visual Arts 291
Language Arts 322
Social Studies 358
Language Arts 391
Visual Arts 411
Social Studies 456
Language Arts 478
Visual Arts 486
Social Studies 510
Language Arts 540
Social Studies 572
Social Studies 600
Visual Arts 631
Social Studies 676
Language Arts 692
Social Studies 730
Social Studies 763

EXPLORING

Visual exploration of concepts

Careers in Life Science .12
The Experiments of Redi and Pasteur 22
Plant and Animal Cells 38
The Cell Cycle 76
Meiosis 105
Protein Synthesis 110
A Pedigree 124
Genetic Engineering 135
Life's History 162
How Viruses Multiply 208
Protozoans 220
Plant Adaptations .250
A Leaf 279
The Life Cycle of a Gymnosperm 287
The Life Cycle of an Angiosperm 292
A Sponge 321
The Life Cycle of a Dog Tapeworm 329
A Snail 343
A Crayfish 351
Insect Metamorphosis 357
A Sea Star 367
A Bony Fish 385
A Frog 393
A Lizard 398
A Bird 413
Birds 418
Placental Mammals .434
A Honeybee Society 455
Movable Joints 485
The Food Guide Pyramid 514
The Heart 539
Blood Cells 550
The Respiratory System 569
A Kidney 582
The Immune Response 602
The Path of a Nerve Impulse 625
The Effects of Alcohol 651
The Endocrine System 660
Defense Strategies 706
A Food Web 720
Endangered Species .772

xxi

Introduction to Life Science

Objectives	Time	Student Edition Activities	Other Activities	
◆ Explain the nature of scientific inquiry. ◆ Describe the skills used by scientists in their work. ◆ Describe the importance of hypotheses and controlled experiments. ◆ Explain the importance of laboratory safety.	2–3 periods/ 1–1½ blocks	**Skills Lab: Designing Experiments** Keeping Flowers Fresh, pp. 10–11	TE TE TE TE LM	Addressing Naive Conceptions, p. 5 Building Inquiry Skills; Developing Hypotheses, p. 6 Demonstration, p. 11 Including All Students, p. 13 Introduction, "Investigating Seeds"

For Standard or Block Schedule The Resource Pro® CD-ROM gives you maximum flexibility for planning your instruction for any type of schedule. Resource Pro® contains Planning Express®, an advanced scheduling program, as well as the entire contents of the Teaching Resources and the Computer Test Bank.

Meeting the National Science Education Standards and AAAS Benchmarks

National Science Education Standards	Benchmarks for Science Literacy	Unifying Themes
Science As Inquiry (Content Standard A) ◆ **Design and conduct a scientific investigation** Students design an experiment about using sugar to keep cut flowers fresh. *(Skills Lab)* ◆ **Use appropriate tools and techniques to gather, analyze, and interpret data** Students collect, graph, and analyze data about cut-flower freshness. *(Skills Lab)* ◆ **Think critically and logically to make the relationships between evidence and explanation** Students use their data to draw a conclusion about the relationship between sugar and cut-flower freshness. *(Skills Lab)* ◆ **Communicate scientific procedures and explanations** Students describe their experimental designs. *(Skills Lab)* **History and Nature of Science** (Content Standard G) ◆ **Science as a human endeavor** Many different types of people are involved in life science and its related fields. ◆ **Nature of science** Life scientists use observation and experimentation to explain the living world around them.	**1B Scientific Inquiry** Students investigate the scientific process. **1C The Scientific Enterprise** Life scientists work in many different places throughout the world. **12D Communication Skills** Students organize data in graphs and identify the relationships they indicate. *(Skills Lab)*	◆ **Systems and Interactions** Environmental factors such as temperature, light, and the amount of available water affect plant growth.

PLANNING GUIDE

Program Resources	Assessment Strategies	Media and Technology
UR Introduction Lesson Plan, p. 2 **UR** Introduction Section Summary, p. 3 **UR** Introduction Review and Reinforce, p. 4 **UR** Introduction Enrich, p. 5 **UR** Introduction Skills Lab, pp. 6–7	**TE** Ongoing Assessment, pp. 5, 7, 9, 13 **TE** Performance Assessment, p. 11 **SE** Study Guide/Assessment, pp. 14–15 **PA** Introduction Performance Assessment, pp. 2–4 **CUT** Introduction Test, pp. 2–3 **CTB** Introduction Test	Science Explorer Internet Site at www.phschool.com Audio CD, English-Spanish Summary Introduction Computer Test Bank, Introduction Test

Key:
- **SE** Student Edition
- **CTB** Computer Test Bank
- **ISAB** Inquiry Skills Activity Book
- **GSW** Guided Study Workbook

- **TE** Teacher's Edition
- **PTA** Product Testing Activities by *Consumer Reports*
- **RCA** Reading in the Content Area
- **PA** Performance Assessment

- **UR** Unit Resources
- **LM** Laboratory Manual
- **IES** Interdisciplinary Explorations Series
- **CUT** Chapter and Unit Tests

Student Edition Activities Planner

ACTIVITY	Time (minutes)	Materials *Quantities for one work group*	Skills
Skills Lab, p. 10–11	40 min Day 1, 5–10 min Days 2–5	**Consumable** cut flowers, water, sugar **Nonconsumable** plastic cups, spoon	**Designing Experiments**

A list of all materials required for the Student Edition activities can be found on pages T25–T33. You can obtain information about ordering materials by calling 1-800-848-9500 or by accessing the Science Explorer Internet site at **www.phschool.com**.

Take It to the Net

 *Interactive text at www.phschool.com*

Science Explorer comes alive with iText.

- **Complete student text** is accessible from any computer with Internet access or a CD-ROM drive.
- **Animations, simulations, and videos** enhance student understanding and retention of concepts.
- **Self-tests and online study tools** assess student understanding.

STAY CURRENT with **SCIENCE NEWS®**

Find out the latest research and information about life science at: **www.phschool.com**

Go to **www.phschool.com** and click on the Science icon. Then click on <u>Science Explorer: Life, Earth, and Physical Science</u> under PH@school.

Disease Detective Solves Mystery

Focus on Public Health

This four-page feature introduces the process of scientific inquiry by involving students in a high-interest, magazine-like feature about a working scientist, physician Cindy Friedman. Using Dr. Friedman's investigation of the source of a salmonella outbreak, the article focuses on persistence, reasoning, and questioning as key elements of scientific inquiry.

Bacteria are presented in Chapter 6. However, students need not have any previous knowledge of that chapter's content to understand and appreciate this article.

Scientific Inquiry

♦ Before students read the article, let them read the title, examine the pictures, and read the captions on their own. Then ask: **What questions came into your mind as you looked at these pictures?** (*Students might suggest questions such as "How did the Colorado Health Department know that the children were sick?"; "Why did they suspect reptiles?"; and "Do all reptiles carry salmonella?"*) Point out to students that just as they had questions about what they were seeing, scientists too have questions about what they observe.

DISEASE DETECTIVE SOLVES
MYSTERY

The Colorado Health Department had a problem.

Seven children had become sick with diarrhea, stomach cramps, fever, and vomiting.

Within days, another 43 people had the same symptoms.

Tests indicated that they all had become infected with salmonella. Salmonella are bacteria that are usually transmitted through foods such as contaminated meat or eggs.

How did these children become infected with salmonella? To find the answer, Colorado health officials called in Dr. Cindy Friedman. Dr. Friedman works at the Centers for Disease Control and Prevention (CDC), a United States government agency that tracks down and studies the transmission of diseases throughout the world.

Cindy Friedman studies outbreaks of diseases in groups of people rather than in individuals. Her specialty is infectious diseases, illnesses that spread from one organism to another. She has investigated outbreaks of disease in such places as rural Bolivia in South America, the Cape Verde Islands off the coast of Africa, and a Vermont farm.

Dr. Cindy Friedman is a physician and investigator in the Foodborne and Diarrheal Diseases Branch of the Centers for Disease Control and Prevention (CDC). The youngest of three sisters, Dr. Friedman is originally from Brooklyn, New York. In her spare time she enjoys horseback riding.

Background

Facts and Figures The Centers for Disease Control and Prevention (CDC) is an agency of the United States Public Health Service. Scientists at CDC perform research to determine how diseases originate and to find ways to control them. The CDC also provides information and training to public health workers. Although CDC is based in Atlanta, Georgia, the agency also conducts international programs.

Salmonella is a type of bacteria commonly found in poultry and eggs. One kind of salmonella causes gastroenteritis. People with this type of food poisoning experience abdominal pain, fever, nausea, vomiting, and diarrhea. There are several things people can do to avoid becoming infected, such as cooking chicken and eggs thoroughly and cleaning cooking surfaces after preparing raw chicken.

An Interview With Dr. Cindy Friedman

Q *How did you get started in science?*

A When I was young, we always had pets around the house and a lot of books about medicine and science. I wanted to be a veterinarian. In college I decided that I loved animals but didn't want to practice medicine on them. I'd rather keep them as a hobby and devote my career to human medicine.

Q *How did you come to specialize in infectious diseases?*

A Out of all the subjects I studied in medical school, I liked microbiology the best—learning about different viruses and bacteria. Then, when I did my medical training in New Jersey, we had a lot of patients from Latin America. So I saw quite a few tropical and exotic diseases, which further heightened my interest.

Q *What do you enjoy about your job?*

A I really like being able to help more than one patient at a time. We do this by figuring out the risk factors for a disease and how to prevent people from getting it. Sometimes the answer is complicated, like adding chlorine to the water Sometimes it's simple measures, like washing your hands or cooking your food thoroughly

Q *What clues did you have in the Colorado case?*

A At first, state investigators thought the bacteria came from some contaminated food. But when they questioned the children, they couldn't identify one place where they had all eaten.

Q *How did you find out what experiences the children had in common?*

A The investigators did a second set of interviews and learned that the children had all visited the zoo the week before they got sick. They didn't eat the same food at the zoo. But they all went to a special exhibit at the reptile house.

How did the children get infected?

Did the salmonella come from infected food?

What common place had the children visited?

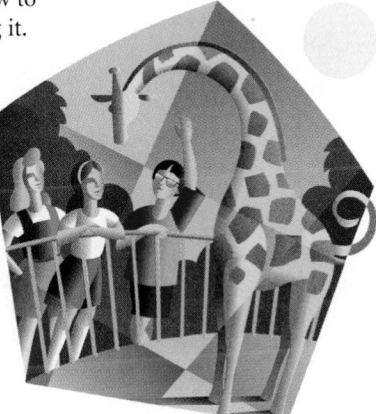

• Explain that public health is the science of preventing disease through organized community efforts.
• Encourage students to tell what they already know about salmonella. Ask students who have ever had food poisoning to describe how they felt. Ask them how they deduced what food had caused their food poisoning.
• Ask students to describe other outbreaks of disease they recall that affected many people. *(Answers may vary from the Black Plague to an outbreak of head lice.)*
• Encourage interested students to find out more about salmonella and ways to avoid being infected by it. Have students make a list of foods that may carry the bacterium. Ask students to share their findings with the class.
• Ask: **Why is it important that doctors in the United States be familiar with the causes of tropical and exotic diseases?** *(Answers may vary. Sample: Tourists may bring these diseases to the United States.)*
• Ask: **Why was it important for the investigators to find out how the children became infected?** *(Answers may vary. Samples: To keep other people from getting sick, to satisfy their curiosity, to learn something new about salmonella, and to prevent future outbreaks.)*
• If students seem particularly interested in the salmonella outbreak, share the information in the Background below. Students with pet reptiles may be particularly concerned. Also suggest that they consult library books to learn more about how scientists track down the cause of disease outbreaks. (See Further Reading, page 3.)

Background

When scientists at CDC examined the Komodo dragon enclosure, they found that touching the wooden barrier was the most likely cause of the infection outbreak. The type of salmonella involved in this outbreak had an unusual appearance. For this reason, scientists could be fairly certain that the bacteria that infected the people came from the reptile display.

The people who became infected were unusually ill. Some victims were hospitalized, and some were still sick nearly a month later.

Only one of the four lizards was infected with the salmonella. The scientists were not able to determine how it became infected. They examined the lizard's food—rats—but found no trace of salmonella there.

1

◆ Ask: **Why did the scientists suspect the reptile exhibit?** *(They knew that reptiles can carry salmonella.)*

◆ Challenge interested students to find out more about Komodo dragons. Ask students to find out how large the lizard on page 2 could be. Invite students to share their findings with the class.

◆ Ask students to think of some event they attended a week ago. Ask them: **Could you recall where you stood, what you touched, and what you ate and drank?** *(Most students would probably not be able to remember.)* The answers to such questions are exactly the kind of information that scientists such as Dr. Friedman would need to track down a disease. Discuss with students why this could make the job of a "disease detective" challenging.

◆ Ask: **Exactly how did all the infected children become infected with the bacteria?** *(By touching a wooden barrier on which the bacteria were growing.)* Help students to realize that any object, such as a barrier, a doorknob, or a stair rail that many people touch every day, is likely to be contaminated with some kind of bacteria. Help students recognize that because many bacteria are spread through touching, hand-washing is an effective way to prevent infection.

◆ Have students use a dictionary or encyclopedia to find out what Dr. Friedman meant by the term *culture*. Because *culture* has several different meanings, students will need to look for the meaning that makes the most sense in context.

Q *Did you think the exhibit might be a new clue?*

A Yes. It was a clue because reptiles frequently carry the salmonella bacteria without becoming ill. In the special exhibit, there were four baby Komodo dragons, meat-eating lizards from the island of Komodo in Indonesia. They were displayed in a pen filled with mulch, surrounded by a wooden barrier about two feet high. We tested the Komodo dragons and found that one of them had salmonella bacteria. But it wasn't a petting exhibit, so I couldn't understand how the children got infected.

Q *How did you gather new data?*

A I questioned the children who became ill and compared their answers with those of children who didn't become ill. I asked about their behavior at the exhibit—where they stood, what they touched, and whether they had anything to eat or drink there. I also asked all the children if they washed their hands after visiting the exhibit. Those who did destroyed the bacteria. It was only the children who didn't wash their hands who became ill.

Q *How did you figure out the source of contamination?*

A I found that anyone who touched the wooden barrier was much more likely to have gotten sick. Children would go up to the barrier and put their hands on it. Then some of them would put their hands in their mouth or would eat without washing their hands first. Those were the children who became infected with salmonella.

Could reptiles provide the clue?

Why did some children get infected and not others?

The Komodo dragon is the largest lizard species in existence. It is found on Komodo Island in Indonesia, and is nearly extinct.

2

Background

The CDC warns that salmonella can be found in the feces of pets, especially those with diarrhea. Reptiles are particularly likely to be infected with salmonella, even if they appear healthy. People should always wash their hands after handling reptiles. The CDC also advises that households with small children and infants should not have reptiles (including turtles) as pets. The CDC suggests that reptiles be kept separated from each other so that they cannot spread salmonella among themselves.

People who have no exposure to reptiles can catch salmonella from contaminated foods. Undercooked meat, poultry, and eggs are especially likely to contain salmonella. Hands, kitchen utensils, and work surfaces that come in contact with raw meat should be washed with soap and warm water as soon as possible.

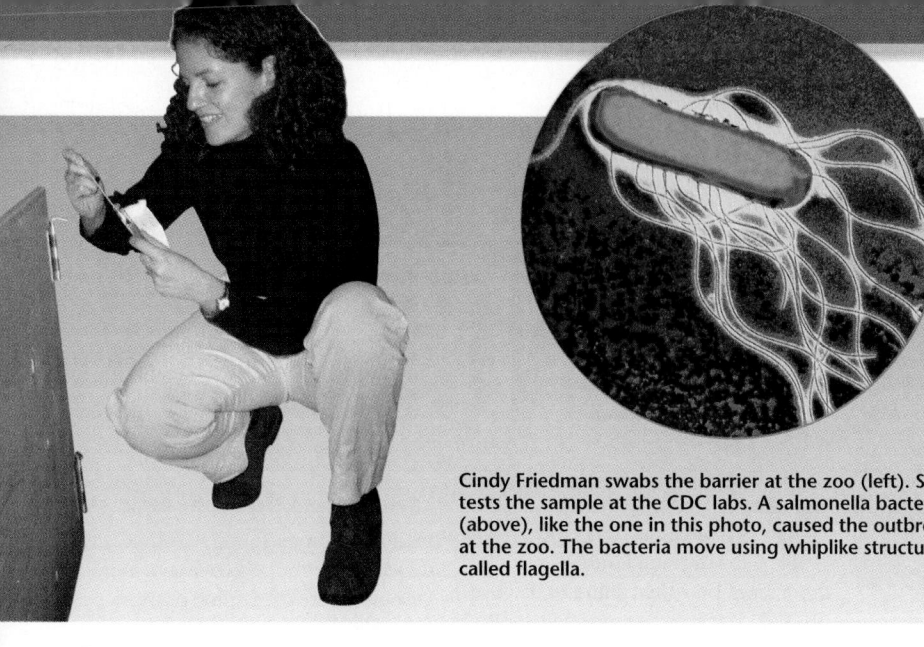

Cindy Friedman swabs the barrier at the zoo (left). She tests the sample at the CDC labs. A salmonella bacterium (above), like the one in this photo, caused the outbreak at the zoo. The bacteria move using whiplike structures called flagella.

◆ Challenge students to brainstorm some ways the zoo could set up the exhibit while protecting the visitors. *(Samples: Raise the barrier so the lizards can't lean on it; replace the wooden barrier with a glass window; build a second barrier so the lizards and visitors do not contact the same barrier; wash the barrier on a regular basis; distribute alcohol wipes at the exhibit.)*

◆ Students who have pet reptiles may wish to learn more about what precautions they should take to avoid infection. Challenge interested students to make a poster or brochure for reptile owners that describes ways that owners can protect themselves from infection.

In Your Journal Have students make a concept map showing all the possible causes of the outbreak and how the scientists narrowed down the options by asking questions. Ask: **If you knew nothing about salmonella but you had to track down the source of an outbreak, what would you do first?** *(Learn all I could about what salmonella is and the conditions and environments in which it grows)* Extend the discussion by asking: **What kind of person do you think would make a good disease investigator?** *(Student answers will vary. Samples: curious, logical, persistent, detailed)*

Q *How did you test your hypothesis?*

A We took cultures—swabs from the top of the barrier where the children put their hands. When we tested those cultures in the lab, we found salmonella bacteria.

Q *What did you conclude about the bacteria on the barrier?*

A The infected Komodo dragon left its droppings in the mulch and the animals walked in it. Then they would stand on their hind legs, bracing themselves by putting their front paws on top of the barrier.

Q *What recommendations did you make?*

A We didn't want to tell zoos not to have reptile exhibits, because they're a good thing. And children should be able to get close to the animals. But at this particular exhibit, the outbreak could have been prevented with a double barrier system, so that the reptiles and the children couldn't touch

the same barrier. And hand-washing is really important. Zoos should have signs instructing people to wash their hands after going to that kind of exhibit. In homes and schools with pet reptiles, hand-washing is very important, too.

Q *What's it like being a disease detective?*

A It's more the old-fashioned idea of medicine. What I do is examine the patients and listen to the stories they tell—where they've traveled, what they ate, and what they were exposed to. Then I try to figure out what caused their illness.

How can the zoo prevent future infections?

In Your Journal

Review the scientific process that Dr. Friedman used to solve the case of salmonella infections. What makes her a disease detective? Write a paragraph or two about the skills and character traits that Cindy Friedman needs to track down the source of an infectious disease.

READING STRATEGIES

Further Reading

◆ Preston, Richard. *The Hot Zone.* Anchor Books, 1995.
◆ Garrett, Laurie. *The Coming Plague: Newly Emerging Diseases in a World Out of Balance.* Penguin USA, 1995.

◆ Regis, Edward. *Virus Ground Zero: Stalking the Killer Viruses With the Centers for Disease Control.* Pocket Books, 1996.
◆ Radetsky, Peter. *The Invisible Invaders: Viruses and the Scientists Who Pursue Them.* Little, Brown and Company, 1995.

What is Science?

Objectives

After completing this introduction, students will be able to
- explain the nature of scientific inquiry;
- describe the skills used by scientists in their work;
- describe the importance of hypotheses and controlled experiments;
- explain the importance of laboratory safety.

Key Terms science, scientific inquiry, observation, data, inference, hypothesis, variable, manipulated variable, responding variable, controlled experiment, scientific theory

1 Engage/Explore

Activating Prior Knowledge

Students have read about Dr. Cindy Friedman and how she solved the mystery of the disease that the Colorado school children had contracted. Ask students: **Can you think of another problem that a scientist might help solve?** *(Sample answer: Why do some plants in the classroom grow better than others?)*

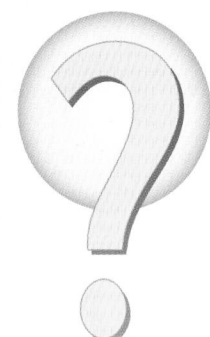

What is SCIENCE?

GUIDE FOR READING

- **What skills do scientists use to find answers and solve problems?**
- **What are the general rules of laboratory safety?**

Reading Tip
As you read, write a definition, in your own words, of each boldfaced term you encounter.

You might think of Dr. Friedman as a detective trying to piece together clues in a mystery. You might think of her as a problem solver, coming up with solutions to help people. Or you might think of her as a biologist, a scientist who studies living things. Which is correct? All of them are! In her job Dr. Friedman plays all of these roles. Dr. Friedman is a scientist.

Science is a way of learning about the natural world. Science also includes all of the knowledge gained through the process of exploring the natural world. This body of knowledge is always growing and changing as scientists ask new questions and explore new ideas.

Another term for the diverse ways in which scientists study the natural world is **scientific inquiry.** Scientific inquiry is used every day by people studying plants and animals, by physicians, and by many others. You may not realize it, but you use this process too, whether you're trying to help a sick pet feel better or to find the best place to plant flowers. Science, as you'll learn, is everywhere.

Thinking Like a Scientist

Dr. Friedman used many skills as she solved the salmonella mystery. You have probably used some of these same skills, while others may be new to you. **Some of the skills that scientists use are posing questions, making observations and inferences, developing hypotheses, designing experiments, making measurements and collecting data, interpreting data, drawing conclusions, and communicating.** Scientists do not always use all of these skills in every investigation.

Figure 1 In studying this pond, these students are using many of the same skills that scientists use.

4

READING STRATEGIES

Reading Tip Suggest that students scan these pages and write each boldface term on an index card. Then, as students read, they should write each definition on the appropriate card. You may wish to use these cards as the basis of a "vocabulary bee." Sample definition: Manipulated variable—in an experiment, the factor that you change to test the hypothesis.

Program Resources

- **Unit 1 Resources** Introduction Lesson Plan, p. 2; Introduction Section Summary, p. 3

Media and Technology

 Audio CD English-Spanish Summary Introduction

Posing Questions Scientific inquiry often begins with a question or a problem. In Dr. Friedman's case, the problem she faced was: What caused the children to get sick?

You can probably think of a question or problem that you would like to investigate further. For example, if you have ever had a garden, you may have wondered whether fertilizer would help your tomato plants grow. Your investigation would begin with the following question: Does adding fertilizer to tomato plants help them grow larger?

Making Observations and Inferences Dr. Friedman used the skill of observation to gather information about the children and the zoo. The skill of **observation** involves using one or more of your senses—sight, hearing, touch, smell, and sometimes taste—to gather information and collect data. **Data** are the facts, figures, and other evidence gathered through observations. Dr. Friedman collected data on such things as the number of children who became infected and the types of animals in the zoo.

Often, a scientist's observations and data lead to an **inference,** which is an interpretation of an observation that is based on evidence or prior knowledge. Some scientists working with Dr. Friedman inferred that the children got sick from eating contaminated food. This inference was based on their knowledge that contaminated food was the cause of salmonella outbreaks they had seen before.

Because an inference is only one of many possible interpretations, it is not a fact. In this case the scientists' inference turned out to be wrong.

Figure 2 Have you ever wondered if fertilizer can help the plants in a garden grow faster? This question can be answered using scientific inquiry.

Like a scientist, you also draw inferences from observations you make. For example, you may notice that plants in your neighbor's garden are growing unusually tall and looking healthy. Because you observed your neighbor applying fertilizer to her plants, you may infer that fertilizer makes tomato plants grow taller. Your inference could prove to be true. Or maybe your neighbor's plants are getting more water and sunlight.

☑ *Checkpoint What senses can the skill of observation involve?*

Figure 3 Imagine that you are a scientist studying these dolphins. *Observing* List five observations that you can make about the dolphins.

Introduction **5**

Thinking Like a Scientist

Addressing Naive Conceptions

The idea of inference may be difficult for some students. Have a student observe a classroom object that only he or she can see. After the student makes three observations about that object, have the other students infer what the object is. Continue adding observations until the object is identified. learning modality: verbal **learning modality: verbal**

ACTIVITY

Including All Students

Some students may not understand that inferring goes beyond observing. An observation or a series of observations combined with the observer's prior knowledge or experience makes an inference. Have students write an equation or statement relating observations and inference. *(Sample answer: observation(s) + experience = inference)* You may wish to have students give examples of observations and inferences. **learning modality: logical/mathematical**

Answers to Self-Assessment

Caption Question

Figure 3 Answers will vary, and can include: dolphins are jumping; dolphins have smooth skin; dolphins are in a group; dolphins have tails and fins; and dolphins appear to be smiling.

☑ *Checkpoint*

Observation can involve sight, hearing, touch, smell, and sometimes taste.

Ongoing Assessment

Writing List two skills that a scientist might use to begin a scientific inquiry. *(Sample answer: Posing questions, making observations and inferences)*

5

Thinking Like a Scientist, continued

Building Inquiry Skills: Developing Hypotheses

ACTIVITY

Set up a situation in the classroom that allows students the opportunity to evaluate a few different hypotheses. Have students assess each choice for validity. For example, show students a dish with a small amount of water in it. Start a hypothesis by saying, **If the water is left out overnight, then….** Invite volunteers to suggest possible endings. *(Accept all reasonable hypotheses. Sample answer: there will be less water the next day.)*
learning modality: logical/ mathematical

Inquiry Challenge

Have students look through magazines or newspapers to identify hypotheses. Then have students decide how they could test each hypothesis. For example, a toothpaste ad might say, "If you brush your teeth with Brand X toothpaste, your teeth will be brighter." *(Try the toothpaste for a period of time to see if the ad is true.)*
learning modality: logical/ mathematical

Developing Hypotheses The next step is to develop a **hypothesis,** which is a possible explanation for a set of observations or answer to a scientific question. In science, a hypothesis must be something that can be tested. A hypothesis can be worded as an *If…then…* statement. For example, you could develop the following hypothesis:

If fertilizer is added to the soil surrounding a tomato plant, then the plant will grow taller.

When a hypothesis is worded in this way, the phrase that begins with the word *If* can serve as a rough outline of your experiment. The phrase that begins with the word *then* suggests a possible outcome of the experiment.

A hypothesis can either be supported or disproved by an experiment. If an experiment supports a hypothesis, many more trials are needed before a hypothesis can be accepted as true.

Designing an Experiment to Test a Hypothesis After you have stated your hypothesis, you are ready to plan an experiment to test it. You know that you will need to grow a tomato plant, give it fertilizer, and observe its growth. But how will you know how tall it would have grown if you hadn't given it fertilizer? To answer this question, you will need another plant to compare it to.

You will need to grow two identical plants under the exact same conditions, except for the amount of fertilizer the plants receive. All other **variables,** or factors that can change in an experiment, need to be the same for both plants. Some other variables are the amounts of water, sunlight, and soil. By keeping all of these variables the same, you will know that any difference in plant growth must be due to the fertilizer alone.

Figure 4 A hypothesis is a possible explanation for a set of observations or answer to a scientific question. *Developing Hypotheses Suppose that the salmon population in an area dwindled. Write a hypothesis about how the grizzly bear population might be affected.*

Figure 5 The tomato plant experiment is an example of a controlled experiment. The two plants received the same amounts of water and sunlight.
Applying Concepts What is the manipulated variable in this experiment?

The one variable that is changed to test a hypothesis is called the **manipulated variable** (sometimes called the independent variable). In your experiment, the manipulated variable would be the fertilizer.

The factor that changes because of the manipulated variable is called the **responding variable** (sometimes called the dependent variable). The height of the tomato plant is the responding variable.

An experiment in which all of the variables except for one remain the same is a **controlled experiment.** You would plant two similar tomato plants in identical pots. You would then add fertilizer to the soil around one tomato plant while leaving the soil around the other tomato plant unfertilized. Both plants would receive the same amounts of water and sunlight throughout the experiment.

✓ *Checkpoint* *What is meant by a controlled experiment?*

Making Measurements and Collecting Data As you observe the tomato plants growing, how will you determine how much each plant has grown? You could measure the height of both plants daily. Or you could select a frequency, such as once a week, to collect your data.

Scientists have developed a standard system of measurement, called the International System of Units, which is abbreviated as SI (for the French, *Système International d'Unités).* SI is based on the metric system of measurement, which is used in many countries of the world. By using SI, scientists from all over the world can communicate their detailed findings with one another.

Can you imagine what it would be like if everyone in the world spoke one language? It would make communication much easier. That's what it's like for scientists using SI. Before you conduct any experiments, review Making Measurements on pages 788–789 of the Skills Handbook.

Figure 6 This scientist is using an instrument called calipers to measure the length of a Virginia rail's beak. By using SI to make scientific measurements, scientists all over the world have a standard "language" of measurement.

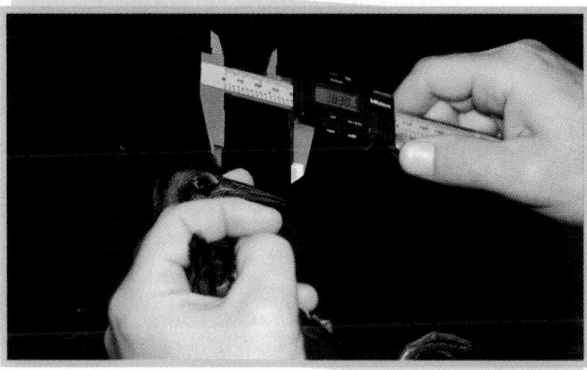

Building Inquiry Skills: Controlling Variables

Ask students: **What happens to milk that is left out of the refrigerator all day?** *(It spoils, or turns sour.)* **Will the same thing happen to milk that is kept in the refrigerator?** *(Yes, but it will take longer.)* **What factor is different in these two cases?** *(The temperature at which the milk is kept)* Discuss with students how they would investigate the relationship between the temperature of the milk and the time it takes for the milk to spoil. Focus on the variables that must be kept constant, such as the amount of milk, kind of container, whether the container is open or closed, and so forth.
learning modality: logical/ mathematical

Answers to Self-Assessment

Caption Question

Figure 4 Sample answer: The grizzly bear population would decrease.
Figure 5 fertilizer

✓ *Checkpoint*

An experiment in which all of the variables except one remain the same

Ongoing Assessment

Oral Presentation Call on students to define or give examples of the terms *manipulated variable* and *responding variable.*

Building Inquiry Skills: Interpreting Data

Have students look at the data table and graph. Ask them to identify the height difference between the two plants on each recorded day. *(Day 0, 0 cm; Day 3, 0 cm; Day 6, 0 cm; Day 9, 1 cm; Day 12, 2 cm; Day 15, 4 cm; Day 18, 5 cm; Day 21, 6 cm)* Ask: **Are both plants growing?** *(Yes)* **Which plant is growing faster?** *(The fertilized plant)* **learning modality: logical/mathematical**

Addressing Naive Conceptions

After looking at the data table or graph, some students may expect the growth of the fertilized plant to continue indefinitely at its rapid rate. Explain that at some point the growth of both plants will taper off as the plant begins to put its nutrients and energy into producing flowers and then fruit. **learning modality: logical/mathematical**

	Height of Tomato Plants (cm)	
Day	Unfertilized plant	Fertilized plant
Day 0	30	30
Day 3	30	30
Day 6	31	31
Day 9	32	33
Day 12	33	35
Day 15	34	38
Day 18	35	40
Day 21	36	42

Figure 7 The data table shows the height of the two tomato plants over a three-week period. A graph was created using this data. *Interpreting Graphs How does the growth of the fertilized plant compare with the growth of the unfertilized plant?*

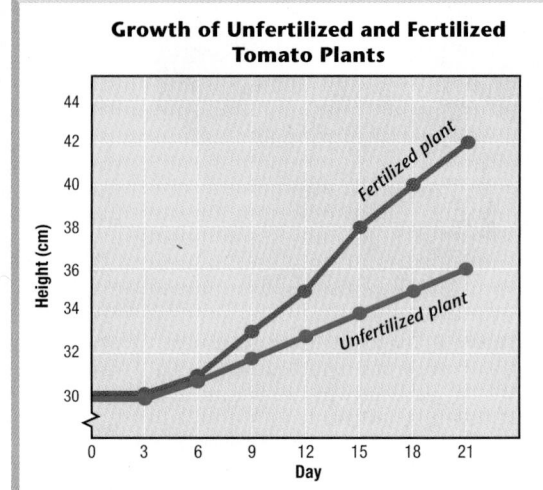

Interpreting Data After all of the data are collected, they need to be interpreted. Interpreting data that you have collected in an experiment means arranging the results in an organized way.

Look at Figure 7 to see how graphing data helps you visualize and organize your findings. By organizing data in this way, you can look for patterns and trends. For example, you can see that the two tomato plants were the same height through the first six days of the experiment. The fertilized plant then grew faster than the unfertilized plant over the next fifteen days. To learn more about data tables and graphs, look at pages 796–798 in the Skills Handbook.

✓ *Checkpoint Why is it necessary to organize the data collected in an experiment?*

Drawing Conclusions After you have organized and interpreted your data, the next step is to draw a conclusion, which means summing up what you learned from the investigation. To draw a conclusion, you need to decide whether or not the data support your original hypothesis.

In the tomato experiment, the data showed that fertilizer did help the tomato plant grow taller. You could say that the evidence supports your hypothesis.

Evidence can either support a hypothesis or prove it to be false. Even if you conclude that your hypothesis was false, you will have learned something important from your experiment. You may have new questions that you want to investigate further. Conclusions often lead to new questions, which lead to new experiments.

The words *inference* and *conclusion* have the same meaning in everyday language, and one term is often defined by using the other term. In science, however, *inference* is often used as the broader term, while *conclusion* is used for the culminating, formal inference of an experiment. For example, researchers often refer to the conclusion of their study. In keeping with this distinction, this book describes *drawing a conclusion* as summarizing whether or not the data collected during an experiment supports the hypothesis tested.

Communicating in Science

For scientists, an important step in the inquiry process is communicating their results and conclusions to other scientists. Communication is the sharing of ideas and experimental findings with others through writing and speaking.

Scientists share their conclusions with one another by writing articles in scientific journals, by attending scientific meetings, and by using the Internet. The Internet is very useful to scientists in communicating with one another and with nonscientists.

When scientists communicate their conclusions to nonscientists, it is important that they use nontechnical terms that can be easily understood. In life science, communicating with nonscientists is especially important. Many experimental findings directly affect the health and safety of people. In these cases, findings must be communicated clearly and quickly.

Communication with the public was very important in Dr. Friedman's work. Once she discovered the source of the salmonella, Dr. Friedman communicated the need for double railings and the importance of hand washing. Her communication skills may have helped prevent future salmonella infections.

Scientific Theories

Often a set of experiments is repeated by many scientists, who all arrive at the same conclusions. This can lead to the development of a scientific theory. A **scientific theory** is a well-tested concept that explains a wide range of observations. You will learn about many important theories in life science as you read this book.

Although a theory is based on thousands of experiments done by different scientists, future testing can still prove a theory to be incorrect. In that case, scientists may revise the theory or abandon it.

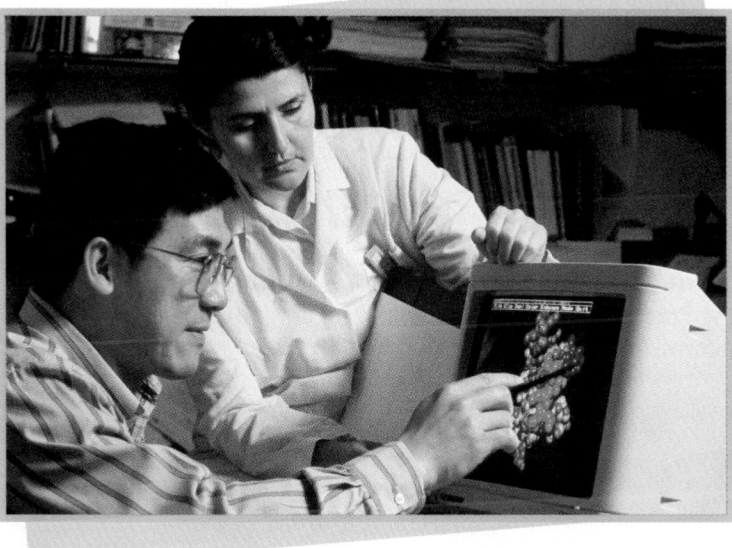

Figure 8 Scientists must communicate their findings to other scientists and to the public. These two scientists are discussing a computer model of a chemical that can be used to fight disease.

Real-Life Learning

Have students use television, newspapers, or magazines to find an example of communicating scientific information. Have them evaluate the communication. For example, is it clear and nontechnical enough for its audience? **learning modality: verbal**

Addressing Naive Conceptions

Be sure students understand that even well tested scientific theories can be revised, discarded, or abandoned. Have students list reasons that might contribute to the revision or abandonment of a theory. *(Sample answer: new information, more accurate testing, change over time.)* **learning modality: logical/mathematical**

Answers to Self-Assessment

Caption Question

Figure 7 The fertilized plant grew taller at a faster rate than the unfertilized one.

☑ *Checkpoint*

It is important in looking for patterns and trends and making interpretations.

Ongoing Assessment

Oral Presentation Ask students to list two ways that scientists display experimental results and state the advantages of each. *(Data table—it is easier to find exact numbers; graph—it is easier to see patterns and changes in the results.)*

9

Keeping Flowers Fresh

Preparing for Inquiry

Key Concept Certain additives can affect how long cut flowers will stay fresh in water.

Skills Objective Students will be able to
◆ design an experiment to test a hypothesis.

Time Day 1, design and set up experiment: 40 minutes; Days 2-5, examine freshness: 5-10 minutes each day.

Guiding Inquiry

Invitation Students are probably aware that cut flowers wilt unless they are put in water. Ask: **How long do cut flowers last in water? Do you think it is possible to make them last longer?**

Introducing the Procedure

You may wish to introduce this activity on the day before you intend to do it. Ask students about their experiences with cut flowers in their homes. Suggest that students bring cut flowers from home, if possible.

Troubleshooting the Experiment

◆ Make sure students re-cut the stems before placing them in the water solutions.
◆ Caution students not to handle the flowers or the vases too frequently.
◆ Prompt students to mark water levels on the vases as markers for maintaining the proper water level.
◆ Make sure students store the flowers out of direct sunlight.

Expected Outcome

The flowers in the sugar water mixture stay fresher longer.

Analyze and Conclude

1. Answers will vary depending on the design of the students' controlled experiments. In general, the manipulated variable will be the sugar additive. The responding variable will be the freshness

---

KEEPING FLOWERS FRESH

You have just been given a bouquet of cut flowers. A friend tells you that the flowers will stay fresh for longer if you add sugar to the water in the vase. You decide to put your friend's idea to the test.

Problem

Do cut flowers stay fresher for a longer time if sugar is added to the water?

Suggested Materials

plastic cups	cut flowers	spoon
water	sugar	

Design a Plan

1. Write a hypothesis for an experiment you could perform to find out whether your friend's advice is correct.
2. Working with a partner, design a controlled experiment to test your hypothesis. Brainstorm a list of all of the variables you will need to control. Discuss how you will control each of the variables. Also decide what data you will need to collect. For example, you could count the number of petals each flower drops. Decide how often you will collect the data. Then write out a detailed experimental plan for your teacher to review.
3. If necessary, revise your plan according to your teacher's instructions. Then set up your experiment and begin collecting your data. Remember to keep careful, accurate records of the data you collect.

Analyze and Conclude

1. What was the manipulated variable in the experiment you performed? What was the responding variable? What variables were kept constant?
2. Use the data you collected to create one or more graphs of your experimental results. (See pages 796–798 of the Skills Handbook for directions on creating graphs.) What patterns or trends do your graphs reveal?
3. Based on your graphs, what conclusion can you draw about sugar and cut flowers? Do your results support your hypothesis? Why or why not?
4. Make a list of some additional questions that you would like to investigate about how to keep cut flowers fresh.
5. **Think About It** What aspects of your experimental plan were difficult to carry out? Were any variables hard to control? Was it difficult to collect accurate data? What changes could you make to improve your experimental plan?

Design an Experiment

Choose one of the questions you listed in response to Question 4 above. Write a hypothesis and design a controlled experiment to test your hypothesis. Obtain your teacher's approval before carrying out the experiment.

---

of the flowers. Students may have chosen different ways to evaluate the freshness. Controlled variables should include the type of flower, the source of water, the type of vase, and the exposure to sunlight.

2. In general, student data tables and graphs should show that the flowers in the sugar water mixture stayed fresher longer.

3. The students should conclude that sugar added to water lengthens the time cut flowers stay fresh. This conclusion either will or will not support the varied students' hypotheses.

4. Answers will vary and may include adding other substances, such as aspirin and fertilizer to the water.

5. Answers will vary depending on the students' experimental designs.

Laboratory Safety

What do you think is the most important part of a scientific experiment? Careful observation? Accurate measurements? Clear communication? All of these skills are very important. But the most important skill in any experiment is following safe laboratory practices.

In general, laboratory safety means following your teacher's instructions and making sure you understand all laboratory procedures before you begin. Laboratory safety also means showing respect and courtesy to your teacher and classmates, wearing proper safety equipment, being careful with lab materials, and keeping your work area neat and clean.

Safe laboratory practices will not only protect you and your classmates from injury, they will also help make your experiments more successful. Before you conduct any experiments, review the laboratory safety symbols and rules in Appendix A on pages 799–801.

☑ *Checkpoint* *Why is laboratory safety important?*

Branches of Life Science

In this book you will explore tiny life forms such as bacteria and larger forms such as plants, reptiles, and mammals. You will learn about the microscopic structures that make up living things and how living things interact with one another and with their environment.

You will also learn about many scientists who have made important

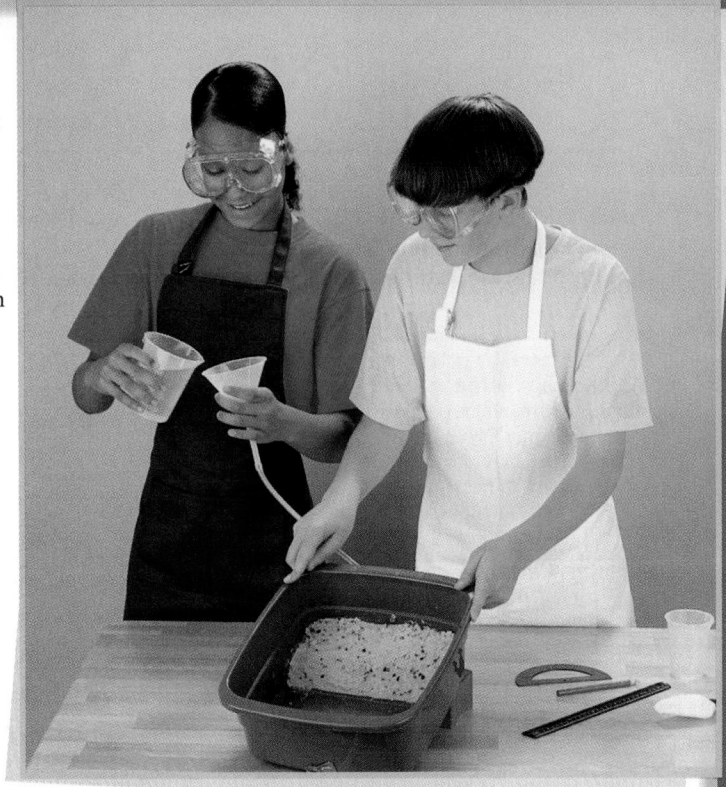

Figure 9 Following safe laboratory practices keeps scientists safe and makes experiments more successful. *Observing What things have these students done to protect themselves while carrying out this experiment?*

discoveries in life science. You will read about biologists such as Cindy Friedman, who are at work today in laboratories, hospitals, jungles, and other places all over the world. Look at *Exploring Careers in Life Science* on the next page to see just some of the things that life scientists do. This year, you too will be a life scientist—thinking like a scientist, carrying out experiments, and gaining new understandings about the living world around you.

Extending the Inquiry

Design an Experiment Some students may be aware that florists add chemicals to water to maintain the freshness of flowers, or that people sometimes add aspirin or glycerin to cut-flower water. Accept all reasonable experimental designs. Supervise students' use of aspirin or other chemical additives.

Laboratory Safety

Including All Students

Have students list one or two safety rules for the Skills Lab on page 10. *(Sample answer: Follow all safety rules for the use of scissors. Check with your teacher before using any chemicals.)* **learning modality: verbal**

Demonstration

Place safety equipment items (goggles, apron, and gloves) and other laboratory equipment (beakers, slides, liquids, and so on) on a table. Have students identify the safety equipment and comment on safety issues concerning the other equipment. You may want students to look through Appendix A on pages 799-801 before doing this exercise. **learning modality: verbal**

ACTIVITY

Branches of Life Science

Real-Life Learning

Ask students why the Skills Lab they just did is considered to be a part of life science. *(Sample answer: Flowers are plants, which are living things.)* **learning modality: logical/mathematical**

Program Resources

◆ **Unit 1 Resources** Introduction Skills Lab, pp. 6–7

Answers to Self-Assessment

Caption Question

Figure 9 They are wearing protective aprons and goggles. The girl's hair is tied back. Their work area is uncluttered and clean.

☑ *Checkpoint*

For preventing injuries and thus helping to ensure successful experiments.

Performance Assessment

Skills Check Have students make concept maps to show different branches of life science.

EXPLORING
Careers in Life Science

Have students look at the photographs of the life scientists. Ask students which of the seven careers shown interests them the most. Divide students into seven groups and assign each group one of the careers highlighted on the page. Encourage each group to list what they know about the work "their scientist" does and what they would like to learn. Have groups share their knowledge and questions. Some questions might be: **Where might each scientist work? What would a day in the life of each scientist be like? What kind of education is needed by each scientist?** Have each group prepare a notebook with information about each scientist. The notebook could contain original writings and drawings along with information from newspapers, magazines, and the Internet. **cooperative learning**

Addressing Naive Conceptions

Some students may not think of physicians and other medical personnel as life scientists. Have these students list at least three ways physicians, emergency medical technicians, veterinarians, or physical therapists use information from or processes of life science. Refer back to the story of Dr. Cindy Friedman on pages xxii–3 for ideas. **learning modality: logical/mathematical**

EXPLORING Careers in Life Science

Life scientists study many things—from the workings of tiny particles inside cells to the interactions of thousands of organisms in a forest. You can find life scientists at work in such diverse places as hospitals, laboratories, tropical rain forests, and national parks.

Physician ▶
Some physicians, such as the one in this photo, examine patients and diagnose illnesses and injuries. They may also design health programs to help patients prevent illness. Other physicians do research to try to find cures for diseases, such as cancer.

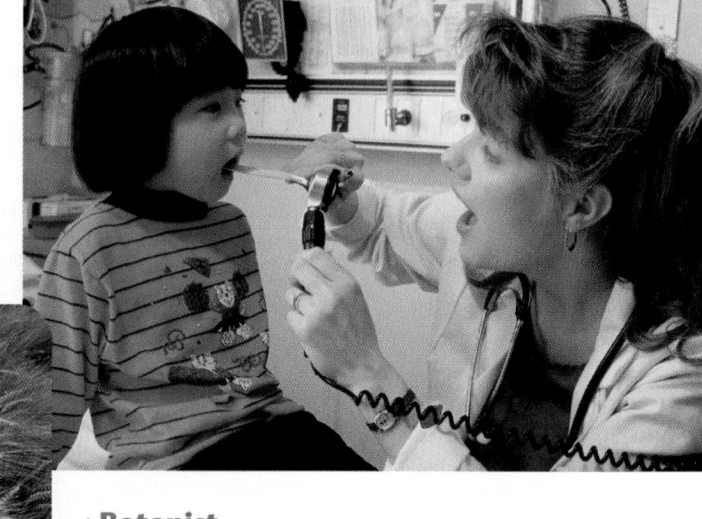

◀ Botanist
Botanists study plants. Many botanists, such as the one shown here, work outdoors, studying plants growing in their natural environment. Other botanists work with farmers to identify ways to increase crop yields. Still others study the relationship between plants and the environment.

Marine ▶ Biologist
Marine biologists study organisms that live in the oceans—from microscopic plankton to giant whales. Many marine biologists spend a lot of time in the water, observing marine animals such as the Florida manatee shown here.

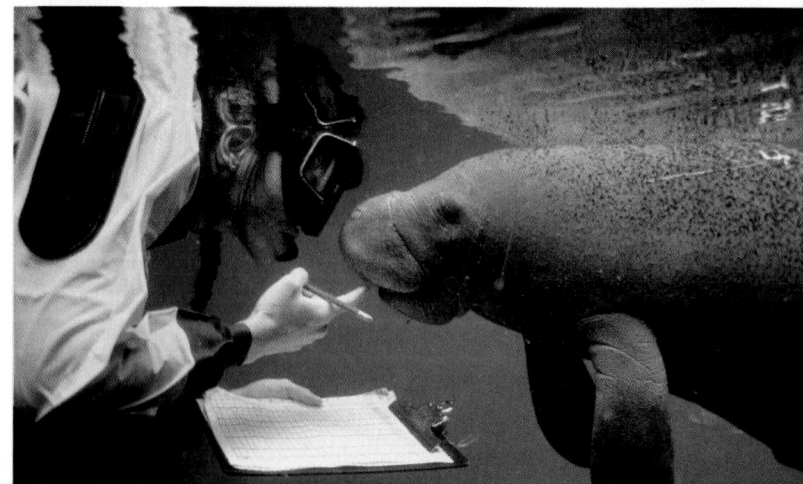

12

Background

Facts and Figures Physicians often have a difficult job with long hours at work and even more hours on call. Their training generally requires four years of medical school and from 3–8 years of internship and residency. They also must pass a licensing exam and continue graduate medical education. However, the work (serving patients) is rewarding both professionally and often financially.

Emergency medical technicians and physical therapists all contribute to the well-being of people. An EMT can be trained in either Basic Life Support or Advanced Life Support. Completing the training may take about 1,000–2,000 hours. Physical therapists must take an accredited educational program and pass an exam. This can be done with college courses or in a special program after college.

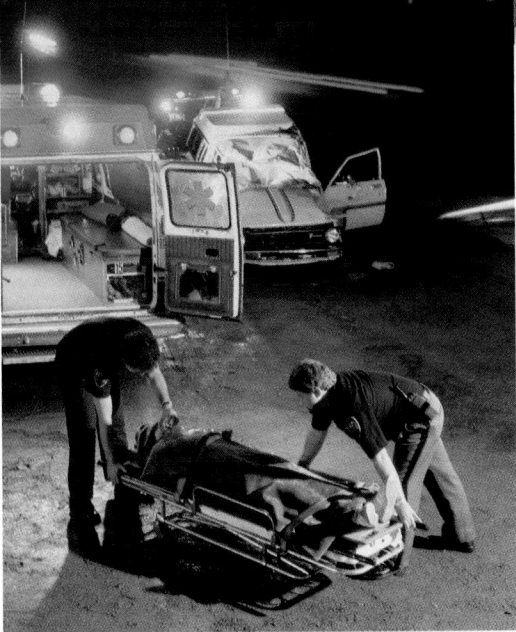

▲ Emergency Medical Technician (EMT)

EMTs play an important role in keeping the public healthy and safe. They ride in ambulances and fire engines, where they provide medical help for sick and injured people. EMTs may transport patients to the hospital by ambulance or helicopter in cases of severe injury.

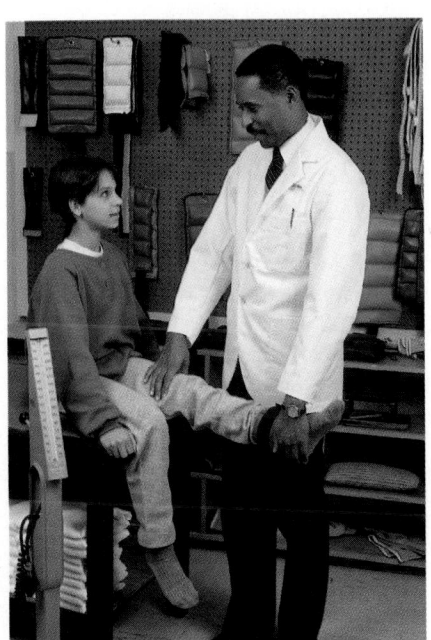

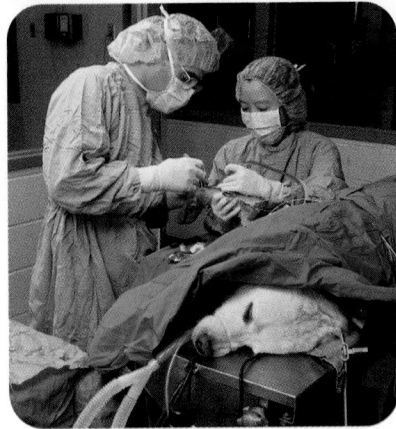

Veterinarian ▲

Veterinarians are animal doctors. Some veterinarians perform surgery on household pets, or on farm and zoo animals. They also perform routine checkups and care for sick and injured animals. Many veterinarians also provide advice to pet owners on animal behavior.

Park Ranger ▲

Park rangers work in government parks. Some rangers record data on animal habitats, populations, and migration. The rangers in this photo are tagging a bird so they can track its migration pattern. Other rangers lead tours for park visitors, educating them about protecting the environment.

◄ Physical Therapist

Physical therapists help people regain their strength and coordination after serious illness or injury. Physical therapists use massage, weight training, and stretching exercises to help a patient recover. The work of physical therapists also helps patients prevent future injuries.

Introduction **13**

Including All Students

Materials *One index card per student*
Time *10 minutes*

ACTIVITY

Have each student choose one of the seven scientific careers shown and draw a picture of one or more things that such scientists might study. Group the cards by field and have groups work together to make a display about working in each of these fields of life science. cooperative learning **cooperative learning**

3 Assess

Ongoing Assessment

Writing Have students list four types of life scientists and an example of one thing each scientist might study.

Reviewing Content

True or False

1. a **2.** b **3.** d **4.** a **5.** b

Multiple Choice

6. observation **7.** True **8.** True
9. Communication **10.** True

Checking Concepts

11. Scientific inquiry is the diverse ways in which scientists study the natural world.
12. A hypothesis is a possible explanation for a set of observations or a scientific question. Examples of hypotheses will vary, but they may be worded as *If…then…* statements. A hypothesis can be tested by designing and carrying out a controlled experiment.
13. In a controlled experiment, all of the variables except for one remain the same.
14. Scientists communicate by writing articles in scientific journals, by attending scientific meetings, and by using the Internet.
15. Answers will vary, but they should include navigational directions and landmarks associated with changes in direction.

Thinking Critically

16. Answers will vary, and may include the following: type of bowl used; feeding time; feeding place; and hours since last meal.
17. In a controlled experiment all of the factors except for one remain the same. This allows the scientist to concentrate on the results brought about by the manipulated variable, and it prevents other variables from interfering with the results. If scientists control all of the other variables, the process of repeating an experiment is much less complicated.
18. Answers will vary. The observation would involve seeing the student with the ice pack on his arm. The inference would be the interpretation of the observation, such as *the boy must have fallen in gym class and hurt his arm.*

Study Guide

Key Ideas

◆ Science is a way of learning about the natural world and the knowledge gained through that process. Another term for the diverse ways in which scientists study the natural world is scientific inquiry.
◆ Some of the skills that scientists use are posing questions, making observations and inferences, developing hypotheses, designing experiments, making measurements and collecting data, interpreting data, drawing conclusions, and communicating.
◆ The International System of Units (SI) is the standard system of measurement in science.
◆ A scientific theory is a well-tested concept that explains a wide range of observations.
◆ Laboratory safety means following your teacher's instructions and making sure you understand all laboratory procedures before you begin.

Key Terms

science	variable
scientific inquiry	manipulated variable
observation	responding variable
data	controlled experiment
inference	scientific theory
hypothesis	

Reviewing Content

 For more review of key concepts, see the Interactive Student Tutorial CD-ROM.

Multiple Choice

Choose the letter of the best answer.

1. The diverse ways in which scientists study the natural world is called
   a. scientific inquiry.   **b.** observation.
   c. data.   **d.** communication.
2. The facts, figures, and other evidence gathered through observations are called
   a. inferences.   **b.** data.
   c. hypotheses.   **d.** variables.
3. A possible explanation for a set of observations or answer to a scientific question is a(n)
   a. variable.   **b.** controlled experiment.
   c. scientific theory. **d.** hypothesis.
4. The factors that can change in an experiment are called
   a. variables.   **b.** inferences.
   c. hypotheses.   **d.** scientific theories.
5. A well-tested concept that explains a wide range of observations is a
   a. variable.
   b. scientific theory.
   c. hypothesis.
   d. controlled experiment.

True or False

If the statement is true, write true. If it is false, change the underlined word or words to make the statement true.

6. The skill of <u>laboratory safety</u> involves using one or more of the senses to gather information and collect data.
7. An <u>inference</u> is an interpretation of an observation that is based on evidence or prior knowledge.
8. The standard system of measurement used in science is called <u>SI</u>.
9. <u>Observation</u> is the sharing of ideas and experimental findings with others.
10. The most important skill in any experiment is <u>laboratory safety</u>.

Checking Concepts

11. What is scientific inquiry?
12. What is a hypothesis? Give an example of a hypothesis. Describe how the hypothesis can be tested.
13. What makes a controlled experiment different from other types of experiments?
14. What are some of the methods that scientists use to communicate their findings with one another?
15. **Writing to Learn** You probably use the same route to travel home from school each day. The next time you make the trip, write down directions home from school. Also, record at least ten things that you observe. Then write a letter to a friend or relative in another town detailing exactly how you get home from school and what you notice along the way.

Thinking Critically

16. **Applying Concepts** Suppose you would like to find out which dog food your dog likes best. What variables would you need to control in your experiment?
17. **Making Judgments** Scientists often perform experiments and make new discoveries. Other scientists must then repeat the experiments and arrive at the same conclusions before the discoveries are widely accepted. Explain how controlled experiments are important in ensuring that experiments are repeatable.
18. **Inferring** While walking by the nurse's office, you notice a student in gym clothes with an ice pack on his arm. What inference could you draw? Explain how your inference differs from an observation.

Test Preparation

19. c 20. b 21. a

Test Preparation   Use these questions to prepare for standardized tests.

Use the information to answer Questions 19–21.
Three students conducted a controlled experiment to find out how walking and running affected their heart rates. Their data are found in the table below.

Effect of Activity on Heart Rate (in beats per minute)			
Student	Heart Rate (at rest)	Heart Rate (walking)	Heart Rate (running)
Student One	70	90	115
Student Two	72	80	110
Student Three	80	100	120

19. Which factor is the manipulated variable in this experiment?
    a. heart rate
    b. breathing rate
    c. the activity the person is doing
    d. the students' ages

20. Which of the following statements would be a good hypothesis for this experiment?
    a. If a person's heart rate increases, then he or she will run.
    b. If a person runs or walks, then his or her heart rate will increase.
    c. If a person's heart rate increases, then he or she is in good shape.
    d. If a person runs or walks, then he or she is in good shape.

21. Based on the data in the table, which statement is true?
    a. Every student's heart rate increased while walking and running.
    b. Heart rates increased while running but not while walking.
    c. Student One's heart rate increased while running, but Student Two's did not.
    d. Student Three's running heart rate was 110.

Introduction **15**

Program Resources

◆ **Unit 1 Resources** Introduction Review and Reinforce, p. 4; Introduction Enrich, p. 5
◆ **Performance Assessment** Introduction, pp. 2–4
◆ **Chapter and Unit Tests** Introduction Test, pp. 2–3

Media and Technology

 Interactive Student Tutorial CD-ROM Introduction

 Computer Test Bank Introduction Test

15

CHAPTER 1
Cells: The Building Blocks of Life

Sections	Time	Student Edition Activities	Other Activities
CHAPTER PROJECT **Mystery Object** p. 17	Ongoing (2 weeks)	Check Your Progress, pp. 25, 33, 46 Present Your Project, p. 49	
1 What Is Life? pp. 18–26 ◆ List the characteristics all living things share. ◆ Explain how scientists used controlled experiments to disprove the idea of spontaneous generation. ◆ Identify what all living things need to survive.	2–3 periods/ 1–1½ blocks	**Discover** Is It Living or Nonliving?, p. 18 **Try This** React!, p. 20 **Sharpen Your Skills** Designing an Experiment, p. 24 **Skills Lab: Designing Experiments** Please Pass the Bread!, p. 26	TE Demonstration, p. 19 TE Building Inquiry Skills: Applying Concepts, p. 20 TE Integrating Chemistry, p. 24
2 Discovering Cells pp. 27–33 ◆ Explain how the invention of the microscope contributed to scientists' understanding of living things. ◆ State the three points of the cell theory. ◆ Describe how a light microscope works, including how a lens magnifies an object.	1–2 periods/ ½–1 block	**Discover** Is Seeing Believing?, p. 27 **Sharpen Your Skills** Observing, p. 32	TE Building Inquiry Skills: Classifying, p. 28 TE Including All Students, p. 31 TE Integrating Physics, p. 32
3 Looking Inside Cells pp. 34–43 ◆ Identify the cell wall, cell membrane, and nucleus, and describe their functions. ◆ Identify other organelles in the cell and describe their functions. ◆ Compare bacterial cells with plant and animal cells. ◆ Describe the role of specialized cells in many-celled organisms.	2–3 periods/ 1–1½ blocks	**Discover** How Large Are Cells?, p. 34 **Try This** Gelatin Cell, p. 40 **Science at Home,** p. 42 **Skills Lab: Observing** A Magnified View of Life, p. 43	TE Building Inquiry Skills: Comparing and Contrasting, p. 36 TE Inquiry Challenge, p. 37 TE Including All Students, p. 39 TE Demonstration, p. 39 TE Demonstration, p. 40 TE Building Inquiry Skills: Observing, p. 41 LM 1, "Cell Membranes and Permeability"
4 *INTEGRATING EARTH SCIENCE* **The Origin of Life** pp. 44–46 ◆ Compare the atmosphere of early Earth with today's atmosphere. ◆ State how scientists hypothesize that life arose on early Earth.	1 period/ ½ block	**Discover** How Can the Composition of Air Change?, p. 44	TE Including All Students, p. 45
Study Guide/Chapter Assessment pp. 47–49	1 period/ ½ block		ISAB Provides teaching and review of all inquiry skills

 For Standard or Block Schedule The Resource Pro® CD-ROM gives you maximum flexibility for planning your instruction for any type of schedule. Resource Pro® contains Planning Express®, an advanced scheduling program, as well as the entire contents of the Teaching Resources and the Computer Test Bank.

CHAPTER PLANNING GUIDE

Program Resources	Assessment Strategies	Media and Technology
UR Chapter 1 Project Teacher Notes, pp. 8–9 **UR** Chapter 1 Project Overview and Worksheets, pp. 10–13	**SE** Performance Assessment: Present Your Project, p. 49 **TE** Check Your Progress, pp. 25, 33, 42 **UR** Chapter 1 Project Scoring Rubric, p. 14	Science Explorer Internet Site at www.phschool.com
UR 1-1 Lesson Plan, p. 15 **UR** 1-1 Section Summary, p. 16 **UR** 1-1 Review and Reinforce, p. 17 **UR** 1-1 Enrich, p. 18 **UR** Chapter 1 Skills Lab, pp. 31–33	**SE** Section 1 Review, p. 25 **TE** Ongoing Assessment, pp. 19, 21, 23 **TE** Performance Assessment, p. 25	Life Science Videotape 1; Videodisc Unit 1 Side 2, "It's Alive!" Audio CD, English-Spanish Summary 1-1 Transparencies 1, "Exploring Redi's Experiment"; 2, "Exploring Pasteur's Experiment"
UR 1-2 Lesson Plan, p. 19 **UR** 1-2 Section Summary, p. 20 **UR** 1-2 Review and Reinforce, p. 21 **UR** 1-2 Enrich, p. 22	**SE** Section 2 Review, p. 33 **TE** Ongoing Assessment, pp. 29, 31 **TE** Performance Assessment, p. 33	Audio CD, English-Spanish Summary 1-2 Transparency 3, "The Compound Microscope"
UR 1-3 Lesson Plan, p. 23 **UR** 1-3 Section Summary, p. 24 **UR** 1-3 Review and Reinforce, p. 25 **UR** 1-3 Enrich, p. 26 **UR** Chapter 1 Skills Lab, pp. 34–35	**SE** Section 3 Review, p. 42 **TE** Ongoing Assessment, pp. 35, 37, 39, 41 **TE** Performance Assessment, p. 42	Life Science Videotape 1; Videodisc Unit 1 Side 2, "What's in a Cell?" Life Science Videotape 1; Videodisc Unit 1 Side 2, "Evolution of Cells" Audio CD, English-Spanish Summary 1-3 Transparencies 4, "Exploring a Plant Cell"; 5, "Exploring an Animal Cell" Interactive Student Tutorial CD-ROM, Chapter 1
UR 1-4 Lesson Plan, p. 27 **UR** 1-4 Section Summary, p. 28 **UR** 1-4 Review and Reinforce, p. 29 **UR** 1-4 Enrich, p. 30	**SE** Section 4 Review, p. 46 **TE** Performance Assessment, p. 46	Life Science Videotape 1; Videodisc Unit 1 Side 2, "Where Did It Come From?" Earth Science Videotape 5; Videodisc Unit 2 Side 2, "Air Today Gone Tomorrow" Audio CD, English-Spanish Summary 1-4
RCA Provides strategies to improve science reading skills **GSW** Provides worksheets to promote student comprehension of content	**SE** Chapter 1 Study Guide/Assessment, pp. 47–49 **PA** Chapter 1 Performance Assessment, pp. 5–7 **CUT** Chapter 1 Test, pp. 4–7 **CTB** Chapter 1 Test	Interactive Student Tutorial CD-ROM, Chapter 1 Computer Test Bank, Chapter 1 Test

Key: **SE** Student Edition   **TE** Teacher's Edition   **UR** Unit Resources
      CTB Computer Test Bank   **PTA** Product Testing Activities by *Consumer Reports*   **LM** Laboratory Manual
      ISAB Inquiry Skills Activity Book   **RCA** Reading in the Content Area   **IES** Interdisciplinary Explorations Series
      GSW Guided Study Worksheets   **PA** Performance Assessment   **CUT** Chapter and Unit Tests

Meeting the National Science Education Standards and AAAS Benchmarks

National Science Education Standards	Benchmarks for Science Literacy	Unifying Themes
Science as Inquiry (Content Standard A) ◆ **Identify questions that can be answered through scientific investigations** Students develop a list of characteristics shared by living things. *(Section 1; Chapter Project)* ◆ **Design and conduct a scientific investigation** Students devise a way to determine if an object is alive. *(Chapter Project)* ◆ **Use appropriate tools and techniques to gather, analyze, and interpret data** Students compare plant and animal cells. *(Skills Lab)* **Life Science** (Content Standard C) ◆ **Reproduction and Heredity** Reproduction is a fundamental characteristic of living things. *(Section 1)* ◆ **Structure and function in living systems** All living things are composed of cells. Each of the various structures in a cell has a different function. *(Sections 2, 3)* **Science and Technology** (Content Standard E) ◆ **Understandings about science and technology** The invention of the microscope made it possible for people to discover and learn about cells. *(Section 2; Science & History)* **History and Nature of Science** (Content Standard G) ◆ **History of science** Redi and Pasteur established that life comes from life. Miller and Urey demonstrated that conditions in Earth's early atmosphere could have produced complex organic molecules. *(Sections 1, 2, 4)*	**1B Scientific Inquiry** Redi and Pasteur established that life comes from life. Students compare plant and animal cells. Miller and Urey demonstrated that conditions in Earth's early atmosphere could have produced organic molecules. *(Sections 1, 4; Skills Lab)* **1C The Scientific Enterprise** The observations and conclusions of many scientists led to the development of the cell theory. *(Section 2)* **3A Technology and Science** The invention of the microscope made it possible for people to discover and learn about cells. Microscopes have improved in many ways over the past 400 years. *(Section 2; Science & History)* **5C Cells** All living things are composed of cells. Each of the various structures in a cell has a different function. The most important groups of organic compounds found in living things are carbohydrates, lipids, proteins, and nucleic acids. Substances can move into and out of a cell by diffusion, osmosis, or active transport. *(Sections 1, 2, 3; Skills Lab)* **5E Flow of Matter and Energy** All living things require energy. The energy is used to grow and reproduce. Different kinds of organisms obtain energy in different ways. *(Section 1)*	◆ **Energy** All living things must have energy to survive. Different organisms obtain energy in different ways. Mitochondria produce most of the energy a cell needs to carry out its functions. Chloroplasts capture energy from the sun and use it to produce food. *(Sections 1, 2, 3)* ◆ **Patterns of Change** The composition of air changed as a result of the presence of living organisms. *(Section 4)* ◆ **Scale and Structure** Cells are the basic unit of structure and function in living things. Cells have different structures that perform different functions. Students compare plant and animal cells. *(Sections 1, 2, 3; Skills Lab)* ◆ **Systems and Interactions** The invention of the microscope made it possible for people to discover and learn about cells. Cell organelles function to produce energy, build and transport needed materials, and store and recycle wastes. *(Sections 2, 3; Science & History)* ◆ **Unity and Diversity** All living things are made of cells. Plant cells have cell walls and chloroplasts, while animal cells do not. *(Sections 1, 2, 3; Skills Lab)*

Take It to the Net

 *Interactive text at www.phschool.com*

Science Explorer comes alive with iText.

- **Complete student text** is accessible from any computer with Internet access or a CD-ROM drive.
- **Animations, simulations, and videos** enhance student understanding and retention of concepts.
- **Self-tests and online study tools** assess student understanding.

STAY CURRENT with **SCIENCE NEWS®**

Find out the latest research and information about cells at:
www.phschool.com

Go to **www.phschool.com** and click on the Science icon. Then click on <u>Science Explorer: Life, Earth, and Physical Science</u> under PH@school.

ACTIVITY	Time (minutes)	Materials _Quantities for one work group_	Skills
Section 1			
Discover, p. 18	10	**Nonconsumable** wind-up toys	Forming Operational Definitions
Try This, p. 20	10	**Consumable** lemon slices **Nonconsumable** small mirrors	Classifying
Sharpen your Skills, p. 24	30	**Consumable** thin potato slices, paper towel **Nonconsumable** hair dryers, balance	Predicting
Skills Lab, p. 26	20 min first day, 5 min per day for the next 5 days or so	**Consumable** paper plates, bread without preservatives, sealable plastic bags, tap water, packing tape **Nonconsumable** plastic dropper	Controlling Variables
Section 2			
Discover, p. 27	10	**Consumable** black and white newspaper photograph **Nonconsumable** scissors, hand lens, microscope	Observing
Sharpen Your Skills, p. 32	15	**Consumable** pond water **Nonconsumable** prepared slide of cork, microscope, plastic dropper, slide, coverslip	Observing
Section 3			
Discover, p. 34	10	**Nonconsumable** calculator, metric ruler	Inferring
Try This, p. 40	10/10	**Consumable** packet of colorless gelatin, warm water, other miscellaneous materials to represent cell structures **Nonconsumable** rectangular or round pan	Making Models
Science at Home, p. 42	home	No special materials are required.	Comparing and Contrasting
Skills Lab, p. 43	40	**Consumable** water, _Elodea_ leaf **Nonconsumable** plastic dropper, microscope slide, microscope, prepared slide of animal cells, colored pencils, forceps, coverslip	Observing, Comparing and Contrasting
Section 4			
Discover, p. 44	10	**Nonconsumable** two covered plastic jars; one containing a plant and the other an animal	Inferring

A list of all materials required for the Student Edition activities can be found on pages T25–T33. You can obtain information about ordering materials by calling 1-800-848-9500 or by accessing the Science Explorer Internet site at **www.phschool.com**.

Mystery Object

It can be difficult to determine whether some objects are alive or not. This project allows students to observe the characteristics that make living things different from nonliving things.

Purpose In this project, students observe an object to determine whether it is alive. Students also develop strategies for distinguishing between living and nonliving objects.

Skills Focus After completing the Chapter 1 Project, students will be able to
◆ brainstorm about the characteristics of life;
◆ observe characteristics of objects to infer whether they are alive;
◆ carry out tests for signs of life;
◆ communicate their findings about their mystery object to the class.

Project Time Line This project requires about two weeks. Some living things, such as small insects and larvae, will show obvious signs of life at first glance. Other objects, such as seeds, brine-shrimp eggs, or plants, may take a week or so to reveal signs of life. During the first two days, students should observe their objects and record their observations. Allow at least three days for students to carry out their tests for life characteristics. Remind them to include data tables as well as drawings in their project notebooks. Finally, give students time to analyze their data, classify their objects, and plan their presentations.

Possible Materials Provide students with living and nonliving objects, and instructions on their care.
◆ Living "mystery objects" may include: brine shrimp; slime mold; bread mold; insect larvae; goldfish; plants; yeast (add one spoonful of baker's yeast and sugar to 250 mL warm water; observe under microscope); and seeds (soak lentil seeds in water overnight then wrap in wet paper towel; place towel in plastic bag and store in dark; observe daily).
◆ Nonliving "mystery objects" may include: pebbles; vermiculite; lead shot (looks like seeds); artificial plants (look real but do not grow or have a

cellular structure); soluble salts in a saturated solution (crystal gardens appear to grow); hair (cellular structure, but no longer living); and toys with microchips (can have complex responses).
◆ Plastic petri dishes and paper towels are useful for germinating seeds. BTB solution (bromthymol blue) can be used to test for the presence of carbon dioxide in water environments.
◆ Provide equipment such as a microscope, glass slides and cover slips, scissors, plastic dropper, hand lens, and a ruler. Show students how to use a microscope and make thin cross-sections.

Safety

CAUTION: Glass and sharp objects can cause injury. Handle with care.

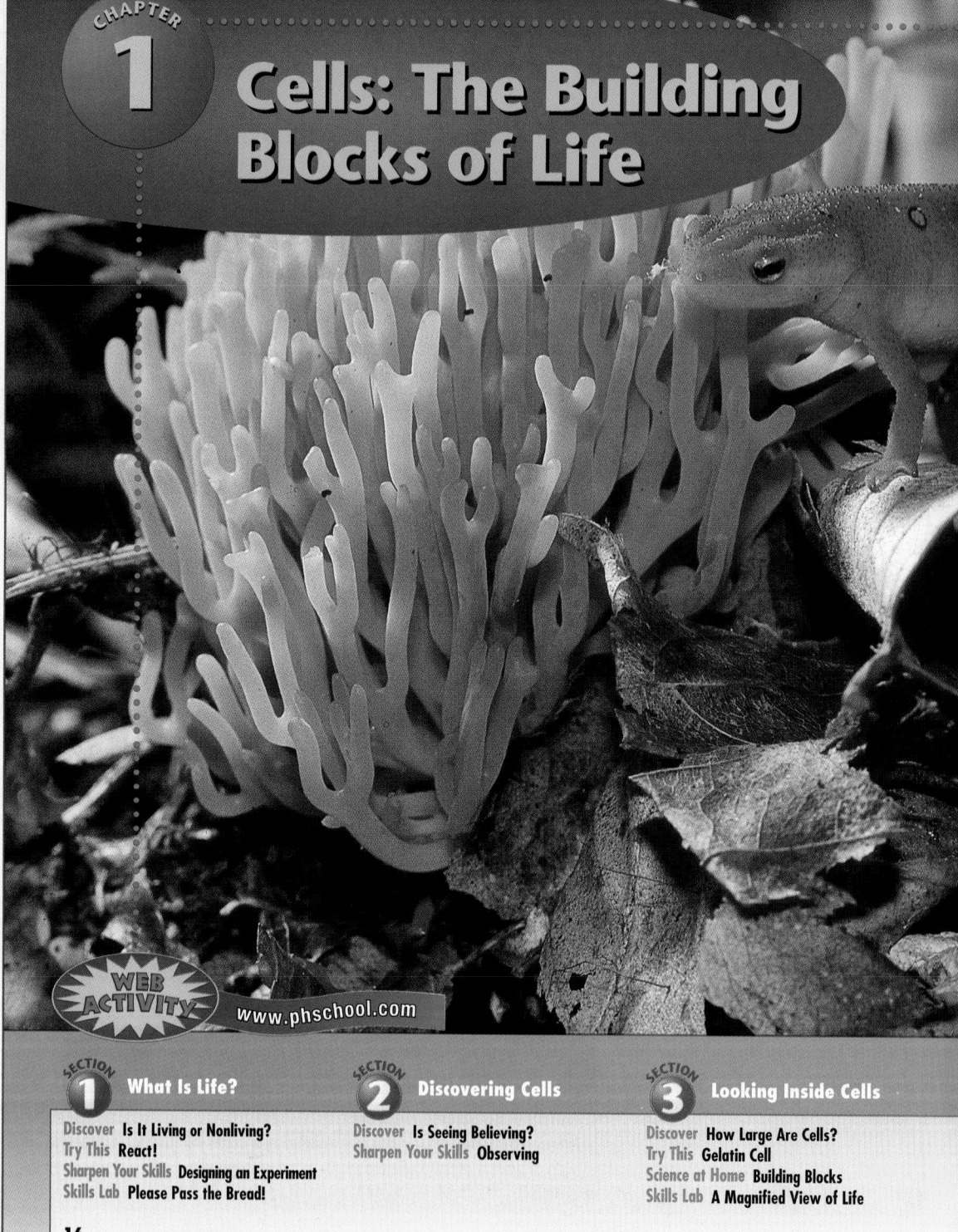

Cells: The Building Blocks of Life

WEB ACTIVITY www.phschool.com

SECTION 1 What Is Life?

Discover **Is It Living or Nonliving?**
Try This **React!**
Sharpen Your Skills **Designing an Experiment**
Skills Lab **Please Pass the Bread!**

SECTION 2 Discovering Cells

Discover **Is Seeing Believing?**
Sharpen Your Skills **Observing**

SECTION 3 Looking Inside Cells

Discover **How Large Are Cells?**
Try This **Gelatin Cell**
Science at Home **Building Blocks**
Skills Lab **A Magnified View of Life**

16

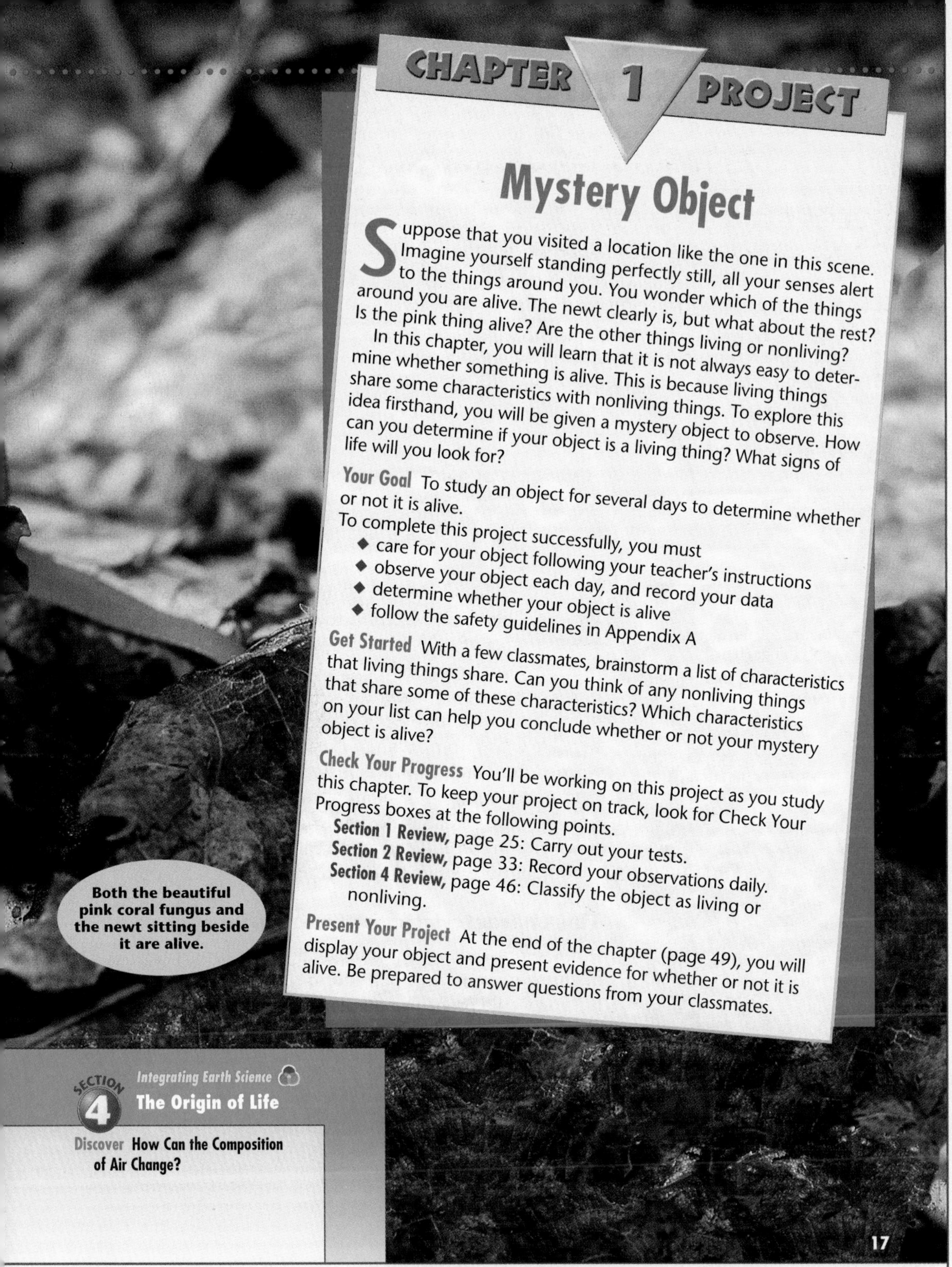

Mystery Object

Suppose that you visited a location like the one in this scene. Imagine yourself standing perfectly still, all your senses alert to the things around you. You wonder which of the things around you are alive. The newt clearly is, but what about the rest? Is the pink thing alive? Are the other things living or nonliving?

In this chapter, you will learn that it is not always easy to determine whether something is alive. This is because living things share some characteristics with nonliving things. To explore this idea firsthand, you will be given a mystery object to observe. How can you determine if your object is a living thing? What signs of life will you look for?

Your Goal To study an object for several days to determine whether or not it is alive.

To complete this project successfully, you must
◆ care for your object following your teacher's instructions
◆ observe your object each day, and record your data
◆ determine whether your object is alive
◆ follow the safety guidelines in Appendix A

Get Started With a few classmates, brainstorm a list of characteristics that living things share. Can you think of any nonliving things that share some of these characteristics? Which characteristics on your list can help you conclude whether or not your mystery object is alive?

Check Your Progress You'll be working on this project as you study this chapter. To keep your project on track, look for Check Your Progress boxes at the following points.
Section 1 Review, page 25: Carry out your tests.
Section 2 Review, page 33: Record your observations daily.
Section 4 Review, page 46: Classify the object as living or nonliving.

Present Your Project At the end of the chapter (page 49), you will display your object and present evidence for whether or not it is alive. Be prepared to answer questions from your classmates.

Both the beautiful pink coral fungus and the newt sitting beside it are alive.

SECTION 4 *Integrating Earth Science*
The Origin of Life

Discover How Can the Composition of Air Change?

17

Program Resources

◆ **Unit 1 Resources** Chapter 1 Project Teacher Notes, pp. 8–9; Chapter 1 Project Overview and Work-sheets, pp. 10–13; Chapter 1 Project Scoring Rubric, p. 14

WEB ACTIVITY www.phschool.com

You will find an Internet activity, chapter self-tests for students, and links to other chapter topics at this site.

Launching the Project Bring a few living organisms, such as a plant, a snail, and a fish, into the classroom to show students. Ask: **What characteristics do these objects have in common?** (*They grow; they respond to changes in the environment.*) Talk about the distinguishing characteristics that scientists use to classify the objects as living. Ask: **What tests could you design that would help you observe the characteristics of these living organisms?** (*Measure size over a period of time.*) Discuss how scientists develop and test hypotheses. Allow students to read the description of the project in their text and in the Chapter 1 Project Overview on pages 10–11 in the Unit 1 Resources. Distribute copies of the Chapter 1 Project Worksheets on pages 12–13 for students to review. Tell students that all tests must be approved so that living organisms are not injured.

Performance Assessment

The Chapter 1 Project Scoring Rubric on page 14 will help you evaluate how well students complete the Chapter 1 Project. Students will be assessed on
◆ the detail of their observations;
◆ how well they design tests to determine whether their object is alive;
◆ the accuracy and organization of their testing and documentation, including how well they follow directions for the care of their objects;
◆ whether they draw appropriate conclusions from their tests and present their results to the class in a clear and organized manner.
By sharing the Chapter 1 Project Scoring Rubric with students at the beginning of the project, you will make it clear to them what they are expected to do.

Objectives

After completing the lesson, students will be able to
- list the characteristics all living things share;
- explain how scientists used controlled experiments to disprove the idea of spontaneous generation;
- identify what all living things need to survive.

Key Terms organism, cell, unicellular, multicellular, development, stimulus, response, reproduce, spontaneous generation, controlled experiment, manipulated variable, autotroph, heterotroph, homeostasis

1 Engage/Explore

Activating Prior Knowledge

Ask students to describe the most unusual living thing they have seen. Ask: **What did it look like? Where did it live? What was so unusual about it?** Write the heading *Living Things* on the board and list the organisms as students identify them. Have students describe whether they thought the organism was a plant, animal, or other form of life such as a mushroom.

DISCOVER

Skills Focus forming operational definitions
Materials *wind-up toys*
Time 10 minutes
Tips Do not wind toys too tightly. Urge students to think of all living things, not just animals, as they make their lists.
Expected Outcome Students could say that because the toy moves it is alive, or because the toy does not eat, grow, or reproduce, it is not alive.
Think It Over Students should conclude that growth is shared by all living things, while characteristics such as sleeping or talking are not.

SECTION 1 What Is Life?

DISCOVER ·········· ACTIVITY

Is It Living or Nonliving?

1. Your teacher will give you and a partner a wind-up toy.
2. With your partner, decide who will find evidence that the toy is alive and who will find evidence that the toy is not alive.
3. Observe the wind-up toy. Record the characteristics of the toy that support your position about whether or not the toy is alive.
4. Share your lists of living and nonliving characteristics with your classmates.

Think It Over
Forming Operational Definitions Based on what you learned from the activity, create a list of characteristics that living things share.

GUIDE FOR READING

- What characteristics do all living things share?
- What do living things need to survive?

Reading Tip As you read, use the headings to make an outline of the characteristics and needs of living things.

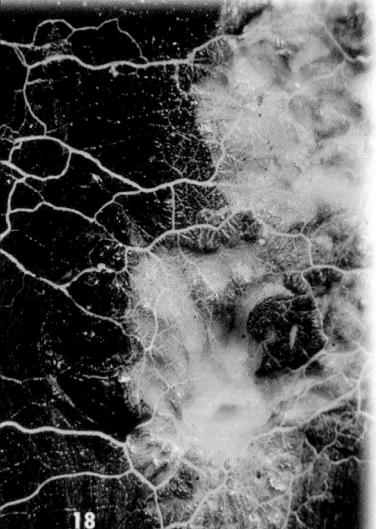

Looking like the slimy creatures that star in horror movies, the "blobs" appeared in towns near Dallas, Texas, in the summer of 1973. Jellylike masses, like the ones in Figure 1, overran yards and porches all over the towns. The glistening blobs oozed slowly along the ground. Terrified homeowners didn't know what the blobs were. Some people thought that they were life forms from another planet. People around Dallas were worried until biologists, scientists who study living things, put their minds at ease. The blobs were slime molds—living things usually found on damp, decaying material on a forest floor. The unusually wet weather around Dallas that year provided ideal conditions for the slime molds to grow in people's yards.

The Characteristics of Living Things

If you were asked to name some living things, or **organisms,** you might name yourself, a pet, and maybe some insects or plants. But you would probably not mention a moss growing in a shady spot, the mildew on bathroom tiles, or the slime molds that oozed across the lawns in towns near Dallas. But all of these things are also organisms that share six important characteristics

Figure 1 Slime molds similar to these grew in yards and porches in towns near Dallas, Texas.

READING STRATEGIES

Reading Tip Remind students that making an outline helps readers organize information so they remember key points and important details. As a guide for students, begin outlining the first main topic on the board. Complete the outline for this heading as a class. Then have students work independently to complete the rest of the outline.

I. The Characteristics of Living Things
  A. Cellular organization
    1. basic unit of structure and function
    2. unicellular or multicellular
  B. The Chemicals of Life
    1. all living cells composed of chemicals
    2. primary chemicals of life: water, carbohydrates, proteins, lipids, and nucleic acids

◄ Animal cells

◄ Plant cells

Figure 2 Like all living things, the butterfly and the leaf are made of cells. Although the cells of different organisms are not identical, they share important characteristics. *Making Generalizations In what ways are cells similar?*

with all other living things. **All living things have a cellular organization, contain similar chemicals, use energy, grow and develop, respond to their surroundings, and reproduce.**

Cellular Organization All organisms are made of small building blocks called cells. A **cell** is the basic unit of structure and function in an organism. The smallest cells are so tiny that you could fit over a million of them on the period at the end of this sentence. To see most cells, you need a microscope—a tool that uses lenses, like those in eyeglasses, to magnify small objects.

Organisms may be composed of only one cell or of many cells. **Unicellular,** or single-celled organisms, include bacteria (bak TEER ee uh), the most numerous organisms on Earth. A bacterial cell carries out all of the functions necessary for the organism to stay alive. **Multicellular** organisms are composed of many cells. The cells of many multicellular organisms are specialized to do certain tasks. For example, you are made of trillions of cells. Specialized cells in your body, such as muscle and nerve cells, work together to keep you alive. Nerve cells carry messages from your surroundings to your brain. Other nerve cells then carry messages to your muscle cells, making your body move.

The Chemicals of Life The cells of all living things are composed of chemicals. The most abundant chemical in cells is water. Other chemicals called carbohydrates (kahr boh HY drayt) are a cell's energy source. Two other chemicals, proteins (PROH teenz) and lipids (LIP idz), are the building materials of cells, much like wood and bricks are the building materials of houses. Finally, nucleic (noo KLEE ik) acids are the genetic material—the chemical instructions that direct the cell's activities.

Program Resources

♦ **Unit 1 Resources** 1-1 Lesson Plan, p. 15; 1-1 Section Summary, p. 16

Media and Technology

 Audio CD English-Spanish Summary 1-1

Answers to Self-Assessment

Caption Question

Figure 2 Cells are the basic building blocks of animal and plant tissues. They are composed of complex chemicals and can perform tasks necessary to life.

2 Facilitate

The Characteristics of Living Things

Using The Visuals: Figure 2

Make sure students understand that the images in the circles are magnified many times. Have students describe differences between the plant and animal cells in the figure. (*Animal cells—rounded, have dark spots in the centers; plant cells—rectangular, have green structures inside them*) Point out that plant and animal cells have more similarities than differences. **learning modality: visual**

Demonstration

Materials *charcoal, piece of chalk, nail, small sack of fertilizer, bottle of carbonated water*
Time 10 minutes

ACTIVITY

Ask if students have heard that all the chemicals in a human body cost only a few dollars. Show the materials, explaining that in simple forms the chemicals would not cost much to buy. Challenge students to identify the chemicals in each item: charcoal (*carbon*); chalk (*calcium*); nail (*iron*); fertilizer (*phosphorus, nitrogen, and potassium*); carbonated water (*carbon dioxide and water*). Explain that the human body can convert these nonliving chemicals into complex arrangements of molecules such as carbohydrates, proteins, lipids, and nucleic acids, which help the body function and provide its structure. **learning modality: verbal**

Ongoing Assessment

Skills Check Have each student choose one living thing and explain how he or she knows it is alive.

The Characteristics of Living Things, continued

Skills Focus classifying

Materials *small mirrors, lemon slices*

Time 10 minutes

Tips Ask: **What does a dog do when it sees a big, juicy steak?** *(Sample: wags tail, acts excited, salivates)* Ask: **Which is the stimulus and which is the response?** *(Stimulus is the steak; response is tail wagging, acting excited, salivating.)* Remind students not to taste the lemon slices.

Expected Outcome clapping hands— sudden motion close to eyes/eyes blink; covering eyes, then uncover—change in light intensity/pupil contracts; lemon— smell/mouth puckers

Extend Challenge students to list at least 5 other stimulus / response actions demonstrated by plants or animals. *(Samples: feel pain—yelp or howl; see a predator—run away; feel heat—pull away; light source—plant stem turns toward)* **learning modality: kinesthetic**

Building Inquiry Skills: Applying Concepts

Materials *crystal "gardens"*

Tips Crystals exhibit growth similar to that of living systems. Inexpensive crystal "gardens" are available from toy stores, novelty shops, and scientific-supply houses. Allow students to construct the gardens and observe crystal growth for a few days. After crystals form, have students list the characteristics of living things, then state whether the crystals have each characteristic. Ask: **Based on your observations, do you think the crystals are alive?** After class discussion, have students write short paragraphs to support their conclusions. **learning modality: logical/mathematical**

Figure 3 Over time, a tiny acorn develops into a giant oak tree. A great deal of energy is needed to produce the trillions of cells that make up the body of an oak tree. *Comparing and Contrasting In what way does the seedling resemble the oak tree? In what ways is it different?*

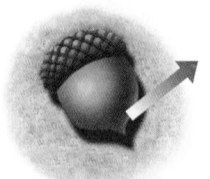 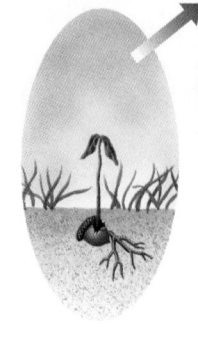 

Acorn   *Seedling*   *Oak tree*

React!

In this activity, you will test your responses to three different stimuli.

1. Have a partner clap his or her hands together about six inches in front of your face. Describe how you react.

2. Look at one of your eyes in a mirror. Cover the eye with your hand for a minute. While looking in the mirror, remove your hand. Observe how the size of your pupil changes.

3. Bring a slice of lemon close to your nose and mouth. Describe what happens.

Classifying For each action performed, name the stimulus and the response.

Energy Use The cells of organisms use energy to do what living things must do, such as grow and repair injured parts. An organism's cells are always hard at work. For example, as you read this paragraph, not only are your eye and brain cells busy, but most of your other cells are working, too. The cells of your stomach and intestine are digesting food. Your blood cells are moving chemicals around your body. If you've hurt yourself, some of your cells are repairing the damage.

Growth and Development Another characteristic of living things is that they grow and develop. Growth is the process of becoming larger. **Development** is the process of change that occurs during an organism's life to produce a more complex organism. For example, as multicellular organisms develop, their cells differentiate, or become specialized. To grow and develop, organisms use energy to create new cells. Look at Figure 3 to see how an acorn develops as it grows into an oak tree.

You may argue that some nonliving things grow and change as they age. For example, a pickup truck rusts as it ages. Icicles grow longer as more water freezes on their tips. But pickup trucks and icicles do not use energy to change and grow. They also don't become more complex over time.

Response to Surroundings If you've ever seen a plant in a sunny window, you may have observed that the plant's stems have bent so that the leaves face the sun. Like a plant bending toward the light, all organisms react to changes in their environment. A change in an organism's surroundings that causes the organism to react is called a **stimulus** (plural *stimuli*). Stimuli include changes in temperature, light, sound, and other factors.

An organism reacts to a stimulus with a **response**—an action or change in behavior. For example, has someone ever leapt out at you from behind a door? If so, it's likely that you jumped or screamed. Your friend's sudden motion was the stimulus that caused your startled response. Nonliving things, such as rocks, do not react to stimuli as living things do.

Reproduction Another characteristic of organisms is the ability to **reproduce,** or produce offspring that are similar to the parents. Robins lay eggs that develop into young robins that closely resemble their parents. Sunflowers produce seeds that develop into sunflower plants, which in turn make more seeds. Bacteria produce other bacteria exactly like themselves.

☑ *Checkpoint* *How do growth and development differ?*

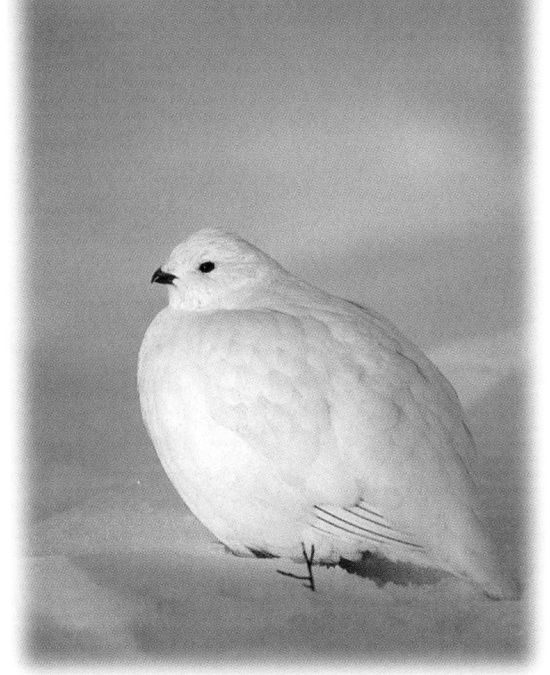

Figure 4 All organisms respond to changes in their surroundings. This willow ptarmigan's feathers have turned white in response to its snowy surroundings. This Alaskan bird's plumage will remain white until spring.

Life Comes From Life

Today, when people observe young plants in a garden or see a litter of puppies, they know that these new organisms are the result of reproduction. Four hundred years ago, however, people believed that life could appear suddenly from nonliving material. For example, when people saw flies swarming around decaying meat, they concluded that flies could arise from rotting meat. When frogs appeared in muddy puddles after heavy rains, people concluded that frogs could sprout from the mud in ponds. The mistaken idea that living things arise from nonliving sources is called **spontaneous generation.**

It took hundreds of years of experiments to convince people that spontaneous generation does not occur. One scientist who did some of these experiments was an Italian doctor, Francesco Redi. In the mid-1600s, Redi designed a controlled experiment to show that flies do not spontaneously arise from decaying meat. In a **controlled experiment,** a scientist carries out two tests that are identical in every respect except for one factor. The one factor that the scientist changes is called the **manipulated variable.** The scientist can conclude that any differences in the results of the two tests must be due to the manipulated variable.

Even after Redi's work, many people continued to believe that spontaneous generation occurred in bacteria. In the mid-1800s,

Life Comes From Life

Building Inquiry Skills: Communicating

To help students better understand the experiments that helped disprove spontaneous generation, tell students they will work in groups to design illustrated posters of Redi and Pasteur's experiments. Divide students into groups. Have them read over the experiments and choose one to illustrate. Suggest they brainstorm how they will present the experiments, perhaps sketching a couple of ideas before they decide on a final model. The illustrations should show all aspects of the experiment, and each of the steps should be labeled or explained. Posters can range from flowcharts to illustrated stories, such as in a comic book format. Tell students to include the scientists' reasoning and conclusions, and a title for the poster. Each of the students in the group should work on producing the poster, such as drawing or coloring the illustrations, or writing captions. They can present their posters as a group to their classmates. Posters can be displayed in the classroom and in the school hall. **learning modality: visual**

Answers to Self-Assessment

Caption Question

Figure 3 The seedling and the tree are both made of cells that contain complex chemicals; use energy, grow and develop; respond to their environment, and are capable of reproduction. Both have stems, roots, and leaves; and are plants. They differ in their size and in their number of cells.

☑ *Checkpoint*

Growth is the process of becoming larger. Development is a process of change that produces a more complex organism.

Ongoing Assessment

Oral Presentation Have students give brief presentations to the class on the topic *How to Design a Controlled Experiment.* Each student should design a different experiment. Encourage students to use visuals in their presentations.

Life Comes From Life, continued

Language Arts Connection

Some students may have problems distinguishing the manipulated variable in an experiment. Write the prefix *vari* on the chalkboard and point out that it means "diverse" or "having different aspects or characteristics." Pair students and have them look up words that begin with *vari*, including *variable*, *variable star*, *variation*, and *vary*. Suggest that students find synonyms that will help them identify the variable being manipulated in an experiment. They should discuss the meanings quietly among themselves. Call on students to share their synonyms and definitions with the class. **limited English proficiency**

The Needs of Living Things

Addressing Naive Conceptions

Students may be confused by the statement that plants make their own food because they are familiar with products marketed as "plant food." Show students the label from a plant-food package. Most of these products contain forms of nitrogen, phosphorus, and potassium. Tell students that these chemicals are not actually food because they are not an energy source, but are nutrients that plants need to convert sunlight, water, and carbon dioxide into food. **learning modality: verbal**

the French chemist Louis Pasteur designed some controlled experiments that finally disproved spontaneous generation. The controlled experiments of Francesco Redi and Louis Pasteur helped to convince people that living things do not arise from nonliving material. Look at *Exploring the Experiments of Redi and Pasteur* to learn more about the experiments they performed.

✓ *Checkpoint* **What is a controlled experiment?**

The Needs of Living Things

Imagine yourself biking through a park on a warm spring day. As you ride by a tree, you see a squirrel running up the tree trunk. Although it may seem that squirrels and trees do not have the

---

EXPLORING the Experiments of Redi and Pasteur

Redi designed one of the first controlled experiments. By Pasteur's time, controlled experiments were standard procedure. As you explore, identify the manipulated variable in each experiment.

FRANCESCO REDI

REDI'S EXPERIMENT

1 Redi placed meat in two identical jars. He left one jar uncovered. He covered the other jar with a cloth that let in air.

2 After a few days, Redi saw maggots (young flies) on the decaying meat in the open jar. There were no maggots on the meat in the covered jar.

3 Redi reasoned that flies had laid eggs on the meat in the open jar. The eggs hatched into maggots. Because flies could not lay eggs on the meat in the covered jar, there were no maggots there. Therefore, Redi concluded that the decaying meat did not produce maggots.

22

Background

History of Science In 1651, an English physician, William Harvey, published a book describing his studies of reproduction. Harvey speculated that insects, worms, and frogs arise from seeds or eggs. Redi had read Harvey's book, so it may have inspired his experiments.

In 1860, the French Academy of Sciences offered a prize to anyone who could "throw new light" on spontaneous generation, and Pasteur responded. He had shown that

organisms in air caused fermentation in milk and alcohol, and decided to investigate whether the organisms were always in the air or arose by spontaneous generation. Pasteur's conclusion that microorganisms develop from other microorganisms in the air was supported in 1876 by another Englishman, physicist John Tyndall. Tyndall was able to show that pure air did not contribute to the production of organisms as regular air did.

same basic needs as you, they do. All organisms need four things to stay alive. **Living things must satisfy their basic needs for energy, water, living space, and stable internal conditions.**

Energy You read earlier that organisms need a source of energy to live. They use food as their energy source. Organisms differ in the ways they obtain their energy. Some organisms, such as plants, capture the sun's energy and use it along with carbon dioxide, a gas found in Earth's atmosphere, and water to make their own food. Organisms that make their own food are called **autotrophs** (AW tuh trawfs). *Auto-* means "self" and *-troph* means "feeder." Autotrophs use the food they make as an energy source to carry out their life functions.

PASTEUR'S EXPERIMENT

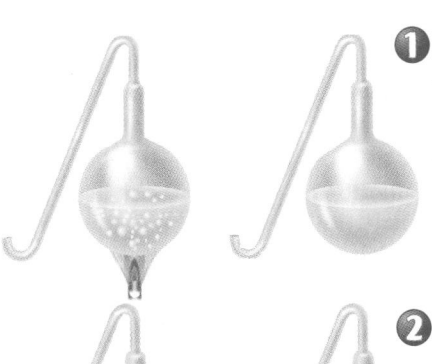

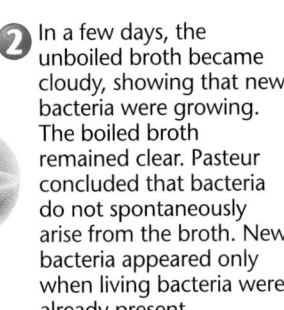

LOUIS PASTEUR

① In one experiment, Pasteur put clear broth into two flasks with curved necks. The necks would let in oxygen but keep out bacteria from the air. Pasteur boiled the broth in one flask to kill any bacteria in the broth. He did not boil the broth in the other flask.

② In a few days, the unboiled broth became cloudy, showing that new bacteria were growing. The boiled broth remained clear. Pasteur concluded that bacteria do not spontaneously arise from the broth. New bacteria appeared only when living bacteria were already present.

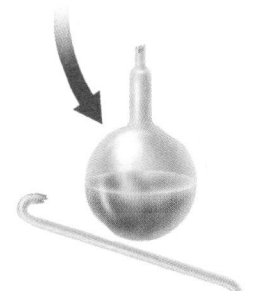

Later, Pasteur took the curve-necked flask containing the broth that had remained clear and broke its long neck. Bacteria from the air could now enter the flask. In a few days, the broth became cloudy. This evidence confirmed Pasteur's conclusion that new bacteria appear only when they are produced by existing bacteria.

Chapter 1 **23**

After students have read about the experiments of Redi and Pasteur, lead students in a discussion of controlled experiments. Draw a compare/contrast table on the chalkboard. Ask: **In Redi's experiment, what factors were identical in each test?** *(Both had meat in a jar and both were exposed to air.)* Invite a volunteer to fill in the compare/contrast table. Ask: **How did the tests differ?** *(Redi covered one of the jars with a cloth.)* Write the answer in the compare/contrast table. Ask: **What factor is the variable?** *(The cloth covering the jar so that flies could not reach the meat. If necessary, remind students that the cloth still allowed the meat to be exposed to air.)* Challenge students to make either a compare/contrast table or a Venn diagram for Pasteur's experiment. When students have finished, ask: **What is the variable in Pasteur's experiment?** *(Whether or not he boiled the broth in the flask to kill any bacteria in the broth)*

Extend Encourage the class to role-play an encounter between the scientists and people who have a strong belief in spontaneous generation. Have two students act as Redi and Pasteur and explain their arguments in answer to questions posed by the class. **learning modality: verbal**

Portfolio Students can save their Venn diagrams or compare/contrast tables in their portfolios.

Media and Technology

 Transparencies "Exploring Redi's Experiment," Transparency 1

 Transparencies "Exploring Pasteur's Experiment," Transparency 2

Answers to Self-Assessment

☑ *Checkpoint*

A controlled experiment involves performing at least two tests that are identical in every respect except for one factor called a variable.

Ongoing Assessment

Writing Ask students to explain how we now know that spontaneous generation does not take place.

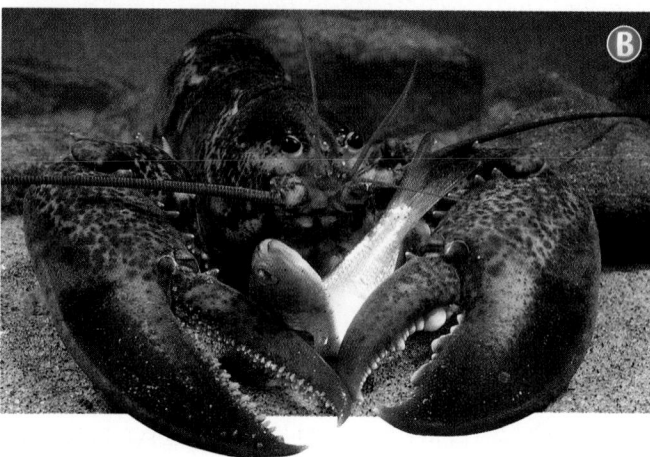

Figure 5 All organisms need a source of energy to live. **A.** *Volvox* is an autotroph that lives in fresh water, where it uses the sun's energy to make its own food. **B.** This American lobster, a heterotroph, is feeding on a herring it has caught. *Applying Concepts How do heterotrophs depend on autotrophs for energy?*

Sharpen your Skills

24

Organisms that cannot make their own food are called **heterotrophs** (HET uh roh trawfs). *Hetero-* means "other." A heterotroph's energy source is also the sun—but in an indirect way. Heterotrophs either eat autotrophs and obtain the energy in the autotroph's stored food, or they consume other heterotrophs that eat autotrophs. Animals, mushrooms, and slime molds are examples of heterotrophs.

Water All living things need water to survive—in fact, most organisms can live for only a few days without water. Organisms need water to do things such as obtain chemicals from their surroundings, break down food, grow, move substances within their bodies, and reproduce.

INTEGRATING CHEMISTRY One important property of water that is vital to living things is its ability to dissolve more chemicals than any other substance on Earth. In your body, for example, water makes up 92 percent of the liquid part of your blood. The food that your cells need dissolves in the blood and is transported throughout your body. Waste from cells dissolves in the blood and is carried away. Your body's cells also provide a watery environment in which chemicals are dissolved. In a sense, you can think of yourself as a person-shaped sack of water in which many substances are dissolved. Fortunately, your body contains some substances that do not dissolve in water, so you hold your shape.

Living Space All organisms need a place to live—a place to get food and water and find shelter. Because there is a limited amount of living space on Earth, some organisms may compete for space. Plants, for example, occupy a fixed living space. Above the ground, their branches and leaves compete for living space with those of other plants. Below ground, their roots compete for water and minerals. Unlike plants, organisms such as animals move around. They may either share living space with others or compete for living space.

Stable Internal Conditions Because conditions in their surroundings can change significantly, organisms must be able to keep the conditions inside their bodies constant. The maintenance of stable internal conditions despite changes in the surroundings is called **homeostasis** (hoh mee oh STAY sis). You know that when you are healthy your body temperature stays constant despite temperature changes in your surroundings. Your body's regulation of temperature is an example of homeostasis.

Other organisms have different mechanisms for maintaining homeostasis. For example, imagine that you are a barnacle attached to a rock at the edge of the ocean. At high tide, the ocean water covers you. At low tide, however, your watery surroundings disappear, and you are exposed to hours of sun and wind. Without a way to keep water in your cells, you'd die. Fortunately, a barnacle can close up its hard outer plates, trapping droplets of water inside. In this way, the barnacle can keep its body moist until the next high tide.

Figure 6 A tree trunk provides these mushrooms with food, water, and shelter.

Section 1 Review

1. Name six characteristics that you have in common with a tree.
2. List the four things that all organisms need to stay alive.
3. How did Pasteur's experiment show that bacteria do not arise spontaneously in broth?
4. **Thinking Critically** **Applying Concepts** You see a crowd of gulls fighting over an object on the wet sand at the ocean's edge. You investigate. The object is a pink blob about as round as a dinner plate. How will you decide if it is a living thing?

Check Your Progress

CHAPTER PROJECT

At this point, you should be ready to carry out your tests for signs of life following your teacher's directions. Before you start, examine your mystery object carefully, and record your observations. Also, decide whether you need to revise the list of life characteristics you prepared earlier. *(Hint: Do not be fooled by the object's appearance—some organisms appear dead during a certain stage of their life.)*

Answers to Self-Assessment

Caption Question

Figure 5 Heterotrophs cannot produce their own food, so they obtain their energy from the food they eat. They either eat autotrophs and directly consume their stored energy, or they eat other heterotrophs that eat autotrophs.

---

3 Assess

Section 1 Review Answers

1. Cellular organization, similar chemicals, use energy, grow and develop, respond to surroundings, and can reproduce.
2. A source of energy, water, living space, and stable internal conditions
3. By heating the broth in one flask, Pasteur killed the bacteria in the broth. No bacteria grew in the heated broth until the broth was exposed to bacteria in the air. Unheated broth was the control.
4. Students might suggest changing a condition in the environment to see if the object responds, examining a sample under the microscope to see if it contains cells, or observing it for a period of time. Accept all answers that describe testing the object to determine whether it has the characteristics of living things.

Check Your Progress

CHAPTER PROJECT

Make sure students are caring for their objects according to your instructions. As you review plans, discuss with students any plans that require deviation from the care instructions. Plans should test for different characteristics and predict how students expect a living thing to respond to each test. Work with students to revise any plans that do not meet your approval.

Performance Assessment

Writing Have students invent a living thing that meets all the criteria outlined in this section. Students should describe their creature and may draw a picture of it.

 Students can save their descriptions and drawings in their portfolios.

Please Pass the Bread!

Preparing for Inquiry

Key Concept Bread mold needs water to grow.

Skills Objective Students will be able to
◆ control variables to determine the effects of different factors;
◆ draw conclusions about how various factors affect the growth of bread mold.

Time 20 minutes first day; 5 minutes per day for the next 5 days or so

Advance Planning The day before, obtain bread without preservatives.

Guiding Inquiry

Troubleshooting the Experiment

◆ Tell students to handle the moist bread gently. Show them how to slide the bread off the side of the plate into a bag.
◆ Students can draw the bread with a grid containing squares of equal size. A 5 × 5 grid contains 25 squares, so each represents 4% of the slice. They can use this drawing to estimate the mold growth.

Expected Outcome

Mold should grow on the moistened bread. Little or no mold should grow on the unmoistened bread.

Analyze and Conclude

1. Mold grows faster with moisture, darkness, and warmth.
2. The variable was moisture. Answers for the manipulated variable in the second experiment will vary.
3. The mold needed water, food (bread), and a place to grow (a dark, warm space).
4. Controlling variables means keeping all conditions the same except the one that the experimenter purposely changes. If variables are not controlled, experimenters cannot be sure which variable caused a specific change.

Extending the Inquiry

Students' designs will vary but should take account of the fact that bread mold spores are in the air.

Please Pass the Bread!

In this lab, you will control variables in an investigation into the needs of living things.

Problem

What factors are necessary for bread molds to grow?

Materials

paper plates	tap water
plastic dropper	packing tape
bread without preservatives	
sealable plastic bags	

Procedure

1. Brainstorm with others to predict which factors might affect the growth of bread mold. Record your ideas.
2. To test the effect of moisture on bread mold growth, place two slices of bread of the same size and thickness on separate, clean plates.
3. Add drops of tap water to one bread slice until the whole slice is moist. Keep the other slice dry. Expose both slices to the air for 1 hour.
4. Put each slice into its own sealable bag. Press the outside of each bag to remove the air. Seal the bags. Then use packing tape to seal the bags again. Store the bags in a warm, dark place.
5. Copy the data table into your notebook.
6. Every day for at least 5 days, briefly remove the sealed bags from their storage place. Record whether any mold has grown. Estimate the area of the bread where mold is present. **CAUTION:** *Do not unseal the bags. At the end of the experiment, give the sealed bags to your teacher.*
7. Choose another factor that may affect mold growth, such as temperature or the amount of light. Set up an experiment to test the factor you choose. Remember to keep all conditions the same except for the one you are testing.

Analyze and Conclude

1. What conclusions can you draw from each of your experiments?
2. What was the variable in the first experiment? In the second experiment?
3. What basic needs of living things were demonstrated in this lab? Explain.
4. **Think About It** What is meant by "controlling variables"? Why is it necessary to control variables in an experiment?

Design an Experiment

Suppose that you lived in Redi's time. A friend tells you that molds just suddenly appear on bread. Design an experiment to show that the new mold comes from existing mold. Consult your teacher before performing the experiment.

DATA TABLE				
	Moistened Bread Slice		**Unmoistened Bread Slice**	
	Mold Present?	Area with Mold	Mold Present?	Area with Mold
Day 1				
Day 2				

Sample Data Table

	Moistened Bread Slice		Unmoistened Bread Slice	
	Mold Present?	Area with Mold	Mold Present?	Area with Mold
Day 1	No		No	
Day 2	No		No	

Safety

Do not open sealed bags. Released mold spores could aggravate allergies, asthma, or other medical problems.

Program Resources

◆ **Unit 1 Resources** Chapter 1 Skills Lab, pp. 31–33
◆ **Inquiry Skills Activity Book** Provides teaching and review of all inquiry skills

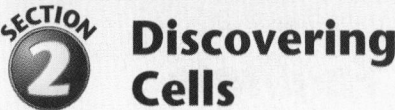
DISCOVER 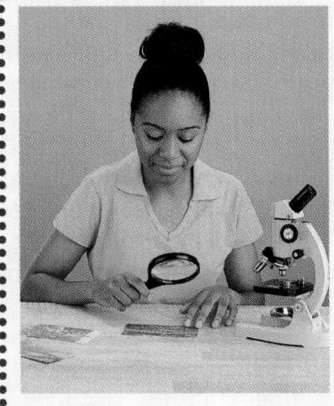 ACTIVITY

Is Seeing Believing?

1. ✂ Cut a black-and-white photograph out of a page in a newspaper. With your eyes alone, closely examine the photo. Record your observations.

2. Examine the same photo with a hand lens. Record your observations.

3. Place the photo on the stage of a microscope. Use the clips to hold the photo in place. Shine a light down on the photo. Focus the microscope on part of the photo. (See Appendix B for instructions on using the microscope.) Record your observations.

Think It Over
Observing What did you see in the photo with the hand lens and the microscope that you could not see with your eyes alone?

A majestic oak tree shades you on a sunny day at the park. A lumbering rhinoceros wanders over to look at you at the zoo. After a rain storm, mushrooms sprout in the damp woods. What do you think an oak tree, a rhinoceros, and a mushroom have in common? You might say that they are all living things. What makes all of these living things alike? If you said that they are made of cells, you are correct.

Cells are the basic units of structure and function in living things. Just as bricks are the building blocks of a house or school, cells are the building blocks of life. Since you are alive, you are made of cells, too. Look closely at the skin on your arm. No

GUIDE FOR READING
◆ How did the invention of the microscope contribute to scientists' understanding of living things?
◆ What is the cell theory?
◆ How does a lens magnify an object?

Reading Tip As you read, make a flowchart showing how the contributions of several scientists led to the development of the cell theory.

Figure 7 This building is made up of individual bricks. Similarly, all living things are made up of individual cells.

READING STRATEGIES

Reading Tip Students should include in their flowcharts contributions made by Janssen, Hooke, Leeuwenhoek, Schlieden, Schwann, and Virchow. Suggest that students illustrate their flowcharts and share them with the class. Also suggest that they save their flowcharts to use as study guides.

You may want to help students construct their flowcharts by writing the first entry or two on the board.

| **Janssen** |
| made one of first compound microscopes |

↓

| **Hooke** |
| saw compartments in cork and called them cells |

Objectives
After completing the lesson, students will be able to
◆ explain how the invention of the microscope contributed to scientists' understanding of living things;
◆ state the three points of the cell theory;
◆ describe how a light microscope works, including how a lens magnifies an object.

Key Terms microscope, compound microscope, cell theory, magnification, convex lens, resolution

1 Engage/Explore

Activating Prior Knowledge
Help students appreciate the large number of cells that make up living things like themselves, by asking: **How many individual grains of sand do you think make up a beach?** (*Students probably will say millions or billions.*) Point out that humans and many other living things are composed of billions of tiny components as well. These components, called cells, are too small to be seen without a microscope.

DISCOVER

Skills Focus observing
Materials *black and white newspaper photograph, scissors, hand lens, microscope*
Time 10 minutes
Tips Set up several microscopes around the room and, if necessary, review with students how to use them.
Expected Outcome With the hand lens and microscope, students should see the individual dots of ink that make up the newspaper photograph. This will help them appreciate how the hand lens and microscope allow them to see objects too small to be seen with the naked eye.
Think It Over Students may say that with the hand lens and microscope they can see that the black and grey shaded areas in the picture actually are made up of separate tiny dots of ink.

2 Facilitate

First Sightings of Cells

Building Inquiry Skills: Classifying

Materials *a collection of several different small items that represent living or nonliving things, such as wood, rubber, cotton, silk, wool, hair, coral, bone, leaves, paper, sand, silt, pebbles, rocks, marbles, and plastic*

Time 10 minutes

Give each student several different items, and instruct students to divide the items into two groups, living things and nonliving things. Tell students to classify as living any item that was part of or is made up of once-living things. Have students compare their groupings and resolve any differences. Ask: **In addition to being composed of cells, can you think of other ways that living things differ from nonliving things?** *(Possible answers are that living things take in energy, give off waste, grow and develop, respond to their environment, and reproduce.)* **learning modality: kinesthetic**

Using the Visuals: Figure 8

Help students appreciate how much Hooke's work contributed to the understanding of the nature of living things. Call their attention to the figure, and then point out that Hooke could not photograph what he saw under the microscope because there were no cameras then. Fortunately, Hooke was a gifted artist, and when he published his book, it became a bestseller. Ask: **Why do you think people were so interested in seeing Hooke's drawings?** *(Because they were drawings of things that up until that time had been invisible, so the book opened up a whole new world to people.)* **learning modality: visual**

matter how hard you look with your eyes alone, you won't be able to see individual skin cells. The reason is that cells are very small. In fact, one square centimeter of your skin's surface contains over 100,000 cells.

First Sightings of Cells

Until the late 1500s there was no way to see cells. No one even knew that cells existed. Around 1590, the invention of the microscope enabled people to look at very small objects. **The invention of the microscope made it possible for people to discover and learn about cells.**

A **microscope** is an instrument that makes small objects look larger. Some microscopes do this by using lenses to focus light. The lenses used in light microscopes are similar to the clear curved pieces of glass used in eyeglasses. A simple microscope contains only one lens. A hand lens is an example of a simple microscope. A light microscope that has more than one lens is called a **compound microscope.**

Robert Hooke One of the first people to observe cells was the English scientist and inventor Robert Hooke. In 1663, Hooke observed the structure of a thin slice of cork using a compound microscope he had built himself. Cork, the bark of the cork oak tree, is made up of cells that are no longer alive. To Hooke, the cork looked like tiny rectangular rooms, which he called *cells*. Hooke described his observations this way: "These pores, or cells, were not very deep...." You can see Hooke's drawings of cork cells in Figure 8. What most amazed Hooke was how many cells the cork contained. He calculated that in a cubic inch there were about 1.2 billion cells—a number he described as "most incredible."

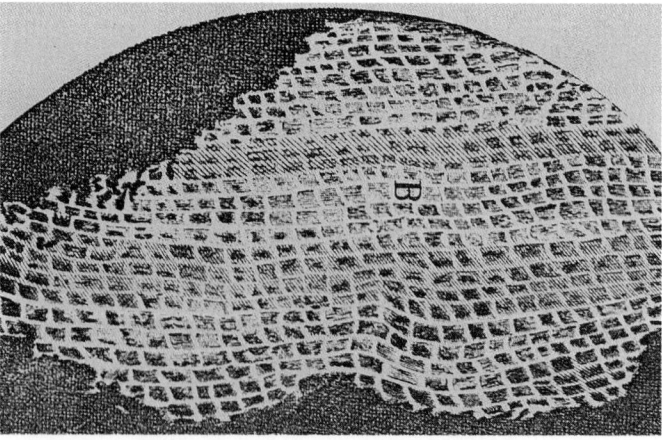

Figure 8 Robert Hooke made this drawing of dead cork cells that he saw through his microscope. Hooke called these structures *cells* because they reminded him of tiny rooms. *Comparing and Contrasting How are cells similar to the bricks in a building? How are they different?*

28

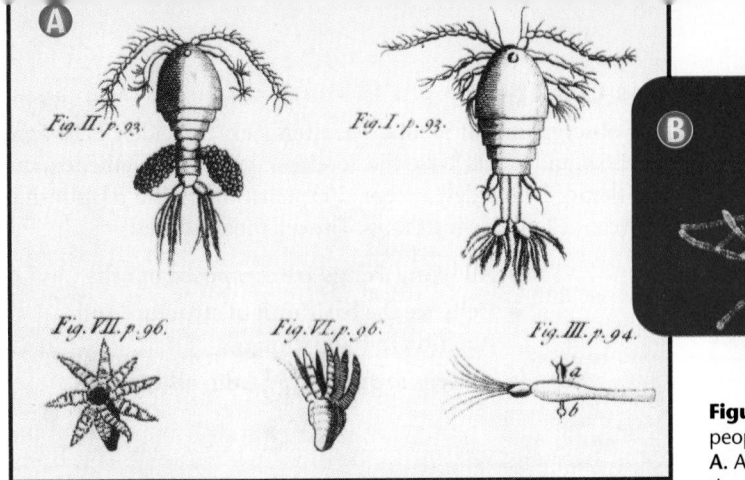

Anton van Leeuwenhoek At about the same time that Robert Hooke made his discovery, Anton van Leeuwenhoek (LAY vun hook) also began to observe tiny objects with microscopes. Leeuwenhoek was a Dutch businessman and amateur scientist who made his own lenses. He then used the lenses to construct simple microscopes.

One of the things Leeuwenhoek looked at was water from a pond. He was surprised to see one-celled organisms, which he called *animalcules* (an uh MAL kyoolz), meaning "little animals."

Leeuwenhoek looked at many other specimens, including scrapings from teeth. When Leeuwenhoek looked at the scrapings, he became the first person to see the tiny single-celled organisms that are now called bacteria. Leeuwenhoek's many discoveries caught the attention of other researchers. Many other people began to use microscopes to see what secrets they could uncover about cells.

Matthias Schleiden and Theodor Schwann Over the years, scientists have continued to use and improve the microscope. They have discovered that all kinds of living things are made up of cells. In 1838, a German scientist named Matthias Schleiden (SHLY dun) concluded that all plants are made of cells. He based this conclusion on his own research and on the research of others before him. The next year, another German scientist, Theodor Schwann, concluded that all animals are also made up of cells. Thus, stated Schwann, all living things are made up of cells.

Schleiden and Schwann had made an important discovery about living things. However, they didn't understand where cells came from. Until their time, most people thought that living things could come from nonliving matter. In 1855, a German doctor, Rudolf Virchow (FUR koh) proposed that new cells are formed only from existing cells. "All cells come from cells," wrote Virchow.

✓ *Checkpoint* What did Schleiden and Schwann conclude about cells?

Figure 9 Microscopes allow people to look at very small objects. **A.** Anton van Leeuwenhoek made these drawings of organisms in the late 1600s after looking through a simple microscope. **B.** This is a hydra, a tiny water organism, as seen through a modern microscope. Compare this hydra to the one Leeuwenhoek drew, which is labeled Fig. III.

Answers to Self-Assessment

Caption Question

Figure 8 Cells are the building blocks of organisms as bricks are the building blocks of buildings. However, bricks, unlike cells, are not alive.

✓ *Checkpoint*

Schleiden concluded that all plants are made of cells. Schwann concluded that all animals are also made of cells.

Building Inquiry Skills: Inferring

Help students infer the nature of the scientific process by asking: **Why do you think it took almost 200 years after cells were discovered for scientists to conclude that all living things consist of cells?** (*Students may say that there were far fewer scientists and microscopes than today, yet scientists had to examine thousands of samples of living things before they could reasonably conclude that all living things are made of cells.*) **learning modality: logical/mathematical**

Using the Visuals: Figure 9

Call students' attention to the figure and ask them to compare and contrast Leeuwenhoek's drawing in Fig. III with the photo of the hydra. Ask: **What are the similarities between the drawing and the photo?** (*They are both of the same organism as seen under a microscope.*) **What are the differences?** (*The drawing shows less detail than the photo.*) Point out that scientists needed the ability to draw accurate sketches before photography was developed in the 19th century. **learning modality: visual**

Ongoing Assessment

Writing Have students explain how the invention of the microscope led to the discovery of the cell.

The Cell Theory

SCIENCE & History

Guide students who need more help in organizing and comprehending the technical information in the feature. First point out that, up until 1933, all microscopes operated under the same general principle: They used lenses to focus light on or through an object in order to magnify it enough to be seen by the human eye. Then ask: **How do electron microscopes differ from light microscopes?** (*Instead of using light, electron microscopes use electrons to "see" an object.*) **How does this difference make electron microscopes better?** (*They can magnify objects much more than light microscopes and provide different views of an object.*) **What are TEMs, SEMs, and STMs?** (*Transmission electron microscope, scanning electron microscope, and scanning tunneling microscope, respectively.*) **How are TEMs, SEMs, and STMs the same, and how are they different?** (*All three use electrons instead of light to view objects. A TEM sends electrons through objects, so it is good for seeing the insides of things. A SEM sends electrons over the surfaces of objects, so it can create three-dimensional images of them. A STM records electrons "leaking" from the surface of objects, so it can show individual molecules on the object's surface.*) **Which type of electron microscope has the greatest magnification?** (*STM, which can magnify an object up to 1,000,000 times its actual size*)

In Your Journal To stimulate ideas in visual learners, have students look at the many figures throughout the chapter that contain pictures of objects as seen through a microscope. Advise students to consider the time period they are writing about if they choose one of the earlier microscopes for their advertisement. Point out that, although Hooke's 17th century sketch of cork cells in Figure 8 looks crude compared with the late 20th century electron microscope photo of the single-celled organism in Figure 16, Hooke's images were novel and exciting to the people who lived at that time.
learning modality: verbal

The Cell Theory
The observations of Hooke, Leeuwenhoek, Schleiden, Schwann, Virchow, and others led to the development of the **cell theory.** The cell theory is a widely accepted explanation of the relationship between cells and living things. **The cell theory states:**

- ◆ **All living things are composed of cells.**
- ◆ **Cells are the basic unit of structure and function in living things.**
- ◆ **All cells are produced from other cells.**

SCIENCE & History

The Microscope— Improvements Over Time

The discovery of cells would not have been possible without the microscope. Microscopes have been improved in many ways over the last 400 years.

1660
Hooke's Compound Microscope

Robert Hooke improved on the compound microscope. The stand at the right holds oil for a flame, which shines light on the specimen under the microscope.

1600 ———————————————— **1750**

1590
First Compound Microscope

Hans Janssen and his son Zacharias, Dutch eyeglass makers, made one of the first compound microscopes. Their microscope was simply a tube with a lens at each end.

1683
Leeuwenhoek's Simple Microscope

Although Leeuwenhoek's simple microscope used only one tiny lens, it could magnify a specimen up to 266 times. Leeuwenhoek was the first person to see many one-celled organisms, including bacteria.

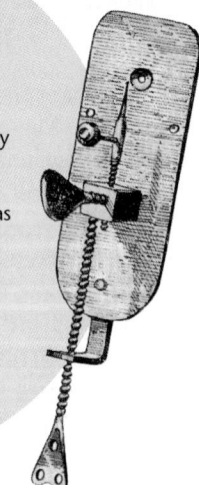

30

Background

Facts and Figures To differentiate among particular cell structures under a microscope, scientists may stain the tissue to be examined. Different stains color different structures inside cells. For example, a stain called hematoxylin colors the cell's nucleus, the area where most nucleic acids in the cell are found.

Before staining the tissue, a scientist shaves off extremely thin slices with a precision cutting instrument called a microtome. The microtome can cut slices so thin that they are less than one cell thick. This allows a clear view of even the tiniest cell structures. When the slices are stained, scientists can differentiate among numerous tiny cell structures.

The cell theory holds true for all living things, no matter how big or small, or how simple or complex. Since cells are common to all living things, they can provide information about all life. And because all cells come from other cells, scientists can study cells to learn about growth, reproduction, and all other functions that living things perform. By learning about cells and how they function, you can learn about all types of living things.

☑ *Checkpoint* *Which scientists contributed to the development of the cell theory?*

In Your Journal

Choose one of the microscopes. Write an advertisement for it that might appear in a popular science magazine. Be creative. Emphasize the microscope's usefulness or describe the wonders that can be seen with it.

1933
Transmission Electron Microscope (TEM)

The German physicist Ernst Ruska created the first electron microscope. TEMs make images by sending electrons through a very thinly sliced specimen. They can only examine dead specimens, but are very useful for viewing internal cell structures. TEMs can magnify a specimen up to 500,000 times.

1981
Scanning Tunneling Microscope (STM)

A STM measures electrons that leak, or "tunnel," from the surface of a specimen. With a STM, scientists can see individual molecules on the outer layer of a cell. STMs can magnify a specimen up to 1,000,000 times.

1900   **2050**

1886
Modern Compound Light Microscope

German scientists Ernst Abbé and Carl Zeiss made a compound light microscope similar to this one. The horseshoe stand helps keep the microscope steady. The mirror at the bottom focuses light up through the specimen. Modern compound light microscopes can magnify a specimen up to 1,000 times.

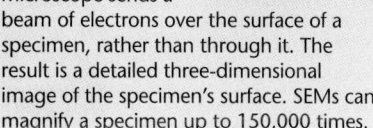

1965
Scanning Electron Microscope (SEM)

The first commercial SEM is produced. This microscope sends a beam of electrons over the surface of a specimen, rather than through it. The result is a detailed three-dimensional image of the specimen's surface. SEMs can magnify a specimen up to 150,000 times.

Chapter 1 **31**

Answers to Self-Assessment

☑ *Checkpoint*

Hooke, Leeuwenhoek, Schleiden, Schwann, and Virchow contributed to the development of the cell theory.

Addressing Naive Conceptions

Students may think the cell theory is not well-established because it is called a theory. Explain that in everyday speech, people often use the word *theory* to mean speculation or conjecture. However, in science a theory is a well-tested concept that consistently explains a wide range of observations and predicts future events. Point out that a theory may be the best explanation to date, but no theory is beyond dispute. Ask: **Do you think the cell theory has been proven conclusively? Explain.** *(No, it is not possible for scientists to examine every single living thing to determine if it is composed of cells, and a single exception would disprove the theory.)* **learning modality: verbal**

Including All Students

Materials *microscope, slide, coverslip*

Time 15 minutes

Let students actually experience the difference that the degree of magnification can make in how objects appear under a microscope. Have students choose a suitable object, such as a strand of human hair, to place on a slide with a coverslip and view under the microscope, first at low and then at high power. For students whose movements are limited, you can use a microprojector to project the images on a screen. Have students draw a simple sketch of what they see under each magnification. Remind them to label their drawings with the magnification. Ask volunteers to share their drawings with the class and have other students try to identify each object from the drawings. **learning modality: visual**

Ongoing Assessment

Oral Presentation Call on students at random to state Leeuwenhoek's contributions to science. *(Leeuwenhoek made microscopes powerful enough to see single-celled organisms, and he was the first person to see bacteria.)*

How a Light Microscope Works

Integrating Physics

Materials *convex lens (hand lens)*

Time 10 minutes

Group students in pairs, and instruct one student to hold a hand lens steady at about 10 cm above a page. Tell the other student to move closer to or farther from the lens until the letters on the page come into focus. At this point, have both students note the relative positions of the eye, lens, and page and compare them with their positions in Figure 10. Ask: **At what position is your eye?** *(At the focal point)* By moving their eye farther back from the lens, students can see the difference between magnification and resolution. Ask: **How does the object appear now?** *(Even larger but blurry, or out of focus)* Have students switch positions and repeat the activity.
learning modality: kinesthetic

Sharpen your *Skills*

Observing

Materials *prepared slide of cork, microscope, pond water, plastic dropper, slide, coverslip*
Time 15 minutes
Tips Make sure students have focused the microscope and can see the cells clearly before they start their drawings.
Expected Outcome Students' drawings of cork cells should resemble Hooke's drawing on page 28. Students' drawings of pond water should show various microorganisms. Leeuwenhoek called the organisms he saw "little animals" because they moved as animals move.
Extend Ask: **What do you think a drop of tap water would look like under the microscope?** *(It would contain few if any microorganisms.)* **learning modality: visual**

32

Observing

1. Place a prepared slide of a thin slice of cork on the stage of a microscope.
2. Observe the slide under low power. Draw what you see.
3. Place a few drops of pond water on another slide and cover it with a coverslip.
4. Observe the slide under low power. Draw what you see. Wash your hands after handling pond water.

Observing How does your drawing in Step 2 compare to Hooke's drawing in Figure 8? Based on your observations in Step 4, why did Leeuwenhoek call the organisms he saw "little animals"?

How a Light Microscope Works

INTEGRATING PHYSICS Microscopes use lenses to make small objects look larger. But simply enlarging a small object is not useful unless you can see the details clearly. For a microscope to be useful to a scientist, it must combine two important properties—magnification and resolution.

Magnification The first property, **magnification,** is the ability to make things look larger than they are. **The lens or lenses in a light microscope magnify an object by bending the light that passes through them.** If you examine a hand lens, you will see that the glass lens is curved, not flat. The center of the lens is thicker than the edges. A lens with this curved shape is called a **convex lens.** Look at Figure 10 to see how light is bent by a convex lens. The light passing through the sides of the lens bends inward. When this light hits the eye, the eye sees the object as larger than it really is.

Because a compound microscope uses more than one lens, it can magnify an object even more. Light passes through a specimen and then through two lenses. Figure 10 also shows the path that light takes through a compound microscope. The first lens near the specimen magnifies the object. Then a second lens near the eye further magnifies the enlarged image. The total magnification of the microscope is equal to the magnifications of the two lenses multiplied together. For example, if the first lens has a magnification of 10 and the second lens has a magnification of 40, then the total magnification of the microscope is 400.

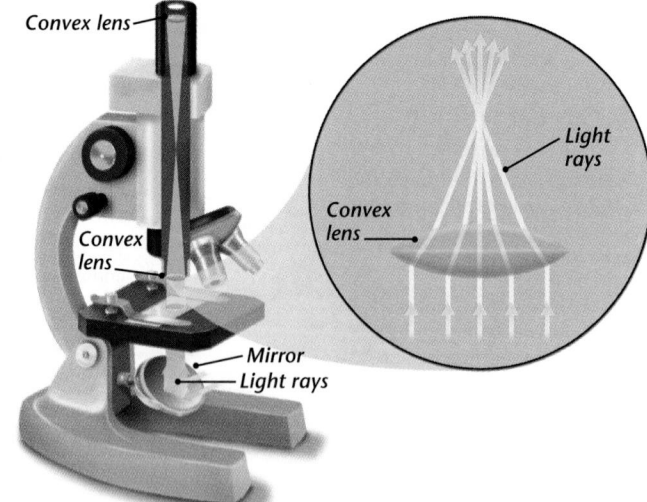

Figure 10 Microscopes use lenses to make objects look larger. A compound microscope has two convex lenses. Each convex lens bends light, making the image larger. *Calculating If one lens had a magnification of 10, and the other lens had a magnification of 50, what would the total magnification be?*

32

Resolution To create a useful image, a microscope must also help you see individual parts clearly. The ability to clearly distinguish the individual parts of an object is called **resolution.** Resolution is another term for the sharpness of an image.

For example, when you use your eyes to look at a photo printed in a newspaper, it looks like a complete picture from one side to the other. That picture, however, is really made up of a collection of small dots. To the unaided eye, two tiny dots close together appear as one. If you put the photo under a microscope, however, you can see the dots. You see the dots not only because they are magnified but also because the microscope improves resolution. Good resolution—being able to see fine detail—is not needed when you are reading the newspaper. But it is just what you need when you study cells.

Electron Microscopes

The microscopes used by Hooke, Leeuwenhoek, and other early researchers were all light microscopes. Since the 1930s, scientists have developed a different type of microscope called an electron microscope. Electron microscopes use a beam of electrons instead of light to examine a specimen. Electrons are tiny particles that are smaller than atoms. The resolution of electron microscopes is much higher than the resolution of light microscopes. As the technology of microscopes keeps improving, scientists will continue to learn more about the structure and function of cells.

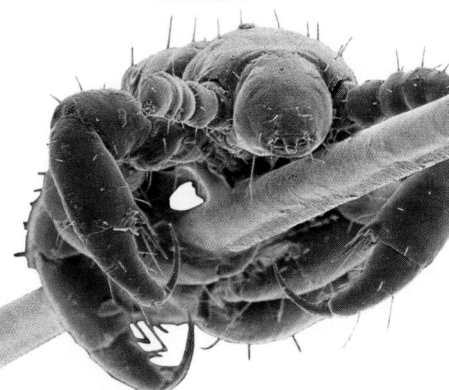

Figure 11 This head louse, shown clinging to a human hair, was photographed through a scanning electron microscope. It has been magnified to about 80 times its actual size.

Section 2 Review

1. How did the invention of the microscope affect scientists' understanding of living things?
2. Explain the three main ideas of the cell theory.
3. How does a compound microscope use lenses to magnify an object?
4. Explain why both magnification and resolution are important when viewing a small object with a microscope.
5. **Thinking Critically** **Applying Concepts** Why do scientists learn more about cells each time the microscope is improved?

Check Your Progress CHAPTER PROJECT
Observe your object at least once a day. Record your observations in a data table. Draw accurate diagrams. *(Hint: Measuring provides important information. Take measurements of your object regularly. If you cannot measure it directly, make estimates.)*

Chapter 1 **33**

Answers to Self-Assessment

Caption Question

Figure 10 The total magnification would be 10×50, or 500.

Electron Microscopes

Including All Students

Urge students who need extra challenges to work together to prepare a presentation on electron microscopes, which may be difficult for some students to understand. The presentation should explain in simple terms how electron microscopes work and why electron microscopes can magnify so greatly. **cooperative learning**

3 Assess

Section 2 Review Answers

1. The invention of the microscope made it possible for people to discover and learn about cells.
2. According to the cell theory, all living things are made of cells, cells are the basic building blocks of life, and they are the only source of new cells.
3. Light passing through the first lens magnifies the object; then light passing through the second lens magnifies the image of the object even more.
4. Both magnification and resolution are important because magnification makes an object larger whereas resolution sharpens the image so you can see details.
5. Each time the microscope is improved, scientists can see structures in cells in greater detail and more clearly.

Check Your Progress CHAPTER PROJECT
Make sure students spend time making observations of their object. If students seem bored because their object is not doing anything, encourage them to consider whether this inactivity proves that the object is not alive, or whether they should revise their methods of observation. For example, encourage students to explain how they could be sure that the object is not breathing or growing.

Performance Assessment

Skills Check Have students compare and contrast light microscopes and electron microscopes.

Objectives

After completing the lesson, students will be able to
◆ identify the cell wall, cell membrane, and nucleus, and describe their functions;
◆ identify other organelles in the cell and describe their functions;
◆ compare bacterial cells with plant and animal cells;
◆ describe the role of specialized cells in many-celled organisms.

Key Terms organelle, cell wall, cell membrane, nucleus, chromatin, cytoplasm, mitochondrion, endoplasmic reticulum, ribosome, Golgi body, chloroplast, vacuole, lysosome, prokaryote, eukaryote

1 Engage/Explore

Activating Prior Knowledge

Introduce students to the division of labor among structures in cells by relating it to the division of labor in a community. Ask: **How are the various jobs in a town divided up among people?** *(Possible answers might include: shopkeepers supply food, police officers enforce laws, and the mayor and city council members make decisions.)* **Why is it effective to divide the labor in this way?** *(By dividing the labor, people can become specialized at the work they do and do it more effectively.)*

DISCOVER

Skills Focus inferring
Materials *calculator, metric ruler*

Time 10 minutes
Tips Have partners measure each other's height with a metric ruler.
Expected Outcome A student who is 1.5 m tall would be the same height as a stack of 1,500 amebas. The same student would be 150,000 body cells tall.
Think It Over Students should infer that they cannot see body cells without a microscope because they are too small.

DISCOVER · ACTIVITY

How Large Are Cells?

1. Look at the organism in the photo. The organism is an ameba, a large single-celled organism. This type of ameba is about 1 millimeter (mm) long.

2. Multiply your height in meters by 1,000 to get your height in millimeters. How many amebas would you have to stack end-to-end to equal your height?

3. Many of the cells in your body are about 0.01 mm long—one hundredth the size of an ameba. How many body cells would you have to stack end-to-end to equal your height?

Think It Over
Inferring Look at a metric ruler to see how small 1 mm is. Now imagine a distance one-hundredth as long, or 0.01 mm. Why can't you see your body's cells without the aid of a microscope?

GUIDE FOR READING

◆ What role do the cell membrane and nucleus play in the cell?

◆ What functions do other organelles in the cell perform?

◆ How do bacterial cells differ from plant and animal cells?

Reading Tip Before you read, preview *Exploring Plant and Animal Cells* on pages 38–39. Make a list of any unfamiliar terms. As you read, write a definition for each term.

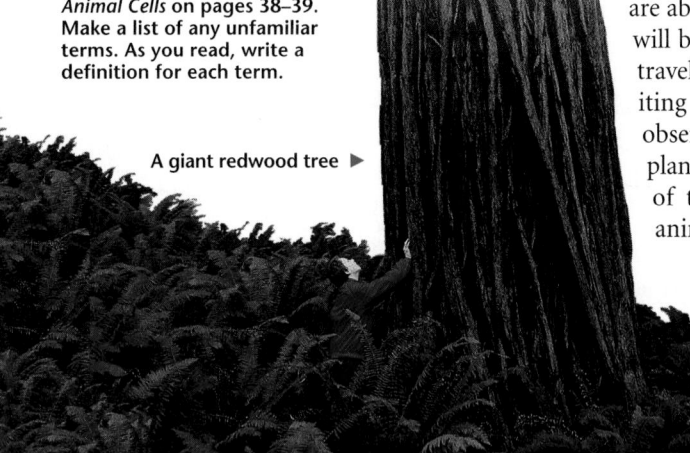

A giant redwood tree ▶

Imagine you're in California standing next to a giant redwood tree. You have to bend your head way back to see the top of the tree. Some of these trees are over 110 meters tall and more than 10 meters in circumference! How do redwoods grow so large? How do they carry out all the functions necessary to stay alive?

To answer these questions, and to learn many other things about living things, you are about to take an imaginary journey. It will be quite an unusual trip. You will be traveling inside a living redwood tree, visiting its tiny cells. On your trip you will observe some of the structures found in plant cells. You will also learn about some of the differences between plant and animal cells.

READING STRATEGIES

Reading Tip Have students list all the unfamiliar boldface terms in *Exploring Plant and Animal Cells*. They will probably include terms such as endoplasmic reticulum and mitochondrion among others. You may want to suggest that they list the words on notecards and write the definition of each word on the other side of the card. They can use the cards to study.

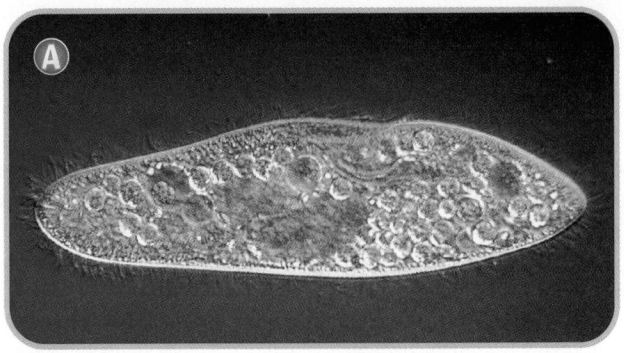

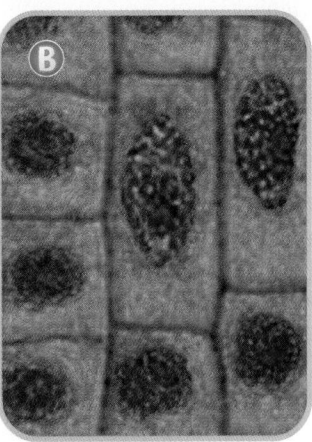

Figure 12 All cells have cell membranes, but not all cells have cell walls. **A.** The cell membrane of this single-celled paramecium controls what substances enter and leave the cell. **B.** The cell walls of these onion root cells have been stained green so you can see them clearly. Cell walls protect and support plant cells.

As you will discover on your journey, cells themselves contain even smaller structures. These tiny cell structures, called **organelles,** carry out specific functions within the cell. Just as your stomach, lungs, and heart have different functions in your body, each organelle has a different function within the cell. You can see the organelles found in plant and animal cells in *Exploring Plant and Animal Cells* on pages 38 and 39. Now it's time to hop aboard your imaginary ship and prepare to enter a typical plant cell.

Cell Wall

Entering a plant's cell is a bit difficult. First you must pass through the cell wall. The **cell wall** is a rigid layer of nonliving material that surrounds the cells of plants and some other organisms. The cell wall is made of a tough, yet flexible, material called cellulose. If you think of a stalk of celery, you will have a good idea of what cellulose is. Celery contains a lot of cellulose.

The cells of plants and some other organisms have cell walls. In contrast, the cells of animals and some other organisms lack cell walls. A plant's cell wall helps to protect and support the cell. In woody plants, the cell walls are very rigid. This is why giant redwood trees can stand so tall. Each cell wall in the tree adds strength to the tree. Although the cell wall is stiff, many materials, including water and oxygen, can pass through the cell wall quite easily. So sail on through the cell wall and enter the cell.

☑ *Checkpoint* What is the function of the cell wall?

Cell Membrane

After you pass through the cell wall, the next structure you encounter is the **cell membrane.** All cells have cell membranes. In cells with cell walls, the cell membrane is located just inside the cell wall. In other cells, the cell membrane forms the outside boundary that separates the cell from its environment.

Chapter 1 **35**

Answers to Self-Assessment

☑ *Checkpoint*
The function of the cell wall is to help protect and support the cell.

2 Facilitate

Cell Wall

Building Inquiry Skills: Inferring

Extend the analogy in the text by first naming several different parts of the body, including the brain, skin, and blood vessels, and challenging students to identify their roles in the body. Point out that each cell, like the body as a whole, has structures that perform similar functions. Then ask: **What are the functions of some organelles you would expect to find in the cell?** *(Answers should include an organelle like the brain to control the rest of the cell, an organelle like the skin to enclose and protect the cell, and an organelle like the blood vessels to carry materials from one part of the cell to another.)* **learning modality: logical/mathematical**

Cell Membrane

Including All Students

Help students still mastering English build language skills and improve their understanding of the cell membrane. First, challenge students to find the origin of the word *membrane* in a dictionary. *(Membrane comes from the Latin word,* membrana, *which means "skin.")* Then ask: **Do you think the skin on your body is a good analogy for the cell membrane? Why or why not?** *(Most students probably will say that the skin is a good analogy for the cell membrane, because both the cell membrane and the skin enclose and protect what's inside.)* **limited English proficiency**

Ongoing Assessment

Oral Presentation Call on students at random to identify differences and similarities between cell walls and cell membranes.

Language Arts
CONNECTION

The analogy in the text, in which the cell membrane is compared with a window screen, is an extended analogy, because it is more than just a brief statement of comparison. Referring to the nucleus as the cell's "brain" is a simple analogy.

In Your Journal Examples of simple analogies in this section include referring to the mitochondria as the cell's "powerhouses" and the ribosomes as the cell's "factories." After students have finished writing in their journals, ask: **Why do analogies help you better understand the parts of a cell?** *(Because they compare them with things that are more familiar or easier to understand.)*
learning modality: verbal

Nucleus

Building Inquiry Skills: Comparing and Contrasting

Time 5 minutes

ACTIVITY

Help students avoid confusing the cell membrane and nuclear membrane by having them form two concentric circles in the classroom and asking: **Which circle represents the nuclear membrane? Which circle represents the cell membrane?** *(The inner circle represents the nuclear membrane. The outer circle represents the cell membrane.)* **How is the nuclear membrane like the cell membrane? How is it different?** *(Both are thin films that enclose and protect what is inside the membrane. However, the nuclear membrane encloses and protects just the cell's nucleus, whereas the cell membrane encloses and protects the entire cell.)*
learning modality: kinesthetic

Language Arts
CONNECTION

Writers often use analogies to help readers understand unfamiliar ideas. In an analogy, a writer explains something by comparing it to something similar with which the reader is more familiar. For example, the author of this textbook describes the cell membrane by making an analogy to a window screen. This analogy helps the readers understand that the cell membrane is a boundary that separates the cell from the outside environment.

In Your Journal

Identify other analogies used by the author. Then choose two cell parts from this section. Write an analogy for each part that helps explain its structure or function.

As your ship nears the edge of the cell membrane, you notice that there are tiny openings, or pores, in the cell membrane. You steer toward an opening. Suddenly, your ship narrowly misses being struck by a chunk of waste material passing out of the cell. **You have discovered one of the cell membrane's main functions: the cell membrane controls what substances come into and out of a cell.**

Everything the cell needs—from food to oxygen—enters the cell through the cell membrane. Harmful waste products leave the cell through the cell membrane. For a cell to survive, the cell membrane must allow these materials to pass into and out of the cell. In a sense, the cell membrane is like a window screen. The screen keeps insects out of a room. But holes in the screen allow air to enter and leave the room.

Nucleus

As you sail inside the cell, a large, oval structure comes into view. This structure, called the **nucleus** (NOO klee us), acts as the "brain" of the cell. **You can think of the nucleus as the cell's control center, directing all of the cell's activities.**

Nuclear Membrane Notice in Figure 13 that the nucleus is surrounded by a nuclear membrane. Just as the cell membrane protects the cell, the nuclear membrane protects the nucleus. Materials pass in and out of the nucleus through small openings, or pores, in the nuclear membrane. So aim for that pore just ahead and carefully glide into the nucleus.

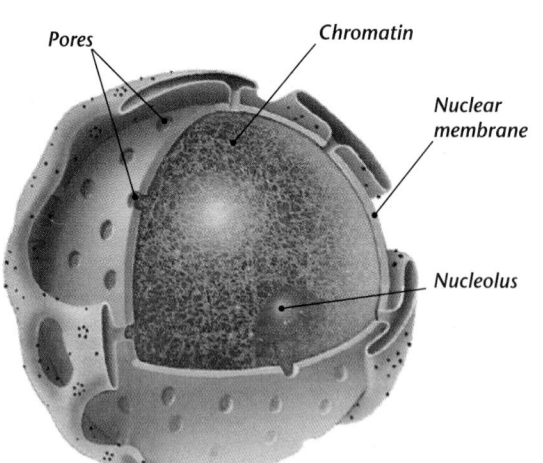

Pores

Chromatin

Nuclear membrane

Nucleolus

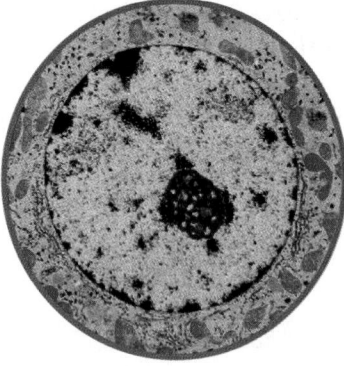

Figure 13 The nucleus is the cell's control center. The chromatin in the nucleus contains instructions for carrying out the cell's activities.

Background

Facts and Figures In both plant and animal cells, mitochondria have a smooth outer membrane and a folded inner membrane with a lot of surface area where chemical reactions take place. Because energy is released during these chemical reactions, mitochondria frequently are called the "powerhouses" of the cell.

Both mitochondria and chloroplasts have a double membrane and the ability to divide. In addition, both contain small amounts of DNA. These three features also characterize some bacteria, leading some biologists to think that mitochondria and chloroplasts are descendants of bacteria that lived as independent organisms long ago.

Chromatin You might wonder how the nucleus "knows" how to direct the cell. The answer lies in those thin strands floating directly ahead in the nucleus. These strands, called **chromatin,** contain the genetic material, the instructions that direct the functions of a cell. For example, the instructions in the chromatin ensure that leaf cells grow and divide to form more leaf cells. The genetic material is passed on to each new cell when an existing cell divides. You'll learn more about how cells divide in Chapter 2.

Nucleolus As you prepare to leave the nucleus, you spot a small object floating by. This structure, the nucleolus, is where ribosomes are made. Ribosomes are the organelles where proteins are produced.

☑ *Checkpoint* *Where in the nucleus is genetic material found?*

Organelles in the Cytoplasm

As you leave the nucleus, you find yourself in the **cytoplasm,** the region between the cell membrane and the nucleus. Your ship floats in a clear, thick, gel-like fluid. The fluid in the cytoplasm is constantly moving, so your ship does not need to propel itself. Many cell organelles are found in the cytoplasm. **The organelles function to produce energy, build and transport needed materials, and store and recycle wastes.**

Mitochondria As you pass into the cytoplasm, you see rod-shaped structures looming ahead. These organelles are called **mitochondria** (my tuh KAHN dree uh) (singular *mitochondrion*). Mitochondria are called the "powerhouses" of the cell because they produce most of the energy the cell needs to carry out its functions. Muscle cells and other very active cells have large numbers of mitochondria.

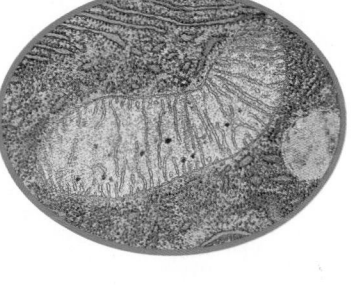

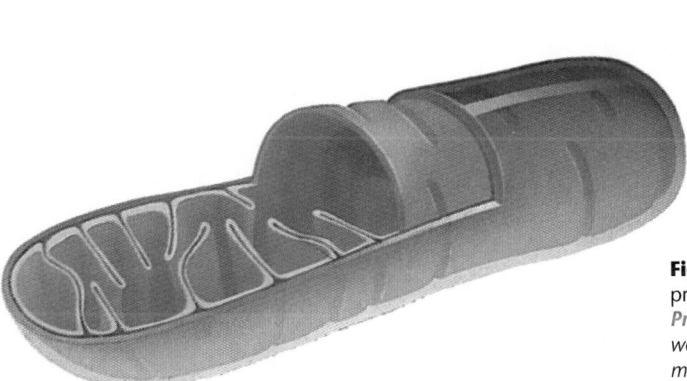

Figure 14 The mitochondria produce most of the cell's energy. *Predicting In what types of cells would you expect to find a lot of mitochondria?*

Chapter 1 **37**

Answers to Self-Assessment

☑ *Checkpoint*
The genetic material in the nucleus is found in strands called chromatin.

Caption Question
Figure 14 You would expect to find a lot of mitochondria in muscle cells and other very active cells.

Addressing Naive Conceptions

Students may think that different types of cells within an organism must contain different genetic material. Point out that the same genetic material is found in every cell of an organism. Explain that different cells, such as skin and blood cells, look and function so differently because they respond to different genetic instructions. Ask: **Can you think of an analogy to cells containing the same genetic material, yet looking and functioning differently because they are following different genetic instructions?** *(One analogy is the same cookbook being used by different cooks to make different recipes.)* **learning modality: verbal**

Organelles in the Cytoplasm

Inquiry Challenge

Materials *sheets of plain white paper, markers, cans of food, bottles of water, batteries, storage boxes, other miscellaneous items*
Time 15 minutes

After students have read about all of the organelles, challenge them to make a human model of a cell that shows how two or more organelles function. One possible way is for one student to represent each type of organelle and the rest of the class to represent the cell and nuclear membranes. Provide students with paper and markers for making signs and with props such as those listed above. Have them demonstrate the functioning of the organelles. *(For example, a sign labeled "protein" might be passed from a student representing a ribosome to a student representing an endoplasmic reticulum, who then carries the "protein" to the students representing the cell membrane, one of whom passes the sign out of the "cell.")* **cooperative learning**

Ongoing Assessment

Communication Ask students to draw a cell and label the three structures of the nucleus.

EXPLORING
Plant and Animal Cells

Call students' attention to the feature, and ask if they have any questions. Point out that some cell structures, including Golgi bodies, ribosomes, and mitochondria, are defined on just one drawing or the other because they are much the same in both plant cells and animal cells. Help students organize the material in the feature by creating a table on the chalkboard titled "Comparison of Plant and Animal Cells." For headings use *Similarities* and *Differences,* and for rows use *Plants* and *Animals.* Encourage students to interpret the diagrams and other information in the feature to help fill in the cells of the table. Stimulate their thinking by asking: **Which organelles are found only in plant cells? Which are found in both plant and animal cells?** (*Except for cell walls and chloroplasts, most organelles are found in both plant and animal cells.*) Complete the table as students volunteer their ideas. When the table is finished, you may want to have students copy it in a notebook and refer to it as they study this section. **learning modality: verbal**

Addressing Naive Conceptions

Emphasize that the drawings of plant and animal cells shown in the feature are generalized representations of cells. In reality, cells can take on many different shapes and sizes. They also can vary in the specific organelles they contain. For comparison, show students drawings of other types of cells, such as leaf and root cells for plants and muscle and bone cells for animals. In each drawing, challenge students to locate the cell membrane and organelles if these are visible. Ask: **Why do you think different cells look so different from each other?** (*Because they play different roles in the organism.*) **learning modality: visual**

EXPLORING Plant and Animal Cells

On these pages, you can compare structures found in two kinds of cells: plant cells and animal cells. As you study these cells, remember that they are generalized cells. In living organisms, cells vary somewhat in shape and structure.

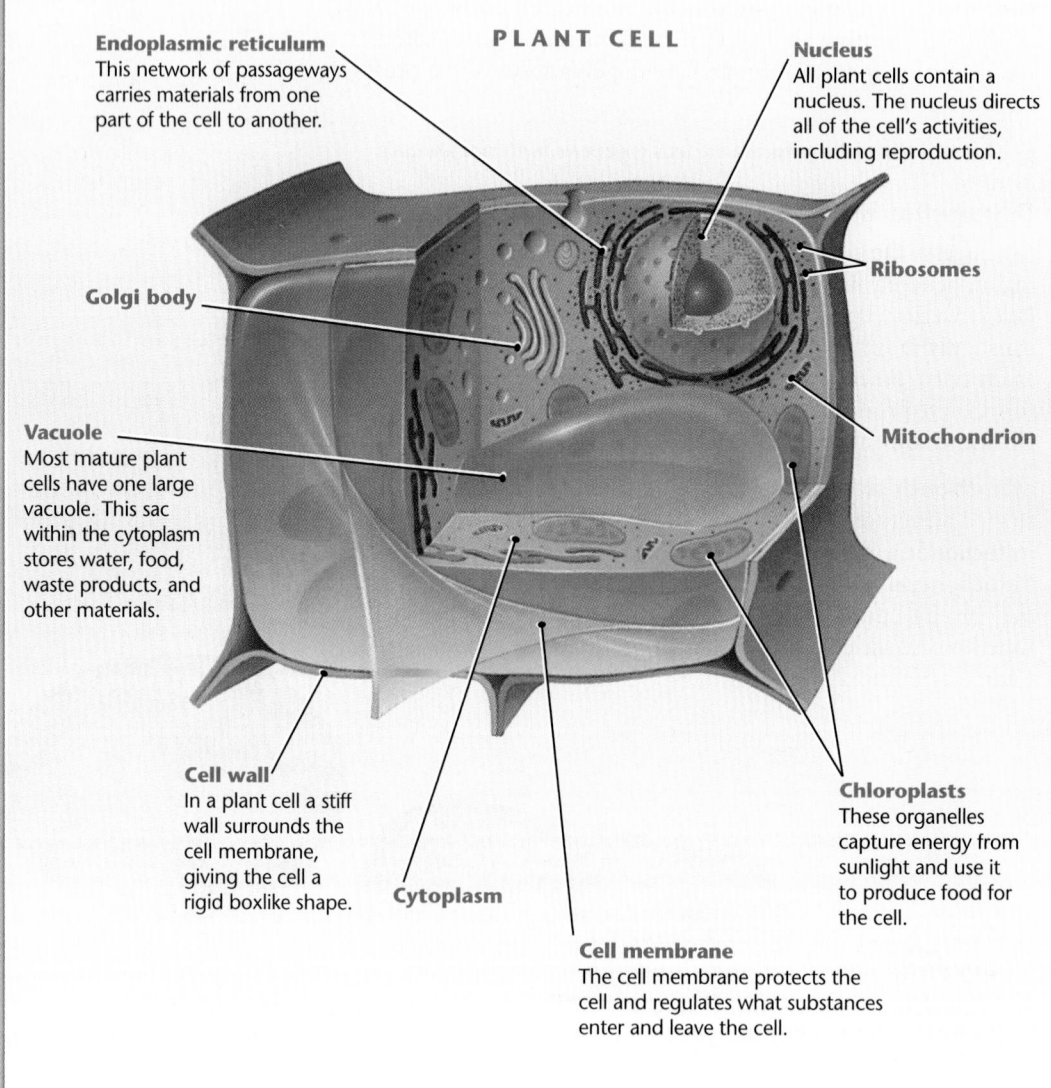

PLANT CELL

Endoplasmic reticulum
This network of passageways carries materials from one part of the cell to another.

Nucleus
All plant cells contain a nucleus. The nucleus directs all of the cell's activities, including reproduction.

Golgi body

Ribosomes

Mitochondrion

Vacuole
Most mature plant cells have one large vacuole. This sac within the cytoplasm stores water, food, waste products, and other materials.

Cell wall
In a plant cell a stiff wall surrounds the cell membrane, giving the cell a rigid boxlike shape.

Cytoplasm

Chloroplasts
These organelles capture energy from sunlight and use it to produce food for the cell.

Cell membrane
The cell membrane protects the cell and regulates what substances enter and leave the cell.

Background

Facts and Figures Many types of organisms are unicellular. Bacteria are single-celled organisms called prokaryotes. Prokaryotic cells do not contain nuclei and most other cell organelles. Many protists, such as paramecia and amebas, are unicellular organisms called eukaryotes. Eukaryotic cells contain nuclei and most cell organelles.

Paramecia have many hairlike projections called cilia that beat rhythmically to propel the paramecia through water. Paramecia also use cilia to obtain food. Amebas move by forming pseudopods, or "false feet"—bulges in their cell membranes into which cytoplasm flows. To feed, amebas surround smaller organisms with their pseudopods, thereby entrapping their prey in vacuoles inside the cytoplasm of their cells.

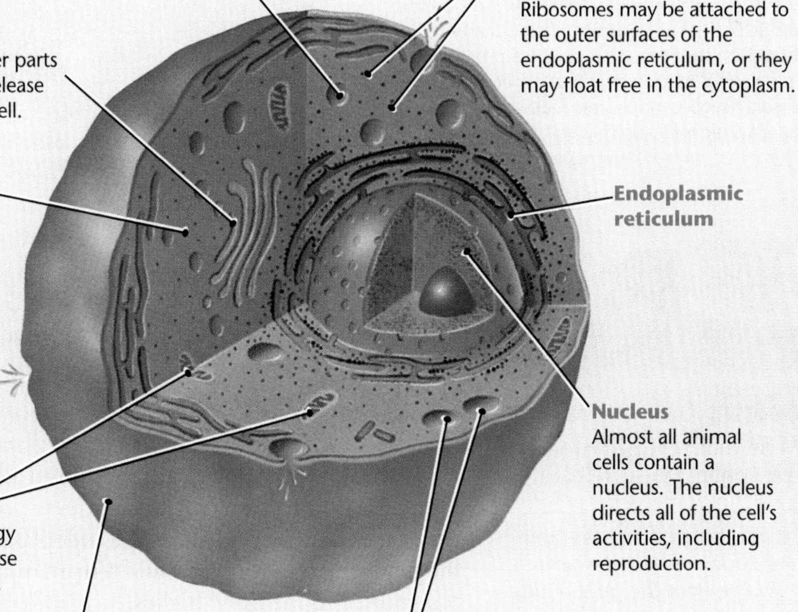

ANIMAL CELL

Vacuole
Some animal cells have vacuoles that store food, water, wastes, and other materials.

Golgi body
The Golgi bodies receive materials from the endoplasmic reticulum and send them to other parts of the cell. They also release materials outside the cell.

Cytoplasm
The cytoplasm is the area between the cell membrane and the nucleus. It contains a gel-like fluid in which many different organelles are found.

Mitochondria
Most of the cell's energy is produced within these rod-shaped organelles.

Cell membrane
Since an animal cell does not have a cell wall, the cell membrane forms a barrier between the cytoplasm and the environment outside the cell.

Ribosomes
These small structures function as factories to produce proteins. Ribosomes may be attached to the outer surfaces of the endoplasmic reticulum, or they may float free in the cytoplasm.

Endoplasmic reticulum

Nucleus
Almost all animal cells contain a nucleus. The nucleus directs all of the cell's activities, including reproduction.

Lysosomes
These small organelles found in many animal cells contain chemicals that break down food particles and worn-out cell parts.

Including All Students

Materials *10 index cards*
Time 20 minutes

Students who are not native English speakers and any other students who are having difficulty with the material on the parts of the cell may benefit from creating and using flash cards. On one side of each flash card, students should write the name of a cell structure. On the other side, they should summarize in their own words the structure's function in the cell. When students have finished, check to make sure they have correctly identified each cell structure. For example, ask: **What does the cell membrane do?** *(It protects the cell and controls what enters and leaves it.)* **What does the nucleus do?** *(It directs all the cell's activities)* Then divide students into pairs and challenge them to use their flash cards to quiz each other. **limited English proficiency**

Demonstration

Materials *microprojector, prepared slide of plant cells, prepared slide of animal cells*
Time 10 minutes

Help students relate the generalized cells shown in *Exploring Plant and Animal Cells* to actual plant and animal cells. Use a microprojector to project first a prepared slide of plant cells and then a prepared slide of animal cells onto a screen. (If a microprojector is not available, use an opaque projector and photographs of plant and animal cells.) Challenge students to locate the cell wall or cell membrane, nucleus, and other organelles on the projected images. Encourage students to describe how the actual cells vary in shape and structure from the generalized cells in the text. **learning modality: visual**

Media and Technology

Transparencies "Exploring a Plant Cell," Transparency 4; "Exploring an Animal Cell," Transparency 5

Ongoing Assessment

Skills Check Have students write two lists, one summarizing the similarities between plant and animal cells, the other summarizing the differences. Students can save their lists in their portfolios.

Organelles in the Cytoplasm, continued

Skills Focus making models

Materials *packet of colorless gelatin, warm water, other miscellaneous materials to represent cell structures, rectangular or round pan*

Time 10 minutes one day; 10 minutes later the same day

Tips Advise students to stir the gelatin until it dissolves completely in the warm water. Suggest that they leave the gelatin in the refrigerator for up to an hour until it starts to thicken before they add the "cell structures." Make sure the water is not too hot for students to work safely.

Expected Outcome Students should create a round gelatin mold to represent an animal cell or a rectangular gelatin mold to represent a plant cell. The gelatin should contain objects to represent each of the cell structures described on pages 38 or 39, and there should be a key identifying and describing each of the structures.

Extend Challenge hands-on learners to make a model of an animal cell with gelatin using a resealable plastic bag instead of a pan for a mold. Give students a chance to handle the plastic bag after the gelatin in it solidifies, then ask: **Why is the plastic-bag model a better representation of an animal cell than the pan model?** *(There is no "cell wall," as there is with the pan, to support the cell and make it rigid.)* **learning modality: kinesthetic**

Demonstration

Materials *wilted houseplant, water*
Time 5 minutes at the beginning of class, 5 minutes at the end of class

Call students' attention to the passage in the text that describes how plants look when their vacuoles are full of water and how they look when their vacuoles do not contain much water. Then show students a wilted coleus or impatiens that is in need of water. Water the plant thoroughly. By the end of class, the plant should no longer be drooping. Ask: **Why is the plant no longer wilted?** *(Its vacuoles have filled up with water.)*
learning modality: visual

Figure 15 The endoplasmic reticulum is a passageway through which proteins and other materials move within the cell. The spots on the outside of the endoplasmic reticulum are ribosomes, structures that produce proteins. An endoplasmic reticulum with attached ribosomes is called a rough endoplasmic reticulum. A smooth endoplasmic reticulum has no attached ribosomes.

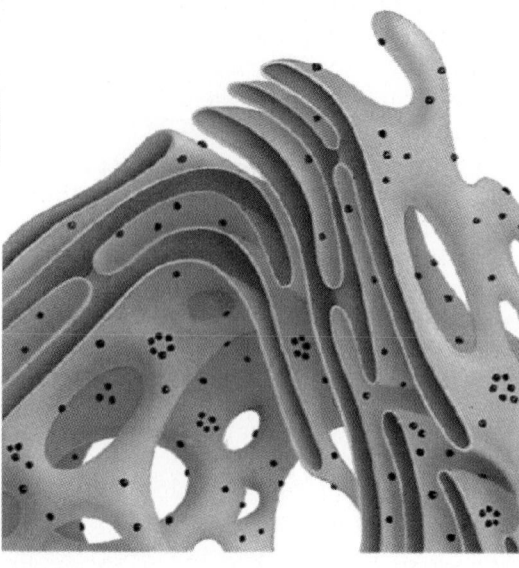

Gelatin Cell

Make your own model of a cell.

1. Dissolve a packet of colorless gelatin in warm water. Pour the gelatin into a rectangular pan (for a plant cell) or a round pan (for an animal cell).
2. Choose different materials that resemble each of the cell structures found in the cell you are modeling. Insert these materials into the gelatin before it begins to solidify.

Making Models On a sheet of paper, develop a key that identifies each cell structure in your model. Describe the function of each structure.

Endoplasmic Reticulum As you sail farther into the cytoplasm, you find yourself in a maze of passageways called the **endoplasmic reticulum** (en duh PLAZ mik rih TIK yuh lum). These passageways carry proteins and other materials from one part of the cell to another.

Ribosomes Attached to the outer surface of the endoplasmic reticulum in Figure 15 are small grainlike bodies known as **ribosomes.** Other ribosomes are found floating in the cytoplasm. Ribosomes function as factories to produce proteins. The ribosomes pass the proteins to the endoplasmic reticulum. From the interior of the endoplasmic reticulum, the proteins will be transported to the Golgi bodies.

Golgi Bodies As you move through the endoplasmic reticulum, you see structures that look like a flattened collection of sacs and tubes. These structures, called **Golgi bodies,** can be thought of as the cell's mailroom. The Golgi bodies receive proteins and other newly formed materials from the endoplasmic reticulum, package them, and distribute them to other parts of the cell. The Golgi bodies also release materials outside the cell.

Chloroplasts Have you noticed the many large green structures floating in the cytoplasm? Only the cells of plants and some other organisms have these structures. These organelles, called **chloroplasts,** capture energy from sunlight and use it to produce food for the cell. It is the chloroplasts that give plants their green color. You will learn more about chloroplasts in Chapter 2.

Vacuoles Steer past the chloroplasts and head for that large, round, water-filled sac floating in the cytoplasm. This sac, called a **vacuole** (VAK yoo ohl), is the storage area of the cell. Most plant cells have one large vacuole. Some animal cells do not have vacuoles; others do.

Vacuoles store food and other materials needed by the cell. Vacuoles can also store waste products. Most of the water in plant cells is stored in vacuoles. When the vacuoles are full of water, they make the cell plump and firm. Without much water in the vacuoles, the plant wilts.

Lysosomes Your journey through the cell is almost over. Before you leave, take another look around you. If you carefully swing your ship around the vacuole, you may be lucky enough to see a lysosome. **Lysosomes** (LY suh sohmz) are small round structures that contain chemicals that break down large food particles into smaller ones. Lysosomes also break down old cell parts and release the substances so they can be used again. In this sense, you can think of the lysosomes as the cell's cleanup crew. Lysosomes are found in both animal cells and plant cells.

Although lysosomes contain powerful chemicals, you need not worry about your ship's safety. The membrane around a lysosome keeps these harsh chemicals from escaping and breaking down the rest of the cell.

Bacterial Cells

The plant and animal cells that you just learned about are very different from the bacterial cell you see in Figure 16. First, bacterial cells are usually smaller than plant or animal cells. A human skin cell, for example, is about 10 times as large as an average bacterial cell.

There are several other ways in which bacterial cells are different from plant and animal cells. **While a bacterial cell does have a cell wall and a cell membrane, it does not contain a nucleus.** Organisms whose cells lack a nucleus are called **prokaryotes** (proh KAR ee ohtz). The bacterial cell's genetic material, which looks like a thick, tangled string, is found in the cytoplasm. Bacterial cells contain ribosomes, but none of the other organelles found in plant or animal cells. Organisms whose cells contain a nucleus and many of the organelles you just read about are called **eukaryotes** (yoo KAR ee ohtz).

Figure 16 This single-celled organism is a type of bacteria. Bacterial cells lack a nucleus and some other organelles.
Applying Concepts Where is the genetic material in a bacterial cell found?

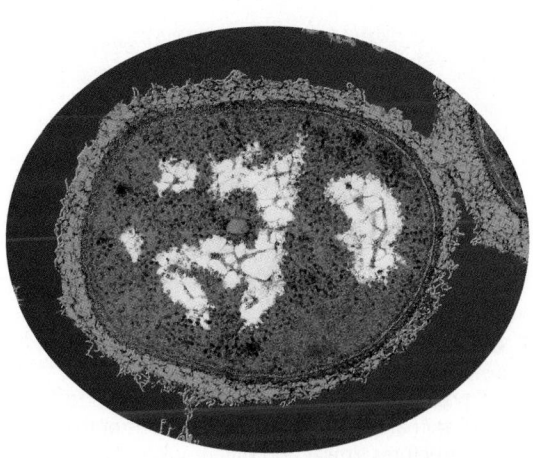

Answers to Self-Assessment

Caption Question

Figure 16 The genetic material in a bacterial cell is found in the cytoplasm.

Bacterial Cells

Using the Visuals: Figure 16

Call students' attention to the figure, and then read the following description from the text of a bacterial cell's genetic material: ". . . a thick, tangled string found in the cytoplasm." Ask: **Can you find this bacterium's genetic material?** *(Help students who cannot find the genetic material locate it in the figure.)* **Besides a nucleus, what organelles does this bacterium appear to be lacking?** *(Possible answers include mitochondria, chloroplasts, and endoplasmic reticulum.)* **learning modality: visual**

Building Inquiry Skills: Observing

Materials *soil, water, plastic dropper, microscope slide, coverslip, microscope*

Time 15 minutes

Have students observe bacterial cells under a microscope. Mix soil into water, and let the mixture sit out in an open, shallow container for several days. Then place drops of the water on microscope slides. Invite students to observe the water under high power and sketch any bacterial cells they find. Have them compare their sketches with photos of bacteria from either textbooks or encyclopedias. **learning modality: visual**

Ongoing Assessment

Skills Check Have each student create a table listing at least five organelles in the cell and summarizing their functions.

Portfolio Students can save their tables in their portfolios.

Specialized Cells

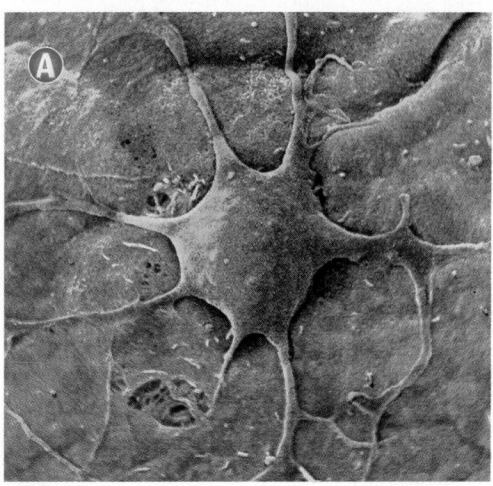
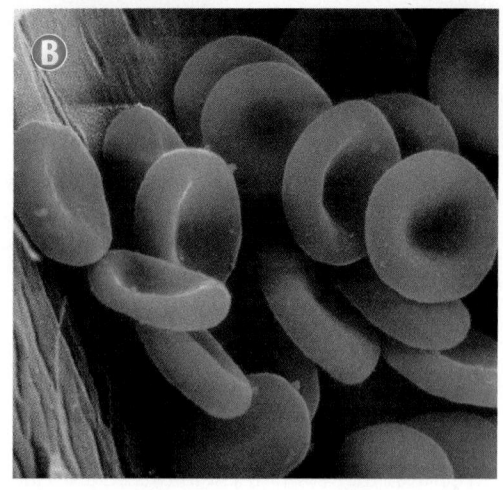

Figure 17 Your body contains a variety of different types of cells. **A.** Nerve cells have long projections through which messages are sent throughout the body. **B.** Red blood cells are thin and flexible, which allows them to fit through tiny blood vessels.

Specialized Cells

Unlike bacteria and other single-celled organisms, plants, animals (including yourself), and other organisms contain many cells. In a many-celled organism, the cells often vary greatly in size and structure. Think of the different parts of your body. You have skin, bones, muscles, blood, a brain, a liver, a stomach, and so on. Each of these body parts carries out a very different function. Yet all of these body parts are made up of cells.

Figure 17 shows two examples of different kinds of cells in your body—nerve cells and red blood cells. The structure of each kind of cell is suited to the unique function it carries out within the organism.

Section 3 Review

1. What is the function of the cell membrane?
2. Why is the nucleus sometimes called the control center of the cell?
3. Name two plant cell parts that are not found in animal cells. What is the function of each part?
4. How do the cells of bacteria differ from those of other organisms?
5. **Thinking Critically Comparing and Contrasting** Compare the functions of the cell wall in a plant cell and the cell membrane in an animal cell. How are the functions of the two structures similar and different?

Science at Home

Building Blocks Ask family members to help you find five items in your house that are made of smaller things. Make a list of the items and identify as many of their building blocks as you can. Be sure to look at prepared foods, furniture, and books. Discuss with your family how these building blocks come together to make up the larger objects. Do these objects or their building blocks possess any characteristics of living things?

42

A Magnified View of Life

Skills Lab

In this lab, you will use your observation skills to compare plant and animal cells.

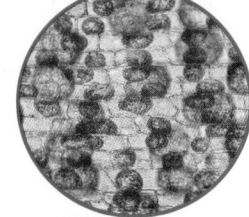

Problem

How are plant and animal cells alike and different?

Materials

plastic dropper
water
microscope slide
microscope
colored pencils
prepared slide of animal cells

Elodea leaf
forceps
coverslip

Procedure

1. Before you start this lab, read *Using the Microscope* (Appendix B) on pages 802–803. Be sure you know how to use a microscope correctly and safely.

Part 1 Observing Plant Cells

2. Use a plastic dropper to place a drop of water in the center of a slide. **CAUTION:** *Slides and coverslips are fragile. Handle them carefully. Do not touch broken glass.*

3. With forceps, remove a leaf from an *Elodea* plant. Place the leaf in the drop of water on the slide. Make sure that the leaf is flat. If it is folded, straighten it with the forceps.

4. Holding a coverslip by its edges, slowly lower it onto the drop of water and *Elodea* leaf. If any air bubbles form, tap the slide gently to get rid of them.

5. Use a microscope to examine the *Elodea* leaf under low power. Then, carefully switch to high power.

6. Observe the cells of the *Elodea* leaf. Draw and label what you see, including the colors of the cell parts. Record the magnification.

7. Discard the *Elodea* leaf as directed by your teacher. Carefully clean and dry your slide and coverslip. Wash your hands thoroughly.

Part 2 Observing Animal Cells

8. Obtain a prepared slide of animal cells. The cells on the slide have been stained with an artificial color.

9. Observe the animal cells with a microscope under both low and high power. Draw and label the cell parts that you see. Record the magnification.

Analyze and Conclude

1. How are plant and animal cells alike?
2. How are plant and animal cells different?
3. What natural color appeared in the plant cells? What structures give the plant cells this color?
4. **Think About It** Why is it important to record your observations while you are examining a specimen?

More to Explore

Observe other prepared slides of animal cells. Look for ways that animal cells differ from each other. Obtain your teacher's permission before carrying out these observations.

Safety

Remind students to handle glass slides and coverslips carefully. Review the safety guidelines in Appendix A.

Observing

A Magnified View of Life

Preparing for Inquiry

Key Concept Plant and animals cells have both similarities and differences.
Skills Objectives Students will be able to
◆ observe and draw cells under the microscope;
◆ compare and contrast plant and animal cells.
Time 40 minutes
Advance Planning You can order prepared slides of animal cells from a biological supply company.
Alternative Materials You may wish to have students use prepared slides of plant cells instead of preparing their own slides.

Guiding Inquiry

Troubleshooting the Experiment

◆ Tell students to raise the lenses before going from low to high power so they do not damage the microscope or slide.
◆ Check to be sure students have focused their microscopes correctly.
◆ Remind students to label their diagrams with the magnification.

Expected Outcome

Students should observe individual plant and animal cells under the microscope and draw diagrams that show their similarities and differences.

Analyze and Conclude

1. Both kinds of cells have a cell membrane, nucleus, and such organelles as mitochondria and ribosomes.
2. Plant cells have a cell wall and chloroplasts, whereas animal cells do not.
3. The color is green; it comes from chloroplasts in the plant cells.
4. So you do not forget details

Extending the Inquiry

More to Explore Provide students with slides of animal cells that look very different, such as red blood cells and muscle cells, and check that students can identify differences among them.

SECTION 4 The Origin of Life

Objectives

After completing the lesson, students will be able to
◆ compare the atmosphere of early Earth with today's atmosphere;
◆ state how scientists hypothesize that life arose on early Earth.

Key Term fossil

1 Engage/Explore

Activating Prior Knowledge

Mention to students that the air around us is composed of gases in varying amounts. Ask students: **What are some of the gases found in air?** (*Sample: oxygen, nitrogen, carbon dioxide, and argon*) Tell students that in this section they will discover how the composition of gases in the atmosphere has changed over time.

DISCOVER

Skills Focus inferring
Materials *two covered plastic jars; one containing a plant and the other, an animal*
Time 10 minutes
Tips Select animals such as snails, insects, or earthworms. Release animals immediately after students observe them. Students may need help to identify factors such as respiration that will change the air inside the containers.
Think It Over Because the animal consumes oxygen and the plant produces oxygen, students will suggest that early organisms either removed things from or put things back into the air so that eventually the atmospheric composition changed.

SECTION 4 The Origin of Life

DISCOVER ······· ACTIVITY

How Can the Composition of Air Change?

1. Your teacher will give you two covered plastic jars. One contains a plant and one contains an animal.

2. Observe the organisms in each jar. Talk with a partner about how you think each organism affects the composition of the air in its jar.

3. Write a prediction about how the amount of oxygen in each jar would change over time if left undisturbed.

4. Return the jars to your teacher.

Think It Over

Inferring Scientists hypothesize that Earth's early atmosphere was different from today's atmosphere. What role might early organisms have played in bringing about those changes?

GUIDE FOR READING

◆ How was the atmosphere of early Earth different from today's atmosphere?

◆ How do scientists hypothesize that life arose on early Earth?

Reading Tip Before you read, write a paragraph stating what you already know about early life on Earth. As you read this section, make changes and additions to your paragraph.

Y ou stare out the window of your time machine. You have traveled back to Earth as it was 3.6 billion years ago. The landscape is rugged, with bare, jagged rocks and little soil. You search for a hint of green, but there is none. You see only blacks, browns, and grays. Lightning flashes all around you. You hear the rumble of thunder, howling winds, and waves pounding the shore.

You neither see nor hear any living things. However, you know that this is the time period when scientists think that early life forms arose on Earth. You decide to explore. To be safe, you put on your oxygen mask. Stepping outside, you wonder what kinds of organisms could ever live in such a place.

Earth's Early Atmosphere

You were smart to put on your oxygen mask before exploring early Earth. Scientists think that early Earth had a different atmosphere than it has today. **Nitrogen, water vapor, carbon dioxide, and methane were probably the most abundant gases in Earth's atmosphere 3.6 billion years ago. Although all these gases are still found in the atmosphere today, the major gases are nitrogen and oxygen.** You, like most of today's organisms, could not have lived on Earth 3.6 billion years ago, because there was no oxygen in the air. Scientists think, however, that the first forms of life on Earth appeared at that time.

44

READING STRATEGIES

Reading Tip Before they write their paragraphs, have students fold their paper in half lengthwise and write in the first column, leaving the second column for revisions. As they read the section, they can add and delete material from their original paragraph.

Program Resources

◆ **Unit 1 Resources** 1-4 Lesson Plan, p. 27; 1-4 Section Summary, p. 28

Media and Technology

 Audio CD English-Spanish Summary 1-4

No one can ever be sure what the first life forms were like, but scientists have formed hypotheses about them. First, early life forms did not need oxygen to survive. Second, they were probably unicellular organisms. Third, they probably lived in the oceans. Many scientists think that the first organisms resembled the bacteria that live today in places without oxygen, such as the polar ice caps, hot springs, or the mud of the ocean bottoms. These bacteria survive in extreme environments—surroundings where temperatures are often above 100°C or below 0°C, or where the water pressure is extremely high.

Life's Chemicals

One of the most intriguing questions that scientists face is explaining how early life forms arose. Although Redi and Pasteur demonstrated that living things do not spontaneously arise on today's Earth, scientists reason that the first life forms probably did arise from nonliving materials.

Two American scientists, Harold Urey and Stanley Miller, provided the first clue as to how organisms might have arisen on Earth. In 1953, they designed an experiment in which they re-created the conditions of early Earth in their laboratory. They placed water (to represent the ocean), and a mixture of the gases thought to compose Earth's early atmosphere into a flask. They were careful to keep oxygen and unicellular organisms out of the mixture. Then, they sent an electric current through the mixture to simulate lightning. Within a week, the mixture darkened. In the dark fluid, Miller and Urey found some small chemical units that, if joined together, could form proteins—one of the building blocks of life.

☑ *Checkpoint* *What did Harold Urey and Stanley Miller model in their experiment?*

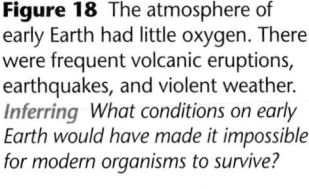
Figure 18 The atmosphere of early Earth had little oxygen. There were frequent volcanic eruptions, earthquakes, and violent weather. *Inferring What conditions on early Earth would have made it impossible for modern organisms to survive?*

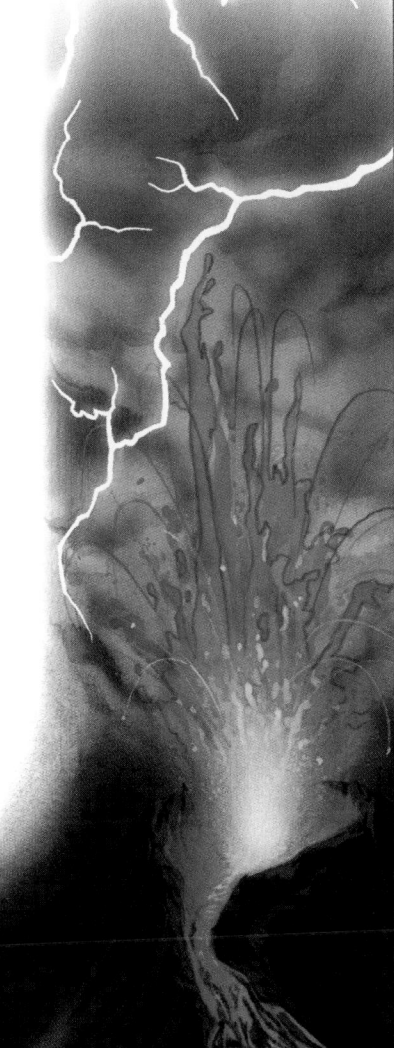

Chapter 1 **45**

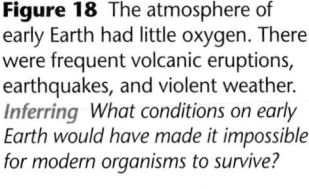

Media and Technology

🔘 **Exploring Earth Science Videodisc**
Unit 2, Side 2,
"Air Today Gone
Tomorrow"
Chapter 2

🔘 **Exploring Life Science Videodisc**
Unit 4, Side 2,
"Where Did It
Come From?"
Chapter 1

Answers to Self-Assessment
Caption Question
Figure 18 Earth lacked oxygen.
☑ *Checkpoint*
Urey and Miller's experiment modeled conditions thought to exist on early Earth.

2 *Facilitate*

Earth's Early Atmosphere

Building Inquiry Skills: Comparing and Contrasting

Ask students to explain why scientists propose that early life forms might be like some anaerobic bacteria that live in extreme habitats. Ask: **What do these specialized bacteria have in common with early life forms?** (*They don't need oxygen, they are unicellular, they can live in extreme environments.*) Point out that scientists use fossils to support their hypotheses that the two life forms share characteristics.
learning modality: visual

Life's Chemicals

Building Inquiry Skills: Organizing Information

Have students make flowcharts to describe Miller and Urey's experiment. Ask: **Why did they make sure there was no oxygen in the flask?** (*Because there was no oxygen in Earth's early atmosphere*) Ask students to speculate about the role of the electric current in the experiment. (*Sample: It adds energy.*)
learning modality: verbal

The First Cells

Including All Students

Materials *clay, prepared plaster of Paris, almond, peanut, walnut, and pecan shells* ACTIVITY
Time 40 minutes

Students who are visually challenged can examine fossil models by touch. Give student pairs one of each kind of shell. Have them make impressions of the shells in clay and compare them and the shells. Students should then fill their impressions with plaster to make casts. When the plaster dries, have them remove the clay and compare the casts with the shells. Tell students that impressions and casts are two types of fossils. **learning modality: kinesthetic**

3 Assess

Section 4 Review Answers

1. There was no oxygen in the atmosphere of early Earth and humans need oxygen to survive.

2. Small chemical units of life formed in Earth's waters over millions of years. Some of these units joined to form large chemical building blocks found in cells today. Some of these large chemicals accumulated to form the forerunners of cells.

3. They placed water and a mixture of gases thought to be present in Earth's early atmosphere in a sealed container and sent an electric current through the mixture over time. After a week, the mixture darkened because it contained chemicals that can form proteins.

4. The fact that organisms can live in such extreme conditions suggests that life forms could have formed under the extreme conditions in Earth's early atmosphere.

CHAPTER PROJECT

Check Your Progress
Remind students they should be designing a display to present to the class. Provide students with guidelines to analyze their data.

Performance Assessment

Writing Have students write paragraphs describing how scientists asked questions, used models, and interpreted experimental data to test their hypotheses about how life began on Earth.

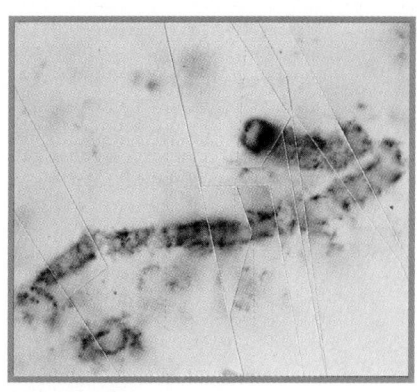

Figure 19 This fossil of bacteria-like cells was found in western Australia. It is the oldest fossil known—about 3.5 billion years old.

The First Cells

In experiments similar to Miller and Urey's, other scientists succeeded in producing chemical units that make up carbohydrates and nucleic acids. **From the results of these experiments, scientists hypothesized that the small chemical units of life formed gradually over millions of years in Earth's waters.** Some of these units joined to form the large chemical building blocks that are found in cells. Eventually, some of these large chemicals accumulated and became the forerunners of the first cells.

These hypotheses are consistent with evidence from fossils. **Fossils** are traces of ancient organisms that have been preserved in rock or other substances. The fossils in Figure 19 are of bacteria-like organisms that were determined to be between 3.4 and 3.5 billion years old. Scientists think that these ancient cells may be evidence of Earth's earliest life forms.

The first cells could not have needed oxygen to survive. They probably were heterotrophs that used the chemicals in their surroundings for energy. As they grew and reproduced, their numbers increased. In turn, the amount of chemicals available to them decreased. At some point, some of the cells may have developed the ability to make their own food. These early ancestors of today's autotrophs had an important effect on the atmosphere. As they made their own food, they produced oxygen as a waste product. As the autotrophs thrived, oxygen accumulated in Earth's atmosphere. Over many, many millions of years, the amount of oxygen increased to its current level.

No one will ever know for certain how life first appeared on Earth. However, scientists will continue to ask questions, construct models, and look for both experimental and fossil evidence about the origin of life on Earth.

Section 4 Review

1. Explain why you could not have survived in the atmosphere of early Earth.
2. Describe how scientists think that life could have arisen on Earth.
3. Describe Urey and Miller's experiment.
4. **Thinking Critically** **Inferring** How is the existence of organisms in hot springs today consistent with the scientific hypothesis of how life forms arose on Earth?

Check Your Progress
CHAPTER PROJECT

Now that you have completed your observations, analyze your data. Arrange your data in a chart or diagram. Find another object that is familiar to you and similar to your mystery object. Compare the two objects. Conclude whether your object is alive.

Program Resources

◆ **Unit 1 Resources** 1-4 Review and Reinforce, p. 29; 1-4 Enrich, p. 30

CHAPTER 1 STUDY GUIDE

SECTION 1 — What Is Life?

Key Ideas
- All living things are made of cells, contain similar chemicals, use energy, grow and develop, respond to their surroundings, and reproduce.
- All living things must satisfy their basic needs for energy, water, living space, and stable internal conditions.

Key Terms

organism · cell · unicellular · multicellular · development · stimulus · response · reproduce · spontaneous generation · controlled experiment · manipulated variable · autotroph · heterotroph · homeostasis

SECTION 2 — Discovering Cells

Key Ideas
- The invention of the microscope made the discovery of the cell possible.
- The cell theory explains the relationship between cells and living things.

Key Terms

microscope · compound microscope · cell theory · magnification · convex lens · resolution

SECTION 3 — Looking Inside Cells

Key Ideas
- The cell membrane protects the cell and controls what substances enter and leave it.
- The nucleus is the cell's control center.
- Organelles in the cytoplasm perform many different vital functions.

Key Terms

organelle · cell wall · cell membrane · nucleus · chromatin · cytoplasm · mitochondrion · endoplasmic reticulum · ribosome · Golgi body · chloroplast · vacuole · lysosome · prokaryote · eukaryote

SECTION 4 — The Origin of Life

INTEGRATING EARTH SCIENCE

Key Ideas
- Nitrogen, water vapor, carbon dioxide, and methane were probably the most abundant gases in Earth's atmosphere 3.6 billion years ago. Today the major gases are nitrogen and oxygen.
- Scientists hypothesize that over millions of years, the small chemical units of life formed in Earth's oceans. Over time, some of these units joined to form the large chemical building blocks found in cells.

Key Term

fossil

Organizing Information

Concept Map Copy the concept map about the needs of organisms onto a separate sheet of paper. Then complete it and add a title. (For more on concept maps, see the Skills Handbook.)

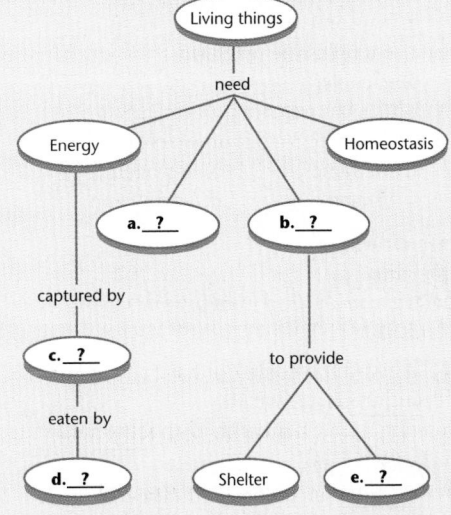

Organizing Information

Concept Map a. water b. living space c. autotrophs d. heterotrophs e. food and water

Program Resources
- **Unit 1 Resources** Chapter 1 Project Scoring Rubric, p. 14
- **Performance Assessment** Chapter 1, pp. 5–7
- **Chapter and Unit Tests** Chapter 1 Test, pp. 4–7

Media and Technology

 Interactive Student Tutorial CD-ROM Chapter 1

 Computer Test Bank Chapter 1 Test

Reviewing Content
Multiple Choice
1. b 2. a 3. c 4. d 5. b

True or False
6. heterotroph 7. compound
8. Mitochondria 9. true 10. autotrophs

Checking Concepts
11. Students might point out that plants will bend toward sunlight and that plants grow, develop, and reproduce.

12. The microscope allowed scientists to observe the cells that make up living things. Over the years, they discovered that all living things are made up of cells.

13. The cell wall is rigid, and it helps to protect and support plant cells.

14. The earliest organisms to live on Earth probably lived in the oceans. They were heterotrophs and took in chemicals.

15. Students' articles should describe the discoveries of either Robert Hooke or Anton van Leeuwenhoek and relate them to the microscope.

Thinking Critically
16. Although all robots use energy and some respond to their surroundings, they do not use energy to grow and develop. Living things are made out of cells and are able to reproduce themselves.

17. This recipe may have worked because the grains attracted mice into the open pot. To disprove this, you could observe the pot to make sure mice did not enter, or cover the pot so air could enter, but mice could not.

18. The cell theory states that all living things are composed of cells, that cells are the basic unit of structure and function in living things, and that all cells are produced from other cells. A dog is a living thing. Therefore, a dog is composed of cells, cells are the basic unit of structure and function in a dog, and all the dog's cells are produced from other cells.

19. A cell could not survive without a cell membrane because it would not have a barrier to control what substances moved into and out of the cell.

Reviewing Content

 For more review of key concepts, see the Interactive Student Tutorial CD-ROM.

Multiple Choice
Choose the letter of the best answer.

1. The idea that life could spring from nonliving matter is called
   a. development.
   b. spontaneous generation.
   c. homeostasis.
   d. evolution.
2. The ability of microscopes to distinguish fine details is called
   a. resolution.
   b. bending.
   c. magnification.
   d. active transport.
3. In plant and animal cells, the control center of the cell is the
   a. chloroplast.
   b. ribosome.
   c. nucleus.
   d. Golgi body.
4. The storage compartment of a cell is the
   a. cell wall.
   b. lysosome.
   c. endoplasmic reticulum.
   d. vacuole.
5. Which gas was not part of Earth's atmosphere 3.6 billion years ago?
   a. methane   b. nitrogen
   c. oxygen   d. water vapor

True or False
If the statement is true, write true. If it is false, change the underlined word or words to make the statement true.

6. When you eat salad, you are acting like an <u>autotroph</u>.
7. Cells were discovered using <u>electron</u> microscopes.
8. <u>Vacuoles</u> are the "powerhouses" of the cell.
9. Bacterial cells differ from the cells of plants and animals in that they lack a <u>nucleus</u>.
10. The first organisms on Earth were probably <u>heterotrophs</u>.

Checking Concepts
11. Your friend thinks that plants are not alive because they do not move. How would you respond to your friend?

12. What role did the microscope play in the development of the cell theory?

13. Describe the function of the cell wall in the cells that have these structures.

14. Describe where Earth's early organisms lived, and how they obtained food.

15. **Writing to Learn** Suppose you had been a reporter assigned to cover early scientists' discoveries about cells. Write a brief article for your daily newspaper that explains one scientist's discoveries. Be sure to explain both how the discoveries were made and why they are important.

Thinking Critically
16. **Classifying** How do you know that a robot is not alive?

17. **Relating Cause and Effect** When people believed that spontaneous generation occurred, there was a recipe for making mice: Place a dirty shirt and a few wheat grains in an open pot; wait three weeks. List the reasons why this recipe might have worked. How could you demonstrate that spontaneous generation was not responsible for the appearance of mice?

18. **Applying Concepts** Explain how the cell theory applies to a dog.

19. **Predicting** Could a cell survive without a cell membrane? Give reasons to support your answer.

20. **Comparing and Contrasting** How are plant and animal cells similar? How are they different? To answer these questions, make a list of the different organelles in each cell. Explain how each organelle is vital to the life and function of a plant or animal.

20. They both have nuclei. Plant cells have cell walls and chloroplasts and animal cells do not.
Mitichondria—produce energy for plant and animal cells
Edoplasmic reticulum—provides an internal transport system for plant and animal cells
Ribosomes—places where proteins are produced in plant and animal cells
Golgi bodies—package and distribute protein made in plant and animal cells
Chloroplasts—make food in plant cells
Vacuole—storage areas in plant and some animal cells
Lysosomes—contain chemicals that break down food particles

Applying Skills

A student designed an experiment to test how light affects the growth of plants. Refer to the illustrations below to answer Questions 21–24.

21. Controlling Variables Is this a controlled experiment? If not, why not? If so, identify the manipulated variable.

22. Developing Hypotheses What hypothesis might this experiment be testing?

23. Predicting Based on what you know about plants, predict how each plant will have changed after two weeks.

24. Designing Experiments Design a controlled experiment to determine whether the amount of water that a plant receives affects its growth.

Performance CHAPTER PROJECT Assessment

Present Your Project Prepare a display presenting your conclusion about your mystery object. Describe the observations that helped you reach your conclusion. Compare your ideas with those of other students. If necessary, defend your work.

Reflect and Record Make a list of the characteristics of life that you observed in your mystery object. Which were hard to study? Explain in your journal why some characteristics were hard to investigate.

Test Preparation

Use these questions to prepare for standardized tests.

Study the table. Then answer Questions 25–29.

Cell	Nucleus	Cell Wall	Cell Membrane
Cell A	Yes	Yes	Yes
Cell B	Yes	No	Yes
Cell C	No	Yes	Yes

25. Which cell is probably an animal cell?
  a. cell A   **b.** cell B
  c. cell C   **d.** none of the above

26. Which cell is probably a plant cell?
  a. cell A   **b.** cell B
  c. cell C   **d.** none of the above

27. Which cell is a prokaryote?
  a. cell A   **b.** cell B
  c. cell C   **d.** none of the above

28. In Cell B, where would the genetic material be found?
  a. in the mitochondria
  b. in the vacuoles
  c. in the nucleus
  d. in the cell membrane

29. Which cell(s) would most likely contain chloroplasts?
  a. cell A   **b.** cell B
  c. cell C   **d.** cell B and cell C

Applying Skills

21. Yes; the light is the manipulated variable.

22. Sample hypothesis: If plants do not have enough light, they will die.

23. In two weeks, the plant on the left will be dead, but the plant on the right will be healthy.

24. Sample experiment: Two plants receive the same light, but one receives one-fourth cup of water a day, and the other one-fourth cup every two days.

Performance CHAPTER PROJECT Assessment

Present Your Project Students' displays should be well organized and describe how students tested their hypotheses. Have each student give a brief presentation to the class describing how the results of their tests support their conclusions. Encourage students to talk about results that they found surprising.

Reflect and Record Students may have had trouble determining whether their object was alive if it was a fungus, a plant, or an animal such as coral that does not move.

Test Preparation

25. b **26.** a **27.** c **28.** c **29.** a

Program Resources

♦ **Inquiry Skills Activity Book** Provides teaching and review of all inquiry skills

Cell Processes and Energy

Sections	Time	Student Edition Activities	Other Activities	
CHAPTER PROJECT **Egg-speriment with a Cell** p. 51	Ongoing (2–3 weeks)	Check Your Progress, p. 60, 65, 79 Present Your Project, p. 83		
1 INTEGRATING CHEMISTRY **Chemical Compounds in Cells** pp. 52–55 ◆ Describe the four main kinds of organic molecules in living things. ◆ Explain how water is essential to the functioning of cells.	1–2 periods/ 1 block	**Discover** What Is a Compound?, p. 52 **Try This** What's That Taste?, p. 54 **Science at Home,** p. 55	TE	Demonstration, p. 54
2 **The Cell in Its Environment** pp. 56–60 ◆ Describe the three methods by which materials move into and out of cells. ◆ Compare passive transport to active transport. ◆ Explain why cells are small.	1 period/ $\frac{1}{2}$ block	**Discover** How Do Molecules Move?, p. 56 **Try This** Diffusion in Action, p. 58	TE TE TE TE TE	Including All Students, p. 57 Integrating Chemistry, p. 57 Demonstration, p. 58 Inquiry Challenge, p. 59 Demonstration, p. 60
3 **Photosynthesis** pp. 61–65 ◆ Describe the process of photosynthesis. ◆ Explain how the sun supplies all living things with the energy they need.	1–2 periods/ $\frac{1}{2}$–1 block	**Discover** Where Does the Energy Come From?, p. 61 **Sharpen Your Skills** Inferring, p. 63	TE TE TE LM	Demonstration, p. 62 Building Inquiry Skills: Observing, p. 63 Building Inquiry Skills: Making Models, p. 64 2, "Stomata Functions"
4 **Respiration** pp. 66–70 ◆ Describe the events that occur during respiration. ◆ Describe the relationship between photosynthesis and respiration. ◆ Describe alcoholic and lactic-acid fermentation.	$1\frac{1}{2}$–2 periods/ $\frac{3}{4}$–1 block	**Discover** What Is a Product of Respiration?, p. 66 **Science at Home,** p. 70 **Real-World Lab: You and Your Environment** Gases in Balance, p. 71	TE IES IES	Inquiry Challenge, p. 68 "Fate of the Rain Forest," pp. 20–21 "Where River Meets Sea," pp. 15–16
5 **Cell Division** pp. 72–80 ◆ Identify the events that take place during the three stages of the cell cycle. ◆ Describe the structure of DNA and DNA replication.	2 periods/ 1 block	**Discover** What Are the Cells Doing?, p. 72 **Try This** Modeling Mitosis, p. 74 **Sharpen Your Skills** Interpreting Data, p. 75 **Skills Lab: Calculating** Multiplying by Dividing, p. 80	TE TE TE TE TE	Building Inquiry Skills: Calculating, p. 74 Demonstration, p. 75 Inquiry Challenge, p. 76 Including All Students, p. 77 Inquiry Challenge, p. 77, 78
Study Guide/Chapter Assessment pp. 81–83	1 period/ $\frac{1}{2}$ block		ISAB	Provides teaching and review of all inquiry skills

For Standard or Block Schedule The Resource Pro® CD-ROM gives you maximum flexibility for planning your instruction for any type of schedule. Resource Pro® contains Planning Express®, an advanced scheduling program, as well as the entire contents of the Teaching Resources and the Computer Test Bank.

CHAPTER PLANNING GUIDE

Program Resources	Assessment Strategies	Media and Technology
UR Chapter 2 Project Teacher Notes, pp. 36–37 **UR** Chapter 2 Project Overview and Worksheets, pp. 38–41	**SE** Performance Assessment: Present Your Project, p. 83 **TE** Check Your Progress, pp. 60, 65, 79 **UR** Chapter 2 Project Scoring Rubric, p. 42	Science Explorer Internet Site at www.phschool.com
UR 2-1 Lesson Plan, p. 43 **UR** 2-1 Section Summary, p. 44 **UR** 2-1 Review and Reinforce, p. 45 **UR** 2-1 Enrich, p. 46	**SE** Section 1 Review, p. 55 **TE** Ongoing Assessment, p. 53 **TE** Performance Assessment, p. 55	Audio CD, English-Spanish Summary 2-1
UR 2-2 Lesson Plan, p. 47 **UR** 2-2 Section Summary, p. 48 **UR** 2-2 Review and Reinforce, p. 49 **UR** 2-2 Enrich, p. 50	**SE** Section 2 Review, p. 60 **TE** Ongoing Assessment, pp. 57, 59 **TE** Performance Assessment, p. 60	Life Science Videotape 1; Videodisc Unit 1 Side 2, "How Does It Get in There?" Audio CD, English-Spanish Summary 2-2 Transparency 6, "Passive and Active Transport" Interactive Student Tutorial CD-ROM, Chapter 2
UR 2-3 Lesson Plan, p. 51 **UR** 2-3 Section Summary, p. 52 **UR** 2-3 Review and Reinforce, p. 53 **UR** 2-3 Enrich, p. 54	**SE** Section 3 Review, p. 65 **TE** Ongoing Assessment, p. 63 **TE** Performance Assessment, p. 65	Audio CD, English-Spanish Summary 2-3 Transparency 7, "Photosynthesis"
UR 2-4 Lesson Plan, p. 55 **UR** 2-4 Section Summary, p. 56 **UR** 2-4 Review and Reinforce, p. 57 **UR** 2-4 Enrich, p. 58 **UR** Chapter 2 Real-World Lab, pp. 63–64	**SE** Section 4 Review, p. 70 **TE** Ongoing Assessment, pp. 67, 69 **TE** Performance Assessment, p. 70	Earth Science Videotape 5; Videodisc Unit 1 Side 1, "Sunny Days" Audio CD, English-Spanish Summary 2-4 Transparency 8, "Respiration"
UR 2-5 Lesson Plan, p. 59 **UR** 2-5 Section Summary, p. 60 **UR** 2-5 Review and Reinforce, p. 61 **UR** 2-5 Enrich, p. 62 **UR** Chapter 2 Skills Lab, pp. 65–67	**SE** Section 5 Review, p. 79 **TE** Ongoing Assessment, pp. 73, 75, 77 **TE** Performance Assessment, p. 79	Audio CD, English-Spanish Summary 2-5 Transparencies 9, "Exploring the Cell Cycle"; 10, "DNA Structure"; 11, "DNA Replication"
RCA Provides strategies to improve science reading skills **GSW** Provides worksheets to promote student comprehension of content	**SE** Chapter 2 Study Guide/Assessment, pp. 81–83 **PA** Chapter 2 Performance Assessment, pp. 8–10 **CUT** Chapter 2 Test, pp. 8–11 **CTB** Chapter 2 Test	Interactive Student Tutorial CD-ROM, Chapter 2 Computer Test Bank, Chapter 2 Test

Key: **SE** Student Edition   **TE** Teacher's Edition   **UR** Unit Resources
     CTB Computer Test Bank   **PTA** Product Testing Activities by *Consumer Reports*   **LM** Laboratory Manual
     ISAB Inquiry Skills Activity Book   **RCA** Reading in the Content Area   **IES** Interdisciplinary Explorations Series
     GSW Guided Study Worksheets   **PA** Performance Assessment   **CUT** Chapter and Unit Tests

Meeting the National Science Education Standards and AAAS Benchmarks

National Science Education Standards	Benchmarks for Science Literacy	Unifying Themes
Science as Inquiry (Content Standard A) ◆ **Think critically and logically to make the relationships between evidence and explanations** Students investigate how various materials enter or leave a cell, using an egg as a model of the cell. *(Chapter Project)* ◆ **Design and conduct a scientific investigation** Students investigate how photosynthesis and respiration are related. *(Real-World Lab)* ◆ **Use appropriate tools and techniques to gather, analyze, and interpret data** Students investigate how long the stages of the cell cycle take. *(Skills Lab)* **Life Science** (Content Standard C) ◆ **Structure and function in living systems** The most important organic compounds found in living things are carbohydrates, lipids, proteins, and nucleic acids. Photosynthesis occurs inside the chloroplasts of plants and some other organisms. During respiration, cells break down food molecules and release the energy they contain. The regular sequence of growth and division that cells undergo is called the cell cycle. *(Chapter Project; Sections 1, 2, 3, 4, 5; Real-World Lab; Skills Lab)* ◆ **Regulation and behavior** Substances can move into and out of a cell by diffusion, osmosis, or active transport. *(Section 2)* ◆ **Populations and ecosystems** Photosynthesis and respiration form a cycle that keeps the levels of oxygen and carbon dioxide fairly constant in the atmosphere. *(Sections 3, 4; Real-World Lab)*	**1B Scientific Inquiry** Students investigate how various materials enter or leave a cell, how photosynthesis and respiration are related, and how long the stages of the cell cycle take. *(Chapter Project; Real-World Lab; Skills Lab)* **5C Cells** The most important groups of organic compounds found in living things are carbohydrates, lipids, proteins, and nucleic acids. Substances can move into and out of a cell by diffusion, osmosis, or active transport. *(Sections 1, 2; Skills Lab)* During respiration, cells break down food molecules and release the energy they contain. The regular sequence of growth and division that cells undergo is called the cell cycle. *(Sections 1, 2, 4, 5; Skills Lab)* **5D Interdependence of Life** Nearly all living things obtain energy either directly or indirectly from the energy of sunlight captured during photosynthesis. Photosynthesis and respiration form a cycle that keeps the levels of oxygen and carbon dioxide fairly constant in the atmosphere. *(Sections 3, 4; Real-World Lab)* **5E Flow of Matter and Energy** During photosynthesis, plants and some other organisms use the sun's energy to make food. *(Section 3)*	◆ **Energy** Carbohydrates and lipids are energy-rich organic compounds. Active transport is the movement of materials through a cell membrane using energy. During photosynthesis, plants and some other organisms use the sun's energy to make food. During respiration, cells break down food molecules and release their energy. *(Real-World Lab; Sections 1, 2, 3, 4)* ◆ **Modeling** Students investigate how various materials enter or leave a cell, using an egg as a model of the cell. *(Chapter Project)* ◆ **Patterns of Change** During photosynthesis, carbon dioxide and water are converted into oxygen and sugars. Cells undergo a regular sequence of growth and division. *(Sections 3, 4, 5; Skills Lab)* ◆ **Scale and Structure** Photosynthesis occurs inside the chloroplasts of plants and some other organisms. Respiration takes place in the cytoplasm and mitochondria of an organism's cells. After a cell has grown to its mature size, it divides. *(Sections 3, 4, 5)* ◆ **Systems and Interactions** Without water, most chemical reactions within cells could not take place. Substances move into and out of a cell by diffusion, osmosis, or active transport. Through photosynthesis and respiration, the sun's energy is converted into energy that living organisms can use. *(Sections 1, 2, 3, 4; Real-World Lab)* ◆ **Stability** Photosynthesis and respiration form a cycle that keeps the levels of oxygen and carbon dioxide fairly constant in the atmosphere. DNA replication ensures that each daughter cell will have all the necessary genetic information. *(Sections 3, 4, 5)*

Take It to the Net

 *Interactive text at www.phschool.com*

Science Explorer comes alive with iText.

- **Complete student text** is accessible from any computer with Internet access or a CD-ROM drive.
- **Animations, simulations, and videos** enhance student understanding and retention of concepts.
- **Self-tests and online study tools** assess student understanding.

STAY CURRENT with **SCIENCE NEWS®**

Find out the latest research and information about cells at: **www.phschool.com**

Go to **www.phschool.com** and click on the Science icon. Then click on <u>Science Explorer: Life, Earth, and Physical Science</u> under PH@school.

ACTIVITY	Time (minutes)	Materials Quantities for one work group	Skills
Section 1			
Discover, p. 52	10	**Consumable** labeled containers of various chemical compounds such as salt, zinc oxide sun block, baking soda, and chalk	Forming Operational Definitions
Try This, p. 54	5	**Consumable** unsalted soda cracker	Inferring
Science at Home, p. 55	home	**Nonconsumable** food packages with "Nutrition Facts" labels	Interpreting Data, Communicating
Section 2			
Discover, p. 56	10	**Consumable** air freshener spray	Developing Hypotheses
Try This, p. 58	10	**Consumable** cold water, food coloring **Nonconsumable** small clear plastic cup, plastic dropper	Inferring
Section 3			
Discover, p. 61	5	**Nonconsumable** solar-powered calculator that does not have batteries	Inferring
Sharpen Your Skills, p. 63	20	**Consumable** coffee filter, leaf, rubbing alcohol **Nonconsumable** scissors, metric ruler, dime, plastic cup	Inferring
Section 4			
Discover, p. 66	20	**Consumable** warm water, 5 mL sugar, 1.0 mL dried yeast, 2 straws **Nonconsumable** 2 test tubes with stoppers, test tube rack	Observing
Science at Home, p. 70	home	**Consumable** ingredients for bread recipe **Nonconsumable** bread recipe	Communicating
Real-World Lab, p. 71	20/15	**Consumable** 2 *Elodea* plants, bromthymol blue solution, straws **Nonconsumable** marking pens, 100-mL plastic graduated cylinder, 3 250-ml flasks with stoppers, light source	Controlling Variables, Interpreting Data
Section 5			
Discover, p. 72	15	**Consumable** yeast culture, methylene blue stain **Nonconsumable** plastic dropper, microscope slide with coverslip, microscope	Developing Hypotheses
Try This, p. 74	10	**Consumable** construction paper, 3 different colored pipe cleaners	Making Models
Sharpen Your Skills, p. 75	5	No special materials are required.	Interpreting Data
Skills Lab, p. 80	40	**Nonconsumable** microscope, colored pencils, calculator, prepared slides of onion root tip cells undergoing cell division	Observing, Calculating, Interpreting Data

A list of all materials required for the Student Edition activities can be found on pages T25–T33. You can obtain information about ordering materials by calling 1-800-848-9500 or by accessing the Science Explorer Internet site at **www.phschool.com**.

Egg-speriment With a Cell

In the Chapter 2 Project, students will learn about an essential structure found in all cells—the cell membrane. During the course of the project, students will carry out experiments, make observations, and draw conclusions about how the cell membrane functions.

Purpose In the Chapter 2 Project, students will observe how fluids move across the semi-permeable membrane surrounding a raw egg.

Skills Focus After completing the Chapter 2 Project, students will be able to
- predict how various liquids will affect an egg;
- observe how the liquids affect the egg;
- measure and record changes in the egg;
- graph data of the egg's circumference;
- draw conclusions about what processes occurred during the experiment.

Project Time Line The entire project will require at least two weeks. It will take longer if students break their eggs and have to start over. On the first day, have students read about the Chapter 2 Project in their text, and ask if they have any questions. Then hand out the Chapter 2 Project Overview and Student Worksheets, pages 38–41 in Unit 1 Resources. You might also wish to give students a copy of the Chapter 2 Project Scoring Rubric, page 42 in Unit 1 Resources, so they know what will be expected of them. Encourage students to read the Overview and do the Worksheets early in the project.

If students will be working in groups, divide the class into groups at this time. Also set aside some class time during the course of the project for group members to work on the project. If students are doing the project individually, allow a few minutes each day for students to share their observations and ask questions. Students might also need class time at the end of the project to prepare their presentations and share their results with the class.

For more detailed information on planning and supervising the Chapter 2 Project, see Chapter 2 Project Teacher Notes, pages 36–37 in Unit 1 Resources.

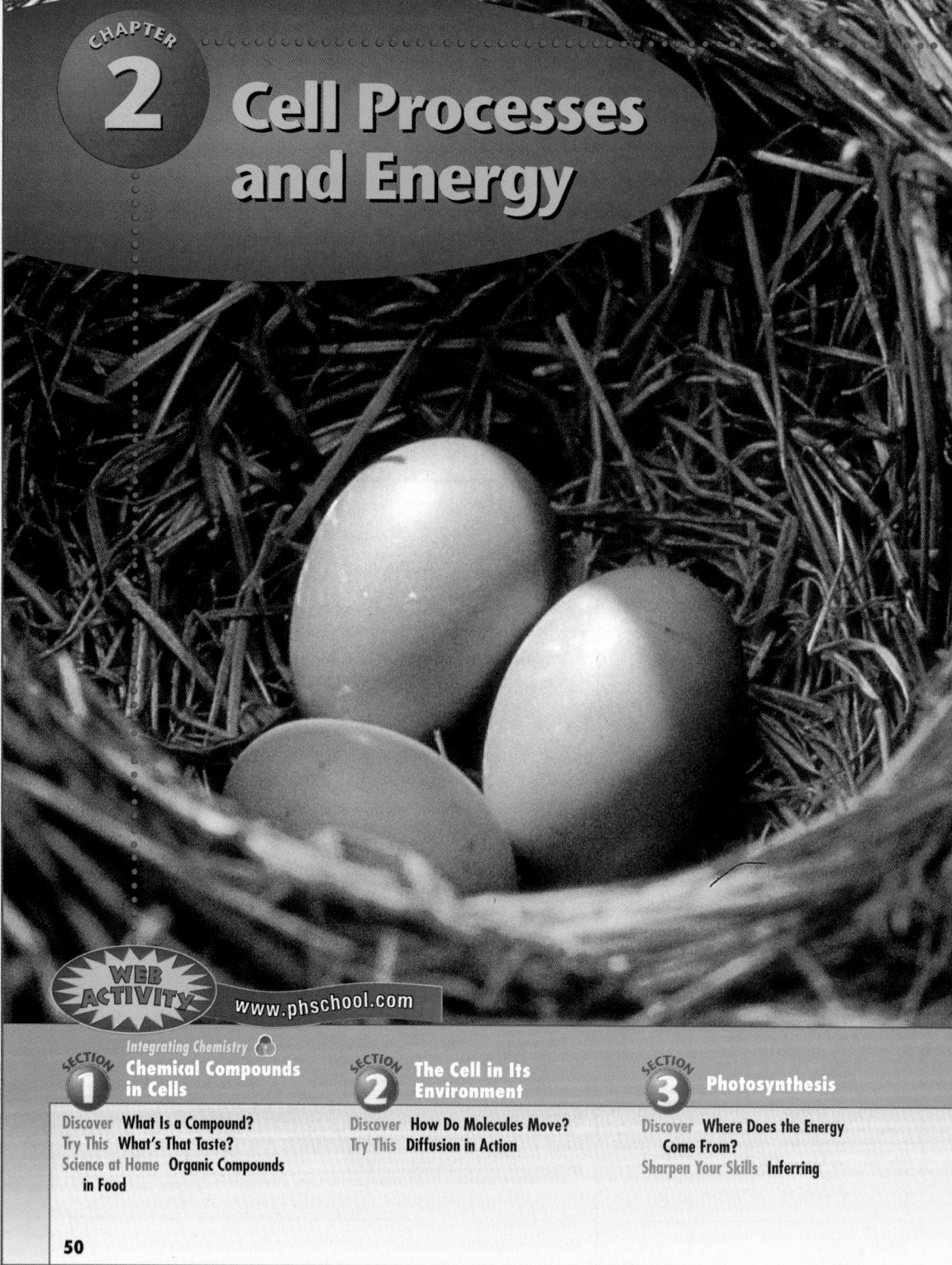

CHAPTER

2 Cell Processes and Energy

WEB ACTIVITY www.phschool.com

SECTION 1 *Integrating Chemistry* **Chemical Compounds in Cells**
Discover **What Is a Compound?**
Try This **What's That Taste?**
Science at Home **Organic Compounds in Food**

SECTION 2 **The Cell in Its Environment**
Discover **How Do Molecules Move?**
Try This **Diffusion in Action**

SECTION 3 **Photosynthesis**
Discover **Where Does the Energy Come From?**
Sharpen Your Skills **Inferring**

50

Suggested Shortcuts To speed up the project, you can have each student soak his or her egg in a different liquid, after first soaking the eggs in vinegar for two days. One student should use water, one student water with food coloring, and one student salt water, but the other students could soak their eggs in a liquid of their choice. Then all students can pool their results.

You can limit the amount of student involvement in the project by doing it as a class project. First have students brainstorm predictions about what will happen to the egg when it is soaked in the various liquids, and record their predictions on the chalkboard. Then set up the experiment with the egg soaking in a container of vinegar, and every other day change the liquid in which the egg is soaking, according to the directions in the text. Assign a different student to measure and record changes in the size of the egg each day, and give all the students a chance to observe how the egg is changing. Have each student create a data table and graph.

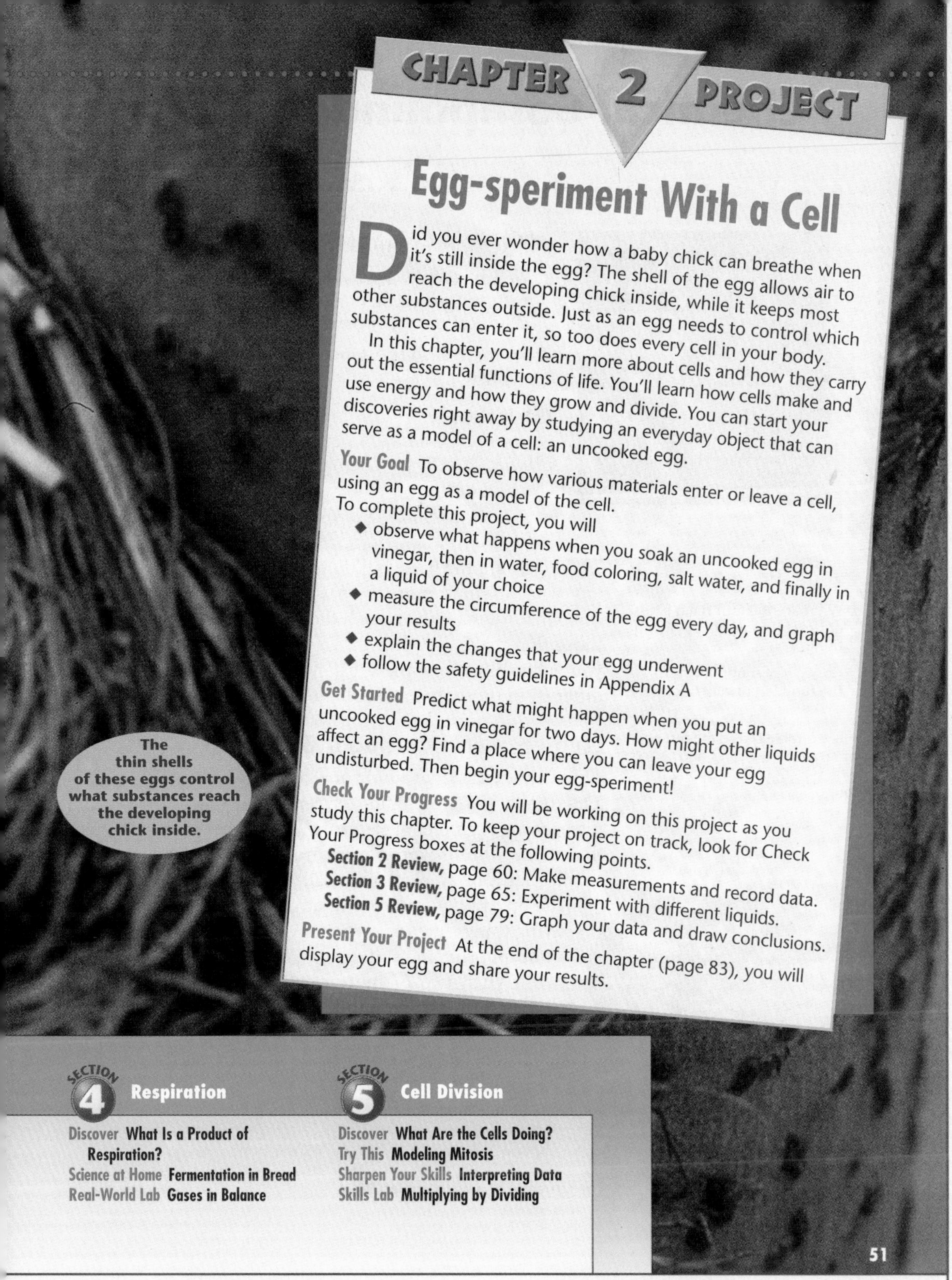

CHAPTER 2 PROJECT

Egg-speriment With a Cell

Did you ever wonder how a baby chick can breathe when it's still inside the egg? The shell of the egg allows air to reach the developing chick inside, while it keeps most other substances outside. Just as an egg needs to control which substances can enter it, so too does every cell in your body.

In this chapter, you'll learn more about cells and how they carry out the essential functions of life. You'll learn how cells make and use energy and how they grow and divide. You can start your discoveries right away by studying an everyday object that can serve as a model of a cell: an uncooked egg.

Your Goal To observe how various materials enter or leave a cell, using an egg as a model of the cell.

To complete this project, you will
◆ observe what happens when you soak an uncooked egg in vinegar, then in water, food coloring, salt water, and finally in a liquid of your choice
◆ measure the circumference of the egg every day, and graph your results
◆ explain the changes that your egg underwent
◆ follow the safety guidelines in Appendix A

Get Started Predict what might happen when you put an uncooked egg in vinegar for two days. How might other liquids affect an egg? Find a place where you can leave your egg undisturbed. Then begin your egg-speriment!

Check Your Progress You will be working on this project as you study this chapter. To keep your project on track, look for Check Your Progress boxes at the following points.

Section 2 Review, page 60: Make measurements and record data.
Section 3 Review, page 65: Experiment with different liquids.
Section 5 Review, page 79: Graph your data and draw conclusions.

Present Your Project At the end of the chapter (page 83), you will display your egg and share your results.

> The thin shells of these eggs control what substances reach the developing chick inside.

SECTION 4 Respiration

Discover **What Is a Product of Respiration?**
Science at Home **Fermentation in Bread**
Real-World Lab **Gases in Balance**

SECTION 5 Cell Division

Discover **What Are the Cells Doing?**
Try This **Modeling Mitosis**
Sharpen Your Skills **Interpreting Data**
Skills Lab **Multiplying by Dividing**

51

Program Resources

◆ **Unit 1 Resources** Chapter 2 Project Teacher Notes, pp. 36–37; Chapter 2 Project Overview and Worksheets, pp. 38–41; Chapter 2 Project Scoring Rubric, p. 42

WEB ACTIVITY www.phschool.com

You will find an Internet activity, chapter self-tests for students, and links to other chapter topics at this site.

Possible Materials Any clean plastic containers can be used to soak the eggs, as long as the containers are large enough for the eggs to be completely covered by liquid. Plastic is better than glass because eggs are less likely to break if they bump against plastic. Containers with tight-fitting lids may help avoid spills and broken eggs, but lids are not necessary.

Students can use either white or brown eggs. Large eggs will show a greater change in size, making it easier for students to observe the results of osmosis. Make sure that none of the eggs is cracked to begin with. Encourage students to use a wide variety of liquids for soaking their eggs, such as corn syrup, milk, orange juice, or shampoo. To measure their egg, students can use a flexible cloth or vinyl tape or a piece of string and a ruler.

Launching the Project Introduce the project by showing students a chicken egg. State that the egg is similar to a single large cell. Point out that in this project, students will study an egg to learn more about how cells function. Ask: **Why do you think you will be using an egg to study the cell instead of an actual cell, such as a human skin cell?** *(Because most cells are too small to be seen without a microscope. Also, unlike most cells mounted on microscope slides, eggs are still alive.)* Say that, although a chicken egg is larger than any of the cells in their own bodies, it has many of the same structures. Explain that the cell membrane is the structure they will focus on in this project.

Performance Assessment

To assess students' performance in this project, use the Chapter 2 Project Scoring Rubric on page 42 of Unit 1 Resources. Students will be assessed on
◆ how accurately and consistently they make measurements and record their data;
◆ the neatness and accuracy of their graphs and diagrams;
◆ how well their conclusions display an understanding of the functions of a cell membrane;
◆ their participation in a group, if they worked in groups.

SECTION
1 Chemical Compounds in Cells

Objectives

After completing the lesson, students will be able to
- describe the four main kinds of organic molecules in living things;
- explain how water is essential to the functioning of cells.

Key Terms element, atom, compound, molecule, organic compound, inorganic compound, protein, amino acid, enzyme, carbohydrate, lipid, nucleic acid, DNA, RNA

1 Engage/Explore

Activating Prior Knowledge

Write this "recipe" for the human body on the board: 50 L of water (hydrogen, oxygen); 16 kg of coal (carbon); and about 5 kg total of fireworks (potassium, nitrogen, carbon, sulfur), chalk (calcium, carbon), matches (phosphorus), salt (sodium, chlorine), and several metals (including iron). Ask **What are the three chief chemical "ingredients" of the body?** (*Hydrogen, oxygen, and carbon*)

 **DISCOVER**

Skills Focus forming operational definitions
Materials *labeled containers of chemical compounds such as salt, zinc oxide sun block, baking soda, and chalk*
Time 10 minutes
Tips Label the compounds with their common and chemical names (sodium chloride for salt, zinc oxide for sun block, sodium bicarbonate for baking soda, and calcium carbonate for chalk).
Expected Outcome Students should discover that all the compounds consist of two or more different elements.
Think It Over Students may say that a chemical compound is something that is made up of more than one substance.

SECTION
1 Chemical Compounds in Cells

DISCOVER •••••••••••••••••••••••••••• **ACTIVITY**

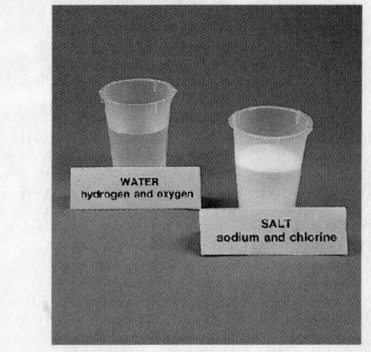

What Is a Compound?

1. Your teacher will provide you with containers filled with various substances. All of the substances are chemical compounds.

2. Examine each substance. Read the label on each container to learn what each substance is made of.

Think It Over
Forming Operational Definitions Write a definition of what you think a chemical compound is.

GUIDE FOR READING

- What are the four main kinds of organic molecules in living things?
- How is water important to the function of cells?

Reading Tip As you read, make a table of the main types of organic molecules and where in the cell each one is found.

I f cells are the basic building blocks of living things, then what substances are the basic building blocks of cells? In what ways are the basic building blocks of cells similar to those that make up other things around you? In this section you will explore how the substances that make up living cells differ from those that make up nonliving things.

Elements and Compounds

Think about the air around you. You probably know that air is a mixture of gases, including oxygen and nitrogen. Oxygen and nitrogen are examples of elements. An **element** is any substance that cannot be broken down into simpler substances. The smallest unit of an element is called an **atom.** An element is made up of only one kind of atom. The elements found in living things include carbon, hydrogen, oxygen, nitrogen, phosphorus, and sulfur.

When two or more elements combine chemically they form a **compound.** Water, for example, is a compound made up of the elements hydrogen and oxygen. The smallest unit of most compounds is called a **molecule.** Each water molecule is made up of two hydrogen atoms and one oxygen atom.

Oxygen
Hydrogen
Hydrogen

◄ The structure of a water molecule

READING STRATEGIES

Reading Tip Have students preview the main headings of the section to identify the four main types of organic molecules. If they need additional help, students should read the boldface sentence on page 53.

Students' tables should have two columns, one for the organic molecules and one for the location in the cell. There should be a row for each of the four organic molecules— carbohydrates, lipids, proteins, and nucleic acids.

Organic and Inorganic Compounds

Many of the compounds found in living things contain the element carbon, which is usually combined with other elements. Most compounds that contain carbon are called **organic compounds.**

The most important groups of organic compounds found in living things are proteins, carbohydrates, lipids, and nucleic acids. As you may know, many of these compounds are found in the foods you eat. This is not surprising, since the foods you eat come from living things.

Compounds that don't contain the element carbon are called **inorganic compounds.** One exception to this definition is carbon dioxide. Although carbon dioxide contains carbon, it is classified as an inorganic compound. Other inorganic compounds include water and sodium chloride, or table salt.

Proteins

What do a bird's feathers, a spider's web, and your fingernails have in common? All of these substances are made mainly of proteins. **Proteins** are large organic molecules made of carbon, hydrogen, oxygen, nitrogen, and, in some cases, sulfur. Foods that are high in protein include meat, eggs, fish, nuts, and beans.

Cells use proteins for many different things. For instance, proteins form parts of cell membranes. Proteins also make up many of the organelles within the cell. Certain cells in your body use proteins to build body structures such as muscles.

Protein Structure Protein molecules are made up of smaller molecules called **amino acids.** Although there are only 20 common amino acids, cells can combine them in different ways to form thousands of different proteins. The kinds of amino acids and the order in which they link together determine the type of protein that forms.

You can think of the 20 amino acids as being like the 26 letters of the alphabet. Those 26 letters can form thousands of words. The letters you use and their order determine the words you form. Even a change in one letter, for example, from *rice* to *mice*, creates a new word. Similarly, changes in the type or order of amino acids result in a different protein.

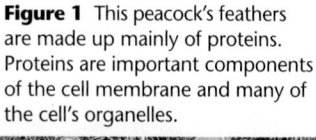

Figure 1 This peacock's feathers are made up mainly of proteins. Proteins are important components of the cell membrane and many of the cell's organelles.

Program Resources

◆ **Unit 1 Resources** 2-1 Lesson Plan, p. 43; 2-1 Section Summary, p. 44

Media and Technology

 Audio CD English-Spanish Summary 2-1

2 Facilitate

Elements and Compounds

Including All Students

For students who need more help, relate atoms to elements by showing them the periodic table of the elements and pointing out that the elements are arranged according to their atomic numbers. Explain that the atomic number is the number of protons, or positively charged particles, in each atom of the element. Add that elements have standard symbols, such as H for hydrogen, O for oxygen, and C for carbon. Ask: **What are the atomic numbers of the three elements that are most common in living things?** *(1 for hydrogen, 8 for oxygen, and 6 for carbon)* **learning modality: visual**

Organic and Inorganic Compounds

Including All Students

Help students understand the difference between the terms organic and inorganic by explaining that the combining form *organ-* means "having to do with life" and the prefix *in-* means "not." Then ask: **Based on these meanings, what does inorganic mean?** *(Not having to do with life.)* Ask: **Can you think of other words that start with *organ-*?** *(organism, organelle)* **Can you think of other words that contain the prefix *in-* meaning "not"?** *(indecent, incredible)* **limited English proficiency**

Ongoing Assessment

Oral Presentation Call on students at random to give examples of organic and inorganic compounds. *(Organic compounds: carbohydrates, lipids, proteins, and nucleic acids. Inorganic compounds: water, salt, carbon dioxide.)*

Proteins

Demonstration

Materials *pot of water, hot plate, pudding mix*
Time 10 minutes

Use a visual analogy to demonstrate how enzymes work to speed up chemical reactions. Mix a package of pudding (not instant) and cook the mixture until it thickens. Explain that heat provides energy to speed up chemical reactions, whereas most enzymes work like chemical "matchmakers," bringing chemicals together so they can interact.
learning modality: visual

TRY THIS

Skills Focus inferring
Materials *unsalted soda cracker*
Time 5 minutes
Expected Outcome After students have chewed the cracker for a minute or two, it should start to taste slightly sweet. Students should infer that enzymes in their saliva helped break down the cracker's starch into sugar.
Extend Ask: **How can you tell that a food is high in sugar?** *(It tastes sweet.)*
learning modality: kinesthetic

Carbohydrates

Real-Life Learning

Point out that carbohydrates are an important source of energy. Then challenge students to describe a healthful high-carbohydrate meal. *(One possible meal is spaghetti with tomato sauce, bread, peas, grape juice, and a banana.)*
learning modality: verbal

Lipids

 Integrating Health

Ask: **Why might you gain weight if you ate a lot of foods high in lipids?** *(You would not need all the energy they provided, and the excess lipids would be stored as fat.)* **learning modality: visual**

54

What's That Taste?

Use this activity to discover one role that enzymes play in your body.

1. Put an unsalted soda cracker in your mouth. Chew it up, but do not swallow. Note what the cracker tastes like.
2. Continue to chew the cracker for a few minutes, mixing it well with your saliva. Note how the taste of the cracker changes.

Inferring Soda crackers are made up mainly of starch, with little sugar. How can you account for the change in taste after you chewed the cracker for a few minutes?

Enzymes An **enzyme** is a type of protein that speeds up a chemical reaction in a living thing. Without enzymes, many chemical reactions that are necessary for life would either take too long or not occur at all. For example, enzymes in your saliva speed up the digestion of food by breaking down starches into sugars in your mouth.

Carbohydrates

A **carbohydrate** is an energy-rich organic compound made of the elements carbon, hydrogen, and oxygen. Sugars and starches are examples of carbohydrates.

Sugars are produced during the food-making process that takes place in plants. Foods such as fruits and some vegetables are high in sugar content. Sugar molecules can combine, forming large molecules called starches. Plant cells store excess energy in molecules of starch.

Carbohydrates are important components of some cell parts. The cellulose found in the cell walls of plants is a type of carbohydrate. Carbohydrates are also found in cell membranes.

Lipids

Have you ever seen a cook trim the fat from a piece of meat before cooking it? The cook is trimming away a lipid. Fats, oils, and waxes are all **lipids.** Like carbohydrates, lipids are energy-rich, organic compounds made of carbon, hydrogen, and oxygen.

Lipids contain even more energy than carbohydrates. Cells store energy in lipids for later use. For example, during winter a dormant bear lives on the energy stored as fat within its cells.

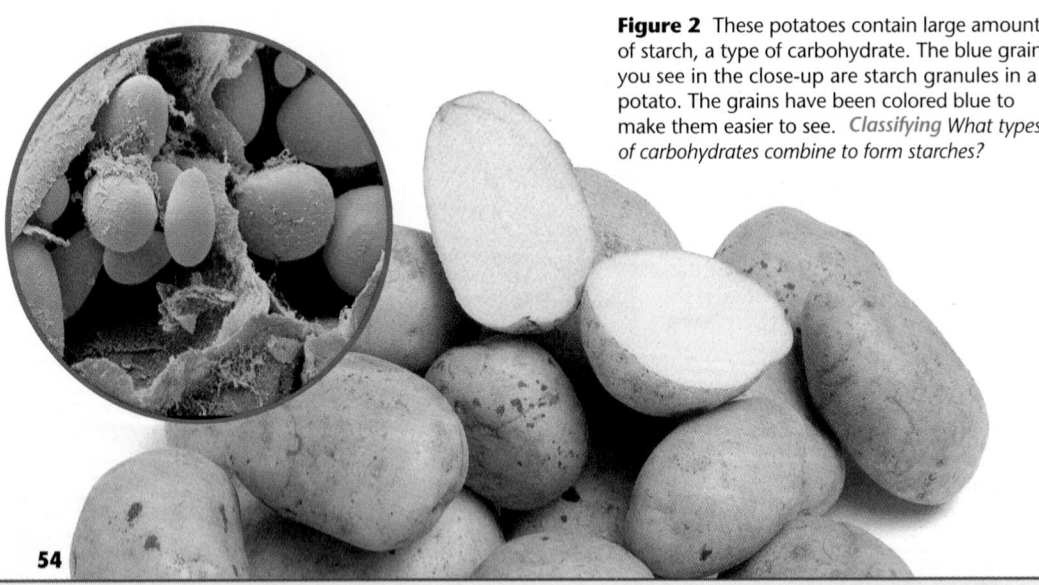

Figure 2 These potatoes contain large amounts of starch, a type of carbohydrate. The blue grains you see in the close-up are starch granules in a potato. The grains have been colored blue to make them easier to see. *Classifying What types of carbohydrates combine to form starches?*

54

Background

Integrating Science One type of lipid is cholesterol. Cholesterol is a waxy, fatlike substance found only in animal cells. A certain amount of cholesterol is needed by the human body to make cell membranes, nerve cells, certain hormones, vitamin D, and bile, an acid that aids in digestion. However, elevated levels of cholesterol are associated with heart disease.

Cholesterol is carried through the bloodstream in large molecules called lipoproteins. There are two main types of lipoproteins—low-density lipoprotein (LDL) and high-density lipoprotein (HDL). LDL, sometimes called "bad cholesterol," increases the tendency for fatty build-up in blood vessels, while HDL, or "good cholesterol," reduces the tendency for fatty build-up. The higher the ratio of LDL to HDL, the greater the risk of heart attack.

Nucleic Acids

Nucleic acids are very large organic molecules made of carbon, oxygen, hydrogen, nitrogen, and phosphorus. Nucleic acids contain the instructions that cells need to carry out all the functions of life.

There are two kinds of nucleic acids. Deoxyribonucleic acid (dee ahk see ry boh noo KLEE ik), or **DNA,** is the genetic material that carries information about an organism that is passed from parent to offspring. The information in DNA also directs all of the cell's functions. Most of the DNA in a cell is found in the chromatin in the nucleus. Ribonucleic acid (ry boh noo KLEE ik), or **RNA,** plays an important role in the production of proteins. RNA is found in the cytoplasm, as well as in the nucleus.

Water and Living Things

Did you know that water makes up about two thirds of your body? Water plays many vital roles in cells. For example, most chemical reactions that take place in cells can occur only when substances are dissolved in water. **Without water, most chemical reactions within cells could not take place.** Also, water molecules themselves take part in many chemical reactions in cells.

Water also helps cells keep their size and shape. In fact, a cell without water would be like a balloon without air. In addition, because water changes temperature slowly, it helps keep the temperature of a cell from changing rapidly.

Figure 3 Water is essential for all living things to survive. The cells of these tulips need water to function.

Section 1 Review

1. Name the four main groups of organic molecules in living things. Describe the function of each type of molecule.
2. What roles does water play in cells?
3. How are elements related to compounds?
4. **Thinking Critically** **Predicting** Suppose a cell did not have a supply of amino acids and could not produce them. What effect might this have on the cell?

Science at Home

Organic Compounds in Food With family members, look at the "Nutrition Facts" labels on a variety of food products. Identify foods that contain large amounts of the following organic compounds: carbohydrates, proteins, and fats. Discuss with your family what elements each of these compounds are made of and what roles they play in cells and in your body.

Chapter 2 **55**

Program Resources

◆ **Unit 1 Resources** 2-1 Review and Reinforce, p. 45; 2-1 Enrich, p. 46

Answers to Self-Assessment

Caption Question

Figure 2 Sugars combine to form starches.

Nucleic Acids

Building Inquiry Skills: Comparing and Contrasting

Ask: **How are DNA and RNA similar?** *(large; contain oxygen, hydrogen, nitrogen, and phosphorus; contain genetic instructions)* **How do they differ?** *(DNA is in the nucleus; RNA is in the cytoplasm)* **learning modality: logical/ mathematical**

Water and Living Things

Building Inquiry Skills: Calculating

Remind students that about two thirds of their body mass is water. Then have them calculate how many kilograms of water their body contains. *(A 45-kg student contains about 30 kg of water.)* **learning modality: logical/ mathematical**

3 Assess

Section 1 Review Answers

1. Carbohydrates provide energy and components of cell membranes and walls; proteins provide components of cell membranes and organelles and speed up chemical reactions; lipids provide components of cell membranes and store energy; nucleic acids contain the instructions for the cell to function.
2. Water helps chemical reactions take place, maintains cell size and shape, keeps cell temperature stable, and helps carry substances into and out of cells.
3. Compounds are made up of two or more elements.
4. The cell could not make proteins.

Science at Home

Tips All contain carbon, hydrogen, and oxygen and provide energy. Proteins also have nitrogen, and sometimes sulfur, and form cell membranes and organelles.

Performance Assessment

Skills Check Have students compare and contrast lipids and nucleic acids.

Objectives

After completing the lesson, students will be able to
◆ describe the three methods by which materials move into and out of cells;
◆ compare passive transport to active transport;
◆ explain why cells are small.

Key Terms selectively permeable, diffusion, osmosis, passive transport, active transport

1 Engage/Explore

Activating Prior Knowledge

Introduce students to the idea of the cell membrane as a gatekeeper by helping them recall how a sieve or colander works. Ask: **Why might you use a sieve or colander?** *(Possible answers might include to strain lumps out of gravy or to drain vegetables or pasta.)* **What do all these things have in common?** *(They involve using a filter to separate large from small particles or solids from liquids.)* Tell students that the cell membrane acts like a filter, too, by allowing some substances, but not others, to pass in and out of the cell.

⋯⋯ DISCOVER ⋯⋯

Skills Focus developing hypotheses **ACTIVITY**
Materials *air freshener spray*
Time 10 minutes
Tips When spraying the air freshener, spray up or down rather than in the direction of students.
Expected Outcome The spray should diffuse evenly throughout the classroom, reaching students at the same distance from the source at about the same time.
Think It Over The farther each student was from the teacher, the longer it took for the student to smell the air freshener. Students may hypothesize that particles in the spray moved from an area of higher concentration to an area of lower concentration.

DISCOVER ⋯⋯⋯⋯⋯⋯⋯⋯⋯⋯⋯⋯ ACTIVITY ⋯

How Do Molecules Move?

1. With your classmates, stand so that you are evenly spaced throughout the classroom.

2. Your teacher will spray an air freshener into the room. When you first begin to smell the air freshener, raise your hand.

3. Note how long it takes for other students in the classroom to smell the scent.

Think It Over
Developing Hypotheses How was each student's distance from the teacher related to when he or she smelled the air freshener? Develop a hypothesis about why this pattern occurred.

GUIDE FOR READING

◆ By what three methods do materials move into and out of cells?

◆ What is the difference between passive transport and active transport?

Reading Tip Before you read, use the headings to make an outline about how materials move into and out of cells. As you read, make notes about each process.

▼ The *Mir* space station

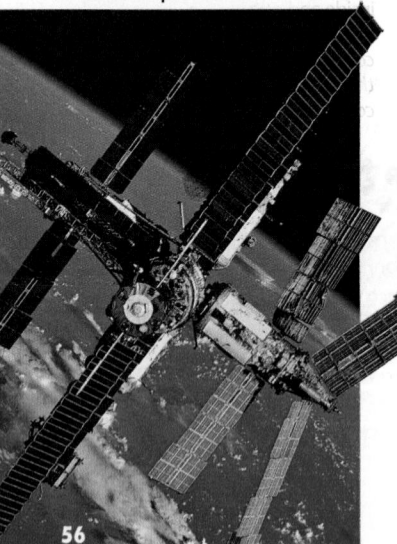

56

How is a cell like a space station? The walls of a space station protect the astronauts inside from the airless vacuum of space. Food, water, and other supplies must be brought to the space station by shuttles from Earth. In addition, the space station needs to be able to get rid of wastes. The doors of the space station allow the astronauts to bring materials in and move wastes out into the shuttle to be returned to Earth.

Like space stations, cells also have structures that protect them from the outside environment. As you learned, all cells are surrounded by a cell membrane that separates the cell from the outside environment. Just like the space station, the cell also has to take in needed materials and get rid of wastes. It is the cell membrane that controls what materials move into and out of the cell.

The Cell Membrane as Gatekeeper

The cell membrane is **selectively permeable,** which means that some substances can pass through it while others cannot. The term *permeable* comes from a Latin word that means "to pass through." You can think of the cell membrane as being like a gatekeeper at an ancient castle. It was the gatekeeper's job to decide when to open the gate to allow people to pass into and out of the castle. The gatekeeper made the castle wall "selectively permeable"—it was permeable to friendly folks but not to enemies.

A cell membrane is usually permeable to substances such as oxygen, water, and carbon dioxide. On the other hand, the cell membrane is usually not permeable to some large molecules and salts. **Substances that can move into and out of a cell do so by one of three methods: diffusion, osmosis, or active transport.**

READING STRATEGIES

Reading Tip Have students preview the main headings of the section. Remind students to leave space between headings so they can add details as they read. Write the main headings of the outline on the board, as shown in the right column. After students have read the section, call on volunteers to add details.

I. The Cell Membrane as Gatekeeper
II. Diffusion: Molecules in Motion
   A. What Causes Diffusion
   B. Diffusion in Cells

Study and Comprehension Encourage visual learners to preview the section by looking at the figures and reading the captions. This is also a good way for them to review after reading the section.

Diffusion—Molecules in Motion

The main method by which small molecules move into and out of cells is diffusion. **Diffusion** (dih FYOO zhun) is the process by which molecules tend to move from an area of higher concentration to an area of lower concentration. The concentration of a substance is the amount of the substance in a given volume.

If you did the Discover activity, you observed diffusion in action. The area where the air freshener was sprayed had many molecules of freshener. The molecules gradually moved from this area of higher concentration to the other parts of the classroom, where there were few molecules of freshener, and thus a lower concentration.

What Causes Diffusion? Molecules are always moving. As

 INTEGRATING CHEMISTRY they move, the molecules bump into one another. The more molecules there are in an area, the more collisions there will be. Collisions cause molecules to push away from one another. Over time, the molecules of a substance will continue to spread out. Eventually they will be spread evenly throughout the area.

Diffusion in Cells Have you ever used a microscope to observe one-celled organisms in pond water? These organisms obtain the oxygen they need to survive from the water around them. Luckily for them, there are many more molecules of oxygen in the water outside the cell than there are inside the cell. In other words, there is a higher concentration of oxygen molecules in the water than inside the cell. Remember that the cell membrane is permeable to oxygen molecules. The oxygen molecules diffuse from the area of higher concentration—the pond water—through the cell membrane to the area of lower concentration—the inside of the cell.

Figure 4 Molecules move by diffusion from an area of higher concentration to an area of lower concentration. **A.** There is a higher concentration of molecules outside the cell than inside. **B.** The molecules diffuse into the cell. Eventually, there is an equal concentration of molecules inside and outside the cell.
Predicting What would happen if the concentration of the molecules outside the cell was lower than the concentration inside?

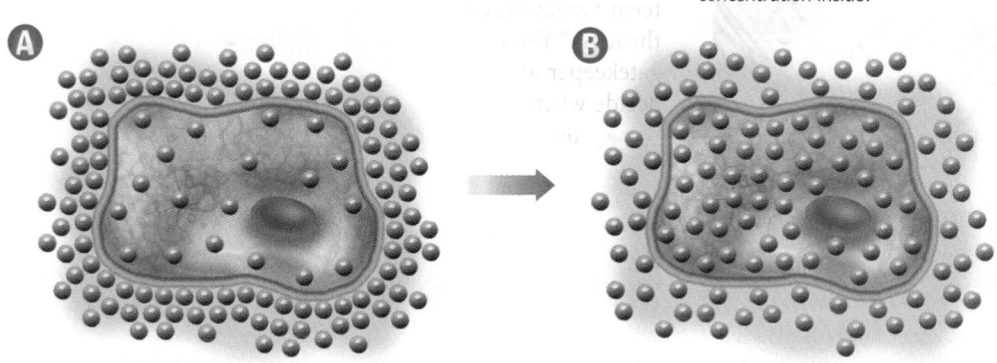

Program Resources

◆ **Unit 1 Resources** 2-2 Lesson Plan, p. 47; 2-2 Section Summary, p. 48

Media and Technology

 Audio CD English-Spanish Summary 2-2

Answers to Self-Assessment

Caption Question

Figure 4 If the concentration of molecules outside the cell was lower than the concentration inside, the molecules would diffuse out of the cell.

---

2 Facilitate

The Cell Membrane as Gatekeeper

Including All Students

Materials *cheesecloth, spoon, applesauce*
Time 10 minutes

Have students place a small amount of applesauce in the middle of a piece of cheesecloth. Have them pull the edges together and, over a sink, try to squeeze the applesauce through the cloth. Have students examine what remains in the pouch, then ask: **How is the cheesecloth like a cell membrane?** *(It allows some but not all substances to pass through.)*
learning modality: kinesthetic

Diffusion—Molecules in Motion

Integrating Chemistry

Materials *tablespoon, cornstarch, two cups, water, resealable plastic bag, plastic dropper, iodine*

Time 15 minutes

To demonstrate diffusion through a selectively permeable membrane, stir a tablespoon of cornstarch into half a cup of water and pour the mixture into a plastic bag. Seal the bag, rinse it off to remove any cornstarch, and place it in a clean cup half full of plain water. Add 20 drops of iodine to the water in the cup. Later, show students the cup and ask. **Why did the water in the bag turn purple?** *(Iodine molecules passed through the plastic into the bag and interacted with the starch.)* **Why didn't the water in the cup turn purple?** *(The starch molecules were too big to pass through the bag.)*
learning modality: visual

Ongoing Assessment

Drawing Have students draw a diagram to show what happens if the concentration outside a cell is lower than the concentration inside.

Osmosis—The Diffusion of Water Molecules

Demonstration

Materials *raw potato, knife, two shallow dishes, tap water, salt*

Time 5 minutes; 5 minutes

Use a potato to demonstrate the process of osmosis. At the beginning of class, cut a raw potato in half and hollow out a small depression in the curved side of each half. Place the halves flat-side down in shallow dishes containing a small amount of tap water. Place a pinch of salt in the depression of one of the potato halves, and then set the two halves aside. At the end of class, have students observe what has happened to the two potato halves. *(The depression without salt has become dried out, whereas the depression with salt has filled with water.)* Ask: **Where did the water in the depression come from?** *(The water moved by osmosis from an area of higher concentration in the potato cells to an area of lower concentration in the depression containing salt.)* **learning modality: visual**

TRY THIS

Skills Focus inferring
Materials *small clear plastic cup, cold water, plastic dropper, food coloring*
Time 10 minutes
Expected Outcome The large drop of food coloring will diffuse throughout the water in the cup, and the water will have an even shade of color.
Extend Encourage students to predict how changing the parameters of the experiment would affect the outcome. For example, ask: **How do you think the results of the activity would be different if you had used a larger amount of water?** *(Diffusion would have taken longer, and the water would have turned a lighter shade of color.)* **learning modality: logical/mathematical**

Diffusion in Action

Here's how you can observe the effects of diffusion.

1. Fill a small clear plastic cup with cold water. Place the cup on a table and allow it to sit until there is no movement in the water.
2. Use a plastic dropper to add one large drop of food coloring to the water.
3. Observe the water every minute. Note any changes that take place. Continue to observe until you can no longer see any changes.

Inferring What role did diffusion play in the changes you observed?

Osmosis—The Diffusion of Water Molecules

Like oxygen, water passes easily into and out of cells through the cell membrane. The diffusion of water molecules through a selectively permeable membrane is called **osmosis.** Osmosis is important to cells because cells cannot function properly without adequate water.

Remember that molecules tend to move from an area of higher concentration to an area of lower concentration. In osmosis, water molecules move by diffusion from an area where they are highly concentrated through the cell membrane to an area where they are less concentrated. This can have important consequences for the cell.

Look at Figure 5 to see the effect of osmosis on cells. In Figure 5A, red blood cells are bathed in a solution in which the concentration of water is the same as it is inside the cells. This is the normal shape of a red blood cell.

Now look at Figure 5B. The red blood cells are floating in water that contains a lot of salt. The concentration of water molecules outside the cells is lower than the concentration of water molecules inside the cells. This is because the salt takes up space in the salt water, so there are fewer water molecules. As a result, water moves out of the cells by osmosis, and the cells shrink.

Finally, consider Figure 5C. The red blood cells are floating in water that contains a very small amount of salt. The water inside the cells contains more salt than the solution they are floating in. Thus, the concentration of water outside the cell is greater than it is inside the cell. The water moves into the cell, causing it to swell.

Checkpoint How is osmosis related to diffusion?

Figure 5 Osmosis is the diffusion of water molecules through a selectively permeable membrane.

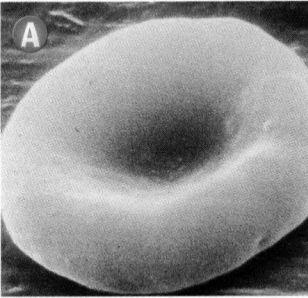
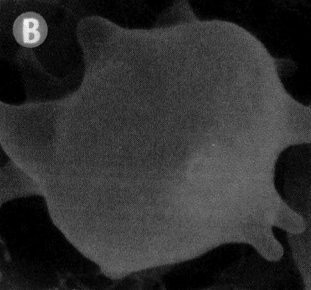

A. This is the normal shape of a red blood cell.

B. This cell has shrunk because water moved out of it by osmosis.

C. This cell is swollen with water that has moved into it by osmosis.

Background

Integrating Science Did you ever wonder why most fish cannot live in both freshwater and salt water? The answer lies in osmosis, which requires freshwater and saltwater fishes to have very different adaptations.

When fishes live in salt water, the water outside their body is saltier than the water inside their cells. Therefore, fishes lose a lot of water into the water around them by osmosis.

To compensate, they must drink a lot of water, use active transport to get rid of the excess salt, and produce very little urine.

In contrast, when fishes live in freshwater, the water inside their body cells is saltier than the water outside. Therefore, they gain a lot of water by osmosis. To compensate, they usually do not drink, and they produce large amounts of very dilute urine.

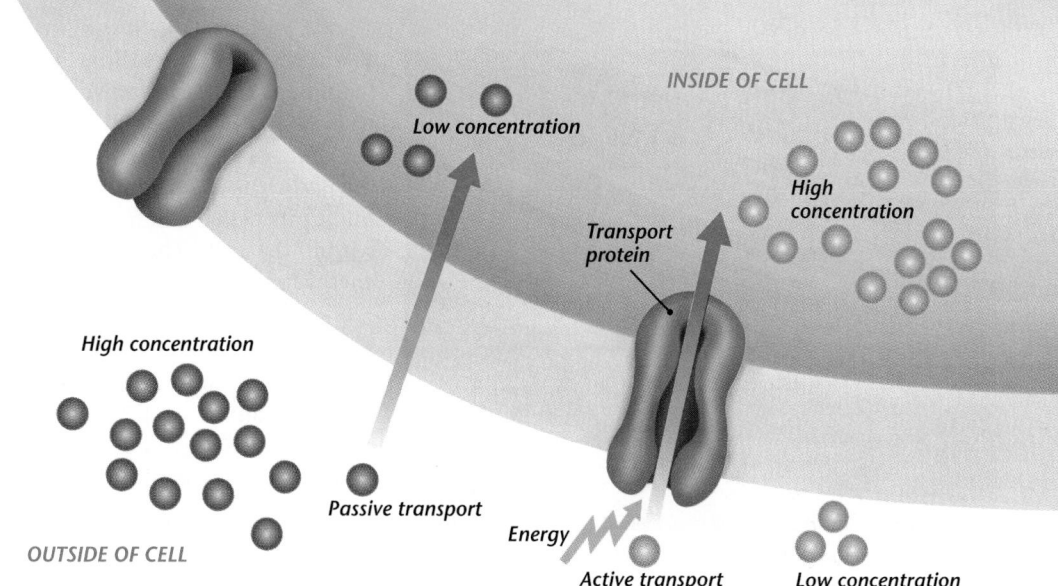

INSIDE OF CELL

Low concentration

High concentration

Transport protein

High concentration

Passive transport

OUTSIDE OF CELL

Energy

Active transport

Low concentration

Active Transport

If you have ever ridden a bicycle down a long hill, you know that it doesn't take any of your energy to go fast. But pedaling back up the hill does take energy. For a cell, moving materials through the cell membrane by diffusion and osmosis is like cycling downhill. These processes do not require the cell to use any energy. The movement of materials through a cell membrane without using energy is called **passive transport.**

What if a cell needs to take in a substance that is in higher concentration inside the cell than outside? The cell would have to move the molecules in the opposite direction than they naturally move by diffusion. Cells can do this, but they have to use energy—just as you would use energy to pedal back up the hill. **Active transport** is the movement of materials through a cell membrane using energy. **The main difference between passive transport and active transport is that active transport requires the cell to use energy while passive transport does not.**

Transport Proteins   A cell has several ways of moving materials by active transport. In one method, transport proteins in the cell membrane "pick up" molecules outside the cell and carry them in, using energy in the process. Transport proteins also carry molecules out of cells in a similar way. Some substances that are carried into and out of cells in this way include calcium, potassium, and sodium.

Figure 6 Diffusion and osmosis are forms of passive transport. These processes do not require the cell to use any energy. Active transport, on the other hand, requires the use of energy.
Interpreting Diagrams How are passive and active transport related to the concentrations of the molecules inside and outside the cell?

Answers to Self-Assessment

☑ *Checkpoint*
Osmosis is water diffusion through a selectively permeable membrane.

Caption Question
Figure 6 Passive transport—molecules move from higher to lower concentration. Active transport—molecules move from lower to higher concentration.

Inquiry Challenge
Materials *small board, stack of books, toy car*
Time 5 minutes

Challenge pairs of students to model active and passive transport using the materials listed above. *(The most likely way is to make an inclined plane with the board and books, and then to roll the toy car down the ramp to simulate passive transport and push it up the ramp to simulate active transport.)* Ask: **Why do you need to supply energy to move the toy car up the ramp?** *(To overcome the force of gravity)* **Why is energy needed to actively transport some substances into the cell?** *(To move the substances from an area of lower to an area of higher concentration)* **cooperative learning**

Building Inquiry Skills: Relating Cause and Effect

Help students better understand the role of transport proteins in active transport by developing the analogy in the text. Ask: **What plays a similar role in active transport as your muscles play when you pedal a bicycle up a hill?** *(Transport proteins, because they require energy to move something that could not move on its own)* **learning modality: logical/ mathematical**

Ongoing Assessment

Skills Check Have students draw a Venn diagram that relates active and passive transport. *(Students' diagrams should show that active transport requires energy and passive transport does not. The overlap area should indicate that in both processes, materials move in and out of cells.)*

Why Are Cells Small?

Demonstration

Materials *one-gallon aquarium, cold and room-temperature water, measuring cup, food coloring*

Time 5 minutes

Demonstrate how materials move through the cell in a stream of moving cytoplasm by creating a convection current in water. Pour half a cup of very cold water mixed with ten drops of food coloring into an aquarium filled with room-temperature water. Ask: **How would increasing the size of the tank affect how long it takes the colored water to reach the bottom?** *(It would take longer.)* **learning modality: visual**

3 Assess

Section 2 Review Answers

1. In diffusion, molecules move from an area of higher to an area of lower concentration. In osmosis, water molecules move by diffusion. In active transport, molecules are helped across cell membranes by transport proteins.

2. Both passive and active transport refer to the movement of substances across cell membranes. Active transport requires energy; passive transport does not.

3. Substances can travel faster through the cytoplasm of small cells.

4. The cell will shrink as it loses water by osmosis.

CHAPTER PROJECT

Check Your Progress

Make sure students have started soaking their eggs in vinegar and are measuring and recording their curcumferences every day. Check that they always measure the eggs in the same way.

Performance Assessment

Concept Map Have students make a concept map that includes the terms diffusion, osmosis, passive transport, and active transport.

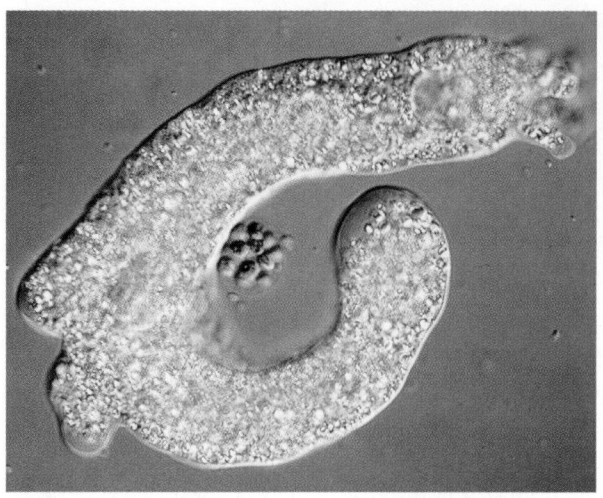

Figure 7 A cell can move some materials into the cell by engulfing them. This single-celled ameba is engulfing a smaller single-celled organism. *Applying Concepts How does this process differ from passive transport?*

Transport by Engulfing You can see another method of active transport in Figure 7. First the cell membrane surrounds, or engulfs, a particle. Once the particle is engulfed, the cell membrane pinches off and forms a vacuole within the cell. The cell must use energy in this process.

Why Are Cells Small?

As you know, most cells are so small that you cannot see them without a microscope. Have you ever wondered why cells are so small? One reason is related to how materials move into and out of cells.

As a cell's size increases, more of its cytoplasm is located farther from the cell membrane. Once a molecule enters a cell, it is carried to its destination by a stream of moving cytoplasm, somewhat like the way currents of water in the ocean move a raft. But in a very large cell, the streams of cytoplasm must travel farther to bring materials to all parts of the cell. It would take much longer for a molecule to reach the center of a very large cell than it would in a small cell. Likewise, it would take a long time for wastes to be removed. If a cell grew too large, it could not function well enough to survive. When a cell reaches a certain size, it divides into two new cells. You will learn more about cell division later in this chapter.

Section 2 Review

1. Describe three methods by which substances can move into and out of cells.
2. How are passive transport and active transport similar? How do they differ?
3. Why is small size an advantage to a cell?
4. **Thinking Critically** **Predicting** A single-celled organism is transferred from a tank of fresh water into a tank of salt water. How will the cell change? Explain.

CHAPTER PROJECT

Check Your Progress

By now you should have started your egg-speriment by soaking an uncooked egg in vinegar. Leave your egg in the vinegar for at least two days. Each day, rinse your egg in water and measure its circumference. Record all of your observations. (*Hint:* Handle the egg gently. If your egg breaks, don't give up or throw away your data. Simply start again with another egg and keep investigating.)

Program Resources

◆ **Unit 1 Resources** 2-2 Review and Reinforce, p. 49; 2-2 Enrich, p. 50

Media and Technology

Interactive Student Tutorial CD-ROM Chapter 2

Answers to Self-Assessment

Caption Question

Figure 7 Engulfing requires energy while passive transport does not.

3 Photosynthesis

DISCOVER

Where Does the Energy Come From?

1. Obtain a solar-powered calculator that does not use batteries. Place the calculator in direct light.

2. Cover the solar cells with your finger. Note how your action affects the number display.

3. Uncover the solar cells. What happens to the number display?

4. Now cover all but one of the solar cells. How does that affect the number display?

Think It Over

Inferring From your observations, what can you infer about the energy that powers the calculator?

I t's a beautiful summer afternoon—a perfect day for a picnic in the park. The aroma of chicken cooking on the grill fills the air. Your dog is busy chasing sticks under a nearby tree. Up above, blue jays swoop down from the tree's branches, hunting for food. "Let's go for a bike ride before lunch," suggests your cousin. "Great idea," you say, and you ride off down the path.

Dogs running, birds flying, people biking—all of these activities require energy. Where do you think this energy comes from? Believe it or not, all the energy used to perform such activities comes from the sun. In fact, the sun provides almost all the energy used by living things on Earth.

GUIDE FOR READING

◆ What happens during the process of photosynthesis?

◆ How does the sun supply living things with the energy they need?

Reading Tip As you read, create a flowchart that shows the steps involved in the process of photosynthesis.

READING STRATEGIES

Reading Tip Students' flowcharts should show photosynthesis as a two-stage process, with the first stage using chlorophyll to capture the sun's energy and the second stage using the captured energy to produce sugars and oxygen from carbon dioxide and water. To improve students' understanding of photosynthesis, challenge them to relate the steps of their flowcharts to the photosynthesis equation on page 64.

Program Resources

◆ **Unit 1 Resources** 2-3 Lesson Plan, p. 51; 2-3 Section Summary, p. 52

Objectives

After completing the lesson, students will be able to

◆ describe the process of photosynthesis;

◆ explain how the sun supplies all living things with the energy they need.

Key Terms photosynthesis, pigment, chlorophyll, stomata

1 Engage/Explore

Activating Prior Knowledge

Ask students: **How many of you have houseplants in your home?** *(Most will probably say they do.)* **Where are houseplants usually placed?** *(Near a window or where they will receive light)* **What happens if a houseplant doesn't get enough light?** *(They get spindly, turn yellow, and may die.)* **Why do plants need light?** *(Some students may know that plants use light energy to make food. Accept all responses without comment at this time.)*

DISCOVER

Skills Focus inferring
Materials *solar-powered calculator that does not use batteries*
Time 5 minutes
Tips If necessary, show students where the solar cells are located on the calculator.
Expected Outcome When all the solar cells are covered, the number display should go blank. When all but one of the solar cells are covered, the number display should flicker and fade.
Think It Over Students should infer that energy to power the calculator comes from sunlight.

2 Facilitate

What Is Photosynthesis?

Demonstration

Materials *green leaf, jar, rubbing alcohol, paper towel, shallow dish, iodine solution*

Time 10 minutes

Demonstrate to students that starch is produced in green leaves. Place a green leaf in a jar of rubbing alcohol and leave it overnight to remove the leaf's waxy covering and most of its chlorophyll. The next day in class, blot the leaf dry with a paper towel and place it in a shallow dish. Tell students that iodine turns purple when it comes into contact with starch, and then cover the leaf with iodine solution. Have students observe how the leaf changes color. Then ask: **Based on these observations, what compound does the leaf contain?** *(starch)* **Why does the leaf contain this compound?** *(It was produced from sugars that were produced by photosynthesis.)* **learning modality: visual**

A Two-Stage Process

Using the Visuals: Figure 8

Make sure students understand that the inset photo is a microscopic view of chloroplasts. Ask: **What makes the chloroplasts green?** *(Chlorophyll, a green pigment)* **What is the role of chlorophyll in photosynthesis?** *(It captures light energy that is used to power the second stage of photosynthesis.)* **learning modality: visual**

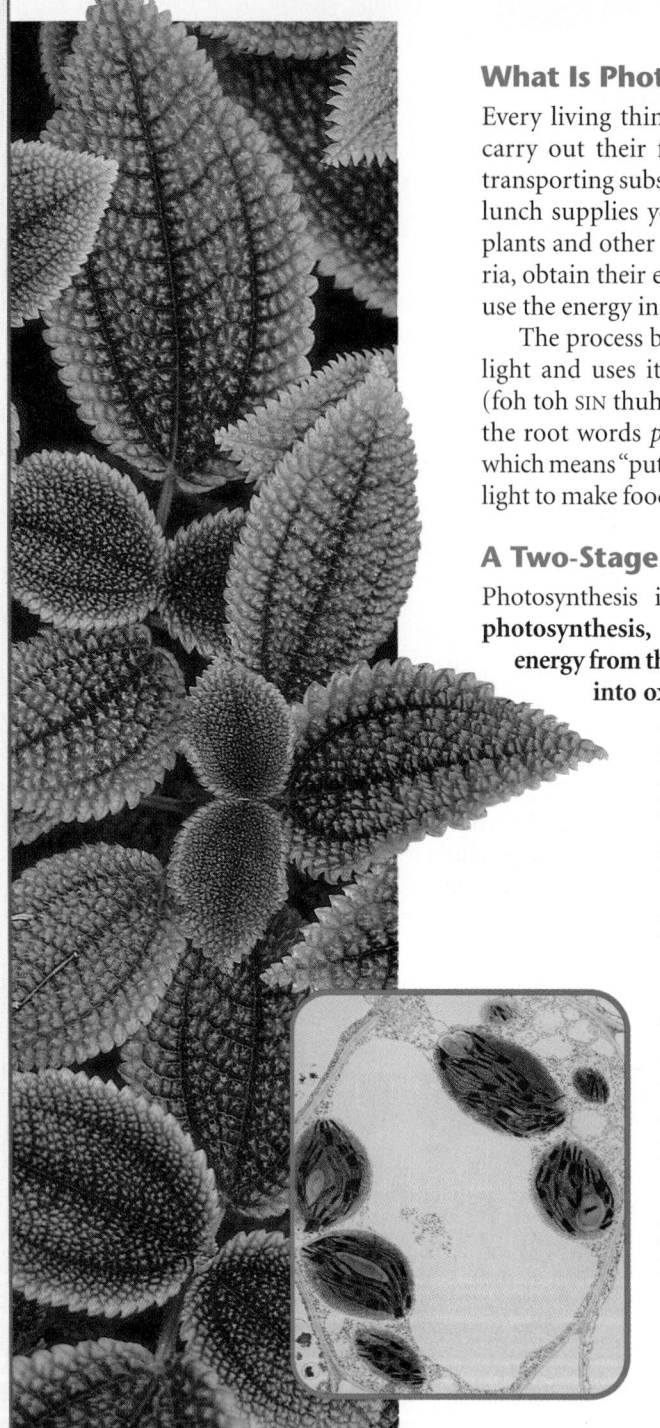

What Is Photosynthesis?

Every living thing needs energy. All cells need energy to carry out their functions, such as making proteins and transporting substances into and out of the cell. Your picnic lunch supplies your cells with the energy they need. But plants and other organisms, such as algae and some bacteria, obtain their energy in a different way. These organisms use the energy in sunlight to make their own food.

The process by which a cell captures the energy in sunlight and uses it to make food is called **photosynthesis** (foh toh SIN thuh sis). The term *photosynthesis* comes from the root words *photo*, which means "light," and *synthesis*, which means "putting together." Photosynthesis means using light to make food.

A Two-Stage Process

Photosynthesis is a very complicated process. **During photosynthesis, plants and some other organisms use energy from the sun to convert carbon dioxide and water into oxygen and sugars, including glucose.** You can think of photosynthesis as taking place in two stages: capturing the sun's energy and producing sugars. You're probably familiar with many two-stage processes. To make a cake, for example, the first stage is to combine the ingredients to make the batter. The second stage is to bake the batter in an oven. To get the desired result—the cake—both stages must occur in the correct order.

Capturing the Sun's Energy The first stage of photosynthesis involves capturing the energy in sunlight. In plants, this energy-capturing process occurs in the leaves and other green parts of the plant. Recall from Chapter 1 that chloroplasts are green organelles inside plant cells. In most plants, leaf cells contain more chloroplasts than do cells in other parts of the plant.

Figure 8 Photosynthesis occurs inside chloroplasts in the cells of plants and some other organisms. The chloroplasts are the green structures in the cell in the inset. *Applying Concepts Where in a plant are cells with many chloroplasts found?*

The chloroplasts in plant cells give plants their green color. The green color comes from **pigments,** colored chemical compounds that absorb light. The main pigment found in the chloroplasts of plants is **chlorophyll.** Chloroplasts may also contain yellow and orange pigments, but they are usually masked by the green color of chlorophyll.

Chlorophyll and the other pigments function in a manner similar to that of the solar "cells" in a solar-powered calculator. Solar cells capture the energy in light and use it to power the calculator. Similarly, the pigments capture light energy and use it to power the second stage of photosynthesis.

Using Energy to Make Food In the second stage of photosynthesis, the cell uses the captured energy to produce sugars. The cell needs two raw materials for this stage: water (H_2O) and carbon dioxide (CO_2). In plants, the roots absorb water from the soil. The water then moves up through the plant's stem to the leaves. Carbon dioxide is one of the gases in the air. Carbon dioxide enters the plant through small openings on the undersides of the leaves called **stomata** (STOH muh tuh)(singular *stoma*). Once in the leaves, the water and carbon dioxide move into the chloroplasts.

Inside the chloroplasts, the water and carbon dioxide undergo a complex series of chemical reactions. The reactions are powered by the energy captured in the first stage. One of the products of the reactions is oxygen (O_2). The other products are sugars, including glucose ($C_6H_{12}O_6$). Recall from Section 1 that sugars are a type of carbohydrate. Cells can use the energy in the sugars to carry out important cell functions.

☑ *Checkpoint* Why are plants green?

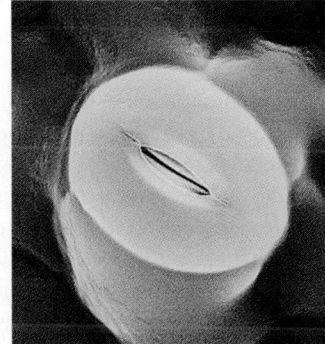

Figure 9 Stomata are small openings on the undersides of leaves. Stomata can open (left) or close (right) to control the movement of carbon dioxide, oxygen, and water vapor.

Inferring ACTIVITY
In this activity, you will observe the pigments in a leaf.

1. Cut a strip 5 cm by 20 cm out of a coffee filter.
2. Place a leaf on top of the paper strip, about 2 cm from the bottom.
3. Roll the edge of a dime over a section of the leaf, leaving a narrow band of color on the paper strip.
4. Pour rubbing alcohol into a plastic cup to a depth of 1 cm. Stand the paper strip in the cup so the color band is about 1 cm above the alcohol. Hook the other end of the strip over the top of the cup.
5. After 10 minutes, remove the paper strip and let it dry. Observe the strip.
6. Wash your hands.

What does the appearance of your paper strip reveal about the presence of pigments in the leaf?

Inferring

Materials *coffee filter, scissors, leaf, metric ruler, dime, rubbing alcohol, plastic cup* ACTIVITY
Time 20 minutes
Tips A geranium will work well. Tell students that chlorophyll and other plant pigments dissolve in alcohol.
Expected Outcome As the alcohol spreads through the green band, it dissolves the plant pigments and carries them up the paper strip. As the paper dries, the heavier pigments separate out first, so students may see separate lines of different pigments on the paper strip.
Extend Point out that, in temperate climates, the amount of chlorophyll in leaves greatly decreases in the fall. Ask: **Why does this cause the leaves to change color?** (*When the leaves contain less chlorophyll, the other pigments they contain can show through.*) **learning modality: kinesthetic**

Building Inquiry Skills: Observing

Materials *forceps, lettuce leaf, water, microscope slide, coverslip, microscope* ACTIVITY
Time 15 minutes

Give students a chance to see stomata on the underside of a leaf. Have students use forceps to gently pull away a small piece of the thin membrane on the underside of a lettuce leaf. Then have students use the piece of leaf to make a slide. Students should scan the leaf under low power to find a few stomata, and then bring the stomata into focus under high power. Urge students to sketch the structures they see. Call their attention to the sausage-shaped guard cells on either side of each stoma, and ask: **What role do you think the guard cells play?** (*They regulate what enters the stomata.*) **What substance enters the leaf through the stomata?** (*Carbon dioxide*) **learning modality: visual**

Ongoing Assessment

Oral Presentation Call on students at random to define photosynthesis and identify its two stages.

Media and Technology

 Audio CD English-Spanish Summary 2-3

 Exploring Earth Science Videodisc Unit 1, Side 1, "Sunny Days"

Chapter 6

Answers to Self-Assessment

☑ *Checkpoint*
Plants are green because their chloroplasts contain the green pigment chlorophyll.

Caption Question
Figure 8 Cells with many chloroplasts are found in the leaves.

The Photosynthesis Equation

Integrating Chemistry

Inform students that chemical equations must balance by having the same number of each type of atom on both sides of the equation. Point out that the subscript numerals show the number of atoms in each molecule in a compound and the numerals in front of the compound show how many molecules of that compound are involved in the reaction. Challenge students to determine if the chemical equation for photosynthesis is balanced by counting the number of each type of atom on the two sides of the equation. Check their counts by asking: **How many oxygen atoms are there on each side of the equation?** *(18)* **learning modality: logical/ mathematical**

Building Inquiry Skills: Making Models

Materials *bingo chips, buttons, cereal or pasta pieces, or other small objects in three different colors or shapes* **Time** 10 minutes

Divide the class into pairs, and provide each pair with enough small objects of each color or shape to represent the carbon, oxygen, and hydrogen atoms on one side of the photosynthesis equation. First have one member of each pair arrange the objects to represent the left side of the equation. Then have the other member of the pair rearrange the same objects to represent the right side of the photosynthesis equation. Urge partners to reverse their roles and repeat the activity. Then ask: **What part of the photosynthesis equation is not represented in the model?** *(The energy required to make the reaction occur)* **learning modality: kinesthetic**

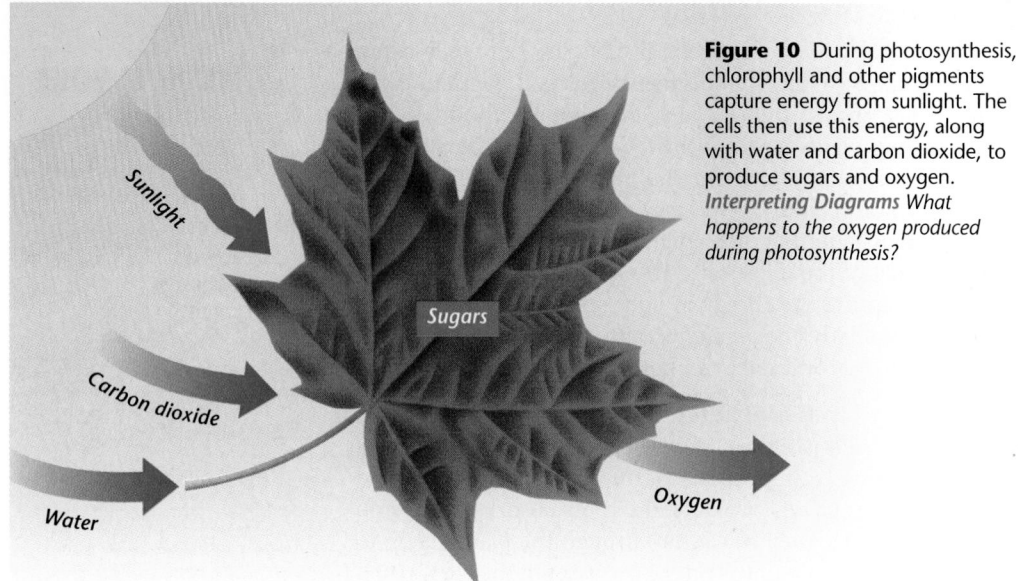

Figure 10 During photosynthesis, chlorophyll and other pigments capture energy from sunlight. The cells then use this energy, along with water and carbon dioxide, to produce sugars and oxygen. *Interpreting Diagrams What happens to the oxygen produced during photosynthesis?*

The Photosynthesis Equation

The events of photosynthesis can be summed up by the following chemical equation:

$$6\ CO_2 + 6\ H_2O \xrightarrow{\text{light energy}} C_6H_{12}O_6 + 6\ O_2$$

carbon dioxide   water   glucose   oxygen

INTEGRATING CHEMISTRY Notice that the raw materials—six molecules of carbon dioxide and six molecules of water—are on the left side of the equation. The products—one molecule of glucose and six molecules of oxygen—are on the right side of the equation. An arrow, which is read as "yields," connects the raw materials to the products. Light energy, which is necessary for the chemical reaction to occur, is written above the arrow.

What happens to the products of photosynthesis? Plant cells use some of the sugar for food. The cells break down the sugar molecules to release the energy they contain. This energy can then be used to carry out the plant's functions. Some sugar molecules are converted into other compounds, such as cellulose. Other sugar molecules may be stored in the plant's cells for later use. When you eat food from plants, such as potatoes or carrots, you are eating the plant's stored food.

The other product of photosynthesis is oxygen. Most of the oxygen passes out of the plant through the stomata and into the air. All organisms that carry out photosynthesis release oxygen.

64

Photosynthesis and Life

Integrating Environmental Science If you were a caterpillar, you might be sitting on a plant chewing on a leaf. The plant is an autotroph, an organism that makes its own food. The plant's leaves contain sugars made during photosynthesis. Leaves also contain starches, cellulose, and other compounds made from sugars. The energy in these compounds originally came from the sun.

The caterpillar is a heterotroph, an organism that cannot make its own food. To live, grow, and perform other caterpillar functions, it needs the energy in the plant's sugars. By eating plants, the caterpillar gets its energy from the sun, although in an indirect way.

Watch out—there's a bird! The bird, a heterotroph, gets its energy by eating caterpillars. Since the energy in caterpillars indirectly comes from the sun, the bird too is living off the sun's energy. **Nearly all living things obtain energy either directly or indirectly from the energy of sunlight captured during photosynthesis.**

Photosynthesis is also essential for the air you breathe. Most living things need oxygen to survive. About 21% of Earth's atmosphere is oxygen—thanks to plants and other organisms that carry out photosynthesis. Almost all the oxygen in Earth's atmosphere was produced by living things through the process of photosynthesis.

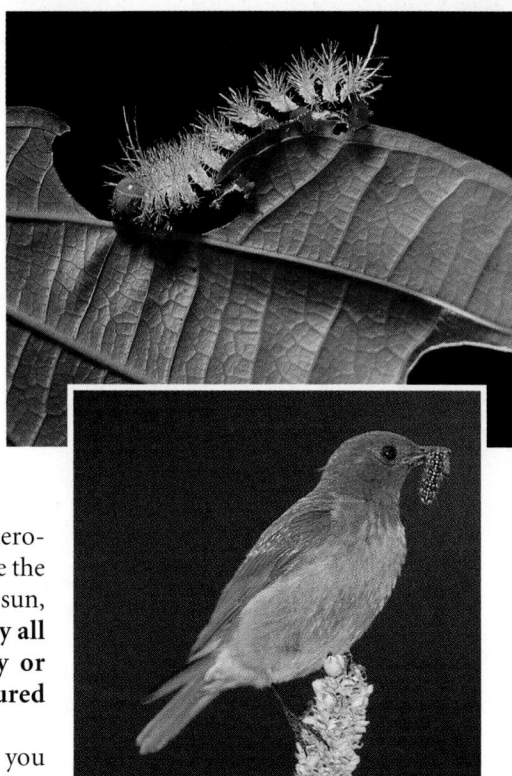

Figure 11 Both the caterpillar and the western bluebird obtain their energy indirectly from the sun.

Section 3 Review

1. What are the raw materials needed for photosynthesis? What are the products?
2. How do plants get energy? How do animals get energy?
3. What role does chlorophyll play in photosynthesis? Where is chlorophyll found?
4. **Thinking Critically Applying Concepts** List three ways that autotrophs were important to you today.

CHAPTER PROJECT

Check Your Progress

At this point, you should soak your egg for one or two days in water, then in water with food coloring, then in salt water, and finally in another liquid of your choice. Continue to rinse your egg and measure and record its circumference every day. Your egg should be going through some amazing changes in appearance.

Program Resources

- **Laboratory Manual** 2, "Stomata Functions"
- **Unit 1 Resources** 2-3 Review and Reinforce, p. 53; 2-3 Enrich, p. 54

Media and Technology

Transparencies "Photosynthesis," Transparency 7

Answers to Self-Assessment

Caption Question

Figure 10 It passes out of the plant through the stomata and into the air.

Photosynthesis and Life

Integrating Environmental Science

Point out that not all the energy converted to food by autotrophs is available to the heterotrophs that depend on them. In fact, only about 10 percent of the energy at a given level in a food chain is available to organisms at the next level of the food chain. Ask: **Why are there fewer caterpillars than the plants they eat, and fewer birds than caterpillars?** *(Because there is less and less energy available to support life as you move up the food chain)* **learning modality: logical/mathematical**

3 Assess

Section 3 Review Answers

1. Raw materials: carbon dioxide, water; products: oxygen, sugars
2. Plants get energy from the sun. Animals get energy by eating plants or animals that eat plants.
3. Chlorophyll absorbs light, which provides the energy for photosynthesis. It is found in chloroplasts, which occur mainly in leaves.
4. Students may say that autotrophs provided them with oxygen, food for themselves, and food for the animals they depend on for food and other purposes.

CHAPTER PROJECT

Check Your Progress

Make sure students are not having problems with the project. Call on volunteers to describe the changes they have noticed in their egg. *(After two days in vinegar, the shell should have dissolved and the egg should have increased in size and become rubbery in texture.)*

Performance Assessment

Writing Have students explain how life on Earth depends on the sun.

SECTION 4 Respiration

Objectives

After completing the lesson, students will be able to
◆ describe the events that occur during respiration;
◆ describe the relationship between photosynthesis and respiration;
◆ describe alcoholic and lactic-acid fermentation.

Key Terms respiration, fermentation

1 Engage/Explore

Activating Prior Knowledge

Introduce students to respiration by relating it to combustion. First help students recall what they know about combustion, by asking: **What does a fire need to burn?** *(fuel and oxygen)* **What is released when fuel is burned?** *(Energy in the form of heat and light)* Then tell students that a similar chemical process, called respiration, "burns" food molecules in cells. Like combustion, respiration uses fuel and oxygen to produce energy. The fuel comes from food, and the energy is used for cellular functions.

•••••••• DISCOVER ••••••••

Skills Focus observing
Materials *2 test tubes*
with stoppers, warm water, 5 mL sugar, test tube rack, 1.0 mL dried yeast, 2 straws
Time 20 minutes
Tips If possible, use fast-acting yeast, which you can purchase at a food store. The water should be warm, but not hot.
Expected Outcome Students should observe bubbles in the sugar water but none in the plain water.
Think It Over Students should infer that the bubbles in the test tube containing the sugar are due to some process involving the yeast and the sugar.

SECTION 4 Respiration

DISCOVER •••••••••••••••••••••••••••••• ACTIVITY

What Is a Product of Respiration?

1. Put on your goggles. Fill two test tubes half full of warm water. Add 5 milliliters of sugar to one of the test tubes. Put the tubes in a test tube rack.

2. Add 0.5 milliliter of dried yeast (a single-celled organism) to each tube. Stir the contents of each tube with a straw. Place a stopper snugly in the top of each tube.

3. Observe any changes that occur in the two test tubes over the next 10 to 15 minutes.

Think It Over
Observing What changes occurred in each test tube? How can you account for any differences that you observed?

GUIDE FOR READING

◆ What events occur during respiration?
◆ How are photosynthesis and respiration related?
◆ What is fermentation?

Reading Tip Before you read, write a definition of *respiration.* After reading this section, revise your definition to include what you've learned.

Your friend stops along the trail ahead of you and calls out, "Let's eat!" He looks around for a flat rock to sit on. You're ready for lunch. You didn't have much breakfast this morning, and you've been hiking for the past hour. As you look around you, you see that the steepest part of the trail is still ahead of you. You'll need a lot of energy to make it to the top.

Everyone knows that food provides energy. But not everyone knows *how* food provides energy. The food you eat does not provide your body with energy immediately after you eat it. First, the food must pass through your digestive system. There, the food is broken down into small molecules. These small molecules can then pass out of the digestive system and into your bloodstream. Next, the molecules travel through the bloodstream to the cells of your body. Inside the cells, the energy in the molecules is released. In this section, you'll learn how your body's cells obtain energy from the food you eat.

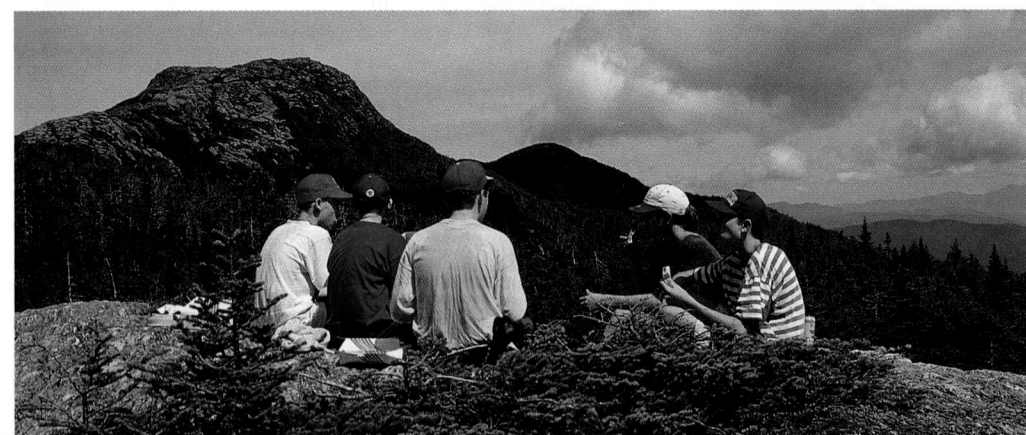

READING STRATEGIES

Reading Tip Most students will think initially that *respiration* just means breathing, which is its common meaning. By the time students have finished reading the section, they should realize that *respiration* also means the breakdown of food molecules in cells to produce energy. Ask volunteers to read their revised definitions aloud. Discuss with the class the dual use of this term.

Program Resources

◆ **Unit 1 Resources** 2-4 Lesson Plan, p. 55; 2-4 Section Summary, p. 56

Figure 12 All organisms need energy to live. A. Although these mushrooms don't move, they still need a continuous supply of energy to grow and reproduce. B. This leopard frog uses the energy stored in carbohydrates to leap great distances.
Applying Concepts What is the name of the process by which cells obtain the energy they need?

Storing and Releasing Energy

To understand how cells use energy, think about how people save money in a bank. You might, for example, put some money in a savings account. Then, when you want to buy something, you withdraw some of the money. Cells store and use energy in a similar way. During photosynthesis, plants capture the energy from sunlight and "save" it in the form of carbohydrates, including sugars and starches. When the cells need energy, they "withdraw" it by breaking down the carbohydrates. This process releases energy. Similarly, when you eat a meal, you add to your body's energy savings account. When your cells need energy, they make a withdrawal and break down the food to release energy.

Respiration

After you eat a meal, your body converts the carbohydrates in the food into glucose, a type of sugar. When cells need energy, they "withdraw" energy from glucose in a process called **respiration. During respiration, cells break down simple food molecules such as glucose and release the energy they contain.** Because living things need a continuous supply of energy, the cells of all living things carry out respiration continuously.

The term *respiration* might be confusing. You have probably used it to mean breathing, that is, moving air in and out of your lungs. Because of this confusion, the respiration process that takes place inside cells is sometimes called *cellular respiration.*

The double use of the term *respiration* does point out a connection that you should keep in mind. Breathing brings oxygen into your lungs, and oxygen is necessary for cellular respiration to occur in most cells. The most efficient means of obtaining energy from glucose requires the presence of oxygen. Some cells, however, can obtain energy from glucose without using oxygen.

Media and Technology

 Audio CD English-Spanish Summary 2-4

 Transparencies "Respiration," Transparency 8

Answers to Self-Assessment

Caption Question

Figure 12 The name of the process is respiration.

2 Facilitate

Storing and Releasing Energy

Building Inquiry Skills: Inferring

Ask students: **When do you think plants would need to "withdraw" the energy stored in their cells as complex carbohydrates?** *(During the winter when plants have lost their leaves and cannot photosynthesize)* **learning modality: logical/mathematical**

Respiration

Building Inquiry Skills: Communicating

Urge a small group of students who need extra challenges to work together to investigate the role of ATP in respiration and to communicate what they learn to the rest of the class. *(ATP, or adenosine triphosphate, is the molecule in which energy is stored during respiration. It is a very reactive molecule that readily breaks down and releases its energy for other cell functions.)* Make sure students fairly share the tasks of researching the problem and communicating the information. Challenge the group to communicate the information in a way that is creative, interesting, and easy to understand, such as a skit, cartoon strip, or illustrated flowchart. **cooperative learning**

Ongoing Assessment

Oral Presentation Call on students to explain the relationship between breathing and cellular respiration. Have them compare and contrast the processes.

Respiration, continued

Including All Students

Guide students who are still mastering English in comparing and contrasting breathing and cellular respiration. Ask: **How are breathing and cellular respiration similar?** *(Both involve using or taking in oxygen and releasing carbon dioxide and water.)* **How are breathing and cellular respiration different?** *(Breathing takes place in the lungs and provides the body with oxygen, whereas cellular respiration takes place inside cells and provides the cells with energy.)* **limited English proficiency**

Inquiry Challenge

Materials *100 mL tap water, flask, phenolpthalein, 0.4% sodium hydroxide solution, 2 plastic droppers*
Time 20 minutes

Inform students that the carbon dioxide in exhaled breath can be measured with the following procedure: breathe for one minute into a flask containing 100 mL of tap water; add five drops of phenolpthalein to the water; add 0.4% sodium hydroxide solution, drop by drop, until the water turns light pink. The more sodium hydroxide that is needed to turn the water pink, the greater the concentration of carbon dioxide. Challenge students to develop and test a hypothesis regarding how exercise affects the amount of carbon dioxide in exhaled breath. (**CAUTION:** *Excuse students with health problems from physical activity.*) Ask: **Why does exhaled breath contain more carbon dioxide after exercise?** *(Because more respiration was needed to provide energy for the activity)* **learning modality: kinesthetic**

The Respiration Equation Although respiration occurs in a series of complex steps, the overall process can be summarized in the following equation:

$$C_6H_{12}O_6 + 6\,O_2 \longrightarrow 6\,CO_2 + 6\,H_2O + energy$$

glucose · · · · oxygen · · · · carbon dioxide · · · water

Notice that the raw materials for respiration are glucose and oxygen. Plants and other organisms that undergo photosynthesis make their own glucose. The glucose in the cells of animals and other organisms comes from the food they consume. The oxygen comes from the air or water surrounding the organism.

The Two Stages of Respiration Like photosynthesis, respiration is a two-stage process. The first stage takes place in the cytoplasm of the organism's cells. There, glucose molecules are broken down into smaller molecules. Oxygen is not involved in this stage of respiration. Only a small amount of the energy in glucose is released during this stage.

The second stage of respiration takes place in the mitochondria. There, the small molecules are broken down into even smaller molecules. These chemical reactions require oxygen, and a great deal of energy is released. This is why the mitochondria are sometimes called the "powerhouses" of the cell.

Figure 13 summarizes the process of respiration. If you trace the steps in the breakdown of glucose, you'll see that energy is released in both stages. Two other products of respiration are carbon dioxide and water. These products diffuse out of the cell. In animals, the carbon dioxide and some water leave the body when they breathe out. Thus, when you breathe in, you take in oxygen, a raw material for respiration. When you breathe out, you release carbon dioxide and water, products of respiration.

✓ *Checkpoint* What are the raw materials for respiration?

Figure 13 The first stage of respiration, which takes place in the cytoplasm, releases a small amount of energy. The second stage takes place in the mitochondria. A large amount of energy is released at this stage.

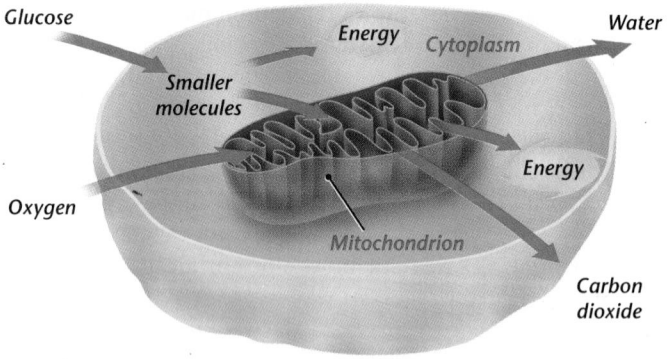

Background

Facts and Figures Respiration is often compared to combustion because both processes involve the breakdown of molecules in the presence of oxygen to produce energy and carbon dioxide. However, respiration is a much slower, more controlled process than combustion. If respiration is like carrying a bundle down five flights of stairs, combustion is like dropping it from a fifth-story window.

History of Science The discovery of the nature of cellular respiration is attributed jointly to the French chemist Antoine Laurent Lavoisier and the French physicist, mathematician, and astronomer Pierre Laplace. In 1780 they published the results of their experiments showing that animal respiration is a form of combustion.

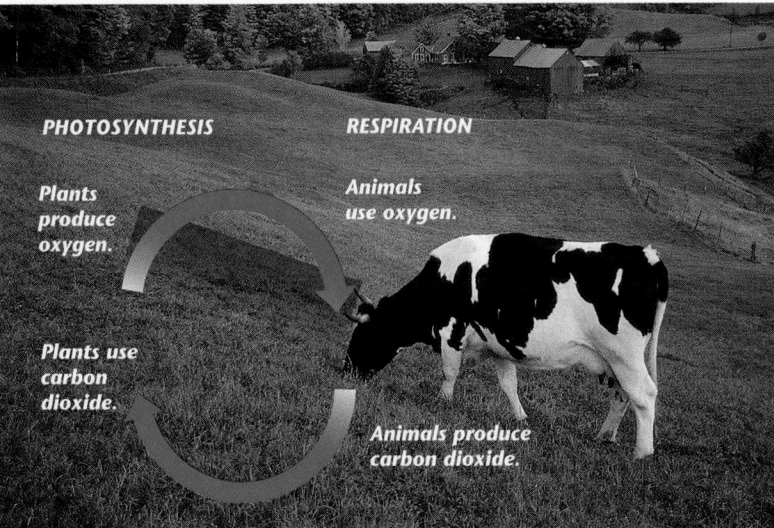

Figure 14 Photosynthesis and respiration can be thought of as opposite processes. *Interpreting Photographs How do these two processes keep the levels of oxygen and carbon dioxide in the atmosphere fairly constant?*

PHOTOSYNTHESIS
Plants produce oxygen.
Plants use carbon dioxide.

RESPIRATION
Animals use oxygen.
Animals produce carbon dioxide.

Comparing Photosynthesis and Respiration

Do you notice anything familiar about the equation for respiration? You are quite right if you said it is the opposite of the equation for photosynthesis. This is an important point to remember. During photosynthesis, carbon dioxide and water are used to produce sugars and oxygen. During respiration, glucose (a sugar) and oxygen are used to produce carbon dioxide and water. **Photosynthesis and respiration can be thought of as opposite processes.** Together, these two processes form a cycle that keeps the levels of oxygen and carbon dioxide fairly constant in the atmosphere. As you can see in Figure 14, living things use both gases over and over again.

Fermentation

Some cells are able to obtain energy from food without using oxygen. For example, some single-celled organisms live where there is no oxygen, such as deep in the ocean or in the mud of lakes or swamps. These organisms obtain their energy through **fermentation,** an energy-releasing process that does not require oxygen. **Fermentation provides energy for cells without using oxygen.** The amount of energy released from each sugar molecule during fermentation, however, is much lower than the amount released during respiration.

Social Studies CONNECTION

Many popular Asian foods are produced by fermentation. Kimchee, for example, is a Korean side dish that is similar to sauerkraut. It is made from Asian cabbage, salt, and spices. Naturally occurring bacteria ferment sugars in the cabbage by lactic-acid fermentation. The lactic acid produced during the fermentation process gives the kimchee a tangy flavor. Other Asian foods produced by fermentation include soy sauce and miso.

In Your Journal

Write an ad for kimchee or another fermented food product. Include information about how the food is made and used.

Comparing Photosynthesis and Respiration

Building Inquiry Skills: Comparing and Contrasting

Urge students to compare the respiration equation on the previous page with the photosynthesis equation on page 64. Ask: **How are the two equations similar?** *(Both involve the same chemical compounds.)* **How are the two equations different?** *(The left and right sides of the equations are reversed; also the photosynthesis reaction uses energy, and the respiration reaction produces energy.)* **Based on your comparison, what can you conclude about the relationship between respiration and photosynthesis?** *(Complex molecules formed during photosynthesis are broken down during respiration to produce energy and simple molecules that are the raw materials for photosynthesis.)* **learning modality: logical/mathematical**

Fermentation

Social Studies CONNECTION

Emphasize that lactic acid is a product of one type of fermentation. Explain that lactic acid, like most other acids, has a sour taste. Bring samples of fermented foods, such as sauerkraut, soy sauce, or miso. Have students taste the foods and describe them. (CAUTION: Check for food allergies.)

In Your Journal In their ads, students should write about one of the fermented foods mentioned in the feature or another fermented food, such as yogurt. Suggest that they try to find a recipe for the foods they have chosen. Their ads should include a clear description of the process of lactic-acid fermentation. **learning modality: verbal**

Ongoing Assessment

Skills Check Have students create a compare and contrast table of the two stages of cellular respiration.

Answers to Self-Assessment

☑ *Checkpoint*

The raw materials for respiration are oxygen and glucose.

Caption Question

Figure 14 Photosynthesis uses carbon dioxide and produces oxygen; respiration uses oxygen and produces carbon dioxide.

Fermentation, continued

 Integrating Health

Tell students that researchers have hypothesized that eating a high-carbohydrate diet before a long race slows the buildup of lactic acid in the muscles and helps prevent muscle soreness and fatigue. Challenge students to design an experiment to test this hypothesis. Call on volunteers to describe their experimental designs. *(The most likely design compares muscle soreness and fatigue in two groups of runners, one group that has been eating a high-carbohydrate diet and one that has been eating a low-carbohydrate diet.)* **learning modality: logical/mathematical**

3 Assess

Section 4 Review Answers

1. It supplies the energy the cell needs.
2. They can be thought of as opposite processes: During photosynthesis, carbon dioxide and water are used to produce sugar and oxygen. During respiration, sugar and oxygen are used to produce carbon dioxide and water.
3. oxygen
4. The level of oxygen in the atmosphere is maintained mainly by plants producing oxygen during photosynthesis and animals using oxygen during respiration.
5. Yes; plant cells carry out respiration to produce energy for cell functions from molecules such as glucose.

Science at Home

Students should explain that yeast uses the sugar in the dough for alcoholic fermentation, which releases carbon dioxide. The carbon dioxide, in turn, causes the dough to rise and small holes to form in the baked bread.

ACTIVITY

Performance Assessment

Writing Have students describe the similarities and differences between alcoholic and lactic-acid fermentation.

Figure 15 When an athlete's muscles run out of oxygen, lactic-acid fermentation occurs. The athlete's muscles feel tired and sore. *Inferring Which muscles in this runner were producing the most lactic acid?*

Alcoholic Fermentation One type of fermentation occurs in yeast and some other single-celled organisms. This process is sometimes called alcoholic fermentation because alcohol is one of the products made when these organisms break down sugars. The other products are carbon dioxide and a small amount of energy.

The products of alcoholic fermentation are important to bakers and brewers. The carbon dioxide produced by yeast causes dough to rise, and it creates the air pockets you see in bread. Carbon dioxide is also the source of bubbles in alcoholic drinks such as beer and sparkling wine.

Lactic-Acid Fermentation Another type of fermentation takes place at times in your body, and you've probably felt its effects. Think of a time when you've run as fast as you could for as long as you could. Your leg muscles were pushing hard against the pavement, and you were breathing quickly. Eventually, however, your legs became tired and you couldn't run any more.

INTEGRATING HEALTH

No matter how hard you breathed, your muscle cells used up the oxygen faster than it could be replaced. Because your cells lacked oxygen, they used the process of fermentation to produce energy. One by-product of this type of fermentation is a substance known as lactic acid. When lactic acid builds up, your muscles feel weak, tired, and sore.

Section 4 Review

1. Why is respiration important for a cell?
2. Explain the relationship between photosynthesis and respiration.
3. Which raw material is *not* needed for fermentation to occur?
4. How do plants and animals maintain the level of oxygen in the atmosphere?
5. **Thinking Critically** **Applying Concepts** Do plant cells need to carry out respiration? Explain.

Science at Home

Fermentation in Bread With an adult family member, follow a recipe in a cookbook to make a loaf of bread using yeast. Explain to your family what causes the dough to rise. After you bake the bread, observe a slice and look for evidence that fermentation occurred.

Program Resources

◆ **Unit 1 Resources** 2-4 Review and Reinforce, p. 57; 2-4 Enrich, p. 58
◆ **Interdisciplinary Exploration Series** "Fate of the Rain Forest," pp. 20–21; "Where River Meets Sea," pp. 15–16

Answers to Self-Assessment

Caption Question

Figure 15 Cells in the runner's leg muscles were producing the most lactic acid.

You and Your Environment

Gases in Balance

Problem

How are photosynthesis and respiration related?

Skills Focus

controlling variables, interpreting data

Materials

marking pens   straws
2 *Elodea* plants   light source
plastic graduated cylinder, 100-mL
bromthymol blue solution
3 flasks with stoppers, 250-mL

Procedure

1. Bromthymol blue can be used to test for carbon dioxide. To see how this dye works, pour 100 mL of bromthymol blue solution into a flask. Record its color. **CAUTION:** *Bromthymol blue can stain skin and clothing. Avoid spilling or splashing it on yourself.*

2. Provide a supply of carbon dioxide by gently blowing into the solution through a straw until the dye changes color. Record the new color. **CAUTION:** *Do not inhale any of the solution through the straw.*

3. Copy the data table into your notebook. Add 100 mL of bromthymol blue to the other flasks. Then blow through clean straws into each solution until the color changes.

4. Now you will test to see what gas is used by a plant in the presence of light. Obtain two *Elodea* plants of about the same size.

5. Place one plant into the first flask. Label the flask "L" for light. Place the other plant in the second flask. Label the flask "D" for darkness. Label the third flask "C" for control. Put stoppers in all three flasks.

DATA TABLE

Flask	Color of Solution	
	Day 1	Day 2
L (light)		
D (dark)		
C (control)		

6. Record the colors of the three solutions under Day 1 in your data table.

7. Place the flasks labeled L and C in a lighted location as directed by your teacher. Place the flask labeled D in a dark location as directed by your teacher. Wash your hands thoroughly when you have finished.

8. On Day 2, examine the flasks and record the colors of the solutions in your data table.

Analyze and Conclude

1. Explain why the color of each solution did or did not change from Day 1 to Day 2.

2. Why was it important to include the flask labeled C as part of this experiment?

3. Predict what would happen if you blew into the flask labeled L after you completed Step 8. Explain your prediction.

4. **Apply** How does this lab show that photosynthesis and respiration are opposite processes? Why are both processes necessary to maintain an environment suitable for living things?

More to Explore

Suppose you were to put an *Elodea* plant and a small fish in a stoppered flask. Predict what would happen to the levels of oxygen and carbon dioxide in the flask. Explain your prediction.

Sample Data Table

Flask	Color of Solution	
	Day 1	Day 2
L (light)	yellow	blue
D (dark)	yellow	yellow
C (control)	yellow	yellow

Program Resources

♦ **Unit 1 Resources** Chapter 2 Real-World Lab, pp. 63–64

Safety

Stress to students that they should not inhale the bromthymol blue solution through the straw. Review the safety guidelines in Appendix A.

You and Your Environment

Gases in Balance

Preparing for Inquiry

Key Concept Photosynthesis and respiration are opposite processes.
Skills Objectives Students will be able to
♦ control other variables while investigating whether photosynthesis requires light;
♦ interpret data on color to detect carbon dioxide in solutions.
Time 20 minutes on Day 1; 15 minutes on Day 2
Advance Planning Purchase *Elodea* plants at an aquarium supply store.

Guiding Inquiry

Troubleshooting the Experiment

♦ Make sure students realize that the solution will turn blue again if the carbon dioxide is used up.

Expected Outcome

The solution in flask L should change from yellow to blue; the solution in flasks D and C should remain yellow.

Analyze and Conclude

1. The solution in flask L changed because photosynthesis used up the carbon dioxide. The solution in flask D remained the same because the plant had no light for photosynthesis. The solution in flask C remained the same because there was no plant to undergo photosynthesis.
2. Flask C was needed to rule out the possibility that the solution in flask L changed color just because it was placed in the light.
3. The solution would turn yellow again because it would contain carbon dioxide.
4. The lab showed that carbon dioxide is given off in respiration and used in photosynthesis. These two processes form a cycle that keeps levels of oxygen and carbon dioxide constant.

Extending the Inquiry

More to Explore The levels would reach a stable balance as the plant and fish recycled the two gases.

SECTION 5 Cell Division

Objectives

After completing the lesson, students will be able to

♦ identify the events that take place during the three stages of the cell cycle;
♦ describe the structure of DNA and DNA replication.

Key Terms cell cycle, interphase, replication, mitosis, chromosome, chromatid, cytokinesis

1 Engage/Explore

Activating Prior Knowledge

Introduce students to the cell cycle by relating it to the human life cycle. Ask: **What are the stages that people go through during their lives, starting with infancy and ending with old age?** *(Students are likely to name or describe the additional stages of childhood, adolescence, and adulthood.)* Point out that cells, like people, undergo a life cycle, called the cell cycle. During the stages of the cell cycle, cells grow and mature. Just as the human life cycle starts again with reproduction, the cell cycle starts over again when the cell divides.

DISCOVER

Skills Focus developing hypotheses
Materials *plastic dropper, yeast culture, stained microscope slide, coverslip, microscope*
Time 15 minutes
Tips You can prepare a yeast culture by stirring dry yeast and sugar into warm water. Stain slides ahead of time by adding a drop of methylene blue to each slide and letting it dry. You could also use prepared slides of yeast cells.
Expected Outcome Students should observe and sketch yeast cells, some of which are in the process of budding to form daughter cells.
Think It Over Students may say that the "double cells" are dividing. The most likely hypothesis is that yeast cells split in two when they reproduce.

SECTION 5 Cell Division

DISCOVER ············ ACTIVITY

What Are the Cells Doing?

1. Use a plastic dropper to transfer some yeast cells from a yeast culture to a microscope slide. Your teacher has prepared the slide by drying methylene blue stain onto it. Add a cover-slip and place the slide under a microscope.

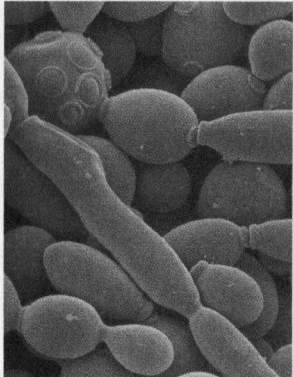

2. Examine the cells on the slide. Use low power first, then high power. Look for what appears to be two cells attached to each other. One cell may be larger than the other. Draw what you see.

Think It Over

Developing Hypotheses What process do you think the "double cells" are undergoing? Develop a hypothesis that might explain what you see.

GUIDE FOR READING

♦ What events take place during the three stages of the cell cycle?
♦ What is the role of DNA replication?

Reading Tip Before you read, use the headings to outline the process of cell division. As you read, draw pictures to help you understand the process.

I n the early autumn, many local fairs run pumpkin contests. Proud growers enter their largest pumpkins, hoping to win a prize. If you've never seen these prize-winning pumpkins, you would be amazed. Some have masses close to 400 kilograms and can be as big as a doghouse. What's even more amazing is that these giant pumpkins began as small flowers on pumpkin plants. How did the pumpkins grow so big?

A pumpkin grows in size by increasing both the size and the number of its cells. A single cell divides, forming two cells. Then two cells divide, forming four, and so on. This process of cell division does not occur only in pumpkins, though. In fact, many cells in your body are undergoing cell division as you read this page.

72

READING STRATEGIES

Reading Tip Suggest to students that each stage of cell division is a main point of their section outline. For each stage, they should sketch the cell undergoing division.

Study and Comprehension Before students read the section, suggest that they reread the material on DNA in Section 1. After students read this section, encourage them to create a concept map using the boldfaced terms. Call on students to name the stage of the cell cycle and the phases of mitosis to make sure they are not confusing the two.

The Cell Cycle

Think about the cells you learned about in Chapter 1. Each cell contains many different structures, including a cell membrane, a nucleus, mitochondria, and ribosomes. To divide into two equal parts, the cell would need to either duplicate the structures or divide them equally between the two new cells. Both cells would then contain everything they need in order to survive and carry out their life functions.

The regular sequence of growth and division that cells undergo is known as the **cell cycle.** You can see details of the cell cycle in *Exploring the Cell Cycle* on pages 76 and 77. Notice that the cell cycle is divided into three main stages. As you read about each stage, follow the events that occur as one "parent" cell divides to form two identical "daughter" cells.

Stage 1: Interphase

The first stage of the cell cycle is called **interphase.** Interphase is the period before cell division occurs. Even though it is not dividing, the cell is quite active during this stage. **During interphase, the cell grows to its mature size, makes a copy of its DNA, and prepares to divide into two cells.**

Growth During the first part of interphase, the cell doubles in size and produces all the structures needed to carry out its functions. For example, the cell enlarges its endoplasmic reticulum, makes new ribosomes, and produces enzymes. Both mitochondria and chloroplasts make copies of themselves during the growth stage. The cell matures to its full size and structure.

DNA Replication After a cell has grown to its mature size, the next part of interphase begins. The cell makes a copy of the DNA in its nucleus in a process called **replication.** Recall that DNA is a nucleic acid found in the chromatin in a cell's nucleus. DNA holds all the information that the cell needs to carry out its functions. The replication of a cell's DNA is very important, since each daughter cell must have a complete set of DNA to survive. At the end of DNA replication, the cell contains two identical sets of DNA. One set will be distributed to each daughter cell. You will learn the details of DNA replication later in this section.

Figure 16 The cells that make up this young monkey are the same size as those that make up its mother. However, the adult has many more cells in its body. *Applying Concepts What is the name of the regular sequence of growth and division that a cell undergoes?*

Chapter 2 **73**

Program Resources

◆ **Unit 1 Resources** 2-5 Lesson Plan, p. 59; 2-5 Section Summary, p. 60

Media and Technology

 Audio CD English-Spanish Summary 2-5

Answers to Self-Assessment

Caption Question

Figure 16 This process is called the cell cycle.

2 Facilitate

The Cell Cycle

Including All Students

Guide students who need more help in organizing the information in this section. Point out that the focus of the section is cell division, but cell division is just part of the cell cycle. Ask: **What are the three stages of the cell cycle?** *(interphase, mitosis, and cytokinesis)* As students identify the names of the three stages, list them on the chalkboard under the heading "Cell Cycle." Point out that the stages of mitosis and cytokinesis, which comprise cell division, are relatively short, whereas interphase is by far the longest stage. **limited English proficiency**

Stage 1: Interphase

Building Inquiry Skills: Inferring

Help students appreciate the role of DNA replication by having them infer what would happen if cell division occurred without DNA replication occurring first during interphase. Ask: **How would this affect the daughter cells?** *(Each daughter cell would have just half the DNA of the parent cell. With only half the DNA, the daughter cells would be unable to direct all cell activities and the cells probably would not survive.)* **learning modality: logical/mathematical**

Language Arts Connection

Tell students that interphase in the cell cycle is like childhood and adolescence in the human life cycle. Ask: **Do you think this is a good analogy? Why or why not?** *(Students may say it is a good analogy because during interphase, like childhood and adolescence, the cell grows and matures.)* **learning modality: verbal**

Ongoing Assessment

Writing Have students write a paragraph explaining the significance of replication in cell division.

Stage 2: Mitosis

Skills Focus making models

Materials *construction paper, different colored pipe cleaners*

Time 10 minutes

Expected Outcome Students should place three pairs of pipe cleaners, which represent three chromosomes, on the construction paper, which represents the cell. In prophase, both pipe cleaners in each pair should be joined at the center, and all the paired pipe cleaners should be clustered together. In metaphase, the paired pipe cleaners should be lined up across the center. In anaphase, the pipe cleaners in each pair should be separated and moved part way toward opposite ends. In telophase, the separated pipe cleaners should be located at opposite ends. Students may say that their model helped them see mitosis as a continuous process.

Extend Ask: **How could you use your model to show the next stage of the cell cycle?** *(Cytokinesis could be modeled by cutting the paper into two equal pieces and placing half the pipe cleaners on each piece.)* **learning modality: kinesthetic**

Building Inquiry Skills: Calculating

Materials *calculator*

Time 5 minutes

Help students appreciate how quickly cell division can lead to a large number of cells. Challenge students to calculate how many cells there would be after a cell divides once, twice, three times, and so on, up to ten times. Then ask: **With each division that occurs, how does the number of cells change?** *(The number doubles.)* **learning modality: logical/mathematical**

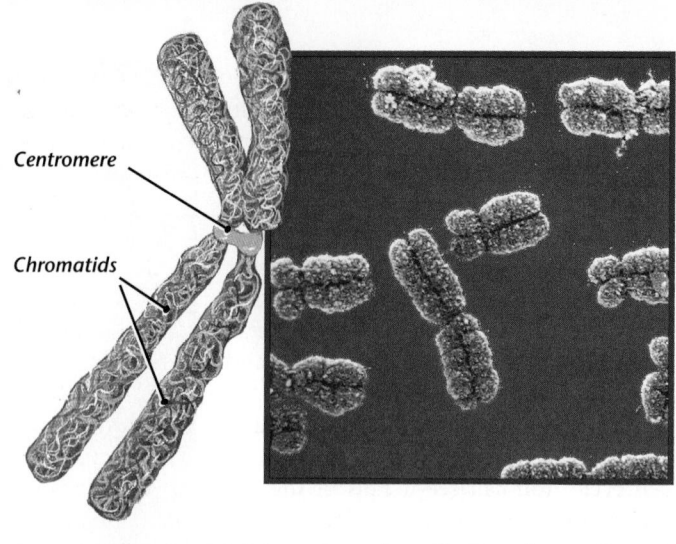
Centromere

Chromatids

Figure 17 During mitosis, the chromatin condenses to form rodlike chromosomes. Each chromosome consists of two identical strands, or chromatids. *Interpreting Diagrams What is the name of the structure that holds the chromatids together?*

Modeling Mitosis

Refer to *Exploring the Cell Cycle* as you carry out this activity.

1. Construct a model of a cell that has three chromosomes. Use a piece of construction paper to represent the cell. Use different colored pipe cleaners to represent the chromosomes. Make sure that the chromosomes look like double rods.

2. Position the chromosomes in the cell where they would be during prophase.

3. Repeat Step 2 for metaphase, anaphase, and telophase.

Making Models How did the model help you understand the events of mitosis?

Preparation for Division Once the cell's DNA has replicated, preparation for cell division begins. The cell produces structures that it will use to divide during the rest of the cell cycle. At the end of interphase, the cell is ready to divide.

Stage 2: Mitosis

Once interphase is complete, the second stage of the cell cycle begins. **Mitosis** (my TOH sis) is the stage during which the cell's nucleus divides into two new nuclei. **During mitosis, one copy of the DNA is distributed into each of the two daughter cells.**

Scientists divide mitosis into four parts, or phases: prophase, metaphase, anaphase, and telophase. During prophase, the threadlike chromatin in the cell's nucleus begins to condense and coil, like fishing line wrapping around a ball. Under a light microscope, the condensed chromatin looks like tiny rods, as you can see in Figure 17. Since the cell's DNA has replicated, each rod has doubled. Each is an exact copy of the other. Scientists call each doubled rod of condensed chromatin a **chromosome.** Each identical rod, or strand, of the chromosome is called a **chromatid.** The two strands are held together by a structure called a centromere.

As the cell progresses through metaphase, anaphase, and telophase, the chromatids separate from each other and move to opposite ends of the cell. Then two nuclei form around the chromatids at the two ends of the cell. You can follow this process in *Exploring the Cell Cycle.*

✓ *Checkpoint During which stage of mitosis does the chromatin condense to form rodlike structures?*

Background

Integrating Science The cells in our body divide at varying rates as we grow older, causing the body not only to grow in size, but also to change in shape. During early life, cells in the head divide rapidly so that by birth, the head is very large relative to the body. During early childhood, the cells in the arms and legs divide rapidly, causing the young child's limbs to grow long relative to the trunk. At puberty, the child's body undergoes another spurt in growth and development. Sex hormones influence cells of the bones and muscles to divide rapidly, and within a few years the child reaches adult body size and proportions. The hormones also stimulate rapid growth and development of the sex organs and the secondary sex characteristics, such as breasts and body hair.

Stage 3: Cytokinesis

After mitosis, the final stage of the cell cycle, called **cytokinesis** (sy toh kih NEE sis), completes the process of cell division. **During cytokinesis, the cytoplasm divides, distributing the organelles into each of the two new cells.** Cytokinesis usually starts at about the same time as telophase.

During cytokinesis in animal cells, the cell membrane squeezes together around the middle of the cell. The cytoplasm pinches into two cells with about half of the organelles in each daughter cell.

Cytokinesis is somewhat different in plant cells. A plant cell's rigid cell wall cannot squeeze together in the same way that a cell membrane can. Instead, a structure called a cell plate forms across the middle of the cell. The cell plate gradually develops into new cell membranes between the two daughter cells. New cell walls then form around the cell membranes.

There are many variations of the basic pattern of cytokinesis. For example, yeast cells divide, though not equally. A small daughter cell, or bud, pinches off of the parent cell. The bud then grows into a full-sized yeast cell.

Cytokinesis marks the end of the cell cycle. Two new cells have formed. Each daughter cell has the same number of chromosomes as the original parent cell. At the end of cytokinesis, each cell enters interphase, and the cycle begins again.

☑️ *Checkpoint* *When in the cell cycle does cytokinesis begin?*

Length of the Cell Cycle

How long does it take for a cell to go through one cell cycle? The answer depends on the type of cell. In a young sea urchin, for example, one cell cycle takes about 2 hours. In contrast, a human liver cell completes one cell cycle in about 22 hours, as shown in Figure 18. The length of each stage in the cell cycle also varies greatly from cell to cell. Some cells, such as human brain cells, never divide—they remain in the first part of interphase for as long as they live.

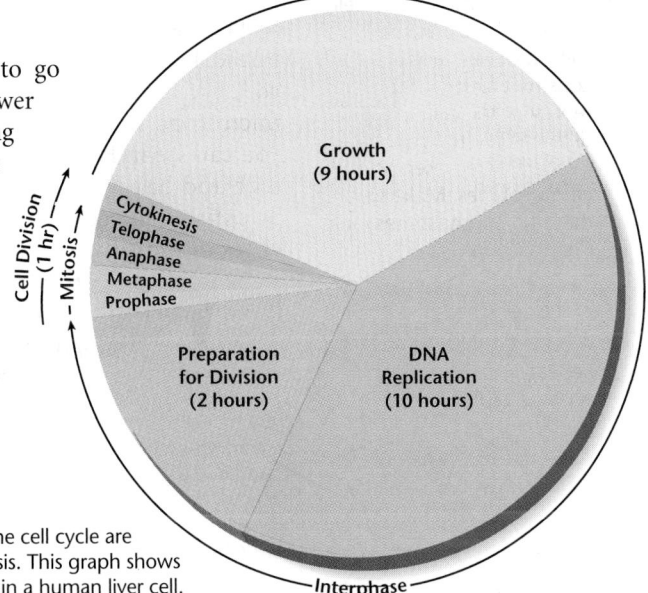

Figure 18 The main stages of the cell cycle are interphase, mitosis, and cytokinesis. This graph shows the average length of each stage in a human liver cell.

EXPLORING
the Cell Cycle

After students have examined the feature, ask: **How are the photographs related to the drawings?** *(They show actual cells at each stage of the cell cycle as they appear under a microscope, whereas the drawings are simplified sketches of the stages.)* Challenge students to find the genetic material in each illustration. Point out that, in prophase, each pair of chromatids consists of the original DNA of the parent cell plus a copy of the DNA, which was made during interphase. To help students appreciate the continuous nature of the cell cycle, tell them that cytokinesis and the last phase of mitosis, telophase, actually overlap in time. Ask: **Why is a circular diagram like this a better way to represent the cell cycle than a straight-line flowchart?** *(Because after the last stage of the cell cycle, the cycle starts over again)* **learning modality: visual**

Inquiry Challenge

Materials *poster board, colored markers, index cards, dice, small objects such as different colored erasers for game tokens*
Time 20 minutes

Divide the class into groups, and provide each group with the materials listed above. Challenge each group to create a board game that models the cell cycle. To get from "start" to "finish" on the game board, players must advance through each stage of the cell cycle by correctly answering questions about that stage. For example, to advance from prophase to metaphase, they might be required to answer: **How does the position of the chromosomes in metaphase differ from their position in prophase?** *(In prophase, the chromosomes are clustered in a group in the nucleus; in metaphase, the chromosomes are lined up across the center of the cell.)* When groups have finished creating their games, have them exchange and play the games. **cooperative learning**

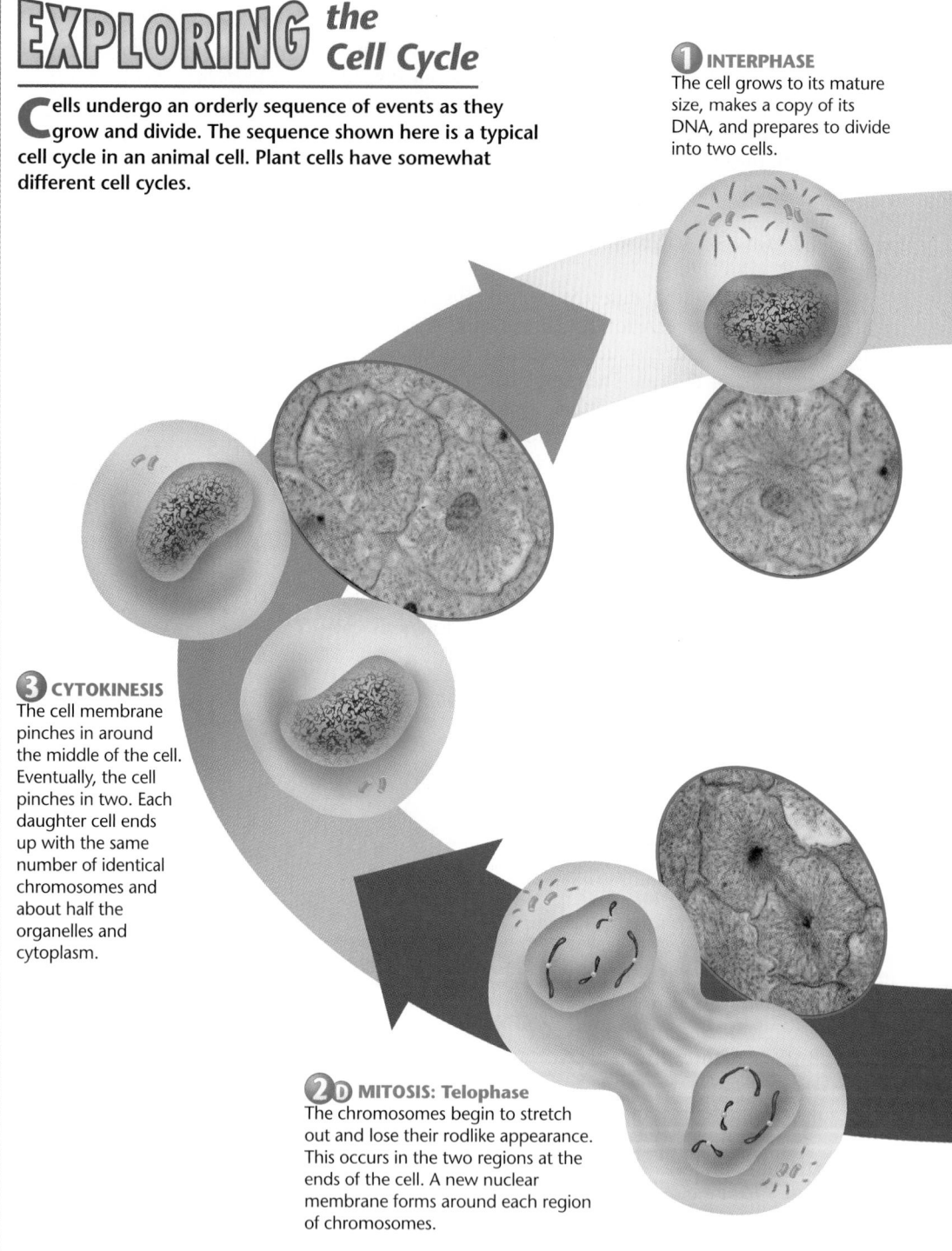

EXPLORING the Cell Cycle

Cells undergo an orderly sequence of events as they grow and divide. The sequence shown here is a typical cell cycle in an animal cell. Plant cells have somewhat different cell cycles.

① INTERPHASE
The cell grows to its mature size, makes a copy of its DNA, and prepares to divide into two cells.

③ CYTOKINESIS
The cell membrane pinches in around the middle of the cell. Eventually, the cell pinches in two. Each daughter cell ends up with the same number of identical chromosomes and about half the organelles and cytoplasm.

② D MITOSIS: Telophase
The chromosomes begin to stretch out and lose their rodlike appearance. This occurs in the two regions at the ends of the cell. A new nuclear membrane forms around each region of chromosomes.

76

Background

History of Science With the development of dyes for staining microscope specimens in the 1800s, scientists could see organelles in the nucleus and learn the details of mitosis. Some of the dyes stained the granular material in the nucleus, so it was given the name *chromatin,* from the Greek word *chroma,* meaning "color." With the dye, chromatin could be seen condensing into rodlike structures during cell division. These rodlike structures were called chromosomes, or "colored bodies" (the Greek word *soma* means "body.") By the late 1800s, German zoologist Theodor Boveri was able to show that, following mitosis, both daughter cells contain an exact copy of the chromosomes of the parent cell.

A MITOSIS: Prophase
The chromatin in the nucleus condenses to form chromosomes. Structures called spindle fibers form a bridge between the ends of the cell. The nuclear membrane breaks down.

Spindle fiber

Centromere

Chromatids

B MITOSIS: Metaphase
The chromosomes line up across the center of the cell. Each chromosome attaches to a spindle fiber at its centromere, which still holds the chromatids together.

C MITOSIS: Anaphase
The centromeres split. The two chromatids separate. One chromatid moves along the spindle fiber to one end of the cell. The other chromatid moves to the opposite end. The cell becomes stretched out as the opposite ends pull apart.

 Transparencies "Exploring the Cell Cycle," Transparency 9

Including All Students

Materials index cards
Time 20 minutes

Urge students who are still mastering English to create flash cards for the stages of the cell cycle and the phases of mitosis. Suggest that they write the name of each stage or phase on one side of an index card, and describe it in their own words on the other side. After students have finished making their flash cards, check to see that they have included all the stages of the cell cycle and all the phases of mitosis. Also make sure that students have correctly described each stage or phase. For example, ask: **What occurs during metaphase?** (*The chromosomes form a line across the middle of the cell, and each chromosome is joined to a spindle fiber.*) Encourage pairs of students to quiz each other using their flash cards. **limited English proficiency**

Inquiry Challenge

Materials *construction paper, colored markers, tape or safety pins*
Time 15 minutes

Challenge the class to make a human model of the nucleus to show how mitosis occurs. (*One possible model is for a few pairs of students, representing paired chromatids, to stand face to face and join hands, while the other students, representing the nuclear membrane, join hands in a circle around them.*) Provide students with the materials listed above so they can make and wear signs that show which part of the nucleus they represent. After the class has formed the model, challenge students to move in ways that demonstrate the major events of mitosis. Ask: **How could you model the chromatin inside the nucleus during the other stages of the cell cycle?** (*To model cytokinesis and interphase, the formerly paired students might stand at random inside the "nuclear membrane" and no longer hold hands.*) **learning modality: kinesthetic**

Ongoing Assessment

Writing Have students write a list, in chronological order, of the major events that occur during mitosis.

DNA Replication

Inquiry Challenge

Materials *toothpicks, white and colored miniature marshmallows*
Time 15 minutes

Challenge hands-on learners to make a three-dimensional model of a DNA molecule using the materials listed above. *(The most likely way is to use toothpicks to join together white marshmallows, representing sugar and phosphate molecules, and colored marshmallows, representing nitrogen bases.)* Suggest to students that they make keys for their models that show which part of the DNA molecule the different components represent. Then ask: **How does your model show that adenine only pairs with thymine and guanine only pairs with cytosine?** *(In their models, students should have joined colored marshmallows representing different bases in the correct pairings.)* **learning modality: kinesthetic**

Building Inquiry Skills: Inferring

Encourage students to infer what would happen if an error in DNA replication occurred. Ask: **What do you think would be the outcome if one or more of the nitrogen bases were assembled in the wrong order in a new DNA molecule?** *(Answers may vary. Students may say that the new DNA molecule might not be able to properly direct cell functions. They also might say that any future copies of the new DNA molecule would contain bases in the wrong order, so the error would spread if the cells survived and divided.)* **learning modality: logical/mathematical**

Figure 19 A DNA molecule is shaped like a twisted ladder. The sides are made up of sugar and phosphate molecules. The rungs are formed by pairs of nitrogen bases. *Classifying Which base always pairs with adenine?*

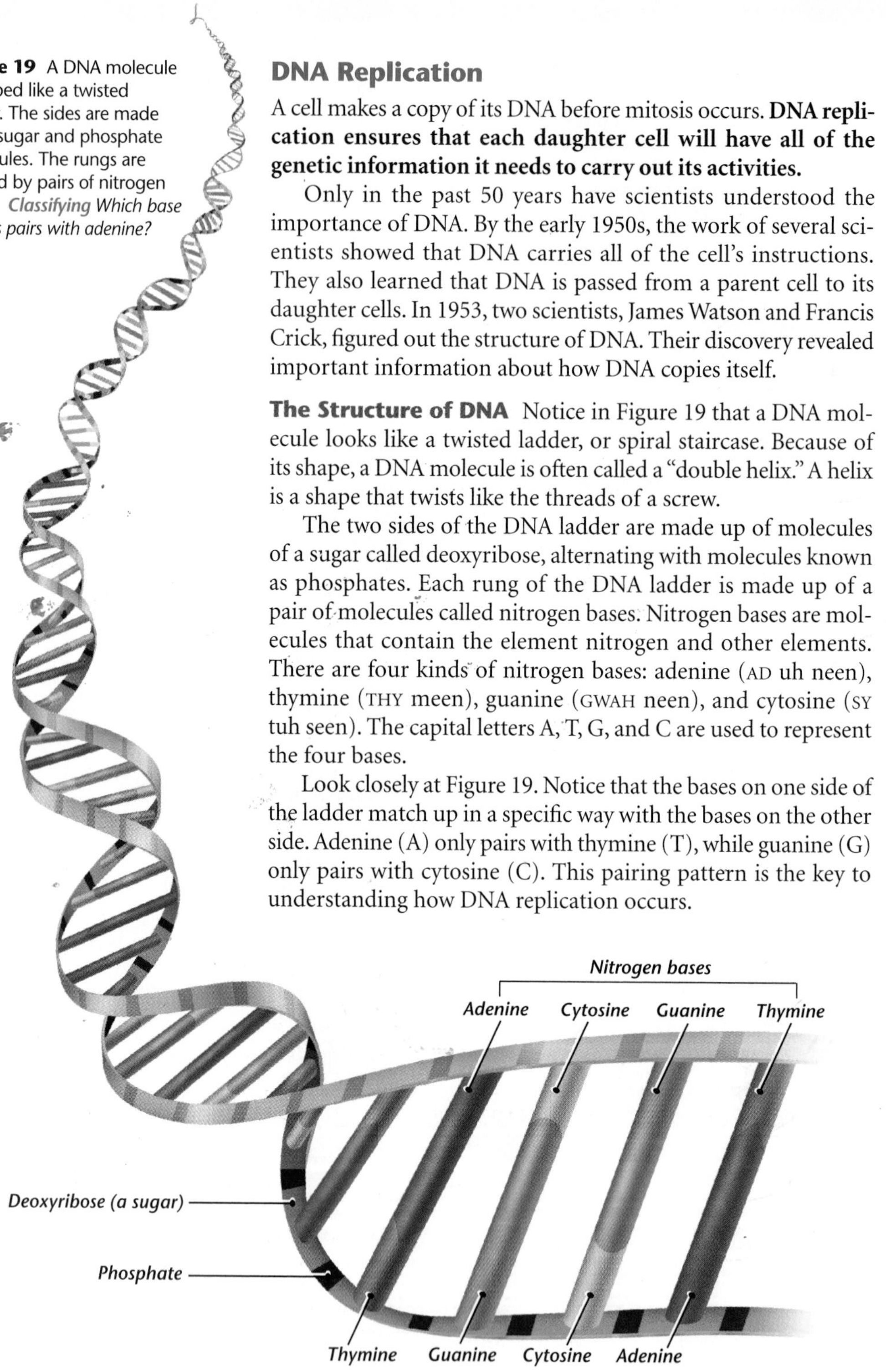

DNA Replication

A cell makes a copy of its DNA before mitosis occurs. **DNA replication ensures that each daughter cell will have all of the genetic information it needs to carry out its activities.**

Only in the past 50 years have scientists understood the importance of DNA. By the early 1950s, the work of several scientists showed that DNA carries all of the cell's instructions. They also learned that DNA is passed from a parent cell to its daughter cells. In 1953, two scientists, James Watson and Francis Crick, figured out the structure of DNA. Their discovery revealed important information about how DNA copies itself.

The Structure of DNA Notice in Figure 19 that a DNA molecule looks like a twisted ladder, or spiral staircase. Because of its shape, a DNA molecule is often called a "double helix." A helix is a shape that twists like the threads of a screw.

The two sides of the DNA ladder are made up of molecules of a sugar called deoxyribose, alternating with molecules known as phosphates. Each rung of the DNA ladder is made up of a pair of molecules called nitrogen bases. Nitrogen bases are molecules that contain the element nitrogen and other elements. There are four kinds of nitrogen bases: adenine (AD uh neen), thymine (THY meen), guanine (GWAH neen), and cytosine (SY tuh seen). The capital letters A, T, G, and C are used to represent the four bases.

Look closely at Figure 19. Notice that the bases on one side of the ladder match up in a specific way with the bases on the other side. Adenine (A) only pairs with thymine (T), while guanine (G) only pairs with cytosine (C). This pairing pattern is the key to understanding how DNA replication occurs.

Nitrogen bases

Adenine   Cytosine   Guanine   Thymine

Deoxyribose (a sugar)

Phosphate

Thymine   Guanine   Cytosine   Adenine

Background

History of Science In 1953, Watson and Crick described the structure of the DNA molecule. To determine DNA's structure, they used English chemist Rosalind Franklin's X-ray photographs showing the helical appearance of DNA along with much other data. Franklin died in 1956, before Watson and Crick were awarded the Nobel Prize for their work on DNA's structure.

Facts and Figures When DNA replicates, the process requires more than 20 different enzymes to separate the strands of parent DNA and join the nucleotides in the correct sequence in the DNA copies. Although mistakes sometimes happen during this process, they are rare, occurring, on average, once in every one billion replications of any given base pair in a DNA molecule.

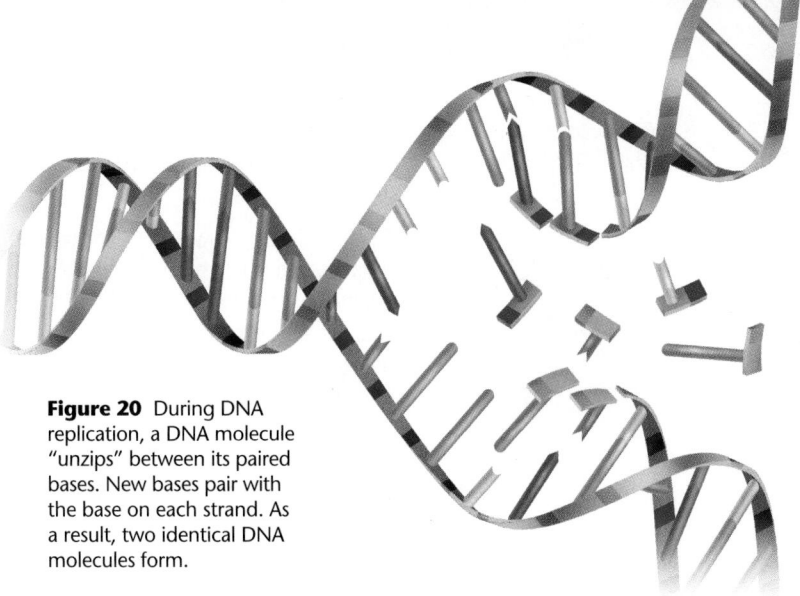

Figure 20 During DNA replication, a DNA molecule "unzips" between its paired bases. New bases pair with the base on each strand. As a result, two identical DNA molecules form.

The Replication Process DNA replication begins when the two sides of the DNA molecule unwind and separate, like a zipper unzipping. As you can see in Figure 20, the molecule separates between the paired nitrogen bases on each rung. Next, nitrogen bases that are floating in the nucleus pair up with the bases on each half of the DNA molecule. Remember that the pairing of bases follows definite rules: A always pairs with T, while G always pairs with C. Once the new bases are attached, two new DNA molecules are formed. The order of the bases in each new DNA molecule will exactly match the order in the original DNA molecule.

 Section 5 Review

1. What are the three main stages of the cell cycle? Briefly describe the events that occur at each stage.
2. Why must the DNA in a cell replicate before the cell divides?
3. How does cytokinesis differ in plant and animal cells?
4. **Thinking Critically Predicting** Suppose that during anaphase, the centromeres did not split, and the chromatids did not separate. Predict the results.

Check Your Progress　CHAPTER PROJECT
Begin to think about why the egg changed as it did at each stage of the project. Consider how each of the different substances affected your egg. (*Hint:* Water plays a crucial role in the activities of a cell. How has water been involved in your investigation?) Organize your results into a report and make a graph of your egg's changing circumference. You may want to include diagrams to explain the processes that took place.

Chapter 2 **79**

Section 5 Review Answers
1. The stages are interphase, mitosis, and cytokinesis. In interphase, the cell grows and DNA replicates; in mitosis, the nucleus divides and a copy of DNA goes to each daughter cell; in cytokinesis, the cytoplasm divides into two new cells.
2. The DNA must replicate so that each daughter cell will have all the genetic information it needs.
3. In plant cells, new cell membranes develop across the middle of the cell and separate the cytoplasm of the daughter cells. In animal cells, the cell membrane squeezes together around the middle of the cell and pinches the cytoplasm into the daughter cells.
4. Both chromatids of a chromosome would go to the same pole, so neither daughter cell would get the correct number of chromosomes. Probably neither cell would survive.

Check Your Progress　CHAPTER PROJECT
Have students graph their egg's diameter on one axis and the date it was measured on the other. They also should indicate on their graphs what liquid the egg was soaking in each day.

Program Resources
◆ **Unit 1 Resources** 2-5 Review and Reinforce, p. 61; 2-5 Enrich, p. 62; Chapter 2 Skills Lab, pp. 65–67

Media and Technology
Transparencies "DNA Structure," Transparency 10; "DNA Replication," Transparency 11

Answers to Self-Assessment
Caption Question
Figure 19 Thymine always pairs with adenine.

Safety
Remind students to handle slides and coverslips carefully. Review the safety guidelines in Appendix A.

Performance Assessment
Writing Have students explain why the pairing of nitrogen bases is the key to understanding DNA replication.

Multiplying by Dividing

Preparing for Inquiry

Key Concept Mitosis occurs quickly, and cells spend most of their time in interphase.

Skills Objectives Students will be able to
◆ observe cells in different stages of the cell cycle;
◆ calculate the amount of time cells spend in each stage of the cell cycle;
◆ interpret data to compare how long cells spend in mitosis with the total time of the cell cycle.

Time 40 minutes

Advance Planning Prepared slides can be purchased from a biological supply company.

Alternative Materials Slides of other rapidly dividing cells undergoing division may be used if nuclear structures show up clearly.

Guiding Inquiry

Troubleshooting the Experiment
◆ Urge students to review the photographs in *Exploring the Cell Cycle* on pages 76–77.

Expected Outcome
Students should observe and sketch cells undergoing interphase and the four phases of mitosis. Most of the cells they count should be in the interphase stage of the cell cycle, but errors in counting and differences in samples may give varying results.

Analyze and Conclude
1. The most likely answer is interphase.
2. Answers will vary depending on students' data. Answers for the sample data are: interphase, 641 minutes; prophase, 50 minutes; metaphase, 14 minutes; anaphase, 7 minutes; telophase, 7 minutes.
3. Based on the sample data, the amount of time spent in mitosis is 11 percent. Students' answers will vary depending on their data.

Multiplying by Dividing

Problem

How long do the stages of the cell cycle take?

Materials

microscope
colored pencils
calculator (optional)
prepared slides of onion root tip cells undergoing cell division

Procedure

1. Place the slide on the stage of a microscope. Use low power to locate a cell in interphase. Then switch to high power, and make a labeled drawing of the cell. **CAUTION:** *Slides and coverslips break easily. Do not allow the objective to touch the slide. If the slide breaks, notify your teacher. Do not touch broken glass.*
2. Repeat Step 1 to find cells in prophase, metaphase, anaphase, and telophase. Then copy the data table into your notebook.
3. Return to low power. Find an area of the slide with many cells undergoing cell division. Switch to the magnification that lets you see about 50 cells at once (for example, 100 ×).

DATA TABLE			
Stage of Cell Cycle	First Sample	Second Sample	Total Number
Interphase			
Mitosis: Prophase			
Metaphase			
Anaphase			
Telophase			
Total number of cells counted			

4. Examine the cells row by row, and count the cells that are in interphase. Record that number in the data table under *First Sample*.
5. Examine the cells row-by-row four more times to count the cells in prophase, metaphase, anaphase, and telophase. Record the results.
6. Move to a new area on the slide. Repeat Steps 3–5 and record your counts in the column labeled *Second Sample*.
7. Fill in the column labeled *Total Number* by adding the numbers across each row in your data table.
8. Add the totals for the five stages to find the total number of cells counted.

Analyze and Conclude

1. Which stage of the cell cycle did you observe most often?
2. The cell cycle for onion root tips takes about 720 minutes (12 hours). Use your data and the formula below to find the number of minutes each stage takes.

$$\text{Time for each stage} = \frac{\text{Number of cells at each stage}}{\text{Total number of cells counted}} \times 720 \text{ min}$$

3. **Think About It** Use the data to compare the amount of time spent in mitosis with the total time for the whole cell cycle.

More to Explore

Examine prepared slides of animal cells undergoing cell division. Use drawings and descriptions to compare plant and animal mitosis.

Extending the Inquiry

More to Explore Interphase and mitosis are very similar in plant and animal cells, except that the centrioles appear during prophase in animal cells. Challenge students to predict whether animal or plant cells spend longer in mitosis. Then have them design an experiment to test their prediction.

Sample Data Table

Stage of Cell Cycle	First Sample	Second Sample	Total Number
Interphase	43	46	89
Mitosis: Prophase	3	4	7
Metaphase	1	1	2
Anaphase	1	0	1
Telophase	0	1	1

CHAPTER 2 STUDY GUIDE

SECTION 1 Chemical Compounds in Cells

INTEGRATING CHEMISTRY

Key Ideas

◆ When two or more elements combine chemically, they form a compound.
◆ Organic compounds in living things include proteins, carbohydrates, lipids, and nucleic acids.
◆ Without water, most chemical reactions within cells could not take place.

Key Terms

element	protein	lipid
atom	amino acid	nucleic acid
compound	enzyme	DNA
molecule	carbohydrate	RNA
organic compound		
inorganic compound		

SECTION 2 The Cell in Its Environment

Key Ideas

◆ Substances can move into and out of a cell by diffusion, osmosis, or active transport.
◆ Active transport requires the cell to use energy while passive transport does not.

Key Terms

selectively permeable	passive transport
diffusion	active transport
osmosis	

SECTION 3 Photosynthesis

Key Ideas

◆ During photosynthesis, plants use energy from the sun to convert carbon dioxide and water into oxygen and sugars.
◆ Chlorophyll and other plant pigments capture energy from sunlight. Cells use the energy to produce sugars from carbon dioxide and water.
◆ Most living things obtain the energy they need either directly or indirectly from the sun.

Key Terms

photosynthesis	chlorophyll	stomata
pigment		

SECTION 4 Respiration

Key Ideas

◆ Respiration is a process in which cells break down simple food substances, such as glucose, and release the energy they contain.
◆ During respiration, glucose and oxygen are converted into carbon dioxide and water.

Key Terms

respiration	fermentation

SECTION 5 Cell Division

Key Ideas

◆ Cells go through a regular cycle of growth and division called the cell cycle.
◆ The major phases of the cell cycle are interphase, mitosis, and cytokinesis.

Key Terms

cell cycle	mitosis	chromatid
interphase	chromosome	cytokinesis
replication		

Organizing Information

Cycle Diagram Copy the cycle diagram about the cell cycle onto a separate sheet of paper. Then complete it and add a title. (For more on cycle diagrams, see the Skills Handbook.)

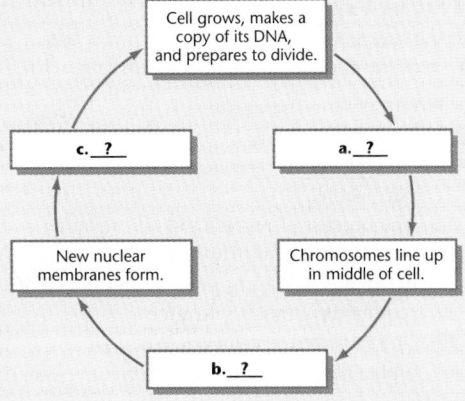

Chapter 2 **81**

Organizing Information

Cycle Diagram **a.** Chromatin condenses to form chromosomes, spindle fibers form, and the nuclear membrane breaks down. **b.** The chromatids separate and move to opposite ends of the cell. **c.** The cell membrane pinches in around the middle of the cell, and the cell divides. Sample title: The Cell Cycle

Program Resources

◆ **Unit 1 Resources** Chapter 2 Project Scoring Rubric, p. 42
◆ **Performance Assessment** Chapter 2, pp. 8–10
◆ **Chapter and Unit Tests** Chapter 2 Test, pp. 8–11

Media and Technology

 Interactive Student Tutorial CD-ROM Chapter 2

 Computer Test Bank Chapter 2 Test

Reviewing Content

Multiple Choice

1. d 2. a 3. a 4. c 5. c

True or False

6. nucleic acids 7. true 8. true
9. fermentation 10. interphase

Checking Concepts

11. Enzymes speed up chemical reactions in living things. Without enzymes, many of the chemical reactions that are necessary for life would either take too long or not occur at all.

12. Diffusion is the process by which molecules tend to move from an area of higher concentration to an area of lower concentration. Diffusion helps the cell take in the substances it needs and get rid of those it does not need.

13. During photosynthesis, energy from sunlight is changed into chemical energy, which is used to convert carbon dioxide and water into oxygen and sugars, including glucose.

14. Heterotrophs get energy by eating plants or other organisms that eat plants. Plants get energy from the sun.

15. Organisms need to carry out respiration in order to provide energy for cell processes.

16. During the cell cycle, the parent cell divides into two identical cells. These daughter cells contain the same DNA and the same organelles. During mitosis each of the chromosome pairs is split, with half of each pair going to each new daughter cell. Organelles and cytoplasm are divided between the two daughter cells during telophase and cytokinesis.

17. Students' paragraphs should include the following points: Respiration and photosynthesis are opposite processes. The raw materials of respiration are the same as the products of photosynthesis. The raw materials of photosynthesis are the same as the products of respiration. Photosynthesis uses carbon dioxide from the atmosphere and produces oxygen. Respiration uses oxygen from the atmosphere and produces carbon dioxide.

Reviewing Content

 For more review of key concepts, see the Interactive Student Tutorial CD-ROM.

Multiple Choice

Choose the letter of the best answer.

1. Starch is an example of a
  a. nucleic acid.
  b. protein.
  c. lipid.
  d. carbohydrate.

2. The process by which water moves across a cell membrane is called
  a. osmosis.
  b. active transport.
  c. diffusion.
  d. resolution.

3. What process is responsible for producing most of Earth's oxygen?
  a. photosynthesis
  b. replication
  c. mutation
  d. respiration

4. The process in which a cell makes an exact copy of its DNA is called
  a. fermentation.
  b. respiration.
  c. replication.
  d. reproduction.

5. Chromatids are held together by a
  a. spindle.   b. chloroplast.
  c. centromere.   d. cell membrane.

True or False

If the statement is true, write true. If it is false, change the underlined word or words to make the statement true.

6. Both DNA and RNA are <u>proteins.</u>
7. The <u>cell membrane</u> is selectively permeable.
8. The process of respiration takes place mainly in the <u>mitochondria.</u>
9. An energy-releasing process that does not require oxygen is <u>replication.</u>
10. The stage of the cell cycle when DNA replication occurs is <u>telophase.</u>

Checking Concepts

11. How are enzymes important to living things?
12. What is diffusion? What role does diffusion play in the cell?
13. Briefly explain what happens to energy from the sun during photosynthesis.
14. Explain how heterotrophs depend on the sun for energy.
15. Why do organisms need to carry out the process of respiration?
16. How do the events of the cell cycle ensure that the daughter cells will be identical to the parent cell?
17. Writing to Learn Write a paragraph comparing and contrasting photosynthesis and respiration. Be sure to discuss how the two processes maintain the oxygen and carbon dioxide balance in the atmosphere.

Thinking Critically

18. Making Generalizations Why is the study of chemistry important to the understanding of living things?
19. Predicting Suppose a volcano spewed so much ash into the air that it blocked most of the sunlight that usually strikes Earth. How might this affect the ability of animals to obtain the energy they need to live?
20. Applying Concepts Explain the relationship between the processes of breathing and respiration.
21. Inferring Suppose one strand of a DNA molecule contained the following bases: A C G T C T G. What would the bases on the other strand be?
22. Problem Solving Explain why it is important that the cell cycle results in daughter cells that are identical to the parent cell.

Thinking Critically

18. The study of chemistry is important to the understanding of living things because chemical elements and compounds make up the cells of living things and carry out their functions.

19. Answers may vary. *Sample answer:* The ash from the volcano would block the sun and prevent plants from using its energy to make food. Plants would die out, and the animals and other organisms that get their energy from plants would die out as well.

20. Breathing brings oxygen into the body for respiration. Respiration uses the oxygen to break down food and provide energy for the body's needs.

21. T G C A G A C

22. The daughter cells need the same genetic material that the parent cell had in order to live.

Applying Skills

Use the table below to answer Questions 23–25.

Percentages of Nitrogen Bases In the DNA of Various Organisms

Nitrogen Base	Human	Wheat	E. coli bacterium
Adenine	30%	27%	24%
Guanine	20%	23%	26%
Thymine	30%	27%	24%
Cytosine	20%	23%	26%

23. Graphing For each organism, draw a bar graph to show the percentages of each nitrogen base in its DNA.

24. Interpreting Data What is the relationship between the amounts of adenine and thymine in the DNA of each organism? Between the amounts of guanine and cytosine?

25. Inferring Based on your answer to Question 24, what can you infer about the structure of DNA in these three organisms?

Performance CHAPTER PROJECT **Assessment**

Present Your Project Bring in your egg, your graph, and any diagrams you made. As a class or in groups, discuss your results and conclusions. Then, as a group, try to agree on answers to these questions: What happened to the eggshell? What process took place at each stage of the experiment?

Reflect and Record In your notebook, describe what you learned from doing this egg-speriment. Which part of the project was the most surprising? Why? When did you begin to understand what was happening to the egg? If you did the project again, what would you do differently? Why?

Test Preparation

Use these questions to prepare for standardized tests.

Study the equations. Then answer Questions 26–28.

Photosynthesis

$$6\ CO_2 + 6\ H_2O \xrightarrow{\text{light energy}} C_6H_{12}O_6 + 6\ O_2$$

Respiration

$$C_6H_{12}O_6 + 6\ O_2 \rightarrow 6\ CO_2 + 6\ H_2O + \text{energy}$$

26. What products are produced during photosynthesis?
a. carbon dioxide and water
b. light energy and carbon dioxide
c. carbon dioxide and sugar
d. sugar and oxygen

27. What raw materials are needed for respiration to occur?
a. energy and water
b. carbon dioxide, water, and energy
c. sugar and oxygen
d. sugar and carbon dioxide

28. Why are the words "light energy" written above the arrow in the photosynthesis equation?
a. Light energy is necessary for the reaction to occur.
b. Light energy is produced during the reaction.
c. Oxygen can exist only in the presence of light.
d. Sugar can exist only in the presence of light.

Program Resources

◆ **Inquiry Skills Activity Book** Provides teaching and review of all inquiry skills

---

Applying Skills

23. The bars in the graph should correspond to the percentages in the table. There should be four bars for each organism.

24. The percents of adenine and thymine are equal. The percents of guanine and cytosine also are equal.

25. In all of the organisms, adenine is paired with thymine and guanine is paired with cytosine.

Performance CHAPTER PROJECT **Assessment**

Present Your Project Have students display their eggs and share their graphs showing how the size of their egg changed and what it was soaking in each day. If students made diagrams showing how water moved into or out of the cell by osmosis, have them share these as well. Guide the class discussion so that students come to the conclusion that the eggshell dissolved in the vinegar, and that the egg increased and decreased in size because of osmosis.

Reflect and Record Students may say that this "egg-speriment" helped them understand the process of osmosis and how impor-tant the cell membrane is to the cell. The most surprising part may have been how the texture of the egg changed. Most students probably began to understand what was happening to the egg when they read about osmosis in Section 2. If they did the project over, students may say they would test a greater variety of liquids.

Test Preparation

26. d **27.** c **28.** a

3 Genetics: The Science of Heredity

	Sections	Time	Student Edition Activities	Other Activities
CHAPTER PROJECT	**All In The Family** p. 85	Ongoing (2–3 weeks)	Check Your Progress, p. 91, 106, 112 Present Your Project, p. 115	
1	**Mendel's Work** pp. 86–93 ◆ Describe Mendel's genetics experiments. ◆ Identify the factors that control the inheritance of traits in organisms. ◆ Explain how geneticists use symbols to represent alleles.	$1\frac{1}{2}$–2 periods/ $\frac{1}{2}$–1 block	**Discover** What Does the Father Look Like?, p. 86 **Skills Lab: Developing Hypotheses** Take a Class Survey, pp. 92–93	TE Building Inquiry Skills: Observing, p. 87 TE Inquiry Challenge, p. 87 TE Demonstration, p. 89 TE Inquiry Challenge, p. 90
2	**INTEGRATING MATHEMATICS** **Probability and Genetics** pp. 94–101 ◆ Describe the principles of probability and how Mendel applied them to inheritance. ◆ State how geneticists use Punnett squares. ◆ Explain the meanings of the terms *phenotype, genotype, homozygous, heterozygous,* and *codominance*.	1 period/ $\frac{1}{2}$ block	**Discover** What's the Chance?, p. 94 **Try This** Coin Crosses, p. 97 **Science at Home,** p. 99 **Skills Lab: Making Models** Make the Right Call!, pp. 100–101	TE Including All Students, p. 95 TE Inquiry Challenge, p. 95 TE Inquiry Challenge, p. 96 TE Demonstration, p. 97 IES "The Power of Patterns," p. 42
3	**The Cell and Inheritance** pp. 102–106 ◆ Describe chromosomes and their role in inheritance. ◆ Identify and describe the events that occur during meiosis.	1–2 periods/ $\frac{1}{2}$–1 block	**Discover** Which Chromosome Is Which?, p. 102	TE Inquiry Challenge, p. 103 TE Building Inquiry Skills: Making Models, p. 104 TE Building Inquiry Skills, Observing, p. 105 TE Including All Students, p. 106 LM 3, "Chromosomes and Inheritance"
4	**The DNA Connection** pp. 107–112 ◆ Explain the term "genetic code." ◆ Describe the process by which a cell produces proteins. ◆ Describe different types of mutations and how they affect organisms.	1–2 periods/ $\frac{1}{2}$–1 block	**Discover** Can You Crack the Code?, p. 107 **Sharpen Your Skills** Predicting, p. 109	TE Inquiry Challenge, p. 109 TE Building Inquiry Skills: Making Models, p. 111
	Study Guide/Chapter Assessment pp. 113–115	1 period/ $\frac{1}{2}$ block		ISAB Provides teaching and review of all inquiry skills.

For Standard or Block Schedule The Resource Pro® CD-ROM gives you maximum flexibility for planning your instruction for any type of schedule. Resource Pro® contains Planning Express®, an advanced scheduling program, as well as the entire contents of the Teaching Resources and the Computer Test Bank.

CHAPTER PLANNING GUIDE

Program Resources	Assessment Strategies	Media and Technology
UR Chapter 3 Project Teacher Notes, pp. 68–69 **UR** Chapter 3 Project Overview and Worksheets, Materials, pp. 70–73	**SE** Performance Assessment: Present Your Project, p. 115 **TE** Check Your Progress, pp. 91, 106, 112 **UR** Chapter 3 Project Scoring Rubric, p. 74	Science Explorer Internet Site at www.phschool.com
UR 3-1 Lesson Plan, p. 75 **UR** 3-1 Section Summary, p. 76 **UR** 3-1 Review and Reinforce, p. 77 **UR** 3-1 Enrich, p. 78 **UR** Chapter 3 Skills Lab, pp. 91–92	**SE** Section 1 Review, p. 91 **TE** Ongoing Assessment, pp. 87, 89 **TE** Performance Assessment, p. 91	Life Science Videotape 1; Videodisc Unit 5 Side 1, "We Are All Heirs" Audio CD, English-Spanish Summary 3-1 Transparency 12, "Genetics of Pea Plants"
UR 3-2 Lesson Plan, p. 79 **UR** 3-2 Section Summary, p. 80 **UR** 3-2 Review and Reinforce, p. 81 **UR** 3-2 Enrich, p. 82 **UR** Chapter 3 Skills Lab, pp. 93–95	**SE** Section 2 Review, p. 99 **TE** Ongoing Assessment, pp. 95, 97 **TE** Performance Assessment, p. 99	Audio CD, English-Spanish Summary 3-2 Transparency 13, "Punnett Square—Pea Plants" Interactive Student Tutorial CD-ROM, Chapter 3
UR 3-3 Lesson Plan, p. 83 **UR** 3-3 Section Summary, p. 84 **UR** 3-3 Review and Reinforce, p. 85 **UR** 3-3 Enrich, p. 86	**SE** Section 3 Review, p. 106 **TE** Ongoing Assessment, pp. 103, 105 **TE** Performance Assessment, p. 106	Life Science Videotape 1; Videodisc Unit 5 Side 1, "The Chromosome Theory" Audio CD, English-Spanish Summary 3-3 Transparency 14, "Exploring Meiosis"
UR 3-4 Lesson Plan, p. 87 **UR** 3-4 Section Summary, p. 88 **UR** 3-4 Review and Reinforce, p. 89 **UR** 3-4 Enrich, p. 90	**SE** Section 4 Review, p. 112 **TE** Ongoing Assessment, pp. 109, 111 **TE** Performance Assessment, p. 113	Life Science Videotape 1; Videodisc Unit 5 Side 1, "DNA: The Double Helix" and "Protein Synthesis" Audio CD, English-Spanish Summary 3-4 Transparency 15, "Exploring Protein Synthesis"
RCA Provides strategies to improve science reading skills. **GSW** Provides worksheets to promote student understanding of content	**SE** Chapter 3 Study Guide/Assessment, pp. 113–115 **PA** Chapter 3 Performance Assessment, pp. 11–13 **CUT** Chapter 3 Test, pp. 12–15 **CTB** Chapter 3 Test	Interactive Student Tutorial CD-ROM, Chapter 3 Computer Test Bank, Chapter 3 Test

Key: **SE** Student Edition   **TE** Teacher's Edition   **UR** Unit Resources
     CTB Computer Test Bank   **PTA** Product Testing Activities by *Consumer Reports*   **LM** Laboratory Manual
     ISAB Inquiry Skills Activity Book   **RCA** Reading in the Content Area   **IES** Interdisciplinary Explorations Series
     GSW Guided Study Worksheets   **PA** Performance Assessment   **CUT** Chapter and Unit Tests

Meeting the National Science Education Standards and AAAS Benchmarks

National Science Education Standards	Benchmarks for Science Literacy	Unifying Themes

Science As Inquiry (Content Standard A)

◆ **Use appropriate tools and technology to gather, analyze, and interpret data** Students investigate genetic traits among classmates. *(Skills Lab)*

◆ **Develop descriptions, explanations, predictions, and models using evidence** Students model genetic crosses. Students predict the possible results of genetic crosses. *(Chapter Project; Skills Lab)*

◆ **Use mathematics in all aspects of scientific inquiry** Geneticists use Punnett squares to determine the probability of a particular outcome. *(Chapter Project; Section 2; Skills Lab)*

Life Science (Content Standard C)

◆ **Structure and function in living systems** Meiosis is the process by which the number of chromosomes is reduced by half to form sex cells. During protein synthesis, the cell uses information from genes to produce proteins. *(Sections 3, 4)*

◆ **Reproduction and heredity** The passing of traits from parents to offspring is called heredity. Genes are carried from parents to offspring on chromosomes. Mutations can be a source of genetic variety. *(Chapter Project; Sections 1, 3, 4; Skills Lab)*

History and Nature of Science (Content Standard G)

◆ **History of science** Many of the genetic principles that Mendel discovered still stand to this day. *(Sections 1, 2)*

1B Scientific Inquiry Students model genetic crosses, investigate genetic traits among classmates, and predict the possible results of genetic crosses. *(Chapter Project; Skills Lab; Skills Lab)*

1C The Scientific Enterprise Many of the genetic principles that Gregor Mendel discovered still stand to this day. Mendel was the first scientist to recognize that the principles of probability can be used to predict the results of genetic crosses. Walter Sutton concluded that chromosomes carry genes from one generation to the next. *(Sections 1, 2, 3)*

5B Heredity The passing of traits from parents to offspring is called heredity. Genes are carried from parents to offspring on chromosomes. Mutations can be a source of genetic variety. *(Chapter Project; Sections 1, 3, 4; Skills Lab)*

5C Cells Meiosis is the process by which the number of chromosomes is reduced by half to form sex cells. During protein synthesis, the cell uses information from a gene to produce a specific protein. *(Sections 3, 4)*

9D Uncertainty Geneticists use Punnett squares to show all the possible outcomes of a genetic cross and to determine the probability of a particular outcome. *(Chapter Project; Section 2; Skills Lab)*

◆ **Evolution** Genes are the basic units of heredity. Genes are carried from parents to offspring on chromosomes. Mutations can be a source of genetic variety. *(Sections 1, 3, 4)*

◆ **Modeling** Students model genetic crosses. *(Chapter Project; Skills Lab)*

◆ **Patterns of Change** Individual alleles control the inheritance of traits. During meiosis, a cell undergoes two divisions to produce sex cells with half the number of chromosomes. Mutations can result in a cell producing an incorrect protein. *(Sections 1, 3, 4)*

◆ **Scale and Structure** Genes are located on chromosomes. Sex cells have half the normal number of chromosomes. DNA and RNA contain nitrogen bases. *(Sections 3, 4)*

◆ **Stability** Heredity is the passing of traits from parents to offspring. A dominant allele is one whose trait always shows up in the organism when the allele is present. Before meiosis begins, every chromosome in the cell is copied. In the genetic code, a group of three bases codes for the attachment of a specific amino acid. *(Sections 1, 3, 4)*

◆ **Systems and Interactions** During meiosis, chromosome pairs separate and are distributed to two different cells. During protein synthesis, the cells use information from a gene to produce specific proteins. *(Sections 2, 3, 4)*

◆ **Unity and Diversity** The different forms of a gene are called alleles. *(Section 1)*

Take It to the Net

 *Interactive text at www.phschool.com*

Science Explorer comes alive with iText.

■ **Complete student text** is accessible from any computer with Internet access or a CD-ROM drive.

■ **Animations, simulations, and videos** enhance student understanding and retention of concepts.

■ **Self-tests and online study tools** assess student understanding.

STAY CURRENT with **SCIENCE NEWS**®

Find out the latest research and information about genetics at: **www.phschool.com**

Go to **www.phschool.com** and click on the Science icon. Then click on <u>Science Explorer: Life, Earth, and Physical Science</u> under PH@school.

ACTIVITY	Time *(minutes)*	Materials *Quantities for one work group*	Skills
Section 1			
Discover, p. 86	10	No special materials are required.	Inferring
Skills Lab, pp. 92–93	40	**Consumable** PTC paper **Nonconsumable** mirror (optional)	Developing Hypotheses, Interpreting Data, Drawing Conclusions
Section 2			
Discover, p. 94	15	**Nonconsumable** coin	Predicting
Try This, p. 97	15	**Consumable** masking tape **Nonconsumable** 2 coins, scissors	Interpreting Data
Science at Home, p. 99	home	No special materials are required.	Predicting
Skills Lab, pp. 100–101	40	**Consumable** 2 small paper bags **Nonconsumable** marking pen, 3 blue marbles, 3 white marbles	Making Models, Predicting, Analyzing Data, Comparing and Contrasting
Section 3			
Discover, p. 102	10	**Consumable** 4 craft sticks **Nonconsumable** 3 pieces of paper, marking pen	Inferring
Section 4			
Discover, p. 107	15	No special materials are required.	Forming Operational Definitions
Sharpen Your Skills, p. 109	10	No special materials are required.	Predicting

A list of all materials required for the Student Edition activities can be found on pages T25–T33. You can obtain information about ordering materials by calling 1-800-848-9500 or by accessing the Science Explorer Internet site at **www.phschool.com**.

All In The Family

Most students are curious about why family members share some physical similarities. Some might even have their own ideas about how physical traits run in families.

Purpose In the Chapter 3 Project, students will create a family of "paper pets" based on phenotypes they have selected. In doing so, students will learn about phenotypes, genotypes, traits, and alleles. They will also learn how traits are passed from parent to offspring and how it is possible to predict the outcomes of genetic crosses.

Skills Focus After completing the Chapter 3 Project, students will be able to
◆ model the inheritance of traits using a paper pet;
◆ infer their pets' genotypes;
◆ predict the genotypes and phenotypes of their pets' offspring;
◆ communicate the results of genetic crosses in a class presentation.

Project Time Line The entire project will require about two or three weeks. See Chapter 3 Project Teacher Notes on pages 68–69 in Unit 1 Resources for more detailed instructions. Begin the project by distributing Chapter 3 Project Overview, pages 70–71 in Unit 1 Resources. Discuss the project with students and begin talking about the materials they will need to decorate their pets. Students will use Chapter 3 Project Worksheet 1, page 72 in Unit 1 Resources, to help them create their pets.

Once they have created their pets, allow class time for students to set up crosses with another pet. After students have found partners, distribute Chapter 3 Project Worksheet 2, page 73 in Unit 1 Resources, to help students determine the results of the crosses between their pets and create the offspring. Student pairs might need class time to prepare displays of their pet families.

Suggested Shortcuts You can simplify this project by having students record the phenotype and genotype of their pets on paper. Student pairs can set up Punnett squares for the crosses without making paper models of the pet parents and

offspring. Each pair can simply assume that one of their pets is female and the other is male.

Possible Materials Students need blue or yellow construction paper for the pet's body. They will also need scissors, colored pencils, glue, and markers to create their pets. Encourage students to decorate their pets with additional materials. You can provide these materials or have students use materials from

home. Materials students might use include glitter, beads, feathers, sequins, yarn, and buttons. Students will need a coin to toss to determine the offspring's genotypes and poster board or other large paper to display their pet families.

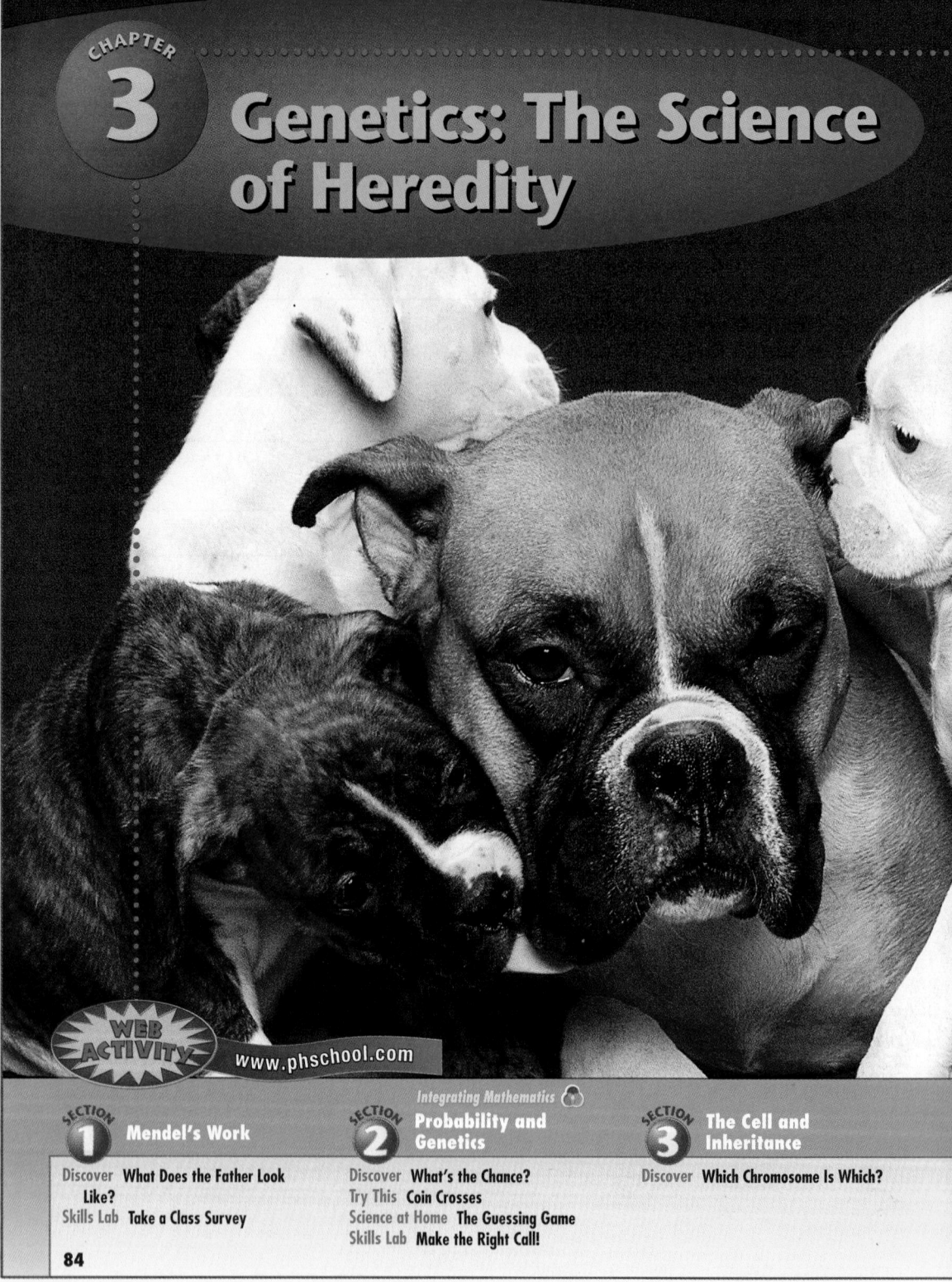

CHAPTER 3 Genetics: The Science of Heredity

WEB ACTIVITY www.phschool.com

Integrating Mathematics

SECTION 1 Mendel's Work
Discover What Does the Father Look Like?
Skills Lab Take a Class Survey

SECTION 2 Probability and Genetics
Discover What's the Chance?
Try This Coin Crosses
Science at Home The Guessing Game
Skills Lab Make the Right Call!

SECTION 3 The Cell and Inheritance
Discover Which Chromosome Is Which?

84

CHAPTER 3 PROJECT

All in the Family

Did you ever wonder why some offspring resemble their parents while others do not? In this chapter, you'll learn how offspring come to have traits similar to those of their parents. In this project, you'll create a family of "paper pets" to explore how traits pass from parents to offspring.

Your Goal To create a "paper pet" that will be crossed with a pet belonging to a classmate, and to determine what traits the offspring will have.

To complete this project successfully, you must
- create your own unique paper pet with five different traits
- cross your pet with another pet to produce six offspring
- determine what traits the offspring will have, and explain how they came to have those traits

Get Started Cut out your pet from either blue or yellow construction paper. Choose other traits for your pet from this list: female or male; square eyes or round eyes; oval nose or triangular nose; pointed teeth or square teeth. Then create your pet using materials of your choice.

Check Your Progress You'll be working on this project as you study this chapter. To keep your project on track, look for Check Your Progress boxes at the following points.
Section 1 Review, page 91: Identify your pet's genotype.
Section 3 Review, page 106: Determine what traits your pet's offspring have.
Section 4 Review, page 112: Make a display of your pet's family.

Present Your Project At the end of the chapter (page 115), you and your partner will display your pet's family and analyze the inheritance patterns.

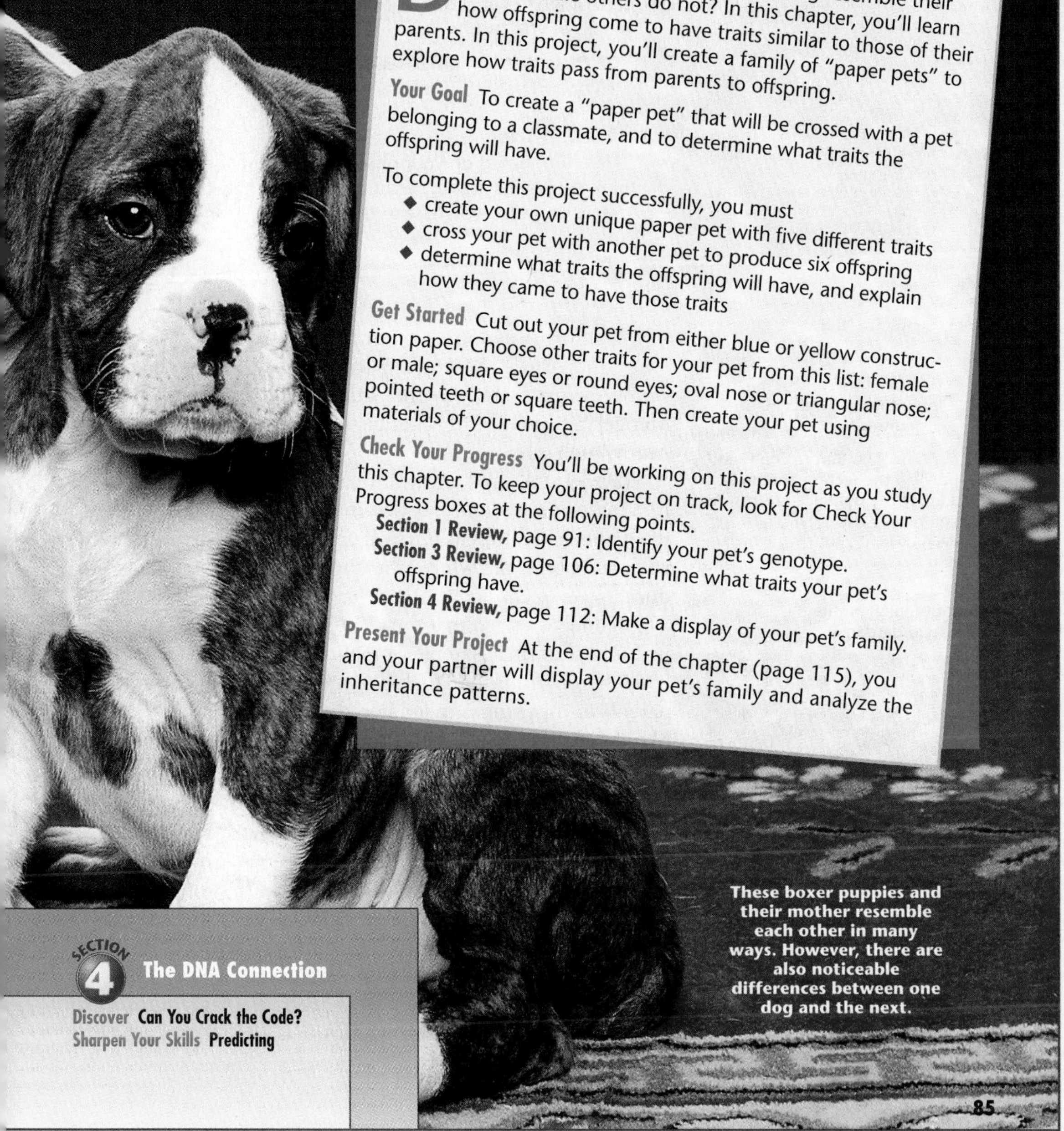

These boxer puppies and their mother resemble each other in many ways. However, there are also noticeable differences between one dog and the next.

85

SECTION 4 The DNA Connection

Discover **Can You Crack the Code?**
Sharpen Your Skills **Predicting**

Program Resources

- **Unit 1 Resources** Chapter 3 Project Teacher Notes, pp. 68–69; Chapter 3 Project Overview and Worksheets, pp. 70–73; Chapter 3 Project Scoring Rubric, p. 74

WEB ACTIVITY www.phschool.com

You will find an Internet activity, chapter self-tests for students, and links to other chapter topics at this site.

Launching the Project To introduce the Chapter 3 Project, invite students to look at the photo of the boxer puppies on these pages. Ask: **How are these puppies similar to each other and to their mother? How are they different?** (*Accept all answers. Most students will describe similarities in the shape of the nose and ears and differences in color.*) Encourage students to offer explanations for these similarities and differences.

Finally, have students read the description of the project in their text and in the Chapter 3 Project Overview. Encourage students to begin thinking about what traits their pets will have without considering which alleles are dominant or recessive.

Performance Assessment

The Chapter 3 Project Scoring Rubric on page 74 of Unit 1 Resources will help you evaluate how well students complete the Chapter 3 Project. Students will be assessed on
- how neatly and creatively they design their paper pets and how correctly they identify the phenotypes and genotypes;
- how accurately they identify the genotypes and phenotypes of their pets' offspring;
- how accurately and completely they design a display of their pets' families.

By sharing the Chapter 3 Project Scoring Rubric with students at the beginning of the project, you will make it clear to them what they are expected to do.

Objectives

After completing the lesson, students will be able to
- describe Mendel's genetics experiments;
- identify the factors that control the inheritance of traits in organisms;
- explain how geneticists use symbols to represent alleles.

Key Terms trait, heredity, genetics, purebred, gene, allele, dominant allele, recessive allele, hybrid

1 Engage/Explore

Activating Prior Knowledge

Invite students to share observations they have made about the physical similarities and differences among family members. Ask: **Have you ever wondered why some family members look very similar while others look very different?** *(Many students will have considered this in one way or another.)* Encourage students to share their ideas about the inheritance of traits in families. Be alert for misconceptions students might have, and address these throughout the section.

DISCOVER

Skills Focus inferring
Time 10 minutes
Expected Outcome Two kittens are mostly white with some black. The third kitten is dark gray with some white. The mother is black with some white.
Think It Over Students will probably infer that the father may be mostly white. They may infer that the white kittens may have inherited their color pattern from the father. They may also infer that the gray kitten is a mixture of the mostly white father and the mostly black mother.

SECTION 1 Mendel's Work

DISCOVER ⋯⋯⋯⋯⋯⋯⋯⋯⋯ ACTIVITY

What Does the Father Look Like?

1. Observe the colors of each kitten in the photo. Record each kitten's coat colors and patterns. Include as many details as you can.

2. Observe the mother cat in the photo. Record her coat color and pattern.

Think It Over

Inferring Based on your observations, describe what you think the kittens' father might look like. Identify the evidence on which you based your inference.

GUIDE FOR READING

- What factors control the inheritance of traits in organisms?

Reading Tip Before you read, preview the section and make a list of the boldfaced terms. As you read, write a definition for each term in your own words.

Gregor Mendel in the monastery garden ▼

The year was 1851. Gregor Mendel, a young priest from a monastery in Central Europe, entered the University of Vienna to study mathematics and science. Two years later, Mendel returned to the monastery and began teaching at a nearby high school.

Mendel also cared for the monastery's garden, where he grew hundreds of pea plants. He became curious about why some of the plants had different physical characteristics, or **traits.** Some pea plants grew tall while others were short. Some plants produced green seeds, while others had yellow seeds.

Mendel observed that the pea plants' traits were often similar to those of their parents. Sometimes, however, the pea plants had different traits than their parents. The passing of traits from parents to offspring is called **heredity.** For more than ten years, Mendel experimented with thousands of pea plants to understand the process of heredity. Mendel's work formed the foundation of **genetics,** the scientific study of heredity.

Mendel's Peas

Mendel made a wise decision when he chose to study peas rather than other plants in the monastery garden. Pea plants are easy to study because they have many traits that exist in only two forms. For example, pea plant stems are either tall or short, but not medium height. Also, garden peas produce a large number of offspring in one generation. Thus, it is easy to collect large amounts of data to analyze.

READING STRATEGIES

Reading Tip Make sure students use their own words to define each boldfaced term. After students have previewed the section, pronounce the boldfaced terms for the class to make sure that students are pronouncing them correctly. Students could write each term on one side of an index card and the definition on the other side. They can then use these cards as study aids.

Concept Mapping Have students make a concept map in which they show the relationships among the terms in the section. Students may include their definitions on the concept maps, if they wish.

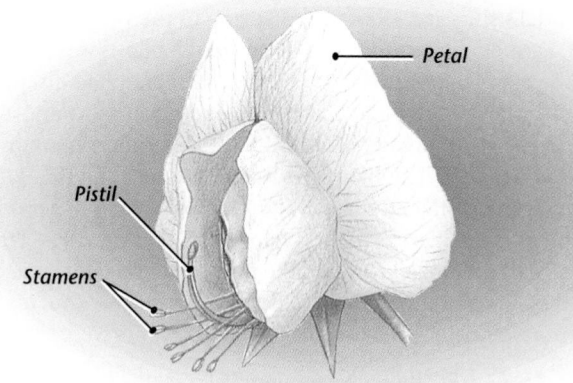

Petal

Pistil

Stamens

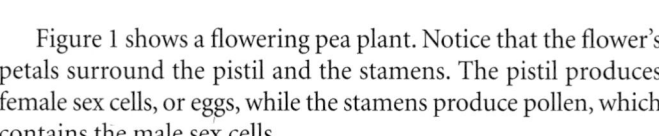

Figure 1 Garden peas usually reproduce by self-pollination. Pollen from a flower's stamens lands on the pistil of the same flower. Plants that result from self-pollination inherit all of their characteristics from the single parent plant. *Relating Cause and Effect Why was it important for Mendel to prevent his pea plants from self-pollinating?*

Figure 1 shows a flowering pea plant. Notice that the flower's petals surround the pistil and the stamens. The pistil produces female sex cells, or eggs, while the stamens produce pollen, which contains the male sex cells.

In nature, pea plants are usually self-pollinating. This means that pollen from one flower lands on the pistil of the same flower. Mendel developed a method by which he could cross-pollinate, or "cross," pea plants. To cross two plants, he removed pollen from a flower on one plant and brushed it onto a flower on a second plant. To prevent the pea plants from self-pollinating, he carefully removed the stamens from the flowers on the second plant.

Mendel's Experiments

Suppose you had a garden full of pea plants, and you wanted to study the inheritance of traits. What would you do? Mendel decided to cross plants with opposite forms of a trait, for example, tall plants and short plants. He started his experiments with purebred plants. A **purebred** plant is one that always produces offspring with the same form of a trait as the parent. For example, purebred short pea plants always produce short offspring. Purebred tall pea plants always produce tall offspring. To produce purebred plants, Mendel allowed peas with one particular trait to self-pollinate for many generations. By using purebred plants, Mendel knew that the offspring's trait would always be identical to that of the parents.

In his first experiment, Mendel crossed purebred tall plants with purebred short plants. He called these parent plants the parental generation, or P generation. He called the offspring from this cross the first filial (FIL ee ul) generation, or the F_1 generation. The word *filial* means "son" in Latin.

Answers to Self-Assessment

Caption Question

Figure 1 Mendel had to be sure of the source of the pollen. By eliminating the possibility of self-pollination, he knew the pollen came from another plant.

2 Facilitate

Mendel's Peas

Building Inquiry Skills: Observing

Materials *tulip or lily flower, hand lens, small blunt-tipped scissors*
Time 15 minutes

Encourage students to closely observe the intact flower with a hand lens. Then instruct students to snip apart the pistil and stamens with scissors and examine these parts individually. Have students draw a labeled diagram of the flower and its parts. Then have them compare their diagrams with the pea flower in Figure 1. Ask: **What makes the pea flower well suited for self-pollination?** *(The petals almost completely enclose the pistil and stamen.)* Tell students that self-pollinating plants are a better choice for studying inheritance because it is easier to obtain purebreeding plants.
learning modality: kinesthetic

Mendel's Experiments

Inquiry Challenge

Materials *posterboard*
Time 20 minutes

Challenge small groups to evaluate Mendel's experimental procedure. Groups should create a poster on which they identify Mendel's question and hypothesis and outline his experimental design. Groups should also include a summary of their opinions about Mendel's procedures. Have them consider why Mendel allowed the F_1 plants to self-pollinate. *(To see if they were purebred)* Groups can present their posters to the class. **cooperative learning**

Ongoing Assessment

Writing Have students identify three characteristics of pea plants that make them useful for studying inheritance. *(Only two forms of many traits, large number of offspring, self-pollinating)*

Other Traits

Language Arts
CONNECTION

Have students compare Mendel's description with the round and wrinkled peas in Figure 3. Invite them to suggest changes to Mendel's description. Then ask: **Why do you think detailed descriptions are important in scientific papers?** *(So readers will clearly understand the author's ideas)*

In Your Journal Before students list the features of their objects, discuss adjectives and adverbs, the kinds of words used to describe objects. Tell students not to use the name of their objects in their paragraphs. Then have students trade paragraphs and guess their partners' objects. **learning modality: verbal**

Dominant and Recessive Alleles

Using the Visuals: Figure 3

Review with students the forms of each trait in the peas that Mendel studied. Ask: **Why are these traits well suited for studying inheritance?** *(The traits are easy to observe and have two distinct forms.)* Then have students solve simple genetic crosses between peas that differ in one trait. For example: **What color seeds will the offspring have when a purebred pea plant with yellow seeds is crossed with a purebred plant with green seeds?** *(yellow seeds)* **learning modality: visual**

Including All Students

Students can add the following terms to their lists of boldfaced terms from the Reading Tip activity to create their own dictionary of genetic terms: *factor, characteristic, self-pollination, cross-pollination, cross, filial, F_1 generation, P generation, inheritance,* and *purebred.* Students should write definitions of these words and include drawings if needed. Allow students whose native language is not English to write definitions in their own language. **limited English proficiency**

Language Arts
CONNECTION

Gregor Mendel presented a detailed description of his observations in a scientific paper in 1866. In the excerpt that follows, notice how clearly he describes his observations of the two different seed shapes in peas.

"These are either round or roundish, the depressions, if any, occur on the surface, being always only shallow; or they are irregularly angular and deeply wrinkled."

In Your Journal Choose an everyday object, such as a piece of fruit or a pen. Make a list of the object's features. Then write a short paragraph describing the object. Use clear, precise language in your description.

You can see the results of Mendel's first cross in Figure 2. To Mendel's surprise, all of the offspring in the F_1 generation were tall. Despite the fact that one of the parent plants was short, none of the offspring were short. The shortness trait had disappeared!

Mendel let the plants in the F_1 generation grow and allowed them to self-pollinate. The results of this experiment also surprised Mendel. The plants in the F_2 (second filial) generation were a mix of tall and short plants. This occurred even though none of the F_1 parent plants were short. The shortness trait had reappeared. Mendel counted the number of tall and short plants in the F_2 generation. He found that about three fourths of the plants were tall, while one fourth of the plants were short.

✓ *Checkpoint* What is a purebred plant?

Other Traits

In addition to stem height, Mendel studied six other traits in garden peas: seed shape, seed color, seed coat color, pod shape, pod color, and flower position. Compare the two forms of each trait in Figure 3. Mendel crossed plants with these traits in the same manner as he did for stem height. The results in each experiment were similar to those that he observed with stem height. Only one form of the trait appeared in the F_1 generation. However, in the F_2 generation the "lost" form of the trait always reappeared in about one fourth of the plants.

Figure 2 When Mendel crossed purebred tall and short pea plants, all the offspring in the F_1 generation were tall. In the F_2 generation, three fourths of the plants were tall, while one fourth were short.

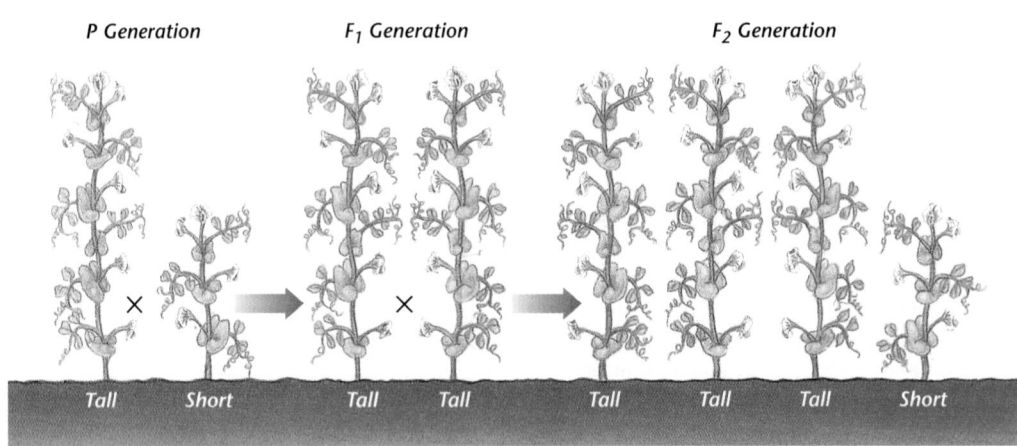

P Generation *F₁ Generation* *F₂ Generation*

Tall Short × Tall Tall × Tall Tall Tall Short

Background

History of Science Mendel's work is relevant today because of his careful experimental design. Unlike other scientists and plant and animal breeders of his time, Mendel carefully chose to study distinct traits. He allowed plants to self-pollinate until he was certain that the plants he used were purebreeding. Most importantly, he applied the principles of statistics when setting up his crosses and interpreting his results. This prevented him from interpreting his results using his personal opinions and beliefs. Other scientists and breeders at that time set up their crosses randomly with parents of unknown breeding and often tried to follow more than one trait at a time. They also thought that inheritance was much too complicated to analyze using the principles of statistics.

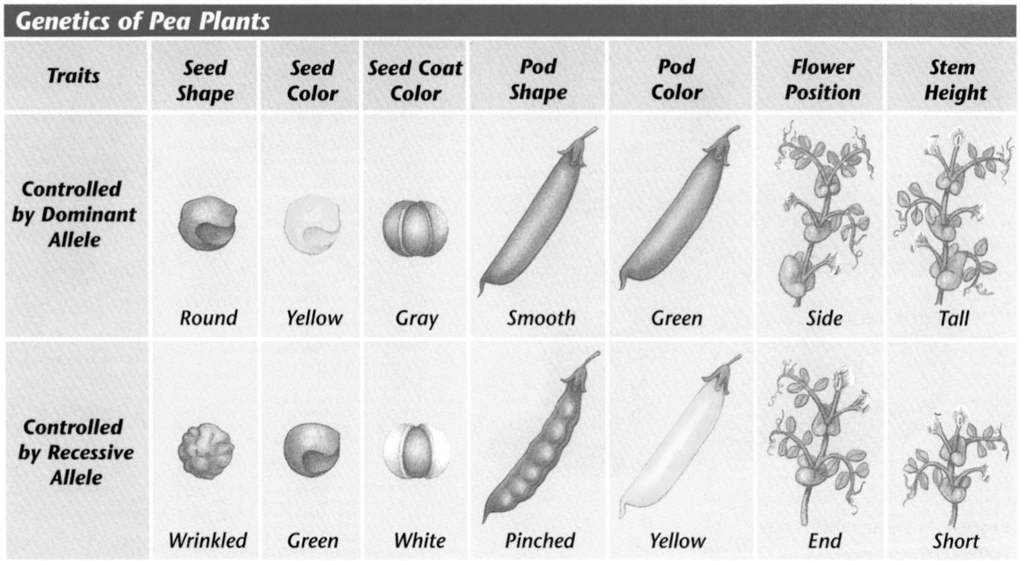

Genetics of Pea Plants

Traits	Seed Shape	Seed Color	Seed Coat Color	Pod Shape	Pod Color	Flower Position	Stem Height
Controlled by Dominant Allele	Round	Yellow	Gray	Smooth	Green	Side	Tall
Controlled by Recessive Allele	Wrinkled	Green	White	Pinched	Yellow	End	Short

Figure 3 Mendel studied seven different traits in pea plants. Each trait has two different forms. *Interpreting Diagrams Is yellow seed color controlled by a dominant allele or a recessive allele? What type of allele controls pinched pod shape?*

Dominant and Recessive Alleles

From his results, Mendel reasoned that individual factors must control the inheritance of traits in peas. The factors that control each trait exist in pairs. The female parent contributes one factor, while the male parent contributes the other factor.

Mendel went on to reason that one factor in a pair can mask, or hide, the other factor. The tallness factor, for example, masked the shortness factor in the F_1 generation.

Today, scientists call the factors that control traits **genes.** They call the different forms of a gene **alleles** (uh LEELZ). The gene that controls stem height in peas, for example, has one allele for tall stems and one allele for short stems. Each pea plant inherits a combination of two alleles from its parents—either two alleles for tall stems, two alleles for short stems, or one of each.

Individual alleles control the inheritance of traits. Some alleles are dominant, while other alleles are recessive. A **dominant allele** is one whose trait always shows up in the organism when the allele is present. A **recessive allele,** on the other hand, is masked, or covered up, whenever the dominant allele is present. A trait controlled by a recessive allele will only show up if the organism does not have the dominant allele.

In pea plants, the allele for tall stems is dominant over the allele for short stems. Pea plants with one allele for tall stems and one allele for short stems will be tall. The allele for tall stems masks the allele for short stems. Only pea plants that inherit two recessive alleles for short stems will be short.

Answers to Self-Assessment

✓ *Checkpoint*

A plant that always produces offspring with the same form of a trait as the parent

Caption Question

Figure 3 a dominant allele; recessive

Demonstration

Materials 2 Drosophila melanogaster *cultures— wild-type and ebony, culture vials and plugs,* Drosophila *media, nonether anesthesia kit, hand lens, paint brush, white index card, marking pen* (NOTE: Drosophila *cultures are available from science supply companies.*)

Time 20 minutes

Advance Preparation Set up the parental cross about two weeks in advance by placing 2 to 3 ebony males with 2 to 3 wild-type virgin females in each of three vials. To collect virgin females, remove all adult flies from the culture vial. Then, within 4 to 6 hours, collect the newly emerged females. Females have pointed abdomens with stripes almost to the end. Males have rounded abdomens that are black at the end. Anesthetize flies to sort them and to set up the crosses. Place vials on their sides until the flies wake up. Remove parent flies from the vials when pupae begin to develop. When F_1 adults begin to emerge, remove the flies daily to prevent F_2 offspring from mixing with F_1 offspring. Dispose of flies in a jar of mineral oil. Empty this "morgue" into a garbage disposal.

Tips Anesthetize the parent flies and place them on index cards for students to examine. Ask: **How do these flies differ?** *(Ebony flies have darker bodies than wild-type flies.)* Challenge students to predict which trait is controlled by a dominant allele and which is controlled by a recessive allele. Then anesthetize the F_1 flies and place them on index cards for students to count. Ask: **Which trait is controlled by a dominant allele?** *(lighter body color)* **How do you know?** *(None of the F_1 flies have ebony bodies.)* **What body color will F_2 flies have?** *(Some will have ebony bodies, but most will have lighter bodies.)* **learning modality: logical/mathematical**

Ongoing Assessment

Drawing Have students diagram Mendel's crosses between tall and short pea plants. Tell them to label the traits controlled by dominant and recessive alleles.

 Students can save their drawings in their portfolios.

Understanding Mendel's Crosses

Building Inquiry Skills: Applying Concepts

Have students choose a pea trait from Figure 3, and challenge them to diagram the crosses that Mendel made. In their diagrams, students should show how dominant and recessive alleles are inherited from the P generation through the F_1 generation to the F_2 generation. Encourage students to share their diagrams with the class. **learning modality: logical/mathematical**

Using Symbols in Genetics

Including All Students

Students who need more help can practice using genetic symbols by assigning letters to the dominant and recessive alleles for each trait that Mendel studied. Students can use any letter to represent each trait, although the convention is to use the letter that begins the word of the dominant allele. For example, *R* stands for round seeds and *r* stands for wrinkled. Dominant alleles must have a capital letter; recessive alleles, lower-case. **learning modality: verbal**

Inquiry Challenge

Materials *F_2 ear of corn with purple and yellow kernels (available from science supply companies)*
Time 15 minutes

Give each small group an ear of corn. Explain that the ears were produced by F_2 generation plants and that kernel color is controlled by dominant and recessive alleles—purple is controlled by the dominant allele, and yellow is controlled by the recessive allele. Then challenge students to trace the inheritance of the dominant and recessive alleles for kernel color by working backward from the F_2 ear to the F_1 cross and finally to the parental cross. Students should use symbols to represent the alleles for kernel color. (*F_1 parents: both purple* (Pp); *P parents: one purple* (PP), *one yellow* (pp)) **learning modality: logical/mathematical**

Figure 4 These rabbits have some traits controlled by dominant alleles and other traits controlled by recessive alleles. For example, the allele for black fur is dominant over the allele for white fur. *Inferring What combination of alleles must the white rabbit have?*

Understanding Mendel's Crosses

You can understand Mendel's results by tracing the inheritance of alleles in his experiments. The purebred plants in the P generation had two identical alleles for stem height. The purebred tall plants had two alleles for tall stems. The purebred short plants had two alleles for short stems. In the F_1 generation, all of the plants received one allele for tall stems from the tall parent. They received one allele for short stems from the short parent. The F_1 plants are called **hybrids** (HY bridz) because they have two different alleles for the trait. All the F_1 plants are tall because the dominant allele for tall stems masks the recessive allele for short stems.

When Mendel crossed the hybrid plants in the F_1 generation, some of the plants inherited two dominant alleles for tall stems. These plants were tall. Other plants inherited one dominant allele for tall stems and one recessive allele for short stems. These plants were also tall. Other plants inherited two recessive alleles for short stems. These plants were short.

☑ *Checkpoint* *If a pea plant has a tall stem, what possible combinations of alleles could it have?*

Using Symbols in Genetics

Geneticists today use a standard shorthand method to write about alleles in genetic crosses. Instead of using words such as "tall stems" to represent alleles, they simply use letters. A

Background

History of Science At the time of Mendel's studies of inheritance, most of the scientific community believed in the blending theory of inheritance. This theory assumed that both parents contributed equally to the characteristics of the offspring. According to the theory, parents of contrasting appearance always produced offspring with an intermediate appearance. When parental traits reappeared in the offspring, it was thought to be due to some genetic disturbance. Mendel also subscribed to the blending theory. When he started working on his experiments with peas, he was not trying to discover the laws of inheritance. Rather, he was trying to find a hybrid that would breed true. This is one reason why his results went unnoticed for some time. The scientific community could not interpret them for what they really showed.

dominant allele is represented by a capital letter. For example, the allele for tall stems is represented by *T*. A recessive allele is represented by the lowercase version of the letter. So, the allele for short stems would be represented by *t*. When a plant inherits two dominant alleles for tall stems, its alleles are written as *TT*. When a plant inherits two recessive alleles for short stems, its alleles are written as *tt*. When a plant inherits one allele for tall stems and one allele for short stems, its alleles are written as *Tt*.

Mendel's Contribution

In 1866, Mendel presented his results to a scientific society that met regularly near the monastery. In his paper, Mendel described the principles of heredity he had discovered. Unfortunately, other scientists did not understand the importance of Mendel's work. Some scientists thought that Mendel had oversimplified the process of inheritance. Others never read his paper, or even heard about his work. Remember, at that time there were no telephones or other types of electronic communication. So scientists in different parts of the world were isolated from each other. Mendel was especially isolated because he wasn't at a university.

Mendel's work was forgotten for 34 years. In 1900, three different scientists rediscovered Mendel's work. They had made many of the same observations as Mendel had. The scientists quickly recognized the importance of Mendel's work. Many of the genetic principles that Mendel discovered still stand to this day. Because of his work, Mendel is often called the Father of Genetics.

Figure 5 The dominant allele for yellow skin color in summer squash is represented by the letter *Y*. The recessive allele for green skin color is represented by the letter *y*.

Section 1 Review

1. Explain how the inheritance of traits is controlled in organisms. Use the terms *genes* and *alleles* in your explanation.
2. What is a dominant allele? What is a recessive allele? Give an example of each.
3. The allele for round seeds is represented by *R*. Suppose that a pea plant inherited two recessive alleles for wrinkled seeds. How would you write the symbols for its alleles?
4. **Thinking Critically Applying Concepts** Can a short pea plant ever be a hybrid? Why or why not?

Check Your Progress
CHAPTER PROJECT
By now you should have constructed your paper pet. On the back, write what alleles your pet has for each trait. Use XX for a female, and XY for a male. The dominant alleles for the other four traits are: *B* (blue skin), *R* (round eyes), *T* (triangular nose), and *P* (pointed teeth). (*Hint:* If your pet has a trait controlled by a dominant allele, you can choose which of the possible combinations of alleles your pet has.)

Answers to Self-Assessment

Caption Question

Figure 4 two alleles for white fur

☑ *Checkpoint*

Two alleles for tall stems or one allele for tall stems and one allele for short stems

Mendel's Contribution

Real-Life Learning

Explain to students that it is not unusual for scientists who have discovered new ideas to be misunderstood or even ridiculed. It is very difficult to change popular opinion. Some ideas that were once controversial include that Earth orbits the sun and that Earth is round. Challenge student groups to work together to write a broadcast news story about a scientific idea that is controversial. Students might choose Mendel's results or another idea, either current or historical. You might wish to videotape the groups' broadcasts in a pretend news show. **cooperative learning**

3 Assess

Section 1 Review Answers

1. Each allele of a gene controls the inheritance of a specific trait.
2. *Dominant:* trait always shows up when the allele is present; tall stems in peas. *Recessive:* trait is covered up whenever dominant allele is present; short pea stems.
3. The symbols would be *rr*.
4. No, it has two recessive alleles (*tt*); hybrids have two different alleles for a trait.

Check Your Progress
CHAPTER PROJECT
Check each paper pet to make sure students have correctly assigned pairs of alleles based on the traits they chose. Monitor the number of male and female pets so that there is an equal number of each. If the class has an odd number of students, create an extra pet. Encourage students to be creative when they decorate their pets.

Performance Assessment

Writing Have students summarize Mendel's experiments and his conclusions about the inheritance of traits.

 Students can save their summaries in their portfolios.

Take a Class Survey

Preparing for Inquiry

Key Concept Human traits are controlled by dominant and recessive alleles, causing many different combinations of traits among a group of people.

Skills Objectives Students will be able to

- develop hypotheses about whether traits controlled by dominant alleles are more common than traits controlled by recessive alleles;
- interpret data about certain traits controlled by dominant and recessive alleles in humans;
- draw conclusions about the frequency and the variation of certain traits in the class.

Time 40 minutes

Advance Planning Purchase PTC paper from a science supply house. Gather mirrors, or invite students to bring some from home. You might wish to make photocopies of the circle chart and the data table.

Alternative Materials If PTC paper is not available, this trait can be omitted. If you do not have mirrors, students can observe each other.

Guided Inquiry

Invitation Help students relate Mendel's conclusions to their own physical characteristics. Ask: **Why do you think people often look very similar to other family members, but also different?** *(Some students might realize that children inherit both dominant and recessive alleles from each parent. The combination of these alleles determines the child's physical appearance.)*

Introducing the Procedure

- Have students read through the entire procedure. Then review with them what each trait looks like. Refer students to the illustrations in the text, or find examples of each trait among the class. Explain that PTC paper tastes bitter to those who can taste it.

Nontasters will not taste anything. Curly hair includes wavy hair or any hair that is not straight.

- Make sure students know how to use the circle of traits in Part 2. Point out how to use the color-coding, starting at the center of the circle.

Troubleshooting the Experiment

- Monitor students as they work to make sure they correctly identify each trait.

- The class can record their results on a large data table on the chalkboard by writing their initials in the appropriate columns.

Expected Outcome

Students will show a great variation in traits. Few, if any, will have the same number on the circle of traits.

Skills Lab

Developing Hypotheses

Take a Class Survey

In this lab, you'll explore how greatly traits can vary in a group of people—your classmates.

Problem

Are traits controlled by dominant alleles more common than traits controlled by recessive alleles?

Materials

mirror (optional)   PTC paper

Procedure

Part 1 Dominant and Recessive Alleles

1. Write a hypothesis reflecting your ideas about the problem question. Then copy the data table.

2. For traits A, B, C, D, and E, work with a partner to determine which trait you have. Circle that trait in your data table.

3. For trait F, wash and dry your hands. Taste the PTC paper your teacher gives you. Circle either "can taste PTC" or "cannot taste PTC" in your data table. **CAUTION:** *Never taste any substance in the lab unless directed to by your teacher.*

4. Count the number of students who have each trait. Record that number in your data table. Also record the total number of students.

DATA TABLE

Total Number _____

	Trait 1	Number	Trait 2	Number
A	Free ear lobes		Attached ear lobes	
B	Hair on fingers		No hair on fingers	
C	Widow's peak		No widow's peak	
D	Curly hair		Straight hair	
E	Cleft chin		Smooth chin	
F	Can taste PTC*		Cannot taste PTC*	

*PTC stands for phenylthiocarbamide.

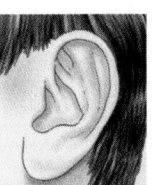
Free ear lobe

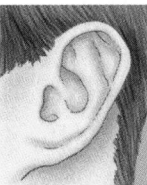
Attached ear lobe

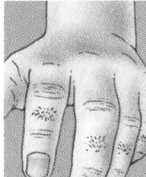
Hair on fingers

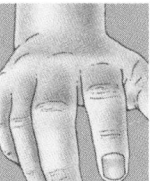
No hair on fingers

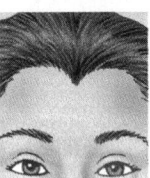
Widow's peak

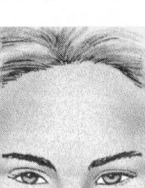
No widow's peak

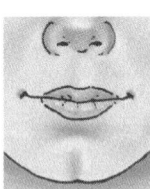
Cleft chin

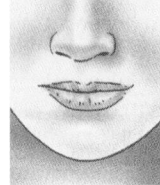
No cleft chin

92

Part 2 Are Your Traits Unique?

5. Look at the circle of traits below. All the traits in your data table appear in the circle. Place the eraser end of your pencil on the trait in the small central circle that applies to you—either free ear lobes or attached ear lobes.

6. Look at the two traits touching the space your eraser is on. Move your eraser to the next description that applies to you. Continue using your eraser to trace your traits until you reach a number on the outside rim of the circle. Share that number with your classmates.

Analyze and Conclude

1. The traits listed under Trait 1 in the data table are controlled by dominant alleles. The traits listed under Trait 2 are controlled by recessive alleles. Which traits controlled by dominant alleles were shown by a majority of students? Which traits controlled by recessive alleles were shown by a majority of students?

2. How many students ended up on the same number on the circle of traits? How many students were the only ones to have their number? What do the results suggest about each person's combination of traits?

3. **Think About It** Do your data support the hypothesis you proposed in Step 1? Explain your answer with examples.

Design an Experiment

Do people who are related to each other show more genetic similarity than unrelated people? Write a hypothesis. Then design an experiment to test your hypothesis.

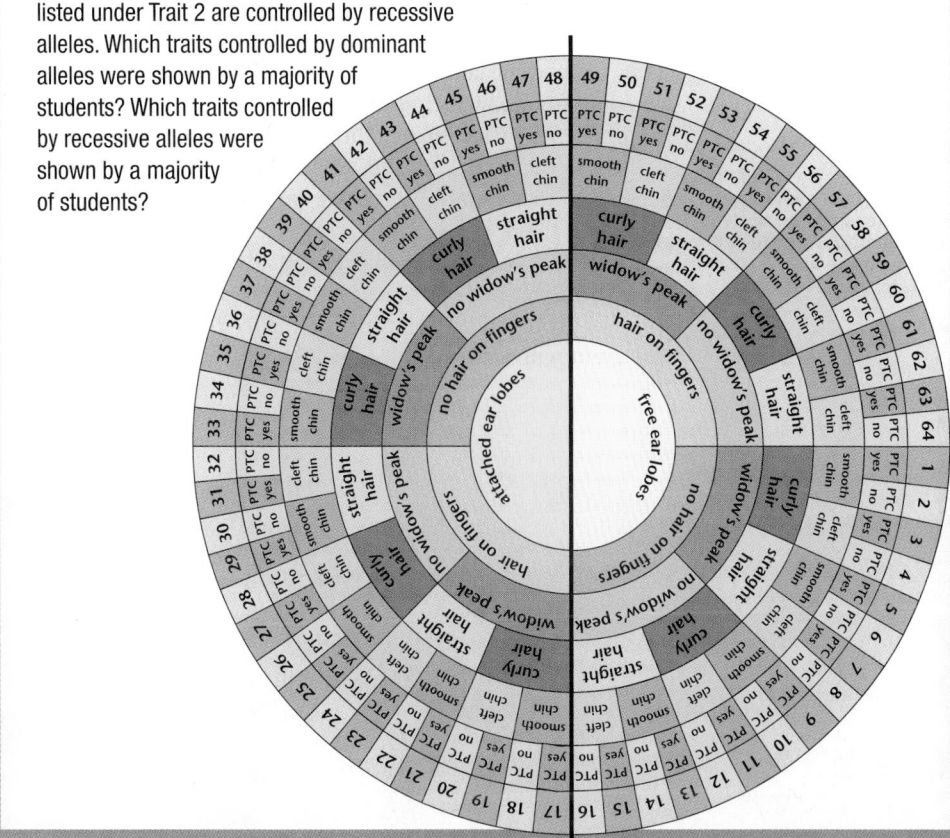

Analyze and Conclude

1. Some traits controlled by dominant alleles that are usually more common include free earlobes and ability to taste PTC. Some traits controlled by recessive alleles that are usually more common include smooth chin, straight hair, no widow's peak, and no mid-finger hair. However, any class's results may vary from the overall population patterns because of the small sample size.

2. Answers will vary, but usually few or no students have the same number when six traits are studied. As more traits are considered, the smaller the chance that any two people in a class will have the same number. Even siblings, except for identical twins, have different combinations of traits.

3. Answers will vary, but students should describe, using examples from the lab, that neither traits controlled by dominant alleles nor traits controlled by recessive alleles are automatically more common in a population.

Extending the Inquiry

Design an Experiment Students' hypotheses will vary. *Sample hypothesis:* A group of related people will share more numbers on the circle of traits than a group of unrelated people. Student experiments can follow the same procedure as this lab, except students should observe the traits in people all from a single family.

◆ **Unit 1 Resources** Chapter 3 Skills Lab, pp. 91–92

Safety

Remind students to wash their hands before tasting the PTC paper. Caution them to never taste any substance in the lab unless you instruct them to. Review the safety guidelines in Appendix A.

SECTION 2 Probability and Genetics

Objectives

After completing the lesson, students will be able to
◆ describe the principles of probability and how Mendel applied them to inheritance;
◆ state how geneticists use Punnett squares;
◆ explain the meanings of the terms *phenotype, genotype, homozygous, heterozygous,* and *codominance.*

Key Terms probability, Punnett square, phenotype, genotype, homozygous, heterozygous, codominance

1 Engage/Explore

Activating Prior Knowledge

Invite students to describe situations in which they have used a coin toss to decide an issue. Ask: **Why did you toss a coin in these situations?** (*Students might mention that it was the fairest way to make a decision.*) **Why is a coin toss fair?** (*Each person has a 50–50 chance of winning.*)

DISCOVER

Skills Focus predicting
Materials *coin*
Time 15 minutes
Expected Outcome The actual outcome of the coin tosses will vary. The more data, the closer the outcome will be to the expected ratio of 1 head: 1 tail.
Think It Over For most students, their results were slightly different from their predictions. The combined class data should be closer to the expected ratio of 1 head to 1 tail. Students might infer that the difference is due to chance or that the more coin tosses they make, the closer they will come to the predicted outcome.

SECTION 2 Probability and Genetics

DISCOVER •••••••••••••••••••••••••••••••••••••• ACTIVITY

What's the Chance?

1. Suppose you were to toss a coin 20 times. Predict how many times the coin would land "heads up" and how many times it would land "tails up."

2. Now test your prediction by tossing a coin 20 times. Record the number of times the coin lands heads up and the number of times it lands tails up.

3. Combine the data from the entire class. Record the total number of tosses, the number of heads, and the number of tails.

Think It Over

Predicting How did your results in Step 2 compare to your prediction? How can you account for any differences between your results and the class results?

GUIDE FOR READING

◆ How do the principles of probability help explain Mendel's results?

◆ How do geneticists use Punnett squares?

Reading Tip Before you read, rewrite the headings in the section as questions that begin with *how, what,* or *why.* As you read, look for answers to these questions.

The city of Portland, Oregon, was founded in the mid-1800s. Two men, Asa L. Lovejoy and Francis W. Pettygrove, owned the land on which the new city was built. Lovejoy, who was from Massachusetts, wanted to name the new town Boston. Pettygrove, however, thought the town should be named after his hometown, Portland, Maine. To settle the dispute, they decided to toss a coin. Pettygrove won, and the new town was named Portland.

What was the chance that Pettygrove would win the coin toss? To answer this question, you need to understand the principles of probability. **Probability** is the likelihood that a particular event will occur.

READING STRATEGIES

Reading Tip Students can write questions for both the major headings and the subheads in the section. For example, a student might write the question "What are the principles of probability?" for the first head. Remind students to leave adequate space after each question to allow room for their answers. Encourage students to keep their questions nearby as they read the section so they can write the answers as they read. Students can use the questions and answers as study guides.

Vocabulary Show students that the term *homozygous* is made up of the Greek words *homos,* meaning "same," and *zygos,* meaning "yoked or paired." Taken together, these words describe a cell formed from two gametes that have the same genetic makeup.

Principles of Probability

If you did the Discover activity, you used the principles of probability to predict the results of a particular event. Each time you toss a coin, there are two possible ways that the coin can land—heads up or tails up. Each of these two events is equally likely to occur. In mathematical terms, you can say that the probability that a tossed coin will land heads up is 1 in 2. There is also a 1 in 2 probability that the coin will land tails up. A 1 in 2 probability can also be expressed as the fraction $\frac{1}{2}$ or as a percent—50 percent.

If you tossed a coin 20 times, you might expect it to land heads up 10 times and tails up 10 times. However, you might not actually get these results. You might get 11 heads and 9 tails, or 8 heads and 12 tails. Remember that the laws of probability predict what is likely to occur, not necessarily what will occur. However, the more tosses you make, the closer your actual results will be to the results predicted by probability.

When you toss a coin more than once, the results of one toss do not affect the results of the next toss. Each event occurs independently. For example, suppose you toss a coin five times and it lands heads up each time. What is the probability that it will land heads up on the next toss? Because the coin landed heads up on the previous five tosses, you might think that it would be likely to land heads up on the next toss. However, this is not the case. The probability of the coin landing heads up on the next toss is still 1 in 2, or 50 percent. The results of the first five tosses do not affect the results of the sixth toss.

✓ *Checkpoint* *Why is there a 1 in 2 probability that a tossed coin will land heads up?*

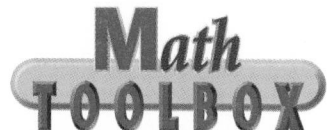

Math TOOLBOX

Calculating Probability

When the probability of an event is 1, the event is *certain* to happen. When the probability of an event is 0, the event is *impossible*. Events with probabilities between 0 and 1 are *possible*.

Suppose that 6 out of 10 marbles in a bag are red. Here's how you can calculate the probability of pulling out a red marble from the bag.

1. There are 10 marbles in the bag, and 6 of them are red.

2. Write this comparison as a fraction.

$$\frac{6 \text{ red marbles}}{10 \text{ marbles total}} = \frac{6}{10} = \frac{3}{5}$$

The probability of choosing a red marble is $\frac{3}{5}$, or 3 out of 5.

If the other 4 marbles in the bag are blue, what is the probability of pulling out a blue marble? What is the probability of pulling out a green marble?

Figure 6 According to the laws of probability, there is a 50 percent probability that the coin will land heads up. *Calculating What is the probability that the coin will land tails up?*

Answers to Self-Assessment

✓ *Checkpoint*

There are two possible ways that the coin can land, and each one has an equal chance of occurring.

Caption Question

Figure 6 50%

2 Facilitate

Principles of Probability

Including All Students

Materials *4 pipe cleaners of different lengths, but all the same color*

To help reinforce the concept of probability, challenge student pairs to use the pipe cleaners to illustrate the two principles of probability: each event has an equal chance of occurring and each event occurs independently. Then ask: **What is the chance that the longest pipe cleaner will be chosen?** *(1 out of 4 or 25%)* **If the longest pipe cleaner is chosen the first time and is replaced, what is the chance that it will be chosen again?** *(Also 25%; each event occurs independently of the results of other events.)* **learning modality: kinesthetic**

Inquiry Challenge

Challenge small groups of students to create a game that uses the principles of probability. Students may use coin tosses, a spinner, or anything else that gives players an equal chance at winning the game. Each group should write rules for its game and teach another group how to play the game. **cooperative learning**

Math TOOLBOX

Time 10 minutes

Tips For the first problem, students should set up the fraction $\frac{4}{10}$ or $\frac{2}{5}$ They should state that there is a 2 in 5 chance of pulling out a blue marble. For the second problem, students should set up the fraction $\frac{0}{10}$ or 0. They should state that the probability of pulling out a green marble is zero. **learning modality: logical/ mathematical**

Ongoing Assessment

Oral Presentation Call on students at random to describe the two principles of probability using a coin toss as an example.

Mendel and Probability

Building Inquiry Skills: Calculating

Using the example from the text, have students calculate the probability that a cross between two hybrid tall pea plants *(Tt)* will produce tall offspring. ($\frac{3}{4} \times 100\% = 75\%$) Ask: **What is the probability that such a cross will produce short offspring?** ($\frac{1}{4} \times 100\% = 25\%$) Extend this by challenging students to calculate the probabilities of tall and short offspring from a cross between a purebred tall pea *(TT)* and a purebred short pea *(tt)*. *(100% of offspring will be tall; 0% will be short.)* **learning modality: logical/mathematical**

Punnett Squares

Using the Visuals: Figure 7

Have students identify in Figure 7 the two alleles that each parent could pass on to the offspring *(Tt)*. Make sure students understand how the alleles combine from each parent to form the different offspring classes. Emphasize that a cross between these two plants will produce more than just four offspring. The Punnett square simply identifies all the *possible* combinations of alleles. In this case, offspring will be either tall or short with three different allele combinations. Ask: **Which of these combinations is more likely to occur than others?** *(Tt)* **What percentage of the offspring will have that combination?** *(50%)* **learning modality: visual**

Inquiry Challenge

Materials *F_2 ear of corn with purple and yellow kernels*

Time 15 minutes

Challenge students to devise a Punnett square that illustrates the possible offspring in a cross between two plants that could produce corn with both purple (dominant allele) and yellow (recessive allele) kernels. *(Pp × Pp)* Then have students set up Punnett squares that show the possible offspring in a cross between a purebred yellow corn plant *(pp)* and a purebred purple corn plant *(PP)*. **learning modality: logical/ mathematical**

Mendel and Probability

How is probability related to genetics? To answer this question, think back to Mendel's experiments with peas. Remember that Mendel carefully counted the offspring from every cross that he carried out. When Mendel crossed two plants that were hybrid for stem height *(Tt)*, three fourths of the F_1 plants had tall stems. One fourth of the plants had short stems.

Each time Mendel repeated the cross, he obtained similar results. Mendel realized that the mathematical principles of probability applied to his work. He could say that the probability of such a cross producing a tall plant was 3 in 4. The probability of producing a short plant was 1 in 4. **Mendel was the first scientist to recognize that the principles of probability can be used to predict the results of genetic crosses.**

Punnett Squares

A tool that can help you understand how the laws of probability apply to genetics is called a Punnett square. A **Punnett square** is a chart that shows all the possible combinations of alleles that can result from a genetic cross. **Geneticists use Punnett squares to show all the possible outcomes of a genetic cross and to determine the probability of a particular outcome.**

The Punnett square in Figure 7 shows a cross between two hybrid tall pea plants *(Tt)*. Each parent can pass either of its alleles, *T* or *t,* to its offspring. The possible alleles that one parent can pass on are written across the top of the Punnett square. The possible alleles that the other parent can pass on are written down the left side of the Punnett square. The boxes in the Punnett square represent the possible combinations of alleles that the offspring can inherit. The boxes are filled in like a multiplication problem, with one allele contributed by each parent.

Using a Punnett Square You can use a Punnett square to calculate the probability that offspring will have a certain combination of alleles. The allele that each parent will pass on is based on chance, just like the toss of a coin. Thus, there are four possible combinations of alleles. The probability that an offspring will

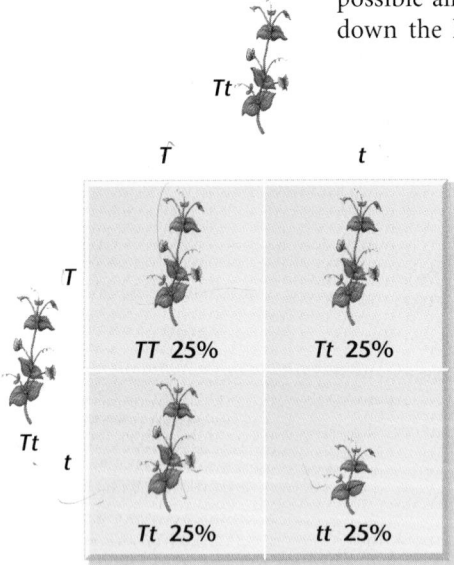

Figure 7 This Punnett square shows a cross between two hybrid tall pea plants. *Interpreting Charts Which allele combinations will result in tall offspring?*

Background

History of Science The Punnett square was devised in the early 1900s by the English geneticist Reginald C. Punnett. Punnett studied at the University of Cambridge under the biologist William Bateson who had recognized that the results of his breeding experiments were perfectly explained by Mendel's principles. Bateson and Punnett studied sweet peas and chickens. Their breeding research further supported Mendel's principles. They were among the first to show that Mendel's principles also applied to animals. Punnett wrote the first textbook on the subject of genetics, called *Mendelism,* in 1905.

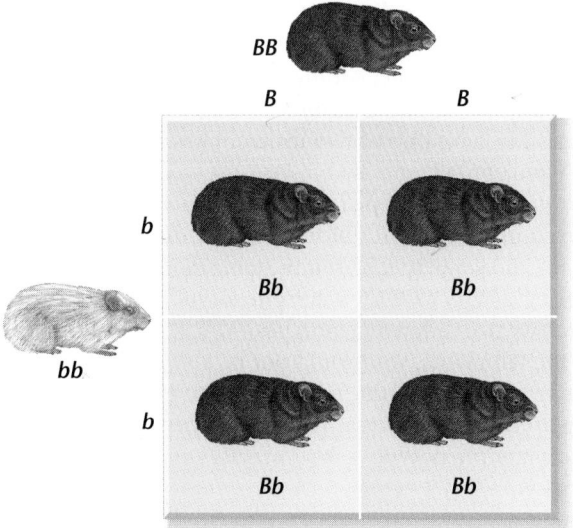

BB

B   B

b

Bb   Bb

bb

b

Bb   Bb

Figure 8 This Punnett square shows a cross between a black guinea pig (*BB*) and a white guinea pig (*bb*). *Calculating What is the probability that an offspring will have white fur?*

be *TT* is 1 in 4, or 25 percent. The probability that an offspring will be *tt* is also 1 in 4, or 25 percent. Notice, however, that the *Tt* allele combination appears in two boxes in the Punnett square. This is because there are two possible ways in which this combination can occur. The probability, then, that an offspring will be *Tt* is 2 in 4, or 50 percent.

Recall that when Mendel performed this cross, he discovered that about three fourths of the plants (75%) had tall stems. The remaining one fourth of the plants (25%) had short stems. Now you can understand why that was true. Plants with the *TT* allele combination would be tall. So too would those plants with the *Tt* allele combination. Remember that the dominant allele masks the recessive allele. Only those plants with the *tt* allele combination would be short.

Predicting Probabilities You can also use a Punnett square to predict probabilities. For example, Figure 8 shows a cross between a purebred black guinea pig and a purebred white guinea pig. The allele for black fur is dominant over the allele for white fur. Notice that only one allele combination is possible in the offspring—*Bb*. All of the offspring will inherit the dominant allele for black fur. Because of this, all of the offspring will have black fur. You can predict that there is a 100% probability that the offspring will have black fur.

☑ *Checkpoint* *If two guinea pigs with the alleles* Bb *are crossed, what is the probability that an offspring will have white fur?*

Coin Crosses

Here's how you can use coins to model Mendel's cross between two *Tt* pea plants.

ACTIVITY

1. Place a small piece of masking tape on each side of two coins.
2. Write a *T* (for tall) on one side of each coin and a *t* (for short) on the other.
3. Toss both coins together 20 times. Record the letter combinations that you obtain from each toss.

Interpreting Data How many of the offspring would be tall plants? (*Hint:* What different letter combinations would result in a tall plant?) How many would be short? Convert your results to percents. Then compare your results to Mendel's.

Demonstration

Materials *F₂ tobacco seeds that produce green (GG, Gg) and albino (gg) seedlings in a ratio of 3:1, seed starting soil, shallow pan, plastic wrap, water*

ACTIVITY

Advance Preparation Order the seeds from a science supply house in plenty of time. Plant the seeds 7 to 14 days in advance, or as directed on the seed packet.

Time 15 minutes

Explain that a cross between two hybrid green tobacco plants (*Gg* and *Gg*) produces both green and white offspring. Help students complete a Punnett square of this cross. Ask: **What percentage of seedlings will be green?** ($\frac{3}{4} \times 100\% = 75\%$) **What percentage will be white?** ($\frac{1}{4} \times 100\% = 25\%$) Then have students count the number of green and white seedlings from the F_2 seeds you planted. Have students compare the actual number of green and white seedlings to the amount predicted. **learning modality: logical/mathematical**

TRY THIS

Skills Focus interpreting data

ACTIVITY

Materials *2 coins, masking tape, scissors*

Time 15 minutes

Expected Outcome 5 *TT*, 10 *Tt*, 5 *tt*; All plants that are *TT* and *Tt* will be tall, approximately 15, or 75%. All *tt* plants will be short, approximately 5, or 25%. Some students might observe that their results are similar to Mendel's results, 75% tall and 25% short.

Extend Let students toss both coins another twenty times and observe whether or not their percentages are closer to Mendel's results. **learning modality: logical/mathematical**

Program Resources

◆ **Interdisciplinary Exploration Series** "The Power of Patterns," p. 42

Media and Technology

 Transparencies "Punnett Square— Pea Plants," Transparency 13

Answers to Self-Assessment

Caption Question

Figure 7 *TT* and *Tt*

Figure 8 0% white fur

☑ *Checkpoint*

25% probability of white fur

Ongoing Assessment

Drawing Have students draw a Punnett square for a cross between any two hybrids (*Aa* × *Aa*). They should include the probabilities of each offspring type.

Phenotypes and Genotypes

Including All Students

For students who need more help, explain that the terms *heterozygous* and *hybrid* are synonyms, as are *purebred* and *homozygous*. To help students remember the meanings of *genotype* and *phenotype*, explain that both *genotype* and *genetics* begin with the same prefix, *gen-*, and *physical* and *phenotype* both begin with *ph*. For *codominance*, tell students that the prefix *co-* means "jointly" or "together." **learning modality: verbal**

Building Inquiry Skills: Classifying

Have students make a chart in which they identify the genotypes and the phenotypes of the seven traits in garden peas that Mendel studied. Also have students include the genotypes and the phenotypes of the organisms from other teaching strategies that you might have used in the first two sections, such as the *Drosophila* body color, kernel color in corn, and the color of tobacco seedlings. In their charts, students should also identify the homozygous and the heterozygous genotypes. **learning modality: logical/mathematical**

Codominance

Addressing Naive Conceptions

Some students may have difficulty with the concept that alleles can be inherited in patterns other than dominance, which Mendel studied in garden peas. One way to help students start thinking about different inheritance patterns is to challenge them to create patterns using two different colored pencils or markers. One pattern should represent the combinations of genotypes and phenotypes in dominance. The other pattern should represent the combination of genotypes and phenotypes in codominance. For ideas on creating these patterns, students can think about the expression of phenotypes in both kinds of inheritance, as well as the phenotypic and genotypic ratios. **learning modality: visual**

Phenotypes and Genotypes	
Phenotype	**Genotype**
Tall	*TT*
Tall	*Tt*
Short	*tt*

Figure 9 The phenotype of an organism is its physical appearance. Its genotype is its genetic makeup.

Phenotypes and Genotypes

Two useful terms that geneticists use to describe organisms are phenotype and genotype. An organism's **phenotype** (FEE noh typ) is its physical appearance, or its visible traits. For example, pea plants can have one of two different phenotypes for stem height—short or tall.

An organism's **genotype** (JEN uh typ) is its genetic makeup, or allele combinations. To understand the difference between phenotype and genotype, look at the table in Figure 9. Although all of the tall plants have the same phenotype (they are all tall), they can have two different genotypes—*TT* or *Tt*. If you were to look at the tall plants, you would not be able to tell the difference between those with the *TT* genotype and those with the *Tt* genotype. The short pea plants, on the other hand, would all have the same phenotype—short stems—as well as the same genotype—*tt*.

Geneticists use two additional terms to describe an organism's genotype. An organism that has two identical alleles for a trait is said to be **homozygous** (hoh moh ZY gus) for that trait. A tall pea plant that has the alleles *TT* and a short pea plant with the alleles *tt* are both homozygous. An organism that has two different alleles for a trait is said to be **heterozygous** (het ur oh ZY gus) for that trait. A tall pea plant with the alleles *Tt* is heterozygous. Mendel used the term *hybrid* to describe heterozygous pea plants.

☑ *Checkpoint* If a pea plant's genotype is Tt, what is its phenotype?

Codominance

For all of the traits that Mendel studied, one allele was dominant while the other was recessive. This is not always the case. For some alleles, an inheritance pattern called codominance exists. In **codominance,** the alleles are neither dominant nor recessive. As a result, both alleles are expressed in the offspring.

Look at the Punnett square in Figure 11. Mendel's principle of dominant and recessive alleles does not explain why the heterozygous chickens have both black and white feathers. The alleles for feather color are

Figure 10 In Erminette chickens, the alleles for black feathers and white feathers are codominant.

Background

Facts and Figures Another pattern of inheritance is called incomplete dominance, in which neither allele is fully dominant. This is different from codominance in which both alleles are fully expressed, resulting in organisms that display the characteristics of both parents. Incomplete dominance results in organisms that have an intermediate phenotype. For example, in four o'clock flowers, a cross between a homozygous red-flowered plant and a homozygous white-flowered plant produces F$_1$ offspring with pink flowers. When the F$_1$ offspring are crossed, the F$_2$ offspring are in a ratio of 1 red : 2 pink : 1 white.

Figure 11 The offspring from the cross in this Punnett square will have both black and white feathers. *Classifying Will the offspring be heterozygous or homozygous? Explain your answer.*

codominant—neither dominant nor recessive. As you can see, neither allele is masked in the heterozygous chickens. Notice also that the codominant alleles are written as capital letters with superscripts—F^B for black feathers and F^W for white feathers. As the Punnett square shows, heterozygous chickens have the $F^B F^W$ allele combination.

Another example of codominance can be found in cattle. Red hair and white hair are codominant. Heterozygous cattle have coats with both white hairs and red hairs. From a distance, heterozygous cattle look pinkish brown, a color called roan.

Section 2 Review

1. What is meant by the term *probability*? How is probability related to genetics?
2. How are Punnett squares useful to geneticists?
3. What is the difference between a phenotype and a genotype? Give an example of each.
4. A white cow is crossed with a red bull. The calf is neither white nor red, but roan. Explain how this happens.
5. **Thinking Critically** **Problem Solving** In pea plants, the allele for round seeds (*R*) is dominant over the allele for wrinkled seeds (*r*). Construct a Punnett square that shows a cross between a heterozygous plant with round seeds (*Rr*) and a homozygous plant with wrinkled seeds (*rr*). What is the probability that an offspring will have wrinkled seeds?

Science at Home

The Guessing Game Have a family member think of a number between 1 and 5. Then try to guess the number. Discuss the probability of guessing the correct number. Then repeat the guessing activity four more times. How did your success rate compare to the probability of guessing correctly? How can you account for any difference between your success rate and the results predicted by probability?

Chapter 3 **99**

Answers to Self-Assessment

☑ *Checkpoint*

It is tall.

Caption Question

Figure 11 Heterozygous; they have alleles for both white feathers and black feathers.

3 Assess

Section 2 Review Answers

1. Probability is the likelihood that a particular event will occur. It can be used to predict the results of genetic crosses.
2. Geneticists use Punnett squares to show all the possible genotypes of the offspring produced in a genetic cross and to help calculate the probability of each outcome.
3. Phenotype is the physical appearance, or visible traits of an organism. Example: tall stems. Genotype is the genetic makeup, or the combinations of alleles in an organism. Example: *Tt*.
4. The alleles for red hair and white hair are codominant. The calf is roan because it has both white and red hairs in its coat; it is heterozygous for coat color.
5.

	R	r
r	Rr	rr
r	Rr	rr

There is a 1 in 2 probability that an offspring will have wrinkled seeds (*rr*).

Science at Home

Tips Review how to calculate probabilities. Ask: **How would you calculate the probability of guessing a number between 1 and 5?** (*There is a 1 in 5 chance of guessing the right number, or $\frac{1}{5} \times 100\% = 20\%$*) Remind students of the coin tosses they made. Emphasize that the laws of probability predict what is *likely* to occur, not what *will* occur. Many students will find that their success rates are different from what the laws of probability predicted.

Performance Assessment

Skills Check Have students construct a Punnett square for a cross between two heterozygous Erminette chickens ($F^B F^W$) that shows all the possible genotypes and phenotypes of the offspring. Students should also calculate the probabilities of each genotype and phenotype. (*$F^B F^B$ 1 in 4; $F^B F^W$ 2 in 4; $F^W F^W$ 1 in 4*)

Make the Right Call!

Preparing for Inquiry

Key Concepts Punnett squares can predict the results of a genetic cross when the genotypes of both parents are known.

Skills Objectives Students will be able to
- model the combination of alleles in a genetic cross;
- predict the offspring of a genetic cross;
- analyze data from models of genetic crosses;
- compare actual data with predicted outcomes.

Time 40 minutes

Alternative Materials Marbles of other colors may be substituted, but use two easily distinguished colors. (Some students may be colorblind.) Other small colored objects that have the same shape and texture, such as buttons, can also be used.

Guiding Inquiry

Invitation Discuss circumstances in which students make predictions in their lives. Talk about the different evidence and ideas that lead to various predictions. Then ask: **Why is it helpful to scientists to make accurate predictions in their experiments?** *(Accurate predictions make scientists more confident that they are asking the right questions and correctly understanding the phenomena that they are studying; they also help scientists to better plan their experiments.)*

Introducing the Procedure

- Have students read the entire procedure. Then ask: **What do the marbles represent?** *(The alleles from each parent)* **Why should you not look inside the bag when you remove the marbles?** *(To make sure the allele combinations occur randomly)*
- Make sure students know the meanings of *homozygous* and *heterozygous.*

MAKE THE RIGHT CALL!

Making Models

You know that making predictions is an important part of science. An accurate prediction can be a sign that you understand the event you are studying. In this lab, you will make predictions as you model the events involved in genetic crosses.

Problem

How can you predict the possible results of genetic crosses?

Materials

2 small paper bags
marking pen
3 blue marbles
3 white marbles

Procedure

1. Label one bag "Bag 1, Female Parent." Label the other bag "Bag 2, Male Parent." Then read over Part 1, Part 2, and Part 3 of this lab. Write a prediction about the kinds of offspring you expect from each cross.

Part 1 Crossing Two Homozygous Parents

2. Copy the data table and label it *Data Table Number 1.* Then place two blue marbles in Bag 1. This pair of marbles represents the female parent's alleles. Use the letter *B* to represent the dominant allele for blue color.

3. Place two white marbles in Bag 2. Use the letter *b* to represent the recessive allele for white color.

4. For Trial 1, remove one marble from Bag 1 without looking in the bag. Record the result in your data table. Return the marble to the bag. Again, without looking in the bag, remove one marble from Bag 2. Record the result in your data table. Return the marble to the bag.

5. In the column labeled *Offspring's Alleles*, write *BB* if you removed two blue marbles, *bb* if you removed two white marbles, or *Bb* if you removed one blue marble and one white marble.

6. Repeat Steps 4 and 5 nine more times.

DATA TABLE

Number _____

Trial	Allele From Bag 1 (Female Parent)	Allele From Bag 2 (Male Parent)	Offspring's Alleles
1			
2			
3			
4			
5			
6			

Troubleshooting the Experiment

- As students perform the different crosses, encourage them to discuss whether only one type of allele can be passed on by a parent or whether either of two alleles can be passed on.
- Monitor students to make sure they correctly identify the dominant and recessive alleles.

Expected Outcome

In the first cross (*BB* × *bb*), students should observe that all offspring are *Bb*. In the second cross (*BB* × *Bb*), all offspring are blue, but some are homozygous (*BB*) and some are heterozygous (*Bb*). In the third cross (*Bb* × *Bb*), some offspring are blue and some are white. All white offspring are homozygous (*bb*). Blue offspring are either homozygous (*BB*) or heterozygous (*Bb*).

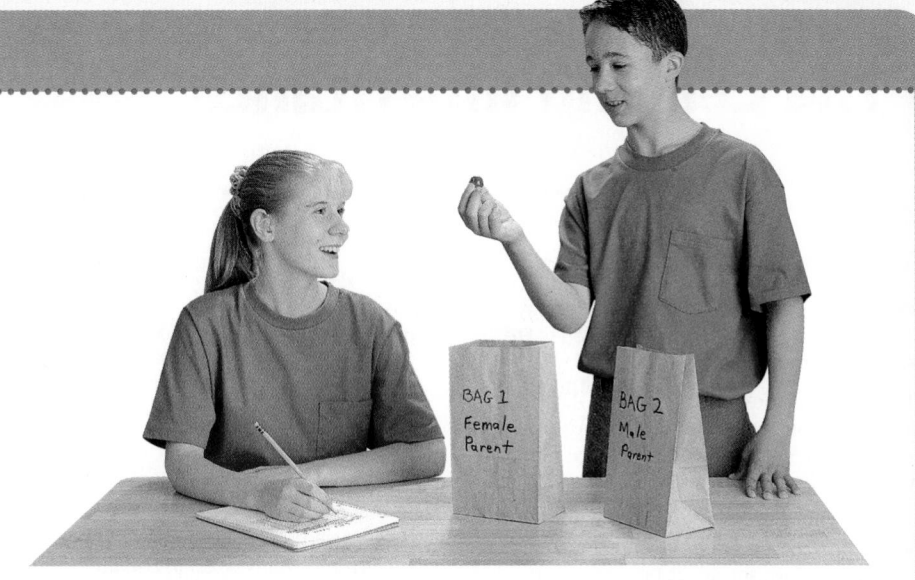

Part 2 Crossing a Homozygous Parent With a Heterozygous Parent

7. Place two blue marbles in Bag 1. Place one white marble and one blue marble in Bag 2. Copy the data table again, and label it *Data Table Number 2.*
8. Repeat Steps 4 and 5 ten times.

Part 3 Crossing Two Heterozygous Parents

9. Place one blue marble and one white marble in Bag 1. Place one blue marble and one white marble in Bag 2. Copy the data table again and label it *Data Table Number 3.*
10. Repeat Steps 4 and 5 ten times.

Analyze and Conclude

1. Make a Punnett square for each of the crosses you modeled in Part 1, Part 2, and Part 3.
2. According to your results in Part 1, how many different kinds of offspring are possible when the homozygous parents (*BB* and *bb*) are crossed? Do the results you obtained using the marble model agree with the results shown by a Punnett square?

3. According to your results in Part 2, what percent of offspring are likely to be homozygous when a homozygous parent (*BB*) and a heterozygous parent (*Bb*) are crossed? What percent of offspring are likely to be heterozygous? Does the model agree with the results shown by a Punnett square?
4. According to your results in Part 3, what different kinds of offspring are possible when two heterozygous parents (*Bb* × *Bb*) are crossed? What percent of each type of offspring are likely to be produced? Does the model agree with the results of a Punnett square?
5. For Part 3, if you did 100 trials instead of 10 trials, would your results be closer to the results shown in a Punnett square? Explain.
6. **Think About It** How does the marble model compare with a Punnett square? How are the two methods alike? How are they different?

Design an Experiment

In peas, the allele for yellow seeds (*Y*) is dominant over the allele for green seeds (*y*). What possible crosses do you think could produce a heterozygous plant with yellow seeds (*Yy*)? Use the marble model and Punnett squares to test your hypothesis.

Analyze and Conclude

1. Punnett square for Part 1:

	b	*b*
B	*Bb*	*Bb*
B	*Bb*	*Bb*

Punnett square for Part 2:

	B	*b*
B	*BB*	*Bb*
B	*BB*	*Bb*

Program Resources

◆ **Unit 1 Resources** Chapter 3 Skills Lab, pp. 93–95

Punnett square for Part 3:

	B	*b*
B	*BB*	*Bb*
b	*Bb*	*bb*

2. Only heterozygous blue offspring (*Bb*) are possible. The Punnett square shows the same results.
3. Student results may produce slightly different answers. As the number of trials increases, the results will show more closely that 50 percent of the offspring are likely to be homozygous (*BB*), while 50 percent are likely to be heterozygous (*Bb*). The Punnett square shows that 50 percent will be homozygous and 50 percent will be heterozygous.
4. Student results may vary due to chance, but all should indicate that three different kinds of offspring are possible: *BB*, *Bb*, and *bb*. From the Punnett square, students can predict that 25 percent are likely to be *BB*, 50 percent are likely to be *Bb*, and 25 percent are likely to be *bb*. The marble model will probably not totally agree with the Punnett square due to chance.
5. Probably, as the number of trials is increased, the results are more likely to match those predicted in a Punnett square because of chance.
6. The marble model and the Punnett square both show the genotypes of the parents and offspring and demonstrate how the parent can donate one of two possible alleles to the offspring. The Punnett square gives all the possible genotypes of the offspring and their probabilities of occurring. The model gives the genotypes of the offspring based on chance, much like the actual combining of alleles in a real genetic cross.

Extending the Inquiry

Design an Experiment Crosses that will produce a heterozygous plant (*Yy*) include *YY* × *yy*, *YY* × *Yy*, *Yy* × *Yy*, and *Yy* × *yy*.

Objectives

After completing the lesson, students will be able to
◆ describe chromosomes and their role in inheritance;
◆ identify and describe the events that occur during meiosis.

Key Terms sperm, egg, meiosis

1 Engage/Explore

Activating Prior Knowledge

Have students recall what they know about cells and cell structure. Based on their knowledge of cell structure, challenge them to predict the location of Mendel's hereditary factors, or genes, within the cell. You might wish to record students' predictions on the board and have the class evaluate them as you study the section.

DISCOVER

Skills Focus inferring
Materials *4 craft sticks, 3 pieces of paper, marking pen*
Time 10 minutes
Expected Outcome Students should realize that parents contribute only one of their two chromosomes to the offspring. The idea is to get students thinking about genes being carried on chromosomes and the cell having some kind of process to make sure only one allele of a gene is contributed to offspring.
Think It Over Students might infer that genes are located on chromosomes and chromosomes must divide and separate in a certain way so that the offspring get only one chromosome, or one allele, from each parent.

SECTION
3 The Cell and Inheritance

DISCOVER .... ACTIVITY

Which Chromosome Is Which?

Mendel did not know that chromosomes play a role in genetics. Today we know that genes are located on chromosomes.

1. Label two craft sticks with the letter *A*. The craft sticks represent a pair of chromosomes in the female parent. Turn the sticks face down on a piece of paper.

2. Label two more craft sticks with the letter *a*. These represent a pair of chromosomes in the male parent. Turn the sticks face down on another piece of paper.

3. Turn over one craft stick "chromosome" from each piece of paper. Move both sticks to a third piece of paper. These represent a pair of chromosomes in the offspring. Note the allele combination that the offspring received.

Think It Over
Inferring Use this model to explain how chromosomes are involved in the inheritance of alleles.

GUIDE FOR READING

◆ What role do chromosomes play in inheritance?
◆ What events occur during meiosis?

Reading Tip As you read, write a sentence that states the main idea of each paragraph.

Sperm cells ▼

102

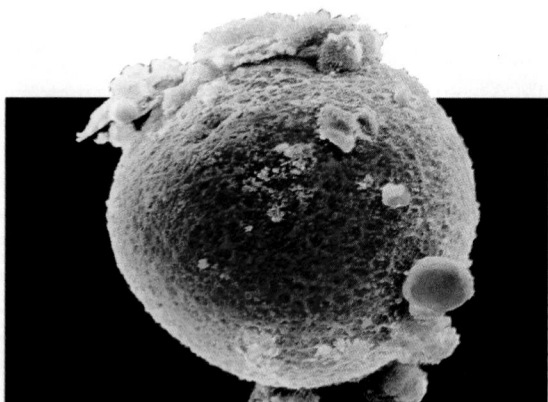

◀ Egg cell

When Mendel's results were rediscovered in 1900, scientists became excited about his principles of inheritance. They were eager to identify the structures that carried Mendel's hereditary factors, or genes.

In 1903, Walter Sutton, an American geneticist, added an important piece of information to the understanding of genetics. Sutton was studying the cells of grasshoppers. He was trying to understand how sex cells—sperm and egg—form. A **sperm** is the male sex cell. An **egg** is the female sex cell. During his studies, Sutton examined sex cells in many different stages of formation. He became particularly interested in the movement of chromosomes during the formation of sex cells. Sutton hypothesized that chromosomes were the key to understanding how offspring come to have traits similar to those of their parents.

READING STRATEGIES

Reading Tip Remind students that the main idea of a paragraph is often stated in the topic sentence, usually the first or last sentence of a paragraph. Sometimes the main idea is not stated but must be inferred. Have students list the main idea of each paragraph, write a sentence about it, and arrange the sentences together to produce a summary of the section.

Vocabulary While studying the process of meiosis, explain to students that the term *meiosis* is a Greek word that means "to diminish or make less." Discuss with students what diminishes during the process of meiosis. *(the number of chromosomes)*

Figure 12 Grasshoppers have 24 chromosomes in each of their body cells. *Applying Concepts How many chromosomes did Sutton observe in the sperm cells and egg cells of grasshoppers?*

Chromosomes and Inheritance

Sutton knew that structures inside cells must be responsible for the inheritance of genes. He needed evidence to support his hypothesis that chromosomes were those structures. Sutton compared the number of chromosomes in a grasshopper's sex cells with the number of chromosomes in the other cells in the grasshopper's body. As you can see in Figure 12, the body cells of grasshoppers have 24 chromosomes. To his surprise, Sutton found that the grasshopper's sex cells have only 12 chromosomes. In other words, a grasshopper's sex cells have exactly half the number of chromosomes found in its body cells.

Sutton knew that he had discovered something important. He observed what happened when a sperm cell (with 12 chromosomes) and an egg cell (with 12 chromosomes) joined. The fertilized egg that formed had 24 chromosomes—the original number. As a result, the grasshopper offspring had exactly the same number of chromosomes in its cells as did each of its parents. The 24 chromosomes existed in 12 pairs. One chromosome in each pair came from the male parent, while the other chromosome came from the female parent.

Sutton concluded that the chromosomes carried Mendel's hereditary factors, or genes, from one generation to the next. In other words, genes are located on chromosomes. Sutton's idea came to be known as the chromosome theory of inheritance. **According to the chromosome theory of inheritance, genes are carried from parents to their offspring on chromosomes.**

Checkpoint How does the number of chromosomes in a grasshopper's sex cells compare to the number in its body cells?

Answers to Self-Assessment

Caption Question

Figure 12 12 chromosomes in each

Checkpoint

The sex cells have exactly half the number of chromosomes as the body cells.

---

2 Facilitate

Chromosomes and Inheritance

Addressing Naive Conceptions

Students might have difficulty visualizing exactly where genes are located on chromosomes and how chromosomes fit inside cells. Review cell structure and encourage students to draw diagrams of the cell in which they show the chromosomes inside the cell nucleus. Until students learn the composition of chromosomes (in Section 4), it will be difficult for them to visualize what kind of structure a gene actually has. Explain that chromosomes are made up of many, many genes. Genes are not separate structures "stuck to" chromosomes; rather chromosomes are long chains of genes. **learning modality: visual**

Inquiry Challenge

Challenge small groups of students to conclude what might happen if sex cells did not have half the number of chromosomes as body cells. Groups should develop a model that illustrates their conclusions. Provide various art materials for students to use, or encourage them to bring materials from home. Have groups present their models to the class and explain why sex cells must have half the chromosomes as body cells. **learning modality: logical/mathematical**

Ongoing Assessment

Drawing Have students draw a diagram of a grasshopper body cell and sex cell and show the number of chromosomes in each of these cells.

EXPLORING
Meiosis

Walk students through each stage in meiosis. Point out that before meiosis occurs, every chromosome is copied, so the cell actually has four copies of each chromosome. Emphasize that during Meiosis I, the chromosome pairs separate. The centromeres are still holding together the chromosome copies. When discussing Meiosis II, point out that this division is similar to the division that occurs during mitosis—the centromeres split and the chromosome copies separate. Ask: **How many sex cells are produced at the end of meiosis?** *(four)* **How do the sex cells differ from the parent cell?** *(The sex cells have half the number of chromosomes of the parent cell.)* **learning modality: visual**

Building Inquiry Skills: Making Models

Materials *8 pipe cleaners—4 of one color and 4 of another, 4 beads*
Time 15 minutes

Challenge students to model the steps in meiosis using the pipe cleaners to represent two chromosomes in a cell. Students should use pipe cleaners of the same color to represent chromosome pairs, with different chromosome pairs having different colors. Monitor students to make sure they double each chromosome before meiosis begins. (They should add another pipe cleaner of the same color to each pipe cleaner chromosome.) Students can use beads to hold the chromosome copies together, or they can simply twist the pipe cleaners together at one point. Make sure students separate the chromosome pairs during Meiosis I and the chromosome copies during Meiosis II. **learning modality: kinesthetic**

Meiosis

How do sex cells end up with half the number of chromosomes as body cells? To answer this question, you need to understand the events that occur during meiosis. **Meiosis** (my OH sis) is the process by which the number of chromosomes is reduced by half to form sex cells—sperm and eggs.

You can trace the events of meiosis in *Exploring Meiosis.* In this example, each parent cell has four chromosomes arranged in two pairs. **During meiosis, the chromosome pairs separate and are distributed to two different cells. The resulting sex cells have only half as many chromosomes as the other cells in the organism.** In *Exploring Meiosis,* notice that the sex cells end up with only two chromosomes each—half the number found in the parent cell. Only one chromosome from each chromosome pair ends up in each sex cell.

When sex cells combine to produce offspring, each sex cell will contribute half the normal number of chromosomes. Thus, the offspring gets the normal number of chromosomes—half from each parent.

✓ *Checkpoint* *What types of cells form by meiosis?*

Meiosis and Punnett Squares

The Punnett squares that you learned about earlier in this chapter are actually a shorthand way to show the events that occur at meiosis. When the chromosome pairs separate into two different sex cells, so do the alleles carried on each chromosome. One allele from each pair goes to each sex cell. In Figure 13, you can see how the Punnett square accounts for the separation of alleles during meiosis.

As shown across the top of the Punnett square, half of the sperm cells from the male parent will receive the chromosome with the *T* allele. The other half of the sperm cells will receive the chromosome with the *t* allele. In this example, the same is true for the egg cells from the female parent, as shown down the left side of the Punnett square. Depending on which sperm cell combines with which egg cell, one of the allele combinations shown in the boxes will result.

Figure 13 This Punnett square shows how alleles separate when sex cells form during meiosis. It also shows the possible allele combinations that can result after fertilization occurs. *Interpreting Charts What is the probability that a sperm cell will contain a T allele?*

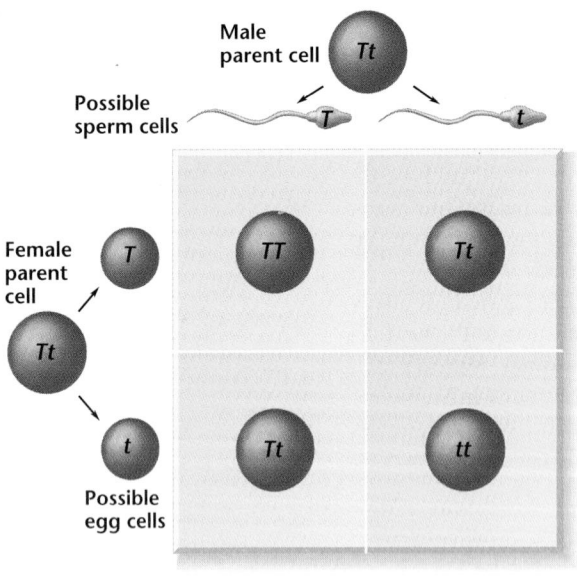

104

Background

Facts and Figures Before the first division of meiosis occurs, an important event, called crossing over, occurs. In crossing over, corresponding segments of chromosome pairs exchange parts. In effect, the organism's maternal and paternal chromosomes exchange some alleles, producing some chromosomes that are genetically different from either parent of the organism. This increases the genetic diversity of a species.

Crossing over occurs randomly, but the farther apart genes are located on their chromosomes, the more often crossing over will occur between them. Geneticists use this principle to help map the location of genes on chromosomes.

EXPLORING Meiosis

During meiosis, a cell undergoes two divisions to produce sex cells that have half the number of chromosomes.

1 Beginning of Meiosis
Before meiosis begins, every chromosome in the cell is copied. As in mitosis, centromeres hold the double-stranded chromosomes together.

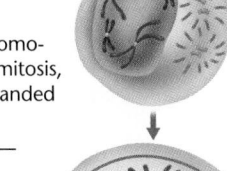

2 Meiosis I
The chromosome pairs line up next to each other in the center of the cell. The pairs then separate from each other and move to opposite ends of the cell. Two cells form, each with half the number of chromosomes. Each chromosome is still double-stranded.

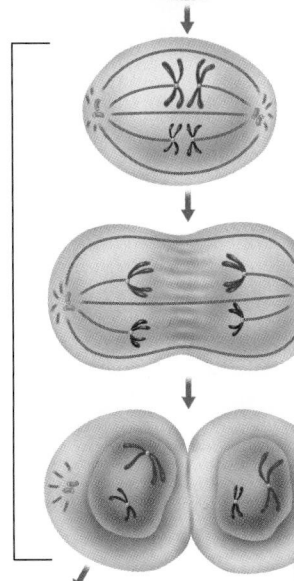

3 Meiosis II
The double-stranded chromosomes move to the center of the cell. The centromeres split and the two strands of each chromosome separate. The two strands move to opposite ends of the cell.

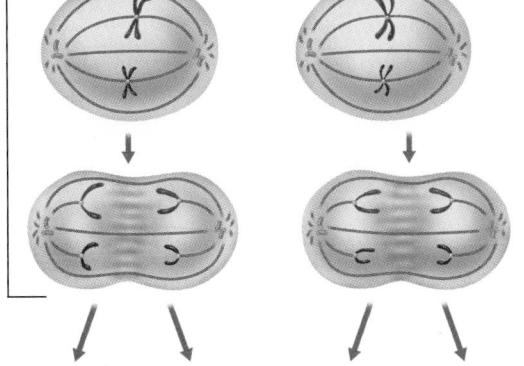

4 End of Meiosis
Four sex cells have been produced. Each cell has only half the number of chromosomes that the parent cell had at the beginning of meiosis. Each cell has only one chromosome from each original pair.

Chapter 3 **105**

Answers to Self-Assessment

☑ *Checkpoint*
Sex cells form by meiosis.

Caption Question
Figure 13 $\frac{1}{2} \times 100\% = 50\%$

Building Inquiry Skills: Observing

Materials *a set of prepared slides showing the stages of meiosis, microscopes*

ACTIVITY

Set up microscope stations at which you place the prepared slides. Depending on the number of microscopes you have and the ability of your students to use microscopes, you could place a whole set of slides at each microscope and allow students to change the slides themselves, or you could place the microscopes in a row with individual slides from a set positioned and focused for students to look at. As students examine the slides, encourage them to compare the *Exploring Meiosis* diagram to what they see. Have students draw their observations, labeling the chromosomes. Emphasize that meiosis is a dynamic process. Each slide represents a snapshot in a continuous event, much like a photograph captures an instant of time in a parade or a soccer game. **learning modality: visual**

Meiosis and Punnett Squares

Using the Visuals: Figure 13

Point out that like other Punnett squares they have studied, the one in Figure 13 also shows all possible allele combinations for the offspring. Make it clear that the cells inside the boxes of the Punnett square represent the body cells of the offspring. This Punnett square goes one step further in showing the genotypes of the parents' body cells. Ask: **What are the possible sex cells produced by each offspring?** (TT *would only produce sex cells with* T; Tt *would produce both* T *and* t *sex cells; and* tt *would produce only sex cells with* t.) **learning modality: visual**

Ongoing Assessment

Writing Have students write an outline of meiosis in which each major step is a main heading in the outline.

 Students can save their outlines in their portfolios.

Chromosomes

Including All Students

Give students who need more help craft sticks to make a model of a chromosome pair based on the diagram in Figure 14. Each chromosome model should have at least six different genes, either homozygous or heterozygous. **learning modality: kinesthetic**

ACTIVITY

3 Assess

Section 3 Review Answers

1. Chromosomes carry the information for the inheritance of traits.
2. Chromosome pairs separate to form sex cells with half the number of chromosomes in each.
3. Genes are located on chromosomes.
4. It shows how the alleles separate when sex cells form during meiosis.
5. 22 chromosomes

CHAPTER PROJECT

Check Your Progress

Students can choose mates for their pets based on phenotypes or by you randomly choosing names out of a hat for males and one for females. Suggest that students first toss the coin to determine the color of each offspring and cut out each offspring from paper of the appropriate color. Then students can determine the genotypes of the other traits and write the genotypes directly on the backs of each offspring.

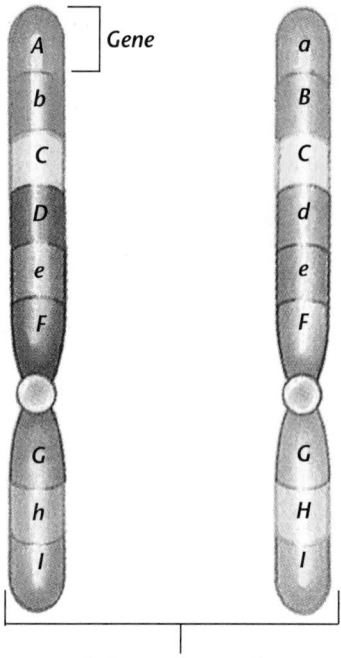

A chromosome pair

Figure 14 Genes are located on chromosomes. The chromosomes in a pair may have different alleles for some genes and the same alleles for others. *Classifying For which genes is this organism homozygous? For which genes is it heterozygous?*

Chromosomes

Since Sutton's time, scientists have studied the chromosomes of many different organisms. The body cells of humans, for example, contain 23 pairs, or 46 chromosomes. The body cells of dogs have 78 chromosomes, while the body cells of silkworms have 56 chromosomes. As you can see, larger organisms don't always have more chromosomes.

Chromosomes are made up of many genes joined together like beads on a string. Sutton reasoned that chromosomes must contain a large number of genes because organisms have so many traits. Although you have only 23 pairs of chromosomes, your body cells contain more than 60,000 genes. Each of the genes controls a particular trait.

Look at the pair of chromosomes in Figure 14. One chromosome in the pair came from the female parent. The other chromosome came from the male parent. Notice that each chromosome in the pair has the same genes. The genes are lined up in the same order from one end of the chromosome to the other. However, the alleles for some of the genes might be different. For example, the organism has the *A* allele on one chromosome and the *a* allele on the other. As you can see, this organism is heterozygous for some traits and homozygous for others.

Section 3 Review

1. Explain the role that chromosomes play in inheritance.
2. Briefly describe what happens to chromosomes during meiosis.
3. On what structures in a cell are genes located?
4. How is a Punnett square a model for what happens during meiosis?
5. **Thinking Critically** **Inferring** The body cells of hamsters have 44 chromosomes. How many chromosomes would the sex cells of a hamster have?

106

CHAPTER PROJECT

Check Your Progress

At this point, you should find a classmate with a paper pet of the opposite sex. Suppose the two pets were crossed and produced six offspring. For each trait, use coin tosses to determine which allele the offspring will inherit from each parent. Construct a paper pet for each offspring, showing the traits each one has inherited. Write the genotype for each trait on their backs.

Performance Assessment

Drawing Have students make a Punnett square for a cross between two heterozygous black guinea pigs, *Bb* × *Bb*. Before they make the Punnett square, students should make a diagram similar to Figure 13, showing how the four sex cells formed for each parent.

Answers to Self-Assessment

Caption Question

Figure 14 The organism is homozygous for genes C, E, F, G, and I. The organism is heterozygous for genes A, B, D, and H.

Program Resources

♦ **Laboratory Manual** 3, "Chromosomes and Inheritance"
♦ **Unit 1 Resources** 3-3 Review and Reinforce, p. 85; 3-3 Enrich, p. 86

SECTION 4 The DNA Connection

DISCOVER · ACTIVITY · · ·

Can You Crack the Code?

A • –	N – •
B – • • •	O – – –
C – • – •	P • – – •
D – • •	Q – – • –
E •	R • – •
F • • – •	S • • •
G – – •	T –
H • • • •	U • • –
I • •	V • • • –
J • – – –	W • – –
K – • –	X – • • –
L • – • •	Y – • – –
M – –	Z – – • •

1. Use the Morse code in the chart to decode the question in the message below. The letters are separated by slash marks.

• – – / • • • • / • / • – • / • / • – • / • – • / • / – – • / • / – • /
• / • • • / • – • • / – – – / – • – • / • – / – / • / – • • /

2. Write your answer to the question in Morse code.

3. Exchange your coded answer with a partner. Then decode your partner's answer.

Think It Over

Forming Operational Definitions Based on your results from this activity, write a definition of the word *code*. Then compare your definition to one in a dictionary.

A white buffalo calf was born on Childs Place Farm near Hanover, Michigan, in 1998. White buffaloes are extremely rare, occurring only once in every 10 million births. Why was this calf born with such an uncommon phenotype? To answer this question, you need to know how the genes on a chromosome control an organism's traits.

The Genetic Code

Today scientists know that the main function of genes is to control the production of proteins in the organism's cells. Proteins help to determine the size, shape, and many other traits of an organism.

Figure 15 The white color of this buffalo calf is very unusual. Both of the calf's parents had brown coats.

Chapter 3 **107**

GUIDE FOR READING

◆ What is meant by the term "genetic code"?

◆ How does a cell produce proteins?

◆ How do mutations affect an organism?

Reading Tip As you read, create a flowchart that shows how a cell produces proteins.

SECTION 4 The DNA Connection

Objectives

After completing the lesson, students will be able to
◆ explain the term "genetic code";
◆ describe the process by which a cell produces proteins;
◆ describe different types of mutations and how they affect organisms.

Key Terms messenger RNA, transfer RNA, mutation

1 Engage/Explore

Activating Prior Knowledge

Invite students to recall what they have learned about inheritance, DNA, and cell division up to this point. Then ask: **How do genes determine the traits of an organism?** Accept all answers, and explain that students will learn more about this process in the section.

· · · · · · · · · DISCOVER · · · · · · · ·

Skills Focus forming operational definitions
Time 15 minutes
Expected Outcome The coded question is "Where are genes located?" The answer, "on chromosomes," is encoded below.

– – – / – • / • – • • / • • • • / • – • / – – – / – – /
– – – / • • • / – – – / – – / • / • • • /

Think It Over Students might define *code* as set of symbols with specific meanings used to send messages. Some dictionaries define *code* as a system of symbols, letters, or words given arbitrary meanings, used for transmitting messages.

Program Resources

◆ **Unit 1 Resources** 3-4 Lesson Plan, p. 87; 3-4 Section Summary, p. 88

Media and Technology

🎧 **Audio CD** English-Spanish Summary 3-4

READING STRATEGIES

Reading Tip Student flowcharts should begin with genes on a chromosome in the nucleus of a cell. Next they should include the production of messenger RNA and its entrance into the cytoplasm to attach to a ribosome. Then transfer RNA brings the amino acid to the growing protein chain. Encourage students to illustrate their flowcharts, define terms, and explain processes that are new to them.

107

2 Facilitate

The Genetic Code

Using the Visuals: Figure 16

Have students trace the relationship between DNA and chromosomes in Figure 16. Explain that a gene is a segment of DNA with a specific sequence of nitrogen bases that codes for a certain protein. Remind students of DNA base pairing from Chapter 2. Ask: **Which nitrogen base always pairs with thymine?** *(adenine)* **Which always pairs with cytosine?** *(guanine)* Then start students thinking about protein synthesis by pointing out that although DNA is located in the cell nucleus, proteins are made in the cytoplasm. **learning modality: visual**

Including All Students

To help students bring together everything they have studied so far, explain that the traits Mendel observed, such as tall plants and short plants, are the results of the action of proteins in an organism. Challenge students to draw a diagram or a concept map that shows the relationships among DNA, genes, proteins, genotypes, and phenotypes. **learning modality: visual**

How Cells Make Proteins

Building Inquiry Skills: Inferring

Discuss the role of messenger RNA. Then ask: **Why do you think the cell sends a coded message for a gene into the cytoplasm instead of sending the gene itself?** *(Some students might infer that by using a coded message for a gene, the cell protects its DNA from damage, ensuring that the cell will always produce the proper proteins throughout its life.)* **learning modality: logical/ mathematical**

Recall from Chapter 2 that DNA is a major component of chromosomes. In Figure 16, you can see the relationship between chromosomes and DNA. Notice that a DNA molecule is made up of four different nitrogen bases—adenine (A), thymine (T), guanine (G), and cytosine (C). These bases form the rungs of the DNA "ladder." A single gene on a chromosome may contain anywhere from several hundred to a million or more of these bases. The bases are arranged in a specific order—for example, ATGACGTAC.

The order of the nitrogen bases along a gene forms a genetic code that specifies what type of protein will be produced. In the genetic code, a group of three bases codes for the attachment of a specific amino acid. Amino acids are the building blocks of proteins. The order of the bases determines the order in which amino acids are put together to form a protein. You can think of the bases as three-letter code words. The code words tell the cell which amino acid to add to the growing protein chain.

☑ *Checkpoint* *What is the main function of genes?*

How Cells Make Proteins

The production of proteins is called protein synthesis. **During protein synthesis, the cell uses information from a gene on a chromosome to produce a specific protein.** Protein synthesis takes place on the ribosomes in the cytoplasm of the cell. As you know, the cytoplasm is outside the nucleus. The chromosomes, however, are found inside the nucleus. How, then, does the information needed to produce proteins get out of the nucleus and into the cytoplasm?

Figure 16 A chromosome contains thousands of genes along its length. The sequence of bases along a gene forms a code that tells the cell what protein to produce. *Interpreting Diagrams Where in the cell are the chromosomes located?*

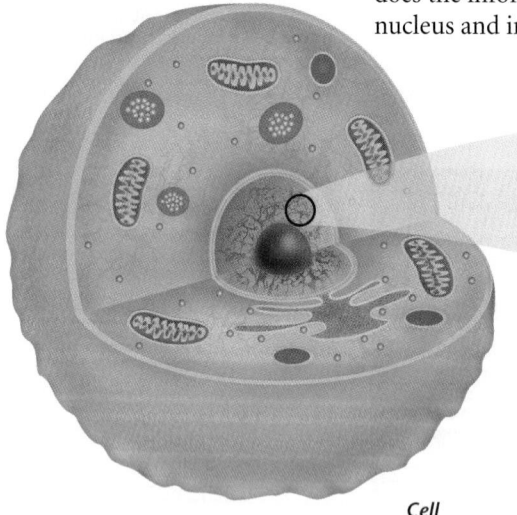

Cell

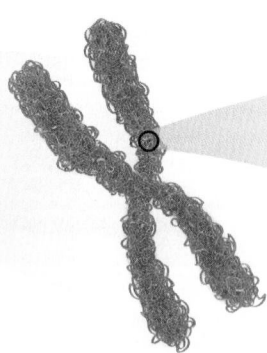

Chromosome

The Role of RNA Before protein synthesis can take place, a "messenger" must first carry the genetic code from the DNA inside the nucleus into the cytoplasm. This genetic messenger is called ribonucleic acid, or RNA.

Although RNA is similar to DNA, the two molecules differ in some important ways. Unlike DNA, which looks like a twisted ladder, an RNA molecule almost always looks like only one side, or strand, of the ladder. RNA also contains a different sugar molecule from the sugar found in DNA. Another difference between DNA and RNA is in their nitrogen bases. Like DNA, RNA contains adenine, guanine, and cytosine. However, instead of thymine, RNA contains uracil (YOOR uh sil).

There are several types of RNA involved in protein synthesis. **Messenger RNA** copies the coded message from the DNA in the nucleus, and carries the message into the cytoplasm. Another type of RNA, called **transfer RNA,** carries amino acids and adds them to the growing protein.

Translating the Code The process of protein synthesis is shown in *Exploring Protein Synthesis* on the next page. The first step is for a DNA molecule to "unzip" between its base pairs. Then one of the strands of DNA directs the production of a strand of messenger RNA. To form the RNA strand, RNA bases pair up with the DNA bases. Instead of thymine, however, uracil pairs with adenine. The messenger RNA then leaves the nucleus and attaches to a ribosome in the cytoplasm. There, molecules of transfer RNA pick up the amino acids specified by each three-letter code word. Each transfer RNA molecule puts the amino acid it is carrying in the correct order along the growing protein chain.

☑ *Checkpoint* *What is the function of transfer RNA?*

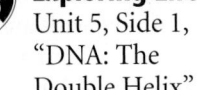

DNA molecule

Nitrogen bases

 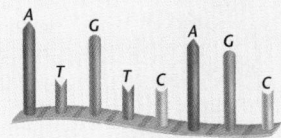

Answers to Self-Assessment

Caption Question

Figure 16 in the nucleus

☑ *Checkpoint*

(p. 108) To control the production of proteins
(p. 109) To carry amino acids and add them to the growing protein chain

How Cells Make Proteins, continued

EXPLORING

Protein Synthesis

Review each step in the process of protein synthesis using the Exploring. Emphasize in Step 1 that DNA always stays inside the cell nucleus. In Step 2, explain that the ribosome has special sites that hold messenger RNA as the ribosome moves along it. The ribosome also has special sites that hold transfer RNA so its amino acid can easily join the growing protein chain. In Step 3, explain that transfer RNA is made in the same way as messenger RNA, but has a region to which amino acids bond. In Step 4, explain that more than one ribosome can attach to a single messenger RNA at one time. **learning modality: visual**

Including All Students

Some students may have difficulty with the terms related to protein synthesis. Help students identify these words and have them add the words to the glossary of genetics terms that they began in Section 1. **learning modality: verbal**

EXPLORING Protein Synthesis

To make proteins, messenger RNA copies information from DNA in the nucleus. Transfer RNA then uses this information to produce proteins in the ribosomes.

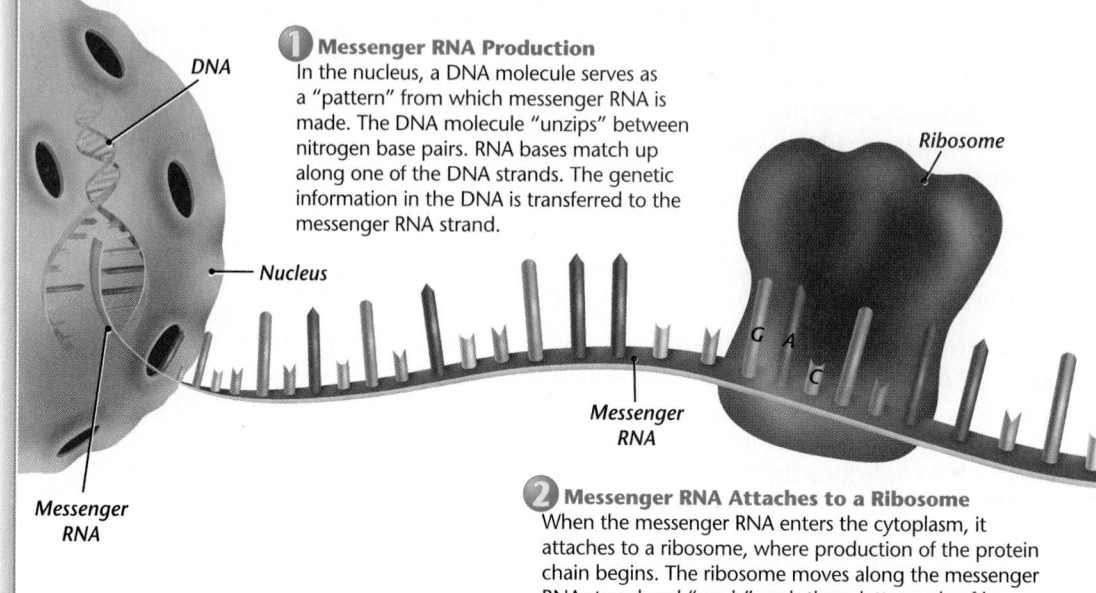

1 Messenger RNA Production
In the nucleus, a DNA molecule serves as a "pattern" from which messenger RNA is made. The DNA molecule "unzips" between nitrogen base pairs. RNA bases match up along one of the DNA strands. The genetic information in the DNA is transferred to the messenger RNA strand.

2 Messenger RNA Attaches to a Ribosome
When the messenger RNA enters the cytoplasm, it attaches to a ribosome, where production of the protein chain begins. The ribosome moves along the messenger RNA strand and "reads" each three-letter code of bases.

Mutations

Suppose that a mistake occurred in one gene of a chromosome. Instead of the base A, for example, the DNA molecule might have the base G. This is one type of mistake that can occur in a cell's hereditary material. Any change that occurs in a gene or chromosome is called a **mutation.** Mutations can cause a cell to produce an incorrect protein during protein synthesis. As a result, the organism's traits, or phenotype, will be different from what it normally would have been. In fact, the term *mutation* comes from a Latin word that means "change."

Types of Mutations Some mutations are the result of small changes in an organism's hereditary material, such as the substitution of a single base for another. This type of mutation can occur during the DNA replication process. The white coat on the

---

Background

Facts and Figures Different types of changes in the base sequence of DNA affect the organism in different ways. If a base is inserted or deleted from a gene, the reading frame for three-letter base code, or codon, is shifted. The result of a frame-shift mutation is a nonfunctional protein.

A point mutation occurs when one base is substituted for another. This kind of mutation affects only one codon, which has variable affects on the protein product. Sometimes it has no effect because most amino acids are encoded by more than one codon. Sometimes the protein will have a reduced function because one amino acid is substituted for the correct one. Other times, the protein will not work at all, either because the codon has been changed to a stop codon or the amino acid that is substituted completely changes the nature of the protein.

3 Transfer RNA Attaches to Messenger RNA

Transfer RNA molecules carry specific amino acids to the ribosome. There they match up with three-letter codes of bases on the messenger RNA. The protein chain grows as each amino acid is attached in the correct sequence.

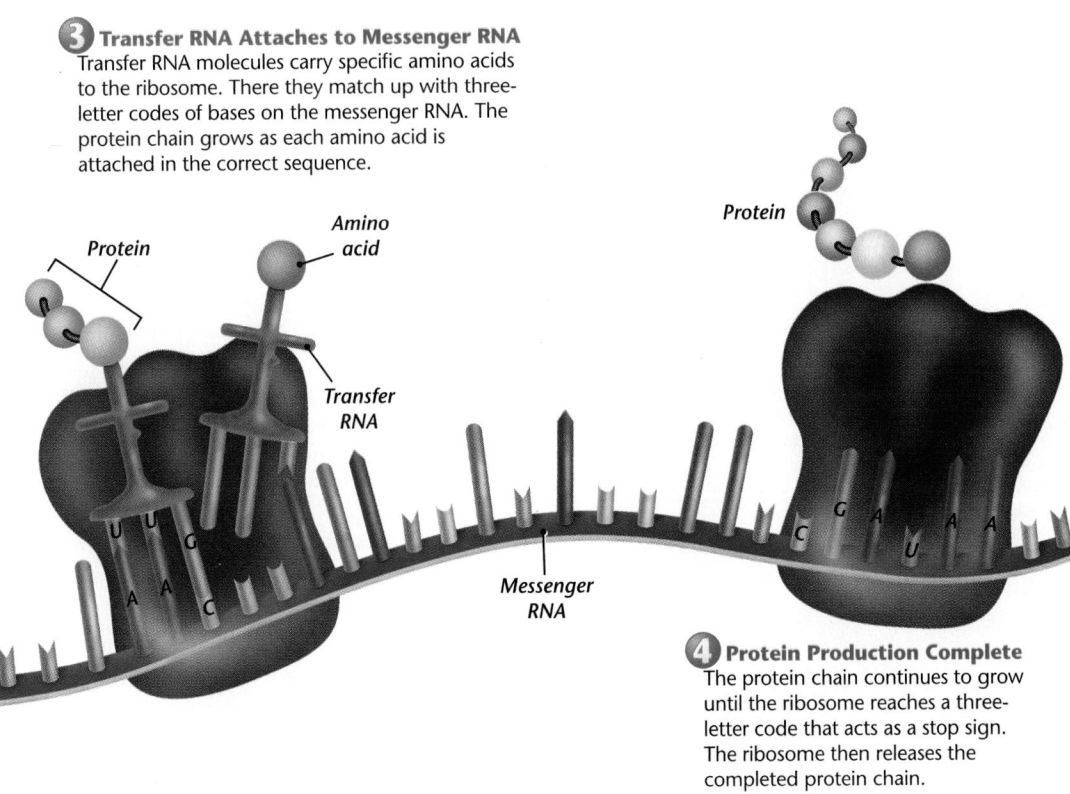

Protein

Amino acid

Transfer RNA

Protein

Messenger RNA

4 Protein Production Complete

The protein chain continues to grow until the ribosome reaches a three-letter code that acts as a stop sign. The ribosome then releases the completed protein chain.

buffalo calf you read about at the start of this section might have resulted from this type of mutation. Other mutations may occur when chromosomes don't separate correctly during meiosis. When this type of mutation occurs, a cell can end up with too many or too few chromosomes.

If a mutation occurs in a body cell, such as a skin cell, the mutation will affect only the cell that carries it. If, however, a mutation occurs in a sex cell, the mutation can be passed on to an offspring and affect the offspring's phenotype.

The Effects of Mutations Because mutations can introduce changes in an organism, they can be a source of genetic variety. **Some of the changes brought about by mutations are harmful to an organism. Other mutations, however, are helpful, and still others are neither harmful nor helpful.** A mutation is

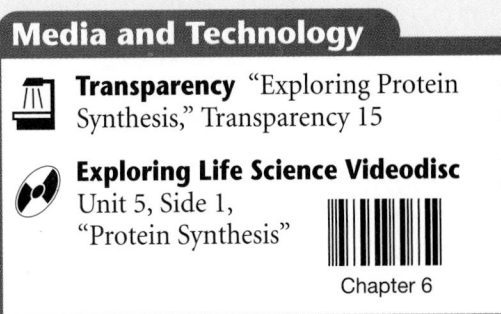

Media and Technology

Transparency "Exploring Protein Synthesis," Transparency 15

Exploring Life Science Videodisc Unit 5, Side 1, "Protein Synthesis"

Chapter 6

Mutations

Building Inquiry Skills: Making Models

Materials *beads of different colors, pipe cleaners*

Time 15 minutes

Challenge students to use the materials to model the two types of mutations described in the text: a point mutation, in which a single base is substituted for another, and a chromosomal mutation, in which chromosomes do not separate correctly during meiosis. The beads should represent nitrogen bases, and the pipe cleaners should be the chromosomes. Check students' models to make sure they are accurate. Remind students that organisms have two copies of each chromosome. You might also challenge students to model why mutations in body cells do not affect offspring. **learning modality: kinesthetic**

Addressing Naive Conceptions

Some students might think that mutations can only harm an organism. To help dispel this misconception, explain that mutations can also provide organisms a means to better adapt to their environment. Then display pictures of a monarch and a viceroy butterfly. Tell students that birds learn to avoid monarchs because of their bitter taste. Birds like the taste of viceroy butterflies, and many years ago, viceroys looked different from monarchs. However over time, various mutations in the appearance of viceroy butterflies have made them look similar to monarchs. Ask: **How have these mutations helped viceroys?** (*Birds also avoid viceroys because they associate their appearance with a bitter taste.*) **learning modality: visual**

Ongoing Assessment

Oral Presentation Call on students at random to explain what a mutation is and how mutations affect organisms.

Mutations, continued

Integrating Health

Ask students: **What is cancer?** (*A disease in which mutated body cells grow out of control*) Explain that the mutation that causes a particular cancer may occur either in a gene that causes cancer cells to grow or in a gene that prevents cancer cells from growing. Emphasize that one of the best ways to stop cancer is by prevention. Eating a healthful diet that is low in fat, high in fiber, and includes plenty of fruits and vegetables is one way to reduce the risk of cancer. Other ways include regular physical exams and cancer screenings and avoiding smoking, unprotected sun exposure, and alcohol.
learning modality: verbal

3 Assess

Section 4 Answers

1. The order of the nitrogen bases forms a genetic code that specifies what type of protein will be produced. Groups of three bases code for specific amino acids, the building blocks of proteins.
2. First, messenger RNA is produced using a strand of DNA as a pattern. Messenger RNA moves into the cytoplasm where it attaches to a ribosome. The ribosome helps match the three-letter code of bases in the messenger RNA to the transfer RNA that carries the specified amino acid. The protein chain continues to grow until the ribosome comes to a stop signal, and then the completed protein chain is released.
3. Some mutations can be helpful to the organism, some are harmful, and others are neither helpful nor harmful.
4. in the cytoplasm
5. Only sex cells can pass on their chromosomes to the offspring. Body cells are not passed to offspring, they remain a part of the parent.

Figure 17 Mutations can affect an organism's traits, or phenotype. The unusually large strawberries on the left are the result of a mutation. The cells of these strawberries have extra sets of chromosomes.

harmful to an organism if it reduces the organism's chance for survival and reproduction.

Whether a mutation is harmful or not depends partly on the organism's environment. The mutation that led to the production of a white buffalo calf would probably be harmful to an organism in the wild. Its white color would make it more visible, and thus easier for predators to find. However, a white buffalo calf raised on a farm has the same chance for survival as a brown buffalo. On the farm, the mutation is neutral—it neither helps nor harms the buffalo.

 INTEGRATING HEALTH Some diseases in humans are caused by harmful mutations. For example, some forms of cancer are caused by mutations in an organism's body cells. Overexposure to the ultraviolet radiation in sunlight, for example, may lead to mutations that could cause skin cancer. In Chapter 4, you will learn more about other diseases that result from harmful mutations.

Helpful mutations, on the other hand, improve an organism's chances for survival and reproduction. Antibiotic resistance in bacteria is an example. Antibiotics are chemicals that kill bacteria. Gene mutations have enabled some kinds of bacteria to become resistant to certain antibiotics—that is, the antibiotics do not kill the bacteria that have the mutations. Since the antibiotic-resistant bacteria are not killed by the antibiotics, the mutations have improved the bacteria's ability to survive and reproduce.

Section 4 Review

1. How do the nitrogen bases along a gene serve as a genetic code?
2. Briefly describe the process by which a cell produces proteins.
3. What possible effects can a mutation have on an organism?
4. Where in a cell does protein synthesis take place?
5. **Thinking Critically** Relating Cause and Effect Why are mutations that occur in an organism's body cells not passed on to its offspring?

112

Check Your Progress **CHAPTER PROJECT**
With your partner, plan a display of your pet's family. Label the parents the P generation. Label the offspring the F₁ generation. Construct a Punnett square for each trait to help explain the inheritance pattern in your pet's family. (*Hint: Attach your pets to the display in a way that lets viewers turn the pets over to read their genotypes.*)

Program Resources

◆ **Unit 1 Resources** 3-4 Review and Reinforce, p. 89; 3-4 Enrich, p. 90

CHAPTER 3 STUDY GUIDE

SECTION 1 Mendel's Work

Key Ideas
◆ Gregor Mendel's work was the foundation for understanding why offspring have traits similar to those of their parents.
◆ Traits are controlled by alleles of genes. Organisms inherit one allele from each parent.
◆ Some alleles are dominant and some alleles are recessive.

Key Terms
trait	purebred	dominant allele
heredity	gene	recessive allele
genetics	allele	hybrid

SECTION 2 Probability and Genetics
INTEGRATING MATHEMATICS

Key Ideas
◆ Probability is the likelihood that a particular event will happen.
◆ Mendel was the first scientist to interpret his data using the principles of probability.
◆ Geneticists use Punnett squares to show all the possible outcomes of a genetic cross.

Key Terms
probability	homozygous
Punnett square	heterozygous
phenotype	codominance
genotype	

SECTION 3 The Cell and Inheritance

Key Ideas
◆ According to the chromosome theory of inheritance, genes are carried from parents to their offspring on chromosomes.
◆ During meiosis, chromosome pairs separate to form sex cells. Only one chromosome from each pair ends up in each sex cell. The sex cells have half the number of chromosomes as the body cells.

Key Terms
sperm	egg	meiosis

SECTION 4 The DNA Connection

Key Ideas
◆ The nitrogen bases along a gene form a code that specifies the order in which amino acids will be put together to produce a protein.
◆ During protein synthesis, messenger RNA copies the coded message from the DNA in the nucleus and carries the message into the cytoplasm. Transfer RNA adds amino acids to the growing protein.
◆ A mutation is a change in a gene or chromosome. Some mutations are harmful, some are helpful, and some are neutral.

Key Terms
messenger RNA
transfer RNA
mutation

Organizing Information

Compare/Contrast Table Copy the table comparing DNA and messenger RNA onto a separate sheet of paper. Then complete the table. (For more about compare/contrast tables, see the Skills Handbook.)

Characteristic	DNA	Messenger RNA
Nitrogen bases	a. ? , b. ? , c. ? , d. ?	Adenine, uracil, guanine, cytosine
Structure	Twisted ladder	e. ?
Function	Forms a genetic code that specifies what type of protein will be produced	f. ?

Chapter 3 **113**

Check Your Progress
CHAPTER PROJECT

Give each student pair poster board on which they can display their pet family. If students don't understand the hint, show them how to attach the pets to the poster board by taping down the left side of the pet so people can easily turn over the pet to read their genotypes, much like turning the page in a book. Check Punnett squares to make sure students have correctly shown all the possible genotypes and phenotypes of the F_1 pets, based on the genotypes of the two parents. Each student pair should construct five Punnett squares, one for each trait—sex, body color, eye shape, nose shape, and teeth shape.

Organizing Information

Compare/Contrast Table
a.–d. adenine, thymine, guanine, cytosine e. one strand of the ladder f. carries the genetic code from the DNA inside the nucleus into the cytoplasm

Program Resources

◆ **Unit 1 Resources** Chapter 3 Project Scoring Rubric, p. 74
◆ **Performance Assessment** Chapter 3, pp. 11–13;
◆ **Chapter and Unit Tests** Chapter 3 Test, pp. 12–15

Media and Technology

 Interactive Student Tutorial CD-ROM Chapter 3

 Computer Test Bank Chapter 3 Test

Performance Assessment

Drawing Have students draw a diagram that shows the process by which a cell produces proteins. In their diagrams, have students indicate where mistakes could occur, leading to mutations.

 Students can save their diagrams in their portfolios.

113

Reviewing Content

Multiple Choice

1. a 2. c 3. b 4. a 5. c

True or False

6. true 7. phenotype 8. true
9. meiosis 10. cytoplasm

Checking Concepts

11. All the first generation offspring were tall.

12. There is a 1 in 2, or 50 percent chance that the coin will land heads up on the sixth toss because each coin toss is an independent event—the result of one toss does not affect the following coin tosses.

13. Punnett squares should look like the following:

	B	b
b	Bb	bb
b	Bb	bb

There is a 50 percent (2 in 4) chance that an offspring will have a white coat (bb).

14. Before meiosis begins, the chromosomes make copies of themselves. During Meiosis I, chromosome pairs separate from each other. In Meiosis II, the chromosome copies separate from each other to form four sex cells, each with half the number of chromosomes as the parent cell.

15. Transfer RNA carries the amino acid that corresponds to the code in the messenger RNA and adds it to the growing protein chain.

16. Student letters should describe Mendel's experiments as outlined in Section 1.

Thinking Critically

17. The solid-colored parent must be homozygous for the recessive allele (ss), and the spotted parent must be homozygous for the dominant allele (SS). If the spotted parent were heterozygous (Ss), then 50% of the offspring would have been solid-colored.

18. The allele for the striped trait is dominant. If it were recessive, all of the offspring would have been solid green.

19. A thicker coat is a helpful mutation in cold environments, because it provides extra insulation to keep the mouse warm.

Reviewing Content

 For more review of key concepts, see the Interactive Student Tutorial CD-ROM.

Multiple Choice

Choose the letter of the best answer.

1. The different forms of a gene are called
   a. alleles.   b. chromosomes.
   c. phenotypes.   d. genotypes.

2. In a coin toss, the probability of the coin landing heads up is
   a. 100 percent.   b. 75 percent.
   c. 50 percent.   d. 25 percent.

3. An organism with two identical alleles for a trait is
   a. heterozygous.
   b. homozygous.
   c. recessive.
   d. dominant.

4. If the body cells of an organism have 10 chromosomes, then its sex cells would have
   a. 5 chromosomes.
   b. 10 chromosomes.
   c. 15 chromosomes.
   d. 20 chromosomes.

5. During protein synthesis, messenger RNA
   a. "reads" each three-letter code of bases.
   b. releases the completed protein chain.
   c. copies information from DNA in the nucleus.
   d. carries amino acids to the ribosome.

True or False

If the statement is true, write true. If it is false, change the underlined word or words to make the statement true.

6. The scientific study of heredity is called genetics.

7. An organism's physical appearance is its genotype.

8. In codominance, neither of the alleles is dominant or recessive.

9. Heredity is the process by which sex cells form.

10. Proteins are made in the nucleus of the cell.

Checking Concepts

11. Describe what happened when Mendel crossed purebred tall pea plants with purebred short pea plants.

12. You toss a coin five times and it lands heads up each time. What is the probability that it will land heads up on the sixth toss? Explain your answer.

13. In guinea pigs, the allele for black fur (B) is dominant over the allele for white fur (b). In a cross between a heterozygous black guinea pig (Bb) and a homozygous white guinea pig (bb), what is the probability that an offspring will have white fur? Use a Punnett square to answer the question.

14. In your own words, describe the sequence of steps in the process of meiosis.

15. Describe the role of transfer RNA in protein synthesis.

16. **Writing to Learn** Imagine that you are a student in the 1860s visiting Gregor Mendel in his garden. Write a letter to a friend describing Mendel's experiments.

Thinking Critically

17. **Applying Concepts** In rabbits, the allele for a spotted coat is dominant over the allele for a solid-colored coat. A spotted rabbit was crossed with a solid-colored rabbit. The offspring all had spotted coats. What were the genotypes of the parents? Explain.

18. **Problem Solving** Suppose you are growing purebred green-skinned watermelons. One day you find a mutant striped watermelon. You cross the striped watermelon with a purebred green watermelon. Fifty percent of the offspring are striped, while fifty percent are green. Is the allele for the striped trait dominant or recessive? Explain.

19. **Predicting** A new mutation in mice causes the coat to be twice as thick as normal. In what environments would this mutation be helpful?

Applying Skills

20. $\frac{9}{12} \times 100\% = 75\%$ green pods;
$\frac{3}{12} \times 100\% = 25\%$ yellow pods

21. Yellow pods: *gg*; green pods: *GG* or *Gg*

22. Both parents are *Gg*. If both parents were *GG*, then none of the offspring would have yellow pods. If one parent were *GG* and the other were *Gg*, then, again, none of the offspring would have yellow pods. Neither parent could be *gg* because that is the genotype for yellow pods, and both parents have green pods.

Applying Skills

In peas, the allele for green pods (G) is dominant over the allele for yellow pods (g). The table shows the phenotypes of the offspring produced from a cross of two plants with green pods. Use the data to answer Questions 20–22.

Phenotype	Number of Offspring
Green pods	9
Yellow pods	3

20. **Calculating** Calculate what percent of the offspring have green pods. Calculate what percent have yellow pods.

21. **Inferring** What is the genotype of the offspring with yellow pods? What are the possible genotypes of the offspring with green pods?

22. **Drawing Conclusions** What are the genotypes of the parents? How do you know?

Performance · CHAPTER PROJECT · Assessment

Present Your Project Finalize your display of your pet's family. Be prepared to discuss the inheritance patterns in your pet's family. Examine your classmates' exhibits, and see which offspring look most like, and least like, their parents. Can you find any offspring that "break the laws" of inheritance?

Reflect and Record How did your paper pets help you learn about genetics? How do the inheritance patterns in your pet's family resemble real-life patterns? How could you use paper pets to help you understand other topics in genetics?

Test Preparation

Use these questions to prepare for standardized tests.

Use the information to answer Questions 23–26.
A pet store's customers prefer pet mice with black fur over mice with white fur. With this in mind, the owner crossed a female with black fur and a male with black fur. When the mice were born, she was surprised that three of the ten offspring had white fur. She did not know that the parents were heterozygous for fur color.

23. Which letters represent the genotype of the female parent?
   a. BB
   b. Bb
   c. B
   d. bb

24. Which letters represent the genotype of the male parent?
   a. BB
   b. Bb
   c. B
   d. bb

25. How could the pet store owner breed a litter of only white mice?
   a. by making sure that either the mother or the father has white fur
   b. by making sure that both the mother and the father have white fur
   c. by making sure that at least one of the grandparents has white fur
   d. She could not breed a litter of only white mice.

26. If the pet store owner were to cross one homozygous black mouse with a heterozygous black mouse, what percentage of the mice would you expect to have white fur?
   a. 0%
   b. 25%
   c. 50%
   d. 75%

Performance · CHAPTER PROJECT · Assessment

Present Your Project Make sure students understand that "breaking the laws" of inheritance refers to proposed inheritance patterns that violate the principles of heredity. This could happen, for example, when students propose that two homozygous recessive parents produce offspring with one or two dominant alleles. Students should review each other's Punnett squares to make sure that no offspring "break the inheritance laws."

Reflect and Record Students should record in their journals how their paper pets helped them understand specific concepts and principles of genetics. For example, students should describe how the inheritance patterns of their paper pets demonstrated the inheritance of dominant and recessive alleles, or showed the relationship between genotype and phenotype. They should also explain how paper pets could be used as models to study other topics in genetics.

Test Preparation

23. b 24. b 25. b 26. a

Program Resources

◆ **Inquiry Skills Activity Book** Provides teaching and review of all inquiry skills

Modern Genetics

Sections	Time	Student Edition Activities	ACTIVITY Other Activities	
CHAPTER PROJECT **A Family Portrait** p. 117	Ongoing (2 weeks)	Check Your Progress, p. 124, 129 Present Your Project, p. 143		
1 **Human Inheritance** pp. 118–124 ◆ Explain what multiple alleles are. ◆ Explain why some human traits show a large variety of phenotypes. ◆ Explain how environmental factors can alter the effects of a gene. ◆ Identify what determines sex, and explain why some sex-linked traits are more common in males than in females. ◆ Describe how geneticists use pedigrees.	1–2 periods/ $\frac{1}{2}$–1 block	**Discover** How Tall Is Tall?, p. 118 **Try This** The Eyes Have It, p. 120 **Try This** Girl or Boy?, p. 122	TE LM	Including All Students, p 123 4, "How Are Genes on Sex Chromosomes Inherited?"
2 **Human Genetic Disorders** pp. 125–131 ◆ Describe the causes and symptoms of five human genetic disorders. ◆ Explain how genetic disorders are diagnosed. ◆ Describe the role of a genetic counselor.	$1\frac{1}{2}$–2 periods/ $\frac{1}{2}$–1 block	**Discover** How Many Chromosomes?, p. 125 **Real-World Lab: Careers in Science** Family Puzzles, pp. 130–131	TE TE	Including All Students, p. 126 Demonstration, p. 128
3 **INTEGRATING TECHNOLOGY** **Advances in Genetics** pp. 132–140 ◆ Describe three ways in which people have developed organisms with desired traits. ◆ Identify some uses of DNA fingerprinting. ◆ State the goal of the Human Genome Project.	$1\frac{1}{2}$–2 periods/ $\frac{1}{2}$–1 block	**Discover** What Do Fingerprints Reveal?, p. 132 **Sharpen Your Skills** Communicating, p. 137 **Science at Home,** p. 138 **Real-World Lab: You Solve the Mystery** Guilty or Innocent?, p. 140	TE TE TE	Real-Life Learning, p. 133 Demonstration, p. 134 Inquiry Challenge, p. 135
Study Guide/Chapter Assessment pp. 141–143	1 period/ $\frac{1}{2}$ block		ISAB	Provides teaching and review of all inquiry skills.

 For Standard or Block Schedule The Resource Pro® CD-ROM gives you maximum flexibility for planning your instruction for any type of schedule. Resource Pro® contains Planning Express®, an advanced scheduling program, as well as the entire contents of the Teaching Resources and the Computer Test Bank.

CHAPTER PLANNING GUIDE

Program Resources	Assessment Strategies	Media and Technology
UR Chapter 4 Project Teacher Notes, pp. 96–97 **UR** Chapter 4 Project Overview and Worksheets, pp. 98–99	**SE** Performance Assessment: Present Your Project, p. 143 **TE** Check Your Progress, pp. 124, 129 **UR** Chapter 4 Project Scoring Rubric, p. 102	Science Explorer Internet Site at www.phschool.com
UR 4-1 Lesson Plan, p. 103 **UR** 4-1 Section Summary, p. 104 **UR** 4-1 Review and Reinforce, p. 105 **UR** 4-1 Enrich, p. 106	**SE** Section 1 Review, p. 124 **TE** Ongoing Assessment, pp. 117, 121, 123 **TE** Performance Assessment, p. 124	Audio CD, English-Spanish Summary 4-1 Transparencies 16, "Punnett Square—Male or Female?"; 17, "Exploring a Pedigree"
UR 4-2 Lesson Plan, p. 107 **UR** 4-2 Section Summary, p. 108 **UR** 4-2 Review and Reinforce, p. 109 **UR** 4-2 Enrich, p. 110 **UR** Chapter 4 Real-World Lab, pp. 115–117	**SE** Section 2 Review, p. 129 **TE** Ongoing Assessment, p. 127 **TE** Performance Assessment, p. 129	Life Science Videotape 1; Videodisc Unit 5 Side 1, "An Unusual Mutation" Audio CD, English-Spanish Summary 4-2
UR 4-3 Lesson Plan, p. 111 **UR** 4-3 Section Summary, p. 112 **UR** 4-3 Review and Reinforce, p. 113 **UR** 4-3 Enrich, p. 114 **UR** Chapter 4 Real-World Lab, pp. 118–119	**SE** Section 3 Review, p. 138 **TE** Ongoing Assessment, pp. 133, 135, 137 **TE** Performance Assessment, p. 138	Life Science Videotape 1; Videodisc Unit 5 Side 1, "Breeding for Dollars" Audio CD, English-Spanish Summary 4-3 Transparency 18, "Exploring Genetic Engineering" Interactive Student Tutorial CD-ROM, Chapter 4
RCA Provides strategies to improve science reading skills **GSW** Provides worksheets to promote student comprehension of content	**SE** Chapter 4 Study Guide/Assessment, pp. 141–143 **PA** Chapter 4 Performance Assessment, pp. 14–16 **CUT** Chapter 4 Test, pp. 16–19 **CTB** Chapter 4 Test	Interactive Student Tutorial CD-ROM, Chapter 4 Computer Test Bank, Chapter 4 Test

Key: **SE** Student Edition
CTB Computer Test Bank
ISAB Inquiry Skills Activity Book
GSW Guided Study Worksheets

TE Teacher's Edition
PTA Product Testing Activities by *Consumer Reports*
RCA Reading in the Content Area
PA Performance Assessment

UR Unit Resources
LM Laboratory Manual
IES Interdisciplinary Explorations Series
CUT Chapter and Unit Tests

Meeting the National Science Education Standards and AAAS Benchmarks

National Science Education Standards	Benchmarks for Science Literacy	Unifying Themes
Science As Inquiry (Content Standard A) ◆ **Develop descriptions, explanations, predictions, and models using evidence** Students create a pedigree for an imaginary family, investigate inheritance patterns in families and model DNA fingerprinting. *(Chapter Project; Real-World Lab)* **Life Science** (Content Standard C) ◆ **Reproduction and heredity** Human traits can be controlled by single genes, multiple alleles, or many genes. A pedigree is used to trace the inheritance of traits. Genetic disorders are caused by mutations. People have used selective breeding, cloning, and genetic engineering to develop organisms with desirable traits. *(Chapter Project; Sections 1, 2, 3; Real-World Lab)* **Science and Technology** (Content Standard E) ◆ **Understandings about science and technology** Doctors use such tools as amniocentesis and karyotypes to help detect genetic disorders. In genetic engineering, genes from one organism are transferred into the DNA of another organism. DNA can be used to identify individuals. *(Sections 2, 3; Real-World Lab)* **Science in Personal and Social Perspectives** (Content Standard F) ◆ **Science and technology in society** Students examine the issue of who should have access to genetic test results. *(Science and Society)*	**1B Scientific Inquiry** Students create a pedigree for an imaginary family. Students investigate inheritance patterns in families. Students model DNA fingerprinting. *(Chapter Project; Real-World Lab)* **3A Technology and Science** Doctors use such tools as amniocentesis and karyotypes to help detect genetic disorders. In genetic engineering, genes from one organism are transferred into the DNA of another organism. DNA can be used to identify individuals. *(Sections 2, 3; Real-World Lab)* **3C Issues in Technology** Students examine the issue of who should have access to genetic test results. *(Science and Society)* **5B Heredity** Human traits can be controlled by single genes, multiple alleles, or many genes. A pedigree is used to trace the inheritance of traits. Genetic disorders are caused by mutations. People have used selective breeding, cloning, and genetic engineering to develop organisms with desirable traits. *(Chapter Project; Sections 1, 2, 3; Real-World Lab)* **12D Communication Skills** Students present their pedigrees and "photo" albums to the class. *(Chapter Project)*	◆ **Evolution** Geneticists use a pedigree to trace the inheritance of traits in humans. People have used selective breeding, cloning, and genetic engineering to develop organisms with desirable traits. *(Chapter Project; Sections 1, 3; Real-World Lab)* ◆ **Patterns of Change** The effects of genes are often altered by the environment. Genetic disorders are caused by mutations. Selective-breeding methods can be used to produce desired characteristics in plants and animals. *(Sections 1, 2, 3)* ◆ **Scale and Structure** The Y chromosome is much smaller than the X chromosome. The 23 pairs of human chromosomes that make up the human genome contain about 60,000 to 80,000 genes. *(Sections 1, 3)* ◆ **Stability** A clone is an organism that is genetically identical to the organism from which it was produced. *(Section 3)* ◆ **Systems and Interactions** Because males have only one X chromosome, males are more likely than females to inherit sex-linked traits controlled by recessive alleles. Doctors use tools such as amniocentesis and karyotypes to help detect genetic disorders. In genetic engineering, genes from one organism are transferred into the DNA of another organism. *(Sections 1, 2, 3)* ◆ **Unity and Diversity** Human traits can be controlled by single genes, multiple alleles, or many genes. A genetic disorder is an abnormal condition that a person inherits through genes or chromosomes. *(Sections 1, 2, 3; Real-World Lab)*

Take It to the Net

 **Interactive text at www.phschool.com**

Science Explorer comes alive with iText.

- **Complete student text** is accessible from any computer with Internet access or a CD-ROM drive.
- **Animations, simulations, and videos** enhance student understanding and retention of concepts.
- **Self-tests and online study tools** assess student understanding.

STAY CURRENT with

Find out the latest research and information about genetics at:
www.phschool.com

Go to **www.phschool.com** and click on the Science icon. Then click on <u>Science Explorer: Life, Earth, and Physical Science</u> under PH@school.

ACTIVITY	Time (minutes)	Materials Quantities for one work group	Skills
Section 1			
Discover, p. 118	15	**Consumable** graph paper **Nonconsumable** tape measure	Inferring
Try This, p. 120	10	No special materials are required.	Designing Experiments
Try This, p. 122	10	**Nonconsumable** 2 paper bags, 3 red marbles, 1 white marble	Making Models
Section 2			
Discover, p. 125	10	No special materials are required.	Inferring
Real-World Lab, pp. 130–131	40	**Consumable** 12 index cards **Nonconsumable** scissors, marker	Interpreting Data, Drawing Conclusions
Section 3			
Discover, p. 132	15	**Consumable** plain white paper **Nonconsumable** ink pad, hand lens	Observing
Science at Home, p. 138	home	No special materials are required.	Observing, Applying Concepts
Real-World Lab, p. 140	20	**Consumable** 4–6 bar codes **Nonconsumable** hand lens	Observing, Making Models, Drawing Conclusions

A list of all materials required for the Student Edition activities can be found on pages T25–T33. You can obtain information about ordering materials by calling 1-800-848-9500 or by accessing the Science Explorer Internet site at **www.phschool.com**.

A Family Portrait

In Chapter 4, students will learn more about human traits and how they are inherited. They also will learn how pedigrees can be used to trace the inheritance of traits in families. The Chapter 4 Project will give students an opportunity to use pedigrees to demonstrate different types of inheritance.

Purpose In the Chapter 4 Project, students will create a pedigree for an imaginary family and use it to show how two different traits have been passed from generation to generation within the family. Students also will create a family album showing how the traits appear in individual family members. Successfully completing the Chapter 4 Project will require students to understand different patterns of inheritance and the concepts of genotype and phenotype.

Skills Focus After completing the Chapter 4 Project, students will be able to
◆ create a model pedigree for an imaginary family;
◆ apply genetic concepts to show the inheritance of two different traits in the family's pedigree;
◆ predict phenotypes of individuals with different genotypes to create a family album;
◆ communicate their work in a class presentation.

Project Time Line The Chapter 4 Project will take about two weeks to complete. On the first day, launch the project and have students read about the project on page 117 in the text. Review the traits controlled by a single gene that are described in Chapters 3 and 4. Tell students to select two of the traits for the project. Distribute the Chapter 4 Project Overview, pages 98–99 in Unit 1 Resources, and give students a chance to read through it and ask questions.

The first day of the project is a good time to hand out the Chapter 4 Project Scoring Rubric, page 102 in Unit 1 Resources, so students will know how their work will be evaluated. If you want students to work in groups, assign them to groups at this time as well, and give groups a chance to meet and plan the

CHAPTER
4 Modern Genetics

WEB ACTIVITY
www.phschool.com

Integrating Technology

SECTION 1 Human Inheritance

Discover How Tall Is Tall?
Try This The Eyes Have It
Try This Girl or Boy?

SECTION 2 Human Genetic Disorders

Discover How Many Chromosomes?
Real-World Lab Family Puzzles

SECTION 3 Advances in Genetics

Discover What Do Fingerprints Reveal?
Sharpen Your Skills Communicating
Science at Home Grocery Genetics
Real-World Lab Guilty or Innocent?

116

project. Distribute Chapter 4 Project Worksheet 1, page 100 in Unit 1 Resources, and instruct students to complete it before they begin their pedigrees.

Give students two or three days to create a pedigree for their imaginary families, following the specifications in *Exploring a Pedigree* on page 124 in their text. After students have completed their pedigrees, check them for errors. Then hand out Chapter 4 Project Worksheet 2, page 101 in Unit 1 Resources, and instruct students to complete the worksheet before they create their

pedigrees for the two traits. When students have finished their pedigrees, check their work before they begin their family albums.

Students may need several days to create their family albums, depending on how they choose to represent their selected traits. Finally, set aside at least one class period at the end of the project for students to present their work to the rest of the class.

For more detailed information on the chapter project, see Chapter 4 Project Teacher Notes, pages 96–97 in Unit 1 Resources.

CHAPTER 4 PROJECT

A Family Portrait

A pedigree, or family tree, is a branched drawing that shows many generations of a family. In some cases, a pedigree may show centuries of a family's history.

In genetics, pedigrees are used to show how traits are passed from one generation to the next. In this project, you will create a genetic pedigree for an imaginary family. Although the family will be imaginary, your pedigree must show how real human traits are passed from parents to children.

Your Goal To create a pedigree for an imaginary family that shows the transfer of genetic traits from one generation to the next.

To complete the project you will
- ◆ choose two different genetic traits, and identify all the possible genotypes and phenotypes
- ◆ create pedigrees that trace each trait through three generations of your imaginary family
- ◆ prepare a family "photo" album to show what each family member looks like

Get Started With a partner, review the human traits described on page 92 in Chapter 3. List what you already know about human inheritance. For example, which human traits are controlled by dominant alleles? Which are controlled by recessive alleles? Then preview Section 1 of this chapter, and list the traits you'll be studying. Choose two traits that you would like to focus on in your project.

Check Your Progress You'll be working on this project as you study this chapter. To keep your project on track, look for Check Your Progress boxes at the following points.
Section 1 Review, page 124: Create a pedigree for the first trait you chose.
Section 2 Review, page 129: Create the second pedigree, and begin your family album.

Present Your Project At the end of the chapter (page 143), you will present your family's pedigrees and "photo" album to the class.

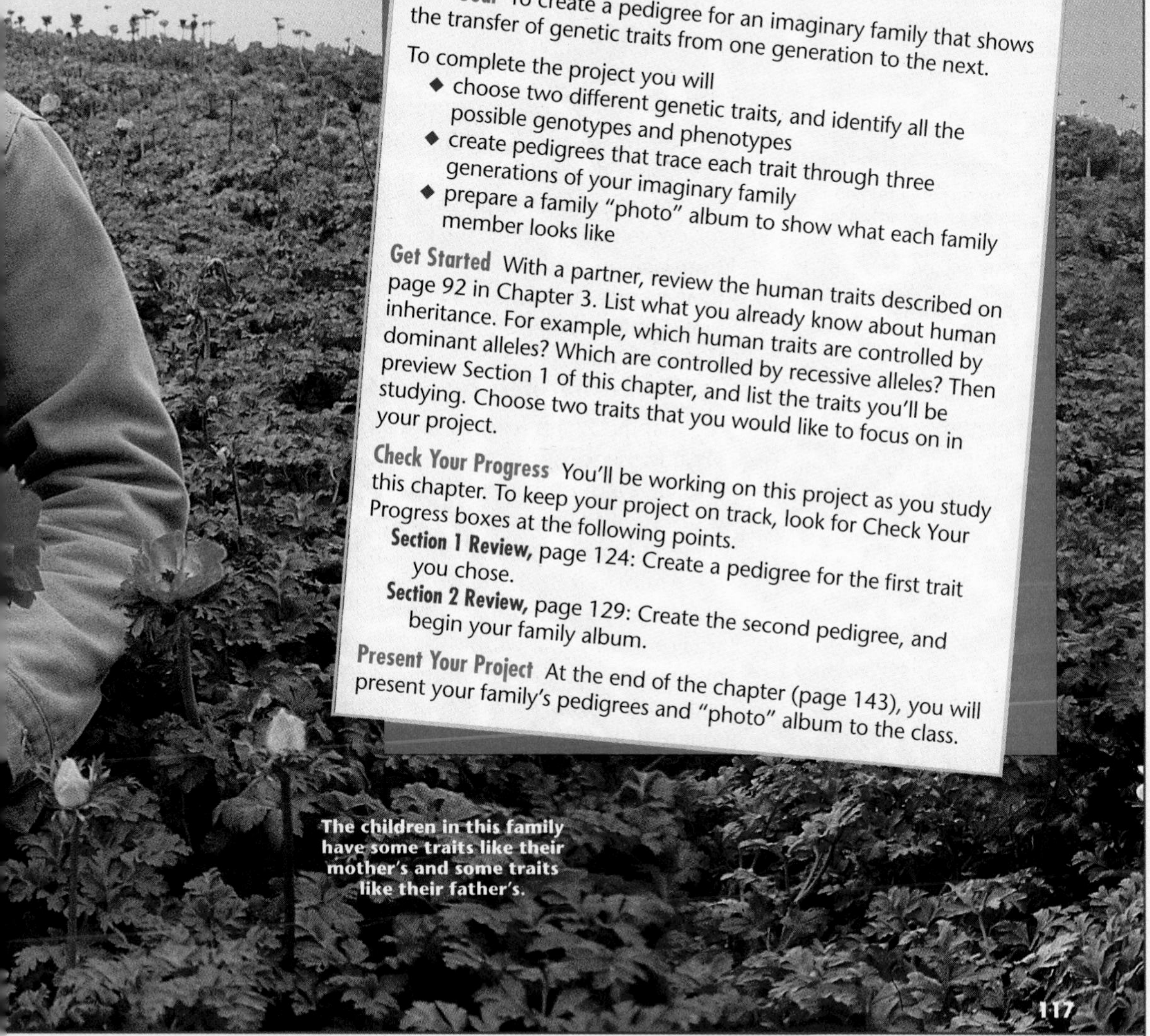

The children in this family have some traits like their mother's and some traits like their father's.

117

Program Resources

◆ **Unit 1 Resources** Chapter 4 Project Teacher Notes, pp. 96–97; Chapter 4 Project Overview and Worksheets, pp. 98–101; Chapter 4 Project Scoring Rubric, p. 102

WEB ACTIVITY www.phschool.com

You will find an Internet activity, chapter self-tests for students, and links to other chapter topics at this site.

Suggested Shortcuts Before students fill in the basic pedigree for a specific trait, make sure it is accurate. Then have students make a photocopy to use for the second trait.

Another possible shortcut is to have each student choose just one trait. Also, instead of having students make oral presentations, you can have them display their work on a bulletin board. Alternatively, you could select just a few students to present their pedigrees and family albums.

Possible Materials For their pedigrees, students can use large sheets of white paper or poster board. For their family albums, students can use a variety of different materials. The album itself may be a real photo album or scrapbook or a sheet of poster board. For pictures, students can use drawings or photographs from magazines or newspapers or sketches of their own. To show traits that are not visible, such as colorblindness or hemophilia, urge students to think of creative ways of depicting individuals with different phenotypes, such as fictitious newspaper articles or letters.

Launching the Project Introduce the project by calling students' attention to the family photograph and asking: **What are some traits that the children in this family appear to share with their parents?** *(Students are likely to name obvious physical traits such as hair color or nose shape.)* Point out that, in addition to traits such as these, children inherit thousands of other traits from their parents, including many that are not so apparent. Tell students that they will create a family tree for an imaginary family and show how genetic traits pass from one generation to the next.

Performance Assessment

To assess students' performance in this project, use the Chapter 4 Project Scoring Rubric on page 102 of Unit 1 Resources. Students will be assessed on
- ◆ the accuracy of their pedigrees;
- ◆ how accurately and creatively they depict the phenotypes of the individuals in their family albums;
- ◆ how complete and prepared their class presentation is;
- ◆ their group participation, if they worked in groups.

Objectives

After completing the lesson, students will be able to
♦ explain what multiple alleles are;
♦ explain why some human traits show a large variety of phenotypes;
♦ explain how environmental factors can alter the effects of a gene;
♦ identify what determines sex, and explain why some sex-linked traits are more common in males than in females;
♦ describe how geneticists use pedigrees.

Key Terms multiple alleles, sex-linked gene, carrier, pedigree

1 Engage/Explore

Activating Prior Knowledge

Help students think of examples of inherited traits by asking: **What are some traits that children may share with one or both of their parents?** (*Students are likely to identify traits such as hair color, nose shape, or eye color.*)

 **DISCOVER**

Skills Focus inferring
Materials *metric ruler, graph paper*
Time 15 minutes
Tips If any students are in wheelchairs, you might want to have the class measure sitting height, which is the height from the base of the spine to the top of the head.
Expected Outcome The graph of students' heights is likely to include several bars, but not as many as there are students in the class.
Think It Over Students may infer that height in humans is controlled by more than one gene because the graph of students' heights has more bars than the two-bar graph Mendel would have drawn.

DISCOVER • • • • • • • • • • • • • • • **ACTIVITY**

How Tall Is Tall?

1. Choose a partner. Measure each other's height to the nearest 5 centimeters. Record your measurements on the chalkboard.

2. Create a bar graph showing the number of students at each height. Plot the heights on the horizontal axis and the number of students on the vertical axis.

Think It Over
Inferring If Gregor Mendel had graphed the heights of his pea plants, the graph would have had two bars—one for tall stems and one for short stems. Do you think height in humans is controlled by a single gene, as it is in peas? Explain your answer.

GUIDE FOR READING

♦ Why do some human traits show a large variety of phenotypes?

♦ Why are some sex-linked traits more common in males than in females?

♦ How do geneticists use pedigrees?

Reading Tip Before you read, rewrite the headings in this section as *how, why,* or *what* questions. As you read, write answers to the questions.

Have you ever heard someone say "He's the spitting image of his dad" or "She has her mother's eyes"? Children often resemble their parents. The reason for this is that alleles for eye color, hair color, and thousands of other traits are passed from parents to their children. People inherit some alleles from their mother and some from their father. This is why most people look a little like their mother and a little like their father.

Traits Controlled by Single Genes

In Chapter 3, you learned that many traits in peas and other organisms are controlled by a single gene with two alleles. Often one allele is dominant, while the other is recessive. Many human traits are also controlled by a single gene with one dominant allele and one recessive allele. As with tall and short pea plants, these human traits have two distinctly different phenotypes, or physical appearances.

For example, a widow's peak is a hairline that comes to a point in the middle of the forehead. The allele for a widow's peak is dominant over the allele for a straight hairline. The Punnett square in Figure 1 illustrates a cross between two parents who are heterozygous for a widow's peak. Trace the possible combinations of alleles that a child may inherit. Notice that each child has a 3 in 4, or 75 percent, probability of having a widow's peak. There is only a 1 in 4, or 25 percent, probability that a child will have a straight hairline. Recall from Chapter 3 that when Mendel crossed peas that were heterozygous for a trait, he obtained similar percentages in the offspring.

READING STRATEGIES

Reading Tip You may wish to help students develop their first question and let them discover the answer as they read the information in the heading aloud. Questions might include, "What traits are controlled by genes?" Students might answer that height in pea plants and widow's peak and dimples in humans all are traits controlled by genes.

Study and Comprehension Before students begin the section, you may want to have them review several of the key terms from Chapter 3 that are important for understanding the concepts in this section. Have them find and read the definition of each of the following: *allele, dominant allele, recessive allele, phenotype, genotype,* and *codominance.*

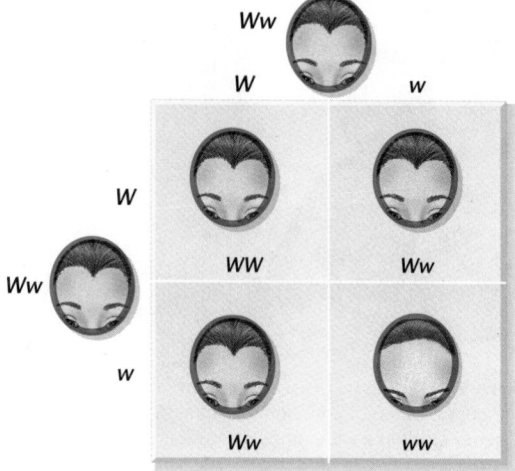

Figure 1 This Punnett square shows a cross between two parents with widow's peaks. *Interpreting Diagrams What are the possible genotypes of the offspring? What percent of the offspring will have each genotype?*

Do you have dimples when you smile? If so, then you have the dominant allele for this trait. Like having a widow's peak, having smile dimples is controlled by a single gene. People who have two recessive alleles do not have smile dimples.

Multiple Alleles

Some human traits are controlled by a single gene that has more than two alleles. Such a gene is said to have **multiple alleles**—three or more forms of a gene that code for a single trait. You can think of multiple alleles as being like flavors of pudding. Pudding usually comes in more flavors than just chocolate and vanilla!

Even though a gene may have multiple alleles, a person can carry only two of those alleles. This is because chromosomes exist in pairs. Each chromosome in a pair carries only one allele for each gene.

One human trait that is controlled by a gene with multiple alleles is blood type. There are four main blood types—A, B, AB, and O. Three alleles control the inheritance of blood types. The allele for blood type A and the allele for blood type B are codominant. The codominant alleles are written as capital letters with superscripts—I^A for blood type A and I^B for blood type B. The allele for blood type O—written i—is recessive. Recall that when two codominant alleles are inherited, neither allele is masked. A person who inherits an I^A allele from one parent and an I^B allele from the other parent will have type AB blood. Figure 2 shows the allele combinations that result in each blood type. Notice that only people who inherit two i alleles have type O blood.

Checkpoint If a gene has multiple alleles, why can a person only have two of the alleles for the gene?

Blood Types

Blood Type	Combination of Alleles
A	$I^A I^A$ or $I^A i$
B	$I^B I^B$ or $I^B i$
AB	$I^A I^B$
O	ii

Figure 2 Blood type is determined by a single gene with three alleles. This chart shows which combinations of alleles result in each blood type.

Program Resources

◆ **Unit 1 Resources** 4-1 Lesson Plan, p. 103; 4-1 Section Summary, p. 104

Media and Technology

 Audio CD English-Spanish Summary 4-1

Answers to Self-Assessment

Caption Question

Figure 1 The possible genotypes of the offspring are *WW*, *Ww*, and *ww*; 25% should have the *WW* genotype, 50% the *Ww* genotype, and 25% the *ww* genotype.

Checkpoint

Chromosomes exist in pairs, and each chromosome in a pair carries only one allele for each gene.

2 Facilitate

Traits Controlled by Single Genes

Addressing Naive Conceptions

Help students avoid the naive conception that the children in families always have genotypes that are in the ratios predicted by Punnett squares. Ask: **Could two parents with a widow's peak have three children without widow's peaks, and only one child with a widow's peak?** *(Students may say that three of the four children should have a widow's peak because the allele for the trait is dominant.)* Explain that three out of four children with a widow's peak is the most likely outcome for this mating. However, due to chance and the small number of offspring, any given family can deviate significantly from ratios determined by a Punnett square, as in the example given here. **learning modality: verbal**

Multiple Alleles

Using the Visuals: Figure 2

Make sure that students understand that the superscripts are not exponents but just labels used to distinguish the two codominant alleles, I^A and I^B. Then check that students understand the relationship between genotype and phenotype for traits controlled by multiple alleles, such as blood type, by asking: **Which column in the table lists the genotypes? Which lists the phenotypes?** *(The right column lists the genotypes; the left column the phenotypes.)* **Why are there more genotypes than phenotypes?** *(Because two different genotypes—$I^A I^A$ and $I^A i$—result in the A phenotype and two other genotypes—$I^B I^B$ and $I^B i$—result in the B phenotype.)* **learning modality: visual**

Ongoing Assessment

Drawing Have students draw a Punnett square that shows a cross between two heterozygotes for smile dimples (a trait controlled by a dominant allele).

Traits Controlled by Many Genes

Building Inquiry Skills: Calculating

Challenge students to identify all the possible genotypes for a hypothetical trait controlled by two genes, each having two alleles, with *A* and *a* representing the two alleles for one gene and *B* and *b* representing the two alleles for the other gene. Ask a volunteer to record students' responses on the chalkboard as they identify all the possible genotypes. (*The possible genotypes are AABB, AABb, AAbb, AaBB, AaBb, Aabb, aaBB, aaBb, and aabb.*) After the list is complete, ask: **How many more genotypes are there for a trait controlled by two genes than for a trait controlled by one gene, if each gene has two alleles?** (*Three times as many*) **learning modality: logical/mathematical**

The Effect of Environment

TRY THIS

Skills Focus designing experiments

ACTIVITY

Time 10 minutes

Tips Make sure students focus on an object that is at least a few meters away from them.

Expected Outcome Students should find that when they close one eye their finger appears to be stationary, but when they close the other eye their finger appears to move. For some students the finger will appear stationary when they look at it with their right eye, meaning their right eye is dominant. For other students the finger will appear stationary when they look at it with their left eye, meaning their left eye is dominant. To test the relationship between eye and hand dominance, students might determine eye and hand dominance for a large sample of people, and then inspect the data to see if a pattern emerges.

Extend Ask: **How is a dominant eye different than a dominant allele?** (*A dominant eye is a trait, whereas a dominant allele controls the inheritance of a trait.*) **learning modality: kinesthetic**

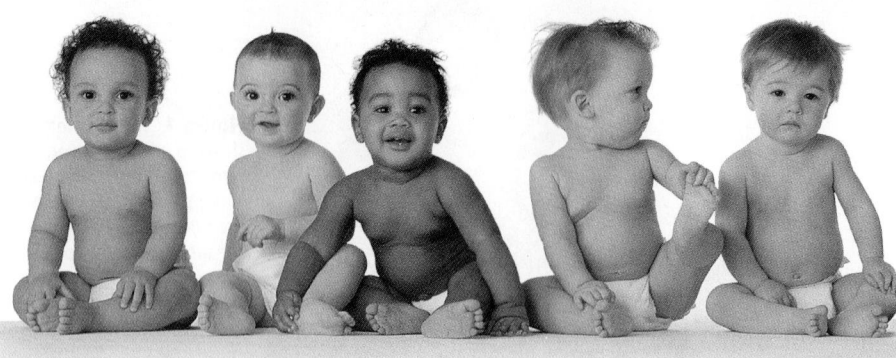

Figure 3 Skin color in humans is determined by three or more genes. Different combinations of alleles at each of the genes result in a wide range of possible skin colors.

TRY THIS

The Eyes Have It

One inherited trait is eye dominance—the tendency **ACTIVITY** to use one eye more than the other. Here's how you can test yourself for this trait.

1. Hold your hand out in front of you at arm's length. Point your finger at an object across the room.

2. Close your right eye. With only your left eye open, observe how far your finger appears to move.

3. Repeat Step 2 with the right eye open. With which eye did your finger seem to remain closer to the object? That eye is dominant.

Designing Experiments Is eye dominance related to hand dominance—whether a person is right-handed or left-handed? Design an experiment to find out. Obtain your teacher's permission before carrying out your experiment.

Traits Controlled by Many Genes

If you did the Discover activity, you observed that height in humans has more than two distinct phenotypes. In fact, there is an enormous variety of phenotypes for height. What causes this wide range of phenotypes? **Some human traits show a large number of phenotypes because the traits are controlled by many genes. The genes act together as a group to produce a single trait.** At least four genes control height in humans, so there are many possible combinations of genes and alleles.

Like height, skin color is determined by many genes. Human skin color ranges from almost white to nearly black, with many shades in between. Skin color is controlled by at least three genes. Each gene, in turn, has at least two possible alleles. Various combinations of alleles at each of the genes determine the amount of pigment that a person's skin cells produce. Thus, a wide variety of skin colors is possible.

The Effect of Environment

The effects of genes are often altered by the environment—the organism's surroundings. For example, people's diets can affect their height. A diet lacking in protein, minerals, and vitamins can prevent a person from growing to his or her potential maximum height. Since the late 1800s, the average height of adults in the United States has increased by almost 10 centimeters. During that time, American diets have become more healthful. Other environmental factors, such as medical care and living conditions, have also improved since the late 1800s.

☑ *Checkpoint* *How can environmental factors affect a person's height?*

Background

History of Science The existence of sex chromosomes was discovered in the late 1800s by Hermann Henking. While studying wasp cells, Henking observed an "accessory chromosome" in each dividing cell that did not have a matching chromosome at prophase. He also noted that male wasps had an uneven number of chromosomes, but females had an even number.

In the early 1900s, the American zoologist Clarence McClung observed "accessory chromosomes" in cells of grasshoppers. McClung's work revealed the significance of the "accessory chromosome," the X chromosome, as a mechanism for the determination of an organism's sex.

Male or Female?

"Congratulations, Mr. and Mrs. Gonzales. It's a baby girl!" What factors determine whether a baby is a boy or a girl? As with other traits, the sex of a baby is determined by genes on chromosomes. Among the 23 pairs of chromosomes in each body cell is a single pair of chromosomes called the sex chromosomes. The sex chromosomes determine whether a person is male or female.

The sex chromosomes are the only pair of chromosomes that do not always match. If you are female, your two sex chromosomes match. The two chromosomes are called X chromosomes. If you are male, your sex chromosomes do not match. One of your sex chromosomes is an X chromosome. The other chromosome is a Y chromosome. The Y chromosome is much smaller than the X chromosome.

What happens to the sex chromosomes when egg and sperm cells form? As you know, each egg and sperm cell has only one chromosome from each pair. Since both of a female's sex chromosomes are X chromosomes, all eggs carry one X chromosome. Males, however, have two different sex chromosomes. This means that half of a male's sperm cells carry an X chromosome, while half carry a Y chromosome.

When a sperm cell with an X chromosome fertilizes an egg, the egg has two X chromosomes. The fertilized egg will develop into a girl. When a sperm with a Y chromosome fertilizes an egg, the egg has one X chromosome and one Y chromosome. The fertilized egg will develop into a boy. Thus it is the sperm that determines the sex of the child, as you can see in Figure 4.

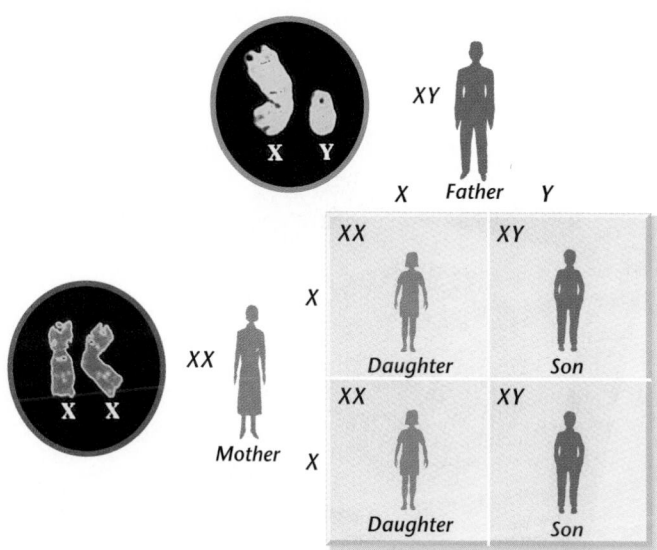

Figure 4 As this Punnett square shows, there is a 50 percent probability that a child will be a girl and a 50 percent probability that a child will be a boy. *Interpreting Diagrams What sex will the child be if a sperm with a Y chromosome fertilizes an egg?*

Chapter 4 **121**

Media and Technology

 Transparencies "Punnett Square–Male or Female?," Transparency 16

Answers to Self-Assessment

☑ *Checkpoint*

Environmental factors such as a poor diet can affect a person's height by preventing the person from reaching his or her potential maximum height.

Caption Question

Figure 4 The child will be male.

Male or Female?

Building Inquiry Skills: Drawing Diagrams

Challenge students to draw two simple diagrams of meiosis, contrasting the formation of sex cells in males and females. Their drawings should show clearly which type of sex chromosome each of the sex cells contains. If students do not remember the details of meiosis, suggest that they refer to *Exploring Meiosis* on page 99, Chapter 3. Explain that the X and Y chromosomes pair up during meiosis. After students have finished their drawings, ask: **How do your drawings demonstrate that the father's sperm determines the sex of a child?** *(The drawings should show that the sex cells produced by a male may contain either an X or a Y chromosome, whereas the sex cells produced by a female may contain only an X chromosome. Thus, the sex of a child is determined by whether an egg is fertilized by an X-bearing or a Y-bearing sperm produced by the father.)*
learning modality: kinesthetic

Using the Visuals: Figure 4

Use the visual to help students understand why an allele on a man's X chromosome cannot be inherited by his sons. Ask: **If the man in the figure had an allele *A* on his X chromosome, which of his offspring—his sons or his daughters—would inherit the allele?** *(The man's daughters)* **Why wouldn't his sons inherit the allele?** *(Because the man's sons inherit only the Y chromosome from their father.)*
learning modality: visual

Ongoing Assessment

Writing Have students explain, in their own words, why about half of all babies are boys and about half are girls. *(Sample answer: A baby's sex depends on whether it receives an X or a Y chromosome from the father. Half the sperm produced by males contain an X chromosome, and the other half contain a Y chromosome. Therefore, about half the time eggs are fertilized by Y-bearing sperm and about half the time they are fertilized by X-bearing sperm. This results in about half the babies being boys and about half being girls.)*

Male or Female?, continued

Skills Focus making models

Materials *two paper bags, three red marbles, one white marble*

Time 10 minutes

Tips Remind students to replace the two marbles in the correct bags each time before they make their next draw.

Expected Outcome About half the time students will draw two red marbles, representing a female, and about half the time they will draw one red and one white marble, representing a male. If you add up the numbers of females and males produced by the whole class, the totals are likely to be even closer to half female and half male.

Extend Ask: **How could you use the same setup to model the inheritance of a trait controlled by a single gene, such as widow's peak?** *(The most likely way is to assume that one color marble represents the dominant allele and the other color represents the recessive allele for the same gene. Students would draw one marble from each bag, as in the original activity.)*
learning modality: kinesthetic

Sex-Linked Genes

Building Inquiry Skills: Inferring

Challenge students to infer how the inheritance of a sex-linked trait controlled by a dominant allele would differ from the inheritance of a sex-linked trait controlled by a recessive allele. First, remind students that a sex-linked trait controlled by a recessive allele is more common in males because males need to inherit just one recessive allele to have the trait. Then ask: **If a sex-linked trait is controlled by a dominant allele, would the trait be more common in males than in females? Why or why not?** *(A trait controlled by a dominant allele would not be more common in males because females, like males, would need to inherit just one dominant allele to have the trait.)* **learning modality: logical/mathematical**

Girl or Boy?

You can model how the sex of an offspring is determined.

1. Label one paper bag "female." Label another paper bag "male."
2. Place two red marbles in the bag labeled "female." The red marbles represent X chromosomes.
3. Place one red marble and one white marble in the bag labeled "male." The white marble represents a Y chromosome.
4. Without looking, pick one marble from each bag. Two red marbles represent a female offspring. One red marble and one white marble represent a male offspring. Record the sex of the "offspring."
5. Put the marbles back in the correct bags. Repeat Step 4 nine more times.

Making Models How many males were produced? How many females? How close were your results to the expected probabilities for male and female offspring?

Program Resources

◆ **Laboratory Manual** 4, "How Are Genes on Sex Chromosomes Inherited?"

Sex-Linked Genes

Some human traits occur more often in one sex than the other. The genes for these traits are often carried on the sex chromosomes. Genes on the X and Y chromosomes are often called **sex-linked genes** because their alleles are passed from parent to child on a sex chromosome. Traits controlled by sex-linked genes are called sex-linked traits.

Like other genes, sex-linked genes can have dominant and recessive alleles. Recall that females have two X chromosomes, whereas males have one X chromosome and one Y chromosome. In females, a dominant allele on one X chromosome will mask a recessive allele on the other X chromosome. The situation is not the same in males, however. In males, there is no matching allele on the Y chromosome to mask, or hide, the allele on the X chromosome. As a result, any allele on the X chromosome—even a recessive allele—will produce the trait in a male who inherits it. **Because males have only one X chromosome, males are more likely than females to have a sex-linked trait that is controlled by a recessive allele.**

One example of a sex-linked trait that is controlled by a recessive allele is red-green colorblindness. A person with red-green colorblindness cannot distinguish between red and green.

Many more males than females have red-green colorblindness. You can understand why this is the case by examining the Punnett square in Figure 6. Both parents in this example have normal color vision. Notice, however, that the mother is a carrier of colorblindness. A **carrier** is a person who has one recessive allele for a trait and one dominant allele. Although a carrier does not have the trait, the carrier can pass the recessive allele on to his or her offspring. In the case of sex-linked traits, only females can be carriers.

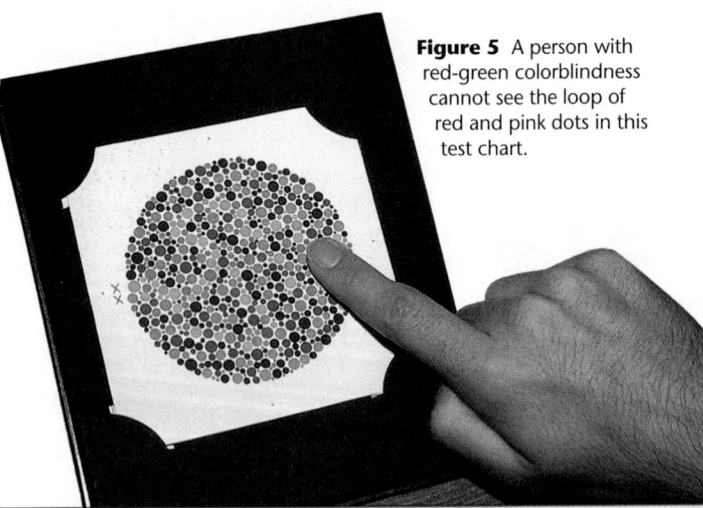

Figure 5 A person with red-green colorblindness cannot see the loop of red and pink dots in this test chart.

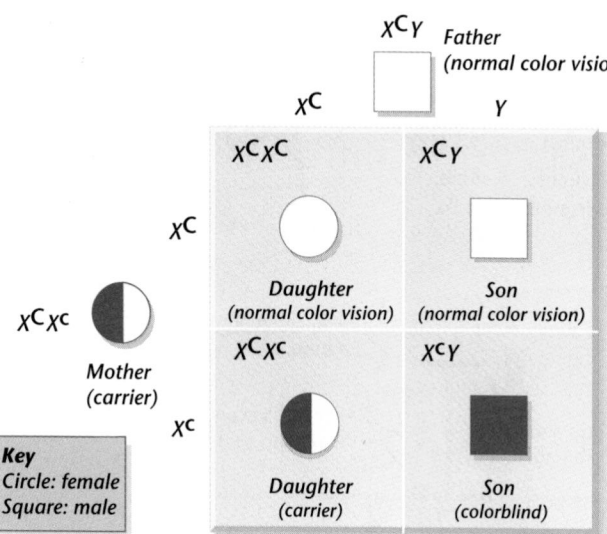

Father
(normal color vision)

$X^C Y$

X^C Y

X^C

$X^C X^C$ $X^C Y$

Daughter
(normal color vision)

Son
(normal color vision)

$X^C X^c$

Mother
(carrier)

X^c

$X^C X^c$ $X^c Y$

Daughter
(carrier)

Son
(colorblind)

Key
Circle: female
Square: male

Figure 6 Red-green color-blindness is a sex-linked trait. A girl who receives only one recessive allele (written X^c) for red-green colorblindness will not have the trait. However, a boy who receives one recessive allele will be colorblind. *Applying Concepts What allele combination would a daughter need to inherit to be colorblind?*

As you can see in Figure 6, there is a 25 percent probability that this couple will have a colorblind child. Notice that none of the couple's daughters will be colorblind. On the other hand, the sons have a 50 percent probability of being colorblind. For a female to be colorblind, she must inherit two recessive alleles for colorblindness, one from each parent. A male needs to inherit only one recessive allele. This is because there is no gene for color vision on the Y chromosome. Thus, there is no allele that could mask the recessive allele on the X chromosome.

Pedigrees

Imagine that you are a geneticist interested in studying inheritance patterns in humans. What would you do? You can't set up crosses with people as Mendel did with peas. Instead, you would need to trace the inheritance of traits through many generations in a number of families.

One tool that geneticists use to trace the inheritance of traits in humans is a pedigree. A **pedigree** is a chart or "family tree" that tracks which members of a family have a particular trait. The trait recorded in a pedigree can be an ordinary trait such as the widow's peak, or it could be a sex-linked trait such as colorblindness. In *Exploring a Pedigree* on page 124, you can trace the inheritance of colorblindness through three generations of a family.

☑ *Checkpoint* How is a pedigree like a "family tree"?

Chapter 4 **123**

Media and Technology

 Transparencies "Exploring a Pedigree," Transparency 17

Answers to Self-Assessment

Caption Question

Figure 6 A daughter would need to inherit two X^c alleles.

☑ *Checkpoint*

A pedigree is like a "family tree" in that it traces the inheritance of a trait through the generations of a family.

Including All Students

Materials *white, red, and green pipe cleaners*
Time 15 minutes

Provide hands-on learners with an opportunity to make a three-dimensional model to help them understand sex-linked inheritance. Have students twist together two white pipe cleaners to represent a normal X chromosome, a red pipe cleaner and a green pipe cleaner to represent an X chromosome with the allele for red-green colorblindness, and a single white pipe cleaner to represent a Y chromosome. Encourage students to use their models to represent several different matings and their expected outcomes. Then ask: **What is the phenotype of each individual represented in your model?** *(Students' answers should show that they understand that males are colorblind when they inherit just one allele for colorblindness.)* **learning modality: kinesthetic**

Pedigrees

EXPLORING
a Pedigree

Check that students understand the symbols in the pedigree by asking: **How many married couples are there in the second generation?** *(three)* **In all three generations, how many males are colorblind?** *(two)* **How many females are carriers?** *(four)* Then check that students understand sex-linked recessive inheritance by asking: **Which third-generation individuals could have colorblind daughters?** *(The two carrier females and the colorblind male, if he marries a colorblind female.)* **learning modality: visual**

Ongoing Assessment

Skills Check Have students solve the following problem: Mary and her mother are both colorblind. Is Mary's father colorblind, too? How do you know? *(Because Mary is colorblind, she must have inherited an X^c allele from each parent. Therefore, Mary's father's genotype must be $X^c Y$, so he is colorblind, too.)*

3 Assess

Section 1 Review Answers

1. Such traits are controlled by many genes and influenced by environment.
2. Because males have one X chromosome, alleles on the X chromosome, whether dominant or recessive, are always expressed. Males will be colorblind if they have one allele, and females need two recessive alleles to be colorblind.
3. It is a chart that tracks which members of a family have a particular trait. They are used by geneticists as tools for tracing inheritance.
4. Yes, if both parents are heterozygous for widow's peak and the child inherits a recessive allele for straight hairline from each parent. No, because the parents each have two recessive alleles for straight hairline, so the child will inherit two recessive alleles.

Check Your Progress

CHAPTER PROJECT

Check that students' pedigrees cover at least three generations and that the second generation consists of five children. Make sure the pedigrees do not contain any errors before students start using them to show inheritance patterns. Also check that students have chosen traits controlled by single genes.

Performance Assessment

Drawing Have students draw a pedigree showing the inheritance of a single recessive allele, starting with first generation genotypes of $Aa \times Aa$ and continuing for three generations.

EXPLORING a Pedigree

This pedigree traces the occurrence of colorblindness in three generations of a family. Colorblindness is a sex-linked trait that is controlled by a recessive allele. Notice that specific symbols are used in pedigrees to communicate genetic information.

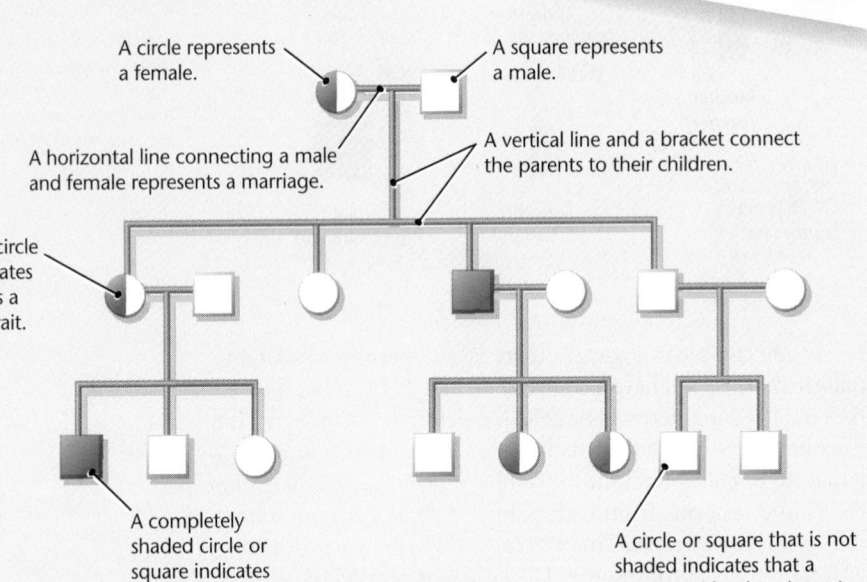

A circle represents a female.

A square represents a male.

A horizontal line connecting a male and female represents a marriage.

A vertical line and a bracket connect the parents to their children.

A half-shaded circle or square indicates that a person is a carrier of the trait.

A completely shaded circle or square indicates that a person has the trait.

A circle or square that is not shaded indicates that a person neither has the trait nor is a carrier of the trait.

Section 1 Review

1. Why do human traits such as height and skin color have many different phenotypes?
2. Explain why red-green colorblindness is more common in males than in females.
3. What is a pedigree? How are pedigrees used?
4. **Thinking Critically Predicting** Could two people with widow's peaks have a child with a straight hairline? Could two people with straight hairlines have a child with a widow's peak? Explain.

124

Check Your Progress

CHAPTER PROJECT

By now, you should be creating your pedigree for the first trait you chose. Start with one couple, and show two generations of offspring. The couple should have five children. It is up to you to decide how many children each of those children has. Use Punnett squares to make sure that your imaginary family's inheritance pattern follows the laws of genetics.

Background

Facts and Figures Traits controlled by sex-linked recessive alleles are unique in appearing to skip generations in a pedigree. Such traits do not pass from a man to his sons. Instead they pass from a man through his daughters, who do not have the trait but are carriers, to his grandsons. When a trait shows this inheritance pattern, it is likely to be controlled by a sex-linked recessive allele.

Program Resources

♦ **Unit 1 Resources** 4-1 Review and Reinforce, p. 105; 4-1 Enrich, p. 106

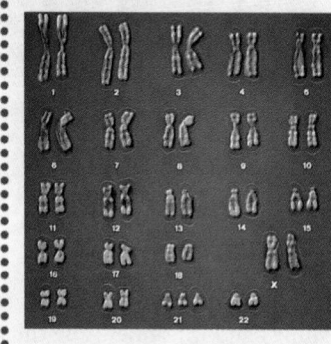

DISCOVER .... ACTIVITY

How Many Chromosomes?

The photo at the left shows the chromosomes from a cell of a person with Down syndrome, a genetic disorder. The chromosomes have been sorted into pairs.

1. Count the number of chromosomes in the photo.

2. How does the number of chromosomes compare to the usual number of chromosomes in human cells?

Think It Over

Inferring How do you think a cell could have ended up with this number of chromosomes? (*Hint:* Think about the events that occur during meiosis.)

The air inside the stadium was hot and still. The crowd cheered loudly as eight runners approached the starting blocks. The runners shook out their arms and legs to loosen up their muscles and calm their jitters. When the starter raised the gun, all eyes focused on the runners. At the crack of the starter's gun, the runners leaped into motion and sprinted down the track.

Seconds later, the race was over. The runners, bursting with pride, hugged each other and their coaches. It didn't matter where each of the runners placed. All that mattered was that they had finished the race and done their best. These athletes were running in the Special Olympics, a competition for people with disabilities.

Many of the athletes who compete in the Special Olympics have disabilities that result from genetic disorders. A **genetic disorder** is an abnormal condition that a person inherits through genes or chromosomes. **Genetic disorders are caused by mutations, or changes in a person's DNA.** In some cases, a mutation occurs when sex cells form during meiosis. In other cases, a mutation that is already present in a parent's cells is passed on to the offspring. In this section, you will learn about some common genetic disorders.

GUIDE FOR READING

◆ What causes genetic disorders?

◆ How are genetic disorders diagnosed?

Reading Tip As you read, make a list of different types of genetic disorders. Write a sentence about each disorder.

A runner at the Special Olympics ▶

Chapter 4 **125**

Objectives

After completing the lesson, students will be able to

◆ describe the causes and symptoms of five human genetic disorders;

◆ explain how genetic disorders are diagnosed;

◆ describe the role of a genetic counselor.

Key Terms genetic disorder, amniocentesis, karyotype

1 Engage/Explore

Activating Prior Knowledge

Introduce human genetic disorders by asking: **What do you think a genetic disorder is?** (*An abnormal condition that is inherited*) **What are some genetic disorders you have heard about?** (*Accept all student responses without comment at this time.*) Write students' suggestions of genetic disorders on the board, so students can reevaluate the list at the end of the section.

.... DISCOVER ....

Skills Focus inferring
Time 10 minutes
Tips Provide any students who have vision problems with a hand lens for examining the photo.
Expected Outcome Students should count 47 chromosomes in the photo, or one more than the 46 chromosomes normally found in human cells, because there is an extra copy of chromosome 21.
Think It Over Students may correctly say that the extra chromosome is due to failure of the chromosomes to separate during meiosis.

Program Resources

◆ **Unit 1 Resources** 4-2 Lesson Plan, p. 107; 4-2 Section Summary, p. 108

Media and Technology

🎧 **Audio CD** English-Spanish Summary 4-2

READING STRATEGIES

Reading Tip Before students begin their lists, write the following terms on the board: *cystic fibrosis, sickle-cell disease, hemophilia,* and *Down syndrome.* Pronounce each term clearly, and have the students repeat it. Also have them write each term, spelling it correctly. Their sentences should distinguish between the diseases. Sample sentence: In cystic fibrosis, the body produces mucus that clogs the lungs and intestines.

2 Facilitate

Cystic Fibrosis

Building Inquiry Skills: Relating Cause and Effect

Point out that cystic fibrosis, like most genetic disorders, can be treated but not cured. Then ask: **What is the difference between a treatment and a cure for a disease like cystic fibrosis?** *(A cure eliminates the disease, and therefore the symptoms, whereas a treatment controls the symptoms without eliminating the disease.)* **What are some ways that cystic fibrosis can be treated?** *(Possible ways include drugs to prevent infections and physical therapy to break up mucus in the lungs.)* **How could a genetic disorder like cystic fibrosis be cured?** *(By changing or replacing the gene that causes the symptoms)* **learning modality: verbal**

Sickle-Cell Disease

Including All Students

Materials *poster board, marker*

ACTIVITY

Time 15 minutes

Reinforce the concept of codominance for hands-on learners by having them draw a two-generation pedigree for sickle-cell disease, starting with the genotypes of *Ss* × *Ss*. Remind students to include a key indicating which individuals in the pedigree have normal hemoglobin, one sickle-cell allele, and sickle-cell disease. Invite students to share their pedigrees with the rest of the class. Follow up by asking: **In terms of the genetics, why is having one sickle-cell allele different from being a carrier of cystic fibrosis?** *(People with one sickle-cell allele have both normal hemoglobin and sickle-cell hemoglobin because the allele for abnormal hemoglobin is codominant with the allele for normal hemoglobin. In contrast, people who are carriers of cystic fibrosis have no signs or symptoms of cystic fibrosis because the allele for cystic fibrosis is recessive to the normal allele.)* **learning modality: logical/mathematical**

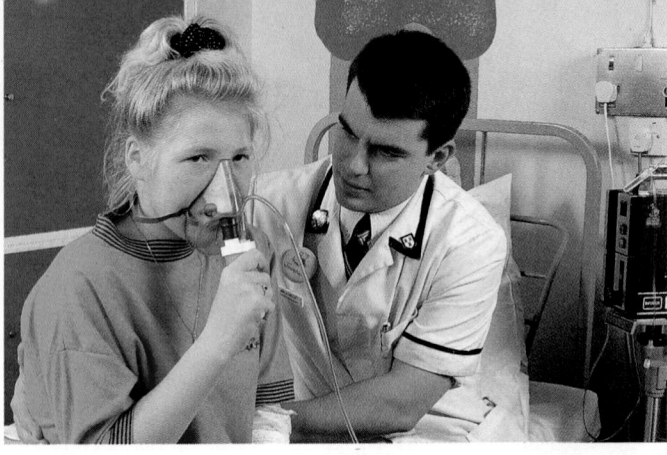

Figure 7 Cystic fibrosis is a genetic disorder that causes thick mucus to build up in a person's lungs and intestines. This patient is inhaling a fine mist that will help loosen the mucus in her lungs.

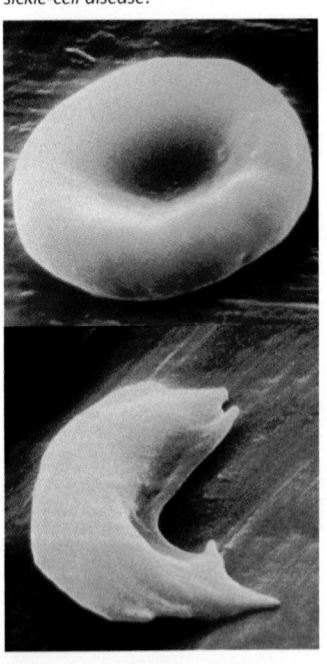

Figure 8 Normally, red blood cells are shaped like round disks (top). In a person with sickle-cell disease, red blood cells can become sickle-shaped (bottom). *Relating Cause and Effect What combination of alleles leads to sickle-cell disease?*

Cystic Fibrosis

Cystic fibrosis is a genetic disorder in which the body produces abnormally thick mucus in the lungs and intestines. The thick mucus fills the lungs, making it hard for the affected person to breathe. Bacteria that grow in the mucus can cause infections and, eventually, lung damage. In the intestines, the mucus makes it difficult for digestion to occur.

The mutation that leads to cystic fibrosis is carried on a recessive allele. The cystic fibrosis allele is most common among people whose ancestors are from Northern Europe. Every day in this country, four babies are born with cystic fibrosis.

Currently there is no cure for cystic fibrosis. Medical treatments include drugs to prevent infections and physical therapy to break up mucus in the lungs. Recent advances in scientists' understanding of the disease may lead to better treatments and longer lifespans for people with cystic fibrosis.

☑ *Checkpoint What are some symptoms of cystic fibrosis?*

Sickle-Cell Disease

Sickle-cell disease is a genetic disorder that affects the blood. The mutation that causes the disorder affects the production of an important protein called hemoglobin. Hemoglobin is the protein in red blood cells that carries oxygen. People with sickle-cell disease produce an abnormal form of hemoglobin. When oxygen concentrations are low, their red blood cells have an unusual sickle shape, as you can see in Figure 8.

Sickle-shaped red blood cells cannot carry as much oxygen as normal-shaped cells. Because of their shape, the cells become stuck in narrow blood vessels, blocking them. People with sickle-cell disease suffer from lack of oxygen in the blood and experience pain and weakness.

126

The allele for the sickle-cell trait is most common in people of African ancestry. About 9 percent of African Americans carry the sickle-cell allele. The allele for the sickle-cell trait is codominant with the normal allele. A person with two sickle-cell alleles will have the disease. A person with one sickle-cell allele will produce both normal hemoglobin and abnormal hemoglobin. This person usually will not have symptoms of the disease.

Currently, there is no cure for sickle-cell disease. People with sickle-cell disease are given drugs to relieve their painful symptoms and to prevent blockages in blood vessels. As with cystic fibrosis, scientists are hopeful that new, successful treatments will soon be found.

Hemophilia

Hemophilia is a genetic disorder in which a person's blood clots very slowly or not at all. People with the disorder do not produce one of the proteins needed for normal blood clotting. A person with hemophilia can bleed to death from a minor cut or scrape. The danger of internal bleeding from small bumps and bruises is also very high.

Hemophilia is an example of a disorder that is caused by a recessive allele on the X chromosome. Because hemophilia is a sex-linked disorder, it occurs more frequently in males than in females. **INTEGRATING HEALTH** People with hemophilia must get regular doses of the missing clotting protein. In general, people with hemophilia can lead normal lives. However, they are advised to avoid contact sports and other activities that could cause internal injuries.

Figure 9 Empress Alexandra of Russia (center row, left) passed the allele for hemophilia to her son Alexis (front).

Social Studies CONNECTION

Hemophilia has affected European history. Queen Victoria of England had a son and three grandsons with hemophilia. Victoria, at least two of her daughters, and four of her granddaughters were carriers of the disease.

As Victoria's descendants passed the hemophilia allele to their offspring, hemophilia spread through the royal families of Europe. For example, Empress Alexandra, Queen Victoria's granddaughter, married the Russian Czar Nicholas II in 1894. Alexandra, a carrier of hemophilia, passed the disease to her son Alexis, who was heir to the throne.

A monk named Rasputin convinced Alexandra that he could cure Alexis. As a result of his control over Alexandra, Rasputin was able to control the Czar as well. The people's anger at Rasputin's influence may have played a part in the Russian Revolution of 1917, in which the Czar was overthrown.

In Your Journal

Imagine that you are Empress Alexandra. Write a diary entry expressing your feelings and unanswered questions about Alexis's condition.

Media and Technology

Exploring Life Science Videodisc
Unit 5, Side 1, "An Unusual Mutation"

Chapter 4

Answers to Self-Assessment

Caption Question

Figure 8 The combination of two recessive alleles leads to sickle-cell disease.

✓ Checkpoint

Some symptoms of cystic fibrosis are difficulty breathing, frequent infections, and difficulty digesting food.

Hemophilia

Integrating Health

Give a group of students who need extra challenges a chance to research and create a flowchart showing how blood clots form. Each group member should research at least one source. Group members should then compile their information and collaborate on creating the flowchart. Have one or more group members explain the flowchart to the rest of the class. Then ask: **How does the hemophilia allele interfere with blood clotting?** (*By leading to the lack of a protein, which is essential for blood to clot*) Challenge group members to point out this step in the flowchart. **cooperative learning**

Social Studies CONNECTION

Provide background for the feature by informing students that the presence of the hemophilia allele in Queen Victoria is believed to have been created by a new mutation. This is based on the fact that neither Victoria's husband nor any of her male relatives in earlier generations had the disorder.

In Your Journal Help students put themselves in Alexandra's place by urging them to imagine what it was like for a child to live with hemophilia, especially in the late 1800s before the development of blood transfusions and blood-clotting proteins. Every cut or nosebleed could cause a life-threatening loss of blood. Ask: **How do you think her son's hemophilia might have affected Alexandra's relationship with him?** (*Alexandra might have been overly protective of her son and very focused on caring for his health and safety.*) Point out that this could have made Alexandra fall more easily under the influence of Rasputin. **learning modality: verbal**

Ongoing Assessment

Skills Check Have students create a table comparing and contrasting cystic fibrosis, sickle-cell disease, and hemophilia.

Huntington's Disease

Building Inquiry Skills: Comparing and Contrasting

Have students use Punnett squares to compare the inheritance pattern of a disorder caused by a dominant allele (such as Huntington's disease) to one caused by a recessive allele (such as cystic fibrosis).

Down Syndrome

Demonstration

Materials *colored chalk*
Time 10 minutes

Demonstrate with a simple drawing how the production of sex cells with an abnormal number of chromosomes can lead to Down syndrome. Start with one parent cell containing two colored Xs to represent a pair of chromosomes that has replicated. Illustrate these chromosomes as the cell goes through Meiosis I and Meiosis II (see page 105). Point out that the pairs can fail to separate in either stage. Then draw four circles to represent sex cells. Distribute the chromosomes among the sex cells unequally, so that one contains two chromosomes and one contains none. Beside each sex cell, draw another small circle containing one white line, to represent a normal sex cell from the other parent. Finally, draw four circles to represent the possible individuals formed when sex cells unite. Two should be normal, one should contain only one white chromosome, and one should contain one white and two colored chromosomes. Ask: **Which individual will have Down syndrome?** (*The one with three chromosomes*) **learning modality: visual**

Diagnosing Genetic Disorders

 Integrating Technology

Tell students that amniocentesis is often recommended for older mothers because they have a greater risk of having babies with Down syndrome. Ask: **For what other women do you think amniocentesis is recommended?** (*Women who have, or whose husbands have, a family history of genetic disorders.*) **learning modality: logical/mathematical**

128

Huntington's Disease

Huntington's disease is an example of a genetic disorder that is caused by a dominant allele. Every individual who inherits the allele develops Huntington's disease. A person who has the allele has a 50 percent chance of passing it on to his or her offspring.

Huntington's disease is fatal, although symptoms do not usually appear until a person is over 30 years old. The disease causes the gradual breakdown of cells in the brain, leading to death.

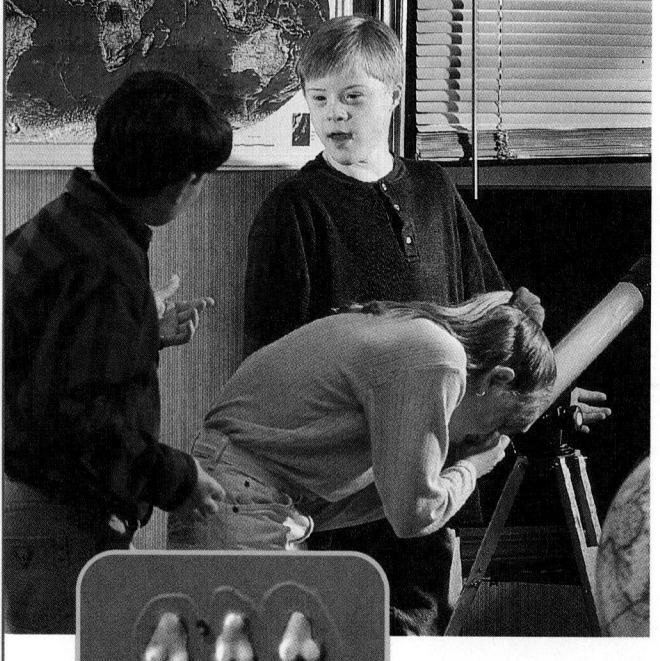

Figure 10 Down syndrome is a genetic disorder in which a person's cells have an extra copy of chromosome 21. Although people with Down syndrome have some mental and physical limitations, they can lead active, productive lives.

128

Down Syndrome

Some genetic disorders are the result of too many or too few chromosomes. In one such disorder, called Down syndrome, a person's cells have an extra copy of chromosome 21. The extra chromosome is the result of an error during meiosis. Recall that in meiosis, cells divide and chromosomes separate to produce sex cells with half the normal number of chromosomes. Down syndrome most often occurs when chromosomes fail to separate properly during meiosis.

People with Down syndrome have a distinctive physical appearance, and have some degree of mental retardation. Heart defects are also common, but can be treated. Despite their limitations, many people with Down syndrome lead full, active lives.

Diagnosing Genetic Disorders

INTEGRATING TECHNOLOGY Years ago, doctors had only Punnett squares and pedigrees to help them predict whether a child might have a genetic disorder. **Today doctors use tools such as amniocentesis and karyotypes to help detect genetic disorders.**

Before a baby is born, doctors can use a procedure called **amniocentesis** (am nee oh sen TEE sis) to determine whether the baby will have some genetic disorders. During amniocentesis, a doctor uses a very long needle to remove a small amount of the fluid that surrounds the developing baby. The fluid contains cells from the baby.

The doctor then examines the chromosomes from the cells. To do this, the doctor creates a karyotype. A **karyotype** (KA ree uh typ) is a picture of all the chromosomes in a cell. The chromosomes in a karyotype are arranged in pairs. A karyotype can reveal whether a developing baby has the correct number of chromosomes in its cells and whether it is a boy or a girl. If you did the Discover activity, you saw a karyotype from a girl with Down syndrome.

Genetic Counseling

A couple that has a family history or concern about a genetic disorder may turn to a genetic counselor for advice. Genetic counselors help couples understand their chances of having a child with a particular genetic disorder. Genetic counselors use tools such as karyotypes, pedigree charts, and Punnett squares to help them in their work.

Suppose, for example, that a husband and wife both have a history of cystic fibrosis in their families. If they are considering having children, they might seek the advice of a genetic counselor. The genetic counselor might order a test to determine whether they are carriers of the allele for cystic fibrosis. The genetic counselor would then apply the same principles of probability that you learned about in Chapter 3 to calculate the couple's chances of having a child with cystic fibrosis.

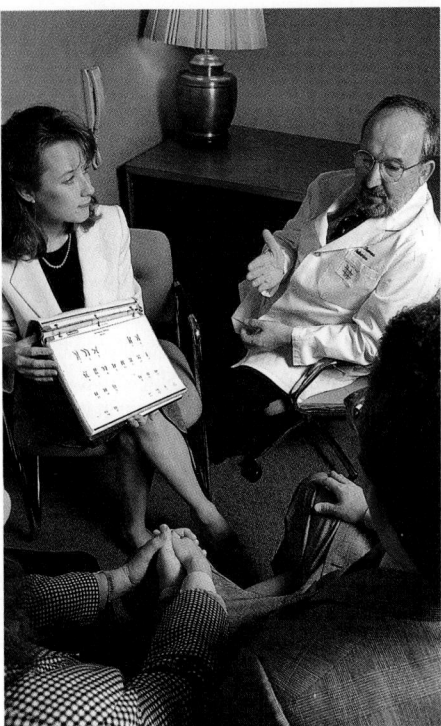

Figure 11 Couples may meet with a genetic counselor and their doctor in order to understand their chances of having a child with a genetic disorder.

Section 2 Review

1. Explain how genetic disorders occur in humans. Give two examples of genetic disorders.
2. Describe two tools that doctors use to detect genetic disorders.
3. How do the cells of people with Down syndrome differ from those of others? How might this difference arise?
4. **Thinking Critically Problem Solving** A couple with a family history of hemophilia is about to have a baby girl. What information about the parents would you want to know? How would this information help you determine whether the baby will have hemophilia?

> **CHAPTER PROJECT**
> ### Check Your Progress
> At this point, you should begin to trace the inheritance of another trait through the same family members that are in your first pedigree. Also, start making your family "photo" album. Will you use drawings or some other method to show what the family members look like? (*Hint:* Photo albums show phenotypes. Remember that more than one genotype can have the same phenotype.)

Program Resources

◆ **Unit 1 Resources** 4-2 Review and Reinforce, p. 109; 4-2 Enrich, p. 110

Inquiry Challenge
Challenge students to assume they are genetic counselors who must determine the chance of a couple having a child with cystic fibrosis, when both husband and wife are carriers. (*Students should draw a Punnett square for two heterozygotes. The Punnett square should show that 25% of the couple's children would be likely to inherit two recessive alleles.*) Ask: **If the couple already has three normal children, what is the chance that their fourth child will have cystic fibrosis?** (*25%; each child has a 25% chance of having cystic fibrosis.*) **learning modality: logical/mathematical**

3 Assess

Section 2 Review Answers
1. Genetic disorders occur when mutations cause changes in DNA. Cystic fibrosis, sickle-cell disease, hemophilia
2. In amniocentesis, cells are removed from the fluid surrounding the baby; in karyotypes, a picture of the chromosomes is analyzed for abnormal chromosomes.
3. They have an extra copy of chromosome 21, which might arise if the chromosomes fail to separate properly during meiosis.
4. You would want to know if the parents have hemophilia or are carriers. This would help you predict the chances of their baby girl having hemophilia.

> **CHAPTER PROJECT**
> ### Check Your Progress
> By now students should be working on their pedigrees for the second trait. Remind them to use the same basic pedigree as they did for the first trait. Ask students how they plan to show individuals in the family album.

Performance Assessment

Skills Check Have students explain how amniocentesis and a karyotype can be used to determine whether a developing baby will have Down syndrome.

Family Puzzles

Preparing for Inquiry

Key Concept By analyzing pedigrees, you can determine the pattern of inheritance of a trait and the chance of any given individual inheriting specific alleles.

Skills Objectives Students will be able to
◆ interpret data on phenotypes to construct family pedigrees;
◆ draw conclusions from the pedigrees about the types of alleles controlling the traits and the chances of given individuals inheriting specific alleles for the traits.

Time 40 minutes

Advance Planning To save time, you can cut and label the index cards for students before class begins.

Alternative Materials Instead of index cards to represent alleles, students can use marbles, game chips, beads, or other similar objects, with different colors representing the two different alleles in each case study.

Guiding Inquiry

Invitation Before students begin, draw a simple pedigree on the chalkboard showing a wife with a genetic disorder and a healthy husband who have an affected daughter and a healthy son. Ask: **Can you tell if the trait shown in this pedigree is controlled by a dominant or recessive allele?** *(No, there isn't enough information.)* Extend the pedigree back one generation by adding two healthy parents for the wife. Then ask: **Now can you tell if the trait is controlled by a dominant or recessive allele?** *(The trait must be controlled by a recessive allele; otherwise, at least one of the wife's parents would also have the trait.)* Point out to students that the more generations there are in a pedigree, the more obvious the pattern of inheritance becomes, as they will see when the do this lab.

Introducing the Procedure

◆ Check that students remember how to draw pedigrees. For example, ask: **How do you show in a pedigree that**

a man and woman are married? *(By linking their symbols with a horizontal line)* If necessary, suggest students review *Exploring a Pedigree* on page 124.

Troubleshooting the Experiment

◆ Before students answer the questions, check that they have drawn their pedigrees correctly and labeled each individual with the appropriate genotype(s). You may want to have pairs of students compare pedigrees to detect any errors.

◆ Tell students they will need to draw Punnett squares to find the answers to Questions 2 and 4.

Expected Outcome

Students should be able to use the data provided to construct a pedigree for each family. From the pedigrees, students should be able to determine the type of allele controlling the skin condition and the probability of particular individuals inheriting each condition.

Family Puzzles

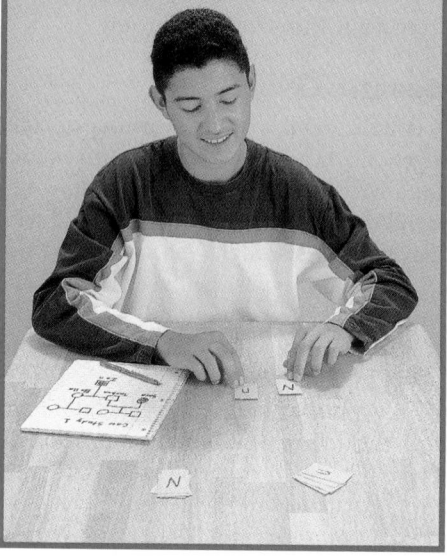

Imagine that you are a genetic counselor. Two couples come to you for advice. Their family histories are summarized in the boxes labeled *Case Study 1* and *Case Study 2*. They want to understand more about certain genetic disorders that run in their families. In this lab, you will find answers to their questions.

Problem

How can you investigate inheritance patterns in families?

Materials

12 index cards
scissors
marker

Procedure

Part 1 Investigating Case Study 1

1. Read over Case Study 1. In your notebook, draw a pedigree that shows all the family members. Use circles to represent the females, and squares to represent the males. Shade in the circles or squares representing the individuals who have cystic fibrosis.

> **Case Study 1: Joshua and Bella**
> ◆ Joshua and Bella have a son named Ian. Ian has been diagnosed with cystic fibrosis.
> ◆ Joshua and Bella are both healthy.
> ◆ Bella's parents are both healthy.
> ◆ Joshua's parents are both healthy.
> ◆ Joshua's sister, Sara, has cystic fibrosis.

2. You know that cystic fibrosis is controlled by a recessive allele. To help you figure out Joshua and Bella's family pattern, create a set of cards to represent the alleles. Cut each of six index cards into four smaller cards. On 12 of the small cards, write *N* to represent the dominant normal allele. On the other 12 small cards, write *n* for the recessive allele.

3. Begin by using the cards to represent Ian's alleles. Since he has cystic fibrosis, what alleles must he have? Write in this genotype next to the pedigree symbol for Ian.

4. Joshua's sister, Sara, also has cystic fibrosis. What alleles does she have? Write in this genotype next to the pedigree symbol that represents Sara.

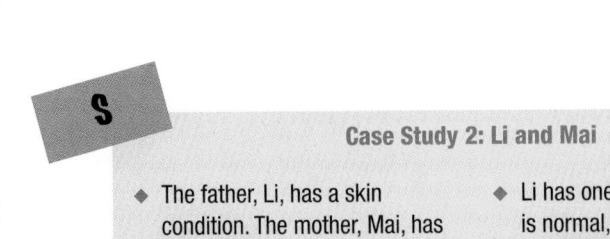

Case Study 2: Li and Mai

- The father, Li, has a skin condition. The mother, Mai, has normal skin.
- Li and Mai's first child, a girl named Gemma, has the same skin condition as Li.
- Mai's sister has a similar skin condition, but Mai's parents do not.

- Li has one brother whose skin is normal, and one sister who has the skin condition.
- Li's mother has the skin condition. His father does not.
- Li's family lives in a heavily wooded area. His family has always thought the skin condition was a type of allergy.

5. Now use the cards to figure out what genotypes Joshua and Bella must have. Write their genotypes next to their symbols in the pedigree.

6. Work with the cards to figure out the genotypes of all other family members. Fill in each person's genotype next to his or her symbol in the pedigree. If more than one genotype is possible, write in both genotypes.

Part 2 Investigating Case Study 2

7. Read over Case Study 2.

8. You suspect that Gemma and Li's skin condition is caused by an inherited recessive allele. Begin to investigate this possibility by drawing a family pedigree in your notebook. Use shading to indicate which individuals have the skin condition.

9. Fill in the genotype *ss* beside each individual who has the skin condition. Then use cards as you did in Case Study 1 to figure out each family member's genotype. If more than one genotype is possible, fill in both genotypes.

Analyze and Conclude

1. In Case Study 1, what were the genotypes of Joshua's parents? What were the genotypes of Bella's parents?

2. In Case Study 1, Joshua also has a brother. What is the probability that he has cystic fibrosis? Explain.

3. Can you conclude that the skin condition in Case Study 2 is most likely an inherited trait controlled by a recessive allele? Explain.

4. What is the probability that Mai and Li's next child will have the skin condition? Explain.

5. Apply Why do genetic counselors need information about many generations of a family in order to draw conclusions about a hereditary condition?

More to Explore

Review the two pedigrees that you just studied. What data suggests that the traits are not sex-linked? Explain.

condition is controlled by a recessive allele. At least one of Mai's parents would have the skin condition if the allele were dominant, but both of the parents have normal skin.

4. Because one of the parents is heterozygous *(Ss)* and one is homozygous *(ss)* for the skin condition, there is a 50 percent chance of each child inheriting two *s* alleles and having the skin condition.

5. Genetic counselors cannot usually draw firm conclusions about a hereditary condition with information about just one or two generations, because more than one inheritance pattern may explain the facts when the information is so limited. For example, if the only information in Case Study 2 were the phenotypes of Li, Mai, and Gemma, sex-linked inheritance could not be ruled out.

Extending the Inquiry

More to Explore Data showing that the traits are not sex-linked include the observation that the traits affect males and females about equally. If the skin condition in Case Study 2 were sex-linked, Li's brother also would have inherited the condition from their mother, but he did not. If cystic fibrosis in Case Study 1 were sex-linked, Ian would have inherited the disorder from his mother's side of the family, not his father's side of the family, as appears to have been the case.

Case Study 1: Joshua and Bella

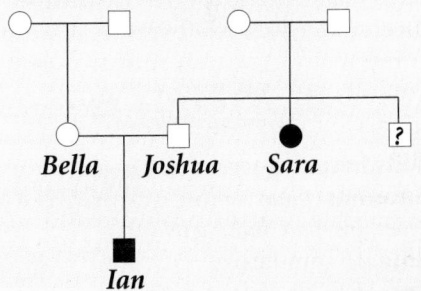

Case Study 2: Li and Mai

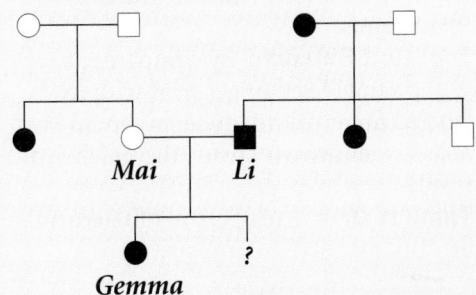

Analyze and Conclude

1. Joshua's parents are both heterozygous *(Nn)*. The genotypes of Bella's parents cannot be determined for certain, but at least one must be heterozygous; the other could be either heterozygous or homozygous *(NN)*.

2. Because both parents are heterozygous *(Nn)*, there is a 25 percent chance of each child inheriting two *n* alleles and having cystic fibrosis.

3. All the evidence in the family's pedigree supports the conclusion that the skin

Program Resources

- **Unit 1 Resources** Chapter 4 Real-World Lab, pp. 115–117

SECTION 3 Advances in Genetics

Objectives

After completing the lesson, students will be able to
♦ describe three ways in which people have developed organisms with desired traits;
♦ identify some uses of DNA fingerprinting;
♦ state the goal of the Human Genome Project.

Key Terms selective breeding, inbreeding, hybridization, clone, genetic engineering, gene therapy, genome

1 Engage/Explore

Activating Prior Knowledge

Introduce the section by helping students appreciate the variation that has been selectively bred into dogs. Ask: **What are some breeds of dogs that have very different characteristics?** (*Possible answers might include dachshund, Chihuahua, and Great Dane.*) Explain that the different breeds were produced by mating animals that have certain desirable traits. In this section, students will learn about selective breeding and other ways of producing organisms with desirable traits.

DISCOVER

Skills Focus observing
Materials *plain white paper, ink pad, hand lens*
Time 15 minutes
Tips Help students recognize similarities and differences among the fingerprints by pointing out examples of whirls, loops, and other standard features of fingerprints.
Expected Outcome By comparing a group's unlabeled fingerprint with its labeled fingerprints, students should be able to identify who made the unlabeled print.
Think It Over Each person's fingerprints are unique.

SECTION 3 Advances in Genetics

DISCOVER ······················· ACTIVITY

What Do Fingerprints Reveal?

1. Label a sheet of paper with your name. Then roll one of your fingers from side to side on an ink pad. Make a fingerprint by carefully rolling your inked finger from side to side on the paper.

2. Divide into groups. Each group should choose one member to use the same finger to make a second fingerprint on a sheet of paper. Leave the paper unlabeled.

3. Exchange your group's fingerprints with those from another group. Compare each labeled fingerprint with the fingerprint on the unlabeled paper. Decide whose fingerprint it is.

4. Wash your hands after completing this activity.

Think It Over
Observing Why are fingerprints a useful tool for identifying people?

GUIDE FOR READING

♦ What are three ways in which an organism's traits can be altered?
♦ What is the goal of the Human Genome Project?

Reading Tip As you read, make a concept map of the methods used to produce organisms with desirable traits. Include at least one example of each technique.

Dolly ▼

In the summer of 1996, a lamb named Dolly was born in Scotland. Dolly was an ordinary lamb in every way except one. The fertilized cell that developed into Dolly was produced in a laboratory by geneticists using experimental techniques. You will learn more about the techniques used by the geneticists later in the section.

Although the techniques used to create Dolly are new, the idea of producing organisms with specific traits is not. For thousands of years, people have tried to produce plants and animals with desirable traits. **Three methods that people have used to develop organisms with desirable traits are selective breeding, cloning, and genetic engineering.**

Selective Breeding

More than 5,000 years ago, people living in what is now central Mexico discovered that a type of wild grass could be used as food. They saved the seeds from those plants that produced the best food, and planted them to grow new plants. By repeating this process over many generations of plants, they developed an early variety of the food crop we now call corn. The process of selecting a few organisms with desired traits to serve as parents of the next generation is called **selective breeding.**

People have used selective breeding with many different plants and animals. Breeding programs usually focus on increasing the value of the plant or animal to people. For

READING STRATEGIES

Reading Tip Help students start their concept maps by drawing the first circle and filling it in. Then help them develop the next row by suggesting verbs that will work. Students' concept maps might begin as follows:

Trait-specific organism
can be produced by

Study and Comprehension Before students read the section, suggest that they make an outline using the boldfaced headings and subheadings. Then, as students read the section, urge them to add a sentence or two under each heading to summarize the main points. Encourage visual learners to preview the section by looking at the figures and reading the captions.

example, dairy cows are bred to produce larger quantities of milk. Many varieties of fruits and vegetables are bred to resist diseases and insect pests.

Inbreeding One useful selective breeding technique is called inbreeding. **Inbreeding** involves crossing two individuals that have identical or similar sets of alleles. The organisms that result from inbreeding have alleles that are very similar to those of their parents. Mendel used inbreeding to produce purebred pea plants for his experiments.

One goal of inbreeding is to produce breeds of animals with specific traits. For example, by only crossing horses with exceptional speed, breeders can produce purebred horses that can run very fast. Purebred dogs, such as Labrador retrievers and German shepherds, were produced by inbreeding.

Unfortunately, because inbred organisms are genetically very similar, inbreeding reduces an offspring's chances of inheriting new allele combinations. Inbreeding also increases the probability that organisms may inherit alleles that lead to genetic disorders. For example, inherited hip problems are common in many breeds of dogs.

Hybridization Another selective breeding technique is called hybridization. In **hybridization** (hy brid ih ZAY shun), breeders cross two genetically different individuals. The hybrid organism that results is bred to have the best traits from both parents. For example, a farmer might cross corn that produces many kernels with corn that is resistant to disease. The result might be a hybrid corn plant with both of the desired traits. Today, most crops grown on farms and in gardens were produced by hybridization.

Figure 12 For thousands of years, people have used selective breeding to produce plants and animals with desirable traits. *Making Generalizations What are some traits for which corn may be bred?*

Chapter 4 **133**

Media and Technology

 Audio CD English-Spanish Summary 4-3

 Exploring Life Science Videodisc Unit 5, Side 1, "Breeding for Dollars"

Chapter 2

Answers to Self-Assessment

Caption Question

Figure 12 Some traits include resistance to disease and the production of ears with many kernels.

Program Resources

◆ **Unit 1 Resources** 4-3 Lesson Plan, p. 111; 4-3 Section Summary, p. 112

2 Facilitate

Selective Breeding

Cultural Diversity

Provide students with additional information about selective breeding to help them appreciate its significance throughout human history. For example, thousands of years ago, some Native Americans began domesticating plant species. They genetically changed plant species by cross-pollinating plants with desired traits. Eventually, more than 100 different species of plants were domesticated, of which maize, or corn, is probably the most important. Maize was selectively bred by Native Americans to have larger, more numerous kernels. Conclude by asking: **How do you think the selective breeding of plants such as maize would have affected the people who depended on the plants for food?** *(It would have increased the amount of food available, so people could have been better fed or more people could have been fed.)* **learning modality: verbal**

Real-Life Learning

Materials *seed catalogs*
Time 10 minutes

Help students appreciate the importance of hybridization in real life by giving them an opportunity to examine seed catalogs and read about hybrid varieties of flowers, vegetables, and fruits that have been developed by plant breeders. Ask: **What are some traits for which hybrids have been bred?** *(Students might name rapid growth or improved flavor, among many other possible traits.)* **learning modality: verbal**

Ongoing Assessment

Drawing Have students draw two Punnett squares, one to represent inbreeding and one to represent hybridization. *(To represent inbreeding, students should show a cross between individuals with the same genotype, such as AA $\times$ AA. To represent hybridization, students should show a cross between individuals with different genotypes, such as AA $\times$ aa.)*

Cloning

Demonstration

Materials *coleus plant, scissors, rooting solution, plant pot, vermiculite, water*
Time 5 minutes; 5 minutes two weeks later

Demonstrate how a plant can be cloned. Take a small cutting from a coleus plant, dip the cut end of the stem in rooting solution, and place the cutting in a pot of vermiculite. Keep the vermiculite moist, and after about two weeks gently pull the cutting out of the pot. Let students observe the tiny roots that have started to grow, and ask: **How is the new plant that grew from the cutting like the original plant from which the cutting was taken?** *(It is genetically identical to the original plant.)* **learning modality: visual**

Social Studies Connection

Inform students that the cloning of Dolly the sheep raised the possibility of large-scale animal cloning, and that this, in turn, raised many ethical issues. Challenge students to use the Internet or other resources to learn more about animal cloning by finding answers to such questions as: **Is animal cloning unnatural? Would it narrow genetic diversity too much? What are some of its possible uses?** Encourage students to form their own opinions on the subject and share their findings in an oral report to the class. **learning modality: verbal**

Genetic Engineering

Addressing Naive Conceptions

The term *genetic engineering* may conjure up images of mad scientists and Frankenstein-type monsters. Address this naive conception by describing one or more real-life examples of genetic engineering, such as the production of bacteria that can manufacture human insulin or corn plants that can resist disease. Then ask: **Why do you think people hold naive conceptions about genetic engineering?** *(Because of fictional accounts in movies and books or lack of knowledge)* **learning modality: verbal**

Figure 13 Plants can be easily cloned by making a cutting. Once the cutting has grown roots, it can be planted and will grow into a new plant. *Applying Concepts Why is the new plant considered to be a clone of the original plant?*

Cloning

One problem with selective breeding is that the breeder cannot control whether the desired allele will be passed from the parent to its offspring. This is because the transmission of alleles is determined by probability, as you learned in Chapter 3. For some organisms, another technique, called cloning, can be used to produce off-spring with desired traits. A **clone** is an organism that is genetically identical to the organism from which it was produced. This means that a clone has exactly the same genes as the organism from which it was produced. Cloning can be done in plants and animals, as well as other organisms.

Cloning Plants One way to produce a clone of a plant is through a cutting. A cutting is a small part of a plant, such as a leaf or a stem, that is cut from the plant. The cutting can grow into an entire new plant. The new plant is genetically identical to the plant from which the cutting was taken.

Cloning Animals Remember Dolly, the lamb described at the beginning of this section? Dolly was the first clone of an adult mammal ever produced. To create Dolly, researchers removed an egg cell from one sheep. The cell's nucleus was replaced with the nucleus from a cell of a six-year-old sheep. The egg was then implanted into the uterus of a third sheep. Five months later, Dolly was born. Dolly is genetically identical to the six-year-old sheep that supplied the nucleus. Dolly is a clone of that sheep.

Since scientists first cloned Dolly, pigs and calves have also been cloned. Scientists hope that cloning animals will allow humans to live healthier lives. For example, pigs that are being cloned have genes that will make their organs suitable for organ transplants into humans.

Checkpoint How can a clone of a plant be produced?

Genetic Engineering

In the past few decades, geneticists have developed another powerful technique for producing organisms with desired traits. In this process, called **genetic engineering,** genes from one organism are transferred into the DNA of another organism. Genetic engineering is sometimes called "gene splicing" because a DNA molecule is cut open and a gene from another organism is spliced into it. Genetic engineering can produce medicines and improve food crops, and may cure human genetic disorders.

Background

History of Science Since the structure of DNA was discovered in 1953, genetic research has advanced significantly. In 1959, Down syndrome was traced to the presence of an extra 21st chromosome, making it the first documented example of a genetic disorder. Geneticists successfully spliced together DNA segments from a toad cell and a bacterial cell, giving rise to the science of genetic engineering in 1973. In 1982, scientists inserted rat growth hormone genes into some fertilized mouse eggs. The eggs developed into mice that grew nearly twice as large as mice without the gene for rat growth hormone. In 1990, researchers successfully inserted a gene needed for the functioning of the human immune system into a patient with ADA, a fatal immune system disorder.

EXPLORING Genetic Engineering

Scientists use genetic engineering to create bacterial cells that produce important human proteins, such as insulin.

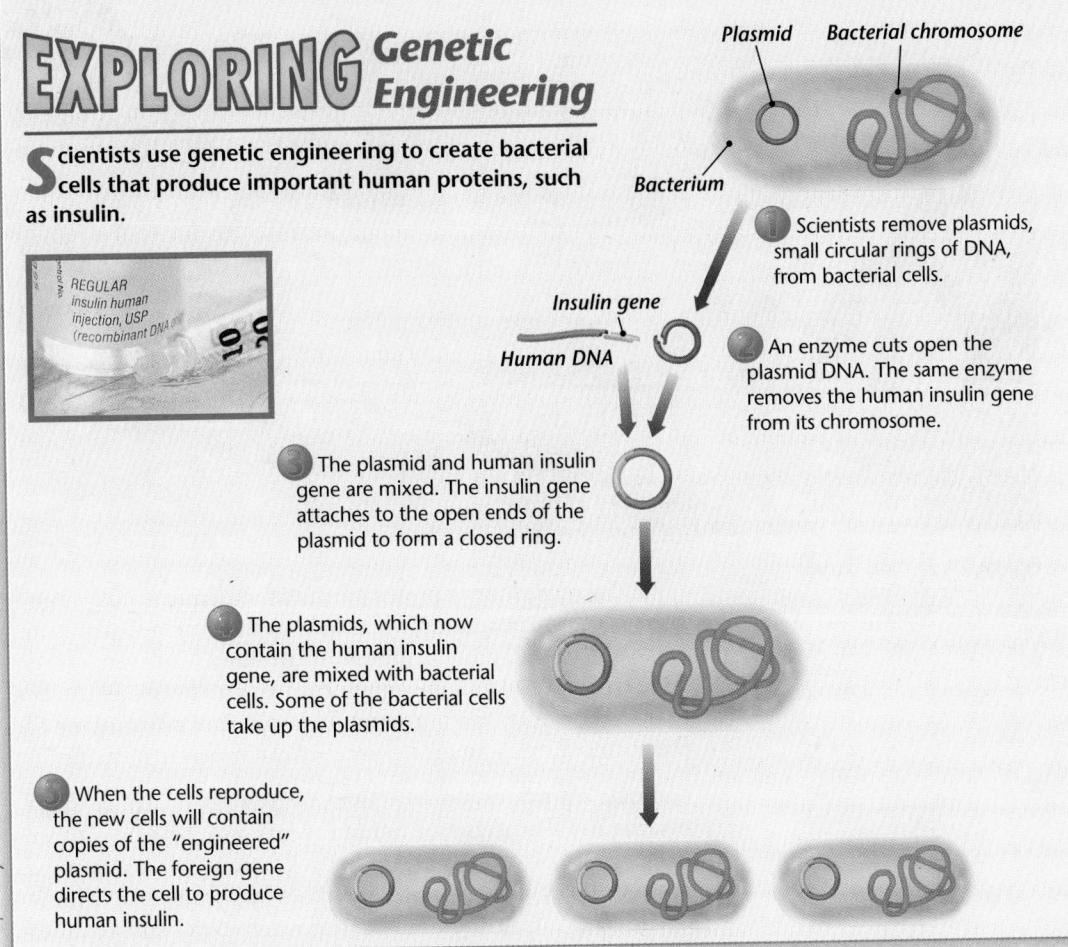

REGULAR insulin human injection, USP (recombinant DNA oris)

Plasmid **Bacterial chromosome**

Bacterium

Insulin gene

Human DNA

1 Scientists remove plasmids, small circular rings of DNA, from bacterial cells.

2 An enzyme cuts open the plasmid DNA. The same enzyme removes the human insulin gene from its chromosome.

3 The plasmid and human insulin gene are mixed. The insulin gene attaches to the open ends of the plasmid to form a closed ring.

4 The plasmids, which now contain the human insulin gene, are mixed with bacterial cells. Some of the bacterial cells take up the plasmids.

5 When the cells reproduce, the new cells will contain copies of the "engineered" plasmid. The foreign gene directs the cell to produce human insulin.

Genetic Engineering in Bacteria Researchers had their first successes with genetic engineering when they inserted DNA from other organisms into bacteria. Recall that the single DNA molecule of bacterial cells is found in the cytoplasm. Some bacterial cells also contain small circular pieces of DNA called plasmids.

In *Exploring Genetic Engineering*, you can see how scientists insert a human gene into the plasmid of a bacterium. Once the DNA is spliced into the plasmid, the bacterial cell and all its offspring will contain this human gene. As a result, the bacteria produce the protein that the human gene codes for, in this case insulin. Because bacteria reproduce quickly, large amounts of insulin can be produced in a short time. The insulin can be collected and used to treat people with diabetes, a disorder in which the body does not produce enough of this protein.

Media and Technology

📽 **Transparencies** "Exploring Genetic Engineering," Transparency 18

Answers to Self-Assessment

Caption Question

Figure 13 The new plant is genetically identical to the original plant.

☑ *Checkpoint*
By growing a cutting of the original plant

EXPLORING
Genetic Engineering

Provide students with background information about diabetes so they can appreciate the importance of genetically engineering bacteria to produce human insulin. Insulin is a hormone that cells need to absorb sugar from the blood for energy. People with Type I, or juvenile onset, diabetes cannot produce insulin. As a result, their cells are unable to absorb sugar from the blood, and the sugar level in their blood can become dangerously high. Taking insulin helps people with Type I diabetes control the level of sugar in their blood.

Guide students who need more help by asking questions that will require them to read the captions carefully. For example, ask: **What is a plasmid, and where is it found?** *(A small circular ring of DNA in a bacterial cell)* **Why are the bacteria in Step 5 able to produce human insulin?** *(Because they contain copies of the human insulin gene.)* **limited English proficiency**

Inquiry Challenge

Materials *two pieces of yarn of different colors, blunt scissors, tape*
Time 10 minutes

Challenge students to create a simple model of DNA with yarn and then to use the model to simulate gene splicing, as illustrated in *Exploring Genetic Engineering.* *(The most likely way is to arrange a piece of yarn of one color in a circle to represent a bacterial plasmid and to use the piece of yarn of the other color to represent a small section of human DNA. Gene splicing can be simulated by cutting both pieces of yarn, taping a piece of the "DNA" yarn to the piece of "plasmid" yarn, and reforming the circle.)* Ask: **What do the scissors represent in your model?** *(The enzyme that cuts the DNA)*
learning modality: kinesthetic

Ongoing Assessment

Skills Check Have students compare and contrast cloning and genetic engineering.

Genetic Engineering, continued

Inquiry Challenge

Challenge students to think of ways that plants could be genetically engineered to increase the production of food. Ask: **How could you genetically engineer a fruit, vegetable, or other food plant so that it would be more likely to survive and thrive?** *(Ways that food plants actually have been genetically engineered include making plants that are able to tolerate poor soil or resist disease.)* **learning modality: logical/mathematical**

Real-Life Learning

Point out that genetic engineering, particularly of food plants, has led to public concern about the potential consequences to consumers and the environment. Urge students who need extra challenges to learn more about the issues and form their own opinions. Then call on these students to debate the issues, with students on one side arguing that the genetic engineering of food plants should be unregulated and students on the other side arguing that the genetic engineering of food plants should be closely regulated or even outlawed. The debate should address such questions as: **What are the potential dangers of genetically engineered foods?** *(Potential dangers include the short and long term human health risks and the ecological impact that genetically engineered foods might have.)* **What are the potential benefits?** *(Foods might be more nutritious, keep longer, or be easier to transport. Also plants and animals can be genetically engineered to be raised under a wider range of conditions.)* After the debate, encourage the rest of the class to comment on which side was more convincing and why. **cooperative learning**

Figure 14 Scientists created this new variety of tomatoes using genetic engineering. The tomatoes taste better and keep longer than other varieties. *Making Judgments What other traits would be desirable in tomatoes?*

Today, many human proteins are produced in genetically engineered bacteria. For example, human growth hormone is a protein that controls the growth process in children. Children whose bodies do not produce enough human growth hormone can be given injections of the hormone. Today, an unlimited supply of the hormone exists, thanks to genetically engineered bacteria.

Genetic Engineering in Other Organisms Genetic engineering has also been used to insert genes into the cells of other organisms. Scientists have inserted genes from bacteria into the cells of tomatoes, wheat, rice, and other important crops. Some of the genes enable the plants to survive in colder temperatures or in poor soil conditions, and to resist insect pests.

Genetic engineering techniques can also be used to insert genes into animals, which then produce important medicines for humans. For example, scientists can insert human genes into the cells of cows. The cows then produce the human protein for which the gene codes. Scientists have used this technique to produce the blood clotting protein needed by people with hemophilia. The protein is produced in the cows' milk, and can easily be extracted and used to treat people with the disorder.

Gene Therapy Researchers are also using genetic engineering to try to correct some genetic disorders. This process, called **gene therapy,** involves inserting working copies of a gene directly into the cells of a person with a genetic disorder. For example, people with cystic fibrosis do not produce a protein that is needed for proper lung function. Both copies of the gene that codes for the protein are defective in these people.

Background

Facts and Figures Two major problems must be solved in developing gene therapy for a particular genetic disorder. The first problem is finding the best way to correct the genetic defect that is causing the disorder. Options may include correcting or increasing the defective cell product, making diseased cells weaker or more vulnerable, or blocking the operation of diseased cells. The other problem that must be solved is finding a way to carry the genetically engineered DNA to target cells. Because of their ability to infect living cells, viruses make excellent candidates for this role. However, before a virus can be used safely, the viral DNA must be genetically engineered to make the virus harmless to the human patient.

Scientists can insert working copies of the gene into harmless viruses. The "engineered" viruses can then be sprayed into the lungs of patients with cystic fibrosis. The researchers hope that the working copies of the gene in the viruses will function in the patient to produce the protein. Gene therapy is still an experimental method for treating genetic disorders. Researchers are working hard to improve this promising technique.

DNA Fingerprinting

In courtrooms across the country, a genetic technique called DNA fingerprinting is being used to help solve crimes. If you did the Discover activity, you know that fingerprints can help to identify people. No two people have the same fingerprints. Detectives routinely use fingerprints found at a crime scene to help identify the person who committed the crime. In a similar way, DNA from samples of hair, skin, and blood can also be used to identify a person. No two people, except for identical twins, have the same DNA.

In DNA fingerprinting, enzymes are used to cut the DNA in the sample found at a crime scene into fragments. An electrical current then separates the fragments by size to form a pattern of bands, like the ones you see in Figure 15. Each person's pattern of DNA bands is unique. The DNA pattern can then be compared to the pattern produced by DNA taken from people suspected of committing the crime.

✓ *Checkpoint* *In what way is DNA like fingerprints?*

Sharpen your **Skills**

Communicating

Imagine that you are an 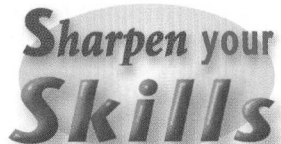ACTIVITY expert witness at a murder trial. You will be called to testify about the DNA evidence found in drops of blood at the crime scene. You will need to explain the process of DNA fingerprinting to the jury. Write a paragraph describing what you would say. How would you convince a jury that DNA fingerprinting is a reliable technique?

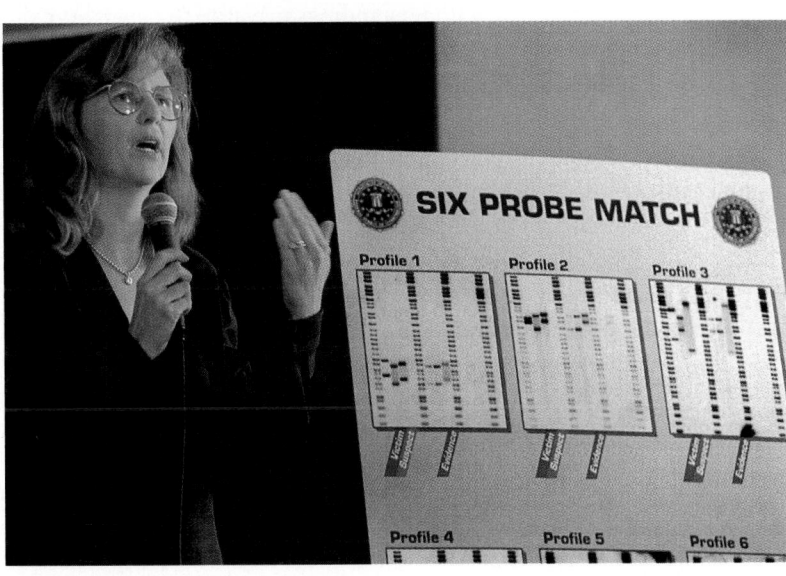

Figure 15 This scientist is explaining how DNA fingerprinting can be used to help solve crimes. DNA from blood or other substances collected at a crime scene can be compared to DNA from a suspect's blood.

Answers to Self-Assessment

Caption Question

Figure 14 Other traits might include deep red color, large size, and firmness.

✓ *Checkpoint*

DNA, like fingerprints, is unique to each person, except for identical twins.

Addressing Naive Conceptions

Students may develop the naive conception that all genetic disorders will soon be cured with gene therapy. Point out that gene therapy is unlikely to be developed, at least not any time soon, for diabetes, heart disease, or most types of cancer, because these diseases are also influenced by the environment. Conclude by asking: **Besides cystic fibrosis, which genetic disorders are good candidates for gene therapy?** (*Students' responses should reflect their understanding that gene therapy is most likely to lead to cures for genetic disorders caused by single genes, such as hemophilia or sickle-cell disease.*) **learning modality: logical/ mathematical**

DNA Fingerprinting

Sharpen your **Skills**

Communicating

Time 15 minutes

Tips Advise students to 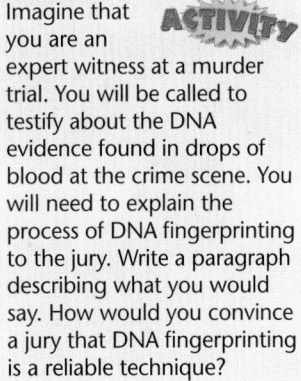ACTIVITY pretend they are explaining DNA fingerprinting to a friend who has no knowledge of genetics.

Expected Outcome Students should write a paragraph explaining the process of DNA fingerprinting in simple terms. Their paragraph should make it clear that each cell contains a complete set of a person's DNA and that each person, with the exception of identical twins, has DNA that is unique.

Extend Tell students that before DNA fingerprinting was developed, blood typing often was used for identification purposes. Ask: **Why is blood typing a less accurate way of identifying an individual?** (*Because many people have the same blood type*) **learning modality: verbal**

Ongoing Assessment

Oral Presentation Call on students at random to describe ways that genetic engineering has been used to treat human disorders.

The Human Genome Project

Building Inquiry Skills: Communicating

Give students who need extra challenges a chance to learn more about the Human Genome Project and communicate what they learn in a report to the class. Students can get up-to-date information on the project from the following Internet site: **www.ornl.gov/TechResources/Human_Genome/ learning modality: verbal**

3 Assess

Section 3 Review Answers

1. Inbreeding, hybridization, and cloning
2. To learn what makes the body work and what causes things to go wrong
3. The process of transferring genes from one organism into the DNA of another organism; produce medicines, improve food crops, treat human genetic disorders
4. It is produced by cutting the DNA from a sample of hair, skin, or blood into fragments and separating the fragments by size to form a pattern of bands. It can reveal who committed a crime by identifying the person who left the sample at the crime scene.
5. Answers may vary. Make sure students give logical, well-founded reasons to support their position.

Science at Home

Tips Other vegetables and fruits that students might focus on because of their variety are squash and pears. Suggest that students ask the store's produce manager what traits each variety is known for.

Performance Assessment

Skills Check Have students infer how the completion of the Human Genome Project might lead to advances in gene therapy.

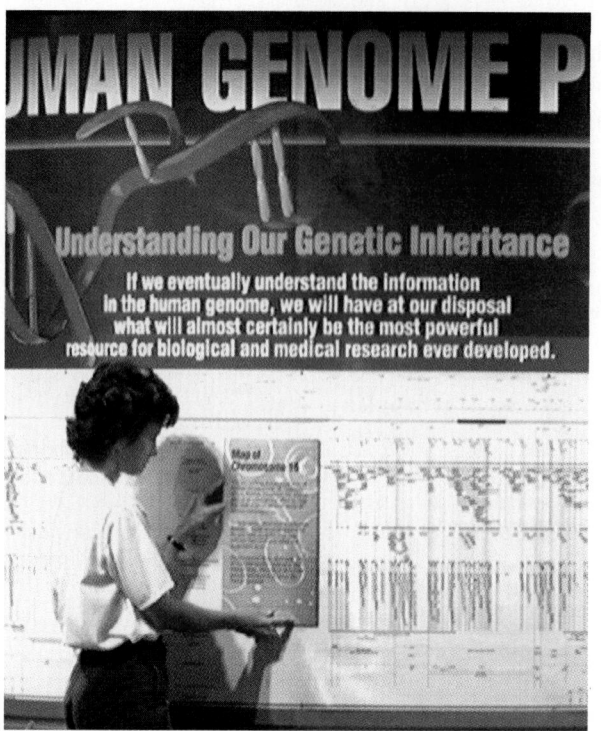

Figure 16 The goal of the Human Genome Project is to identify the sequence of every DNA base pair in the human genome.

The Human Genome Project

Imagine trying to crack a code that is 3 billion characters long. Then imagine working with people all over the world to accomplish this task. That's exactly what scientists working on the Human Genome Project are doing. A **genome** is all the DNA in one cell of an organism. Researchers estimate that the 23 pairs of chromosomes that make up the human genome contain about 3 billion DNA base pairs—or about 30,000 to 35,000 genes.

The main goal of the Human Genome Project is to identify the DNA sequence of every gene in the human genome. The Human Genome Project will provide scientists with an encyclopedia of genetic information about humans. Scientists will know the DNA sequence of every human gene, and thus the amino acid sequence of every protein.

With the information from the Human Genome Project, researchers may gain a better understanding of how humans develop from a fertilized egg to an adult. They may also learn more about what makes the body work, and what causes things to go wrong. New understandings may lead to new treatments and prevention strategies for many genetic disorders and for diseases such as cancer.

Section 3 Review

1. Name three techniques that people have used to produce organisms with desired traits.
2. Why do scientists want to identify the DNA sequence of every human gene?
3. What is genetic engineering? Describe three possible benefits of this technique.
4. Explain how a DNA fingerprint is produced. What information can a DNA fingerprint reveal?
5. **Thinking Critically** **Making Judgments** Do you think there should be any limitations on genetic engineering? Give reasons to support your position.

138

Science at Home

Grocery Genetics With a parent or other adult family member, go to a grocery store. Look at the different varieties of potatoes, apples, and other fruits and vegetables. Discuss how these varieties were created by selective breeding. Then choose one type of fruit or vegetable and make a list of different varieties. If possible, find out what traits each variety was bred for.

Background

Facts and Figures The Human Genome Project was started in 1990. By late 1999, scientists estimated that they were about 40 percent of the way to the goal of mapping the 3 billion base pairs of the human genome. When completed, a listing of all the base pairs in the human genome will fill many volumes of an encyclopedia.

Program Resources

◆ **Unit 1 Resources** 4-3 Review and Reinforce, p. 113; 4-3 Enrich, p. 114

Media and Technology

 Interactive Student Tutorial CD-ROM Chapter 4

Who Should Have Access to Genetic Test Results?

Scientists working on the Human Genome Project have identified many alleles that put people at risk for certain diseases, such as breast cancer and Alzheimer's disease. Through techniques known as genetic testing, people can have their DNA analyzed to find out whether they have any of these alleles. If they do, they may be able to take steps to prevent the illness or to seek early treatment.

Some health insurance companies and employers want access to this type of genetic information. However, many people believe that genetic testing results should be kept private.

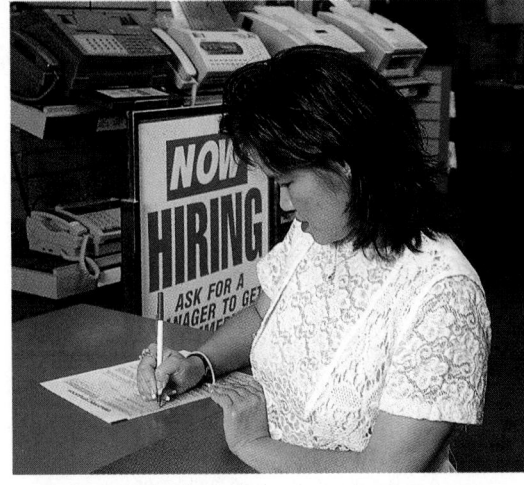

The Issues

Why Do Insurance Companies Want Genetic Information? Health insurance companies set their rates based on a person's risk of health problems. To determine a person's insurance rate, insurance companies often require that a person have a physical examination. If the examination reveals a condition such as high blood pressure, the company may charge that person more for an insurance policy. This is because he or she would be more likely to need expensive medical care.

Insurance companies view genetic testing as an additional way to gather information about a person's health status. Insurers argue that if they were unable to gather this information, they would need to raise rates for everyone. This would be unfair to people who are in good health.

Why Do Employers Want Genetic Information? Federal laws forbid employers with 15 or more workers from choosing job applicants based on their health status. These laws do not apply to smaller companies, however. Employers may not want to hire employees with health problems because they often miss more work time than other employees. In addition, employers who hire people with health problems may be charged higher health insurance rates. Many small companies cannot afford to pay these higher rates.

Should Genetic Information Be Kept Private? Some people think that the government should prohibit all access to genetic information. Today, some people fear that they will be discriminated against as a result of genetic test results. Because of this fear, some people avoid genetic testing—even though testing might allow them to seek early treatment for a disorder. These people want tighter control of genetic information. They want to be sure that insurers and employers will not have access to genetic test results.

You Decide

1. Identify the Problem
In your own words, explain the problem of deciding who should have access to genetic test results.

2. Analyze the Options
Examine the pros and cons of keeping genetic test results private. List reasons to maintain privacy. List reasons why test results should be shared.

3. Find a Solution
Create a list of rules to control access to genetic information. Who should have access, and under what circumstances? Explain your reasoning.

SCIENCE AND SOCIETY

Who Should Have Access to Genetic Test Results?

Purpose To provide students with an introduction to the ethical problems raised by genetic testing.

Panel Discussion

Time a day to prepare; 30 minutes for panel discussion

Choose students to play the following roles in a panel discussion: the CEO of a health insurance company, the president of an association of small business owners, the doctor who presides over the American Medical Association, the spokesperson for a patients' rights group, the director of a diabetes foundation, and the president of a worker's union. Urge each panel member to take the point of view they believe the person they represent would actually take on issues relating to genetic testing. Other students should take notes during the discussion and ask questions afterward. The panel discussion should begin with each panel member briefly stating his or her position regarding who should have access to genetic test results. Then panel members should take turns presenting arguments in support of their statements.

Extend Challenge students to find out more about genetic testing by interviewing a lab technician, nurse, or doctor. Suggest that they ask such questions as: **What genetic tests are commonly performed today? What are some reasons genetic testing is done?**

You Decide

Help students keep to the point by challenging them to explain the problem in a single sentence. Reasons for sharing genetic test results can be found in the first two paragraphs. Reasons for keeping genetic test results private can be found in the last paragraph. In addition, encourage students to think of reasons of their own. If students are having difficulty creating a list of rules, suggest that they first decide what they believe are acceptable uses for genetic information. This will help them decide who should control it and under what circumstances.

You Solve the Mystery

Guilty or Innocent?

Preparing for Inquiry

Key Concept A person's DNA forms a unique pattern of bands that can be used to identify the person.

Skills Objectives Students will be able to
◆ use bar codes as models of DNA fingerprints;
◆ observe similarities and differences in the patterns of bands on the bar codes;
◆ draw conclusions about which suspect was present at the crime scene based on the comparisons.

Time 20 minutes

Advance Planning Remove bar codes from commercial products and cut the numbers from them. Each students' set of bar codes should contain one that is identical to the bar code from the crime scene. You could mount the bar codes on heavy paper so they can be reused.

Alternative Materials If you can obtain actual DNA fingerprints, the lab will be more realistic. Provide a hand lens for any student who has vision problems.

Guiding Inquiry

Troubleshooting the Experiment
◆ Advise students to examine the patterns of bands very carefully, because the differences may be minor and easily overlooked.

Expected Outcome
Students should find that one of the suspect DNA samples is identical to the DNA sample from the crime scene.

Analyze and Conclude
1. The suspect whose DNA sample matches the DNA sample from the crime scene must have been present at the crime scene.
2. DNA patterns differ so greatly because no two people, except for identical twins, have the same sequence of bases in their DNA.
3. The twin's DNA pattern would be identical to the suspect's, making it impossible to conclude which individual

---

Real-World Lab

Guilty or Innocent?

In this lab, you will investigate how DNA fingerprinting can be used to provide evidence related to a crime.

Problem

How can DNA be used to identify individuals?

Skills Focus

observing, making models, drawing conclusions

Materials

4–6 bar codes   hand lens

Procedure

1. Look at the photograph of DNA band patterns shown at right. Each person's DNA produces a unique pattern of these bands.
2. Now look at the Universal Product Code, also called a bar code, shown below the DNA bands. A bar code can be used as a model of a DNA band pattern. Compare the bar code with the DNA bands to see what they have in common. Record your observations.
3. Suppose that a burglary has taken place, and you're the detective leading the investigation. Your teacher will give you a bar code that represents DNA from blood found at the crime scene. You arrange to have DNA samples taken from several suspects. Write a sentence describing what you will look for as you try to match each suspect's DNA to the DNA sample from the crime scene.
4. You will now be given bar codes representing DNA samples taken from the suspects. Compare those bar codes with the bar code that represents DNA from the crime scene.

5. Use your comparisons to determine whether any of the suspects were present at the crime scene.

Analyze and Conclude

1. Based on your findings, were any of the suspects present at the crime scene? Support your conclusion with specific evidence.
2. Why do people's DNA patterns differ so greatly?
3. How would your conclusions be affected if you learned that the suspect whose DNA matched the evidence had an identical twin?
4. **Apply** In everyday life, do you think that DNA evidence is enough to determine that a suspect committed the crime? Explain.

More to Explore

Do you think the DNA fingerprints of a parent and a child would show any similarities? Draw what you think they would look like. Then explain your thinking.

---

had been at the crime scene.
4. Students may say that DNA evidence alone is not enough, because it only identifies who was at the crime scene and not who actually committed the crime. Students also may say that errors can be made in analyzing the DNA evidence.

Extending the Inquiry

More to Explore The DNA fingerprints of a parent and a child should look more similar than the DNA fingerprints of unrelated people, because parents and children share many of the same genes.

Program Resources

◆ **Unit 1 Resources** Chapter 4 Real-World Lab, pp. 118–119

SECTION 1 Human Inheritance

Key Ideas
◆ Some human traits are controlled by a single gene that has multiple alleles—three or more forms.
◆ Some human traits show a wide range of phenotypes because these traits are controlled by many genes. The genes act together as a group to produce a single trait.
◆ Traits are often influenced by the organism's environment.
◆ Males have one X chromosome and one Y chromosome. Females have two X chromosomes. Males are more likely than females to have a sex-linked trait controlled by a recessive allele.
◆ Geneticists use pedigrees to trace the inheritance pattern of a particular trait through a number of generations of a family.

Key Terms
multiple alleles   carrier
sex-linked gene   pedigree

SECTION 2 Human Genetic Disorders

Key Ideas
◆ Genetic disorders are abnormal conditions that are caused by mutations, or DNA changes, in genes or chromosomes.
◆ Common genetic disorders include cystic fibrosis, sickle-cell disease, hemophilia, and Down syndrome.
◆ Amniocentesis and karyotypes are tools used to diagnose genetic disorders.
◆ Genetic counselors help couples understand their chances of having a child with a genetic disorder.

Key Terms
genetic disorder   karyotype
amniocentesis

SECTION 3 Advances in Genetics

INTEGRATING TECHNOLOGY

Key Ideas
◆ Selective breeding is the process of selecting a few organisms with desired traits to serve as parents of the next generation.
◆ Cloning is a technique used to produce genetically identical organisms.
◆ Genetic engineering can be used to produce medicines and to improve food crops. Researchers are also using genetic engineering to try to cure human genetic disorders.
◆ DNA fingerprinting can be used to help determine whether material found at a crime scene came from a particular suspect.
◆ The goal of the Human Genome Project is to identify the DNA sequence of every gene in the human genome.

Key Terms
selective breeding   genetic engineering
inbreeding   gene therapy
hybridization   genome
clone

Organizing Information

Concept Map Copy the concept map about human traits onto a separate sheet of paper. Then complete it and add a title. (For more on concept maps, see the Skills Handbook.)

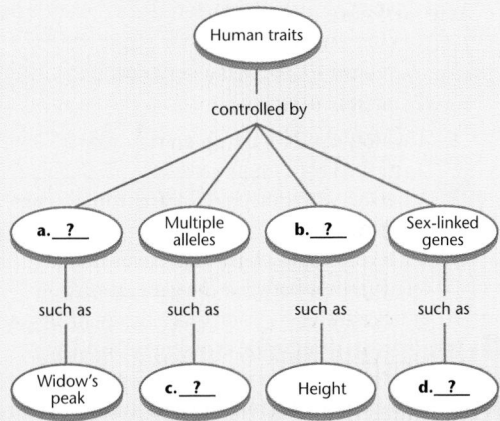

Chapter 4 **141**

Organizing Information

Concept Map **a.** Single genes **b.** Many genes **c.** Blood type **d.** Colorblindness (or Hemophilia) *Sample title:* The Inheritance of Human Traits

Program Resources
◆ **Unit 1 Resources** Chapter 4 Project Scoring Rubric, p. 102
◆ **Performance Assessment** Chapter 4, pp. 14–16
◆ **Chapter and Unit Tests** Chapter 4 Test, pp. 16–19

Media and Technology

 Interactive Student Tutorial CD-ROM Chapter 4

 Computer Test Bank Chapter 4 Test

Reviewing Content

Multiple Choice

1. b 2. c 3. a 4. d 5. c

True or False

6. true 7. female 8. pedigree
9. Inbreeding 10. true

Checking Concepts

11. The four or more genes that control height determine the maximum height that a person can attain. The environment, particularly diet, medical care, and living conditions, determines whether or not the person reaches the potential maximum height.

12. Males need to inherit just one allele to have the trait, whereas females need to inherit two alleles.

13. Sickle-cell disease is a genetic disorder in which red blood cells contain an abnormal form of hemoglobin. People who have the disease inherit a copy of the affected allele from each parent.

14. In amniocentesis, a doctor removes fluid surrounding a growing baby so that the baby's chromosomes can be analyzed. Down syndrome is present if there is an extra copy of chromosome 21.

15. The horse breeder would mate only horses that have golden coats.

16. Doctors would give the person with hemophilia a virus containing the normal gene for the missing blood-clotting protein. The viral DNA would infect the person's cells and lead to the production of the missing protein.

17. Students should identify the genetic disorder they chose and then describe its symptoms, how it is inherited, and how it is treated. Check that students' answers reflect the information in the text.

Thinking Critically

18. Two alleles are needed for the trait to be expressed. If the person has only one recessive allele for the trait, he or she will not have the trait, but will be a carrier. However, a person cannot be a carrier of a trait caused by a dominant allele because if the person has only one dominant allele, he or she will have the trait.

Reviewing Content

 For more review of key concepts, see the Interactive Student Tutorial CD-ROM.

Multiple Choice

Choose the letter of the best answer.

1. A human trait that is controlled by multiple alleles is
   a. dimples.   b. blood type.
   c. height.   d. skin color.
2. A genetic disorder caused by a sex-linked gene is
   a. cystic fibrosis.
   b. sickle-cell disease.
   c. hemophilia.
   d. Down syndrome.
3. Sickle-cell disease is characterized by
   a. abnormally shaped red blood cells.
   b. abnormally thick body fluids.
   c. abnormal blood clotting.
   d. an extra copy of chromosome 21.
4. Inserting a human gene into a bacterial plasmid is an example of
   a. inbreeding.
   b. selective breeding.
   c. DNA fingerprinting.
   d. genetic engineering.
5. DNA fingerprinting is a way to
   a. clone organisms.
   b. breed organisms with desirable traits.
   c. identify people.
   d. map and sequence human genes.

True or False

If the statement is true, write true. If it is false, change the underlined word or words to make the statement true.

6. A widow's peak is a human trait that is controlled by a single gene.
7. A person who inherits two X chromosomes will be male.
8. A karyotype is a chart that shows the relationships between the generations of a family.
9. Hybridization is the crossing of two genetically similar organisms.
10. A clone is an organism that is genetically identical to another organism.

Checking Concepts

11. Explain how both genes and the environment determine how tall a person will be.

12. Explain why traits controlled by recessive alleles on the X chromosome are more common in males than in females.

13. What is sickle-cell disease? How is this disorder inherited?

14. How can amniocentesis be used to detect a disorder such as Down syndrome?

15. Explain how a horse breeder might use selective breeding to produce horses that have golden coats.

16. Describe how gene therapy might be used in the future to treat a person with hemophilia.

17. **Writing to Learn** As the webmaster for a national genetics foundation, you must create a Web site to inform the public about genetic disorders. Choose one human genetic disorder discussed in this chapter. Write a description of the disorder that you will use for the Web site.

Thinking Critically

18. Applying Concepts Why can a person be a carrier of a trait caused by a recessive allele but not of a trait caused by a dominant allele?

19. Problem Solving A woman with normal color vision has a colorblind daughter. What are the genotypes and phenotypes of both parents?

20. Calculating If a mother is a carrier of hemophilia, what is the probability that her son will have the trait? Explain your answer.

21. Inferring How could ancient people selectively breed corn if they didn't know about genes and inheritance?

22. Comparing and Contrasting How are selective breeding and genetic engineering different? How are they similar?

---

19. The mother has normal color vision but is a carrier of the colorblindness allele. Her genotype is $X^C X^c$. The father is colorblind. His genotype is $X^c Y$.

20. If the mother is a carrier of hemophilia, one of her X chromosomes has the allele for normal clotting and the other X chromosome has the allele for hemophilia. The son has a 50 percent chance of inheriting an X chromosome that carries the allele for hemophilia, and therefore of having hemophilia.

21. Selective breeding is based on phenotypes. Therefore, ancient people could selectively breed corn without knowing about genes and inheritance by using seeds only from the plants that had the traits they desired.

22. Both selective breeding and genetic engineering are ways of producing organisms with desirable traits. Selective breeding involves restricting matings to those individuals who have the desirable traits. Genetic engineering involves inserting genes for the desirable traits into an individual's genome.

Applying Skills

Use the information below to answer Questions 23–25.

- Bob and Helen have three children.
- Bob and Helen have one son who has albinism, an inherited condition in which the skin does not have brown pigments.
- Bob and Helen have two daughters who do not have albinism.
- Neither Bob nor Helen has albinism.
- Albinism is neither sex-linked nor codominant.

23. **Interpreting Data** Use the information to construct a pedigree. If you don't know whether someone is a carrier, leave their symbol empty. If you decide later that a person is a carrier, change your pedigree.

24. **Drawing Conclusions** Is albinism controlled by a dominant allele or by a recessive allele? Explain your answer.

25. **Predicting** Suppose Bob and Helen were to have another child. What is the probability that the child will have albinism? Explain.

Performance CHAPTER PROJECT Assessment

Present Your Project Before displaying your project, exchange it with another group to check each other's work. Make any necessary corrections, and then display your materials to the class. Be ready to explain the inheritance patterns shown in your pedigrees.

Reflect and Record In your journal, describe what you learned by creating the pedigrees. What questions do you have as a result of the project?

Test Preparation

Use these questions to prepare for standardized tests.

Use the information to answer Questions 26–29. The Punnett square below shows how muscular dystrophy, a sex-linked recessive disorder, is inherited.

Key
X^M = normal allele
X^m = muscular dystrophy allele

Father (normal)
$X^M Y$

	X^M	Y
X^M	$X^M X^M$	$X^M Y$
X^m	$X^M X^m$	$X^m Y$

Mother
$X^M X^m$
(carrier)

26. What is the probability that a daughter of these parents will have muscular dystrophy?
   a. 0%   b. 25%
   c. 50%   d. 100%

27. What is the probability that a son of these parents will have muscular dystrophy?
   a. 0%   b. 25%
   c. 50%   d. 100%

28. What is the probability that a daughter of these parents will be a carrier of the disease?
   a. 0%   b. 25%
   c. 50%   d. 100%

29. Which of the following statements is true of muscular dystrophy?
   a. More men than women have muscular dystrophy.
   b. More women than men have muscular dystrophy.
   c. More men than women are carriers of muscular dystrophy.
   d. No women can have muscular dystrophy.

Chapter 4 **143**

Applying Skills

23. The top row of the pedigree should show a half-shaded circle (Helen) connected with a half-shaded square (Bob), indicating that both parents are carriers for albinism. The second row should show two unshaded circles (the two daughters) and a shaded square (the affected son).

24. Albinism must be controlled by a recessive allele, because otherwise either Bob or Helen also would have the condition.

25. Both Bob and Helen must be carriers of the albinism allele in order to have an affected child, so there is a 25 percent chance that any child would have albinism.

Performance CHAPTER PROJECT Assessment

Present Your Project Before students make their presentations, give them a chance to exchange their pedigrees and family albums with other students for feedback and to make any corrections or other changes. Have students trace each of their family's traits through the pedigree from generation to generation and point out individuals in the family album with each possible phenotype for the two traits. Make sure that the family album is consistent with the information in the pedigrees.

Reflect and Record After all the students have presented their projects, encourage students to compare the different patterns of inheritance shown in the pedigrees. Challenge them to identify ways that the patterns differ. Conclude by saying that detecting such patterns in pedigrees is how geneticists have determined which type of gene controls different traits.

Program Resources

- **Inquiry Skills Activity Book** Provides teaching and review of all inquiry skills

Test Preparation

26. a   27. c   28. c   29. a

Changes Over Time

Sections	Time	Student Edition Activities		Other Activities
CHAPTER PROJECT **Life's Long Calendar** p. 145	Ongoing (2 weeks)	Check Your Progress, p. 156, 169 Present Your Project, p. 173		
1 **Darwin's Voyage** pp. 146–156 ◆ State how Darwin explained variations among similar species. ◆ Explain how natural selection leads to evolution, and explain the role of genes in evolution. ◆ Describe how new species form.	2 periods/ 1 block	**Discover** How Do Living Things Vary?, p. 146 **Try This** Bird Beak Adaptations, p. 149 **Sharpen Your Skills** Inferring, p. 151 **Skills Lab: Making Models** Nature at Work, pp. 152–153	TE TE TE LM	Demonstration, p. 147 Building Inquiry Skills: Observing, p. 148 Inquiry Challenge, p. 154 5, "Variation in a Population"
2 *INTEGRATING EARTH SCIENCE* **The Fossil Record** pp. 157–164 ◆ Describe how most fossils form. ◆ Explain how a scientist determines a fossil's age. ◆ Explain what fossils reveal. ◆ Describe the main events of the Geologic Time Scale. ◆ Distinguish between gradualism and punctuated equilibria.	1–2 periods/ $\frac{1}{2}$–1 block	**Discover** What Can You Learn From Fossils?, p. 157 **Try This** Preservation in Ice, p. 159 **Sharpen Your Skills** Calculating, p. 160 **Science at Home,** p. 164	TE TE TE TE IES	Demonstration, p. 158 Including All Students, p. 158 Inquiry Challenge, p. 163 Including All Students, p. 163 "The Glory of Ancient Rome," pp. 26–27
3 **Other Evidence for Evolution** pp. 165–169 ◆ State evidence from modern-day organisms that scientists use to determine evolutionary relationships among groups. ◆ Explain what a branching tree diagram is.	1 period/ $\frac{1}{2}$ block	**Discover** How Can You Classify Species?, p. 165 **Sharpen Your Skills** Drawing Conclusions, p. 166 **Skills Lab: Interpreting Data** Telltale Molecules, p. 170	TE TE TE	Building Inquiry Skills: Observing, p. 166 Inquiry Challenge, p. 167 Building Inquiry Skills: Interpreting Data, p. 168
Study Guide/Chapter Assessment pp.171–173	1 period/ $\frac{1}{2}$ block		ISAB	Provides teaching and review of all inquiry skills

 For Standard or Block Schedule The Resource Pro® CD-ROM gives you maximum flexibility for planning your instruction for any type of schedule. Resource Pro® contains Planning Express®, an advanced scheduling program, as well as the entire contents of the Teaching Resources and the Computer Test Bank.

CHAPTER PLANNING GUIDE

Program Resources	Assessment Strategies	Media and Technology
UR Chapter 5 Project Teacher Notes, pp. 120–121 **UR** Chapter 5 Project Overview and Worksheets, pp. 122–125	**SE** Performance Assessment: Present Your Project, p. 173 **TE** Check Your Progress, pp. 156, 169 **UR** Chapter 5 Project Scoring Rubric, p.126	Science Explorer Internet Site at www.phschool.com
UR 5-1 Lesson Plan, p. 127 **UR** 5-1 Section Summary, p. 128 **UR** 5-1 Review and Reinforce, p. 129 **UR** 5-1 Enrich, p. 130 **UR** Chapter 5 Skills Lab, pp. 139–141	**SE** Section 1 Review, p. 156 **TE** Ongoing Assessment, pp. 147, 149, 151, 155 **TE** Performance Assessment, p. 156	Earth Science Videotape 5; Videodisc Unit 4 Side 2, "Hot, Cold, Wet, Dry" Life Science Videotape 1; Videodisc Unit 5 Side 2, "The Drifters" Audio CD, English-Spanish Summary 5-1
UR 5-2 Lesson Plan, p. 131 **UR** 5-2 Section Summary, p. 132 **UR** 5-2 Review and Reinforce, p. 133 **UR** 5-2 Enrich, p. 134	**SE** Section 2 Review, p. 164 **TE** Ongoing Assessment, pp. 159, 161, 163 **TE** Performance Assessment, p. 164	Life Science Videotape 1; Videodisc Unit 5 Side 2, "Fossils" Life Science Videotape 1; Videodisc Unit 5 Side 2, "The Earth Library" Life Science Videotape 1; Videodisc Unit 5 Side 2, "Extinction" Life Science Videotape 1; Videodisc Unit 5 Side 2, "Geologic Time" Audio CD, English-Spanish Summary 5-2 Transparencies 19, "How Fossils Form"; 20, "Exploring Life's History (1)"; 21, "Exploring Life's History (2)" Interactive Student Tutorial CD-ROM, Chapter 5
UR 5-3 Lesson Plan, p. 135 **UR** 5-3 Section Summary, p. 136 **UR** 5-3 Review and Reinforce, p. 137 **UR** 5-3 Enrich, p. 138 **UR** Chapter 5 Skills Lab, pp. 142–143	**SE** Section 3 Review, p. 169 **TE** Ongoing Assessment, pp. 167 **TE** Performance Assessment, p. 169	Audio CD, English-Spanish Summary 5-3 Transparency 22, "Homologous Structures"
RCA Provides strategies to improve science reading skills **GSW** Provides worksheets to improve student comprehension of content	**SE** Chapter 5 Study Guide/Assessment, pp. 171–173 **PA** Chapter 5 Performance Assessment, pp. 17–19 **CUT** Chapter 5 Test, pp. 20–23 **CTB** Chapter 5 Test	Interactive Student Tutorial CD-ROM, Chapter 5 Computer Test Bank, Chapter 5 Test

Key: **SE** Student Edition
CTB Computer Test Bank
ISAB Inquiry Skills Activity Book
GSW Guided Study Worksheets

TE Teacher's Edition
PTA Product Testing Activities by *Consumer Reports*
RCA Reading in the Content Area
PA Performance Assessment

UR Unit Resources
LM Laboratory Manual
IES Interdisciplinary Explorations Series
CUT Chapter and Unit Tests

Meeting the National Science Education Standards and AAAS Benchmarks

National Science Education Standards	Benchmarks for Science Literacy	Unifying Themes
Science As Inquiry (Content Standard A) ◆ **Develop descriptions, explanations, predictions, and models using evidence** Students create time lines of Earth's history. Students model how natural selection leads to changes in a species over time. Students compare the structure of a protein in several animals to determine their evolutionary relationships. *(Chapter Project; Skills Lab; Skills Lab)* **Life Science** (Content Standard C) ◆ **Diversity and adaptations of organisms** Over a long period of time, natural selection can lead to evolution. A species is extinct if no members of that species are still alive. Scientists compare body structures, early development, and DNA sequences to determine evolutionary relationships. *(Sections 1, 2, 3; Skills Lab; Skills Lab)* **Earth and Space Science** (Content Standard D) ◆ **Earth's history** The fossil record provides clues about how and when new groups of organisms evolved. *(Chapter Project; Sections 1, 2)* **History and Nature of Science** (Content Standard G) ◆ **History of science** Charles Darwin explained that evolution occurs by means of natural selection. *(Section 1)*	**1B Scientific Inquiry** Students create time lines of Earth's history. Students model how natural selection leads to changes in a species over time. Students compare the structure of a protein in several animals to determine their evolutionary relationships. *(Chapter Project; Skills Lab; Skills Lab)* **1C The Scientific Enterprise** Charles Darwin explained that evolution occurs by means of natural selection. *(Section 1)* **4C Processes that Shape the Earth** Most fossils form when organisms that die become buried in sediments. *(Section 2)* **5A Diversity of Life** Any difference between individuals of the same species is called a variation. *(Section 1)* **5F Evolution of Life** Over a long period of time, natural selection can lead to evolution. The fossil record provides clues about how and when new groups of organisms evolved. Scientists compare body structures, early development, and DNA sequences to determine the evolutionary relationships among organisms. *(Chapter Project, Sections 1, 2, 3; Skills Lab; Skills Lab)*	◆ **Evolution** Over a long period of time, natural selection can lead to evolution. The fossil record provides clues about how and when new groups of organisms evolved. Scientists compare body structures, early development, and DNA sequences to determine evolutionary relationships. *(Chapter Project, Sections 1, 2, 3; Skills Lab; Skills Lab)* ◆ **Patterns of Change** A new species can form when a group of individuals is isolated from the rest of the species. Most fossils form when organisms that die become buried in sediments. *(Sections 1, 2)* ◆ **Scale and Structure** Scientists can determine a fossil's age through relative dating and absolute dating. Similar structures that related species have inherited from a common ancestor are called homologous structures. Protein structures can reveal evolutionary relationships among organisms. *(Sections 2, 3; Skills Lab)* ◆ **Stability** Natural selection is the survival and reproduction of those organisms best adapted to their environment. The half-life of a radioactive element is the time it takes for half of the atoms in a sample to decay. *(Sections 1, 2)* ◆ **Unity and Diversity** A species is a group of similar organisms that can mate and produce fertile offspring. Two theories of how quickly evolution occurs are gradualism and punctuated equilibria. *(Sections 1, 2)*

Take It to the Net

 *Interactive text at www.phschool.com*

Science Explorer comes alive with iText.

- **Complete student text** is accessible from any computer with Internet access or a CD-ROM drive.
- **Animations, simulations, and videos** enhance student understanding and retention of concepts.
- **Self-tests and online study tools** assess student understanding.

STAY CURRENT with

Find out the latest research and information about evolution at:
www.phschool.com

WEB ACTIVITY www.phschool.com

Go to **www.phschool.com** and click on the Science icon. Then click on <u>Science Explorer: Life, Earth, and Physical Science</u> under PH@school.

Student Edition Activities Planner

ACTIVITY	Time (minutes)	Materials *Quantities for one work group*	Skills
Section 1			
Discover, p. 146	15	**Consumable** 10 sunflower seeds **Nonconsumable** metric ruler, hand lens	Classifying
Try This, p. 149	10	**Consumable** bird seed, paper plate, 20 raisins, paper cup **Nonconsumable** tweezers, hair clips, hairpins, clothespins, stopwatch	Inferring
Skills Lab, p. 152–153	40	**Consumable** 2 colors of construction paper **Nonconsumable** scissors, marking pen	Making Models, Observing, Predicting
Section 2			
Discover, p. 157	5	No special materials are required.	Inferring
Try This, p. 159	10	**Consumable** fresh fruit, water **Nonconsumable** 2 plastic containers	Inferring
Science at Home, p. 164	home	**Consumable** mud **Nonconsumable** shallow, flat-bottomed pan	Making Models
Section 3			
Discover, p. 165	10	**Nonconsumable** 6-8 pens	Classifying
Skills Lab, p. 170	30	No special materials are required.	Interpreting Data, Comparing and Contrasting, Drawing Conclusions

A list of all materials required for the Student Edition activities can be found on pages T25–T33. You can obtain information about ordering materials by calling 1-800-848-9500 or by accessing the Science Explorer Internet site at **www.phschool.com**.

Life's Long Calendar

Understanding evolution through natural selection requires an appreciation for the great age of Earth and for the vast span of time involved in the development of Earth's diverse species. The Chapter 5 Project is designed to help students understand the large numbers involved in geologic time and place significant evolutionary events within an accurate model of Earth's history: a time line drawn to scale. The project works best with small groups.

Sometimes illustrations of the history of life on Earth, including the main section on pages 162–163 of this book, are not drawn to scale. (The time line that runs across the top of the spread *is* drawn to scale.) Illustrations that are not drawn to scale do not give an accurate image of the relative amounts of time occupied by different eras and periods in geologic history. However, a single time line to scale would devote most of the line to the Precambrian and squeeze the evolution of all plants and animals into a very small portion. To avoid this problem, students will make two time lines in this project: one showing Earth's history from 5 billion years ago to the present, and the other from 600 million years ago to the present.

Purpose Students will construct scale models of Earth's history by converting geological units of millions of years to more manageable units of either length or time. Students will mark both lines to show important events in Earth's history.

Skills Focus After completing the Chapter 5 Project, students will be able to
◆ calculate the scale of a model;
◆ make scale models representing the history of life on Earth, with major evolutionary events included;
◆ communicate the model-making procedures and results to others.

Project Time Line The Chapter 5 Project requires about two weeks to complete, depending on how detailed you want the time lines to be. If students label only the major evolutionary events shown on the textbook's time line, less than two weeks should be sufficient.

CHAPTER 5 Changes Over Time

WEB ACTIVITY www.phschool.com

Integrating Earth Science

SECTION 1 Darwin's Voyage
Discover **How Do Living Things Vary?**
Try This **Bird Beak Adaptations**
Sharpen Your Skills **Inferring**
Skills Lab **Nature at Work**

SECTION 2 The Fossil Record
Discover **What Can Fossils Tell You?**
Try This **Preservation in Ice**
Sharpen Your Skills **Calculating**
Science at Home **Make Your Mark**

SECTION 3 Other Evidence for Evolution
Discover **How Can You Classify Species?**
Sharpen Your Skills **Drawing Conclusions**
Skills Lab **Telltale Molecules**

144

Possible Materials
◆ Students could use calculators to determine the scale of each model and the placement of each evolutionary event.
◆ Meter sticks and metric tape measures will be needed to construct all models that use units of length to represent millions of years.
◆ Other materials will vary depending on the formats that students choose.
◆ If you want students to research additional evolutionary events to include in their time lines, provide a variety of source materials.

Launching the Project Ask students to read the project description on page 145 and examine the time line on pages 162–163. Then draw a long line across the board, and label the left end *Beginning of Earth* and the right end *Present*. Ask: **How long ago did Earth begin?** *(4.6 billion years ago)* Write *4,600,000,000* on the board. **When did the first animals appear on Earth?** *(600 million years ago)* Write *600,000,000* below the first number with the place values aligned. Ask: **Where should the line be marked to show when the first animals appeared on Earth?**

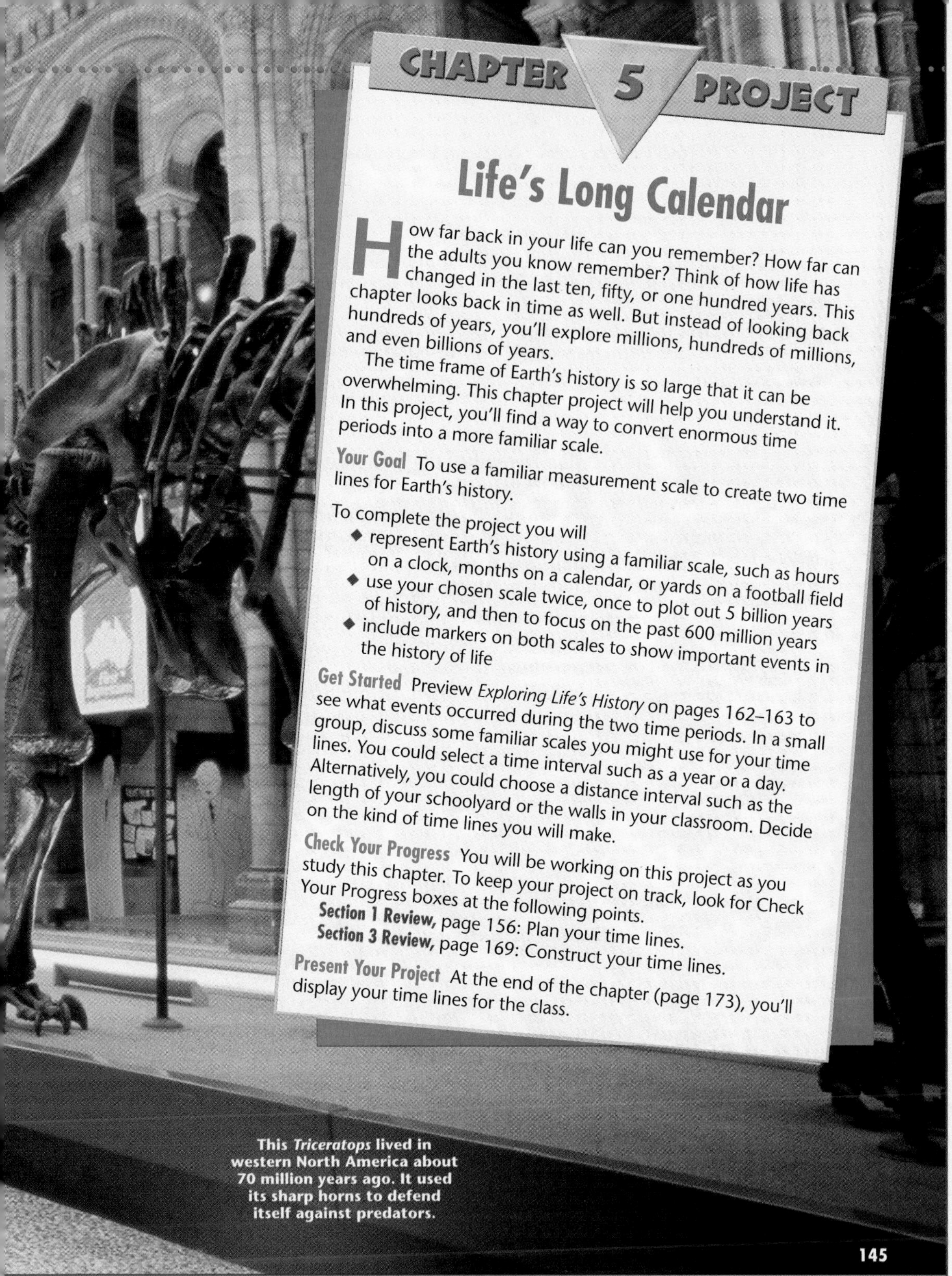

CHAPTER 5 PROJECT

Life's Long Calendar

How far back in your life can you remember? How far can the adults you know remember? Think of how life has changed in the last ten, fifty, or one hundred years. This chapter looks back in time as well. But instead of looking back hundreds of years, you'll explore millions, hundreds of millions, and even billions of years.

The time frame of Earth's history is so large that it can be overwhelming. This chapter project will help you understand it. In this project, you'll find a way to convert enormous time periods into a more familiar scale.

Your Goal To use a familiar measurement scale to create two time lines for Earth's history.

To complete the project you will
- represent Earth's history using a familiar scale, such as hours on a clock, months on a calendar, or yards on a football field
- use your chosen scale twice, once to plot out 5 billion years of history, and then to focus on the past 600 million years of history
- include markers on both scales to show important events in the history of life

Get Started Preview *Exploring Life's History* on pages 162–163 to see what events occurred during the two time periods. In a small group, discuss some familiar scales you might use for your time lines. You could select a time interval such as a year or a day. Alternatively, you could choose a distance interval such as the length of your schoolyard or the walls in your classroom. Decide on the kind of time lines you will make.

Check Your Progress You will be working on this project as you study this chapter. To keep your project on track, look for Check Your Progress boxes at the following points.
Section 1 Review, page 156: Plan your time lines.
Section 3 Review, page 169: Construct your time lines.

Present Your Project At the end of the chapter (page 173), you'll display your time lines for the class.

This *Triceratops* lived in western North America about 70 million years ago. It used its sharp horns to defend itself against predators.

145

Have a volunteer mark the line. (*The mark should be close to the "Present" end of the line. If it is not, ask the rest of the class to comment on the mark's place-ment.*) Point out that if students made only one time line to scale, all the events that happened from the beginning of the Paleozoic Era to the present would have to be crowded into a very small section of the line. Explain that this is why they will make two time lines.

Distribute the Chapter 5 Project Overview on pages 122–123 of Unit 1 Resources, and have students review the project rules and procedures. Then divide the class into groups of three or four students to discuss the types of time lines they could make.

When students are ready to make the first time line at the end of Section 1, distribute Worksheet 1 on page 124 of Unit 1 Resources. This worksheet will provide practice in making a time line to scale. At the end of Section 3, distribute Worksheet 2, on page 125 in Unit 1 Resources. This worksheet lists other evolutionary events that could be included in the time lines.

Additional information on guiding the project is provided in Chapter 5 Project Teacher Notes on pages 120–121 of Unit 1 Resources.

Program Resources

- **Unit 1 Resources** Chapter 5 Project Teacher Notes, pp. 120–121; Chapter 5 Project Overview and Worksheets, pp. 122–125; Chapter 5 Project Scoring Rubric, p. 126

WEB ACTIVITY www.phschool.com

You will find an Internet activity, chapter self-tests for students, and links to other chapter topics at this site.

Performance Assessment

The Chapter 5 Project Scoring Rubric on page 126 in Unit 1 Resources will help you evaluate how well students complete the Chapter 5 Project. You may want to share the scoring rubric with students so they are clear about what will be expected of them. Students will be assessed on
- their accuracy in calculating the scales for the two models;
- their ability to construct two scale models of Earth's history with important evolutionary events accurately marked;
- their effectiveness in communicating the model-making process and results to others;
- their participation in their groups.

Objectives

After completing the lesson, students will be able to

◆ state how Darwin explained variations among similar species;

◆ explain how natural selection leads to evolution, and explain the role of genes in evolution;

◆ describe how new species form.

Key Terms species, adaptation, evolution, scientific theory, natural selection, variation

1 Engage/Explore

Activating Prior Knowledge

Most students will have read articles or seen television specials about Darwin or the Galapagos Islands. Help them recall what they know by asking: **Who was Charles Darwin?** *(A scientist who came up with the idea of evolution by natural selection)* **What is special about the Galapagos Islands?** *(They have a lot of unusual organisms, such as giant lizards and tortoises.)*

·········· DISCOVER ··········

Skills Focus classifying
Materials *metric ruler,*
10 sunflower seeds, hand lens
Time 15 minutes
Tips Tell students that differences among seeds in their sample may be slight and hard to detect, so they should examine the seeds very carefully.
Expected Outcome Students should observe that the seeds in their sample differ in such traits as size, shape, color, or number of stripes.
Think It Over The seeds in each sample may differ in some traits and be similar in others. Depending on the makeup of their sample, students may group together seeds that are similar in size, shape, color, number of stripes, or other traits.

SECTION 1 Darwin's Voyage

DISCOVER ·· ACTIVITY

How Do Living Things Vary?

1. Use a metric ruler to measure the length and width of 10 sunflower seeds. Record each measurement.

2. Now use a hand lens to carefully examine each seed. Record each seed's shape, color, and number of stripes.

Think It Over
Classifying In what ways are the seeds in your sample different from one another? In what ways are they similar? How could you group the seeds based on their similarities and differences?

GUIDE FOR READING

◆ How did Darwin explain the differences between species on the Galapagos Islands and on mainland South America?

◆ How does natural selection lead to evolution?

◆ How do new species form?

Reading Tip As you read, make a list of main ideas and supporting details about evolution.

In December 1831, the British naval ship HMS *Beagle* set sail from England on a five-year-long trip around the world. On board was a 22-year-old named Charles Darwin. Darwin eventually became the ship's naturalist—a person who studies the natural world. His job was to learn as much as he could about the living things he saw on the voyage.

During the voyage, Darwin observed plants and animals he had never seen before. He wondered why they were so different from those in England. Darwin's observations led him to develop one of the most important scientific theories of all time: the theory of evolution by natural selection.

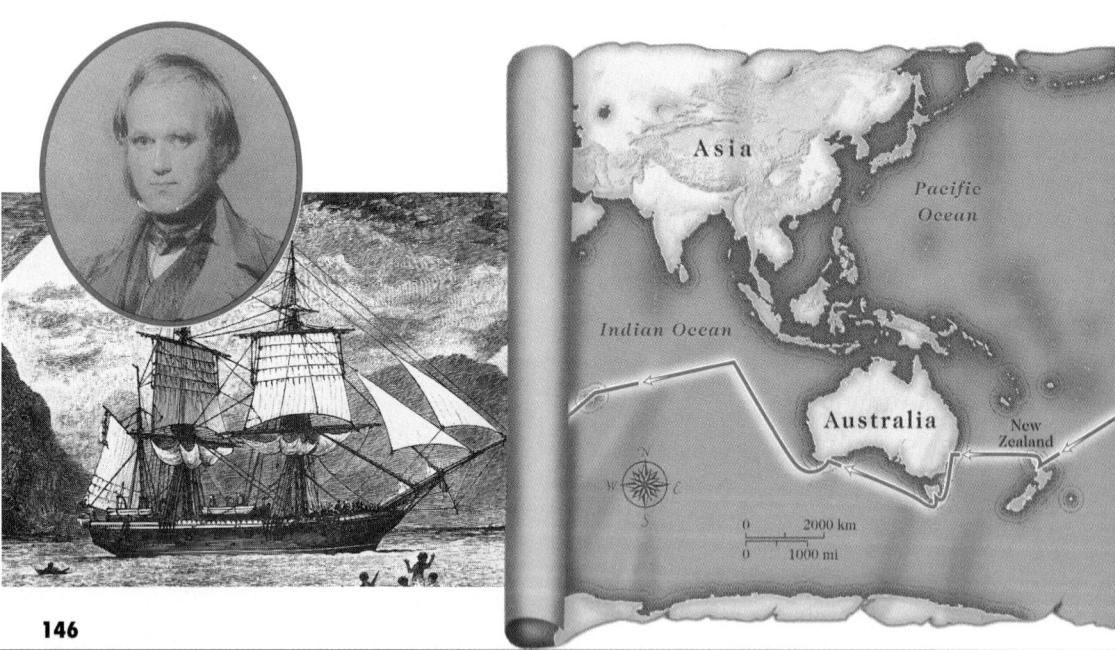

146

READING STRATEGIES

Reading Tip To find the main ideas and details, students can first read each paragraph carefully, then write its main idea in a sentence, and finally identify the supporting details. Use the first paragraph under **Darwin's Observations** as an example. Main idea: In South America, Darwin saw a great variety of animals. Details: flowerlike insects, huge armies of ants, animals covered with bony plates, sloths hanging upside down.

Students should include all six Key Terms as they write their paragraphs.

Vocabulary Students may think that the term *species* is plural and that the singular form is *specie*. Explain that the term *species* is both singular and plural. Then use the word in a sentence to illustrate. For example, say: "All humans belong to one species, but humans and chimpanzees belong to two different species."

Darwin's Observations

One of the *Beagle*'s first stops was the coast of South America. In Brazil, Darwin saw insects that looked like flowers, and ants that marched across the forest floor like huge armies. In Argentina, he saw armadillos—burrowing animals covered with small, bony plates. He also saw sloths, animals that moved very slowly and spent much of their time hanging upside down in trees.

Darwin was amazed by the tremendous diversity, or variety, of living things he saw. Today scientists know that living things are even more diverse than Darwin could ever have imagined. Scientists have identified more than 1.7 million species of organisms on Earth. A **species** is a group of similar organisms that can mate with each other and produce fertile offspring.

Darwin saw something else in Argentina that puzzled him: the bones of animals that had died long ago. From the bones, Darwin inferred that the animals had looked like the sloths he had seen. However, the bones were much larger than those of the living sloths. He wondered why only smaller sloths were alive today. What had happened to the giant creatures from the past?

In 1835, the *Beagle* reached the Galapagos Islands, a group of small islands in the Pacific Ocean off the west coast of South America. It was on the Galapagos Islands that Darwin observed some of the greatest diversity of life forms. He saw large numbers of giant tortoises, or land turtles, which he described as immense in size. There were also seals covered with fur, and lizards that ate cactus for food and water.

Figure 1 Charles Darwin sailed on HMS *Beagle* from England to South America and then to the Galapagos Islands. He saw many unusual organisms on the Galapagos Islands.

Galapagos hawk ▼

▲ *Giant tortoise*

▲ *Sally light-foot crab*

◄ *Blue-footed booby*

---

2 Facilitate

Darwin's Observations

Using the Visuals: Figure 1

Have students use their fingers to trace the route of Darwin's voyage. When they have traced Darwin's route as far as the Galapagos Islands, ask: **About how far are the Galapagos Islands from mainland South America?** *(About 1,000 km)* Help students appreciate how far away from the mainland that is, and therefore how isolated the islands are, by equating the distance to a distance with which they are more familiar, such as from Seattle to Sacramento, Detroit to Boston, or Indianapolis to Washington, D.C. **learning modality: kinesthetic**

Demonstration

Materials *taxonomic chart*
Time 10 minutes

Show students a taxonomic chart, either a chart from a biology book or encyclopedia, or a simple chart that you have drawn on the chalkboard. Point out that the taxonomic categories group together organisms based on the degree to which they are similar, with the largest, most inclusive category being the kingdom. Explain that humans belong to the animal kingdom, because, like other animals, humans are multicellular and do not make their own food. Ask: **What other organisms are in the animal kingdom?** *(Accept any type of animal in response, and use students' responses to illustrate how diverse the animal kingdom is.)* Then point out that at the other end of the taxonomy is the species, the smallest, most exclusive category, containing only those organisms that can reproduce together. **learning modality: visual**

Ongoing Assessment

Writing Have students describe in their own words the insight into the nature of living things Darwin gained from his voyage.

Similarities and Differences

Building Inquiry Skills: Observing

Materials *drawings of related bird species from a field identification guide*

Time 10 minutes

Point out to students that much of Darwin's time during the voyage of the *Beagle* was spent observing and comparing different organisms. Add that Darwin was a keen observer, and he noticed many details that other people might have overlooked. Give students a chance to see how difficult Darwin's job was, as well as to improve their own observation skills. Provide students with drawings from a field guide that show several related species of birds, such as several species of ducks, warblers, herons, or woodpeckers. Have students examine the drawings carefully and make lists of all the similarities and differences they observe among the species pictured. Then, have pairs of students compare lists. Emphasize that being a good observer requires care and skill. Be sensitive to visually challenged students by asking: **What are some other ways these birds might be similar or different that you cannot observe visually?** *(Possible ways include their songs and the texture of their feathers.)* **learning modality: visual**

Using the Visuals: Figure 2

Call students' attention to the figure and have them answer the caption question. Most students will respond that one way the two species differ is in color. Point out that variations in a trait such as this may make organisms better suited for their environment. Ask: **What difference in the environment do you think might explain the difference in color between the two species of iguanas?** *(Students may say the colors in the environment: the green iguana's color helps it blend in with its leafy environment, and the marine iguana's color helps it blend in with its rocky environment.)* **learning modality: logical/mathematical**

Similarities and Differences

Darwin was surprised that many of the plants and animals on the Galapagos Islands were similar to organisms on mainland South America. For example, many of the birds on the islands, including hawks, mockingbirds, and finches, resembled those on the mainland. Many of the plants were also similar to plants Darwin had collected on the mainland.

However, there were also important differences between the organisms on the islands and those on the mainland. Large sea birds called cormorants, for example, lived in both places. The cormorants on the mainland were able to fly, while those on the Galapagos Islands were unable to fly. The iguanas on the Galapagos Islands had large claws that allowed them to keep their grip on slippery rocks, where they fed on seaweed. The iguanas on the mainland had smaller claws. Smaller claws allowed the mainland iguanas to climb trees, where they ate leaves.

From his observations, Darwin inferred that a small number of different plant and animal species had come to the Galapagos Islands from the mainland. They might have been blown out to sea during a storm or set adrift on a fallen log. Once the plants and animals reached the islands, they reproduced. Eventually, their offspring became different from their mainland relatives.

Darwin also noticed many differences among similar organisms as he traveled from one Galapagos island to the next. For example, the tortoises on one island had dome-shaped shells. Those on another island had saddle-shaped shells. The governor of one of the islands told Darwin that he could tell which island a tortoise came from just by looking at its shell.

☑ *Checkpoint* *How did Darwin think plants and animals had originally come to the Galapagos Islands?*

Figure 2 Darwin observed many differences between organisms in South America and similar organisms on the Galapagos Islands. For example, green iguanas (left) live in South America. Marine iguanas (right) live on the Galapagos Islands. *Comparing and Contrasting How are the two species similar? How are they different?*

148

Background

Facts and Figures Ever since Darwin's time, scientists have suggested that one way species can become dispersed around the world is on natural rafts of fallen trees blown out to sea during storms. However, until recently there was virtually no direct evidence to support this idea. Then, in 1995, two powerful hurricanes passed through the Caribbean Sea, and a large clump of trees was blown into the sea from the island of Guadeloupe. Storm winds blew the natural raft across more than 300 km of sea, and it eventually washed ashore on the island of Anguilla. On the raft were 15 green iguanas, native to Guadeloupe but, until that time, not found on Anguilla. Most of the iguanas survived the journey and within a few months started reproducing. Scientists speculate that green iguanas eventually will become established on Anguilla.

Figure 3 Darwin made these drawings of four species of Galapagos finches. The beak of each finch is adapted to the type of food it eats.

Adaptations

Like the tortoises, the finches on the Galapagos Islands were noticeably different from one island to another. The most obvious differences were the varied sizes and shapes of the birds' beaks. As Darwin studied the different finches, he noticed that each species was well suited to the life it led. Finches that ate insects had sharp, needlelike beaks. Finches that ate seeds had strong, wide beaks. Beak shape is an example of an **adaptation,** a trait that helps an organism survive and reproduce.

Evolution

After he returned home to England, Darwin continued to think about what he had seen during his voyage on the *Beagle.* Darwin spent the next 20 years consulting with many other scientists, gathering more information, and thinking through his ideas. He especially wanted to understand how the variety of organisms with different adaptations arose on the Galapagos Islands.

Darwin reasoned that plants or animals that arrived on one of the Galapagos Islands faced conditions that were different from those on the mainland. **Perhaps, Darwin thought, the species gradually changed over many generations and became better adapted to the new conditions.** The gradual change in a species over time is called **evolution.**

Darwin's ideas are often referred to as the theory of evolution. A **scientific theory** is a well-tested concept that explains a wide range of observations.

It was clear to Darwin that evolution had occurred on the Galapagos Islands. He did not know, however, how this process had occurred. Darwin had to draw on other examples of changes in living things to help him understand how evolution occurs.

Bird Beak Adaptations

Use this activity to explore adaptations in birds.

1. Scatter a small amount of bird seed on a paper plate. Scatter 20 raisins on the plate to represent insects.

2. Obtain a variety of objects such as tweezers, hair clips, clothes pins, and hairpins. Pick one object to use as a "beak."

3. See how many seeds you can pick up and drop into a cup in 10 seconds.

4. Now see how many "insects" you can pick up and drop into a cup in 10 seconds.

5. Use a different "beak" and repeat Steps 3 and 4.

Inferring What type of beak worked well for seeds? For insects? How are different-shaped beaks useful for eating different foods?

Adaptations

TRY THIS

Skills Focus inferring
Materials *bird seed, paper plate, 20 raisins, tweezers, hair clips, hairpins, clothes pins, stopwatch, paper cup*
Time 10 minutes
Tips Have students work with partners so one student can pick up the seeds or raisins while the partner watches the clock.
Expected Outcome Students will find that some objects are better for picking up seeds and others for picking up raisins. Students should infer that some bird beaks are better for picking up seeds and others for picking up insects.
Extend Ask: **Which species in Figure 3 appear to be adapted to a diet of seeds, and which to a diet of insects?** (*Species 1, 2, and possibly 3 appear to be adapted to a diet of seeds, and species 4 to a diet of insects.*) **learning modality: kinesthetic**

Evolution

Addressing Naive Conceptions

People often say, "It's only a theory," and this may lead students to believe that a theory is just any idea. Address this naive conception by asking: **What makes an idea a theory?** (*It is well-tested and explains many observations.*) **How is a theory different from a fact?** (*A fact is a specific observation, known to be true; a theory is a broad concept, thought to be true because it explains many facts.*) **Upon which facts did Darwin base his theory of evolution?** (*The similarities and differences he observed among living things*) **learning modality: verbal**

Answers to Self-Assessment

Caption Question

Figure 2 Both species have spines, claws, and scaly skin. Green iguanas are green, have smaller claws, and live in trees. Marine iguanas are gray, have larger claws, and live on rocks near the ocean.

☑ *Checkpoint*

Perhaps by being blown out to sea during a storm or set adrift on a fallen log

Ongoing Assessment

Oral Presentation Call on students at random to define each term in their own words: *species, adaptation, evolution,* and *scientific theory.*

Evolution, continued

Including All Students

Support students who need more help in understanding natural selection by relating it to selective breeding, which they learned about in Chapter 4. Create a simple compare/contrast table on the chalkboard and call on students to help you complete it. The table should have two rows, one for selective breeding and one for natural selection. It also should have columns such as: **Type of Traits Selected** *(Selective breeding: traits that benefit humans; natural selection: traits that benefit the organism);* **Examples of Traits Selected** *(Selective breeding: fine wool in sheep or many kernels in corn; natural selection: ability to escape predators or resist drought);* **How Traits Are Selected** *(Selective breeding: by humans, who allow only organisms with the traits to reproduce; natural selection: by natural events, which allow organisms with the traits to produce more offspring)* After the table is completed, ask: **Why would *artificial* selection be a good term for selective breeding?** *(Because, like natural selection, selective breeding leads to changes in a species' traits, but artificial human choices, not natural events, control the process)* **learning modality: logical/mathematical**

Natural Selection

Building Inquiry Skills: Communicating

Encourage students who need extra challenges to learn about and then communicate to the rest of the class how natural selection has resulted in the viceroy butterfly bearing a close but superficial resemblance to the monarch butterfly. Urge students to use diagrams and illustrations to communicate what they learn. After students have communicated their findings, ask: **Why is the result of this type of natural selection called mimicry?** *(Because natural selection results in one species looking like, or mimicking, another species)* **learning modality: verbal**

Darwin knew that people used selective breeding to produce organisms with desired traits. For example, English farmers used selective breeding to produce sheep with fine wool. Darwin himself had bred pigeons with large, fan-shaped tails. By repeatedly allowing only those pigeons with many tail feathers to mate, Darwin produced pigeons with two or three times the usual number of tail feathers. Darwin thought that a process similar to selective breeding must happen in nature. But he wondered why certain traits were selected for, and how.

☑ *Checkpoint* **What observations led Darwin to propose his theory of evolution?**

Natural Selection

In 1858, Darwin and another British biologist, Alfred Russel Wallace, proposed an explanation for how evolution occurs. The next year, Darwin described this mechanism in a book entitled *The Origin of Species.* In his book, Darwin explained that evolution occurs by means of natural selection. **Natural selection** is the process by which individuals that are better adapted to their environment are more likely to survive and reproduce than other members of the same species. Darwin identified a number of factors that affect the process of natural selection: overproduction, competition, and variations.

Overproduction Most species produce far more offspring than can possibly survive. In many species, so many offspring are produced that there are not enough resources—food, water, and living space—for all of them. For example, each year a female sea turtle may lay more than 100 eggs. If all the young turtles survived, the sea would soon be full of turtles. Darwin knew that this doesn't happen. Why not?

Figure 4 Most newborn loggerhead sea turtles will not survive to adulthood. *Making Generalizations What factors limit the number of young that survive?*

150

Figure 5 The walruses lying on this rocky beach in Alaska must compete for resources. All organisms compete for limited resources such as food.

Competition Since food and other resources are limited, the offspring must compete with each other to survive. Competition does not usually involve direct physical fights between members of a species. Instead, competition is usually indirect. For example, some turtles may fail to find enough to eat. Others may not be able to escape from predators. Only a few turtles will survive long enough to reproduce.

Variations As you learned in your study of genetics, members of a species differ from one another in many of their traits. Any difference between individuals of the same species is called a **variation.** For example, some newly hatched turtles are able to swim faster than other turtles.

Selection Some variations make certain individuals better adapted to their environment. Those individuals are more likely to survive and reproduce. When those individuals reproduce, their offspring may inherit the allele for the helpful trait. The offspring, in turn, will be more likely to survive and reproduce, and thus pass on the allele to their offspring. After many generations, more members of the species will have the helpful trait. In effect, the environment has "selected" organisms with helpful traits to be the parents of the next generation—hence the term "natural selection." **Over a long period of time, natural selection can lead to evolution. Helpful variations gradually accumulate in a species, while unfavorable ones disappear.**

For example, suppose a new fast-swimming predator moves into the turtles' habitat. Turtles that are able to swim faster would be more likely to escape from the new predator. The faster turtles would thus be more likely to survive and reproduce. Over time, more and more turtles in the species would have the "fast-swimmer" trait.

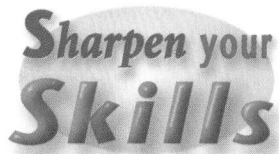

Sharpen your Skills

Inferring   ACTIVITY

Scatter 15 black buttons and 15 white buttons on a sheet of white paper. Have a partner time you to see how many buttons you can pick up in 10 seconds. Pick up the buttons one at a time.

Did you collect more buttons of one color than the other? Why? How can a variation such as color affect the process of natural selection?

Program Resources

◆ **Laboratory Manual** 5, "Variation in a Population"

Answers to Self-Assessment

☑ *Checkpoint*

Darwin proposed his theory of evolution based on observations of similarities and differences among species in nature and observations of domestic animals selectively bred to have desired traits.

Caption Question

Figure 4 Factors include predators and limited resources.

Cultural Diversity

Point out to students that human beings are unusual among living things in the variation of their behavior. Explain that the ability of humans to adapt their behavior has allowed them to move into a wide range of environments without evolving specific physical adaptations. In very cold climates, for example, animals such as polar bears have evolved thick fur to stay warm. Humans, on the other hand, have been able to use behavioral means, such as making and wearing clothing, to stay warm. As a result, humans do not have any special physical adaptations to extreme cold. Ask: **What are some behavioral means that humans use to protect themselves from predators?** *(Possible ways might include making and using weapons and living in groups.)* **learning modality: verbal**

Sharpen your Skills

Inferring

Materials *15 black buttons, 15 white buttons, large sheet of plain white paper, stopwatch*   ACTIVITY
Time 10 minutes
Tips Have students work in pairs so one student can focus on picking up buttons while the other keeps track of the time. All the buttons should be identical except for color.
Expected Outcome Students are likely to pick up more black buttons than white buttons. They should infer that a variation such as color can affect natural selection by making an organism more or less likely to be seen and captured by a predator.
Extend Ask: **Besides color, what are some other variations that might affect whether or not an organism is seen and captured by a predator?** *(Accept any reasonable responses, such as other physical traits, intelligence, and acuity of senses.)* **learning modality: kinesthetic**

Ongoing Assessment

Writing Have students explain how overproduction, competition, and variations lead to natural selection.

Nature at Work

Preparing for Inquiry

Key Concept Natural selection can lead to changes in a species' traits over time.
Skills Objectives Students will be able to
◆ make a dynamic model of natural selection in mice;
◆ observe how selection changes a species;
◆ predict how changing environmental conditions will affect natural selection in the model.
Time 40 minutes
Advance Planning To save time, before class begins you can prepare enough mouse and event cards so there is a complete set of cards for each group of students.

Guiding Inquiry

Invitation Tell students that in this lab they will simulate natural selection in mice of two different colors. Ask: **How do you think variation of color in a species might affect natural selection?** (*Some colors might make individuals better able to hide from predators, making them more likely to survive and reproduce. Other colors might make it more difficult for individuals to hide from predators, making them less likely to survive and reproduce.*)

Introducing the Procedure

Make sure students understand the rationale behind each step of the procedure. It may not be obvious to them, for example, why they cannot simply use cards representing mice of each color, rather than cards representing alleles. Ask: **Why do the mouse cards represent alleles rather than phenotypes?** (*Because alleles are passed on to the next generation, not phenotypes*) Point out that choosing alleles to make up the next generation is a realistic way to model reproduction and the inheritance of traits while choosing phenotypes is not.

Nature at Work

In this lab, you will investigate how natural selection can lead to changes in a species over time. You'll explore how both genetic and environmental factors play a part in natural selection.

Problem

How do species change over time?

Materials

scissors
marking pen
construction paper, 2 colors

Procedure

1. Work on this lab with two other students. One student should choose construction paper of one color and make the team's 50 "mouse" cards, as described in Table 1. The second student should choose a different color construction paper and make the team's 25 "event" cards, as described in Table 2. The third student should copy the data table and record all the data.

Part 1 A White Sand Environment

2. Mix up the mouse cards.
3. Begin by using the cards to model what might happen to a group of mice in an environment of white sand dunes. Choose two mouse cards. Allele pairs *WW* and *Ww* produce a white mouse. Allele pair *ww* produces a brown mouse. Record the color of the mouse with a tally mark in the data table.

4. Choose an event card. An "S" card means the mouse survives. A "D" or a "P" card means the mouse dies. A "C" card means the mouse dies if its color contrasts with the white sand dunes. (Only brown mice will die when a "C" card is drawn.) Record each death with a tally mark in the data table.
5. If the mouse lives, put the two mouse cards in a "live mice" pile. If the mouse dies, put the cards in a "dead mice" pile. Put the event card at the bottom of its pack.
6. Repeat Steps 3 through 5 with the remaining mouse cards to study the first generation of mice. Record your results.
7. Leave the dead mice cards untouched. Mix up the cards from the live mice pile. Mix up the events cards.
8. Repeat Steps 3 through 7 for the second generation. Then repeat Steps 3 through 6 for the third generation.

Table 1: "Mouse" Cards		
Number	**Label**	**Meaning**
25	*W*	Dominant allele for white fur
25	*w*	Recessive allele for brown fur

Table 2: "Event" Cards		
Number	**Label**	**Meaning**
5	S	Mouse survives.
1	D	Disease kills mouse.
1	P	Predator kills mice of all colors.
18	C	Predator kills mice that contrast with the environment.

Troubleshooting the Experiment

◆ Divide students into groups of three before they start the lab, and make sure group members divide the tasks as specified in the text.
◆ Check that students are assigning the right phenotype to each genotype. Remind them that the *W* allele for white fur is dominant to the *w* allele for brown fur.

Expected Outcome

Groups should find that the number of mice declines each generation, with the number of brown mice declining faster than the number of white mice in Part 1, and the number of white mice declining faster than the number of brown mice in Part 2.

DATA TABLE

Type of Environment: _____

Generation	White Mice	Brown Mice	Deaths	
			White Mice	Brown Mice
1				
2				
3				

Part 2 A Forest Floor Environment

9. How would the data differ if the mice in this model lived on a dark brown forest floor? Record your prediction in your notebook.

10. Make a new copy of the data table. Then use the cards to test your prediction. Remember that a "C" card now means that any mouse with white fur will die.

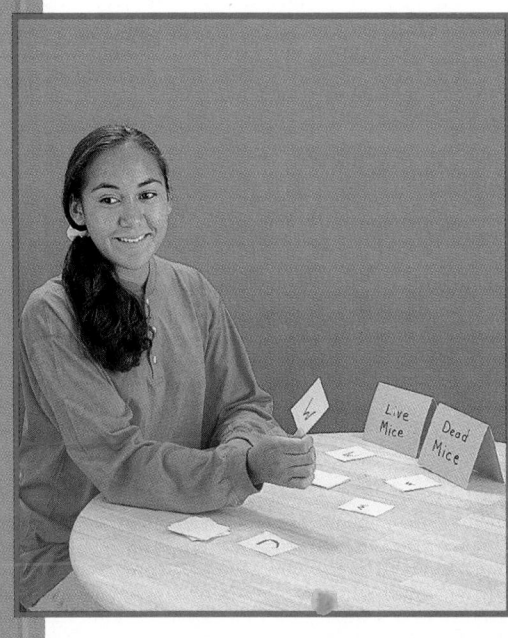

Analyze and Conclude

1. In Part 1, how many white mice were there in each generation? How many brown mice? In each generation, which color mouse had the higher death rate? (*Hint:* To calculate the death rate for white mice, divide the number of white mice that died by the total number of white mice, then multiply by 100%.)

2. If the events in Part 1 occurred in nature, how would the group of mice change over time?

3. How did the results in Part 2 differ from those in Part 1?

4. What are some ways in which this investigation models natural selection? What are some ways in which natural selection differs from this model?

5. **Think About It** How would it affect your model if you increased the number of "C" cards? If you decreased the number?

Design an Experiment

Choose a different species with a trait that interests you. Make a set of cards similar to these cards to investigate how natural selection might bring about the evolution of that species.

Sample Data Table

Type of Environment: White Sand

Generation	White Mice	Brown Mice	Deaths of White Mice	Deaths of Brown Mice
1	18	7	2	5
2	16	2	2	1
3	14	1	1	1

Program Resources

◆ **Unit 1 Resources** Chapter 5 Skills Lab, pp. 139–141

Safety

Review the safety guidelines in Appendix A.

Analyze and Conclude

1. Answers will depend on the genotypes of the mice in each generation and the order in which the mouse and event cards are drawn. For the sample data, there were 18 white mice in the first generation, of which 2 died, yielding a death rate of 11% for the white mice. There were also 7 brown mice in the first generation, of which 5 died, yielding a death rate of 71% for the brown mice.

2. The population of mice would contain more and more mice with white fur.

3. In Part 2, the population contains more brown mice each generation because white mice are selected against, whereas in Part 1, the population contains more white mice each generation because the brown mice are selected against.

4. This investigation models natural selection in that an organism's chances of surviving and reproducing depend both on the organism's inherited traits and on the environment in which the organism lives. Natural selection differs from the model in that other environmental factors besides predators and disease, and other traits besides fur color, are likely to influence an organism's chances of surviving and reproducing.

5. If you increased the number of "C" cards, natural selection against mice that contrast with the environment would be stronger and contrasting-color mice would decrease in number more quickly. If you decreased the number of "C" cards, natural selection against mice that contrast with the environment would be weaker and contrasting-color mice would decrease in number more slowly.

Extending the Inquiry

Design an Experiment Urge students to select a trait that is controlled by a recessive allele so they can see how dominance affects the rate at which natural selection changes the genetic makeup of the population. The trait they choose to model may be real or hypothetical.

The Role of Genes in Evolution

Inquiry Challenge

Time 10 minutes

ACTIVITY

Divide the class into groups, and challenge students in each group to brainstorm an experiment to demonstrate that only inherited traits are affected by natural selection. You may wish to share the information on Lamarck in the Background below to stimulate students' thinking. *(One way is to change experimental organisms in some way, for example, by dyeing the hair of lab rats, and then observing whether the changed trait appears in their offspring.)* Have each group elect a spokesperson to describe its plan to the rest of the class, and urge the class to give the group feedback on its ideas. Then ask: **Why are only inherited traits affected by natural selection?** *(Because only genes are passed from parents to their offspring)* **cooperative learning**

Evolution in Action

Social Studies
CONNECTION

Give students a context for the feature by explaining that the type of natural selection it describes is called *industrial melanism.* Explain that melanism refers to the pigment melanin, which gives many organisms—from peppered moths to humans—their color. The change in color of moths was documented in several unrelated species and in several different places, all of which were heavily industrialized. Point out that industrial melanism is one of the best analyzed examples of natural selection in action in the real world.

In Your Journal Students should (correctly) predict that strict pollution laws since the 1950s would lead to trees returning to their light gray color and natural selection favoring light-colored moths. This, in turn, would result in peppered moth populations becoming mostly light-colored again. **learning modality: logical/mathematical**

Social Studies
CONNECTION

The case of the English peppered moth is an example of how human actions can affect natural selection. In the late 1700s, most English peppered moths were light gray in color. The light-colored moths had an advantage over black peppered moths because birds could not see them against the light-gray trees. Natural selection favored the light-colored moths over the black moths.

The Industrial Revolution began in England in the late 1700s. People built factories to make cloth and other goods. Over time, smoke from the factories blackened the trunks of the trees. Now the light-colored moths were easier to see than the black ones. As a result, birds caught more light-colored moths. Natural selection favored the black moths. By about 1850, almost all the peppered moths were black.

In Your Journal

Since the 1950s, strict pollution laws have reduced the amount of smoke released into the air in England. Predict how this has affected the trees and the moths.

Figure 6 The Industrial Revolution affected natural selection in peppered moths in England. As pollution blackened the tree trunks, black moths became more likely to survive and reproduce.

The Role of Genes in Evolution

Without variations, all the members of a species would have the same traits. Evolution by natural selection would not occur because all individuals would have an equal chance of surviving and reproducing. But where do variations come from? How are they passed on from parents to offspring? Darwin could not answer these questions.

Darwin did not know anything about genes or mutations. It is not surprising that he could not explain what caused variations or how they were passed on. As scientists later learned, variations can result from mutations in genes or from the shuffling of alleles during meiosis. Only genes are passed from parents to their offspring. Because of this, only traits that are inherited, or controlled by genes, can be acted upon by natural selection.

Evolution in Action

Since Darwin published his book, scientists have observed many examples of evolution in action. In a 1977 study of the finches on Daphne Major, one of the Galapagos Islands, scientists observed that beak size could change very quickly by natural selection. That year, little rain fell on the island—only 25 millimeters instead of the usual 130 millimeters or so. Because of the lack of rain, many plants died. Fewer of the seeds that the finches usually ate were available. Instead, the birds had to eat large seeds that were enclosed in tough, thorny seed pods.

Finches with larger and stronger beaks were better able to open the tough pods than were finches with smaller, weaker beaks. Many of the finches with smaller beaks did not survive the drought. The next year, more finches on the island had larger and stronger beaks. Evolution by natural selection had occurred in just one year.

Background

History of Science Darwin was not the first person to propose a theory of evolution. In the early 1800s, a well-known French naturalist named Jean-Baptiste Lamarck also developed a theory of evolution to explain changes in a species' traits through time. Lamarck thought that changes in an organism during its lifetime could be passed on to its offspring. For example, dog breeders cut off parts of the ears of some breeds of dogs to make the ears stand up. According to Lamarck, the offspring of the dogs with cropped ears would also have cropped ears. This idea is often called "the inheritance of acquired characteristics," and it is now known to be incorrect. Changes in an organism cannot be passed on to its offspring unless they are controlled by genes.

How Do New Species Form?

Darwin's theory of evolution by natural selection explains how variations can lead to changes in a species. But how does an entirely new species evolve? Since Darwin's time, scientists have come to understand that geographic isolation is one of the main ways that new species form. Isolation, or complete separation, occurs when some members of a species become cut off from the rest of the species.

Sometimes a group is separated from the rest of its species by a river, volcano, or mountain range. Even an ocean wave can separate a few individuals from the rest of their species by sweeping them out to sea and later washing them ashore on an island. This may have happened on the Galapagos Islands. Once a group becomes isolated, members of the isolated group can no longer mate with members of the rest of the species.

A new species might form when a group of individuals remains separated from the rest of its species long enough to evolve different traits. The longer the group remains isolated from the rest of the species, the more likely it is to evolve into a new species. For example, Abert's squirrel and the Kaibab squirrel live in forests in the Southwest. About 10,000 years ago both types of squirrels were members of the same species. About that time, however, a small group of squirrels became isolated in a forest on the north side of the Grand Canyon in Arizona. Over time, this group evolved into the Kaibab squirrel, which has a distinctive black belly. Scientists are not sure whether the Kaibab squirrel has become different enough from Abert's squirrel to be considered a separate species.

☑ *Checkpoint* *How did geographic isolation affect the Kaibab squirrel?*

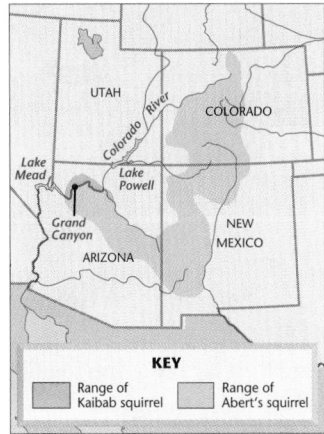

Figure 7 About 10,000 years ago, a group of squirrels became isolated from the rest of the species. As a result, the Kaibab squirrel (left) has become different from Abert's squirrel (right).
Interpreting Maps *What geographic feature separates the range of the Kaibab squirrel from that of Abert's squirrel?*

KEY
Range of Kaibab squirrel   Range of Abert's squirrel

Continental Drift

Demonstration

Display a map of Pangaea. Point out that Australia broke away from Pangaea 250 million years ago, while other continents were still joined as recently as 50 million years ago. This isolated marsupials in Australia from competition with other mammals. Ask: **What are some other Australian marsupials?** *(kangaroo, koala, wombat)* **learning modality: visual**

3 Assess

Section 1 Review Answers

1. Evolution is the gradual change in a species over time. Darwin observed different adaptations among organisms.
2. Otherwise all individuals would be equally adapted to their environment and equally likely to survive and reproduce.
3. A new species can form when a group of individuals becomes isolated from the rest of its species and remains separated long enough to evolve different traits.
4. Insects that look like sticks are camouflaged among twigs and may be overlooked by predators. If the trait increases the insect's chances of surviving and reproducing, then insects with the trait would become more common than insects without it.

┄┄┄┄┄┄┄┄┄┄┄┄┄┄ **CHAPTER PROJECT** ▼

Check Your Progress
Review students' plans to make sure they have chosen workable models. Distribute Worksheet 1, and guide students through the procedure of making a scale model of their own life history to date. When students are comfortable with the process, let each group start its first time line.

Performance Assessment

Skills Check Have students explain how continental drift led to the evolution of many different marsupials in Australia.

Continental Drift

Geographic isolation has also occurred on a worldwide scale. For example, hundreds of millions of years ago all of Earth's landmasses were connected as one landmass. It formed a supercontinent called Pangaea. Organisms could migrate from one part of the supercontinent to another. Over millions of years, Pangaea gradually split apart in a process called continental drift. As the continents separated, species became isolated from one another and began to evolve independently.

Perhaps the most striking example of how continental drift affected the evolution of species is on the continent of Australia. The organisms living in Australia have been isolated from all other organisms on Earth for millions of years. Because of this, unique organisms have evolved in Australia. For example, most mammals in Australia belong to the group known as marsupials. Unlike other mammals, a marsupial gives birth to very small young that continue to develop in a pouch on the mother's body. Figure 8 shows two of the many marsupial species that exist in Australia. In contrast, few species of marsupials exist on other continents.

Figure 8 As a result of continental drift, many species of marsupials evolved in Australia. Australian marsupials include the numbat (top) and the spotted cuscus (bottom).

 ### Section 1 Review

1. What is evolution? What did Darwin observe on the Galapagos Islands that he thought was the result of evolution?
2. Explain why variations are needed for natural selection to occur.
3. Describe how geographic isolation can result in the formation of a new species.
4. **Thinking Critically** **Applying Concepts** Some insects look just like sticks. How could this be an advantage to the insects? How could this trait have evolved through natural selection?

156

Check Your Progress
CHAPTER PROJECT
You should now be ready to submit your plans for your time lines to your teacher. Include a list of the major events you will include on your time lines. Remember, you want to emphasize the life forms that were present at each period. When your plans are approved, begin to construct your time lines. (*Hint:* You will need to divide your time lines into equal-sized intervals. For example, if you use a 12-month calendar to represent 5 billion years, calculate how many months will represent 1 billion years.)

Program Resources

◆ **Unit 1 Resources** 5-1 Review and Reinforce, p. 129; 5-1 Enrich, p. 130

Media and Technology

 **Exploring Life Science Videodisc**
Unit 5, Side 2, "The Drifters"

Chapter 6

SECTION 2 The Fossil Record

DISCOVER ••••••••••••••••••••••••••••••••• ACTIVITY

What Can Fossils Tell You?

1. Look at the fossil in the photograph. Describe the fossil's characteristics in as much detail as you can.

2. From your description in Step 1, try to figure out how the organism lived. How did it move? Where did it live?

Think It Over
Inferring What type of present-day organism do you think is related to the fossil? Why?

A crime has been committed. You and another detective arrive at the crime scene after the burglar has fled. To piece together what happened, you begin searching for clues. First you notice a broken first-floor window. Leading up to the window are footprints in the mud. From the prints, you can infer the size and type of shoes the burglar wore. As you gather these and other clues, you slowly piece together a picture of what happened and who the burglar might be.

To understand events that occurred long ago, scientists act like detectives. Some of the most important clues to Earth's past are fossils. A **fossil** is the preserved remains or traces of an organism that lived in the past. A fossil can be formed from a bone, tooth, shell, or other part of an organism. Other fossils can be traces of the organism, such as footprints or worm burrows left in mud that later turned to stone.

How Do Fossils Form?

Very few fossils are of complete organisms. Often when an animal dies, the soft parts of its body either decay or are eaten before a fossil can form. Usually only the hard parts of the animal, such as the bones or shells, remain. Plants also form fossils. The parts of plants that are most often preserved as fossils include leaves, stems, roots, and seeds.

The formation of any fossil is a rare event. The conditions must be just right for a fossil to form. **Most fossils form when organisms that die become buried in sediments.** Sediments are

Chapter 5 **157**

GUIDE FOR READING

◆ How do most fossils form?

◆ How can scientists determine a fossil's age?

Reading Tip As you read, write four multiple-choice questions about the content in this section. Exchange questions with a partner and answer each other's questions.

A fossilized shark tooth ▼

READING STRATEGIES

Reading Tip Students can choose from among the 13 boldface terms in this section for their multiple choice questions. Point out that the definitions of the key terms come just before or just after the term appears in boldface. An example of a question might be: The remains of organisms that are changed to rock are called (a) petrified fossils, (b) molds, (c) casts, (d) sedimentary rock.

SECTION 2 The Fossil Record

Objectives

After completing the lesson, students will be able to

◆ describe how most fossils form;
◆ explain how a scientist determines a fossil's age;
◆ explain what fossils reveal;
◆ describe the main events of the Geologic Time Scale;
◆ distinguish between gradualism and punctuated equilibria.

Key Terms fossil, sedimentary rock, petrified fossil, mold, cast, relative dating, absolute dating, radioactive element, half-life, fossil record, extinct, gradualism, punctuated equilibria

1 Engage/Explore

Activating Prior Knowledge

Most students are likely to know a lot about dinosaurs. Ask: **How do we know so much about dinosaurs if there are no longer any of them left alive?** (*From their remains, which have been preserved as fossils*) Tell students they will learn in this section how fossils are formed and how they are used by scientists to understand extinct organisms and their evolution.

•••••••• DISCOVER ••••••••

Skills Focus inferring
Time 5 minutes
Tips It may be helpful to provide a hand lens for any students with vision problems. After the activity, inform students that the fossil pictured is a trilobite, an ocean-bottom-dwelling animal that existed about 540 to 250 million years ago.
Expected Outcome Students are likely to describe the overall shape and obvious physical features of the fossil, including what appear to be a shell and numerous legs.
Think It Over Students may say the fossil is related to present-day insects or crabs, because it resembles them in its physical features.

2 Facilitate

How Do Fossils Form?

Demonstration

Materials *clear plastic container, sand, soil, shells, other small objects*
Time 10 minutes

Demonstrate how most fossils form by gradually layering sand and soil in a clear container and scattering small shells or other objects throughout the layers to represent organic remains. As you add the layers of sediment, point out to students how the gradual accumulation of sediment buries and helps preserve the remains of organisms. Relate the demonstration to the actual formation of fossils by asking: **How would real animal remains become buried in this way?** (*By wind or water dropping sand and soil on them*) **How might the fossils become uncovered again?** (*Answers may vary. Usually erosion wears away layers of rock.*) **learning modality: visual**

Including All Students

Materials *baking sheet, modeling clay, prepared gelatin, shell or other small object*
Time 5 minutes one day; 5 minutes the next day

Give hands-on learners an opportunity to experience how molds and casts are formed. Instruct students to lay a flat piece of clay on a baking sheet and make an impression in the clay with a small object such as a shell. Then have students pour a small amount of prepared gelatin into the depression and put the baking sheet in a refrigerator overnight. The next day, advise students to gently dislodge the hardened gelatin from the clay. The gelatin should have the same shape as the object that made the depression in the clay. Ask: **Which part of your model represents a mold? Which part represents a cast?** (*The depression in the clay represents a mold; the gelatin shape represents a cast.*) **learning modality: kinesthetic**

1. Two dinosaurs are buried by ash from an erupting volcano.

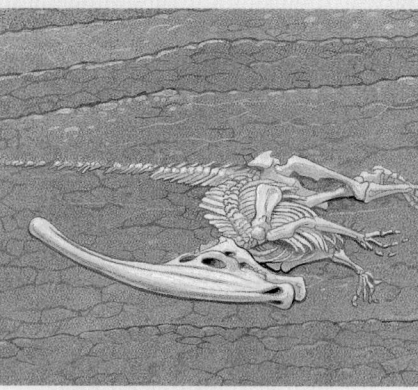

2. Minerals gradually replace the remains. Over millions of years, the fossils become buried by sediments.

Figure 9 Fossils are the preserved remains or traces of organisms that lived in the past. Fossils can form when organisms that die become buried in sediments.
Interpreting Diagrams What is one way in which a buried fossil can become uncovered?

particles of soil and rock. When a river flows into a lake or ocean, the sediments carried by the river settle to the bottom. Layers of sediments build up and cover the dead organisms. Over millions of years, the layers harden to become **sedimentary rock.**

Petrified Fossils Some remains that become buried in sediments are actually changed to rock. Minerals dissolved in the water soak into the buried remains. Gradually, the minerals replace the remains, changing them into rock. Fossils that form in this way are called **petrified fossils.**

Molds and Casts Sometimes shells or other hard parts buried by sediments are gradually dissolved. An empty space remains in the place the part once occupied. A hollow space in sediment in the shape of an organism or part of an organism is called a **mold.**

Sometimes a mold becomes filled in with hardened minerals, forming a **cast.** A cast is a copy of the shape of the organism that made the mold. If you have ever made a gelatin dessert in a plastic mold, then you can understand how a cast forms.

Preserved Remains Organisms can also be preserved in substances other than sediments. Entire organisms, such as the huge elephant-like mammoths that lived thousands of years ago, have been preserved in ice. The low temperatures preserved the mammoths' soft parts.

The bones and teeth of other ancient animals have been preserved in tar pits. Tar is a dark, sticky form of oil. Tar pits formed when tar seeped up from under the ground to the surface. The tar pits were often covered with water. Animals that came to drink the water became stuck in the tar.

158

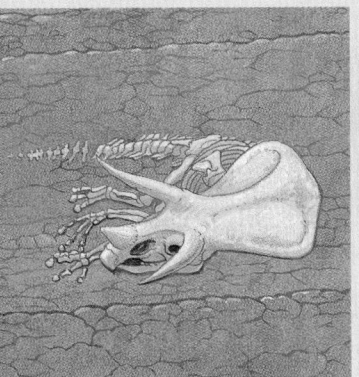
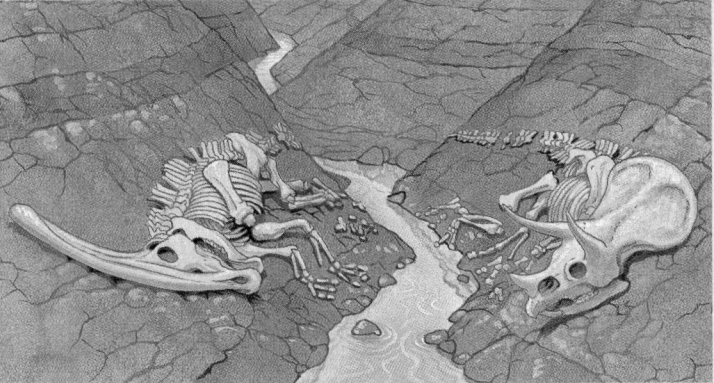

3. Running water cuts through the sedimentary rock layers, exposing the fossils.

Tips Make sure students find a place to put the container of fruit that is left out so it will not be disturbed. Warn students not to eat the fruit that has been left out.

Expected Outcome The frozen fruit is well preserved, whereas the fruit that was left out is starting to spoil. Students should infer that freezing prevents the soft parts from drying out and/or rotting.

Extend Ask: **How do you think a mammoth or other animal might get preserved in this way?** *(Accept any reasonable response, such as an avalanche burying the animal or the animal falling into a crevasse in a glacier.)* **learning modality: kinesthetic**

Determining a Fossil's Age

Building Inquiry Skills: Problem Solving

Have students assume they are scientists who have excavated two fossil reptile skulls. Tell them that one skull was found 20 m below the surface and the other was found 30 m below the surface. Then ask: **Based on this information alone, what can you infer about the age of the two skulls?** *(The skull found nearer the surface is most likely younger than the skull found farther down in the ground.)* Urge students to draw a diagram to illustrate the problem and its solution. **learning modality: logical/mathematical**

Insects and some other organisms can become stuck in the sticky sap that some evergreen trees produce. The sap then hardens, forming amber. The amber protects the organism's body from decay.

Determining a Fossil's Age

To understand how living things have changed through time, scientists need to be able to determine the ages of fossils. They can then determine the sequence in which past events occurred. This information can be used to reconstruct the history of life on Earth. **Scientists can determine a fossil's age in two ways: relative dating and absolute dating.**

Relative Dating Scientists use **relative dating** to determine which of two fossils is older. To understand how relative dating works, imagine that a river has cut down through layers of sedimentary rock to form a canyon. If you look at the canyon walls, you can see the layers of sedimentary rock piled up one on top of another. The layers near the top of the canyon were formed most recently. These layers are the youngest rock layers. The lower down the canyon wall you go, the older the layers are. Therefore, fossils found in layers near the top of the canyon are younger than fossils found near the bottom of the canyon.

Relative dating can only be used when the rock layers have been preserved in their original sequence. Relative dating can help scientists determine whether one fossil is older than another. However, relative dating does not tell scientists the fossil's actual age.

☑ *Checkpoint* Which rock layers contain younger fossils?

TRY THIS

Preservation in Ice

1. Place fresh fruit, such as apple slices, strawberries, and blueberries, in an open plastic container.

2. Completely cover the fruit with water. Put the container in a freezer.

3. Place the same type and amount of fresh fruit in another open container. Leave it somewhere where no one will disturb it.

4. After three days, observe the fruit in both containers.

Inferring Use your observations to explain why fossils preserved in ice are more likely to include soft, fleshy body parts.

Exploring Life Science Videodisc
Unit 5, Side 2, "Fossils"

Chapter 1

Exploring Life Science Videodisc
Unit 5, Side 2, "The Earth Library"

Chapter 3

Answers to Self-Assessment

Caption Question

Figure 9 A buried fossil can become uncovered when running water cuts through sedimentary rock layers.

☑ *Checkpoint*
The rock layers nearer the surface contain younger fossils.

Oral Presentation Call on students at random to describe how petrified fossils, molds, and casts form.

Integrating Chemistry

Reinforce students' understanding of absolute dating by calling their attention to Figure 10 and asking: **If the sample contains one eighth of the original amount of potassium-40, how old is it?** (*Three half-lives, or 3.9 billion years, old*) **What proportion of the same sample would be argon-40?** (*seven eighths*) **learning modality: logical/ mathematical**

Sharpen your Skills

Calculating

Materials *calculator*
Time 10 minutes
Tips Remind students that for each half-life that passes, half of the sample will break down.
Expected Outcome Three half-lives will have gone by after 2,139 million years ($2,139 \div 713 = 3$). One-eighth ($\frac{1}{2} \times \frac{1}{2} \times \frac{1}{2}$) of the original 16-gram sample, or 2 grams, will remain after 2,139 million years.
Extend Explain that other radioactive elements have longer or shorter half-lives than potassium-40. Ask: **How does the length of an element's half-life relate to its usefulness for dating purposes?** (*Very old rocks can be dated using an element with a long half-life.*) **learning modality: logical/mathematical**

What Do Fossils Reveal?

Addressing Naive Conceptions

Explain that of the millions of extinct species, only a fraction of one percent are likely to have been preserved as fossils. Ask: **Which organisms are most likely to be found as fossils: those that lived when much of Earth was covered by shallow seas or those that lived when Earth's mountain ranges were being formed?** (*Those that lived when much of Earth was covered by shallow seas*) **learning modality: verbal**

160

Figure 10 The half-life of potassium-40, a radioactive element, is 1.3 billion years. This means that half of the potassium-40 in a sample will break down into argon-40 every 1.3 billion years. *Interpreting Charts If a sample contains one fourth of the original amount of potassium-40, how old is the sample?*

Decay of Potassium-40 (Half-life = 1.3 billion years)		
Time	**Amount of Potassium-40**	**Amount of Argon-40**
2.6 billion years ago	4 g	0 g
1.3 billion years ago	2 g	2 g
Present	1 g	3 g

Sharpen your Skills

Calculating

A radioactive element has a half-life of 713 million years. After 2,139 million years, how many half-lives will have gone by?

Calculate how much of a 16-gram sample of the element will remain after 2,139 million years.

Absolute Dating Another technique, called **absolute dating,** allows scientists to determine the actual age of fossils. The rocks that fossils are found near contain **radioactive elements,** unstable elements that decay, or break down, into different elements. The **half-life** of a radioactive element is the time it takes for half of the atoms in a sample to decay. Figure 10 shows how a sample of potassium-40, a radioactive element, breaks down into argon-40 over time.

Scientists can compare the amount of a radioactive element in a sample to the amount of the element into which it breaks down. As you can see in Figure 10, this information can be used to calculate the age of the rock, and thus the age of the fossil.

☑ *Checkpoint* What is a half-life?

What Do Fossils Reveal?

Like pieces in a jigsaw puzzle, fossils help scientists piece together information about Earth's past. The millions of fossils that scientists have collected are called the **fossil record.** The fossil record, however, is incomplete. Many organisms die without leaving fossils behind. Despite gaps in it, the fossil record has given scientists a lot of important information about past life on Earth.

Almost all of the species preserved as fossils are now extinct. A species is **extinct** if no members of that species are still alive. Most of what scientists know about extinct species is based on the fossil record. Scientists use fossils of bones and teeth to build models of extinct animals. Fossil footprints provide clues about how fast an animal could move and how tall it was.

160

Background

Facts and Figures Another element used in absolute dating is carbon-14. All plants and animals contain some radioactive carbon-14. As plants and animals grow, carbon atoms are added to their tissues. After the organism dies, no more carbon-14 is added and the carbon-14 in the organism's body decays. To determine the absolute age of a sample, scientists measure the amount of carbon-14 that is left in the organism's remains.

Carbon-14 has been used to date frozen mammoths and the skeletons of prehistoric humans, as well as pieces of wood and bone.

Carbon-14 is very useful in dating materials from plants and animals that lived up to about 50,000 years ago. Since carbon-14 has a half-life of only 5,730 years, it can't be used to date really ancient fossils or rocks. The amount of carbon-14 left would be too small to measure accurately.

The fossil record also provides clues about how and when new groups of organisms evolved. The first animals appeared in the seas about 540 million years ago. These animals included worms, sponges, and other invertebrates—animals without backbones. About 500 million years ago, fishes evolved. These early fishes were the first vertebrates—animals with backbones.

The first land plants, which were similar to mosses, evolved around 410 million years ago. Land plants gradually evolved strong stems that held them upright. These plants were similar to modern ferns and cone-bearing trees. Look at *Exploring Life's History* on pages 162 and 163 to see when other groups of organisms evolved.

The Geologic Time Scale

Using absolute dating, scientists have calculated the ages of many different fossils and rocks. From this information, scientists have created a "calendar" of Earth's history that spans more than 4.6 billion years. Scientists have divided this large time period into smaller units called eras and periods. This calendar of Earth's history is sometimes called the Geologic Time Scale.

The largest span of time in the Geologic Time Scale is Precambrian Time. This span of time is sometimes referred to simply as the Precambrian (pree KAM bree un). It covers the first 4 billion years of Earth's history. Scientists know very little about the Precambrian because there are few fossils from these ancient times. After the Precambrian, the Geologic Time Scale is divided into three major blocks of time, or eras. Each era is further divided into shorter periods. In *Exploring Life's History,* you can see the events that occurred during each time period.

Figure 11 Complete skeletons of animals that lived thousands of years ago have been found in the Rancho La Brea tar pits in Los Angeles, California. The photo shows a model of an elephant-like animal. Scientists created the model based on information learned from the fossils.

Students are referred in the text to the *Exploring Life's History* on pages 162 and 163. Check that they are interpreting the diagram correctly and extracting the most important information from the feature by asking them the following series of questions: **When did the first amphibians evolve?** *(During the Devonian Period, about 380 million years ago)* **When did the earliest reptiles appear on Earth?** *(During the Carboniferous Period, about 320 million years ago)* **When did the first dinosaurs and mammals evolve?** *(In the Triassic Period, about 220 million years ago)* **When did the first birds appear?** *(During the Jurassic Period, about 150 million years ago)* **When did the first primates appear?** *(During the Tertiary Period, about 66 million years ago)* **When did humans evolve?** *(During the Quaternary Period, about 1.5 million years ago)* **learning modality: verbal**

The Geologic Time Scale

Including All Students

Support students who need more help in learning the names of the eras in the Geologic Time Scale by explaining the words' roots. The combining form *-zoic* comes from the Greek word for "life," *paleo-* from the Greek word for "ancient," *meso-* from the Greek word for "middle," and *ceno-* from the Greek word for "recent." After students have learned the meanings of the combining forms, check their understanding by asking: **What do the terms *Paleozoic, Mesozoic,* and *Cenozoic* mean?** *(Ancient life, middle life, and recent life, respectively)* **learning modality: verbal**

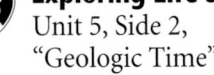

Answers to Self-Assessment

Caption Question

Figure 10 The sample is two half-lives, or 2.6 billion years, old.

 *Checkpoint*

A half-life is the time it takes for half the atoms in a sample of a radioactive element to break down, or decay.

Ongoing Assessment

Skills Check Have students create a table that compares and contrasts relative and absolute dating.

 Students can save their tables in their portfolios.

The Geologic Time Scale, continued

EXPLORING
Life's History

Call students' attention to the feature and stress that the captions at the bottom summarize the important evolutionary events in each time period. Make sure that students understand the time line that runs across the top of the feature. Explain that the Precambrian actually covers most of Earth's *total* history, but because there were few living things during the Precambrian, it makes up very little of Earth's *life* history. Add that almost one-quarter of Earth's history passed before the first life forms appeared around 3.5 billion years ago. Inform students that the earliest life forms on Earth were confined to the water. Then ask: **When did the first land plants and animals appear on Earth?** *(During the Silurian Period, about 430 million years ago)* The amount of detail in the feature may overwhelm some students, so make sure you are clear about how much detail you expect them to learn. **learning modality: visual**

Building Inquiry Skills: Communicating

Challenge students to imagine that they are in a machine traveling back in time from the present to another period in Earth's history. Then have them write an eyewitness report, modeled on a television or newspaper story, relaying what they might observe in their time travels. In their report, they should address such questions as: **What would it be like to live during another time period? What type of organisms would you see? What familiar species of today would you not see?** Encourage students who need extra challenges to use outside sources in addition to *Exploring Life's History* for more information, such as descriptions of climate or land forms. Ask volunteers to share their reports with the rest of the class, and challenge other students to identify each time period as it is described in the reports. **learning modality: verbal**

162

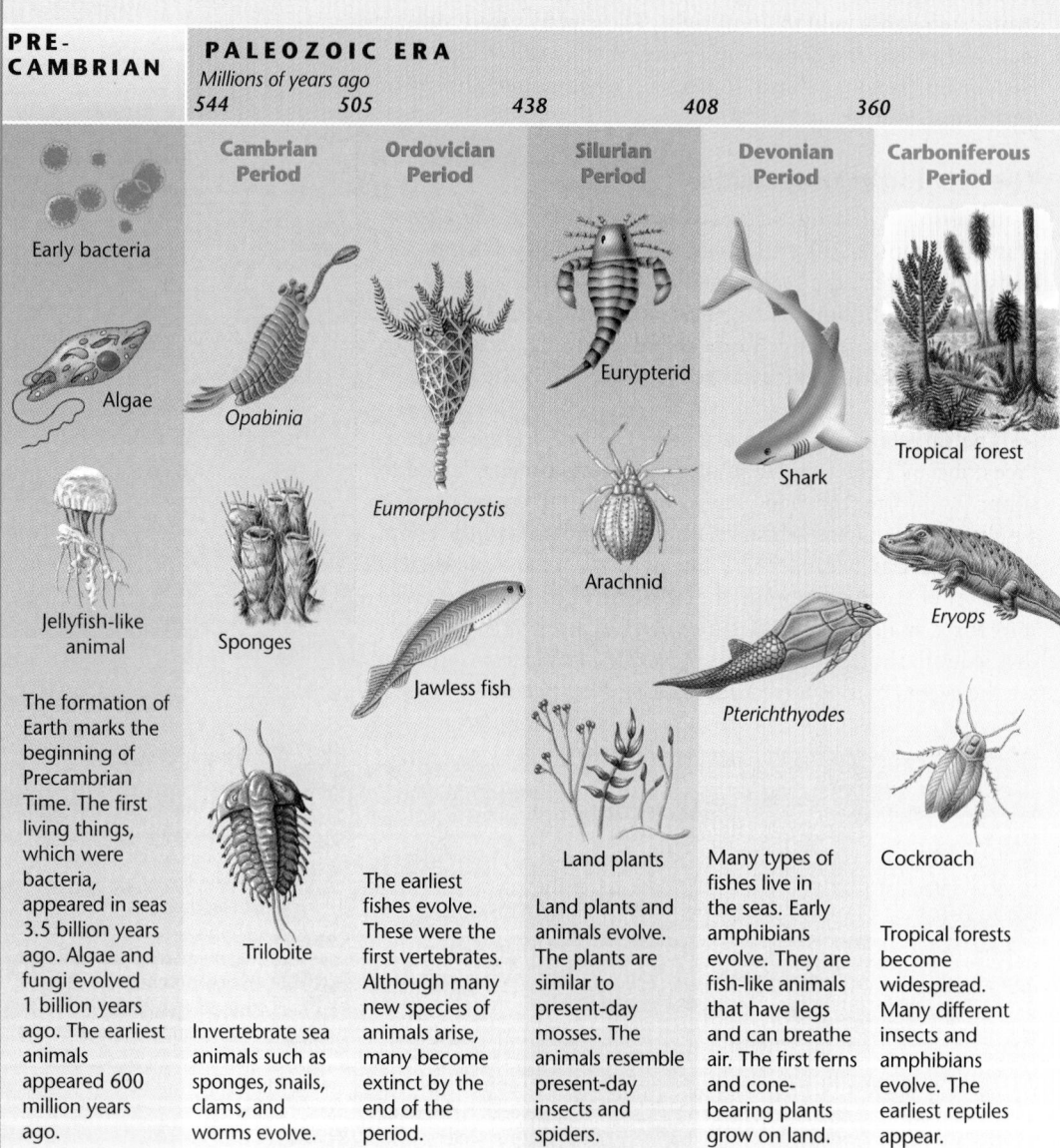

EXPLORING *Life's History*
Take a trip through time to see how life on Earth has changed.

PRECAMBRIAN TIME The Precambrian covers about 87 percent of Earth's history.

4.6 billion years ago

PRE-CAMBRIAN

PALEOZOIC ERA
Millions of years ago

| 544 | 505 | 438 | 408 | 360 |

Cambrian Period — **Ordovician Period** — **Silurian Period** — **Devonian Period** — **Carboniferous Period**

Early bacteria

Algae

Jellyfish-like animal

Opabinia

Sponges

Trilobite

Eumorphocystis

Jawless fish

Eurypterid

Arachnid

Land plants

Shark

Pterichthyodes

Tropical forest

Eryops

Cockroach

The formation of Earth marks the beginning of Precambrian Time. The first living things, which were bacteria, appeared in seas 3.5 billion years ago. Algae and fungi evolved 1 billion years ago. The earliest animals appeared 600 million years ago.

Invertebrate sea animals such as sponges, snails, clams, and worms evolve.

The earliest fishes evolve. These were the first vertebrates. Although many new species of animals arise, many become extinct by the end of the period.

Land plants and animals evolve. The plants are similar to present-day mosses. The animals resemble present-day insects and spiders.

Many types of fishes live in the seas. Early amphibians evolve. They are fish-like animals that have legs and can breathe air. The first ferns and cone-bearing plants grow on land.

Tropical forests become widespread. Many different insects and amphibians evolve. The earliest reptiles appear.

162

	CENOZOIC
PALEOZOIC	MESOZOIC
544 million years ago	245 million years ago	66.4 million years ago

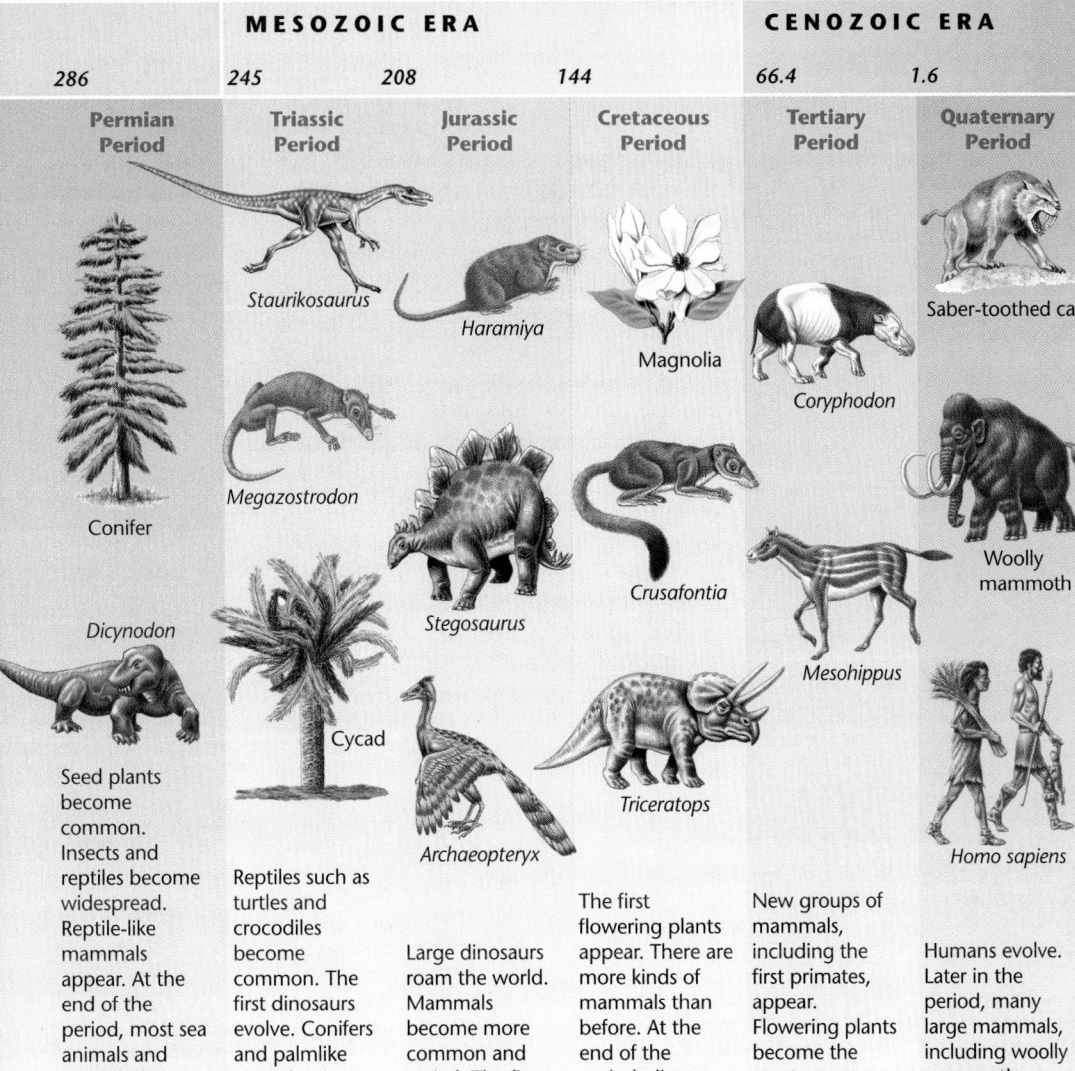

MESOZOIC ERA

| 286 | 245 | 208 | 144 |
| Permian Period | Triassic Period | Jurassic Period | Cretaceous Period |

CENOZOIC ERA

| 66.4 | 1.6 |
| Tertiary Period | Quaternary Period |

Staurikosaurus

Haramiya

Magnolia

Coryphodon

Saber-toothed cat

Megazostrodon

Conifer

Dicynodon

Stegosaurus

Crusafontia

Woolly mammoth

Cycad

Mesohippus

Archaeopteryx

Triceratops

Homo sapiens

Seed plants become common. Insects and reptiles become widespread. Reptile-like mammals appear. At the end of the period, most sea animals and amphibians become extinct.

Reptiles such as turtles and crocodiles become common. The first dinosaurs evolve. Conifers and palmlike trees dominate forests.

Large dinosaurs roam the world. Mammals become more common and varied. The first birds appear.

The first flowering plants appear. There are more kinds of mammals than before. At the end of the period, dinosaurs become extinct.

New groups of mammals, including the first primates, appear. Flowering plants become the most common kind of plant.

Humans evolve. Later in the period, many large mammals, including woolly mammoths, become extinct.

Chapter 5 **163**

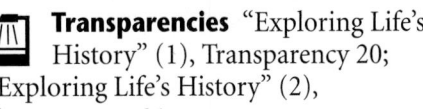

Media and Technology

📽 **Transparencies** "Exploring Life's History" (1), Transparency 20; "Exploring Life's History" (2), Transparency 21

Inquiry Challenge

Materials poster board, dice, index cards, markers, small toys or other items for game tokens
Time 30 minutes

Divide the class into groups, and challenge each group to create a board game, called *A Trip Through Geologic Time,* to reinforce their knowledge of Earth's life history. The game board should start in the Precambrian and continue on to the present. To advance around the game board (and through time), players should be required to answer questions, perhaps written on chance cards, about each period. Escaping from carnivorous dinosaurs, skirting around treacherous tar pits, or avoiding similar relevant obstacles in particular time periods might be included on the game board to add excitement to the game and require students to apply more of the information from *Exploring Life's History.* After students have created their games, urge groups to exchange and play each other's games. **cooperative learning**

Including All Students

Materials index cards
Time 30 minutes

Pair students who are having difficulty or who are still mastering English with other students who have strong verbal skills. Then have the members of each pair work together to make flash cards for the periods of the Geologic Time Scale. On each card, they should include the dates for the period and the most important life history events. Challenge pairs to exchange flash cards and use them to quiz each other on the material. **limited English proficiency**

Ongoing Assessment

Oral Presentation Call on students at random to describe an event in the evolution of plants or animals, based on the information in *Exploring Life's History.*

How Fast Does Evolution Occur?

Building Inquiry Skills: Inferring

Ask students: **Why are fossils of intermediate life forms likely to be rare if the theory of punctuated equilibria explains how evolution occurs?** *(The theory proposes that new species evolve rapidly over a short period of time, so the chances of fossils of intermediate species forming are greatly reduced.)* **learning modality: logical/mathematical**

3 Assess

Section 2 Review Answers

1. Most fossils form when organisms that die become buried in layers of sediment and the layers harden to become sedimentary rock.

2. Scientists compare the amount of a radioactive element in a sample to the amount of the element into which it breaks down and then calculate the age of the fossil based on the element's constant rate of decay.

3. The fossil record refers to the millions of fossils scientists have collected. It reveals how extinct species looked, behaved, and evolved.

4. Both theories attempt to explain the fossil record. Gradualism proposes that evolution occurs slowly and steadily. Punctuated equilibria proposes that evolution occurs during short periods of rapid change separated by long periods of little or no change.

Science at Home

Tips Advise students to use mud that contains a lot of clay and enough water to make it the consistency of yogurt or pudding.

Performance Assessment

Skills Check Have students make a table to compare and contrast the theories of gradualism and punctuated equilibria.

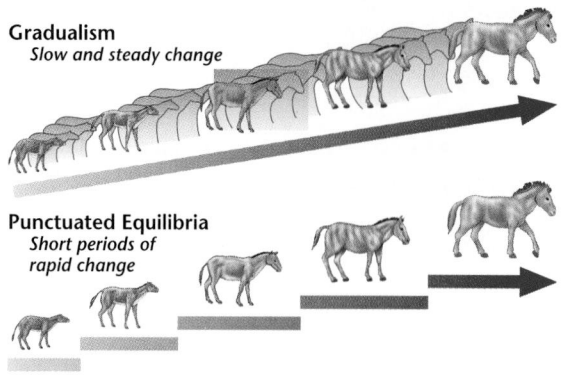

Gradualism
Slow and steady change

Punctuated Equilibria
Short periods of rapid change

— Time —→

Figure 12 According to the theory of gradualism, new species of horses evolved slowly and continuously. Intermediate forms were common. According to punctuated equilibria, new species evolved rapidly during short periods of time. Intermediate forms were rare.

How Fast Does Evolution Occur?

Because the fossil record is incomplete, many questions about evolution remain unanswered. For example, scientists cannot always tell from the fossil record how quickly a particular species evolved.

One theory, called **gradualism,** proposes that evolution occurs slowly but steadily. According to this theory, tiny changes in a species gradually add up to major changes over very long periods of time. This is how Darwin thought evolution occurred.

If the theory of gradualism is correct, intermediate forms of all species should have existed. However, the fossil record often shows no intermediate forms for long periods of time. Then, quite suddenly, fossils appear that are distinctly different. One possible explanation for the lack of intermediate forms is that the fossil record is incomplete. Scientists may eventually find more fossils to fill the gaps.

Rather than assuming that the fossil record is incomplete, two scientists, Stephen Jay Gould and Niles Eldridge, have developed a theory that agrees with the fossil data. According to the theory of **punctuated equilibria,** species evolve during short periods of rapid change. These periods of rapid change are separated by long periods of little or no change. According to this theory, species evolve quickly when groups become isolated and adapt to new environments.

Today most scientists think that evolution can occur gradually at some times and fairly rapidly at others. Both forms of evolution seem to have occurred during Earth's long history.

Section 2 Review

1. Describe how fossils form in sedimentary rock.
2. Explain the process of absolute dating.
3. What is the fossil record? What does the fossil record reveal about extinct species?
4. **Thinking Critically Comparing and Contrasting** How are the theories of gradualism and punctuated equilibria similar? How are they different?

164

Science at Home

Make Your Mark With a family member, spread some mud in a shallow flat-bottomed pan. Smooth the surface of the mud. Use your fingertips to make "footprints" across the mud. Let the mud dry and harden, so that the footprints become permanent. Explain to your family how this is similar to the way some fossils form.

Background

Facts and Figures Just how short are the periods of rapid change proposed by supporters of the punctuated equilibria theory? Generally, they are on the order of 50,000 to 100,000 years, which is very short indeed compared with the billions of years of the Geologic Time Scale. The best data in support of the theory come from the fossilized remains of invertebrates, or animals without backbones, such as snails.

Program Resources

◆ **Unit 1 Resources** 5-2 Review and Reinforce, p. 133; 5-2 Enrich, p. 134

Media and Technology

Interactive Student Tutorial CD-ROM Chapter 5

3 Other Evidence for Evolution

DISCOVER •• **ACTIVITY** ••••

How Can You Classify Species?

1. Collect six to eight different pens. Each pen will represent a different species of similar organisms.

2. Choose a trait that varies among your pen species, such as size or ink color. Using this trait, try to divide the pen species into two groups.

3. Now choose another trait. Divide each group into two smaller groups.

Think It Over

Classifying Which of the pen species share the most characteristics? What might the similarities suggest about how the pen species evolved?

Do you know anyone who has had their appendix out? The appendix is a tiny organ attached to the large intestine. You might think that having a part of the body removed would cause a problem. After all, you need your heart, lungs, stomach and other body parts to live. However, this is not the case with the appendix. In humans, the appendix does not seem to have much function. In some other species of mammals, though, the appendix is much larger and plays an important role in digestion. To scientists, this information about modern-day organisms provides clues about their ancestors and their relationships.

The appendix is just one example of how modern-day organisms can provide clues about evolution. By comparing organisms, scientists can infer how closely related the organisms are in an evolutionary sense. **Scientists compare body structures, development before birth, and DNA sequences to determine the evolutionary relationships among organisms.**

Similarities in Body Structure

Scientists long ago began to compare the body structures of living species to look for clues about evolution. In fact, this is how Darwin came to understand that evolution had occurred on the Galapagos Islands. An organism's body structure is its basic body plan, such as how its bones are arranged. Fishes, amphibians, reptiles, birds, and mammals, for example, all have a similar body

> **GUIDE FOR READING**
>
> ◆ What evidence from modern-day organisms can help scientists determine evolutionary relationships among groups?
>
> *Reading Tip* As you read, use the headings to make an outline about the different types of evidence for evolution.

Chapter 5 **165**

Program Resources

◆ **Unit 1 Resources** 5-3 Lesson Plan, p. 135; 5-3 Section Summary, p. 136

Media and Technology

🎧 **Audio CD** English-Spanish Summary 5-3

📽 **Transparencies** "Homologous Structures," Transparency 22

READING STRATEGIES

Reading Tip Students can use the text headings as the main topics in their outlines. Sample:
I. Similarities in Body Structure
   A. Body structure: basic plan, e.g., how bones are arranged
   B. Homologous structures: similar structures that different organisms have inherited from a common ancestor

---

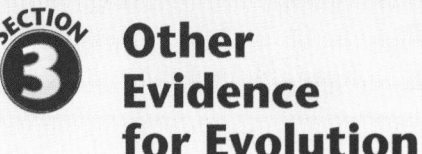

3 Other Evidence for Evolution

Objectives

After completing the lesson, students will be able to
◆ state evidence from modern-day organisms that scientists use to show evolutionary relationships among groups;
◆ explain what a branching tree diagram is.

Key Terms homologous structure, branching tree

1 Engage/Explore

Activating Prior Knowledge

On the chalkboard write the following list: *horse, rabbit, zebra, squirrel, donkey, deer, chipmunk,* and *mouse.* Then ask: **Which animals would you group together based on their similarities?** *(Students are likely to place the horse, zebra, donkey, and deer in one group and the rabbit, squirrel, chipmunk, and mouse in another.)* Tell students that, in this section, they will see how scientists use similarities among living species to infer how the species evolved.

•••••••• **DISCOVER** ••••••••

Skills Focus classifying
Materials *6 to 8 pens*
Time 10 minutes
Tips Have extra pens to guarantee that each student has enough. Include pens that are somewhat different from each other.
Expected Outcome How students classify their pens will depend on their particular sample of pens and the traits they choose for classification.
Think It Over Students may say that the pen species that are most similar evolved from a common ancestor.

165

2 Facilitate

Similarities in Body Structure

Sharpen your *Skills*

Drawing Conclusions

Time 5 minutes
Tips If students have 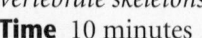 difficulty identifying similarities between the crocodile's leg and the legs of the animals shown in Figure 13, advise them to focus on the number and arrangement of bones.
Expected Outcome Students are likely to say that crocodiles share a common ancestor with birds, dolphins, and dogs because of the similar structure of the bones in their legs.
Extend Ask: **What other animals do you think would have forelimbs similar in structure to those of crocodiles, birds, dolphins, and dogs?** (*Possible answers include any reptile, bird, or mammal.*) **learning modality: logical/mathematical**

Building Inquiry Skills: Observing

Materials *illustrations of* *vertebrate skeletons*
Time 10 minutes

Show students illustrations of skeletons from a variety of vertebrates, such as fish, reptiles, birds, and mammals. (Illustrations can be found in zoology and anatomy textbooks, as well as in general reference books such as encyclopedias.) Challenge students to compare the skeletal structures, then ask: **What evidence suggests that all of these animals share a common ancestor?** (*Students should point out ways that the skeletal structures are similar in the number and arrangement of bones. They should also explain how such similarities are used to infer evolutionary relationships.*) **learning modality: visual**

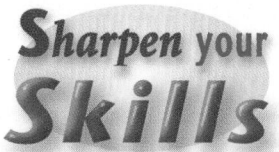

Drawing Conclusions

Look at the drawing 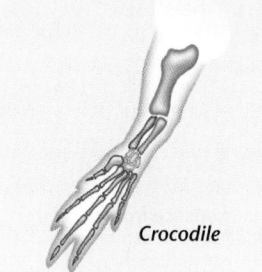 below of the bones in a crocodile's leg. Compare this drawing to Figure 13. Do you think that crocodiles share a common ancestor with birds, dolphins, and dogs? Support your answer with evidence.

Crocodile

Figure 13 A bird's wing, dolphin's flipper, and dog's leg are all adapted to performing different tasks. However, the structure of the bones in each forelimb is very similar. These homologous structures provide evidence that these animals evolved from a common ancestor. *Observing What similarities in structure do the three forelimbs share?*

---

structure—an internal skeleton with a backbone. This is why scientists classify all five groups of animals together as vertebrates. Presumably, these groups all inherited these similarities in structure from an early vertebrate ancestor that they shared.

Look closely at the structure of the bones in the bird's wing, dolphin's flipper, and dog's leg shown in Figure 13. Notice that the bones in the forelimbs of these three animals are arranged in a similar way. These similarities provide evidence that these three organisms all evolved from a common ancestor. Similar structures that related species have inherited from a common ancestor are called **homologous structures** (hoh MAHL uh gus).

Sometimes scientists find fossil evidence that supports the evidence provided by homologous structures. For example, scientists have recently found fossils of ancient whale-like creatures. The fossils show that the ancestors of today's whales had legs and walked on land. This evidence supports other evidence that whales and humans share a common ancestor.

✓ *Checkpoint* *What information do homologous structures reveal?*

Similarities in Early Development

Scientists can also make inferences about evolutionary relationships by comparing the early development of different organisms. Suppose you were asked to compare an adult turtle, a chicken, and a rat. You would probably say they look quite different from each other. However, during early development, these three organisms go through similar stages, as you can see

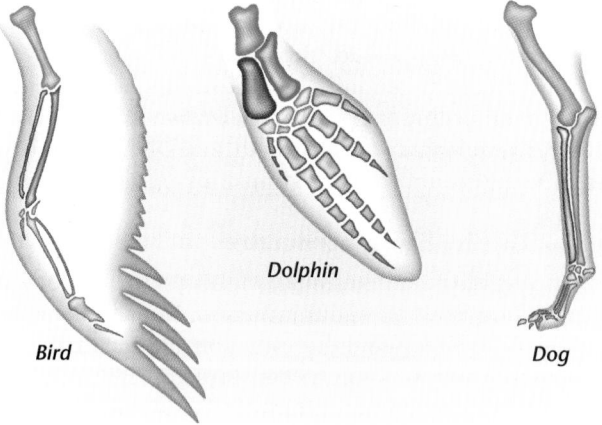

Bird   *Dolphin*   *Dog*

Background

Facts and Figures The system of classification based on homologous structures is believed to have been developed by Carolus Linnaeus, the eighteenth century Swedish botanist who developed the taxonomic system for classifying living things that is still in use today. Based on homologous structures, humans are classified as primates along with monkeys and apes, and lions are classified as cats along with tigers and leopards.

Sometimes species have similar structures that reflect parallel adaptations but not a common ancestor. Such structures are called analogous structures. A good example is the wing of a bird and the wing of a butterfly. The wings of both animals perform the same function, but their internal structures are quite different because the animals evolved from different ancestors.

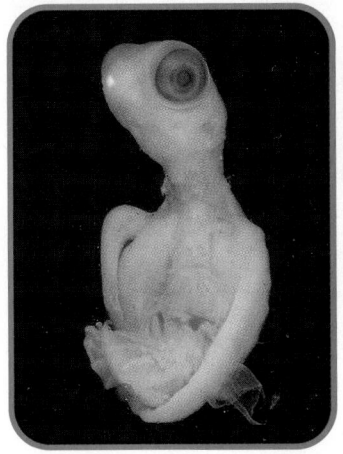
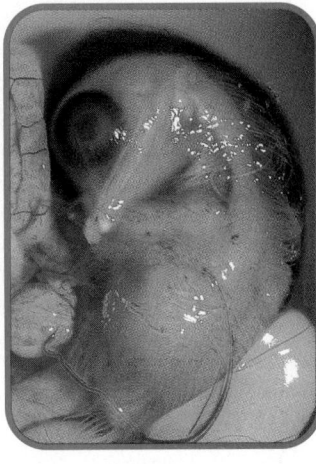
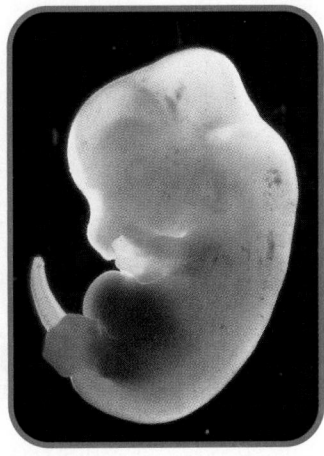

in Figure 14. For example, during the early stages of development all three organisms have a tail and tiny gill slits in their throats. These similarities suggest that these three vertebrate species are related and share a common ancestor.

When scientists study early development more closely, they notice that the turtle appears more similar to the chicken than it does to the rat. This evidence supports the conclusion that turtles are more closely related to chickens than they are to rats.

Similarities in DNA

Why do related species have similar body structures and development patterns? Scientists infer that the species inherited many of the same genes from a common ancestor. Recently, scientists have begun to compare the genes of different species to determine how closely related the species are.

Recall that genes are made of DNA. By comparing the sequence of nitrogen bases in the DNA of different species, scientists can infer how closely related the species are. The more similar the sequences, the more closely related the species are.

Recall also that the DNA bases along a gene specify what type of protein will be produced. Thus, scientists can also compare the order of amino acids in a protein to see how closely related two species are.

Sometimes DNA evidence does not confirm earlier conclusions about relationships between species. For example, aside from its long nose, the tiny elephant shrew looks very similar to rodents such as mice. Because of this, biologists used to think that the elephant shrew was closely related to rodents. But when scientists compared DNA from elephant shrews to that of both

Figure 14 Turtles (left), chickens (center), and rats (right) look similar during the earliest stages of development. These similarities provide evidence that these three animals evolved from a common ancestor.

Chapter 5 **167**

Answers to Self-Assessment

✓ Checkpoint
Homologous structures reveal that organisms share a common ancestor.

Caption Question
Figure 13 The three forelimbs share a similar number and arrangement of bones.

Similarities in Early Development

Using the Visuals: Figure 14
Challenge students to detect ways that the three embryos are similar and different. *(Similarities might include tails and a curved shape; differences might include shape of head and body.)* Point out that scientists have concluded, on the basis of such similarities and differences, that turtles are more closely related to chickens than to rats. Then ask: **In what ways do the turtle and chicken appear to be more similar than the turtle and rat?** *(Students may say that the turtle and chicken both have large eyes and a pointed mouth.)* **learning modality: visual**

Similarities in DNA

Inquiry Challenge
Challenge pairs of students to draw short sections of DNA base sequences for three hypothetical related species to illustrate how DNA similarities can be used to infer evolutionary relationships. Remind students that there are four bases in DNA: adenine, thymine, guanine, and cytosine, which they can abbreviate as A, T, G, and C, respectively. After students have finished their drawings, urge volunteers to share their work with the class. Have other students try to infer from the DNA base sequences how the three species are related. *(They should infer that the more similar the DNA base sequences, the more closely related the species.)* Conclude by asking: **How do you think the amino acid sequences in the proteins of the three species would compare? Why?** *(Students should say that the amino acid sequences in the proteins would reflect the same evolutionary relationships as the DNA base sequences. This is because the amino acid sequences are encoded in the DNA.)* **learning modality: logical/mathematical**

Ongoing Assessment

Oral Presentation Call on students at random to describe the three kinds of similarities in living species that scientists use to reconstruct evolutionary relationships.

Similarities in DNA, continued

Integrating Technology

Encourage students to think about how recent advances in DNA technology may affect the way scientists study evolutionary relationships. Ask: **What can scientists learn from fossil DNA that they could not learn by studying the physical structure of the fossils?** *(DNA provides more direct evidence of genetic relationships.)* **Will the ability to extract DNA from fossils mean that scientists will no longer have to compare living species in order to reconstruct evolutionary relationships?** *(The fossil record is incomplete, so being able to extract DNA from fossils will not add any new information about many extinct species. Therefore, scientists will still have to compare living species to reconstruct evolutionary relationships.)* **learning modality: logical/mathematical**

Combining the Evidence

Building Inquiry Skills: Interpreting Data

Time 10 minutes

ACTIVITY

Have students interpret data to infer how three hypothetical species—A, B, and C—are related. First tell students that A and C appear to be more similar in body structure than A and B or B and C. Then tell students that A and B appear to be more similar in their early development than A and C or B and C. Finally, tell students that the DNA base sequences of A and B are more similar than the DNA base sequences of A and C or B and C. After providing students with this information, challenge them to combine and weigh the evidence. Then ask: **What are the evolutionary relationships among the three species?** *(Species A and B are more closely related to each other than either species is related to species C because of the similarities in their early development and DNA.)* Challenge students to draw a branching tree to illustrate the evolutionary relationships among the three species. **learning modality: logical/mathematical**

Figure 15 Because of its appearance, the tiny elephant shrew was thought to be closely related to mice and other rodents. Surprisingly, DNA comparisons showed that the elephant shrew is actually more closely related to elephants.

rodents and elephants, they got a surprise. The elephant shrew's DNA was more similar to the elephant's DNA than it was to the rodent's DNA. Scientists now think that elephant shrews are more closely related to elephants than to rodents.

INTEGRATING TECHNOLOGY Recently, scientists have developed techniques that allow them to extract, or remove, DNA from fossils. Using these techniques, scientists have now extracted DNA from fossils of bones, teeth, and plants, and from insects trapped in amber. The DNA from fossils has provided scientists with new evidence about evolution.

Combining the Evidence

Scientists have combined evidence from fossils, body structures, early development, and DNA and protein sequences to determine the evolutionary relationships among species. In most cases, DNA and protein sequences have confirmed conclusions based on earlier evidence. For example, recent DNA comparisons show that dogs are more similar to wolves than they are to coyotes. Scientists had already reached this conclusion based on similarities in the structure and development of these three species.

Another example of how scientists combined evidence from different sources is shown in the branching tree in Figure 16. A **branching tree** is a diagram that shows how scientists think different groups of organisms are related. Based on similar body structures, lesser pandas were thought to be closely related to giant pandas. The two panda species also resemble both bears and raccoons. Until recently, scientists were not sure how these four groups were related. DNA analysis and other methods have shown that giant pandas and lesser pandas are not closely related. Instead, giant pandas are more closely related to bears, while lesser pandas are more closely related to raccoons.

168

Background

Integrating Science Similarities and differences in DNA base sequences are assessed using a technique called DNA hybridization. In this technique, double strands of DNA from two different species are separated and then recombined into a new molecule called hybrid DNA. The genetic similarity of the two species is then measured by calculating the number of base pairs that do not match along the hybrid sequence, that is, pairs in which adenine is not matched with thymine or cytosine is not matched with guanine.

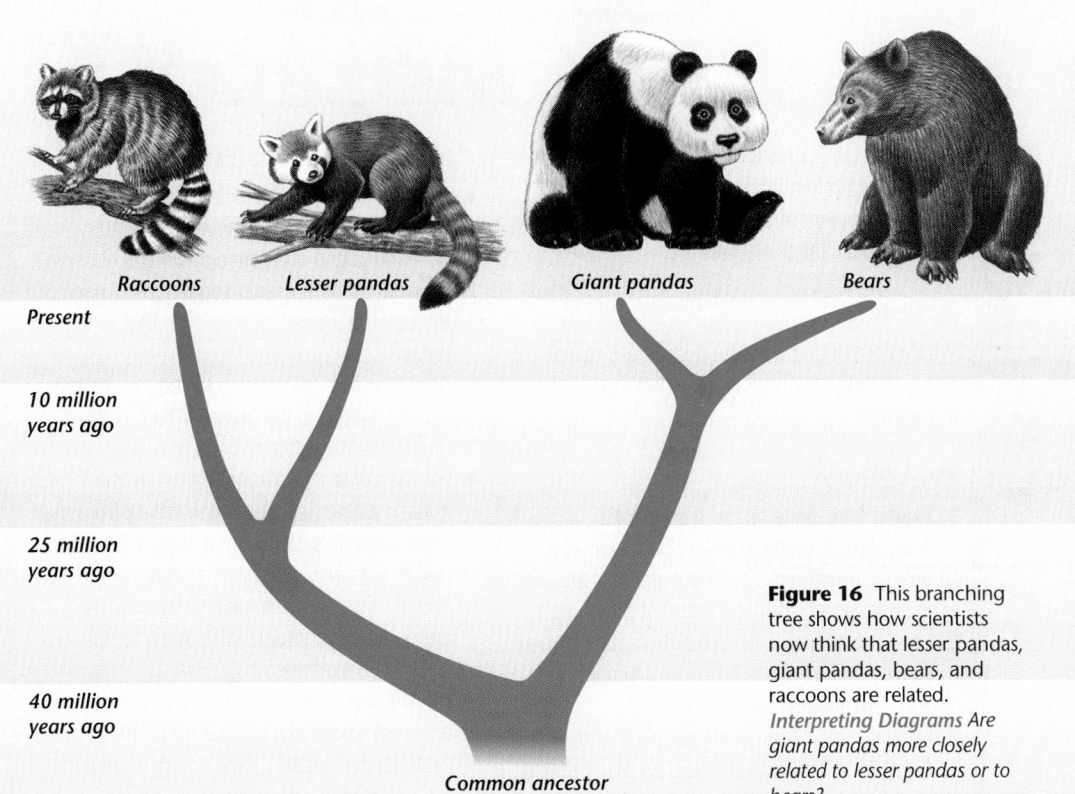

Raccoons   Lesser pandas   Giant pandas   Bears

Present

10 million
years ago

25 million
years ago

40 million
years ago

Common ancestor

Figure 16 This branching tree shows how scientists now think that lesser pandas, giant pandas, bears, and raccoons are related. *Interpreting Diagrams Are giant pandas more closely related to lesser pandas or to bears?*

 Section 3 Review

1. Name three types of evidence from modern-day organisms that scientists use to determine evolutionary relationships.
2. What are homologous structures?
3. What information did scientists learn by comparing the early developmental stages of turtles, chickens, and rats?
4. If two species are closely related, what would you expect a comparison of their DNA base sequences to reveal?
5. **Thinking Critically Making Judgments** Most scientists today consider similarities in DNA to be the best indicator of how closely two species are related. Why do you think this is the case?

Check Your Progress
You should be completing construction of the time line that covers 5 billion years. Now begin work on the time line showing 600 million years. This version is a magnified view of one part of the first time line. It will give you additional space to show what happened in the more recent years of Earth's history. (*Hint:* Prepare drawings to show how life forms on Earth were changing. Also, try to include three or more events not mentioned in the text.)

CHAPTER PROJECT

Program Resources

◆ **Unit 1 Resources** 5-3 Review and Reinforce, p. 137; 5-3 Enrich, p. 138

Answers to Self-Assessment

Caption Question

Figure 16 Giant pandas are more closely related to bears than to lesser pandas.

Using the Visuals: Figure 16
Reinforce students' understanding of branching trees and evolutionary relationships. Ask: **When did giant pandas and bears evolve from their common ancestor?** (*About 10 million years ago*) **When did raccoons and lesser pandas evolve from their common ancestor?** (*About 25 million years ago*) **Which are more closely related, raccoons and lesser pandas, or giant pandas and bears?** (*Giant pandas and bears*) **learning modality: visual**

3 Assess

Section 3 Review Answers

1. Similarities in body structure, similarities in early development, and similarities in DNA base sequences
2. Similar structures that related species have inherited from a common ancestor
3. Scientists learned that these animals evolved from a common ancestor.
4. You would expect the base sequences to be very similar.
5. DNA similarities are the most direct indicator that species inherited their genes from a common ancestor.

Check Your Progress
Review each group's first time line, and offer comments before the group starts its second time line. Make sure students understand that because the second time line is an enlargement of one section of the first time line, its scale will be different. Distribute Worksheet 2, which lists additional evolutionary events not in the text. Provide source materials for students to use.

CHAPTER PROJECT

Performance Assessment

Drawing Have students draw a branching tree that shows how dogs, wolves, and coyotes are related. (*Students' drawings should show that dogs and wolves shared a common ancestor more recently than either species did with coyotes.*)

Telltale Molecules

Preparing for Inquiry

Key Concept The more similar the amino acid sequence in proteins of different species, the more closely the species are related.

Skills Objectives Students will be able to
- interpret data on amino acid sequences in proteins;
- compare and contrast amino acid sequences in the same protein for different species;
- draw conclusions about how the species are related based on the amino acid comparisons.

Time 30 minutes

Advance Planning You may need to review with students what they learned about protein synthesis in Chapter 3.

Alternative Materials You may want to provide students with copies of tables comparing actual amino acid sequences from a genetics textbook to show how similar the data in the lab are to data scientists actually use to reconstruct evolutionary relationships.

Guiding Inquiry

Invitation Ask students: **What is a genetic code?** (*It is the order of the nitrogen bases along a gene.*) **How do cells use a genetic code to make proteins?** (*The nitrogen bases code for the production of specific amino acids, which are the building blocks of proteins.*) **What are genes made of?** (*DNA*)

Introducing the Procedure

- Have students read the entire lab, then ask: **What is the objective of this lab activity?** (*To use the amino acid sequence of a protein to determine the evolutionary relationship among several animals*) **What do the letters in the table represent?** (*Each letter represents a different amino acid.*)
- Suggest that students create a table to record the number of differences between the horse and each of the other animals.

Troubleshooting the Experiment
- Make sure students understand how to read the table correctly before they compare the different species.

Expected Outcome
Students should infer from the amino acid comparisons which species are most closely related and which are least closely related to the horse.

Skills Lab

Interpreting Data

TELLTALE MOLECULES

In this lab, you will compare the structure of one protein in a variety of animals. You'll use the data to draw conclusions about how closely related those animals are.

Problem

What information can protein structure reveal about evolutionary relationships among organisms?

Procedure

1. Examine the table below. It shows the sequence of amino acids in one region of a protein, cytochrome c, for six different animals. Each letter represents a different amino acid.
2. Predict which of the five other animals is most closely related to the horse. Which animal do you think is most distantly related?
3. Compare the amino acid sequence of the horse to that of the donkey. How many amino acids differ between the two species? Record that number in your notebook.
4. Compare the amino acid sequences of each of the other animals to that of the horse. Record the number of differences in your notebook.

Analyze and Conclude

1. Which animal's amino acid sequence was most similar to that of the horse? What similarities and difference(s) did you observe?
2. How did the amino acid sequences of each of the other animals compare with that of the horse?
3. Based on this data, which species is the most closely related to the horse? Which is the most distantly related?
4. For the entire cytochrome c protein, the horse's amino acid sequence differs from the other animals as follows: donkey, 1 difference; rabbit, 6; snake, 22; turtle, 11; and whale, 5. How do the relationships indicated by the entire protein compare with those for the region you examined?
5. **Think About It** Explain why data about amino acid sequences can provide information about evolutionary relationships among organisms.

More to Explore

Use the amino acid data to construct a branching tree that includes horses, donkeys, and snakes. The tree should show one way that the three species could have evolved from a common ancestor.

Section of Cytochrome c Protein in Animals															
	Amino Acid Position														
Animal	39	40	41	42	43	44	45	46	47	48	49	50	51	52	53
Horse	A	B	C	D	E	F	G	H	I	J	K	L	M	N	O
Donkey	A	B	C	D	E	F	G	H	Z	J	K	L	M	N	O
Rabbit	A	B	C	D	E	Y	G	H	Z	J	K	L	M	N	O
Snake	A	B	C	D	E	Y	G	H	Z	J	K	W	M	N	O
Turtle	A	B	C	D	E	V	G	H	Z	J	K	U	M	N	O
Whale	A	B	C	D	E	Y	G	H	Z	J	K	L	M	N	O

Program Resources

- **Unit 1 Resources** Chapter 5 Skills Lab, pp. 142–143

SECTION 1 Darwin's Voyage

Key Ideas
- Darwin thought that species gradually changed over many generations as they became better adapted to new conditions. This process is called evolution.
- Darwin's observations led him to propose that evolution occurs through natural selection. Natural selection occurs due to overproduction, competition, and variations.
- Only traits controlled by genes can change over time as a result of natural selection.
- If a group of individuals remains separated from the rest of its species long enough to evolve different traits, a new species can form.

Key Terms

species	evolution	natural selection
adaptation	scientific theory	variation

SECTION 2 The Fossil Record
INTEGRATING EARTH SCIENCE

Key Ideas
- Most fossils form when organisms die and sediments bury them. The sediments harden, preserving parts of the organisms.
- Relative dating determines which of two fossils is older and which is younger. Absolute dating determines the actual age of a fossil.
- Fossils help scientists understand how extinct organisms looked and evolved.
- The Geologic Time Scale shows when during Earth's 4.6-billion-year history major groups of organisms evolved.
- Evolution has occurred gradually at some times and fairly rapidly at other times.

Key Terms

fossil	radioactive element
sedimentary rock	half-life
petrified fossil	fossil record
mold	extinct
cast	gradualism
relative dating	punctuated equilibria
absolute dating	

SECTION 3 Other Evidence for Evolution

Key Ideas
- By comparing modern-day organisms, scientists can infer how closely related they are in an evolutionary sense.
- Homologous structures can provide evidence of how species are related and of how they evolved from a common ancestor.
- Similarities in early developmental stages are evidence that species are related and shared a common ancestor.
- Scientists can compare DNA and protein sequences to determine more precisely how species are related.
- A branching tree is a diagram that shows how scientists think different groups of organisms are related.

Key Terms
homologous structure
branching tree

Organizing Information

Flowchart Copy the flowchart about natural selection onto a separate sheet of paper. Complete the flowchart by writing a sentence describing each factor that leads to natural selection. Then add a title. (For more on flowcharts, see the Skills Handbook.)

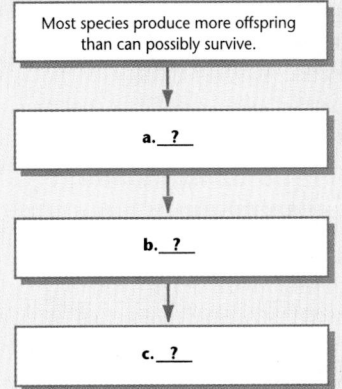

Analyze and Conclude

1. The donkey's amino acid sequence was most similar to that of the horse, differing only in the amino acid in position 47.
2. The rabbit and whale differed from the horse in two amino acids. The snake and turtle differed from the horse in three amino acids.
3. Based on this data, the donkey is most closely related to the horse and the turtle and snake are least closely related to the horse.
4. The relationships indicated by the entire protein are similar to the relationships indicated by the region of the protein examined in the lab.
5. As two or more species evolve from a common ancestor, their DNA may undergo different mutations, causing changes in the amino acids making up common proteins. The fewer differences in the amino acids, the more closely the given species are related.

Extending the Inquiry

More to Explore Students' branching trees should show that the horse and donkey have the most recent common ancestor and that the horse and snake have the most distant common ancestor.

Organizing Information

Flowchart *Sample title:* How Natural Selection Works
a. Since food and other resources are limited, the offspring must compete with each other to survive.
b. The offspring will have variations that make some of them better adapted to their environment.
c. Better adapted offspring are more likely to survive and reproduce, and after many generations more members of the species will have the adaptive variations.

Program Resources

- **Unit 1 Resources** Chapter 5 Project Scoring Rubric, p. 126
- **Performance Assessment** Chapter 5, pp. 17–19
- **Chapter and Unit Tests** Chapter 5 Test, pp. 20–23

Media and Technology

Interactive Student Tutorial CD-ROM Chapter 5

Computer Test Bank Chapter 5 Test

Reviewing Content

Multiple Choice

1. b 2. b 3. b 4. c 5. c

True or False

6. true 7. true 8. true
9. absolute dating 10. true

Checking Concepts

11. The overproduction of offspring leads to competition in which only the better adapted organisms survive and reproduce.

12. Examples will vary. *Sample answer:* A large number of turtles are born every year but only a few will be able to swim fast enough to escape predators. Because being able to swim faster makes the turtles more likely to survive and reproduce, natural selection leads to an increase through time in the fast-swimming trait.

13. Fossils found in layers of rock nearer the surface are younger than fossils found in deeper layers.

14. According to the theory of punctuated equilibria, the fossil record includes very few intermediate forms because new species evolve so rapidly that there is very little chance that such intermediate forms will be preserved as fossils.

15. Related species inherit the same basic developmental plan from their common ancestor.

16. Students' questions and answers will vary, but they should demonstrate clearly that students understand Darwin's theory of evolution by natural selection.

Thinking Critically

17. The islands were characterized by a great diversity of species that had developed different adaptations.

18. Natural selection would favor members of the species that were better adapted to the new climate. For example, in a species of mammal, a colder climate might lead to natural selection for animals with thicker fur.

19. Geographic isolation prevents mating between members of the isolated population and the rest of the species. This, in turn, allows natural selection to lead to the evolution of different traits in the isolated population.

Reviewing Content

 For more review of key concepts, see the Interactive Student Tutorial CD-ROM.

Multiple Choice

Choose the letter of the best answer.

1. Changes in a species over long periods of time are called
   a. relative dating.
   b. evolution.
   c. homologous structures.
   d. developmental stages.

2. A trait that helps an organism survive and reproduce is called a(n)
   a. variation.   b. adaptation.
   c. species.   d. selection.

3. The type of fossil formed when an organism dissolves and leaves an empty space in a rock is called a
   a. cast.   b. mold.
   c. trace.   d. petrified fossil.

4. The rate of decay of a radioactive element is measured by its
   a. year.   b. era.
   c. half-life.   d. period.

5. Which of these is *not* used as evidence for evolution?
   a. DNA sequences
   b. stages of development
   c. body size
   d. body structures

True or False

If the statement is true, write true. If it is false, change the underlined word or words to make the statement true.

6. Darwin's idea about how evolution occurs is called <u>natural selection</u>.

7. Most members of a species show differences, or <u>variations</u>.

8. A footprint of an extinct dinosaur is an example of a <u>fossil</u>.

9. The technique of <u>relative dating</u> can be used to determine the actual age of a fossil.

10. <u>Homologous structures</u> are similar structures in related organisms.

Checking Concepts

11. What role does the overproduction of offspring play in the process of natural selection?

12. Use an example to explain how natural selection can lead to evolution.

13. How are rock layers used to determine the relative ages of fossils?

14. According to the theory of punctuated equilibria, why does the fossil record include very few intermediate forms?

15. Explain why similarities in the early development of different species suggest that the species are related.

16. **Writing to Learn** You are a young reporter for a local newspaper near the home of Charles Darwin. You have been asked to interview Darwin about his theory of evolution. Write three questions that you would ask Darwin. Then choose one question and answer it as Darwin would have.

Thinking Critically

17. **Applying Concepts** Why did Darwin's visit to the Galapagos Islands have such an important influence on his development of the theory of evolution by natural selection?

18. **Predicting** Predict how an extreme change in climate might affect natural selection in a species.

19. **Relating Cause and Effect** What is the role of geographic isolation in the formation of new species?

20. **Comparing and Contrasting** How does relative dating differ from absolute dating?

21. **Applying Concepts** A seal's flipper and a human arm have very different functions. What evidence might scientists look for to determine whether both structures evolved from the forelimb of a common ancestor?

---

20. Relative dating determines which of two fossils is older and which is younger based on their relative positions in layers of sedimentary rock. Absolute dating determines the actual age of fossils in years based on the amount of decay of radioactive elements in the fossils.

21. Scientists might look for evidence that the structures are homologous, for example, whether they have the same number and arrangement of bones.

Applying Skills

22. Based on the positions of the fossils in the rock layers, B is the youngest, C is intermediate in age, and A is the oldest.

23. Based on the carbon-14 and nitrogen data, A is 17,190 years old, B is 5,730 years old, and C is 11,460 years old.

24. Students should say that the answers based on the two methods of dating are in agreement.

Applying Skills

Radioactive carbon-14 decays to nitrogen with a half-life of 5,730 years. Use this information and the table below to answer Questions 22–24.

Fossil	Amount of Carbon-14 in Fossil	Amount of Nitrogen in Fossil	Position of Fossil in Rock Layers
A	1 gram	7 grams	bottom layer
B	4 grams	4 grams	top layer
C	2 grams	6 grams	middle layer

22. Inferring Use the positions of the fossils in the rock layers to put the fossils in order from youngest to oldest.

23. Calculating Calculate the age of each fossil using the data about carbon-14 and nitrogen.

24. Drawing Conclusions Do your answers to Questions 22 and 23 agree or disagree with each other? Explain.

Performance ▼ Assessment
CHAPTER PROJECT

Present Your Project Display your completed time lines for the class. Be prepared to explain why you chose the scale that you did. Also, describe how your time lines are related to each other.

Reflect and Record In your notebook, describe how the time lines helped you understand the long periods involved in the evolution of life. Were you surprised to see how far apart some of the events were? What surprised you the most? What did making two time lines enable you to see that you might have missed with only one?

Performance ▼ Assessment
CHAPTER PROJECT

Present Your Project Give each group an opportunity to show its two time lines to the rest of the class, describe how the models were made, and explain how the second time line relates to the first time line. Ask each group to point out any evolutionary events that were not included in the textbook's time line. Encourage the rest of the class to ask questions.

Reflect and Record Students' responses to these questions will vary, but students should realize that making a second time line for the past 600 millions years allowed them to see the time spans and placements of evolutionary events much more clearly. Let students share their ideas in a class discussion.

Test Preparation *Use these questions to prepare for standardized tests.*

Use the illustration to answer Questions 25–28.

25. What is the best title for this illustration?
  a. Plant Growth Over Time
  b. Branching Tree of Plant Evolution
  c. Mosses and Ferns, the Oldest Plants
  d. Flowering Plants, the Youngest Plants

26. About how long ago did mosses evolve?
  a. 100 million years ago
  b. 150 million years ago
  c. 350 million years ago
  d. 450 million years ago

27. Which group of plants would have DNA that is most similar to the DNA of flowering plants?
  a. mosses
  b. ferns
  c. conifers
  d. They would all be equally alike.

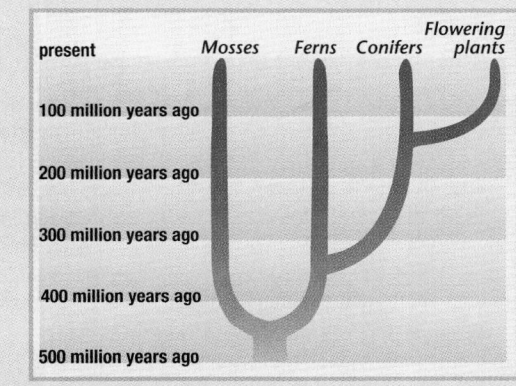

28. Which group of plants would have DNA that is least similar to the DNA of flowering plants?
  a. mosses
  b. ferns
  c. conifers
  d. They would all be equally alike.

Chapter 5 **173**

Test Preparation
25. b **26.** d **27.** c **28.** a

Program Resources

◆ **Inquiry Skills Activity Book** Provides teaching and review of all inquiry skills

Dogs—Loyal Companions

This interdisciplinary feature presents the central theme of dogs and the traits of various breeds that make them similar and different by connecting four different disciplines: science, social studies, language arts, and mathematics. The four explorations are designed to capture students' interest and help them see how the content they are studying in science relates to other school subjects and to real-world events. This exploration is particularly suitable for team teaching.

1 Engage/Explore

Activating Prior Knowledge

Help students recall what they learned in Chapter 3, Genetics: The Science of Heredity, by asking questions such as: **How are traits inherited by offspring from parents?** *(The alleles of genes are carried from parents to their offspring on chromosomes.)* **Why do offspring sometimes look different from parents?** *(Offspring inherit different combinations of alleles from parents; therefore, they might express a trait controlled by a recessive allele that is masked in the parents or inherit a trait controlled by a dominant allele that is expressed in one parent, but not the other.)*

Introducing the Exploration

Invite students who own dogs to share the characteristics of their dogs with the class. Separately list on the board each dog's characteristics, and have students compare the characteristics of each dog. Ask: **How are these dogs different?** *(Differences might include size, temperament, length and color of fur, type of ears, and length of tail.)* **What causes these differences?** *(The combination of alleles that each dog inherited from its parents)*

DOGS
LOYAL COMPANIONS

WHAT'S YOUR IMAGE OF A DOG?

✦ A small, floppy-eared spaniel?

✦ A large, powerful Great Dane?

✦ A protective German shepherd guide dog?

✦ A shaggy sheepdog?

✦ A tiny, lively Chihuahua?

✦ A friendly, lovable mutt?

The gray wolf is the ancestor of most modern breeds of dogs.

More than 3,000 years ago, an artist in ancient Egypt drew three dogs chasing a hyena. ▼

Most dogs are descendants of the gray wolf, which was originally found throughout Europe, Asia, and North America. Dogs were the first animals to be domesticated, or tamed. As far back as 9,000 years ago, farmers who raised sheep, cattle, and goats tamed dogs to herd and guard the livestock.

After taming dogs, people began to breed them for traits that people valued. Early herding dogs helped shepherds. Speedy hunting dogs learned to chase deer and other game. Strong, sturdy working dogs pulled sleds and even rescued people. Small, quick terriers hunted animals, such as rats. "Toy" dogs were companions to people of wealth and leisure. More recently, sporting dogs were trained to flush out and retrieve birds. Still others were bred to be guard dogs. But perhaps the real reason people bred dogs was for their loyalty and companionship.

174

Program Resources

◆ **Interdisciplinary Exploration** Science, pp. 2–4; Social Studies, pp. 5–7; Language Arts, pp. 8–10; Mathematics, pp. 11–13

From Wolf to Purebred

About ten thousand years ago, some wolves may have been attracted to human settlements. They may have found it easier to feed on food scraps than to hunt for themselves. Gradually the wolves came to depend on people for food. The wolves, in turn, kept the campsites clean and safe. They ate the garbage and barked to warn of approaching strangers. These wolves were the ancestors of the dogs you know today.

Over time dogs became more and more a part of human society. People began to breed dogs for the traits needed for tasks such as herding sheep and hunting. Large, aggressive dogs, for example, were bred to be herding dogs, while fast dogs with a keen sense of smell were bred to be hunting dogs. Today there are hundreds of breeds. They range from the tiny Chihuahua to the massive Saint Bernard, one of which can weigh as much as fifty Chihuahuas.

Today, people breed dogs mostly for their appearance and personality. Physical features such as long ears or a narrow snout are valued in particular breeds of dogs. To create "pure" breeds of dogs, breeders use a method known as inbreeding. Inbreeding involves mating dogs that are genetically very similar. Inbreeding is the surest way to produce dogs with a uniform physical appearance.

One undesirable result of inbreeding is an increase in genetic disorders. Experts estimate that 25 percent of all purebred dogs have a genetic disorder. Dalmatians, for example, often inherit deafness. German shepherds may develop severe hip problems. Mixed-breed dogs, in contrast, are less likely to inherit genetic disorders.

In Labrador retrievers, the allele for dark-colored fur is dominant over the allele for yellow fur.

Science Activity

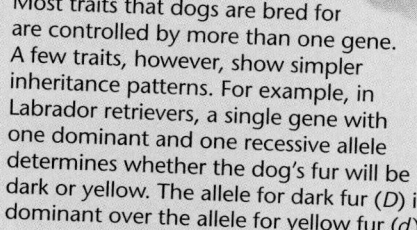

Most traits that dogs are bred for are controlled by more than one gene. A few traits, however, show simpler inheritance patterns. For example, in Labrador retrievers, a single gene with one dominant and one recessive allele determines whether the dog's fur will be dark or yellow. The allele for dark fur (D) is dominant over the allele for yellow fur (d).

- Construct a Punnett square for a cross between 2 Labrador retrievers that are both heterozygous for dark fur (Dd).

- Suppose there were 8 puppies in the litter. Predict how many would have dark fur and how many would have yellow fur.

- Construct a second Punnett square for a cross between a Labrador retriever with yellow fur (dd) and one with dark fur (Dd). In a litter with 6 puppies, predict how many would have dark fur and how many would have yellow fur.

175

---

2 Facilitate

- Point out the role of genetics in the development of dog breeds. Ask: **What are some traits that people select for when breeding dogs?** (*Size, sense of smell, aggressiveness, personality, speed, appearance*) Remind students that genes control these traits.

- Ask students: **Why does inbreeding cause an increase in genetic disorders?** (*Since inbred dogs are genetically similar, there is a greater chance that breeders will unknowingly cross two carriers to produce offspring with the disorder.*) **Why are mixed-breed dogs less likely to have genetic disorders?** (*Mixed breeds are hybrids. They usually have two different alleles for most traits, so an allele for a genetic disorder would probably be masked by the normal allele.*)

Science Activity

Have students complete the activity on their own. Suggest that students calculate the probability for each color of offspring before they calculate the number of puppies with a certain color. **Interdisciplinary Explorations** The following worksheets correlate with these pages: Developing a Classification System, page 2; Breeding the Spinone, page 3; Identifying Dog Adaptations, page 4.

3 Assess

Activity Assessment

Punnett square for $Dd \times Dd$ has offspring DD, Dd, Dd, dd. Out of 8 puppies, the ratio is 6 with dark fur (8×0.75) and 2 with yellow fur (8×0.25). Punnett square for $dd \times Dd$ has offspring Dd, dd, Dd, dd. Out of 6 puppies, the ratio is 3 with dark fur (6×0.5) and 3 with yellow fur (6×0.5).

Background

Facts and Figures Some people still raise wild wolf puppies to keep in captivity. For example, Aleuts in Alaska and northern Canada often breed wolves with their own dogs to improve stamina. They also use tamed wolves, as well as wolf-dog mixes, for their dogsled teams. A tamed wolf, however, can be very dangerous. Because wolves are still instinctively wild animals, they tend to react defensively in unfamiliar situations—being around new people or in a new place. When a wolf reacts defensively, it usually attacks whatever it feels is threatening it. Several generations of breeding in captivity, isolated from the wild species, are required to remove this defensive instinct.

2 Facilitate

- After students have read about each dog breed, discuss how people have developed each breed to fit a particular role. Ask: **Which breeds are hunters?** *(Golden retriever, chow chow, Akita, basset hound, dachshund, greyhound)* **Which were bred for herding?** *(Border collie, chow chow)* **Which were bred for guarding?** *(Chow chow, Akita, Lhaso apso)* **Which were bred for pulling sleds?** *(Siberian husky)* **Which were bred for companionship?** *(Pekingese)* Point out that each breed has certain traits that make it well suited for its role in people's lives. Some dogs are still used as working dogs, but most dogs now are simply companions.

- Invite students to locate on the map the places of origin for each breed shown. Explain that breeds have also originated in the United States, such as the Alaskan malamute and the bluetick coonhound, and in Australia, such as the silky terrier and the Australian kelpie. Point out that the origins of the older breeds coincide with the locations of ancient civilizations. **Which breed is the oldest?** *(greyhound)* **In which ancient civilization did it originate?** *(ancient Egypt)*

- Encourage students to identify working roles that dogs play in the lives of people today. *(Modern roles played by dogs include search and rescue; finding drugs, explosives, or weapons; assisting people with disabilities; tracking criminals; hunting game; herding livestock; and guarding property or people.)* As students identify roles, challenge them to identify traits that make the dogs well suited for their roles.

Golden Retriever
Great Britain, A.D. 1870s
Lord Tweedsmouth developed this breed to help hunters retrieve waterfowl and other small animals.

Border Collie
Great Britain, after A.D. 1100
This breed was developed in the counties near the border of England and Scotland for herding sheep. The Border collie's ancestors were cross-breeds of local sheepdogs and dogs brought to Scotland by the Vikings.

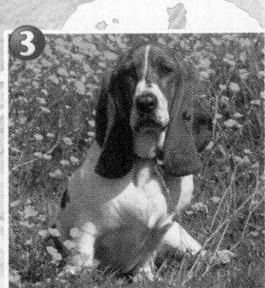

Dachshund
Germany, A.D. 1700s
These dogs were bred to catch badgers or rats. Their short legs and long body can fit into a badger's burrow. In fact, in German the word *Dachshund* means "badger dog."

Basset Hound
France, A.D. 1600s
Second only to the bloodhound at following a scent, the basset hound has short legs and a compact body that help it run through underbrush.

Greyhound
Egypt, 3500 B.C.
These speedy, slender hounds were bred for chasing prey. Today, greyhounds are famous as racers.

176

Background

Facts and Figures The American Kennel Club divides dog breeds into seven groups. These groups are sporting dogs, hounds, working dogs, terriers, toy dogs, nonsporting dogs, and herding dogs. Sporting dogs were bred to assist hunters who use guns. Hounds were bred to hunt for prey by catching it themselves or by cornering it until the hunter arrives. Working dogs were bred for specific jobs, such as guarding, hauling, pulling sleds, or rescuing people and other animals. Terriers were bred to dig into the ground in pursuit of prey, mostly rodents. Toy dogs are small dogs that are companions. Nonsporting dogs are large companion dogs. Herding dogs were bred to protect and herd livestock, such as sheep.

Dogs and People

Over thousands of years, people have developed many different breeds of dogs. Each of the dogs shown on the map was bred for a purpose—hunting, herding, guarding, pulling sleds—as well as companionship. Every breed has its own story.

Siberian Husky
Siberia, 1000 B.C.
The Chukchi people of northeastern Siberia used these strong working dogs to pull sleds long distances across the snow.

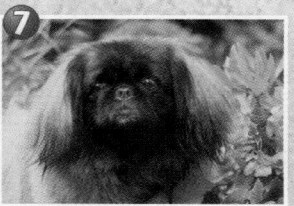

Pekingese
China, A.D. 700s
These lapdogs were bred as pets in ancient China. One Chinese name for a Pekingese means "lion dog," which refers to the dog's long, golden mane.

Chow Chow
China, 150 B.C.
Chow chows, the working dogs of ancient China, worked as hunters, herders, and guard dogs.

Akita
Japan, A.D. 1600s
This breed was developed in the cold mountains of northern Japan as a guard dog and hunting dog. The Akita is able to hunt in deep snow and is also a powerful swimmer.

Lhasa Apso
Tibet, A.D. 1100
This breed has a long, thick coat to protect it from the cold air of the high Tibetan plateau. In spite of its small size, the Lhasa apso guarded homes and temples.

Social Studies Activity

Draw a time line that shows the approximate date of origin of different breeds of domestic dogs from 7000 B.C. to the present. Use the information on the map to fill out your time line. Include information about where each breed was developed.

177

◆ Extend this exploration by encouraging interested students to find the place and time of origin for their favorite breed of dog. Students can find this kind of information in encyclopedias of dog breeds.

Social Studies Activity

Students can work individually or in small groups. Provide students with shelf paper or butcher's paper so that they have adequate space to draw and label the time lines. Encourage students to add drawings or pictures of the different dog breeds. Remind students to make the divisions in time equal in length on the time line. They can do this by first calculating the total number of years in the time line.

Interdisciplinary Explorations The following worksheets correlate with these pages: Reading a Data Table, page 5; Finding Your Way Around a Sheepdog Trial, page 6; The Responsibilities of Owning a Dog, page 7.

3 Assess

Activity Assessment

Display the time lines in the classroom and in the hallway. You might consider allowing class time for students to present their time lines. Each time line should be divided into equal increments with the origins of all dog breeds clearly and accurately labeled. Students should also include information about each dog breed as presented in the text, especially where each breed was developed. Excellent time lines will also be illustrated with the dog breeds.

2 Facilitate

◆ Before students read this section, ask if they are familiar with James Herriot and have read any of his books or watched the television series based on his books. If so, let these students describe what the books are about.

◆ After students have read the excerpt, ask: **How does Herriot feel about getting a Border terrier?** *(He was happy, excited, and content.)* **What do you think Herriot meant when he wrote, "The wheel had indeed turned?"** *(He finally felt complete because he finally found the dog that he had wanted for so long.)*

Language Arts Activity

Before students begin writing their narratives, encourage them to think about their lives and choose one event that is particularly memorable to them. Instruct students to write down why this particular event was so memorable to them. Did they overcome a problem, for example, or were they recognized for their special efforts? Then encourage students to list the emotions they felt during this event and record why they felt those emotions.
Interdisciplinary Explorations The following worksheets correlate with this page: Developing Dialog, page 8; Practicing Point of View, page 9; Researching for the Right Dog, page 10.

3 Assess

Activity Assessment

Invite students to read their narratives aloud to the rest of the class. Evaluate students' narratives based on their use of first-person point of view, the use of dialog, and the clarity with which they expressed their emotions.

Picking a Puppy

People look for different traits in the dogs they choose. Here is how one expert selected his dog based on good breeding and personality.

James Herriot, a veterinarian in England, had owned several dogs during his lifetime. But he had always wanted a Border terrier. These small, sturdy dogs are descendants of working terrier breeds that lived on the border of England and Scotland. For centuries they were used to hunt foxes, rats, and other small animals. In this story, Herriot and his wife Helen follow up on an advertisement for Border terrier puppies.

Language Arts Activity

James Herriot describes this scene using dialog and first-person narrative. The narrative describes Herriot's feelings about a memorable event—finally finding the dog he had wanted for so long. Write a first-person narrative describing a memorable event in your life. You might choose a childhood memory or a personal achievement at school. What emotions did you feel? How did you make your decision? If possible, use dialog in your writing.

Border terrier ▶

S he [Helen, his wife] turned to me and spoke agitatedly, "I've got Mrs. Mason on the line now. There's only one pup left out of the litter and there are people coming from as far as eighty miles away to see it. We'll have to hurry. What a long time you've been out there!"

We bolted our lunch and Helen, Rosie, granddaughter Emma and I drove out to Bedale. Mrs. Mason led us into the kitchen and pointed to a tiny brindle creature twisting and writhing under the table.

"That's him," she said.

I reached down and lifted the puppy as he curled his little body round, apparently trying to touch his tail with his nose. But that tail wagged furiously and the pink tongue was busy at my hand. I knew he was ours before my quick examination for hernia and overshot jaw.

The deal was quickly struck and we went outside to inspect the puppy's relations. His mother and grandmother were out there. They lived in little barrels which served as kennels and both of them darted out and stood up at our legs, tails lashing, mouths panting in delight. I felt vastly reassured. With happy, healthy ancestors like those I knew we had every chance of a first rate dog.

As we drove home with the puppy in Emma's arms, the warm thought came to me. The wheel had indeed turned. After nearly fifty years I had my Border terrier.

James Herriot was a country veterinarian in Yorkshire, England. In several popular books published in the 1970s and 1980s, he wrote warm, humorous stories about the animals he cared for. His book *All Creatures Great and Small* was the basis for a television series.

178

Facts and Figures James Herriot was the pen name of James Alfred Wight, a British veterinarian and writer. Herriot began practicing veterinary medicine in North Yorkshire, England, after he graduated from veterinary school in 1937. In his practice, he cared for cows, horses, and sheep, as well as dogs and cats. He began writing about his experiences with people and animals in his practice when he was 50 years old. His first book, *All Creatures Great and Small*, was published in 1972. He published three other books *All Things Bright and Beautiful*, *All Things Wise and Wonderful*, and *The Lord God Made Them All*, as well as children's stories and a book of photographs describing the Yorkshire countryside. James Herriot died in 1995 at the age of 78.

Breed	1970	1980	1990	1997
Poodle	265,879	92,250	71,757	54,773
Labrador Retriever	25,667	52,398	99,776	158,366
Cocker Spaniel	21,811	76,113	105,642	41,439

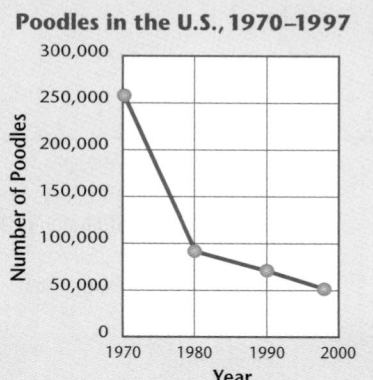

Poodles in the U.S., 1970–1997

Number of Poodles (y-axis): 0, 50,000, 100,000, 150,000, 200,000, 250,000, 300,000

Year (x-axis): 1970, 1980, 1990, 2000

Math Activity

The popularity of different breeds of dogs changes over time. For example, the line graph shows how the number of poodles registered with the American Kennel Club changed between 1970 and 1997. Use the table to create your own line graph for Labrador retrievers and cocker spaniels.

Which breed was more popular in 1980, Labrador retrievers or cocker spaniels? How has the number of Labrador retrievers changed from 1970 to 1997? How has the number of cocker spaniels changed over the same time?

Tie It Together

Best of Breed Show

In many places proud dog owners of all ages bring their animals to compete in dog shows. Organize your own dog show. With a partner, choose one specific breed of dog. Pick a breed shown on the map on pages 176–177, or use library resources to research another breed.

- Find out what the breed looks like, the time and place where it originated, and what traits it was first bred for.
- List your breed's characteristics, height, weight, and coloring.
- Research the breed's personality and behavior.
- Find out your breed's strengths. Learn what weakness may develop as a result of inbreeding.
- Make a poster for your breed. Include a drawing or photo and the information that you researched.
- With your class, organize the dog displays into categories of breeds, such as hunting dogs, herding dogs, and toy dogs.

179

2 Facilitate

- To assess students' understanding of the data, ask questions such as: **What breed was most popular in 1980?** *(poodle)* **Which breed is most popular now?** *(Labrador retriever)*
- Ask students questions about the graph, such as: **How has the number of poodles changed from 1970 to 1997?** *(There has been a sharp decrease.)*

Mathematics Activity

Have students complete the activity on their own. Provide them with graph paper. Students may draw separate graphs for each breed or combine the breeds on one graph. Encourage students to use the graph on this page as a guide for their own graphs.
Interdisciplinary Explorations The following Worksheets correlate with this page: Making a Bar Graph, page 11; The Costs of Owning a Dog, page 12; Calculating Points in Obedience Trials, page 13.

3 Assess

Activity Assessment

Students' graphs should look similar to the graph for poodles on this page. In 1980, cocker spaniels were more popular. Labrador retrievers have increased steadily in popularity from 1970 to 1997. Cocker spaniel popularity increased steadily until 1990, when it began to decrease sharply.

Tie It Together

Time 1 week (2 days for research, 2 days for the poster, 1 day for the show)
Tips With supervision, students can learn about specific dog breeds on the Internet. They can use the breed name as the search word. Have the class vote for their favorite breed to determine "Best of Show."

179

	Sections	Time	Student Edition Activities		Other Activities
CHAPTER PROJECT	**Be a Disease Detective** p. 181	Ongoing (1½ weeks)	Check Your Progress, pp. 191, 211 Present Your Project, p. 215		
1	**Classifying Organisms** pp. 182–188 ◆ Explain why scientists organize living things into groups. ◆ Describe early classification systems, including that of Linneaus. ◆ Name the seven levels of classification used by scientists. ◆ Explain the relationship between classification and evolution.	2–3 periods/ 1–1½ blocks	**Discover** Can You Organize a Junk Drawer?, p. 182 **Sharpen Your Skills** Observing, p. 186 **Science at Home,** p. 188	TE TE TE	Inquiry Challenge, pp. 183, 184 Including All Students, p. 185 Building Inquiry Skills: Making Models, p. 186
2	**The Six Kingdoms** pp. 189–191 ◆ Name and describe the six kingdoms into which organisms are grouped.	1 period/ ½ block	**Discover** Which Organism Goes Where?, p. 189	TE TE TE	Real-Life Learning, p. 190 Demonstration, p. 190 Building Inquiry Skills: Classifying, p. 191
3	**Bacteria** pp. 192–203 ◆ Describe ways in which bacteria cells are different from all other organisms' cells. ◆ Name the two kingdoms of bacteria, and explain how bacteria reproduce and survive. ◆ List positive roles that bacteria play in people's lives.	2 periods/ 1 block	**Discover** How Fast Do Bacteria Multiply?, p. 192 **Sharpen Your Skills** Graphing, p. 195 **Try This** Bacteria for Breakfast, p. 197 **Science at Home,** p. 201 **Real-World Lab: You, the Consumer** Do Disinfectants Work?, pp. 202–203	TE TE LM IES PTA	Building Inquiry Skills: Classifying, p. 193; Designing Experiments, p. 196; Drawing Conclusions, p. 199 Demonstration, p. 200 9, "Eubacteria That Dine on Vegetables" "Riddles of the Pharaohs," p. 38 "Testing Yogurt," pp. 1–8
4	**INTEGRATING HEALTH** **Viruses** pp. 204–212 ◆ Give reasons why viruses are considered to be nonliving. ◆ Describe the sizes and shapes of viruses. ◆ Describe the basic structure of a virus. ◆ Explain how viruses multiply.	2 periods/ 1 block	**Discover** Can You Cure a Cold?, p. 204 **Try This** Modeling a Virus, p. 207 **Skills Lab: Making Models** How Many Viruses Fit on a Pin?, p. 212	TE TE	Inquiry Challenge, p. 206 Including All Students, p. 207
	Study Guide/Chapter Assessment pp. 213–215	1 period/ ½ block		ISAB	Provides teaching and review of all inquiry skills

For Standard or Block Schedule The Resource Pro® CD-ROM gives you maximum flexibility for planning your instruction for any type of schedule. Resource Pro® contains Planning Express®, an advanced scheduling program, as well as the entire contents of the Teaching Resources and the Computer Test Bank.

CHAPTER PLANNING GUIDE

Program Resources	Assessment Strategies	Media and Technology
UR Chapter 6 Project Teacher Notes, pp. 2–3 **UR** Chapter 6 Project Overview and Worksheets, pp. 4–7	**SE** Performance Assessment: Present Your Project, p. 215 **TE** Check Your Progress, pp. 191, 211 **UR** Chapter 6 Project Scoring Rubric, p. 8	Science Explorer Internet Site at www.phschool.com
UR 6-1 Lesson Plan, p. 9 **UR** 6-1 Section Summary, p. 10 **UR** 6-1 Review and Reinforce, p. 11 **UR** 6-1 Enrich, p. 12	**SE** Section 1 Review, p. 188 **TE** Ongoing Assessment, pp. 183, 185, 187 **TE** Performance Assessment, p. 188	Life Science Videotape 2; Videodisc Unit 2 Side 2, "*Pantera leo?*" Audio CD, English-Spanish Summary 6-1 Transparency 23, "Seven Levels of Classification" Interactive Student Tutorial CD-ROM, Chapter 6
UR 6-2 Lesson Plan, p. 13 **UR** 6-2 Section Summary, p. 14 **UR** 6-2 Review and Reinforce, p. 15 **UR** 6-2 Enrich, p. 16	**SE** Section 2 Review, p. 191 **TE** Performance Assessment, p. 191	Audio CD, English-Spanish Summary 6-2
UR 6-3 Lesson Plan, p. 17 **UR** 6-3 Section Summary, p. 18 **UR** 6-3 Review and Reinforce, p. 19 **UR** 6-3 Enrich, p. 20 **UR** Chapter 6 Real-World Lab, pp. 25–27	**SE** Section 3 Review, p. 201 **TE** Ongoing Assessment, pp. 193, 195, 197, 199 **TE** Performance Assessment, p. 201	Life Science Videotape 2; Videodisc Unit 2 Side 2, "Positive Bacteria" Audio CD, English-Spanish Summary 6-3 Transparency 24, "The Structure of a Bacterial Cell"
UR 6-4 Lesson Plan, p. 21 **UR** 6-4 Section Summary, p. 22 **UR** 6-4 Review and Reinforce, p. 23 **UR** 6-4 Enrich, p. 24 **UR** Chapter 6 Skills Lab, pp. 28–29	**SE** Section 4 Review, p. 211 **TE** Ongoing Assessment, pp. 205, 207, 209 **TE** Performance Assessment, p. 211	Life Science Videotape 2; Videodisc Unit 2 Side 2, "On the Trail of a Disease"; Videodisc Unit 2 Side 2, "Have You Had Your Shots?" Audio CD, English-Spanish Summary 6-4 Transparencies 25, "How a Virus Attaches to a Host Cell"; 26, "Exploring How Active Viruses Multiply"; 27, "Exploring How Hidden Viruses Multiply"
RCA Provides strategies to improve science reading skills **GSW** Provides worksheets to promote student comprehension of content	**SE** Chapter 6 Study Guide/Assessment, pp. 213–215 **PA** Chapter 6 Performance Assessment, pp. 20–22 **CUT** Chapter 6 Test, pp. 28–31 **CTB** Chapter 6 Test	Interactive Student Tutorial CD-ROM, Chapter 6 Computer Test Bank, Chapter 6 Test

Key: **SE** Student Edition   **TE** Teacher's Edition   **UR** Unit Resources
      CTB Computer Test Bank   **PTA** Product Testing Activities by *Consumer Reports*   **LM** Laboratory Manual
      ISAB Inquiry Skills Activity Book   **RCA** Reading in the Content Area   **IES** Interdisciplinary Explorations Series
      GSW Guided Study Worksheets   **PA** Performance Assessment   **CUT** Chapter and Unit Tests

Meeting the National Science Education Standards and AAAS Benchmarks

National Science Education Standards	Benchmarks for Science Literacy	Unifying Themes
Science as Inquiry (Content Standard A) ◆ **Use appropriate tools and techniques to gather, analyze, and interpret data** Students investigate how well disinfectants control the growth of bacteria. *(Real-World Lab)* ◆ **Use mathematics in scientific inquiry** How many viruses fit on a pin? *(Skills Lab)* **Life Science** (Content Standard C) ◆ **Diversity and adaptations of organisms** Students learn the main characteristics of bacteria and how they reproduce. *(Section 3)* Students learn the main characteristics of viruses and how they reproduce. *(Section 4)* ◆ **Populations and ecosystems** Students learn that bacteria function as decomposers of dead organic matter. *(Section 3)* ◆ **Structure and function in living systems** Students learn that the cells of bacteria are different from those of other living organisms. *(Section 3)* Students learn that disease is often the result of infection by bacteria and viruses. *(Section 3, 4)*	**1B Scientific Inquiry** Students compare the effects of two disinfectants and make inferences about which is more effective by gathering and analyzing data. *(Real-World Lab)* **2C Mathematical Inquiry** Students use models to investigate the size of viruses. *(Skills Lab)* **3C Issues in Technology** Students learn that technology has influenced the development of helpful antibiotics and study how antibiotic resistance affects society. *(Section 3, Science and Society)* **5A Diversity of Life** Organisms share common characteristics, allowing them to be placed in groups. Differences between organisms establish different groups. *(Sections 1, 2)* Positive roles that bacteria play in people's lives are presented as well as a discussion of bacteria's role as a decomposer and recycler of organic matter. *(Section 2)* **5D Interdependence of Life** The relationship between viruses and their host cells are discussed. *(Section 1)* **12D Communication** Students organize information in data tables and use the results to make inferences about the relative effectiveness of two disinfectants. *(Real-World Lab)*	◆ **Scale and Structure** Classification groups form a hierarchy in which the largest groups are the most general and the smallest are the most specific. The smallest classification group (species) refers to just one kind of organism. *(Section 1)* Viruses are considered to be nonliving, but have genetic material necessary to reproduce. Bacteria are different in structure from other cells. *(Sections 3, 4)* ◆ **Unity and Diversity** Different organisms in each classification group share important characteristics. Differences between organisms are used as a means of classifying them into different groups. *(Section 1)* There are many types of viruses and bacteria, but they all share basic characteristics. *(Sections 3, 4)* ◆ **Evolution** Life has evolved over time. Modern classification systems are based on evolutionary history. *(Section 1)* The first forms of life on Earth may have been similar to bacteria. *(Section 3)* ◆ **Patterns of Change** Bacteria are responsible for altering Earth's early atmosphere. *(Section 3)* ◆ **System and Interactions** Bacteria interact with their environment in many ways. Some are producers, some are decomposers, some are parasites. Early bacteria probably altered Earth's atmosphere. *(Sections 3, 4)* ◆ **Stability** Binomial nomenclature gives every organism a name that can be understood by everyone, regardless of individual differences. *(Section 2)*

Take It to the Net

 *Interactive text at* www.phschool.com

Science Explorer comes alive with iText.
- **Complete student text** is accessible from any computer with Internet access or a CD-ROM drive.
- **Animations, simulations, and videos** enhance student understanding and retention of concepts.
- **Self-tests and online study tools** assess student understanding.

STAY CURRENT with

Find out the latest research and information about bacteria and viruses at: **www.phschool.com**

WEB ACTIVITY www.phschool.com

Go to **www.phschool.com** and click on the Science icon. Then click on <u>Science Explorer: Life, Earth, and Physical Science</u> under PH@school.

ACTIVITY	Time (minutes)	Materials Quantities for one work group	Skills
Section 1			
Discover, p. 182	15	**Nonconsumable** items such as scotch tape, pencils, rubber bands, stamps, markers, erasers, rulers, envelopes, paper clips, paper	Classifying
Sharpen Your Skills, p. 186	20	No special materials are required.	Observing
Science at Home, p. 188	home	No special materials are required.	Classifying
Section 2			
Discover, p. 189	15	**Nonconsumable** mushroom, small green plant, a worm or insect, sea animal such as an urchin, anemone, or cultivated coral	Classifying
Section 3			
Discover, p. 192	20	**Nonconsumable** paper cups; dried lima, kidney, or navy beans	Inferring
Sharpen Your Skills, p. 195	20	**Consumable** graph paper **Nonconsumable** pencil	Graphing
Try This, p. 197	20	**Consumable** unpasteurized yogurt, methylene blue **Nonconsumable** plastic dropper, glass slide, cover slip, microscope, lab apron	Observing
Science at Home, pp. 201	home	**Nonconsumable** original packaging from foods	Communicating
Real-World Lab, pp. 202–203	30	**Nonconsumable** original packaging from foods	Observing, Inferring, Drawing, Conclusions
Section 4			
Discover, p. 204	20	**Nonconsumable** assortment of containers or over-the-counter cold medications (pills and liquids) such as decongestants, pain relievers, cough medicines	Inferring
Try This, p. 207	20	**Consumable** pipe cleaners, string, thread, rubber bands, construction paper, aluminum foil, straws, plastic wrap, glue, tape	Inferring
Skills Lab, p. 212	45	**Consumable** long strips of paper, tape **Nonconsumable** straight pin, pencil, scissors, calculator, meter stick	Inferring

A list of all materials required for the Student Edition activities can be found on pages T25–T33. You can obtain information about ordering materials by calling 1-800-848-9500 or by accessing the Science Explorer Internet site at **www.phschool.com**.

Be a Disease Detective

In this chapter, students will be introduced to viruses and bacteria and their importance in human health. This project will give them an opportunity to explore how perceptions of a common childhood disease have changed between generations.

Purpose In this project, students will have the opportunity to investigate a childhood disease by doing research in a library or on the Internet as well as preparing, conducting, and analyzing the results of a survey.

Skills Focus Students will be able to
◆ ask questions so they can research a particular disease, then prepare and conduct a survey asking people about their experience and knowledge of a disease;
◆ draw conclusions concerning how the incidence of a childhood disease and people's knowledge of the disease have changed over time.

Project Time Line Before the project, check with the librarian and the school nurse to find out whether they are willing to help students during the research phase of the project. The entire project will take four weeks. During the first week, students will research a childhood disease. During the second and third weeks, students will write and conduct their surveys. In week four, students will analyze the results of their surveys and present their report to the class. Before beginning the project, see Chapter 6 Project Teacher Notes on pages 2–3 in Unit 2 Resources for more details on carrying out the project. Also distribute to students the Chapter 6 Project Overview, Worksheets, and Scoring Rubric on pages 4–8 in Unit 2 Resources.

Suggested Shortcuts You can simplify the project by allowing students to work in pairs or small groups. Students should work together to plan their surveys and should each interview several people, making sure that the total group includes people of different ages.

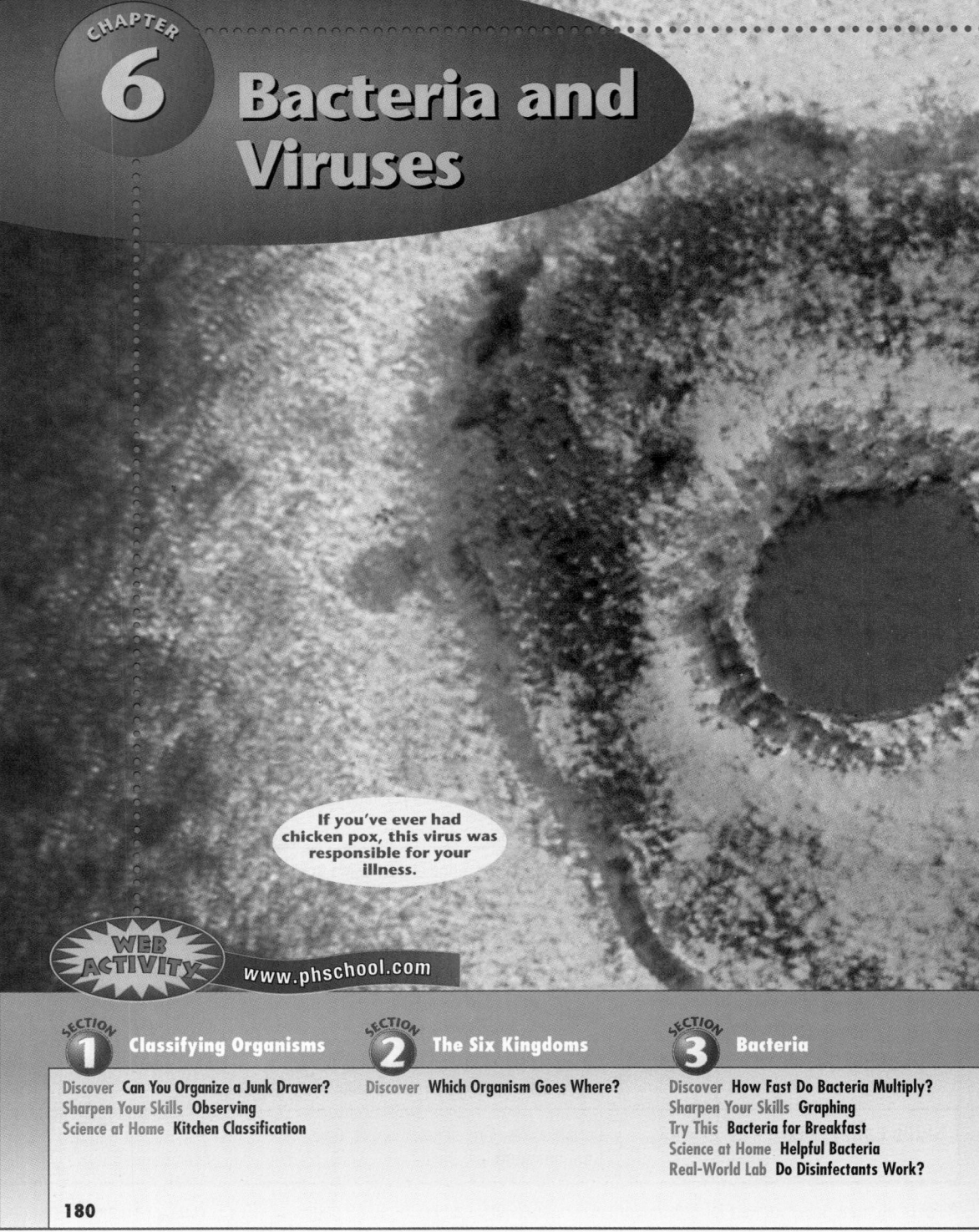

CHAPTER 6 Bacteria and Viruses

If you've ever had chicken pox, this virus was responsible for your illness.

WEB ACTIVITY www.phschool.com

SECTION 1 Classifying Organisms
Discover Can You Organize a Junk Drawer?
Sharpen Your Skills Observing
Science at Home Kitchen Classification

SECTION 2 The Six Kingdoms
Discover Which Organism Goes Where?

SECTION 3 Bacteria
Discover How Fast Do Bacteria Multiply?
Sharpen Your Skills Graphing
Try This Bacteria for Breakfast
Science at Home Helpful Bacteria
Real-World Lab Do Disinfectants Work?

180

Possible Materials In addition to the librarian and school nurse, students could talk to their doctors to research their diseases.

Launching the Project To introduce the project and to stimulate student interest, ask: **What vaccinations did you have when you were younger?** (*Sample: diphtheria, tetanus, pertussis [whooping cough], influenza, polio, measles, mumps, rubella*) Ask students: **What are the symptoms of these diseases?** (*Students may have difficulty describing the symptoms because these diseases are quite rare, due in part*

to the use of vaccines.) Tell students that the vaccinations for these diseases were introduced after 1920. Also discuss the chickenpox (*Varicella*) vaccine, which was introduced in the United States in 1995. Some students in your class may have had chicken pox and will be able to describe the symptoms accurately. Ask: **Do you think students ten years from now will be able to describe the symptoms of chicken pox?** (*Probably not, since few will have had the disease growing up.*)

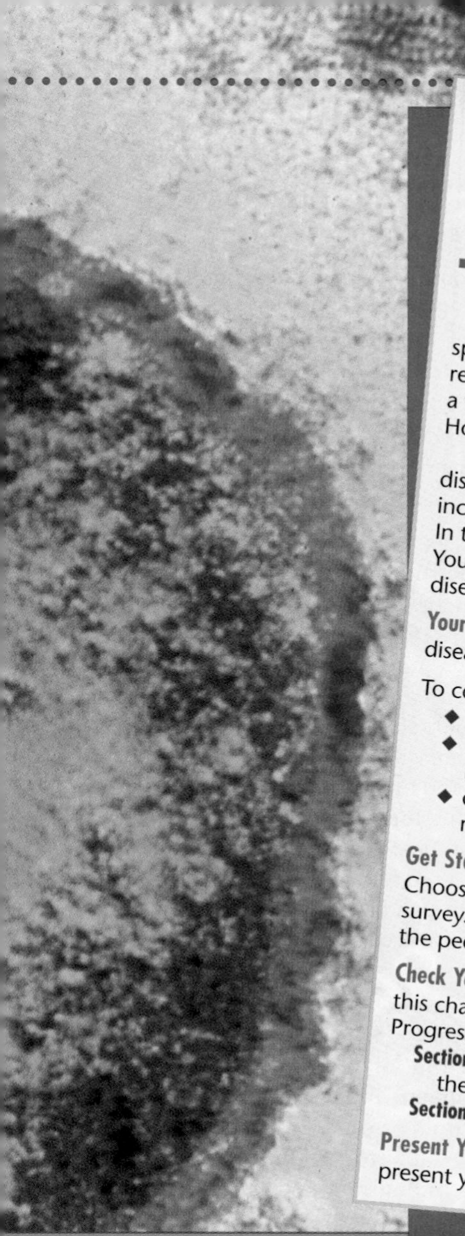

CHAPTER 6 PROJECT

Be a Disease Detective

The virus pictured on this page may look harmless, but it's not. If you've ever had chicken pox, you've experienced it firsthand. Soon after the virus enters your body, red spots appear on your skin, and you begin to itch. As the virus reproduces inside your body, you become sick. But even though a virus can reproduce, scientists do not consider it a living thing. However, bacteria, which can also cause disease, are living things.

Not too long ago, catching viral and bacterial "childhood diseases" was a routine part of growing up. Those diseases included chicken pox, mumps, and pertussis (whooping cough). In this project, you will select a childhood disease to investigate. You'll then survey people to learn what they know about the disease.

Your Goal To survey people of different ages about a childhood disease.

To complete this project successfully, you must
- ◆ select and research one disease to learn more about it
- ◆ prepare a questionnaire to survey people about their knowledge and experience with the disease
- ◆ question a total of 30 people in different age groups, and report any patterns that you find

Get Started With classmates, make a list of childhood diseases. Choose one disease to research. Also list the steps involved in a survey. What questions will you need to ask? How will you select the people for your survey? Draft your questionnaire.

Check Your Progress You'll be working on this project as you study this chapter. To keep your project on track, look for Check Your Progress boxes at the following points.

Section 2 Review, page 191: Write your questionnaire, and identify the people to survey.
Section 4 Review, page 211: Analyze your survey results.

Present Your Project At the end of the chapter (page 215), you will present your survey results to your classmates.

SECTION 4

Integrating Health
Viruses

Discover **Can You Cure a Cold?**
Try This **Modeling a Virus**
Skills Lab **How Many Viruses Fit on a Pin?**

181

Program Resources

- ◆ **Unit 2 Resources** Chapter 6 Project Teacher Notes, pp. 2–3; Chapter 6 Project Overview and Worksheets, pp. 4–7; Chapter 6 Project Scoring Rubric, p. 8

www.phschool.com

You will find an Internet activity, chapter self-tests for students, and links to other chapter topics at this site.

Allow time for students to read the description of the project in their text and the Chapter Project Overview on pages 4–5 in Unit 2 Resources. Then encourage discussions on childhood diseases, reference materials that could be used, and any initial questions students may have. Pass out copies of the Chapter 6 Project Worksheets on pages 6–7 in Unit 2 Resources for students to review.

Performance Assessment

The Chapter 6 Project Scoring Rubric on page 8 of Unit 2 Resources will help you evaluate how well students complete the Chapter 6 Project. Students will be assessed on
- ◆ the thoroughness of their research on the disease;
- ◆ how well-organized, complete, and informative the survey is and whether it is given to 30 individuals of different ages;
- ◆ the clarity, thoroughness, and organization of their survey analysis and written reports;
- ◆ their presentations and how well they use their results to explain a change in the occurrence of, or the knowledge about, the disease.

By sharing the Chapter 6 Project Scoring Rubric with students at the beginning of the project, you will make it clear to them what they are expected to do.

Objectives

After completing the lesson, students will be able to

◆ explain why scientists organize living things into groups;

◆ describe early classification systems, including that of Linnaeus;

◆ name the seven levels of classification used by scientists;

◆ explain the relationship between classification and evolution.

Key Terms classification, taxonomy, binomial nomenclature, genus, species, taxonomic key

1 Engage/Explore

Activating Prior Knowledge

Ask students: **How do libraries organize their books?** (*First by whether they are fiction or nonfiction, then by subject matter, then in alphabetical order by author's last name, first name, and finally title*) Discuss with students how difficult it would be to find a book in the library without some sort of organizing system.

DISCOVER

Skills Focus classifying

Materials *items such as scotch tape, pencils, rubber bands, stamps, markers, erasers, rulers, envelopes, paper clips, paper*

Time 15 minutes

Tips Avoid using sharp objects. Stress that items in a set must share at least one common trait.

Expected Outcome A variety of classification systems may be proposed. For example, students may group by function (items you write with) or by shape (round).

Think It Over Each grouping system will have strengths and weaknesses. Criteria for usefulness will vary. Possibilities include systems that emphasize similar functions or systems that allow objects to be found quickly.

DISCOVER ·········· ACTIVITY

Can You Organize a Junk Drawer?

1. Your teacher will give you some items that you might find in the junk drawer of a desk. Your job is to organize the items.

2. Examine the objects and decide on three groups into which you can sort them.

3. Place each object into one of the groups based on how the item's features match the characteristics of the group.

4. Compare your grouping system with those of your classmates.

Think It Over

Classifying Explain which grouping system seemed most useful.

GUIDE FOR READING

◆ Why do scientists organize living things into groups?

◆ What is the relationship between classification and evolution?

Reading Tip Before you read, make a list of the boldfaced vocabulary terms. As you read, write the meaning of each term in your own words.

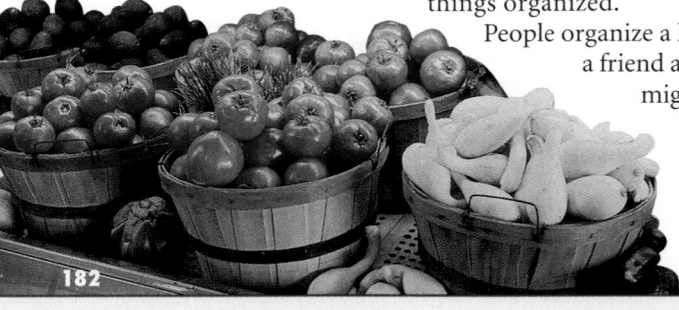

▼ Vegetables organized by type

182

Suppose you had only ten minutes to run into a supermarket to get what you need—milk and tomatoes. Could you do it? In most supermarkets this would be an easy task. First, you might go to the dairy aisle and find the milk. Then you'd go to the produce aisle and find the tomatoes. Finally, you'd pay for the items and leave the store.

Now imagine shopping for these same items in a market where the shelves were organized in a random manner. To find what you need, you'd have to search through boxes of cereal, cans of tuna, bins of apples, and much more. You could be there for a long time!

Why Do Scientists Classify?

Just as shopping can be a problem in a disorganized store, finding information about one of the millions of kinds of organisms can also be a problem. Today, scientists have identified at least 1.7 million kinds of organisms on Earth. This number includes all forms of life, from plants and animals to bacteria. It is important for biologists to have all these living things organized.

People organize a lot of things into groups. For example, if a friend asks you what kind of music you like, you might say that you like country or rock and roll music. Although you may not know it, you have grouped the music you like. **Classification** is the process of grouping things based on their similarities.

READING STRATEGIES

Reading Tip Have students write the vocabulary words on the fronts of index cards and their definitions on the backs. Students can work in pairs to quiz each other and practice pronouncing the words. Sample definition: Classification—a system of grouping living things according to their similarities.

Study and Comprehension Before students read the section, have them write the six main section headings in their notebooks, leaving enough space between headings to write at least three sentences. As students read each section, they should summarize it before reading the next section. Remind students to identify the main idea and restate it in their own words.

Biologists use classification to organize living things into groups so that organisms are easier to study. The scientific study of how living things are classified is called **taxonomy** (tak SAHN uh mee). Taxonomy is useful because once an organism is classified, a scientist knows a lot about that organism. For example, if you know that crows are classified as birds, you know that crows have wings, feathers, and beaks.

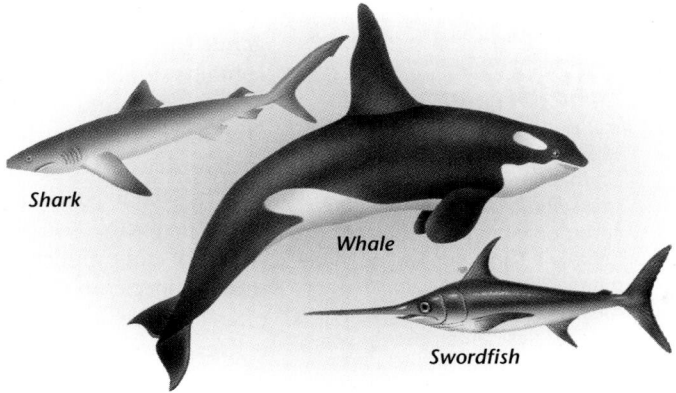

Shark

Whale

Swordfish

Figure 1 Aristotle would have classified this shark, whale, and swordfish together because they all swim. However, he would have separated them into subgroups because they differ from one another in many ways. *Classifying List two differences that would place these animals into separate subgroups.*

Early Classification Systems

The first scientist to develop a classification system for organisms was the Greek scholar Aristotle. In the fourth century B.C., Aristotle observed many animals. He recorded each animal's appearance, behavior, and movement. Then he divided animals into three groups: those that fly, those that swim, and those that walk, crawl, or run.

Aristotle could see that even though all the organisms in a group moved in a similar way, they were different in many other ways. So he used their differences to further divide each group into subgroups—smaller groups of organisms that shared other similarities.

Aristotle's method of using careful observations as the basis for classification and his idea of creating subgroups are still used today. However, organisms are no longer classified into large groups on the basis of how they move or where they live.

☑ *Checkpoint* *What were the three major groups of animals in Aristotle's system of classification?*

The Classification System of Linnaeus

In the 1750s, a Swedish scientist named Carolus Linnaeus expanded on Aristotle's ideas of classification. Like Aristotle, Linnaeus used observations as the basis of his system. He wrote descriptions of organisms from his observations, and placed organisms in groups based on their observable features.

Linnaeus also used his observations to devise a naming system for organisms. In Linnaeus's naming system, called **binomial nomenclature** (by NOH mee ul NOH men klay chur), each organism is given a two-part name.

Answers to Self-Assessment

Caption Question

Figure 1 Answers will vary but might include gills or lungs and horizontal or vertical caudal fins.

☑ *Checkpoint*

Animals that fly; those that swim; and those that crawl, walk, or run

2 *Facilitate*

Why Do Scientists Classify?

Inquiry Challenge

Materials *igneous, metamorphic, and sedimentary rocks; three labeled boxes*
Time 20 minutes

ACTIVITY

Display a specimen of each rock type in front of a labeled box. Pass out rocks to small groups of students so that every group has one of each kind to examine and classify. Have groups classify their rocks. **limited English proficiency**

Early Classification Systems

Building Inquiry Skills: Thinking Critically

Challenge students to think of some examples of animals that Aristotle would have classified in the same group but that today's scientists classify in very different groups. *(Sample: ostrich, cheetah, and lizard)* **learning modality: verbal**

The Classification System of Linnaeus

Building Inquiry Skills: Applying Concepts

Write these scientific names on the board: *Perognathus californicus, Perognathus nelsoni, Perognathus spinatus.* Challenge students to see how much information they can infer about these North American pocket mice just from their names. *(They are from the same genus. Students may also infer that* nelsoni *was discovered by someone named Nelson, or* californicus *is found in California.* **learning modality: logical/mathematical**

Ongoing Assessment

Writing Have students describe the difference between classification and taxonomy.

The Classification System of Linnaeus, continued

Language Arts
CONNECTION

Ask students to consider the term *binomial nomenclature*. *Bi* translates as "two" or "twice" while *nomen* means "name." Ask: **How does English provide hints about the meanings of Latin terms?** *(Sample: In the term "Viola missouriensis," English helps identify Missouri as a location of the plant.)*

In Your Journal Provide biology textbooks, dictionaries, and encyclopedias. *(Musca domestica: housefly; Hirudo medicinalis: medicinal leech. Students may recognize the words* domestic *or* medicine.) **learning modality: verbal**

Inquiry Challenge

Materials *index cards or small pieces of paper, tape, markers*

Time 15 minutes

Ask: **What would happen if scientists used only one word to name organisms?** *(They might run out of names, and they would not be able to express relationships between similar organisms.)* Challenge small groups of students to use the numbers from zero to nine to classify objects in the classroom by genus and species. Have students write each digit on 10 pieces of paper. A typical system includes assigning one number for the genus and a second number for the species. Allow students to tape the labels onto the objects to identify the genus and species. Challenge groups to identify the system used by other groups. *(A sample system would place all furniture with legs in a genus, with individual species such as tables, desks, and chairs.)* Ask: **How many different species names could you have?** *(100)* Encourage students to think of ways to increase the number of names they could have. *(By using more than one digit for each name.)* **learning modality: logical/mathematical**

Language Arts
CONNECTION

You don't have to understand Latin to know that you should avoid an organism named *Ursus horribilis. Ursus horribilis* is commonly known as a grizzly bear. The Latin word *ursus* means "bear" and *horribilis* means "horrible or feared."

A species name describes an organism like an adjective describes the noun it modifies. Some names describe a specific trait; others tell who discovered the organism. Other names tell you where the organism lives. Guess where you'd find the plant *Viola missouriensis.*

In Your Journal

Look up the meanings of these species names: *Musca domestica* and *Hirudo medicinalis.* Then find some English words derived from the Latin terms.

The first part of an organism's scientific name is its genus. A **genus** (JEE nus) (plural *genera*) is a classification grouping that contains similar, closely related organisms. For example, pumas, ocelots, and house cats are all classified in the genus *Felis.* Organisms that are classified in the genus *Felis* share features such as sharp, retractable claws and behaviors such as hunting.

The second part of an organism's scientific name is its species name. A **species** (SPEE sheez) is a group of similar organisms that can mate and produce fertile offspring in nature. A species name sets one species in a genus apart from another. The species name often describes a distinctive feature of an organism, such as where it lives or its color. For example, the scientific name for many pumas, or mountain lions, is *Felis concolor. Concolor* means "the same color" in Latin. The scientific name for some ocelots is *Felis pardalis.* The word *pardalis* means "spotted like a panther" in Latin. The scientific name for house cats is *Felis domesticus.* The species name *domesticus* means "of the house" in Latin.

Linnaeus's system might remind you of the way you are named because you, also, have a two-part name made up of your first name and your family name. Your two-part name distinguishes you from others. In a similar way, binomial nomenclature ensures that a combination of two names distinguishes one kind of organism from another. Together, a genus and a species name identify one kind of organism.

Figure 2 These animals belong to the genus *Felis.* Their species names distinguish them from one another. **A.** This puma's coat is one color, as indicated by its species name *concolor.* **B.** This ocelot has a spotted coat, described by its species name *pardalis.* **C.** The species name of this kitten is *domesticus,* which indicates that it is a house cat.

Background

Facts and Figures Latin was originally spoken by small groups that lived near the Tiber River in Italy. As the power and territory of the Roman Empire spread, so did the Latin language. The spoken language of various parts of the Empire developed into the modern Romance languages, which include French, Italian, Spanish, Portuguese, and Romanian.

The name *Romance* comes from an old French form of the Latin word *Romanticus.* This word was used in the Middle Ages to refer to a popular form of Latin speech, rather than the form used by the church. By the end of the twentieth century, more than 1 billion people spoke a Romance language.

Romance languages share a high proportion of basic vocabulary and many grammatical forms with the language of the Roman empire.

Notice that both the genus and species names are Latin words. Linnaeus used Latin words in his naming system because Latin was the language that scientists communicated in during that time. Notice also that a complete scientific name is written in italics. The genus is capitalized while the species name begins with a small letter.

Binomial nomenclature makes it easy for scientists to communicate about an organism because everyone uses the same name for the same organism. For example, people call the tree shown in Figure 3 by any one of a number of common names: loblolly pine, longstraw pine, or Indian pine. Fortunately, this tree has only one scientific name, *Pinus taeda*.

☑ *Checkpoint* *Which part of a scientific name is like your first name? Your family name?*

Classification Today

At the time that Linnaeus developed his classification system, people thought that species never change. They could see that some organisms were similar. They thought that these organisms had always been similar, yet distinct from each other.

The theory of evolution changed the way biologists think about classification. Today, scientists understand that certain organisms are similar because they share a common ancestor. When organisms share a common ancestor, they share an evolutionary history. Today's system of classification considers the history of a species when classifying the species. **Species with similar evolutionary histories are classified more closely together.**

Levels of Classification

The classification system that scientists use today is based on the contributions of both Aristotle and Linnaeus. But today's classification system uses a series of seven levels to classify organisms. To help you understand the levels in classification, imagine a room filled with everybody who lives in your state. First, all of the people who live in your *town* raise their hands. Next, those people who live in your *neighborhood* raise their hands. Then, those who live on your *street* raise their hands. Finally, those who live in your *house* raise their hands. Each time, fewer people raise their hands. But you would be in all of the groups. The most general group you belong to is the state. The most specific group is the house. The more levels you share with others, the more you have in common with them.

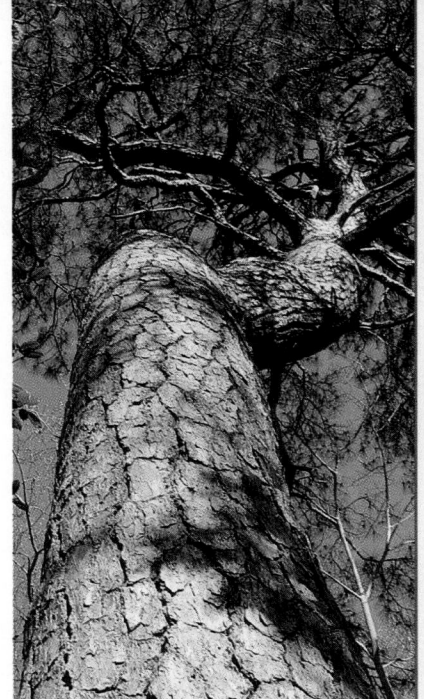

Figure 3 Although there are many common names for this tree, it has only one scientific name. *Making Generalizations What is the advantage of having scientific names for organisms?*

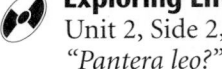
Answers to Self-Assessment
Caption Question
Figure 3 Using scientific names makes it easy for scientists to communicate about organisms, because everyone uses the same name for the same organism.

☑ *Checkpoint*
Genus name —family name; species name —given name.

Classification Today

Building Inquiry Skills: Comparing and Contrasting
Display pictures of the bones in a bat's wing, a whale's flipper, and a human's arm and hand. Draw students' attention to the long upper bone (humerus) of the human arm and ask them to compare the bones in similar locations in the other animals. Ask: **How does this bone compare to the bone in the same location in the bat? The whale?** (*Bat: wider at the shoulder and narrower at the elbow; whale: proportionately much shorter and heavier*) This questioning strategy may be applied to the lower arm bones (radius and ulna), the wrist bones (carpels), hand (metacarpals) and fingers (phalanges). **learning modality: visual**

Levels of Classification

Including All Students
Give students index cards  and ask them to visually depict the levels of where they live as if they were using a classification system. (*Visual representations might include a series of concentric circles to show the increasingly specific levels of country, state, county, city, street, and house number.*) **learning modality: visual**

Ongoing Assessment

Skills Check Tell students that the scientific name for dogs is *Canis familiaris*. Call on students to identify the parts of the name. (*Canis is the genus;* familiaris *is the species.*) List the following binomial names on the board and have students identify the genus and species and then describe the animal by comparing it to an animal of the same genus from p. 184: *Felis onca, Ursus arctos, Canis latrans.*

Levels of Classification, continued

Sharpen your *Skills*

Observing

Time 10 minutes

Tips If students have difficulty finding common traits of animals at the kingdom level, ask: **Are these animals unicellular or multicellular?** *(multicellular)* **Are they autotrophs or heterotrophs?** *(heterotrophs)* Next, have students compare and contrast the birds pictured at the class and genus levels. Point out that structural adaptations for movement and obtaining food are often used in assigning classification.

Expected Outcome The closer to the species level, the longer the list of shared characteristics. *(Kingdom: multicellular heterotrophs; Class: multicellular heterotrophs with wings, feathers, a beak, feet made to grip; Genus: multicellular heterotrophs with wings, feathers, feet made to grip, similar body shape, tufts of feathers, hooked beak, flat, round face, forward facing eyes, and talons)*

Extend Challenge students to describe some shared characteristics of humans. *(Samples: multicellular heterotroph, walks on two legs, has hair, opposable thumb, stands upright)* **learning modality: visual**

Building Inquiry Skills: Making Models

Materials *posterboard or other heavyweight paper, pen, ruler, colored pencils, glue, scissors, nature magazines, dictionaries*

Time 50 minutes

Direct students to create model classification charts for their pets similar to the one shown in Figure 4 for the owl. Provide students with lists of the class, order, and family of several common pets, and encourage them to find the genus and species. Some students might like to attach pictures of their pets at the species level. **learning modality: visual**

Sharpen your Skills

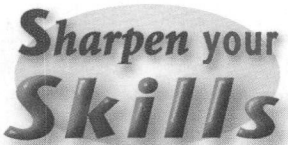

Observing **ACTIVITY**

Test your observational skills using Figure 4. Look carefully at the organisms pictured together at the kingdom level. Make a list of the characteristics that the organisms share. Then make two more lists of shared characteristics—one for the organisms at the class level and the other for those at the genus level. How does the number of characteristics on your lists change at each level?

The Seven Levels of Classification Modern biologists classify organisms into the seven levels shown in Figure 4. Of course, organisms are not grouped by where they live but rather by their shared characteristics. First an organism is placed in a broad group, which in turn is divided into more specific groups.

A kingdom is the broadest level of organization. Within a kingdom, there are phyla (FY luh) (singular *phylum*). Within each phylum are classes. Each class is divided into orders. Each order contains families, and each family contains at least one genus. Finally, within a genus, there are species. The more classification levels that two organisms share, the more characteristics they have in common.

Classifying an Owl Take a closer look at Figure 4 to see how the levels of classification apply to the great horned owl, a member of the animal kingdom. Look at the top row of the figure. As you can see, a wide variety of organisms also belong to the animal kingdom. Now, look at the phylum, class, and order levels. Notice that as you move down the levels in the figure, there are fewer kinds of organisms in each group. More importantly, the organisms in each group look similar and have more in common with one another. For example, the class Aves includes all birds, while the order Strigiformes includes only owls. Different owls have more in common with each other than they do with other birds.

☑ *Checkpoint* **List the seven levels of classification from the broadest to the most specific.**

Using the Classification System

You may be wondering why you should care about taxonomy. Suppose you wake up and feel something tickling your ankle. You fling back the covers and stare at a tiny creature crouching in the sheets by your right foot. Although it's only the size of a small melon seed, you don't like the looks of its two claws waving at you. Then, in a flash, it's gone—darting off under the safety of your covers.

How could you learn the identity of the organism that woke you? One way to identify it would be to use a field guide. Field guides are books with illustrations that highlight differences between similar-looking organisms.

Another tool you could use to identify the organism is called a taxonomic key. A **taxonomic key** is a series of paired statements that describe the physical characteristics of different organisms.

Background

Facts and Figures The name *horned owl* can refer to any owl in the genus *Bubo*, but usually relates to the great horned owl (*Bubo virginianis*) of the Americas. The great horned owl ranges from the Arctic to the Strait of Magellan at the tip of South America. It is adapted to deserts and forests, and migrates only when food is scarce.

Great horned owls can be more than 60 cm long and weigh as much as 2 kilos. The female can have a wingspan of 200 cm. These owls are often called "tigers of the sky," because they are so large and aggressive. They have been known to evict eagles from their nests. Although great horned owls prefer prey like rabbits, they are one of the few predators that prey on skunks.

Kingdom Animalia

Phylum Chordata

Class Aves

Order Strigiformes

Family Strigidae

Genus *Bubo*

Species *Bubo virginianus*

Figure 4 Scientists use seven levels to classify organisms such as the great horned owl. Notice that, as you move down the levels, the number of organisms decreases. The organisms at lower levels share more characteristics with each other. *Interpreting Diagrams* How many levels do a robin and the great horned owl share?

Chapter 6 **187**

Using the Visuals: Figure 5

Have students work in groups to study Figure 5 on page 188. Have them use the taxonomic key to draw a picture of each organism listed. When students have drawn all the organisms, have groups compare their drawings for each type. The reporter from each group should explain how the group used the key to determine what features each should have. Ask: **What other information did you need to draw your pictures but could not find in the taxonomic key?** *(Answers will vary, but some students may want to know what color the organisms are, what kind of legs they have, or where their eyes are located.)* Ask students: **Are the characteristics that are not mentioned in the key necessary to identify an organism? Explain.** *(No, the information in the key is enough to identify it even if the key does not describe everything about it.)* **cooperative learning**

Media and Technology

 Transparencies "Seven Levels of Classification," Transparency 23

Answers to Self-Assessment

Caption Question

Figure 4 The robin and the great horned owl share three levels: kingdom, phylum, and class.

☑ *Checkpoint*

kingdom, phylum, class, order, family, genus, species

Ongoing Assessment

Skills Check Ask students to tell you which classification level will always have the greatest number of organisms and which level will always have the smallest number and why. *(Kingdom, species; because kingdom contains all organisms in that category and species is a specific organism)*

3 Assess

Section 1 Review Answers

1. Scientists classify living things into groups because it makes it easier for the scientists to study them.

2. An organism's evolutionary history determines how it is classified.

3. Linnaeus devised the naming system, binomial nomenclature, which classifies organisms into genus and species.

4. Sample taxonomic key:

Step 1	
1a. Fruit is red	Go to Step 2.
1b. Fruit is not red	Go to Step 3.
Step 2	
2a. Fruit has smooth skin with seeds inside	Apple
2b. Fruit has little seeds scattered over the skin	Strawberry
Step 3	
3a. Fruit is yellow, elongated	Banana
3b. Fruit is orange, round	Orange

Science at Home

Remind students to identify the criteria used to classify kitchen objects in their houses. Families may have organized items by size, by function, or by location of use. Ask students whether their family members agreed with their classification systems.

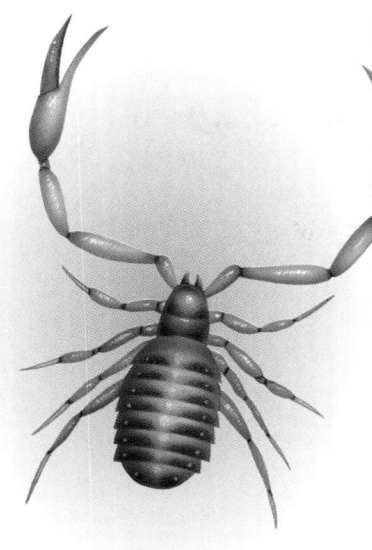

Figure 5 A taxonomic key is a series of paired statements that describe the physical characteristics of different organisms. There are six pairs of statements in this key. *Drawing Conclusions What is the identity of the organism shown in the picture?*

Taxonomic Key

Step 1	
1a. Has 8 legs	Go to Step 2.
1b. Has more than 8 legs	Go to Step 3.
Step 2	
2a. Has one oval-shaped body region	Go to Step 4.
2b. Has two body regions	Go to Step 5.
Step 3	
3a. Has one pair of legs on each body segment	Centipede
3b. Has two pairs of legs on each body segment	Millipede
Step 4	
4a. Is less than 1 millimeter long	Mite
4b. Is more than 1 millimeter long	Tick
Step 5	
5a. Has clawlike pincers	Go to Step 6.
5b. Has no clawlike pincers	Spider
Step 6	
6a. Has a long tail with a stinger	Scorpion
6b. Has no tail or stinger	Pseudoscorpion

The taxonomic key in Figure 5 can help you identify the organism in your bed. First, read the paired statements numbered 1a and 1b. Notice that the two statements are opposites. Decide which of the two statements applies to the organism. Then, follow the direction at the end of that statement. For example, if the organism has 8 legs, follow the direction at the end of statement 1a, which says "Go to Step 2." Continue this process until you learn the identity of the organism.

Section 1 Review

1. Why is it important for biologists to classify organisms into groups?

2. How is an organism's evolutionary history related to the way in which it is classified?

3. Explain Linnaeus's contribution to taxonomy.

4. **Thinking Critically** **Applying Concepts** Create a taxonomic key that could help identify a piece of fruit as either an apple, an orange, a strawberry, or a banana.

Science at Home

Kitchen Classification With a family member, go on a "classification hunt" in the kitchen. Look in your cabinets, refrigerator, and drawers to discover what classification systems your family uses to organize items. Discuss the advantages of organizing items in your kitchen in the way that you do. Then explain to your family member the importance of classification in biology.

Performance Assessment

Skills Check Write this list on the board: *bed, dining table, recliner, dresser, sofa, cabinet, bookshelf.* Instruct students to create a seven-level classification system that includes all of these items. (*Sample: Kingdom Furniture, Phylum Household Furniture, Class Legged, Order Seats, Family Individual, Genus Chair, Species Recliner*)

Program Resources

◆ **Unit 2 Resources** 6-1 Review and Reinforce, p. 11; 6-2 Enrich, p. 12

Media and Technology

Interactive Student Tutorial CD-ROM Chapter 6

Answers to Self-Assessment

Caption Question
Figure 5 A pseudoscorpion

DISCOVER •••••••••••••••••••••••••••••••• ACTIVITY ••••

Which Organism Goes Where?

1.  Your teacher will give you some organisms to observe. Two of the organisms are classified in the same kingdom.

2. Observe the organisms. Decide which organisms might belong in the same kingdom. Write the reasons for your decision. Wash your hands after handling the organisms.

3. Discuss your decision and reasoning with your classmates.

Think It Over
Forming Operational Definitions What characteristics do you think define the kingdom into which you placed the two organisms?

When Linnaeus developed his system of classification, there were two kingdoms: plant and animal. But, the use of the microscope led to the discovery of new organisms and the identification of differences among cells. A two-kingdom system was no longer useful.

Until recently, most scientists classified organisms into five kingdoms, with all bacteria in a single kingdom called Monerans. **Today, the system of classification includes six kingdoms: archaebacteria, eubacteria, protists, fungi, plants, and animals.** Organisms are placed into kingdoms based on their type of cells, their ability to make food, and the number of cells in their bodies.

Archaebacteria

In 1983, scientists took a water sample from a spot deep in the Pacific Ocean where hot gases and molten rock boiled into the ocean from Earth's interior. To their surprise, they discovered some unicellular organisms in the water sample. Today, scientists classify these tiny organisms in a kingdom called Archaebacteria (ahr kee bak TEER ee uh), which means "ancient bacteria." Archaebacteria already existed on Earth for billions of years before dinosaurs appeared. Scientists think that today's archaebacteria might resemble some of Earth's early life forms.

> **GUIDE FOR READING**
>
> ◆ What are the six kingdoms into which all organisms are grouped?
>
> *Reading Tip* Before you read the section, make a list of the headings. As you read, list the characteristics of organisms in each kingdom.

Figure 6 Heat-loving archaebacteria thrive in this hot spring in Yellowstone National Park.

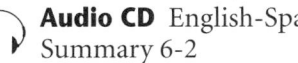
189

READING STRATEGIES

Reading Tip Provide each student with six note cards. Instruct students to write a kingdom name on one side of each card. As students read the section, have them list, on the opposite side of each card, the characteristics of organisms in the kingdom. Then have partners take turns using their sets of note cards as flashcards for testing their knowledge about the six kingdoms.

Program Resources

◆ **Unit 2 Resources** 6-2 Lesson Plan, p. 13; 6-2 Section Summary, p. 14

Media and Technology

🎧 **Audio CD** English-Spanish Summary 6-2

SECTION
2 The Six Kingdoms

Objective

After completing the lesson, students will be able to
◆ name and describe the six kingdoms into which all organisms are grouped.

1 Engage/Explore

Activating Prior Knowledge

Have students list different genres of movies. (*Sample: action, mystery, comedy, romance, western, foreign*) Invite them to consider how using these categories helps them describe movies.

•••••••• DISCOVER ••••••••

Skills Focus classifying
Materials *mushroom, small green plant, a worm or insect, sea animal such as an urchin, anemone, or cultivated coral*
Time 15 minutes
Tips Tropical fish stores carry coral and sea animals. Caution students to be careful handling the animals and to wash their hands after the activity.
Expected Outcome Students may place all the organisms in the same kingdom. Biologists classify the sea animal and the worm or insect in the same kingdom.
Think It Over Defining characteristics will vary but may focus on movement. Discuss features biologists use to classify living things such as cell type, food-making ability, and number of cells.

2 Facilitate

Archaebacteria

Language Arts Connection

Ask: **Why do you think archaebacteria have that name?** (*The name means "ancient bacteria," and these bacteria may be among the earliest life forms.*)
learning modality: verbal

Eubacteria

Real-Life Learning

Materials *plastic bucket* 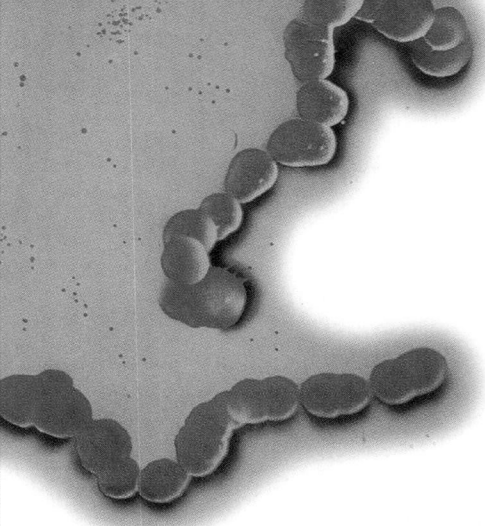 *with dilute suspension of blue tempera and water, soap, paper towels, plastic dropcloth*

Time 30 minutes

Direct students to dip their hands in the bucket of diluted tempera and let them air-dry. Then students should close their eyes and wash their hands without looking. Students should see if they have removed all the "bacteria." Ask: **What can you infer about washing your hands from this experiment?** *(If blue stain remains on their hands, they have not removed all the bacteria.)* **learning modality: kinesthetic**

Protists

Cultural Diversity

In Japan, different seaweeds are used as sources of nutrition. For example, nori, wakame, kombu, and laver are used in soups, salads, tea, and sushi. **learning modality: verbal**

Fungi

Real-Life Learning

Encourage students to contact local organic gardening centers to find out more about the role of fungi in the decay process in a compost pile. **learning modality: verbal**

Plants

Demonstration

Soak a light green leaf in alcohol for 24 hours. Dry the leaf, place it in a glass dish, and cover it with iodine. Explain that iodine darkens when it contacts starch, a type of food. Have students examine the leaf. Ask: **What can you conclude about plants from this demonstration?** *(They have starch in their leaves.)* **How did it get there?** *(The plant made it using the sun's energy, carbon dioxide, and water.)* **limited English proficiency**

Figure 7 Most eubacteria are helpful. However, these eubacteria are *Streptococci,* which can give you strep throat! *Classifying What characteristics do eubacteria share?*

Archaebacteria can be either autotrophic or heterotrophic. Some live on the ocean floor, some in salty water, and some in hot springs. Don't be alarmed, but some even live inside you.

Archaebacteria are prokaryotes. As you read in Chapter 1, prokaryotes are organisms whose cells lack a nucleus. In prokaryotes, nucleic acids—the chemical instructions that direct the cell's activities—are not contained within a nucleus.

Eubacteria

What do the bacteria that produce yogurt have in common with the bacteria that give you strep throat? They both belong to the kingdom known as Eubacteria (yoo bak TEER ee uh). Like archaebacteria, eubacteria are unicellular prokaryotes. And like archaebacteria, some eubacteria are autotrophs while others are heterotrophs. Eubacteria are classified in their own kingdom, however, because their chemical makeup is different from that of archaebacteria. You will learn more about eubacteria in the next section.

☑ *Checkpoint* How are eubacteria similar to archaebacteria? How are they different?

Protists

Have you ever walked along a beach scattered with dark clumps of seaweed? The tangled piles of seaweed are classified in the same kingdom as the unicellular organism in Figure 8. Both are protists (PROH tists). The protist kingdom is sometimes called the "odds and ends" kingdom because its organisms are very different from one another. For example, some protists are autotrophs, while others are heterotrophs. Also, although most protists are unicellular, some, such as the organisms that are commonly called seaweeds, are multicellular.

You may be wondering why those protists that are unicellular are not classified in one of the kingdoms of bacteria. It is because, unlike bacteria, protists are eukaryotes—organisms with cells that contain nuclei.

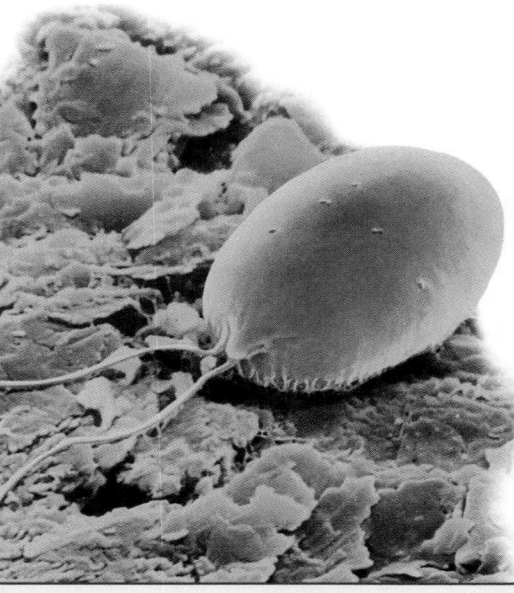

Figure 8 The protist kingdom contains diverse organisms. This unicellular green protist, which lives in fresh water, is called *Chlamydomonas.*

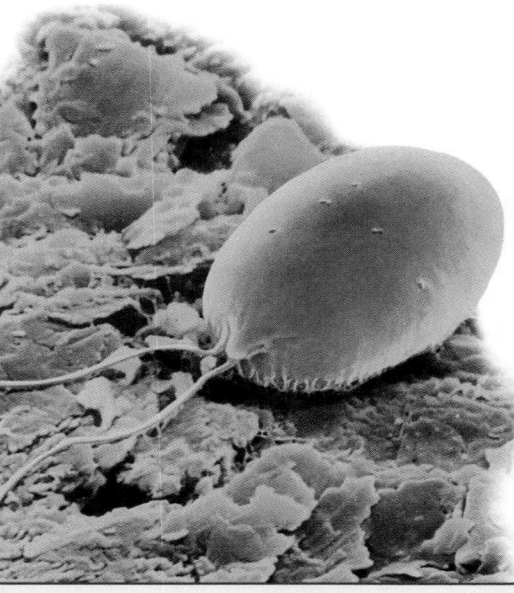

Background

History of Science The terms prokaryotic and eukaryotic were first used by Eduoard Chatton, a French marine biologist. In 1937, he published an article in which he suggested the use of *procariotique* for organisms that were then classified as bacteria and blue-green algae. He derived this term from the Greek prefix *pro-,* which means "before," and *karyon,* which means "kernel," or "nucleus."

Prokaryotes are organisms that are similar to more primitive life forms that existed before the evolution of the nucleus. Chatton suggested the use of *eucariotique* for organisms whose cells contain a nucleus. The Greek prefix *eu-* means "true." So eukaryotes are organisms whose cells contain a true nucleus, as opposed to genetic material in the cytoplasm.

Fungi

If you have ever seen mushrooms, you have seen fungi (FUN jy). Mushrooms, molds, and mildew are all fungi. Most fungi are multicellular eukaryotes. A few, such as yeast, are unicellular eukaryotes. Fungi are found almost everywhere on land, but only a few live in fresh water. All fungi are heterotrophs. Most fungi feed on dead or decaying organisms. The cuplike fungus you see in Figure 9 obtains its food from the parts of plants that are decaying in the soil.

Plants

Dandelions on a lawn, mosses in a forest, and tomatoes in a garden are familiar kinds of plants. All plants are multicellular eukaryotes. In addition, plants are autotrophs that make their own food. Without plants, life on Earth would not exist. Plants feed almost all of the heterotrophs on Earth. The plant kingdom includes a variety of organisms. Some plants produce flowers, while others do not. Some plants, such as giant sequoia trees, can grow very tall. Others, like mosses, never grow taller than a few centimeters.

Animals

A dog, a flea on the dog's ear, and a rabbit the dog chases have much in common because all are animals. All animals are multicellular eukaryotes. In addition, all animals are heterotrophs. Animals have different adaptations that allow them to locate food, capture it, eat it, and digest it. You will learn more about these adaptations in Chapters 10 through 14 of this book. Members of the animal kingdom are found in diverse environments on Earth.

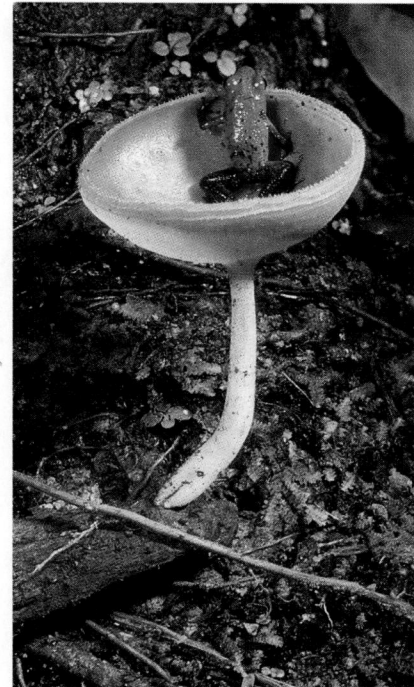

Figure 9 The animal you see peeking out of this cuplike fungus is a poison arrow frog. These organisms live in the forests of Central America.
Interpreting Photographs Which organisms in the photograph are heterotrophs?

Section 2 Review

1. List the six kingdoms into which all organisms are classified.
2. Which two kingdoms include only prokaryotes?
3. Which kingdoms include only heterotrophs?
4. **Thinking Critically Classifying** In a rain forest, you see an unfamiliar green organism. As you watch, an ant walks onto one of its cuplike leaves. The leaf closes and traps the ant. Do you have enough information to classify this organism? Why or why not?

Check Your Progress

CHAPTER PROJECT

By now, you should have a draft of the questions you will ask in your survey. Have your teacher review your questions. (*Hint*: Design the questionnaire so that you can easily record and tally the responses. Test your survey on a friend to make sure the questions are clear.)

Program Resources

◆ **Unit 2 Resources** 6-2 Review and Reinforce, p. 15; 6-2 Enrich, p. 16

Answers to Self-Assessment

Caption Questions

Figure 7 Eubacteria are unicellular prokaryotes that are either autotrophs or heterotrophs.
Figure 9 Both the frog and the fungus are heterotrophs.

☑ *Checkpoint*

Both are unicellular prokaryotes that are either autotrophs or heterotrophs. Their chemical makeups differ.

Animals

Building Inquiry Skills: Classifying

Materials *prepared slides of different bacteria in plant or animal cells, microscopes* **ACTIVITY**
Time 20 minutes

Demonstrate how to use a microscope, and direct students to examine the slides and sketch the cells. Then have them decide which cells are bacteria and which are plant or animal. (*Cells with a nucleus are animals or plants, those without are bacteria.*) **learning modality: visual**

3 Assess

Section 2 Review Answers

1. Archaebacteria, eubacteria, protists, fungi, plants, animals
2. Archaebacteria and eubacteria
3. Fungi and animals
4. Some kingdoms can be eliminated, but there is not enough information to make a definite identification. The organism is multicellular, so it is not an archaebacteria or a eubacteria. It is green, so it may be an autotroph, but because it is trapping food, it may be a heterotroph. So it might be a plant or an animal or a multicellular protist because it is in a moist environment.

Check Your Progress

CHAPTER PROJECT

Make sure students' survey questions will elicit relevant information. Encourage them to ask questions requiring yes/no or numerical answers. For other questions, students should devise a tally system to record the most common responses. Encourage students to test and revise the questions.

Performance Assessment

Drawing Invite students to sketch a member of each kingdom and describe the characteristics that place it in that kingdom.

 Students can save their sketches in their portfolios.

191

SECTION 3 Bacteria

Objectives

After completing the lesson, students will be able to

◆ describe ways in which bacteria cells are different from all other organisms' cells;

◆ name the two kingdoms of bacteria, and explain how bacteria reproduce and survive;

◆ list positive roles that bacteria play in people's lives.

Key Terms flagellum, binary fission, asexual reproduction, sexual reproduction, conjugation, endospore, decomposer, infectious disease, toxin, antibiotic

1 Engage/Explore

Activating Prior Knowledge

Display samples of yogurt and Swiss cheese. Ask students what these foods have in common, then record their responses on the board. Tell students that these products are all produced with the help of certain kinds of bacteria. Ask: **What other foods can you think of that might be prepared with the aid of bacteria?** *(Sample: Buttermilk, sauerkraut, sour cream)*

Materials *paper cups; dried lima, kidney, or navy beans*

Time 20 minutes

Tips Remind students to calculate the elapsed time based on the fact that it takes 20 minutes for bacteria to divide.

Expected Outcome Cup 1–1 bean; Cup 2–2 beans; Cup 3–4 beans; Cup 4–8 beans; Cup 5–16 beans; Cup 6–32 beans; Cup 7–64 beans; Cup 8–128 beans. There are 128 cells in the eighth generation. Two hours and twenty minutes have passed since there was only 1 bacterium.

Think It Over Students will probably infer that the numbers increase rapidly because each bacterium can double every 20 minutes.

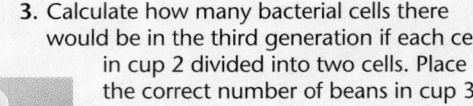

How Fast Do Bacteria Multiply?

1. Your teacher will give you some beans and paper cups. Number the cups 1 through 8. Each bean will represent a bacterial cell.

2. Put one bean into cup 1 to represent the first generation of bacteria. Approximately every 20 minutes, a bacterial cell reproduces by dividing into two cells. Put two beans into cup 2 to represent the second generation of bacteria.

3. Calculate how many bacterial cells there would be in the third generation if each cell in cup 2 divided into two cells. Place the correct number of beans in cup 3.

4. Repeat Step 3 five more times. All the cups should now contain beans. How many cells are in the eighth generation? How much time has elapsed since the first generation?

Think It Over

Inferring Based on this activity, explain why the number of bacteria can increase rapidly in a short period of time.

GUIDE FOR READING

◆ How are the cells of bacteria different from those of all other organisms?

◆ What roles do bacteria play in people's lives?

Reading Tip Before you read, make a list of the boldfaced vocabulary words in the section. Predict the meaning of each word. As you read, check your predictions.

You may not know it, but seconds after you were born, tiny organisms surrounded and invaded your body. Today, millions of these organisms coat your skin. As you read this page, they swarm inside your nose, throat, and mouth. In fact, there are more of these organisms living in your mouth than there are people who are living on Earth. You don't see or feel these organisms because they are very small. But you cannot escape them. They are found nearly everywhere on Earth—in soil, rocks, Arctic ice, volcanoes, and in all living things. These organisms are bacteria.

The Bacterial Cell

Although there are many bacteria on Earth, they were not discovered until the late 1600s. In Chapter 1 you read about Anton van Leeuwenhoek, who built microscopes as a hobby. One day, while he was using one of his microscopes to look at scrapings from his teeth, he saw some tiny organisms in the sample. However, because his microscopes were not very powerful, Leeuwenhoek could not see any details inside these tiny organisms.

◀ **Bacteria on the surface of a human tooth**

READING STRATEGIES

Reading Tip Suggest that students create charts with the headings *Word, What I Think It Means*, and *What It Means* on which to record boldface words and make their predictions. Remind students to study the parts of each word and to think of words they already know that have the same word roots or parts. For example, students may predict that binary fission has something to do with two parts.

Study and Comprehension As students read, remind them of these strategies for breaking down information:

◆ Read the title, headings, subheadings, and captions to get an overview.

◆ Read one section of text at a time, line by line. Reread parts you did not understand fully.

◆ Jot down unfamiliar words. Try to determine the meanings or look them up.

If Leeuwenhoek had owned one of the high-powered microscopes in use today, he would have seen the single-celled organisms that are known as **bacteria** (singular *bacterium*) in detail. As you learned in Section 2, the cells of bacteria differ from the cells of other organisms in many ways. **Bacteria are prokaryotes. The genetic material in their cells is not contained in a nucleus.** In addition to lacking a nucleus, the cells of prokaryotes also lack many other structures that are found in the cells of eukaryotes. However, regardless of the structure of their cells, prokaryotes accomplish all tasks necessary for life. That is, each bacterial cell uses energy, grows and develops, responds to its surroundings, and reproduces.

Cell Shapes If you were to look at bacterial cells under a microscope, you would notice that bacterial cells have one of three basic shapes: spherical, rodlike, or spiral shaped. The shape of a bacterial cell helps scientists identify the type of bacteria. For example, bacteria that cause strep throat are spherical. Figure 10 shows the different shapes of bacterial cells.

Cell Structures The shape of a bacterial cell is determined by the chemical makeup of its outermost structure—the cell wall. Cell walls surround most bacterial cells. A bacterium's rigid cell wall helps to protect the cell.

Bacterial cells contain many of the other structures you learned about in Chapter 1. Inside the cell wall is the cell membrane, which controls what materials pass into and out of the cell. Inside the cell membrane, the cytoplasm contains a gel-like material. Ribosomes, the sites where proteins are produced, are located in the cytoplasm. The cell's genetic material, which looks like a thick, tangled string, is also located in the cytoplasm. If you could untangle this genetic material, you would see that it forms a circular shape. The genetic material contains the instructions for all the cell's functions, such as how to produce proteins on the ribosomes.

Figure 10 Bacteria have three basic shapes. **A.** Like the bacteria that cause strep throat, these *Staphylococcus aureus* bacteria are spherical. They represent over 30 percent of the bacteria that live on your skin. **B.** *Escherichia coli* bacteria have rodlike shapes. These bacteria are found in your intestines. **C.** *Borrelia burgdorferi* bacteria, which cause Lyme disease, are spiral-shaped.

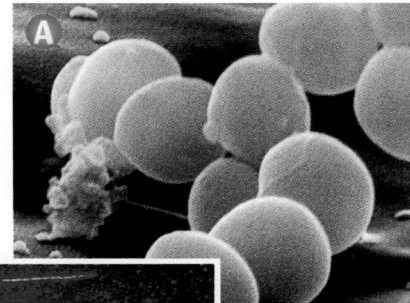

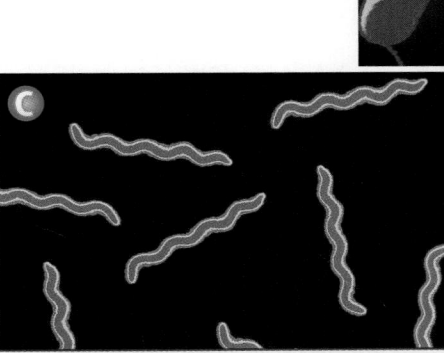

Chapter 6 **193**

Program Resources

◆ **Unit 2 Resources** 6-3 Lesson Plan, p. 17; 6-3 Section Summary, p. 18

Media and Technology

Audio CD English-Spanish Summary 6-3

2 Facilitate

The Bacterial Cell

Building Inquiry Skills: Comparing and Contrasting

Write the terms *prokaryote* and *eukaryote* on the board and invite students to recall their meanings. Challenge them to explain the differences and similarities between the two types of cells. (*Both have genetic material and reproduce by cell division. Prokaryotes do not have a nucleus or other cell structures.*)
learning modality: verbal

Building Inquiry Skills: Classifying

Materials *light microscope, prepared slides of cocci, bacilli, and spirilla*
Time 20 minutes
Tips Provide students with the materials and tell them they are going to observe and identify the three main bacterial cell shapes. As students view the various slides, have them sketch what they observe. Have pairs of students compare sketches and classify the bacteria as rod-shaped (*bacilli*), spherical (*cocci*), or spiral-shaped (*spirilla*). **learning modality: visual**

Using the Visuals: Figure 10

As students compare the bacteria shown, ask: **How many cells does each bacterium have?** (*one*) Point out to students that some of the bacteria in the picture are dividing. Remind students that bacteria are unicellular, and that each image shows several bacteria.
learning modality: visual

Ongoing Assessment

Writing Have students write sentences explaining in their own words the function of each of these structures: cell wall, cell membrane, ribosome, cytoplasm.

Two Kingdoms of Bacteria

Addressing Naive Conceptions

Students who are accustomed to classifying organisms as plants or animals may need extra help to understand that bacteria are not animals or plants. Ask students: **What do bacteria have in common with animals?** *(They are alive, some are heterotrophs.)* **How are they different?** *(Bacteria are one-celled organisms, while animals have many cells that are highly organized.)* **learning modality: verbal**

Including All Students

Students just learning English may have difficulty with the names of the two kingdoms, Archaebacteria and Eubacteria. Have students look up the definitions of the prefixes *archaeo-* (ancient) and *eu-* (good or true). Ask them to find other words that begin with each prefix used in the same sense *(archaeology, archaeopteryx, eukaryote, eulogy, euphony, euphoria)* **learning modality: verbal**

Integrating Earth Science

Ask students: **Why do scientists think the bacteria that originally began to alter Earth's atmosphere were similar to autotrophic eubacteria?** *(To alter the atmosphere, the first organisms had to produce oxygen.)* **Why do scientists think the first life forms on Earth were similar to archaebacteria?** *(The conditions on ancient Earth may have been too extreme for ordinary bacteria to survive.)* **learning modality: verbal**

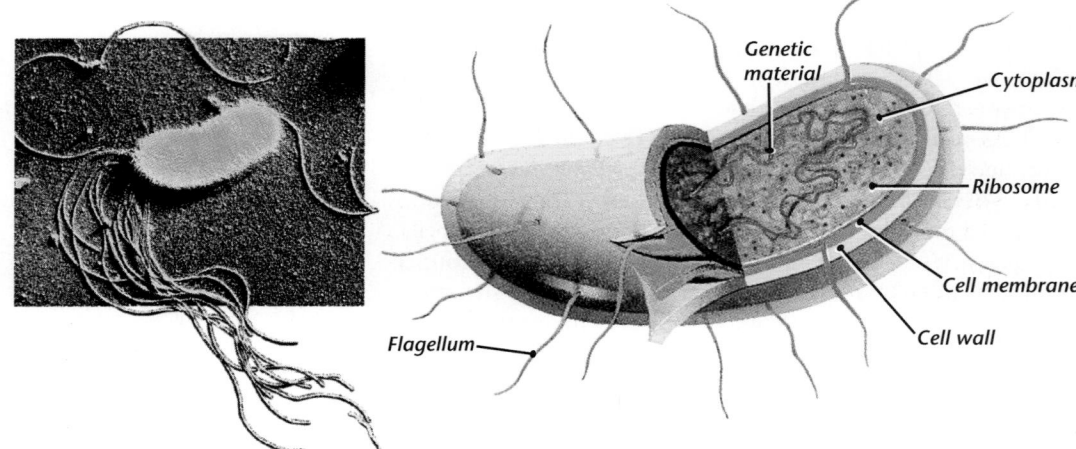

Figure 11 The diagram shows the structures found in a typical bacterial cell. *Interpreting Photographs Which structures can you locate in the photograph of the bacterium? What roles do these structures play?*

You can see the cell wall, cytoplasm, ribosomes, and genetic material in the bacterial cell in Figure 11. Another structure you see is a flagellum. A **flagellum** (fluh JEL um) (plural *flagella*) is a long, whiplike structure that extends from the cell membrane and passes out through the cell wall. A flagellum helps a cell to move by spinning in place like a propeller. A bacterial cell can have many flagella, one, or none. Most bacteria that do not have flagella cannot move on their own. Instead, they depend on air, water currents, clothing, and other objects to carry them.

✓ *Checkpoint* *What structure determines the shape of a bacterial cell?*

Two Kingdoms of Bacteria

Until recently, biologists grouped all bacteria together in a single kingdom called Monerans on the basis of their similar cellular structure. However, although all bacteria look similar, some differ chemically. After analyzing the chemical differences, scientists have reclassified bacteria into two separate kingdoms—archaebacteria and eubacteria.

Archaebacteria Many archaebacteria live in extreme environments. Some thrive in hot springs, where the water can be as hot as 110°C. Others live in environments that are as acidic as lemon juice. Archaebacteria also live in the intestines of animals, the mud in swamps, and in sewage. These bacteria produce the foul odors that you may associate with these places.

Eubacteria Unlike archaebacteria, most eubacteria do not live in extreme environments. However, they live everywhere else. For example, millions of eubacteria live on and in your body. Eubacteria coat your skin and swarm in your nose. Don't be alarmed. Most of them are either useful or harmless to you.

Background

Integrating Science Because of the large number of bacteria with different characteristics, scientists have changed the classifications of bacteria several times. Although bacteria-like organisms are believed to be the earliest life forms, the evolutionary relationships among bacteria have been very difficult to study, partly because the fossil record of bacteria is difficult to analyze.

A new approach to classification of bacteria was developed in the 1980s, based on the amount of time that has passed since two organisms developed from a common ancestor. Scientists are now able to classify bacteria according to how closely they are related. Based on these studies, scientists now believe that eubacteria and archaebacteria evolved from a common ancestor.

Eubacteria help maintain some of Earth's physical conditions and thus help other organisms to survive. For example, some eubacteria are autotrophs that float near the surfaces of Earth's waters. These bacteria use the sun's energy to produce food and oxygen. Scientists think that billions of years ago autotrophic bacteria were responsible for adding oxygen to Earth's atmosphere. Today, the distant offspring of those bacteria help to keep Earth's current level of oxygen at about 20 percent.

Reproduction in Bacteria

When bacteria have plenty of food, the right temperature, and other suitable conditions, they thrive and reproduce frequently. Under these ideal conditions, some bacteria can reproduce as often as once every 20 minutes. Fortunately, growing conditions for bacteria are rarely ideal. Otherwise, there would soon be no room on Earth for other organisms!

Asexual Reproduction Bacteria reproduce by **binary fission**, a process in which one cell divides to form two identical cells. Binary fission is a form of **asexual reproduction**. Asexual reproduction is a reproductive process that involves only one parent and produces offspring that are identical to the parent. In binary fission, the cell first duplicates its genetic material and then divides into two separate cells. Each new cell gets its own complete copy of the parent cell's genetic material as well as some of the parent's ribosomes and cytoplasm. Figure 12 shows a parent cell forming two new cells by binary fission.

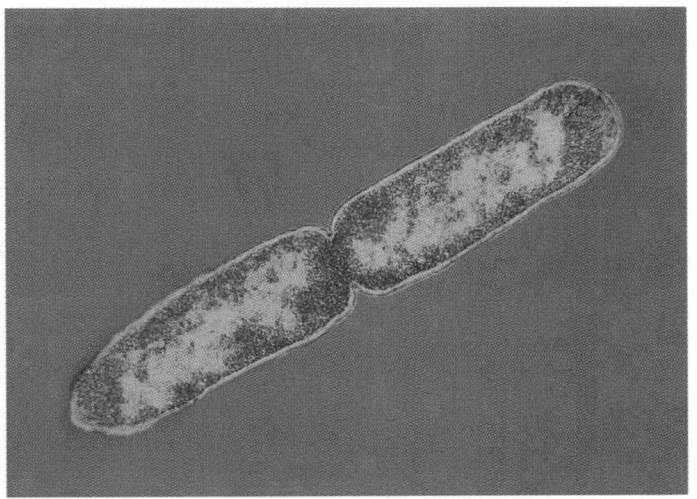

Figure 12 Bacteria, such as this *Escherichia coli,* reproduce by binary fission. Each new cell is identical to the parent cell.

Sharpen your Skills

Graphing ACTIVITY

Suppose a bacterium reproduces by binary fission every 20 minutes. The new cells reproduce at the same rate. The table shows how many bacteria there would be each hour over a 5-hour period.

Bacterial Reproduction	
Time	**Number of Bacteria**
Start	1
1 hour	8
2 hours	64
3 hours	512
4 hours	4,096
5 hours	32,768

Construct a line graph using the information in the table. Plot time on the horizontal axis and the number of bacteria on the vertical axis. Use the graph to explain why the number of bacteria grows more rapidly over time.

Reproduction in Bacteria

Sharpen your Skills

Graphing

Materials *graph paper and pencil* **ACTIVITY**
Time 20 minutes
Tips Have students predict how their line graphs will look after they have finished plotting data.
Expected Outcome Students' graphs should show that bacterial numbers remain relatively steady for almost 3 hours. The numbers increase slightly between 3 and 4 hours, then increase sharply because the bacteria are reproducing exponentially.
Extend Challenge students to calculate the number of bacteria there would be after 24 hours. (8^{24}, *or approximately* 4.722×10^{21}) **learning modality: logical/mathematical**

Using the Visuals: Figures 12 and 13

As students study the forms of bacterial reproduction shown in both figures, ask: **What main difference can you see between conjugation and binary fission?** *(Binary fission—only one cell is involved; conjugation—two cells are involved.)* Then ask: **How does conjugation result in the production of new bacteria?** *(After conjugation, the original cells have new combinations of genetic material.)* **learning modality: visual**

Answers to Self-Assessment

Caption Question
Figure 11 Flagellum—helps the bacterium move. Cell wall—protects bacterium.

 Checkpoint
The cell wall determines the shape.

Ongoing Assessment

Skills Check Have students create Venn diagrams that compare and contrast archaebacteria and eubacteria. *Portfolio* Students can save their diagrams in their portfolios.

Reproduction in Bacteria, continued

Building Inquiry Skills: Inferring

Allow students to form small groups and discuss the possible evolutionary advantage of different individuals or populations of bacteria exchanging genetic information. *(By exchanging genetic information, bacteria may find better combinations that will enhance survival or increase reproductive success.)*
learning modality: logical/ mathematical

Survival Needs

Building Inquiry Skills: Designing Experiments

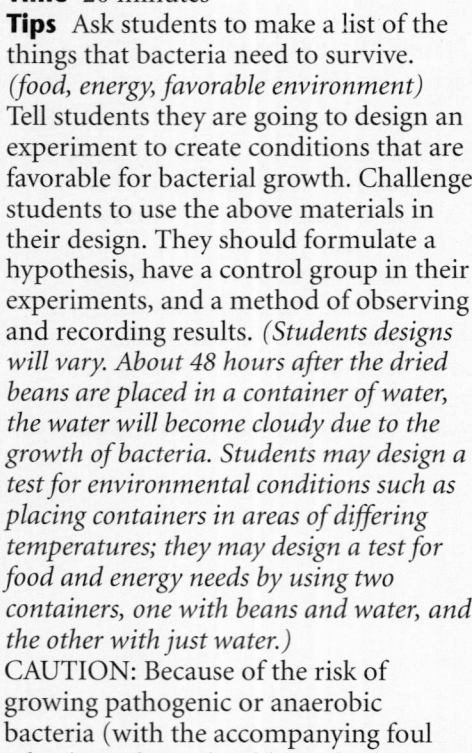

Materials *beakers, dried beans, water*
Time 20 minutes
Tips Ask students to make a list of the things that bacteria need to survive. *(food, energy, favorable environment)* Tell students they are going to design an experiment to create conditions that are favorable for bacterial growth. Challenge students to use the above materials in their design. They should formulate a hypothesis, have a control group in their experiments, and a method of observing and recording results. *(Students designs will vary. About 48 hours after the dried beans are placed in a container of water, the water will become cloudy due to the growth of bacteria. Students may design a test for environmental conditions such as placing containers in areas of differing temperatures; they may design a test for food and energy needs by using two containers, one with beans and water, and the other with just water.)*
CAUTION: Because of the risk of growing pathogenic or anaerobic bacteria (with the accompanying foul odors), students should not do the experiment. You may wish to demonstrate an experimental design using sealed petri dishes. Be sure to follow district and state guidelines for disposing of the petri dishes.

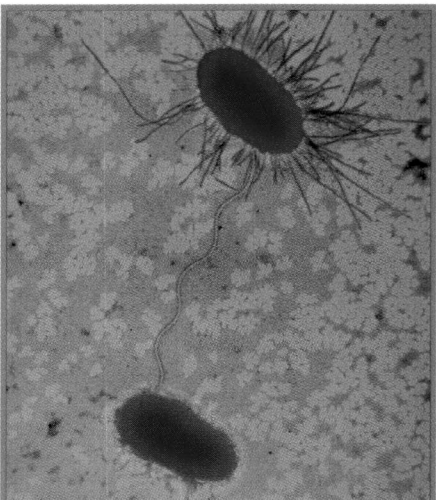

Figure 13 In conjugation, one bacterium transfers some of its genetic material into another bacterium. *Observing What structure allows the cells to transfer genetic material?*

Sexual Reproduction Some bacteria, such as the ones in Figure 13, may at times undergo a simple form of sexual reproduction called conjugation. **Sexual reproduction** involves two parents who combine their genetic material to produce a new organism, which differs from both parents. During **conjugation** (kahn juh GAY shun), one bacterium transfers some of its genetic material into another bacterial cell through a thin, threadlike bridge that joins the two cells. After the transfer, the cells separate.

Conjugation results in bacteria with new combinations of genetic material. When these bacteria divide by binary fission, the new genetic material passes to the new cells. Conjugation does not increase the number of bacteria. However, it does result in the production of new bacteria, which are genetically different than the parent cells.

Survival Needs

From the bacteria that live inside the craters of active volcanoes to those that live in the pores of your skin, all bacteria need certain things to survive. Bacteria must have a source of food, a way of breaking down the food to release the food's energy, and survival techniques when conditions in their surroundings become unfavorable.

Obtaining Food Some bacteria are autotrophs and make their own food. Autotrophic bacteria make food in one of two ways. Some autotrophic bacteria make food by capturing and using the sun's energy as plants do. Other autotrophic bacteria, such as those that live deep in the ocean, do not use the sun's energy. Instead, these bacteria use the energy from chemical substances in their environment to make their food.

Some bacteria are heterotrophs that obtain food by consuming autotrophs or other heterotrophs. Heterotrophic bacteria may consume a variety of foods—from milk and meat, which you might also eat, to the decaying leaves on a forest floor.

Respiration Like all organisms, bacteria need a constant supply of energy to carry out their functions. This energy comes from food. As you learned in Chapter 2, the process of breaking down food to release its energy is called respiration. Like many other organisms, most bacteria need oxygen to break down their food. But a few kinds of bacteria do not need oxygen for respiration. In fact, those bacteria die if oxygen is present in their surroundings. For them, oxygen is a poison that kills!

Background

Integrating Science The tomb of the Egyptian pharaoh Tutankhamen was discovered by the archaeologist Howard Carter in 1922. In the seven years following the discovery, eleven people, including Lord Carnarvon (who had paid for the excavation), died. Although the story of a curse was cooked up by security guards to keep away looters, others have speculated that bacteria sealed up in the tomb formed endospores and survived. Because there are few similarities between the deaths of the individuals, disease from ancient spores seems unlikely. However, it is possible for some bacterial spores to survive for a long time. *Bacillus anthracis*, the bacteria that causes anthrax, can live in the soil for many decades or longer. Archaeologists who excavate in areas where anthrax is known to have occurred must take precautions.

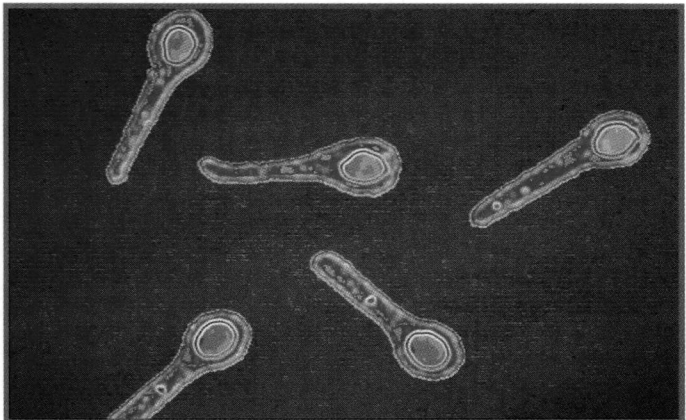

Figure 14 When conditions in the environment become unfavorable for growth, some bacteria form endospores. These endospores of *Clostridium tetani* can survive for years.

Endospore Formation Sometimes the conditions in the environment become unfavorable for the growth of bacteria. For example, food sources can disappear or wastes can poison the bacteria. Some bacteria can survive these harsh conditions by forming endospores like the ones you see in Figure 14. An **endospore** is a small, rounded, thick-walled, resting cell that forms inside a bacterial cell. It contains the cell's genetic material and some of its cytoplasm. Because endospores can resist freezing, heating, and drying, they can survive for many years. Endospores are also light—a breeze can lift and carry them to new places. If an endospore lands in a place where conditions are suitable, it opens up. Then the bacterium can begin to grow and multiply.

☑ *Checkpoint* How do autotrophic bacteria obtain energy?

Bacteria and The Living World

When you think about bacteria in your life, you might think of strep throat or ear infections before you think of cheese or fertile soil. But most of the ways that bacteria interact with living organisms are harmless or positive, not harmful. **Bacteria are involved in fuel and food production as well as in environmental recycling and cleanup. However, some bacteria do cause diseases and other harmful effects.**

Fuel The next time you use natural gas to boil an egg, grill a hamburger, or heat your house, think of archaebacteria. The archaebacteria that live in oxygen-free environments, such as the thick mud at the bottom of a lake or swamp, produce a gas called methane during respiration. The methane produced by archaebacteria that died millions of years ago is the major component in about 20 percent of Earth's deposits of natural gas.

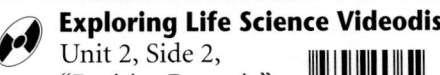

Bacteria for Breakfast

In this activity, you will observe helpful bacteria in a common food.

1. Put on your apron. Add water to plain yogurt to make a thin mixture.
2.  With a plastic dropper, place a drop of the mixture on a glass slide.
3. Use another plastic dropper to add one drop of methylene blue dye to the slide. **CAUTION:** *This dye can stain your skin.*
4. Put a coverslip on the slide.
5. Observe the slide under both the low and high power lenses of a microscope.

Observing Draw a diagram of what you see under high power. Label any cell structures that you see.

Bacteria and the Living World

TRY THIS

Skills Focus observing ACTIVITY
Materials *unpasteurized yogurt, plastic dropper, methylene blue, glass slide, cover slip, microscope, lab apron*
Time 20 minutes
Tips Students will need to observe with the highest powers of the microscope. As they observe the bacteria in yogurt, have students classify the bacteria according to their shape: spherical, rod, or spiral. Caution them to not drop the glass slides, and to avoid getting methylene blue on their skin or clothing.
Observing The bacteria appear as dark-blue capsule-shaped dots against a cloudy, pale blue background. Bacteria are so small that students will be unable to see them unless they are using high-powered microscopes.
Extend Challenge students to observe yogurt that contains added *Lactobacillus acidophilus* (the contents will be listed on the label) and to draw what they observe under the microscope. **learning modality: visual**

Media and Technology

🔘 **Exploring Life Science Videodisc**
Unit 2, Side 2,
"Positive Bacteria"

Chapter 4

Answers to Self-Assessment

Caption Question

Figure 13 A thin, threadlike bridge that joins the two cells during conjugation allows for the transfer of genetic material.

☑ *Checkpoint*

Some autotrophic bacteria obtain the energy to make food from the sun. Others obtain food-making energy from chemical substances in their environment.

Ongoing Assessment

Oral Presentation Ask students to describe the conditions bacteria need in order to survive and explain one way bacteria can survive when the conditions are not present. (*Food, a way of breaking down food for energy; some bacteria form endospores*)

Bacteria and the Living World, continued

SCIENCE & History

Materials *globe or world map*
Time 15 minutes
Tips Have a world map or globe available for students to use to locate the places discussed in the feature. Invite volunteers to read aloud the annotations to the time line. For each food preservation method, encourage students to draw conclusions about the environment in which the bacteria grew and how they affected the food. Ask: **Do you think these methods of food preservation and preparation are still used today? What examples have you seen?** (*Responses will vary. These methods are still used.*)

In Your Journal Suggest students keep the following questions in mind as they do their research.

◆ What techniques were used in the food production method?
◆ What environment existed in the geographical region where the method was developed?
◆ Did the environment have any effect on the development of the method?

Many different cultures have used foods that have been altered by bacteria. You may want to have students do research and write in their journals about such a food from their own culture. Encourage students to share their reports with the class.

 Students can save their reports in their portfolios.

Food Do you like cheese, yogurt, and apple cider? What about olives and sauerkraut? The activities of helpful bacteria produce all of these foods and more. For example, bacteria that grow in a liquid poured around fresh cucumbers turn the cucumbers into pickles. Bacteria that grow in apple cider change the cider to vinegar. Bacteria that grow in milk produce dairy products such as buttermilk, sour cream, yogurt, and cheeses.

However, some bacteria cause food to spoil when they break down the food's chemicals. Spoiled food usually smells or tastes foul and can make you very sick. Since ancient times, people have

SCIENCE & History

Bacteria and Foods of the World

Ancient cultures lacked refrigeration and other modern methods of preventing food spoilage. People in these cultures developed ways to use bacteria to preserve foods. You may enjoy some of these foods today.

1000 B.C. China
The Chinese salted vegetables and packed them in containers. Naturally occurring bacteria fed on the vegetables and produced a sour taste. The salt pulled water out of the vegetables and left them crisp. These vegetables were part of the food rations given to workers who built the Great Wall of China.

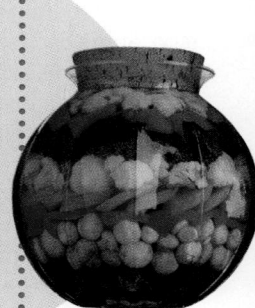

3000 B.C.	2000 B.C.	1000 B.C.

2300 B.C. Egypt
Ancient Egyptians made cheese from milk. Cheesemaking begins when bacteria feed on the sugars in milk. The milk separates into solid curds and liquid whey. The curds are processed into cheeses, which keep longer than milk.

500 B.C. Mediterranean Sea Region
People who lived in the region around the Mediterranean Sea chopped meat, seasoned it with salt and spices, rolled it, and hung it to dry. Bacteria in the drying meat gave unusual flavors to the food. The rolled meat would keep for weeks in cool places.

198

Background

History of Science Canning as a method of food preservation was developed in 1810 by a Frenchman named Nicolas Appert. The first food-processing plant began operating in England in 1813. The plant sealed meats, vegetables, and soups in tin canisters, then heated the "cans" to a certain temperature for the correct amount of time.

Freezing food to preserve it was not possible until mechanical refrigeration systems were perfected About 1880, fish were frozen and sold in the United States and Europe. At that time, New Zealand began to freeze mutton and ship it to England. Frozen fruits appeared in the United States in 1905 and frozen vegetables in 1923.

Dehydration, or drying food, became commercially important during World War I, when soldiers were given dehydrated foods.

developed ways to slow down food spoilage. They have used such methods as heating, refrigerating, drying, salting, or smoking foods. These methods help to preserve food by preventing the bacteria that cause spoiling from growing in the food.

Environmental Recycling Do you recycle plastic, glass, and other materials? If you do, you have something in common with some heterotrophic eubacteria. These bacteria, which live in the soil, are **decomposers**—organisms that break down large chemicals in dead organisms into small chemicals. Decomposers are

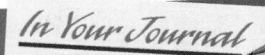

In Your Journal

Find out more about one of these ancient food production methods and the culture that developed it. Write a report about the importance of the food to the culture.

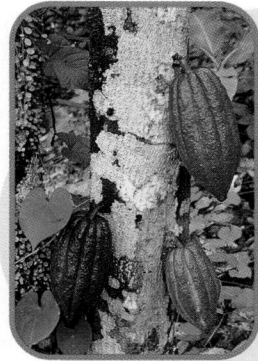

A.D. 1500
The West Indies

People in the West Indies mixed beans from the cocoa plant with bacteria and other microorganisms, then dried and roasted them. The roasted beans were then brewed to produce a beverage with a chocolate flavor. The drink was served cold with honey, spices, and vanilla.

A.D. 1　　　　**A.D. 1000**　　　　**A.D. 2000**

A.D. 500
China

The Chinese crushed soybeans with wheat, salt, bacteria, and other microorganisms. The microorganisms fed on the proteins in the wheat and soybeans. The salt pulled water out of the mixture. The protein-rich soy paste that remained was used to flavor foods. The soy sauce you may use today is made in a similar manner.

A.D. 1850
United States of America

Gold prospectors in California ate a bread called sourdough bread. The bacteria *Lactobacillus san francisco* gave the bread its sour taste. Each day before baking, cooks would set aside some dough that contained the bacteria to use in the next day's bread.

Chapter 6 **199**

Program Resources

◆ **Laboratory Manual** 6, "Eubacteria That Dine on Vegetables"

Including All Students

Before refrigeration was common, milk had to be delivered fresh each day. Even then, milk would occasionally spoil. Frugal housekeepers would not discard the sour milk, but would use it in cooking and baking. Have students discuss and infer why it was probably safe to use sour milk in baking biscuits. *(Heat would destroy the bacteria.)* **learning modality: logical/ mathematical**

Building Inquiry Skills: Drawing Conclusions

Materials *empty cans, bottles, jars, freezer wraps, boil-in-bags, and packages from a variety of prepared foods with labels included*

ACTIVITY

Time 20 minutes

Tips Prior to the activity, ask students to bring in a variety of empty food packages. Tell students they are going to examine some modern ways to preserve food. Organize students into small groups, and provide each group with two or three packages. CAUTION: *Make sure packaging materials are clean. Have students wash their hands with antibacterial soap after handling the packaging materials.* Challenge students to draw conclusions about how the foods were prepared and what was done to prevent them from spoiling. Ask students to infer how the method used to prevent spoilage inhibited the growth of bacteria. Have a reporter from each group share findings with the class. **cooperative learning**

Ongoing Assessment

Skills Check Call on students to give examples of how bacteria are beneficial in food production and how they are harmful.

Bacteria and the Living World, continued

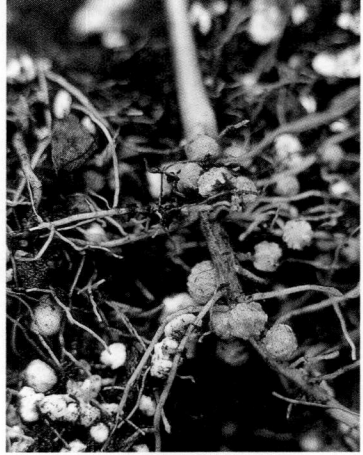

Figure 15 Bacteria live in the swellings on the roots of this soybean plant. The bacteria convert nitrogen from the air into substances the plant needs. *Applying Concepts Why might farmers plant soybeans in a field that is low in nitrogen?*

Figure 16 Scientists use bacteria such as these *Ochrobactrum anthropi* to help clean up oil spills.

"nature's recyclers"—they return basic chemicals to the environment for other living things to reuse. For example, in the fall, the leaves of many trees die and fall to the ground. Decomposing bacteria spend the next months breaking down the chemicals in the dead leaves. The broken-down chemicals mix with the soil, and can then be absorbed by the roots of nearby plants.

Other recycling eubacteria live in swellings on the roots of some plants, such as peanuts and soybeans. There, they convert nitrogen gas from the air into nitrogen compounds that the plants need to grow. The plants cannot convert nitrogen from the air into the nitrogen compounds they need. The bacteria that live in the roots of plants help the plants to survive.

Environmental Cleanup Some bacteria help to clean up Earth's land and water. Can you imagine having a bowl of oil for dinner? Well, there are some bacteria that feast on oil. They convert the dangerous chemicals in oil into harmless substances. Scientists have put these bacteria to work cleaning up oil spills in oceans and gasoline leaks around gas stations.

Illness and Health Most people have experienced a disease caused by bacteria, such as strep throat or food poisoning. These and many other diseases are called **infectious diseases**—illnesses that pass from one organism to another. Viruses can also cause infectious diseases, as you will read in Section 4.

Infectious diseases can spread in many ways. One way is direct contact, such as touching, hugging, or kissing an infected person. Indirect contact, such as inhaling the drops of moisture from an infected person's sneeze or sharing food and drink, can also spread disease. Some disease-causing bacteria are found naturally in the environment. An example is the bacterium *Clostridium tetani,* which lives in the soil. This bacterium can enter your body through an open wound. It produces a poison known as a **toxin,** which causes the disease tetanus.

200

Bacterial Infectious Diseases

Disease	Symptoms	How Spread	Treatment	Prevention
Food poisoning	Vomiting; cramps; diarrhea; fever	Eating foods containing the bacteria	Antitoxin medicines; rest	Properly cook and store foods; avoid foods in rusted and swollen cans
Lyme disease	Rash at site of tick bite; chills; fever; body aches; joint swelling	Animal bite	Antibiotic	Tuck pants into socks; wear long-sleeved shirt; vaccine
Strep throat	Fever; sore throat; swollen glands	Inhale droplets; contact with infected object	Antibiotic	Avoid contact with infected people
Tetanus (lockjaw)	Stiff jaw and neck muscles; spasms; difficulty swallowing	Deep puncture wound	Antibiotic; opening and cleaning wound	Vaccine
Tuberculosis (TB)	Fatigue; mild fever; weight loss; night sweats; cough	Inhale droplets	Antibiotic	Vaccine (for those in high-risk occupations only)

Figure 17 This table lists some diseases caused by bacteria. *Interpreting Charts How can you avoid catching Lyme disease?*

Fortunately, many bacterial diseases can be cured with medications known as antibiotics. An **antibiotic** is a chemical that can kill bacteria without harming a person's own cells. Penicillin is a familiar antibiotic that works by weakening the cell walls of certain bacteria until the cells burst.

 INTEGRATING HEALTH You may find it hard to believe that many of the bacteria living in your body actually keep you healthy. In your digestive system, for example, your intestines teem with bacteria. This is a natural and healthy situation. Some of the bacteria help you digest your food. Some make vitamins that your body needs. Others compete for space with disease-causing organisms. They prevent the harmful bacteria from attaching to your intestines and making you sick.

 Section 3 Review

1. How is a bacterial cell different from the cells of other kinds of organisms?
2. List four ways in which bacteria interact with people.
3. What happens during binary fission?
4. **Thinking Critically Applying Concepts** Why are some foods, such as milk, heated to high temperatures before they are bottled?

Science at Home

Helpful Bacteria With a family member, look around your kitchen for foods that are made using bacteria. Read the labels on the foods to see if the role of bacteria in the food's production is mentioned. Discuss with your family member the helpful roles that bacteria play in people's lives.

Chapter 6 **201**

Program Resources

♦ **Unit 2 Resources** 6-3 Review and Reinforce, p. 19; 6-3 Enrich, p. 20

Answers to Self-Assessment

Caption Question

Figure 15 The bacteria that live on the roots of soybeans can convert the nitrogen compounds into a form that can be used by the plant.

Figure 17 Preventative actions include covering your body as much as possible and getting a vaccination.

 Integrating Health

Ask: **Have you ever been told to eat yogurt after having taken a prescription for antibiotics?** *(Some students may have had this experience.)* Tell students that antibiotics get rid of bacteria that make you sick but may also kill helpful bacteria in the intestines. Yogurt contains bacteria, so eating yogurt replaces the helpful bacteria. **learning modality: visual**

3 Assess

Section 3 Review Answers

1. Bacterial cells are prokaryotic; cells of other organisms are eukaryotic.
2. fuel, food, environmental cleanup, disease
3. During binary fission, a cell divides to produce two new cells that are identical to each other.
4. High temperatures kill any disease-causing bacteria in the milk.

Science at Home

Provide students with a list of keywords to look for on product labels to help them identify bacteria in products. For example, *live* or *active cultures, enzymes*. Encourage students to share their findings from home with classmates.

Performance Assessment

Writing Have students write two or three paragraphs describing bacteria that are either helpful or harmful to humans.

201

Do Disinfectants Work?

Preparing for Inquiry

Key Concept The growth of bacteria can be controlled through the use of disinfectants.

Skills Objective Students will be able to
◆ observe bacterial growth on petri dishes;
◆ infer how well a disinfectant controls bacterial growth;
◆ draw conclusions regarding the best way to use disinfectants.

Time 30 minutes first day, 15 minutes for each of the next three days

Advance Planning Bring disinfectants, such as pine-scented cleaners or bleach, to class that contain different active ingredients. Dilute disinfectants at least tenfold to reduce the possibility of injury to students. Make sure the room is well ventilated. Review the use of the eyewash apparatus in case disinfectant is accidentally splashed into the eye of a student. Because disinfectants may stain clothes, students may want to bring an old shirt or apron to wear over their clothes during the lab. After opening a package of agar plates, use all the plates right away or dispose of leftover plates, because they will not remain sterile.

Guiding Inquiry

Invitation

Ask students why some cleaning products contain disinfectants. Students should discuss the fact that bacteria are present everywhere around them. Controlling bacteria using disinfectants helps prevent disease transmission and food spoilage. Students should be able to explain how they will test the ability of a disinfectant to control bacteria in this lab.

Introducing the Procedure

◆ Pour out enough of each disinfectant into small containers so that students can fill their droppers without inserting them into the bottle of disinfectant. Caution students not to mix samples.

Do Disinfectants Work?

When your family goes shopping, you may buy cleaning products called disinfectants. Disinfectants kill microorganisms such as bacteria, which may cause infection or decay. In this lab, you will compare the effects of two different disinfectants.

Problem

How well do disinfectants control the growth of bacteria?

Skills Focus

observing, inferring, drawing conclusions

Materials

clock   wax pencil
2 plastic droppers   transparent tape
2 household disinfectants
3 plastic petri dishes with sterile nutrient agar

Procedure

1. Copy the data table into your notebook.
2. Work with a partner. Obtain 3 petri dishes containing sterile agar. Without opening them, use a wax pencil to label the bottoms "A," "B," and "C." Write your initials beside each letter.
3. Wash your hands thoroughly with soap, then run a fingertip across the surface of your worktable. Your partner should hold open the cover of petri dish A while you run that fingertip gently across the agar in a zig-zag motion. Close the dish immediately.
4. Repeat Step 3 for dishes B and C.
5. Use a plastic dropper to transfer 2 drops of one disinfectant to the center of petri dish A. Open the cover just long enough to add the disinfectant to the dish. Close the cover immediately. Record the name of the disinfectant in your data table. **CAUTION:** *Do not inhale vapors from the disinfectant.*
6. Repeat Step 5 for dish B but add 2 drops of the second disinfectant. **CAUTION:** *Do not mix any disinfectants together.*
7. Do not add any disinfectant to dish C.
8. Tape down the covers of all 3 petri dishes so that they will remain tightly closed. Allow the 3 dishes to sit upright on your work surface for at least 5 minutes. **CAUTION:** *Do not open the petri dishes again.* Wash your hands with soap and water.
9. As directed by your teacher, store the petri dishes in a warm, dark place where they can remain for at least 3 days. Remove them only to make a brief examination each day.

DATA TABLE				
Petri Dish	Disinfectant	Day 1	Day 2	Day 3
A				
B				
C				

Program Resources

◆ **Unit 2 Resources** Chapter 6 Real-World Lab, pp. 25–27

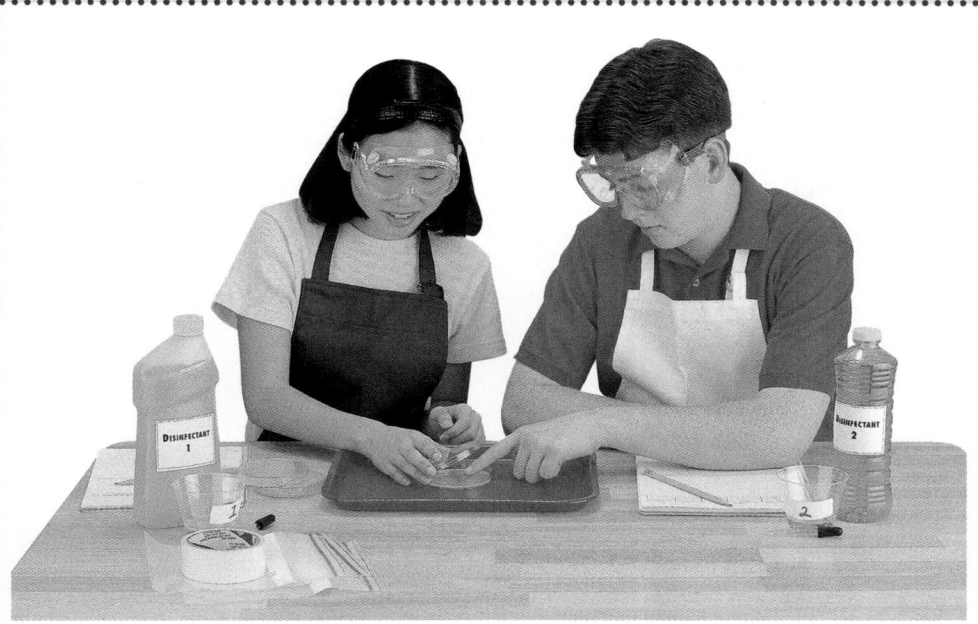

10. After one day, observe the contents of each dish without removing the covers. Estimate the percentage of the agar surface that shows any changes. Record your observations. Return the dishes to their storage place when you have finished making your observations. Wash your hands with soap.

11. Repeat Step 10 after the second day and again after the third day.

12. After you and your partner have made your last observations, return the petri dishes to your teacher unopened.

Analyze and Conclude

1. How did the appearance of dish C change during the lab?
2. How did the appearance of dishes A and B compare with dish C? Explain any similarities or differences.

3. How did the appearance of dishes A and B compare with each other? How can you account for any differences?
4. Why was it important to set aside one petri dish that did not contain any disinfectant?
5. **Apply** Based on the results of this lab, what recommendation would you make to your family about the use of disinfectants? Where in the house do you think these products would be needed most?

Design an Experiment

Go to a store and look at soap products that claim to be "antibacterial" soaps. How do their ingredients differ from other soaps? How do their prices compare? Design an experiment to test how well these products control the growth of bacteria.

◆ Explain that students will store petri dishes upside down so that any condensed water will collect on the inside cover of the dish instead of dropping into the agar.

Troubleshooting the Experiment
Stress the safety procedures associated with any lab dealing with bacteria. Emphasize that students must not open the petri dishes after the initial procedures.

Expected Outcome
Several colonies of bacteria should grow on the control dish C. Dishes A and B should have fewer colonies, smaller colonies, or both.

Analyze and Conclude
1. Answers will vary, but students should report numerous bacterial colonies growing on the agar surface.
2. Dishes A and B should have fewer colonies, smaller colonies, or both.
3. Answers will vary depending on the disinfectants used. Any differences between A and B may be due to the relative effectiveness of the two disinfectants. They could also be due to other factors such as the distribution of different kinds of bacteria picked up off the work surface.
4. The dish without disinfectant, dish C, was the control. It shows how bacteria grew when no disinfectant was applied.
5. Students may mention using disinfectants to clean locations and implements associated with food preparation, bathroom facilities, children's rooms, and in cases of family illness.

Extending the Inquiry

Design an Experiment Encourage students to compare the labels of antibacterial soaps with the labels of disinfectants to look for any common ingredients. Students' plans should include clear and safe procedures and should clearly identify the control and the variables to be tested.

Safety

Dilute the bleach at least tenfold to reduce the chances of injury to students. Caution students to use care when working with the disinfectants. Keep an eyewash apparatus on hand in case disinfectant is accidentally splashed into a student's eye. Tell students to inform you immediately if a spill occurs.

Review the safety guidelines in Appendix A. Dispose of the petri dishes and all other materials according to the proper procedures. Be sure to check your district's and state's guidelines for the proper disposal of bacterial cultures.

SECTION 4 Viruses

Objectives

After completing the lesson, students will be able to
- give reasons why viruses are considered to be nonliving;
- describe the sizes and shapes of viruses;
- describe the basic structure of a virus;
- explain how viruses multiply.

Key Terms virus, host, parasite, bacteriophage, vaccine

1 Engage/Explore

Activating Prior Knowledge

Invite students to name diseases they are familiar with. List the diseases on the board. Tell students that viruses are the cause of some diseases. Encourage them to identify any diseases on the list that they know are caused by viruses.
(Sample: cold, flu, smallpox, measles, mumps, polio)

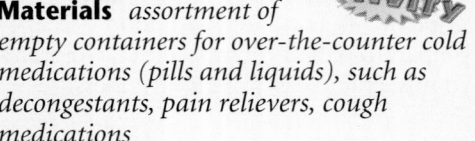

DISCOVER

Skills Focus inferring
Materials *assortment of empty containers for over-the-counter cold medications (pills and liquids), such as decongestants, pain relievers, cough medications*
Time 20 minutes
Tips Have students list some symptoms of colds. Guide students to read the labels critically. The labels generally specify the active ingredients, those ingredients that actually have an effect on the body. Guide students to associate the active ingredients with the product's claims.
Think It Over Students should conclude that none of the products can cure colds, although they can relieve cold symptoms.

204

INTEGRATING HEALTH

SECTION 4 Viruses

DISCOVER · ACTIVITY

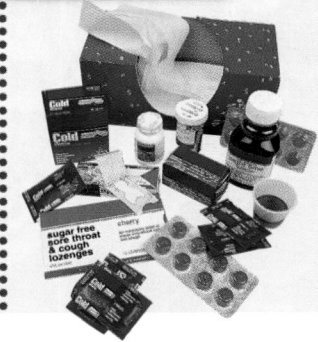

Can You Cure a Cold?

1. Look at the cold medications that your teacher displays. You may have used some of these products when you had a cold.
2. Read the ingredient labels on the products. Read the product claims.
3. Decide which medication you would use if you had a cold. Record the reasons for your choice of product.

Think It Over
Inferring Do medications cure colds? Explain your answer.

GUIDE FOR READING

- Why are viruses considered to be nonliving?
- What is the basic structure of a virus?
- How do viruses multiply?

Reading Tip As you read, use the headings to outline information about the characteristics of viruses.

It is a dark and quiet night. An enemy spy slips silently across the border. Invisible to the guards, the spy creeps cautiously along the edge of the road, heading toward the command center. Undetected, the spy sneaks by the center's security system and reaches the door. Breaking into the control room, the spy takes command of the central computer. The enemy is in control.

Moments later the command center's defenses finally activate. Depending on the enemy's strength and cunning, the defenses may squash the invasion before much damage is done. Otherwise the enemy will win and take over the territory.

What Is a Virus?

Although this spy story may read like a movie script, it describes events that can occur in your body. The spy acts very much like a virus invading an organism. A **virus** is a small, nonliving particle that invades and then reproduces inside a living cell.

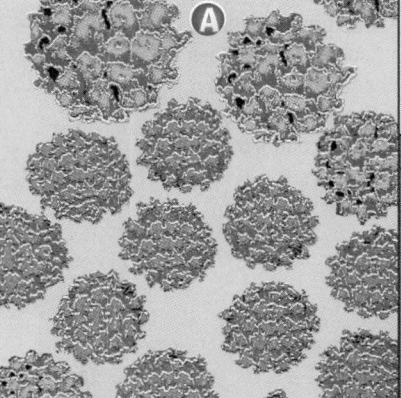
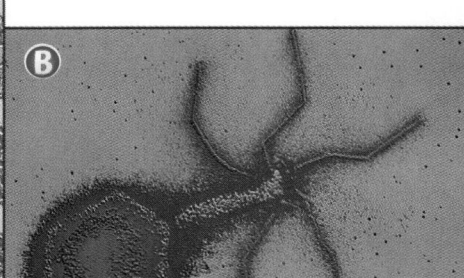
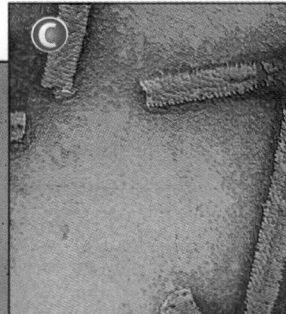

READING STRATEGIES

Reading Tip Before students read, remind them that an outline is one way to organize main ideas and details in order to remember key points about a selection. Write the following outline guide on the board to remind students how to construct an outline. Encourage students to use the guide while they read to outline information about the characteristics of viruses.

I. First Main Idea
  A. First supporting idea or fact
    1. detail or example
    2. detail or example

Sample outline:
I. What is a Virus?
  A. Nonliving
    1. Cannot take in food
    2. Needs a host to reproduce
  B. Parasitic (outline will continue)

Biologists consider viruses to be nonliving because viruses are not cells. Viruses do not use energy to grow or to respond to their surroundings. Viruses also cannot make food, take in food, or produce wastes.

The only way in which viruses are like organisms is in their ability to multiply. But, although viruses can multiply, they do so differently than organisms. Viruses can only multiply when they are inside a living cell. The organism that a virus enters and multiplies inside is called a host. A **host** is a living thing that provides a source of energy for a virus or an organism. Organisms that live on or in a host and cause harm to the host are called **parasites** (PA ruh syts). Almost all viruses act like parasites because they destroy the cells in which they multiply.

No organisms are safe from viruses. Viruses can infect the organisms of all six kingdoms—archaebacteria, eubacteria, protists, fungi, plants, and animals. Each virus, however, can enter, or infect, only a few types of cells in a few specific species. For example, most cold viruses only infect cells in the nose and throat of humans. The tobacco mosaic virus only infects the leaf cells of tobacco plants.

☑ *Checkpoint* *When you have a cold, are you the host or the parasite?*

Naming Viruses

Because viruses are not alive, scientists do not use binomial nomenclature to name them. Instead, scientists may name a virus, such as the polio virus, after the disease it causes. Other viruses are named for the organisms they infect, as is the case with the tomato mosaic virus, which infects tomato plants. Scientists named the Ebola virus after the place in Africa where it was first found. And scientists sometimes name viruses after people. The Epstein-Barr virus, for example, was named for the two scientists who first identified the virus that causes the disease known as infectious mononucleosis.

Figure 18 Viruses are tiny nonliving particles that invade and reproduce inside living cells. Viruses can infect the organisms of all six kingdoms. **A.** Papilloma viruses cause warts to form on human skin. **B.** This virus, called a bacteriophage, infects bacteria. **C.** Tobacco mosaic viruses infect tobacco plants. **D.** The rabies virus infects nerve cells in certain animals. **E.** The blue circles in this photo are viruses that cause German measles in humans.

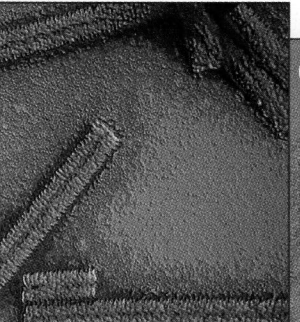
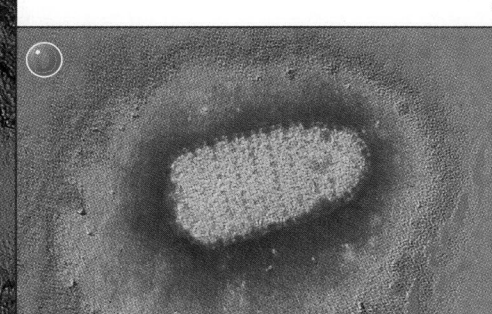
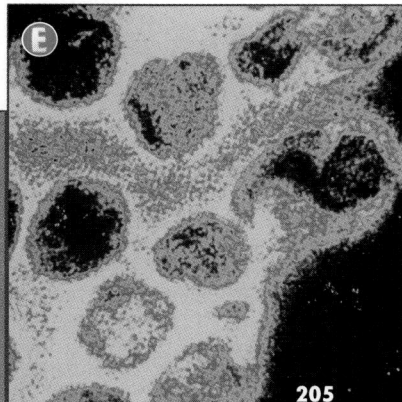

205

Program Resources

◆ **Unit 2 Resources** 6-4 Lesson Plan, p. 21; 6-4 Section Summary, p. 22

Media and Technology

 Audio CD English-Spanish Summary 6-4

Answers to Self-Assessment

☑ *Checkpoint*

You are the host because you provide cells in which the cold viruses can multiply.

2 Facilitate

What Is a Virus?

Using the Visuals: Figure 18

Point out that the viruses in these photos are magnified many thousands of times. Invite students to read the captions carefully and compare and contrast the appearance of the different viruses. *(Students may notice that each virus has a distinct shape or some kind of organization. Viruses can infect organisms of all six kingdoms.)* **learning modality: visual**

Naming Viruses

Building Inquiry Skills: Comparing and Contrasting

Ask students to recall why scientists use binomial nomenclature to name living organisms. *(It allows scientists to make sure they all use the same name to refer to a specific species.)* Challenge students to compare this with the methods used for naming viruses. Ask: **What can you tell about a virus from its name?** *(Sometimes you can tell where it was discovered, what kind of organism it infects, or what disease it causes.)* Encourage students to speculate about problems with how viruses are named. **learning modality: verbal**

Ongoing Assessment

Writing Have students write two sentences explaining why viruses must invade cells in order to multiply.

205

The Shapes and Sizes of Viruses

Using the Visuals: Figure 19

As students compare the sizes of the viruses and the bacterial cell, explain that the bacteria are much smaller than most body cells. Encourage students to speculate on how having so many different sizes and shapes could influence how viruses affect the bodies of their hosts. *(Students might say that it is hard for the body to fight them because they are so different.)* **learning modality: visual**

Structure of Viruses

Inquiry Challenge

Materials *construction paper in different colors, scissors, glue, posterboard*

Time 30 minutes

Tips To help students who have difficulty grasping the meaning of the text, before class, cut out four large circles to represent four different types of cells. Use scissors to notch the edges of the circles so that each circle has a distinct pattern. Divide the class into four groups and give each group one cell model. Challenge groups to create model viruses to attach to their type of cell. Tell students to imagine that they are trying to make a puzzle piece that will fit into the cell. Encourage students to refer to the viruses shown in Figure 18 for inspiration. You may want to challenge each student in the group to make at least one model virus, so that groups can develop the greatest variety of viruses that can attach to one type of cell. When students have completed their models, each group can make a poster showing the cell and the viruses. Ask: **If each virus can only attach to one kind of cell, does that mean that each cell can only be attacked by one kind of virus?** *(No, viruses of different sizes with different structures can attach to the same type of cell.)* **limited English proficiency**

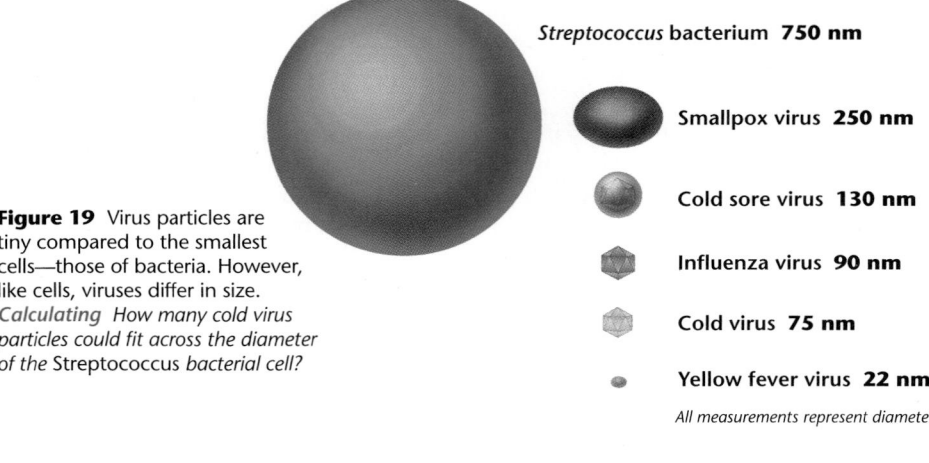

Streptococcus bacterium **750 nm**

Smallpox virus **250 nm**

Cold sore virus **130 nm**

Influenza virus **90 nm**

Cold virus **75 nm**

Yellow fever virus **22 nm**

All measurements represent diameters.

Figure 19 Virus particles are tiny compared to the smallest cells—those of bacteria. However, like cells, viruses differ in size. *Calculating How many cold virus particles could fit across the diameter of the* Streptococcus *bacterial cell?*

The Shapes and Sizes of Viruses

As you can see from the photographs on the previous pages, viruses vary widely in shape. Some viruses are round, while some others are rod-shaped. Other viruses have bricklike, threadlike, or bulletlike shapes. There are even some viruses, such as the bacteriophage in Figure 18B, that have complex, robotlike shapes. A **bacteriophage** (bak TEER ee oh fayj) is a virus that infects bacteria. In fact, its name means "bacteria eater."

Just as viruses vary in shape, they also vary in size. Viruses are smaller than cells and cannot be seen with the microscopes you use in school. Viruses are so small that they are measured in units called nanometers (nm). One nanometer is one billionth of a meter (m). The smallest viruses, such as yellow fever viruses, are about 22 nanometers in diameter. The largest viruses, such as smallpox viruses, are about 250 nanometers in diameter. Most viruses measure between 50 and 60 nanometers in diameter. The smallest cells, those of bacteria, are much larger than the average virus, as you can see in Figure 19 above.

Structure of Viruses

Although viruses may look very different from one another, they all have a similar structure. **All viruses have two basic parts: an outer coat that protects the virus and an inner core made of genetic material.** A virus's genetic material contains the instructions for making new viruses. Figure 20 shows the basic structure of a virus. The structure might remind you of a chocolate-covered candy. The outer coat of a virus is like the chocolate on the outside of a candy. The inner core is like the gooey filling inside the candy.

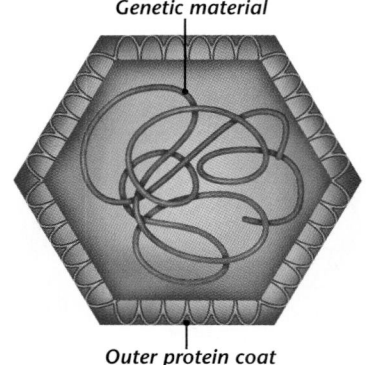

Genetic material

Outer protein coat

Figure 20 All viruses have a similar structure. They have an outer coat made of protein and an inner core that contains genetic material.

Background

Facts and Figures Scientists can now use a virus's ability to get inside cells as a way to alleviate the symptoms of disease. In one instance, scientists studying the painful and disabling disease, rheumatoid arthritis, discovered that its symptoms were caused by a high level of a substance called interleukin-1(IL-1). Scientists isolated a gene that programs the manufacture of a substance that blocks IL-1. But the problem was how to get the gene into the cells around the affected joint. The vector (gene-delivery vehicle) they decided to use was a replication-defective virus. This is a virus that still has the biological mechanism for injecting genetic material into a cell, but cannot reproduce itself in tissues. When the technique was tested on rabbits with arthritic knee joints, the rabbit's symptoms were much reduced.

The coat of a virus plays an important role during the invasion of a host cell. This coat is made of proteins. Each virus contains unique proteins in its coat. The shape of the proteins allows the virus's coat to attach to, or lock onto, certain cells in the host. Like keys, a virus's proteins only fit into certain "locks," or proteins, on the surface of a host's cells. Figure 21 shows how the lock-and-key action works. Because this action is highly specific, a certain virus will attach to only one or a few types of cells. For example, the human immunodeficiency virus, or HIV, can only attach to specific cells in the human body. These human cells have proteins on their surfaces that complement, or "fit," those on the virus.

✓ *Checkpoint* *Why does a virus only invade a specific kind of cell?*

How Viruses Multiply

After a virus attaches to a cell, it enters the cell. **Once inside, a virus's genetic material takes over the cell's functions. The genetic material directs the cell to produce the virus's proteins and genetic material. These proteins and genetic material are then assembled into new viruses.** Some viruses take over the cell's functions immediately. Other viruses wait for a while.

Active Viruses After entering a cell, an active virus immediately goes into action. The virus's genetic material takes over the cell's functions, and the cell quickly begins to produce the virus's proteins and genetic material. Then these parts assemble into new viruses. Like a photocopy machine left in the "on" position, the invaded cell makes copy after copy of new viruses. When it

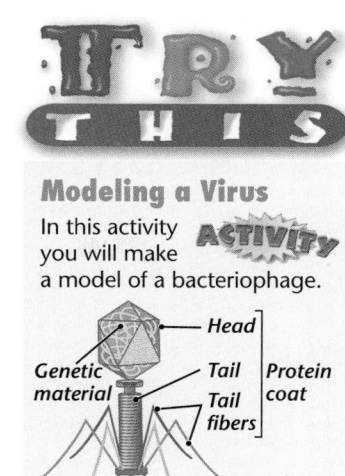

TRY THIS

Modeling a Virus

In this activity **ACTIVITY** you will make a model of a bacteriophage.

Head
Genetic material
Tail
Tail fibers
Protein coat

1. Sketch the bacteriophage above in your notebook.
2. Decide what materials you will use to model the virus.
3. Build your model.

Making Models Label your model. On each label, state the role that the part plays in infecting a host cell.

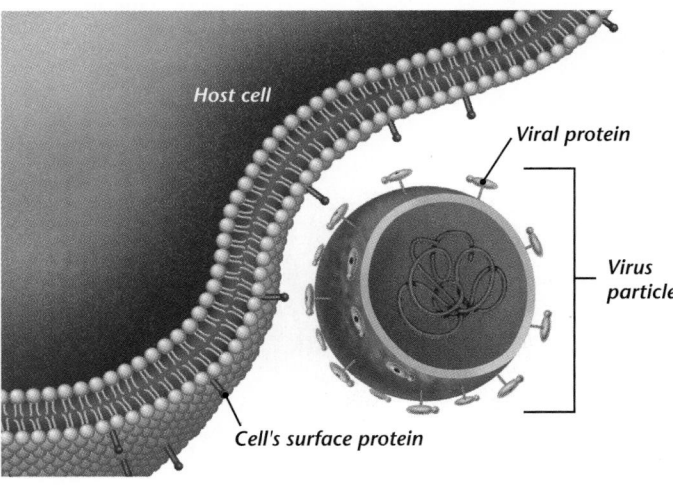

Figure 21 The shape of the proteins in a virus's coat determines what type of cell the virus will infect. The proteins fit together with the cell's proteins in the same way that a key fits a lock. Once attached, the virus can release its genetic material into the cell.

Host cell
Viral protein
Virus particle
Cell's surface protein

Chapter 6 **207**

Answers to Self-Assessment

Caption Question

Figure 19 About ten

✓ *Checkpoint*

A virus only invades a specific kind of cell because its coat has unique proteins that attach only to proteins of a particular host cell.

TRY THIS

Skills Focus making models **ACTIVITY**

Materials *model-making materials such as pipe cleaners, string, thread, rubber bands, paper clips, construction paper, aluminum foil, straws, plastic wrap, clay, glue, tape, scissors*

Time 20 minutes

Tips Encourage students to make a second sketch after they have decided what materials to use, showing the model they are going to build.

Expected Outcome Students should label the outer protein coat, the genetic material, the tail, and the tail fibers.

Extend Challenge students to model what happens when a bacteriophage attacks a bacterial cell. **learning modality: kinesthetic**

Including All Students

Some students may have difficulty understanding **ACTIVITY** the structure of a virus. Distribute a peanut in the shell to each student. CAUTION: *Some students may be allergic to peanuts.* Ask: **How is the structure of a virus similar to a peanut?** (*The shell is like the protein coat; the nut is like the genetic material.*) **learning modality: visual**

How Viruses Multiply

Building Inquiry Skills: Comparing and Contrasting

Have students compare and contrast the operation of a photocopier stuck in the "on" position with the operation of an active virus that has invaded a host cell. (*The photocopier will make copies until it runs out of paper. The virus will make copies until the cell bursts. The photocopies do not infect other copy machines. The new viruses go on to attack other cells.*) **learning modality: logical/ mathematical**

Ongoing Assessment

Drawing Have students draw a flowchart illustrating the steps a virus uses to invade a cell.

How Viruses Multiply
continued

EXPLORING
How Viruses Multiply

Have students work in cooperative groups. While volunteers read aloud the descriptions of the active virus, have each group create a flowchart that shows each step and its result. Repeat the process for the hidden virus. Have a reporter from each group present that group's flowchart to the class. Ask: **At what stage in the flowchart do the cycles of the two viruses begin to differ?** *(In Stage 3)* **What does the active virus do at that point?** *(Its host cell begins to produce the virus's proteins and genetic material.)* **What does the hidden virus do before it becomes active?** *(Its genetic material becomes part of the host's genetic material.)* **cooperative learning**

Building Inquiry Skills: Communicating

Challenge students to apply the concept of how viruses multiply by writing a creative story about a hidden or active virus that invades a human body cell. Students should take the virus through each step in its cycle, explaining what happens and the effect on the host cell. **learning modality: verbal**

208

is full of new viruses, the host cell bursts open and releases the new viruses. In *Exploring How Viruses Multiply*, below, you can follow how an active virus multiplies.

Hidden Viruses Some viruses function differently than active viruses after entering a cell—at least for a while. The genetic material of these viruses enters a host cell. Then, instead of going into action like an active virus does, the virus's genetic material becomes part of the cell's genetic material. The virus does not appear to affect the cell's functions. The virus's genetic material may stay in this inactive state for a long time. Then, for reasons that scientists do not yet fully understand, the virus's genetic material suddenly becomes active. It takes over the cell's

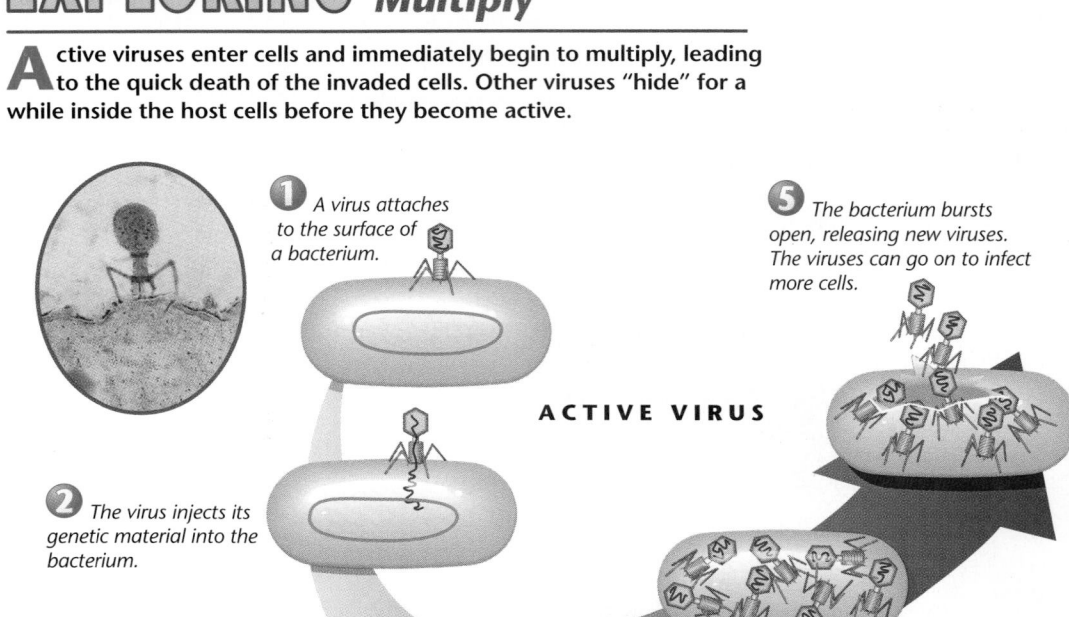

EXPLORING How Viruses Multiply

Active viruses enter cells and immediately begin to multiply, leading to the quick death of the invaded cells. Other viruses "hide" for a while inside the host cells before they become active.

1 A virus attaches to the surface of a bacterium.

2 The virus injects its genetic material into the bacterium.

3 The virus's genetic material takes over the cell functions of the bacterium. The cell starts to produce the virus's proteins and genetic material.

4 The proteins and genetic material assemble into new viruses that fill the bacterium.

5 The bacterium bursts open, releasing new viruses. The viruses can go on to infect more cells.

ACTIVE VIRUS

208

Background

Facts and Figures The hidden, or latent, virus that causes cold sores is called *Herpes simplex*. Another *Herpes* virus is *cytomegalovirus*. This virus rarely causes symptoms in healthy adults. However, infants who are infected by the virus can become deaf, blind, or retarded. Adults with compromised immune systems can become infected and develop an inflammation of the retina that leads to blindness.

Another serious illness, SSPE, is caused by a measles virus that remains dormant in brain cells for many years until it is reactivated in adolescence. Scientists do not know why hidden viruses, which are present in the tissues of most adults, reactivate and cause diseases in some people, but not in others.

functions in much the same way that active viruses do. In a short time, the cell is full of new viruses, and it bursts open to release them. Look at *Exploring How Viruses Multiply* to see how a hidden virus multiplies.

The virus that causes cold sores in humans is an example of a hidden virus. The virus can remain inactive for months or years inside the nerve cells in the face. While hidden, the virus causes no symptoms. When it becomes active, the virus causes a swollen, painful sore to form near the mouth. Strong sunlight and stress are two factors that scientists believe may activate a cold sore virus. After an active period, the virus once again "hides" in the nerve cells until it becomes active once again.

☑ *Checkpoint* **Give one example of a hidden virus.**

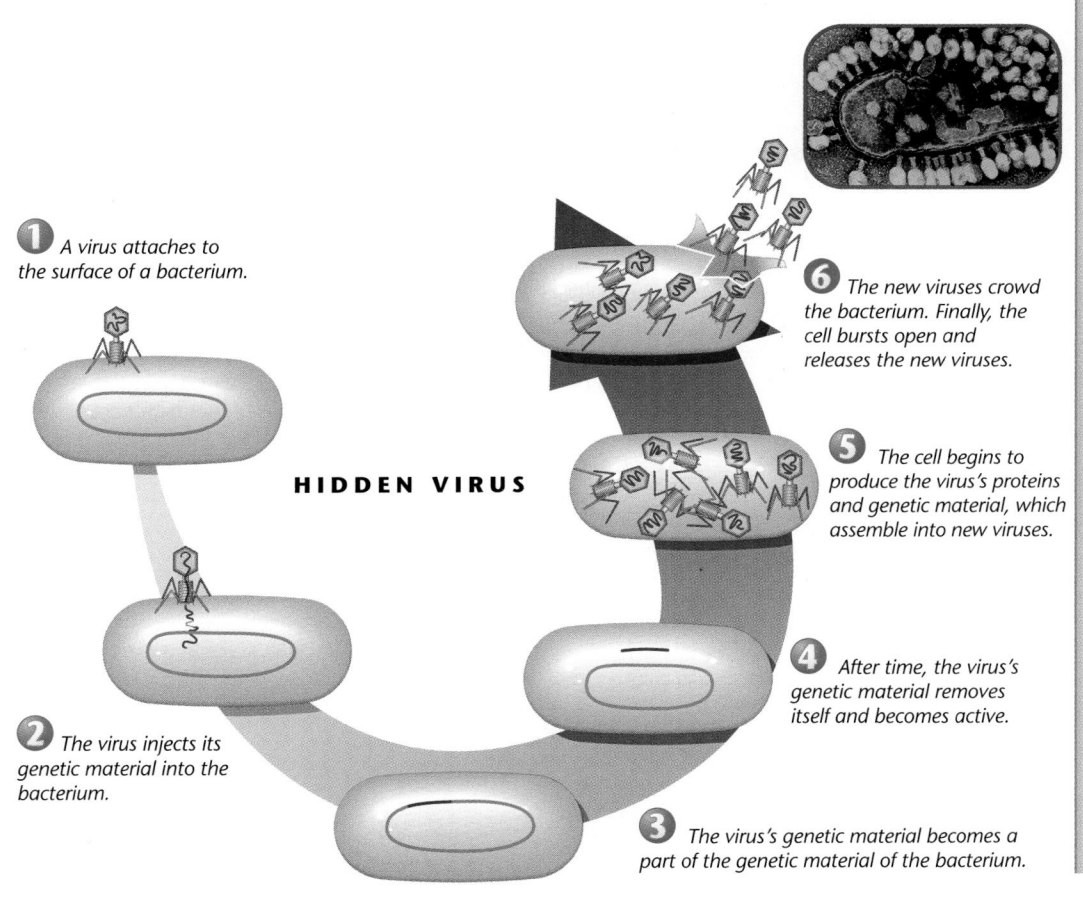

① *A virus attaches to the surface of a bacterium.*

HIDDEN VIRUS

⑥ *The new viruses crowd the bacterium. Finally, the cell bursts open and releases the new viruses.*

⑤ *The cell begins to produce the virus's proteins and genetic material, which assemble into new viruses.*

④ *After time, the virus's genetic material removes itself and becomes active.*

② *The virus injects its genetic material into the bacterium.*

③ *The virus's genetic material becomes a part of the genetic material of the bacterium.*

Chapter 6 **209**

Answers to Self-Assessment

☑ *Checkpoint*
The virus that causes cold sores

Social Studies Connection

Tell students that descriptions of viral diseases date to the 10th century B.C., but the concept of viruses was not proposed until the 1890s, when two different researchers proposed an infectious agent so small that it would pass through a filter that would not allow the passage of bacteria. Viruses could not be examined in detail until the 1940s. In 1952, Alfred Hershey and Martha Chase demonstrated how viruses multiply. Ask: **Why do you think it took so long for scientists to study viruses?** (*Because viruses are so small, scientists could not isolate them until powerful microscopes and other equipment were invented.*) **learning modality: verbal**

Real-Life Learning

Computer viruses are quite different from biological viruses. Invite a computer science instructor or software programmer to talk to the class about computer viruses. Before the visit, explain to students that when a computer virus enters a computer via a disk, the computer may infect all other disks with which it comes into contact by copying the virus onto them. Encourage students to develop a list of questions about computer viruses before the visit. Help students come up with questions that will help them understand the difference between computer viruses and viruses that invade cells. **learning modality: verbal**

Ongoing Assessment

Skills Check Have students make a poster illustrating the differences between what happens when an active virus attaches to a cell and what happens when a hidden virus attaches to a cell, with accompanying explanations on the poster.

209

Viral Diseases

Using the Visuals: Figure 22

Ask students to imagine that they are doctors examining a patient with a rash and a fever. Ask: **Which diseases could these symptoms be caused by?** *(Sample: Chicken pox, measles, Lyme disease)* **What questions could you ask the patient to determine which disease he or she had?** *(Samples: Were you immunized against measles? Have you been in the woods lately?)* **learning modality: verbal**

Preventing Infectious Diseases

Real-Life Learning

Have students contact a public-health agency or their school administration to learn more about vaccinations. Some topics students might research include making a list of all vaccines that are required for school children, or the schedule for receiving immunizations in childhood. Have students make posters or prepare presentations to share their findings. **learning modality: verbal**

Viral Diseases

If you've ever had a cold sore or been sick with a cold or flu, you know that viruses can cause disease in organisms. Some diseases, such as colds, are mild—people are sick for a short time but soon recover. Other diseases, such as acquired immunodeficiency syndrome, or AIDS, can cause death.

Viral infectious diseases can spread in many of the same ways as the bacterial infectious diseases described in Section 3. The table in Figure 22 below lists some familar viral diseases and how they are spread.

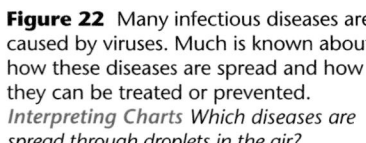

Figure 22 Many infectious diseases are caused by viruses. Much is known about how these diseases are spread and how they can be treated or prevented. *Interpreting Charts Which diseases are spread through droplets in the air?*

Viral Infectious Diseases

Disease	Symptoms	How Spread	Treatment	Prevention
Acquired immuno-deficiency syndrome (AIDS)	Weight loss; chronic fatigue; fever; diarrhea; frequent infections	Sexual contact; contact with blood; pregnancy, birth, and breast-feeding	Drugs to slow viral multiplication	Avoid contact with infected body fluids
Chicken Pox	Fever; red itchy rash	Contact with rash; inhale droplets	Antiviral drug (for adults)	Vaccine
Influenza (flu)	High fever; sore throat; headache; cough	Contact with contaminated objects; inhale droplets	Bed rest; fluids	Vaccine (mainly for high-risk ill, elderly, and young)
Measles	High fever; sore throat; cough; white spots on cheek lining; rash; puffy eyelids	Inhale droplets	Bed rest, cough medicine	Vaccine
Poliomyelitis (polio)	Fever; muscle weakness; headache; difficulty swallowing	Inhale droplets	Bed rest	Vaccine
Rabies	Drooling; skin sensitivity; alternating periods of rage and calm; difficulty swallowing	Animal bite	Vaccine	Avoid wild animals and pets that act abnormally; keep track of pets outside

---

Background

Facts and Figures Most vaccinations involve injections, ingestions, or most recently, inhalations. However, researchers at Washington University in Missouri have found a better way.

The most common cause of salmonella poisoning is through eating uncooked eggs, either directly or in other foods. To prevent salmonella in humans, the researchers

decided to vaccinate the chickens that lay the eggs. From 1990–1997, they worked to make a live salmonella strain harmless by deleting two critical genes. These genes regulate the expression of other genes that make the bacteria harmful. The vaccine can be administered in aerosol form or in drinking water, at a cost of less than a penny per bird.

Unfortunately, there are no medications that can cure viral infections. However, there are many over-the-counter medications that treat the symptoms. These medications are available without a prescription. Over-the-counter medications can make you feel better. But, they can delay your recovery if you resume your normal routine too soon. They can also hide symptoms that would normally cause you to go to a doctor. For most infectious diseases, the best treatment is bed rest. Indeed, resting, drinking lots of fluids, and eating healthy meals may be all you can do while you recover from some infectious diseases.

Preventing Infectious Diseases

One important tool that helps to prevent the spread of some viral and bacterial infectious diseases is vaccines. A **vaccine** is a substance that stimulates the body to produce chemicals that destroy viruses or bacteria. A vaccine may be made from dead or altered viruses or bacteria. The viruses or bacteria in the vaccine do not cause disease, but instead activate the body's natural defenses. In effect, the altered viruses or bacteria put the body "on alert." If that virus or bacterium ever invades the body, it is destroyed before it can produce disease. You may have been vaccinated against diseases such as tetanus, pertussis, measles, mumps, and polio. Now there is also a vaccine available for the viral disease chicken pox.

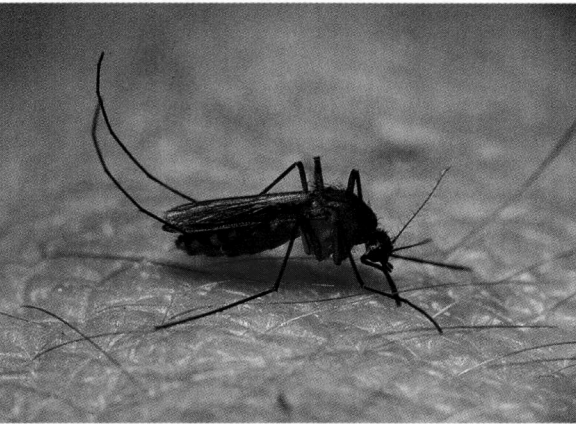

Figure 23 This mosquito, *Culex nigripalpus*, is feeding on human blood. If this mosquito contains the virus that causes encephalitis, it can transmit the disease through its bite.

Section 4 Review

1. Explain why viruses are considered nonliving.
2. Describe the basic structure of a virus.
3. Describe how viruses multiply.
4. **Thinking Critically Making Judgments** You have a case of the flu. A friend recommends a new treatment advertised in a magazine. The ad states that the treatment works by "deactivating the virus's nucleus so it can't reproduce." Could this treatment cure you? Explain.

Check Your Progress CHAPTER PROJECT
By now you should have nearly all of your questionnaires answered. You should be ready to tally your responses. Begin to think about how you will use graphs or other visual ways to organize your results. (*Hint:* You may need to review the research you did earlier to help you make sense of some survey data.)

Chapter 6 **211**

Answers to Self-Assessment

Caption Question

Figure 22 Chicken pox, influenza, measles, and poliomyelitis

3 Assess

Section 4 Review Answers

1. Viruses are not cells, and they do not respond to their surroundings or use energy to grow.
2. Viruses have an outer protein coat surrounding a core of genetic material.
3. An active virus takes over the host's genetic material and uses it to make new viruses. A hidden virus is incorporated into the host's genetic material, but seems to have no effect on the cell. At any time, the hidden virus can become active and multiply.
4. Probably not, because viruses do not have nuclei.

Check Your Progress CHAPTER PROJECT
Make sure students have collected most of their survey results, and that they are keeping organized records of their data. Review with the class some of the ways (line graphs, bar charts) in which data can be visually presented.

Performance Assessment

Oral Presentation Tell students to choose one infectious disease and explain what causes the disease, what its symptoms are, how it is spread, its treatment, and how they could prevent the disease.

How Many Viruses Fit on a Pin?

Preparing for Inquiry

Key Concept To help appreciate the small size of viruses, people often compare them to other known objects.
Skills Objective Students will be able to
◆ make models to illustrate the size of a virus relative to the head of a pin;
◆ calculate the number of viruses that could fit on the head of a pin.
Time 45 minutes
Alternative Materials To make the 10-m strip, obtain long rolls of paper such as adding machine tape.

Guiding Inquiry

Invitation
Point out that referring to how many items fit on a pinhead often occurs when discussing things that are very small or very numerous.

Introducing the Procedure
◆ Review the idea of scale.
◆ Review metric measurements, if necessary.

Troubleshooting the Experiment
◆ Remind students that there are often different ways to solve specific calculation problems. Match up students using similar methods, then let different groups share their strategies with the class.

Expected Outcome
Area of the enlarged pinhead: $\pi \times$ radius^2 = 3.1 × 25 = 77.5 m²; area of enlarged virus: 0.002 × 0.002 = 0.000004 m²; could fit 77.5/0.000004 = 19,375,000 viruses on pinhead

Analyze and Conclude
1. About 20 million
2. Students should explain whether their predictions were based on reasoning or whether they "just guessed."
3. Although the magnified pinhead became very large, the magnified virus size was still quite small.

Skills Lab

How Many Viruses Fit on a Pin?

In this lab, you will make models to help you investigate the size of viruses.

Problem
How many viruses could fit on the head of a pin?

Materials
straight pin   long strips of paper
pencil   meter stick
scissors   tape
calculator (optional)

Procedure
1. Examine the head of a straight pin. Write a prediction about the number of viruses that could fit on the pinhead. **CAUTION:** *Avoid pushing the pin into anyone's skin.*
2. Assume that the pinhead has a diameter of about 1 mm. If the pinhead were enlarged 10,000 times, its diameter would measure 10 m. Create a model of the pinhead by cutting and taping together narrow strips of paper to make a strip that is 10 m long. The strip of paper represents the diameter of the enlarged pinhead.
3. Lay the 10-m strip of paper on the floor of your classroom or in the hall. Imagine creating a large circle that had the strip as its diameter. The circle would be the pinhead at the enlarged size. Calculate the area of the enlarged pinhead using this formula:
   $$\text{Area} = \pi \times \text{radius}^2$$
   Remember that you can find the radius by dividing the diameter by 2.

4. A virus particle may measure 200 nm on each side (1 nm equals a billionth of a meter). If the virus were enlarged 10,000 times, each side would measure 0.002 m. Cut out a square 0.002 m by 0.002 m to serve as a model for a virus. *(Hint:* 0.002 m = 2 mm)
5. Next, find the area in meters of one virus particle at the enlarged size. Remember that the area of a square equals side × side.
6. Now divide the area of the pinhead that you calculated in Step 3 by the area of one virus particle to find out how many viruses could fit on the pinhead.
7. Exchange your work with a partner, and check each other's calculations. Make any corrections that are necessary.

Analyze and Conclude
1. Approximately how many viruses can fit on the head of a pin?
2. How did your calculation compare with your prediction? If the two numbers were very different, explain why they were different.
3. What did you learn about the size of viruses by magnifying both the viruses and pinheads to 10,000 times their actual size?
4. **Think About It** Why do scientists sometimes make and use enlarged models of very small things such as viruses?

More to Explore
Think of another everyday object that you could use to model some other facts about viruses, such as their shapes or how they infect cells. Describe your model and explain why the object would be a good choice.

212

---

4. The enlarged models help them to understand details of structure.

Extending the Inquiry

More to Explore Encourage students to explain how they chose their models. Ask students to compare their models to what they know about viruses to determine the strengths and weaknesses of the model.

Safety

Remind students not to push the pin against anyone's skin. Caution students not to lose any of the pins.

Program Resources

◆ **Unit 2 Resources** Chapter 6 Skills Lab, pp. 28–29

SECTION 1 — Classifying Organisms

Key Ideas

◆ Biologists use classification to organize living things into groups.

◆ Species with similar evolutionary histories are classified more closely together.

◆ Today, organisms are classified into seven levels: kingdom, phylum, class, order, family, genus, and species.

Key Terms

classification   genus
taxonomy   species
binomial nomenclature   taxonomic key

SECTION 2 — The Six Kingdoms

Key Ideas

◆ The six kingdoms are: archaebacteria, eubacteria, protists, fungi, plants, and animals.

◆ Organisms are classified into kingdoms based on cell structure, ability to make food, and number of cells.

SECTION 3 — Bacteria

Key Ideas

◆ Bacteria are prokaryotes.

◆ Bacteria reproduce asexually by binary fission, which results in the production of two cells exactly like the parent cell. Some bacteria have a simple form of sexual reproduction called conjugation. This process results in a cell with a new combination of genetic information.

◆ Bacteria play both beneficial and harmful roles in the lives of humans.

Key Terms

bacterium   endospore
flagellum   decomposer
binary fission   infectious disease
asexual reproduction toxin
sexual reproduction   antibiotic
conjugation

SECTION 4 — Viruses

INTEGRATING HEALTH

Key Ideas

◆ Viruses are considered to be nonliving because viruses are not cells, and they do not use energy to grow and develop or to respond to their surroundings.

◆ All viruses have two basic parts: an outer coat that protects the virus and an inner core made of genetic material.

◆ Once inside a cell, a virus uses the host cell's functions to make its own proteins and genetic material. The proteins and genetic material assemble into new viruses, which burst out, destroying the host.

◆ There is no cure for viral diseases. Vaccines can prevent some viral and bacterial diseases.

Key Terms
virus
host
parasite
bacteriophage
vaccine

Organizing Information

Venn Diagram Copy the Venn diagram comparing viruses and bacteria onto a separate sheet of paper. Then complete the Venn diagram. (For more on Venn diagrams, see the Skills Handbook.)

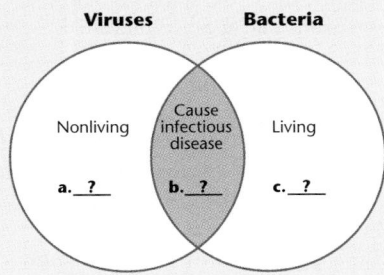

Viruses   Bacteria

Nonliving   Cause infectious disease   Living

a. ?   b. ?   c. ?

Organizing Information

Venn Diagram a. Can only multiply inside a cell or not treated with antibiotics **b.** Microscopic **c.** Can multiply by itself or treated with antibiotics

Program Resources

◆ **Unit 2 Resources** Chapter 6 Project Scoring Rubric, p. 8

◆ **Performance Assessment** Chapter 6, pp. 20–22

◆ **Chapter and Unit Tests** Chapter 6 Test, pp. 28–31

Media and Technology

Interactive Student Tutorial CD-ROM Chapter 6

Computer Test Bank Chapter 6 Text

Reviewing Content

Multiple Choice

1. c 2. a 3. b 4. a 5. c

True or False

6. Linneaus 7. True 8. True 9. bacteria
10. Active viruses

Checking Concepts

11. A scientific name gives information about an organism's characteristics and avoids confusion about the identity of the organism.

12. Fungi are heterotrophs; plants are autotrophs.

13. Cell wall – protects the cell; cytoplasm – contains ribosomes and genetic material; ribosomes – produce protein; genetic material – contains instruction for the cell's functions; flagellum – helps cell to move

14. Most bacteria reproduce asexually by binary fission, in which one cell divides into two cells. Some bacteria have a simple form of sexual reproduction called conjugation, in which some genetic material from one cell is transferred into another cell, eventually resulting in different cells.

15. Answers may vary. Student descriptions may be on making dairy products, such as yogurt, or vinegar, pickles, and sauerkraut.

16. Antibiotics kill bacteria without harming body cells. For example, penicillin weakens the cell wall of some bacteria and cause them to burst.

17. Viruses do not have cell structures. Viruses do not carry on the functions of cells, such as food getting and respiration. Viruses cannot reproduce on their own.

18. The proteins in the coat of the virus will only fit within certain proteins on the surface of the cell.

19. Vaccines prevent the spread of infectious diseases by stimulating people who receive them to produce chemicals that fight off invading viruses and bacteria.

20. Students' essays should include the idea that once the virus is suspended in the air it could land on many different kinds of surfaces, many different times, before it finds itself in a person's moist nose and throat. They should

Reviewing Content

 For more review of key concepts, see the Interactive Student Tutorial CD-ROM.

Multiple Choice

Choose the letter of the best answer.

1. The science of placing organisms into groups based on shared characteristics is called
   a. development.   b. biology.
   c. taxonomy.   d. evolution.

2. A genus is divided into
   a. species.   b. phyla.
   c. families.   d. classes.

3. Which organisms have cells that do not contain nuclei?
   a. protists
   b. archaebacteria
   c. plants
   d. fungi

4. Most bacteria are surrounded by a rigid protective structure called the
   a. cell wall.
   b. cell membrane.
   c. protein coat.
   d. flagellum.

5. Viruses multiply
   a. by conjugation.
   b. by binary fission.
   c. by taking over a cell's functions.
   d. both asexually and sexually.

True or False

If the statement is true, write true. If it is false, change the underlined word or words to make the statement true.

6. <u>Aristotle</u> devised a system of naming organisms that is called binomial nomenclature.

7. Most <u>archaebacteria</u> live in extreme environments.

8. Bacteria form <u>endospores</u> to survive unfavorable conditions in their surroundings.

9. Bacteriophages are viruses that attack and destroy <u>other viruses</u>.

10. <u>Hidden viruses</u> enter a cell and immediately begin to multiply.

Checking Concepts

11. What are the advantages of identifying an organism by its scientific name?

12. What is the major difference between fungi and plants?

13. What are the parts of a bacterial cell? Explain the role of each part.

14. Describe how bacteria reproduce.

15. Describe an example of how bacteria are used in food production.

16. Explain how antibiotics kill bacteria.

17. List three ways that viruses are different from cells.

18. Explain why a certain virus will attach to only one or a few types of cells.

19. How do vaccines prevent the spread of some infectious diseases?

20. **Writing to Learn** Imagine you are a cold virus. The student you infected just sneezed you into the air in the cafeteria. Write a description of what happens to you until you finally attach to a cell in another student.

Thinking Critically

21. **Classifying** Which two of the following organisms are most closely related: *Entamoeba histolytica, Escherichia coli, Entamoeba coli*? Explain your answer.

22. **Problem Solving** Bacteria will grow in the laboratory on a gelatin-like substance called agar. Viruses will not grow on agar. If you needed to grow viruses in the laboratory, what kind of substance would you have to use? Explain.

23. **Classifying** You know that viruses vary in shape, size, and the kinds of organisms they infect. Which one of these three characteristics would you use as a basis for a classification system for viruses? Explain your answer.

24. **Comparing and Contrasting** Describe the similarities of and differences between active and hidden viruses.

---

demonstrate knowledge of how viruses are spread and should mention the selectivity of viruses for a host.

Thinking Critically

21. *Entamoeba histolytica* and *Entamoeba coli*; they are in the same genus.

22. A substance that includes living cells would have to be used to grow viruses in a laboratory, because viruses need to infect living cells in order to increase their numbers.

23. Students might choose any of the three methods to classify viruses. Be sure they explain their choice. Scientists usually classify viruses on the basis of the organisms they infect.

24. All viruses invade the host cell and cause it to start producing new viruses. With an active virus, the takeover occurs immediately after the entry into the cell. With hidden viruses, the genetic material of the virus is incorporated into the cell's genetic material and it can be years before the virus actively takes over the cell.

Applying Skills

The graph shows how the number of bacteria that grow on a food source changes over time. Use the graph to answer Questions 25–27.

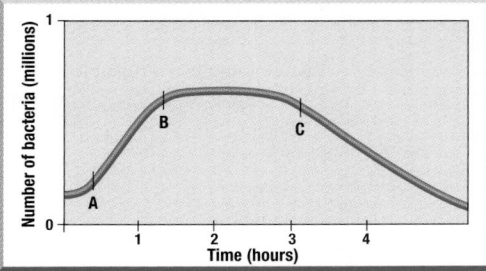

25. **Interpreting Data** Explain what is happening between points A and B.
26. **Developing Hypotheses** Develop a hypothesis to explain why the number of bacteria stays constant between points B and C.

27. **Designing Experiments** How could you test the hypothesis you developed in Question 26? What would your results show?

Performance ▼ Assessment

Present Your Project Lead your audience through your project from your survey to your conclusions. Be sure to explain why you chose the questions and survey group that you did. Use graphs or other visual displays to highlight important similarities or differences you found. Be sure to support your conclusions with data.

Reflect and Record Do you think that a survey like this one is similar to a science experiment? What makes them alike or different? In your journal, describe what you did to make your survey accurate and complete.

Test Preparation   *Use these questions to prepare for standardized tests.*

Read the passage. Then answer Questions 28–30.

Summer is a time for picnics, hiking, and camping. But many people are afraid to go out in the woods or fields for fear they'll catch Lyme disease.

The symptoms of Lyme disease often resemble those of other ailments. A victim may suffer from flu-like symptoms, such as headaches, fatigue, and chills. Many also develop a rash.

It took scientists many years to figure out that Lyme disease is caused by a bacterium that is spread by the bite of a tiny tick. The tick, although called a deer tick, can live on mice, raccoons, and birds, as well as on deer.

Although Lyme disease is difficult to diagnose, it is fairly easy to prevent. People can wear long-sleeved shirts, long pants, and hats when they are in wooded areas or open fields. Most people, however, become infected near their homes, in their own yards. Frequently checking yourself and your pets for deer ticks is the best precaution against Lyme disease.

28. What is the main idea of this passage?
    a. Deer ticks live on many wild animals.
    b. Lyme disease is caused by a bacterium.
    c. Lyme disease is a summertime disease.
    d. Although Lyme disease can be difficult to diagnose, it is fairly easy to prevent.
29. Based on this passage, which of the following statements is true?
    a. The symptoms of Lyme disease are similar to those of some other ailments.
    b. Lyme disease is caused by a virus.
    c. Lyme disease is easy to diagnose.
    d. Some people are immune to Lyme disease.
30. Why is Lyme disease most often contracted in the summer?
    a. Ticks die in autumn and new eggs don't hatch until July.
    b. Deer feed only during the summer.
    c. People are outdoors in the summer more often than in any other season.
    d. Bacteria live only during summer.

Applying Skills

25. Bacteria are rapidly growing because they have plenty of food available.
26. Sample: The number of bacteria stays constant between points B and C because the amount of food available to the bacteria can only support this number of bacteria.
27. Students might suggest testing their hypothesis from Question 26 by preparing petri dishes with different amounts of food and graphing the growth patterns of the bacteria.

Performance ▼ Assessment

Present Your Project Have students present their projects while their classmates take notes. Students' conclusions must be drawn from the results of their own surveys. Encourage students to compare their data with other sources. Prepare classroom space for students to display their posters or visual aids.

Reflect and Record Students should realize that a survey is similar to a science experiment in that they both require careful analysis. Students may express frustration that it is much more difficult to control variables in their surveys.

Test Preparation

28. d 29. a 30. c

Program Resources

◆ **Inquiry Skills Activity Book** Provides teaching and review of all inquiry skills

CHAPTER 7

Protists and Fungi

Sections	Time	Student Edition Activities	Other Activities
CHAPTER PROJECT **A Mushroom Farm** p. 217	Ongoing (1½ weeks)	Check Your Progress, pp. 230, 242 Present Your Project, p. 245	**TE** Chapter 7 Project Notes, pp. 216–217
1 Protists pp. 218–227 ◆ Describe the characteristics of animal-like, funguslike, and plantlike protists.	2½ periods/ 1 block	**Discover** What Lives in a Drop of Pond Water?, p. 218 **Try This** Feeding Paramecia, p. 222 **Sharpen Your Skills** Predicting, p. 225 **Science at Home,** p. 227	**TE** Inquiry Challenge, p. 219 **TE** Inquiry Challenge, p. 221 **TE** Building Inquiry Skills: Making Models, p. 223 **TE** Inquiry Challenge, p. 224 **TE** Building Inquiry Skills: Making Models, p. 224 **TE** Demonstration, p. 226 **LM** 7, "Comparing Protists"
2 _INTEGRATING ENVIRONMENTAL SCIENCE_ **Algal Blooms** pp.228–232 ◆ Describe how red tides occur and explain why they are dangerous. ◆ Explain how the rapid growth of algae affects a pond or lake.	1 period/ ½ block	**Discover** How Can Algal Growth Affect Pond Life?, p. 228 **Real-World Lab: You and Your Environment** An Explosion of Life, p. 231	**TE** Building Inquiry Skills: Making Models, p. 229 **TE** Including All Students, p. 230 **IES** "Where River Meets Sea," pp. 28–30
3 Fungi pp. 233–242 ◆ Name the characteristics that all fungi share. ◆ Describe how fungi obtain food. ◆ List the roles fungi play in the living world. ◆ Describe the ways that fungi reproduce.	2 periods/ 1 block	**Discover** Do All Models Look Alike?, p. 233 **Try This** Making Spore Prints, p. 235 **Try This** Spreading Spores, p. 236 **Skills Lab: Drawing Conclusions** What's for Lunch?, pp. 238–239	**TE** Building Inquiry Skills: Observing, p. 234 **TE** Building Inquiry Skills: Observing, p. 236 **TE** Demonstration, p. 237 **TE** Building Inquiry Skills: Designing Experiments, p. 240 **TE** Integrating Earth Science, p. 242 **IES** "A Nation of Immigrants," pp. 12–13
Study Guide/Chapter Assessment pp. 243–245	1 period/ ½ block		**ISAB** Provides teaching and review of all inquiry skills

For Standard or Block Schedule The Resource Pro® CD-ROM gives you maximum flexibility for planning your instruction for any type of schedule. Resource Pro® contains Planning Express®, an advanced scheduling program, as well as the entire contents of the Teaching Resources and the Computer Test Bank.

CHAPTER PLANNING GUIDE

Program Resources	Assessment Strategies	Media and Technology
UR Chapter 7 Project Teacher Notes, pp. 30–31 **UR** Chapter 7 Project Overview and Worksheets, pp. 32–35	**SE** Performance Assessment: Present Your Project, p. 245 **TE** Check Your Progress, pp. 230, 242 **UR** Chapter 7 Project Scoring Rubric, p. 36	Science Explorer Internet Site at www.phschool.com
UR 7-1 Lesson Plan, p. 37 **UR** 7-1 Section Summary, p. 38 **UR** 7-1 Review and Reinforce, p. 39 **UR** 7-1 Enrich, p. 40	**SE** Section 1 Review, p. 227 **TE** Ongoing Assessment, pp. 219, 221, 223, 225 **TE** Performance Assessment, p. 227	Life Science Videotape 2; Videodisc Unit 2 Side 2, "Fungi and Algae" Audio CD, English-Spanish Summary 7-1 Transparency 28, "Exploring Protozoans— Ameba" Transparency 29, "Exploring Protozoans— Paramecium" Transparency 30, "The Structure of a Euglena" Interactive Student Tutorial CD-ROM, Chapter 7
UR 7-2 Lesson Plan, p. 41 **UR** 7-2 Section Summary, p. 42 **UR** 7-2 Review and Reinforce, p. 43 **UR** 7-2 Enrich, p. 44 **UR** Chapter 7 Real-World Lab, pp. 49–50	**SE** Section 2 Review, p. 230 **TE** Ongoing Assessment, p. 229 **TE** Performance Assessment, p. 230	Life Science Videotape 2; Videodisc Unit 2 Side 2, "Fungi and Algae" Audio CD, English-Spanish Summary 7-2
UR 7-3 Lesson Plan, p. 45 **UR** 7-3 Section Summary, p. 46 **UR** 7-3 Review and Reinforce, p. 47 **UR** 7-3 Enrich, p. 48 **UR** Chapter 7 Skills Lab, pp. 51–53	**SE** Section 3 Review, p. 242 **TE** Ongoing Assessment, pp. 235, 237, 241 **TE** Performance Assessment, p. 242	Audio CD, English-Spanish Summary 7-3 Transparency 31, "The Structure of a Mushroom"
RCA Provides strategies to improve science reading skills **GSW** Provides worksheets to promote student comprehension of content	**SE** Chapter 7 Study Guide/Assessment, pp. 243–245 **PA** Chapter 7 Performance Assessment, pp. 23–25 **CUT** Chapter 7 Test, pp. 32–35 **CTB** Chapter 7 Test	Interactive Student Tutorial CD-ROM, Chapter 7 Computer Test Bank, Chapter 7 Test

Key: **SE** Student Edition **TE** Teacher's Edition **UR** Unit Resources
CTB Computer Test Bank **PTA** Product Testing Activities by *Consumer Reports* **LM** Laboratory Manual
ISAB Inquiry Skills Activity Book **RCA** Reading in the Content Area **IES** Interdisciplinary Explorations Series
GSW Guided Study Worksheets **PA** Performance Assessment **CUT** Chapter and Unit Tests

Meeting the National Science Education Standards and AAAS Benchmarks

National Science Education Standards	Benchmarks for Science Literacy	Unifying Themes
Science as Inquiry (Content Standard A) ◆ **Identify questions that can be answered through scientific investigations** How does the amount of fertilizer affect algae growth? (*Real-World Lab*) How does the presence of sugar or salt affect the activity of yeast? (*Skills Lab*) ◆ **Use mathematics in all aspects of scientific inquiry** Students use mathematics as variables in scientific investigations. (*Real-World Lab, Skills Lab*) ◆ **Design and conduct a scientific investigation** Students design and conduct an investigation about how light and moisture affect the growth of mushrooms. (*Section 2; Chapter Project*) **Life Science** (Content Standard C) ◆ **Structure and function in living systems** Students learn the main characteristics of protists and the differences among the protist groups. (*Section 1*) Students learn the characteristics of fungi, how they obtain food, and their role in the living world. (*Section 3; Chapter Project*) ◆ **Populations and ecosystems** Students learn about the effects of the rapid growth of algae on a pond or a lake. (*Section 2*) ◆ **Diversity and adaptations of organisms** Students learn about the diversity among protists and fungi. (*Sections 1 and 3*)	**1B Scientific Inquiry** Students control variables to see the effect of fertilizer on algae growth. Students control variables to see the effect of sugar or salt on yeast. (*Real-World Lab; Skills Lab*) **5A Diversity of Life** Characteristics that describe protists, algae, and fungi are presented in a general format. (*Sections 1, 2, 3*) **5D Interdependence of Life** Interactions between fungi and food, fungi and their relationship to diseases, and fungi and their relationship to the environment are explored. (*Section 3*) **11D Scale** Students organize the results of investigations in data tables and interpret their results. (*Real-World Lab; Skills Lab*)	◆ **Scale and Structure** Protists are unicellular organisms that contain nuclei. Most are microscopic and cannot be seen without the aid of a microscope. Fungi are made of threadlike fibers called *hyphae*. (*Sections 1, 3*) ◆ **Unity and Diversity** There are many types of protists, but they all share basic characteristics. Fungi are alike in the way they reproduce and obtain food. (*Sections 1, 3*) ◆ **Systems and Interactions** Some protists are parasitic in nature and can harm crops and cause disease in humans. Fungi interact with the living world in a variety of ways. (*Section 3*) ◆ **Energy** Animal-like protists are heterotrophic, obtaining food by consuming other organisms; funguslike protists are heterotrophs; and plantlike protists and algae are autotrophs. Fungi are heterotrophs, obtaining energy by absorbing food from living organisms. (*Sections 1, 2, 3*)

Take It to the Net

 *Interactive text at www.phschool.com*

Science Explorer comes alive with iText.

- **Complete student text** is accessible from any computer with Internet access or a CD-ROM drive.
- **Animations, simulations, and videos** enhance student understanding and retention of concepts.
- **Self-tests and online study tools** assess student understanding.

STAY CURRENT with **SCIENCE NEWS**®

Find out the latest research and information about protists and fungi at: **www.phschool.com**

Go to **www.phschool.com** and click on the Science icon. Then click on <u>Science Explorer: Life, Earth, and Physical Science</u> under PH@school.

ACTIVITY	Time (minutes)	Materials *Quantities for one work group*	Skills
Section 1			
Discover, p. 218	25	**Consumable** pond dropper **Nonconsumable** plastic dropper, microscope slide, cover slip, microscope	Observing
Try This, p. 222	15	**Consumable** paramecium culture, Chlorella culture, cotton fibers **Nonconsumable** plastic dropper, microscope slide, microscope	Inferring
Sharpen your Skills, p. 225	20	**Consumable** euglena culture, aluminum foil **Nonconsumable** plastic petri dish, compound microscope	Predicting
Science at Home, p.227	home	No special materials are required.	Communicating
Section 2			
Discover, p. 228	15	**Consumable** water **Nonconsumable** clear plastic container, green paper punches, spoons	Predicting
Real-World Lab, p. 231	30 min first day, 10 min subsequent days	**Consumable** aged tap water, aquarium water, liquid fertilizer **Nonconsumable** 4 glass jars with lids, graduated cylinder, marking pen	Controlling Variables, Predicting, Drawing Conclusions
Section 3			
Discover, p. 233	15	**Consumable** self-seal bags, tape, old bread, fruit **Nonconsumable** hand lens	Observing
Try This, p. 235	10 min; 15 min for observations two days later	**Consumable** mushroom cap, white paper **Nonconsumable** large plastic container	Predicting
Try This, p. 236	25	**Consumable** tape **Nonconsumable** round balloon, cotton balls, stick or ruler about 30 cm long, modeling clay, pin	Making Models
Skills Lab, pp. 238–239	45	**Consumable** 5 plastic straws, salt, sugar, warm water (40–45°C), dry powdered yeast **Nonconsumable** marking pen, beaker, graduated cylinder, 5 narrow-necked bottles, 5 round balloons	Drawing Conclusions

A list of all materials required for the Student Edition activities can be found on pages T25–T33. You can obtain information about ordering materials by calling 1-800-848-9500 or by accessing the Science Explorer Internet site at **www.phschool.com**.

A Mushroom Farm

Although most students are probably familiar with mushrooms, they may not know very much about their structure or how they grow.

Purpose In this project, students will determine the effect of changing a single variable on the growth of mushrooms.

Skills Focus After completing the Chapter 7 Project, students will be able to
◆ develop a hypothesis concerning how a variable affects mushroom growth;
◆ design and perform an experiment to test their hypothesis;
◆ draw conclusions based on their results;
◆ communicate their results in the form of a poster.

Project Time Line This project will take four to five weeks. It will take one class period to introduce the project, discuss mushrooms, and have students decide what variable to test. Allow students a day or two to come up with an experimental design to test their chosen variables. The experiment will take between two and four weeks, depending on the conditions being tested. Allow one week following the end of the project for data analysis and poster preparation. Before beginning the project, see Chapter 7 Project Teacher Notes on pages 30–31 in Unit 2 Resources for more details on carrying out the project. Also, distribute to students the Chapter 7 Project Overview, Worksheets, and Scoring Rubric on pages 32–36 in Unit 2 Resources.

Possible Materials It is difficult to grow mushrooms from spores you collect yourself. Mushroom growing kits are available from most biological supply companies. They provide all the materials necessary to complete this project. You may need additional pots and peat moss. You can use milk cartons, two-liter plastic bottle bottoms, or other such containers with holes cut in the bottom. A spray bottle works well for watering the containers.

CHAPTER 7 Protists and Fungi

WEB ACTIVITY www.phschool.com

SECTION 1 Protists

Discover **What Lives in a Drop of Water?**
Try This **Feeding Paramecia**
Sharpen Your Skills **Predicting**
Science at Home **Kitchen Algae**

SECTION 2 *Integrating Environmental Science* **Algal Blooms**

Discover **How Can Algal Growth Affect Pond Life?**
Real-World Lab **An Explosion of Life**

SECTION 3 Fungi

Discover **Do All Molds Look Alike?**
Try This **Making Spore Prints**
Try This **Spreading Spores**
Skills Lab **What's for Lunch?**

216

For testing variables you will need
◆ a dark location and a light source (to test light);
◆ a thermometer and a warm and a cool location (to test temperature);
◆ substrate lacking nutrients and some fertilizer (to test nutrients).

Launching the Project To introduce the project and to stimulate interest, ask students: **How do you think mushrooms grow? Are they like plants?** Students will probably describe mushrooms growing somewhere damp and warm, such as in the forest after a rain. Students may know that mushrooms are fungi, but may also think of them as plants because they grow out of the ground in a similar way. Encourage students to discuss similarities and differences between mushrooms and plants.

Allow time for students to read the description of the project in their text and the Chapter 7 Project Overview on pages 32–33 in Unit 2 Resources. Then discuss experimental design. Make sure students understand the difference between the manipulated and

CHAPTER 7 PROJECT

A Mushroom Farm

Have you ever seen mushrooms growing in a local park or on a forest floor? Over the centuries, people have been curious about these organisms because they seem to sprout up without warning, often after a rainfall. Mushrooms are the most familiar type of fungi. In some ways, they resemble plants, often growing near or even on them like small umbrellas. But mushrooms are very different from plants in some important ways. In this project, you'll learn these differences.

As you read the chapter, you'll also learn about other fungi and about the diverse kingdom known as protists. You'll find out how these organisms carry out their life activities and how important they are to people and to the environment.

Your Goal To determine the conditions needed for mushrooms to grow.

To complete this project successfully, you must
◆ choose one variable, and design a way to test how it affects mushroom growth
◆ make daily observations, and record them in a data table
◆ prepare a poster that describes the results of your experiment
◆ follow the safety guidelines in Appendix A

Get Started With your partners, brainstorm possible hypotheses about the way variables such as light or moisture could affect the growth of mushrooms. Write your own hypothesis and the reasons why you chose it. Write out a plan for testing the variable that you chose. Then start growing your mushrooms!

Check Your Progress You'll be working on this project as you study the chapter. To keep your project on track, look for Check Your Progress boxes at the following points.
Section 2 Review, page 230: Make observations and collect data.
Section 3 Review, page 242: Plan a poster about your discoveries.

Present Your Project At the end of the chapter (page 245), you will display your poster that details what you learned about mushroom growth.

Although these scarlet waxy cap mushrooms are quite tasty, beware. There are poisonous mushrooms that look just like them.

responding variables, and why other variables must be controlled. Pass out copies of the Chapter 7 Project Worksheets on pages 34–35 in Unit 2 Resources for students to review.

Have students form groups and choose their variables. Check that some groups choose different variables. Students should develop hypotheses about how mushroom growth will be affected by their variable.

Performance Assessment

The Chapter 7 Project Scoring Rubric on page 36 of Unit 2 Resources will help you evaluate how well students complete the Chapter 7 Project. Students will be assessed on
◆ how well they define and control the variables in their experiment;
◆ how well their experimental design tests their hypothesis, and the thoroughness of their data collection;
◆ their analysis of the results, and the clarity and organization of their poster;
◆ their ability to work cooperatively in a group.
By sharing the Chapter 7 Scoring Rubric with students at the beginning of the project, you will make it clear to them what they are expected to do.

Program Resources

◆ **Unit 2 Resources** Chapter 7 Project Teacher Notes, pp. 30–31; Chapter 7 Project Overview and Worksheets, pp. 32–35; Chapter 7 Project Scoring Rubric, p. 36

WEB ACTIVITY www.phschool.com

You will find an Internet activity, chapter self-tests for students, and links to other chapter topics at this site.

SECTION 1 Protists

Objective

After completing the lesson, students will be able to
◆ describe the characteristics of animal-like, funguslike, and plantlike protists.

Key Terms protozoan, pseudopod, contractile vacuole, cilia, symbiosis, mutualism, spore, algae, pigment

1 Engage/Explore

Activating Prior Knowledge

Before class, place several drops of vegetable oil in a small dish of water. Add a few drops of green food coloring to the water. To begin, place the dish on an overhead projector. Ask students: **How can you tell whether the blobs you see are alive?** (*Sample: Check for reaction to stimuli, taking in food, breathing, movement*)

•••••••• DISCOVER ••••••••

Skills Focus observing
Materials *plastic dropper, pond water, microscope slide, cover slip, microscope*
Time 25 minutes
Tips Have students predict what they might observe in the water. Suggest students use their high-power objective lenses if they have them.
Expected Outcome Both algae and protozoans should be visible. Green algae have a greenish tint, but most organisms appear colorless. Organisms with flagella or pseudopods could be either protozoans or algae.
Think It Over Students will probably associate movement with life.

SECTION 1 Protists

DISCOVER •••••••••••••••••••••••• ACTIVITY

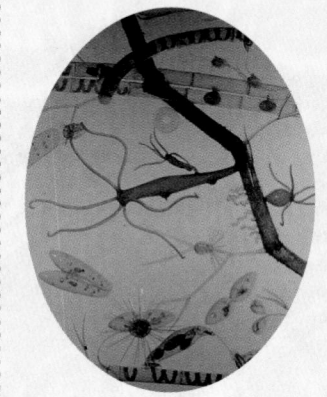

What Lives in a Drop of Water?

1. Use a plastic dropper to place a drop of pond water on a microscope slide.

2. Put the slide under your microscope's low-power lens. Focus on the objects you see.

3. Find at least three different objects that you think might be organisms. Observe them for a few minutes.

4. Draw the three organisms in your notebook. Below each sketch, describe the movements or behaviors of the organism. Wash your hands thoroughly when you have finished.

Think It Over
Observing What characteristics did you observe that made you think that each organism was alive?

GUIDE FOR READING

◆ What are the characteristics of animal-like, funguslike, and plantlike protists?

Reading Tip As you read, use the headings to make an outline of the different kinds of protists.

Look at the objects in Figure 1. What do they look like to you? Jewels? Stained glass windows? Crystal ornaments? You might be surprised to learn that these beautiful, delicate structures are the walls of unicellular organisms called diatoms. Diatoms live in both salt water and fresh water. These tiny organisms are at the base of the food web that provides food for some of Earth's largest organisms—whales.

What Is a Protist?

Diatoms are only one type of organism classified in the protist kingdom. Protists are so different from each other that you can think of this kingdom as the "junk drawer" kingdom. You may have a drawer in your room where you store ticket stubs, postcards, and other odds and ends. Just as these items don't really fit anywhere else in your room, protists don't really fit into any other biological kingdom. Protists do share some characteristics. They are all eukaryotes, or organisms that have cells with nuclei. In addition, all protists live in moist surroundings.

Despite these common characteristics, the word that best describes the protist kingdom is diversity. For example, most protists are unicellular like the diatoms. On the other hand, some

Figure 1 These delicate-looking diatoms are classified in the protist kingdom.

READING STRATEGIES

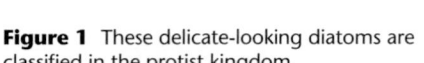

Reading Tip Review outlines. Explain that main topics should be written with Roman numerals, subtopics should be written with capital letters, and important details should be written with numerals. Use an example such as the following partial outline for the first main topic in the section.
I. Animal-like Protists
  A. Protozoans with Pseudopods
  B. Protozoans with Cilia

After students read the information under topics A and B, discuss key details that should be included under these headings.

Study and Comprehension Have students make compare/contrast tables to list characteristics of animal-like, funguslike, and plantlike protists. Suggest they list the three types of protists across the top of the table and the characteristics in the left-hand column.

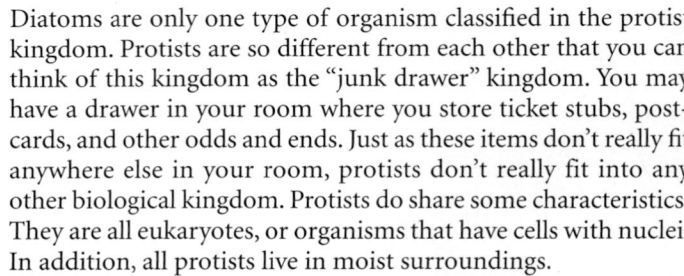

218

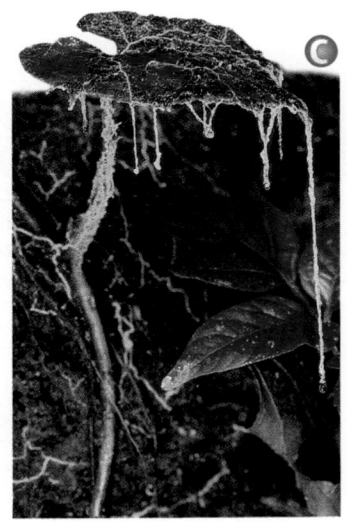

protists are multicellular. In fact, the protists known as giant kelps can be over 100 meters long. Protists also vary in how they obtain food—some are heterotrophs, some are autotrophs, and others are both. Some protists cannot move, while others zoom around their moist surroundings.

Because of the great variety of protists, scientists have proposed different ways of grouping these organisms. One useful way of grouping protists is to divide them into three categories: animal-like protists, funguslike protists, and plantlike protists.

☑️ *Checkpoint* *What characteristics do all protists share?*

Animal-like Protists

What image pops into your head when you think of an animal? A tiger chasing its prey? A snake slithering onto a rock? Most people immediately associate animals with movement. In fact, movement is often involved with an important characteristic of animals—obtaining food. All animals are heterotrophs that must obtain food by consuming other organisms.

Like animals, animal-like protists are heterotrophs. And most animal-like protists, or **protozoans** (proh tuh ZOH unz), are able to move from place to place to obtain their food. Unlike animals, however, protozoans are unicellular. Some scientists distinguish between four types of protozoans based on the way these organisms move and live.

Protozoans With Pseudopods The ameba in *Exploring Protozoans* on the next page belongs to the group of protozoans called sarcodines. Sarcodines move and feed by forming **pseudopods** (SOO doh pahdz)—temporary bulges of the cell membrane that fill with cytoplasm. The word *pseudopod* means "false foot." Pseudopods form when the cell membrane pushes outward in one location. The cytoplasm flows into the bulge

Figure 2 The protist kingdom includes animal-like, plantlike, and funguslike organisms. **A.** These shells contained unicellular, animal-like protists called foraminifera. **B.** This red alga is a multicellular, plantlike protist that lives on ocean floors. **C.** This yellow slime mold is a funguslike protist.
Comparing and Contrasting In what way are animal-like protists similar to animals? How do they differ?

2 Facilitate

What Is a Protist?

Building Inquiry Skills: Forming Operational Definitions

Display pictures of protists such as slime molds, paramecia, euglenoids, diatoms, and algae in stations around the room. Have small groups list the characteristics they observe. Ask students if it is possible to create an operational definition of a protist. Have students consider this as they read the rest of the section.
learning modality: visual

Animal-like Protists

Inquiry Challenge

Materials *plastic dropper, ameba culture, microscope slide, cover slip, microscope*
ACTIVITY
Time 20 minutes
Tips Challenge students to identify the pseudopod action of an ameba they observe. Have them place a drop of the ameba culture on a slide and carefully add a cover slip, then observe the organisms under low and high power. Ask: **Can you tell when the ameba is using its pseudopods to eat and when it is using them to move?** (*Students may say that when the ameba is eating, it wraps two pseudopods around the food; when it is moving, it puts out a pseudopod and flows into it.*) Students can sketch what they observe and label the parts of the ameba. Observations should include the organism's shape, size, and motion.
learning modality: visual

Program Resources

◆ **Unit 2 Resources** 7-1 Lesson Plan, p. 37; 7-1 Section Summary, p. 38

Media and Technology

🎧 **Audio CD** English-Spanish Summary 7-1

Answers to Self-Assessment

Caption Question

Figure 2 Animal-like protists are like animals in that they are heterotrophs, moving from place to place to obtain food. They are different in that they are unicellular.

☑️ *Checkpoint*

All protists are eukaryotes and live in moist surroundings.

Ongoing Assessment

Writing Have students explain why protists are thought of as the "junk drawer" kingdom by describing characteristics, categories, and examples of protists.

Animal-like Protists,
continued

EXPLORING
Protozoans

Ask students: **What do these protists have in common?** *(They eat the same things, they both have nuclei, cytoplasm, food vacuoles, and contractile vacuoles.)*
Ask: **What is different about them?** *(Amebas live in soil and water, paramecia only in water; paramecia move with cilia, amebas move with pseudopods; paramecia ingest food into an oral groove, amebas surround food with pseudopods; amebas have one nucleus, paramecia have two.)* As students list the similarities and differences, include them in a Venn diagram on the board. Then draw students' attention to the number and shapes of the contractile vacuoles in the two protists. Remind students that amebas live in soil or water, and paramecia live only in the water. Then ask: **What characteristics of the ameba do you think make it suited to living in either soil or water?** *(Sample: They can take any shape and flow easily through different substances. The contractile vacuole allows excess water to be expelled.)*
What characteristics of the paramecium do you think make it suited to living only in water? *(Sample: The cilia act like tiny oars to move the paramecium through the water and sweep food into the oral groove. The cilia may not be as effective in a solid environment such as soil. Their rigid shape may make it difficult to move through compacted soil. The two contractile vacuoles remove excess water from the cell.)*
learning modality: logical/ mathematical

and the rest of the organism follows. Pseudopods enable sarcodines to move in response to changes in the environment. For example, amebas use psuedopods to move away from bright light. Sarcodines also use pseudopods to trap food. The organism extends a pseudopod on each side of the food particle. The two pseudopods then join together, trapping the particle inside.

Organisms that live in fresh water, such as amebas, have a problem. Small particles, like those of water, pass easily through the cell membrane into the cytoplasm. If the excess water were to build up inside the cell, the ameba would burst. Fortunately, amebas have a **contractile vacuole** (kun TRAK til VAK yoo ohl), a structure that collects the extra water and then expels it from the cell.

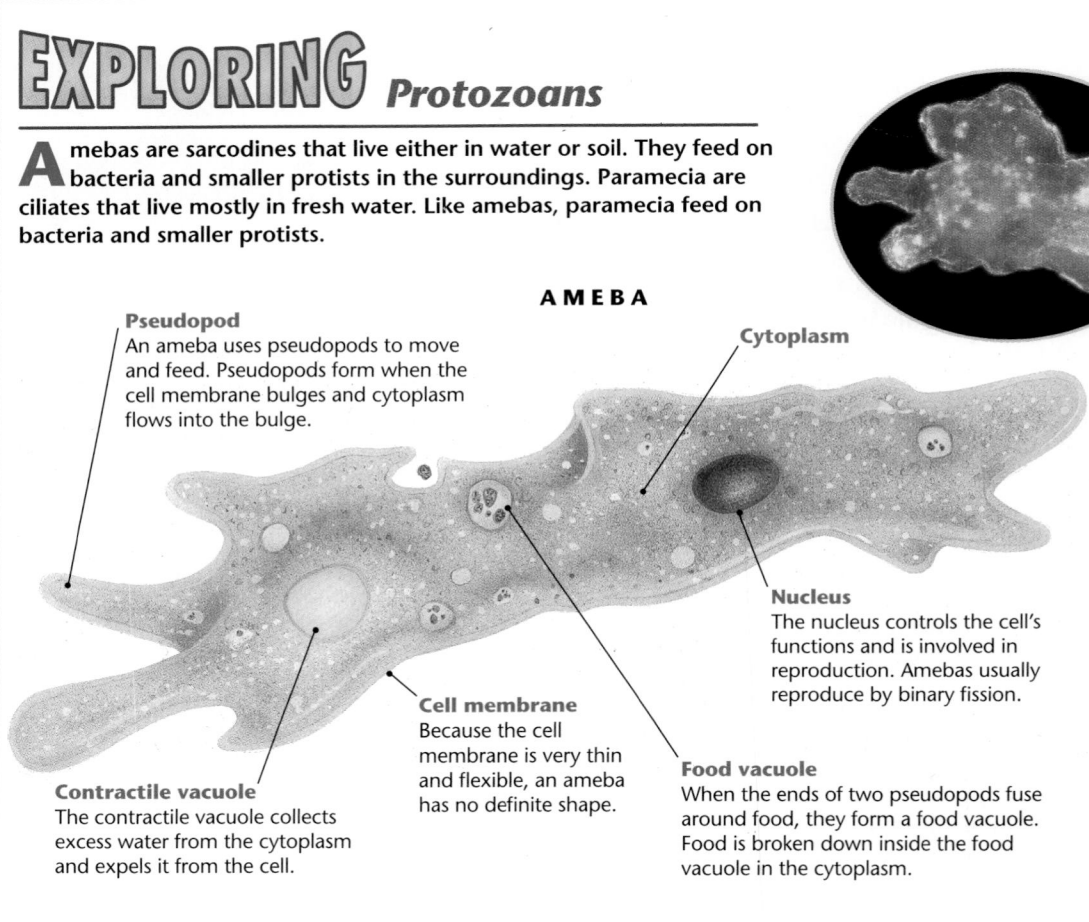

EXPLORING Protozoans

Amebas are sarcodines that live either in water or soil. They feed on bacteria and smaller protists in the surroundings. Paramecia are ciliates that live mostly in fresh water. Like amebas, paramecia feed on bacteria and smaller protists.

AMEBA

Pseudopod
An ameba uses pseudopods to move and feed. Pseudopods form when the cell membrane bulges and cytoplasm flows into the bulge.

Cytoplasm

Nucleus
The nucleus controls the cell's functions and is involved in reproduction. Amebas usually reproduce by binary fission.

Cell membrane
Because the cell membrane is very thin and flexible, an ameba has no definite shape.

Food vacuole
When the ends of two pseudopods fuse around food, they form a food vacuole. Food is broken down inside the food vacuole in the cytoplasm.

Contractile vacuole
The contractile vacuole collects excess water from the cytoplasm and expels it from the cell.

220

Background

Facts and Figures Free-living protists encounter changes in temperature, water acidity, food supply, moisture, and light. Many survive during these changes by entering a dormant stage—forming cysts with tough walls that act as protective coverings. During encystment, protozoans that have flagella and cilia lose them, and the contractile vacuole and food vacuoles

disappear. Many protozoans can form cysts, and biologists believe this ability formed early in their evolutionary history.

Some parasitic protozoans, such as the one that causes amebic dysentery, also form cysts. The cysts are excreted and survive in the soil or water, and humans who come into contact with the cysts can be infected.

Protozoans With Cilia The second type of animal-like protist is the ciliate. Ciliates have structures called **cilia** (SIL ee uh) which are hairlike projections from cells that move with a wavelike pattern. They use cilia to move, obtain food, and sense the environment. Cilia act something like tiny oars to move a ciliate. Their movement also sweeps food into the organism.

Ciliates have complex cells. In *Exploring Protozoans*, you see a ciliate called a paramecium. Notice that the paramecium has two nuclei. The large nucleus controls the everyday tasks of the cell. The small nucleus functions in reproduction. Paramecia usually reproduce asexually by binary fission. Sometimes, they reproduce by conjugation. This occurs when two paramecia join together and exchange genetic material.

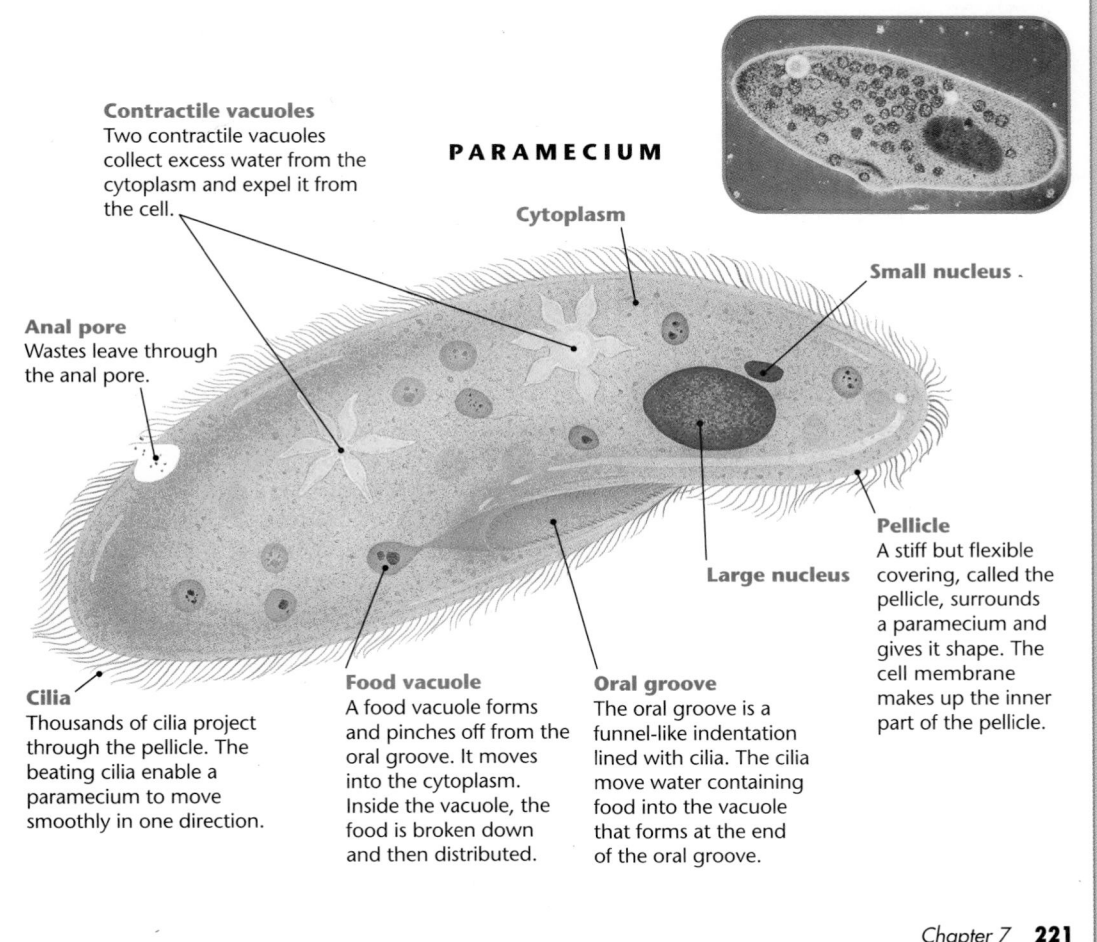

PARAMECIUM

Contractile vacuoles
Two contractile vacuoles collect excess water from the cytoplasm and expel it from the cell.

Cytoplasm

Small nucleus

Anal pore
Wastes leave through the anal pore.

Pellicle
A stiff but flexible covering, called the pellicle, surrounds a paramecium and gives it shape. The cell membrane makes up the inner part of the pellicle.

Large nucleus

Cilia
Thousands of cilia project through the pellicle. The beating cilia enable a paramecium to move smoothly in one direction.

Food vacuole
A food vacuole forms and pinches off from the oral groove. It moves into the cytoplasm. Inside the vacuole, the food is broken down and then distributed.

Oral groove
The oral groove is a funnel-like indentation lined with cilia. The cilia move water containing food into the vacuole that forms at the end of the oral groove.

Materials *microscope, slide and cover slip, water, plastic dropper, paramecium culture, ice*
Time 30 minutes

ACTIVITY

Challenge students to form hypotheses about how water temperature affects the activity level of a paramecium, then design experiments using the materials above to test their hypotheses. *(Sample design: materials— two or more paramecium cultures, plastic dropper, microscope, slides, cover slips; procedure— put the paramecia in water of varying temperatures, then examine them under the microscope; results— paramecia are active at room temperature and slow down at about 2°C.)* After you review their designs, have students carry out their experiments and report their findings to the class. **learning modality: logical/mathematical**

Media and Technology

 Transparencies "Exploring Protozoans—Ameba," Transparency 28

 Transparencies "Exploring Protozoans—Paramecium," Transparency 29

Ongoing Assessment

Oral Presentation Have students compare and contrast the characteristics of an ameba and a paramecium.

221

Animal-like Protists, continued

Skills Focus inferring
Materials *plastic dropper, paramecium culture,* Chlorella *culture, microscope slide, cotton fibers, microscope*
Time 15 minutes
Tips As well as using cotton fibers, students can slow down the paramecia by placing a cover slip over the drop of culture and absorbing some of the water by holding the edge of a piece of lens paper against the edge of the cover slip. Another option is to add one drop of a 2–3% solution of clear gelatin to the drop of culture on the slide. Make sure students wash their hands immediately after the activity.
Inferring Students should see green food vacuoles form inside the paramecia. Students should conclude that paramecia are heterotrophs because they ingest the *Chlorella. Chlorella* behave like autotrophs because they do not seem to be ingesting food and are green like plants.
Extend Have students predict how long it will take the paramecia to ingest all the *Chlorella,* then check their slides at regular intervals to test their predictions. Have students turn off the lights on the microscopes when they are not making observations to avoid overheating the paramecia. **learning modality: visual**

 Integrating Health

Ask students to describe ways that hikers can avoid ingesting *Giardia.* (*Samples: carrying enough water; using purifying treatments; boiling water before using*) Inform students that the safest way to purify water of organisms is to boil it for at least three minutes. This will kill the organisms, but it will not necessarily make the water safe if the water also contains chemical pollutants. **learning modality: verbal**

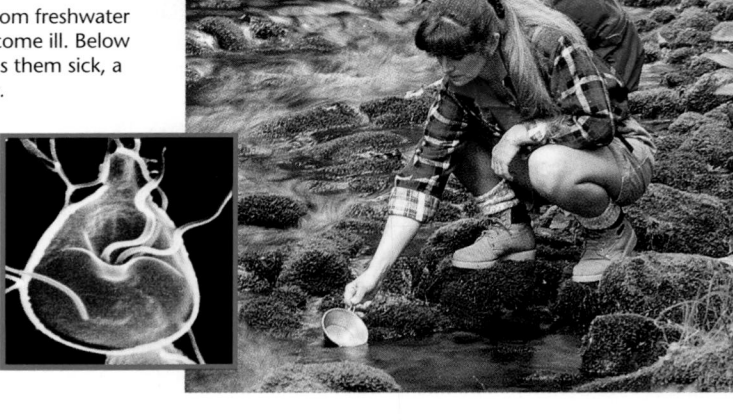

Figure 3 When people drink from freshwater streams and lakes, they may become ill. Below you see the organism that makes them sick, a protozoan called *Giardia lamblia.*

Feeding Paramecia

In this activity you will feed *Chlorella,* a plantlike protist, to paramecia.

1. Use a plastic dropper to place one drop of paramecium culture on a micrscope slide. Add some cotton fibers to slow down the paramecia.

2. Use the microscope's low-power objective to find some paramecia.

3. Add one drop of *Chlorella* to the paramecium culture on your slide.

4. Switch to high power and locate a paramecium. Observe what happens. Then wash your hands.

Inferring What evidence do you have that paramecia are heterotrophs? That *Chlorella* are autotrophs?

222

Protozoans With Flagella The third type of protozoans are called zooflagellates (zoh uh FLAJ uh lits)—animal-like protists that use flagella to move. Most zooflagellates have one to eight long, whiplike flagella that help them move.

Many zooflagellates live inside the bodies of other organisms. For example, one type of zooflagellate lives in the intestines of termites. The zooflagellates digest the wood that the termites eat, producing sugars for themselves and for some termites. In turn, the termites protect the zooflagellates. The interaction between these two species is an example of **symbiosis** (sim bee OH sis)—a close relationship where at least one of the species benefits. When both partners benefit from living together, the relationship is a type of symbiosis called **mutualism.**

INTEGRATING HEALTH Sometimes a zooflagellate harms the animal in which it lives. In Figure 3 you see a zooflagellate called *Giardia.* This zooflagellate is a parasite in humans. When a person drinks water containing *Giardia,* the zooflagellates attach to the person's intestine, where they feed and reproduce. The person develops a serious intestinal condition. This can occur even in unpopulated areas where wild animals, such as beavers, deposit *Giardia* into streams, rivers, and lakes.

Other Protozoans The fourth type of protozoans, the sporozoans, are characterized more by the way they live than by the way they move. Sporozoans are parasites that feed on the cells and body fluids of their hosts. They move in a variety of ways. Some have flagella and some depend on hosts for transport. One even slides from place to place on a layer of slime that it produces.

Many sporozoans have more than one host. For example, *Plasmodium* is a sporozoan that causes malaria, a serious disease

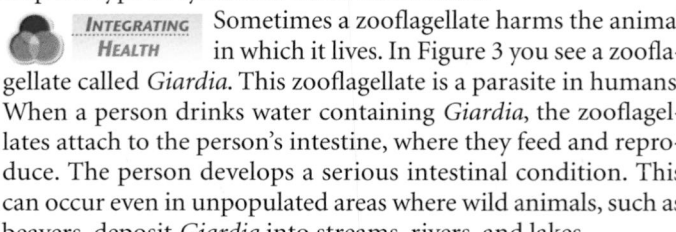

Background

History of Science Malarial infection, mentioned in medical records as early as the fifth century B.C., has plagued human populations since ancient times. Early doctors knew that malaria was associated with swampy and marshy areas, but they did not know about *Plasmodium* and the *Anopheles* mosquito.

A French army surgeon, Alphonse Laveran, was working in Algeria in 1880 when he became the first person to discover that the sporozoan *Plasmodium* was the parasite that causes human malaria. A British army doctor, Sir Ronald Ross, was in India in 1892. He was able to demonstrate that malaria was transmitted from infected birds to healthy ones by the bite of the mosquito, suggesting that the same transmission was possible in humans.

of the blood. Two hosts are involved in *Plasmodium's* life cycle—humans and a species of mosquitoes found in tropical areas. The disease spreads when a healthy mosquito bites a person with malaria, becomes infected, and then bites a healthy person. Symptoms of malaria include high fevers that alternate with severe chills. These symptoms can last for weeks, then disappear, only to reappear a few months later.

☑ *Checkpoint* *What structures do protozoans use to move?*

Funguslike Protists

The second group of protists are the funguslike protists. Recall from Chapter 6 that fungi include organisms such as mushrooms and yeast. Until you learn more about fungi in Section 3, you can think of fungi as the "sort of like" organisms. Fungi are "sort of like" animals because they are heterotrophs. They are "sort of like" plants because their cells have cell walls. In addition, most fungi use spores to reproduce. A **spore** is a tiny cell that is able to grow into a new organism.

Like fungi, funguslike protists are heterotrophs, have cell walls, and use spores to reproduce. Unlike fungi, however, all funguslike protists are able to move at some point in their lives. The three types of funguslike protists are water molds, downy mildews, and slime molds.

Water Molds and Downy Mildews Most water molds and downy mildews live in water or in moist places. These organisms grow as tiny threads that look like a fuzzy covering. Figure 5 shows a fish attacked by a water mold.

Water molds and downy mildews also attack food crops, such as potatoes, cabbages, corn, and grapes. A water mold destroyed the Irish potato crops in 1845 and 1846. The loss of these crops led to a famine that resulted in the deaths of over one million Irish people. Many others left Ireland and moved to other countries, such as Canada and the United States.

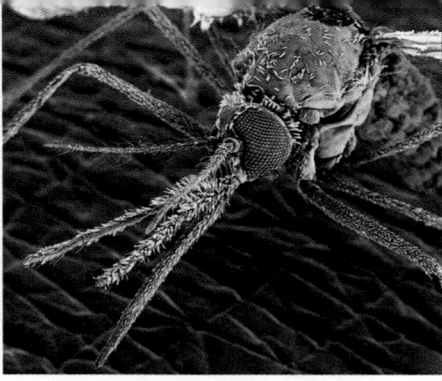

Figure 4 *Anopheles* mosquitoes can carry a sporozoan, *Plasmodium*, which causes malaria in people. *Relating Cause and Effect Why do you think it is difficult to control the spread of malaria?*

Figure 5 This threadlike water mold is a parasite that grows on fish. The water mold eventually kills the fish.

Chapter 7 **223**

Answers to Self-Assessment

Caption Question

Figure 4 It is difficult to control the populations of mosquitoes that carry the parasite.

☑ *Checkpoint*

Protozoans use pseudopods, cilia, or flagella to move.

Building Inquiry Skills: Making Models

Materials *clay, paint, string, pipe cleaners, cardboard, and other materials of students' choice*

ACTIVITY

Time 30 minutes

Tips Challenge small groups to design models of one of the four kinds of animal-like protists. Have students consult photos in the text or in reference materials. Models should include the details of each organism that make it unique, with labels. Have students compare and contrast the models, explaining similarities and differences. They should note the structures, shapes, and methods of movement of the various animal-like protozoans. Challenge groups to use their models to demonstrate how these organisms move, eat, or reproduce. **cooperative learning**

Funguslike Protists

Building Inquiry Skills: Organizing Information

On the board, write the headings *Plants and Animals.* Then call on students to tell you the characteristics of each type of organism and list them under the appropriate heading. Then ask a volunteer to put a star next to each item that is a characteristic of a funguslike protist. *(Heterotrophs, cells have cell walls, reproduce by spores)* **learning modality: verbal**

Ongoing Assessment

Writing Ask students to describe the characteristics of zooflagellates, sporozoans, or funguslike protists.

Funguslike Protists, continued

Inquiry Challenge

Materials *compound microscope, slime mold culture, plastic petri dish with cover, oatmeal*

Time 15 minutes for setup, 10 minutes for observation after 24 hours

Tips Pair students. Give each pair a covered petri dish containing slime mold culture to observe under the microscope. Partners can take turns observing and sketching what they see. Ask students to predict how slime molds will react when oatmeal is placed in the dish. They can test their predictions by uncovering the dish, putting a few flakes about one mm from a branch of the slime mold and putting the cover back on. Allow students to place the dish in a cool, dark place. After 24 hours, the slime mold should increase in size, spread across, then engulf the oatmeal flakes. Ask: **What did you observe that suggests the slime mold is alive?** *(It moved toward the oatmeal and engulfed it.)* **How is a slime mold similar to an ameba?** *(It engulfs its food with pseudopods.)* Caution students to wash their hands thoroughly after the activity. Review the safety guidelines in Appendix A. Dispose of the petri dishes and all other materials according to the proper procedures. Be sure to check your district's and state's guidelines for the proper disposal of fungal cultures.
learning modality: visual

Plantlike Protists

Building Inquiry Skills: Making Models

Divide the class into three groups: unicellular algae, multicellular algae, and a colony of algae. Have each student act out the role of an individual algae cell. Give each group a deck of cards to use as a food source, and encourage the "cells" to act out how each organism accomplishes food intake and waste elimination. *(Sample: unicellular: individual students pick up and put down cards without interacting; multicellular: cooperative model; one student picks up a card and passes it on; another puts it down; colony: individual and cooperative)*
learning modality: kinesthetic

Figure 6 Slime molds, like the chocolate tube slime mold (left), feed on microorganisms on the surfaces of decaying materials. When food runs low, they grow stalks that produce spores (right).

Slime Molds Slime molds live in moist soil and on decaying plants and trees. Slime molds are often beautifully colored. Many are bright yellow, like the one in Figure 6. Their glistening bodies creep over fallen logs and dead leaves on shady, moist forest floors. They move in an amebalike way by forming pseudopods and oozing along the surfaces of decaying materials. Slime molds feed on bacteria and other microorganisms.

Some slime molds are large enough to be seen with the naked eye. Many, however, are so small that you need a microscope to see them. When the food supply decreases or other conditions change, some tiny slime molds creep together and form a multicellular mass. Spore-producing structures grow out of the mass and release spores, which can develop into a new generation of slime molds.

☑ *Checkpoint* In what environments are slime molds found?

Plantlike Protists

If you've ever seen seaweed at a beach, then you are familiar with a type of plantlike protist. Plantlike protists, which are commonly called **algae** (AL jee), are even more varied than the animal-like and funguslike protists. **The one characteristic that all algae share is that, like plants, they are autotrophs.**

Some algae live in the soil, others live on the barks of trees, and still others live in fresh water and salt water. Algae that live on the surface of ponds, lakes, and oceans are an important food source for other organisms in the water. In addition, most of the oxygen in Earth's atmosphere is made by these algae.

Algae range greatly in size. Some algae, such as diatoms, are unicellular. Others are groups of unicellular organisms that live together in colonies. Still others, such as seaweeds, are multicellular. Recall from Chapter 1 that a unicellular organism carries

---

Background

Facts and Figures The cryophyte alga *Chlamydomonas nivalis* is one of several responsible for a phenomenon known as red (or pink) snow. During the late spring or the summer, snowbanks in mountain regions all over the world may be colored beautiful shades of red by "blooms" or patches of various snow algae. Scientists estimate that one teaspoon of melted snow may contain more than a million cells of algae.

Although *Chlamydomonas nivalis* is classified as a green alga, its color comes from a bright red carotenoid pigment that probably helps to protect the algae from intense solar radiation at high altitudes. The nutrients for the algae are minerals leached from boulders and soil, as well as organic material that blows onto the snow from nearby plants.

out all the functions necessary for life. But the cells of a multi-cellular organism are specialized to do certain tasks. When single-celled algae come together to form colonies, some of the cells may become specialized to perform certain functions, such as reproduction. However, most cells in a colony continue to carry out all functions. Colonies can contain from four up to thousands of cells.

Algae exist in a wide variety of colors because they contain many types of **pigments**—chemicals that produce color. Depending on their pigments, algae can be green, yellow, red, brown, orange, or even black. Read on to learn about the types of algae that live on Earth.

Euglenoids Euglenoids are green, unicellular algae that are found mostly in fresh water. Unlike other algae, euglenoids have one animal-like characteristic—they can be heterotrophs under certain conditions. When sunlight is available, euglenoids are autotrophs that produce their own food. However, when sunlight is not available, euglenoids will act like heterotrophs by finding and taking in food from their environment.

In Figure 7 you see a euglena, which is a common euglenoid. Notice the long whiplike flagellum that helps the organism move. Locate the eyespot near the flagellum. Although the eyespot is not really an eye, it contains pigments. These pigments are sensitive to light and help a euglena recognize the direction of a light source. You can imagine how important this response is to an organism that needs light to make food.

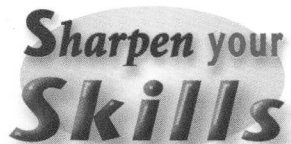

Sharpen your Skills

Predicting ACTIVITY

Predict what will happen when you pour a culture of euglenas into a petri dish, then cover half the dish with aluminum foil. Give a reason for your prediction.

Then carry out the experiment with a culture of euglenas in a plastic petri dish. Cover half the dish with aluminum foil as shown. After 10 minutes, uncover the dish. What do you observe? Was your prediction correct? Explain why euglenas behave this way.

Figure 7 Euglenas are unicellular algae that live in fresh water. In sunlight, euglenas make their own food. Without sunlight, they obtain food from their environment. *Interpreting Diagrams What structures help a euglena find and move toward light?*

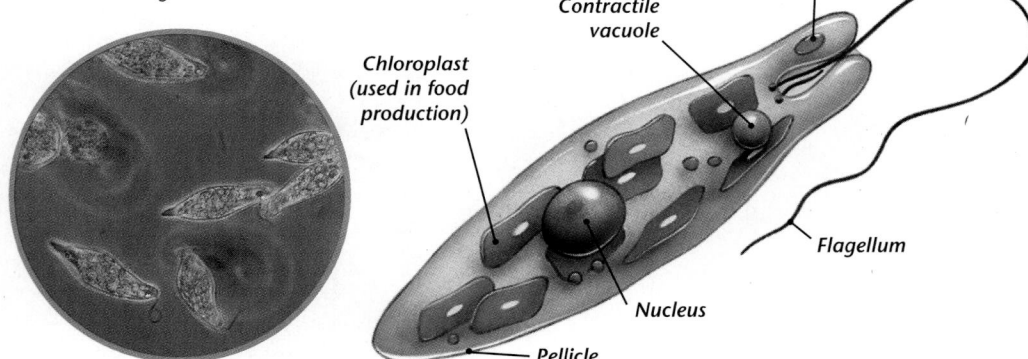

Contractile vacuole

Eyespot

Chloroplast (used in food production)

Flagellum

Nucleus

Pellicle

Using the Visual: Figure 7

Ask students: **How many cells does a Euglena have?** *(one)* Point out that the structures such as flagella, the eyespot, and the chloroplast are all part of the same cell. Some students may be confused that a unicellular organism has so many parts. Explain that cells are the smallest structures capable of performing all the functions required for life. Ask: **Is the cell shown in the figure specialized to do certain tasks?** *(No, it performs all the functions necessary to maintain the Euglena's life.)* **learning modality: visual**

Sharpen your Skills

Predicting

Materials *euglena culture, plastic petri dish, aluminum foil, compound microscope*
Time 20 minutes
Tips Tell students to record their predictions and the reasons for them.
Expected Outcome Students will probably predict that the euglena will move toward the light because it needs light to make food. The result of the experiment will confirm this prediction. The covered area will no longer be green, because the euglena have moved to the uncovered area and the light.
Extend Ask students to identify the source of the green tint of the euglena culture. *(chloroplasts)* **learning modality: visual**

Answers to Self-Assessment

Caption Question

Figure 7 The eyespot helps the euglena find light, and the flagellum helps the euglena move toward light.

☑ Checkpoint

Slime molds are found in moist soil and on decaying plants and trees.

Ongoing Assessment

Oral Presentation Ask students to name the types of funguslike protists. Ask them what plantlike protists are called. *(Funguslike—water molds, downy mildews, slime molds; plantlike—algae)*

Plantlike Protists,
continued

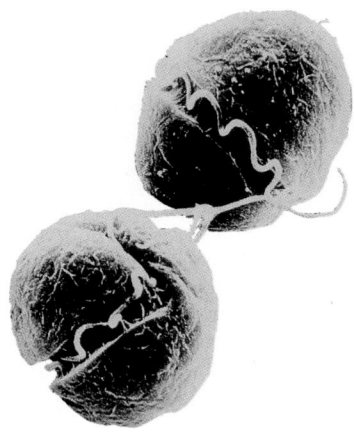

Figure 8 Dinoflagellates, such as these *Gonyaulax,* have rigid plates for protection. They use flagella to move through the water.

Figure 9 Green algae range in size from unicellular organisms to multicellular seaweeds. **A.** The multicellular sea lettuce, *Ulva,* lives in oceans. **B.** This unicellular alga, *Closterium,* lives in fresh water.

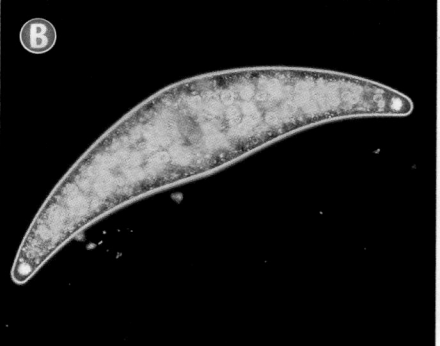

Dinoflagellates Dinoflagellates are unicellular algae covered by stiff plates that look like a suit of armor. Because they have different amounts of green, red, and other pigments, dinoflagellates exist in a variety of colors.

All dinoflagellates have two flagella held in grooves between their plates. When the flagella beat, the dinoflagellates twirl like toy tops through the water. Many glow in the dark and look like miniature fireflies dancing on the ocean's surface at night.

Diatoms Diatoms are unicellular protists with beautiful glasslike cell walls. Some float on the surface of freshwater and saltwater environments. Others attach to objects such as rocks in shallow water. Diatoms move by oozing slime out of slits in their cell walls. They then glide in the slime. Diatoms are a food source for heterotrophs in the water.

INTEGRATING TECHNOLOGY When diatoms die, their cell walls collect on the bottoms of oceans and lakes. Over time, they form layers of a coarse material called diatomaceous (dy uh tuh MAY shus) earth. This makes a good polishing agent. Manufacturers add diatomaceous earth to most toothpastes. Diatomaceous earth is also used in many household scouring products as well as in swimming pool filters. It is even used as an insecticide. The sharp edges puncture the bodies of insects.

Green Algae As their name suggests, all green algae contain green pigments. Otherwise, green algae are quite diverse, as you can see in Figure 9. Although most green algae are unicellular, some form colonies, and a few are multicellular. You might have seen multicellular green algae, or green seaweed, washed up on a beach. Most green algae live in either freshwater or saltwater surroundings. The few that live on land are found along the bases of trees or in moist soils.

226

Red Algae Almost all red algae are multicellular seaweeds. Divers have found red algae growing at depths greater than 260 meters below the ocean's surface. Their red pigments are especially good at absorbing the small amount of light that enters deep ocean waters.

Red algae are used by humans in a variety of ways. Carrageenan (kar uh JEE nun), a substance extracted from red algae, is used in products such as ice creams and hair conditioners. For people in many Asians cultures, red algae is a nutrient-rich delicacy that is eaten fresh, dried, or toasted.

Brown Algae Many of the organisms that are commonly called seaweeds are brown algae. In addition to their brown pigment, brown algae also contain green, yellow, and orange pigments. As you can see in Figure 10, a typical brown alga has many plantlike structures. Holdfasts anchor the alga to rocks. Stalks support the blades, which are the leaflike structures of the alga. Brown algae also have gas-filled sacs called bladders that allow the algae to float upright in the water.

Brown algae flourish in cool, rocky waters. Brown algae called rockweed live along the Atlantic coast of North America. Giant kelps, which can grow to 100 meters in length, live in some Pacific coastal waters. The giant kelps form large underwater "forests" where many organisms, including sea otters and abalone, live. Some people eat brown algae for their nutrients. Substances called algins are extracted from brown algae and used as thickeners in foods such as puddings and salad dressings.

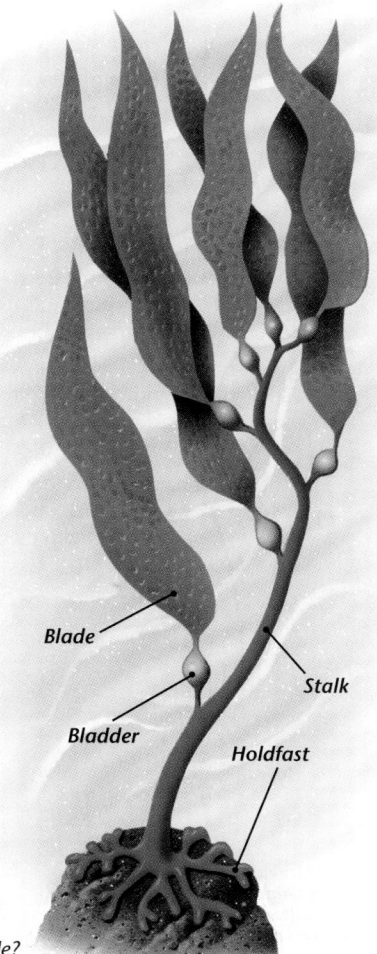

Blade

Stalk

Bladder

Holdfast

Figure 10 Giant kelps have many plantlike structures. *Applying Concepts What plant structures do the holdfasts and blades resemble?*

Section 1 Review

1. What characteristic do all protozoans share?
2. What are three characteristics of the funguslike protists?
3. What characteristic do algae share with plants?
4. **Thinking Critically Making Judgments** Would you classify a euglena as an animal-like protist or as a plantlike protist? Explain your answer.

Science at Home

Kitchen Algae Look through your kitchen with a family member to find products that contain substances made from algae. Look for both food and non-food items. First tell your family member that words such as diatomaceous earth, algin, and carrageenan are substances that come from algae. Make a list of the products and the algae-based ingredient they contain. Share your list with the class.

Section 1 Review Answers

1. All protozoans are unicellular heterotrophs.
2. Funguslike protists have cell walls, use spores to reproduce, are heterotrophs, and are able to move at some point in their lives.
3. Both plants and algae are autotrophs that use sunlight to make their food.
4. Students may argue that euglena are either plantlike or animal-like protists. They are animal-like because they can feed like heterotrophs when there is no light. They are plantlike because they can make their own food and are usually green.

Science at Home

Encourage students to explain to family members that algae can be found in many products such as ice cream, hair conditioners, toothpaste, and scouring products. They may wish to see who can find the most products containing algae.

Program Resources

◆ **Unit 2 Resources** 7-1 Review and Reinforce, p. 39; 7-1 Enrich, p. 40
◆ **Laboratory Manual** 7, "Comparing Protists"

Answers to Self-Assessment

Caption Question
Figure 10 The holdfasts resemble roots and the blades resemble leaves.

Media and Technology

 Interactive Student Tutorial CD-ROM Chapter 7

Performance Assessment

Writing Ask students to imagine they are the size of a protozoan. Have them write a short story of their encounters with other microscopic life forms such as amebas, euglenoids, slime molds, and other protists. Encourage students to describe how these organisms behave and how they identify them. *Portfolio* Students can save their stories in their portfolios.

227

SECTION 2 Algal Blooms

Objectives

After completing the lesson, students will be able to

◆ describe how red tides occur and explain why they are dangerous;

◆ explain how the rapid growth of algae affects a pond or lake.

Key Terms algal bloom, red tide, eutrophication

1 Engage/Explore

Activating Prior Knowledge

Remind students that in Section 1, they learned that algae live on the surface of ponds, lakes, and oceans. Ask: **What do you think would happen if there were so many algae on the water's surface that they blocked sunlight from getting into the water?** (*Sample: The organisms in the water that need sunlight to make food will die.*)

· · · · · · · · DISCOVER · · · · · · · ·

Skills Focus predicting
Materials *clear plastic container, water, green paper punches, spoons*
Time 15 minutes
Tips Use a hole punch to make green paper punches. After students complete their models, ask: **What does your model show about how algae can grow on a pond?** (*How rapidly the number of algae can increase*)
Expected Outcome The green paper punches will eventually cover the surface of the water.
Think It Over If algae cover the pond's surface, less light and air will reach the bottom, and organisms deep in the pond will die.

SECTION 2 Algal Blooms

DISCOVER · ACTIVITY

How Can Algal Growth Affect Pond Life?

1. Pour water into a plastic petri dish until the dish is half full. The petri dish will represent a pond.

2. Sprinkle a spoonful of green paper punches into the water in the petri dish to represent green algae growing in the pond water.

3. Sprinkle two more spoonfuls of paper punches into the water to represent one cycle of algae reproduction.

4. Sprinkle four more spoonfuls of paper punches into the water to represent the next reproduction cycle of the algae.

Think It Over
Predicting How might algae growing on the surface affect organisms living deep in a pond?

GUIDE FOR READING

◆ What makes red tides dangerous?

◆ How does the rapid growth of algae affect a pond or lake?

Reading Tip As you read, look for evidence of the dangers of algal blooms. Make a list of sentences from the text that provide this evidence.

◄ A humpback whale

Over a five week period one year, the bodies of 14 humpback whales washed up along beaches on Cape Cod, Massachusetts. The whales showed no outward signs of sickness. Their stomachs were full of food. Their bodies contained plenty of blubber to insulate them from changes in water temperature. What caused such healthy-looking animals to die?

When biologists examined the dead whales' tissues, they identified the cause of the puzzling deaths. The whales' cells contained a deadly toxin produced by a dinoflagellate called *Alexandrium tamarense*. For reasons that scientists don't fully understand, the population of these algae grew rapidly in the ocean waters through which the whales were migrating. When the whales fed on the toxin-producing algae or on fishes that had eaten the algae, the toxins reached a deadly level and killed the whales.

Algae are common in both saltwater and freshwater environments on Earth. They float on the surface of the waters and use sunlight to make food. The rapid growth of a population of algae is called an **algal bloom.** The deaths of the humpbacks is one example of the damage that an algal bloom can cause.

READING STRATEGIES

Reading Tip As students read, instruct them to list the dangers of algal blooms on a sheet of notebook paper. Suggest to students that they divide their paper into two columns with the headings Saltwater Blooms and Freshwater Blooms. Sentences may include "When the whales fed on the toxin-producing algae or on fishes that had eaten the algae, the toxins reached a deadly level and killed the whales."

Study and Comprehension After students read the section, have them imagine that they are newspaper or television reporters. Direct them to write news stories about an algal bloom. Ask students to include the most important points about the rapid growth of algae populations. Suggest that students use their notes from the Reading Tip to help them decide what information to include about the dangers of algal blooms.

Saltwater Blooms

In Figure 11, you see an algal bloom in ocean water. Saltwater algal blooms are commonly called **red tides.** This is because the algae that grow rapidly often contain red pigments and turn the color of the water red. But red tides do not always look red. Some red tides are brown, green, or colorless depending on the species of algae that blooms. Dinoflagellates and diatoms are two algae that frequently bloom in red tides.

Scientists are not sure why some saltwater algal populations increase rapidly at times. But red tides occur most often when there is an increase in nutrients in the water. Increases in ocean temperature due to climate changes also affect the occurrence of red tides. Some red tides occur regularly in certain seasons. The cold bottom layers of the ocean contain a lot of nutrients. When the cold water mixes with the surface waters, more nutrients become available to surface organisms. With excess nutrients present in the surface waters, blooms of algae occur.

Red tides are dangerous when the toxins that the algae produce become concentrated in the bodies of organisms that consume the algae. Shellfish feed on large numbers of the algae and store the toxins in their cells. Fishes may also feed on the algae and store the toxins. When people or other large organisms eat these shellfish and fishes, it may lead to serious illness or even death. Public health officials close beaches in areas of red tides and prohibit people from gathering shellfish or fishing.

INTEGRATING TECHNOLOGY Red tides occur more frequently worldwide today than they did a decade ago. Scientists cannot yet predict when red tides will occur. They use images taken by satellites in space to track how red tides move with ocean currents. Satellite images can also detect increases in ocean temperatures, which may put an area at risk for red tide.

☑️ *Checkpoint* What gives red tides their color?

Figure 11 Rapid algae growth has caused a red tide in this small bay off the coast of California. *Relating Cause and Effect What organisms are most often responsible for causing red tides?*

---

2 Facilitate

Saltwater Blooms

Building Inquiry Skills: Making Models

Materials *index cards, red and black markers*

In this activity, students role-play how toxic algae in a red tide eventually affect humans. Divide the class into several groups, choosing one "fish," one "shellfish," and one "person" from each group. The rest of the students in each group will be algae. Give each "alga" three cards, and have the "algae" write *Nutrient* on two cards in black and *Toxin* on the third card in red. Then direct the "fish" and "shellfish" to "eat" all the "algae" in their group by taking their cards. Ask: **What do the fish and shellfish gain from eating algae?** *(Lots of nutrients and a little bit of toxins)* Instruct the fish and shellfish to discard two out of every three *Nutrient* cards. Ask: **What happens to the nutrients?** *(They get used up.)* **What happens to the toxins?** *(They stay in the bodies of the fish and shellfish.)* Now instruct the "person" in each group to eat the fish and shellfish by taking all their cards. Ask: **What does the human gain from eating the toxic fish?** *(A little nutrients and a lot of toxins)* **cooperative learning**

Integrating Technology

Ask students why satellite images are used to study activity, such as oil spills, in the oceans. *(Sample: Satellite images show large parts of the ocean, which are difficult for scientists on Earth to observe.)*

Answers to Self-Assessment

Caption Question

Figure 11 Dinoflagellates and diatoms are the algae most often responsible for causing red tides.

☑️ *Checkpoint*

The algae that form the red tides often contain red pigments that change the color of the water to red.

Ongoing Assessment

Writing Have students explain how red tides can affect the health of people in a shore community.

Freshwater Blooms

Including All Students

This activity will benefit students who need extra help. Challenge groups of students to create wall-size flowcharts that show the process of eutrophication, including both the natural events and the human activities that affect the rate of eutrophication. **learning modality: logical/mathematical**

3 Assess

Section 2 Review Answers

1. Toxins that the algae produce become concentrated in the bodies of the organisms that consume the algae.
2. An increase of nutrients in the water causes an increase in algae growth, beginning a series of events that affect all organisms in the lake or pond.
3. When bottom plants die, organisms break them down, using up the oxygen in the water in the process. Without oxygen, fishes die.
4. Sample: Plan a good sewage system so that excess nutrients do not get into the lake and increase the rate of eutrophication. Design landscaping to prevent runoff into the lake, and encourage residents to limit use of fertilizers.

Check Your Progress

CHAPTER PROJECT
Encourage students to develop a standard procedure to make sure they measure from the same place every day.

Performance Assessment

Writing Have students describe each step in the processes involved in red tides or freshwater blooms.
 Students can save their descriptions in their portfolios.

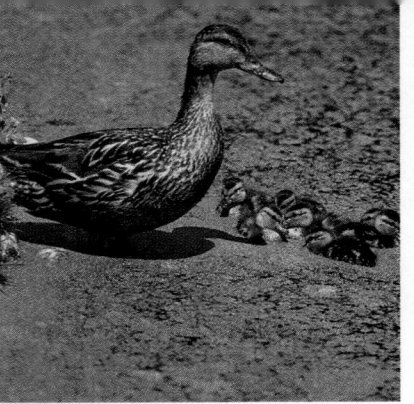

Figure 12 Increased nutrient levels in lakes and ponds can lead to algal blooms. The thick layer of algae on the surface can threaten other organisms in the water. *Problem Solving Outline a series of steps that could help slow down the rapid growth of algae in a lake.*

Freshwater Blooms

Algal blooms also occur in bodies of fresh water. Have you ever seen a pond or lake that looked as if it was coated with a layer of green paint? The green layer of surface scum usually consists of huge numbers of unicellular green algae.

Lakes and ponds undergo natural processes of change over time. In a process called **eutrophication** (yoo troh fih KAY shun), nutrients such as nitrogen and phosphorus build up in a lake or pond over time, causing an increase in the growth of algae.

Certain natural events and human activities can increase the rate of eutrophication. For example, when farmers spread fertilizers on fields, some of these chemicals can run off into nearby lakes and ponds. In addition, poorly designed or aging septic systems can leak their contents into the soil. The nutrients make their way from the soil into water that leads into lakes and ponds. These events cause a rapid increase in algae growth.

The rapid growth of algae in a pond or lake triggers a series of events with serious consequences. First, the layer of algae prevents sunlight from reaching plants and other algae beneath the surface. Those organisms die and sink to the bottom. Then organisms, such as bacteria, which break down the bodies of the dead plants and algae, increase in number. Soon the bacteria use up the oxygen in the water. Fishes and other organisms in the water die without the oxygen they need to survive. About the only life that survives is the algae on the surface.

Algal blooms in fresh water can be easier to control than those in salt water because lakes and ponds have definite boundaries. To slow eutrophication, scientists first need to find the sources of the excess nutrients and then eliminate them. If the source can be eliminated and the nutrients used up, eutrophication slows to its natural rate.

Section 2 Review

1. Why are red tides dangerous?
2. What causes a freshwater bloom?
3. How does the death of bottom plants in a shallow pond affect the rest of the pond?
4. **Thinking Critically Problem Solving** A new housing development is to be built along a recreational lake. What factors should the developers consider to protect the lake from rapid eutrophication?

Check Your Progress

CHAPTER PROJECT
By now, you should have your teacher's approval for your plan, and you should have started growing your mushrooms. Make careful observations of growth every day. Include sketches and measurements as appropriate. Use a data table to organize the data you collect. *(Hint: As you make your observations, be careful not to disturb the experiment or introduce any new variables.)*

Media and Technology

 Audio CD English-Spanish Summary 7-2

 Exploring Life Science Videodisc Unit 2, Side 2, "Fungi and Algae"

Chapter 5

Answers to Self-Assessment

Caption Question

Figure 12 Find and eliminate sources of excess nutrients, including excessive soil fertilization and leaking septic systems.

Program Resources

◆ **Teaching Resources** 7-2 Review and Reinforce, p. 43; 7-2 Enrich, p. 44

AN EXPLOSION OF LIFE

Living things are interconnected with their surroundings in many ways. In this lab, you will investigate how one change in a freshwater environment can affect everything that lives in that environment.

Problem

How does the amount of fertilizer affect algae growth?

Skills Focus

controlling variables, predicting, drawing conclusions

Materials

4 glass jars with lids	marking pen
aged tap water	aquarium water
graduated cylinder	liquid fertilizer

Procedure

1. Read through the steps in the procedure. Then write a prediction describing what you think will happen in each of the four jars.
2. Copy the data table into your notebook. Be sure to allow enough lines to make entries for a two-week period.
3. Label four jars A, B, C, and D. Fill each jar half full with aged tap water.
4. Add aquarium water to each jar until the jar is three-fourths full.
5. Add 3 mL of liquid fertilizer to jar B; 6 mL to jar C; and 12 mL to jar D. Do not add any fertilizer to jar A. Loosely screw the lid on each jar. Place all the jars in a sunny location where they will receive the same amount of direct sunlight.

DATA TABLE

Date	Observations			
	Jar A no fertilizer	Jar B 3 mL fertilizer	Jar C 6 mL fertilizer	Jar D 12 mL fertilizer
Day 1				
Day 2				

6. Observe the jars every day for two weeks. Compare the color of the water in the four jars. Record your observations in your data table.

Analyze and Conclude

1. How did the color in the four jars compare at the end of the two-week period? How can you account for any differences that you observed?
2. What was the purpose of jar A?
3. Describe the process that led to the overall color change in the water. What organisms were responsible for causing that color change?
4. Predict what would have happened if you placed the four jars in a dark location instead of in sunlight. Explain your prediction.
5. **Apply** What do you think might happen to fish and other living organisms when fertilizer gets into a body of fresh water? What are some ways that fertilizer might get into a body of water?

Design an Experiment

Some detergents contain phosphates, which are an ingredient in many kinds of fertilizer. Design an experiment to compare how regular detergent and low-phosphate detergent affect the growth of algae.

Safety

Remind students to wear safety goggles, handle the glass jars with care, and wash their hands immediately after setting up the activity and making observations. Review the safety guidelines in Appendix A. Dispose of the algae and all other materials according to the proper procedures. Be sure to check your district's and state's guidelines for the proper disposal of algal cultures.

Program Resources

♦ **Unit 2 Resources** Chapter 7 Real-World Lab, pp. 49–50

You and Your Environment

An Explosion of Life

Preparing for Inquiry

Key Concept Algae grow better in the presence of fertilizer.

Skills Objective Students will be able to
♦ control variables;
♦ predict relative algae growth;
♦ draw conclusions about nutrient use.

Time 30 minutes first day, 10 minutes subsequent days

Advance Planning The tap water should stand for 3 days before the lab.

Alternative Materials You can use pond water or algae cultures from a biological supply house.

Guiding Inquiry

Invitation

Ask students what agricultural runoff after a rainstorm might contain. *(Soil, fertilizers)* Students will test the effect of fertilizer on algal growth.

Analyze and Conclude

1. Jar D was the darkest green, with jars C and B increasingly lighter, and jar A the lightest. The difference: fertilizer.

2. Jar A served as the control.

3. Algae in the water used the nutrients to grow. The intensity of the green color also increased with the numbers of algae.

4. Without light to make food, the jars would stay the same as the first day.

5. Reproduction of algae would use up oxygen in the water. Organisms would die without sufficient oxygen. Fertilizer could get into the water in runoff from farm fields or golf courses.

Extending the Inquiry

Design an Experiment Use regular detergent in one set of jars and low-phosphate detergent in another.

Eutrophication— The Threat to Clear, Clean Water

Purpose

Discuss the problems associated with eutrophication in Weiss Lake. Identify the pros and cons of different plans and consider their implementation.

Panel Discussion

Time 45 minutes to prepare, 30 minutes for panel discussion.

Review eutrophication and ask students to explain why adding nutrients to rivers and lakes is harmful. Divide the class into five groups: farmers, residents, environmentalists, local officials, and industry representatives. Encourage groups to identify the problem and discuss the nutrient sources that are polluting Weiss Lake. Have each group choose a spokesperson and prepare their viewpoints. In the panel discussion, each spokesperson should assess the problem by presenting his or her concerns and possible solutions, along with the economic impact of the final proposal. Students may choose to consider restricting fertilizer use, reducing factory emissions of phosphorus, additional processing of wastewater, or landscaping to prevent soil erosion.

Extend Encourage students to research pollution issues for a local body of water. If possible, have students watch local proceedings in which community members address this problem.

You Decide

Students should complete the first part with their interest groups as they prepare for the discussion. The second part could be completed after the panel discussion. Then have students create a prevention plan based on what they learn in the discussion. Students should indicate an understanding of how each solution will affect different groups of people.

SCIENCE AND SOCIETY

Eutrophication — The Threat to Clear, Clean Water

Weiss Lake, on the Georgia-Alabama border, is a popular vacation area. People come to this lake to fish, boat, and swim. But every year about two million pounds of phosphorus pour into Weiss Lake from rivers. These excess nutrients are threatening the lake's good fishing and clean, clear water.

Weiss Lake is just one of thousands of lakes and ponds in the United States threatened by eutrophication. The threat is not just to recreation. Drinking water for nearly 70 percent of Americans comes from lakes, reservoirs, and other surface water.

The Issues

Where Does the Pollution Come From?
The two main sources of excess nutrients are wastes and fertilizers from farms and wastewater from sewage treatment plants. When farmers fertilize crops, the plants absorb only some of these nutrients. The excess nutrients can be washed with soil into lakes and ponds. When wastewater from homes and factories is treated, large amounts of nutrients still remain in the water. For example, about 380 million liters of treated wastewater flow toward Weiss Lake daily. This treated wastewater still contains large amounts of phosphorus produced by many factories.

What Are the Costs of Eutrophication?
People who live near Weiss Lake depend on the lake for jobs and money. But as the fish die in the oxygen-poor waters, swimming and boating in the murky water become less appealing and possibly unsafe. Over 4,000 jobs and millions of dollars each year would be lost if Weiss Lake were to close down. But upgrading or building new water-treatment plants would cost millions of dollars in higher taxes to citizens.

What Can Be Done? Even as cities, farms, and factories grow, the amount of nutrients reaching lakes and ponds can be reduced. Factories can install water-treatment facilities that remove more nitrogen and phosphorus from their wastewater. Farmers can often reduce the use of fertilizers. People can plant trees along the banks of lakes to reduce the amount of soil entering the lake. These solutions can cost millions of dollars, but they can reverse the problem.

You Decide

1. Identify the Problem
In your own words, describe the eutrophication issues that affect Weiss Lake.

2. Analyze the Options
Make a chart of different ways to slow the eutrophication process. How would each work? What groups of people would be affected?

3. Find a Solution
Create a "prevention plan" advising town leaders how to reduce eutrophication in lakes and ponds.

Background

Although most commonly seen in lakes, the problems of eutrophication are also present in oceans. In general, coastal areas that do not have strong winds or tides to mix the sea water, such as bays and gulfs, are most at risk. In these areas, freshwater runoff tends to float on top of the denser sea water. Without being mixed, the water on the surface begins to develop a rich overabundance of life forms. The bottom layers fill with dead plant matter, which decomposes and rapidly consumes oxygen. Entire bays can suffer from the suffocation below the surface. In the Gulf of Mexico, an 18,000-sq km area goes through this deadly process every summer. This lifeless region in open waters is known as the "dead zone."

DISCOVER •• ACTIVITY

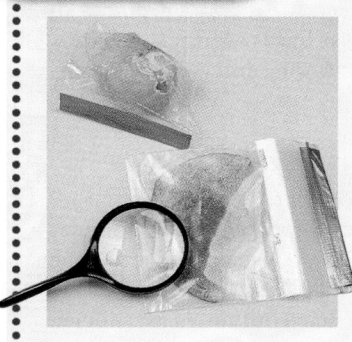

Do All Molds Look Alike?

1. Your teacher will give you two sealed, clear plastic bags—one containing moldy bread and another containing moldy fruit. **CAUTION:** *Do not open the sealed bags at any time.*

2. Examine each mold. In your notebook, describe what you see.

3. Then, use a hand lens to examine each mold. Sketch each mold in your notebook and list its characteristics.

4. Return the sealed bags to your teacher. Wash your hands.

Think It Over
Observing How are the molds similar? How do they differ?

U nnoticed, a speck of dust lands on a cricket's back. But this is no ordinary dust—it is alive! Tiny glistening threads emerge from the dust and begin to grow into the cricket's moist body. As they grow, the threads release chemicals that slowly dissolve the cricket's living tissues. The threads continue to grow deeper into the cricket's body. Within a few days, the cricket's body is little more than a hollow shell filled with a tangle of the deadly threads. Then the threads begin to grow up and out of the dead cricket. They produce long stalks with knobs at their tips. When one of the knobs breaks open, it will release thousands of dustlike specks, which the wind can carry to new victims.

What Are Fungi?

The strange cricket-killing organism is a member of the fungi kingdom. Although you may not have heard of a cricket-killing fungus before, you are probably familiar with other kinds of fungi. For example, the molds that grow on stale bread or on decaying fruit are all fungi. Mushrooms that sprout in forests or yards are also fungi.

> ### GUIDE FOR READING
> ◆ What characteristics do fungi share?
> ◆ How do fungi obtain food?
> ◆ What roles do fungi play in the living world?
>
> *Reading Tip* Before you read, preview the headings. Record them in outline form, leaving space for writing notes.

▼ A bush cricket attacked by a killer fungus

Chapter 7 **233**

Objectives

After completing the lesson, students will be able to
◆ name the characteristics that all fungi share;
◆ describe how fungi obtain food;
◆ list the roles fungi play in the living world;
◆ describe the ways that fungi reproduce.

Key Terms hypha, fruiting body, budding, lichen

1 Engage/Explore

Activating Prior Knowledge

Ask students to describe what they know about how mushrooms grow. Some students may have seen mushrooms growing in the woods, while others may have seen cultivated mushrooms. Encourage students to think about how mushrooms are similar to plants.

•••••••• DISCOVER ••••••••

Skills Focus observing
Materials *self-seal bags, tape, hand lens, old bread, fruit*
Time 15 minutes
Tips At least one week before the activity, place pieces of moist bread and fruit in separate self-seal bags. Seal the bags, then make an extra seal with tape. Keep them in a dark place at room temperature. Make sure students do not open the bags. Dispose of the sealed bags and all other materials according to the proper procedures. Be sure to check your district's and state's guidelines for the proper disposal of fungal cultures.
Expected Outcome Observations will depend on the kinds of fungi that grow on the foods. Students should see more detail with the hand lens.
Think It Over The molds will probably have similar threadlike appearances and fruiting bodies but will probably be of different colors.

2 Facilitate

What Are Fungi?

Using the Visuals: Figures 13 and 14

As students study the two figures, ask: **How are the hyphae of the mushroom similar to those of the mold growing on the orange?** (*Both make up the bodies of the organism, and both grow down into the nutrient source.*) In each example, the hyphae within the body of the organism are more tightly packed than the hyphae under the surface. **learning modality: visual**

Cell Structure

Building Inquiry Skills: Observing

Materials *various types of mushrooms from the grocery store, hand lens*

ACTIVITY

Time 15 minutes

Tips Give groups of students a selection of mushrooms to observe. Caution students not to eat any part of the mushrooms. Challenge them to identify mushroom structures including gills, cap, and stalk, then sketch the mushrooms and label each part. Encourage each group to compare and contrast the different fruiting bodies. Finally, have students gently twist off the cap of one mushroom and break open the stalk from end to end. Ask: **Can you pull any threadlike structures from the stalk?** (*Answers may vary depending on the mushroom.*) **Using your knowledge of mushrooms, what do you think these threadlike structures are? What are they made of?** (*Hyphae; the cells of the fungus*) Make sure students wash their hands immediately after the activity. **learning modality: visual**

234

Fungi vary in size from the unicellular yeasts to the multicellular fungi, such as mushrooms and the bracket fungi that look like shelves growing on tree trunks. **Most fungi share three important characteristics: They are eukaryotes, use spores to reproduce, and are heterotrophs that feed in a similar way.** In addition, fungi need moist, warm places in which to grow. They thrive on moist foods, damp tree barks, lawns coated with dew, damp forest floors, and even wet bathroom tiles.

Cell Structure

Except for yeast cells, which are unicellular, the cells of fungi are arranged in structures called hyphae. **Hyphae** (HY fee) (singular *hypha*) are the branching, threadlike tubes that make up the bodies of multicellular fungi. The hyphae of some fungi are continuous threads of cytoplasm that contain many nuclei. Substances move quickly and freely through the hyphae.

The appearance of a fungus depends on how its hyphae are arranged. In some fungi, the threadlike hyphae are loosely tangled. Fuzzy-looking molds that grow on old foods have loosely tangled hyphae. In other fungi, hyphae are packed tightly together. For example, the stalk and cap of the mushrooms in Figure 13 are made of hyphae packed so tightly that they appear solid. Underground, however, a mushroom's hyphae form a loose, threadlike maze in the soil.

☑ *Checkpoint* *What structures make up the bodies of multicellular fungi?*

Cap

Gills

Stalk

Hyphae

Underground hyphae

234

Figure 13 The hyphae in the stalk and cap of a mushroom are packed tightly to form very firm structures. Underground hyphae, on the other hand, are arranged loosely. *Inferring What function do you think the underground hyphae perform?*

234

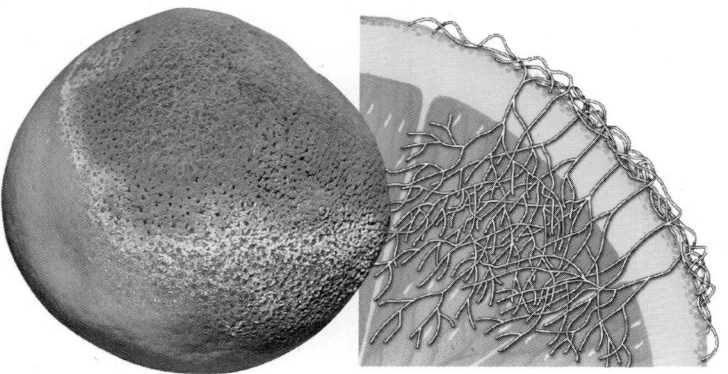

Figure 14 The mold *Penicillium* often grows on old fruits such as this orange. Notice that some hyphae grow deep inside the orange. These hyphae digest the food and absorb the smaller chemicals.

How Do Fungi Obtain Food?

Although fungi are heterotrophs, they do not take food into their bodies as you do. Instead fungi absorb food through hyphae that grow into the food source.

Look at Figure 14 to see how a fungus feeds. **First, the fungus grows hyphae into a food source. Then digestive chemicals ooze from the hyphae into the food. The digestive chemicals break down the food into small substances that can be absorbed by the hyphae.** Imagine yourself sinking your fingers down into a chocolate cake and dripping digestive chemicals out of your fingertips. Then imagine your fingers absorbing the digested particles of the cake. That's how a fungus feeds.

Some fungi feed on the remains of dead organisms. Other fungi are parasites that break down the chemicals in living organisms. For example, athlete's foot is a disease caused by a fungus that feeds on chemicals in a person's skin. Dutch elm disease is caused by a fungus that feeds on elm trees and eventually kills the trees.

Reproduction in Fungi

Like it or not, fungi are everywhere. The way they reproduce guarantees their survival and spread. Fungi usually reproduce by producing lightweight spores that are surrounded by a protective covering. Spores can be carried easily through air or water to new sites. Fungi produce many more spores than will ever grow into new fungi. Only a few of the thousands of spores that a fungus releases will fall where conditions are right for them to grow into new organisms.

Making Spore Prints

In this activity, you will examine the reproductive structures of a mushroom.

1. Place a fresh mushroom cap, gill side down, on a sheet of white paper. **CAUTION:** *Do not eat the mushroom.*

2. Cover the mushroom cap with a plastic container. Wash your hands with soap.

3. After two days, carefully remove the container and then the cap. You should find a spore print on the paper.

4. Examine the print with a hand lens. Then wash your hands with soap.

Predicting Use your spore print to estimate how many spores a mushroom could produce. Where would spores be most likely to grow into new mushrooms?

Answers to Self-Assessment

Caption Question

Figure 13 Students may suspect that the underground hyphae hold the mushroom in place and help it get water, or they may suggest that the hyphae help absorb food.

✓ *Checkpoint*

hyphae

How Do Fungi Obtain Food?

Using the Visuals: Figure 14

Have students note the way hyphae grow from the surface of the orange into the inner part of the orange. Ask: **Why do the hyphae grow deeper and deeper into the orange?** *(As they consume the food in one part of the orange, they grow into another part to get more food.)* **learning modality: visual**

Reproduction in Fungi

Skills Focus predicting
Materials *mushroom cap, white paper, large plastic container*
Time 10 minutes; 15 minutes for observations two days later
Tips Use only mushrooms from a grocery store. Carefully twist the caps off the stalks. The color of spores is a characteristic used to identify mushrooms. Using white paper will help ensure accurate observations.
Expected Results Students should obtain a spore print consisting of lines radiating outward like spokes. Students can estimate the number of spores in a radiating line and multiply the estimate by the number of lines. Spores would grow in a moist warm place with adequate food.
Extend Provide students with different varieties of edible mushrooms and allow them to compare spore prints.

 Students can save their spore prints in their portfolios.

Ongoing Assessment

Writing Have students briefly describe the structure and function of hyphae.

Reproduction in Fungi, continued

Building Inquiry Skills: Observing

Materials *mushroom spores, eyedropper, water, microscope, slide, and cover slip*

Tips Students can observe the spores they collected in the Try This activity on the previous page. Have them use the eyedropper to place a drop of water on the spore print. Then, they can draw up the water with the dropper, place a drop on a microscope slide, and cover it with a cover slip. Allow them to observe the spores under a microscope. Encourage students to sketch their observations and include the color and shape of the spores. Ask: **What is the function of these spores?** (*Spores are the reproductive cells that will produce new mushrooms.*)
learning modality: visual

TRY THIS

Skills Focus making models

Materials *round balloon, cotton balls, tape, stick or ruler about 30 cm long, modeling clay, pin*
Time 25 minutes

Tips If possible, blow up the balloons with a pump or compressed air so that the cotton balls do not get wet. Suggest students make the cotton balls as small as possible so the balls will not just fall to the ground when expelled from the balloon.

Expected Outcome The "spores" should fly out from the balloons and land in many directions and fairly far from the balloons. Students should explain that, just like air in the balloon scattered the cotton balls from the balloon, air currents catch and carry spores from the tall fruiting bodies.

Extend Allow students to repeat the activity in front of a fan to model the effects of wind on the dispersal of the spores. **learning modality: visual**

TRY THIS

Spreading Spores

In this activity you will make a model of a fruiting body.

1. Break a cotton ball into five equal-sized pieces. Roll each piece into a tiny ball.

2. Insert the cotton balls into a balloon through the opening in its neck.

3. Repeat Steps 1 and 2 until the balloon is almost full.

4. Inflate the balloon. Tie a knot in its neck. Tape the knotted end of the balloon to a stick.

5. Stand the stick upright in a mound of modeling clay.

6. Pop the balloon with a pin. Observe what happens.

Making Models Draw a diagram of the model you made. Label the stalk, the spore case, and the spores. Use your model to explain why fungi are found just about everywhere.

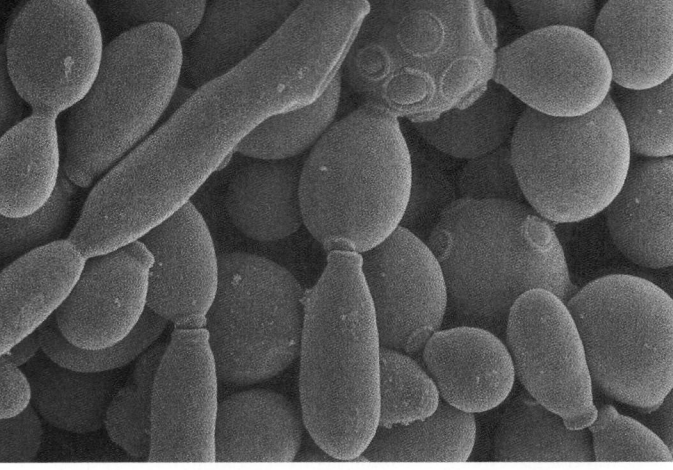

Figure 15 Budding is a form of asexual reproduction that occurs in yeast. The small yeast cell that grows from the body of a parent cell is identical to the parent.

Fungi produce spores in structures called **fruiting bodies,** which are reproductive hyphae that grow out of a fungus. The appearances of fruiting bodies vary from one type of fungus to another. For some fungi, such as mushrooms and puffballs, the part of the fungus that you see is the fruiting body. In other fungi, such as bread molds, the stalklike fruiting bodies grow upward from the hyphae on the surface of the bread. The knoblike structure, or spore case, at the tip of a stalk contains the spores.

Asexual Reproduction Most fungi reproduce both asexually and sexually. When there is adequate moisture and food, most fungi reproduce asexually by growing fruiting bodies that release thousands of spores.

Unicellular yeast cells undergo a form of asexual reproduction called **budding.** In budding, no spores are produced. Instead, a small yeast cell grows from the body of a large, well-fed parent cell in a way that might remind you of a bud forming on the branch of a tree. The new cell then breaks away and lives on its own.

Sexual Reproduction When growing conditions become unfavorable, fungi may reproduce sexually. In sexual reproduction, the hyphae of two fungi grow together and genetic material is exchanged. A new spore-producing structure grows from the joined hyphae. The new structure produces spores, which can develop into fungi that differ from either parent.

✓ Checkpoint *What is a fruiting body?*

Background

Classification of Fungi

Fungi are classified into groups based on the shape of the spore-producing structures and on their ability to reproduce sexually. The four groups of fungi—the threadlike fungi, the sac fungi, the club fungi, and the imperfect fungi—are shown in Figure 16.

▲ **Threadlike Fungi**

This group contains about 600 different species of molds, including many common bread molds, such as this *Rhizopus*. These fungi produce spores in their threadlike hyphae.

▲ **Sac Fungi**

This group contains over 30,000 diverse species of fungi, including yeast, morels, truffles, and some fungi that cause plant diseases, such as Dutch elm disease. They are called sac fungi because they produce spores in structures that look like sacks. The sac fungi in the photo are called bird's nest fungi.

◀ **Club Fungi**

This group includes about 25,000 species of mushrooms, bracket fungi, plant parasites, and puffballs. Club fungi produce spores in structures that look like clubs. One of the puffballs in the photo is shooting out its spores.

Figure 16 The four groups of fungi differ in the appearance of their spore-producing structures and in how they reproduce.
Classifying To which group do mushrooms belong?

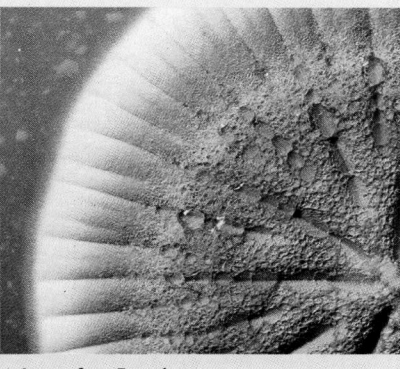

▲ **Imperfect Fungi**

The 25,000 species in this group include this *Penicillium*, the source of an important antibiotic. The fungi in this group are not known to reproduce sexually.

Demonstration

Materials *warm water (40°C–45°C), large beaker, package of dry yeast, sugar, tablespoon, iodine, high-power microscope*

Time 20 minutes for setup; 10 minutes for observations about 30 minutes later

Tips To encourage students who may be having difficulty understanding the text, demonstrate how yeast reproduce by budding. Dissolve several tablespoons of sugar in a jar that is about one-quarter full of warm water. Pour the yeast into the water. Ask students to predict what will happen. Set the jar aside for about 30 minutes. At that time, collect a small sample of yeast from the water. Place the sample on a slide, stain it with a drop of iodine, and cover with a cover slip. Set up the microscope at a central location and allow students to make observations. *(Students should be able to see buds on some yeasts.)* **limited English proficiency**

Classification of Fungi

Using the Visuals: Figure 16

Students may be confused when they look at the puffball, because it does not resemble a club. Inform them that the club-shaped spore cases are located inside the puffball. Point out that the *Penicillium* is classified as an imperfect fungus because sexual reproduction has never been observed in *Penicillium*. Then ask: **What questions would a scientist have to ask to classify a fungus he or she found?** *(Sample: Does it have a spore case, and if so, what shape is it?)* **learning modality: verbal**

Answers to Self-Assessment

Caption Question

Figure 16 Mushrooms are a kind of club fungi.

☑ *Checkpoint*

A fruiting body is a reproductive hypha that grows out of a fungus.

Ongoing Assessment

Writing Have students explain why and how fungi reproduce asexually and sexually.

Drawing Conclusions

What's for Lunch?

Preparing for Inquiry

Key Concept The activity of yeast varies, depending on the amount of available food.

Skills Objective Students will be able to
◆ draw conclusions about whether sugar and salt act as food sources for yeast.

Time 45 minutes

Advance Planning Before the lab, check a sample of yeast in warm water with sugar for 20 minutes to make sure the yeasts are alive.

Guiding Inquiry

Invitation

Tell students that yeasts produce carbon dioxide when they break down food. Carbon dioxide production can be measured to determine whether yeasts are feeding. Have students explain how carbon dioxide production will be measured in this lab.

Introducing the Procedure

Help students understand that when carbon dioxide gas forms in water, much of it will escape from the water's surface.

Troubleshooting the Experiment

◆ Have groups walk through Steps 5–11 before they actually carry them out so that they will be sure what to add to each bottle. Have students use the data table as a guide.
◆ Do not let students overfill the bottles.
◆ Caution students to use a fresh straw for each mixing. This is particularly important when mixing bottle E, because students must not introduce yeast by accident.
◆ Balloons may pop off the bottles during the lab.

Expected Outcome

Balloon D should inflate the most. Balloon C should also inflate but noticeably less than balloon D. Balloons A, B, and E should not inflate.

Skills Lab

What's for Lunch?

In this lab, you will draw conclusions about the effects of two substances on the activity of yeast.

Problem

How does the presence of sugar or salt affect the activity of yeast?

Materials

marking pen
5 plastic straws
salt
beaker
graduated cylinder
5 small narrow-necked bottles
5 round balloons
sugar
warm water (40–45°C)
dry powdered yeast

Procedure

1. Copy the data table into your notebook. Then read over the entire procedure to see how you will test the activity of the yeast cells in bottles A through E. Write a prediction about what will happen in each bottle.

2. Gently stretch each of the 5 balloons so that they will inflate easily.

3. Using the marking pen, label the bottles A, B, C, D, and E.

4. Use a beaker to fill each bottle with the same amount of warm water. **CAUTION:** *Glass is fragile. Handle the bottles and beaker gently to avoid breakage. Do not touch broken glass.*

5. Put 5 mL of salt into bottle B.

6. Put 5 mL of sugar into bottles C and E.

7. Put 30 mL of sugar into bottle D.

8. Put 2 mL of powdered yeast into bottle A, and stir the mixture with a clean straw. Remove the straw and discard it.

9. Immediately place a balloon over the opening of bottle A. Make sure that the balloon opening fits very tightly around the neck of the bottle.

10. Repeat Steps 8 and 9 for bottle B, bottle C, and bottle D.

DATA TABLE			
Bottle	Contents	Prediction	Observations
A	Yeast alone		
B	Yeast and 5 mL of salt		
C	Yeast and 5 mL of sugar		
D	Yeast and 30 mL of sugar		
E	No yeast and 5 mL of sugar		

Sample Data Table

Bottle	Contents	Prediction	Observations
A	Yeast alone	Balloon will inflate	Did not inflate
B	Yeast and 5 mL of salt	Balloon will not inflate	Did not inflate
C	Yeast and 5 mL of sugar	Balloon will inflate	Inflated to small size
D	Yeast and 30 mL of sugar	Balloon will inflate	Inflated to large size
E	No yeast and 5 mL of sugar	Balloon will not inflate	Did not inflate

Analyze and Conclude

11. Place a balloon over bottle E without adding yeast to the bottle.
12. Place the 5 bottles in a warm spot away from drafts. Observe and record what happens.

Analyze and Conclude

1. Which balloons changed in size during this lab? How did they change?
2. Explain why the balloon changed size in some bottles and not in others. What caused that change in size?
3. Do yeast cells use sugar as a food source? How do you know?

4. Do yeast cells use salt as a food source? How do you know?
5. What did the results from bottle C show, compared with the results from bottle D?
6. **Think About It** If you removed bottle E from your experiment, would you be able to conclude whether or not sugar is a food source for the yeast cells? Why or why not?

Design an Experiment

Develop a hypothesis about whether yeast cells need light to carry out their life activities. Then design an experiment to test your hypothesis. Obtain your teacher's permission before you carry out the experiment.

Program Resources

◆ **Unit 2 Resources** Chapter 7 Skills Lab, pp. 51–53
◆ **Inquiry Skills Activity Book** Provides teaching and review of all inquiry skills

Safety

Students should wear safety goggles in case a balloon pops off a bottle or a bottle is accidentally dropped. Review the safety guidelines in Appendix A.

Analyze and Conclude

1. Balloons C and D changed during the lab. Balloon C filled up a little, and balloon D filled up a lot.
2. Some balloons were inflated by carbon dioxide gas. Other balloons remained unchanged because no carbon dioxide gas was produced by the yeast.
3. Yes. Balloons C and D inflated, indicating that the yeast was using the sugar as a source of energy.
4. No. Bottle B produced no gas, indicating that the yeast was not active.
5. The balloon on bottle C did not inflate as much as the balloon on bottle D. When less sugar was available to the yeast (5 mL in bottle C versus 30 mL in D), the yeast gave off less carbon dioxide.
6. No, because there would be no way of knowing whether the gas was being produced by the sugar alone as it dissolved in the water.

Extending the Inquiry

Design an Experiment Students could prepare another bottle D and place it in the dark. They would find that yeasts (unlike algae) do not require light to carry out their basic life processes.

Fungi and the Living World

Real-Life Learning

Ask students: **Does your family or anyone you know have a compost pile?** Explain that compost piles are made by alternating layers of soil, animal manure, and vegetable materials such as weeds, grass clippings, leaves, and food waste. After several months, the material in a compost pile becomes a rich mixture that can be used to supply nutrients necessary for the plants in a garden to grow. Ask: **How do fungi help to produce compost?** (*Fungi are decomposers. They live in the soil in the compost pile and break down the chemicals in the dead plant matter.*) Students interested in gardening may want to find out more about composting. **learning modality: verbal**

Building Inquiry Skills: Designing Experiments

Challenge small groups of students to work together to design experiments that show how yeast reacts with other ingredients to make bread. Suggest that students find simple bread recipes and vary the ingredients for their experiments. Students can make predictions about how different quantities of ingredients will affect the outcome of the baked bread. Bring a bread machine into class so students can try out their recipes. **cooperative learning**

Integrating Health

Encourage students to share what they know about athlete's foot. Ask: **How do you get athlete's foot?** (*Spores fall off infected feet and are picked up by your feet.*) **Where does this usually occur?** (*Public showers, gyms, etc.*) **What can you do to avoid getting athlete's foot?** (*Dry between your toes; wear shoes in public areas.*) **How would you treat this fungus if you got it?** (*With a fungicide*) **learning modality: verbal**

Fungi and the Living World

Fungi affect humans and other organisms in many ways. **Fungi play an important role as decomposers on Earth. In addition, many fungi provide foods for people. Some cause disease and some fight disease. Still other fungi live in symbiosis with other organisms.**

Environmental Recycling Like bacteria, many fungi are decomposers—organisms that break down the chemicals in dead organisms. For example, many fungi live in the soil and break down the chemicals in dead plant matter. This process returns important nutrients to the soil. Without fungi and bacteria, Earth would be buried under dead plants and animals.

Food and Fungi When you eat a slice of bread, you benefit from the work of yeast. Bakers add yeast to bread dough to make it rise. Yeast cells use the sugar in the dough for food and produce carbon dioxide gas as they feed. The gas forms bubbles, which cause the dough to rise. You see these bubbles as holes in a slice of bread. Without yeast, bread would be flat and solid. Yeast is also used to make wine from grapes. Yeast cells feed on the sugar in the grapes and produce carbon dioxide and alcohol.

Other fungi are also important sources of foods. Molds are used in the production of foods such as some cheeses. The blue streaks in blue cheese, for example, are actually growths of *Penicillium roqueforti*. People enjoy eating mushrooms in salads and soups and on pizza. Because some mushrooms are poisonous, however, you should never pick or eat wild mushrooms.

☑ *Checkpoint* *What are three foods that fungi help to produce?*

Disease-Causing Fungi Many fungi cause serious diseases in plants that result in huge crop losses every year. Corn smut and wheat rust are two club fungi that cause diseases in important food crops. Fungal plant diseases also affect other crops, including rice, cotton, and soybeans.

INTEGRATING HEALTH Some fungi cause diseases in humans as well. Athlete's foot causes an itchy irritation in the damp places between toes. Ringworm, another fungal disease, causes an itchy, circular rash on the skin. Because the fungi that cause these

Figure 17 Many food crops are lost each year due to fungal diseases. The ear of corn in the photo has been attacked by a fungus called corn smut. *Making Generalizations Why is the spread of fungal diseases difficult to control?*

Background

Facts and Figures Many species of soil fungi have their hyphae attached to the roots of forest trees. These associations, called *mycorrhizae,* can benefit both the fungi and the tree.

Because hyphae grow very rapidly under favorable conditions, mycorrhizae can be enormous. In northern Michigan, a single *Armillaria bulbosa* fungus has been

discovered that continues under more than 30 acres of forest. Although this may be one of the world's largest organisms, scientists think it came from a single spore released thousands of years ago. In Washington State, another *Armillaria* fungus—consisting of an underground network of hyphae and aboveground mushrooms—covers more than 1,000 acres.

diseases produce spores at the site of infection, the diseases can spread easily from person to person. Both diseases can be treated with antifungal medications.

Disease-Fighting Fungi In 1928 a Scottish biologist, Alexander Fleming, was examining petri dishes in which he was growing bacteria. To his surprise, Fleming noticed a spot of a bluish-green mold growing in one dish. Curiously, no bacteria were growing near the mold. Fleming hypothesized that the mold, a fungus named *Penicillium*, produced a substance that killed the bacteria growing near it. Fleming's work led to the development of the first antibiotic, penicillin. It has saved the lives of millions of people with bacterial infections. Since the discovery of penicillin, many additional antibiotics have been isolated from both fungi and eubacteria.

Fungus-Plant Root Associations Some fungi help plants grow larger and healthier when their hyphae grow among the plant's roots. The hyphae spread out underground and absorb water and nutrients from the soil for the plant. With more water and nutrients, the plant grows larger than it would have grown without its fungal partner. The plant is not the only partner that benefits. The fungi get to feed on the extra food that the plant makes and stores.

Many plants are so dependent on their fungal partners that they cannot survive well without them. For example, orchids cannot grow without their fungal partners.

Figure 18 The fruiting bodies of these mushrooms have emerged in an almost perfect circular pattern. This pattern is called a fairy ring. The mushrooms share the same network of underground hyphae.

Language Arts
CONNECTION

Folk tales are ancient stories that were passed down by word of mouth over many generations. Folk tales often involve magical elements, such as fairies—supernatural beings with powers to become invisible, change form, and affect the lives of people.

The circle of mushrooms in Figure 18 was often mentioned in folk tales. These circles were said to be the footprints of fairies who danced there at midnight. These mushroom circles were given the name "fairy rings"—a name that is still used today. People believed that the area inside a fairy ring was a magical location. Cutting down the tree inside a fairy ring was believed to bring bad luck.

In Your Journal

A type of mushroom called a toadstool is mentioned in some folk tales. Write a paragraph that could be part of a folk tale that reveals how toadstools got their name.

Language Arts
CONNECTION

Ask students if they know of other mushrooms with interesting names. Some are named for their appearance, like the bird's nest, cauliflower, earthstar, old-man-of-the-woods, parasol, squirrel's bread, and thimble mushrooms. Chicken-of-the-woods and milk cap are named for their taste, and destroying angel, fly agaric, and inky cap are named for distinguishing traits or uses. Others, like fairy cups, elves' saddle, and morel have names rooted in folklore.

In Your Journal Students' paragraphs may include the idea that a toad used a "toadstool" to sit upon. Students should try to include a magical element in their paragraphs. Inform students that although the word *toadstool* commonly refers to poisonous mushrooms, there is no scientific distinction between mushrooms and toadstools. Many families of fungi include both edible and poisonous mushrooms. **learning modality: verbal**

Answers to Self-Assessment
Caption Question
Figure 17 Disease-causing fungi produce spores at the site of infection. The spores are easily dispersed, so disease spreads rapidly.

✓ *Checkpoint*
Fungi help produce bread, cheese, and wine.

Ongoing Assessment

Skills Check Have students list ways that fungi affect humans and identify each as beneficial or harmful.

Integrating Earth Science

ACTIVITY

Provide students with hand lenses and samples of lichens on rocks or tree bark. As students observe the lichens, challenge them to infer why lichens are sensitive to environmental pollution. *(Lichens rapidly absorb substances directly from rainwater, so they are very susceptible to airborne pollutants.)* **learning modality: visual**

3 Assess

Section 3 Review Answers

1. Fungi are eukaryotes, reproduce by spores, and are heterotrophs that feed in a similar way. They also live in warm, moist places.
2. Hyphae secrete digestive chemicals into a food source. The chemicals break down the food into smaller chemicals which the hyphae absorb. Fungi feed on dead organisms or are parasites in living organisms.
3. Fungi recycle chemical substances on Earth. They may cause human diseases, help cure diseases, provide a source of food, or live in symbiotic relationships with plants.
4. Mushrooms cannot make their own food so they are not classified as plants.

Check Your Progress

CHAPTER PROJECT

Students will need help drawing conclusions about their results. As you review students' sketches, point out questions that are not addressed by the poster. If necessary, list some ideas for information students should include on their posters before they make their sketches.

Performance Assessment

Oral Presentation Have small groups make presentations on the structure of fungi, how they obtain food, their reproduction, types of fungi, or how fungi interact with the living world. Presentations should include labeled sketches.

Figure 19 Lichens consist of a fungus living together with either algae or autotrophic bacteria. **A.** This lichen—a British soldier—probably gets its name from its scarlet red tops, which stand upright. **B.** The lichens covering these rocks are slowly breaking down the rocks to create soil.

Lichens A **lichen** (LY kun) consists of a fungus and either algae or autotrophic bacteria that also live together in a mutualistic relationship. You have probably seen some familiar lichens—irregular, flat, crusty patches that grow on tree barks or rocks. The fungus benefits from the food produced by the algae or bacteria. The algae or bacteria, in turn, obtain water and minerals from the fungus.

 INTEGRATING EARTH SCIENCE Lichens are often called "pioneer" organisms because they are the first organisms to appear on the bare rocks in an area after a volcano, fire, or rock slide has occurred. Over time, the lichens break down the rock into soil in which other organisms can grow. Lichens are also useful as indicators of air pollution. Many species of lichens are very sensitive to pollutants and die when pollution levels rise. By monitoring the growth of lichens, scientists can assess the air quality in an area.

Section 3 Review

1. List three characteristics that fungi share.
2. Explain how a fungus feeds. What do fungi feed on?
3. Describe three roles that fungi play in the world.
4. **Thinking Critically Classifying** Explain why mushrooms are classified as fungi rather than as plants.

Check Your Progress

CHAPTER PROJECT

Continue to observe your mushrooms and collect data. Begin to review your data to see which conditions favored mushroom growth. How do your results compare with your hypothesis? Begin to plan your poster now. Think about how you can use graphs and diagrams to display your results. *(Hint: Draw a rough sketch of your poster, and show it to your teacher. Include a labeled drawing of a mushroom.)*

Background

History of Science Beatrix Potter (the creator of Peter Rabbit) thought that lichens were composed of algae and fungi living in a mutualistic relationship. Potter was an avid naturalist and scientific illustrator. She wrote a paper that included drawings of her observations of lichens through the microscope. The paper was read at a scholarly society in the 1890s, but because she was a woman, Potter was not allowed to appear.

Program Resources

◆ **Unit 2 Resources** 7-3 Review and Reinforce, p. 47; 7-3 Enrich, p. 48

Protists

Key Ideas
◆ Animal-like protists, or protozoans, include sarcodines, ciliates, zooflagellates, and sporozoans. Like animals, these protists are heterotrophs. Most protozoans move by using pseudopods, cilia, or flagella.
◆ Funguslike protists include water molds, downy mildews, and slime molds. Like fungi, these protists are heterotrophs, have cell walls, and use spores to reproduce.
◆ Plantlike protists, or algae, include euglenoids, dinoflagellates, diatoms, green algae, red algae, and brown algae. Like plants, these organisms are autotrophs.

Key Terms
protozoan
pseudopod
contractile vacuole
cilia
symbiosis
mutualism
spore
algae
pigment

Algal Blooms
INTEGRATING ENVIRONMENTAL SCIENCE

Key Ideas
◆ Red tides occur when a population of algae increases quickly in ocean waters. Some algae can secrete toxins that poison animals.
◆ Nutrients in a lake or pond build up over time, causing an increase in the numbers of algae. An accelerated rate of eutrophication can lead to the deaths of many organisms in the lake or pond.

Key Terms
algal bloom   eutrophication
red tide

Fungi

Key Ideas
◆ Most fungi are eukaryotes, use spores to reproduce, and are heterotrophs.
◆ Most fungi feed by absorbing food through their hyphae. The hyphae secrete digestive chemicals into a food source, which is broken down into small substances that are absorbed by the hyphae.
◆ Fungi produce spores in fruiting bodies. Most fungi reproduce both asexually and sexually.
◆ Fungi are decomposers that recycle Earth's chemicals.

Key Terms
hypha   budding
fruiting body   lichen

Organizing Information

Flowchart Copy this flowchart about changes in a lake onto a separate sheet of paper. Then complete the flowchart and add a title. (For more on flowcharts, see the Skills Handbook.)

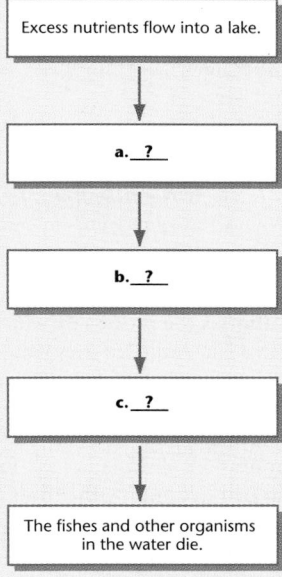

Excess nutrients flow into a lake.

↓

a. _?_

↓

b. _?_

↓

c. _?_

↓

The fishes and other organisms in the water die.

Chapter 7 **243**

Organizing Information

Flow Chart Sample title: The Effect of Excess Nutrients in a Lake; **a.** Algal bloom occurs. **b.** Excess algae block the sun, and plants on the bottom die. **c.** As decomposers feed on the dead bodies, they use up the oxygen in the water.

Program Resources

◆ **Unit 2 Resources** Chapter 7 Project Scoring Rubric, p. 36
◆ **Performance Assessment** Chapter 7, pp. 23–25
◆ **Chapter and Unit Tests** Chapter 7 Test, pp. 32–35

Media and Technology

 Interactive Student Tutorial CD-ROM Chapter 7

 Computer Test Bank Chapter 7 Test

Reviewing Content
Multiple Choice
1. c 2. c 3. d 4. c 5. b

True or False
6. pseudopods 7. true 8. true 9. club
10. true

Checking Concepts
11. An ameba extends pseudopods on each side of a food particle to engulf it.
12. Algae range greatly in size. Some are unicellular, others are multicellular, and some form large colonies.
13. Animal-like and funguslike protists are heterotrophs. Plantlike protists are autotrophs, but some can also be heterotrophs.
14. An algal bloom in the ocean can cause a red tide to occur. Red tides are dangerous because the toxins that the algae produce can become concentrated in the bodies of organisms that consume the algae. An algal bloom in a lake can increase the rate of eutrophication.
15. In sexual reproduction, two hyphae grow together and produce a fruiting body.
16. The fungus benefits from food produced by the algae or bacteria, which obtains water and minerals from the fungus.
17. Students should explain that the puffball is the fruiting body and that the spores are spread by wind, water, or other organisms. They should also know that spores will only germinate in a suitable environment.

Thinking Critically
18. Amebas and paramecia are both unicellular heterotrophs that move. Amebas move with pseudopods, but paramecia move with cilia.
19. Keep it aired out, dry, and cool. Mildew is a funguslike protist that thrives in moist, warm environments.
20. Most other life forms would probably disappear also. Algae provide food and oxygen for water animals and help maintain the oxygen in the atmosphere.
21. There could be excess nutrients in the water, or it may be old and need to be changed. The scum could be from eutrophication, a natural process that occurs over time.

Reviewing Content
 For more review of key concepts, see the Interactive Student Tutorial CD-ROM.

Multiple Choice
Choose the letter of the best answer.

1. Which of the following characteristics describes *all* protists?
   a. They are unicellular.
   b. They can be seen with the unaided eye.
   c. Their cells have nuclei.
   d. They are unable to move on their own.
2. Which protist uses cilia to move?
   a. euglena b. ameba
   c. paramecium d. diatom
3. Which statement is true of slime molds?
   a. They are always unicellular.
   b. They are autotrophs.
   c. They are animal-like protists.
   d. They use spores to reproduce.
4. An overpopulation of saltwater algae is called a(n)
   a. pigment.
   b. lichen.
   c. red tide.
   d. eutrophication.
5. A lichen is a symbiotic association between which of the following?
   a. fungi and plant roots
   b. algae and fungi
   c. algae and bacteria
   d. protozoans and algae

True or False
If the statement is true, write true. If it is false, change the underlined word or words to make the statement true.

6. Sarcodines use <u>flagella</u> to move.
7. <u>Eutrophication</u> is the process by which nutrients in a lake build up over time, causing an increase in the growth of algae.
8. Most fungi are made up of threadlike structures called <u>hyphae</u>.
9. All mushrooms are classified as <u>sac</u> fungi.
10. Most fungi that live among the roots of plants are <u>beneficial</u> to the plants.

Checking Concepts
11. Describe the process by which an ameba obtains its food.
12. Describe the differences among algae in terms of their sizes.
13. Compare how animal-like, funguslike, and plantlike protists obtain food.
14. What problems can an algal bloom cause in an ocean? What problems can an algal bloom cause in a lake?
15. How does sexual reproduction occur in fungi?
16. Explain how both organisms that make up a lichen benefit from their symbiotic relationship.
17. **Writing to Learn** Imagine you are a spore inside a ripe puffball. An animal passing by brushes against the puffball and punctures the outer covering of your spore case. Write a description about what happens to you next.

Thinking Critically
18. **Comparing and Contrasting** Describe the ways in which amebas and paramecia are similar to one another. How are they different?
19. **Problem Solving** What are some actions that homeowners could take to discourage the growth of mildew in their basement? Explain why these actions might help solve the problem.
20. **Predicting** If all algae suddenly disappeared from Earth's waters, what would happen to living things on Earth? Explain your answer.
21. **Relating Cause and Effect** You see some green scumlike material growing on the walls of your freshwater aquarium at home. List some possible reasons why this growth has occurred.

Applying Skills
22. The amount of carbon dioxide produced is highest between 20°C and 30°C. As the temperature gets cooler or warmer than this range, the carbon dioxide production decreases sharply. Below 0°C and above 50°C, no carbon dioxide is produced.

23. Yeast must be active and produce carbon dioxide so the dough will rise, and yeast is more active in warm water.
24. No. For the most part the dough would not continue to rise because yeast are usually inactive at that temperature.

Applying Skills

When yeast is added to bread dough, the yeast cells produce carbon dioxide, which causes the dough to rise. The graph below shows how temperature affects the amount of carbon dioxide that is produced. Use the graph to answer Questions 22–24.

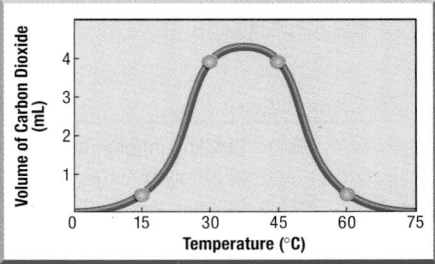

22. **Interpreting Data** Explain how temperature affects the amount of carbon dioxide that the yeast cells produce.

23. **Inferring** Use the graph to explain why yeast is dissolved in warm water rather than cold water when it is used to make bread.

24. **Predicting** Based on the graph, would you expect bread dough to continue to rise if it were placed in a refrigerator (about 2°–5°C)? Explain.

Performance ▼ CHAPTER PROJECT Assessment

Present Your Project Now it's time to finalize your poster. Include your hypothesis, and describe the conditions that produced the best mushroom growth. Make sure your graph is easy to understand. Check that your drawing of a mushroom is clearly labeled.

Reflect and Record What did you learn about mushrooms from this project? Did you encounter and solve any problems? Did the project raise new questions for you? If so, how could you answer those questions?

Test Preparation
Use these questions to prepare for standardized tests.

Study the graph. Then answer Questions 25–28.

25. What is the best title for this graph?
   a. The Growth Rates of Trees
   b. The Heights of Four Tree Species
   c. The Effect of Root-Associated Fungi on Tree Growth
   d. The Growth of Root-Associated Fungi

26. Which of the following statements is supported by the graph's data?
   a. All trees grew equally well.
   b. Trees with root-associated fungi grew taller than similar trees without such fungi.
   c. Yellow poplars are the tallest tree species.
   d. The data support none of the statements.

27. Based on the graph, which type of tree had the largest growth change with root-associated fungi?
   a. pine
   b. sour orange
   c. avocado
   d. yellow poplar

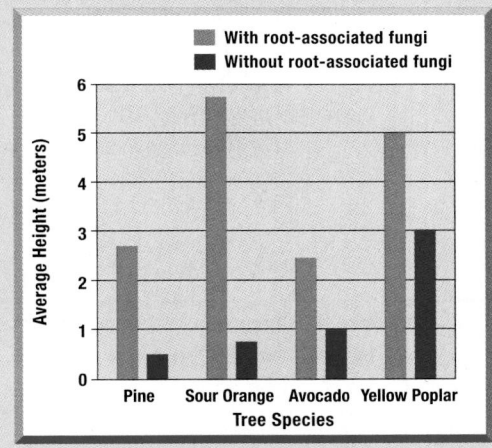

28. What is the average height difference between avocado trees that grew with root-associated fungi and those that grew without such fungi?
   a. 1.5 meters
   b. 2.0 meters
   c. 2.25 meters
   d. 5.0 meters

Performance ▼ CHAPTER PROJECT Assessment

Present Your Project Provide students with materials for making the posters. Set aside time for them to work on posters during class, and allow them to look at each other's posters for ideas. Students should organize information on their posters in a clear manner.

Reflect and Record Some students may have found it difficult to organize their results because they changed the variables too often or were not confident of their results. Students may propose another experiment or talking to an expert as a way of answering their questions.

Test Preparation
25. c 26. b 27. b 28. a

Program Resources
◆ **Inquiry Skills Activity Book** Provides teaching and review of all inquiry skills.

Introduction to Plants

Sections	Time	Student Edition Activities	Other Activities
Become a Moss Expert p. 246	Ongoing (2 weeks)	Check Your Progress, pp. 259, 265, 268 Present Your Project, p. 271	
1 The Plant Kingdom pp. 248–255 ◆ Identify the characteristics that all plants share. ◆ Name all the things that plants need to live successfully and describe the plant life cycle.	$2\frac{1}{2}$ periods/ 1 block	**Discover** What Do Leaves Reveal About Plants?, p. 248 **Sharpen Your Skills** Interpreting Data, p. 249 **Science at Home,** p. 253 **Skills Lab: Designing Experiments** Eye on Photosynthesis, pp. 254–255	TE Building Inquiry Skills: Inferring, p. 249 TE Building Inquiry Skills: Observing, pp. 250, 252 TE Demonstration, p. 252 LM 8, "Investigating Stomata"
2 Mosses, Liverworts, and Hornworts pp. 256–260 ◆ Name some nonvascular plants, and list the characteristics that they all share. ◆ Describe the structure of a moss plant and the importance of mosses on Earth.	1 period/ $\frac{1}{2}$ block	**Discover** Will Mosses Absorb Water? p. 256 **Skills Lab: Observing** Masses of Mosses, p. 260	TE Demonstration, p. 257 TE Building Inquiry Skills: Observing, p. 258
3 Ferns and Their Relatives pp. 261–265 ◆ Name some seedless vascular plants, and list the characteristics that they share. ◆ Describe the structure of a fern plant, how a fern plant reproduces, and the importance of ferns on Earth.	1 period/ $\frac{1}{2}$ block	**Discover** How Quickly Can Water Move Upward?, p. 261 **Try This** Examining a Fern, p. 262	TE Visual Arts Connection, p. 263 TE Building Inquiry Skills: Classifying, p. 264 IES "Fate of the Rain Forest," pp. 12–13
4 INTEGRATING TECHNOLOGY **Feeding the World** pp. 266–268 ◆ Describe some methods that might help farmers produce more crops.	1 period/ $\frac{1}{2}$ block	**Discover** Will There Be Enough to Eat?, p. 266	IES "Fate of the Rain Forest," pp. 6–9; 17–19
Study Guide/Assessment pp. 269–271	1 period/ $\frac{1}{2}$ block		ISAB Provides teaching and review of all inquiry skills

For Standard or Block Schedule The Resource Pro® CD-ROM gives you maximum flexibility for planning your instruction for any type of schedule. Resource Pro® contains Planning Express®, an advanced scheduling program, as well as the entire contents of the Teaching Resources and the Computer Test Bank.

CHAPTER PLANNING GUIDE

Program Resources	Assessment Strategies	Media and Technology
UR Chapter 8 Project Teacher Notes, pp. 54–55 **UR** Chapter 8 Project Overview and Worksheets, pp. 56–57	**SE** Performance Assessment: Present Your Project, p. 271 **TE** Check Your Progress, pp. 259, 265, 268 **UR** Chapter 8 Project Scoring Rubric, p. 60	Science Explorer Internet Site at www.phschool.com
UR 8-1 Lesson Plan, p. 61 **UR** 8-1 Section Summary, p. 62 **UR** 8-1 Review and Reinforce, p. 63 **UR** 8-1 Enrich, p. 64 **UR** Chapter 8 Skills Lab, pp. 77–79	**SE** Section 1 Review, p. 253 **TE** Ongoing Assessment, pp. 249, 251 **TE** Performance Assessment, p. 253	Audio CD, English-Spanish Summary 8-1 Transparency 32, "A Plant Cell" Transparency 33, "The Life Cycle of Plants" Interactive Student Tutorial CD-ROM, Chapter 8
UR 8-2 Lesson Plan, p. 65 **UR** 8-2 Section Summary, p. 66 **UR** 8-2 Review and Reinforce, p. 67 **UR** 8-2 Enrich, p. 68	**SE** Section 2 Review, p. 259 **TE** Ongoing Assessment, p. 257 **TE** Performance Assessment, p. 259	Life Science Videotape 2; Videodisc Unit 1 Side 2, "Space Shuttle Air Systems" Audio CD, English-Spanish Summary 8-2
UR 8-3 Lesson Plan, p. 69 **UR** 8-3 Section Summary, p. 70 **UR** 8-3 Review and Reinforce, p. 71 **UR** 8-3 Enrich, p. 72 **UR** Chapter 8 Skills Lab, pp. 80–81	**SE** Section 3 Review, p. 265 **TE** Ongoing Assessment, p. 262, 264 **TE** Performance Assessment, p. 265	Audio CD, English-Spanish Summary 8-3
UR 8-4 Lesson Plan, p. 73 **UR** 8-4 Section Summary, p. 74 **UR** 8-4 Review and Reinforce, p. 75 **UR** 8-4 Enrich, p. 76	**SE** Section 4 Review, p. 268 **TE** Ongoing Assessment, p. 267 **TE** Performance Assessment, p. 268	Audio CD, English-Spanish Summary 8-4
RCA Provides strategies to improve science reading skills **GSW** Provides worksheets to promote student comprehension of content	**SE** Chapter 8 Study Guide/Assessment, pp. 269–271 **PA** Chapter 8 Performance Assessment, pp. 26–28 **CUT** Chapter 8 Test, pp. 36–39 **CTB** Chapter 8 Test	Interactive Student Tutorial CD-ROM, Chapter 8 Computer Test Bank, Chapter 8 Test

Key: **SE** Student Edition
CTB Computer Test Bank
ISAB Inquiry Skills Activity Book
GSW Guided Study Worksheets

TE Teacher's Edition
PTA Product Testing Activities by *Consumer Reports*
RCA Reading in the Content Area
PA Performance Assessment

UR Unit Resources
LM Laboratory Manual
IES Interdisciplinary Explorations Series
CUT Chapter and Unit Tests

Meeting the National Science Education Standards and AAAS Benchmarks

National Science Education Standards	Benchmarks for Science Literacy	Unifying Themes
Science as Inquiry (Content Standard A) ◆ **Design and conduct a scientific investigation** Students design experiments to identify the raw materials and conditions that are involved in photosynthesis. *(Skills Lab: Designing Experiments)* ◆ **Communicate scientific procedures and explanations** Students create a brochure describing how to grow moss. *(Chapter Project)* **Physical Science** (Content Standard B) ◆ **Transfer of energy** The energy from the sun is stored in plants during photosynthesis. *(Skills Lab: Designing Experiments)* **Life Science** (Content Standard C) ◆ **Structure and function in living systems** Plants are multicellular and have a variety of structures that carry out life functions. *(Sections 1, 2, 3, 4; Chapter Project; Skills Lab: Designing Experiments; Skills Lab: Observing)* ◆ **Reproduction and heredity** Plants have life cycles that include gametophyte and sporophyte stages. *(Sections 1, 2, 3)* ◆ **Diversity and adaptations of organisms** There are many kinds of plant species. Mosses and ferns evolved adaptations that allowed them to survive on land. *(Sections 1, 2, 3; Skills Lab)* **Science in Personal and Social Perspectives** (Content Standard F) ◆ **Populations, resources, and environments** Overpopulation may lead to food shortage. *(Section 4)*	**1A The Scientific World View** Knowledge about photosynthesis has been repeatedly modified as scientists learn more about the process. *(Section 2)* **1B Scientific Inquiry** Controlling variables and conducting experiments are emphasized as students investigate photosynthesis. *(Skills Lab: Designing Experiments)* **3C Issues in Technology** Technological advances in food production may reduce world hunger. *(Section 4)* **5A Diversity of Life** Plants have a wide array of adaptations. All plants share certain characteristics. *(Sections 1, 2, 3; Chapter Project; Skills Lab: Observing)* **5E Flow of Matter and Energy** Plants store energy from the sun as carbohydrates. *(Section 2; Skills Lab: Designing Experiments)* **8A Agriculture** Agricultural technology, such as genetic engineering, hydroponics, and precision farming, can improve crop growth. *(Section 4)*	◆ **Energy** Plants use energy from sunlight to make food during photosynthesis. Peat and coal resources formed from the ancient remains of mosses and ferns. *(Sections 3, 4; Skills Lab: Designing Experiments)* ◆ **Evolution** Land plants evolved from green algae. Land plants evolved in ways that made them better suited to life on land. Vascular plants are better suited to drier conditions than are nonvascular plants. *(Section 1)* ◆ **Scale and Structure** All plants have adaptations for obtaining and transporting water and other materials, support, and reproduction. *(Sections 1, 2, 3; Chapter Project; Skills Lab: Observing)* ◆ **Unity and Diversity** Although each kind of plant has unique adaptations, all plants share basic characteristics. *(Sections 1, 2, 3; Chapter Project; Skills Lab: Observing; Skills Lab: Designing Experiments)*

Take It to the Net

 *Interactive text at www.phschool.com*

Science Explorer comes alive with iText.

- **Complete student text** is accessible from any computer with Internet access or a CD-ROM drive.
- **Animations, simulations, and videos** enhance student understanding and retention of concepts.
- **Self-tests and online study tools** assess student understanding.

STAY CURRENT with

Find out the latest research and information about plants at:
www.phschool.com

Go to **www.phschool.com** and click on the Science icon. Then click on Science Explorer: Life, Earth, and Physical Science under PH@school.

ACTIVITY	Time (minutes)	Materials Quantities for one work group	Skills
Section 1			
Discover, p. 248	10	**Consumable** leaf from a jade plant or a plant with thick, fleshy leaves; leaf of a temperate-climate plant, such as a maple, oak, or common garden plant **Nonconsumable** hand lens	Inferring
Sharpen your Skills, p. 249	15	No special materials are required.	Interpreting Data
Science at Home, p. 253	home	**Consumable** art supplies	Communicating
Skills Lab, pp. 254–255	45	**Consumable** *Elodea* plants, water (boiled, then cooled), sodium bicarbonate solution **Nonconsumable** wide-mouthed container, 2 test tubes, 2 wax pencils, lamp (optional)	Designing Experiments
Section 2			
Discover, p. 256	15	**Consumable** 20 mL sand, 20 mL peat moss, water **Nonconsumable** 3 plastic graduated cylinders, dropper, stopwatch	Predicting
Skills Lab, p. 260	45	**Consumable** clump of moss, toothpicks, water **Nonconsumable** metric ruler, plastic dropper, hand lens	Observing
Section 3			
Discover, p. 261	10	**Consumable** water, food coloring **Nonconsumable** goggles, plastic petri dish, narrow glass tube, dropper	Inferring
Try This, p. 262	20	**Consumable** fern plant, water **Nonconsumable** hand lens, plastic	Inferring
Section 4			
Discover, p. 266	15	**Consumable** cooked rice, peanuts, or cereal **Nonconsumable** bag, tags	Predicting

A list of all materials required for the Student Edition activities can be found on pages T25–T33. You can obtain information about ordering materials by calling 1-800-848-9500 or by accessing the Science Explorer Internet site at **www.phschool.com**.

Become a Moss Expert

Mosses are so low growing, soft, and velvety that students may not realize they are plants at all. By growing mosses in a terrarium, students will be able to make detailed observations of mosses and learn more about plant structure.

Purpose In this project, students construct a terrarium, observe and record the growth of a moss, and determine the requirements for mosses to grow.

Skills Focus After completing the Chapter 8 Project, students will be able to

◆ plan and construct a terrarium and provide the necessary conditions for growth;

◆ observe the response of the moss and determine the growth requirements for mosses;

◆ communicate their results in a brochure describing how to grow mosses;

Project Time Line The entire project will take three to four weeks. Spend one or two days introducing and planning the project. Students may need a day or two to find and collect mosses for their terrariums. It will take one class period to build and set up the terrariums. Mosses should be observed in the terrariums for two to three weeks. Afterward, a few days will be needed for students to write their brochures and prepare their presentations. Before beginning the project, see Chapter 8 Project Teacher Notes on pages 54–55 in Unit 2 Resources for more details on carrying out the project. Also distribute to students the Chapter 8 Project Overview and Worksheets and Scoring Rubric on pages 56–60 in Unit 2 Resources.

Possible Materials

◆ Provide materials for construction of the terrarium. Each group could use a 2-liter soda bottle, a nail (to punch open a cutting hole), scissors, gravel, sand, soil, and charcoal.

◆ Have students collect mosses, or provide the mosses for them. If

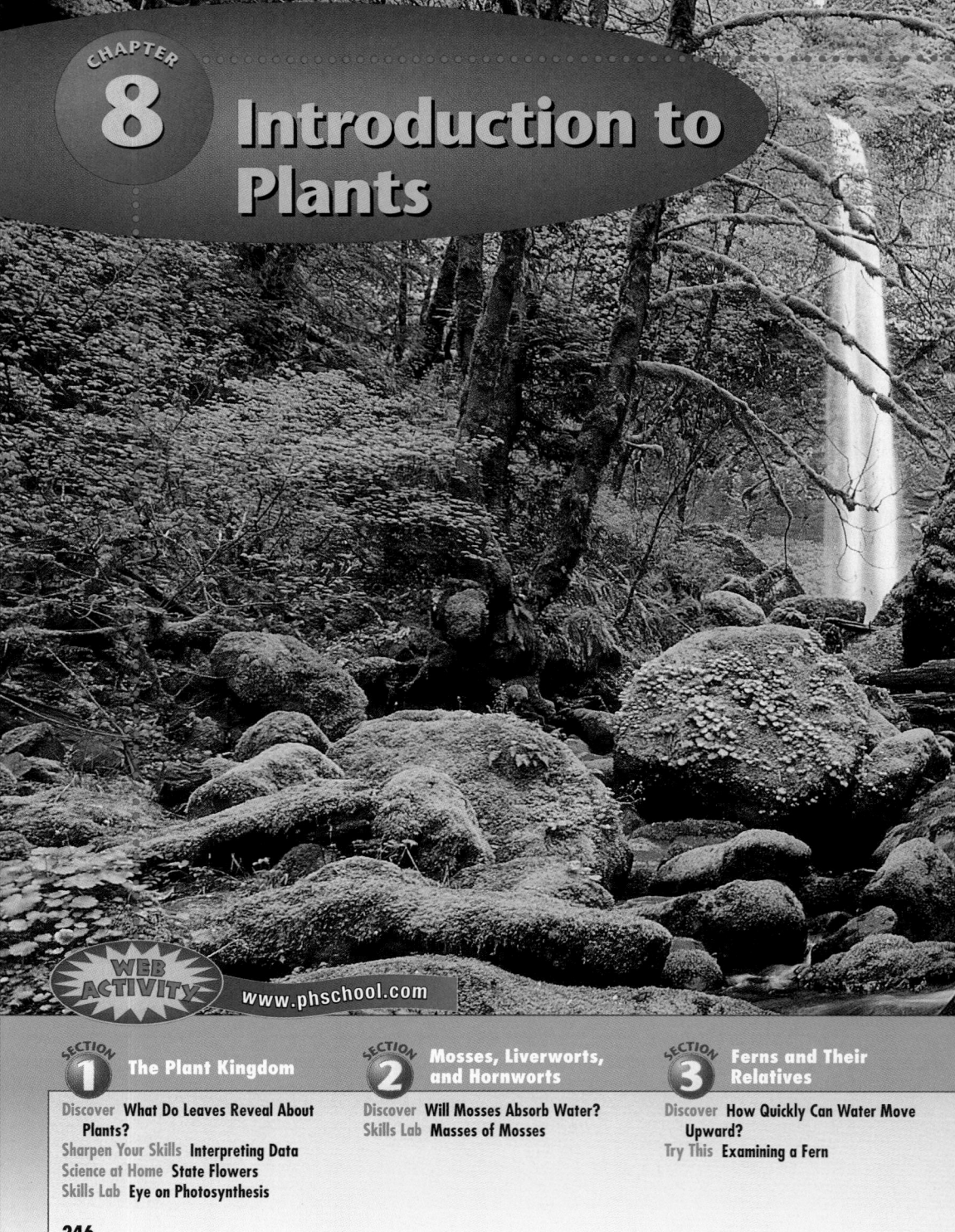

WEB ACTIVITY www.phschool.com

SECTION **1** The Plant Kingdom

Discover **What Do Leaves Reveal About Plants?**
Sharpen Your Skills **Interpreting Data**
Science at Home **State Flowers**
Skills Lab **Eye on Photosynthesis**

SECTION **2** Mosses, Liverworts, and Hornworts

Discover **Will Mosses Absorb Water?**
Skills Lab **Masses of Mosses**

SECTION **3** Ferns and Their Relatives

Discover **How Quickly Can Water Move Upward?**
Try This **Examining a Fern**

246

students collect the mosses themselves, caution them to make sure to remove the plant carefully, including rhizoids, and to take only a small sample.

◆ Supply materials for the presentations including poster board, graphing paper, and unlined paper.

◆ Provide research material for students who wish to include additional information on mosses in their brochures.

Launching the Project Have students discuss where they have seen mosses and brainstorm a list of conditions that are present in all these locations. Once they have identified the conditions they think are suitable, they can use that information to plan their terrariums.

Allow time for students to read the description of the project in their text and the Chapter Project Overview on pages 56–57 in Unit 2 Resources. Explain to students that, unlike most plants, mosses do not have vascular tissue. Vascular tissue functions in support and

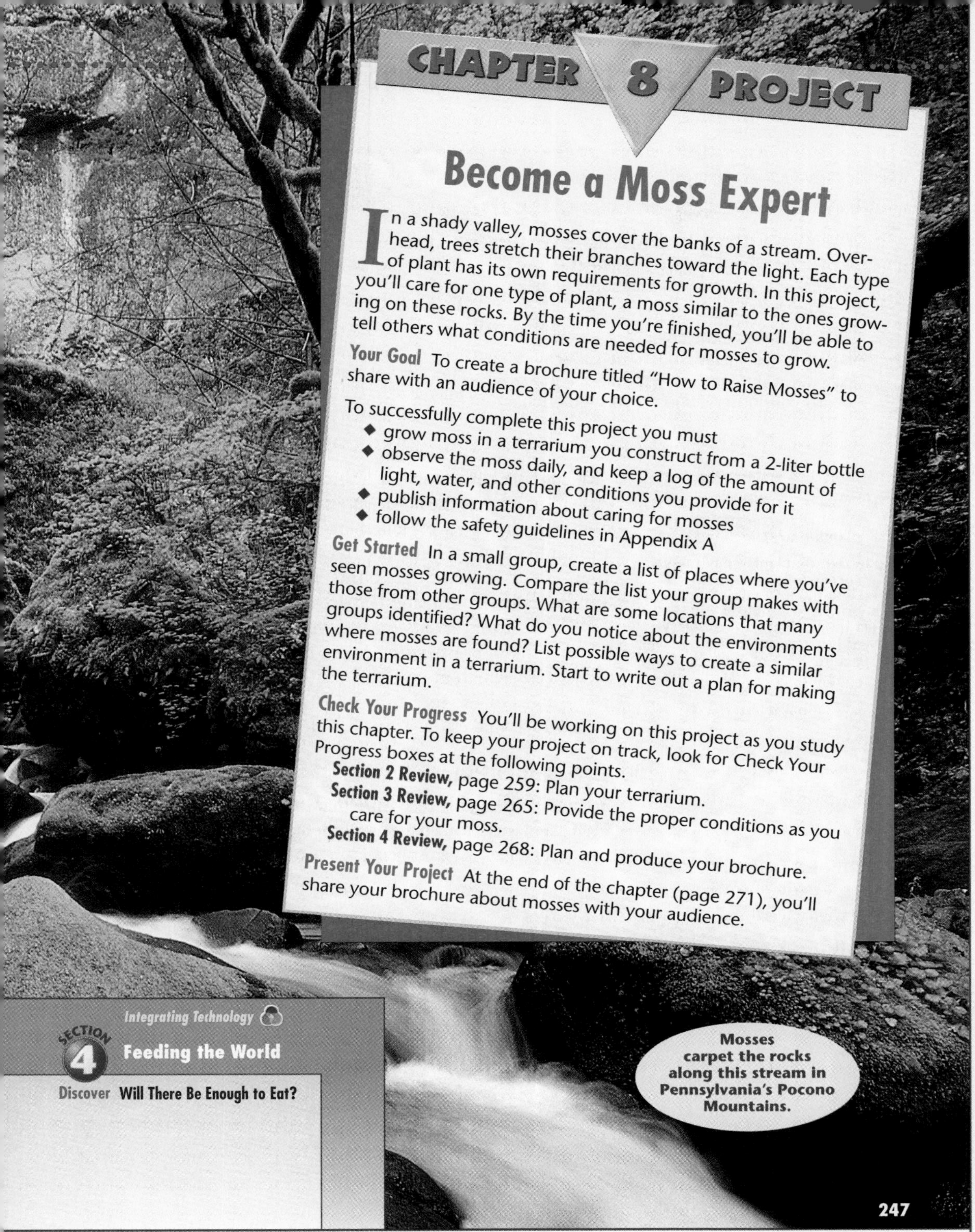

CHAPTER 8 PROJECT

Become a Moss Expert

In a shady valley, mosses cover the banks of a stream. Overhead, trees stretch their branches toward the light. Each type of plant has its own requirements for growth. In this project, you'll care for one type of plant, a moss similar to the ones growing on these rocks. By the time you're finished, you'll be able to tell others what conditions are needed for mosses to grow.

Your Goal To create a brochure titled "How to Raise Mosses" to share with an audience of your choice.

To successfully complete this project you must
◆ grow moss in a terrarium you construct from a 2-liter bottle
◆ observe the moss daily, and keep a log of the amount of light, water, and other conditions you provide for it
◆ publish information about caring for mosses
◆ follow the safety guidelines in Appendix A

Get Started In a small group, create a list of places where you've seen mosses growing. Compare the list your group makes with those from other groups. What are some locations that many groups identified? What do you notice about the environments where mosses are found? List possible ways to create a similar environment in a terrarium. Start to write out a plan for making the terrarium.

Check Your Progress You'll be working on this project as you study this chapter. To keep your project on track, look for Check Your Progress boxes at the following points.

Section 2 Review, page 259: Plan your terrarium.
Section 3 Review, page 265: Provide the proper conditions as you care for your moss.
Section 4 Review, page 268: Plan and produce your brochure.

Present Your Project At the end of the chapter (page 271), you'll share your brochure about mosses with your audience.

> Mosses carpet the rocks along this stream in Pennsylvania's Pocono Mountains.

247

SECTION **4**

Integrating Technology

Feeding the World

Discover **Will There Be Enough to Eat?**

Program Resources

◆ **Unit 2 Resources** Chapter 8 Project Teacher Notes, pp. 54–55; Chapter 8 Project Overview and Worksheets, pp. 56–59; Chapter 8 Project Scoring Rubric, p. 60

WEB ACTIVITY www.phschool.com

You will find an Internet activity, chapter self-tests for students, and links to other chapter topics at this site.

---

in transport of water. Without it, mosses cannot grow tall and must transport water from cell to cell. Caution students to be careful when using scissors to cut the top off the 2-liter plastic bottle. Address any initial questions students may have. Pass out copies of the Chapter 8 Project Worksheets on pages 58–59 in Unit 2 Resources for students to review.

You can have students work in small groups as a cooperative learning task. To ensure that every student will have ample opportunity to participate in terrarium construction, data recording, and brochure preparation, each group should consist of no more than four students.

Performance Assessment

The Chapter 8 Project Scoring Rubric on page 60 of Unit 2 Resources will help you evaluate how well students complete the Chapter 8 Project. Students will be assessed on
◆ how well they construct their terrarium, and the clarity of their procedure;
◆ the completeness of their daily observations and how well they follow their procedure;
◆ the quality of their brochure and presentation;
◆ their group participation (optional).
By sharing the Chapter 8 Project Scoring Rubric with students at the beginning of the project, you will make it clear to them what they are expected to do.

247

Objectives

After completing the lesson, students will be able to
◆ identify the characteristics that all plants share;
◆ name all the things that plants need to live successfully and describe the plant life cycle.

Key Terms cuticle, tissue, vascular tissue, fertilization, zygote, sporophyte, gametophyte, gamete

1 Engage/Explore

Activating Prior Knowledge

Show students a potted plant and ask them to name two ways that it is different from an animal. *(Sample: It cannot make noise and does not walk around.)*

DISCOVER

Skills Focus inferring
Materials *hand lens, leaf from a jade plant or a plant with thick, fleshy leaves; leaf of a temperate-climate plant, such as a maple, oak, or common garden plant*
Time 10 minutes
Tips Select leaves that display adaptations easily associated with protection from bright sun and dry weather. Both leaves should be green in color.
Expected Outcome Students should observe a difference in leaf thickness, texture, and size.
Think It Over Students should infer that the plant with the small, thick, fleshy leaf lives in the desert, and that the plant with the larger, thinner, more delicate leaf lives in an area of average rainfall. Students will probably say that the thick leaf looks like it has water in it.

DISCOVER ··············· ACTIVITY

What Do Leaves Reveal About Plants?

1. Your teacher will give you two leaves from plants that grow in two very different environments: a desert and an area with average rainfall.

2. Carefully observe the color, size, shape, and texture of the leaves. Touch the surfaces of each leaf. Examine each leaf with a hand lens. Record your observations in your notebook.

3. When you have finished, wash your hands thoroughly with soap and water.

Think It Over
Inferring Use your observations to determine which plant lives in the desert and which does not. Give at least one reason to support your inference.

GUIDE FOR READING

◆ What characteristics do all plants share?
◆ What do plants need to live successfully on land?

Reading Tip Before you read, list the boldfaced vocabulary words in your notebook. Leave space to add notes as you read.

▼ The Hoh rain forest

Imagine a forest where a thick growth of fungi, mosses, and ferns carpets the floor. Because there is no bare soil, seedlings start their lives on fallen logs. Ferns hang like curtains from the limbs of giant hemlock trees. Douglas fir trees grow taller than 20-story buildings. Other plants with strange names—vanilla leaf, self-heal, and licorice fern—also grow in the forest.

Such a forest exists on the western slopes of the Olympic Mountains in Washington State. Native Americans named the forest *Hoh*, which means "fast white water," after a river there. In some areas of the forest, over 300 centimeters of rain fall each year, which makes the area a rain forest.

What Is a Plant?

You would probably recognize many of the plants that grow in the Hoh rain forest. You encounter other familiar plants when you pick flowers, run across freshly cut grass, or eat vegetables such as peas.

248

READING STRATEGIES

Reading Tip After students have made their lists, ask if they recognize any of the terms. Ask if they have already studied any of these terms. Suggest that they attempt to define words they've seen before and modify their definitions as they read.

Study and Comprehension Instruct students to use the headings in the section to create an outline that shows main points and key details. Start an outline, such as the one shown below, to guide students.
I. What is a Plant?
  A. a eukaryote that contains many cells

Members of the plant kingdom share some important characteristics. **All plants are eukaryotes that contain many cells. In addition, plants are autotrophs, which produce their own food.**

In Chapter 2, you learned that plants carry out the process called photosynthesis to make their food. During photosynthesis, a plant uses carbon dioxide gas and water to make food and oxygen. Sunlight provides the energy that powers the entire process.

Living on Land

Unlike algae, most plants live on land. How is living on land different from living in water? Imagine multicellular green algae floating in the ocean. Their bodies are held up toward the sunlight by the water around them. The algae obtain water and other materials directly from their watery surroundings. When algae reproduce, sperm cells swim to egg cells through the water.

On land, plants are not surrounded by water. **For plants to survive on land, they must have ways to obtain water and other materials from their surroundings, retain water, transport materials throughout the plant, support their bodies, and reproduce successfully.** In *Exploring Plant Adaptations* on the next page, you can see some of the ways in which plants are adapted to live on land.

Obtaining Water and Other Materials Recall that all organisms need water to survive. Obtaining water is easy for algae because water surrounds them. To live on land, though, plants need adaptations for obtaining water from the soil. Plants must also have ways of obtaining other nutrients from the soil.

Retaining Water Have you ever noticed that a puddle of rainwater gradually shrinks and then disappears after the rain stops? This happens because there is more water in the puddle than in the air. As a result, the water evaporates into the air. The same principle explains why a plant on land can dry out. Because there is more water in plant cells than in air, water evaporates into the air. Plants need adaptations to reduce water loss to the air. One common adaptation is a waxy, waterproof layer called the **cuticle** that covers the leaves of most plants.

Figure 1 Plants have adaptations that help them retain water. The shiny, waterproof cuticle on this leaf slows down evaporation.

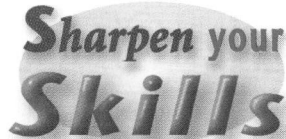

Chapter 8 **249**

Sharpen your Skills

Interpreting Data

The table shows how much water a certain plant loses during the hours listed.

Time	Water Loss (grams)
7 to 8 AM	190
9 to 10 AM	209
11 to Noon	221
1 to 2 PM	233
3 to 4 PM	227
5 to 6 PM	213
7 to 8 PM	190
9 to 10 PM	100
11 to Midnight	90

When does the plant lose the most water? The least water? How could you account for the pattern you see?

---

2 Facilitate

What is a Plant?

Including All Students

Give students who need extra help time to review terms such as *autotroph, eukaryote, photosynthesis, cellulose,* and *chloroplast.* Suggest students create a glossary of words that includes the phonetic English pronunciation and the definition in English. Encourage students to use clues to unlock the meaning of the terms. For example, the term *autotroph* can be broken down into *auto,* which means "from the self," and *troph,* which means "nutrition." **limited English proficiency**

Living on Land

Sharpen your Skills

Interpreting Data

Time 15 minutes

Have students compare the water lost in each time interval. Make sure students understand that the numbers in the right column do not represent the mass of the plant. Ask: **What measurements are used to find these numbers?** *(The mass of the plant is measured every hour, then the mass is subtracted from the measurement made an hour before.)* The plant loses the most water during the hottest part of the day. **Extend** Suggest students graph the data in the table and predict how the line graph would change if the data were collected during a hot summer day or during a cold, rainy day. **learning modality: logical/mathematical**

Ongoing Assessment

Organizing Information Have students create Venn diagrams that show the similarities and differences between green algae and plants.

Program Resources

◆ **Unit 2 Resources** 8-1 Lesson Plan, p. 61; 8-1 Section Summary, p. 62

Media and Technology

 Audio CD English-Spanish Summary 8-1

EXPLORING
Plant Adaptations

After students examine the visual essay, ask them to infer the answers to the following questions:

◆ **Considering that the Venus fly trap catches and digests insects, why do you think scientists classify it as a plant?** *(Sample: Although it gets nitrogen from insects, its leaves perform photosynthesis to make food.)*

◆ **How could water lilies be used to judge whether excess salt water was migrating into a freshwater coastal marsh?** *(Sample: Water lilies only live in fresh water; if the water becomes too salty, they will die.)*

◆ **What is the long-term effect of mangrove roots trapping soil and sand?** *(Sample: The island or beach gradually increases in size.)* **learning modality: visual**

Building Inquiry Skills: Observing

Materials *notebook, pencil*

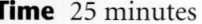

Time 25 minutes

Invite students to explore the diversity of plants in your area. Take students on a walk around the school and have them record descriptions of ten different plants that they see. Each description should include the place where they found the plant, the plant's estimated size, any distinguishing characteristics, and a sketch or photograph of the plant. Make sure students describe at least one adaptation the helps the plant to live in its environment. **learning modality: visual**

EXPLORING *Plant Adaptations*

Today, plants are found in almost every environment on Earth—deserts, lakes, jungles, and even the polar regions. As you read about each plant, notice how it is adapted to living in its specific environment.

◀ **Pasque Flower**
Pasque flowers, such as this *Anemone patens,* often grow on cold, rocky mountain slopes. The flower's petals trap sunlight, keeping the flower up to 10º C warmer than the surrounding air. This feature enables the plant to survive in cold environments.

Staghorn Fern ▶
Staghorn ferns do not grow in soil. Instead, they cling to the bark of trees in tropical areas. The leaves that hug the bark store water and nutrients. The leaves that hang down are involved in reproduction.

▲ **Bristlecone Pine**
Because the needles of bristlecone pines live more than 15 years, the trees survive long periods of drought. Bristlecone pine trees can live more than 4,000 years. This is because they grow slowly in high altitude areas where there are few harmful insects or other disease-causing organisims.

◀ **Water Lily**
Water lilies live only in fresh water. Large, flat leaves and sweet-smelling flowers float on the water's surface. The plants have long stems under the water. Roots anchor the plant in the mud at the bottom of the pond.

250

Background

Facts and Figures Humans use a wide variety of plants to treat pain and disease. These plants are often helpful if used in small amounts or special preparations, but can be deadly or dangerous if used otherwise. The opium poppy is used to make morphine and codeine, which physicians use to treat pain. However, the illegal drug heroin can also be derived from the plant. Similarly, the leaves of the coca plant contain small amounts of cocaine. They have been used as a painkiller for thousands of years. However, in larger doses, cocaine is dangerously addictive. The foxglove plant produces digitalis. In small doses, digitalis is a useful treatment for heart conditions, but in large doses it can be fatal. A plant called belladonna, or deadly nightshade, is lethal when swallowed, but is also the source of atropine, used to dilate the eyes in eye examinations.

Rafflesia ▶
The rafflesia plant produces the largest flowers on Earth. This flower that grew in Borneo measures over 83 centimeters in diameter. Rafflesia flowers have a foul odor—something like rotting meat. The odor attracts insects that help the plant reproduce.

▲ Mangrove
Mangrove trees, such as these on Guadalcanal Island in the Pacific Ocean, grow in salt water in tropical areas. The tree's huge root system makes the tree appear as if it is on stilts. The roots trap soil and sand around them, providing a material in which to anchor as they grow.

◀ Date Palm
Date palms, such as these growing on a date farm in southern California, grow in warm climates. These flowering trees can grow up to 23 meters tall. The leaves are long and narrow, reducing the amount of surface area for evaporation. The female trees produce dates that hang from the stems in large clusters.

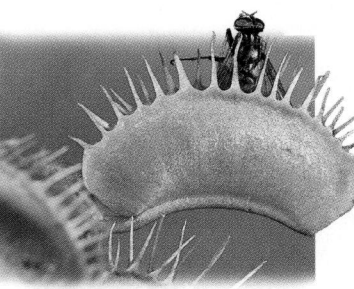

◀ Venus Fly Trap
The Venus fly trap can grow in soil that is low in nitrogen. This is because the plant obtains its nitrogen by digesting insects that it traps. When an insect touches sensitive hairs on the inner surface of a leaf, the two parts of the leaf quickly snap shut. It takes about ten days for the plant to digest an insect.

Chapter 8 **251**

Program Resources

◆ **Laboratory Manual** 8, "Investigating Stomata"

Cultural Diversity

Every culture relies on plants as a resource for food, construction materials, medicines, clothing, and decoration. Date palms are very important in North Africa and the Middle East, where the dates are used for food and the leaves and stalks are woven into baskets, furniture, rugs, and rope. Mangrove trees are used for their wood and sweet fruit, as well as for an astringent tanning solution produced by the bark. Assign students a country or region to investigate. Students should prepare a display showing the kinds of plants that grow in that region and how the plants are used by native populations. Some areas to assign include the Philippine Islands, the Amazon River basin, Kenya, Puerto Rico, and Thailand. **learning modality: verbal**

Building Inquiry Skills: Observing

Suggest students make detailed observations of a common indoor houseplant, such as a rubber plant (*Ficus elastica*). They should describe what adaptations make it a desirable indoor plant. (*Tolerant of low light levels*) Then have them find out the plant's natural environment. (*Tropical forests*) Ask: **How would the feature that makes this plant a desirable houseplant help it in its natural environment?** (*In the plant's natural environment, tolerance of low light levels allowed it to thrive in the limited light beneath the forest canopy.*) **learning modality: visual**

Ongoing Assessment

Oral Presentation Ask students to describe a plant they know or one from Exploring Plant Adaptations and tell about one adaptation that helps the plant survive in its environment. (*Sample: Petals of the Pasque flower help the flower stay warm in a cold environment. Date palms have long, narrow leaves that reduce water loss in a hot environment.*)

Living on Land, continued

Demonstration

Materials *clear vase, blue food coloring, white carnation*

Time 10 minutes for setup and observation, 24 hours waiting time

Help students see how a plant's vascular system works. Fill the vase with water and 10 drops of the food coloring. Cut the stem of the carnation. Place the carnation in the vase. Then ask students to predict what will happen if the carnation sits overnight. The next day, have students describe the carnation. *(It has blue streaks on the leaves.)* Allow them to examine the flower closely. They should notice thin veins of color in the petals. Ask: **How did the color move up the flower?** *(Through the tubes of the vascular system)* **learning modality: visual**

Building Inquiry Skills: Observing

Materials *hand lens, celery leaf stalk, dissecting knife*

Time 20 minutes

Explain to students that they will analyze the transport and support systems in a celery leaf stalk. Give each student a celery leaf stalk to examine. Students should cut the base of the stalk cleanly with a knife. CAUTION: *Knives are sharp and should be handled with care.* Students can then look at different parts of the stalk using a hand lens. Allow them to pull off strands of the stalk or cut the stalk lengthwise to make observations. Ask: **What is the function of the long fibers in a celery stalk?** *(The stalk is made up of long, narrow tubes or fibers that are bundled together. These carry materials and provide support.)* **learning modality: visual**

Figure 2 The vascular tissue in these tree ferns transports water and nutrients inside the plants. *Inferring What additional function might vascular tissue have in these tree ferns?*

252

Transporting Materials A plant needs to transport food, water, minerals, and other materials from one part of its body to another. In general, water and minerals are taken up by the bottom part of the plant. Food is made in the top part. But all the plant's cells need water, minerals, and food. To supply all cells with the materials they need, water and minerals must be transported up to the top of the plant. Then food must be transported throughout the plant.

Most plants that live on land have tissues that transport materials throughout their bodies. **Tissues** are groups of similar cells that perform a specific function in an organism. Some plants have transporting tissue called **vascular tissue.** Vascular tissue is an internal system of tubelike structures through which water and food move inside the plant. Plants that have vascular tissue are called vascular plants. Vascular plants can grow quite tall because they have an effective way of transporting substances to distant cells.

Support While algae are supported by the surrounding water, a plant on land must support its own body. Because plants need sunlight for photosynthesis, the food-making parts of the plant must be exposed to as much sunlight as possible. In vascular plants, vascular tissue strengthens and supports the large bodies of the plants.

Reproduction All plants undergo sexual reproduction that involves fertilization. **Fertilization** occurs when a sperm cell unites with an egg cell. The fertilized egg is called a **zygote.** For algae and some plants, fertilization can occur only if there is water in the environment. This is because sperm cells swim through the water to egg cells. Other plants, however, have an adaptation that make it possible for fertilization to occur in dry environments. You will learn more about this adaptation in the next chapter.

✓ *Checkpoint* Why do plants need adaptations to prevent water loss?

Background

Facts and Figures Certain plant species have remarkable growth rates or growth patterns. The average plant grows about 1 centimeter per day. Some plants, however, grow much faster. For example, the titan arum has a flowering structure that may grow as much as 10 centimeters per day. In the spring, some bamboo shoots can grow as fast as 0.3 meters per day.

While many plants live for a year or two, others continue living and growing for much longer. A bristlecone pine tree in California is estimated to be over 4,600 years old—and it is still alive!

California also has the tallest and biggest trees in the world. Some coast redwoods are up to 112 meters tall, but the biggest living plant on Earth is a giant sequoia that is 83 meters tall with a trunk that is 31 meters in circumference at its base.

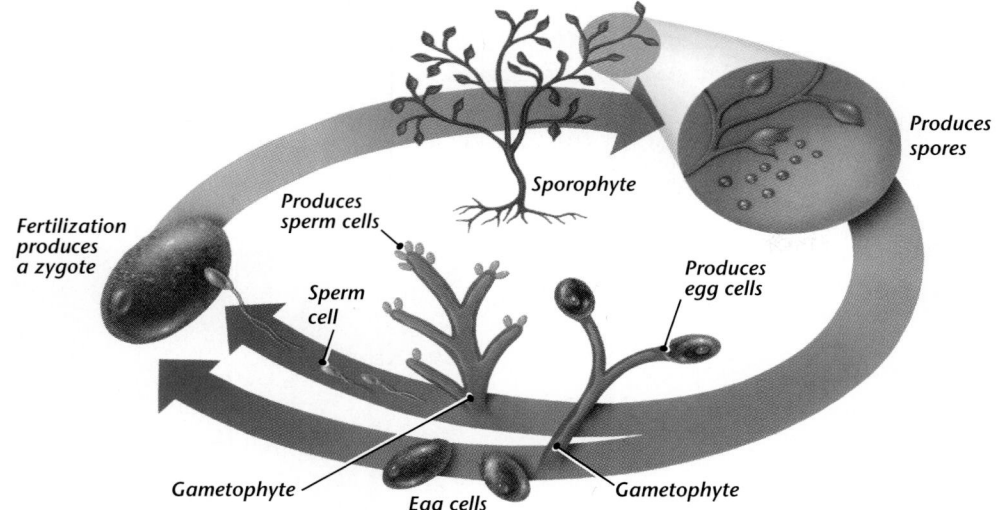

Fertilization produces a zygote

Produces sperm cells

Sperm cell

Sporophyte

Produces spores

Produces egg cells

Gametophyte

Egg cells

Gametophyte

Complex Life Cycles

Unlike most animals, plants have complex life cycles that are made up of two different stages, or generations. In one stage, called the **sporophyte** (SPAWR uh fyt), the plant produces spores, the tiny cells that can grow into new organisms. A spore develops into the plant's other stage, called the gametophyte. In the **gametophyte** (guh MEE tuh fyt) stage, the plant produces two kinds of sex cells, or **gametes**—sperm cells and egg cells.

Figure 3 shows a typical plant life cycle. A sperm cell and egg cell join to form a zygote. The zygote then develops into a sporophyte. The sporophyte produces spores, which develop into the gametophyte. Then the gametophyte produces sperm cells and egg cells and the cycle starts again. The sporophyte of a plant usually looks quite different from the gametophyte.

Figure 3 Plants have complex life cycles that consist of two stages—the sporophyte stage and the gametophyte stage. *Interpreting Diagrams During which stage are sperm and egg cells produced?*

 Section 1 Review

1. List three characteristics that all plants share.
2. What are five adaptations that plants need to survive on land?
3. Distinguish between a sporophyte and a gametophyte.
4. **Thinking Critically Classifying** Suppose you found a tall plant living in the desert. Do you think it would be a vascular plant? Explain.

Science at Home

State Flowers Choose any state in the United States. With a family member, find out the name of the state's official plant. Research why that plant was chosen to represent the state. Then gather information about the plant. Make an illustrated poster to display in your school that includes the information you gather.

Program Resources

◆ **Unit 2 Resources** 8-1 Review and Reinforce, p. 63; 8-1 Enrich, p. 64

Media and Technology

Transparencies "A Plant Cell," Transparency 32; "The Life Cycle of Plants," Transparency 33

Interactive Student Tutorial CD-ROM Chapter 8

Answers to Self-Assessment

Caption Question

Figure 2 The vascular tissue also strengthens and supports the plant's stems and leaves.

Figure 3 Sperm and egg cells are produced during the gametophyte stage.

✓ Checkpoint

Plants need adaptations to prevent water loss because every cell of a plant needs water to live.

Using the Visuals: Figure 3

Point out that plants have both a sexual and an asexual phase in their life cycles. Ask students: **Which stage involves asexual reproduction? How can you tell?** *(The sporophyte stage; the plant produces spores that develop into new organisms.)* Ask: **Which stage involves sexual reproduction?** *(Gametophyte, when sperm cells and egg cells are produced)* **learning modality: logical/mathematical**

3 Assess

Section 1 Review Answers

1. All plants are multicellular, autotrophic eukaryotes.
2. To survive on land, plants must be able to obtain water and other materials from their environment, retain moisture, support their bodies, transport materials throughout their bodies, and reproduce.
3. The sporophyte is the generation in a plant's life that produces spores and the gametophyte is the generation that produces sex cells, or gametes.
4. Yes. Due to the scarcity of water in the desert, a tall plant living in the desert must have vascular tissue to supply its cells with water.

Science at Home

Students may find that many states list two plants—a state flower and a state tree. State-by-state lists can be found in many almanacs and dictionaries. Additional information can be found in reference books and CD-ROM encyclopedias.

Performance Assessment

Writing Have students write paragraphs identifying several ways that an oak tree is adapted to live on land.

Eye on Photosynthesis

Preparing for Inquiry

Key Concept Plants require several factors to be present before they can perform photosynthesis.

Skills Objective Students will be able to
- design experiments to investigate what substances and conditions are necessary for photosynthesis;
- perform tests on several variables;
- analyze the results of their tests and draw conclusions.

Time 45 minutes

Advance Planning Obtain *Elodea* plants. Prepare the sodium bicarbonate solution by using 0.5 g of sodium bicarbonate for each 100 mL of water. Boil water for Part 2 and let it cool.

Alternative Materials If *Elodea* plants are not available, you may be able to find appropriate small water plants at a tropical fish supply fish store.

Guiding Inquiry

Invitation Ask students to describe what might happen to a plant to make it turn brown instead of green. *(Sample: Too much sun, not enough water, disease, change of seasons, poor soil)* Then have them describe the things plants need in order to be green and healthy.

Introducing the Procedure
- Have students use water to perfect their techniques of immersing a filled test tube before they use the sodium bicarbonate solution or boiled water.
- As students read through Steps 3 and 4, make sure they refer to the photograph on page 254.

Troubleshooting the Experiment
- Make sure students do not grip the test tubes too tightly. Remind students to inform you of any breakage immediately.
- Tell students not to expect dramatic results. Have them look for small bubbles of oxygen.
- Remind students to move on to the next procedure while they are waiting for results.

Skills Lab

Eye on Photosynthesis

I n this lab, you'll design an experiment to investigate what substances and conditions are needed for photosynthesis.

Problem

What raw materials and conditions are involved in photosynthesis?

Materials

Elodea plants   2 test tubes
water (boiled, then cooled)   2 wax pencils
wide-mouthed container   lamp (optional)
sodium bicarbonate solution

Procedure

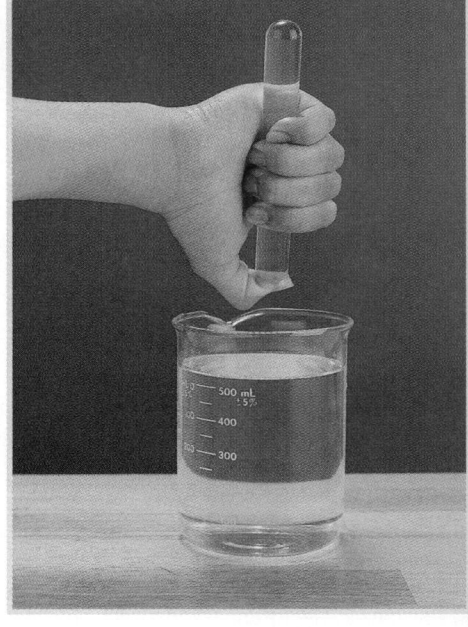

Part 1 Observing Photosynthesis
1. Use a wax pencil to label two test tubes *1* and *2*. Fill test tube 1 with sodium bicarbonate solution, which provides a source of carbon dioxide.
2. Fill the container about three-fourths full of sodium bicarbonate solution.
3. Hold your thumb over the mouth of test tube 1. Turn the test tube over, and lower the tube to the bottom of the container. Do not let in any air. If necessary, repeat this step so that test tube 1 contains no air pockets.
   CAUTION: *Glass test tubes are fragile. Handle the test tubes carefully. Do not touch broken glass.*
4. Fill test tube 2 with sodium bicarbonate solution. Place an *Elodea* plant in the tube with the cut stem at the bottom. Put your thumb over the mouth of the test tube, and lower it into the container without letting in any air. Wash your hands.

5. Place the container with the two test tubes in bright light. After a few minutes, examine both test tubes for bubbles.
6. If bubbles form in test tube 2, observe the *Elodea* stem to see if it is producing the bubbles. The bubbles are oxygen bubbles. The production of oxygen signals that photosynthesis is taking place.
7. Leave the setup in bright light for thirty minutes. Observe what happens to any bubbles that form. Record your observations.

Expected Outcome

Students should observe tiny bubbles forming along the stems or leaves of the plant in Part 1. These bubbles will grow larger with time. If no bubbles are present, review the variables and make a fresh cut in the *Elodea* stem. Make sure all variables, such as sunlight, are at their maximum.

Observations will support or reject students' hypotheses on whether a particular variable is important in photosynthesis.

Analyze and Conclude

1. photosynthesis
2. It was a control, to show whether the bubbles were really related to the plant.
3. Yes. Students' answers should reveal that no bubbles were formed when the plant was not exposed to a source of carbon dioxide.
4. Answers will depend on students' procedures, but students should realize that the most important factors for photosynthesis are light and the presence of CO_2.

Part 2 Is Carbon Dioxide Needed for Photosynthesis?

8. Your teacher will provide a supply of water that has been boiled and then cooled. Boiling drives off gases that are dissolved in the water, including carbon dioxide.
9. Based on what you learned in Part 1, design an experiment to show whether or not carbon dioxide is needed for photosynthesis. Obtain your teacher's approval before carrying out your experiment. Record all your observations.

Part 3 What Other Conditions Are Needed for Photosynthesis?

10. Make a list of other factors that may affect photosynthesis. For example, think about conditions such as light, the size of the plant, and the number of leaves.
11. Choose one factor from your list. Then design an experiment to show how the factor affects photosynthesis. Obtain your teacher's approval before carrying out your experiment. Record all your observations.

Analyze and Conclude

1. What process produced the bubbles you observed in Part 1?
2. In Part 1, what was the purpose of test tube 1?
3. Based on your results in Part 2, is carbon dioxide necessary for photosynthesis?
4. Explain what you learned about photosynthesis from the investigation you did in Part 3.
5. **Think About It** For the experiments you carried out in Parts 2 and 3, identify the manipulated variable and the responding variable. Explain whether or not your experiments were controlled experiments.

More to Explore

A small animal in a closed container will die, even if it has enough water and food. A small animal in a closed container with a plant, water, and food will not die. Use what you have learned from this experiment to explain those facts.

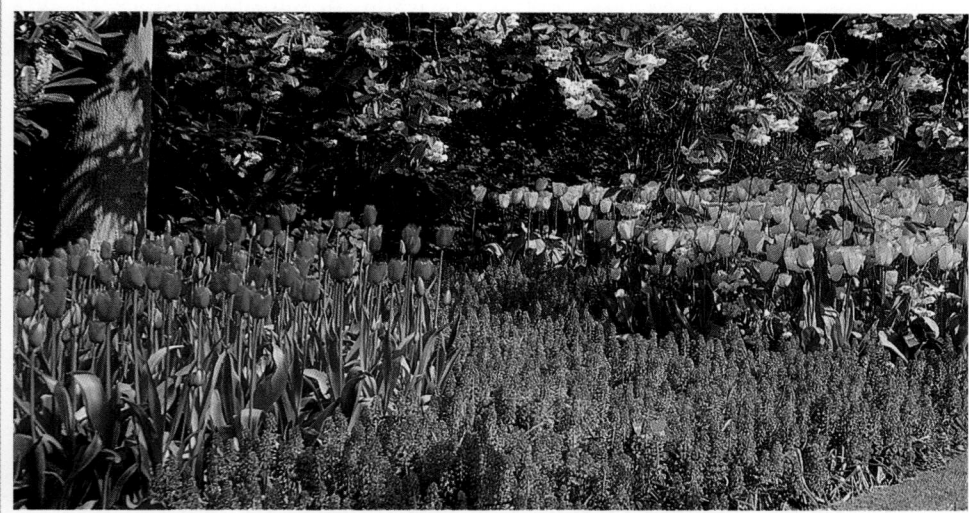

5. Sample answer: The manipulated variable was the presence or absence of sunlight. The responding variable was the production of oxygen. The experiment was controlled because all other variables were kept the same for both test tubes.

Extending the Inquiry

More to Explore Sample experiment: Place a candle securely in each of two identical jars. Place a small green plant in one jar. Light both candles and close the jars tightly. The candle in the jar without the plant will stop burning, but the other candle will continue to burn. Because candles need oxygen to burn, students will know that the oxygen being used in the first container is not being replaced. They should infer that the plant is producing oxygen.

Program Resources

◆ **Unit 2 Resources** Chapter 8 Skills Lab, pp. 77–79
◆ **Inquiry Skills Activity Book** Provides teaching and review of all inquiry skills

Objectives

After completing the lesson, students will be able to

◆ name some nonvascular plants and list the characteristics that they all share;

◆ describe the structure of a moss plant and the importance of mosses on Earth.

Key Terms nonvascular plant, rhizoid, bog, peat

1 Engage/Explore

Activating Prior Knowledge

Ask students to describe mosses they know about. *(Some may know about peat moss, or have seen moss growing on rocks or in the woods.)* Ask: **What was the moss like?** *(Most students will say green, spongy, soft, and moist.)* Explain that not all the things people call mosses actually are mosses, and that in this section, they learn the characteristics of plants scientists classify as mosses.

· · · · · · · · **DISCOVER** · · · · · · · ·

Skills Focus predicting ACTIVITY
Materials *3 plastic graduated cylinders, 20 mL sand, 20 mL peat moss, water, dropper, stopwatch*
Time 15 minutes
Tips Suggest that students use a dropper to slowly add water to the sand and the peat moss. The peat moss absorbs water more readily when it is already damp.
Expected Outcome Students should find that the peat moss absorbs much more water than the sand.
Think It Over Some students will predict that the peat moss will absorb more water, others will predict that the sand will absorb more water. Students should learn that peat moss absorbs water well, better than sand does.

256

DISCOVER ·ACTIVITY

Will Mosses Absorb Water?

1. Place 20 milliliters (mL) of sand into a plastic graduated cylinder. Place 20 mL of peat moss into a second plastic graduated cylinder.

2. Predict what would happen if you were to slowly pour 10 mL of water into each of the two graduated cylinders and then wait five minutes.

3. To test your prediction, use a third graduated cylinder to slowly add 10 mL of water to the sand. Then add 10 mL of water to the moss. After 5 minutes, record your observations.

Think It Over

Predicting How did your prediction compare with your results? What did you learn about moss from this investigation?

GUIDE FOR READING

◆ What characteristics do nonvascular plants share?

Reading Tip As you read, make a table comparing and contrasting mosses, liverworts, and hornworts.

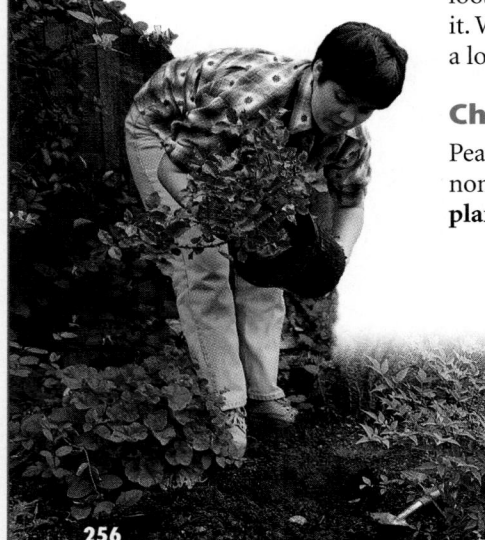

I f you enjoy gardening, you know that a garden requires time, effort, and knowledge. Before you start to plant your garden, you need to know how much water and sun your plants will need. You also need to know whether the soil in your garden can supply the plants with the water and nutrients they need.

Many gardeners add peat moss to the soil in their gardens. Peat moss improves the texture of soil and increases the soil's ability to hold water. When peat moss is added to claylike soil, it loosens the soil so that the plant's roots can easily grow through it. When peat moss is added to sandy soil, the soil stays moist for a longer time after it is watered.

Characteristics of Nonvascular Plants

Peat moss contains one type of **nonvascular plant.** Some other nonvascular plants are liverworts and hornworts. **All nonvascular plants are low-growing plants that lack vascular tissue.**

READING STRATEGIES

Reading Tip Help students prepare their tables by drawing a table on the board. The four columns should have the following heads: Characteristics, Mosses, Liverworts, and Hornworts. Invite volunteers to suggest characteristics to compare. Characteristics of these plants can include their size and structure, where they grow relative to the ground, how they transport water and food through their bodies, environments in which they live, and number of species.

Nonvascular plants do not have vascular tissue—a system of tubelike structures that transport water and other materials. Nonvascular plants can only pass materials from one cell to the next. That means that the materials do not travel very far or very quickly. Also, these plants have only their rigid cell walls to provide support. With this type of structure, these plants cannot grow very wide or tall. As a result, nonvascular plants are small and grow low to the ground.

Like all plants, nonvascular plants require water to survive. These plants lack roots, but they can obtain water and minerals directly from their surroundings. Many nonvascular plants live where water is plentiful. But even nonvascular plants that live in drier areas need enough water to let the sperm cells swim to the egg cells during reproduction.

Mosses

Have you ever seen mosses growing in the crack of a sidewalk, on a tree trunk, or on rocks that are misted by waterfalls? With over 10,000 species, mosses are by far the most diverse group of nonvascular plants.

The Structure of a Moss If you were to look closely at a moss, you would see a plant that looks something like the one in Figure 4. The familiar green fuzzy moss is the gametophyte generation of the plant. Structures that look like tiny leaves grow off a small stemlike structure. Thin rootlike structures called **rhizoids** anchor the moss and absorb water and nutrients from the soil. The sporophyte generation grows out of the gametophyte. It consists of a slender stalk with a capsule at the end. The capsule contains spores.

Figure 4 A moss gametophyte is low-growing and has structures that look like roots, stems, and leaves. The stalklike sporophyte generation remains attached to the gametophyte. *Interpreting Diagrams* What structure anchors the gametophyte in the soil?

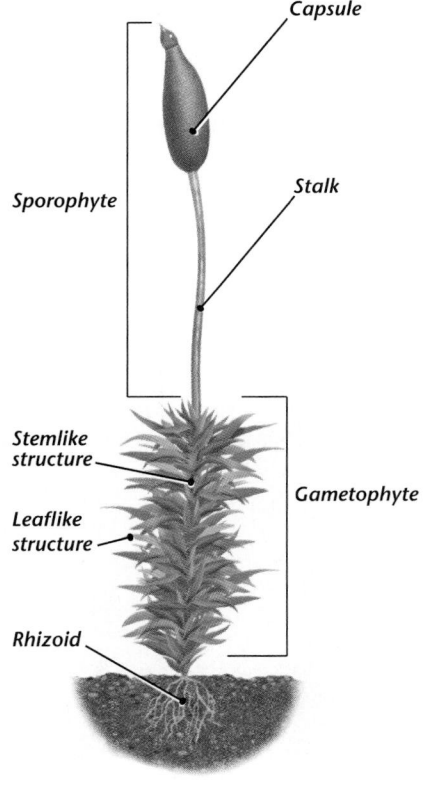

Capsule

Sporophyte

Stalk

Stemlike structure

Leaflike structure

Gametophyte

Rhizoid

Characteristics of Nonvascular Plants

Demonstration

Materials *plastic ice cube tray, paper towel, water, plastic dropper, food coloring*
Time 10 minutes

Model the way that materials pass through nonvascular plants. Tear off a 5-cm wide strip of paper towel and roll it tightly lengthwise. Fill a beaker with about 250 mL of water and 5–10 drops of food coloring. Using a dropper, carefully fill one section of an ice cube tray with colored water. Place one end of the rolled paper towel in the colored water and the other end in another section of the tray. Ask students to predict what will happen to the colored water. Then allow them to watch the movement of the water from one section to another. Ask: **How is this similar to the way that nonvascular plants transport materials?** *(Nonvascular plants move materials from one cell to the next through their bodies.)* **learning modality: visual**

Mosses

Using the Visuals: Figure 4

As they look at the figure, have students describe the life cycle of the moss. Ask: **How is the sporophyte created?** *(Gametophytes produce sperm cells and egg cells. When these are fertilized, a sporophyte develops.)* **What is the function of the sporophyte?** *(It contains spores which can develop into new gametophytes.)* **learning modality: visual**

Ongoing Assessment

Writing Have students write one or two sentences to describe the function of rhizoids.

Program Resources

♦ **Unit 2 Resources** 8-3 Lesson Plan, p. 65; 8-3 Section Summary, p. 66

Media and Technology

 Audio CD English-Spanish Summary 8-2

Answers to Self-Assessment

Caption Question
Figure 4 Rhizoids anchor the gametophyte in the soil.

Mosses, continued

Building Inquiry Skills: Observing

Materials *hand lens, peat moss, white paper*

Time 10 minutes

Invite students to closely examine small clumps of peat moss. They should place a sample on white paper. Using a hand lens, students should examine the rhizoids, and the leaflike and stemlike structures. They should sketch their samples and label the parts.

Portfolio Students can save their sketches in their portfolios. **limited English proficiency**

Social Studies CONNECTION

Help students recognize the historical importance of finding artifacts in bogs. Ask students: **What might be learned from studying these artifacts?** *(Sample: We can learn about the clothes that people wore, and about some of the tools and technology that they used.)*

In Your Journal Encourage students to provide a clear, concise explanation of the conditions found in a bog. Ask volunteers to share their letters with the class. **learning modality: verbal**

Integrating Earth Science

Tell students that moss not only traps soil but also traps water that might wash the soil away otherwise. Ask: **What traits does moss have that would help other plants grow?** *(Sample: It traps water so it helps to keep the ground moist.)* **learning modality: verbal**

Social Studies CONNECTION

Historians have found many items preserved in the acidic water of peat bogs. Weapons more than 1,600 years old have been recovered from bogs in northern Europe. In addition, about 700 human bodies have been found in bogs. Most of the bodies are as well preserved as the one that you see in the photo. This man, who lived 2,000 years ago, was found in a bog in Denmark.

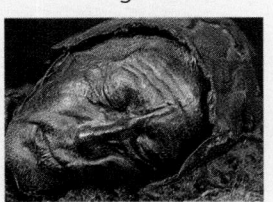

In Your Journal

Imagine that you have just recovered an old wooden tool from a bog. Write a letter to a natural history museum explaining why the tool is so well preserved.

The Importance of Mosses Many people use peat moss in agriculture and gardening. The peat moss that gardeners use contains sphagnum (SFAG num) moss. Sphagnum moss grows in a type of wetland called a **bog.** The still water in a bog is so acidic that decomposing organisms cannot live in the water. Thus when the plants die, they do not decay. Instead, the dead plants accumulate at the bottom of the bog. Over time, the mosses become compressed into layers and form a blackish-brown material called **peat.** Large deposits of peat exist in North America, Europe, and Asia. In Europe and Asia, people use peat as a fuel to heat homes and to cook food.

INTEGRATING EARTH SCIENCE Like the lichens you learned about in Chapter 7, many mosses are pioneer plants. They are among the first organisms to grow in areas destroyed by volcanoes or in burnt-out forests. Like lichens, mosses trap wind-blown soil. Over time, enough soil accumulates to support the growth of other plants whose spores or seeds are blown there.

✓ Checkpoint What does a moss sporophyte look like?

Figure 5 The sphagnum moss that grew in this bog is being harvested as peat.

258

258

Liverworts and Hornworts

Figure 6 shows examples of two other groups of nonvascular plants—liverworts and hornworts. There are more than 8,000 species of liverworts. This group of plants is named for the shape of the plant's body, which looks somewhat like a human liver. *Wort* is an old English word for "plant." Liverworts are often found growing as a thick crust on moist rocks or soil along the sides of a stream. Unlike mosses, most liverworts grow flat along the ground. In Figure 6, you can see the gametophyte generation of one type of liverwort.

There are fewer than 100 species of hornworts. At first glance, these plants resemble liverworts. But if you look closely, you can see slender, curved structures that look like horns growing out of the gametophytes. These hornlike structures, which give these plants their names, are the sporophytes. Unlike mosses or liverworts, hornworts are seldom found on rocks or tree trunks. Instead, hornworts live in moist soil, often mixed in with grass plants.

Figure 6 Like mosses, hornworts and liverworts are nonvascular plants. **A.** Hornworts grow only in soil and are often found growing among grasses. **B.** Liverworts grow flat along the ground on moist soil and rocks.

Section 2 Review

1. Describe two characteristics that nonvascular plants share. Explain how the two characteristics are related.
2. Describe the structure of a moss plant.
3. How does peat form?
4. **Thinking Critically Comparing and Contrasting** In what ways are mosses, liverworts, and hornworts similar? How do they differ?

Check Your Progress
At this point, your plan for creating a terrarium should be complete. On a sheet of paper, list the conditions that will affect moss growth. Explain how you'll provide those conditions in your terrarium. (*Hint:* Use a sketch to show what your bottle terrarium will look like.)

CHAPTER PROJECT

Program Resources

◆ **Unit 2 Resources** 8-2 Review and Reinforce, p. 67; 8-2 Enrich, p. 68

Answers to Self-Assessment

✓ Checkpoint
A moss sporophyte consists of a thin brownish stalk with a spore-containing capsule at the end. It grows out of the gametophyte.

Liverworts and Hornworts

Using the Visuals: Figure 6
Have students identify the plant parts shown. Ask: **What part of the liverwort is the gametophyte?** (*The liver-shaped leaflike structures*) **What part of the hornwort is the sporophyte?** (*The horn-shaped structures*) **learning modality: visual**

3 Assess

Section 2 Review Answers
1. Nonvascular plants are low growing and lack vascular tissue. They do not have vascular tissue for support and movement of materials and therefore are low growing.
2. A moss gametophyte has rhizoids, a stemlike part, and leaflike parts. The sporophyte grows out of the top of the gametophyte.
3. Peat forms from dead moss plants in a bog. The layers of dead moss do not decompose because the water is so acidic; they become compressed and form peat.
4. Mosses, liverworts, and hornworts are all nonvascular plants. Moss grows in soil and on rocks and trees. Liverworts live in very moist areas near streams. Hornworts live on moist soil.

Check Your Progress
Make sure students' sketches of the terrariums show details of their construction. Students' plans should indicate how much water will be given and the location of the terrarium. Students should realize that they do not need to add food to the terrarium because mosses make their own food.

CHAPTER PROJECT

Performance Assessment

Organizing Information Have students make Venn diagrams to compare and contrast the three types of nonvascular plants. (*Venn diagrams should show the similarities between mosses, liverworts, and hornworts, as well as the specific characteristics of each.*)

Masses of Mosses

Preparing for Inquiry

Key Concept Students will observe a moss and describe its structures.
Skills Objective Students will be able to
◆ make detailed observations of a moss and communicate their observations;
◆ measure the structures of a moss and calculate class averages.
Time 45 minutes
Advance Planning Provide a variety of species of mosses. If possible, obtain some moss clumps with sporophytes present.
Alternative Materials If you have microscopes available, allow students to use them.

Guiding Inquiry

Troubleshooting the Experiment
Clumps of moss obtained from nature may contain more than one type. You may wish to have a field guide to the mosses available for students to consult.

Expected Outcome
◆ Students should be able to identify all the parts of the plant.
◆ Measurements will vary, depending on the type of moss.

Analyze and Conclude
1. Leaflike: a few millimeters long, by a fraction of a millimeter thick; stemlike: up to 15-cm high, often much shorter; rootlike: very short. Some mosses are only a few millimeters tall.
2. The green parts (leaflike and stemlike); only the green parts, which contain chlorophyll, can carry out photosynthesis.
3. Mosses cannot transport water quickly over long distances.
4. Sample: You can see that a moss is made of many small plants.

Extending the Inquiry

More to Explore Show students how to gently crush the moss capsules to release the spores. Students can then observe these structures with a microscope.

Masses of Mosses

In this lab, you will look closely at some tiny members of the plant kingdom.

Problem

How is a moss plant adapted to carry out its life activities?

Materials

clump of moss	hand lens
metric ruler	toothpicks
plastic dropper	water

Procedure

1. Your teacher will give you a clump of moss. Examine the clump from all sides. Draw a diagram of what you see. Measure the size of the overall clump and the main parts of the clump. Record your observations.
2. Using toothpicks, gently separate five individual moss plants from the clump. Be sure to pull them totally apart so that you can observe each plant separately. If the moss plants appear to dry up as you are working, moisten them with a few drops of water.
3. Measure the length of the leaflike, stemlike, and rootlike structures on each plant. If brown stalks and capsules are present, measure them. Find the average length of each structure.
4. Make a life-size drawing of a moss plant. Label the parts, give their sizes, and record the color of each part. When you are finished observing the moss, return it to your teacher. Wash your hands thoroughly.
5. Obtain class averages for the sizes of the structures you measured in Step 3. Also, if the moss that you observed had brown stalks and capsules, share your observations about those structures.

Analyze and Conclude

1. Describe the typical size of the leaflike portion of moss plants, the typical height of the stemlike portion, and the typical length of the rootlike portion.
2. In which part(s) of the moss does photosynthesis occur? How do you know?
3. Why are mosses unable to grow very tall?
4. **Think About It** What did you learn by observing a moss up close and in detail?

More to Explore

Select a moss plant with stalks and capsules. Use toothpicks to release some of the spores, which can be as small as dust particles. Examine the spores under a microscope.

Safety

Students should wash their hands thoroughly after finishing the lab. If students use microscopes, review all relevant safety procedures. Review the safety guidelines in Appendix A.

Program Resources

◆ **Unit 2 Resources** Chapter 8 Skills Lab, pp. 80–81
◆ **Inquiry Skills Activity Book** Provides teaching and review of all inquiry skills

DISCOVER ·············· ACTIVITY

How Quickly Can Water Move Upward?

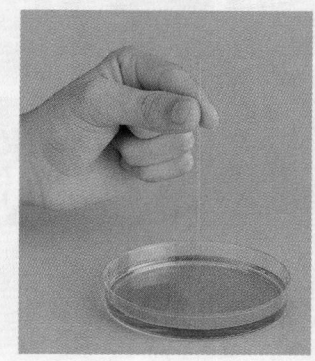

1. Put on your goggles. Your teacher will give you a plastic petri dish as well as a narrow glass tube that is open at both ends.

2. Fill the petri dish half full of water. Add a drop of food coloring to the water.

3. Stand the tube on end in the water and hold it upright. Observe what happens. Record your observations.

Think It Over

Inferring Why might it be an advantage for the transporting cells of plants to be arranged in a tubelike way?

The time is 340 million years ago—long before the dinosaurs lived. The place is somewhere in the forests that covered most of Earth's land. If you could have walked through one of these ancient forests, it would have looked very strange to you.

You might have recognized the mosses and liverworts that carpeted the moist soil. But overhead you would have seen odd-looking trees, some towering as high as 25 meters above the ground. Among the trees were ancient ferns— huge versions of the ferns you find in today's florist shops. Other trees resembled giant stick figures with leaves up to one meter long. The huge leaves hugged the branches, looking something like the scales that cover a fish.

GUIDE FOR READING

◆ What are the main characteristics of seedless vascular plants?

Reading Tip As you read, create a table comparing ferns, club mosses, and horsetails.

Chapter 8 **261**

Objectives

After completing the lesson, students will be able to
◆ name some seedless vascular plants and list the characteristics that they share;
◆ describe the structure of a fern plant, how a fern plant reproduces, and the importance of ferns on Earth.

Key Terms vascular plant, frond

1 Engage/Explore

Activating Prior Knowledge

Ask students to draw and label a picture of a plant that includes leaves, stems, and roots. Then show students a potted fern and ask them to point out the leaves, stems, and roots on the fern.

········· DISCOVER ·········

Skills Focus inferring
Materials *goggles, plastic petri dish, narrow glass tube, water, food coloring, dropper*
Time 10 minutes
Tips Caution students to handle the glass tube gently. If they roughly push the glass tube onto the bottom of the petri dish, the tube may shatter.
Expected Outcome The colored water should move quickly up the glass tube.
Think It Over Students should infer that a tubelike arrangement of cells will help water move quickly up the plant.

READING STRATEGIES

Reading Tip Have students work in pairs to set up their tables. Tables should have four columns: Characteristics, Ferns, Club Mosses, and Horsetails. Suggest that students scan the section if they are having trouble thinking of charcteristics to compare. Characteristics can include size, where they grow, how they reproduce and special characteristics.

Program Resources

◆ **Unit 2 Resources** 8-3 Lesson Plan, p. 69; 8-3 Section Summary, p. 70

Media and Technology

Audio CD English-Spanish Summary 8-3

Ask students to explain where the energy in coal comes from. *(The plants that eventually become coal contained energy that they received from the sun.)* **learning modality: verbal**

Characteristics of Seedless Vascular Plants

Including All Students

Students who are visually impaired and those who need extra help may benefit from exploring the structure of vascular tissue by feeling a bunch of celery. Ask: **What do you feel on the outside of the stalks?** *(Narrow ridges)* Explain that these are bundles of vascular tissue. Have students hold the base of the celery bunch in one hand and apply pressure to the top of the stalks with the other. Ask: **Why couldn't you crush the bunch of celery?** *(The vascular tissue is strong enough to resist the force of a hand pressing down on it.)* **learning modality: kinesthetic**

Figure 7 These fossils are from two plants that lived about 300 million years ago. The larger fossil is of a fern's leaf. The small star-shaped fossil is of a plant called a horsetail.

Examining a Fern **ACTIVITY**

1. Your teacher will give you a fern plant to observe.
2. Draw a diagram of the plant and label the structures that you see.
3. Use a hand lens to observe the top and lower surfaces of the leaf. Run a finger over both surfaces.
4. With a plastic dropper, add a few drops of water to the top surface of the leaf. Note what happens.

Inferring Use your observations to explain how ferns are adapted to life on land.

INTEGRATING EARTH SCIENCE As the trees and other plants died, they formed thick layers and partially decomposed. Over millions of years, the layers became compressed under the weight of the layers above them. Eventually, these layers became the coal deposits that we use for fuel today.

Characteristics of Seedless Vascular Plants

The odd-looking plants in the ancient forests were the ancestors of three groups of plants that are alive today—ferns, club mosses, and horsetails. **Ferns and their relatives share two characteristics. They have vascular tissue and use spores to reproduce.**

Vascular Tissue What adaptations allowed plants to grow very tall? Unlike the mosses, the ancient trees were **vascular plants**—plants that have vascular tissue. Vascular plants are better suited to life on land than are nonvascular plants. This is because vascular tissue solves the problems of support and transportation. Vascular tissue transports water quickly and efficiently throughout the plant's body. It also transports the food produced in the leaves to other parts of the plant, including the roots.

In addition, vascular tissue strengthens the plant's body. Imagine a handful of drinking straws bundled together with rubber bands. The bundle of straws would be stronger and more

Background

Integrating Science The vascular tissue of a plant supports the plant because of the strength of the cell walls. In herbaceous plants, such as grasses, dandelions, and tulips, the cell walls are made mainly of a complex carbohydrate called cellulose. When the plant has enough water, the cytoplasm presses against the cell wall, making the cell rigid. If the plant does not have enough water, the cytoplasm shrinks, and the

pressure on the cell walls decreases. The cells lose their rigidity, and the plant wilts.

In woody plants, such as trees and shrubs, the cell walls of trunks and branches are strengthened by a compound called lignin. The hard cell walls of woody plants support the plant even when there is insufficient water. In a drought, the leaves of a tree may wilt, but the trunk will not lose its strength.

stable than a single straw would be. In a similar way, vascular tissue provides strength and stability to a plant.

Spores for Reproduction Ferns, club mosses, and horsetails still need to grow in moist surroundings. This is because the plants release spores into their surroundings, where they grow into gametophytes. When the gametophytes produce egg cells and sperm cells, there must be enough water available for fertilization to occur.

☑ *Checkpoint* *What adaptation allowed plants to grow tall?*

Ferns

Fossil records indicate that ferns first appeared on land about 400 million years ago. There are over 12,000 species of ferns alive today. They range in size from tiny plants about the size of this letter "M" to large tree ferns that grow up to 5 meters tall in moist, tropical areas.

The Structure of Ferns Like other vascular plants, ferns have true stems, roots, and leaves. The stems of most ferns are underground. Leaves grow upward from the top side of the stems, and roots grow downward from the bottom of the stems. Roots are structures that anchor the fern to the ground and absorb water and nutrients from the soil. These substances enter the root's vascular tissue and travel through the tissue into the stems and leaves. In Figure 8 you can see the fern's structure.

Figure 8 Most ferns have underground stems in addition to underground roots. The leaves, or fronds, grow above ground.

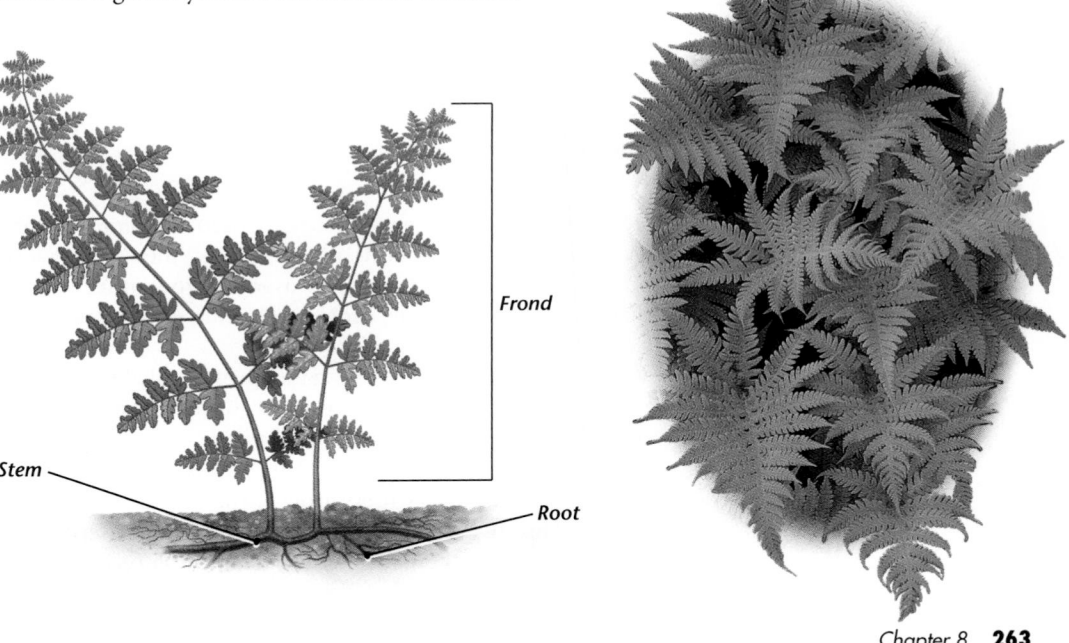

Frond

Stem

Root

Chapter 8 **263**

Answers to Self-Assessment

☑ *Checkpoint*
Vascular tissue allowed plants to grow tall.

Ferns

TRY THIS

Skills Focus inferring
Materials *fern plant, hand lens, plastic dropper, water*
Time 20 minutes
Tips Students should observe the fronds, the stem, and the roots. They should notice that the upper surface of a frond is smooth and shiny compared to the lower surface. Spore cases may be visible on the underside of the blade. Water dropped onto the upper surface of the frond should run off.
Inferring The roots anchor the plant on land and absorb water. The cuticle on the upper surface reduces water loss.
Extend Suggest students closely examine a spore case, then release the spores from the case with a dissecting knife and examine them with a hand lens. **learning modality: visual**

Visual Arts Connection

Rubbings of fern fronds are attractive to look at and can be useful for making scientific observations. To make a rubbing, students can place tracing paper on top of a frond and rub the tracing paper with charcoal. Have students examine the rubbings to see if they can identify any features that were difficult to see on the plant. Keep rubbings for classroom display. **learning modality: kinesthetic**

Portfolio Students can save their rubbings in their portfolios.

Ongoing Assessment

Skills Check Have students list two functions of vascular tissue.
(*Transports food and transports water through the plant's body, provides support*)

Ferns, continued

Building Inquiry Skills: Drawing Conclusions

Describe the reproductive cycle of ferns to students: the mature plant releases spores that grow into gametophytes; the gametophytes develop egg cells and free-swimming sperm that fertilize the egg cells. The fertilized egg cells develop into mature fern plants. Have students discuss the importance of water to this cycle. Ask: **During which part of the cycle does the fern plant require water?** *(The free-swimming sperm must have water to swim in.)* **How would a fern plant survive in a climate that was mostly arid with only seasonal rains?** *(Plants could have evolved a cycle that was synchronized with the seasons so liquid water was available for the free-swimming sperm.)* **learning modality: logical/mathematical**

Club Mosses and Horsetails

Building Inquiry Skills: Classifying

Materials *samples of ferns, club mosses, moss, liverworts or hornworts, and horsetails*
Time 10 minutes

ACTIVITY

Provide samples for students to examine. Have students work in pairs to compare the plants and identify structures. Challenge each pair to classify these plants according to their similarities. Then have students diagram the plants and explain their classifications.
learning modality: visual

Figure 9 Spores are produced on the undersides of mature fronds. *Applying Concepts What happens to spores that are released?*

Figure 10 Fiddleheads are the developing leaves of a fern.

Look closely at the fern's leaves, or **fronds.** Notice that the frond is divided into many smaller parts that look like small leaves. Many other ferns have a similar divided-leaf structure. The upper surface of each frond is coated with a cuticle that helps the plant retain water. In many types of ferns, the developing leaves are coiled at first. Because they resemble the top of a violin, these young leaves are often called fiddleheads. As they mature, the fiddleheads uncurl.

Reproduction in Ferns The familiar fern with its visible fronds is the sporophyte stage of the plant. On the underside of mature fronds, spores develop in tiny spore cases. When the spores are released, wind and water can carry them great distances. If a spore lands in moist, shaded soil, it develops into a gametophyte. Fern gametophytes are tiny plants that grow low to the ground.

The Importance of Ferns Ferns are useful to people in many ways. They are popular houseplants because they are attractive and easy to grow. Ferns are also used to grow other kinds of houseplants. For example, orchids are often grown on the tangled masses of fern roots.

People eat some ferns. During the spring, fiddleheads are sold in supermarkets and farm stands. Fiddleheads make a nutritious vegetable dish. But because some ferns are not safe to eat, you should never gather wild fiddleheads for food.

In Southeast Asia, farmers grow a small aquatic fern alongside rice plants in their rice fields. Tiny pockets in the fern's leaves provide a home for some bacteria. The bacteria produce a natural fertilizer that helps the rice plants grow.

264

Background

Facts and Figures The small aquatic fern mentioned on page 264 is called *Azolla.* Its benefit as a fertilizer is due to the mutualistic relationship it shares with a cyanobacterium (blue-green alga) called *Anabaena azollae.* Filaments of *Anabaena* live inside ovoid cavities within the leaves of *Azolla.* The cyanobacterium provides the *Azolla* with a source of usable nitrogen in the form of ammonia. Nitrogen fixation makes nitrogen available to autotrophic plants, such as rice. *Azolla* and its partner *Anabaena* have been used to fertilize rice paddies in China and other Asian countries for centuries. Some reports suggest that *Azolla* can increase rice yields by as much as 158 percent per year. Because the soil is not depleted of nutrients, rice can be grown in the same fields year after year with no loss of productivity.

Club Mosses and Horsetails

Two other groups of seedless, vascular plants are the club mosses and horsetails. Like ferns, club mosses and horsetails have true leaves, stems, and roots. They also have a similar life cycle. However, there are relatively few species of club mosses and horsetails alive today.

Unlike their larger ancestors, today's club mosses are small. Do not be confused by the name *club mosses*. Unlike the true mosses, the club mosses have vascular tissue. You may be familiar with the club moss you see in Figure 11. The plant, which looks like the small branch of a pine tree, is sometimes called ground pine or princess pine. It grows in moist woodlands and near streams.

There are 30 species of horsetails on Earth today. As you can see in Figure 11, the stems of horsetails are jointed. Long, coarse, needlelike branches grow in a circle around each joint. Small leaves grow flat against the stem just above each joint. The stems contain silica, a gritty substance also found in sand. During colonial times, Americans called horsetails "scouring rushes" because they used the plants to scrub their pots and pans.

Figure 11 Horsetails and club mosses are other seedless vascular plants. **A.** These horsetail plants have jointed stems. Needle-like branches grow out of each joint. **B.** This club moss looks like a tiny pine tree.

Section 3 Review

1. What two characteristics do ferns, club mosses, and horsetails share? How do these characteristics differ from those of mosses?
2. Describe the structure of a fern plant. What do its leaves, stems, and roots look like?
3. List three ways that ferns are useful to people today.
4. **Thinking Critically** **Applying Concepts** Although ferns have vascular tissue, they still must live in moist, shady environments. Explain why this is true.

> **Check Your Progress** CHAPTER PROJECT
> You should now be caring for your moss, and providing the best conditions for its survival and growth. Be sure to keep in mind how mosses differ from other familiar kinds of plants. (*Hint:* Keep your terrarium warm, but not hot, and make sure it remains moist.)

Program Resources

- **Unit 2 Resources** 8-3 Review and Reinforce, p. 71; 8-3 Enrich, p. 72
- **Interdisciplinary Exploration Series** "Fate of the Rain Forest," pp. 6–9, 17–19

Answers to Self-Assessment

Caption Question

Figure 9 Spores that are released are carried by wind and water. If they land in a suitable spot, the spore develops into a gametophyte.

3 Assess

Section 3 Review Answers

1. Ferns and their relatives have two common characteristics: vascular tissue and the use of spores to reproduce. Mosses do not have vascular tissue.
2. The leaves, or fronds, of ferns have vascular tissue and a cuticle that helps prevent water loss. The stems have vascular tissue and are underground. Leaves grow upward and roots grow downward from the stems.
3. Any three: People use some ferns as house plants. Some ferns are eaten. Some ferns help rice grow. The remains of ancient ferns are used as fuel in the form of coal.
4. Ferns need to live in moist, shady places in order to reproduce.

> **Check Your Progress** CHAPTER PROJECT
> Check students' observation records on a regular basis. Students should record observations daily and include details about changes in the size of the moss and the growth of new structures.

Performance Assessment

Organizing Information Ask students to create Venn diagrams that compare ferns, club mosses, and horsetails. (*Venn diagrams should indicate that all three have vascular tissue and reproduce without seeds. Ferns have fronds and underground stems. Club mosses have needlelike leaves. Horsetails have jointed stems with branches growing in a circle around each joint.*)

SECTION 4 Feeding the World

Objective

After completing the lesson, students will be able to
◆ describe some methods that might help farmers produce more crops.

Key Term hydroponics

1 Engage/Explore

Activating Prior Knowledge

Ask students to describe a typical farm from 100 years ago. *(Most will say small, one family worked on it, only grew enough food for the family.)* Then have students describe a farm today. *(Large, may be run by a company, grows enough food for many people.)* Then ask students to imagine what a farm will be like 100 years from now.

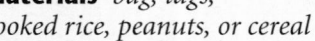

DISCOVER

Skills Focus predicting
Materials *bag, tags, cooked rice, peanuts, or cereal*
Time 20 minutes
Tips For a class of 30, create three number 1 tags, five number 2 tags, and twenty-two number 3 tags. Divide the food into three equal portions, and present one portion to each student, depending on the group. Group 1 should have the largest portion. Group 3 should have the smallest portion. Check for food allergies among students. Encourage but don't require students to eat their portion.
Expected Outcome Students may feel guilt, self-righteousness, pity, envy, anger, resentment, or gratefulness.
Think It Over Food is already scarce in some countries. If the world's population increases, there will be even less food in many places.

SECTION 4 Feeding the World

DISCOVER ⋯⋯⋯⋯⋯⋯⋯⋯⋯⋯ ACTIVITY ⋯

Will There Be Enough to Eat?

1. Choose a numbered tag from the bag that your teacher provides. If you pick a tag with the number 1 on it, you're from a wealthy country. If you pick a tag with the number 2, you're from a middle-income country. If you pick a tag with the number 3, you're from a poor country.

2. Find classmates that have the same number on their tag. Sit down as a group.

3. Your teacher will serve your group a meal. The amount of food you receive will depend on the number on your tag.

4. As you eat, observe the people in your group and in the other groups. After you eat, record your observations. Also, record how you felt and what you were thinking during the meal.

Think It Over
Predicting Based on this activity, predict what effect an increase in the world's population would have on the world's food supply.

GUIDE FOR READING

◆ What methods may help farmers produce more crops?

Reading Tip As you read, make a list of the technologies being used to increase Earth's food supply.

Today, about six billion people live on Earth. Some scientists predict that by the year 2050 the population will grow to ten billion people. Think about how much additional food will be needed to feed the growing population. How will farmers be able to grow enough food?

Fortunately, both scientists and farmers are already hard at work trying to find answers to this question. **In laboratories, scientists are developing plants that are more resistant to insects, disease, and drought. They are also developing plants that produce more food per plant. On farms, new, efficient, "high-tech" farming practices are being used.**

266

READING STRATEGIES

Reading Tip Before students begin reading, encourage them to preview the section by reading the headings, captions, and boldfaced terms and looking at the photographs. Then have students make their lists of technologies as they read, summarizing each one in their own words. Sample answer: Genetic engineering is being used to develop plants that produce more food.

Study and Comprehension Arrange students in groups of three or four. Have students in each group use the information in the section to write a list of questions about feeding the world's population. Encourage students to read the section to find the answers to their questions. Students may want to do additional research in the school media center.

Producing Better Plants

Wheat, corn, rice, and potatoes are the major sources of food for people on Earth today. To feed more people, then, the production, or yields, of these crops must be increased. This is not an easy task. One challenge facing farmers is that these crops grow only in certain climates. Another challenge is that the size and structure of these plants limit how much food they can produce.

Today scientists are using new technologies to address these challenges. Recall from Chapter 4 that scientists can manipulate the genetic material of certain bacteria to produce human insulin. The process that these scientists use is called genetic engineering. In genetic engineering, scientists alter an organism's genetic material to produce an organism with qualities that people find useful.

Scientists are using genetic engineering to produce plants that can grow in a wider range of climates. They are also engineering plants to be more resistant to damage from insects. For example, scientists have inserted genetic material from a bacterium into corn and tomato plants. The new genetic material enables the plants to produce substances that kill insects. Caterpillars or other insects that bite into the leaves of these plants are killed. Today, many kinds of genetically engineered plants are grown on experimental farms. Some of these plants may produce the crops of the future.

✓ **Checkpoint** *What are the four crops on which people depend?*

Improving the Efficiency of Farms

On the farms of the future, satellite images and computers will be just as important as tractors and harvesters. These new tools will allow farmers to practice "precision farming"—knowing just how much water and fertilizer different fields require. First, satellite images of the farmer's fields are taken. Then, a computer analyzes the images to determine the makeup of the soil in different fields on the farm. The computer uses the data to prepare a watering and fertilizing plan for each field. Precision farming benefits farmers because it saves time and money. It also increases crop yields by helping farmers maintain ideal conditions in all fields.

Figure 12 In this high-tech greenhouse, scientists control the environmental conditions as they develop new types of plants. *Applying Concepts How might new plant types lead to increased crop yields in the future?*

Program Resources

◆ **Unit 2 Resources** 8-4 Lesson Plan, p. 73; 8-4 Section Summary, p. 74

Media and Technology

 Audio CD English-Spanish Summary 8-4

Answers to Self-Assessment

Caption Question

Figure 12 New plant types that were resistant to pests or disease and able to grow in a variety of climates would result in higher crop yields.

✓ *Checkpoint*

Wheat, corn, rice, and potatoes

2 *Facilitate*

Producing Better Plants

Building Inquiry Skills: Making Judgments

Inform students that scientists have genetically engineered rice plants, using genes from the potato to make the rice resist insects and genes from barley plants to make it salt—and drought—tolerant. The scientists decided to give this technology to developing countries for free, but to sell it to developed countries such as Japan and the United States. Use this information to stimulate class discussion. Encourage the class to make judgments about the scientists' decision. **learning modality: verbal**

Improving the Efficiency of Farms

 Integrating Environmental Science

If possible, visit a local farm or invite a farmer or farm manager to talk to the class. Direct students to prepare questions about the size and layout of the farm, the crops produced, the quality of the soil, and the methods used to protect plants from disease and pests. After the visit, ask students: **How could precision farming both improve the efficiency of this farm and protect the environment?** *(Sample: Precision farming could keep farmers from using more water and fertilizer than necessary.)* **learning modality: verbal**

Ongoing Assessment

Oral Presentation Ask students to explain why it is necessary to produce better plants and increase the efficiency of farms. *(Answers should include that the world's population is growing and more food will be needed.)*

Hydroponics

Ask students to infer some benefits of growing food crops hydroponically. *(Hydroponics allows plants to be grown in conditions where it would be difficult to grow plants in soil.)* **learning modality: logical/mathematical**

3 Assess

Section 4 Review Answers

1. Genetic engineering, precision farming, and hydroponics
2. It can produce plants that are resistant to disease, insects, and drought; can produce more food; and can grow in a wider range of climates.
3. It saves time and money and helps improve crop yields. It benefits the environment because less fertilizer is used.
4. They can survive without soil because they absorb water and nutrients directly from the nutrient-rich water that bathes their roots.

Check Your Progress

CHAPTER PROJECT

Tell students that their brochures should outline the steps needed to construct a terrarium and summarize the growth requirements for mosses, based on their observations. The directions must be clear enough that an individual from another class could set up a terrarium and successfully grow mosses using only the brochure. Students should also describe the general characteristics and life cycle of mosses.

Performance Assessment

Oral Presentation Have students work in groups to make displays and present to show how genetic engineering, precision farming, or hydroponics can help farmers increase food production.

Figure 13 The map on the computer screen of this tractor shows the makeup of the soil in a farm's fields. The map was obtained by satellite imaging.

 INTEGRATING ENVIRONMENTAL SCIENCE Precision farming also benefits the environment because farmers use only as much fertilizer as the soil needs. When less fertilizer is used, fewer nutrients wash off the land into lakes and rivers. As you read in Chapter 7, reducing the use of fertilizers is one way to prevent algal blooms from damaging bodies of water.

Hydroponics

In some areas of the world, poor soil does not support the growth of crops. For example, on some islands in the Pacific Ocean, the soil contains large amounts of salt from the surrounding ocean. Food crops will not grow in the salty soil.

On these islands, people can use hydroponics to grow food crops. **Hydroponics** (hy druh PAHN iks) is a method by which plants are grown in solutions of nutrients instead of in soil. Usually, the plants are grown in containers in which their roots are anchored in gravel or sand. The nutrient-rich water is pumped through the gravel or sand. Unfortunately, hydroponics is a costly method of growing food crops. But, the process allows people to grow crops in areas with poor farmland to help feed a growing population.

Section 4 Review

1. List three methods that farmers can use to increase crop yields.
2. Explain how genetic engineering may help farmers grow more food.
3. How does precision farming benefit farmers? How does it benefit the environment?
4. **Thinking Critically** **Applying Concepts** How are plants that are grown using hydroponics able to survive without soil?

Check Your Progress

CHAPTER PROJECT

Begin planning your brochure as you continue caring for your moss. What's the best way to give clear directions for making a terrarium? What must you say about the amount of light, water, and other conditions that mosses need to survive? (*Hint:* Be sure to include important information about mosses, such as how tall they grow and how they reproduce.)

Program Resources

- **Interdisciplinary Exploration Series** "Fate of the Rain Forest," p. 42
- **Unit 2 Resources** 8-4 Review and Reinforce, p. 75; 8-4 Enrich, p. 76

Media and Technology

Exploring Life Science Videodisc Unit 1, Side 2, "Can We Still Get What We Need?"  Chapter 4

CHAPTER 8 STUDY GUIDE

SECTION 1 The Plant Kingdom

Key Ideas
◆ Plants are multicellular eukaryotes and autotrophs.
◆ For plants to survive on land, they need ways to obtain water and other materials from their surroundings, retain moisture, support their bodies, transport materials throughout the plant, and reproduce successfully.
◆ All plants have complex life cycles. In the sporophyte stage, plants produce spores. In the gametophyte stage, plants produce sperm cells and egg cells.

Key Terms
cuticle   zygote
tissue   sporophyte
vascular tissue   gametophyte
fertilization   gamete

SECTION 2 Mosses, Liverworts, and Hornworts

Key Ideas
◆ Nonvascular plants are small, low-growing plants that lack vascular tissue. Most nonvascular plants transport materials by passing them from one cell to the next.
◆ Mosses, liverworts, and hornworts are three types of nonvascular plants.

Key Terms
nonvascular plant   bog
rhizoid   peat

SECTION 3 Ferns and Their Relatives

Key Ideas
◆ Seedless vascular plants have vascular tissue and use spores to reproduce. These plants include ferns, club mosses, and horsetails.
◆ Although seedless vascular plants grow taller than nonvascular plants, they still need to live in moist places. The plants' spores are released into the environment, where they grow into gametophytes.

Key Terms
vascular plant   frond

SECTION 4 Feeding the World
INTEGRATING TECHNOLOGY

Key Idea
◆ Genetic engineering, precision farming, and hydroponics can help farmers produce more crops to feed the world's growing population.

Key Term
hydroponics

Organizing Information

Compare/Contrast Table Copy the table comparing mosses and ferns onto a separate sheet of paper. Complete the table by filling in the missing information. Then add a title. (For more on compare/contrast tables, see the Skills Handbook.)

Characteristic	Moss	Fern
Size	a. __?__	Can be tall
Environment	Moist	b. __?__
Body parts	Rootlike, stemlike, and leaflike	c. __?__
Familiar generation	d. __?__	sporophyte
Vascular tissue present?	e. __?__	f. __?__

Chapter 8 **269**

Organizing Information

Compare/Contrast Table
Sample title: Comparing Mosses and Ferns **a.** Small and low **b.** Moist
c. Fronds, stems, and roots
d. Gametophyte **e.** No **f.** Yes

Reviewing Content
Multiple Choice
1. c 2. d 3. c 4. c 5. b

True or False
6. true 7. true 8. nonvascular
9. ferns 10. true

Checking Concepts
11. Photosynthesis is a plant's foodmaking process. The plant uses carbon dioxide and water and chemically changes them into sugars and oxygen using the energy in sunlight. Because plants make their own food, they do not have to find food to eat like animals do.
12. Vascular tissue enables a plant to efficiently transport water and food to all its cells and supports plants so they can grow large.
13. Plants have complex life cycles in which a sporophyte generation produces spores that develop into a gametophyte. The gametophyte plant produces egg cells and sperm cells. Fertilization occurs when a sperm cell fuses with an egg cell to form a zygote. The zygote develops into a new sporophyte plant.
14. Ferns must live in moist areas because they don't produce seeds and therefore need moisture in the environment to enable their gametes to join.
15. Mosses are nonvascular plants; club mosses are vascular. Both mosses and club mosses need to grow in moist environments because they use spores for reproduction.
16. Using hydroponics, food can be grown in areas with poor or contaminated soil.
17. Student letters should include the information that precision farming can pinpoint which fields need fertilizer and what kind of fertilizers they need. Also, the method will provide information about watering needs so that all plants get adequate amounts of water.

Thinking Critically
18. The sporophyte generation produces spores. The spore develops into the gametophyte stage. The gametophyte generation produces two kinds of gametes—sperm cells and egg cells.
19. Students should indicate that their friend is probably mistaken. Mosses are

---

Reviewing Content

 For more review of key concepts, see the Interactive Student Tutorial CD-ROM.

Multiple Choice
Choose the letter of the best answer.

1. The products of photosynthesis are
   a. food and carbon dioxide.
   b. food and water.
   c. food and oxygen.
   d. water and oxygen.
2. Mosses and ferns are both
   a. vascular plants.
   b. nonvascular plants.
   c. seed plants.
   d. plants.
3. The familiar green, fuzzy moss is the
   a. frond.
   b. rhizoid.
   c. gametophyte.
   d. sporophyte.
4. The leaves of ferns are called
   a. rhizoids.
   b. sporophytes.
   c. fronds.
   d. cuticles.
5. The process of growing crops in a nutrient solution is called
   a. genetic engineering.
   b. hydroponics.
   c. precision farming.
   d. satellite imaging.

True or False
If the statement is true, write true. If it is false, change the underlined word or words to make the statement true.

6. Plants are <u>autotrophs</u>.
7. <u>Tissues</u> are groups of similar cells that perform a specific function in an organism.
8. Mosses are <u>vascular</u> plants.
9. The young leaves of <u>liverworts</u> are known as fiddleheads.
10. The four basic food crops of the world are wheat, corn, rice, and <u>potatoes</u>.

Checking Concepts
11. Describe the process of photosynthesis. Explain why it is an important process for a plant.
12. In what two ways is vascular tissue important to a plant? Give an example of a plant that has vascular tissue.
13. Briefly describe the life cycle of a typical plant.
14. Explain why fern plants are found in moist areas.
15. In what ways do mosses and club mosses differ from each other? In what ways are they similar?
16. How can the use of hydroponics help increase the amount of food that can be grown on Earth?
17. **Writing to Learn** Suppose you are living in a farming community. Write a letter to the editor of the local newspaper that explains how precision farming can increase crop yields. Also explain the other benefits of precision farming to farmers and to the environment.

Thinking Critically
18. **Comparing and Contrasting** How does the sporophyte generation of a plant differ from the gametophyte generation?
19. **Applying Concepts** A friend tells you that he has seen moss plants that are about 2 meters tall. Is your friend correct? Explain your reasoning.
20. **Relating Cause and Effect** People have observed that mosses tend to grow on the north side of a tree rather than the south side. Why do you think this is so?
21. **Making Judgments** Suppose you were a scientist using genetic engineering to increase crop yields. What improvements would you try to introduce? How would they be beneficial?

---

nonvascular plants and cannot grow tall. They can neither support, nor transport material through, large bodies.
20. The north sides are cooler and get less sunlight. Therefore, the north sides of trees should be more moist and provide the moisture mosses need to grow.
21. Answers will vary, but students should be able to explain how their improvements would increase crop yield. They should also be able to identify the benefits of their suggestions.

Applying Skills
22. It is alwasy higher.
23. One possible answer is that there might have been a heavy rainfall for a few days. Accept all reasonable answers.
24. Growing plants in soil covered with mulch seems more reasonable because plants need moisture to grow and soil that is mulched holds more moisture than soil that is not mulched.

Applying Skills

Some gardeners spread a protective layer of mulch—plant material such as wood chips, peat moss, or straw—on the soil around plants. The graph below compares how much moisture is retained by soil covered with mulch and by soil without mulch. Use the graph to answer Questions 22–24.

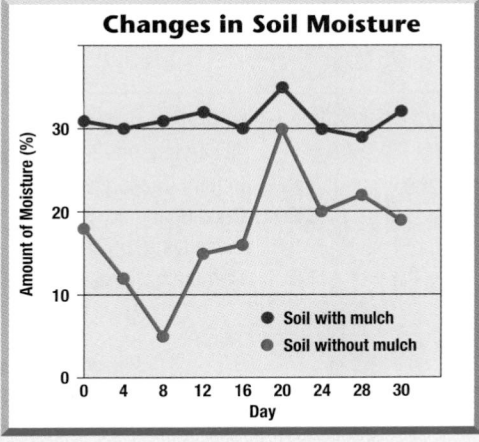

Changes in Soil Moisture

● Soil with mulch
● Soil without mulch

22. **Comparing and Contrasting** How does the amount of moisture in soil covered with mulch differ from the amount of moisture in the uncovered soil?

23. **Inferring** The amount of moisture in both soils increased greatly between days 16 and 20. Explain why this might have happened.

24. **Drawing Conclusions** If you were a gardener, would you grow your plants in soil covered with mulch or in soil that was uncovered? Explain.

Performance CHAPTER PROJECT Assessment

Present Your Project It's time to share your "How to Raise Mosses" brochure with others. Be prepared to explain the information in your brochure. Ask other students about their work.

Reflect and Record What did you learn by keeping the terrarium and making the brochure? Did you discover new ideas from brochures made by others? If you were to repeat this project, how could you improve your work?

Performance CHAPTER PROJECT Assessment

Present Your Project Students' brochures should be well organized and should contain detailed pictures and/or drawings of mosses. Students' presentations should include what they learned about growing mosses and how mosses compare with other plants.

Reflect and Record As students give their reports, have their classmates take brief notes. After all the reports have been given, encourage students to discuss any differences that were apparent among the groups. Have students evaluate their own brochures. Encourage them to decide whether they would change the information presented in their brochure or whether they would present information differently.

Test Preparation   *Use these questions to prepare for standardized tests.*

Use the information to answer Questions 25–27. When bracken ferns grow, their underground stems grow outward and produce new plants. As the map below shows, the new ferns spread into nearby open areas. The bands of color indicate the areas where bracken ferns grew over a four-year period.

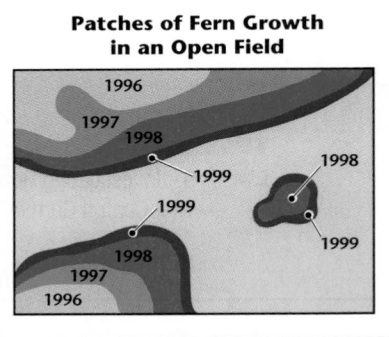

Patches of Fern Growth in an Open Field

25. During which year did the ferns grow most slowly?
    a. 1996   b. 1997
    c. 1998   d. 1999

26. In how many areas in the field were bracken ferns growing in 1997?
    a. one   b. two
    c. three   d. four

27. The underground stems of bracken ferns do not grow far before producing new plants. What is the most likely explanation for how bracken ferns began to grow in the middle of the field in 1998?
    a. It rained less than usual.
    b. The temperatures were higher than normal.
    c. The whole field was fertilized.
    d. Spores blew into a moist part of the field.

Chapter 8 **271**

Test Preparation

25. d **26.** b **27.** d

Program Resources

◆ **Inquiry Skills Activity Book** Provides teaching and review of all inquiry skills

Seed Plants

Sections	Time	Student Edition Activities		Other Activities
CHAPTER PROJECT **Cycle of a Lifetime** p. 273	Ongoing (2½ weeks)	Check Your Progress, pp. 288, 296, 299 Present Your Project, p. 303		
1 The Characteristics of Seed Plants pp. 274–283 ◆ List the characteristics that seed plants share. ◆ Name the main parts of a seed, identify the function of each part of the seed, and describe how seeds disperse and germinate. ◆ Describe the functions of leaves, stems, and roots.	2½ periods/ 1¼ blocks	**Discover** Which Plant Part Is It?, p. 274 **Try This** The In-Seed Story, p. 276 **Sharpen Your Skills** Calculating, p. 280 **Science at Home,** p. 283	TE TE TE TE	Building Inquiry Skills: Observing, pp. 275, 281 Inquiry Challenge, p. 277 Building Inquiry Skills: Classifying, p. 278 Demonstrations, pp. 280, 282
2 Gymnosperms pp. 284–288 ◆ Give examples of gymnosperms and list the characteristics they share. ◆ Describe how gymnosperms reproduce.	1½ periods/ ¾ block	**Discover** Are All Leaves Alike?, p. 284 **Try This** The Scoop on Cones, p. 286	TE	Social Studies Connection, p. 285
3 Angiosperms pp. 289–296 ◆ Name types of angiosperms and list the characteristics that they all share. ◆ Describe the structure and function of a flower. ◆ Describe the life cycle of an angiosperm. ◆ Compare monocots and dicots.	2 periods/ 1 block	**Discover** What Is a Fruit?, p. 289 **Real-World Lab: How It Works** A Close Look at Flowers, pp. 294–295	TE TE TE PTA	Building Inquiry Skills: Comparing and Contrasting, p. 292 Including All Students, p. 293 Integrating Health, p. 293 Testing Jeans, pp. 1–8
4 *INTEGRATING CHEMISTRY* **Plant Responses and Growth** pp. 297–300 ◆ Identify three stimuli that produce plant responses. ◆ List the functions that plant hormones control.	1 period/ ½ block	**Discover** Can a Plant Respond to Touch?, p. 297 **Skills Lab: Developing Hypotheses** Which Way Is Up?, p. 300	TE TE LM	Demonstration, p. 298 Inquiry Challenge, p. 298 9, "Investigating Hormones That Control Germination"
Study Guide/Chapter Assessment pp. 301–303	1 period/ ½ block		ISAB	Provides teaching and review of all inquiry skills

For Standard or Block Schedule The Resource Pro® CD-ROM gives you maximum flexibility for planning your instruction for any type of schedule. Resource Pro® contains Planning Express®, an advanced scheduling program, as well as the entire contents of the Teaching Resources and the Computer Test Bank.

CHAPTER PLANNING GUIDE

Program Resources	Assessment Strategies	Media and Technology
UR Chapter 9 Project Teacher Notes, pp. 82–83 **UR** Chapter 9 Project Overview and Worksheets, pp. 84–87	**SE** Performance Assessment: Present Your Project, p. 303 **TE** Check Your Progress, pp. 288, 296, 299 **UR** Chapter 9 Project Scoring Rubric, p. 88	Science Explorer Internet Site at www.phschool.com
UR 9-1 Lesson Plan, p. 89 **UR** 9-1 Section Summary, p. 90 **UR** 9-1 Review and Reinforce, p. 91 **UR** 9-1 Enrich, p. 92	**SE** Section 1 Review, p. 283 **TE** Ongoing Assessment, pp. 275, 277, 279, 281 **TE** Performance Assessment, p. 283	Life Science Videotape 2; Videodisc Unit 2 Side 2, "Xeriscape" Audio CD, English-Spanish Summary 9-1 Transparencies 34, "The Structure of Seeds"; 35, "Exploring a Leaf"; 36, "The Parts of a Woody Stem" Interactive Student Tutorial CD-ROM, Chapter 9
UR 9-2 Lesson Plan, p. 93 **UR** 9-2 Section Summary, p. 94 **UR** 9-2 Review and Reinforce, p. 95 **UR** 9-2 Enrich, p. 96	**SE** Section 2 Review, p. 288 **TE** Ongoing Assessment, pp. 285, 287 **TE** Performance Assessment, p. 288	Audio CD, English-Spanish Summary 9-2 Transparency 37, "Exploring the Life Cycle of a Gymnosperm"
UR 9-3 Lesson Plan, p. 97 **UR** 9-3 Section Summary, p. 98 **UR** 9-3 Review and Reinforce, p. 99 **UR** 9-3 Enrich, p. 100 **UR** Chapter 9 Real-World Lab, pp. 105–107	**SE** Section 3 Review, p. 296 **TE** Ongoing Assessment, pp. 291, 293 **TE** Performance Assessment, p. 296	Audio CD, English-Spanish Summary 9-3 Transparencies 38, "The Structure of a Flower"; 39, "Exploring the Life Cycle of an Angiosperm"
UR 9-4 Lesson Plan, p. 101 **UR** 9-4 Section Summary, p. 102 **UR** 9-4 Review and Reinforce, p. 103 **UR** 9-4 Enrich, p. 104 **UR** Chapter 9 Skills Lab, pp. 108–109	**SE** Section 4 Review, p. 299 **TE** Performance Assessment, p. 299	Life Science Videotape 2; Videodisc Unit 2 Side 2, "Fertilizers" Audio CD, English-Spanish Summary 9-4
RCA Provides strategies to improve science reading skills **GSW** Provides worksheets to promote student comprehension of content	**SE** Chapter 9 Study Guide/Assessment, pp. 171–173 **PA** Chapter 9 Performance Assessment, pp. 29–31 **CUT** Chapter 9 Test, pp. 40–43 **CTB** Chapter 9 Test	Interactive Student Tutorial CD-ROM, Chapter 9 Computer Test Bank, Chapter 9 Test

Key: **SE** Student Edition
   CTB Computer Test Bank
   ISAB Inquiry Skills Activity Book
   GSW Guided Study Worksheets

TE Teacher's Edition
PTA Product Testing Activities by *Consumer Reports*
RCA Reading in the Content Area
PA Performance Assessment

UR Unit Resources
LM Laboratory Manual
IES Interdisciplinary Explorations Series
CUT Chapter and Unit Tests

Meeting the National Science Education Standards and AAAS Benchmarks

National Science Education Standards	Benchmarks for Science Literacy	Unifying Themes
Science as Inquiry (Content Standard A) ◆ **Think critically and logically to make the relationships between evidence and explanations** Students examine plant responses to gravity. *(Skills Lab)* **Life Science** (Content Standard C) ◆ **Structure and function in living systems** Seed plants have specialized tissues, such as xylem and phloem, that carry out specific functions. *(Section 1)* Gymnosperms and angiosperms have different structures involved in reproduction. *(Sections 2, 3; Real-World Lab)* Hormones are chemicals that govern growth and development. *(Section 4; Skills Lab)* ◆ **Reproduction and heredity** Seeds are specialized structures for reproduction. *(Section 1)* Most gymnosperms reproduce sexually using cones. *(Section 2)* Angiosperms reproduce sexually using flowers and fruit. *(Section 3; Chapter Project; Real-World Lab)*	**5A Diversity of Life** Seed plants have vascular tissue and seeds. Gymnosperms and angiosperms are two types of seed plants with different reproductive structures. *(Sections 1, 2, 3; Chapter Project; Real-World Lab)* **5C Cells** Pollen releases male sperm cells that unite with a female egg cell to form a seed. *(Section 1, 2, 3; Chapter Project)* Actively dividing cells are found in the root cap and cambium of a seed plant. *(Section 1)* **8A Agriculture** Many varieties of angiosperms produce edible food for humans. *(Section 3)* **11C Constancy and Change** Seed plants have predictable life cycles. *(Sections 1, 2, 3; Chapter Project)* Tropisms are predictable responses plants have to stimuli, such as light, gravity, and touch. Angiosperms may have annual, biennial, or perennial life spans. *(Section 4; Skills Lab)*	◆ **Energy** Plants use light energy to change water and carbon dioxide into carbohydrates and oxygen. Plants store energy in their roots, stems, leaves, fruits, and seeds. *(Section 1)* ◆ **Evolution** Gymnosperms were the first group of seed plants to evolve. Angiosperms first appeared about 100 million years ago. Seed plants have evolved adaptations to many different environments. *(Sections 2, 3)* ◆ **Patterns of Change** The life cycle of seed plants involves pollination, fertilization, seed development, dispersal of seeds, and growth of a new plant. Angiosperms have different life spans. *(Sections 1, 2, 3, 4; Chapter Project)* ◆ **Scale and Structure** All seed plants have vascular tissue and seeds that allow seed plants to grow tall and survive in many different environments. *(Sections 1, 2, 3; Real-World Lab)* ◆ **Unity and Diversity** While all seed plants share specific characteristics and responses to stimuli, many different species of seed plants exist. *(Sections 1, 2, 3, 4; Chapter Project; Skills Lab; Real-World Lab)* ◆ **Systems and Interactions** Many angiosperms rely on animals for pollination and seed dispersal. *(Section 1)* ◆ **Stability** Photosynthesis helps to maintain the atmospheric balance of oxygen and carbon dioxide. *(Section 1)*

Take It to the Net

 *Interactive text at* www.phschool.com

Science Explorer comes alive with iText.

- **Complete student text** is accessible from any computer with Internet access or a CD-ROM drive.
- **Animations, simulations, and videos** enhance student understanding and retention of concepts.
- **Self-tests and online study tools** assess student understanding.

STAY CURRENT with **SCIENCE NEWS**®

Find out the latest research and information about plants at:
www.phschool.com

Go to **www.phschool.com** and click on the Science icon. Then click on <u>Science Explorer: Life, Earth, and Physical Science</u> under PH@school.

Student Edition Activities Planner

ACTIVITY	Time (minutes)	Materials — Quantities for one work group	Skills
Section 1			
Discover, p. 274	10	**Nonconsumable** foods such as carrots, parsnips, broccoli, cabbage, lettuce, celery, parsley, potato, onion	Classifying
Try This, p. 276	10	**Nonconsumable** hand lens; dried kidney, lima, or black beans; dried yellow or green peas; shelled peanuts	Observing
Sharpen Your Skills, p. 280	15 min, plus 20 min after 2 h for observation	**Consumable** water, food coloring, celery stalk **Nonconsumable** plastic container, dropper, spoon, metric ruler, clock or stopwatch, lab apron	Calculating
Science at Home, p. 283	home	**Consumable** corn kernels or lima bean seeds, water, soil, paper cup	Observing
Section 2			
Discover, p. 284	10	**Consumable** 2 or 3 leaves from different angiosperms, such as an oak tree, maple tree, day lily, and rose; 2 or 3 leaves from different gymnosperms, such as pine, yew, and spruce **Nonconsumable** hand lens, metric ruler	Classifying
Try This, p. 286	10	**Nonconsumable** mature female pine cone, hand lens, piece of white paper	Inferring
Section 3			
Discover, p. 289	15	**Nonconsumable** hand lens; metric ruler; three different fruits, such as apples, cherries, peaches, plums, tomatoes, or peppers	Forming Operational Definitions
Real-World Lab, pp. 294–295	40	**Consumable** paper towels, tape, large flower, water, lens paper **Nonconsumable** hand lens, slide, cover slip, metric ruler, plastic dropper, microscope, scalpel	Observing, Measuring, Inferring
Section 4			
Discover, p. 297	10	**Nonconsumable** sensitive plant such as a Venus' flytrap or mimosa, common house plant such as a geranium or impatiens	Inferring
Skills Lab, p. 300	30 min, plus a few minutes each day for a week	**Consumable** 4 corn seeds, paper towels, water, masking tape **Nonconsumable** marking pencil, plastic petri dish, scissors, clay	Developing Hypotheses

A list of all materials required for the Student Edition activities can be found on pages T25–T33. You can obtain information about ordering materials by calling 1-800-848-9500 or by accessing the Science Explorer Internet site at **www.phschool.com**.

Cycle of a Lifetime

Although most students are aware that plants grow from seeds, they may never have observed each stage in the life of a seed plant. This project will allow students to observe a plant's growing cycle.

Purpose In this project, students will grow plants from seeds and make detailed observations of the plant's life cycle from germination through growth, flowering, and pollination.

Skills Focus After completing the Chapter 9 Project, students will be able to

◆ pose questions about how plants grow and reproduce;

◆ observe different parts of the seed plant life cycle;

◆ communicate their findings about seed plants to their classmates.

Project Time Line This project will take 4–5 weeks to complete. Students should plant their seeds as soon as possible; germination will take several days. During this time, students should discuss the life cycle of plants and what they expect to observe. They should set up their data tables and prepare to take measurements. Around week three, the plants should have flowers that are ready for pollination. Students should be able to collect new seeds by the fourth week. At this time they should prepare their displays and work on their class presentations. Before beginning the project, see Chapter 9 Project Teacher Notes on pages 82–83 in Unit 2 Resources for more details on carrying out the project. Also, distribute to students the Chapter 9 Project Overview, Worksheets, and Scoring Rubric on pages 84–88 in Unit 2 Resources.

Possible Materials Students will need basic gardening supplies: fast-growing seeds (seeds that flower in about 28 days, such as seeds from fast-growing plants from biological suppliers or from tomatoes, peas, etc.), potting trays, potting soil, water, and cotton swabs for transferring pollen.

Launching the Project To introduce the project and to stimulate student interest, ask: **How do we get more**

CHAPTER
9 Seed Plants

WEB ACTIVITY www.phschool.com

SECTION 1 The Characteristics of Seed Plants

Discover **Which Plant Part Is It?**
Try This **The In-Seed Story**
Sharpen Your Skills **Calculating**
Science at Home **Seed Germination**

SECTION 2 Gymnosperms

Discover **Are All Leaves Alike?**
Try This **The Scoop on Cones**

SECTION 3 Angiosperms

Discover **What Is a Fruit?**
Real-World Lab **A Close Look at Flowers**

272

plants? *(Discussion should lead to the answer "seeds.")* Then ask: **How do we get seeds?** This should lead to a discussion of seed production.

Allow time for students to read the description of the project in their text and the Chapter Project Overview on pages 84–85 in Unit 2 Resources. Then encourage discussions on the life cycle of seed plants and the materials that students will use. Make sure students understand that the most important activity in this project is caring for the plant so that it will grow well and provide useful information

for their observations. Answer any initial questions students may have, and distribute copies of the Chapter 9 Project Worksheets on pages 86–87 in Unit 2 Resources for students to review.

You may want to have students work in small groups as a cooperative learning task. To ensure that every student will have ample opportunity to care for the plants, each group should consist of no more than three students.

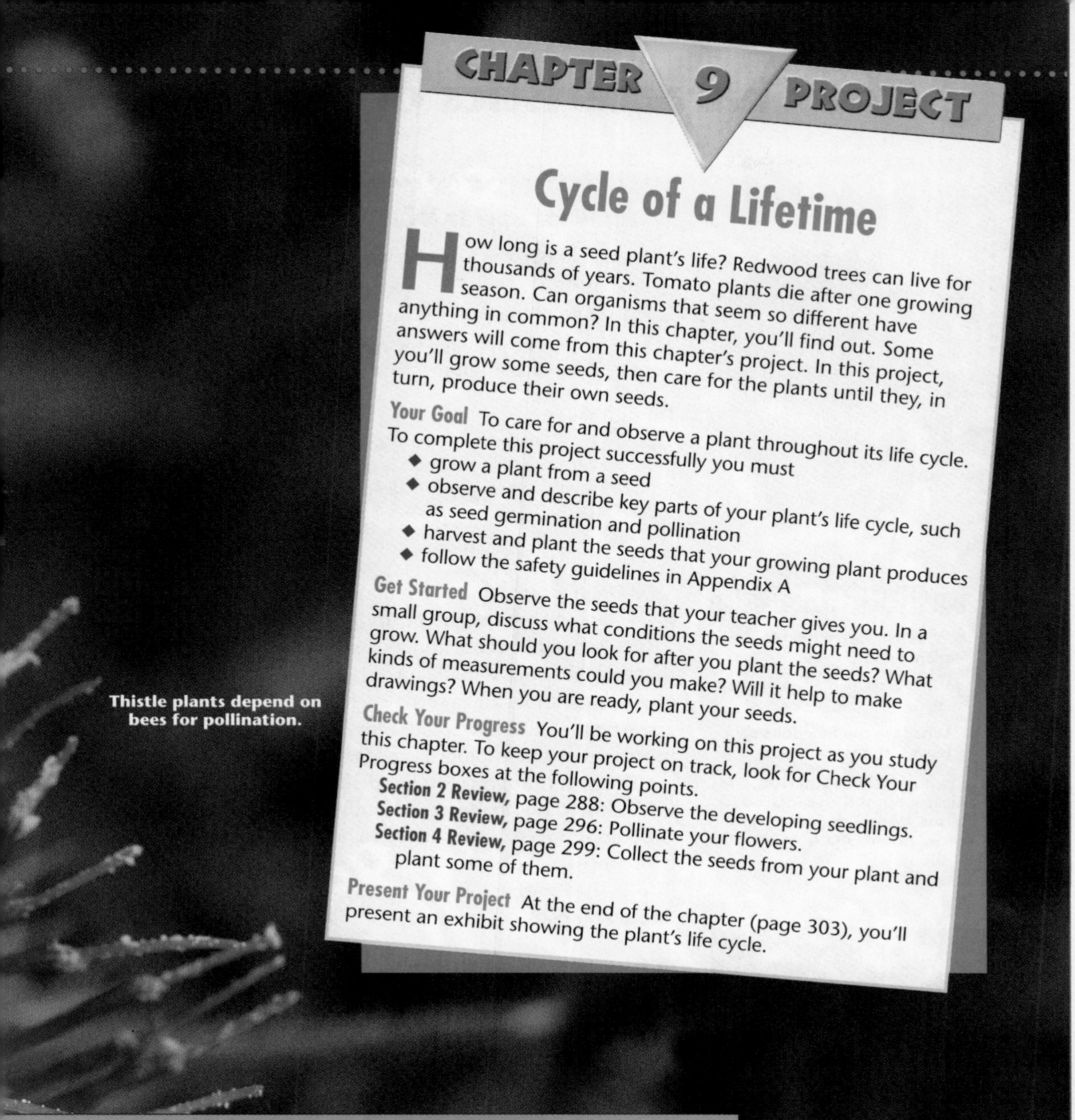

Cycle of a Lifetime

How long is a seed plant's life? Redwood trees can live for thousands of years. Tomato plants die after one growing season. Can organisms that seem so different have anything in common? In this chapter, you'll find out. Some answers will come from this chapter's project. In this project, you'll grow some seeds, then care for the plants until they, in turn, produce their own seeds.

Your Goal To care for and observe a plant throughout its life cycle. To complete this project successfully you must

◆ grow a plant from a seed
◆ observe and describe key parts of your plant's life cycle, such as seed germination and pollination
◆ harvest and plant the seeds that your growing plant produces
◆ follow the safety guidelines in Appendix A

Get Started Observe the seeds that your teacher gives you. In a small group, discuss what conditions the seeds might need to grow. What should you look for after you plant the seeds? What kinds of measurements could you make? Will it help to make drawings? When you are ready, plant your seeds.

Thistle plants depend on bees for pollination.

Check Your Progress You'll be working on this project as you study this chapter. To keep your project on track, look for Check Your Progress boxes at the following points.
Section 2 Review, page 288: Observe the developing seedlings.
Section 3 Review, page 296: Pollinate your flowers.
Section 4 Review, page 299: Collect the seeds from your plant and plant some of them.

Present Your Project At the end of the chapter (page 303), you'll present an exhibit showing the plant's life cycle.

Integrating Chemistry
SECTION **4** **Plant Responses and Growth**

Discover Can a Plant Respond to Touch?
Skills Lab Which Way Is Up?

273

Program Resources

◆ **Unit 2 Resources** Chapter 9 Project Teacher Notes, pp. 82–83; Chapter 9 Project Overview and Worksheets, pp. 84–87; Chapter 9 Project Scoring Rubric, p. 88

WEB ACTIVITY www.phschool.com

You will find an Internet activity, chapter self-tests for students, and links to other chapter topics at this site.

Performance Assessment

The Chapter 9 Project Scoring Rubric on page 88 of Unit 2 Resources will help you evaluate how well students complete the Chapter 9 Project. Students will be assessed on

◆ how well and consistently they care for their plants;
◆ the completeness of their observation entries, including measurements of stem, leaves, and flowers;
◆ how well they apply chapter concepts to their observations;
◆ the thoroughness and organization of their presentations.

By sharing the Chapter 9 Project Scoring Rubric with students at the beginning of the project, you will make it clear to them what they are expected to do.

SECTION 1 The Characteristics of Seed Plants

Objectives

After completing the lesson, students will be able to

- list the characteristics that seed plants share;
- name the main parts of a seed, identify the function of each part of the seed, and describe how seeds disperse and germinate;
- describe the functions of leaves, stems, and roots.

Key Terms phloem, xylem, seed, embryo, cotyledon, germination, stomata, transpiration, cambium, root cap

1 Engage/Explore

Activating Prior Knowledge

Have students brainstorm a list of plants they encounter everyday and classify each plant on the board under the headings *Have Seeds* and *No Seeds*. Note that most of the plants they encounter have seeds.

•••••••• DISCOVER ••••••••

Skills Focus classifying **ACTIVITY**
Materials *foods such as carrots, parsnips, broccoli, cabbage, lettuce, celery, parsley, potato, onion (do not use fruits—they form from flowers)*
Time 10 minutes
Tips Mention that underground plant parts are not necessarily roots. For example, potatoes and onions are underground stems. Celery is not a true stem but a petiole, a leaf stalk.
Expected Outcome Students should identify carrots and parsnips as roots, lettuce and cabbage as leaves, and broccoli as stems.
Think It Over Students should classify foods from roots, stems, and leaves in separate categories.

DISCOVER **ACTIVITY**
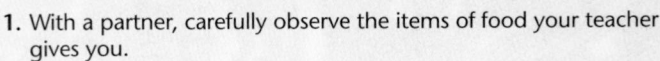

Which Plant Part Is It?

1. With a partner, carefully observe the items of food your teacher gives you.
2. Make a list of the food items.
3. For each food item, write the name of the part of the plant—root, stem, or leaf—from which you think the food is obtained.

Think It Over
Classifying Classify the items into groups depending on the plant part from which the food is obtained. Compare your groupings with those of your classmates.

GUIDE FOR READING

- What characteristics do seed plants share?
- What are the main parts of a seed?
- What are the functions of leaves, stems, and roots?

Reading Tip As you read, make a list of the boldfaced terms. Write a definition for each term in your own words.

Chances are you've seen dandelions. But how much do you know about these common plants? For example, do you know that dandelion blossoms open only in sunlight? Or that each blossom is made up of hundreds of tube-shaped flowers? Do you know that a seed develops in each of these tiny flowers? And that, just like apple seeds, dandelion seeds are enclosed in structures that biologists call fruits?

The next time you see a dandelion's fluffy "seed head," examine it closely. It is made up of hundreds of individual fruits, each containing a seed. Each fruit has a hooklike structure at one end. Like tiny parachutes, the fruits ride in currents of air. When one hooks into moist soil, the seed inside can grow into a new dandelion plant.

What Is a Seed Plant?

Dandelions are seed plants. So are most of the other plants on Earth. In fact, seed plants outnumber seedless plants by more than ten to one. You eat many seed plants—rice, tomatoes, peas, and squash, for example. You may also eat the meat of animals that eat seed plants. You wear clothes made from seed plants, such as cotton and flax. You may even live in a home built from seed plants—oak, pine, or maple trees. In addition, seed plants produce much of the oxygen you breathe.

Figure 1 Some of these dandelions are releasing tiny parachute-like fruits, which carry the seeds inside to new areas.

274

READING STRATEGIES

Reading Tip As students write definitions for the boldfaced terms, encourage them to add sketches or examples that will help them remember the meanings of the words. Have students work in pairs to quiz each other on the key terms using their definitions. Sample definition: Seed—a structure that has a tiny plant and stored food.

Study and Comprehension After students read the section, have them work in small groups to write ten questions about characteristics of seed plants. Suggest that they write a mixture of short-answer, fill-in-the-blank, and matching questions. Remind them to create answer keys. Then have groups exchange worksheets and questions and complete them. Instruct students to check their answers against the answer keys.

All seed plants share two characteristics. They have vascular tissue and use seeds to reproduce. In addition, they all have body plans that include leaves, stems, and roots. Like seedless plants, seed plants have complex life cycles that include the sporophyte and the gametophyte. In seed plants, the plants that you see are the sporophytes. The gametophytes are microscopic.

Vascular Tissue

Most seed plants live on land. Recall from Chapter 8 that land plants face many challenges, including standing upright and supplying all their cells with water and food. Like ferns, seed plants meet these two challenges with vascular tissue. The thick walls of the cells in the vascular tissue help support the plants. In addition, water, food, and nutrients are transported throughout the plants in vascular tissue.

There are two types of vascular tissue. **Phloem** (FLOH um) is the vascular tissue through which food moves. When food is made in the plant's leaves, it enters the phloem and travels to the plant's stems and roots. Water and nutrients, on the other hand, travel in the vascular tissue called **xylem** (ZY lum). The plant's roots absorb water and nutrients from the soil. These materials enter the root's xylem and move upward into the plant's stems and leaves.

☑ *Checkpoint* *What material travels in phloem? What materials travel in xylem?*

Figure 2 Seed plants are diverse and live in many environments.
A. Wheat is an important food for people. **B.** Organpipe cacti, here surrounded by other flowering plants, live in deserts. **C.** Lodgepole pines thrive in the mountains of the western United States.
Applying Concepts *What two roles does vascular tissue play in these plants?*

What Is a Seed Plant?

Building Inquiry Skills: Comparing and Contrasting

Have students discuss similarities and differences among some seed plants—real ones or photos from magazines and other sources. Ask: **How are these plants all alike?** *(They all have leaves, stems, and roots.)* Then ask: **How are they different?** *(Samples: Appearance, uses, life span, seed dispersal method)* **learning modality: verbal**

Vascular Tissue

Building Inquiry Skills: Observing

Materials *large tree leaf, scissors or lab knife, food coloring, large test tube, water*

Time 5 minutes on each of 4 days

Have students carefully cut the end of the stem of the leaf. They should fill a large test tube with water, add 15 drops of food coloring, and put the stem in the water. Ask students to observe the stem over 3 days, looking for uptake of dye. If the water level drops, students can add small amounts of colored water to the test tube. Ask: **Is the dye moving through the xylem or the phloem? Explain.** *(The dye moves through the xylem with the water.)* **learning modality: visual**

Answers to Self-Assessment

Caption Question

Figure 2 Vascular tissue provides transportation and support, making it possible for plants to grow large.

☑ *Checkpoint*

Food travels in phloem. Water and nutrients travel in xylem.

Ongoing Assessment

Organizing Information Have students make flowcharts showing the movement of food, water, and nutrients through a vascular plant. *(Phloem—food moves from the leaves to the roots and stem; xylem—water and nutrients travel from the roots into the stems and leaves.)*

275

Seeds

Using the Visuals: Figure 3

As students study the visual, ask them to compare and contrast the seeds. *(Samples: The seed coat covers the exterior of each seed. The cotyledon in the bean stores food.)* **learning modality: visual**

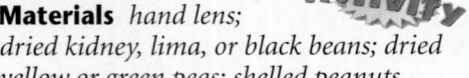

Skills Focus observing
Materials *hand lens; dried kidney, lima, or black beans; dried yellow or green peas; shelled peanuts*
Time 10 minutes
Tips Soak the beans in water for 2 hours before the activity. Soak the peas for 24 hours. Remove peanuts from their shells 3 or 4 days before the activity, and store them in a moist place so the cotyledons will open.
Expected Outcome Students should notice that each of these seeds is composed of two sections that can be easily separated. After they separate the seed, students should see the tiny leaves and root (and possibly the miniature stem) of the embryo plant.
Observing Students' sketches should include the seed coat, which protects the embryo and food from drying out; the cotyledons, which contain stored food; and the embryo, which will develop into a mature plant.
Extend Challenge students to repeat the activity with other kinds of seeds.
learning modality: visual

Portfolio Students can save their drawings in their portfolios.

The In-Seed Story

1. Your teacher **ACTIVITY** will give you a hand lens and two different seeds that have been soaked in water.

2. Carefully observe the outside of each seed. Draw what you see.

3. Gently remove the coverings of the seeds. Then carefully separate the parts of each seed. Use a hand lens to examine the inside of each seed. Draw what you see.

Observing Based on your observations, label the parts of each seed. Then describe the function of each part next to its label.

Seeds

One reason why seed plants are so numerous is that they produce seeds. **Seeds** are structures that contain a young plant inside a protective covering. As you learned in Chapter 8, seedless plants need water in the surroundings for fertilization to occur. Seed plants do not need water in the environment to reproduce. This is because the sperm cells are delivered directly to the regions near the eggs. After sperm cells fertilize the eggs, seeds develop and protect the young plant from drying out.

If you've ever planted seeds in a garden, you know that seeds look different from each other. Despite their differences, however, all seeds have a similar structure. **A seed has three important parts—an embryo, stored food, and a seed coat.**

The young plant that develops from the zygote, or fertilized egg, is called the **embryo.** The embryo already has the beginnings of roots, stems, and leaves. In the seeds of most plants, the embryo stops growing when it is quite small. When the embryo begins to grow again, it uses the food stored in the seed until it can make its food. In some plants, food is stored inside one or two seed leaves, or **cotyledons** (kaht uh LEED unz). You can see the cotyledons in the seeds in Figure 3.

The outer covering of a seed is called the seed coat. Some familiar seed coats are the "skins" on lima beans, peanuts, and peas. The seed coat acts like plastic wrap, protecting the embryo and its food from drying out. This allows a seed to remain inactive for a long time. For example, after finding some 10,000-year-old seeds in the Arctic, scientists placed them in warm water. Two days later, the seeds began to grow!

☑ *Checkpoint* *What is the function of the seed coat?*

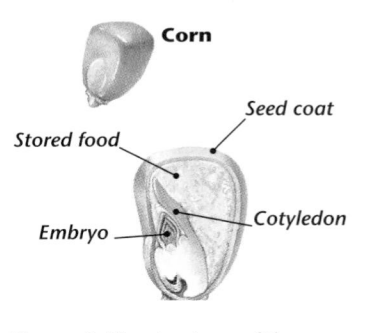
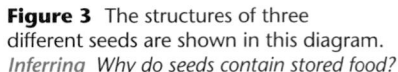
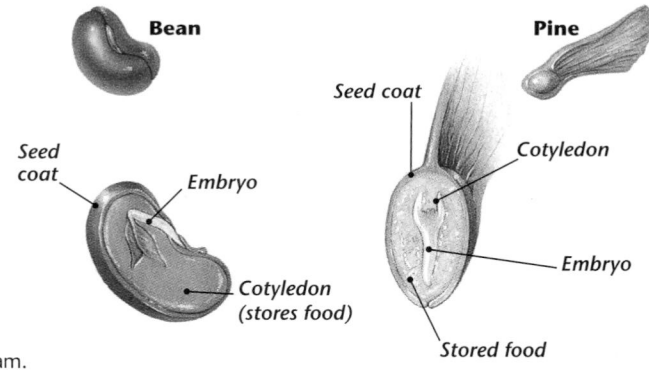

Figure 3 The structures of three different seeds are shown in this diagram. *Inferring Why do seeds contain stored food?*

Background

Facts and Figures Many plants have interesting adaptations for dispersing seeds. Plants that live in or near water often release the seeds into the water, which carries them away. Ocean currents have carried coconuts from island to island throughout the tropics.

The lotus plant, which lives in water, has a flattened seed head that holds several seeds in individual cases. When the seeds ripen, the entire structure breaks off and floats away from the plant. Eventually, the seeds sink to the bottom and germinate.

In the Amazon, the seeds of many plants are dispersed by fish. During times of high water, the fish eat the fruits and disperse the seeds.

The ivy-leaved toad flax grows on rocks and walls. As the seeds ripen, the stem grows away from sunlight, pushing the seed heads into dark cracks in the rock.

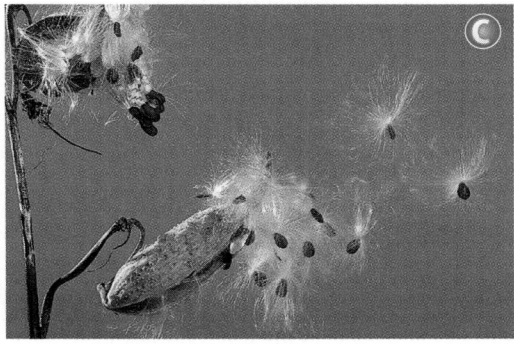
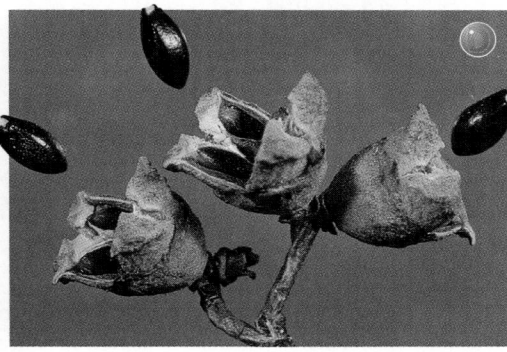

Seed Dispersal

To develop into a new plant, a seed needs light, water, and nutrients. After seeds have formed, they are usually scattered, sometimes far from where they were produced. When seeds land in a suitable area, they can sprout, or begin to grow.

The scattering of seeds is called seed dispersal. Seeds, or the fruits that enclose the seeds, are dispersed in many ways. One method involves animals. Some animals eat fruits, such as cherries and grapes. The seeds inside pass through the animal's digestive system and are deposited in new areas. Other seeds are enclosed in barblike structures that hook onto an animal's fur or a person's clothes. The structures then fall off in a new area. Water disperses other seeds when the seeds float in oceans, rivers, and streams. The seeds inside coconuts, for example, are carried from one area to another by ocean currents.

A third dispersal method involves wind. Wind disperses lightweight seeds, such as those of milkweed plants and pine trees. Finally, some plants shoot out their seeds, in a way that might remind you of popping popcorn. For example, the seedpods of wisteria and impatiens plants burst suddenly. The force scatters the seeds away from the pods in many directions.

Figure 4 Plants have different ways of dispersing their seeds. **A.** Both grass seeds and spiny parsley seeds are hitching a ride on this dog's fur. **B.** Water transports coconut palm seeds to new areas. **C.** The wind carries milkweed seeds through the air. **D.** Witch hazel plants shoot out seeds when their pods explode.

Chapter 9 **277**

Media and Technology

 Transparencies "The Structure of Seeds," Transparency 34

 Exploring Life Science Videodisc
Unit 2, Side 2, "Xeriscape"

Chapter 7

Answers to Self-Assessment

Caption Question

Figure 3 The stored food provides the energy needed for the embryo's early growth.

☑ *Checkpoint*

The seed coat protects the seed from temperature and moisture extremes until the seed grows.

Seed Dispersal

Inquiry Challenge

Time 25 minutes
Materials *modeling materials such as tissue paper, modeling clay, plastic foam balls, plastic spoons, cotton swabs, table tennis balls, hook-and-loop fastener strips*

ACTIVITY

This activity allows students to examine seed shapes and different forms of seed dispersal. Have students work together to build model seeds that can be dispersed by wind, water, or by sticking to clothes or animal fur. Groups should choose the materials for the models, collaborate on seed design, and assign roles for testing the seeds. Ask students to predict how far their model seeds will travel. After they test their predictions, have students identify how their model seeds are similar to real seeds and how their models could be improved. **cooperative learning**

Building Inquiry Skills: Predicting

Have students examine Figure 4 and predict which method would distribute seeds farthest. What characteristic would be important for seeds distributed by each method? (*Dog's fur—stick to fur; water—seed floats; wind—light weight; mechanical—small, dense seed*)

Ongoing Assessment

Drawing Have students draw a seed and label the embryo, stored food, and seed coat. Then have students describe the labeled parts.

 Students can save their drawings and descriptions in their portfolios.

Germination

Real-Life Learning

In 1982, plant physiologist Jane Shen-Miller obtained seven lotus seeds that had been found at the site of an ancient lotus lake. Shen-Miller took four seeds and filed through their seed coats. Three sprouted into tiny plants. When Shen-Miller used radiocarbon dating to determine how old the seeds were, she discovered that they ranged in age from 684 to 1,288 years old! In 1994, she dated the remaining seeds, then planted one 332-year-old seed at her house. It sprouted vigorously and looked like a modern lotus plant. Ask students: **How could having seeds that can remain inactive for so long benefit a plant?** *(Sample: Travelers could carry seeds with them to new places. The seeds may survive for an extended time in a harsh environment even if the plant cannot.)* **learning modality: verbal**

Leaves

Figure 5 The embryo in this peanut seed uses stored food to germinate. **A.** The peanut's root is the first structure to begin growing. **B.** After the root anchors the germinating plant, the peanut's stem and first two leaves emerge from the seed.

Germination

After seeds are dispersed, they may remain inactive for a while, or they may begin to grow immediately. **Germination** (jur muh NAY shun) is the early growth stage of the embryo. Germination begins when the seed absorbs water from the environment. Then the embryo uses its stored food to begin to grow. First, the embryo's roots grow downward, then its leaves and stem grow upward.

Seeds that are dispersed far away from the parent have a better chance of survival. This is because these young plants do not have to compete with their parent for light, water, and nutrients as they begin to grow.

✓ *Checkpoint* *What must happen before germination can begin?*

Leaves

The most numerous parts on many plants are their leaves. Plant leaves vary greatly in size and shape. Pine trees, for example, have needle-shaped leaves. Birch trees have small rounded leaves with jagged edges. Yellow skunk cabbages, which grow in the northwestern United States, have oval leaves that can be more than one meter wide. No matter what their shape, leaves play an important role in a plant. **Leaves capture the sun's energy and carry out the food-making process of photosynthesis.**

The Structure of a Leaf If you were to cut through a leaf and look at the edge under a microscope, you would see the structures in *Exploring a Leaf.* The leaf's top and bottom surface layers protect the cells inside. Between the layers of cells inside the leaf are veins that contain xylem and phloem. The underside of the leaf has small openings, or pores, called **stomata** (STOH muh tuh) (singular *stoma*). The Greek word *stoma* means "mouth"—and stomata do look like tiny mouths. The stomata open and close to control when gases enter and leave the leaf. When the stomata are open, carbon dioxide enters the leaf and oxygen and water vapor exit.

The Leaf and Photosynthesis The structure of a leaf is ideal for carrying out photosynthesis. Recall from Chapter 2 that photosynthesis occurs in the chloroplasts of plant cells. The cells that contain the most chloroplasts are located near the leaf's upper surface, where they are exposed to the sun. The chlorophyll in the chloroplasts traps the sun's energy.

278

Background

Carbon dioxide enters the leaf through open stomata. Water, which is absorbed by the plant's roots, travels up the stem to the leaf through the xylem. During photosynthesis, sugar and oxygen are produced from the carbon dioxide and water. Oxygen passes out of the leaf through the open stomata. The sugar enters the phloem and then travels throughout the plant.

EXPLORING a Leaf

A leaf is a well-adapted food factory. Each structure helps the leaf produce food.

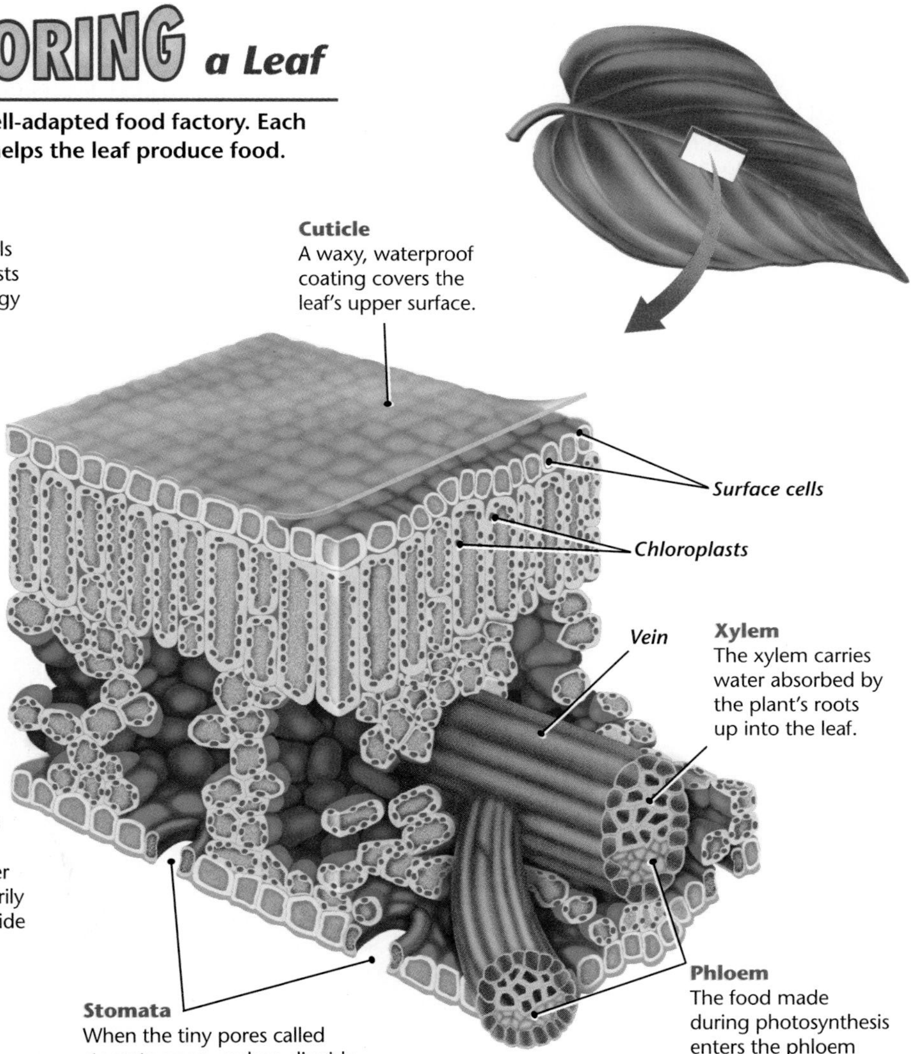

Upper leaf cells
The upper leaf cells contain chloroplasts that trap the energy in sunlight for photosynthesis.

Cuticle
A waxy, waterproof coating covers the leaf's upper surface.

Surface cells

Chloroplasts

Vein

Xylem
The xylem carries water absorbed by the plant's roots up into the leaf.

Lower leaf cells
The many spaces between the lower leaf cells temporarily store carbon dioxide and oxygen.

Stomata
When the tiny pores called stomata open, carbon dioxide enters the leaf while oxygen and water vapor move out.

Phloem
The food made during photosynthesis enters the phloem and travels throughout the plant.

Chapter 9 **279**

Answers to Self-Assessment

☑ *Checkpoint*
The seed must absorb water from the environment.

Language Arts Connection

Point out that the terms *chloroplast* and *chlorophyll* share the prefix *chloro,* which comes from the Greek word for "greenish-yellow." Have students use a good dictionary to find out what the Greek words *phyll* and *plast* mean. (*Phyll comes from the word for "leaf," and* plast *comes from the word for "molded."*) Challenge students to define *chloroplast* and *chlorophyll* using the Greek root words. **learning modality: verbal**

EXPLORING
a Leaf

Materials *large leaf, hand lens*
Time 20 minutes

As students examine the visual essay, encourage them to locate some of the labeled structures on a real leaf. Have students wash their hands thoroughly after handling the leaves. First, direct them to feel the cuticle on the leaf's upper surface and compare the cuticle to the drawing. Then have students look at the leaf with a hand lens. When they have identified the external structures, such as the cuticle and veins, call students' attention back to the visual. Ask: **How does it benefit the plant to have upper leaf cells that are long, rather than round?** (*The long cells provide more surface area and thus more exposure to the sun for photosynthesis.*)
Extend Obtain prepared slides from a biological supply house showing tissue from the underside of a leaf, the top side of a leaf, and a cross section of a leaf. Students can view the slides with a microscope and draw and label the structures they see. **learning modality: visual**

Ongoing Assessment

Writing Ask students to choose a structure found in a leaf and explain the function of that structure.

Leaves, continued

Demonstration

Materials *large potted plant such as a geranium*

Time 15 minutes setup; 10 minutes on each of two subsequent days

Allow the class to observe evidence of transpiration. Place a clear plastic bag over a cluster of leaves attached to the same stem of the plant. Seal the bag around the stem with masking tape. Students should observe the plant over 2 days. After the second day, remove the bag. Ask: **What formed on the inside of the bag?** *(Water droplets)* Have students explain how the water droplets got into the sealed plastic bag. *(As the plant carried out transpiration, it released water through its leaves, and the water formed droplets inside the bag.)* **learning modality: visual**

Stems

Sharpen your Skills

Calculating

Materials *plastic container, water, food coloring, dropper, spoon, celery stalk, metric ruler, clock or stopwatch, lab apron*

Time 15 minutes, plus 20 minutes after 2 hours for observation

Tips Choose stalks that are 15–30 cm tall. Before the activity, cut the ends of each stalk, and strip a thin layer of tissue off the back of each.

Answers In 20 minutes, the water should rise about 30 mm.

Speed = 30 mm ÷ 20 min = 1.5 mm/min
After 2 hours, the water should rise 180 mm:
(120 min)(1.5 mm/min) = 180 mm
(or 18 cm)

Extend Have students repeat the activity with another plant, such as a green onion or a leek. **learning modality: logical/ mathematical**

Sharpen your Skills

Calculating

In this activity you will calculate the speed at which fluid moves up a celery stalk.

1. Put on your apron. Fill a plastic container halfway with water. Stir in a drop of red food coloring.

2. Place the freshly cut end of a celery stalk in the water. Lean the stalk against the container's side.

3. After 20 minutes, remove the celery. Use a metric ruler to measure the height of the water in the stalk.

4. Use the measurement and the following formula to calculate how fast the water moved up the stalk.

$$\text{Speed} = \frac{\text{Height}}{\text{Time}}$$

Based on your calculation, predict how far the water would move in 2 hours. Then test your prediction.

Figure 6 This road in Madagascar is called Baobab Avenue. Tall, fat stems and stubby branches give baobab trees an unusual appearance.

Controlling Water Loss Because such a large area of a leaf is exposed to the air, water can quickly evaporate, or be lost, from a leaf into the air. The process by which water evaporates from a plant's leaves is called **transpiration.** A plant can lose a lot of water through transpiration. A corn plant, for example, can lose as much as 3.8 liters of water on a hot summer day. Without a way to slow down the process of transpiration, a plant would shrivel up and die.

Fortunately, plants have ways to slow down transpiration. One way that plants retain water is by closing the stomata. The stomata often close when the temperature is very hot.

✓ *Checkpoint* How does carbon dioxide get into a leaf?

Stems

The stem of a plant has two important functions. **The stem carries substances between the plant's roots and leaves. The stem also provides support for the plant and holds up the leaves so they are exposed to the sun.** In addition, some stems, such as those of asparagus, also store food.

Stems vary in size and shape. Some stems, like those of the baobab trees in Figure 6, are a prominent part of the plant. Other stems, like those of cabbages, are short and hidden.

The Structure of a Stem Stems can be either herbaceous (hur BAY shus) or woody. Herbaceous stems are soft. Dandelions, dahlias, peppers, and tomato plants have herbaceous stems.

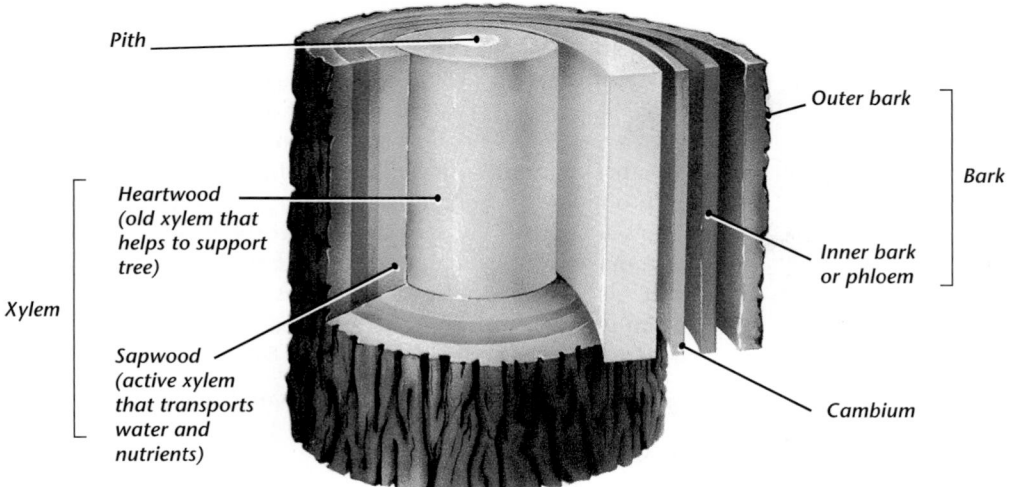

Pith

Outer bark

Bark

Heartwood
(old xylem that
helps to support
tree)

Inner bark
or phloem

Xylem

Sapwood
(active xylem
that transports
water and
nutrients)

Cambium

Figure 7 A typical woody stem
is made up of many cell layers.
*Interpreting Diagrams Where is the
cambium located? What is the
function of this layer of cells?*

In contrast, woody stems are hard and rigid. Maple trees, pine trees, and roses all have woody stems.

Herbaceous and woody stems consist of phloem and xylem tissue as well as many other supporting cells. However, unlike herbaceous stems, woody stems have an outer layer of material called bark, which helps protect the cells inside it, and inner layers of heartwood for additional support.

In Figure 7 you can see the inner structure of a woody stem. Bark covers the outer part of the stem. Just inside the outer bark layer is the phloem. Inside the phloem is a layer of cells called the **cambium** (KAM bee um). The cells of the cambium divide to produce new phloem and xylem. This process increases the stem's width. Just inside the cambium is a layer of active xylem that transports water and nutrients. Inside that layer is a layer of xylem cells that no longer carries water and nutrients. This layer, which is called heartwood, strengthens the stem, providing it with additional support. In the center of the stem is a material called the pith. In young trees, the pith stores food and water.

Annual Rings Have you ever looked at a tree stump and seen a pattern of circles that looks something like a target? These circles are called annual rings because they represent one year of a tree's growth. Annual rings are made of xylem. Xylem cells that form in the spring are large and have thin walls because they grow rapidly. They produce a wide, light brown ring. Xylem cells that form in the summer grow slowly and, therefore, are small and have thick walls. They produce a thin, dark ring. One pair of

Using the Visuals: Figure 7

Have students place a finger in the center of the woody stem shown in the visual. As they move their finger slowly from the figure's center to its outer edge, have them state the functions of each layer in the stem. *(Sample: Pith—stores food and water in young trees)* Then ask them to list *cambium, phloem,* and *xylem* in the order they appear from the pith outward. *(Xylem, cambium, phloem)* **learning modality: visual**

Including All Students

Ask students who speak Spanish to translate the English verb *to change* into Spanish. *(cambiar)* Point out that *cambiar* and *cambium* share similar roots; both come from the Latin word for "exchange." Have students discuss how the function of a stem's cambium relates to its Latin root. *(The cells in the cambium change by dividing to produce new xylem and phloem.)* **limited English proficiency**

Building Inquiry Skills: Observing

Materials *cross-sectional slice of tree trunk; hand lens*

Time 15 minutes

Have students carefully examine the rings in the trunk and sketch what they see. Challenge students to find three pairs of dark and light rings of different widths. Ask students to infer which pair of rings represents the year of heaviest rainfall and which pair of rings represents the year of lightest rainfall. *(The ring with the greatest width is from the year of heaviest rainfall. The ring with the smallest width is from the year of lightest rainfall.)* **learning modality: visual**

Answers to Self-Assessment

Caption Question

Figure 7 The cambium is inside the inner bark or phloem. It divides to produce new xylem and phloem cells.

☑ *Checkpoint*

Carbon dioxide enters the leaf through the open stomata.

Ongoing Assessment

Drawing Have students sketch and label the layers in a woody stem.

Stems, continued

Addressing Naive Conceptions

Students may not realize that trees grow by adding layers to the outside of the stem, so that the outer rings are newer than the inner rings. Point out that the heartwood, the old xylem, is at the center of the trunk. Contrast this with the apical growth that causes trees to increase in height: A nail driven into the bark of a tree will not move up as the tree grows, but will remain at the same height as the tree grows upward above it. **learning modality: verbal**

Integrating Earth Science

Have students calculate the average number of years between the droughts in the southwestern United States. $(227 + 312 + 253) \div 3 = 264\ years$ Then have them calculate the average time between droughts if the next severe drought were to occur in 2022. *(298)* **learning modality: logical/mathematical**

Roots

Demonstration

Materials *small potted plant with a fibrous root system such as a geranium* **Time** 10 minutes

Gently loosen the plant from the container. Hold the plant over newspapers or paper towels, so that spilled dirt can be removed easily. Gently tap or shake the soil around the roots until the root system is clearly visible. Show students the roots and ask: **What kind of root system do you see?** *(fibrous)* Have students sketch the root system and label where the root cap and root hairs can be found. After the activity, carefully return the plant to its container and wash your hands thoroughly. **learning modality: visual**

Figure 8 Tree rings tell more than just the age of a tree. For example, thick rings that are far apart indicate years in which growing conditions were favorable. *Interpreting Photographs What was the weather like during the early years of this locust tree's life?*

light and dark rings represents one year's growth. You can estimate a tree's age by counting its annual rings.

INTEGRATING EARTH SCIENCE The width of a tree's annual rings can provide important clues about past weather conditions, such as rainfall. In rainy years, more xylem is produced, so the tree's annual rings are wide. In dry years, rings are narrow. By examining a tree's annual rings, scientists can make inferences about the weather conditions during the tree's life. For example, when scientists examined annual rings from trees in the southwestern United States, they inferred that severe droughts occurred in the years 840, 1067, 1379, and 1632.

☑ *Checkpoint* **What function does bark perform?**

Roots

Have you ever tried to pull a dandelion out of the soil? It's not easy, is it? That is because most roots are good anchors. **Roots anchor a plant in the ground and absorb water and nutrients from the soil.** The more root area a plant has, the more water and nutrients it can absorb. The roots of an oak tree, for example, may be twice as long as the aboveground tree. In addition, for plants such as carrots and beets, roots function as a storage area for food.

Types of Roots As you can see in Figure 9, there are two types of root systems: taproot and fibrous. A taproot system consists of a long, thick main root. Thin, branching roots grow off the main root. Turnips, radishes, dandelions, and cacti have taproots. In contrast, fibrous root systems consist of several main roots that branch

Figure 9 A plant's roots anchor the plant and absorb substances from the soil. **A.** A taproot grows deep into the soil. The plant is hard to pull out of the ground. **B.** Fibrous roots consist of several main roots that repeatedly branch. They take soil with them when you pull them out of the ground.

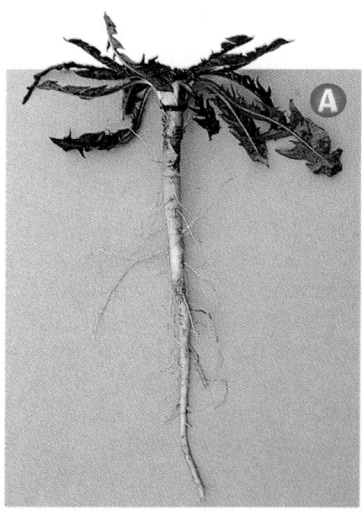

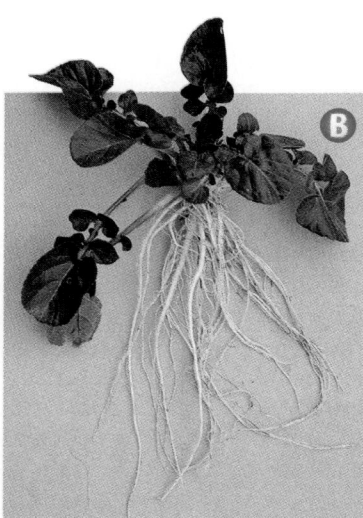

Background

Facts and Figures A traditional Polynesian dish called *poi* is made from the root of the taro plant. Poi is made by pounding cooked taro root and mixing it with water until it forms a thin, starchy, bluish paste. In Hawaii, taro root is usually the main ingredient in poi, but on other Pacific Islands poi often contains mashed pineapple or banana mixed with coconut cream in addition to the taro root.

When European settlers arrived in the northeastern United States, Native American healers shared their knowledge of local plants with the colonists. The roots of milkweed plants were boiled to produce an extract believed to help bowel and kidney disorders. The roots of a poisonous plant called green false hellebore were applied to snakebite wounds.

repeatedly to form a tangled mass of roots and soil. Lawn grass, corn, and most trees have fibrous roots.

The Structure of a Root In Figure 10 you see the structure of a typical root. Notice that the tip of the root is rounded and is covered by a structure called the **root cap.** The root cap, which contains dead cells, protects the root from injury from rocks and other material as the root grows through the soil. Behind the root cap are cells that divide to form new root cells.

Root hairs grow out of the root's surface. These hairs increase the surface area of the root that touches the soil. When more surface area is in contact with the soil, more water and nutrients can be absorbed. The root hairs also help to anchor the plant in the soil.

Locate the vascular tissue in the center of the root. The water and nutrients that are absorbed from the soil quickly move into the xylem. From there, these substances are transported upward to the plant's stems and leaves.

Phloem tissue transports food manufactured in the leaves to the root. The root tissues may then use the food for growth or store it for future use by the plant. The root also contains a layer of cambium, which produces new xylem and phloem.

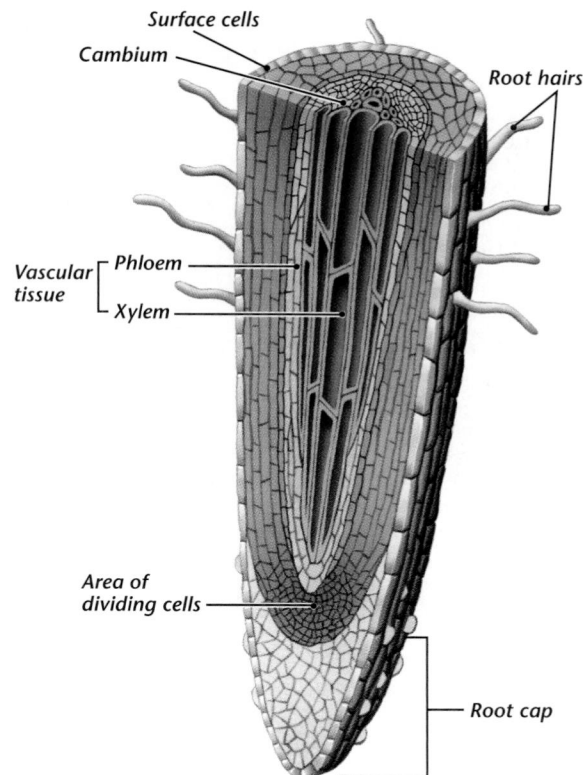

Surface cells
Cambium
Root hairs
Vascular tissue — Phloem
Xylem
Area of dividing cells
Root cap

Figure 10 The root cap protects the root as it grows into the soil. Root hairs absorb water and nutrients, which are transported through the root's vascular tissue.

![Section 1 Review icon] **Section 1 Review**

1. What two characteristics do all seed plants share?
2. List the three main parts of a seed. Describe the function of each part in producing a new plant.
3. What are the main functions of a plant's leaves, stems, and roots?
4. **Thinking Critically Predicting** Predict what would happen to a plant if you were to coat the underside of each leaf with wax. Explain your prediction.

Science at Home

Seed Germination With a family member, soak some corn seeds or lima bean seeds in water overnight. Then push them gently into some soil in a paper cup until they are just covered. Keep the soil moist. When you see the stems break through the soil, remove the seeds and examine them. Explain what you see to your family member.

Chapter 9   **283**

---

3 Assess

Section 1 Review Answers

1. All seed plants have vascular tissue and use seeds to reproduce.
2. Seed coat—protects seed from unfavorable conditions in the environment; embryo plant—grows into new plant; stored food—used by embryo to grow until it can make its own food.
3. Leaves—capture the sun's energy and carry out photosynthesis; stems—carry substances between roots and leaves, provide support for plant; roots—anchor plant, absorb water and nutrients from soil.
4. Coating the underside of a leaf with wax would clog the stomata. Carbon dioxide could not get into the plant for photosynthesis and oxygen could not escape. The plant would be unable to make food and would die.

Science at Home

Materials *corn kernels or lima bean seeds, water, soil, paper cup*
Tips Students should be able to identify the leaves, stem, and root of the plant. Ask: **Where did the plant get the nourishment it needed to grow?** (*from the stored food in the seed*)

Program Resources

◆ **Unit 2 Resources** 9-1 Review and Reinforce, p. 91; 9-1 Enrich, p. 92

Media and Technology

 Interactive Student Tutorial CD-ROM Chapter 9

Answers to Self-Assessment

Caption Question

Figure 8 The narrow inner rings indicate dry years and the wider rings indicate wetter years. Both conditions existed during the tree's early years.

☑ *Checkpoint*

Bark protects the inner cells of woody plants.

Performance Assessment

Oral Presentation Have groups of students make posters showing how leaves, stems, or roots function to produce or transport food and water. Then have them present their posters to the class.

283

Objectives

After completing the lesson, students will be able to

- give examples of gymnosperms and list the characteristics they share;
- describe how gymnosperms reproduce.

Key Terms gymnosperm, cone, pollen, ovule, pollination

1 Engage/Explore

Activating Prior Knowledge

Ask students to name trees that they know stay green during the winter. *(Sample: Pine and fir)* Have students compile a list of the trees' additional characteristics. *(Sample: Cones, leaves like needles)*

DISCOVER

Skills Focus classifying
Materials *hand lens; metric ruler; 2 or 3 leaves from different angiosperms, such as an oak tree, maple tree, day lily, and rose; 2 or 3 leaves from different gymnosperms, such as pine, yew, and spruce*
Time 10 minutes
Tips Encourage students to include a detailed description of the leaves' features beneath their sketches. Instruct students to wash their hands thoroughly after handling the leaves.
Expected Outcome Students should observe differences in size, length, width, and thickness.
Think It Over Students should group the leaves into needlelike shapes and broad leaves. Their reasons may include the marked difference in thickness and broadness of the leaves.

DISCOVER ····················· ACTIVITY

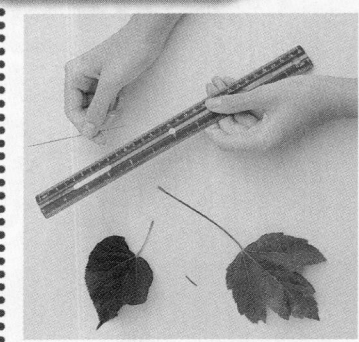

Are All Leaves Alike?

1. Your teacher will give you a hand lens, a ruler, and the leaves from some seed plants.

2. Using the hand lens, examine each leaf. Sketch each leaf in your notebook.

3. Measure the length and width of each leaf. Record your measurements in your notebook.

Think It Over

Classifying Divide the leaves into two groups on the basis of your observations. Explain why you grouped the leaves as you did.

GUIDE FOR READING

- What are the characteristics of gymnosperms?
- How do gymnosperms reproduce?

Reading Tip Before you read, preview *Exploring the Life Cycle of a Gymnosperm* on page 287. List any unfamiliar terms. As you read, write definitions for the terms.

Have you ever seen a tree that has grown wider than a car? Do trees this huge really exist? The answer is yes. Some giant sequoia trees, which grow almost exclusively in central California, are over ten meters wide. You can understand why giant sequoias are commonly referred to as "big trees." It takes a long time for a tree to grow so big. Scientists think that the largest giant sequoias may be about 2,000 years old. One reason they live so long is because their bark is fire-resistant.

What Are Gymnosperms?

The giant sequoia trees belong to the group of seed plants known as gymnosperms. A **gymnosperm** (JIM nuh spurm) is a seed plant that produces naked seeds. The seeds of gymnosperms are "naked" because they are not enclosed by any protective covering.

Every gymnosperm produces naked seeds. In addition, many gymnosperms also have needlelike or scalelike leaves, and deep-growing root systems. Although a few kinds of gymnosperms are shrubs or vines, most are trees.

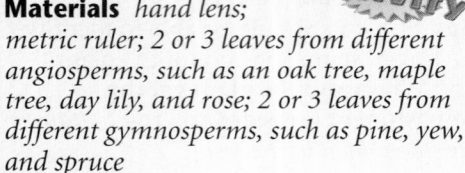

◄ A giant sequoia in California

284

READING STRATEGIES

Reading Tip As students preview *Exploring the Life Cycle of a Gymnosperm,* have them write each unfamiliar term on the front of a card. Students may recognize the terms *scale* and *pollen,* but they may not understand their use in this context. As students read the section, they can write each term's definition on the back of the appropriate card. Then direct students to quiz partners on the terms, using the cards as flashcards.

Study and Comprehension Have students write brief summaries of the information under each heading. Remind students to include only main ideas and key details in their summaries. Students can then use the summaries as study guides.

Types of Gymnosperms

Gymnosperms are the oldest type of seed plant. According to fossil evidence, gymnosperms first appeared on Earth about 360 million years ago. Fossils also indicate that there were many more species of gymnosperms in the past than today. Today, gymnosperms are classified into four groups—the cycads, the ginkgo, the gnetophytes, and the conifers.

Cycads About 175 million years ago, the majority of plants on Earth were cycads (SY kadz). Today, cycads grow mainly in tropical and subtropical areas. As you can see in Figure 11, cycads look like palm trees with cones. A cycad cone can grow as large as a football. In Mexico people grind seeds from the cones of one cycad to make a type of flour for tortillas.

Ginkgo Like cycads, ginkgoes (GING kohz) are also hundreds of millions of years old. Only one species of ginkgo, *Ginkgo biloba*, exists today. It probably survives only because the Chinese and Japanese cared for the species in their gardens. Ginkgoes can grow as tall as 25 meters. Today, ginkgo trees are planted along many city streets because they can tolerate the air pollution produced by city traffic.

Gnetophytes Gnetophytes (NEE tuh fyts) are the gymnosperms that you are least likely to see. These gymnosperms live only in the hot, dry deserts of southern Africa, the deserts of the western United States, and the tropical rain forests. Some gnetophytes are trees, some are shrubs, and others are vines.

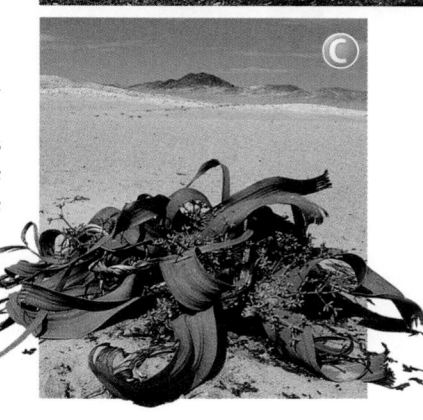

Figure 11 Gymnosperms are the oldest seed plants. **A.** Cycads, similar to this sago palm, were quite common during the age of dinosaurs. **B.** Only one kind of ginkgo, *Ginkgo biloba*, lives today. **C.** Gnetophytes, such as *Welwitschia mirabilis* shown here, grow in the very dry deserts of west Africa.

Chapter 9 **285**

2 Facilitate

What Are Gymnosperms?

Building Inquiry Skills: Making Models

Have students draw a picture of a gymnosperm based on the description in the text. (*Students' drawings should include needlelike or scalelike leaves, deep-growing root systems, and an indication that the seeds produced are not protected.*) Encourage students to include something in their drawings that will help them remember the main characteristics. (*Samples: A needle for needlelike leaves, a marble for unprotected seeds, a ladder for deep-growing root systems*) **learning modality: visual**

Types of Gymnosperms

Social Studies Connection

Materials *state map, map pins*

Time 15 minutes

To help students visualize the geographical distribution of gymnosperms in your state, allow them to first research gymnosperms in the library or on the Internet. Then have students place pins on the map (one color for each type of gymnosperm) as they locate the areas where each type grows. Ask: **Which type of gymnosperm is the most common in your state?** (*Answers will vary.*) **learning modality: visual**

285

Types of Gymnosperms, continued

Real-Life Learning

Materials *magazine pictures of various types of conifers growing*
Time 15 minutes
As students examine the pictures, ask:
What properties of these conifers make them a good source of wood for building? *(Sample: Conifers are tall and straight, so they make good boards; many of them grow in one place, so they are easy to harvest. Some students may know that conifers are also fast-growing.)* **learning modality: verbal**

Reproduction

Using the Visuals: Figure 12

Encourage students to carefully examine the photographs of the male cones and female cones. Ask students to explain why it is important that the scales on the female cone open and close. *(When the scales are open, pollen can enter the female cone. Then the scales close to seal in the pollen. The scales open again when the seeds are mature.)* Then ask students:
How is pollen transferred from the male cone to the female cone? *(wind)*
learning modality: visual

Skills Focus inferring **ACTIVITY**
Materials *mature female pine cone, hand lens, piece of white paper*
Time 10 minutes
Tips Make sure the cones still have some seeds inside the scales. Check for allergies before allowing students to perform this lab. Remind students to wash their hands after the activity.
Expected Outcome The scales of the cone provide some protection for the seeds that develop inside them. For example, the scales probably protect developing seeds from wind, rain, and very cold temperatures.
Extend Have students compare, then sketch, male and female pine cones. Sketches should indicate differences in size, shape, and structure of the scales.
learning modality: visual
Portfolio Students can save their sketches in their portfolios.

286

Figure 12 Both the male cones (**A**) and female cones (**B**) of a Ponderosa pine are produced on a single tree. *Comparing and Contrasting How do the male and female cones differ?*

The Scoop on Cones **ACTIVITY**

1. Use a hand lens to look at a female cone. Gently shake the cone over a piece of white paper. Observe what happens.
2. Break off one scale from the cone. Examine its base. If the scale contains a seed, remove the seed.
3. With a hand lens, examine the seed from Step 2, or examine a seed that fell on the paper in Step 1.
4. Wash your hands.

Inferring How does the cone protect the seeds?

286

Conifers Conifers (KAHN uh furz), or cone-bearing plants, are the largest and most diverse group of gymnosperms on Earth today. Most conifers, such as pines, redwoods, cedars, hemlocks, and junipers, are evergreen plants. Evergreen plants keep their leaves, or needles, year-round. Old needles drop off and are replaced by new ones throughout the life of the plant.

Reproduction

Most gymnosperms have reproductive structures called **cones.** Cones are covered with scales. Most gymnosperms produce two types of cones: male cones and female cones. Usually, a single plant produces both male and female cones. In some types of gymnosperms, however, individual trees produce either male cones or female cones. A few types of gymnosperms produce no cones at all.

Figure 12 shows the male and female cones of a Ponderosa pine. Notice that the male cones are smaller than the female cones. Male cones produce tiny grains of pollen. **Pollen** contains the microscopic cells that will later become sperm cells.

Female cones contain at least one ovule at the base of each scale. An **ovule** (OH vyool) is a structure that contains an egg cell. After fertilization occurs, the ovule develops into a seed.

You can learn how gymnosperms reproduce in *Exploring the Life Cycle of a Gymnosperm.* **First, pollen falls from a male cone onto a female cone. In time, a sperm cell and an egg cell join together in an ovule on the female cone.** After fertilization occurs, the zygote develops into the embryo part of the seed.

EXPLORING the Life Cycle of a Gymnosperm

Pine trees have a typical life cycle for a gymnosperm. Follow the steps of pollination, fertilization, and seed development in the pine tree.

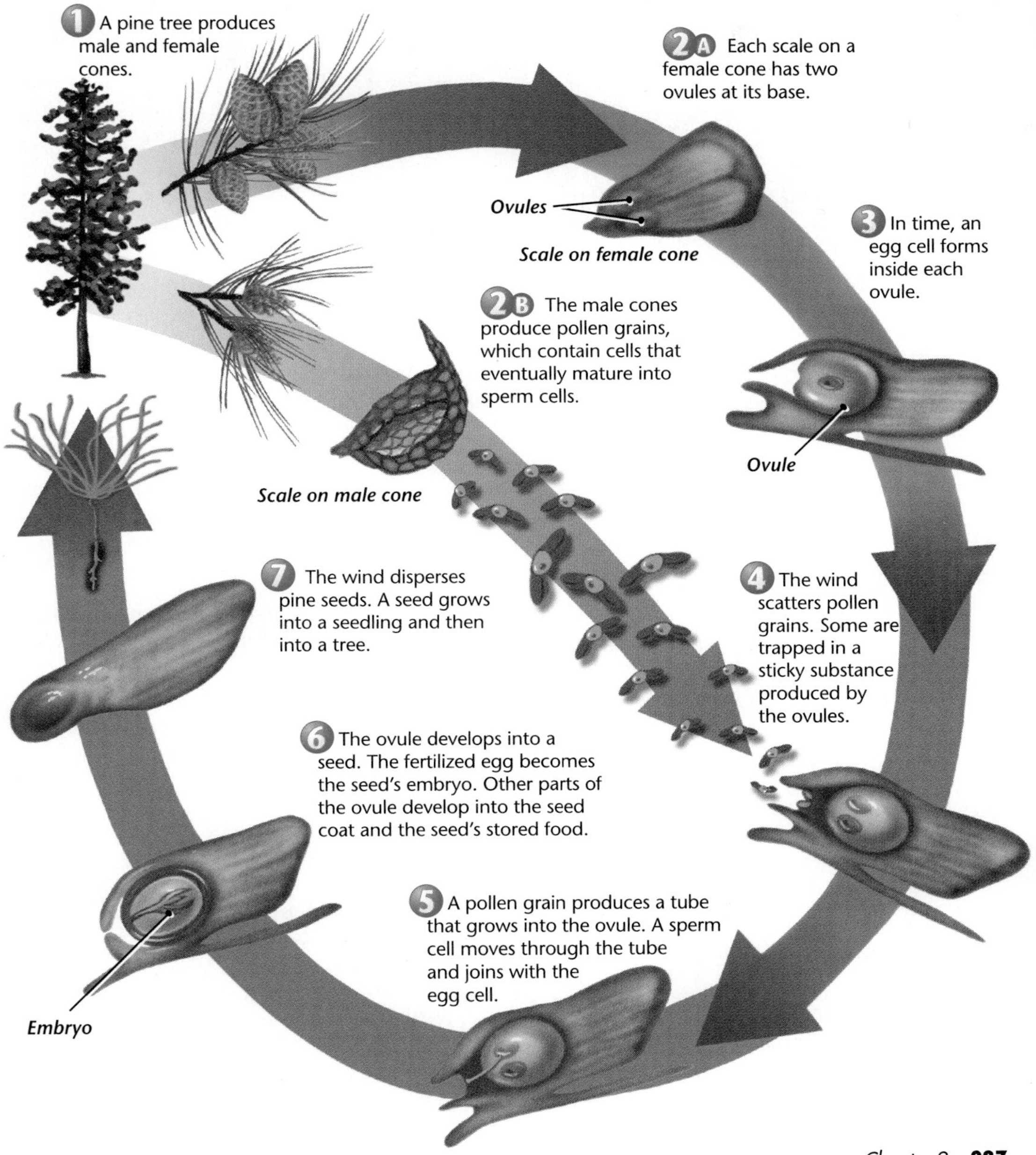

1 A pine tree produces male and female cones.

2A Each scale on a female cone has two ovules at its base.

Ovules

Scale on female cone

2B The male cones produce pollen grains, which contain cells that eventually mature into sperm cells.

Scale on male cone

3 In time, an egg cell forms inside each ovule.

Ovule

4 The wind scatters pollen grains. Some are trapped in a sticky substance produced by the ovules.

7 The wind disperses pine seeds. A seed grows into a seedling and then into a tree.

6 The ovule develops into a seed. The fertilized egg becomes the seed's embryo. Other parts of the ovule develop into the seed coat and the seed's stored food.

Embryo

5 A pollen grain produces a tube that grows into the ovule. A sperm cell moves through the tube and joins with the egg cell.

Media and Technology

 Transparencies "Exploring the Life Cycle of a Gymnosperm," Transparency 37

Answers to Self-Assessment

Caption Question

Figure 12 Male cones are smaller than female cones and produce tiny grains of pollen. Female cones have an ovule at the base of each scale.

EXPLORING the Life Cycle of a Gymnosperm

As students read through the descriptions on the visual essay, ask them to think about how the shape and size of each structure is suited to its function. Ask students: **How do you think the shape of the seed affects its motion in the wind?** *(The shape of the seed allows the wind to carry the seed and prevents the seed from falling directly under the tree.)* Discuss other adaptations that enhance the tree's ability to produce seeds, such as the position of the male cones at the tips of branches *(for efficient pollen distribution)* and growth of male and female cones on the same tree *(increases the probability of fertilization).*
Extend Have students toss a pine seed into the air to see how it travels when released from the female cone. **learning modality: visual**

Gymnosperms and the Living World

 Integrating Environmental Science

Tell students that one alternative to clear cutting, *sustained yield,* allows foresters to harvest timber year after year indefinitely. Based on the time it takes a tree to grow to maturity and other factors, the trees managed by sustained yield are cut down no faster than they can be replaced by new trees. For example, pines take about 20 years to mature, so one twentieth (5 percent) of the pine trees in a forest can be cut every year. Ask students to infer how much of a forest could be cut if the trees required 100 years to grow. *(One-hundredth, or 1 percent)* **learning modality: logical/mathematical**

Ongoing Assessment

Writing Have students use the following words in paragraphs to describe gymnosperm reproduction: ovule, pollen, fertilization, seed, and scales.

3 Assess

Section 2 Review Answers

1. All produce unprotected seeds; many have needlelike or scalelike leaves and grow deep root systems

2. Pollen falls from a male cone onto a female cone. In time, the sperm cell and egg cell join together in the ovule and eventually develop into the embryo of the seed. When the seed is mature, it falls out and is carried by the wind.

3. The four groups of gymnosperms are cycads, ginkgo, gnetophytes, and conifers.

4. The function of both types of cones is to produce reproductive cells. Male cones produce pollen grains while female cones have ovules in which eggs are produced.

Check Your Progress   CHAPTER PROJECT

By now, seeds should have germinated and students should be making their observations. If some seeds have not germinated, allow students to start over or to observe seeds that have germinated. Make sure students make detailed diagrams, drawings, or photographs of their observations.

Figure 13 Conifers provided the lumber for this playground. The sap produced by some conifers is used to make turpentine and the rosin used by baseball pitchers and musicians.

Pollination and Fertilization The transfer of pollen from a male reproductive structure to a female reproductive structure is called **pollination.** In gymnosperms, wind often carries the pollen from the male cones to the female cones. The pollen collects in a sticky substance produced by each ovule. The scales of the female cone close and seal in the pollen. Inside the closed scale, fertilization occurs. The seed then develops on the scale.

Female cones stay on the tree until the seeds mature. It can take up to two years for the seeds of some gymnosperms to mature. Male cones, however, usually fall off the tree after they have shed their pollen.

Seed Dispersal As the seeds develop, the female cone increases in size. The cone's position on the branch may change as well. Cones that contain immature seeds point upward, while cones that contain mature seeds point downward. When the seeds are mature, the scales open. The wind shakes the seeds out of the cone and carries them away. Only a few seeds will land in a suitable place and grow into new plants.

Section 2 Review

1. What are three characteristics of many gymnosperms?
2. Describe how gymnosperms reproduce.
3. What are the four groups of gymnosperms?
4. **Thinking Critically Comparing and Contrasting** Compare the functions of male and female cones.

288

Check Your Progress   CHAPTER PROJECT

If your seeds haven't germinated yet, they soon will. For the next few days keep a close watch on your young plants to see how they grow. How do they change in height? How do the leaves appear and grow? (*Hint:* Consider using drawings or photographs as part of your record keeping.)

Performance Assessment

Oral Presentation Have students work in groups to make presentations about gymnosperms that grow in their area. Suggest students show a photograph or videotape of a gymnosperm in its natural environment as they explain what type of gymnosperm it is, how it reproduces, and what products are made from it.

Portfolio Students can save their photographs or videotapes in their portfolios.

Background

Facts and Figures Some of the most important products obtained from gymnosperms are resins, used for everything from turpentine to the production of medicine. Natural resin is a thick, yellowish liquid that is exuded from trees. Pine and fir trees are the source of most natural resin. Resin forms when the bark of the tree is injured, such as when it is affected by severe winds, fire, or lightning.

Program Resources

◆ **Unit 2 Resources** 9-2 Review and Reinforce, p. 95; 9-2 Enrich, p. 96

SECTION
3 Angiosperms

DISCOVER ·· ACTIVITY ····

What Is a Fruit?

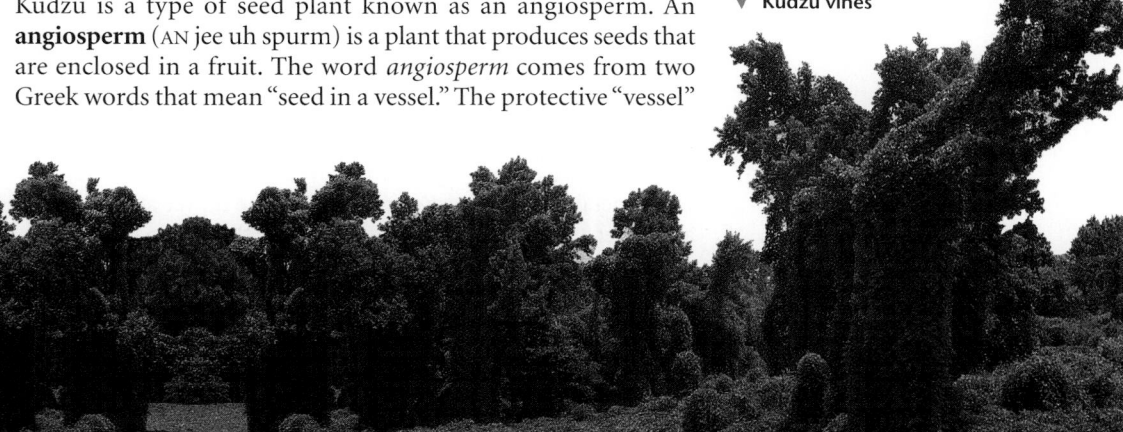

1. Your teacher will give you three different fruits that have been cut in half.

2. Use a hand lens to carefully observe the outside of each fruit. For each fruit, record its color, shape, size, and external features. Record your observations in your notebook.

3. Carefully observe the structures inside the fruit. Record your observations.

Think It Over
Forming Operational Definitions Based on your observations, how would you define the term *fruit*?

A mericans who visited the Japanese pavilion at the United States Centennial Exhibition in 1876 were introduced to kudzu, an attractive Asian vine. Soon, many Americans began planting kudzu in their communities. Little did they know that this creeping vine would become a huge problem.

Kudzu is one of the world's fastest-growing plants. Although it is nicknamed the "mile-a-minute vine," kudzu really does not grow that fast. But it can grow as much as 30 centimeters a day. In the southern United States, kudzu now covers an area twice the size of Connecticut. Unfortunately, there is no effective way to control the growth of this fast-growing plant.

What Are Angiosperms?

Kudzu is a type of seed plant known as an angiosperm. An **angiosperm** (AN jee uh spurm) is a plant that produces seeds that are enclosed in a fruit. The word *angiosperm* comes from two Greek words that mean "seed in a vessel." The protective "vessel"

> ### GUIDE FOR READING
> ◆ What characteristics do angiosperms share?
> ◆ How do angiosperms reproduce?
>
> *Reading Tip* Before you read, preview the photographs in this section. Write a prediction about how angiosperms differ from gymnosperms.

▼ Kudzu vines

Chapter 9 **289**

Objectives
After completing the lesson, students will be able to
◆ name types of angiosperms and list the characteristics that they all share;
◆ describe the structure and function of a flower;
◆ describe the life cycle of an angiosperm;
◆ compare monocots and dicots.

Key Terms angiosperm, ovary, flower, petal, sepal, stamen, pistil, fruit, monocot, dicot

1 Engage/Explore

Activating Prior Knowledge

Ask students to describe how the flowering plants or trees they are familiar with change throughout the year. Encourage students to use specific examples, such as a tree in the schoolyard, a house plant, or a cactus on the bus route. Have students describe the changes in chronological order. Prompt students to include times of increased insect or animal activity in their descriptions, if applicable.

········· DISCOVER ·········

Skills Focus forming operational definitions
Materials *hand lens; metric rule; three different fruits, such as apples, cherries, peaches, plums, tomatoes, or peppers*
Time 15 minutes
Tips Students may not think that vegetables such as tomatoes or peppers are fruits. Begin by challenging students to determine why scientists consider the foods they are examining to be fruits.
Think It Over Sample definition: Fruits contain seeds and have a fleshy edible part. They vary in color, shape, and the number of seeds they contain.

2 Facilitate

What Are Angiosperms?

Building Inquiry Skills: Inferring

Make sure students understand the relationship between the flowers and fruit in an angiosperm. Ask: **If you have an apple tree that has not flowered in over a year, would you expect to be able to get fruit from it?** *(No, because the fruit develops from the ovary, and the flower contains the ovaries.)* **learning modality: verbal**

The Structure of Flowers

Using the Visuals: Figure 14

As students examine the figure, ask them to identify the reproductive parts as male or female. Point out the different parts of the pistil and stamen. Tell students that while most flowers contain both male and female reproductive parts, some flowers contain only one or the other. Ask: **What role do the nonreproductive parts (such as sepals and petals) play?** *(Attract insects)* **learning modality: visual**

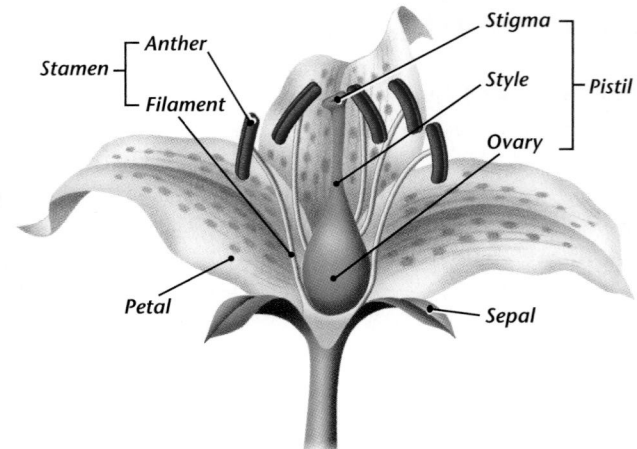

Figure 14 Like most flowers, this lily contains both male and female reproductive structures. *Interpreting Photographs What structures in the diagram can you find in the photograph?*

where seeds develop is called the **ovary.** The ovary is located within an angiosperm's **flower**—the reproductive structure of an angiosperm. **Two characteristics of angiosperms are that they produce flowers and fruits.**

Most of the familiar plants around you are angiosperms. Angiosperms live almost everywhere on Earth. They grow in frozen areas in the Arctic, tropical jungles, and barren deserts. A few angiosperms, such as mangrove trees and some sea grasses, even live in the oceans.

The Structure of Flowers

Like the plants that produce them, flowers come in all sorts of shapes, sizes, and colors. But all flowers have the same function—reproduction. Look at Figure 14 to see the parts of a typical flower. As you read about the parts, keep in mind that the description does not apply to all flowers. For example, some flowers have only male reproductive parts, and some flowers lack **petals**—the colorful structures that you see when flowers open.

When a flower is still a bud, it is enclosed by leaflike structures called **sepals** (SEE pulz). Sepals protect the developing flower. After the sepals fold back, the petals are revealed. The colors and shapes of the petals and the odors produced by the flower attract insects and other animals. These organisms ensure that pollination occurs.

Within the petals are the flower's male and female reproductive parts. Locate the thin stalks topped by small knobs inside the flower in Figure 14. These are the **stamens** (STAY munz), the male reproductive parts. The thin stalk is called the filament. Pollen is produced in the knob, or anther, at the top of the stalk.

Background

Integrating Science Many of the adaptations that attract pollinators to flowers—such as fragrance and color—also attract humans. For example, the flowers of many plants, such as jasmine, rose, and lavender, are used to create strong and attractive scents.

The art of making perfume requires knowledge of both chemistry and botany. For the best perfume, the flowers must be gathered at exactly the right time in the plant's life cycle. Isolating floral compounds often requires a large number of flowers. It takes approximately 113 kg of rose petals to make one ounce of attar of rose.

In addition to flowers, other parts of angiosperms are often valued for their scents. The seeds of the musk mallow tree of India are used for perfume.

The female parts, or **pistils** (PIS tulz), are usually found in the center of the flower. Some flowers have two or more pistils; others have only one. The sticky tip of the pistil is called the stigma. A slender tube, called a style, connects the stigma to a hollow structure at the base of the flower. This hollow structure is the ovary, which contains one or more ovules.

Reproduction

You can learn how angiosperms reproduce in *Exploring the Life Cycle of an Angiosperm* on the next page. **First, pollen falls on a stigma. In time, the sperm cell and egg cell join together in the flower's ovule. The zygote develops into the embryo part of the seed.**

Pollination and Fertilization A flower is pollinated when a grain of pollen falls on the stigma. Like gymnosperms, some angiosperms are pollinated by the wind. But most angiosperms rely on birds, bats, or insects for pollination. Nectar, a sugar-rich food, is located deep inside a flower. When an animal enters a flower to obtain the nectar, it brushes against the anthers and becomes coated with pollen. Some of the pollen can drop onto the flower's stigma as the animal leaves the flower. The pollen can also be brushed onto the sticky stigma of the next flower the animal visits. If the pollen falls on the stigma of a similar plant, fertilization can occur. The zygote then begins to develop into the seed's embryo. Other parts of the ovule develop into the rest of the seed.

Seed Dispersal As the seed develops, the ovary changes into a **fruit**—a ripened ovary and other structures that enclose one or more seeds. Apples and cherries are fruits. So are many foods you usually call vegetables, such as tomatoes and squash. For an angiosperm, a fruit is a way to disperse its seeds. Animals that eat fruits help to disperse their seeds.

☑ *Checkpoint* What attracts pollinators to angiosperms?

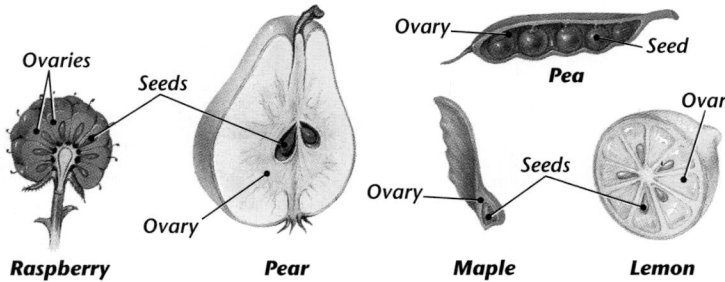

Raspberry • Ovaries • Seeds • Ovary
Pear
Pea • Ovary • Seed
Maple • Ovary • Seeds
Lemon • Ovary

Figure 15 The seeds of angiosperms are enclosed within fruits, which protect and disperse the seed.

Chapter 9 **291**

 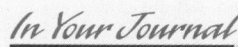
Reproduction

Visual Arts
CONNECTION

Check out art books from the library and provide them for students to use in class. Allow students to compare the paintings of Georgia O'Keeffe with other paintings of flowers by artists such as Van Gogh, Monet, and Picasso. Ask: **What makes Georgia O'Keeffe's paintings different from those of another painter?** (*Sample: O'Keeffe's paintings include accurate details of the parts of a flower. Van Gogh chose to use interpretative colors and limit detail.*)

In Your Journal Encourage students to include at least two adaptations in their paragraphs. Guide student reasoning by asking: **How does a poppy's color help it reproduce?** (*The color attracts insects, which land on the flower and help transfer pollen from stamens to pistils.*) **learning modality: visual**

Addressing Naive Conceptions

Some students may think that pollination and fertilization are the same process. Point out that pollination is necessary for fertilization, but they are not the same. In fact, there is a time delay after pollination occurs before fertilization occurs. Ask students to explain the two processes. (*In pollination, pollen is dusted onto the flower's stigma. In fertilization, an egg and a sperm unite.*) **learning modality: verbal**

Using the Visuals: Figure 15

Have students study the fruits in the figure. Ask them to describe the relationship between an ovary and a fruit. (*An ovary develops into a fruit.*) Then ask: **How is this similar to the relationship between an ovule and a seed?** (*An ovule develops into a seed.*) **learning modality: logical/mathematical**

Ongoing Assessment

Drawing Have students sketch a flower and label the sepal, petals, stamens, and pistil.

Portfolio Students can save their sketches in their portfolios.

291

Media and Technology

 Transparencies "The Structure of a Flower," Transparency 38

 Audio CD English-Spanish Summary 9-3

Program Resources

◆ **Unit 2 Resources** 9-3 Lesson Plan, p. 97; 9-3 Section Summary, p. 98

Answers to Self-Assessment

Caption Question
Figure 14 Petals, stamens, sepals, pistil

☑ *Checkpoint*
The colors and shapes of the petals and the fragrance of the flowers.

EXPLORING
the Life Cycle of an Angiosperm

Explain to students that different parts of an angiosperm produce the different structures needed for reproduction. As students review the steps in the visual, have them record what each of these structures produces and its role in the life cycle: anther *(pollen grains)*, ovule *(egg cell, seed)*, pollen grain *(pollen tube, etc.)*, ovule's wall *(seed coat)*, and ovary *(fruit)*. Make sure students can identify the ovary and anther in the figure at step 1. Ask: **What is the relationship between step 1 and steps 2A and 2B?** *(The ovary in step 2A is shown in the center of step 1; the anther in step 2B is the circled structure.)*

Extend Have students find local examples of an angiosperm, then explain its life cycle in a diagram similar to that in the visual essay. **learning modality: visual**

Building Inquiry Skills: Comparing and Contrasting

Materials *fruits from different plants*
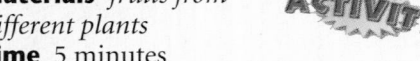
Time 5 minutes

Encourage students to feel the shape, weight, and texture of several fruits, such as grapes, coconuts, apples, bananas, tomatoes, etc. Ask them to infer how the physical characteristics of each fruit are related to the way its seeds are dispersed. CAUTION: *Check for allergies before conducting the activity.* **learning modality: kinesthetic**

EXPLORING the Life Cycle of an Angiosperm

All angiosperms have a similar life cycle. Follow the steps of pollination, fertilization, and fruit development in this typical angiosperm.

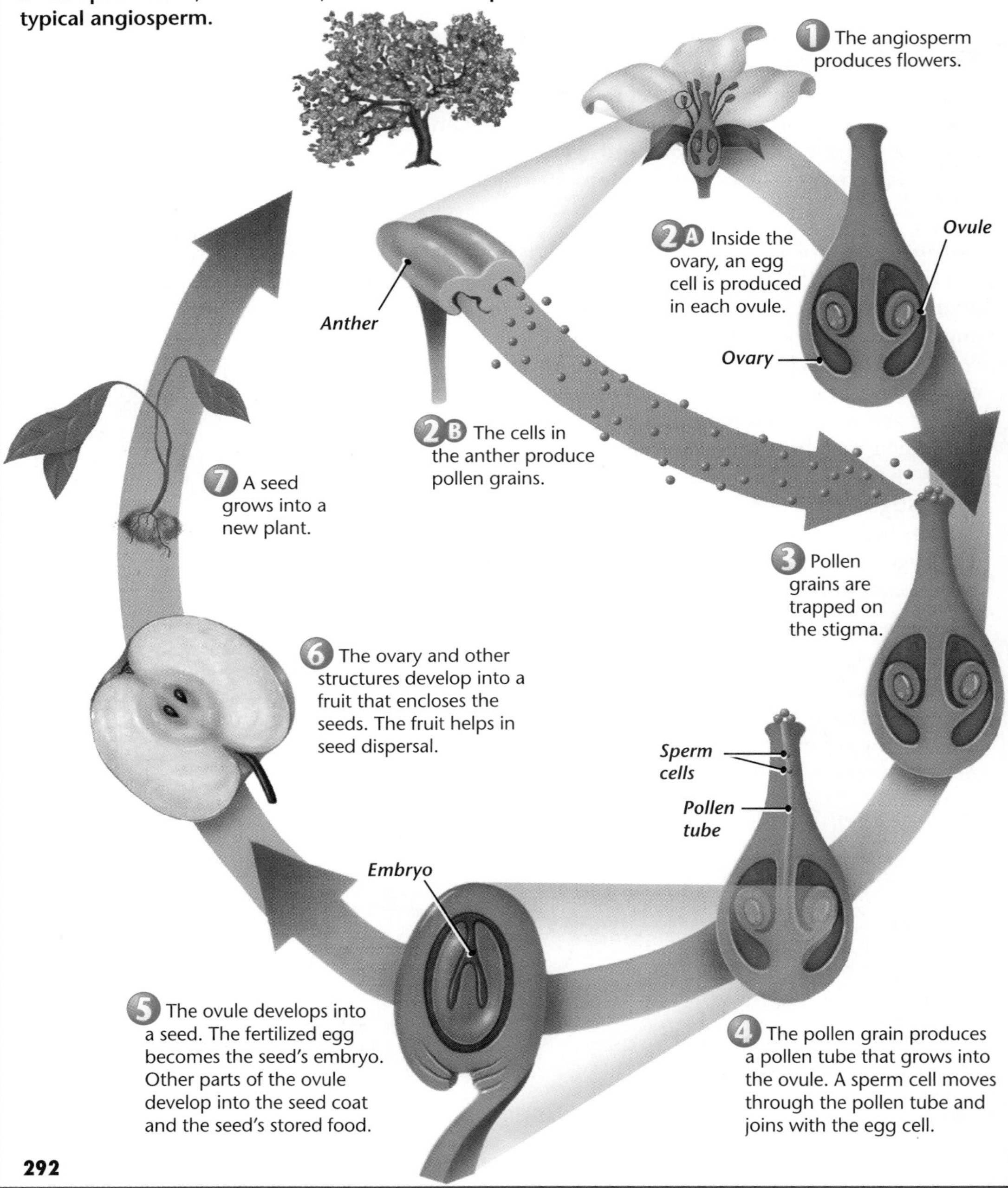

1 The angiosperm produces flowers.

2A Inside the ovary, an egg cell is produced in each ovule.

Ovule

Ovary

Anther

2B The cells in the anther produce pollen grains.

7 A seed grows into a new plant.

3 Pollen grains are trapped on the stigma.

6 The ovary and other structures develop into a fruit that encloses the seeds. The fruit helps in seed dispersal.

Sperm cells

Pollen tube

Embryo

5 The ovule develops into a seed. The fertilized egg becomes the seed's embryo. Other parts of the ovule develop into the seed coat and the seed's stored food.

4 The pollen grain produces a pollen tube that grows into the ovule. A sperm cell moves through the pollen tube and joins with the egg cell.

292

Background

Facts and Figures Some of the most unusual angiosperms are insect-eating plants. These plants generally live in nitrogen-poor soils and receive vital nutrients from their prey.

The bogs of North Carolina house the well-known Venus flytrap. Each plant grows several kidney-shaped leaves with sensitive inner bristles. When a moving insect touches a bristle, the leaf halves snap together.

Enzymes flood the inside of the trap and slowly digest the prey. Special glands absorb the nutrients. When the insect is fully digested, the trap opens again.

The pitcher plant uses a narrow, juglike structure to lure and trap insects. The pitcher has a strong scent and attractive color. Insects slip down the side of the pitcher and fall into a bath of water and digestive juices.

Monocots

Seed	Leaf	Stem	Flower

One cotyledon	*Parallel veins*	*Scattered bundles of vascular tissue*	*Flower parts in threes*

Dicots

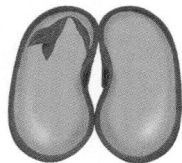			
Two cotyledons	*Branching veins*	*Circle of vascular tissue*	*Flower parts in fours or fives*

Types of Angiosperms

Angiosperms are divided into two major groups: monocots and dicots. "Cot" is short for *cotyledon*. Recall from Section 1 that the cotyledon, or seed leaf, provides food for the embryo. *Mono* means "one" and *di* means "two." **Monocots** are angiosperms that have only one seed leaf. **Dicots,** on the other hand, produce seeds with two seed leaves. Look at Figure 16 to compare the characteristics of monocots and dicots.

Monocots Grasses, including corn, wheat, and rice, and plants such as lilies and tulips are monocots. The flowers of a monocot usually have either three petals or a multiple of three petals. Monocots usually have long, slender leaves with veins that run parallel to one another like train rails. The bundles of vascular tissue in monocot stems are usually scattered randomly throughout the stem.

Dicots Dicots include plants such as roses and violets, as well as dandelions. Both oak and maple trees are dicots, as are food plants such as beans and apples. The flowers of dicots often have either four or five petals or multiples of these numbers. The leaves are usually wide, with veins that branch off from one another. Dicot stems usually have bundles of vascular tissue arranged in a circle.

 Checkpoint How do the petals of monocots and dicots differ in number?

Figure 16 Monocots and dicots are the two groups of angiosperms. The groups differ in the number of cotyledons, the arrangement of veins and vascular tissue, and the number of petals. *Classifying Would a plant whose flowers have 20 petals be a monocot or a dicot?*

Chapter 9 **293**

Types of Angiosperms

Including All Students

Materials *cuttings or cut flowers from several plants, including monocots (corn, wheat, grasses, lilies, tulips) and dicots (roses, violets, dandelions, oak, maple, apples, bean plants), dissecting knife, hand lens*
Time 20 minutes

Students with limited English proficiency may benefit from comparing real plants to the description in the text. Have small groups compare different plants and classify them as monocots or dicots. Students should sketch the parts of the plants they examine and compare them to the diagrams shown in Figure 16. Caution students to be careful when using the knife. **limited English proficiency**

Angiosperms and the Living World

Real-Life Learning

Have students brainstorm a list of items in the classroom that are made from angiosperms. Encourage students to think about items in different categories, such as food, furniture, clothing, school supplies. Write responses on the board. Ask: **Which items are you surprised come from angiosperms?** *(Students may mention paper, dyes, or chemicals in household products.)* **learning modality: logical/mathematical**

 Integrating Health

Students may believe that only "natural" or "herbal" medicines are made from plants. Point out that many prescription medications are made from angiosperms. Interested students may want to research other medicines made from angiosperms. **learning modality: verbal**

Ongoing Assessment

Oral Presentation Have students describe the roles of an orange blossom and an orange in the reproduction of an orange tree.

Media and Technology

Transparencies "Exploring the Life Cycle of an Angiosperm," Transp. 39

Answers to Self-Assessment

Caption Question
Figure 16 A dicot

Checkpoint
Monocot petals are in multiples of three. Dicot petals are in multiples of four or five.

293

How It Works

A Close Look at Flowers

Preparing for Inquiry

Key Concept Flowers contain several distinct parts whose structures can be studied for a more complete understanding of their functions.

Skills Objectives Students will be able to
- observe the structures of a flower;
- measure petal size, and the heights of the pistil and stamen;
- infer the method of pollination and whether the plant is a monocot or dicot.

Time 40 minutes

Advance Planning Provide a variety of flowers so that students can observe more than one type. Use large- or medium-sized flowers that have all the essential structures, such as tulips, lilies, gladiolas, daffodils, petunias, and others. Find out in advance of doing the lab which students may be allergic to pollen. Provide a substitute activity for these students and make any other necessary arrangements.

Guiding Inquiry

Invitation Angiosperms are seed plants that produce flowers. Ask: **What is the function of the flower?** *(reproduction)* Ask students to think about how each structure of the flower relates to the two stages of reproduction in angiosperms—pollination and fertilization.

Introducing the Procedure

- Teach students how to use a scalpel safely. Scissors can be substituted for a scalpel in some steps.
- Introduce or review the use of a microscope and how to make a wet mount. Remind students that slides and cover slips are fragile and they should alert you immediately if anything breaks in the lab.
- To obtain pollen samples, students can simply tap the stamen if the flower is sufficiently developed. If the flower has just opened, demonstrate how to crush the stamen against the slide.

A Close Look at Flowers

In this lab, you will examine a flower in order to understand how it works.

Problem

What is the function of a flower, and what roles do its different parts play?

Skills Focus

observing, measuring, inferring

Materials

paper towels	plastic dropper
hand lens	microscope
slide	large flower
coverslip	scalpel
tape	water
metric ruler	lens paper

Procedure

Part 1 The Outer Parts of the Flower

1. Tape 4 sheets of paper towel on your work area. Obtain a flower from your teacher. While handling the flower gently, observe its shape and color. Use the ruler to measure it. Notice whether the petals have any spots or other markings. Does the flower have a scent? Record your observations with sketches and descriptions.

2. Observe the sepals. How many are there? How do they relate to the rest of the flower? (*Hint:* The sepals are often green, but not always.) Record your observations.

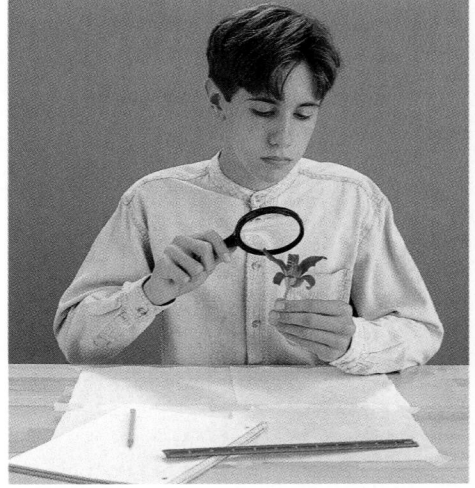

3. Use a scalpel to carefully cut off the sepals without damaging the structures beneath them. **CAUTION:** *Scalpels are sharp. Cut in a direction away from yourself and others.*

4. Observe the petals. How many are there? Are all the petals the same, or are they different? Record your observations.

Part 2 The Male Part of the Flower

5. Carefully pull off the petals to examine the male part of the flower. Try not to damage the structures beneath the petals.

6. Observe the stamens. How many are there? How are they shaped? How tall are they? Record your observations.

7. Use a scalpel to carefully cut the stamens away from the rest of the flower without damaging the structures beneath them. Lay the stamens on the paper towel.

Troubleshooting the Experiment

If pollen begins to fall off as students handle the flowers, they can collect it on a piece of paper and put it aside for Steps 8–9.

Expected Outcome

- The top of the pistil (the stigma) may be rough, smooth, sticky, branched, or feathery.
- The number of chambers in the ovary is equal to or is a multiple of the number of petals and stamens.

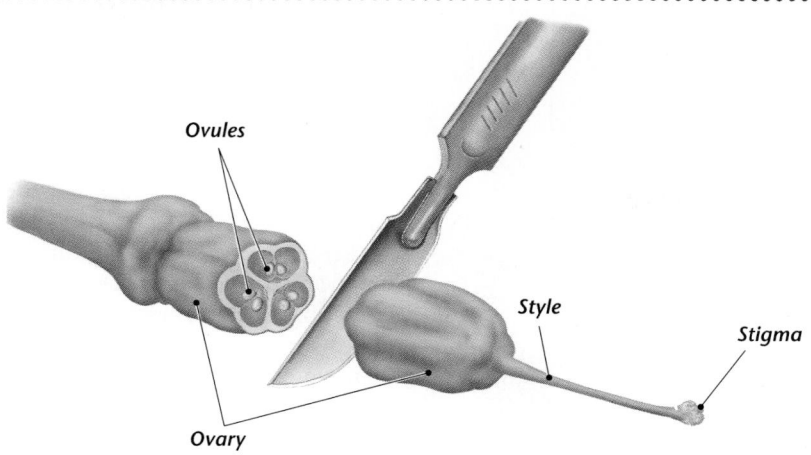

Ovules

Style

Stigma

Ovary

8. Obtain a clean slide and coverslip. Hold a stamen over the slide, and gently tap some pollen grains from the anther onto the slide. Add a drop of water to the pollen. Then place the coverslip over the water and pollen.

9. Observe the pollen under both the low-power objective and the high-power objective of a microscope. Draw and label a pollen grain.

Part 3 The Female Part of the Flower

10. Use a scalpel to cut the pistil away from the rest of the flower. Measure the height of the pistil. Examine its shape. Observe the top of the pistil. Determine if that surface will stick to and lift a tiny piece of lens paper. Record your observations.

11. Lay the pistil on the paper towel. Holding it firmly at its base, use a scalpel to cut the pistil in half at its widest point, as shown in the diagram above. **CAUTION:** *Cut away from your fingers.* How many compartments do you see? How many ovules do you see? Record your observations.

Analyze and Conclude

1. Based on your observations, describe how the petals, pistils, sepals, and stamens of a flower are arranged.

2. What is the main function of a flower? How are the sepals, petals, stamens, and pistil involved in that function?

3. How does a flower produce seeds?

4. Did your flower show any patterns in the number of sepals, petals, stamens, or other structures? If so, describe that pattern. Is your flower a monocot or a dicot?

5. **Apply** How do you think the flower you examined is pollinated? Use your observations, including the heights of the pistil and stamens, to support your answer.

More to Explore

Some kinds of flowers do not have all the parts found in the flower in this lab. Obtain a different flower. Find out which parts this flower has, and which parts are missing. Get your teacher's approval before carrying out this investigation.

Analyze and Conclude
1. In circles, in this order: sepals on the outside, then petals, then stamens, then the pistil at the center.
2. The main function of a flower is reproduction. The sepals protect the flower as it develops and support the base of the flower. The petals may attract the attention of animals by color or scent. Stamens produce pollen, which releases sperm cells. Pistils hold the egg cells.
3. The flower produces seeds when sperm cells from pollen fertilize egg cells inside the ovary.
4. Flower parts of monocots are usually in threes or multiples of threes. Flower parts of dicots are usually in fives or fours, or in multiples of those numbers.
5. Answers will vary. For example, colorful petals suggest the flower is pollinated by organisms with color vision. A pistil that is taller than the stamens may suggest that the flower does not self-pollinate. A flower structure in which the anthers and stigma are located deep within the flower suggests pollination by small pollinators, such as insects or hummingbirds.

Extending the Inquiry

More to Explore Make sure students' second flower is different from the first flower they dissected. Students should compare flowers and discover that flowers vary greatly in structure. For example, some plants have separate male and female flowers. Students should make sketches and should point out the differences between the flowers they studied.

Safety

Provide a substitute activity for any student who is allergic to pollen. Make sure all students wash their hands immediately after this activity. Teach scalpel safety. Substitute scissors for scalpels whenever possible. Students should take care not to drop the glass microscope slides. Review the safety guidelines in Appendix A.

Program Resources

◆ **Unit 2 Resources** Chapter 9 Real-World Lab, pp. 105–107

Section 3 Review Answers

1. All angiosperms produce flowers and fruits. Both are important in reproduction.

2. First, pollen falls on a stigma. In time, the sperm cell and egg cell join together in the flower's ovule. The zygote develops into the embryo part of the seed.

3. Sepals—protect the developing flower; petals—attract pollinators; stamen—consists of an anther and filament, produces pollen; pistil—consists of a stigma, a style, and an ovary that contains one or more ovules; ovule—egg cells are made in ovule

4. The plant is probably pollinated by the wind. If it had to be pollinated by animals, its flowers would probably have an odor and bright colors that attract animals.

Check Your Progress

CHAPTER PROJECT

Check the growth of the plants. If you observe that some of the plants are dying, discuss their care with students. When the plants flower, help students pollinate them. The two best methods are to use the bee parts that come in a seed-growing kit, or to tap the flower gently and collect the pollen on a piece of paper. The pollen can then be placed on the stigma. A third method is to use cotton swabs, but this may not be as successful. Discuss with students how these methods compare to the ways plants are pollinated in nature.

Performance Assessment

Organizing Information Have students draw flowcharts showing the processes involved in the reproduction of angiosperms.

Angiosperms and the Living World

Angiosperms are an important source of food, clothing, and medicine for other organisms. Plant-eating animals, such as cows, elephants, and beetles, eat flowering plants such as grasses as well as the leaves of trees. People eat vegetables, fruits, and cereals, all of which are angiosperms.

People also produce clothing and other products from angiosperms. For example, the seeds of cotton plants, like the ones you see in Figure 17, are covered with cotton fibers. The stems of flax plants provide linen fibers. The sap of tropical rubber trees is used to make rubber for tires and other products. Furniture is often made from the wood of maple, cherry, and oak trees.

INTEGRATING HEALTH Some angiosperms are used in the making of medicine. For example, aspirin was first made from a substance found in the leaves of willow trees. Digitalis, a heart medication, comes from the leaves of the foxglove plant. Cortisone is a medicine made from the roots of the Mexican yam. It is used to treat arthritis and other joint problems. These medicines have helped improve the health of many people.

Figure 17 Cotton seeds, which develop in structures called bolls, are covered with fibers that are manufactured into cotton fabric.

Section 3 Review

1. What two characteristics do all angiosperms share? Explain the importance of those characteristics.

2. Give a brief description of how reproduction occurs in angiosperms.

3. List the parts of a typical flower. What is the function of each part?

4. Thinking Critically Inferring A certain plant has small, dull-colored flowers with no scent. Do you think the plant is pollinated by animals or by the wind? Explain.

Check Your Progress

CHAPTER PROJECT

Your plants should now have, or will soon have, flowers. Make a diagram of the flower's structure. When the flowers open, you'll have to pollinate them. This work is usually done by insects or birds. After pollination, watch how the flower changes. (*Hint:* Discuss with your teacher and classmates how to pollinate the flowers.)

296

Program Resources

- **Unit 2 Resources** 9-3 Review and Reinforce, p. 99; 9-3 Enrich, p. 100
- **Product Testing Activities by** *Consumer Reports* "Testing Jeans," pp. 1–8

SECTION 4 Plant Responses and Growth

DISCOVER •••••••••••••••••••••••••••••••••• ACTIVITY

Can a Plant Respond to Touch?

1. Your teacher will give you two plants. Observe the first plant. Gently touch a leaf and observe what happens over the next three minutes. Record your observations.

2. Repeat Step 1 with the second plant. Record your observations.

3. Wash your hands with soap and water.

Think It Over
Inferring What advantage might a plant have if its leaves responded to touch?

The bladderwort is a freshwater plant with small yellow flowers. Attached to its floating stems are open structures called bladders. When a water flea touches a sensitive hair on a bladder, the bladder flicks open. Faster than you can blink, the water flea is sucked inside, and the bladder snaps shut. The plant then digests the trapped flea.

A bladderwort responds quickly—faster than many animals respond to a similar stimulus. You may be surprised to learn that some plants have lightning-quick responses. In fact, you might have thought that plants do not respond to stimuli at all. But plants do respond to some stimuli, although they usually do so more slowly than the bladderwort.

Tropisms

Animals usually respond to stimuli by moving. Unlike animals, plants commonly respond by growing either toward or away from a stimulus. A plant's growth response toward or away from a stimulus is called a **tropism** (TROH pihz uhm). If a plant grows toward the stimulus, it is said to show a positive tropism. If a plant grows away from a stimulus, it shows a negative tropism. **Touch, light, and gravity are three important stimuli to which plants respond.**

Touch Some plants, such as bladderworts, show a response to touch called thigmotropism. The term *thigmo* comes from a Greek word that means "touch." The stems of many vines, such as grapes and morning glories, show a positive thigmotropism. As the vines grow, they coil around any object that they touch.

GUIDE FOR READING

◆ What are three stimuli that produce plant responses?

◆ What functions do plant hormones control?

Reading Tip As you read, use the headings to make an outline about plant responses and growth.

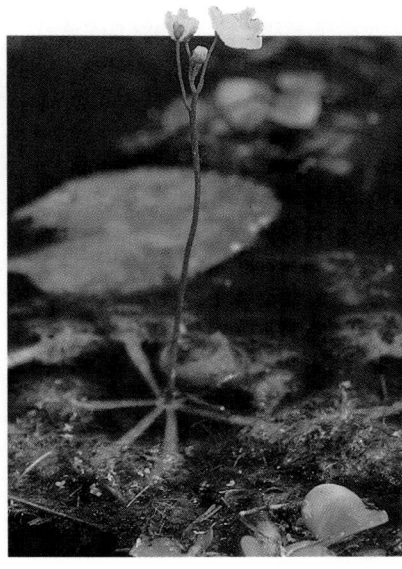

◀ A floating bladderwort

Chapter 9 **297**

READING STRATEGIES

Reading Tip As a class, outline the information under the first section heading, incorporating headings in complete sentences.
I. Plants grow toward or away from stimuli (tropism).
   A. Plants respond to touch (thigmotropism).
   B. Plants respond to light (phototropism).
   C. Plants respond to gravity (gravitropism).

Program Resources

◆ **Unit 2 Resources** 9-4 Lesson Plan, p. 101; 9-4 Section Summary, p. 102

Media and Technology

 Audio CD English-Spanish Summary 9-4

SECTION 4 Plant Responses and Growth

Objectives

After completing the lesson, students will be able to
◆ identify three stimuli that produce plant responses;
◆ list the functions that plant hormones control.

Key Terms tropism, hormone, auxin

1 Engage/Explore

Activating Prior Knowledge

Ask students to describe the usual direction of root and stem growth for plants on Earth. *(Roots point down; stems point up.)* Tell students that scientists and astronauts are studying how plants grow in space, particularly in the apparent weightless conditions in the orbiting space shuttle. Challenge them to speculate how the absence of Earth's gravity might affect plant growth. *(Sample: Without Earth's gravity, plants might not be able to achieve the same orientation.)*

•••••• DISCOVER ••••••••

Skills Focus inferring
Materials *sensitive plant such as a Venus' flytrap or mimosa; common houseplant such as a geranium or impatiens*
Time 10 minutes
Tips If you have difficulty finding sensitive plants, contact a biological supply house or specialty gardening shop. Remind students to wash their hands after touching the plants.
Expected Outcome The leaf of the sensitive plant closes after it is touched. The leaf of the houseplant does not respond.
Think It Over Students might infer that having sensitive leaves helps to protect a plant from predators and environmental conditions.

2 Facilitate

Tropisms

Demonstration

Materials *small potted plant, such as a bean plant; materials to support the pot*

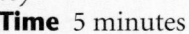

Time 10 minutes, with observations one week later

Students who are mastering English will benefit from this dramatic presentation. Place the plant on a ledge near a window or light. Ask: **In what direction is the plant growing? Why?** *(The stem is growing upward, toward the light and away from the pull of gravity.)* Support the pot on its side so the stem is parallel to the floor. Ask students to predict what the plant will look like in a week. After one week, the plant's new growth should be pointing up, with a bend between the old and new growth. Ask the students to explain what happened in terms of the plant's tropisms. *(The plant's positive phototropism and negative gravitropism caused it to grow upward.)* **limited English proficiency**

Plant Hormones

Inquiry Challenge

Materials *coiled spring toy*

Time 5 minutes

Students may have difficulty understanding how auxin's effect on plant cells controls how a plant responds to light. Have them model this by holding a coiled spring toy and causing one side to elongate, or "grow." The spring toy will bend away from the elongated side. Ask students: **Which side represents the shaded side of the plant?** *(The elongated side)* **learning modality: kinesthetic**

Figure 18 The face of this sunflower turns on its stalk throughout the day so that it always faces the sun.
Making Generalizations How does a positive phototropism help a plant survive?

298

Light All plants exhibit a response to light called phototropism. The leaves, stems, and flowers of plants grow toward light, showing a positive phototropism. For example, as the sun's position changes during the day, sunflowers move on their stalks so that they are always facing the sun.

Gravity Plants also respond to gravity. This response is called gravitropism. Roots show positive gravitropism—they grow downward, with the pull of gravity. Stems, on the other hand, show negative gravitropism—they grow upward.

Plant Hormones

Plants are able to respond to touch, light, and gravity because they produce hormones. A plant **hormone** is a chemical that affects how the plant grows and develops. **In addition to tropisms, plant hormones also control germination, the formation of flowers, stems, and leaves, the shedding of leaves, and the development and ripening of fruit.**

One important plant hormone is named **auxin** (AWX sin). Auxin speeds up the rate at which a plant's cells grow. Auxin controls a plant's response to light. When light shines on one side of a plant's stem, auxin moves to the shaded side of the stem. The cells on that side begin to grow faster. Eventually, the cells on the stem's shady side are longer than those on its sunny side. So the stem bends toward the light.

☑ *Checkpoint* What role does the hormone auxin play in a plant?

Life Spans of Angiosperms

If you've ever planted a garden, you know that many flowering plants grow, flower, and die in a single year. Flowering plants that complete a life cycle within one growing season are called annuals. The word annual comes from the Latin word *annus,* which means "year." Most annuals have herbaceous stems. Annuals include many garden plants, such as marigolds, petunias, and pansies. Wheat, tomatoes, and cucumbers are also annuals.

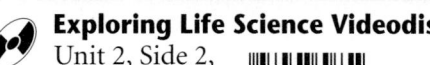

Figure 19 A flowering plant is classified as an annual, biennial, or perennial depending on the length of its life cycle. **A.** These morning glories are annuals. **B.** Foxglove, like this *Digitalis purpurea*, is a biennial. **C.** This peony, a perennial, will bloom year after year.

Angiosperms that complete their life cycle in two years are called biennials (by EN ee ulz). The Latin prefix *bi* means "two." In the first year, biennials germinate and grow roots, very short stems, and leaves. During their second year, biennials grow new stems and leaves and then produce flowers and seeds. Once the flowers produce seeds, the plant dies. Parsley, celery, and foxglove are biennials.

Flowering plants that live for more than two years are called perennials. The Latin word *per* means "through." Perennials usually live through many years. Some perennials, such as peonies and asparagus, have herbaceous stems. The leaves and stems above the ground die each winter. New ones are produced each spring. Most perennials, however, have woody stems. Bristlecone pines, oak trees, and honeysuckle are examples of woody perennials.

Section 4 Review

1. Name three stimuli to which plants respond.
2. What is a plant hormone? List four processes that a plant's hormones control.
3. Suppose you are growing a plant on a windowsill. After a few days, you notice that the plant's leaves and flowers are facing the window. Explain why this has occurred.
4. **Thinking Critically** **Applying Concepts** Is the grass that grows in most lawns an annual, a biennial, or a perennial? Explain.

CHAPTER PROJECT

Check Your Progress
Your plants should be near the end of their growth cycle. Continue to observe them. Harvest the seeds carefully, observe them, and compare them with the original seeds. If you have time, plant a few of these new seeds to begin the life cycle again.

Program Resources

◆ **Unit 2 Resources** 9-4 Review and Reinforce, p. 103; 9-4 Enrich, p. 104
◆ **Laboratory Manual** 9, "Investigating Hormones That Control Germination"

Answers to Self-Assessment

Caption Question

Figure 18 Positive phototropism keeps a plant facing toward light so that it gets enough energy to make its food.

☑ *Checkpoint*
Auxin speeds up the rate at which plant cells grow.

Life Spans of Angiosperms

Language Arts Connection

Students may be familiar with the word *perennial* from phrases such as "the perennial favorite." Ask students to think of other phrases using *annual, biennial, perennial,* or similar words. Have students compose sentences using these words. Groups can share their sentences, then work as a class to come up with three phrases that help them remember the life spans of each type of plant.
cooperative learning

3 Assess

Section 4 Review Answers

1. Light, gravity, and touch
2. A plant hormone is a chemical that affects how a plant grows and develops. Hormones control tropisms, germination, the formation of flowers, stems, and leaves, the shedding of leaves, and the development of fruit.
3. The plant's leaves and flowers show a positive phototropism, so they grow toward the light.
4. The grass that grows in most lawns is a perennial; it lives through many years.

CHAPTER PROJECT

Check Your Progress
Help students collect seeds. Collect data from each student or group and find the average number of seeds produced per plant. If time permits, have students plant these seeds to begin the life cycle again. Emphasize that this second cycle should be similar to the one they just observed. Check student's data tables for completeness and make sure their diagrams are labeled appropriately.

Which Way Is Up?

Preparing for Inquiry

Key Concept When the new root emerges from a germinating seed, it always grows downward; the new stem always grows upward.

Skills Objective Students will be able to
◆ develop hypotheses that explain how the growth of a seed is affected by gravity.

Time 30 minutes, plus a few minutes each day for a week

Advance Planning Make sure there are enough corn seeds for you to give four seeds to each student or group. Soak the seeds in water for 24 hours before the lab.

Alternative Materials Other seeds that can be used include lima beans, sunflowers, squash, oats, and cucumbers. If you use glass petri dishes, remind students to follow all the safety procedures associated with the use of glass.

Guiding Inquiry

Invitation Ask students to imagine what the world would be like if gravity did not influence the growth of plants. Ask: **If you planted a seed in the ground, would the plant always grow up out of the ground?** (*The plant might sometimes grow up, other times grow in other directions.*)

Introducing the Procedure

Make sure students understand that the seeds must be kept in exactly the same position throughout the experiment. Show two sample petri dishes, one in which the positions of the seeds can shift and one that is properly packed.

Analyze and Conclude

1. Roots grew from the pointed tip of the seed, while the stem grew from the rounded part. The roots always grew downward, and the stems always grew upward, bending if necessary.
2. Students should be able to use what they learned in this lab to explain any inconsistencies between their hypotheses and the evidence.
3. Plants usually grow toward light; it was necessary to exclude light as a

---

Which Way is Up?

In this lab, you will use your knowledge of germination to develop a hypothesis about seedlings and gravity.

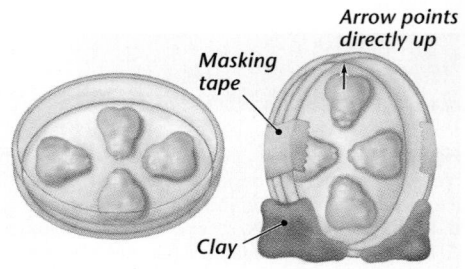

Masking tape
Arrow points directly up
Clay

Problem

How is the growth of a seed affected by gravity?

Materials

4 corn seeds	plastic petri dish
paper towels	scissors
water	masking tape
marking pencil	clay

Procedure

1. With your classmates, discuss how gravity affects objects. Then, with your group, develop a hypothesis that explains how gravity affects the direction of seedling growth.
2. Arrange four seeds that have been soaked in water for 24 hours in a petri dish. The pointed ends of the seeds should face the center of the dish, as shown in the illustration.
3. Place a circle cut from a paper towel over the seeds. Moisten one or more paper towels with water so that they are wet but not dripping. Pack them in the dish to hold the seeds firmly in place. Cover the dish, and seal it with tape.
4. Lay the dish upside down so the seeds show. Use a marking pencil to draw a small, outward-facing arrow over one of the seeds, as shown in the illustration. Turn the dish over and write your name and the date on it.
5. Use clay to stand up the petri dish so that the arrow points upward. Put the petri dish in a dark place.

6. Once a day for a week, remove the petri dish and check it. Do not open the dish. Observe and sketch the seeds. Note the seeds' direction of growth. Then return the dish, making sure that the arrow points upward.

Analyze and Conclude

1. What new structures emerged as the seeds developed? How did the direction of growth compare from seed to seed?
2. Did your results confirm your hypothesis? If not, describe any differences between your hypothesis and your results.
3. Why was it necessary to grow these seeds in the dark?
4. **Think About It** What evidence or ideas did you consider when you wrote your hypothesis? Did any of your ideas change as a result of this experiment? Explain.

Design an Experiment

How will your seedlings respond if you now allow them to grow in the light? Design an experiment to find out. Obtain your teacher's approval before carrying out your experiment.

---

variable so the direction of growth was affected only by gravity. The dark also simulates the underground environment in which seeds usually germinate.

4. Answers will vary. Students should realize that the results show that the direction of growth is influenced by gravity, not the direction in which the seeds are planted.

Extending the Inquiry

Design an Experiment Students may want to place their petri dish so that it is exposed to

light on only one side to observe any differences in the growth of the four plants. Remind them to take gravity into account.

Program Resources

◆ **Unit 2 Resources** Chapter 9 Skills Lab, pp. 108–109
◆ **Inquiry Skills Activity Book** Provides teaching and review of all inquiry skills

SECTION 1 The Characteristics of Seed Plants

Key Ideas
◆ All seed plants have vascular tissue and produce seeds.
◆ A seed has three important parts: an embryo, stored food, and a seed coat.
◆ Photosynthesis occurs mainly in leaves. Stems support plants and transport materials. Roots anchor plants and absorb water and minerals.

Key Terms
phloem	cotyledon	transpiration
xylem	germination	cambium
seed	stomata	root cap
embryo		

 SECTION 2 Gymnosperms

Key Ideas
◆ All gymnosperms produce naked seeds. Many gymnosperms also have needlelike or scalelike leaves, and grow deep root systems.
◆ To reproduce, pollen falls onto a female cone. A sperm cell and an egg cell join. The zygote develops into the seed's embryo.

Key Terms
gymnosperm	pollen	pollination
cone	ovule	

 SECTION 3 Angiosperms

Key Ideas
◆ Angiosperms produce flowers and fruits.
◆ To reproduce, pollen falls on the stigma. In time, the sperm cell and egg cell join in the ovule. The zygote develops into the seed's embryo.

Key Terms
angiosperm	sepal	fruit
ovary	stamen	monocot
flower	pistil	dicot
petal		

SECTION 4 Plant Responses and Growth
INTEGRATING **CHEMISTRY**

Key Ideas
◆ A tropism is a plant's growth response toward or away from a stimulus. Plants respond to touch, light, and gravity.
◆ Plant hormones control tropisms and many other plant functions.

Key Terms
tropism
hormone
auxin

Organizing Information

Concept Map Copy the concept map about seed plants onto a separate piece of paper. Then complete the map and add a title. (For more on concept maps, see the Skills Handbook.)

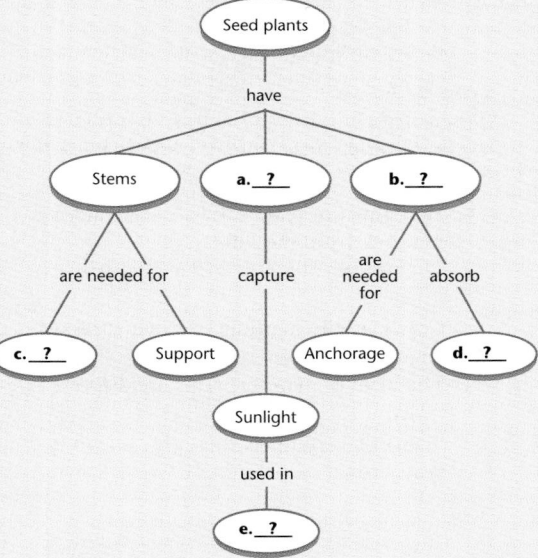

Organizing Information

Concept Map a. Leaves **b.** Roots **c.** Transportation **d.** Water and Nutrients **e.** Photosynthesis

Program Resources

◆ **Unit 2 Resources** Chapter 9 Project Scoring Rubric, p. 88
◆ **Performance Assessment** Chapter 9, pp. 29–31
◆ **Chapter and Unit Tests** Chapter 9 Test, pp. 40–43

Media and Technology

 Interactive Student Tutorial CD-ROM Chapter 9

 Computer Test Bank Chapter 9 Test

Reviewing Content
Multiple Choice
1. d 2. b 3. b 4. c 5. a

True or False
6. roots 7. true 8. gymnosperms
9. angiosperms 10. biennials

Checking Concepts

11. Phloem is the vascular tissue through which food moves, and xylem is the tissue through which water and nutrients move. These tissues allow plants to efficiently transport these essentials substances to all cells of the plant.

12. Seeds can be dispersed by wind, water, or animals. Some plants shoot out their seeds.

13. Stomata open and allow carbon dioxide to enter the leaf and also allow the oxygen and water vapor produced during photosynthesis to escape into the air. Stomata close and retain water in leaf cells during warm temperatures.

14. Annual rings are the circular pattern of xylem cells that form each year in a woody plant stem. Xylem cells that grow in the spring are large and have thin walls because they grow rapidly, producing a wide light-brown ring. Xylem cells that grow in the summer are small and have thick walls because they grow slowly, producing a thin dark ring.

15. Female cones are larger than male cones. The outside is covered by scales which contain at least one ovule at the base of their inner side. The scales close after pollination, and fertilization occurs inside. When the seeds are ready, the scales open, and the cones often hang upside-down on a branch.

16. Pollination is the process by which pollen, containing male reproductive cells, is transferred to the female reproductive structures. Fertilization is the joining of a sperm and egg cell.

17. The plant hormone auxin is involved in phototropism. Auxin speeds up the rate at which plant cells grow. Auxin moves into stem cells on the shadier side of a plant, causing those cells to grow faster than the cells on the sunny side of the plant. With longer cells on one side than the other, the stem bends toward the light.

Reviewing Content

 For more review of key concepts, see the Interactive Student Tutorial CD-ROM.

Multiple Choice
Choose the letter of the best answer.

1. The process by which a seed sprouts is called
  a. pollination. **b.** fertilization.
  c. dispersal. **d.** germination.

2. Which of the following is the process by which water evaporates from leaves?
  a. pollination
  b. transpiration
  c. transportation
  d. dispersal

3. In woody stems, new xylem cells are produced by
  a. bark. **b.** cambium.
  c. phloem. **d.** pith.

4. Which of the following is the male part of the flower?
  a. pistil **b.** ovule
  c. stamen **d.** petal

5. What kind of tropism do roots display when they grow into the soil?
  a. positive gravitropism
  b. negative gravitropism
  c. positive phototropism
  d. negative thigmotropism

True or False
If the statement is true, write true. If it is false, change the underlined word or words to make the statement true.

6. <u>Stems</u> anchor plants and absorb water and minerals from the soil.

7. The needles of a pine tree are actually its <u>leaves</u>.

8. Cones are the reproductive structures of <u>angiosperms</u>.

9. The seeds of <u>gymnosperms</u> are dispersed in fruits.

10. Plants that complete their life cycle in two years are called <u>perennials</u>.

Checking Concepts

11. What is the difference between phloem and xylem? Why are these tissues important to plants?

12. Describe four different ways that seeds can be dispersed.

13. Explain the role that stomata play in a plant's leaves.

14. What are annual rings? Explain how they form.

15. Describe the structure of a female cone.

16. What is the difference between pollination and fertilization?

17. What role do plant hormones play in phototropism?

18. Writing to Learn Imagine that you are a seed inside a plump purple fruit that is floating in a stream. Describe your experiences on the journey you take to the place where you germinate.

Thinking Critically

19. Relating Cause and Effect When a strip of bark is removed all the way around the trunk of a tree, the tree dies. Explain why this happens.

20. Classifying Suppose you find an unusual freshly cut flower on the ground. You discover the flower has 27 petals. What does this information tell you about the plant that produced this flower? What would the plant's leaves, stems, and seeds look like?

21. Predicting Pesticides are designed to kill harmful insects. Sometimes, however, pesticides kill helpful insects as well. What effect could this have on angiosperms? Explain.

22. Applying Concepts Explain why people who grow houseplants on windowsills should turn the plants every week or so.

---

18. Answers will vary. Students should describe how the seed is removed from the fruit and should include a description of the conditions under which the seed finally germinates.

Thinking Critically

19. The innermost part of bark is phloem. If the bark is stripped around the entire base of a tree, all the phloem is removed in that space. Food made in the leaves can no longer reach the lower stem cells and root cells. These cells die, followed by the entire tree.

20. It tells you that the plant is a monocot. The leaves would be long, slender, and have parallel veins. The stems would have scattered vascular bundles. The seeds would have one cotyledon.

21. If helpful insects are killed by a pesticide, the plants that depend on these insects for pollination may not be pollinated.

22. If plants near the window are not turned often, they will not grow evenly, and all their leaves will grow toward the window.

Applying Skills

A scientist measured the rate of transpiration in an ash tree over an 18-hour period. She also measured how much water the tree's roots took up during the same period. Use the data in the graph below to answer Questions 23–25.

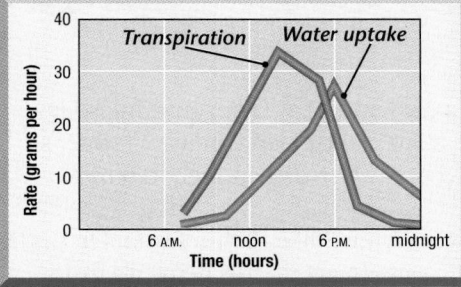

23. Interpreting Data At what time is transpiration at its highest? At what time is water uptake at its highest?

24. Inferring Why do you think the transpiration rate increases and decreases as it does during the 18-hour period?

25. Drawing Conclusions Based on the graph, what is one possible conclusion you can reach about the pattern of water loss and gain in the ash tree?

Performance ▼ Assessment

Present Your Project Design a poster that shows the results of your investigation. You may wish to use a cycle diagram to show the main events in the plant's life. Do you think that the later generations of plants will go through a similar life cycle? Why or why not?

Reflect and Record What new information did you learn about seed plants by doing this project? If you could do another investigation using these plants, what would you do? Why?

Test Preparation

Use these questions to prepare for standardized tests.

Use the information to answer Questions 26–29. One hundred radish seeds were planted in each of two identical trays of soil. Over the next 25 days, one tray was kept at 10°C. The other tray was kept at 20°C. The trays received equal amounts of water and sunlight. The data collected are shown below.

Day	Seeds That Germinated at:	
	10°C	20°C
0	0	0
5	0	5
10	20	35
15	45	75
20	50	85
25	50	85

26. What is the manipulated variable in this experiment?
- **a.** light
- **b.** water
- **c.** seeds
- **d.** temperature

27. What was the purpose of this experiment?
- **a.** to germinate radish seeds
- **b.** to determine whether radish seeds need light to germinate
- **c.** to determine whether radish seeds prefer a specific temperature to germinate
- **d.** to determine whether radish seeds need water to germinate

28. On day 15, what was the difference in the number of seeds that had germinated in the two trays?
- **a.** 15   **b.** 20   **c.** 30   **d.** 35

29. Which statement is a correct conclusion based on the data gathered from this experiment?
- **a.** The experiment failed because some seeds did not germinate.
- **b.** Temperature does not affect germination.
- **c.** More seeds germinate at a temperature of 20°C than at 10°C.
- **d.** Radish seeds need water and sunlight to germinate.

Applying Skills

23. Transpiration is at its highest at about 1:00 P.M. Water uptake is at its highest at about 6:00 P.M.

24. The transpiration rate increases throughout the morning until early afternoon, then starts to decrease because most evaporation occurs during the hot middle part of the day. Not much water evaporates in the cool evening.

25. The maximum amount of transpiration occurs about 5 hours before the peak in water uptake.

Performance ▼ Assessment

Present Your Project Encourage students to use the cycle diagram to describe their observations during the life span of the plant in this project. Remind students to include what will happen after the new seeds are germinated. Find a space for students to display their exhibits.

Reflect and Record Discuss the project with students. Make sure they understand the cyclic nature of plant life. Students may suggest using their plants to investigate tropisms or hydroponics. If there is time, allow students to try their new experiments after you approve their plans.

Test Preparation

26. d **27.** c **28.** c **29.** c

Program Resources

◆ **Inquiry Skills Activity Book** Provides teaching and review of all inquiry skills

From Plants to Chemicals

Focus on Chemistry

This four-page feature introduces the process of scientific inquiry by involving students in a high-interest, magazine-like article about a working scientist, Dr. Rathin Datta. Using Dr. Datta's discoveries of chemicals that can be obtained from plants, the article focuses on persistence, experimentation, and thinking about things in new ways as key elements of scientific inquiry.

Scientific Inquiry

◆ Before students read the article, let them read the title, examine the pictures, and read the captions on their own. Then ask: **What questions came into your mind as you looked at these pictures?** (*Students might suggest questions such as "Is spandex really made from corn? Why aren't we using more corn-based fuel instead of petroleum? How do scientists discover all these products that can be made from corn?"*) Point out to students that, just as they had questions about what they were seeing, scientists too have questions about what they observe.

◆ Ask: **What medicinal products do you know that come from plants?** (*Samples: aloe, echinacea, ginkgo, garlic, ginseng*) **What nonmedicinal products can you think of that come from plants?** (*Samples: cotton, rayon, rubber*)

From Plants to CHEMICALS

Can you power a car with corn? Can you drink soda from a bottle made from plants? Can you use a farmer's corn crop to make chemicals strong enough to remove paint?

You can, thanks to scientists like Rathin Datta. Dr. Datta specializes in finding ways to get useful chemicals from plants. His discoveries will help make the environment cleaner for all of us.

Rathin is a chemical engineer at the Argonne National Laboratory in Illinois. For years, he has been finding ways to make useful products from substances found naturally in plants. He's helped find ways to turn corn into an automobile fuel called gasohol. He's researched plants that can be used to produce powerful medicines. He even worked on a way to use corn to make a stretchy fabric that athletes wear.

"I've always been interested in the plant and biological side of chemistry," says Rathin, who grew up in northern India. Even in grade school, he was interested in science. "That's because I've always been concerned about the effect of chemicals on the environment."

Rathin Datta was born in India, just north of Delhi. His interest in science was inspired in part by his father, who was a mathematician. Rathin came to the United States in 1970 to get a doctorate in chemical engineering at Princeton University. He works now at Argonne National Laboratory in Argonne, Illinois. In his free time, he enjoys tennis, hiking, and biking. He plays the sitar, an Indian lute, and has a special interest in opera.

304

Background

Chemistry is the study of properties of materials, such as their structure and composition. Chemists also study how different materials interact and how adding or removing energy from materials changes them.

Chemical engineering is related to chemistry. Chemical engineers, like Rathin Datta, design and manage facilities in which chemical reactions take place. The chemical engineer chooses the equipment and processes that are most appropriate for the chemistry involved. Chemical engineers were among the first to introduce automated control processes into industrial design.

Talking with Rathin Datta

Are Plant-Based Chemicals Safer?

Chemicals that come from crop plants are called *agrochemicals*, meaning "chemicals from agriculture," Rathin explains. Many agrochemicals are much less dangerous to the environment than chemicals made from petroleum. For one thing, although some agrochemicals can be poisonous to humans, most are not.

Because agrochemicals are made from plant materials, nature usually recycles them just as it recycles dead plants. Think of what happens to a tree after it falls to the ground. Tiny microbes work on its leaves and branches until the tree has rotted completely away. Much the same thing happens to products made from agrochemicals. A bag made from corn-based chemicals will break down and disappear after only a few weeks of being buried. In contrast, a plastic bag made from *petrochemicals*—chemicals made from petroleum—can survive hundreds of years.

Converting Carbohydrates

The starting ingredients in many agrochemicals are energy-rich substances called carbohydrates. Sugar and starch are carbohydrates. Rathin Datta converts, or changes, carbohydrates from corn into an agrochemical that can be used to make plastic. To do this, he needs help from tiny organisms—bacteria. First, he explains, he puts particular bacteria into a big vat of ground-up corn. The bacteria convert the corn's carbohydrates into acids through a

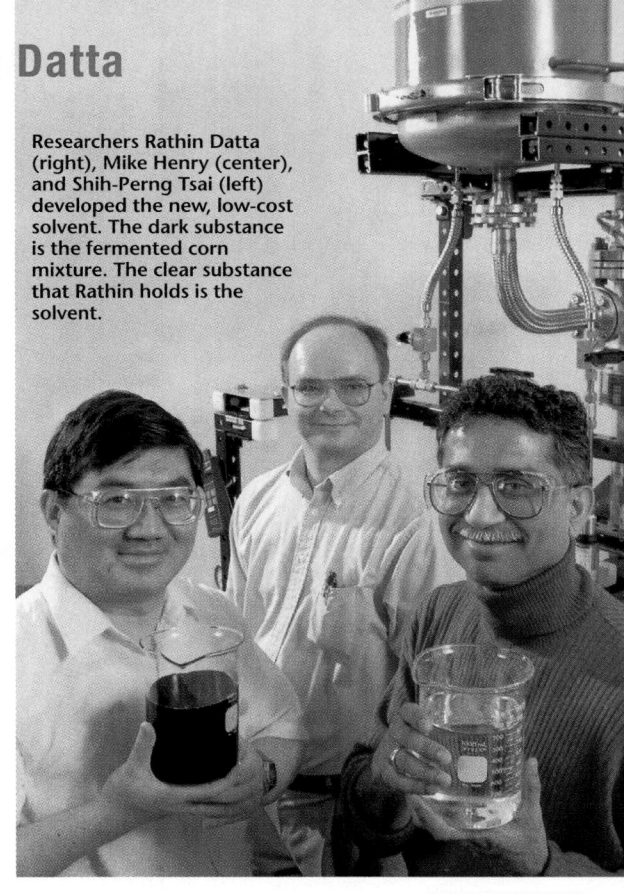

Researchers Rathin Datta (right), Mike Henry (center), and Shih-Perng Tsai (left) developed the new, low-cost solvent. The dark substance is the fermented corn mixture. The clear substance that Rathin holds is the solvent.

natural process called fermentation. Rathin then uses the acids to make agrochemical plastic.

"The bacteria do all the work of converting the carbohydrates into useful molecules," says Rathin. "The hardest part for us comes afterward. The fermentation process produces a brew that contains a whole mix of materials. We have to find ways to separate out the one kind of material that we want to use from all the others."

This sign on a gasoline pump advertises gasohol.

- Ask students if they know what a solvent is. Explain that a solvent is a liquid that helps some other substance dissolve. Water is a solvent because many substances dissolve in it, such as table salt. Solvents are used in numerous commercial and industrial products and processes, and are an important part of products such as paints and drugs.
- Have students locate a specific problem identified by Dr. Datta, then describe how his team solved the problem. *(Sample: Finding a way to separate one kind of material from the fermented mixture; 2 years of research to refine a plastic filter)*
- If students want to know more about fermentation, share with them the background information on page 306. Observe fermentation in the classroom by letting a glass of milk sit at room temperature for a few days. Encourage students to monitor changes in odor, texture, and color of the milk.
- Extend this exploration by challenging students to find out why plastic bags made from petroleum-based products do not decompose.

305

Background

Gasohol is a mixture of gasoline and ethanol. Ethanol, an alcohol, can come from coal, organic wastes, wood products, grain, sugar crops, or almost any starchy plant.

Gasoline-alcohol mixtures have been used as petroleum alternatives since the internal-combustion engine was first developed in the 1870s. However, because these mixtures are expensive to produce, they cannot compete successfully with gasoline unless oil shortages raise the price of gasoline. One advantage of gasohol over pure alcohol fuel is that most of a car's fuel system does not have to be modified for the new fuel.

- Ask: **If petrochemicals are cheaper than agrochemicals, why do we bother researching agrochemicals?** *(Samples: Petrochemicals are often poisonous. Petroleum-based products don't break down quickly. There is a limited supply of petroleum. Agrochemicals may pollute less than petrochemicals.)*
- Direct students' attention to the flow-chart at the top of these pages. Ask: **What does *biodegradable* mean?** *(Capable of being broken down by bacteria and other decomposers.)* Challenge interested students to find out about other products that are made from corn. Invite students to create a classroom display.
- Ask: **Why is it so important to Dr. Datta to find a corn-based solvent?** *Because solvents are found everywhere, and he is concerned about how widespread use of such chemicals affects the environment.*
- Ask a volunteer to research spandex and find out what it is made of.
- To confirm that many solvents are poisonous, students can read the warning labels on the back of products such as cleaners, paint thinners, or nail polish remover.
- Ask students: **If you knew that a product you used was not biodegradable and hurt the environment, how much more money would you be willing to pay for an environmentally friendly, biodegradable alternative?** *(This question may result in a lively debate. Encourage students to express their opinions while respecting those of others.)*
- Interested students may wish to find out what solvent nail polish remover contains, and why Dr. Datta wants to replace it with an alternative.
- Ask: **What does Dr. Datta mean by a chemical being "safe"?** *(A person is less likely to be hurt by using the product.)*

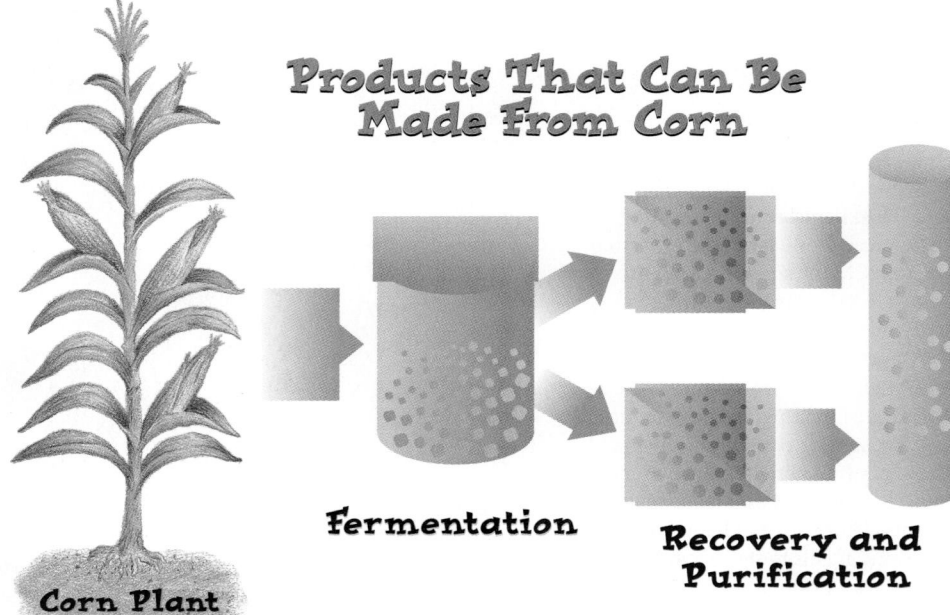

Products That Can Be Made From Corn

Corn Plant

Fermentation

Recovery and Purification

Making Paint Remover From Corn

Rathin Datta's most recent discovery is a good example of how agrochemicals can replace petrochemicals. He and his team have found a new way to use corn to make powerful solvents. Solvents are used to dissolve other substances.

"Solvents are found everywhere," says Rathin. "For example, factories use them in many processes to clean electronic parts or to remove ink from recycled newspapers. Households use them in grease-cleaning detergents and in paint removers."

Almost 4 million tons of solvents are used in the United States every year. Most are made from petro-chemicals and can be very poisonous.

"Scientists have known for a long time that much safer solvents can be made from agrochemicals," says Rathin. "But the process has been too expensive. It doesn't do any good to make something that is environmentally sound if it costs too much for people to use," says Rathin. "Our challenge as chemical engineers

Spandex was used to make the blue tops these dancers are wearing.

Background

Scientists usually use the term *fermentation* to refer to chemical reactions caused by microscopic organisms such as bacteria, molds, and yeasts.

Fermentation is a natural phenomenon. Fermentation causes milk to sour and wine to become vinegar. Fermentation in milk also occurs when bacteria change milk sugar into lactic acid. Kinds of milk products such as yogurt and acidophilus milk are products

of fermentation.

A product of fermentation usually has a simpler structure than that of the substance that was fermented. Fermentation of sugars by yeasts results in ethanol, glycerol, and carbon dioxide. The products of mold fermentation include citric acid, antibiotics, and vitamin B_{12}. The products of bacteria fermentation include acetone, monosodium glutamate, and acetic acid.

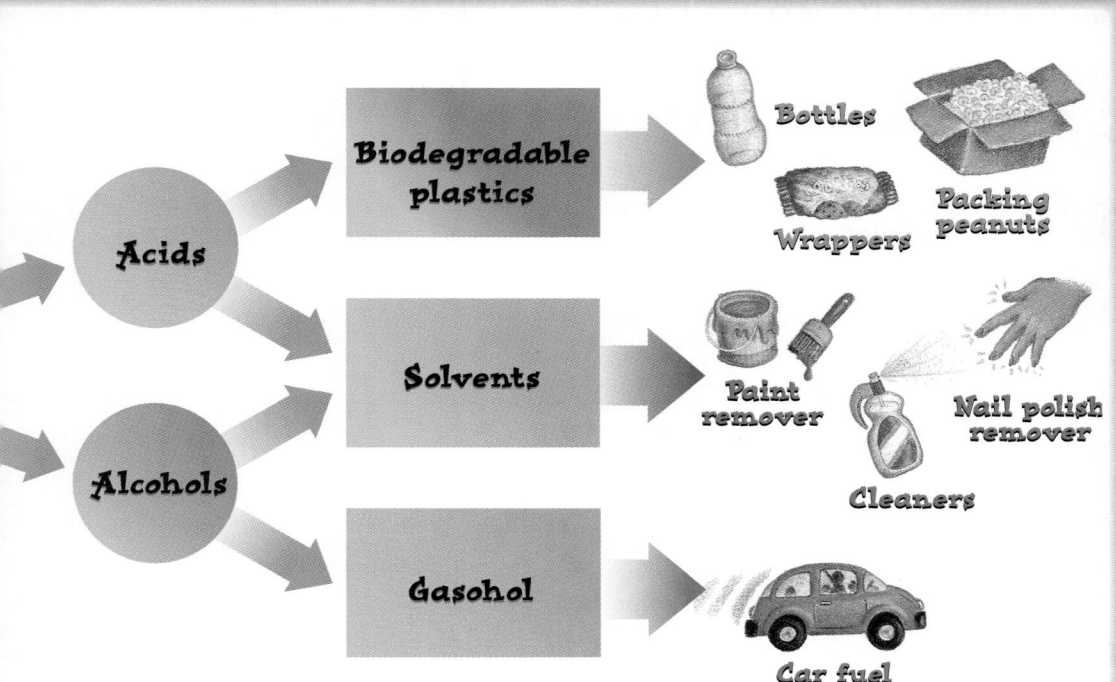

Acids → Biodegradable plastics → Bottles, Wrappers, Packing peanuts

Alcohols

Solvents → Paint remover, Cleaners, Nail polish remover

Gasohol → Car fuel

In Your Journal Ask students what they think motivated the scientists to persevere with finding a cheaper way to make a safe solvent. Then encourage volunteers to describe how persistence and determination has allowed them to solve specific problems they have encountered.

was to think about an old process in an entirely new way. We had to find a less expensive way to make these solvents."

Discovering a New Process

Rathin needed a new process to separate the solvents he wanted from a mixture. "I started working with a new kind of plastic that acts like a very fine filter. When we pass the fermented corn over this plastic, it captures the acids we want to keep and lets the other material pass through."

After two years of experimenting, Rathin perfected his process of making agrochemical solvents. His process works for less than half the cost of the old method. It also uses 90 percent less energy. Soon, most of the solvents used in the United States

could be this cleaner, safer kind made from corn. "It even makes a a great fingernail polish remover," says Datta.

"It's very satisfying to take a natural product like corn and use it to produce a chemical that will replace a less safe chemical," says Rathin. "It's rare to find a compound that can do everything that this corn solvent can do and still be nonpoisonous and easily break down in the environment."

In Your Journal

Rathin Datta and his team had discovered years ago how to make a solvent that was safer for the environment. But it was very expensive to make. Rathin could have stopped his research at that point. Instead, he chose to continue. What does this action tell you about how scientists like Datta meet challenges?

307

READING STRATEGIES

Further Reading

- Montgomery, John H. *Agrochemicals Desk Reference.* CRC Press, 1997.
- Powledge, Fred. *Pharmacy in the Forest: How Medicines are Found in the Natural World.* School and Library Binding, 1998.
- *Discover* magazine, 1998 Environmental Awards, or online at **www.discover.com/july_issue/environment98.html**.
- Argonne National Laboratory's newsletters online at **www.anl.gov/OPA/local/news/an980615.html**.

Sections	Time	Student Edition Activities	Other Activities	
CHAPTER PROJECT **Alive and Well** p. 309	Ongoing (3 weeks)	Check Your Progress, pp. 314, 325, 333 Present Your Project, p. 337		
1 **What is an Animal?** pp. 310–314 ◆ List and describe four major characteristics that all animals share. ◆ Describe what animals need from their environment in order to live. ◆ Describe animal adaptations for getting food and escaping predators.	2 periods/ 1 block	**Discover** Is It an Animal? p. 310 **Sharpen Your Skills** Inferring, p. 312	TE TE	Including All Students, p. 311 Building Inquiry Skills: Classifying, p. 313
2 **INTEGRATING MATHEMATICS** **Symmetry** pp. 315–319 ◆ Distinguish between bilateral and radial symmetry, and describe how animals exhibit these kinds of symmetry.	$1-1\frac{1}{2}$ periods/ $\frac{1}{2}-\frac{3}{4}$ block	**Discover** How Many Ways Can You Fold It? p. 315 **Science at Home,** p. 317 **Real-World Lab: You Solve the Mystery** A Tale Told by Tracks, pp. 318–319	TE TE	Building Inquiry Skills: Applying Concepts, p. 316 Using the Visuals: Figures 6 and 7, p. 316
3 **Sponges and Cnidarians** pp. 320–326 ◆ Describe the organization of a sponge's body. ◆ Identify the main characteristics of cnidarians. ◆ Describe how a coral reef is formed and the life that exists on a coral reef.	2 periods/ 1 block	**Discover** How Do Natural and Synthetic Sponges Compare? p. 320 **Try This** Hydra Doing? p. 324 **Science and Society** Coral Reefs in Danger, p. 326	TE TE TE TE IES	Integrating Chemistry , p. 322 Language Arts Connection, p. 322 Demonstration, p. 323 Including All Students, p. 324 "Where River Meets Sea," pp. 33–34
4 **Worms** pp. 327–334 ◆ Identify the three main groups of worms. ◆ List and identify the characteristics of the three groups of worms.	2 periods/ 1 block	**Discover** What Can You See in a Worm? p. 327 **Sharpen Your Skills** Communicating, p. 331 **Sharpen Your Skills** Observing, p. 332 **Skills Lab: Developing Hypotheses** Earthworm Responses, p. 334	TE TE TE TE LM	Inquiry Challenge, pp. 228, 330 Real-Life Learning, p. 329 Including All Students, p. 331 Integrating Earth Science, p. 332 10, "Observing Flatworms and Roundworms"
Study Guide/Chapter Assessment pp. 335–337	1 period/ $\frac{1}{2}$ block		ISAB	Provides teaching and review of all inquiry skills.

For Standard or Block Schedule The Resource Pro® CD-ROM gives you maximum flexibility for planning your instruction for any type of schedule. Resource Pro® contains Planning Express®, an advanced scheduling program, as well as the entire contents of the Teaching Resources and the Computer Test Bank.

CHAPTER PLANNING GUIDE

Program Resources	Assessment Strategies	Media and Technology
UR Chapter 10 Project Teacher Notes, pp. 2–3 **UR** Chapter 10 Project Overview and Worksheets, pp. 4–7	**SE** Performance Assessment: Present Your Project, p. 337 **TE** Check Your Progress, pp. 314, 325, 333 **UR** Chapter 10 Project Scoring Rubric, p. 8	Science Explorer Internet Site at www.phschool.com
UR 10-1 Lesson Plan, p. 9 **UR** 10-1 Section Summary, p. 10 **UR** 10-1 Review and Reinforce, p. 11 **UR** 10-1 Enrich, p. 12	**SE** Section 1 Review, p. 314 **TE** Ongoing Assessment, pp. 311, 313 **TE** Performance Assessment, p. 314	Life Science Videotape 3; Videodisc Unit 3 Side 2, "Through Their Eyes" Audio CD, English-Spanish Summary 10-1 Transparency 40, "Levels of Organization in the Body" Transparency 41, "Animal Classification Tree"
UR 10-2 Lesson Plan, p. 13 **UR** 10-2 Section Summary, p. 14 **UR** 10-2 Review and Reinforce, p. 15 **UR** 10-2 Enrich, p. 16 **UR** Chapter 10 Real-World Lab, pp. 25–26	**SE** Section 2 Review, p. 317 **TE** Performance Assessment, p. 317	Audio CD, English-Spanish Summary 10-2
UR 10-3 Lesson Plan, p. 17 **UR** 10-3 Section Summary, p. 18 **UR** 10-3 Review and Reinforce, p. 19 **UR** 10-3 Enrich, p. 20	**SE** Section 3 Review, p. 325 **TE** Ongoing Assessment, pp. 321, 323 **TE** Performance Assessment, p. 325	Life Science Videotape 3; Videodisc Unit 3 Side 2, "Spineless" Audio CD, English-Spanish Summary 10-3 Transparency 42, "Exploring a Sponge"
UR 10-4 Lesson Plan, p. 21 **UR** 10-4 Section Summary, p. 22 **UR** 10-4 Review and Reinforce, p. 23 **UR** 10-4 Enrich, p. 24 **UR** Chapter 10 Skills Lab, pp. 27–29	**SE** Section 4 Review, p. 333 **TE** Ongoing Assessment, pp. 329, 331 **TE** Performance Assessment, p. 333	Life Science Videotape 3; Videodisc Unit 3 Side 2, "Spineless" Audio CD, English-Spanish Summary 10-4 Transparency 43, "Exploring the Life Cycle of a Dog Tapeworm" Transparency 44, "Earthworm Anatomy" Interactive Student Tutorial CD-ROM, Chapter 10
RCA Provides strategies to improve science reading skills **GSW** Provides worksheets to promote student comprehension of content	**SE** Chapter 10 Study Guide/Assessment, pp. 335–337 **PA** Chapter 10 Performance Assessment, pp. 32–34 **CUT** Chapter 10 Test, pp. 48–51 **CTB** Chapter 10 Test	Interactive Student Tutorial CD-ROM, Chapter 10 Computer Test Bank, Test 10

Key: **SE** Student Edition **TE** Teacher's Edition **UR** Unit Resources
CTB Computer Test Bank **PTA** Product Testing Activities by *Consumer Reports* **LM** Laboratory Manual
ISAB Inquiry Skills Activity Book **RCA** Reading in the Content Area **IES** Interdisciplinary Explorations Series
GSW Guided Study Worksheets **PA** Performance Assessment **CUT** Chapter and Unit Tests

Meeting the National Science Education Standards and AAAS Benchmarks

National Science Education Standards	Benchmarks for Science Literacy	Unifying Themes
Science as Inquiry (Content Standard A) ◆ **Ask questions that can be answered by scientific investigations** What can be learned about animals by studying their tracks? *(Real-World Lab)* Do earthworms prefer dry or moist conditions? Do they prefer light or dark conditions? *(Skills Lab)* ◆ **Design and conduct a scientific investigation** Students design a plan to investigate whether earthworms prefer smooth or rough surfaces. *(Skills Lab)* **Life Science** (Content Standard C) ◆ **Diversity and adaptations of organisms** Students learn the main characteristics of animals and some of the adaptations animals use to get food and escape predators. *(Section 1)* Students learn the characteristics and adaptations of sponges and cnidarians. *(Section 3)* Students learn the characteristics and adaptations of the three main groups of worms. *(Section 4)* Students research the adaptations of a particular animal. *(Chapter Project)* ◆ **Populations and ecosystems** Students learn about the effects humans can have on coral reefs. *(Section 3)* ◆ **Structure and function of living systems** The bodies of complex animals all have either radial or bilateral symmetry. *(Section 2)*	**1B Scientific Inquiry** Students infer animal activities by the indirect evidence of animal tracks. They test hypotheses by conducting an experiment on earthworm responses to light. *(Real-World Lab; Skills Lab)* **5A Diversity of Life** Students learn the general characteristics of animals. Then they learn the specific characteristics of sponges, cnidarians, and worms. *(Sections 1, 3, 4)* **5D Interdependence of Life** Environmental interactions and dependence are presented. Parasite and host relationships are explained. *(Section 3, 4; Chapter Project; Science and Society)* **11C Constancy and Change** Bilateral and radial symmetry in animals is explored in detail. *(Sections 2, 3, 4)*	◆ **Patterns of Change** Adaptations of animals are the result of change over time. *(Section 1)* ◆ **Scale and Structure** While some animals are asymmetrical, most have radial or bilateral symmetry. Sponges, cnidarians, and worms all have specific body structures. *(Sections 2, 3, 4)* ◆ **Unity and Diversity** There are many types of animals, but they all share basic characteristics. *(Sections 1, 3, 4)* ◆ **Systems and Interactions** Students investigate the interactions of three animals by examining their tracks in the snow. *(Real-World Lab)* ◆ **Evolution** The wide variety of animals are classified into phyla that are related to each other in an evolutionary tree.

Take It to the Net

 *Interactive text at www.phschool.com*

Science Explorer comes alive with iText.

- **Complete student text** is accessible from any computer with Internet access or a CD-ROM drive.
- **Animations, simulations, and videos** enhance student understanding and retention of concepts.
- **Self-tests and online study tools** assess student understanding.

STAY CURRENT with

Find out the latest research and information about animals at:
www.phschool.com

Go to **www.phschool.com** and click on the Science icon. Then click on <u>Science Explorer: Life, Earth, and Physical Science</u> under PH@school.

ACTIVITY	Time (minutes)	Materials *Quantities for one work group*	Skills
Section 1			
Discover, p. 310	15	**Consumable** organisms that students can safely observe, such as earthworms, minnows, pill bugs, crickets, potted plants, ferns, and sponges	Forming Operational Definitions, Observing, Classifying
Sharpen Your Skills, p. 313	15	No special materials are required.	Inferring
Section 2			
Discover, p. 315	10	**Consumable** tracing paper **Nonconsumable** scissors, pen or pencil, circular object	Classifying, Observing, Drawing Conclusions, Forming Operational Definitions
Science at Home, p. 317	home	No special materials are required.	Observing, Classifying
Real-World Lab, pp. 318–319	30	**Consumable** No special materials are required.	Observing, Inferring
Section 3			
Discover, p. 320	20	**Consumable** natural sponges, synthetic kitchen sponges **Nonconsumable** scissors, hand lens or microscope	Observing, Classifying
Try This, p. 324	25	**Consumable** live hydra, toothpick **Nonconsumable** small glass bowl or petri dish, hand lens or microscope	Classifying, Observing
Section 4			
Discover, p. 327	15	**Consumable** live planarian, bottled water, toothpick **Nonconsumable** small paintbrush, small transparent container or petri dish, plastic dropper, hand lens	Observing, Classifying
Sharpen Your Skills, p. 331	30	**Consumable** art supplies, construction paper or posterboard	Communicating
Sharpen Your Skills, p. 332	15 minutes per day over several days	**Consumable** earthworm, construction paper, soil, poster **Nonconsumable** transparent container, hand lens	Observing
Skills Lab, p. 334	15	**Consumable** water, paper towels **Nonconsumable** plastic dropper, cardboard, clock or watch, flashlight, 2 earthworms in a storage container, tray	Developing Hypotheses

A list of all materials required for the Student Edition activities can be found on pages T25–T33. You can obtain information about ordering materials by calling 1-800-848-9500 or by accessing the Science Explorer Internet site at **www.phschool.com**.

Alive and Well

Purpose By caring for an animal during this project, students will learn more about what animals need. They will also learn how to make careful observations.

Skills Focus Students will be able to
◆ pose questions about how to meet the needs of an animal;
◆ observe the behaviors and characteristics of their animal;
◆ communicate their findings about the animal to their classmates.

Project Time Line The project requires about five weeks. See Chapter 10 Project Teacher Notes on pages 2–3 in Unit 3 Resources for hints and detailed directions. Also give students the Chapter 10 Project Overview, Worksheets, and Scoring Rubric on pages 4–8 in Unit 3 Resources. During week one, students should choose their animals, design the habitats, and obtain approval for their plans. At the end of week one, students should have habitats ready for the animals to live in and can obtain the animal and place it in its new habitat.

During weeks two through four, students should place the animals in their habitats and observe their behaviors.

During week five, students should prepare their reports. Have students present their findings to the class.

Suggested Shortcuts Simplify the project by placing students in groups. Have students complete Project Worksheets 1 and 2 with their groups.

You may also wish to choose the animals for the students. Alternatively, keep one animal for the entire class and have groups of students observe and take care of it on different days. To shorten the project time line, have students observe their animals for only one week.

Possible Materials Suitable project animals include slugs, snails, earthworms, pill bugs, spiders, millipedes, fruit flies, crickets, guppies, and anole lizards. Before students consider what animal to choose, explain any restrictions related to school policy on live animals in the classroom; limited classroom storage space, and local

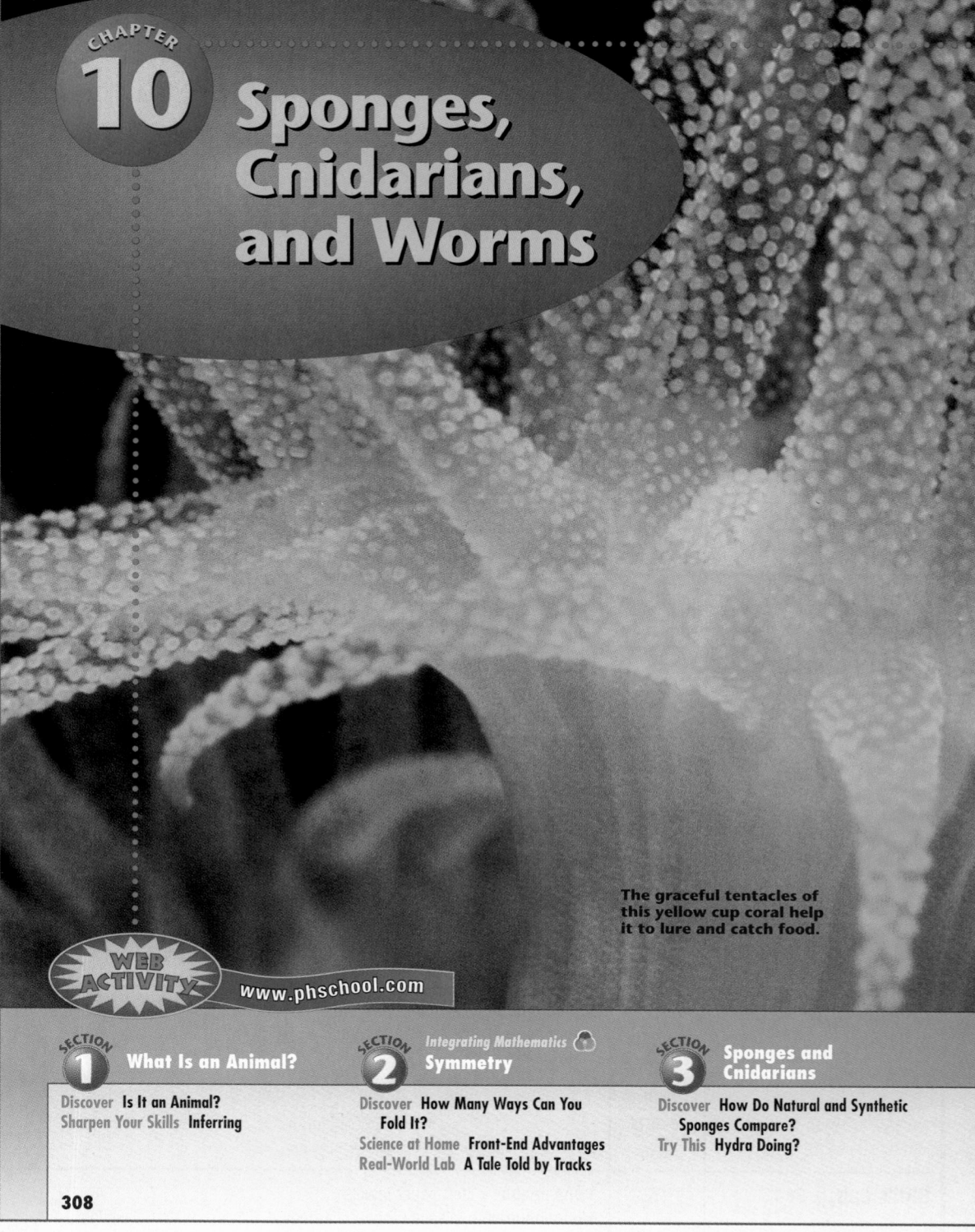

CHAPTER
10 Sponges, Cnidarians, and Worms

The graceful tentacles of this yellow cup coral help it to lure and catch food.

WEB ACTIVITY www.phschool.com

SECTION **1** What Is an Animal?
Discover Is It an Animal?
Sharpen Your Skills Inferring

SECTION **2** *Integrating Mathematics*
Symmetry
Discover How Many Ways Can You Fold It?
Science at Home Front-End Advantages
Real-World Lab A Tale Told by Tracks

SECTION **3** Sponges and Cnidarians
Discover How Do Natural and Synthetic Sponges Compare?
Try This Hydra Doing?

308

conditions such as nighttime and weekend temperatures. Food for the animals will vary depending on the chosen animal's requirements. Leaves, vegetable trimmings, and insects are some possibilities. All habitats must have an adequate supply of water, moisture, and hiding places.

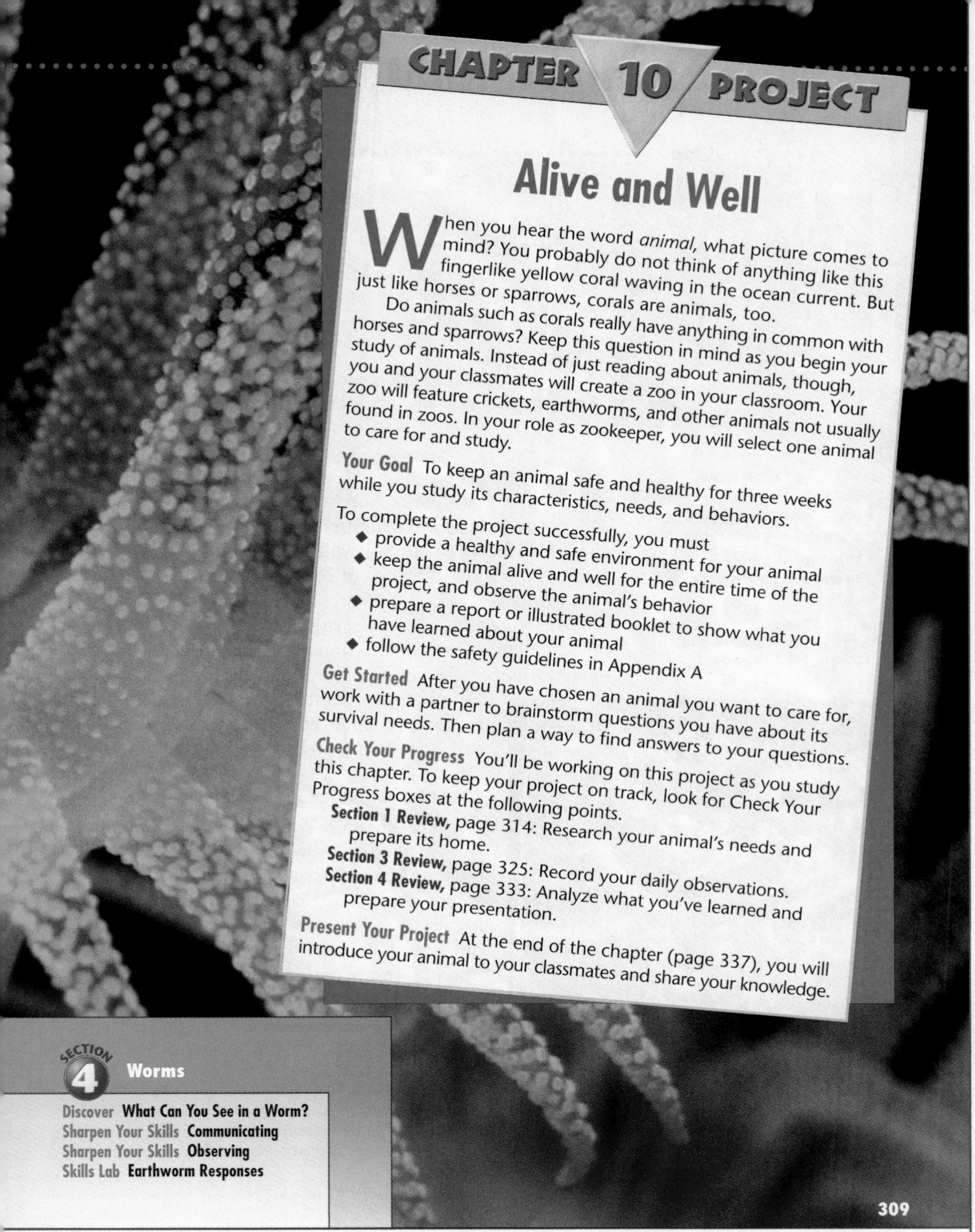

Alive and Well

When you hear the word *animal*, what picture comes to mind? You probably do not think of anything like this fingerlike yellow coral waving in the ocean current. But just like horses or sparrows, corals are animals, too.

Do animals such as corals really have anything in common with horses and sparrows? Keep this question in mind as you begin your study of animals. Instead of just reading about animals, though, you and your classmates will create a zoo in your classroom. Your zoo will feature crickets, earthworms, and other animals not usually found in zoos. In your role as zookeeper, you will select one animal to care for and study.

Your Goal To keep an animal safe and healthy for three weeks while you study its characteristics, needs, and behaviors.

To complete the project successfully, you must
◆ provide a healthy and safe environment for your animal
◆ keep the animal alive and well for the entire time of the project, and observe the animal's behavior
◆ prepare a report or illustrated booklet to show what you have learned about your animal
◆ follow the safety guidelines in Appendix A

Get Started After you have chosen an animal you want to care for, work with a partner to brainstorm questions you have about its survival needs. Then plan a way to find answers to your questions.

Check Your Progress You'll be working on this project as you study this chapter. To keep your project on track, look for Check Your Progress boxes at the following points.

Section 1 Review, page 314: Research your animal's needs and prepare its home.
Section 3 Review, page 325: Record your daily observations.
Section 4 Review, page 333: Analyze what you've learned and prepare your presentation.

Present Your Project At the end of the chapter (page 337), you will introduce your animal to your classmates and share your knowledge.

SECTION 4 Worms

Discover What Can You See in a Worm?
Sharpen Your Skills Communicating
Sharpen Your Skills Observing
Skills Lab Earthworm Responses

309

Program Resources

◆ **Unit 3 Resources** Chapter 10 Project Teacher Notes, pp. 2–3; Chapter 10 Project Overview and Worksheets, pp. 4–7; Chapter 10 Project Scoring Rubric, p. 8

WEB ACTIVITY   www.phschool.com

You will find an Internet activity, chapter self-tests for students, and links to other chapter topics at this site.

Students should construct a suitable habitat for their animals. A 2-liter soda bottle could serve as a nice terrarium for an insect. Students can carefully cut the top off the bottle, then fill it with soil, leaf litter, twigs, and plants for their animals. They can then cover the bottle with plastic wrap and cut tiny holes in the plastic wrap for ventilation.

Launching the Project When introducing the project, bring an animal into the classroom to show the students. Ask: **What kinds of things do you think this animal needs to live?** *(Food, water, a place to live)* Talk about where the animal lives, what it eats, and how to take care of it. Ask: **Where would you find this kind of information if you did not already know it?** *(In the library, on the Internet, or in a pet store)* **What kinds of things do you think you can find out by watching this animal's behavior?** *(Students may mention how and what the animal eats, how it moves, when it is quiet or active, where it stays in its habitat, and the characteristics of its body.)*

Allow students to read the description of the project in their text and in the Chapter 10 Project Overview on pages 4–5 in Unit 3 Resources. Distribute copies of the Chapter 10 Project Worksheets on pages 6–7 for students to complete.

Performance Assessment

The Chapter 10 Project Scoring Rubric on page 8 of Unit 3 Resources will help you evaluate how well students complete the Chapter 10 Project. Students will be assessed on
◆ how well they plan for their animals' care;
◆ whether they observe and record their animals' behavior daily;
◆ the thoroughness and organization of their presentations, and
◆ how well they participate in group activities associated with the project.
By sharing the Chapter 10 Project Scoring Rubric with students at the beginning of the project, you will make it clear to them what they are expected to do.

Objectives

After completing the lesson, students will be able to
◆ list and describe four major characteristics that all animals share;
◆ describe what animals need from their environment in order to live;
◆ describe animal adaptations for getting food and escaping predators.

Key Terms organ, adaptation, herbivore, carnivore, predator, prey, omnivore, invertebrate, vertebrate

1 Engage/Explore

Activating Prior Knowledge

Ask: **What does an animal look like? How is it different from a flower or a tree?** Have students brainstorm ideas. Have students sketch an animal on a piece of paper and list three things that make it an animal. *(Sample answer: An animal must eat other living things.)* Lead students to realize that there is tremendous diversity among animals.

········ **DISCOVER** ·········

Skills Focus forming operational definitions

Materials *organisms that students can safely observe such as earthworms, minnows, pill bugs, crickets, potted plants, ferns, and sponges*
Time 15 minutes
Tips Make sure students record whether or not each specimen is an animal while looking at that specimen. Ask students to give at least one reason for their choice. Invite them to discuss their decisions in small groups. Remind students to treat all living things with care.
Expected Outcome Students should recognize animals such as earthworms and minnows. They may not recognize sponges as animals.
Think It Over Students may note behavioral characteristics such as eating and movement or physical features such as mouths, hair, legs, fins, or wings.

310

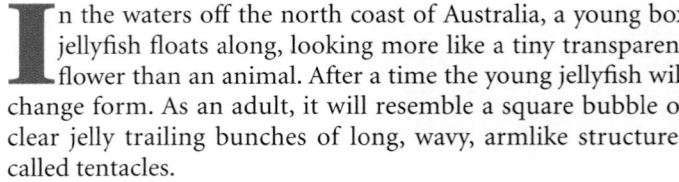

Is It an Animal?

1. Carefully examine each of the organisms that your teacher gives you.
2. Decide which ones are animals. Think about the reasons for your decision. Wash your hands after handling each of the organisms.

Think It Over
Forming Operational Definitions What characteristics did you use to decide whether each organism was an animal?

GUIDE FOR READING

◆ What characteristics do all animals have in common?
◆ What three things do animals need from their environment?

Reading Tip **Before you begin to read, write your own definition of** *animal.* **Add to it or change it as you read.**

Figure 1 Don't be fooled by the delicate-looking tentacles of the Australian box jellyfish. Animals that brush against them can be killed by their venom—and become the jellyfish's next meal.

I n the waters off the north coast of Australia, a young box jellyfish floats along, looking more like a tiny transparent flower than an animal. After a time the young jellyfish will change form. As an adult, it will resemble a square bubble of clear jelly trailing bunches of long, wavy, armlike structures called tentacles.

To capture food, a box jellyfish's tentacles fire deadly venom at unlucky animals that happen to touch them. Humans are no exception. A swimmer who brushes the tentacles of a box jellyfish can die in only four minutes. In spite of their harmless appearance, adult box jellyfish have one of the strongest venoms on Earth.

Characteristics of Animals

The box jellyfish may not look like most animals you are familiar with, but it is indeed an animal. Biologists have described over 1 million different animal species, and there are certainly many more. Recall that a species is a group of organisms that can mate with each other and produce offspring, who in turn can mate and reproduce.

310

READING STRATEGIES

Reading Tip When defining the term *animal*, students may find it helpful to list some characteristics they have noticed in animals. Remind students to modify their definitions as they read. Suggest that they note the subhead titles under *Characteristics of Animals* to help them add to their definitions.

Study and Comprehension Have students outline the main ideas of the section. Outlines should include the characteristics of animals (multicellular, heterotroph, sexual reproduction, movement); adaptations for getting food; and adaptations for escaping predators.

All species of animals, including the beautiful but deadly box jellyfish, are similar in some important ways. **Animals are many-celled organisms that must obtain their food by eating other organisms.** In addition, most animals reproduce sexually and can move from place to place. Biologists look for these characteristics in deciding whether an organism is an animal.

How Animal Cells Are Organized All animals are multicellular organisms. The cells of most animals are grouped together to form different kinds of tissue. A tissue is a group of similar cells that perform a specific job. For example, muscle tissue allows animals to move, while nerve tissue carries messages from one part of the body to another. Tissues may combine to form an **organ**, which is a group of different tissues that work together to perform a specific job that is more complex than the functions of each tissue by itself. Organs are made up of different types of tissue—your thigh bone, for example, is an organ that contains bone tissue, nerve tissue, and blood. In most animals, different organs combine to form an organ system, such as your skeletal system, shown in Figure 2.

How Animals Obtain Food Earlier chapters of this book described autotrophs, organisms that make their own food, and heterotrophs, organisms that cannot make their own food. Every animal is a heterotroph—it must obtain food by eating other organisms. Most animals take food into a cavity inside their bodies. Inside this cavity, the food is digested, or broken down into substances that the animal's body can absorb and use.

How Animals Reproduce Animals typically reproduce sexually. You have learned that sexual reproduction is the process by which a new organism forms from the joining of two organisms' sex cells. When a male sperm cell and a female egg cell unite, the resulting new individual has a combination of characteristics from both parents. Some animals can also reproduce asexually. Recall that asexual reproduction is the process by which a single organism produces a new organism identical to itself. A tiny animal called a hydra, for example, reproduces asexually by forming buds that eventually break off to form new hydras.

How Animals Move Many animal movements are related to obtaining food, reproducing, or escaping danger. Barnacles, for example, wave feathery arms through the water to collect tiny food particles. Some geese fly long distances each spring to the place where they mate and lay eggs. And you've probably seen a cat climb a tree to escape a snarling dog.

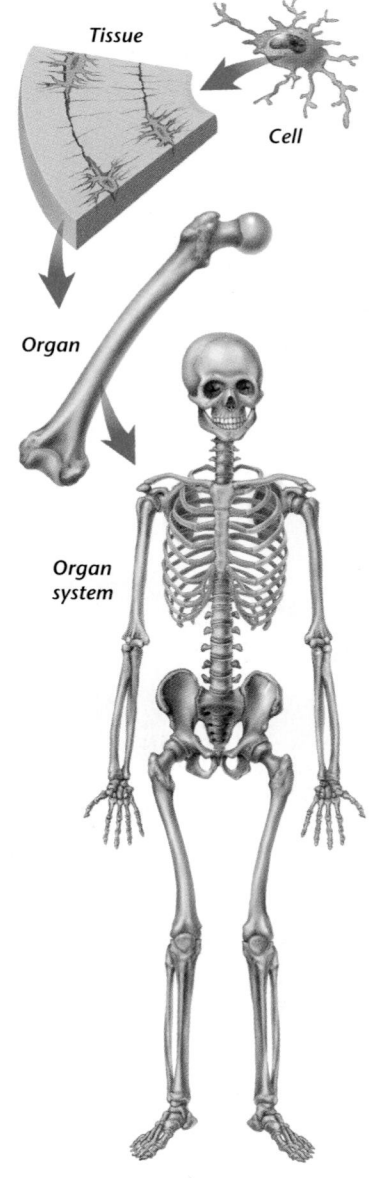

Tissue

Cell

Organ

Organ system

Figure 2 An animal's skeletal system has different levels of organization. Bone cells make up tissues, and tissues make up organs such as the thigh bone.
Classifying Is the skull best classified as an organ or as a tissue?

2 Facilitate

Characteristics of Animals

Using The Visuals: Figure 1
Draw students' attention to the jellyfish. Then ask: **Is this a picture of an animal? How can you tell?** Elicit information on what characteristics students used to form their answer. Finally, tell students to read the caption and describe how the jellyfish obtains its food. **learning modality: visual**

Including All Students
To provide students who need extra challenges with the opportunity to observe details of tissues and organs, give them an uncooked chicken drumstick with the thigh still attached, a dissection kit, and hand lenses. **CAUTION:** Beforehand, soak chicken overnight in dilute bleach solution; then rinse. Students should wear disposable gloves. Dissecting probes and scalpels are sharp. Urge students to use them carefully.

ACTIVITY

   Remind students that muscles are part of the system that provides support for the animal. Have students carefully remove the skin and notice the fat, muscle, and connective tissue. Ask students to carefully disassemble, sketch, and count the muscles of the thigh and lower leg. Have students carefully slice through one of the larger muscles in cross section and observe the structure with a hand lens.
learning modality: visual

Portfolio Students can save sketches of their work and written observations in their portfolios.

Program Resources

◆ **Unit 3 Resources** 10-1 Lesson Plan, p. 9; 10-1 Section Summary, p. 10

Media and Technology

Transparencies "Levels of Organization in the Body" Transparency 40

Audio CD English-Spanish Summary 10-1

Answers to Self-Assessment
Caption Question
Figure 2 Like the thigh bone, the skull is an organ.

Ongoing Assessment

Writing Have each student list the major characteristics of animals. (*Multicellular, heterotrophs, typically reproduce sexually, most move freely*)

How Animals Meet Their Needs

Cultural Diversity

Help students to brainstorm a list of animals that people of cultures throughout the world use for transport. *(Samples: horse, camel, elephant, donkey, llama)* Explain that each culture uses transport animals that are adapted to their region's climate. Ask students to name characteristics that help specific animals survive in their environments. *(Sample: Camels can go without water for a long time in hot, dry climates.)*
learning modality: verbal

Adaptations for Getting Food

Including All Students

For the benefit of students who are learning English, contrast the meanings, spellings, and pronunciations of *predator* and *prey*. Point out that both words derive from the Latin word *praedari*, meaning "to plunder." **limited English proficiency**

Sharpen your *Skills*

Inferring

Time 15 minutes

ACTIVITY

Tips Have students describe the shape of the teeth in each picture. Ask: **What do you think the sharp, pointed teeth in A are adapted to do?** *(Tear skin or flesh)* Then ask: **What do you think the broad, flat teeth in B are adapted to do?** *(To grind or shred plants)* Remind students that animals that eat flesh are carnivores and those that eat plants are herbivores.

Expected Outcome Students should say that the animal in A eats meat and the animal in B eats plants.

Extend Have students compare their own teeth and jaws to those shown in the pictures. Have students describe their own teeth. *(Sample: Some of my front teeth are sharp and pointed like a carnivore's. Some of my back teeth are broad and flat like an herbivore's.)*
learning modality: visual

312

Some animals don't move from place to place. Adult oysters, sponges, and corals all stick firmly to underwater rocks. But most animals move freely at some point in their lives. For example, for its first few weeks of life, an oyster is a tiny swimmer. Then the young oyster swims to a solid surface. It glues itself in place and changes into an adult oyster within a shell.

How Animals Meet Their Needs

Animals need to obtain water, food, and oxygen from their environment, or surroundings. Animals need water because the chemical reactions that keep them alive, such as the breakdown of food, take place in water. Food provides animals with raw materials for growth and with energy for their bodies' activities, such as moving and breathing. To release that energy, the body's cells need oxygen. Some animals get oxygen from air; others absorb it from water.

An animal also needs to be able to respond to its environment—for example, to find food or to run away from danger. Animals' bodies and behaviors are adapted for such tasks. An **adaptation** is a characteristic that helps an organism survive in its environment or reproduce.

Adaptations for Getting Food

Unlike plants that make their own food using sunlight, animals must obtain their food. Some animals eat plants, other animals eat animals, and still others eat both plants and animals.

Herbivores Animals that eat only plants are called **herbivores.** Grasshoppers, termites, and garden snails are some common small herbivores. Larger herbivores include cows, horses, and pandas. Herbivores have adaptations such as teeth with broad, flat surfaces that are good for grinding tough plants.

Figure 3 Animals have different methods of obtaining food.
A. A macaw uses its curved beak to feed on fruits and seeds.
B. A carpet snake uses its body to strangle a lizard for a meal.
Applying Concepts What do these animals obtain from food?

312

Carnivores Animals that eat only other animals are **carnivores.** Many carnivores are **predators** that hunt and kill other animals. Predators have adaptations that help them capture the animals they feed upon, their **prey.** Wolves, for example, run down their prey. A wolf's adaptations include sharp claws, speed, and excellent hearing and eyesight. The teeth of most carnivores are sharp and pointed—they are adapted for cutting and stabbing.

Unlike wolves, "sit-and-wait" predators hide and attack suddenly. Most blend in with their surroundings. Think of a frog sitting by a pond. An insect flying by doesn't see the frog. Suddenly the frog flicks out its tongue and catches the unsuspecting insect.

Omnivores An animal that eats both plants and animals is an **omnivore.** A grizzly bear eats berries and roots, as well as insects, fish, and other small animals. Humans are also omnivores, as you know if you like hamburgers with tomato.

☑ *Checkpoint* *Describe some feeding adaptations of carnivores.*

Adaptations for Escaping Predators

In addition to feeding adaptations, animals have adaptations that help them avoid being eaten by predators. Some animals, such as box turtles and hedgehogs, have hard shells or spiny skins. Opossums and pill bugs "play dead" when they are attacked, so their predators lose interest. Stingers, claws, bitter-tasting flesh, or smelly sprays protect other animals. If you see a skunk, you stay far away from it. So do most predators.

Classification of Animals

Biologists classify animals in the animal kingdom into about 35 phyla, or major groups. The branching tree on page 314 shows how biologists think some of the phyla are related. For example, from their positions on the tree, you can see that segmented worms are more closely related to arthropods than to sponges. The tree also shows the order in which biologists think animal life has evolved, or changed over time.

One important characteristic used to classify animals is the presence or absence of a backbone. An animal that does not have a backbone is called an **invertebrate.** Jellyfishes, worms, snails, crabs, spiders, and insects are all invertebrates. Most animal species—about 95 percent—are invertebrates. In contrast, a **vertebrate** is an animal that has a backbone. Fishes, amphibians, reptiles, birds, and mammals are all vertebrates.

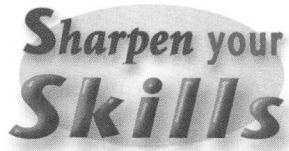

Sharpen your Skills

Inferring *ACTIVITY*

The pictures show the jawbones of two animals. Look at the pictures carefully, and decide what types of food each animal probably eats. List the observations on which you base your inferences.

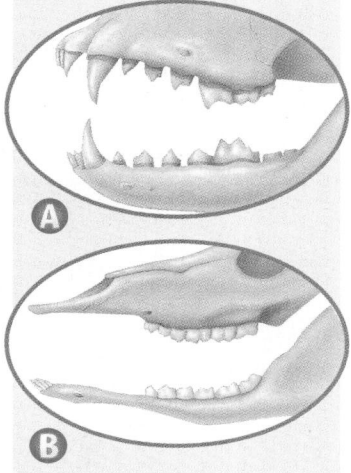

A

B

Figure 4 This African pygmy hedgehog can roll up into a spiny ball to protect itself from predators.

Chapter 10 **313**

Adaptations for Escaping Predators

Building Inquiry Skills: Classifying

Materials: *Pictures of animals from various sources*
Obtain several photographs or drawings of prey animals and predators. If pictures are not available that show both in the same picture, use separate pictures and match them up, as in lion—zebra, fox—rabbit. Divide the class into groups and distribute a set of matching pictures to each group. Have the group make a list of adaptations the prey animals have, such as big horns or long legs. They should then classify these as adaptations for getting food or adaptations for escaping predators. Then have them make a list of adaptations the predators have that allow them to capture prey. **cooperative learning**

Classification of Animals

Using the Visuals: Figure 5

Have students read aloud the names on the limbs of the branching tree. Some of the names may be unfamiliar to students. Tell them they will learn more about these animals as they study this book. Ask: **Are insects more closely related to spiders or to mollusks?** *(spiders)* Then ask: **Which group probably arose earlier, crustaceans or echinoderms?** *(echinoderms)* Continue in this fashion with other animal groups. Explain that this family tree shows rough evolutionary relationships among the major animal groups. **learning modality: visual**

Answers to Self-Assessment

Caption Question

Figure 3 Animals obtain raw materials for growth and energy for their bodies' activities.

☑ *Checkpoint*

Students may note the wolf's adaptations mentioned in the text—sharp claws, speed, and keen senses. Students may also mention snakes that constrict prey.

Ongoing Assessment

Oral Presentation Have each student choose an animal and give a brief oral presentation, describing its adaptations for feeding or protection.

3 Assess

Section 1 Review Answers

1. Multicellular; obtain food by eating other organisms (heterotrophic)
2. Animals need water, food, and oxygen to survive.
3. An invertebrate, such as a jellyfish, does not have a backbone. A vertebrate, such as a frog, has a backbone.
4. The wolf actively pursues its prey while the cow grazes and is a large herbivore. Students should name one adaptation each for the wolf and frog. The wolf has sharp, pointed teeth, keen senses, and speed. The cow has broad, flat teeth that are good for chewing plants.

....

Check Your Progress CHAPTER PROJECT

Before students obtain their animals, group students who have researched and planned habitats for the same kind of animal. Have these students discuss plans for acquiring, housing, and caring for the animal. Visit groups and verify that all students meet the planning requirements of the project and will be able to care for the needs of their animals. After this initial approval, allow students to prepare the habitats. Check habitats for safety before allowing students to obtain their animals.

Performance Assessment

Oral Presentation Provide students with magazines or books containing photographs of animals. Ask each student to choose a photograph of an animal. Have students present their photographs to the class and describe at least two characteristics a scientist would use to classify the organism as an animal. Then show students a plant or a photograph of a plant. Ask them to explain why that organism is *not* an animal.

314

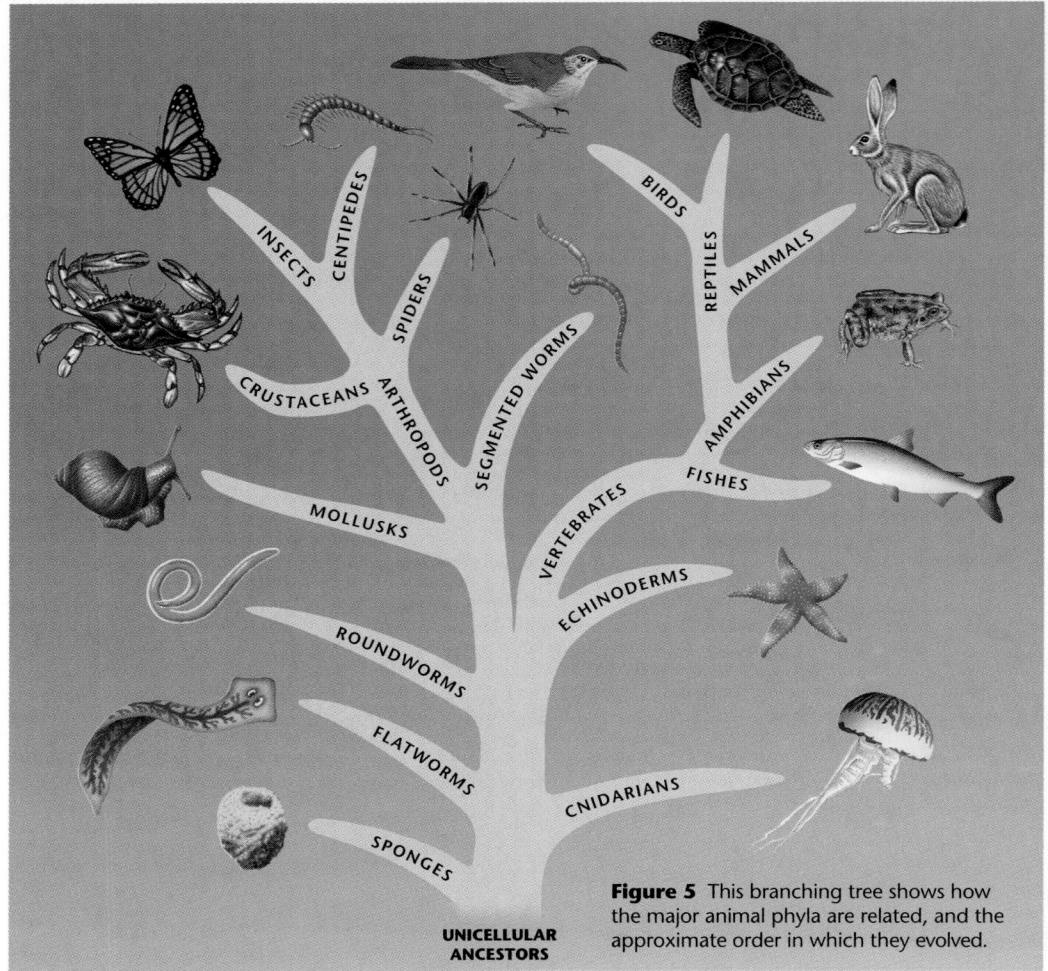

Figure 5 This branching tree shows how the major animal phyla are related, and the approximate order in which they evolved.

UNICELLULAR ANCESTORS

 ## Section 1 Review

1. Describe two characteristics of all animals.
2. List three needs that all animals must meet in order to survive.
3. Define *invertebrate* and *vertebrate*. Give an example of each.
4. **Thinking Critically Comparing and Contrasting** Contrast the ways in which wolves and cows obtain their food, and identify one food-getting adaptation of each animal.

314

....

Check Your Progress CHAPTER PROJECT

By now, you should have chosen an animal and researched how to meet its needs. Discuss with your teacher your plans for housing and caring for your animal. After preparing your animal's home and obtaining some food for it, put the animal in its new home. (*Hint:* Make a plan for your animal for holidays and weekends.)

Program Resources

◆ **Unit 3 Resources** 10-1 Review and Reinforce, p. 11; 10-1 Enrich, p. 12

INTEGRATING MATHEMATICS

SECTION 2 Symmetry

DISCOVER

ACTIVITY

How Many Ways Can You Fold It?

1. Trace the triangle onto a sheet of paper and cut it out. Then draw a circle by tracing the rim of a glass or other round object. Cut out the circle.

2. Fold the triangle so that one half matches the other. Do the same with the circle.

3. See how many different ways you can fold each figure so that the two halves are identical.

Think It Over

Classifying Can you think of animals whose body shape could be folded in the same number of ways as the triangle? As the circle?

With its wings closed, a bright and colorful butterfly perches lightly on a flower, drinking nectar. Its delicate but strong wings are motionless as it drinks. Then, suddenly, those fragile-looking wings begin to move, and they lift the butterfly, seemingly effortlessly, into the air.

As you can see from the photo of the large copper butterfly in Figure 6, a butterfly's body has two halves, and each half looks almost like a reflection of the other. This balanced arrangement, called symmetry, is characteristic of many animals. A butterfly's symmetry contributes to its pleasing appearance. More importantly, the balanced wings help the butterfly to fly more easily.

GUIDE FOR READING

◆ What types of symmetry do complex animals exhibit?

Reading Tip Before you read, preview the illustrations in Figures 6 and 7. Write a few sentences comparing and contrasting the organisms in the illustrations.

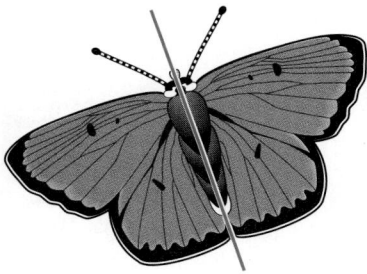

Figure 6 If you could draw a line through this butterfly's body, it would divide the animal into two mirror-image halves. *Applying Concepts* What is this balanced arrangement called?

Chapter 10 **315**

READING STRATEGIES

Reading Tip Students may say that body shape is important because some body shapes include a head with senses and a brain. Students may think of the sea urchin as "inferior" because it has no head. Have students update their comparisons as they read and learn new content.

Vocabulary Point out that the word *bilateral* comes from Latin words meaning "two-sided." Ask students to list other English words that include the root *bi-* and discuss their meanings. *(Sample: Bicycle means "two-wheeled.")* Ask students to think of words similar to the word *radial. (Sample: radius, radiation)* Suggest that when students read the section, they look for a connection between these words and the definition of radial symmetry.

INTEGRATING MATHEMATICS

SECTION 2 Symmetry

Objective

After completing the lesson, students will be able to

◆ distinguish between bilateral and radial symmetry, and describe how animals exhibit these kinds of symmetry.

Key Terms bilateral symmetry, radial symmetry

1 Engage/Explore

Activating Prior Knowledge

Bring to class a selection of bilaterally symmetrical and asymmetrical shapes, pictures, or objects such as leaves, shells, keys, gloves, and scissors. Show students each object, then sort the objects into two groups—symmetrical and asymmetrical. Ask students what characteristic you used to group the shapes. Accept all reasonable answers. Leave the objects in their groups until after the section content has been introduced. Then make sure students understand you sorted the objects based on symmetry.

DISCOVER

Skills Focus classifying
Materials *tracing paper, scissors, pen or pencil, circular object*
ACTIVITY
Time 10 minutes
Tips Suggest that students first determine how many ways the triangle can be folded before they attempt to fold the circle.
Expected Outcome Students should conclude that the triangle can be folded one way into identical halves, and that the circle could be folded in an infinite number of ways.
Think It Over Students may say that the body shapes of butterflies, tigers, and dogs could be folded the same number of ways as a triangle. The body shapes of a sea urchin and jellyfish could be folded the same number of ways as a circle.

315

2 Facilitate

The Mathematics of Symmetry

Building Inquiry Skills: Applying Concepts

Materials *magazines, tape, colored pencils, white paper*

Time 15 minutes

Tips Cut magazine pictures of symmetrical objects in half and give them to students. Objects could include such things as a basketball, a human face, a car, or a pizza. Have students tape their pictures onto pieces of paper, then use what they know about symmetry to draw the complete object. Ask students to identify the objects as radially or bilaterally symmetrical. **learning modality: visual**

Students can save their finished pictures in their portfolios.

Including All Students

Point out that the prefix *bi-* in *bilateral* means "two," and relate this to the concept of bilateral symmetry. Ask the class to identify and define other words with the prefix *bi-*. (*Examples: bicycle, binoculars*) **limited English proficiency**

Symmetry in Animals

Using the Visuals: Figures 6 and 7

Draw students' attention to the photographs of the animals and their diagrams. Organize students in small groups and give each group a small hand mirror. Direct students to hold the mirror along the lines of symmetry and examine the mirror images produced. Ask them to predict what would happen if they held the mirror somewhere else on the drawing of the butterfly. (*The image would not exactly match the butterfly's shape.*) **cooperative learning**

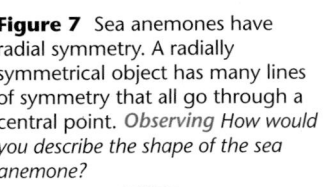

Figure 7 Sea anemones have radial symmetry. A radially symmetrical object has many lines of symmetry that all go through a central point. *Observing How would you describe the shape of the sea anemone?*

The Mathematics of Symmetry

In Figure 6 on page 315, you can see that a line drawn down the middle of the butterfly produces two halves that are the same—they are mirror images. This dividing line is called a line of symmetry. An object has line symmetry, or **bilateral symmetry,** if there is a line that divides it into halves that are mirror images. A large copper butterfly has bilateral symmetry, as do an oak leaf, a spoon, and a pair of eyeglasses.

Contrast the butterfly's symmetry to that of a sea anemone. A sea anemone is circular if you look at it from the top, as in Figure 7. Any line drawn through its center will divide the sea anemone into two symmetrical halves. Like the sea anemone, many circular objects exhibit **radial symmetry**—they have many lines of symmetry that all go through a central point. Pie plates and bicycle wheels have radial symmetry.

☑ *Checkpoint* *How is radial symmetry different from bilateral symmetry?*

Symmetry in Animals

There are a few animals, such as most sponges, that exhibit no symmetry. These asymmetrical animals generally have very simple body plans. Sponges, for example, have no hearts, brains, kidneys, or nerve cells. **The bodies of complex animals all have either radial or bilateral symmetry.**

Animals with Radial Symmetry The external body parts of animals with radial symmetry are equally spaced around a central point, like spokes on a bicycle wheel. Because of the circular arrangement of their parts, radially symmetrical animals, such as jellyfishes, sea anemones, and sea urchins, do not have distinct front or back ends.

Animals with radial symmetry have several characteristics in common. All of them live in water. Most of them do not move very fast—they either stay in one spot, are moved along by water currents, or creep along the bottom. Few radially symmetrical animals are able to go out in search of prey. Instead, their watery environment carries food to them.

For a water animal that does not actively chase prey, the absence of a front end creates no disadvantage. Animals with radial symmetry learn about their environment primarily through senses of touch and taste, which function on the surfaces of their bodies. Because the animals are able to sense their environment in all directions, they can be ready to grab food coming from any direction.

Background

Facts and Figures There are three basic kinds of symmetry among living things—spherical, radial, and bilateral. Animals that lack these basic symmetries, such as sponges, are said to be asymmetrical.

Spherical symmetry is rare and is typical of free-floating organisms that do not move under their own power, such as protozoans. Amebas become spherical when at rest.

The octopus has an unusual symmetry. It is basically bilaterally symmetrical, but its arms are arranged radially around its mouth. Its body is streamlined so that when the octopus swims rapidly, its head follows along behind.

No one kind of symmetry is better or more advanced than any other. Each has advantages and disadvantages, depending on the animal's habits and environment.

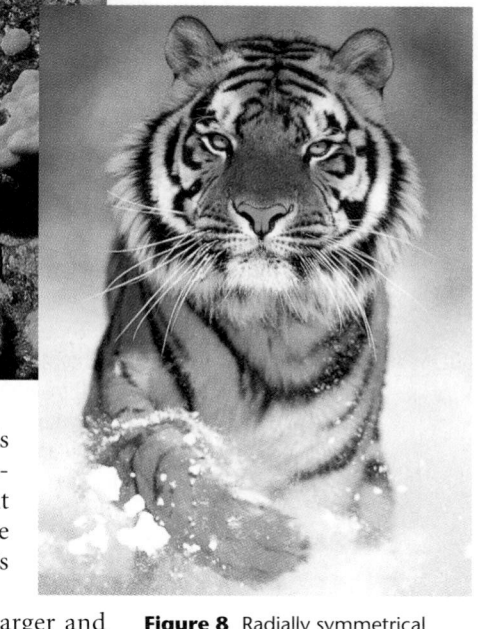

Animals with Bilateral Symmetry Most animals you are familiar with have bilateral symmetry. For example, a fish has only one line of symmetry that divides it into mirror images. Each half of a fish has one eye, one nostril, half of a mouth, and one of each of the fish's pairs of fins. Your body also has bilateral symmetry.

In general, bilaterally symmetrical animals are larger and more complex than those with radial symmetry. Animals with bilateral symmetry have a front end that goes first as the animal moves along. These animals move more quickly and efficiently than most animals with radial symmetry. This is partly because bilateral symmetry allows for a streamlined, balanced body. In addition, most bilaterally symmetrical animals have sense organs in their front ends that pick up information about what is in front of them. Swift movement and sense organs help bilaterally symmetrical animals get food and avoid enemies.

Figure 8 Radially symmetrical animals, like the sea urchin at left, have no distinct front or back ends. In contrast, bilaterally symmetrical animals, like the tiger above, have a front end with sense organs that pick up information. Because of its balanced body plan, a tiger can also move quickly.

Section 2 Review

1. What two types of symmetry do complex animals exhibit? Describe each type.
2. How can bilateral symmetry be an advantage to a predator?
3. Draw a view of a bilaterally symmetrical animal to show its symmetry. Draw the line of symmetry.
4. **Thinking Critically Applying Concepts** Which capital letters of the alphabet have bilateral symmetry? Radial symmetry?

Science at Home

Front-End Advantages With a family member, observe as many different animals as possible in your yard or at a park. Look in lots of different places, such as in the grass, under rocks, and in the air. Explain to your family member the advantage to an animal of having a distinct front end. What is this type of body arrangement called?

Answers to Self-Assessment

Caption Question

Figure 7 The sea anemone is circular when viewed from the top.

☑ *Checkpoint*

A radially symmetrical shape has many lines of symmetry. A bilaterally symmetrical shape has one line of symmetry.

---

3 Assess

Section 2 Review Answers

1. Complex animals exhibit bilateral or radial symmetry. An object has bilateral symmetry if one line can be drawn that divides it into two symmetrical halves. It has radial symmetry if any line drawn through the center divides it into two symmetrical halves.
2. Bilateral symmetry allows animals to have balanced body plans with distinct front and back ends. This body plan enables fast, purposeful movement.
3. Students' drawings should show a bilaterally symmetrical animal with the line of symmetry marked.
4. Bilaterally symmetrical capital letters are A, B, C, D, E, H, I, K, M, T, U, V, W, and Y. Radially symmetrical capital letters are O and X.

Science at Home

Ask a volunteer to read *Science at Home* aloud to the class. Direct students' attention to the paragraph in the text that explains the advantages of having a distinct front end. Ask students to list these advantages. *(Animals move more quickly because of streamlined, balanced bodies. Sense organs in the front end pick up information about what is in front of the animal, such as food or predators.)* Suggest students show their lists to a family member when explaining bilateral symmetry. When observing animals at home, students can sketch the animals they see.

Performance Assessment

Drawing Have each student sketch two familiar objects or living things in the classroom. One should be bilaterally symmetrical, the other radially symmetrical. Ask students to mark the line of bilateral symmetry on the first sketch and the center point on the second sketch.

 Students can save their sketches in their portfolios.

A Tale Told by Tracks

Preparing for Inquiry

Key Concept Animal behavior can be inferred by studying animal tracks.

Skills Objectives Students will be able to
◆ observe tracks left by animals;
◆ infer animal behavior from the tracks.

Time 30 minutes

Advance Planning
◆ If you have not yet taught the skills of observing and inferring, see page 758 of the Skills Handbook.

Alternative Materials Allowing students to examine photographs or drawings of additional animal tracks, which can often be found in field guides, will reinforce and enrich this lab.

Guiding Inquiry

Invitation
◆ Prior to the lab, prepare an outdoor area with damp sand or soil, or undisturbed snow. The area should be about 2 to 3 meters wide and 5 meters long. Invite one student to walk through that area before the class arrives. Then lead the rest of the students to the area.
◆ Have students examine the tracks. Ask: **What observations can you make about these tracks?** *(Sample: The tracks were made by two feet, the feet were a certain size, and the feet were going in a certain direction.)* Next, have students run and hop through the same area. Ask: **How can you tell running tracks from walking tracks? Running tracks from hopping tracks?** *(Accept all reasonable descriptions. The depth and shape of the tracks will be different.)*

Introducing the Procedure
◆ Before students begin the procedure, suggest they make a list of their own questions about the illustrations such as: "How many animals were there?" and "What were the animals doing in each section?"

A TALE TOLD BY TRACKS

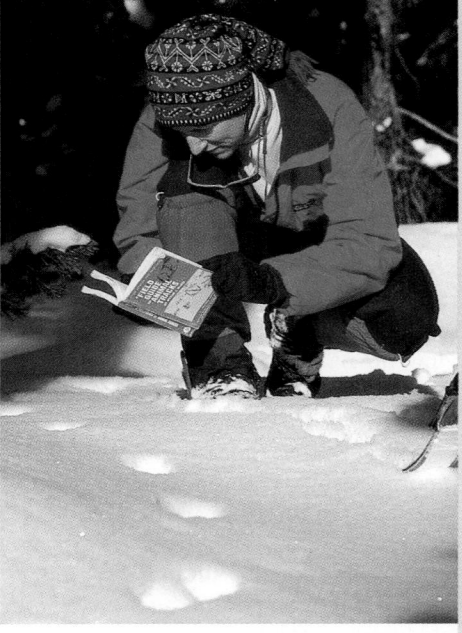

Suppose that, on a chilly winter day, you hike through a park. You suspect that many animals live there, but you don't actually see any of them. Instead, you see signs that the animals have left behind, such as mysterious tracks in the snow. These tracks are evidence you can use to draw inferences about the animals, such as what size they are and what they were doing. Inferences are interpretations of observations that help you to explain what may have happened in a given situation.

Problem

What can you learn about animals by studying their tracks?

Skill Focus

observing, inferring

Procedure

1. Copy the data table into your notebook.
2. The illustration at the top of the next page shows the tracks, or footprints, left in the snow by animals living in a park. The illustration has been divided into three sections. Focus on the tracks in Section 1.
3. Make two or more observations about the tracks and record them in your data table.
4. For each observation you listed, write one or more inferences that could be drawn from that observation.

DATA TABLE

Section	Observations	Inferences
Section 1		
Section 2		
Section 3		

Troubleshooting the Experiment
◆ Students may have difficulty distinguishing observations and inferences.
◆ Students may think there is only one "correct" inference for an observation. Give examples of different, even conflicting, inferences that can be made from a given observation.

Expected Outcome
Students should observe that there are different sets of tracks, probably made by three different animals. Since the tracks and strides are the same, the animals are probably about the same size. They should infer that two of the animals interacted in some way, probably as predator and prey.

Analyze and Conclude
1. Three animals
2. Answers will vary. Sample: All the animals appear to be approximately similar in size.
3. Answers will vary. Sample: The animal entering from the upper left (pink circle) appears to be walking, then it turns direction and begins to run (longer distances between

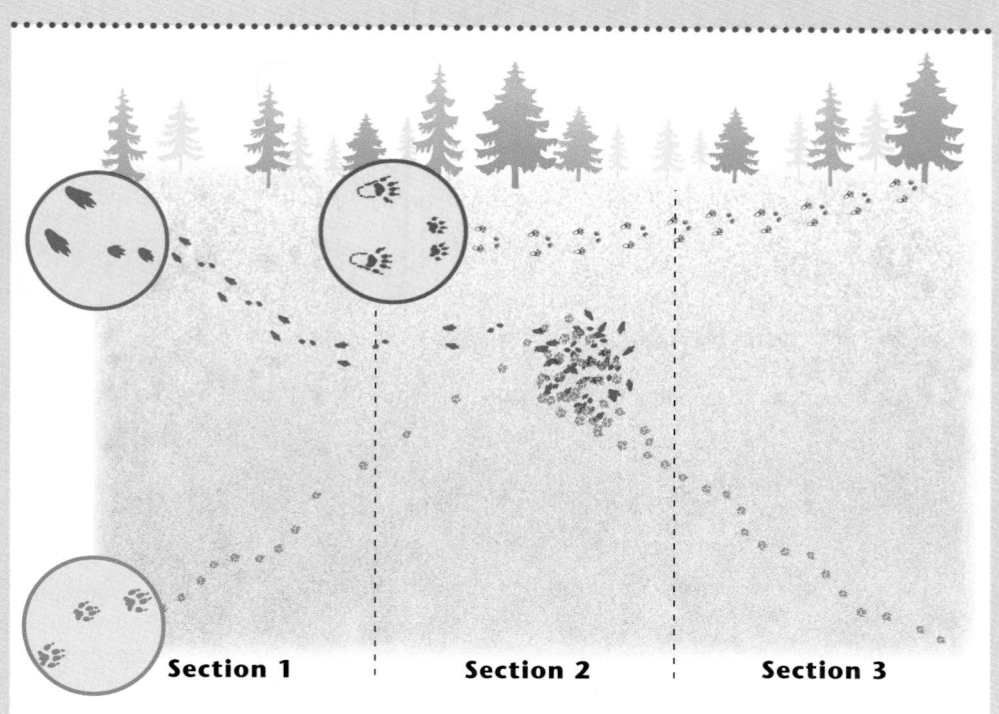

Section 1   **Section 2**   **Section 3**

5. Now look at the tracks in Section 2. Write two or more observations in the data table. For each observation, write one or more inferences.

6. Study the tracks in Section 3. Write two or more observations in the data table. Write at least one inference for each observation.

Analyze and Conclude

1. How many types of animals made the tracks shown in the illustration? Explain.

2. What inferences, if any, can you make about the relative sizes of the animals based on their tracks? Explain.

3. What can you infer about the speed of the animals' movements? Are they walking? Running? How can you tell?

4. In a paragraph, explain what you think happened to the animals and the order in which the events happened.

5. What inference do you feel most confident about and why? Which inference do you feel least confident about and why?

6. **Apply** How might making inferences be important in the work of a real detective? Explain.

More to Explore

Take a walk around your community looking for indirect evidence of animal life such as tracks, feathers, empty nests, and holes in the ground or in dead trees. For each discovery, record its location, at least two observations, and one or more inferences to explain each observation.

prints); then it encounters another animal. The animal entering from the lower left (green circle) appears to walk, then run, before the encounter; it then walks away. The third animal appears to be walking the whole time (small, evenly spaced distances between prints) and was not present during the encounter.

4. Answers will vary. See previous answer.

5. Answers will vary. Sample: Most confident: the predator caught its prey because the tracks of the other animal end. Least confident: deciding what the third animal was doing because the tracks don't provide enough information.

6. Answers will vary. Sample: Making inferences from clues helps a detective figure out what happened during a past event.

Extending the Inquiry

More to Explore Provide field guides to aid student observation, and suggest that students bring a field notebook along with them for quick notes and drawings. Encourage students to make a written record of their findings to bring to class. You may want to put up a map of your community and have students mark and label where they went and what they saw.

Sample Data Table

Section	Observations	Inferences
Section 1	two sets of footprints	Two animals don't see each other
Section 2	three sets of footprints; two sets come together	Two animals meet
Section 3	two sets of footprints	One animal was eaten

Program Resources

◆ **Unit 3 Resources** Chapter 10 Real-World Lab, pp. 25–26
◆ **Inquiry Skills Activity Book** Provides teaching and review of all inquiry skills

Safety

Make sure students are appropriately dressed for the outdoor activity in the Invitation. Review the safety guidelines in Appendix A.

Objectives

After completing the lesson, students will be able to
◆ describe the organization of a sponge's body;
◆ identify the main characteristics of cnidarians;
◆ describe how a coral reef is formed and the life that exists on a coral reef.

Key Terms larva, cnidarian, polyp, medusa

1 Engage/Explore

Activating Prior Knowledge

Bring in a basin of water and a sponge. Ask students to tell you ways sponges are used around the house. (*Mopping floors, wiping up spills, washing dishes*) Ask: **What feature of sponges makes them useful?** (*They soak up liquids.*) Inform students that natural sponges were once live animals, and that divers have harvested sponges for thousands of years.

DISCOVER

Skills Focus observing
Materials *natural sponges, synthetic kitchen sponges, scissors, hand lens or microscope*
Time 20 minutes
Tips Natural sponges can often be found in cosmetic departments or ordered from a biological supply house. Direct students' attention to the pores on the surfaces of the sponges. Tell them that pores in a natural sponge are the openings of pathways through the sponge. Openings on a synthetic sponge are not connected by regular pathways. Students can draw diagrams to compare and contrast features of natural and synthetic sponges.
Expected Outcome Students will observe similarities and differences between natural and artificial sponges.
Think It Over Both have pores, hold liquid, and are soft. They are different in material, color, texture, and shape.

SECTION
3 Sponges and Cnidarians

DISCOVER ••••••••••••••••••••••••••••••••• ACTIVITY

How Do Natural and Synthetic Sponges Compare?

1. Examine a natural sponge, and then use a hand lens or a microscope to take a closer look at its surface. Look carefully at the holes in the sponge. Draw what you see through the lens.
2. Cut out a small piece of sponge and examine it with a hand lens. Draw what you see.
3. Repeat Steps 1 and 2 with a synthetic kitchen sponge.

Think It Over
Observing What are three ways a natural and synthetic sponge are similar? What are three ways they are different?

GUIDE FOR READING

◆ How is the body of a sponge organized?

◆ What are the main characteristics of cnidarians?

Reading Tip As you read, create a compare/contrast table about sponges and cnidarians. Include information on body plans, feeding methods, defense, and reproduction.

Eagerly but carefully, you and the others in your group put on scuba gear, preparing to dive into the ocean and see firsthand what lies beneath the surface. Over the side of the boat you go; the salty ocean water feels cool on your skin. As you slowly descend, you notice that you are surrounded by animals. You see many kinds of fishes, of course, but as you get to the ocean bottom, you notice other animals, too, some as strange as creatures from a science fiction movie. Some of these strange creatures may be sponges.

Sponges live all over the world—mostly in oceans, but also in freshwater rivers and lakes. Sponges are attached to hard surfaces underwater, and they are well adapted to their watery life. Moving currents carry food and oxygen to them, and these same currents take away their waste products. Water plays a role in their reproduction and helps their young find new places to live.

Sponges

Sponges don't look or act like most animals you know. In fact, they are so different that for a long time, people thought that sponges were plants. Like plants, adult sponges stay in one place. But unlike most plants, sponges take food into their bodies, which qualifies them for membership in the animal kingdom. These strange animals have been on Earth for about 540 million years.

◄ Pink sponges on a Caribbean coral reef

READING STRATEGIES

Reading Tip Suggest that students set up their compare/contrast tables before they read. Students can fill in each box as they find the relevant information. Encourage students to read their completed charts as a way to review the section.

Characteristic	Sponges	Cnidarians
Body plan	Asymmetrical	Radically symmetrical
Feeding methods		
Defense		
Reproduction		

The bodies of most sponges have irregular shapes, with no symmetry. While some of their cells do specialized jobs, sponges lack the tissues and organs that most other animals have.

The Structure of a Sponge You might use a brightly colored, synthetic sponge to mop up a spill. That sponge is filled with holes, and so are the animals called sponges. **The body of a sponge is something like a bag that is pierced all over with openings called pores.** In fact, the name of the phylum to which sponges belong—phylum Porifera—means "having pores." Notice the many pores in the sponge in *Exploring a Sponge*.

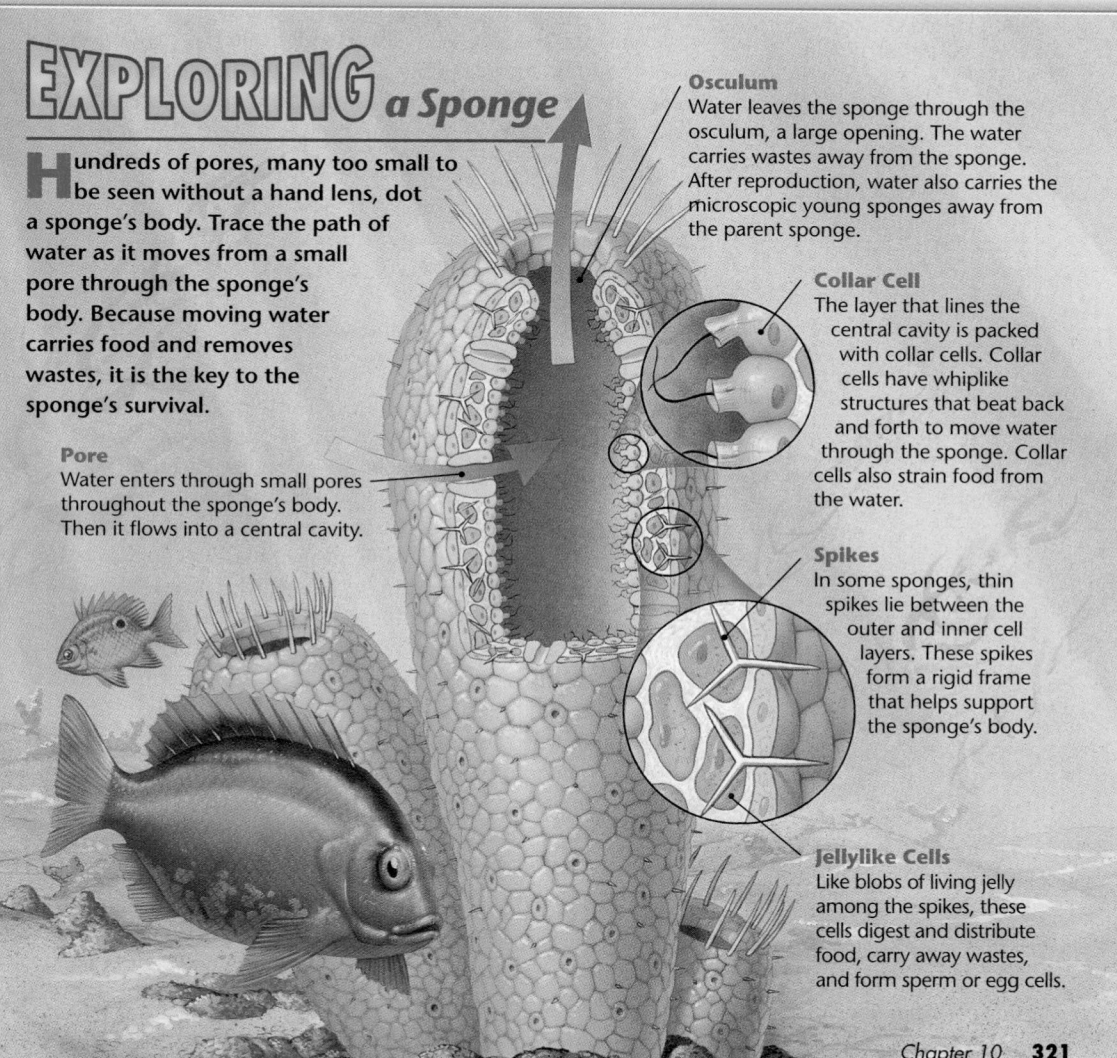

EXPLORING *a Sponge*

Hundreds of pores, many too small to be seen without a hand lens, dot a sponge's body. Trace the path of water as it moves from a small pore through the sponge's body. Because moving water carries food and removes wastes, it is the key to the sponge's survival.

Pore
Water enters through small pores throughout the sponge's body. Then it flows into a central cavity.

Osculum
Water leaves the sponge through the osculum, a large opening. The water carries wastes away from the sponge. After reproduction, water also carries the microscopic young sponges away from the parent sponge.

Collar Cell
The layer that lines the central cavity is packed with collar cells. Collar cells have whiplike structures that beat back and forth to move water through the sponge. Collar cells also strain food from the water.

Spikes
In some sponges, thin spikes lie between the outer and inner cell layers. These spikes form a rigid frame that helps support the sponge's body.

Jellylike Cells
Like blobs of living jelly among the spikes, these cells digest and distribute food, carry away wastes, and form sperm or egg cells.

Chapter 10 **321**

Program Resources

◆ **Unit 3 Resources** 10-3 Lesson Plan, p. 17; 10-3 Section Summary, p. 18

Media and Technology

 Audio CD English-Spanish Summary 10-3

 Transparencies "Exploring a Sponge," Transparency 42

---

2 *Facilitate*

Sponges

EXPLORING
a Sponge

Begin your discussion of the illustration by making certain that students understand what each enlargement shows. Ask a volunteer to describe the structure of a collar cell. Students should observe that a whiplike flagellum is part of the cell. Then have students trace the path of water through the sponge. Help students understand that water enters only through pores, not through the osculum.

After students have examined the illustration, ask: **How do pores help a sponge feed?** *(They allow water into the sponge; the water contains food.)* **How do collar cells help a sponge feed?** *(Move water through the sponge)* **What is the function of the osculum?** *(Allows water to leave the sponge)* **learning modality: visual**

Ongoing Assessment

Oral Presentation Ask students to compare and contrast the pores and osculum of a sponge. *(Water enters the sponge through pores and exits through the larger osculum.)*

Sponges, continued

Integrating Chemistry

Materials *large plastic beaker, water, plastic dropper, food coloring, clock or watch*

Time 20 minutes

Tips Place students in groups and invite them to investigate how oxygen in the water diffuses into a sponge's cells. First have them fill a beaker three-quarters full of water and allow the water to stand for 2 minutes. Then put eight drops of food coloring into the water. Ask students to describe what the food coloring looks like as it enters the water. *(The food coloring is dark and concentrated at the point it enters the beaker.)* Have students observe the water every 2 minutes over a 10-minute period. Ask: **What happened to the food coloring?** *(The food coloring spread evenly throughout the water.)* Tell students the way the food coloring spreads throughout the water is diffusion, and is similar to the way oxygen in water diffuses into a sponge's cells. **learning modality: visual**

Language Arts
CONNECTION

Organize students into small groups. Ask students to make lists of familiar animals and their characteristics. Then have students choose a characteristic, and name several objects or processes that also have this characteristic. Direct students to write a simile about the animal they chose, comparing it to what they named. *(Samples: The cheetah runs as fast as lightning. An elephant's back is as broad as a barn.)* After students make similes for several animals, have them share with group members. Groups can share similes with the class.
cooperative learning

In Your Journal In addition to recording the similes they wrote with their groups, students can look for similes in their favorite books about animals and share them with the class. **Portfolio** Students can save their similes in their portfolios.

Language Arts
CONNECTION

In the paragraph that describes how sponges defend themselves, notice how the author says that a sponge dinner would be "like a sandwich made of thorns, sand, and cement, with a little awful-tasting goo mixed in." The author's description is a simile, which is a comparison using the word *like* or *as*. Writers use similes to paint lively word pictures and create vivid impressions.

In Your Journal

You can use similes in your own writing. For instance, you might say that a racehorse launches itself from the starting line like a rocket. Choose three different animals and write a simile describing each one. For each simile, identify the characteristic that you are trying to convey.

Getting Food and Oxygen from Water Sponges feed by straining food particles from water. As water enters a sponge, it carries tiny organisms such as bacteria and protists. Collar cells on the inside of the central cavity trap these food particles and digest them. Sponges are very efficient at removing food particles from water. A sponge the size of a teacup is able to remove food from 5,000 liters of water per day. That's enough water to fill a truckload of two-liter soft-drink bottles!

INTEGRATING CHEMISTRY A sponge gets its oxygen from water too. The water contains oxygen, which moves from the water into the sponge's cells in a process known as diffusion. In diffusion, molecules of a substance move from an area in which they are highly concentrated to an area in which they are less concentrated. Oxygen is more highly concentrated in the water than it is in the sponge's cells. So the oxygen moves from the water into the sponge. Diffusion also carries waste products from the sponge's cells into the water.

Spikes The soft bodies of most sponges are supported by a network of spikes. Those spikes can be as sharp as needles, as anyone who has touched a live sponge knows. In addition, many sponges are tougher than wood, and some produce irritating substances. Even so, some fish eat sponges. A sponge dinner is probably like a sandwich made of thorns, sand, and cement, with a little awful-tasting goo mixed in.

Sponge Reproduction Sponges reproduce both asexually and sexually. Budding is one form of asexual reproduction in sponges. In budding, small new sponges grow from the sides of an adult sponge. Eventually these tiny sponges detach and begin life on their own. Sponges reproduce sexually too. Sponges do not have separate sexes—a single sponge forms eggs at one time of the year and sperm at a different time. At any one time of the year, some sponges are producing eggs and others are producing sperm. When a sponge produces sperm, the water currents that move through the sponge carry sperm from the sponge into the open water. The sperm may then enter the pores of another sponge and fertilize egg cells in that sponge.

After fertilization, a larva develops. A **larva** (plural *larvae*) is the immature form of an animal that looks very different from the adult. A sponge larva is a hollow ball of cells that swims through the water. Eventually the larva attaches to a surface and develops into a nonmoving adult sponge.

☑ *Checkpoint* As water flows through a sponge's body, what functions does it enable the sponge to perform?

Background

Facts and Figures If a sponge is ground up in a food processor, the individual sponge cells are capable of living independently. When large numbers of sponge cells come near each other, they tend to join together to form new sponges. If cells of several species of sponges are mixed together in the same water, sponge cells will join only with other cells of the same species to form new sponges.

Program Resources

- **Interdisciplinary Exploration Series** "Where River Meets Sea," pp. 33–34

Cnidarians

Some other organisms you might notice on an underwater dive are jellyfishes, sea anemones, and corals. At first glance, those animals look like they could be creatures from another planet. Most jellyfishes look like transparent bubbles that trail curtains of streamerlike tentacles. Sea anemones look like odd, underwater flowers. Some corals have branches that make them look like trees. Jellyfishes, sea anemones, and corals are **cnidarians** (nih DAIR ee uhnz), animals that have stinging cells and take their food into a hollow central cavity. **Members of the phylum Cnidaria are carnivores that use their stinging cells to capture their prey and to defend themselves.** The stinging cells are located on the long, wavy tentacles.

Unlike sponges, cnidarians have specialized tissues. For example, because of muscle-like tissues, many cnidarians can move in interesting ways. Jellyfishes swim through the water, and hydras turn slow somersaults. Anemones stretch out, shrink down, and bend slowly from side to side. These movements are directed by nerve cells that are spread out like a spider web, or net. This nerve net helps the cnidarian respond quickly to danger or the presence of food.

Cnidarian Body Plans Cnidarians have two different body plans. Both body plans have radial symmetry. As you read about these two body plans, refer to Figure 10 on page 324. A **polyp** (PAHL ip), such as a hydra, sea anemone, or coral, is shaped something like a vase, with the mouth opening at the top. Most polyps do not move around; they are

Figure 9 All cnidarians live in watery environments. **A.** Hydras live in freshwater ponds and lakes, where they reproduce by budding. **B.** The Portuguese man-of-war is actually a colony of cnidarians living together. **C.** Sea anemones are large cnidarians that often live in groups in the ocean. *Comparing and Contrasting What characteristics do these three cnidarians share?*

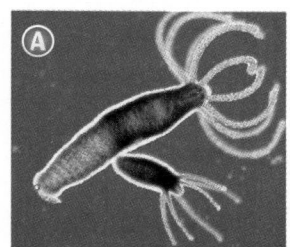

323

Answers to Self-Assessment

Caption Question

Figure 9 All the cnidarians are carnivores and have mouths and tentacles with stinging cells. Cnidarians also have a hollow, central cavity and specialized tissues. They live in water.

☑ *Checkpoint*

The water enables a sponge to feed, get oxygen, discharge waste, and reproduce.

Demonstration

Materials *large jar such as a mayonnaise jar, 50% solution of bleach, natural dried sponge, microscope*

Time 10 minutes for setup, 1 or 2 days to complete demonstration

Tips Prepare about 600 mL of bleach solution by pouring bleach into an equal amount of water. **CAUTION:** *Bleach can damage eyes and clothing. Wear goggles and a lab apron while preparing the bleach solution.*

Fill the jar with the bleach solution and place a sponge in the jar. Seal the jar and let it stand overnight or over a weekend. The bleach will dissolve most of the sponge, leaving the spikes in a gel on the bottom of the jar. Carefully pour the liquid from the jar, making sure not to pour out the gel containing the spikes. Place some of the gel under a binocular microscope and allow students to examine the spikes. To increase learning, students can draw the shapes of the spikes they observe. **learning modality: visual**

Cnidarians

Including All Students

Students may have difficulty remembering that the *c* in cnidarians is silent. Pair students whose first language is not English with native English speakers. Instruct each pair to find three other English words that begin with a silent consonant, such as *knot, know,* and *knuckle.* Pairs can make a table of the words and their pronunciations, and share tables with the class. **limited English proficiency**

Ongoing Assessment

Skills Check Have students compare and contrast how jellyfishes, sea anemones, corals, and hydras move.

323

Cnidarians, continued

TRY THIS

Skills Focus classifying **ACTIVITY**
Materials *live hydra, small glass bowl or petri dish, hand lens or microscope, toothpicks*
Time 25 minutes
Tips You can order hydras from a biological supply house. Guide students to observe characteristics of a cnidarian.
Expected Outcome The hydras will respond by wrapping their tentacles around the toothpick.
Classifying A hydra is a polyp. It moves from place to place in a somersaulting fashion.
Extend Ask if anyone sees a hydra with a bulb or bud developing on its stalk. If so, explain that the hydra is reproducing asexually. **learning modality: visual**

Life on a Coral Reef

Including All Students

Materials *balloon, newspaper strips, flour, water, bowl, straight pins* **ACTIVITY**
Time 20 minutes on 2 days
Tips Some students may need extra help understanding how coral reefs form. To help these students visualize the process, allow them to model a reef by covering balloons with papier mâché. Provide each student with a balloon, newspaper strips, and a flour and water paste made by mixing 3 parts water to 2 parts flour. Direct students to dip newspaper strips into a bowl of paste, then cover the balloon with strips except for a circle about 1 inch in diameter at one end. Students can let the strips dry for one day, then apply another layer and allow to dry for one more day. Ask: **If the balloon represents the soft coral polyp, what does the newspaper shell represent?** (*The coral's hard skeleton*) To model the building of a coral reef, students stack their balloons together while the second layer is wet. Students can demonstrate what happens when the coral polyp dies by popping the balloons with the pins. **CAUTION:** *Pins are a safety hazard.* **learning modality: kinesthetic**

TRY THIS

Hydra Doing?

In this activity, **ACTIVITY** you will observe hydras in action.

1. Put a drop of water that contains hydras in a small unbreakable bowl or petri dish. Allow it to sit for about 15 minutes.
2. Use a hand lens to examine the hydras as they swim. Then gently touch the tentacles of a hydra with the end of a toothpick. Watch what happens.
3. Return the hydras to your teacher, and wash your hands.

Classifying Is a hydra a polyp or a medusa? Describe its method of movement.

adapted for a life attached to an underwater surface. In contrast, the bowl-shaped **medusa** (muh DOO suh), such as a jellyfish, is adapted for a free-swimming life. Medusas, unlike polyps, have mouths that open downward. Some cnidarians go through both a polyp stage and a medusa stage during their lives. Others are polyps or medusas for their whole lives.

How Cnidarians Feed A cnidarian captures its prey by using its stinging cells to inject venom, a poisonous substance that paralyzes fish and other prey. Then the cnidarian's tentacles pull the prey animal to its mouth. From there the food passes into a body cavity where it is digested. Because cnidarians have a digestive system with only one opening, undigested food is expelled through the mouth.

Cnidarian Reproduction Cnidarians reproduce both asexually and sexually. For polyps, budding is the most common form of asexual reproduction. Amazingly, in some polyps the entire animal splits into pieces. Each piece then forms a new polyp. Both kinds of asexual reproduction allow the numbers of cnidarians to increase rapidly in a short time.

Sexual reproduction in cnidarians occurs in a variety of ways. Some species of cnidarians have both sexes within one individual. In others, the sexes are in separate individuals, as in humans.

☑ *Checkpoint* How does a cnidarian obtain and digest food?

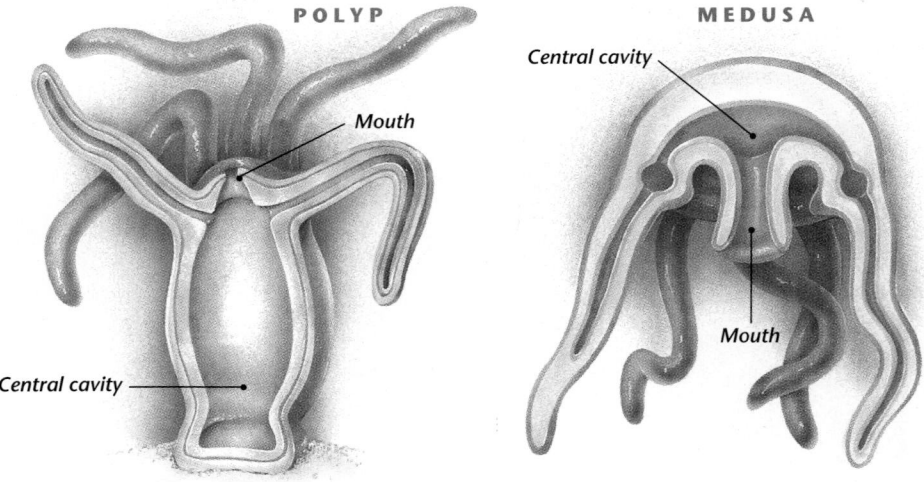

Figure 10 Cnidarians have two basic body forms, the vase-shaped polyp and the bowl-shaped medusa. *Comparing and Contrasting Contrast the location of the mouth in the polyp and the medusa.*

Background

Facts and Figures Cnidarians that live in colonies, such as the Portuguese man-of-war, can be surprisingly complex. The colony consists of polyps and medusas that are specialized for certain functions. Some polyps capture and digest prey, while others produce reproductive cells. Other individuals within the colony act as swimming organs that can contract rhythmically to propel the colony, or as with the Portuguese man-of-

war, act as a float, or air-filled sac.

This form of colony is rarely found in animals. Because the fossils of soft bodied animals are so rare, scientists do not know precisely when the Portuguese man-of-war first formed this unusual colonial relationship. However, the Portuguese man-of-war remains a fascinating example of how specialized function can be an advantage to colonial organisms.

Life on a Coral Reef

In some warm, shallow ocean waters, just below the surface, you can find one of the most diverse ocean environments—a coral reef. Coral reefs seem to be made of stone. But in fact, coral reefs are built by cnidarians. At the beginning of its life, a free-swimming coral larva attaches to a solid surface. A broken shell, a sunken ship, or the skeleton of a once-living coral animal will do just fine. The coral polyp then produces a hard, stony skeleton around its soft body.

The coral polyp reproduces asexually, and then its offspring reproduce asexually, too. Over time, that polyp may give rise to thousands more, each with a hard skeleton. When the coral polyps die, their skeletons remain behind. Over thousands of years, as live corals add their skeletons to those that have died, rocklike masses called reefs grow up from the sea floor. Coral reefs can become enormous. The Great Barrier Reef near Australia is about 2,000 kilometers long.

Coral reefs, like the one in Figure 11, are home to more species of fishes and invertebrates than any other environment on Earth. Hundreds of sponge species live among the corals, constantly filtering water through their bodies. Worms burrow into the coral reef. Giant clams lie with their huge shells slightly open. Shrimp and crabs edge out of hiding places below the corals. At night, bright blue damsel fish settle into pockets in the coral. At dawn and dusk, sea turtles, sea snakes, and sharks all visit the reef, hunting for prey. These living things interact in complex ways, creating an environment that is rich and beautiful.

Figure 11 Coral reefs provide homes and hunting grounds for a vast variety of sea animals. The bottom photo is a close-up of a group of individual coral polyps.

Section 3 Review

1. Describe the structure of a sponge's body.
2. Explain how cnidarians capture prey and defend themselves. In your explanation, refer to specific body structures.
3. Draw a diagram to show how water travels through a sponge. Show the path with an arrow.
4. **Thinking Critically Classifying** Why is a sponge classified as an animal?

Check Your Progress
CHAPTER PROJECT

You should be observing your animal every day and writing your observations in your journal. Record how the animal looks, feeds, and behaves. Note any changes in the animal. Talk to your teacher before making any changes to your animal's home, feeding schedule, or other living conditions.

Answers to Self-Assessment

Caption Question

Figure 10 Polyps have mouths that face upward; medusas have mouths that face downward.

☑ *Checkpoint*

A cnidarian injects venom into its prey. Then it uses its tentacles to pull the food into its mouth. Digestion occurs in the body cavity.

3 Assess

Section 3 Review Answers

1. The body of a sponge is shaped like a hollow bag. Its sides are pierced with openings called pores that lead to a central cavity.
2. Cnidarians obtain food and defend themselves with tentacles covered with stinging cells.
3. Diagrams should show water passing through the pores in the sides of the sponge into a central cavity, then exiting through the osculum at the top of the sponge.
4. Sponges have the characteristics of animals. They are multicellular, take food into their bodies, can reproduce sexually, and are mobile during the early stages of their lives.

Check Your Progress
CHAPTER PROJECT

Give students time in class to study their animals and write down their observations. Suggest that students keep their journal notes in a loose-leaf project notebook so that they can insert drawings and photographs. Review students' observation records on a regular basis. Be sure students include details of any changes in the health and behavior of their animals. Check the health of the animals periodically.

Performance Assessment

Writing Ask students to write two diary entries, the first from the viewpoint of a sponge, and the second from the viewpoint of a cnidarian. Entries should include what and how the animals eat, and a description of the animals' physical features.

 Students can save their diary entries in their portfolios.

Coral Reefs in Danger

Purpose

To provide students with an understanding of the issues involved in diving into coral reefs.

Debate

Time one class period for research and preparation, 30 minutes to conduct the debate

◆ Explain to students that they will be debating the proposition that "Diving near coral reefs should be banned to protect the reefs from ecological damage."

◆ Separate the class into two groups: one to support the proposition, the other to oppose it. Have groups review and investigate the issue from their respective points of view.

◆ Encourage students in the pro-diving group to explore ideas such as education and environmental awareness as an alternative to banning diving. Encourage students in the other group to think realistically and offer alternatives for those affected by a diving ban.

Extend Have students contact a local aquarium, university biology department, or diving organization to obtain relevant background information. Encourage students to prepare questions in advance.

You Decide

Have groups of students complete Steps 1 and 2 before the debate to prepare their arguments. After the debate, direct students to write their editorials using the points they raised during the debate. Give them examples of newspaper editorials to use as models. Consider submitting the most polished articles to a local or school newspaper for possible publication.

Portfolio Students can save their editorials in their portfolios.

Coral Reefs in Danger

Coral reefs off the coasts of many nations are endangered, damaged, or threatened with destruction. Reefs house and protect many species of sea animals, including sponges, shrimp, sea turtles, and fishes. In addition, reefs protect coastlines from floods caused by ocean storms.

Although coral reefs are hard as rocks, the coral animals themselves are quite delicate. Recreational divers can damage the fragile reefs. Is it possible to protect the reefs while still allowing divers to explore them?

The Issues

What's the Harm in Diving? About 3.5 million recreational divers live in the United States. With so many divers it is hard to guarantee that no harm will occur to the coral reefs. In fact, divers can cause significant damage by standing on or even touching these fragile reefs. Carelessly dropping a boat anchor can crush part of a reef. Although most divers are careful, not all are, and accidents can always happen.

Harm to the reefs is even more likely to occur when divers collect coral for their own enjoyment or to sell for profit. You can see brightly colored coral from the sea in jewelry and in decorations.

Should Reefs Be Further Protected? The United States government has passed laws making it illegal, under most circumstances, to remove coral from the sea. Because a few divers break these laws, some people want to ban diving altogether. However, many divers say it's unfair to ban diving just because of a few lawbreakers.

Many divers consider coral reefs the most exciting and beautiful places in the ocean to explore. As recreational divers, photographers, scientists, and others visit and learn more about these delicate coral reefs, they increase their own and other's awareness of them. Public awareness may be the best way to ensure that these rich environments are protected.

More Than a Diving Issue Coral reefs in the Western Atlantic—such as those in Bermuda, the Bahamas, the Caribbean Islands, and Florida—are major tourist attractions that bring money and jobs to people in local communities. If diving were banned, local businesses would suffer significantly. Also, although divers can harm coral reefs, other human activities, such as ocean pollution, oil spills, and fishing nets, can also cause harm. In addition, natural events, such as tropical storms, changes in sea level, and changes in sea temperature, can also damage the fragile reefs.

You Decide

1. Identify the Problem

In your own words, explain the controversy surrounding diving near coral reefs.

2. Analyze the Options

List the arguments on each side of the issue. Note the pros and cons. How well would each position protect the reefs? Who might be harmed or inconvenienced?

3. Find a Solution

Write a newspaper editorial stating your position on whether diving should be allowed near coral reefs. State your position and reasons clearly.

Background

Facts and Figures Coral reefs have extremely high levels of animal diversity—nowhere else in the ocean can you find so many kinds of fish and invertebrates. Like rain forests, coral reefs contain many animals and plants that produce potentially valuable chemicals. For this reason, it is important to protect the reefs from damage from the environment.

But reefs are in danger from natural disasters and from humans. Natural forces, such as water that is too warm, can kill corals and produce a phenomenon called coral bleaching. Organisms that eat living corals, such as the crown-of-thorns sea star, can greatly damage reefs.

In addition to the destruction they cause when diving, people can harm reefs through construction projects on islands near coral reefs.

DISCOVER ···················· ACTIVITY ····

What Can You See in a Worm?

1. Your teacher will give you a planarian, a kind of flatworm. Pick the worm up with the tip of a paintbrush. Place it gently in a small, clear container. Use a dropper to cover the planarian with spring water.

2. Observe the planarian with a hand lens. Look for a head and tail region. Look for two spots in the head region. Draw what you see.

3. Observe and describe how the planarian moves.

4. Gently touch the planarian with a toothpick and observe how it behaves. Then return the planarian to your teacher, and wash your hands.

Think It Over
Observing How is a planarian different from a sponge?

Y ou might think that all worms are small, slimy, and wriggly. But many worms do not fit that description. Some worms are almost three meters long and are as thick as your arm. Others look like glowing, furry blobs. Worms can flutter and glide or climb around with paddle-like bristles. Still others are very small and live in white tubes cemented to rocks.

What Worms Have in Common

It's hard to say exactly what worms are, because there are many kinds of worms, all with their own characteristics. **Biologists classify worms into several phyla—the three major ones are flatworms, roundworms, and segmented worms.** Flatworms belong to the phylum Platyhelminthes (plat ee HEL minth eez); roundworms belong to the phylum Nematoda; segmented worms belong to the phylum Annelida.

GUIDE FOR READING

◆ What are the three main groups of worms?

◆ What are the characteristics of each group of worms?

Reading Tip As you read, list the characteristics of flatworms, roundworms, and segmented worms.

Figure 12 The ocean flatworm, left, and the segmented Christmas tree worm, right, show some of the wide variety of ocean worms.

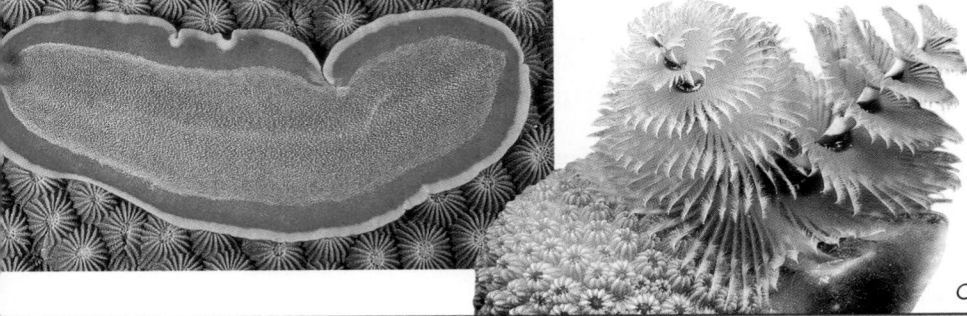

Chapter 10 **327**

Objectives

After completing the lesson, students will be able to
◆ identify the three main groups of worms;
◆ list and identify the characteristics of the three groups of worms.

Key Terms regeneration, anus

1 Engage/Explore

Activating Prior Knowledge

Ask students if they have ever:
◆ used worms as fishing bait;
◆ dug up worms in a garden.
Encourage students to share any observations they have made about the appearance and behavior of worms. Then ask them what words they would use to describe worms. (*Sample: slimy, creepy, crawly*) Inform students that in this section they will learn about the characteristics and nature of worms.

········· DISCOVER ·········

Skills Focus observing **ACTIVITY**
Materials *live planarian, small paintbrush, small transparent container or petri dish, plastic dropper, bottled water, hand lens, toothpick*
Time 15 minutes
Tips Ask students to discuss what the planarians do and how they behave. Direct them to sketch the planarian and make notes of what they see. Check students' sketches and ask them about their observations. Verify that students note the bilateral symmetry of planarians.
Expected Outcome Planarians should visibly react to being touched by recoiling from the toothpick.
Think It Over Suggest students refer back to Section 3 to help them answer this question. Planarians have bilateral symmetry and distinct head and tail ends. Sponges are asymmetrical and do not have head and tail ends.

---

2 Facilitate

What Worms Have in Common

Using the Visuals: Figure 13

For students who have difficulty understanding how the worm in Figure 13 could be an animal, ask: **If you didn't know this was an animal, how could you figure it out?** *(Sample: If the organism can move by itself, it is probably an animal.)* **learning modality: visual**

Including All Students

Point out that the terms *flatworm*, *roundworm*, and *segmented worm*, which were introduced on page 327, all describe major visible characteristics of the groups—all flatworms have flat bodies, and so forth. If students know the meanings of the words *flat*, *round*, and *segmented*, they will also know the major distinguishing characteristics of each group. **limited English proficiency**

Inquiry Challenge

Materials *planarians, small flashlights, transparent containers, bottled water, dark paper or foil*

ACTIVITY

Time 30 minutes

Tips This activity may also be done as a demonstration. It will work better in a partially darkened room. Divide the class into groups and distribute a petri dish (or other small transparent container) to each group. Place a planarian in each dish and cover it with a few drops of water. Have students predict how the planarians will react to light and record their prediction. Have students cover half the container with paper or foil and then shine the flashlight on the container. Students should observe that the planarians move out of the light.
cooperative grouping

Portfolio Students can save their observation notes in their portfolios.

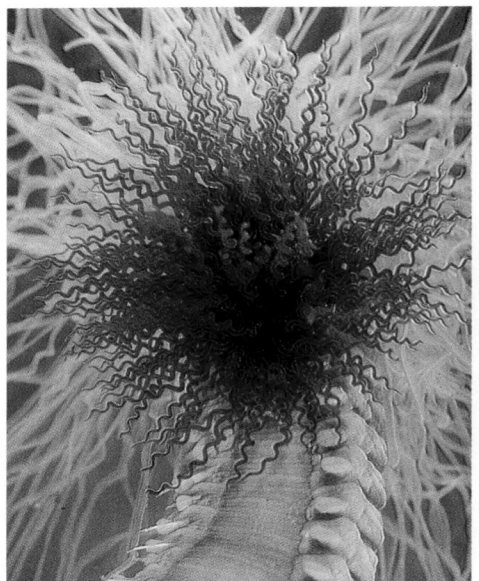

Figure 13 As you can tell from this spectacular spaghetti worm, not all worms are gray and tube shaped.

All worms have some characteristics in common. All worms are invertebrates, and they all have long, narrow bodies without legs. In addition, all worms have tissues, organs, and organ systems. Also, all worms have bilateral symmetry. Unlike sponges or cnidarians, worms have head and tail ends.

Response to the Environment Worms are the simplest organisms with a brain, which is a knot of nerve tissue located in the head end. Because a worm's brain and some of its sense organs are located in its head end, the worm can detect objects, food, mates, and predators quickly, and it can respond quickly, too. Sense organs, such as organs sensitive to light and touch, pick up information from the environment. The brain interprets that information and directs the animal's response. For example, if an earthworm on the surface of the ground senses a footstep, the worm will quickly return to its underground burrow.

Reproduction Both sexual and asexual reproduction are found in the worm phyla. In many species of worms, there are separate male and female animals, as in humans. In other species each individual has both male and female sex organs. A worm with both sexes does not usually fertilize its own eggs. Instead, two worms mate and exchange sperm. Many worms reproduce asexually by methods such as breaking into pieces. In fact, if you cut some kinds of worms into several pieces, a whole new worm will grow from each piece. Earthworms cannot do this, but if you cut off the tail end of an earthworm, the front end will probably grow a new tail. This ability to regrow body parts is called **regeneration.**

✓ Checkpoint *What type of symmetry do worms exhibit?*

Flatworms

As you'd expect from their name, flatworms are flat. The bodies of flatworms, such as planarians, flukes, and tapeworms, are soft as jelly. Although tapeworms can grow to be 10 to 12 meters long, other flatworms are almost too small to be seen.

Most flatworms are parasites that obtain their food from their hosts. As you read in Chapter 6, a parasite is an organism that lives inside or on another organism. The parasite takes its food from the organism in or on which it lives, called the host. Parasites may rob their hosts of food and make them weak. They

---

Background

Facts and Figures The longest animal on Earth is an ocean-dwelling worm called a ribbon worm. The longest ribbon worm measured 54 meters. It was found living in the ocean near Scotland. Some of the smallest animals on Earth are also worms. Turbellarian flatworms are less than 1 centimeter long. They live in the deep mud of oceans and some freshwater lakes.

Trichinella roundworms are among the smallest worms that are parasitic in humans. The mature male is only 1.5 millimeters long. The female Trichinella, which is about 3 to 4 millimeters long, gives birth to between 1,000 to 2,000 larvae. These larvae measure only 7 by 120 microns. (A micron is one-thousandth of a millimeter.)

may injure the host's tissues or organs. Sometimes a parasite will kill its host, but usually the host survives.

Tapeworms Tapeworms are one kind of parasitic flatworm. A tapeworm's body is adapted to absorbing food from the host's digestive system. Some kinds of tapeworms can live in human hosts. Many tapeworms live in more than one host during their lifetime. Notice that in *Exploring the Life Cycle of a Dog Tapeworm*, the tapeworm has two different hosts—a rabbit and a dog.

EXPLORING the Life Cycle of a Dog Tapeworm

As an adult, the tapeworm lives in the digestive tract of a dog. The tapeworm has no mouth or digestive system; instead, it absorbs food directly through its body wall.

1 Dogs can become infected with tapeworms in different ways. One way is by eating the meat of an animal, such as a rabbit, that is infected with tapeworm larvae.

2 Once inside the dog's digestive tract, the immature tapeworm emerges. The tapeworm uses hooks and suckers on its head to dig into the lining of the dog's digestive system.

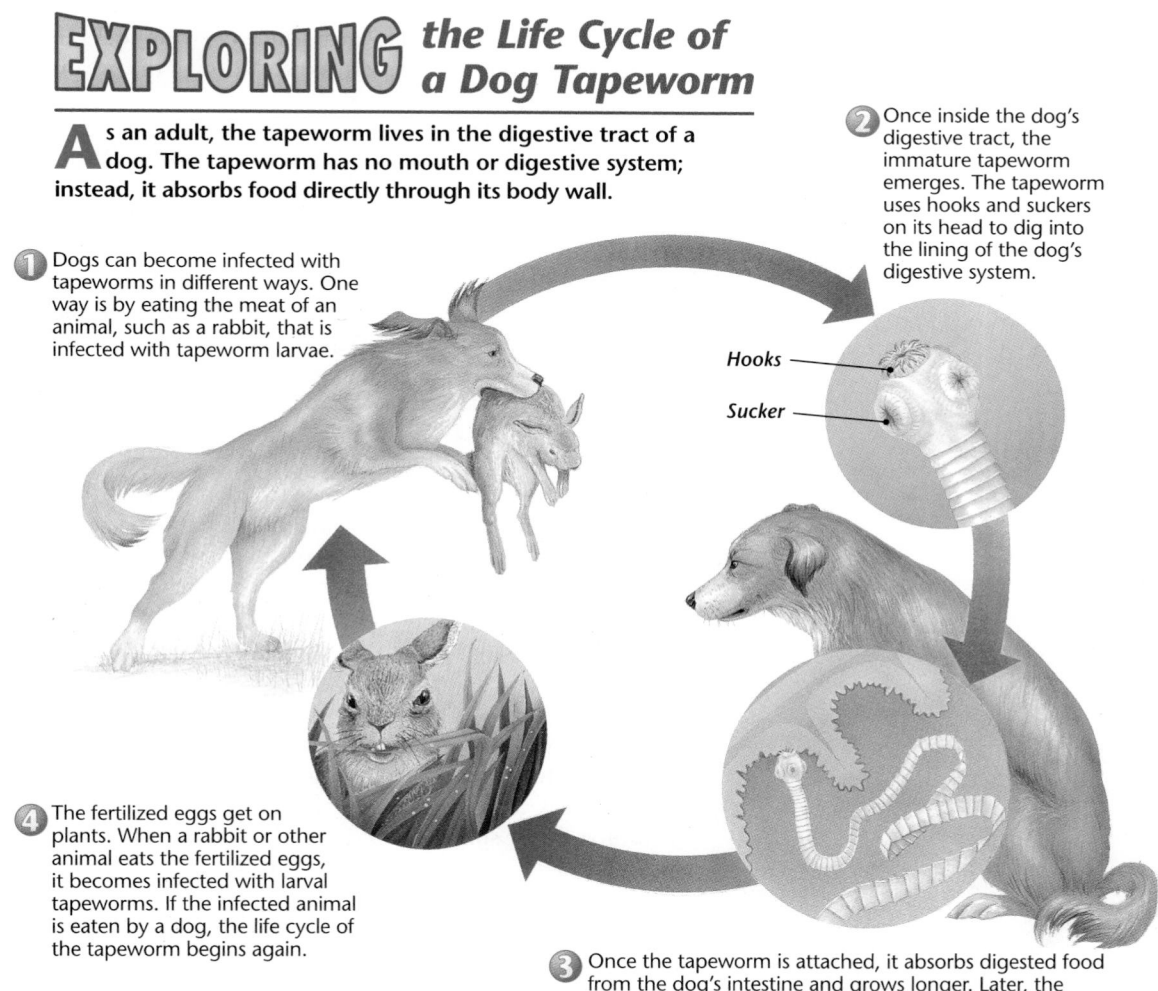

Hooks

Sucker

4 The fertilized eggs get on plants. When a rabbit or other animal eats the fertilized eggs, it becomes infected with larval tapeworms. If the infected animal is eaten by a dog, the life cycle of the tapeworm begins again.

3 Once the tapeworm is attached, it absorbs digested food from the dog's intestine and grows longer. Later, the tapeworm produces eggs and sperm. Fertilized eggs leave the dog's digestive tract along with wastes.

Chapter 10 **329**

Flatworms

EXPLORING
the Life Cycle of a Dog Tapeworm

Discuss each stage in the tapeworm life cycle with students. Remind students that eating a rabbit is only one way a dog can become infected. Have students identify the parasite and the hosts. *(Parasite: tapeworm; hosts: dog and rabbit)* Ask: **Why are the pictures arranged in a cycle?** *(To emphasize that the sequence of events is continuous.)* **Why do you think the tapeworm must attach itself to the dog's digestive system?** *(Its body is adapted to absorbing digested food)* **learning modality: visual**

Building Inquiry Skills: Predicting

Ask students to predict what might happen to a host animal that was infected with tapeworms. *(Sample: Since tapeworms absorb digested food from their host's intestine, the animal might become weak because it is not getting enough food.)* **learning modality: logical/mathematical**

Real-Life Learning

Veterinarians regularly treat household pets for tapeworm infections. Invite a local veterinarian to visit. Prior to the visit, have each student prepare one question to ask the veterinarian. **learning modality: verbal**

ACTIVITY

Portfolio Students can save their questions and the veterinarian's answers in their portfolios.

Answers to Self-Assessment

☑ *Checkpoint*
Worms exhibit bilateral symmetry.

Ongoing Assessment

Writing Ask students to list the distinguishing characteristics of flatworms. *(Bilateral symmetry; a brain; flat bodies; most are parasitic; some are predators)*

Flatworms, continued

Inquiry Challenge

Materials *petri or small plastic dish, bottled water, ground meat, lettuce, live planarian, soft paintbrush, hand lens*

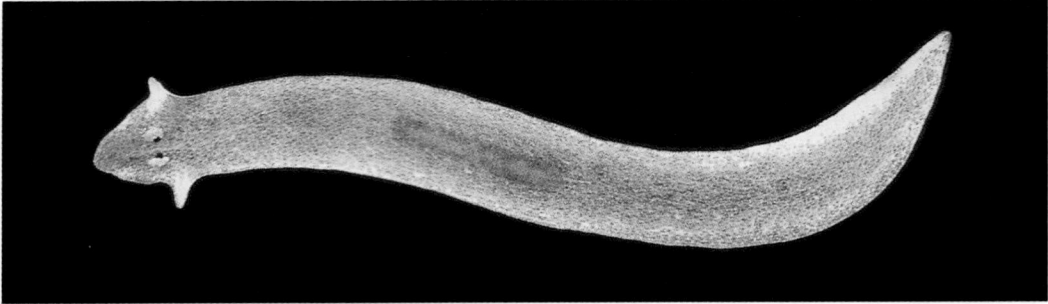

Time 50 minutes

Tips Have students observe planarians to draw conclusions about which food they prefer. Withhold feeding for a day before the class activity to make sure the planarians are hungry at the start of the activity. To begin the activity, have students pour water into the dish until the bottom is completely covered. Then, they should place a small piece of ground meat and a piece of lettuce in one side of the dish about 1 inch apart. Students can then use the paintbrush to carefully place the planarian at the other side of the dish. Have students observe how long it takes a planarian to start moving and whether it moves toward the lettuce or the meat. (Planarians are mainly carnivorous and probably will move toward meat rather than lettuce.) If the planarians are slow to respond, place a dark cover over the dish to reduce the light in the environment. Leave it on for about 10 minutes. Then remove the cover and observe any movement. Students should wash their hands after they finish.

Extend Ask: **How did the planarian locate the food?** *(It used its sense of smell.)* **Where are its sense organs located?** *(The front end of its body)* **Is having sense organs at the front end of its body related to the type of symmetry the planarian has?** *(Yes. Planarians are bilaterally symmetrical. Most bilaterally symmetrical animals have their sense organs at the front ends of their bodies.)*

learning modality: visual

Figure 14 Planarians are flatworms that live in ponds, streams, and oceans. The eyespots on the planarian's head can distinguish between light and dark. *Inferring How is having a distinct head end an advantage to a planarian?*

Figure 15 The transparent bodies of these roundworms have been stained for better viewing under a microscope.

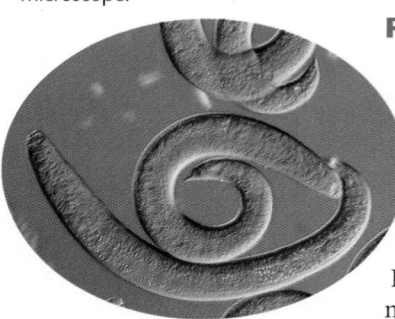

Planarians Some flatworms are nonparasitic, or free-living. Unlike parasites, free-living organisms do not live in or on other organisms. Small free-living flatworms glide over the rocks in ponds, slide over damp soil, or swim slowly through the oceans like ruffled, brightly patterned leaves.

Planarians, such as the one in Figure 14, are scavengers—they feed on dead or decaying material. But they are also predators and will attack any animal smaller than they are.

If you look at a planarian's head, you can see two big dots that look like eyes. These dots are called eyespots, and they function something like eyes, although they cannot see a specific image like human eyes can. A planarian's head also has cells that pick up odors. Planarians rely mainly on smell to locate food. When a planarian smells food, it moves toward the food and glides onto it.

A planarian feeds like a vacuum cleaner. The planarian inserts a feeding tube into its food. Digestive juices flow out into the food, where they begin to break down the food while it is still outside the worm's body. Then the planarian sucks up the partly digested bits of food. Digestion is then completed within a cavity inside the planarian. Food is distributed to body cells by diffusion. Like cnidarians, planarians have one opening in their digestive system. Undigested wastes exit through the feeding tube.

Roundworms

The next time you walk along a beach, consider that about a million roundworms live in each square meter of damp sand. Roundworms can live in nearly any moist environment—including forest soils, Antarctic sands, and even pools of super-hot water. Most are tiny and hard to see, but roundworms may be the most abundant animals on Earth.

Unlike flatworms, roundworms have cylindrical bodies. If you were to look at the roundworms in Figure 15 under a microscope, you'd see their bodies thrashing from side to side.

Background

Facts and Figures Parasitic flatworms and roundworms are major causes of serious disease in humans and livestock. One parasitic roundworm, *Trichinella*, lives in the muscle tissue of pigs and game animals. Humans can become a host for this roundworm if they eat undercooked meat. When a human eats meat that contains Trichinella larvae, the larvae pass in the circulatory system to all parts of the body. Once in the muscle tissue, the larvae enclose themselves in a capsule, where they can remain inactive for a long time. The meat industry has been successful in controlling the spread of this parasite in animals raised for food. However, pork and game should always be thoroughly cooked.

While many roundworms are carnivores or herbivores, others are parasites. Have you given worm medicine to a pet dog or cat? The medicine was probably meant to kill roundworm parasites, such as hookworms.

Unlike cnidarians or flatworms, roundworms have a digestive system that is like a tube, open at both ends. Food enters at the animal's mouth and wastes exit through an opening, called the **anus,** at the far end of the tube. Food travels in one direction through the roundworm's digestive system, as it does in most complex animals.

A one-way digestive system has certain advantages. It is something like an assembly line, with a different part of the digestive process happening at each place along the line. Digestion happens in orderly stages. First food is broken down by digestive juices. Then the digested food is absorbed into the animal's body. Finally wastes are eliminated. The advantage of this type of digestive process is that it enables the animal's body to use foods efficiently, by enabling it to absorb a large amount of the needed substances in foods.

☑ *Checkpoint* *You are using a microscope to look at a tiny worm. What would you look for to tell whether it is a roundworm?*

Segmented Worms

If you have ever dug in a garden in the spring, you have probably seen earthworms wriggling through the moist soil. Those familiar soil inhabitants are segmented worms. So are the exotic sea-floor worms that you see in Figure 16. Parasitic blood-sucking leeches are also segmented worms. Since their bodies are long and narrow, some segmented worms look a bit like flatworms and roundworms. But segmented worms may be more closely related to crabs and snails.

Figure 16 These segmented sea-floor worms belong to the same phylum as earthworms.

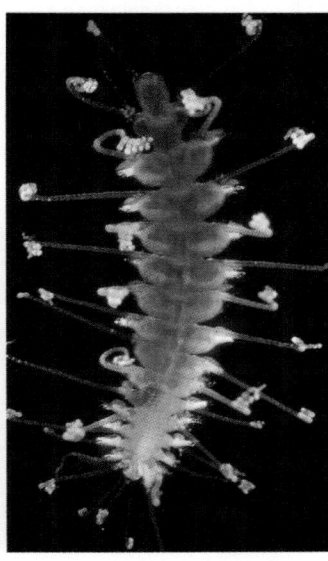

Chapter 10 **331**

Answers to Self-Assessment

Caption Question

Figure 14 Having a distinct head end is an advantage because the planarian can pick up information about what is in front of it and move forward.

☑ *Checkpoint*

To determine whether a worm is a roundworm, you would look for a cylindrical body that thrashes from side to side.

Roundworms

Including All Students

Some students may need extra help to understand the difference between digestive systems with one or two openings. Show students two cardboard tubes, one open at both ends, the other sealed at one end. Ask: **What animal's digestive system could the sealed tube represent?** *(planarian, cnidarian)* **What animal's digestive system could the open tube represent?** *(roundworm, human, dog)* Show students marbles or small pebbles and tell them these items represent food. Fill the sealed tube with "food." Then pass "food" through the open tube. Lead students to understand that one advantage of a digestive system with two openings is that the animal can continue to eat while food eaten earlier passes through its digestive tract. **learning modality: kinesthetic**

Sharpen your Skills

Communicating

Materials *art supplies, construction paper or posterboard*
Time 30 minutes
Tips You may wish to invite a veterinarian or pet-store owner to visit the class to tell students how to protect pets from parasitic worms. Provide old magzines for students to cut out pictures of dogs or cats to decorate their posters.
Extend Interested students can contact a veterinarian to find out what treatments are used to rid a pet of worms. Students can report their findings to the class.

Ongoing Assessment

Oral Presentation Have students identify the distinguishing characteristics of roundworms and contrast roundworms to flatworms. *(Roundworms have cylindrical bodies and a one-way digestive system; in contrast, flatworms have flat bodies and a digestive system in which food and wastes move through the same opening.)*

331

Segmented Worms

Sharpen your *Skills*

Observing

Materials *earthworm, transparent container, construction paper, soil*
Time 15 minutes per day over several days
Tips Fill the container with loose, moist soil. Mist the soil if it starts to dry out. Keep the container out of direct sunlight. Have students wrap the jar walls with dark construction paper. That way the worms, which naturally avoid the light, may burrow along the outside wall of the jar. Have students note the earthworm's location in the soil. Ask: **When the segments at the front end of the worm contract, do the segments at the back end contract at the same time?** (*No, segments contract independently.*)
Expected Outcome Students may say that an earthworm's tunneling behavior is adaptive to the environment because tunneling helps the worm find food.
Extend If feasible, suggest that students raise earthworms in the classroom. They will need to add a food source to the soil such as vegetable waste or leaf litter.
learning modality: visual

Integrating Earth Science

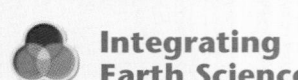

Materials *transparent container, potting soil, light-colored sand, drinking straw*
Time 15 minutes

Have students place a layer of potting soil, then a layer of sand, in the container. Instruct students to stick the straw through the layers to the bottom of the container. Then cover the upper opening of the straw with a finger and withdraw the straw. Remove the finger from the straw and allow the contents to pile up on the surface of the sand. Repeat several times. Ask: **What kind of earthworm behavior does this model?** (*As earthworms move through the soil, they mix it up and loosen it.*) **learning modality: kinesthetic**

Sharpen your Skills

Observing ACTIVITY

Observe earthworms in a container filled with soil. Make your observations on several different days—if possible, at different times in the day. Note the worms' general sizes, colors, and appearances. Also observe their behavior—for example, how the worms move and how they tunnel through the soil. How is an earthworm's behavior adapted to surviving in its environment?

Figure 17 An earthworm's body is divided into over 100 segments. Some organs are repeated in most of those segments; others exist in only a few. *Interpreting Diagrams How does blood move through an earthworm's body?*

Segmented worms occupy nearly all environments, and most live in burrows or tubes. The burrow helps the worm hide both from possible predators and from possible prey. Many segmented worms that live in water are "sit-and-wait" predators. They leap out of their burrows to attack their prey.

Segmentation When you look at an earthworm, you notice that its body seems to consist of a series of rings separated by grooves, something like a vacuum-cleaner hose. **Earthworms and other segmented worms have bodies made up of many linked sections called segments.** An earthworm usually has more than 100 segments. On the outside, the segments look nearly identical. On the inside, some organs are repeated in most segments. For example, each segment has tubes that remove wastes. Other organs, however, such as the worm's reproductive organs, are found only in some segments. Nerve cords and a digestive tube run along the length of the worm's body. Like roundworms, earthworms have a one-way digestive system with two openings.

A Closed Circulatory System Segmented worms have a closed circulatory system. In a closed circulatory system, like your own, blood moves only within a connected network of tubes called blood vessels. In contrast, some animals, such as insects, have an open circulatory system in which blood leaves the blood vessels and sloshes around inside the body. A closed circulatory system can move blood around an animal's body much more quickly than an open circulatory system can. Blood quickly carries oxygen and food to cells. Because of this, an animal with a closed circulatory system can be larger and more active than one with an open circulatory system.

A long blood vessel runs along the top of the earthworm's body. That blood vessel pumps blood through five arches, shown in Figure 17. From the arches, the blood passes into a blood vessel that runs along the lower part of the earthworm.

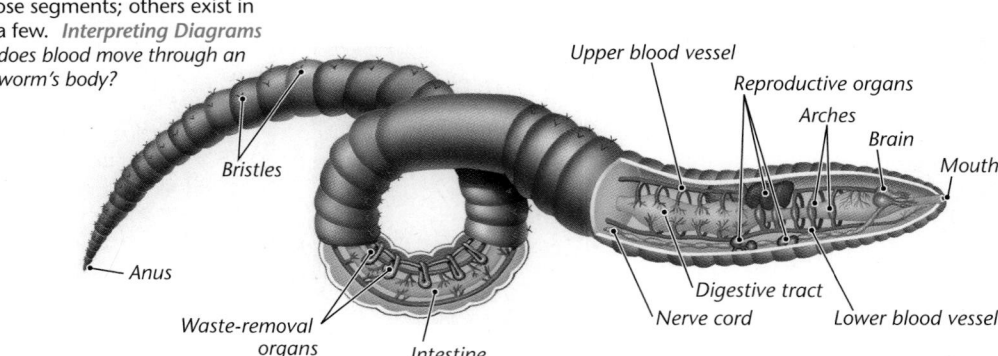

Upper blood vessel
Reproductive organs
Arches
Brain
Mouth
Bristles
Anus
Waste-removal organs
Intestine
Digestive tract
Nerve cord
Lower blood vessel

Background

Facts and Figures Doctors sometimes use leeches, a type of segmented worm, to stimulate blood flow or to keep blood from clotting during surgery. Leeches have a chemical in their saliva called hirudin that prevents blood clotting. In nature, if the blood of the host organism were to clot, the leech could not continue to feed.

Program Resources

◆ **Laboratory Manual** 10, "Observing Flatworms and Roundworms"

How Earthworms Live Earthworms tunnel for a living. They are scavengers that eat decayed plant and animal remains in the soil. On damp nights earthworms come up out of their burrows. They crawl on the surface of the ground, seeking leaves and soft fruits to drag underground and eat.

Night is a safe time for an earthworm to crawl on the surface, because many worm predators are asleep then. At night the air is damp, and this dampness helps keep the worm's skin moist. If a worm dries out, it will die, because it obtains oxygen through moisture on its skin.

Well-developed muscles let an earthworm move through its burrow. Stiff bristles stick out from each of the worm's segments. To crawl forward, an earthworm sticks its bristles in the ground and pulls itself along, much as a mountain climber uses an ice ax. Mountain climbers drive ice axes into a slippery slope and then pull themselves up.

Earthworms and Soil Earthworms are among the most **INTEGRATING EARTH SCIENCE** helpful inhabitants of garden and farm soil. They benefit people by improving the soil in which plants grow. Earthworm droppings make the soil more fertile. Earthworm tunnels loosen the soil and allow air, water, and plant roots to move through it. You have probably seen earthworm tunnel entrances without realizing what they were—they are extremely common in lawns. To find one, look for a small, round hole in the ground with little balls of soil next to it.

Section 4 Review

1. List the three major phyla of worms and give an example of each.
2. How does a dog tapeworm obtain its food?
3. Contrast a roundworm's digestive system to that of a planarian.
4. Describe the structure of an earthworm's body.
5. **Thinking Critically Relating Cause and Effect** How does keeping a dog on a leash reduce its risk for getting a tapeworm?

Check Your Progress
CHAPTER PROJECT

Begin to analyze what you have learned about your animal from your observations. Did you see a daily pattern to the animal's behavior? Think about what each kind of behavior accomplishes—whether it helps the animal obtain food or escape from danger, for example. Choose how you are going to present what you have learned—a written report, a talk, captioned illustrations, or some other method. Prepare charts or other visual aids.

Program Resources

◆ **Unit 3 Resources** 10-4 Review and Reinforce, p. 23; 10-4 Enrich, p. 24

Media and Technology

 Interactive Student Tutorial CD-ROM Chapter 10

 Transparencies "Earthworm Anatomy," Transparency 44

Answers to Self-Assessment

Caption Question

Figure 17 A long blood vessel that runs along the top of the earthworm pumps blood through five arches. The blood then passes into a blood vessel that runs along the lower part of the earthworm.

3 Assess

Section 4 Review Answers

1. Flatworms: planarians, tapeworms; roundworms: hookworms; segmented worms: earthworms.
2. The tapeworm lives in the dog's intestine where it is bathed in food. It absorbs the food.
3. A roundworm has a one-way digestive system in which food enters through a mouth and wastes exit through an anus. A planarian has a digestive system in which undigested wastes exit through its feeding tube.
4. An earthworm's body is divided into many segments. Some organs, such as those that dispose of waste material, are present in each segment. Others, such as the arches and reproductive organs, occupy only specialized segments. Organs such as those in the digestive and nervous systems run the length of the earthworm's body.
5. If a dog is kept on a leash, it is less likely to kill and eat an infected rabbit.

Check Your Progress
CHAPTER PROJECT

Tell students that analyzing their data means summarizing their observations, looking for patterns of behavior, then deciding what the patterns tell them about the animal.

Performance Assessment

Drawing Ask students to draw a flatworm, a roundworm, and a segmented worm. Have them label:
◆ the characteristics shared by all worms; (*Brain, bilateral symmetry*)
◆ the characteristics found only in flatworms; (*Flat body, feeding tube*)
◆ the main characteristics of roundworms; (*Cylindrical body, one-way digestive system*)
◆ the unique characteristics of segmented worms. (*Segmentation, closed circulatory system, bristles*)

333

Developing a Hypothesis

Earthworm Responses

Preparing for Inquiry

Key Concept A hypothesis is a prediction about the outcome of an experiment.

Skills Objective Students will be able to
◆ develop hypotheses.

Time 30 minutes

Advance Planning You can get worms from a biological supply company, a bait shop, or loose garden soil. Keep earthworms moist at all times. You may want to try this experiment before class to anticipate and understand the possible results.

Alternative Materials Cake pans can be used for trays. Do not substitute tissues for paper towels; they are too absorbent and will not last.

Guiding Inquiry

Invitation To help students form a hypothesis, ask: **Think about the places you are likely to see an earthworm. Would these places likely be dry or moist?** (*moist*) **Light or dark?** (*dark*)

Introducing the Procedure

◆ Give students time to read through the procedure and ask questions to clarify any steps they do not understand.
◆ Invite students to look at and thoroughly examine their earthworms on the paper towels before they begin to write a hypothesis.
◆ Have students review the diagram of the setup so they understand how to position the worms.
◆ Suggest that students conduct a trial one time before they actually collect data.

Earthworm Responses

In this lab, you will practice the skill of making hypotheses to learn more about earthworms.

Earthworms

Dry paper towel

Wet paper towel

Tray

Problem

Do earthworms prefer dry or moist conditions? Do they prefer light or dark conditions?

Materials

plastic dropper	water	cardboard
clock or watch	paper towels	flashlight
2 earthworms	storage container	tray

Procedure

1. Which environment do you think earthworms prefer—dry or moist? Record your hypothesis in your notebook.
2. Use the dropper to sprinkle water on the worms. Keep the worms moist at all times.
3. Fold a dry paper towel and place it on the bottom of one side of your tray. Fold a moistened paper towel and place it on the other side.
4. Moisten your hands. Then place the earthworms in the center of the tray. Make sure that half of each earthworm's body rests on the moist paper towel and half rests on the dry towel. Handle the worms gently.
5. Cover the tray with the piece of cardboard. After five minutes, remove the cardboard and observe whether the worms are on the moist or dry surface. Record your observations.
6. Repeat Steps 4 and 5.
7. Return the earthworms to their storage container. Moisten the earthworms with water.
8. Which do you think earthworms prefer—strong light or darkness? Record your hypothesis in your notebook.
9. Cover the whole surface of the tray with a moistened paper towel.
10. Place the earthworms in the center of the tray. Cover half of the tray with cardboard. Shine a flashlight onto the other half.
11. After five minutes, note the locations of the worms. Record your observations.
12. Repeat Steps 10 and 11.
13. Moisten the earthworms and put them in the location designated by your teacher. Wash your hands after handling the worms.

Analyze and Conclude

1. Which environment did the worms prefer—moist or dry? Bright or dark? Did the worms' behavior support your hypotheses?
2. Use what you know about earthworms to explain how their responses to moisture and light help them survive.
3. **Think About It** What knowledge or experiences helped you make your hypotheses at the start of the experiments?

Design an Experiment

Do earthworms prefer a smooth or rough surface? Write your hypothesis. Then design an experiment to answer the question. Check with your teacher before carrying out your experiment.

Troubleshooting the Experiment

◆ Worms are delicate animals. Be sure they are handled gently. Rough handling can harm the worms and prevent them from moving.
◆ The dry paper towel may absorb some water if the wet paper towel is too wet. Have students check to make sure their dry paper towel remains dry. If a dry paper towel becomes damp, have the student replace it with another dry towel.

Safety

◆ Handle the earthworms gently.
◆ Keep the earthworms from drying out by misting them frequently with cool water in a spray bottle.
◆ Do not leave the earthworms unattended. Return them to their container when you are finished with them.
◆ Wash your hands after the experiment.
◆ Review the safety guidelines in Appendix A.

1 What Is an Animal?

Key Ideas
◆ Animals are multicellular organisms that obtain food by eating other organisms.
◆ Animals need water, food, and oxygen to survive. Some animals are carnivores, or meat eaters. Others are herbivores, or plant eaters. Omnivores eat both plants and animals.
◆ Some animals are vertebrates; most animal species are invertebrates.

Key Terms

organ	carnivore	omnivore
adaptation	predator	invertebrate
herbivore	prey	vertebrate

2 Symmetry

INTEGRATING MATHEMATICS

Key Ideas
◆ The bodies of complex animals all have either radial or bilateral symmetry.
◆ Animals with radial symmetry have body parts arranged around a central point.
◆ Animals with bilateral symmetry have one line that divides them into two mirror images.

Key Terms
bilateral symmetry   radial symmetry

3 Sponges and Cnidarians

Key Ideas
◆ A sponge obtains food by straining water taken in through its pores.
◆ Cnidarians are carnivores with stinging cells that help capture prey. Cnidarians have two body plans—polyp and medusa.
◆ Corals are cnidarians with hard skeletons around their soft bodies. Over time, the skeletons of some corals form coral reefs.

Key Terms

larva	polyp
cnidarian	medusa

4 Worms

Key Ideas
◆ The three major worm phyla are flatworms, roundworms, and segmented worms.
◆ Most flatworms are parasites that obtain food from their hosts. Planarians are nonparasitic flatworms.
◆ Roundworms have a digestive system that is a tube open at both ends.
◆ Segmented worms have bodies made up of many segments. Segmented worms have a closed circulatory system in which blood is contained in blood vessels.

Key Terms
regeneration   anus

Organizing Information

Flowchart The flowchart below shows how water travels through a sponge. Copy the flowchart onto a sheet of paper. Then complete it and add a title. (For more on flowcharts, see the Skills Handbook.)

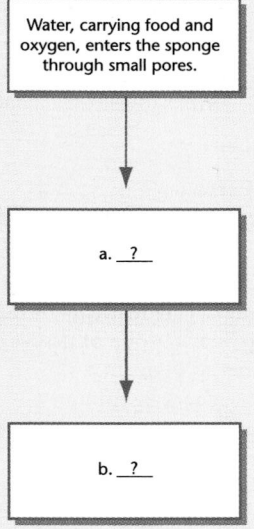

Water, carrying food and oxygen, enters the sponge through small pores.

a. _?_

b. _?_

Sample Data Table for Entire Class

Trial Number	Minutes	Moved to Moist Towel	Moved to Dry Towel	% of worms that prefer the moist towel
1	5	16	4	80%
2	5	17	3	85%

Program Resources

◆ **Unit 3 Resources Chapter 10** Skills Lab, pp. 27–29.

Expected Outcome
◆ The worms generally prefer the moist towel and move toward it, though some worms may move to the dry towel. Students should record all the data and represent the number of times the worm moved towards the moist towel as a percent.
◆ Worms usually prefer a dark environment and move toward it.

Analyze and Conclude
1. Moist; dark; if students predicted these results, their hypotheses were supported.
2. Answers will vary. Sample: Earthworms live in dark, moist soil. They will dry out without water. For an earthworm, light usually means it is in the sun where it could dry out.
3. A typical response might suggest that earthworms are usually found in dark, moist places.

Extending the Inquiry
Design an Experiment Remind students that a hypothesis is a prediction about the outcome of an experiment. For example, if earthworms can move to either a rough or smooth surface, they will move to the rough surface. To test this hypothesis, students might suggest using a rough surface such as sandpaper on one side of a tray and a smooth surface such as ceramic tile on the other. Remind students they must make sure other factors (variables) such as temperature are consistent on the different sides of the tray. Their experiments must only test one factor at a time.

Organizing Information

Flowchart a. Whiplike structures on collar cells beat to move water through the sponge. Collar cells also strain food from the water. Oxygen from the water diffuses into the sponge's cells. **b.** Water leaves the sponge through the osculum, carrying waste products. Sample title: Water Movement Through a Sponge

Reviewing Content

Multiple Choice

1. b **2.** b **3.** b **4.** b **5.** a

True or False

6. true
7. true
8. bilateral symmetry
9. sponges
10. segmented worms

Checking Concepts

11. A cell is the smallest working unit of a living thing. Tissues are made up of similar cells that work together to perform a specific job. Organs are made up of different types of tissues.

12. The oxygen molecule probably diffused into the sponge's cell from the water. In diffusion, molecules of a substance move from an area where they are highly concentrated to an area where they are less concentrated.

13. Sample answer: A polyp is usually attached to a surface. Its mouth is at the top of its body. A medusa is free swimming. Its mouth is at the bottom of its body. Polyps and medusas are similar in that they are both radially symmetrical.

14. Humans are free-living animals because they do not live on or in the bodies of other organisms and take food from them.

15. There would probably be more roundworms—they are very abundant in soil.

16. Responses may vary. Accept any response that states there would be a wide variety of animals—from corals, sponges, and worms to shrimp, crabs, and fish. Dangers to watch out for include predators such as larger fish.

Thinking Critically

17. Bright orange; this color would make it easier to approach their prey without being seen.

18. Radially symmetrical—sea stars, hydras; bilaterally symmetrical—frogs, sharks, humans; asymmetrical—sponges

19. Collar cells in the sponge trap food and digest it. A planarian spits out digestive juice on its food, sucks up the partially digested bits of food, and absorbs the food. A roundworm has a

---

Reviewing Content

 For more review of key concepts, see the Interactive Student Tutorial CD-ROM.

Multiple Choice

Choose the letter of the best answer.

1. Organisms that eat both plants and animals are called
   a. autotrophs.
   b. omnivores.
   c. heterotrophs.
   d. carnivores.

2. An animal without a backbone is called a(n)
   a. vertebrate.
   b. invertebrate.
   c. herbivore.
   d. carnivore.

3. An animal with many lines of symmetry
   a. is bilaterally symmetrical.
   b. is radially symmetrical.
   c. has no symmetry.
   d. has line symmetry.

4. Which animal is a medusa?
   a. coral
   b. jellyfish
   c. planarian
   d. sea anemone

5. Which animal has a one-way digestive system?
   a. earthworm
   b. planarian
   c. sponge
   d. jellyfish

True or False

If the statement is true, write true. If it is false, change the underlined word or words to make the statement true.

6. <u>All</u> animals are made up of many cells.

7. An <u>organ</u> is a group of tissues that work together to perform a job.

8. Fish have <u>radial symmetry</u>.

9. The bodies of <u>cnidarians</u> contain many pores.

10. The bodies of <u>roundworms</u> are segmented.

Checking Concepts

11. Explain the relationship among cells, tissues, and organs.

12. An oxygen molecule has just passed into a sponge's cell. Describe how it probably got there.

13. Compare and contrast a medusa and a polyp.

14. Are humans parasitic or free-living animals? Explain.

15. You dig up a handful of damp soil from the floor of a forest and examine it with a microscope. What kind of animal would probably be there in the greatest numbers? Explain.

16. Writing to Learn You are a small fish visiting a coral reef for the first time. What interesting sights would you see? Are there any dangers you need to watch out for? In a paragraph, describe your adventures at the coral reef.

Thinking Critically

17. Predicting The sand in a desert is bright orange. What color would predators in that desert probably be? Explain.

18. Classifying Classify each of the following animals as either radially symmetrical, bilaterally symmetrical, or asymmetrical: sea stars, frogs, sponges, sharks, humans, and hydras.

19. Comparing and Contrasting Compare and contrast the ways in which a sponge, a planarian, and a roundworm digest their food.

20. Relating Cause and Effect If a pesticide killed off many of the earthworms in a garden, how might that affect the plants growing in that soil? Explain why the plants would be affected in that way.

---

one-way digestive system. The food is digested and absorbed along the way.

20. Answers may vary. Sample: Although there may be fewer insects eating the plants, the plants may be less healthy because there are fewer earthworms. The earthworms break up the soil so that air, water, and plant roots can more easily move through it. They also fertilize the soil.

Applying Skills

21. The manipulated variable is whether the field is treated with pesticide or not. The responding variable is the number of worms in the soil.

22. The average number of worms per cubic meter in the treated fields is 436.4. The average number in the untreated field is 722.4.

23. The number of worms in the soil goes down when the soil is treated with pesticide.

Applying Skills

A scientist used a pesticide on one field and left a nearby field untreated. Next, she marked off five plots of equal size in each field. Then she dug up a cubic meter of soil beneath each plot, and counted the earthworms in the soil. The table below shows her data. Use the table to answer Questions 21–23.

Field with Pesticide		Untreated Field	
Plot	Worms per cubic meter	Plot	Worms per cubic meter
A	730	F	901
B	254	G	620
C	319	H	811
D	428	I	576
E	451	J	704

21. **Controlling Variables** Identify the manipulated and responding variables in this experiment.

22. **Calculating** Calculate the average number of worms per cubic meter in the treated field. Then do the same for the untreated field.

23. **Drawing Conclusions** How did this pesticide affect the population of worms?

Performance ▼ Assessment
CHAPTER PROJECT

Present Your Project Write a summary explaining what you have learned about your animal—its physical characteristics, its habitat, the food it eats, and its behavior. Describe any surprising observations. Then introduce your animal to your classmates and share what you have discovered.

Reflect and Record Was the animal you selected a good choice? Why or why not? How might you have taken better care of your animal? What advice would you give to another student who wants to study this animal?

Test Preparation   *Use these questions to prepare for standardized tests.*

Read the passage. Then answer Questions 24–26.

Cnidarians use stinging cells to obtain food and to protect themselves. The stinging cells contain harpoonlike barbs at the end of coiled, hollow threads. When a cnidarian is touched by another organism, the threads of thousands of its stinging cells uncoil and shoot their barbs into its victim. Then, a paralyzing or deadly poison passes through the hollow threads and into the victim's tissues.

The stinging cells of many cnidarians are too weak to pierce human skin. However, some cnidarian species, such as the jellyfishes commonly called lion's mane and sea nettle, can harm people. A cnidarian known as the Portuguese man-of-war also has a painful and sometimes deadly sting.

It's best to avoid cnidarians. But, if you are stung, apply vinegar, meat tenderizer, or a baking soda and water paste to the stung area. Applying ice to the area can lessen the sting's pain.

24. What is the best title for this passage?
    a. The Portuguese Man-of-War
    b. The Stinging Cells of Cnidarians
    c. How to Avoid Cnidarians
    d. How Cnidarians Obtain Food

25. Which of the following objects would most closely resemble a barb?
    a. a straw   b. a string
    c. a jack-in-the-box spring   d. an arrowhead

26. What is the correct order in which a stinging cell reacts to the touch of another organism?
    a. poison passes through thread; poison enters victim; thread uncoils; barb pierces victim
    b. barb pierces victim; thread uncoils; poison passes through thread; poison enters victim
    c. thread uncoils; barb pierces victim; poison passes through thread; poison enters victim
    d. thread uncoils; poison passes through thread; barb pierces victim; poison enters victim

Chapter 10 **337**

Performance ▼ Assessment
CHAPTER PROJECT

Present Your Project Some students may be shy about presenting their projects to the class. Tell them all they have to do is to thoughtfully write their summaries and then share their summaries with the class. As students give their reports, ask their classmates to take brief notes, writing down the major characteristics of each animal. After students complete their presentations, have them turn in any written work you require. They should also move the animals to their new homes.

Reflect and Record After all presentations have been made, have students evaluate their projects. Students should decide what animals were best for the projects and what were the best methods for taking care of the animals.

Test Preparation
24. b **25.** d **26.** c

Media and Technology

Interactive Student Tutorial CD-ROM Chapter 10

Computer Test Bank Chapter 10 Test

Program Resources

◆ **Unit 3 Resources** Chapter 10 Project Scoring Rubric, p. 8
◆ **Performance Assessment** Chapter 10, pp. 32–34
◆ **Chapter and Unit Tests** Chapter 10 Test, pp. 48–51
◆ **Inquiry Skills Activity Book** Provides teaching and review of all inquiry skills

Sections	Time	Student Edition Activities	Other Activities
CHAPTER PROJECT ▼ **Going Through Changes** p. 339	Ongoing (3–4 weeks)	Check Your Progress, pp. 353, 359, 368 Present Your Project, p. 371	
1 Mollusks pp. 340–345 ◆ Describe the main characteristics of mollusks and the evidence of their early existence on Earth. ◆ Describe the major groups of mollusks.	$1\frac{1}{2}$ periods/ $\frac{3}{4}$ block	**Discover** How Can You Classify Shells? p. 340 **Sharpen Your Skills** Classifying, p. 342 **Science at Home,** p. 344 **Skills Lab: Measuring** A Snail's Pace, p. 345	TE Integrating Earth Science, p. 341 TE Exploring a Snail, p. 343 TE Building Inquiry Skills: Observing, p. 343 TE Integrating Physics, p. 344 IES "Where River Meets Sea," pp. 15–16
2 Arthropods pp. 346–353 ◆ Describe the major characteristics of arthropods. ◆ Identify and describe the main groups of arthropods.	2 periods/ 1 block	**Discover** Will It Bend and Move? p. 346 **Try This** Pill Bugs—Wet or Dry? p. 350	TE Including All Students, p. 347 TE Integrating Chemistry, p. 347 TE Building Inquiry Skills: Modeling, p. 348; Observing, p. 350; Making Generalizations, p. 352 TE Using the Visuals, p. 353
3 Insects pp. 354–361 ◆ Describe the characteristics of insects, including their body structure, how they feed, and how they defend themselves. ◆ Explain metamorphosis. ◆ Describe the overall impact of insects on humans.	2 periods/ 1 block	**Discover** What Kinds of Appendages Do Insects Have? p. 354 **Sharpen Your Skills** Graphing, p. 356 **Real-World Lab: You and Your Environment** What's Living in the Soil? pp. 360–361	TE Building Inquiry Skills: Interpreting Diagrams, p. 355 TE Integrating Environmental Science, p. 359
4 *INTEGRATING* **CHEMISTRY** **The Chemistry of Communication** pp. 362–364 ◆ Describe how animals use pheromones to communicate. ◆ Explain bioluminescence.	1 period/ $\frac{1}{2}$ block	**Discover** Can You Match the Scents? p. 362 **Science at Home,** p. 364	TE Activating Prior Knowledge, p. 362 TE Building Inquiry Skills: Inferring, pp. 363, 364
5 Echinoderms pp. 365–368 ◆ Describe the typical echinoderm characteristics. ◆ Name and describe some types of echinoderms.	1–$1\frac{1}{2}$ periods/ $\frac{1}{2}$–$\frac{3}{4}$ block	**Discover** How Do Sea Stars Hold On? p. 365	TE Including All Students, p. 366 TE Inquiry Challenge, p. 366 LM 11, "Characteristics of Sea Stars"
Study Guide/Chapter Assessment pp. 369–371	1 period/ $\frac{1}{2}$ block		ISAB Provides teaching and review of all inquiry skills

 For Standard or Block Schedule The Resource Pro® CD-ROM gives you maximum flexibility for planning your instruction with a standard or a block schedule. Resource Pro® contains Planning Express®, an advanced scheduling program, as well as the entire contents of the Teaching Resources and the Computer Test Bank.

CHAPTER PLANNING GUIDE

Program Resources	Assessment Strategies	Media and Technology
UR Chapter 11 Project Teacher Notes, pp. 30–31 **UR** Chapter 11 Project Overview and Worksheets, pp. 32–35	**SE** Performance Assessment: Present Your Project, p. 371 **TE** Check Your Progress, pp. 353, 359, 368 **UR** Chapter 11 Project: Scoring Rubric, p. 36	Science Explorer Internet Site at www.phschool.com
UR 11-1 Lesson Plan, p. 37 **UR** 11-1 Section Summary, p. 38 **UR** 11-1 Review and Reinforce, p. 39 **UR** 11-1 Enrich, p. 40 **UR** Chapter 11 Skills Lab, pp. 57–58	**SE** Section 1 Review, p. 344 **TE** Ongoing Assessment, pp. 341, 343 **TE** Performance Assessment, p. 344	Audio CD, English-Spanish Summary 11-1 Life Science Videotape 3; Videodisc Unit 3 Side 2, "Spineless" Transparency 45, "Exploring a Snail"
UR 11-2 Lesson Plan, p. 41 **UR** 11-2 Section Summary, p. 42 **UR** 11-2 Review and Reinforce, p. 43 **UR** 11-2 Enrich, p. 44	**SE** Section 2 Review, p. 353 **TE** Ongoing Assessment, pp. 347, 349, 351 **TE** Performance Assessment, p. 353	Audio CD, English-Spanish Summary 11-2 Life Science Videotape 3; Videodisc Unit 3 Side 2, "Spineless" Transparency 46, "Exploring a Crayfish"
UR 11-3 Lesson Plan, p. 45 **UR** 11-3 Section Summary, p. 46 **UR** 11-3 Review and Reinforce, p. 47 **UR** 11-3 Enrich, p. 48 **UR** Chapter 11 Real-World Lab, pp. 59–61	**SE** Section 3 Review, p. 359 **TE** Ongoing Assessment, pp. 355, 357 **TE** Performance Assessment, p. 359	Audio CD, English-Spanish Summary 11-3 Life Science Videotape 3; Videodisc Unit 3 Side 2, "Insect Success Stories"; "The Good Bugs" Transparency 47, "Grasshopper Anatomy"; Transparency 48, "Exploring Insect Metamorphosis" Interactive Student Tutorial CD-ROM, Chapter 11
UR 11-4 Lesson Plan, p. 49 **UR** 11-4 Section Summary, p. 50 **UR** 11-4 Review and Reinforce, p. 51 **UR** 11-4 Enrich, p. 52	**SE** Section 4 Review, p. 364 **TE** Ongoing Assessment, p. 363 **TE** Performance Assessment, p. 364	Audio CD, English-Spanish Summary 11-4
UR 11-5 Lesson Plan, p. 53 **UR** 11-5 Section Summary, p. 54 **UR** 11-5 Review and Reinforce, p. 55 **UR** 11-5 Enrich, p. 56	**SE** Section 5 Review, p. 368 **TE** Ongoing Assessment, p. 367 **TE** Performance Assessment, p. 368	Audio CD, English-Spanish Summary 11-5 Life Science Videotape 3; Videodisc Unit 3 Side 2, "Spineless" Transparency 49, "Exploring a Sea Star"
RCA Provides strategies to improve science reading skills **GSW** Provides worksheets to promote student comprehension of content	**SE** Chapter 11 Study Guide/Assessment, pp. 369–371 **PA** Chapter 11 Performance Assessment, pp. 35–37 **CUT** Chapter 11 Test, pp. 52–55 **CTB** Chapter 11 Test	Interactive Student Tutorial CD-ROM, Chapter 11 Computer Test Bank, Chapter 11 Test

Key: **SE** Student Edition **TE** Teacher's Edition **UR** Unit Resources
CTB Computer Test Bank **PTA** Product Testing Activities by *Consumer Reports* **LM** Laboratory Manual
ISAB Inquiry Skills Activity Book **RCA** Reading in the Content Area **IES** Interdisciplinary Explorations Series
GSW Guided Study Worksheets **PA** Performance Assessment **CUT** Chapter and Unit Tests

Meeting the National Science Education Standards and AAAS Benchmarks

National Science Education Standards	Benchmarks for Science Literacy	Unifying Themes
Science as Inquiry (Content Standard A) ◆ **Identify questions that can be answered through scientific investigations** How do different conditions affect mealworm development? *(Chapter Project)* ◆ **Design and conduct a scientific investigation** Students design a plan to investigate mealworm development. *(Chapter Project)* **Life Science** (Content Standard C) ◆ **Diversity and adaptations of organisms** Students learn the characteristics and adaptations of mollusks, arthropods, insects, and echinoderms. Many insects use chemical communication. *(Sections 1–5)* ◆ **Populations and ecosystems** The vast majority of insects are harmless or beneficial to humans. Students examine the animal life of a specific soil environment. *(Section 3; Real-World Lab)*	**1B Scientific Inquiry** Scientific investigations usually involve the collection of relevant evidence, the use of logical reasoning, and the application of imagination in devising hypotheses and explanations to make sense of the collected evidence. *(Skills Lab; Real-World Lab; Chapter Project)* **3A Technology and Science** Pheromone chemistry is the basis for the development of new technologies in controlling insect pests. *(Section 4)* **5A Diversity of Life** Animals have a great variety of body plans and internal structures that contribute to their ability to make or find food and reproduce. In classifying organisms, biologists consider details of internal and external structures. *(Sections 1–5)* **5D Interdependence of Life** In any environment, the growth and survival of organisms depend on the physical conditions. Two organisms may interact with one another in several ways: producer/consumer, predator/prey, parasite/host, etc. *(Sections 1– 3, 5; Real-World Lab; Chapter Project)* **12D Communication Skills** Organize information in simple graphs and identify relationships they reveal. *(Skills Lab; Chapter Project)*	◆ **Evolution** The natural history of mollusks is recorded by fossils that date as far back as 600 million years. Most of the fossils occur as shells in limestone rocks. *(Section 1)* ◆ **Unity and Diversity** Mollusks, arthropods, and echinoderms are grouped according to anatomical characteristics. Individual groups within these phyla are differentiated by specific characteristics. *(Sections 1–3, 5; Real-World Lab)* ◆ **Energy** Various feeding strategies of major groups of animals are explained. Specific feeding strategies are described and clarified with examples. Animals' use of chemical communication is examined. *(Sections 1–5)* ◆ **Patterns of Change** Students learn about metamorphosis as a developmental pattern in arthropods. *(Sections 2, 3)*

Take It to the Net

 *Interactive text at www.phschool.com*

Science Explorer comes alive with iText.

- **Complete student text** is accessible from any computer with Internet access or a CD-ROM drive.
- **Animations, simulations, and videos** enhance student understanding and retention of concepts.
- **Self-tests and online study tools** assess student understanding.

STAY CURRENT with **SCIENCE NEWS**®

Find out the latest research and information about animals at:
www.phschool.com

 WEB ACTIVITY www.phschool.com

Go to **www.phschool.com** and click on the Science icon. Then click on <u>Science Explorer: Life, Earth, and Physical Science</u> under PH@school.

ACTIVITY	Time (minutes)	Materials *Quantities for one work group*	Skills
Section 1			
Discover, p. 340	20	**Nonconsumable** mollusk shells such as clams, mussels, oysters, land and marine snails, and nautiluses	Inferring
Sharpen Your Skills, p. 342	10	No special materials are required.	Classifying
Science at Home, p. 344	home	No special materials are required.	Observing, Communicating
Skills Lab, p. 345	60	**Consumable** spring water at three temperatures: cool (9–13ºC); medium (18–22ºC); warm (27–31ºC), graph paper **Nonconsumable** freshwater snail, plastic petri dish, thermometer, ruler, timer	Measuring
Section 2			
Discover, p. 346	15	**Consumable** sheets of heavy cardboard about 30 x 45 cm, tape	Inferring
Try This, p. 350	20	**Consumable** aluminum foil, paper towels, masking tape, water **Nonconsumable** shoe box, live pill bugs	Interpreting Data
Section 3			
Discover, p. 354	20	**Nonconsumable** insect collection, hand lenses	Observing
Sharpen Your Skills, p. 356	20	**Nonconsumable** protractor, compass, calculator	Graphing
Real World Lab, pp. 360–361	15; 45	**Consumable** 2-liter plastic bottle, coarse steel wool, cheesecloth, fresh sample of soil and leaf litter **Nonconsumable** gooseneck lamp; large, wide-mouthed jar; large scissors; trowel; large rubber band; hand lens; small jar	Observing, Classifying, Inferring
Section 4			
Discover, p. 362	20	**Nonconsumable** pairs of small, foil-covered containers holding a variety of nontoxic substances with distinctive scents	Observing
Science at Home, p. 364	home	No special materials are required.	Communicating
Section 5			
Discover, p. 365	5	**Consumable** water **Nonconsumable** plastic dropper	Predicting

A list of all materials required for the Student Edition activities can be found on pages T25–T33. You can obtain information about ordering materials by calling 1-800-848-9500 or by accessing the Science Explorer Internet site at **www.phschool.com**.

Going Through Changes

Many students may have heard about the metamorphosis of insects. In this project, they'll have the chance to observe that process.

Purpose In this project, students will observe metamorphosis while examining conditions (variables) that may affect the process.

Skills Focus Students will be able to
- observe how different conditions affect mealworm development;
- design experiments to test the effect of an environmental variable on metamorphosis;
- control the variable being tested;
- create data tables to record daily mealworm observations;
- draw conclusions regarding the effect of the environmental change on metamorphosis.

Project Time Line The larval stage of mealworms lasts for 10 weeks. However, mealworms obtained from a pet store are probably partly through the larval period. Larger larvae are generally older. Acquire mealworms in advance of the project. If necessary for scheduling purposes, keep the mealworms at a warm temperature to accelerate development or a cold temperature to delay development. Each day for the next few weeks, students count how many larvae, pupae, and adults they have in each container. Students may wish to continue collecting data until half the mealworms have become adults. Generally, pupae become adults in 2 to 3 weeks.

Before beginning the project, see Chapter 11 Project Teacher Notes on pages 30–31 in Unit 3 Resources for more details on carrying out the project. Also give students the Chapter 11 Project Overview, Worksheets 1 and 2, and Scoring Rubric on pages 32–36 in Unit 3 Resources.

Possible Materials
- You can obtain mealworms from local pet stores that sell reptile and amphibian food. Make sure they are well fed and have a moisture source until the project launch day.

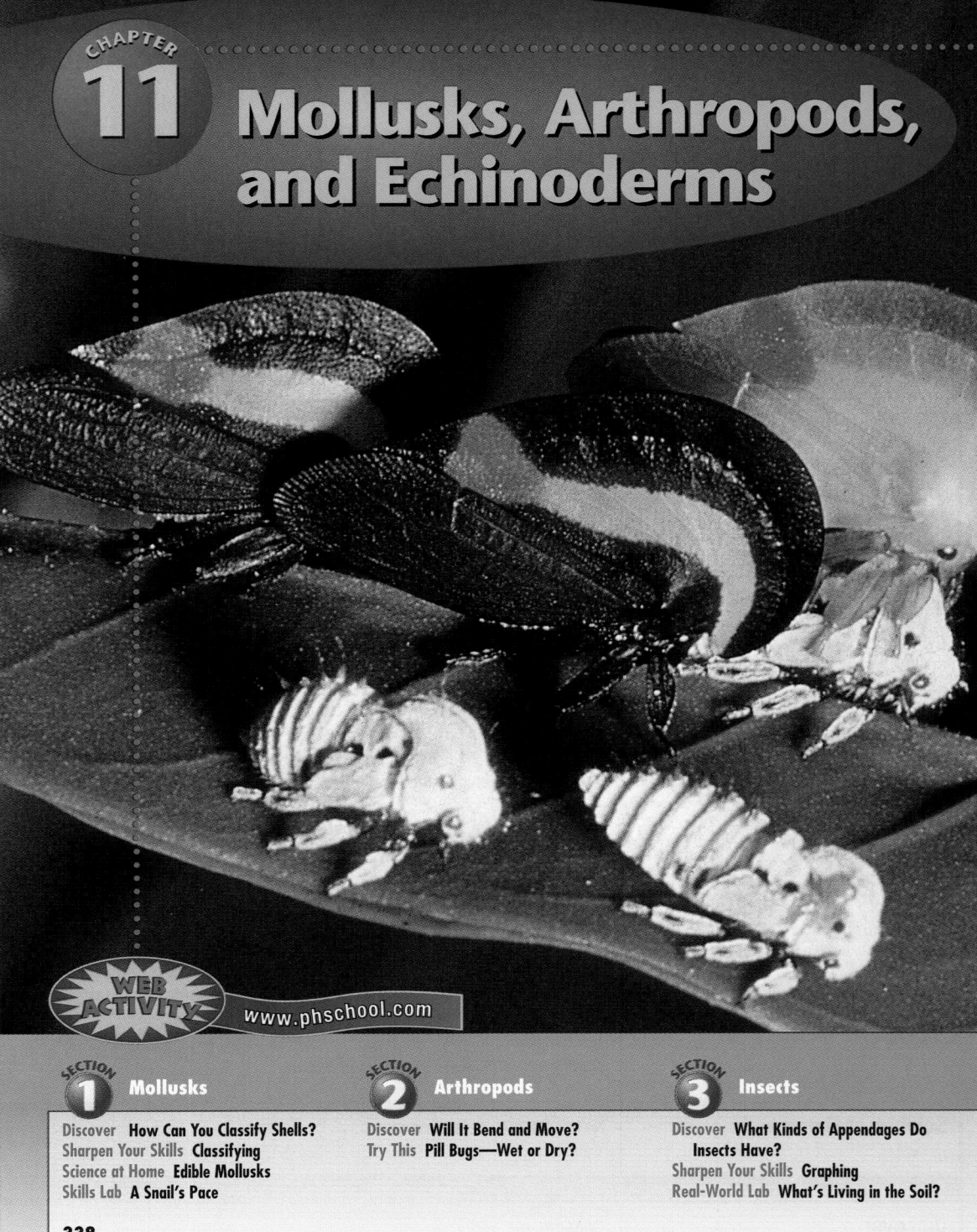

WEB ACTIVITY www.phschool.com

SECTION **1** Mollusks
Discover **How Can You Classify Shells?**
Sharpen Your Skills **Classifying**
Science at Home **Edible Mollusks**
Skills Lab **A Snail's Pace**

SECTION **2** Arthropods
Discover **Will It Bend and Move?**
Try This **Pill Bugs—Wet or Dry?**

SECTION **3** Insects
Discover **What Kinds of Appendages Do Insects Have?**
Sharpen Your Skills **Graphing**
Real-World Lab **What's Living in the Soil?**

338

- Tell students to bring in plastic containers with lids, such as empty margarine tubs. The slippery plastic makes it difficult for the mealworms to escape.
- Students can bring in dry cereal or uncooked oatmeal for mealworm food.
- Slices of apple, potato, carrot, or over-ripe banana can be used as moisture sources.
- Students can use plastic spoons, Popsicle sticks, or wooden splints to transfer the cereal to the containers and to count the mealworms.

Launching the Project Obtain the mealworms in advance and have students begin to collect the materials. To introduce the project and to stimulate interest, ask: **Have any of you seen a caterpillar turn into a butterfly?** *(Answers may vary.)* **What are the major differences and similarities between caterpillars and butterflies?** *(Sample answer: differences—wings; similarities—legs)* Tell students the mealworms will turn into beetles. Reassure them that the beetles will not fly out when the lid of the container is removed.

Going Through Changes

Look at the changes a treehopper insect goes through in its lifetime! In its white nymph stage, it doesn't look anything like an adult treehopper. Most of the animals you will read about in this chapter also change their form during their life cycles. In this project, you will view these kinds of changes firsthand as you observe mealworm development.

Your Goal To observe how different conditions affect mealworm development.

To complete this project successfully, you must

♦ compare mealworm development under two different conditions
♦ record your mealworm observations daily for several weeks
♦ draw conclusions about the effects of those conditions on development
♦ follow the safety guidelines in Appendix A

Get Started Find two containers, such as clean margarine tubs with lids, in which to keep the mealworms. Get some mealworm food, such as cornflakes, and a plastic spoon to transfer the food and count the mealworms. Choose two conditions, such as two different temperatures or food sources, and plan how to test the two conditions.

Check Your Progress You'll be working on this project as you study this chapter. To keep your project on track, look for Check Your Progress boxes at the following points.

Section 2 Review, page 353: Record your daily observations.
Section 3 Review, page 359: Sketch the stages of development.
Section 5 Review, page 368: Draw conclusions about mealworm development under each of the conditions.

Present Your Project At the end of the chapter (page 371), you will report on your results.

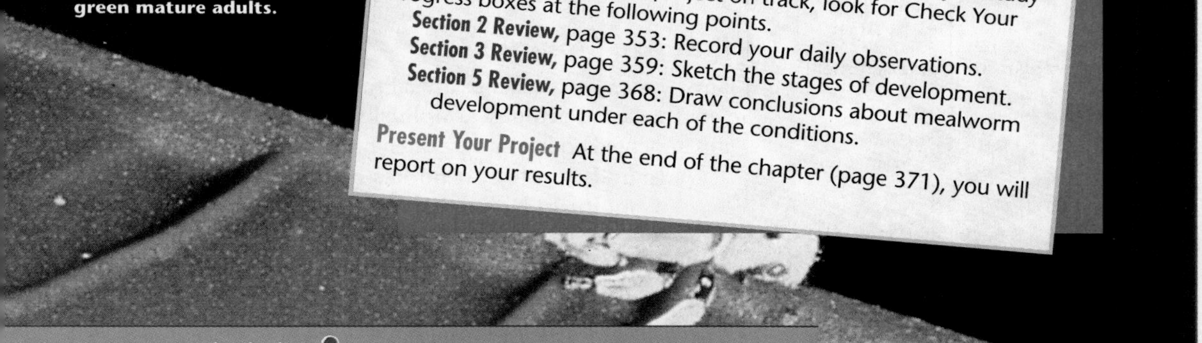

Treehoppers undergo dramatic changes in form during their lives. The whitish nymphs gradually turn into light green young adults. The young adults gradually change into dark green mature adults.

SECTION 4 — Integrating Chemistry
The Chemistry of Communication

Discover **Can You Match the Scents?**
Science at Home **Chemicals and Insect Pests**

SECTION 5
Echinoderms

Discover **How Do Sea Stars Hold On?**

339

Program Resources

♦ **Unit 3 Resources** Chapter 11 Project Teacher Notes, pp. 30–31; Chapter 11 Project Overview and Worksheets, pp. 32–35; Chapter 11 Project Scoring Rubric, p. 36

WEB ACTIVITY www.phschool.com

You will find an Internet activity, chapter self-tests for students, and links to other chapter topics at this site.

Allow time for students to read the description of the project in their text and the Chapter Project Overview on pages 32–33 in Unit 3 Resources. Then encourage discussions on the environmental factors that might affect metamorphosis such as temperature, light, and type of food supplied. Also discuss materials that could be used, and any initial questions students may have. Distribute copies of the Chapter 11 Project Worksheets on pages 34–35 in Unit 3 Resources for students to review.

Students can work in small groups as a cooperative learning task. To ensure that every student will have ample opportunity to participate in designing an experiment, you may wish to limit groups to three students.

On the launch day, have students prepare two containers. They will need to put food (such as cornflakes) and a moisture source (such as a piece of fruit or vegetable) in each container. Direct students to select and set up the two conditions they want to test. You may wish to have students write a hypothesis. Then distribute the mealworms.

Students can interpret their data on the number of larvae, pupae, and adult mealworms in each container by drawing graphs to compare the different conditions. They can then use these graphs to evaluate their hypotheses.

Performance Assessment

The Chapter 11 Project Scoring Rubric on page 36 of Unit 3 Resources will help you evaluate how well students complete the Chapter 11 Project. Students will be assessed on
♦ how well they describe the two conditions that they are comparing;
♦ how well they identify and observe the larval, pupal, and adult stages of mealworm development;
♦ how clearly the data sheets show the number of larvae, pupae, and adults in their samples;
♦ how correctly the graphs show the numbers of mealworm larvae, pupae, and adult beetles.

By sharing the Chapter 11 Project Scoring Rubric with students at the beginning of the project, you will make it clear to them what they are expected to do.

Objectives

After completing this lesson, students will be able to
◆ describe the main characteristics of mollusks and the evidence of their early existence on Earth;
◆ describe the major groups of mollusks.

Key Terms mollusk, kidney, gill, radula, gastropod, bivalve, cephalopod

1 Engage/Explore

Activating Prior Knowledge

Ask students if they have ever eaten a mollusk. Students may not know what a mollusk is. Then, ask if any student has ever eaten clams, oysters, or squid. If students answer yes, inform them that all these animals are mollusks.

DISCOVER

Skills Focus inferring
Materials *mollusk shells such as those from clams, mussels, oysters, land and marine snails, and nautiluses*
Time 20 minutes
Tips Place the shells at stations around the room. Group students at each station. Help students develop a set of characteristics to use for grouping the shells. Remind students to handle specimens carefully as they may be fragile. Tell students to describe some features of the shells. Guide them to notice shiny and rough surfaces, the composition and color of shell material, and possible signs of growth, such as rings. Be sure that students write down the characteristics they used to group the shells. Let each group select a representative to describe the characteristics to the class.
Expected Outcome Students should become aware of the wide diversity of shells.
Think It Over It might help an animal to have a shell because the shell could protect it from predators and support its body.

SECTION 1 Mollusks

DISCOVER ······································ ACTIVITY

How Can You Classify Shells?

1. Obtain an assortment of shells from your teacher. Examine each one carefully. Look at the shells and feel their surfaces.
2. Compare the outer surface of each shell to the inner surface.
3. Classify the shells into two or more groups based on the characteristics you observe.

Think It Over
Inferring How might it help an animal to have a shell?

GUIDE FOR READING

◆ What are the main characteristics of mollusks?
◆ What are the major groups of mollusks?

Reading Tip As you read, make a compare/contrast table to distinguish among the different mollusk groups.

▼ Wampum string and clamshell

From the shells of clams, Native Americans in the Northeast carved purple and white beads called wampum. They wove these beads into belts with complex designs that often had special, solemn significance. A wampum belt might record a group's history. When warring groups made peace, they exchanged weavings made of wampum. Iroquois women would honor a new chief with gifts of wampum strings.

The hard shells of clams provided the material for wampum, and the soft bodies within the shells were a major source of food for Native Americans who lived along the seacoast. Today, clams and similar animals, such as scallops and oysters, are still valuable sources of food for people in many parts of the world.

What Are Mollusks?

Clams, oysters, and scallops are all mollusks (phylum Mollusca). So are snails and octopuses. **Mollusks** are invertebrates with soft, unsegmented bodies that are often protected by hard outer shells. **In addition to soft bodies often covered with shells, mollusks have a thin layer of tissue called a mantle, which covers their internal organs.** The mantle also produces the mollusk's shell. Most mollusks move with a muscular structure called a foot. The feet of different kinds of mollusks are adapted for various uses, such as crawling, digging, or catching prey.

Mollusks live nearly everywhere on Earth. Most live in water, from mountain streams to the deep ocean, but some live on land, usually in damp places.

340

READING STRATEGIES

Reading Tip Help students set up tables with four columns. The first column should be labeled *Characteristics*. Students can add the name of each mollusk group as they read about it. Make sure students include rows in their tables for number of shells, type of foot, and complexity of nervous system for each group of mollusks.

Vocabulary Tell students that *gastropod* means "stomach-footed," *cephalopod* means "head-footed," and *bivalve* means "two-shelled." Have students write down the name of each group of mollusks, what each name means, and a sentence describing why they think each group was given its name.

Like segmented worms, mollusks have bilateral symmetry. However, unlike segmented worms, the body parts of mollusks are not repeated. Instead, their internal organs, such as the stomach and reproductive organs, are all located together in one area. A mollusk's internal organs include a pair of **kidneys,** organs that remove the wastes produced by an animal's cells.

Most water-dwelling mollusks have **gills,** organs that remove oxygen from water. The gills are attached to the mantle and have a rich supply of blood vessels. Within these thin-walled blood vessels, oxygen from the surrounding water diffuses into the blood, while carbon dioxide diffuses out. The gills of most mollusks are covered by tiny, hairlike structures called cilia. The beating movement of these cilia makes water flow over the gills.

Many mollusks have an organ called a **radula** (RAJ oo luh) (plural *radulae*), which is a flexible ribbon of tiny teeth. Acting like sandpaper, the tiny teeth scrape food from a surface such as a leaf. A radula may have as many as 250,000 teeth. Biologists use the arrangement of teeth in the radula to help classify mollusks.

☑ *Checkpoint* How is the body structure of a mollusk different from that of a segmented worm?

Evidence of Early Mollusks

INTEGRATING EARTH SCIENCE Mollusks were living in Earth's oceans about 540 million years ago. Much evidence for this comes from fossil shells in limestone rocks. Some kinds of limestone are partially made from the shells of ancient, ocean-dwelling mollusks. After the mollusks died, their shells were broken into tiny pieces by waves and water currents. These shell pieces, along with the hard remains of other organisms, piled up on the ocean floor. These hard materials then underwent a chemical change in which they became cemented together to form limestone. During this process, some shells—or parts of shells—remained unbroken and eventually became fossils.

Figure 1 Some mollusks, like the chambered nautilus, left, are protected by shells. Other mollusks, like the nudibranch, right, do not have shells. *Classifying What characteristics do these two organisms share?*

Answers to Self-Assessment

Caption Question

Figure 1 Both the nautilus and the nudibranch are invertebrates with soft bodies and a mantle that covers their internal organs.

☑ *Checkpoint*

The bodies of mollusks are not segmented; their internal organs are all in one area.

---

2 *Facilitate*

What Are Mollusks?

Building Inquiry Skills: Classifying

Have students list the characteristics mollusks and segmented worms have in common and those that are unique to each organism. Then ask: **Based on this information, do you think mollusks and segmented worms are closely related? Why?** *(Answers will vary. Be sure students support their answer.)* **learning modality: logical/mathematical**

Evidence of Early Mollusks

 Integrating Earth Science

Materials *pieces of granite, limestone, marine snail or clam shells; 10% hydrochloric acid (HCl) solution; plastic dropper*

ACTIVITY

Time 15 minutes
Tips This demonstration shows students that limestone and marble both contain calcium carbonate.
CAUTION: *Hydrochloric acid can burn skin and clothing. Avoid direct contact. Neutralize spills and splashes with plenty of water. Wear safety goggles, gloves, and a lab apron. After the demonstration, dispose of the acid solution by diluting it with lots of water and pouring it down the sink.* Inform students that materials that contain calcium carbonate fizz when hydrochloric acid is applied to them. Then apply a few drops of acid solution to the granite, then the limestone, and finally the shell. Students should watch for a reaction. The granite will not react; the limestone and shell should fizz. Thoroughly rinse each specimen. Students should infer that both limestone and the shells contain calcium carbonate. **learning modality: visual**

Ongoing Assessment

Writing Have students create a checklist of characteristics that identify an animal as a mollusk.

Snails and Their Relatives

Sharpen your Skills

Skills Focus classifying
Time 10 minutes

Tips Remind students that there are three subgroups of mollusks. Have students review the text for the characteristics biologists use to classify mollusks.

Expected Outcome To decide to which of the major groups the unknown mollusk belongs, students should look for the following characteristics: presence of shell; nature of shell (single or bivalve); type of foot; presence and type of radula; presence of tentacles; and complexity of nervous system.

Extend Ask students: **Do you think the mollusk you stepped on could be a slug?** (*No, because most slugs do not have external shells*) **learning modality: verbal**

Cultural Diversity

Regions with such diverse cultures as Japan, France, and Brazil possess unique methods of flavoring and cooking mollusks, such as oysters, clams, squid, and mussels. Have students research ethnic cookbooks and find out how mollusks are prepared and eaten in different cultures. Students should bring a copy of a recipe to class. If possible, have students prepare the recipes at home and describe the experience of cooking and eating the mollusk dish. **learning modality: kinesthetic**

Including All Students

Students acquiring English may have difficulty pronouncing *gastropod, cephalopod,* and *bivalve.* Pronounce each word clearly and slowly. Suggest that students write each term in their notebooks, define the terms in their own words, and draw a sketch of a representative of each group. **limited English proficiency**

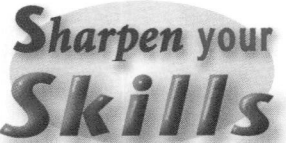

Classifying

While wading in a stream, you almost step on a small animal with a hard external covering. When you examine the animal, you discover that it has a soft body inside its shell. It appears to be a mollusk. What characteristics would help you determine the major group of mollusks to which it belongs?

Figure 2 The two shells of a bivalve are held together by hinges and strong muscles. Giant clams like this one are among the largest bivalves in the world.

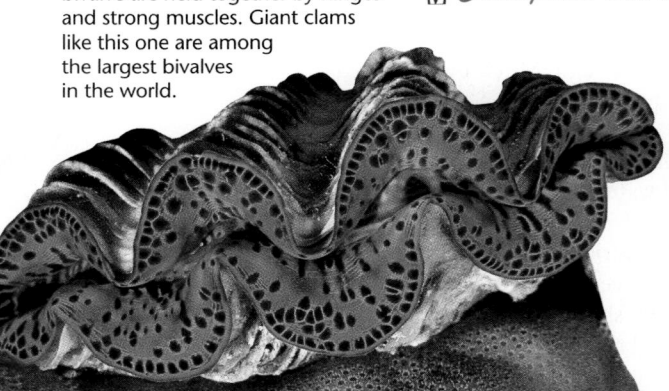

Snails and Their Relatives

Biologists classify mollusks into groups based on physical characteristics such as the presence of a shell, the type of shell, the type of foot, the arrangement of teeth in the radula, and the complexity of the nervous system. **The three major groups of mollusks are gastropods, bivalves, and cephalopods.**

The most numerous mollusks are the gastropods. **Gastropods,** which include snails and slugs, are mollusks that have a single shell or no shell at all. Most snails have a single, coiled shell, while many slugs have no shell. Gastropods usually creep along on a broad foot. Gastropods get their name, which means "stomach foot," from the fact that most of them have their foot on the same side of their body as their stomach. To learn more about the body of a gastropod, look at *Exploring a Snail* on page 343.

You can find gastropods nearly everywhere on Earth. They live in oceans, on rocky shores, in fresh water, and on dry land, too. Some snails even live in treetops.

Some gastropods are herbivores, while others are scavengers that feed on decaying material. Still others are carnivores. For example, the oyster drill is a snail that makes a hole in an oyster's shell by releasing acid and then boring a hole with its radula. The oyster drill then scrapes away the oyster's soft body.

Many snails have a tight-fitting plate or trapdoor on their foot that fits securely into the opening of their shell. When this kind of snail is threatened by a predator, it withdraws into its shell and tightly closes its trapdoor. Snails also pull back into their shells when conditions are dry and then come out when conditions are moist again. When they are sealed up in this way, gastropods can survive incredibly long times. In one museum the shells of two land snails, presumed to be dead, were glued to a piece of cardboard. Four years later, when someone put the cardboard in water, one of the snails crawled away!

☑ *Checkpoint* *How did gastropods get their name?*

Two-Shelled Mollusks

Clams, oysters, scallops, and mussels are **bivalves,** mollusks that have two shells held together by hinges and strong muscles. Unlike other mollusks, bivalves do not have radulae. Instead, most are filter feeders; they strain their food from water. Bivalves use their gills to capture food as they breathe. Food particles stick to mucus

Background

Facts and Figures Many gastropod shells, especially those from the oceans, are valued by collectors. Cone shells are some of the rarest and most beautiful of gastropod shells. However, the animals in cone shells can be very dangerous. Cones capture prey by injecting a paralyzing toxin. A few of the larger species, such as *Conus geographus,* have been reported to cause death in humans.

Program Resources

◆ **Interdisciplinary Exploration Series** "Where River Meets Sea," pp. 15–16
◆ **Unit 3 Resources** 11-1 Review and Reinforce, p. 39; 11-1 Enrich, p. 40

EXPLORING a Snail

Like other gastropods, a snail has a head with sense organs, and it has a wide, muscular foot. The snails shown here live in a pond.

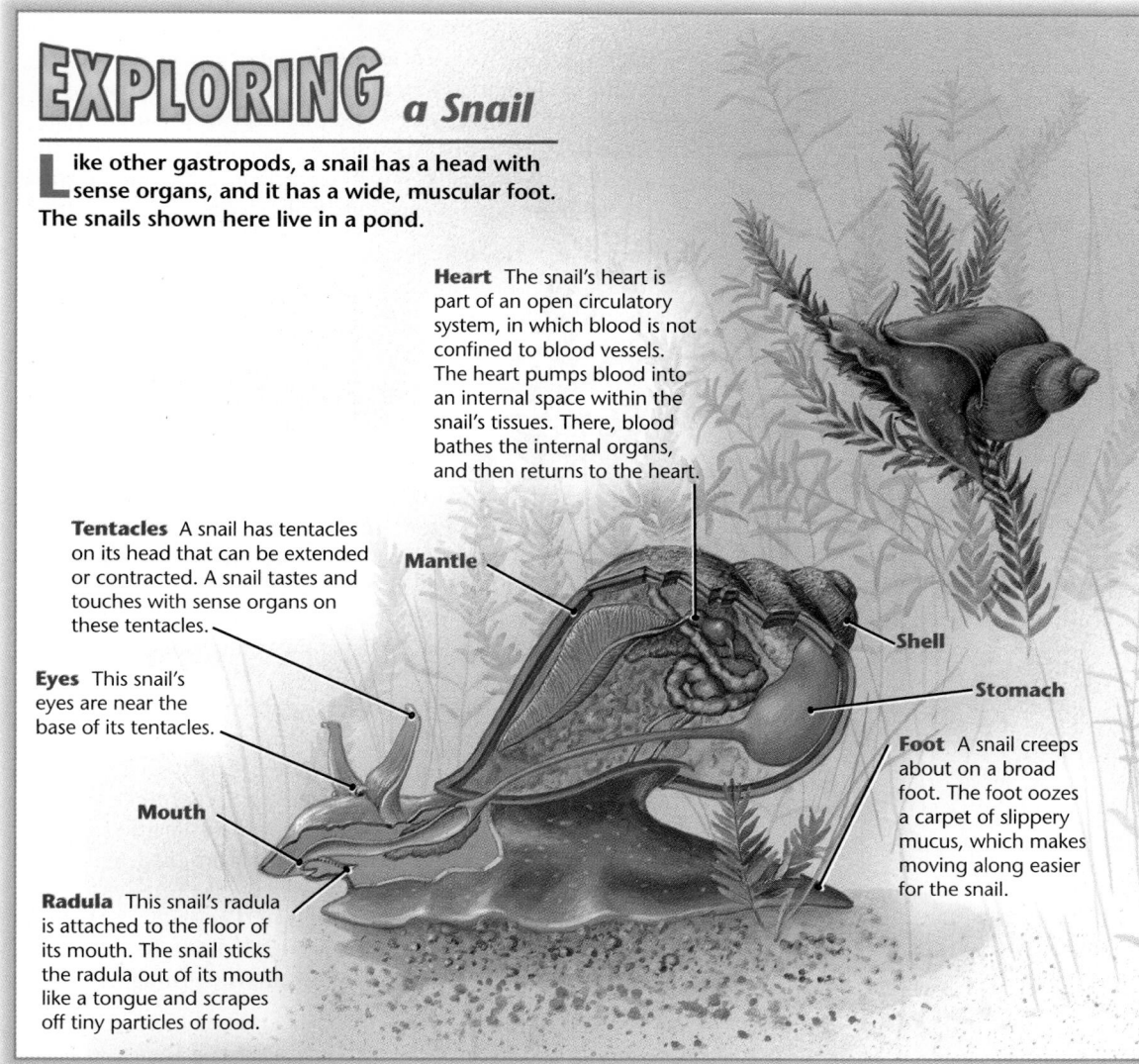

Heart The snail's heart is part of an open circulatory system, in which blood is not confined to blood vessels. The heart pumps blood into an internal space within the snail's tissues. There, blood bathes the internal organs, and then returns to the heart.

Tentacles A snail has tentacles on its head that can be extended or contracted. A snail tastes and touches with sense organs on these tentacles.

Eyes This snail's eyes are near the base of its tentacles.

Mouth

Radula This snail's radula is attached to the floor of its mouth. The snail sticks the radula out of its mouth like a tongue and scrapes off tiny particles of food.

Mantle

Shell

Stomach

Foot A snail creeps about on a broad foot. The foot oozes a carpet of slippery mucus, which makes moving along easier for the snail.

---

that covers the gills. The cilia on the gills then move the food particles into the bivalve's mouth.

Bivalves are found in all kinds of watery environments. As adults, most bivalves stay in one place or move slowly. After their larval stage, for example, oysters and mussels attach themselves to an underwater surface. Clams, in contrast, are active; they use a thin foot to burrow down into the sand or mud. Scallops can also move from place to place. In fact, when startled, scallops clap their shells together and leap rapidly in the water over the sand.

Answers to Self-Assessment

☑ Checkpoint

Gastropod means "stomach foot." Gastropods were given this name because a gastrophod's foot is on the same side of its body as its stomach.

Materials *live snails in an aquarium, hand lens*

Time 20 minutes

Tips Reinforce the information presented in the visual essay by allowing students to observe live snails in an aquarium. Ask students to examine the snail in the visual essay and compare to the snails in the aquarium. Caution them not to touch the snails or tap on the sides of the aquarium. Have students look for the parts of the snail that are labeled in the visual essay. *(Students should be able to see the tentacles, mouth, foot, and shell. They may be able to see the eyes.)* **learning modality: visual**

Two-Shelled Mollusks

Building Inquiry Skills: Observing

Materials *a closed oyster, an opened oyster*

Time 30 minutes

Tips Obtain oysters from a seafood market, and request that half the oysters be opened. Refrigerate the oysters to avoid spoilage. Have students work in pairs. One student should examine the closed bivalve, identify each half of the shell, and explore the texture of the outer covering. The other student should examine the opened oyster and identify as many internal parts as possible. The two students should then compare observations. Students should wash their hands after handling the oysters. **cooperative learning**

Ongoing Assessment

Writing Ask students to write short paragraphs that compare gastropods and bivalves, and include an example of each. *(Gastropods, such as snails and slugs, have one shell or no shell, creep on a broad foot, and scrape food with their radulas. Bivalves, such as clams and oysters, have two shells and are filter feeders. Some use a foot to dig into the sand.)*

Mollusks with Tentacles

Integrating Physics

Materials *balloon, aquarium or sink, water*

Time 10 minutes

Tips To demonstrate how cephalopods move using jet propulsion, fill the balloon with water. Pinch the neck to keep water from squirting out. Immerse the balloon in an aquarium or sink and release the neck. Students will observe the balloon shooting through the water.
learning modality: visual

3 Assess

Section 1 Review Answers

1. Soft bodies, mantle, muscular foot; many have shells.
2. Gastropods have one shell or no shell; most creep on a broad foot. Bivalves have two shells, are filter feeders, and often have one foot adapted for digging. Cephalopods have a complex nervous system, swim using jet propulsion, and have tentacles around their mouths.
3. By straining food from water.
4. No. Gills must have many blood vessels to pick up enough oxygen.

Science at Home

Ask students which animals they expect to find (*Snails, oysters, clams, squid, canned clams, smoked oysters*). If possible, suggest students visit a seafood store with a large variety of seafood.

Sometimes sand or grit becomes lodged between a bivalve's mantle and its shell, irritating the soft mantle. Just as you might put smooth tape around rough bicycle handlebars to protect your hands, the bivalve's mantle produces a smooth, pearly coat to cover the irritating object. Eventually a pearl forms around the grit. Some oysters make pearls so beautiful that they are used in jewelry.

Mollusks with Tentacles

Octopuses, cuttlefish, nautiluses, and squids are **cephalopods,** mollusks whose feet are adapted to form tentacles around their mouths. Some octopuses have tentacles almost 5 meters long! While nautiluses have an external shell, squids and cuttlefish have a small shell within the body. Octopuses do not have shells.

Cephalopods capture food with their flexible, muscular tentacles. Sensitive suckers on the tentacles receive sensations of taste as well as touch. A cephalopod doesn't have to touch something to taste it; the suckers respond to chemicals in the water. For example, when an octopus feels beneath a rock, its tentacle may find a crab by taste before it touches it.

Cephalopods have large eyes and excellent vision. They also have the most complex nervous system, including a large brain, of any invertebrate. Cephalopods are highly intelligent animals that can remember things they have learned. In captivity, octopuses quickly learn when to expect deliveries of food and how to escape from their tanks.

 **INTEGRATING PHYSICS** All cephalopods live in the ocean, where they swim by jet propulsion. They squeeze a current of water out of the mantle cavity through a tube, and like rockets, shoot off in the opposite direction. By turning the tube around, they can steer in any direction.

Figure 3 Octopuses live in coral reefs where they hide when they are not hunting crabs and other small animals. *Observing What structures cover the octopus's tentacles?*

Section 1 Review

1. What characteristics do most mollusks have in common?
2. List the three main groups of mollusks. Describe the main characteristics of each group.
3. Explain how bivalves obtain food.
4. **Thinking Critically Predicting** Would gills function well if they had few blood vessels? Explain.

344

Science at Home

Edible Mollusks Visit a supermarket with a family member. Identify any mollusks that are being sold as food. Be sure to look in places other than the fish counter, such as the canned-foods section. Discuss the parts of the mollusks that are used for food and the parts that are not edible.

Performance Assessment

Drawing Have students draw one mollusk from each major group. Then they should list the three characteristics that make these animals mollusks. Finally, have students label one characteristic that distinguishes each group.

 Students can save their drawings in their portfolios.

344

Background

Facts and Figures Bioluminescence is the ability of an animal to produce light. Many squids are bioluminescent. Squids who live deep in the ocean where there is little light are protected from predators by their bioluminescence. Some squids emit a burst of light that startles an approaching predator; others give off a continuous glow. Ocean predators may have difficulty seeing their prey against the ocean surface.

Answers to Self-Assessment

Caption Question

Figure 3 The tentacles of the octopus are covered with suckers.

A Snail's Pace

Skills Lab

I n this lab, you will use the skill of measuring to investigate how fast a snail moves in different water temperatures.

Problem

How do changes in environmental temperature affect the activity level of a snail?

Materials

freshwater snail	thermometer	ruler
plastic petri dish	graph paper	timer

spring water at three temperatures:
cool (9–13°C); medium (18–22°C);
warm (27–31°C)

Procedure

1. Create a data table for recording the water temperatures and the distance the snail travels at each temperature.
2. On one sheet of graph paper labeled *Snail,* trace a circle using the base of an empty petri dish. Divide and label the circle as shown in the illustration. On a second sheet of graph paper labeled *Data,* draw three more circles like the one in the illustration.
3. Place the petri dish over the circle on the Snail page, fill it with cool water, and record the water temperature. Then place the snail in the water just above the "S" in the circle. Be sure to handle the snail gently.
4. For five minutes, observe the snail. Record its movements by drawing a line that shows its path in the first circle on the Data page.
5. Find the distance the snail moved by measuring the line you drew. You may need to measure all the parts of the line and add them together. Record the distance in your data table.

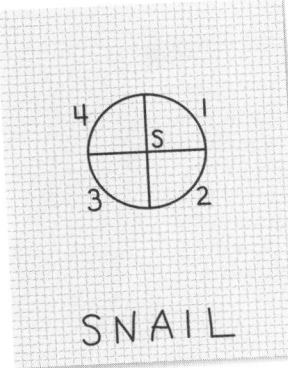

SNAIL

6. Repeat Steps 3 through 5, first with medium-temperature water and then with warm water. Record the snail's paths in the second circle and third circle on the Data page.
7. Return the snail to your teacher when you are done. Wash your hands thoroughly.
8. For each temperature, compute the class average for distance traveled.

Analyze and Conclude

1. Make a bar graph showing the class average for each temperature. How does a snail's activity level change as temperature increases?
2. Do you think the pattern you found would continue at higher temperatures? Explain.
3. **Think About It** What factors in this lab were difficult to measure? How could you change the procedure to obtain more accurate measurements? Explain.

Design an Experiment

Design an experiment to measure the rate at which a snail moves in an aquarium with gravel on the bottom. Obtain your teacher's permission before trying your experiment.

Safety

Students should be very careful with the thermometers. Make sure they do not let them roll off a table top.
- Remind students to treat snails gently and disturb them as little as possible.
- Prepare the cool, medium, and warm water yourself.

Program Resources

- **Unit 3 Resources Chapter 11** Skills Lab, pp. 57–58
- **Inquiry Skills Activity Book** Provides teaching and review of all inquiry skills

---

Skills Lab

Measuring

A Snail's Pace

Preparing for Inquiry

Key Concept The activity of some animals can be affected by the temperature of their environment.
Skills Objective Students will be able to
- measure activity using distance traveled in a specific time.

Time 45 minutes
Advance Planning Place the snails in a small aquarium of pond water. Aerate the aquarium if the snails will be kept more than a few days. For the lab, use the most active snails. For safety reasons, prepare the cool, medium, and warm water yourself.

Guiding Inquiry

Invitation Ask students to give examples of animals that seem to be more active on warm days (such as mosquitoes). Contrast these to animals whose activities seem less dependent on temperature (such as birds).

Introducing the Procedure

Remind students not to leave snails out of the water for very long.

Troubleshooting the Experiment

Do not allow students to tap the petri dish to get the snail moving.

Expected Outcome

Snails usually move more slowly in colder water than in warmer water.

Analyze and Conclude

1. Answers will vary. Plot temperature on *x*-axis and distance moved on *y*-axis.
2. Snails move more in warmer water, but hot water will kill them.
3. Sample: Distance; videotape snails and measure distance on the screen.

Extending Inquiry

Design an Experiment Sample: Tape rulers to the side and rear of the aquarium. Look from front of aquarium and record snail's position using rear ruler; look from side and record position using side ruler.

Objectives

After completing this lesson, students will be able to
◆ describe the major characteristics of arthropods;
◆ identify and describe the main groups of arthropods.

Key Terms arthropod, exoskeleton, chitin, molting, antenna, crustacean, metamorphosis, arachnid, abdomen

1 Engage/Explore

Activating Prior Knowledge

Ask students whether they have ever seen spiders, scorpions, insects, crabs, crayfish, or lobsters. Ask volunteers to describe these animals. Use leading questions to prompt students to mention the external shells and jointed limbs of these animals. Tell students that the features they described are characteristics of arthropods, which they will learn about in this section.

••••••• DISCOVER •••••••

Skills Focus inferring
Materials *sheets of heavy cardboard, about 30 × 45 cm; tape*
Time 15 minutes
Tips Use cardboard that is flexible enough to roll into a tube and tape that is strong enough to stay attached when students attempt to bend their elbows. Students whose partners already have an arm wrapped in cardboard will need assistance when putting on their own tubes.
Expected Outcome Students will find that restricting their joints makes it impossible for them to bend their elbows.
Think It Over Joints in skeletons allow movement.

SECTION 2 Arthropods

◆ DISCOVER •••••••••••••••••••••••• ACTIVITY

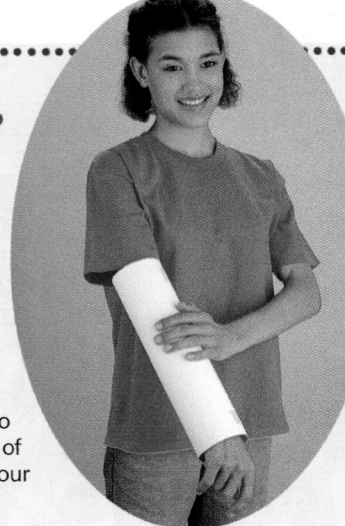

Will It Bend and Move?

1. Have a partner roll a piece of cardboard around your arm to form a tube that covers your elbow. Your partner should put three pieces of tape around the tube to hold it closed— one at each end and one in the middle.

2. With the tube in place, try to write your name on a piece of paper. Then try to scratch your head.

3. Keep the tube on your arm for 10 minutes. Observe how the tube affects your ability to do things.

Think It Over
Inferring Insects and many other animals have rigid skeletons on the outside of their bodies. Why do their skeletons need joints?

GUIDE FOR READING

◆ What are the major characteristics of arthropods?
◆ What are the main groups of arthropods?

Reading Tip Before you read, rewrite the headings in this section as questions. Answer the questions as you read.

On a moonless night at the edge of a wooded area, a moth flits from flower to flower, drinking nectar. Nearby, a hungry spider waits in its web that stretches, nearly invisible, between bushes. Suddenly, the moth gets caught by the spider web. The sticky threads of the web trap one of the moth's wings. As the trapped moth struggles to free itself, the spider rushes toward it. At the last second, the moth gives a strong flap, breaks free, and flutters away—safe! Next time, the moth may not be so lucky.

The hungry spider and lucky moth are both arthropods. Insects and spiders are probably the arthropods you are most familiar with, but the phylum also includes animals such as crabs, lobsters, centipedes, and scorpions. Scientists have identified about 875,000 different species of arthropods, and there are probably many more that have not yet been discovered. Earth has more species of arthropods than of all other animals combined.

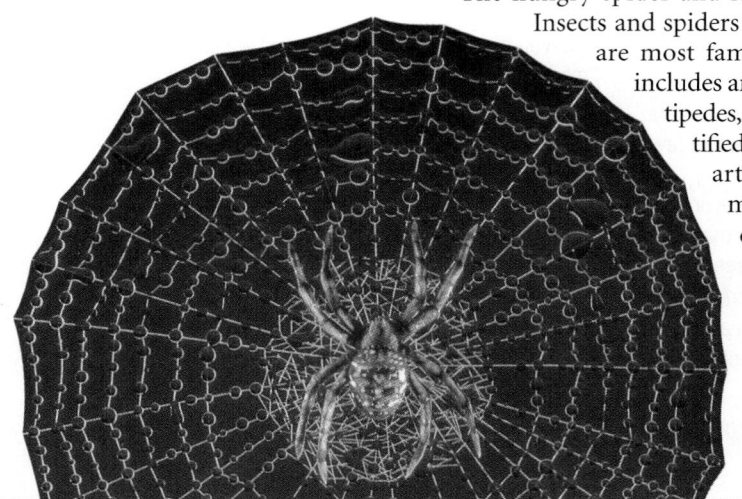

◀ Spider awaiting prey

READING STRATEGIES

Reading Tip Pair students after they have read the sections and rewritten the headings. Have them try to answer each other's questions without referring to the section. Then, have students compare answers and check them with the text. Sample questions: What are the important characteristics of arthropods? Where did arthropods come from?

Vocabulary Point out that both *pod* in arthropod and *pede* in centipede come from roots meaning "foot." *Podos* is a Greek root, *ped* is Latin. Challenge students to think of more words containing these roots. *(Sample: tripod, pedal, pedestal)*

Figure 4 Some arthropods, like the Sally lightfoot crab at left, have a hard exoskeleton. Others, like the Promethea moth caterpillar below, have a leathery exoskeleton. *Making Generalizations What role does an exoskeleton play?*

Characteristics of Arthropods

Members of the **arthropod** phylum (phylum Arthropoda) share certain important characteristics. **An arthropod is an invertebrate that has an external skeleton, a segmented body, and jointed attachments called appendages.** Wings, mouthparts, and legs are all appendages. Jointed legs are such a distinctive characteristic that the arthropod phylum is named for it. *Arthros* means "joint" in Greek, and *podos* means "foot" or "leg."

Arthropods have additional characteristics in common, too. Arthropods have open circulatory systems—the blood leaves the blood vessels and bathes the internal organs. Most arthropods reproduce sexually. Unlike an earthworm, which has both male and female organs in its body, most arthropods are either male or female. Most arthropods have internal fertilization—sperm and egg unite inside the body of the female. This contrasts to external fertilization, which takes place outside an animal's body.

A Skeleton on the Outside If you were an arthropod, you would be completely covered by a waterproof shell. This waxy **exoskeleton,** or outer skeleton, protects the animal and helps prevent evaporation of water. Water animals are surrounded by water, but land animals need a way to keep from drying out. Arthropods were the first animals to move out of water and onto land, and their exoskeletons probably enabled them to do this.

 INTEGRATING CHEMISTRY Arthropod exoskeletons are made of a material called **chitin** (KY tin). Chitin is made of long molecules that are built from many smaller building blocks, like links in a chain. Long-chain molecules like chitin are called polymers. Cotton fibers and rubber are polymers, too. For any

Chapter 11 **347**

---

2 Facilitate

Characteristics of Arthropods

Including All Students

Materials *fresh or frozen whole crab leg; whole shrimp with head from supermarket or seafood store*

Time 20 minutes

Tips Some students may need extra help to identify the features of an arthropod's exoskeleton. Allow them to handle and examine the two specimens. Help students see that both exoskeletons are jointed and made of chitin. Make sure students wash their hands after handling the specimens.

Extend Have students compare the exoskeleton of the shrimp to that of the crab. Ask students: **Which of the two animals has the more flexible exoskeleton?** *(Shrimp)* **The stronger exoskeleton?** *(Crab)* **learning modality: kinesthetic**

Integrating Chemistry

Materials *binocular microscope, fingernail clipper*

Time 10 minutes

 Explain to students that humans produce a polymer similar to chitin called *keratin.* Tell them hair and fingernails are made of keratin. Have students examine a strand of hair and a fingernail clipping under the microscope. Ask them to describe the material that makes up the hair and fingernail. *(Strong and flexible)* **learning modality: visual**

Answers to Self-Assessment

Caption Question

Figure 4 An exoskeleton prevents water loss and provides protection.

Ongoing Assessment

Writing Have students describe three characteristics of arthropods. *(Invertebrates; have jointed appendages, exoskeletons, segmented bodies, open circulatory systems; reproduce sexually)*

Characteristics of Arthropods, continued

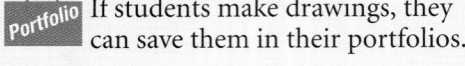

Figure 5 This rainforest cicada has just molted. You can see its old exoskeleton still hanging on the leaf below it. *Applying Concepts Why must arthropods molt?*

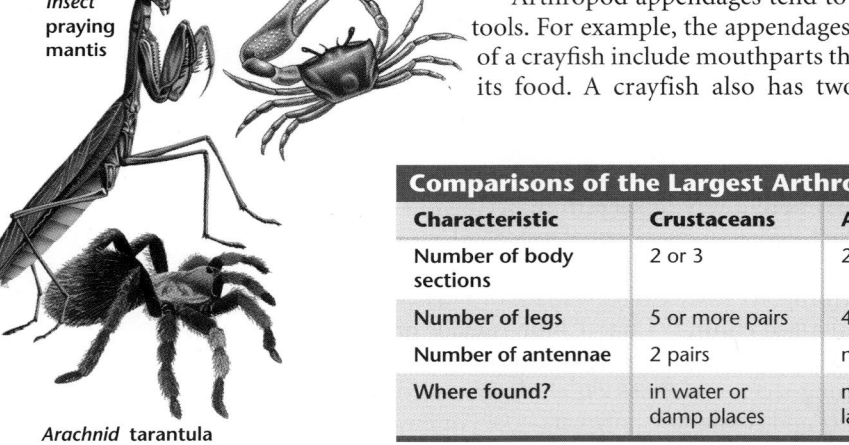

Figure 6 Arthropod groups differ in the numbers of body sections, legs, and antennae, and in where they are found. *Interpreting Charts Which group of arthropods has no antennae?*

Crustacean fiddler crab

Insect praying mantis

Arachnid tarantula

polymer, the kinds, numbers, and the arrangement of its small building blocks determine its characteristics. Chitin's building blocks make it tough and flexible.

As an arthropod grows larger, its exoskeleton cannot expand. The growing arthropod is trapped within its exoskeleton, like a knight in armor that is too small for him. Arthropods solve this problem by occasionally shedding their exoskeletons and growing new ones that are larger. The process of shedding an outgrown exoskeleton is called **molting.** After an arthropod has molted, its new skeleton is soft for a time. During that time, the arthropod has less protection from danger than it does after its new skeleton has hardened.

Segmented Bodies Arthropods' bodies are segmented, something like an earthworm's. The segmented body plan is easiest to see in centipedes and millipedes, which have bodies made up of many identical-looking segments. You can also see segments on the tails of shrimp and lobsters.

In some groups of arthropods, several body segments become joined into distinct sections, with each section specialized to perform specific functions. Figure 6 shows the number of body sections and other physical characteristics that are typical of the three largest groups of arthropods.

Appendages Just as your fingers are appendages attached to your palms, many arthropods have jointed appendages attached to their bodies. The joints in the appendages give the animal flexibility and enable it to move. If you did the Discover activity, you saw how important joints are for allowing movement.

Arthropod appendages tend to be highly specialized tools. For example, the appendages attached to the head of a crayfish include mouthparts that it uses for crushing its food. A crayfish also has two pairs of antennae.

Comparisons of the Largest Arthropod Groups			
Characteristic	**Crustaceans**	**Arachnids**	**Insects**
Number of body sections	2 or 3	2	3
Number of legs	5 or more pairs	4 pairs	3 pairs
Number of antennae	2 pairs	none	1 pair
Where found?	in water or damp places	mostly on land	mostly on land

348

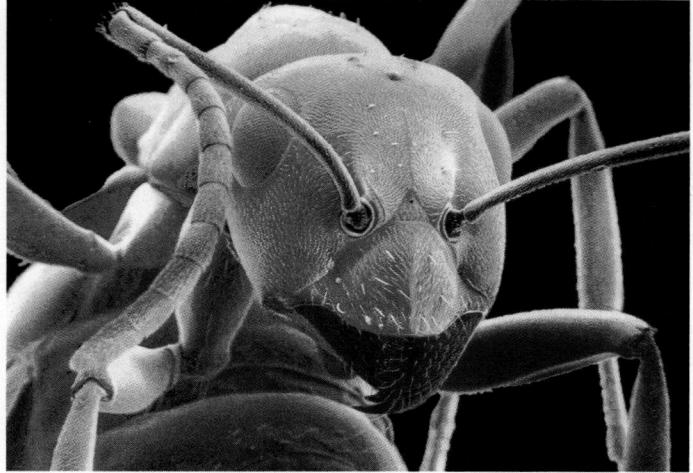

Figure 7 This wood ant's appendages include its antennae, legs, and mouthparts. It uses its mouthparts first to saw its food into small pieces and then to chew it.

An **antenna** (plural *antennae*) is an appendage on the head that contains sense organs. A crayfish's antennae have organs for smelling, tasting, touching, and keeping balance. Legs are also appendages. Most of the crayfish's legs are adapted for walking, but the crayfish uses its first pair of legs, which have claws, for catching prey and defending against predators. The wings that most insects have are also appendages.

✓ *Checkpoint* How do exoskeletons enable many arthropods to live on land?

Origin of Arthropods

Because both segmented worms and arthropods have segmented bodies with appendages attached to some segments, many biologists have inferred that these two groups of animals have a common ancestor. However, DNA evidence indicates that arthropods and segmented worms may not be so closely related.

Arthropods have been on Earth for about 540 million years. Like most other animal groups, arthropods first arose in the oceans. Today, however, they live almost everywhere. Some kinds of arthropods, like crayfish and crabs, are adapted to live in fresh or salt water. Very few insects, in contrast, live in salt water, but they live just about everywhere else.

Crustaceans

The major groups of arthropods are crustaceans, arachnids, centipedes, millipedes, and insects. If you've ever eaten shrimp cocktail or crab cakes, you've dined on crustaceans. A **crustacean** is an arthropod that has two or three body sections and usually has three pairs of appendages for chewing. In addition,

Some students may need extra help to understand how arthropod antennae work. Explain that antennae on arthropods are similar to the antennae on a radio or television set in that they detect information in the surroundings and transfer it to a central receiving point. Arthropod antennae detect the vibration of sound or movement. In addition, certain places on the antennae can sense chemicals in the air or water. The antennae help the arthropod "smell" and "taste" things in its environment. Antennae can also be sensitive to touch and therefore help the organism move around in its environment. **learning modality: logical/mathematical**

Origin of Arthropods

Building Inquiry Skills: Inferring

Tell students that the oldest rocks scientists have found that contain fossils of arthropods are about 540 million years old. Ask students to infer what characteristic the first arthropods had that enabled them to become fossils. *(A hard exoskeleton)* **learning modality: verbal**

Ongoing Assessment

Writing Ask students to write down the following arthropod characteristics: exoskeleton, segmented bodies, appendages. Have them write a sentence describing what they have learned about each characteristic. *(Sample answers: An exoskeleton is a hard covering made of chitin. An arthropod's body has segments that form body sections specialized to do different things. An arthropod's appendages are jointed.)*

Answers to Self-Assessment

Caption Questions

Figure 5 Because their exoskeletons cannot expand when the animals grow, arthropods must molt their outgrown exoskeletons.

Figure 6 Arachnids

✓ *Checkpoint*

An exoskeleton keeps water inside the arthropod, preventing it from drying out.

349

Crustaceans

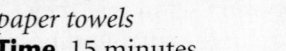

Building Inquiry Skills: Observing

Materials *crustacean, paper towels*

Time 15 minutes

Tips Allow students to observe the parts of a crustacean by examining a specimen. Have students place their crustaceans on paper towels. Sketch and label the body, tail, antennae, and legs. Ask: **What parts of the body help the crustacean protect itself?** *(Hard exoskeleton, claws or pincers)* Be sure students wash their hands after they have handled the crustacean.

learning modality: kinesthetic

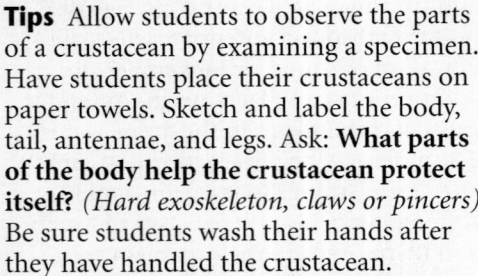

Skills Focus interpreting data

Materials *shoe box, aluminum foil, paper towels, masking tape, live pill bugs, water*

Time 20 minutes

Tips Group students. During the first trial, have them design their data table. During the second and third trials, have students reread the text information on crustaceans.

Interpreting Data The pill bugs will prefer the moist environment.

Extend Challenge students to design and carry out an experiment which tests whether pill bugs prefer a warm or cool environment. Check students' plans to ensure that they are logical and safe.

learning modality: logical/ mathematical

Spiders and Their Relatives

Addressing Naive Conceptions

Clear up some misconceptions about spiders by asking students to decide if the following statements are true or false.

◆ **All spiders catch their prey in webs.** *(False. Some spiders use webs, but others chase or trap their prey.)*

◆ **Spiders' bites are extremely dangerous to people.** *(False. Spiders rarely bite people, and most spider bites are uncomfortable but not dangerous.)*

learning modality: verbal

Pill Bugs—Wet or Dry?

Pill bugs are crustaceans that roll up in a ball when they're disturbed. In this activity, you will find out whether they prefer a moist or dry environment.

1. Line a shoe box with aluminum foil. Tape down two paper towels side by side in the box. Tape a strip of masking tape between the two towels. Carefully moisten one of the paper towels. Keep the other towel dry.

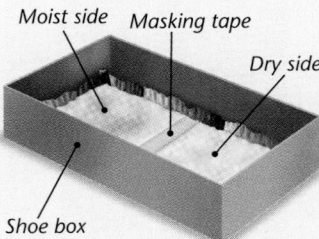

Moist side   *Masking tape*

Dry side

Shoe box

2. Put ten pill bugs on the masking tape. Then put a lid on the box.

3. After 5 minutes, lift the lid and quickly count the pill bugs on the dry towel, the moist towel, and the masking tape. Record your results in a data table.

4. Repeat Steps 2 and 3 two more times. Then average the results of the three trials. Wash your hands after handling the pill bugs.

Interpreting Data Do pill bugs prefer a moist or dry environment?

crustaceans always have five or more pairs of legs; each body segment has a pair of legs or modified legs attached to it. Crustaceans are the only arthropods that have two pairs of antennae. *Exploring a Crayfish* on page 351 shows a typical crustacean.

Life Cycle Most crustaceans, such as crabs, barnacles, and shrimp, begin their lives as microscopic, swimming larvae. The bodies of these larvae do not resemble those of adults. Crustacean larvae develop into adults by **metamorphosis** (met uh MAWR fuh sis), a process in which an animal's body undergoes dramatic changes in form during its life cycle.

Environments Nearly every kind of watery environment is home to crustaceans, which usually obtain their oxygen through gills. Crustaceans thrive in freshwater lakes and rivers, and even in puddles that last a long time. You can find crustaceans in the deepest parts of oceans, floating in ocean currents, and crawling along coastlines. A few crustaceans live in damp areas on land, too. Some huge crabs even live in the tops of palm trees!

Feeding Crustaceans obtain food in many ways. Many eat dead plants and animals. Others are predators, eating animals they have killed. The pistol shrimp is a predator with an appendage that moves with such force that it stuns its prey. Krill, which are shrimplike crustaceans found in huge swarms in cold ocean waters, are herbivores that eat plantlike microorganisms. Krill, in turn, are eaten by predators such as fishes, penguins, seals, sea birds, and even by great blue whales, the world's largest animals.

☑ *Checkpoint* An animal has an exoskeleton, two body sections, and eight legs. Is it a crustacean? Why or why not?

Spiders and Their Relatives

Spiders, mites, and ticks are the arachnids that people most often encounter. To qualify as an **arachnid** (uh RAK nid), an arthropod must have only two body sections. The first section is a combined head and chest. The hind section, called the **abdomen,** contains the arachnid's reproductive organs and part of its digestive tract. Arachnids have eight legs, but no antennae. They breathe with organs called book lungs or with a network of tiny tubes that lead to openings on the exoskeleton.

Spiders Spiders are the most familiar, most feared, and most fascinating kind of arachnid. All spiders are predators, and most of them eat insects. Some spiders, such as tarantulas and wolf spiders, run down their prey, while others, such as golden garden spiders, spin webs and wait for their prey to become entangled.

EXPLORING a Crayfish

Crayfish are crustaceans that live in ponds, streams, or rivers, where they hide beneath rocks and burrow in the mud. Some build a tall mud "chimney" around their burrow entrance. Crayfish will eat nearly any animal or plant, dead or alive, including other crayfish.

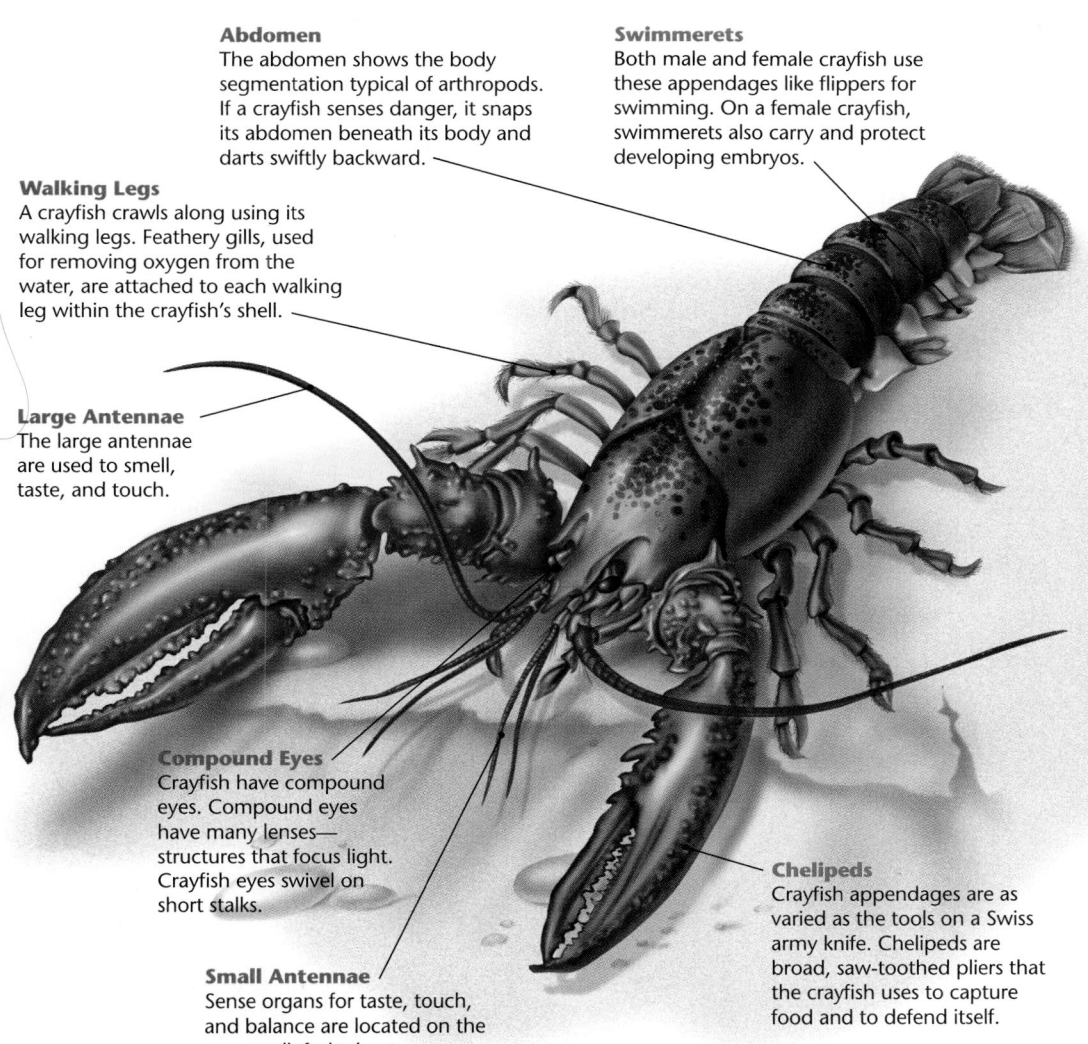

Abdomen
The abdomen shows the body segmentation typical of arthropods. If a crayfish senses danger, it snaps its abdomen beneath its body and darts swiftly backward.

Swimmerets
Both male and female crayfish use these appendages like flippers for swimming. On a female crayfish, swimmerets also carry and protect developing embryos.

Walking Legs
A crayfish crawls along using its walking legs. Feathery gills, used for removing oxygen from the water, are attached to each walking leg within the crayfish's shell.

Large Antennae
The large antennae are used to smell, taste, and touch.

Compound Eyes
Crayfish have compound eyes. Compound eyes have many lenses—structures that focus light. Crayfish eyes swivel on short stalks.

Small Antennae
Sense organs for taste, touch, and balance are located on the two small, forked antennae.

Chelipeds
Crayfish appendages are as varied as the tools on a Swiss army knife. Chelipeds are broad, saw-toothed pliers that the crayfish uses to capture food and to defend itself.

Chapter 11 **351**

Media and Technology

 Transparencies "Exploring a Crayfish," Transparency 46

 Exploring Life Science Videodisc
Unit 3, Side 2, "Spineless"

Chapter 2

Answers to Self-Assessment

☑ Checkpoint

The animal is not a crustacean. Although crustaceans have exoskeletons and sometimes have only two body sections, they always have at least ten legs. The animal described in the question is an arachnid.

EXPLORING
a Crayfish

Begin by asking students to observe the segmentation in the crayfish's abdomen. Make certain that students distinguish between the locations and functions of the small and large antennae. Ask: **How are the chelipeds different from the walking legs?** (*The chelipeds are much larger and have pincers.*)

Extend After students study the visual essay, have them write paragraphs describing a typical day in the life of a crayfish. In their paragraphs, they should infer how a crayfish uses the body parts listed in the visual essay. Paragraphs should also include where crayfish live and hide, and what they eat. (*Students' paragraphs might include the following: large antennae, walking legs, swimmerets—to move around; small antennae, compound eyes—to find food; chelipeds—to eat; chelipeds, tail, swimmerets, walking legs—to escape predators. Crayfish live in ponds, streams, or rivers; hide beneath rocks and burrow in the mud. They eat nearly any animal or plant.*)

 Students can save their paragraphs in their portfolios.

learning modality: logical/ mathematical

Ongoing Assessment

Oral Presentation Provide each student with a photograph or drawing of an unfamiliar crustacean or arachnid. Ask students to decide to which group their animals belong, and to label all major appendages. Then randomly choose students to present their animals to the class and to explain why they classified them as crustaceans or arachnids.

Spiders and Their Relatives, continued

Building Inquiry Skills: Making Generalizations

Materials *oranges, plastic drinking straws* **ACTIVITY**

Time 15 minutes

Tips Allow students to simulate how spiders eat. This activity works best with juicy oranges with thin skins. The area in which students work needs to be clean. Have students wash their hands. Then give each student two clean oranges. Tell students to position the straws at the side of the orange, not at the ends. Have students insert a straw into one orange and try to drink the juice. They should get very little juice from this orange. Next, tell them to take the other orange and roll it on the top of their desk while pushing down on it, but without breaking the skin. Tell students that rolling the orange will mash up the pulp of the orange. Then have them insert the straws and try to drink the juice. They may have to remove the straw and reinsert it several times. Ask: **How is eating the orange with a straw similar to how a spider eats?** (*A spider inserts its fangs into prey to suck in its food.*) Pair students to discuss this activity. Direct the discussion by telling students that before a spider can eat its prey, it injects it with venom that turns its tissues into mush. Then ask: **How did you simulate what a spider's venom does?** (*By rolling and mashing the orange so that the pulp turned to mush*) **learning modality: kinesthetic**

Real-Life Learning

Although we rarely see them, mites are everywhere. Dust mites eat tiny particles of human skin. They like warm, sheltered places where particles of shed skin accumulate, such as in our houses. Ask: **Where in your house do you think dust mites live?** (*Students may mention couches, mattresses, or pillows.*) Remind students some people are allergic to the exoskeletons and droppings of dust mites. Have students brainstorm ways to reduce dust mites. (*Students may suggest vacuuming frequently or covering mattresses and pillows with plastic covers.*) **learning modality: logical/mathematical**

352

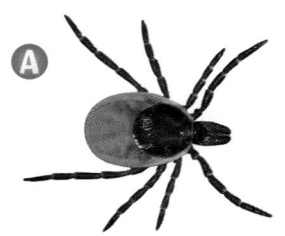

Figure 8 Arachnids are arthropods with two body sections, eight legs, and no antennae. **A.** A tick is a parasite that attaches itself to its prey to feed upon its blood. **B.** A scorpion is a carnivore that injects venom from a stinger at the end of its abdomen. **C.** The Honduran tarantula, a spider, uses its fangs to inject venom into a racer snake.

352

Spiders have hollow fangs, which are organs that inject venom into prey. Spider venom turns the tissues of the prey into mush. Later the spider uses its fangs like drinking straws, sucking in the mush. In spite of what some people might think, spiders rarely bite people. When they do, most spider bites are painful but not life-threatening. However, the bites of the brown recluse or the black widow may require hospital care.

Mites If chiggers have ever given you an itchy rash, you've had an unpleasant encounter with tiny arachnids called mites. Chiggers and many other mites are parasites. Ear mites, for example, give dogs and cats itchy ears. Mites are everywhere. Even the cleanest houses have microscopic dust mites. If you are allergic to dust, you may actually be allergic to the exoskeletons of dust mites. Mites also live in fresh water and in the ocean.

Ticks Ticks are parasites that live on the outside of a host animal's body. Nearly every kind of land animal has a species of tick that sucks its blood. Some ticks that attack humans can carry diseases. Lyme disease, for example, is spread by the bite of an infected deer tick.

Scorpions Scorpions, which live mainly in hot climates, are also arachnids. Usually active at night, scorpions hide in cool places during the day—under rocks and logs, or in holes in the ground, for example.

At the end of its abdomen, a scorpion has a spinelike stinger. The scorpion uses the stinger to inject venom into its prey, which is usually a spider or insect. Sometimes scorpions sting people. These stings, while painful, usually do not cause serious harm.

☑ *Checkpoint* How do spiders obtain and digest their food?

Figure 9 Centipedes and millipedes are arthropods with many body segments. Centipedes, left, are carnivores, while millipedes, right, are herbivores. *Comparing and Contrasting How can you tell the difference between these two organisms?*

Centipedes and Millipedes

Centipedes and millipedes have highly segmented bodies, as you can see in Figure 9. Centipedes have one pair of legs attached to each segment, and some centipedes have over 100 segments. In fact, the word *centipede* means "hundred feet." Centipedes are swift predators with sharp jaws. They inject venom into the smaller animals that they catch for food.

Millipedes, which may have more than 80 segments, have two pairs of legs on each segment—more legs than any other arthropod. Though *millipede* means "thousand feet," they don't have quite that many legs. Most millipedes are herbivores that graze on partly decayed leaves. When they are disturbed, millipedes can curl up into an armored ball and squirt an awful-smelling liquid at a potential predator.

Section 2 Review

1. Identify four characteristics that all arthropods share.
2. List the major groups of arthropods.
3. What characteristic distinguishes crustaceans from all other arthropods?
4. What are the main characteristics of arachnids?
5. **Thinking Critically Applying Concepts** Some seafood restaurants serve a dish called soft-shelled crab. What do you think happened to the crab just before it was caught? Why is that process important?

Check Your Progress
Construct a data table in your notebook. Each day, observe both groups of mealworms. Record how many mealworms in each group are still wormlike larvae, how many have formed motionless pupae, and how many, if any, have become adult insects. (*Hint:* You will learn about the stages of insect metamorphosis in Section 3. You may find it helpful to refer to *Exploring Insect Metamorphosis* on page 357 as you fill in your data table.)

Program Resources

◆ **Unit 3 Resources** 11-2 Review and Reinforce, p. 43; 11-2 Enrich, p. 44

Answers to Self-Assessment

Caption Question
Figure 9 The centipede has one pair of legs on each segment; the millipede has two.

☑ *Checkpoint*
Spiders inject venom into their prey by using hollow fangs. The venom liquefies the tissues of the prey, which are then sucked up by the spider.

Centipedes and Millipedes

Using the Visuals: Figure 9

To help students compare **ACTIVITY** and contrast the millipede and centipede, have them draw each organism. Instruct them to label characteristics specific to centipedes and to millipedes. (*Centipedes—one pair of legs on each segment, sharp jaws; on millipedes—two pairs of legs on each segment*)

Portfolio Students can save their drawings in their portfolios.
learning modality: visual

3 Assess

Section 2 Review Answers

1. External skeleton, segmented bodies, jointed appendages, and an open circulatory system.
2. Crustaceans, arachnids, insects, centipedes, millipedes
3. Two pairs of antennae
4. Two body sections, eight legs, no antennae
5. It had just molted. Molting is important because it allows arthropods to shed exoskeletons they have outgrown.

Check Your Progress
Ensure each mealworm container has food and a source of moisture. Ask students to record their observations along with counts of the larvae, pupae, and adults.

Performance Assessment

Writing Have students describe one distinguishing characteristic of each of the following groups: crustaceans, arachnids, centipedes, and millipedes. (*Crustaceans—two pairs of antennae; arachnids—two body sections; centipedes—two pairs of legs per body segment; millipedes—one pair of legs per body segment*)

Objectives

After completing this lesson, students will be able to
◆ describe the characteristics of insects, including their body structure, how they feed, and how they defend themselves;
◆ explain metamorphosis;
◆ describe the overall impact of insects on humans.

Key Terms insect, thorax, complete metamorphosis, pupa, gradual metamorphosis, nymph, camouflage

1 Engage/Explore

Activating Prior Knowledge

Ask students to name as many insects as they can. *(Samples: ant, mosquito, fly, grasshopper, butterfly, bee)* Ask: **What do these animals have in common?** *(Sample: antennae)* Tell students that they will learn the characteristics insects share in this section.

DISCOVER

Skills Focus observing
Materials *insect collection, hand lenses*
Time 20 minutes
Tips Facilitate careful observation of the specimens by asking students to describe one or two insects that they find particularly interesting. Ask students to point out several characteristics that the insects have in common.
Expected Outcome Students should observe that all the insects have the same number of legs (six) and body sections (three).
Think It Over Encourage students to compare insects that are very different. Consider grouping similar insects and asking students to choose insects from different groups to compare. *(Answers may vary. Sample: A grasshopper and a dragonfly both have six jointed legs and two pairs of wings. The grasshopper has large hind legs that it uses to jump. The dragonfly has large flat wings that it uses to fly.)*

354

SECTION 3 Insects

DISCOVER • ACTIVITY

What Kinds of Appendages Do Insects Have?

1. Your teacher will give you a collection of insects. Examine them carefully.

2. Note the physical characteristics of each insect's body covering.

3. Count the legs, wings, body sections, and antennae on each insect.

4. Carefully observe the appendages—antennae, mouthparts, wings, and legs. Contrast the appendages on different insects. Then return the insects to your teacher and wash your hands.

Think It Over
Observing Compare the legs and wings of two different species of insect. What kind of movements is each insect adapted to perform?

GUIDE FOR READING

◆ What are the characteristics of insects?
◆ What is the overall impact of insects on humans?

Reading Tip As you read, make an outline of this section using the headings as the main topics.

Monarch butterflies, with their beautiful orange and black wings, may seem delicate, but they are champion travelers. Every autumn, about 100 million of these butterflies fly south from southeastern Canada and the eastern United States, heading for the mountains of central Mexico. Some monarch butterflies fly thousands of kilometers before they reach their destination.

The monarch butterflies who make this long journey have never been to Mexico before. But somehow they find their way to the same trees where their ancestors, now dead, spent the previous winter. No one is certain how they are able to do this.

In the spring, the butterflies fly northward. After flying a few hundred miles, they stop, mate, lay eggs, and die. But their children—and later, their grandchildren and great-grandchildren—continue the northward journey. Eventually, monarch butterflies reach the area their ancestors left the previous fall.

Wintering monarch butterflies ▼

READING STRATEGIES

Reading Tip Remind students that the major headings in the text should be the major topics in the outline. If students have trouble recognizing subtopics, suggest that they write a subhead for each paragraph. These can be the subtopics in their outlines. For example:
I. The Insect Body
  A. Body regions and appendages
    1. Three body regions
    2. Six legs
    3. One pair of antennae
    4. One or two pairs of wings
  B. Compound and simple eyes
  C. Oxygen tubes

Study and Comprehension As students complete the chapter, have them create an illustration to accompany each subheading. Illustrations should contain relevant information covered in the paragraphs.

The Insect Body

The monarch butterfly is an **insect**, as is a dragonfly, cockroach, or bee. You can identify insects, like other arthropods, by counting their body sections and legs. **Insects are arthropods with three body sections, six legs, one pair of antennae, and usually one or two pairs of wings.** The three body regions are the head, thorax, and abdomen. An insect's **thorax**, or midsection, is the section to which wings and legs are attached. Sense organs, such as the eyes and antennae, are located on an insect's head. The abdomen contains many of the insect's internal organs. You can see all three body sections on the grasshopper in Figure 11.

Like most crustaceans, insects usually have two large compound eyes, which contain many lenses. Compound eyes are especially keen at seeing movement. Most insects also have small simple eyes, which can distinguish between light and darkness.

Insects obtain oxygen through a system of tubes. These tubes lead to openings on the insect's exoskeleton. Air, which contains oxygen, enters the insect's body through these tubes and travels directly to the insect's body cells.

☑ Checkpoint How are an insect's compound eyes different from its simple eyes?

From Egg to Adult

Insects begin life as tiny, hard-shelled, fertilized eggs. After they hatch, insects begin a process of metamorphosis that eventually produces an adult insect. Each insect species undergoes one of two different types of metamorphosis.

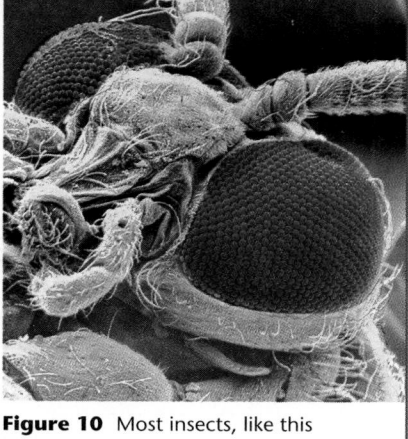

Figure 10 Most insects, like this black fly, have compound eyes with many lenses. Because compound eyes are very effective at seeing movement, insects can quickly escape from potential predators.

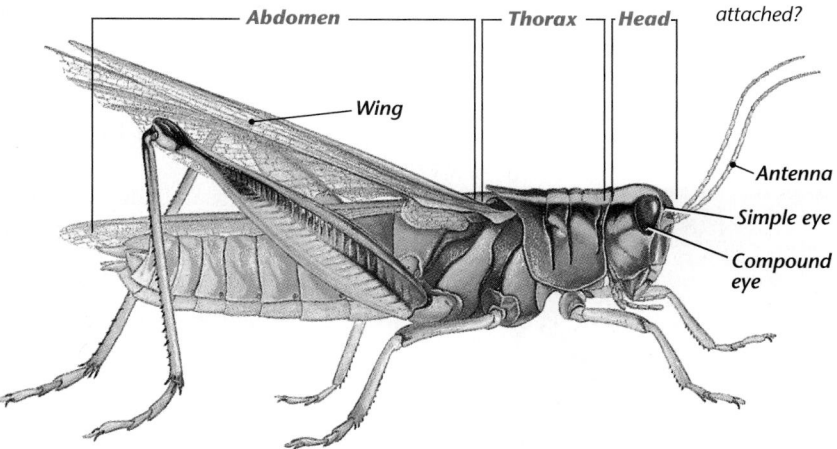

Figure 11 A grasshopper's body, like that of every insect, consists of three sections.
Interpreting Diagrams To which section are the grasshopper's legs attached?

Abdomen — Thorax — Head

Wing

Antenna

Simple eye

Compound eye

Program Resources

 Unit 3 Resources 11-3 Lesson Plan, p. 45; 11-3 Section Summary, p. 46

Media and Technology

 Audio CD English-Spanish Summary 11-3

Transparencies "Grasshopper Anatomy," Transparency 47

Answers to Self-Assessment

Caption Question

Figure 11 The grasshopper's legs are attached to its thorax.

☑ Checkpoint

An insect's compound eyes are made up of many individual lenses and are adapted for sensing motion. Simple eyes are adapted for distinguishing between light and darkness.

---

2 *Facilitate*

The Insect Body

Building Inquiry Skills: Interpreting Diagrams

Obtain intact dead grasshoppers from a pet or bait shop. Have students review each external feature from Figure 11 and work together to identify that feature on their specimens. Students should wash hands after finishing. **cooperative learning**

Addressing Naive Conceptions

Students may think spiders are insects. Ask: **How can you identify an animal as an insect by looking at its body?** (*If it is an insect, it has three body sections.*) Show students pictures of spiders and have them try to identify the head, thorax, and abdomen. Ask: **Are these animals insects?** (*No*) **How do you know?** (*They have only two body sections.*) (*Sample: ticks, scorpions*) **learning modality: visual**

From Egg to Adult

Building Inquiry Skills: Comparing and Contrasting

Have students make Venn diagrams to compare and contrast gradual and complete metamorphosis. **learning modality: logical/mathematical**

Ongoing Assessment

Skills Check Ask students: **If you saw an animal in the woods, how would you decide whether it could be classified as an insect?** (*Accept answers that describe major characteristics of insects. Sample: If the animal had an exoskeleton, three main body parts, six jointed legs, a pair of antennae, and wings, it is probably an insect.*)

From Egg to Adult, continued

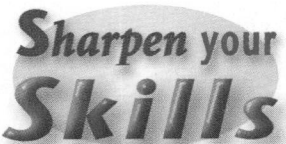

Sharpen your Skills

Graphing ACTIVITY

Approximately 760,000 species of insects have been identified so far. The table gives an approximate species count for the major groups. Use the data to construct a circle graph that shows the percentage of total insect species in each group. (To review circle graphs, see the Skills Handbook.)

Insect Groups	
Group	**Number of Species**
Ants, bees, and wasps	100,000
Beetles and weevils	300,000
Butterflies and moths	110,000
Flies and mosquitoes	100,000
Other insect groups	150,000

The two types of insect metamorphosis are shown in *Exploring Insect Metamorphosis* on page 357. The first type, which is called **complete metamorphosis,** has four dramatically different stages: egg, larva, pupa, and adult. As you learned in Chapter 10, a larva is an immature form of an animal that looks significantly different from the adult. Insect larvae, such as the caterpillars of butterflies and moths, usually look something like worms. Larvae are specialized for eating and growing. After a time, the larva goes into the second stage of complete metamorphosis and becomes a **pupa** (plural *pupae*). During the pupal stage, the insect is enclosed in a protective covering and gradually changes from a larva to an adult. A butterfly in a chrysalis and a moth in a cocoon are examples of insect pupae. When it has completed its development, an adult insect emerges from the protective pupa. Beetles, butterflies, houseflies, and ants all undergo complete metamorphosis.

In contrast, the second type of metamorphosis, called **gradual metamorphosis,** has no distinctly different larval stage—an egg hatches into a stage called a **nymph,** which often resembles the adult insect. A nymph may molt several times before becoming an adult. Grasshoppers, termites, cockroaches, and dragonflies go through gradual metamorphosis.

✓ *Checkpoint* *List the stages of complete metamorphosis.*

How Insects Feed

The rule seems to be this: If it is living, or if it once was living, some kind of insect will eat it. Everyone knows that insects eat plants and parts of plants, such as leaves and nectar. But insects also eat products that are made from plants, such as paper. The next time you open a very old book, watch for book lice. These very small insects live in old books, chewing tiny crooked tunnels through the pages.

Insects feed on animals, too. Some, like fleas and mosquitoes, feed on the blood of living animals. Others, like dung beetles, feed on animal droppings. Still others, like burying beetles, feed on the decaying bodies of dead animals.

Insect mouthparts are adapted for a highly specific way of getting food. For example, a bee has a bristly tongue that laps nectar from flowers, and a mosquito has sharp mouthparts for jabbing and sucking blood.

Figure 12 This caterpillar feeds almost continuously. As a larva, it must store all the energy it will need for its pupal stage.

EXPLORING Insect Metamorphosis

Depending on the species, an insect develops into an adult through one of the two processes shown here. Fireflies undergo complete metamorphosis, while grasshoppers undergo gradual metamorphosis.

COMPLETE METAMORPHOSIS

Adult male firefly

1 Egg Female fireflies lay their eggs in moist places. The eggs of fireflies glow in the dark.

4 Adult When its development is complete, an adult firefly crawls out of its pupal case and unfurls its crumpled wings. After its exoskeleton hardens, the adult begins a life centered around feeding, flying into new areas, and mating. Adult fireflies flash their light to attract mates.

2 Larva The eggs hatch into larvae that feed on snails and slugs. Firefly larvae are called glowworms because they give off light.

3 Pupa After a time, the firefly larva becomes a pupa. Inside the protective pupal case, wings, legs, and antennae form.

GRADUAL METAMORPHOSIS

Adult male grasshopper

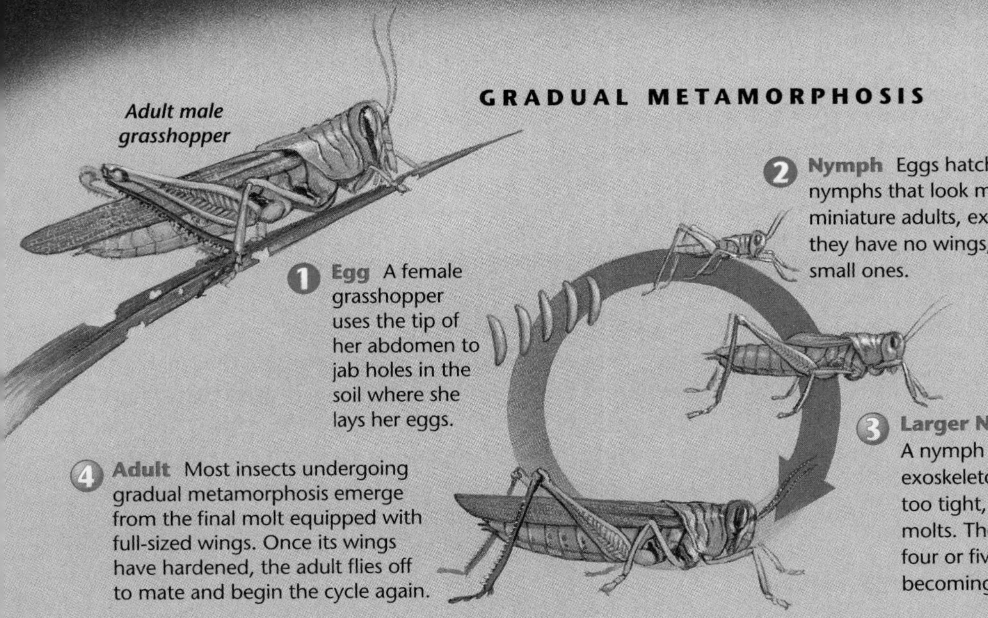

1 Egg A female grasshopper uses the tip of her abdomen to jab holes in the soil where she lays her eggs.

2 Nymph Eggs hatch into nymphs that look much like miniature adults, except that they have no wings, or only small ones.

4 Adult Most insects undergoing gradual metamorphosis emerge from the final molt equipped with full-sized wings. Once its wings have hardened, the adult flies off to mate and begin the cycle again.

3 Larger Nymph A nymph feeds until its exoskeleton becomes too tight, and then it molts. The nymph molts four or five times before becoming an adult.

Chapter 11 **357**

Point out that the visual essay contrasts the metamorphoses of a firefly and a grasshopper. The insects are similar in that they lay eggs. However, once the eggs hatch, the insects develop quite differently. Ask: **How is a firefly's metamorphosis different from a grasshopper's?** *(A firefly goes through four distinct stages, whereas a grasshopper changes its form gradually.)* **When does the grasshopper acquire wings?** *(After the final molt)* **What do adults do that larvae and nymphs do not?** *(Reproduce)*
Extend Have students who are cultivating mealworms for the chapter project describe the kind of metamorphosis the mealworm undergoes. *(Complete)* Challenge them to compare the different stages of mealworm development with the different stages of firefly development.
learning modality: visual

Media and Technology

 Transparencies "Exploring Insect Metamorphosis," Transparency 48

 Exploring Life Science Videodisc Unit 3, Side 2, "Insect Success Stories"

Chapter 5

Answers to Self-Assessment

☑ *Checkpoint*
The stages of complete metamorphosis are egg, larva, pupa, and adult.

Ongoing Assessment

Skills Check Have students list stages of gradual and complete metamorphosis. *(Gradual metamorphosis—egg, nymph, adult; complete metamorphosis—egg, larva, pupa, adult)*

Defending Themselves

Including All Students

In this activity, all students, including those who have difficulty hearing, will be able to access information about camouflage by viewing pictures and discriminating between various classes of defense. Bring to class several color pictures of interesting insects with different types of defenses. Camouflage is the most obvious. Walking sticks are great subjects. Many moths blend in with the bark of trees. Other types of pictures can be of wasp stingers or large eyelike spots on the open wings of butterflies. Wings or large jumping legs help insects avoid predators. Number the pictures, then pass them around. Each student can write a numbered list of the types of defenses employed by each insect. When students have finished making their lists, review the pictures with the entire class.
learning modality: visual

Insects and Humans

Social Studies
CONNECTION

Have students consult social studies textbooks and other references to learn more about the Black Death. You might point out that the plague bacteria have two intermediate hosts before infecting humans. Rats and other rodents can become infected with the bacteria. If a flea bites an infected rodent, the flea may acquire the bacteria. When an infected flea bites a human, the bacteria may pass into the person's body and cause disease.

In Your Journal Students can use what they learn in their research to help them write their journal entries.
learning modality: verbal

Portfolio Students can save their journal entries in their portfolios.

Figure 13 The well-camouflaged thorn insect, left, and leaf insect, right, have very effective built-in defenses against predators.
Observing Why do you think the insect on the left is called a thorn insect?

Social Studies
CONNECTION

In the fall of 1347, a ship sailed from a port on the Black Sea to the European island of Sicily. That ship carried insects that helped change the course of history. The insects were fleas, and their bite passed a deadly disease known as bubonic plague, or the Black Death, on to humans.

People who caught the plague usually died quickly. A Frenchman named Jean de Venette wrote, "He who was well one day was dead the next." The Black Death rapidly spread all over Europe, killing about a third of the people. Because so many died, the plague caused serious economic problems and led to great social unrest.

In Your Journal

Imagine that the year is 1380. You lived through the plague epidemic and are now 45 years old. Write about how the plague epidemic has changed your village.

Defending Themselves

Insects have many defenses against predators, including a hard exoskeleton that helps protect them. Many insects can run quickly or fly away from danger, as you know if you've ever tried to swat a fly. Some insects, such as stinkbugs, smell or taste bad to predators. Other insects, such as bees and wasps, defend themselves with painful stings.

One of the most common defenses is **camouflage,** or protective coloration, in which the insect blends with its surroundings so perfectly that it is nearly invisible to a predator. Test yourself by trying to find the camouflaged insects in Figure 13. Walking sticks, many caterpillars, and grasshoppers are just a few insects that use camouflage as a defense.

Other insects are protected by their resemblance to different animals. The spots on the wings of certain moths, for example, resemble large eyes; predators who see these spots often avoid the moths, mistaking them for much larger animals.

☑ *Checkpoint* What are four defenses used by insects?

Insects and Humans

For every person alive today, scientists estimate that there are at least 200 million living insects. Many of those insects have an impact on people's lives. Some species of insects do major damage to crops. In addition, insects such as flies, fleas, and mosquitoes can carry microorganisms that cause diseases in humans. For example, when they bite humans, some mosquito species can transmit the microorganism that causes malaria.

Background

History of Science Entomology, or the study of insects, was extremely popular in Europe during the 1800s. The French scientist Jean Henri Fabre (1823–1915) became renowned for his study of the structure and behavior of insects. Fabre studied social insects such as bees and wasps as well as other insects, observing them in their natural environments. One of his discoveries involved the predation of stinging wasps. Fabre found that wasps target their stingers for their prey's nerve centers so that the prey becomes paralyzed and cannot move. This allows the wasp to save the prey for later. The work of Henri Fabre greatly enhanced understanding and appreciation of these insects.

The vast majority of insects, however, are harmless or beneficial to humans. Bees make honey, and the larvae of the silkworm moth spin the fibers used to make silk cloth. Some insects prey on harmful insects, helping to reduce those insect populations. And while some insects destroy food crops, many more insects, such as butterflies and flies, enable food crops and other plants to reproduce by carrying pollen from one plant to another. If insects were to disappear from Earth, you would never get a mosquito bite. But you wouldn't have much food to eat, either.

Controlling Insect Pests

INTEGRATING ENVIRONMENTAL SCIENCE People have tried to eliminate harmful insects by applying chemicals, called pesticides, to plants. However, pesticides also kill helpful insects, such as bees, and can harm other animals, including some birds. And after a time, insect populations become resistant to the pesticides—the pesticides no longer kill the insects.

Scientists are searching for other ways to deal with harmful insects. One method is the use of biological controls. Biological controls introduce natural predators or diseases into insect populations. For example, ladybug beetles can be added to fields where crops are grown. Ladybugs prey on aphids, which are insects that destroy peaches, potatoes, and other crop plants. Soil also can be treated with bacteria that are harmless to humans but cause diseases in the larvae of pest insects such as Japanese beetles. These biological controls kill only one or a few pest species. Because biological controls kill only specific pests, they are less damaging to the environment than insecticides.

Figure 14 Bees and other pollinators are among the most beneficial of all insects. As a bee drinks nectar from a flower, pollen sticks to its body. When the insect carries that pollen to the next plant it eats from, it helps that plant to reproduce.

Controlling Insect Pests

Integrating Environmental Science

Bring a Japanese beetle trap, an aphid trap, or an apple maggot trap to class. Ask students to infer how these traps work. Many traps are designed to look like food to the insects. When the insects land on a trap, they are caught in a sticky substance, as on the aphid traps, or lured into a bag they cannot escape from, as in the Japanese beetle trap. Do not allow students to handle the traps, since they may get chemical attractants on their hands. **learning modality: visual**

3 Assess

Section 3 Review Answers

1. Three body sections; six legs; one pair of antennae; usually wings
2. Accept any two: insects pollinate crops; make products such as silk and honey; prey on pests.
3. Complete metamorphosis—four distinct stages: egg; wormlike larva; nonmoving pupa enclosed in a case; adult. Gradual metamorphosis—the newly hatched insect, called a nymph, changes gradually as it goes through a series of molts.
4. Predators mistake the hover fly for a honeybee and avoid it, fearing to be stung.

Check Your Progress CHAPTER PROJECT
Verify that students' data are being collected on time and appear reasonable. Check students' sketches. Tell students they must be able to identify the stages of mealworm development from their sketches.

 Section 3 Review

1. List the characteristics that insects share.
2. Identify two ways in which insects benefit humans.
3. Compare and contrast complete and gradual metamorphosis.
4. **Thinking Critically** **Inferring** Honeybees sting predators that try to attack them. Hover flies, which do not sting, resemble honeybees. How might this resemblance be an advantage to the hover fly?

Check Your Progress CHAPTER PROJECT
Continue observing the mealworms every day. Update the data table with your observations. As you observe the mealworms at different stages of development, make a sketch of a larva, a pupa, and an adult.

Program Resources

◆ **Unit 3 Resources** 11-3 Review and Reinforce, p. 47; 11-3 Enrich, p. 48

Media and Technology

Interactive Student Tutorial CD-ROM Chapter 11

Answers to Self-Assessment

Caption Question

Figure 13 The insect is called a thorn insect because it looks like a thorn.

☑ *Checkpoint*

Answers may include exoskeleton, ability to escape quickly, bad odor, bad taste, sting, camouflage, look like another organism.

Performance Assessment

Drawing Have students sketch an insect and label three major characteristics that classify it as an insect. (*Three body sections, one pair of antennae, and wings*)

What's Living in the Soil?

Preparing for Inquiry

Key Concept Soil and leaf litter make up a miniature environment that contains a variety of organisms.

Skills Objectives Students will be able to

◆ observe soil, leaf litter, and the organisms they contain;
◆ classify organisms into phyla based on key distinguishing characteristics;
◆ infer the quantity and types of organisms living in the soil.

Time 15 minutes on the first day, 45 minutes on the second day

Advance Planning Try the lab in advance to ensure that there are enough organisms present. Three or four days before the lab, go to two different sites. Try to select sites that are moist but not too wet. Collect leaf litter and the first inch or so of soil in buckets. Keep the buckets covered to keep contents moist. Set up the lamp and jars, and test a soil sample from each site. If you do not obtain enough organisms, collect more material from another site.

Alternative Materials Two weeks before the lab, ask students to bring their own wide mouth jars, such as mayonnaise jars. Baby food jars work well as the small inside jars.

Guiding Inquiry

Invitation Have students think about how many animals might be present in soil. Ask: **What advantage do you think living in the soil gives some animals?** *(Moist environment, decaying organic matter for food, protection from predators)* Invite students to write predictions about the number and kind of organisms they will see in a few scoops of soil.

Introducing the Procedure

◆ Tell students not to disturb the funnel once they have placed soil and leaf litter in it. If they do, soil may run into the collection jar.

What's Living in the Soil?

The soil beneath a tree, in a garden, or under a rock is home to many organisms, including a variety of arthropods. Each of these patches of soil can be thought of as a miniature environment with its own group of living residents. In this lab, you will examine one specific soil environment.

Problem

What kinds of animals live in soil and leaf litter?

Skills Focus

observing, classifying, inferring

Materials

2-liter plastic bottle	large scissors
coarse steel wool	trowel
cheesecloth	large rubber band
gooseneck lamp	hand lens
large, wide-mouthed jar	small jar
fresh sample of soil and leaf litter	

Procedure

1. Select a location where your equipment can be set up and remain undisturbed for about 24 hours. At that location, place the small jar inside the center of the large jar as shown in the photograph.
2. Use scissors to cut a large plastic bottle in half. **CAUTION:** *Cut in a direction away from yourself and others.* Turn the top half of the bottle upside down to serve as a funnel.
3. Insert a small amount of coarse steel wool into the mouth of the funnel to keep the soil from falling out. Do not pack the steel wool too tightly. Leave spaces for small organisms to crawl through. Place the funnel into the large jar as shown in the photograph.
4. Using the trowel, fill the funnel with soil and surface leaf litter. When you finish handling the leaves and soil, wash your hands thoroughly.
5. Look closely to see whether the soil and litter are dry or wet. Record your observation.
6. Make a cover for your sample by placing a piece of cheesecloth over the top of the funnel. Hold the cheesecloth in place with a large rubber band. Immediately position a lamp about 15 cm above the funnel, and turn on the light. Allow this setup to remain undisturbed for about 24 hours. **CAUTION:** *Hot light bulbs can cause burns. Do not touch the bulb.*
7. When you are ready to make your observations, turn off the lamp. Leave the funnel and jar in place while making your observations. Use a hand lens to examine each organism in the jar. **CAUTION:** *Do not touch any of the organisms.*
8. Use a data table like the one on the next page to sketch each type of organism and to record other observations. Be sure to include evidence that will help you classify the organisms. (*Hint:* Remember that some animals may be at different stages of metamorphosis.)

◆ Warn students only to observe the animals, not to handle them, since some might bite or sting.
◆ Students should find that millipedes and other small animals (including worms) are best viewed with a hand lens.
◆ The types and numbers of soil organisms found will vary in different regions of the country. Help students familiarize themselves with the animals they might find.

Sample Data Table

Name of Animal	Sketch of Animal	Number Found	Size (mm)	Important Characteristics	Probable Phylum
Roundworm		2	2.5	no legs, moves by wriggling	Roundworms
Earthworm		1	100	no legs, bristles on sides	Segmented Worms
Spider		1	20	4 pairs of legs, exoskeleton	Arthropods
Millipede		2	30	many legs, exoskeleton	Arthropods
Beetle		1	25	3 pairs of legs, hard outer wings	Arthropods

DATA TABLE				
Sketch of Organism	Number Found	Size	Important Characteristics	Probable Phylum

9. Examine the soil and leaf litter, and record whether this material is dry or wet.
10. When you are finished, follow your teacher's directions about returning the organisms to the soil. Wash your hands with soap.

Analyze and Conclude

1. Describe the conditions of the soil environment at the beginning and end of the lab. What caused the change?
2. What types of animals did you collect in the small jar? What characteristics did you use to identify each type of animal? Which types of animals were the most common?
3. Why do you think the animals moved down the funnel away from the soil?
4. **Apply** Using what you have learned about arthropods and other animals, make an inference about the role that each animal you collected plays in the environment.

Design an Experiment

What kinds of organisms might live in other soil types—for example, soil at the edge of a pond, dry sandy soil, or commercially prepared potting soil? Design an experiment to answer this question.

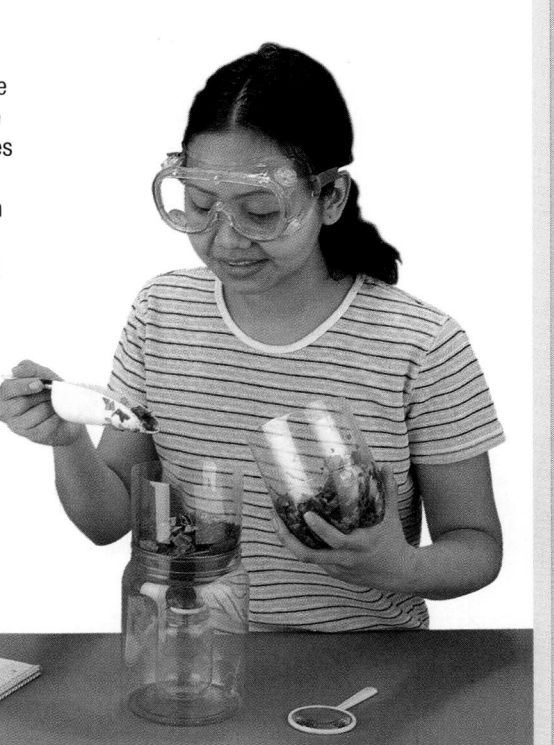

Program Resources

◆ **Unit 3 Resources** Chapter 11 Real-World Lab, pp. 59–61

Media and Technology

 Exploring Life Science Videodisc
Unit 3, Side 2,
"The Good Bugs"

Chapter 6

Safety

Emphasize to students that no organisms should be handled because animals such as centipedes and ants may sting or bite. Students should always wash their hands carefully with antibacterial soap after handling soil or leaf litter. Explain that there may be pathogens in organic matter collected outdoors. To avoid danger of fire, keep the light bulb at a safe distance from the leaf litter.

Troubleshooting the Experiment

◆ If students have trouble classifying the organisms, have them list the features of worms and arthropods. Features include the presence or absence of an exoskeleton, the presence or absence of legs and wings, and the number of pairs of legs.
◆ Certain times of the year are better than others for finding a greater variety and abundance of organisms. If students find only a few organisms, tell them not to be discouraged. The scarcity of organisms may be the result of seasonal conditions.
◆ Make sure students return the leaf litter and organisms to the bucket after use.

Expected Outcome

◆ Several kinds of organisms may be present, and distinguishing among them may be difficult. Have students count the number of pairs of legs, number of body segments and, if possible, observe how the organism moves. See the table for some animals likely to be encountered.

Analyze and Conclude

1. At first the soil was damp and clumped together. At the end of the lab, it was dry and loose. The heat from the lamp dried out the soil.
2. Answers will vary. Students should refer to the animals listed in their data tables. These will most likely be worms and arthropods.
3. The animals moved away from the heat and drying soil.
4. Answers will vary. Sample: Some animals are important as decomposers (for example, worms and some insects). Some are predators (for example, pseudoscorpions and spiders).

Extending Inquiry

Design an Experiment To find out which types of organisms live in other types of soil, students can repeat the lab with those other soil types.

SECTION 4 The Chemistry of Communication

Objectives

After completing the lesson, students will be able to

◆ describe how animals use pheromones to communicate;

◆ explain bioluminescence

Key Terms pheromone, bioluminescence

1 Engage/Explore

Activating Prior Knowledge

Place a strong-but pleasant-smelling object **ACTIVITY** somewhere in the classroom. Tell students you have hidden an object in the room and they are to find it by some sense other than sight. After they have located the object, ask them what sense they used. Tell them that many animals use scent as a means of communication.

DISCOVER

Skills Focus observing **ACTIVITY**
Materials *pairs of small, foil-covered containers holding a variety of nontoxic substances with distinctive scents*
Time 20 minutes
Tips Emphasize that students should not sniff the materials directly, and demonstrate the technique for wafting fumes under the nose. **CAUTION:** *Strong scents are known to trigger migraine headaches and asthma attacks.* Excuse students with known reactions to smells from this activity or ask them to act as observers. Kitchen spices are the safest and easiest to use.
Expected Outcome Students should eventually locate the matching scents.
Think It Over Depending on the materials, it should be fairly easy for students to find the matching scents. Identifying and detecting scents helps an animal to locate food, to find mates, and to identify other individuals or their territories.

SECTION 4 The Chemistry of Communication

DISCOVER ·························· ACTIVITY

Can You Match the Scents?

1. From your teacher, obtain a container covered with aluminum foil with holes punched in it.

2. Carefully sniff the contents of the container. **CAUTION:** *Never sniff an unknown substance directly. When testing an odor, use a waving motion with your hand to direct the vapor toward your nose.*

3. One other person in your class has a container with the same substance. Use your sense of smell to find the container whose scent matches the one in your container.

Think It Over

Observing How easy was it for you and your classmates to match scents? What advantage might identifying or detecting scents have to an animal?

GUIDE FOR READING

◆ How do animals use pheromones to communicate?

Reading Tip As you read, make a list of main ideas and supporting details about pheromones and bioluminescence.

Figure 15 These ants are finding their way to the sugar by following a pheromone trail. The first ant to find the sugar began the trail, and each ant adds to its strength.

362

Oh no—ants have gotten into the sugar! As you watch in dismay, a stream of ants moves along the kitchen counter, heading right for the sugar bowl. Using their sense of smell, the ants follow a chemical trail that was first laid down by the ant that discovered the sugar. Each ant contributes to the trail by depositing a tiny droplet of scent onto the counter. If you watch carefully, you may see the ants doing this. The droplet quickly evaporates, making an invisible cloud of scent that hangs in the air above the path of the ants.

All the ants running to and from the sugar bowl are enveloped in an ant-sized tunnel of scent. It's like an invisible ant highway. The ants hold their antennae forward and use them to sniff their way to the sugar bowl. Then they turn around and follow the same chemical signal back to their nest.

Pheromones

The scent tunnel that leads ants to the sugar bowl is made of pheromones. A **pheromone** (FER uh mohn) is a chemical released by one animal that affects the behavior of another animal of the same

---

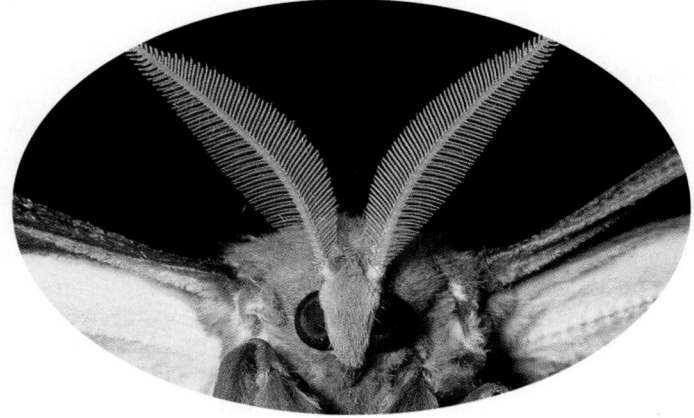

Figure 16 The antennae of this male Atlas silkworm moth allow him to find females that are ready to mate. Sense organs on the antennae pick up the female pheromone scent. The male then follows the scent to the female.
Predicting How might injured antennae affect a male moth's ability to find a mate?

species. **Animals communicate with pheromones to locate food, attract mates, and distinguish members of their own group from members of other groups.** Animals release these very powerful chemicals only in tiny quantities.

Why Pheromones Are Specific Most pheromones are chemical compounds that are made up of long chains of atoms. Each pheromone has a unique combination of atoms in it. Because the atoms join together in specific ways, each pheromone has a different chemical shape. The different shapes of pheromones make them highly specific—when an animal releases a pheromone, it usually only causes a response in other animals of the same species. Just as the key to your front door will not work in the lock of your neighbor's door, the pheromones released by a luna moth will not trigger a response in a gypsy moth.

Pheromones and Behavior Pheromones enable many animals to recognize group members. Every ant colony, for example, has its own pheromones that identify colony members. If an ant wanders into a colony other than its own, the intruder ant's pheromones will be recognized as foreign. The intruder will be attacked and killed.

Pheromones also play an important role in mating and reproduction. A female silkworm moth, for example, releases a pheromone when she is ready to mate. When the sense organs on a male's antennae pick up the scent of the pheromone, the male flies toward the scent to mate with the female.

☑ *Checkpoint How do pheromones enable ants to identify members of another ant colony?*

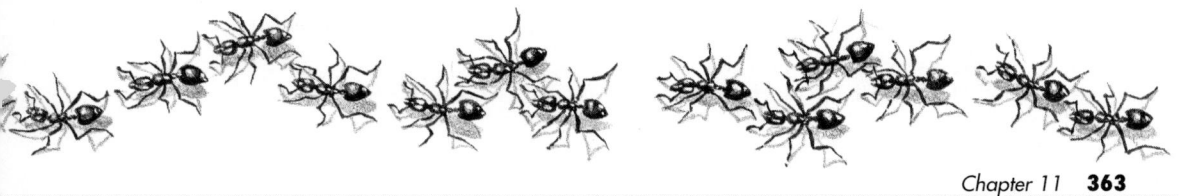

2 *Facilitate*

Pheromones

Including All Students

The key terms in this section are *pheromone* and *bioluminescence.* Explain to students that the term *bioluminescence* comes from the Greek root *bios,* meaning "life," and the Latin root *lumen,* meaning "light." Challenge students to think of other words using those roots. (*Samples: biology, illuminate*) Allow students to use a dictionary to determine how the word pheromone was formed. (*From combining the Greek word* pherein, *"to bear," with* hormone) **limited English proficiency**

Building Inquiry Skills: Inferring

Obtain a number of index cards equal to half the number of students in class. Cut each card in two parts following a random, zigzag line. Place all the pieces in a paper sack and shuffle them. Have students draw one piece. After all pieces are drawn, have the students find the matching pieces. Ask: **How does this model the behavior of pheromones?** (*Pheromones are chemical compounds that have unique shapes that only match the proper receptors.*) **learning modality: kinesthetic**

Answers to Self-Assessment

Caption Question

Figure 16 Injured antennae might be less sensitive to pheromones and make it difficult for the male to find a mate.

☑ *Checkpoint*

The ants in each colony have a unique pheromone. When ants sense another ant's unfamiliar pheromone, they know the ant is foreign.

Ongoing Assessment

Oral Presentation Have students describe two situations in which animals use pheromones. (*Samples: A male cat may mark his territory by spraying a scent containing pheromones. An ant colony can detect an intruder ant because the intruder has different pheromones.*)

363

Pheromones, continued

Integrating Environmental Science

Discuss with students the advantage of pheromone-based pest traps. *(They do not poison beneficial animals.)* **learning modality: verbal**

Communicating with Light

Building Inquiry Skills: Inferring

Have groups devise a code using flashlights. Allow the groups to attempt to communicate with each other across the room. Have a spokesperson report to the class on their success. **cooperative learning**

ACTIVITY

3 Assess

Section 4 Review Answers

1. Establish territories (male cat), attract mates (silkworm moths), distinguish their own group (ants), locate food (ants following trail)

2. Pheromones are used to bait traps.

3. Their readiness to mate

4. The ants will be unable to follow the scent trail.

Science at Home

In addition to their local Board of Health, students can contact their county Agricultural Extension Service or the United States Department of Agriculture. Licensed local exterminators can provide additional information.

Performance Assessment

Writing Have students write fictional accounts of a day in the life of an animal. Accounts should include at least one of the four ways animals communicate with pheromones.

 Students can save their accounts in their portfolios.

Pheromones and Pest Control Some pheromones can be 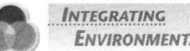 made in laboratories and then used to attract and eliminate pest insects. Manufactured pheromones lure insects into traps. In some cases, the insects are killed in the traps. In some other cases, male insects that collect in these traps can be exposed to X-rays that kill their sperm cells. Even though these altered males will mate with females after they are released, no offspring will result. The population of the insects will eventually decrease. A common pheromone trap lures Japanese beetles, which damage rosebushes. They are lured into a bag from which they can't escape. They can then be killed or relocated.

Figure 17 Fireflies use bioluminescence to find and attract mates.

Communicating with Light

Pheromones are only one form of chemical communication used by animals. Some animals, such as fireflies, use light to communicate. **Bioluminescence** (by oh loo muh NEHS uhns) is the production of light by a living organism. That light is generated by chemical reactions that take place in the organism's cells.

On a warm summer night, when you see a meadow lit up with fireflies, you are actually watching fireflies using bioluminescence in courtship. A male firefly sends a blinking signal to female fireflies in the grass below. Each species of firefly has a distinctive signal. When an interested female sees the signal of a male of her species, she flashes a reply. If the male sees her signal, he will land near her and they may mate.

Section 4 Review

1. List three things that animals communicate with pheromones. Using a specific animal, give an example of each type of communication.
2. How are pheromones used to control insect pests?
3. What do fireflies communicate with their bioluminescence?
4. **Thinking Critically Predicting** While a stream of ants is traveling to and from the sugar bowl, you take a sponge and wash away a six-inch section of their path. Predict how the ants will respond.

364

Science at Home

Chemicals and Insect Pests
Contact your local Board of Health to learn what, if any, measures your community takes to deal with insect pests. Do any of the methods mimic natural pheromones? If your community sprays pesticides, ask what pesticides are used and what measures are taken to protect people and wildlife.

Program Resources

◆ **Unit 3 Resources** 11-4 Review and Reinforce, p. 51; 11-4 Enrich, p. 52

SECTION 5 **Echinoderms**

DISCOVER

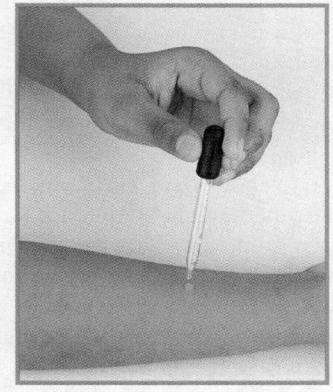

How Do Sea Stars Hold On?

1. Sea stars use hundreds of tiny structures on their arms to cling to rocks and move across underwater surfaces. Use a plastic dropper to see how these structures work. Fill the dropper with water, and then squeeze out most of the water.

2. Squeeze one last drop of water onto the inside of your arm. Then, while squeezing the bulb, touch the tip of the dropper into the water drop. With the dropper tip against your skin, release the bulb.

3. Hold the dropper by the tube and lift it slowly, paying attention to what happens to your skin.

Think It Over
Predicting Besides moving and clinging to surfaces, what might sea stars use their suction structures for?

They look like stars, pincushions, coins, and cucumbers—are these creatures really animals? Sea stars, brittle stars, and basket stars have star-shaped bodies. Sea urchins look like living pincushions, while sand dollars are flat, round discs. Sea cucumbers, with green algae growing within their tissues, look like dill pickles—until they slowly start to crawl along the sand. All of these odd animals belong to the same phylum.

The "Spiny Skinned" Animals

Biologists classify sea stars, sea urchins, sand dollars, and sea cucumbers as echinoderms (phylum Echinodermata). An **echinoderm** (ee KY noh durm) is a radially symmetrical invertebrate that lives on the ocean floor. *Echinoderm* means "spiny skinned." This name is appropriate because the skin of most of these animals is supported by a spiny internal skeleton, or **endoskeleton,** made of plates that contain calcium.

Adult echinoderms have a unique kind of radial symmetry in which body parts, usually in multiples of five, are arranged like spokes on a wheel. If you count the legs on a sea star or the body sections of a sea urchin, you will almost always get five or a multiple of five.

GUIDE FOR READING

◆ What characteristics are typical of echinoderms?

Reading Tip Before you read, preview the photographs in this section. Write a description of the similarities you observe among these organisms.

▼ Magnificent sea urchin

365

READING STRATEGIES

Reading Tip Guide students to list the major characteristics they see when they examine the photographs. Examples might include five-part radial symmetry ("petals" in the sand dollar), and endoskeletons. After students read the section, have them add to their list. Have them note with an asterisk characteristics that are shared by all echinoderms.

Study and Comprehension Group students. Give each group five note cards. Ask students to use their list to write five questions about echinoderms, one on each note card. Students can write the answers on the back of the note cards. Each student in the group should be familiar with the questions and the correct answers. Collect the cards and use them as flash cards for periodic review sessions.

Objectives
After completing this lesson, students will be able to
◆ describe the typical echinoderm characteristics;
◆ name and describe some types of echinoderms.

Key Terms echinoderm, endoskeleton, water vascular system,

1 Engage/Explore

Activating Prior Knowledge

Ask students to name and describe the two kinds of symmetry. *(Bilateral: one line of symmetry; radial: many lines of symmetry through a central point)* Have students examine the figures in this section. Ask: **Which kind of symmetry do the animals in these figures display?** *(Radial symmetry)* Have students name an animal with radial symmetry they learned about in the symmetry section of Chapter 10. *(Sample: Sea anemone)*

DISCOVER

Skills Focus predicting
Materials *plastic dropper, water*
Time 5 minutes
Tips If students have trouble creating suction against their arm, have them practice the activity without using water. Tell them to squeeze the bulb, press the dropper tip against their skin, and then release the bulb. After a few tries, have them try the activity again with a drop of water.
Expected Outcome The droppers will briefly attach to the students' skins.
Think It Over Sea stars might use their suction structures to pry open mollusk shells.

2 Facilitate

The "Spiny Skinned" Animals

Including All Students

In this section, students encounter terms that are difficult to pronounce and understand. Guide students whose native language is not English in the pronunciation of words such as *vascular* and *echinoderm*. Allow them to practice saying the words with a partner until they master the pronunciation. **limited English proficiency**

Inquiry Challenge

Materials *surgical gloves*
Time 20 minutes
Challenge students to see how a water vascular system works by allowing them to make their own simple tube system. First, ask students to suggest ways they could model a water vascular system using the surgical gloves. When students have finished making suggestions, propose this model. Students can fill surgical gloves with water without stretching the gloves. Then they can tie off the openings with rubber bands, and squeeze the gloves in various ways to make different fingers stand up or droop down. Inform students that the muscles surrounding the tubes in an echinoderm's water vascular system squeeze to move water through the tubes and create suction in the tube feet. Ask students: **In this activity, what models the action of these muscles?** *(Hands squeezing the fingers of the glove)* Collect gloves and rubber bands at the end of the activity. **learning modality: kinesthetic**

In addition to five-part radial symmetry and an endoskeleton, echinoderms also have an internal fluid system called a water vascular system. The **water vascular system** consists of fluid-filled tubes within the echinoderm's body. Portions of the tubes can contract, squeezing water into structures called tube feet, which are external parts of the water vascular system. The ends of tube feet are sticky and, when filled with water, they act like small, sticky suction cups. The stickiness and suction enable the tube feet to grip the surface beneath the echinoderm. Most echinoderms also use their tube feet to move along slowly and to capture food. If you turn a sea star upside down, you will see rows of moving tube feet.

Echinoderms crawl about on the bottom of the ocean, seeking food, shelter, and mates. Like other radially symmetrical animals, echinoderms do not have a head end where sense organs and nerve tissue are found. Instead, they are adapted to respond to food, mates, or predators coming from any direction.

Most echinoderms are either male or female. Eggs are usually fertilized right in the seawater, after the female releases her eggs and the male releases his sperm. The fertilized eggs develop into tiny, swimming larvae that eventually undergo metamorphosis and become adult echinoderms.

☑ *Checkpoint* *What is the function of an echinoderm's tube feet?*

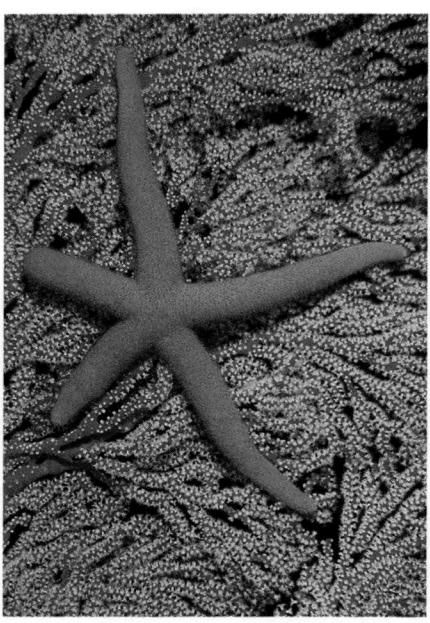

Figure 18 This red sea star is in the process of regenerating two of its arms, possibly lost in a struggle with a predator.

Sea Stars

Sea stars are predators that eat mollusks, crabs, and even other echinoderms. A sea star uses its arms and tube feet, shown in *Exploring a Sea Star* on page 367, to capture prey. The sea star grasps a clam with all five arms. Then it pulls on the tightly closed shells with its tube feet. When the shells open, the sea star forces its stomach out through its mouth and into the opening between the clam's shells. Digestive chemicals break down the clam's tissues, and the sea star sucks in the partially digested body of its prey. Sea star behavior is quite impressive for an animal that doesn't have a brain.

If a sea star loses an arm, it can grow a replacement. The process by which an animal grows a new part to replace a lost one is called regeneration. Figure 18 shows a sea star with two partially regenerated arms. A few species of sea stars can even grow a whole animal from a single arm. Some sea stars reproduce by splitting into many parts. The arms pull the sea star apart in five different directions and five new sea stars regenerate!

366

Background

Facts and Figures Fossil records show that echinoderms have existed for hundreds of millions of years. During the age before the dinosaurs lived, crinoids, or sea lilies, were common. Crinoids still exist today. These enchinoderms live in deeper regions on the ocean floor. Crinoids are filter-feeding animals with five or more long, feathery arms. They are usually attached to the sea floor by a long stem. Many people once thought they were plants because they resemble beautiful flowers.

EXPLORING a Sea Star

S ea stars, which are also called starfishes, usually have five arms. However, some have as many as 50 arms.

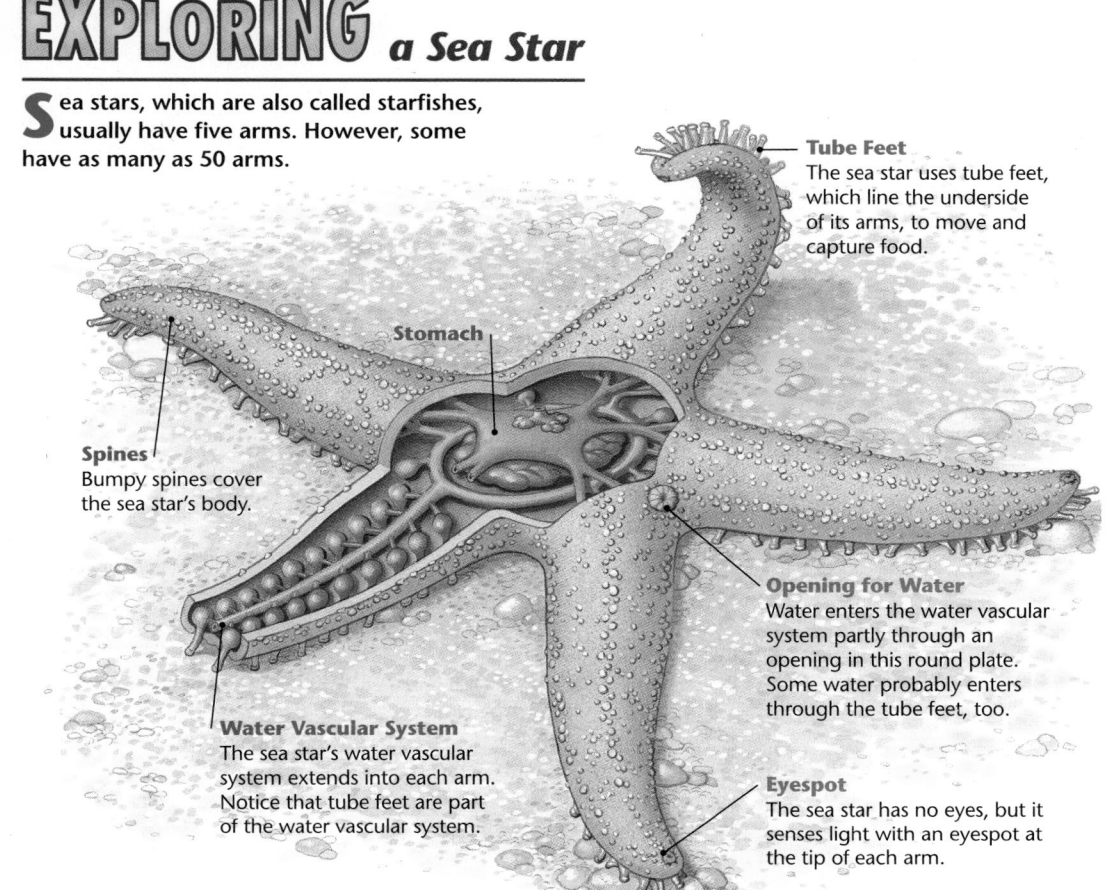

Tube Feet
The sea star uses tube feet, which line the underside of its arms, to move and capture food.

Stomach

Spines
Bumpy spines cover the sea star's body.

Opening for Water
Water enters the water vascular system partly through an opening in this round plate. Some water probably enters through the tube feet, too.

Water Vascular System
The sea star's water vascular system extends into each arm. Notice that tube feet are part of the water vascular system.

Eyespot
The sea star has no eyes, but it senses light with an eyespot at the tip of each arm.

Other Echinoderms

Brittle stars are close relatives of sea stars. Like sea stars, brittle stars have five arms, but their arms are long and slender, with flexible joints. Like sea stars, brittle stars can regenerate lost arms. Brittle stars' tube feet, which have no suction cups, are used for catching food but not for moving. Instead, brittle stars propel themselves along the ocean bottom by moving their giant arms against the ground. They are among the most mobile of all the echinoderms.

Unlike sea stars and brittle stars, sand dollars and sea urchins have no arms. Sand dollars look like large coins. Their flat bodies are covered with very short spines that help them burrow into sand.

Program Resources

◆ **Unit 3 Resources** 11-5 Lesson Plan, p. 53; 11-5 Section Summary, p. 54

Media and Technology

 Audio CD English-Spanish Summary 11-5

 Transparencies "Exploring a Sea Star," Transparency 49

Answers to Self-Assessment

☑ *Checkpoint*
Tube feet allow echinoderms to grip a surface, move along the sea floor, and capture prey.

EXPLORING a Sea Star

Direct students' attention to the labeled parts of the sea star. Point out that the parts labeled Tube Feet, Opening for Water, and Water Vascular System are *all* parts of the water vascular system. Have students work in pairs. One student should trace a finger along a pathway water might travel through the sea star and describe the pathway to a partner. The partner should listen for accuracy and clarity. (*The water goes into the opening for water, through the water vascular tubes, into tube feet, back into the tubes, into other tube feet, and eventually exits from the opening.*) **cooperative learning**

Other Echinoderms

Building Inquiry Skills: Interpreting a Photograph

The five-part symmetry of echinoderms, especially sea urchins and sea cucumbers, is sometimes difficult to see if the animal is viewed from certain angles. Invite students to imagine what the sea cucumber in Figure 19 looks like when viewed from the top. Tell students that the five-part radial symmetry would be evident from this angle. Have them draw a sketch showing what they think the sea cucumber looks like from the top. **learning modality: visual**

 Students can save their paragraphs in their portfolios.

Ongoing Assessment

Writing Give each student a piece of paper labeled Sea Star, Brittle Star, Sand Dollar, Sea Urchin, or Sea Cucumber. Have students write a paragraph describing the animal. Students' paragraphs should mention the general characteristics of echinoderms and the specific characteristics of their animals.

 Students can save their paragraphs in their portfolios.

3 Assess

Section 5 Review Answers

1. Echinoderms are radially symmetrical invertebrates with an endoskeleton. They have five-part symmetry and a water vascular system. Most are spiny.

2. Regeneration is the process by which an animal grows a new part to replace a lost one. When a sea star loses an arm, it can regenerate a new one.

3. Both sea stars and sea urchins have five-part radial symmetry. Both move with tube feet. Sea stars have five arms. Sea urchins have no arms; they are covered with spines and resemble pin-cushions.

4. Tube feet operate by suction. Each time the animal moves, it must pull its feet up by releasing the suction, and then put them down again. Because this process is slow, tube feet are adapted to slow movement.

Check Your Progress
CHAPTER PROJECT

When one-half of a student's mealworms have reached the adult stage, have the student write a simple summary of his or her observations. To draw conclusions, students can make a bar graph comparing the numbers of mealworms in different stages of development under the two conditions. Tell students their conclusions must be based on data they have collected. Have follow-up discussions with students who made inappropriate conclusions. When the project is finished, collect the insects from students.

Figure 19 The blue-and-red sea cucumber (A), spiny brittle stars (B), and sand dollar (C) are all echinoderms.
Observing What type of symmetry do these organisms exhibit?

Movable spines cover and protect the bodies of sea urchins, making them look like pincushions or round brushes. The spines cover a central shell that is made of plates joined together. Sea urchins move by using bands of tube feet that extend out between the spines. With the five strong teeth that can be projected from their mouths, sea urchins can scrape algae, chew seaweed, and crush pieces of coral and the shells of small mollusks. Some sea urchins use their teeth and spines to dig themselves into rock crevices to hide from predators.

As you might expect from their name, sea cucumbers look a little bit like leathery-skinned cucumbers—but you won't see one in a tossed salad. These strange animals, which live on the sandy or rocky ocean floor, can be red, brown, blue, or green. Their bodies are soft, flexible, and muscular. Sea cucumbers have rows of tube feet on their underside, enabling them to crawl slowly along the ocean bottom. At one end of a sea cucumber is a mouth surrounded by tentacles. The sea cucumber, which is a filter feeder, can lengthen its tentacles to sweep food toward its mouth, and then pull the tentacles back into its tough skin.

Section 5 Review

1. Identify the main characteristics of echinoderms.

2. Define *regeneration* and explain how it applies to sea stars.

3. Compare and contrast sea urchins and sea stars.

4. **Thinking Critically Inferring** How are tube feet adapted to slow, rather than rapid, movement?

Check Your Progress
CHAPTER PROJECT

Continue to examine the mealworm containers every day and record your data. In your notebook, record any differences between the two groups of mealworms. Begin to draw conclusions about how the different conditions affected metamorphosis. When you have finished working with the insects, return them to your teacher.

Performance Assessment

Drawing Have students sketch a hypothetical echinoderm. Be sure students' sketches include the major characteristics of echinoderms. *(Students' sketches should include five-part radial symmetry, a water vascular system, and an endoskeleton.)*

Media and Technology

Exploring Life Science Videodisc
Unit 3, Side 2, "Spineless"

Chapter 2

Program Resources

◆ **Unit 3 Resources** 11-5 Review and Reinforce, p. 55; 11-5 Enrich, p. 56
◆ **Laboratory Manual** 11, "Characteristics of Sea Stars"

Answers to Self-Assessment

Caption Question

Figure 18 These organisms exhibit five-part radial symmetry.

SECTION 1 Mollusks

Key Ideas

◆ Most mollusks have shells, soft bodies, a mantle covering internal organs, and a muscular foot.
◆ Major groups of mollusks include gastropods, bivalves, and cephalopods.

Key Terms

mollusk	radula	bivalve
kidney	gastropod	cephalopod
gill		

SECTION 2 Arthropods

Key Ideas

◆ Arthropods have an exoskeleton, jointed appendages, and a segmented body.
◆ Major groups of arthropods include crustaceans, arachnids, centipedes, millipedes, and insects.

Key Terms

arthropod	molting	metamorphosis
exoskeleton	antenna	arachnid
chitin	crustacean	abdomen

SECTION 3 Insects

Key Ideas

◆ Insects are arthropods with three body sections, six legs, one pair of antennae, and usually one or two pairs of wings.
◆ An insect undergoing complete metamorphosis goes through four distinct stages—egg, larva, pupa, and adult. An insect undergoing gradual metamorphosis hatches from an egg to a nymph; the nymph may molt several times before becoming an adult.

Key Terms

insect	pupa
thorax	gradual metamorphosis
complete metamorphosis	nymph
	camouflage

SECTION 4 The Chemistry of Communication

INTEGRATING **CHEMISTRY**

Key Ideas

◆ Pheromones are chemicals that animals use to establish a territory, locate food, attract a mate, and identify group members.
◆ Male fireflies use bioluminescence, or the production of light by a living organism, to attract mates.

Key Terms

pheromone	bioluminescence

SECTION 5 Echinoderms

Key Ideas

◆ Echinoderms have an endoskeleton, five-part radial symmetry, and a water vascular system.
◆ Echinoderms include sea stars, sea urchins, brittle stars, and sea cucumbers.

Key Terms

echinoderm	water vascular system
endoskeleton	

Organizing Information

Concept Map The concept map below shows the classification of arthropods. Copy the map and complete it. (For more on concept maps, see the Skills Handbook.)

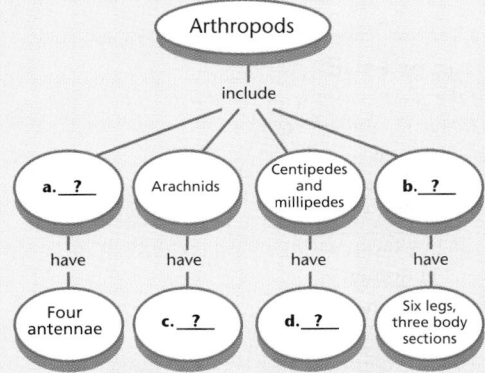

Organizing Information

Concept Map a. crustaceans **b.** insects **c.** eight legs, two body segments **d.** highly segmented body, one or two pairs of legs on each segment

Program Resources

◆ **Unit 3 Resources** Chapter 11 Project Scoring Rubric, p. 36
◆ **Performance Assessment** Chapter 11, pp. 35–37
◆ **Chapter and Unit Tests** Chapter 11 Test, pp. 52–55
◆ **Inquiry Skills Activity Book** Provides teaching and review of all inquiry skills

Media and Technology

 Interactive Student Tutorial CD-ROM Chapter 11

 Computer Test Bank Chapter 11 Test

Reviewing Content
Multiple Choice
1. a 2. d 3. c 4. d 5. c

True or False
6. true 7. crustaceans 8. thorax 9. true
10. true

Checking Concepts
11. A snail uses its radula like a tongue to scrape up tiny particles of food.
12. A cephalopod swims by using jet propulsion. It does not move by using a foot like most mollusks do.
13. Accept any five: antennae smell, taste, touch, and balance; legs walk; swimmerets function in swimming; swimmerets of female hold eggs; plierlike appendages catch food and defend crayfish.
14. Both digest the food outside their bodies and then suck the digested food inside.
15. Centipedes are carnivores and have one pair of legs per body segment. Most millipedes are herbivores; all millipedes have two pairs of legs per body segment.
16. Insects damage crops and carry diseases such as malaria.
17. Unlike other arthropods, all insects have six legs and one pair of antennae. In addition, most have wings.
18. The pheromones of each species have a unique chemical structure, so they usually cause a response only in animals of the same species.
19. An echinoderm's radial symmetry is a 5-part symmetry, while a jellyfish's symmetry is not 5-part.
20. Answers will vary. Students should focus on the new, soft exoskeleton of the animal that is exposed to fish or other predators before it hardens.

Thinking Critically
21. Alike: Bivalves and cephalopods have mantle covering internal organs; have soft bodies; live in water. Different: Bivalves have two shells, but many cephalopods have no shell; cephalopod feet are adapted to form tentacles; cephalopods move by jet propulsion, while bivalves move slowly with feet; cephalopods have complex nervous systems, but bivalves do not.

Reviewing Content

 For more review of key concepts, see the Interactive Student Tutorial CD-ROM.

Multiple Choice
Choose the letter of the best answer.

1. Mollusks with tentacles are known as
   a. cephalopods.
   b. gastropods.
   c. bivalves.
   d. sea stars.
2. Which of these is true of the legs of arthropods?
   a. They always number six.
   b. They are always attached to the abdomen.
   c. They are rigid.
   d. They are jointed.
3. At which stage of its development is a moth enclosed in a cocoon?
   a. egg
   b. larva
   c. pupa
   d. adult
4. Chemicals released by insects that affect other insects of the same species are called
   a. camouflages.
   b. pupae.
   c. pesticides.
   d. pheromones.
5. A sea star is a(n)
   a. mollusk.
   b. arthropod.
   c. echinoderm.
   d. sponge.

True or False
If the statement is true, write true. If it is false, change the underlined word or words to make the statement true.

6. All <u>arthropods</u> have an exoskeleton.
7. All <u>sea urchins</u> have two pairs of antennae.
8. An insect's midsection is called an <u>abdomen</u>.
9. The production of light by an organism is called <u>bioluminescence</u>.
10. All echinoderms have an <u>endoskeleton</u>.

22. The cub looks similar to the adult lion from the time it is born. It grows larger, but it does not change its form.
23. No. All insects have six legs and one pair of antennae.
24. Any argument presented by students is acceptable as long as it is supported by facts.
25. The sea star population increased because new sea stars could regenerate from the pieces thrown into the water.

Checking Concepts
11. Explain how a snail uses its radula.
12. How is a cephalopod's way of moving different from that of most mollusks?
13. Describe five things that a crayfish can do with its appendages.
14. How is the process by which a spider digests its food similar to that of a sea star?
15. How are centipedes different from millipedes?
16. Identify some ways insects harm people.
17. How are insects different from other arthropods?
18. How does a pheromone's structure account for the fact that it usually affects the behavior of only one species?
19. How is an echinoderm's radial symmetry different from that of a jellyfish?
20. **Writing to Learn** Imagine that you are a lobster that has just molted. Using vivid, precise words, describe a dangerous situation that you might encounter before your new exoskeleton has hardened.

Thinking Critically

21. **Comparing and Contrasting** Compare and contrast bivalves and cephalopods.
22. **Applying Concepts** Explain why the development of a lion, which grows larger as it changes from a tiny cub to a 200-pound adult, is not metamorphosis.
23. **Classifying** Your friend said he found a dead insect that had two pairs of antennae and eight legs. Is this possible? Why or why not?
24. **Making Judgments** Do you think that pesticides should be used to kill harmful insects? Support your ideas with facts.
25. **Relating Cause and Effect** Sea stars sometimes get caught in fishing nets. At one time, in an attempt to protect clams from their natural predators, workers on fishing boats cut the sea stars into pieces and threw the pieces back in the water. What do you think happened to the sea star population? Explain.

Applying Skills
26.

Insect	Wing-Beat Rate (times/sec)	Flight Speed (kph)
Hummingbird Moth	85	17.8
Bumblebee	250	10.3
Housefly	190	7.1

Applying Skills

The following information appeared in a book on insects. Use it to answer Questions 26–29.

"A hummingbird moth beats its wings an average of 85 times per second, and it flies at a speed of about 17.8 kilometers per hour (kph). A bumblebee's wings beat about 250 times per second, and it flies about 10.3 kph. A housefly's wings beat about 190 times per second, and it flies about 7.1 kph."

26. Creating Data Tables Make a data table to organize the wing-beat rate and flight speed information above.

27. Graphing Use the data to construct two bar graphs: one showing the three insect wing-beat rates and another showing the flight speeds.

28. Interpreting Data Which of the three insects has the highest wing-beat rate? Which insect flies the fastest?

29. Drawing Conclusions On the basis of the data, do you see any relationship between the rate at which an insect beats its wings and the speed at which it flies? Explain. What factors besides wing-beat rate might affect an insect's flight speed?

Performance CHAPTER PROJECT **Assessment**

Present Your Project Prepare a display with diagrams to show how you set up your experiment and what your results were. Construct and display graphs to show the data you collected. Include pictures of the mealworms in each stage of development.

Reflect and Record In your journal, write your conclusion of how the experimental conditions affected the growth and development of the mealworms. Also suggest some possible explanations for your results.

Test Preparation

Use these questions to prepare for standardized tests.

Study the graph. Then answer Questions 30–33.

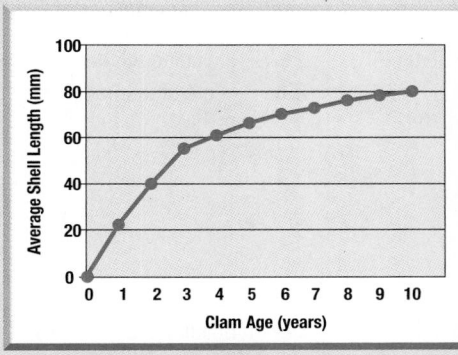

30. What is the best title for this graph?
a. Clam Shell Growth over Time
b. The Ages of a Clam
c. The Maximum Size of Clams
d. The Life Span of Clams

31. In some states, the minimum harvesting size for clams is 40 millimeters. Approximately how long does it take new clams to reach this size?
a. 1 year   **b.** 2 years
c. 3 years   **d.** 4 years

32. Based on the graph, which generalization about clam growth is correct?
a. Clam growth is most rapid during years 5 through 10.
b. Clam growth is most rapid during years 0 through 5.
c. Clam growth is equally rapid each year.
d. Clam growth is very slow.

33. How many millimeters larger was the average clam at age 2 compared to age 1?
a. 8 millimeters
b. 15 millimeters
c. 18 millimeters
d. 25 millimeters

Chapter 11 **371**

---

29. There is no trend in the data to support any relationship between wing-beat rate and speed of flight. Other factors might include mass and shape of the insect and shape of the insect's wings.

Performance CHAPTER PROJECT **Assessment**

Present Your Project Remind students to include illustrations of their setup, data, graph, and results. They must also include diagrams of the larvae, pupae, and adults, with arrows between these diagrams to illustrate the sequence of complete metamorphosis.

Students can evaluate their displays by showing them to a friend or family member who is unfamiliar with the project. Suggest that students update their displays using this feedback before showing them to the class.

Consider grouping students according to the variable they tested. Direct each group to discuss their results. Have them combine their data, create a graph to display the data, and then summarize their results. Instruct each group to present its graph and results to the rest of the class.

Reflect and Record Ask students to discuss their conclusions. Encourage discussion of why metamorphosis was or was not affected by the variables they tested.

Test Preparation

30. a **31.** b **32.** b **33.** c

27.

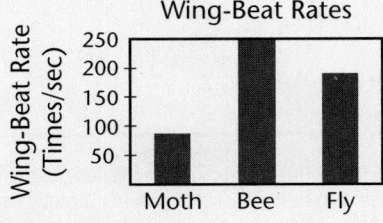

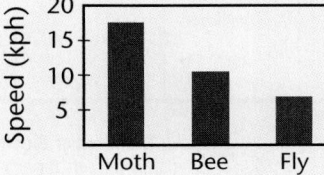

28. The bumblebee has the highest wing-beat rate. The hummingbird moth flies the fastest.

Fishes, Amphibians, and Reptiles

Sections	Time	Student Edition Activities	Other Activities	
CHAPTER PROJECT **Animal Adaptations** p. 373	Ongoing (3 weeks)	Check Your Progress, pp. 387, 394, 404 Present Your Project, p. 407		
1 *INTEGRATING EARTH SCIENCE* **Evolution of Vertebrates** pp. 374–380 ◆ Describe the main characteristics that vertebrates share. ◆ Describe how vertebrates differ in the way they control body temperatures. ◆ Explain what fossil evidence indicates about vertebrate evolution.	$1\frac{1}{2}$ periods/ $\frac{3}{4}$ block	**Discover** How Is an Umbrella like a Skeleton?, p. 374 **Try This** Bead-y Bones, p. 376 **Science at Home** p. 380	TE TE TE	Demonstration, p. 375 Building Inquiry Skills: Relating Cause and Effect, p. 376 Including All Students, p. 378
2 **Fishes** pp. 381–388 ◆ Explain how fish use their gills, move, feed, and reproduce. ◆ Describe the three major groups of fish.	2 periods/ 1 block	**Discover** How Does Water Flow over a Fish's Gills?, p. 381 **Sharpen your Skills** Communicating, p. 382 **Real-World Lab: How It Works** Home Sweet Home, p. 388	TE TE IES LM	Building Inquiry Skills: Observing, p. 384, 386 Integrating Physics, p. 385 "Where River Meets Sea," pp. 13–14, 22–23 12, "Adaptations of Fish"
3 **Amphibians** pp. 389–394 ◆ Describe the characteristics of amphibians and their life cycles. ◆ Explain how amphibians are adapted for land and current threats to their survival. ◆ Identify and describe the groups of amphibians.	$1\frac{1}{2}$ periods/ $\frac{3}{4}$ block	**Discover** What's the Advantage of Being Green?, p. 389 **Try This** Webbing Through Water, p. 392	TE IES	Including All Students, p. 390 "Fate of the Rain Forest," p. 11
4 **Reptiles** pp. 395–404 ◆ Describe some adaptations that allow reptiles to live on dry land. ◆ State how reptiles' eggs are different from amphibians' eggs. ◆ Describe the major groups of reptiles.	2 periods/ 1 block	**Discover** How Do Snakes Feed?, p. 395 **Skills Lab: Interpreting Data** Soaking Up Those Rays, pp. 400–401 **Sharpen your Skills** Drawing Conclusions, p. 403	TE TE IES	Building Inquiry Skills: Inferring, p. 396 Including All Students, p. 402 "Sleuth's Supper," p. 20
Study Guide/Chapter Assessment pp. 405–407	1 period/ $\frac{1}{2}$ block		ISAB	Provides teaching and review of all inquiry skills

For Standard or Block Schedule The Resource Pro® CD-ROM gives you maximum flexibility for planning your instruction for any type of schedule. Resource Pro® contains Planning Express®, an advanced scheduling program, as well as the entire contents of the Teaching Resources and the Computer Test Bank.

CHAPTER PLANNING GUIDE

Program Resources	Assessment Strategies	Media and Technology
UR Chapter 12 Project Teacher Notes, pp. 62–63 **UR** Chapter 12 Project Overview and Worksheets, pp. 64–67	**SE** Performance Assessment: Present Your Project, p. 407 **TE** Check Your Progress, pp. 387, 394, 404 **UR** Chapter 12 Project Scoring Rubric, p. 68	Science Explorer Internet Site at www.phschool.com
UR 12-1 Lesson Plan, p. 69 **UR** 12-1 Section Summary, p. 70 **UR** 12-1 Review and Reinforce, p. 71 **UR** 12-1 Enrich, p. 72	**SE** Section 1 Review, p. 380 **TE** Ongoing Assessment, pp. 375, 377, 379 **TE** Performance Assessment, p. 380	Life Science Videotape 3; Videodisc Unit 3 Side 2, "Backbones"; "How Does Everything Fit?" Life Science Videotape 3; Videodisc Unit 3 Side 2, "Fossils"; "The Earth Library" Audio CD, English-Spanish Summary 12-1 Transparency 50, "Vertebrate Evolution"
UR 12-2 Lesson Plan, p. 73 **UR** 12-2 Section Summary, p. 74 **UR** 12-2 Review and Reinforce, p. 75 **UR** 12-2 Enrich, p. 76 **UR** Chapter 12 Real-World Lab, pp. 85–86	**SE** Section 2 Review, p. 387 **TE** Ongoing Assessment, pp. 383, 385 **TE** Performance Assessment, p. 387	Audio CD, English-Spanish Summary 12-2 Transparency 51, "Exploring a Bony Fish"
UR 12-3 Lesson Plan, p. 77 **UR** 12-3 Section Summary, p. 78 **UR** 12-3 Review and Reinforce, p. 79 **UR** 12-3 Enrich, p. 80	**SE** Section 3 Review, p. 394 **TE** Ongoing Assessment, pp. 391, 393 **TE** Performance Assessment, p. 394	Audio CD, English-Spanish Summary 12-3 Transparencies 52, "Frog Metamorphosis"; 53, "Exploring a Frog" Interactive Student Tutorial CD-ROM, Chapter 12
UR 12-4 Lesson Plan, p. 81 **UR** 12-4 Section Summary, p. 82 **UR** 12-4 Review and Reinforce, p. 83 **UR** 12-4 Enrich, p. 84 **UR** Chapter 12 Skills Lab, pp. 87–89	**SE** Section 4 Review, p. 404 **TE** Ongoing Assessment, pp. 397, 399, 403 **TE** Performance Assessment, p. 404	Life Science Videotape 3; Videodisc, Unit 3 Side 2, "Travelin' Along" Audio CD, English-Spanish Summary 12-4 Transparencies 54, "A Reptile Egg"; 55, "Exploring a Lizard"
RCA Provides strategies to improve science reading skills **GSW** Provides worksheets to promote student comprehension of content	**SE** Chapter 12 Study Guide/Assessment, pp. 405–407 **PA** Chapter 12 Performance Assessment, pp. 38–40 **CUT** Chapter 12 Test, pp. 56–59 **CTB** Chapter 12 Test	Interactive Student Tutorial CD-ROM, Chapter 12 Computer Test Bank, Chapter 12 Test

Key: **SE** Student Edition
CTB Computer Test Bank
ISAB Inquiry Skills Activity Book
GSW Guided Study Worksheets

TE Teacher's Edition
PTA Product Testing Activities by *Consumer Reports*
RCA Reading in the Content Area
PA Performance Assessment

UR Unit Resources
LM Laboratory Manual
IES Interdisciplinary Explorations Series
CUT Chapter and Unit Tests

Meeting the National Science Education Standards and AAAS Benchmarks

National Science Education Standards	Benchmarks for Science Literacy	Unifying Themes

Science as Inquiry (Content Standard A)

◆ **Communicate scientific procedures and explanations** Students report on how successfully they were able to create an artificial environment for organisms (snails and guppies) and determine how the environment meets the needs of the organisms. *(Real-World Lab)*

◆ **Design and conduct a scientific investigation** Students create an artificial environment for two organisms and monitor the organisms' behavior. They also design an extension to the activity allowing more organisms to be added. *(Real-World Lab)*

Earth and Space Science (Content Standard D)

◆ **Earth's history** The fossils found in sedimentary rocks reveal the history of vertebrate evolution through time. *(Section 1)*

Life Science (Content Standard C)

◆ **Diversity and adaptations of organisms** The specialized characteristics of vertebrates reveal great diversity of form. Adaptations allow vertebrates to occupy many different habitats. *(Sections 1–4)*

◆ **Structure and function of living systems** Vertebrates have similar structures to perform similar functions. Different vertebrate groups have specialized structures, such as a two-loop circulatory system and three-chambered heart. *(Sections 1–4)*

5A Diversity of Life Fishes, amphibians, and reptiles show great diversity of form but share common characteristics that allow them to be grouped together as vertebrates. Within each group, there are many variations on the vertebrate theme, ranging from the tiniest salamander to the largest dinosaur. Specialized adaptations allowed some vertebrates to move from the oceans and become land dwellers. *(Sections 1–4; Real-World Lab; Skills Lab; Chapter Project)*

5D Interdependence of Life Predators and prey are interconnected through complex relationships. Organisms depend on their environment to supply needs. *(Sections 2, 3; Real-World Lab)*

5F Evolution of Life Vertebrates evolved from the first chordates. Vertebrate evolution shows over time an increasing variety of specialized adaptations allowing exploitation of many different habitats. This history of change is revealed in the fossil record. *(Section 1)*

11B Models Students create models showing a particular adaptation in fishes, amphibians, and reptiles. *(Chapter Project)*

12D Communication Skills Students interpret pictures of lizard behavior and transfer the information to data tables. *(Skills Lab)*

◆ **Modeling** Students construct models of reptiles, amphibians, and fishes, in order to understand how adaptations aid survival. *(Chapter Project)*

◆ **Patterns of Change** The fossil record shows how changes in reproduction, the skeletal system, respiration, and the circulatory system have allowed animals to move out of the water and populate dry land. *(Sections 1–4)*

◆ **Evolution** Populations of organisms have successfully adapted to many different environments. In vertebrate evolution, this includes a set of adaptations, such as a stronger skeleton and lungs, that have allowed species to become land dwellers. *(Section 1)*

◆ **Structure** Fish, reptiles, and amphibians possess many similar structures. Specialization in the skeletal system and the respiratory system has allowed some animals to adapt to life on dry land. *(Sections 1–4; Chapter Project)*

◆ **Unity and Diversity** Fish, reptiles, and amphibians are all vertebrates, because they all possess a backbone. Each group is distinguished from the others by specialized features. Within each group there is great diversity of size and other variations. *(Sections 1–4; Chapter Project)*

◆ **Systems and Interactions** Organisms interact as part of the environment. Artificial environments must supply all of an animal's needs. *(Real-World Lab)*

Take It to the Net

 *Interactive text at www.phschool.com*

Science Explorer comes alive with iText.

- **Complete student text** is accessible from any computer with Internet access or a CD-ROM drive.
- **Animations, simulations, and videos** enhance student understanding and retention of concepts.
- **Self-tests and online study tools** assess student understanding.

STAY CURRENT with **SCIENCE NEWS®**

Find out the latest research and information about animals at: **www.phschool.com**

Go to **www.phschool.com** and click on the Science icon. Then click on Science Explorer: Life, Earth, and Physical Science under PH@school.

Student Edition Activities Planner

ACTIVITY	Time (minutes)	Materials *Quantities for one work group*	Skills
Section 1			
Discover, p. 374	15	**Nonconsumable** umbrella	Inferring
Try This, p. 376	10	**Consumable** short lengths of string **Nonconsumable** enough beads (in two different sizes) to cover the length of the string	Making Models
Science at Home, p. 380	home	No special materials are required.	Observing
Section 2			
Discover, p. 381	10	**Nonconsumable** a live fish, in an aquarium or fishbowl	Observing
Sharpen Your Skills, p. 382	50	**Consumable** preserved fish, disposable gloves **Nonconsumable** goggles, dissecting tray, blunt probe, hand lens	Communicating
Real-World Lab, p. 388	30 min set up; 10 min per day for 2 wk	**Consumable** gravel, snails, tap water, guppy food, guppies, water plants **Nonconsumable** aquarium filter, rectangular aquarium tank (15 to 20 liters) with cover, metric ruler, thermometer, aquarium heater, dip net	Making Models, Posing Questions
Section 3			
Discover, p. 389	10	**Nonconsumable** dried yellow and green peas; paper cup; green construction paper, approximately 1 m x 1 m; clock or watch with second hand	Inferring
Try This, p. 392	15	**Consumable** plastic bags **Nonconsumable** heavy rubber bands, pail of water or sink	Making Models
Section 4			
Discover, p. 395	10	**Consumable** grapefruit **Nonconsumable** sock with ribbed cuff, strong rubber band	Inferring
Skills Lab, pp. 400–401	30	**Consumable** paper **Nonconsumable** pencil	Interpreting Data, Interpreting Diagrams, Drawing Conclusions
Sharpen your Skills, p. 403	15	No special materials are required.	Drawing Conclusions

A list of all materials required for the Student Edition activities can be found on pages T25–T33. You can obtain information about ordering materials by calling 1-800-848-9500 or by accessing the Science Explorer Internet site at **www.phschool.com**.

Animal Adaptations

Adaptations have evolved over time in species because the adaptations allow individual organisms to be more successful at acquiring food, escaping predators, or reproducing. In this project, students will select one adaptation to model in three different animals: a reptile, an amphibian, and a fish.

Purpose In this project, students will investigate and model how adaptations enable animals to survive in their environments.

Skills Focus Students will be able to
◆ make models of adaptations that perform similar functions in three different kinds of organisms;
◆ compare and contrast the adaptations of the three organisms;
◆ communicate to their classmates their findings about the adaptations they model.

Project Time Line Before beginning the project, see Chapter 12 Project Teacher Notes on pages 62–63 in Unit 3 Resources for more details on carrying out the project. Distribute to students Chapter 12 Project Overview, Worksheets, and Scoring Rubric on pages 64–68 in Unit 3 Resources. This project should progress in several stages and will take 4–5 weeks to complete. During the first week, students get together with a partner or in small groups and skim the chapter and any other sources of relevant information such as books and magazines. By the beginning of the second week, students should have selected an adaptation to model. As students complete each chapter section, they should begin to construct a model of one type of organism they studied in the section. To save time and keep students on track, have them work on their projects at home as well as in the classroom. Students should be given about one week to build the model for each organism and then a few days to prepare their class presentation.

Possible Materials Provide a wide variety of materials from which students can choose. Have students bring extra

CHAPTER 12 Fishes, Amphibians, and Reptiles

This three-horned chameleon has just invited a cricket to lunch.

WEB ACTIVITY www.phschool.com

SECTION 1 *Integrating Earth Science* 🌐 **Evolution of Vertebrates**

Discover **How Is an Umbrella Like a Skeleton?**
Try This **Bead-y Bones**
Science at Home **Focus on Backbones**

SECTION 2 Fishes

Discover **How Does Water Flow Over a Fish's Gills?**
Sharpen Your Skills **Communicating**
Real-World Lab **Home Sweet Home**

SECTION 3 Amphibians

Discover **What's the Advantage of Being Green?**
Try This **Webbing Through Water**

372

materials that they might have at home for others in the class to use. Some possibilities are listed below.
◆ For model building, include toothpicks, pipe cleaners, Styrofoam, cardboard, construction paper, chicken wire, balsa wood, balloons, modeling clay, papier mâché, glue, tape, scissors, paints, markers, and other decorating materials.
◆ For information about organisms, students can consult nature magazines and refererence books.

Launching the Project Allow time for students to read the description of the project in their texts and the Chapter 12 Project Overview on pages 64–65 in Unit 3 Resources. To begin the project, allow students to work with others and think about various adaptations. Suggest that they skim the chapter, books, and magazines to help them think about the ways fishes, amphibians, and reptiles are different. Students can discuss the characteristics that allow fishes, amphibians, and reptiles to move, feed, and protect

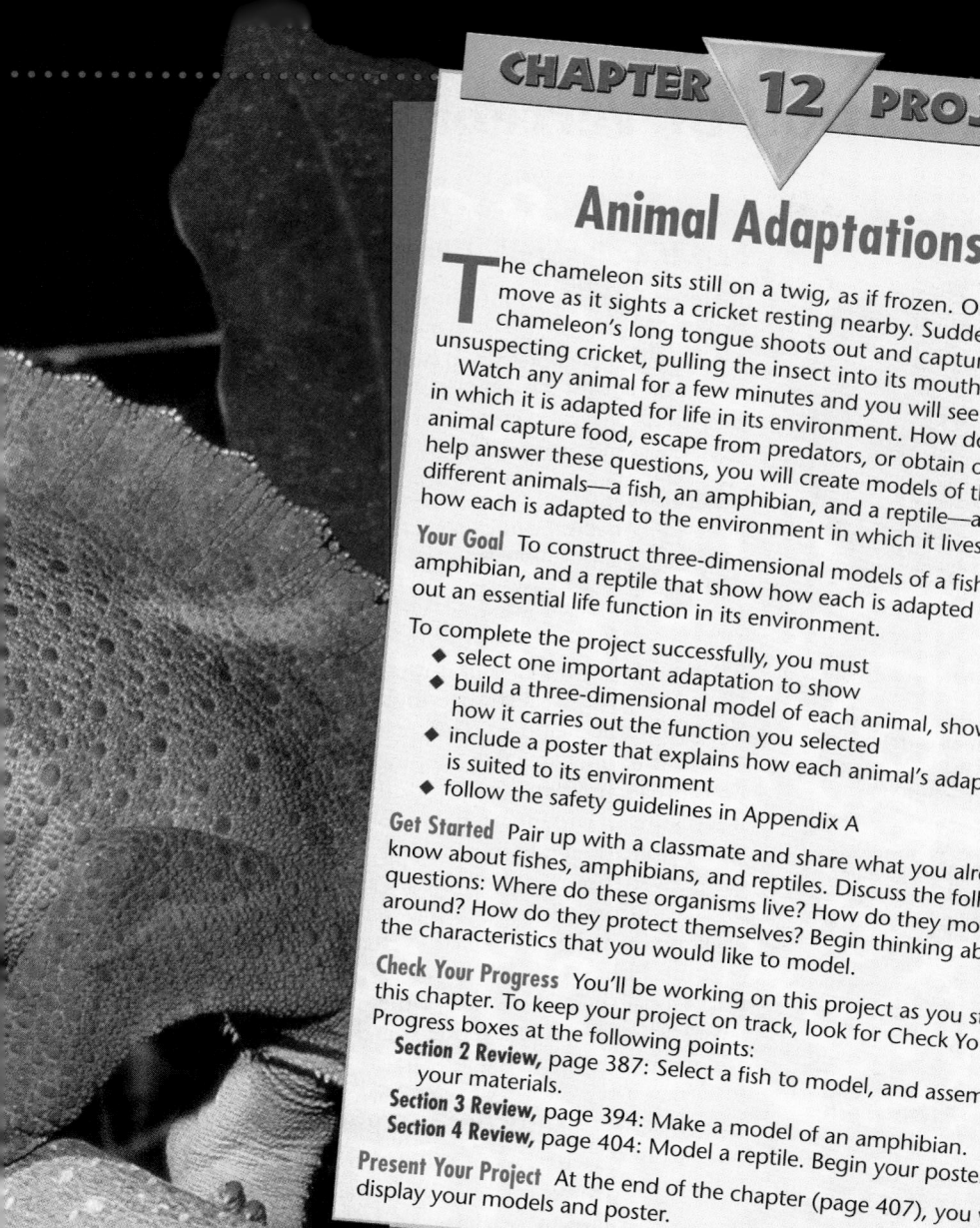

CHAPTER 12 PROJECT

Animal Adaptations

The chameleon sits still on a twig, as if frozen. Only its eyes move as it sights a cricket resting nearby. Suddenly, the chameleon's long tongue shoots out and captures the unsuspecting cricket, pulling the insect into its mouth.

Watch any animal for a few minutes and you will see many ways in which it is adapted for life in its environment. How does the animal capture food, escape from predators, or obtain oxygen? To help answer these questions, you will create models of three different animals—a fish, an amphibian, and a reptile—and show how each is adapted to the environment in which it lives.

Your Goal To construct three-dimensional models of a fish, an amphibian, and a reptile that show how each is adapted to carry out an essential life function in its environment.

To complete the project successfully, you must
◆ select one important adaptation to show
◆ build a three-dimensional model of each animal, showing how it carries out the function you selected
◆ include a poster that explains how each animal's adaptation is suited to its environment
◆ follow the safety guidelines in Appendix A

Get Started Pair up with a classmate and share what you already know about fishes, amphibians, and reptiles. Discuss the following questions: Where do these organisms live? How do they move around? How do they protect themselves? Begin thinking about the characteristics that you would like to model.

Check Your Progress You'll be working on this project as you study this chapter. To keep your project on track, look for Check Your Progress boxes at the following points:
Section 2 Review, page 387: Select a fish to model, and assemble your materials.
Section 3 Review, page 394: Make a model of an amphibian.
Section 4 Review, page 404: Model a reptile. Begin your poster.

Present Your Project At the end of the chapter (page 407), you will display your models and poster.

SECTION 4 Reptiles

Discover **How Do Snakes Feed?**
Skills Lab **Soaking Up Those Rays**
Sharpen Your Skills **Drawing Conclusions**

373

themselves. Suggest that students choose adaptations that are quite different in at least two of the three organisms. To make sure everyone is on track and understands the project, you may wish to hold a class discussion after this brainstorming period. As students complete each section, they should begin to construct models of the type of organisms they just studied. Before they construct their models, students should sketch the design and think about the materials they will need to complete the model. Where appropriate, suggest that students model only a part of the organisms. For example, if they are modeling feeding behaviors, they could model the mouths. Pass out copies of the Chapter 12 Project Worksheets on pages 66–67 in Unit 3 Resources for students to review.

You could have students work in small groups as a cooperative learning task. To ensure that every student will have ample opportunity to participate in model planning and building, each group should consist of three to four students.

Performance Assessment

The Chapter 12 Project Scoring Rubric on page 68 of Unit 3 Resources will help you evaluate how well students complete the Chapter 12 Project. You may wish to share the scoring rubric with your students so they are clear about what is expected of them. Students will be assessed on
◆ the thoroughness of their research into the adaptation that they model, and the appropriateness and accuracy of their sketches;
◆ the size, proportion, and accuracy of their models;
◆ the clarity and thoroughness of their posters;
◆ the thoroughness and organization of their presentations.

Program Resources

◆ **Unit 3 Resources** Chapter 12 Project Teacher Notes, pp. 62–63; Chapter 12 Project Overview and Worksheets, pp. 64–67; Chapter 12 Project Scoring Rubric, p. 68

WEB ACTIVITY www.phschool.com

You will find an Internet activity, chapter self-tests for students, and links to other chapter topics at this site.

Evolution of Vertebrates

Objectives

After completing this lesson, students will be able to
◆ describe the main characteristics that vertebrates share;
◆ describe how vertebrates differ in the way that they control body temperatures;
◆ explain what fossil evidence indicates about vertebrate evolution.

Key Terms chordate, notochord, cartilage, vertebra, ectotherm, endotherm, fossil, sedimentary rock

1 Engage/Explore

Activating Prior Knowledge

Ask students to recall what they learned about vertebrates and invertebrates in Chapter 10. Then ask a volunteer to list on the board all the kinds of vertebrates and invertebrates the students see in a single day. Once the lists are completed, have them compare and contrast several obvious ways vertebrates and invertebrates are similar and ways they are different.

 **DISCOVER**

Skills Focus inferring
Materials *umbrella*
Time 15 minutes
Tips To avoid injuries, make sure students are standing in an open area away from others when they open the umbrella.
Expected Outcome Students should understand that, without its ribs, an umbrella loses its support and cannot function.
Think It Over The umbrella's ribs provide support to the umbrella and give it shape, just as bones support and give shape to the human body. The ribs of an umbrella are different from human bones in that they are near the surface, rather than deep within the body and covered by soft tissue. **learning modality: kinesthetic**

---

① Evolution of Vertebrates

DISCOVER ·· **ACTIVITY**

How Is an Umbrella Like a Skeleton?

1. Open an umbrella. Turn it upside down and examine how it is made.
2. Now fold the umbrella, and watch how the braces and ribs collapse against the central pole.
3. Think of what would happen if you removed the ribs from the umbrella and then tried to use it during a rainstorm.

Think It Over
Inferring What is the function of the ribs of an umbrella? How are the ribs of the umbrella similar to the bones in your skeleton? How are they different?

GUIDE FOR READING

◆ What main characteristic is shared by all vertebrates?
◆ How do vertebrates differ in the way in which they control body temperature?

Reading Tip As you read, write a definition, in your own words, of each boldfaced science term.

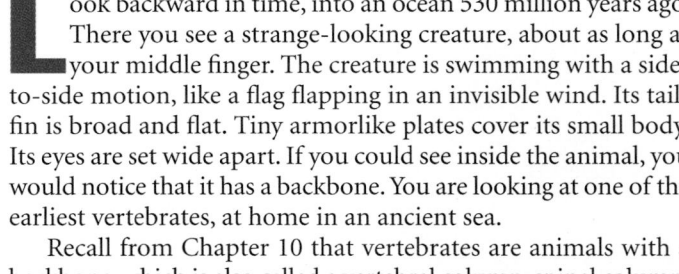

▼ Jawless fish

L ook backward in time, into an ocean 530 million years ago. There you see a strange-looking creature, about as long as your middle finger. The creature is swimming with a side-to-side motion, like a flag flapping in an invisible wind. Its tail-fin is broad and flat. Tiny armorlike plates cover its small body. Its eyes are set wide apart. If you could see inside the animal, you would notice that it has a backbone. You are looking at one of the earliest vertebrates, at home in an ancient sea.

Recall from Chapter 10 that vertebrates are animals with a backbone, which is also called a vertebral column, spinal column, or spine. Fishes were the first vertebrates to appear, and they still thrive today in Earth's waters. Other vertebrates include amphibians, such as frogs, and reptiles, such as snakes, as well as birds and mammals.

The Chordate Phylum

Vertebrates are a subgroup in the phylum Chordata. Members of this phylum, called **chordates** (KAWR daytz), share these characteristics: at some point in their lives, they have a notochord, a nerve cord, and slits in their throat area. The phylum name comes from the **notochord,** a flexible rod that supports the animal's back. Some chordates, like the lancelet in Figure 1, keep the notochord all their lives. Others, such as tunicates, have a notochord as larvae, but not as adults. In vertebrates, part or all of the notochord is

374

READING STRATEGIES

Reading Tip Before they write their definitions, encourage students to read the text definition at least twice and to examine any diagrams, illustrations, or photographs that might further clarify the term. (Sample: *cartilage*—the tough but bendable tissue that connects parts of a body.)

Program Resources

◆ **Unit 3 Resources** 12-1 Lesson Plan, p. 69; 12-1 Section Summary, p. 70

Media and Technology

 Audio CD English-Spanish Summary 12-1

replaced by a backbone. A few vertebrates have backbones made of **cartilage,** a connective tissue that is softer than bone, but flexible and strong. Most vertebrates have backbones made of hard bone.

Besides a notochord, all chordates have a nerve cord that runs down their back—your spinal cord is such a nerve cord. The nerve cord is the connection between the brain and the nerves, on which messages travel back and forth. Many other groups of animals—crustaceans and worms, for example—have nerve cords, but their nerve cords do not run down their backs.

In addition, chordates have slits in their throat area called pharyngeal (fayr uhn JEE uhl) slits. Fishes keep these slits as part of their gills for their entire lives, but in many vertebrates, including humans, pharyngeal slits disappear before birth.

☑ *Checkpoint* **What characteristics do all chordates share?**

The Backbone and Endoskeleton

A vertebrate's backbone runs down the center of its back. The backbone is formed by many similar bones, called **vertebrae** (singular *vertebra*), lined up in a row, like beads on a string. Joints between the vertebrae give the vertebral column flexibility. You are able to bend over and tie your sneakers partly because your backbone is flexible. Each vertebra has a hole in it that allows the spinal cord to pass through it. The spinal cord fits into the vertebrae like fingers fit into rings.

A vertebrate's backbone is part of an endoskeleton, or internal skeleton. The endoskeleton supports and protects the body, helps give it shape, and gives muscles a place to attach. In addition to the backbone, the vertebrate's endoskeleton includes

Figure 1 This lancelet exhibits all the typical characteristics of a chordate. It has a notochord that helps support its body, pharyngeal slits that help it to breathe, and a nerve cord.

Figure 2 The bodies of all vertebrates are supported by an endoskeleton with a backbone. *Comparing and Contrasting What are two ways in which the cow and chicken skeletons are similar? What are two ways in which they are different?*

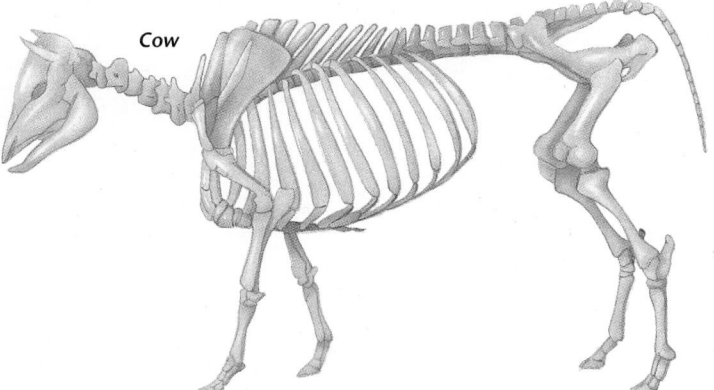
Cow

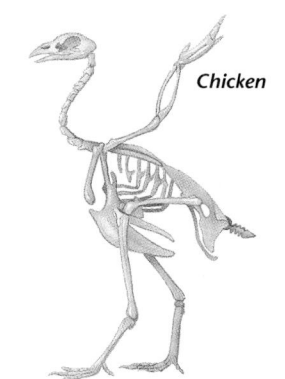
Chicken

Chapter 12 **375**

Media and Technology

▶ **Exploring Life Science Videodiscs**
Unit 3, Side 2,
"Backbones"

Chapter 3

▶ **Exploring Life Science Videodiscs**
Unit 3, Side 2,
"How Does
Everything Fit?"

Chapter 4

Answers to Self-Assessment

Caption Question

Figure 2 Both skeletons have backbones, ribs, legs. A chicken skeleton is small, has wings, and is built for standing on two legs, whereas a cow skeleton is large and is built for standing on four legs.

☑ *Checkpoint*

All chordates have a notochord, a nerve cord, and pharyngeal slits.

2 *Facilitate*

The Chordate Phylum

Demonstration

To help students visualize the notochord, give them semirigid plastic rulers. Allow students to manipulate the rulers to see that they have some flexibility, but not a lot. Explain that notochords, too, have some flexibility. **learning modality: kinesthetic**

The Backbone and Endoskeleton

Using the Visuals: Figure 2

Students whose comprehension of English is poor may not understand the text explanation of the relationship between the backbone and the endoskeleton. Instruct students to place a finger where the neck starts on the cow skeleton and trace along the vertebrae until they come to where the tail begins. Help them trace the backbone on the chicken skeleton. **limited English proficiency**

Ongoing Assessment

Drawing Provide students with unlabeled diagrams of vertebrate skeletons. Ask them to label the skull, backbone, and ribs.

The Backbone and Endoskeleton, continued

TRY THIS

Skills Focus making models
Materials *short lengths of string, enough beads to cover the length of the string*
Time 10 minutes
Tips Direct students to pack the beads tightly along the string. Ask: **What gives the beads and string flexibility?** *(The spaces between the beads)*
Making Models The string represents the spinal cord, and the beads represent the vertebrae.
Extend Have students tape or glue three consecutive beads together. Ask how this affects the flexibility of the model. *(The model is less flexible.)* Then ask students what might happen if three vertebrae in a person's backbone were fused. *(The person's back would be less flexible.)*
learning modality: kinesthetic

Maintaining Body Temperature

Building Inquiry Skills: Relating Cause and Effect

Materials *thermometer, two small cans, small bag of down feathers, string, 150-W light bulb and fixture*
Time 15 minutes

CAUTION: *Make sure students do not touch the light bulb.* Divide students into small groups. Give each group a thermometer, a cloth bag filled with down feathers, some string, and two small cans. Have students put the thermometer into one of the cans and place it under the light bulb. After about 5 minutes, record the temperature. Instruct students to tie the down-filled bag around the other can, put the thermometer in it, and place this can under the same source of heat for about 5 minutes. Record the temperature. Invite students to discuss why the two temperature readings were different. *(The feathers acted as insulation.)*
learning modality: logical/mathematical

TRY THIS

Bead-y Bones

You can use a string and beads to model the structure of a vertebrate's backbone.

1. Tie a large knot at one end of a piece of string.
2. Slide beads onto the string, stopping when there is just enough string left to tie another large knot.
3. Tie a knot in the unknotted end of the string.
4. Try to bend the string of beads at different places.

Making Models What does the string represent in your model? What do the beads represent?

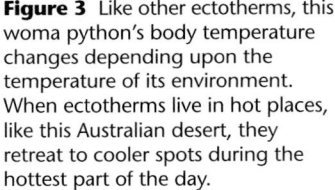

Figure 3 Like other ectotherms, this woma python's body temperature changes depending upon the temperature of its environment. When ectotherms live in hot places, like this Australian desert, they retreat to cooler spots during the hottest part of the day.

the skull and ribs. The skull protects the brain and sense organs. The ribs attach to the vertebrae and protect the heart, lungs, and other internal organs. Many vertebrates also have arm and leg bones adapted for a variety of movements.

A vertebrate's endoskeleton has several important characteristics. For one thing, unlike an arthropod's exoskeleton, it grows as the animal grows. It also forms an internal frame that supports the body against the downward pull of gravity, while allowing easy movement. Because of these endoskeleton characteristics, vertebrates can grow bigger than animals with exoskeletons or no skeletons at all.

☑ *Checkpoint* *What functions does a vertebrate's skeleton perform?*

Maintaining Body Temperature

One characteristic that distinguishes the major groups of vertebrates from one another is the way in which they control their body temperature. **Most fishes, amphibians, and reptiles have a body temperature that is close to the temperature of their environment. In contrast, birds and mammals have a stable body temperature that is typically much warmer than their environment.** Fishes, amphibians, and reptiles are ectotherms. An **ectotherm** is an animal whose body does not produce much internal heat—its body temperature changes depending upon the temperature of its environment. For example, when a turtle is lying in the sun on a riverbank, it has a higher body temperature than when it is swimming in a cool river. Ectotherms are sometimes called "coldblooded," but this term is misleading because the blood of ectotherms is often quite warm.

Figure 4 Though Antarctic winter temperatures can fall to −50°C, a dense coat keeps adult penguins warm. A thick, fluffy baby coat keeps a penguin chick warm until it gets its adult coat.
Inferring Do you think the emperor penguin is an ectotherm or an endotherm?

In contrast to a turtle, a beaver would have the same body temperature whether it was in cool water or on warm land. The beaver is a mammal, and mammals and birds are endotherms. An **endotherm** is an animal whose body controls and regulates its temperature by controlling the internal heat it produces. An endotherm's body temperature usually does not change much, even when the temperature of its environment changes.

Endotherms also have other adaptations, such as fur or feathers and sweat glands, for maintaining their body temperature. Fur and feathers keep endotherms warm on cool days. On hot days, on the other hand, some endotherms sweat. As the sweat evaporates, the animal is cooled. Because endotherms can keep their body temperatures stable, they can live in a greater variety of environments than ectotherms can.

Vertebrate History in Rocks

The information scientists have about early vertebrates comes from fossils. A **fossil** is the hardened remains or other evidence of a living thing that existed a long time in the past. Sometimes a fossil is an imprint in rock, such as an animal's footprint or the outline of a leaf. Other fossils are the remains of bones or other parts of living things—a chemical process has taken place in which the organism's tissues have become replaced by hard minerals. Because most living tissues decay rapidly, only a very few organisms become preserved as fossils.

Figure 5 The diagram shows fossils in sedimentary rock layers.
Interpreting Diagrams Which rock layer probably contains the oldest fossils? Explain.

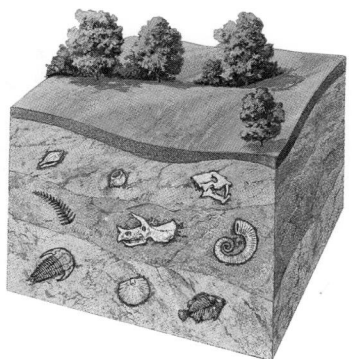

Program Resources

◆ **Unit 3 Resources** 12-1 Review and Reinforce, p. 71; 12-1 Enrich, p. 72

Media and Technology

 Transparencies "Vertebrate Evolution," Transparency 50

Answers to Self-Assessment

Caption Questions

Figure 4 The penguin is an endotherm.
Figure 5 The deepest rock layer probably contains the oldest fossils. In most cases, older layers are covered with newer layers of sedimentary rock.

☑ *Checkpoint*

It supports and protects the body, gives the body shape, and provides the muscles with places for attachment.

Addressing Naive Conceptions

Students may think that "coldblooded" animals are always cold. In fact, the body temperature of an ectotherm can be greater than that of the typical endotherm. The body temperature of an ectotherm reflects the temperature of its environment and whether it has been in the sun, shade, or underground. Point out that land-dwelling, "coldblooded" animals are rare in cold regions, but common in the tropics and other warm zones. Invite the class to speculate on why this might be so. Remind students that for ectotherms to keep their body temperatures high, they must have external sources of warmth. Lead students to understand that in winter in colder climates, the body temperature of an ectotherm would rarely reach a height sufficient for basic life processes.
learning modality: verbal

Vertebrate History in Rocks

Building Inquiry Skills: Calculating

Sedimentary deposits can be thousands of meters thick. For example, part of the Florida Peninsula consists of limestone deposits more than 4,000 meters thick. Ask students to consider the following: Suppose this limestone accumulated at a rate of 1 cm every 50 years. How many years did it take for 4,000 meters of limestone to accumulate? *(4,000 m × 100 cm/m × 50 yr/cm = 20 million years)*
learning modality: logical/mathematical

Ongoing Assessment

Drawing Have each student draw a picture of an ectotherm (except the turtle mentioned in the text) in an environment that would cause its body temperature to be high and that same animal in an environment that would lower its body temperature. These should be environments where the chosen animal might actually live.

 Students can save their drawings in their portfolios.

Vertebrate History in Rocks, continued

Including All Students

Materials *plastic jar with lid, marbles, pea gravel, sand, powdered clay*

Time 10 minutes

If students who lack proficiency in English have difficulty understanding the text description of sedimentary rock formation, this activity will help them understand the process. Students will simulate the effect of moving water on different sizes of rocks. Have students half-fill the jar with the pebbles, gravel, sand, and clay. Tell students these represent different sizes of rocks. Then, have them fill the jar with water and securely fasten the lid. Students should shake the jar until the solid contents are suspended. Then they should quickly set the jar down and record the order in which the materials settle to the bottom. *(Pebbles first, then the gravel, then the sand, then much later, the clay)* Ask: **What is the relationship between the size of the rock and the length of time it takes to settle?** *(The larger the rock, the faster it settles.)* **limited English proficiency**

Fossils occur most frequently in the type of rock known as sedimentary rock. **Sedimentary rock** is made of hardened layers of sediments—particles of clay, sand, mud, or silt. Sediments build up in many ways. For example, wind can blow a thick layer of sand onto dunes. Sediments can also form when muddy water stands in an area for a long time. Muddy sediment in the water will eventually settle to the bottom and build up.

Over a very long time, layers of sediments can be pressed and cemented together to form rock. As sedimentary rock forms, traces of living things that have been trapped in the sediments are sometimes preserved as fossils.

SCIENCE & History

Discovering Vertebrate Fossils

People have been discovering fossils since ancient times. However, it is only within the last few centuries that people have understood that fossils are the remains of organisms. Here are some especially important fossil discoveries.

1822
Dinosaur Tooth

In a quarry near Lewes, England, Mary Ann Mantell discovered a strange-looking tooth embedded in stone. Her husband Gideon drew the picture of the tooth shown here. The tooth belonged to the dinosaur *Iguanodon*.

| 1675 | 1725 | 1775 | 1825 |

1677
Dinosaur-Bone Illustration

Robert Plot, the head of a museum in England, published a book that had an illustration of a huge fossilized thighbone. Plot thought that the bone belonged to a giant human, but it probably was the thighbone of a dinosaur.

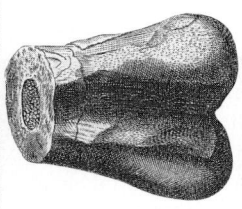

1811
Sea Reptile

Along the cliffs near Lyme Regis, England, 12-year-old Mary Anning discovered the fossilized remains of the giant sea reptile now called *Ichthyosaurus*. Mary became one of England's first professional fossil collectors.

378

Background

History of Science Aristotle recognized that fossils were evidence of past life, but he thought the organisms had grown in the rocks. During medieval times, from about A.D. 500 to 1500, the belief that Earth was created in six days led to the dismissal of fossils as simply odd mineral formations that happened to resemble living things by chance.

Leonardo da Vinci was one of the first scholars to understand how fossils were formed. He noticed that certain fossils he was studying not only looked like the live animal but also were buried in the rock in lifelike positions.

It was not until the late eighteenth century, when the English engineer William Smith recognized that certain fossils are limited to particular layers in the Earth's crust, that paleontology became the study of the development of organisms over time.

Scientists compare fossil structures to present-day organisms. This information, together with the fossil's approximate age, provides clues to the history of animal groups on Earth. If you look at Figure 6 on the next page, you will see that the pattern of vertebrate evolution looks something like a branching tree. Fossil evidence indicates that the earliest vertebrates were fishes, which first appeared about 530 million years ago. Amphibians are descended from fishes. Then, about 320 million years ago, amphibians gave rise to reptiles. Both mammals and birds, which you will learn about in Chapter 13, are descended from reptiles.

☑️ *Checkpoint* **What are two ways in which fossils form?**

In Your Journal

If you could interview the discoverer of one of these fossils, what questions would you ask about the fossil and how it was found? Write a list of those questions in your journal. Then use reference materials to try to find the answers to some of them.

1902
Tyrannosaurus

A tip from a local rancher sent Barnum Brown, a fossil hunter, to a barren, rocky area near Jordan, Montana. There Brown found the first relatively complete *Tyrannosaurus rex* skeleton.

1991
Dinosaur Eggs in China

Digging beneath the soil surface, a farmer on Green Dragon Mountain in China uncovered what may be the largest nest of fossil dinosaur eggs ever found. Here a paleontologist chips carefully to remove one of the eggs from the rock.

| 1875 | 1925 | 1975 | 2025 |

1861
Bird Bones

A worker in a stone quarry in Germany discovered *Archaeopteryx*, a feathered, birdlike animal that also had many reptile characteristics.

1964
Deinonychus

In Montana, paleontologist John Ostrom discovered the remains of a small dinosaur, *Deinonychus*. This dinosaur was probably a predator that could move rapidly. This fossil led scientists to hypothesize that dinosaurs may have been endotherms.

Chapter 12   **379**

Answers to Self-Assessment

☑️ *Checkpoint*

Fossils can form as impressions of living things or from the preserved remains of living things.

Media and Technology

 Exploring Life Science Videodisc
Unit 5, Side 2, "Fossils"

Chapter 1

 Exploring Life Science Videodisc
Unit 5, Side 2, "The Earth Library"

Chapter 3

SCIENCE & History

This *Science and History* feature presents a time line of major events in vertebrate paleontology. Help students relate these events to other events in world history. Have them reproduce the time line without the descriptive paragraphs, then add the following major events in world history:
◆ The signing of the Declaration of Independence (1776)
◆ The end of the American Civil War (1865)
◆ The end of World War II (1945)
◆ The first moon landing (1969)
◆ The breakup of the Soviet Union (1991)

Extend News of paleontological discoveries is often reported in newspapers. Ask students if they have read of recent discoveries that they might include on the time line. Suggest the discovery in China in 1996 of a *Sinosauropteryx*. This dinosaur was small and upright, with short arms covered with what look like feathers. The discovery of *Sinosauropteryx* is significant because the dinosaur may represent an intermediate form between dinosaurs and birds.

In Your Journal Students might ask the fossil discoverers questions such as these: Where and under what circumstances did you find the fossil? What did you think it was at first? What observations did you make later? Encourage students to share their questions and research with the class.
learning modality: visual

Ongoing Assessment

Writing Have students write paragraphs describing how sedimentary rock is formed.

 Students can save their paragraphs in their portfolios.

To help students understand the visual, ask: **Which evolved first, amphibians or reptiles?** (*Amphibians*) **When did mammals first evolve?** (*About 220 million years ago*) **learning modality: visual**

3 Assess

Section 1 Review Answers

1. The backbone supports the body, gives the body flexibility, and protects the spinal cord.

2. The body temperature of ectotherms (e.g., goldfish and frogs) changes depending on the temperature of the environment. Endotherms (e.g., robins and mice) have bodies that control internal body heat and therefore maintain nearly constant body temperatures.

3. Birds and mammals

4. Over time sedimentary rock can be pressed together to form rock. Traces of living things that have been trapped in the sediments can be preserved as fossils.

5. Endotherms would probably be more active at night, because they would not be slowed down by the drop in environmental temperature as much as ectotherms would be.

Science at Home

If a whole fish is available, encourage the student to examine the fish skeleton and to point out the backbone. Have the student note how the skeleton gives the fish its distinctive shape and how it forms the frame that protects the internal organs.

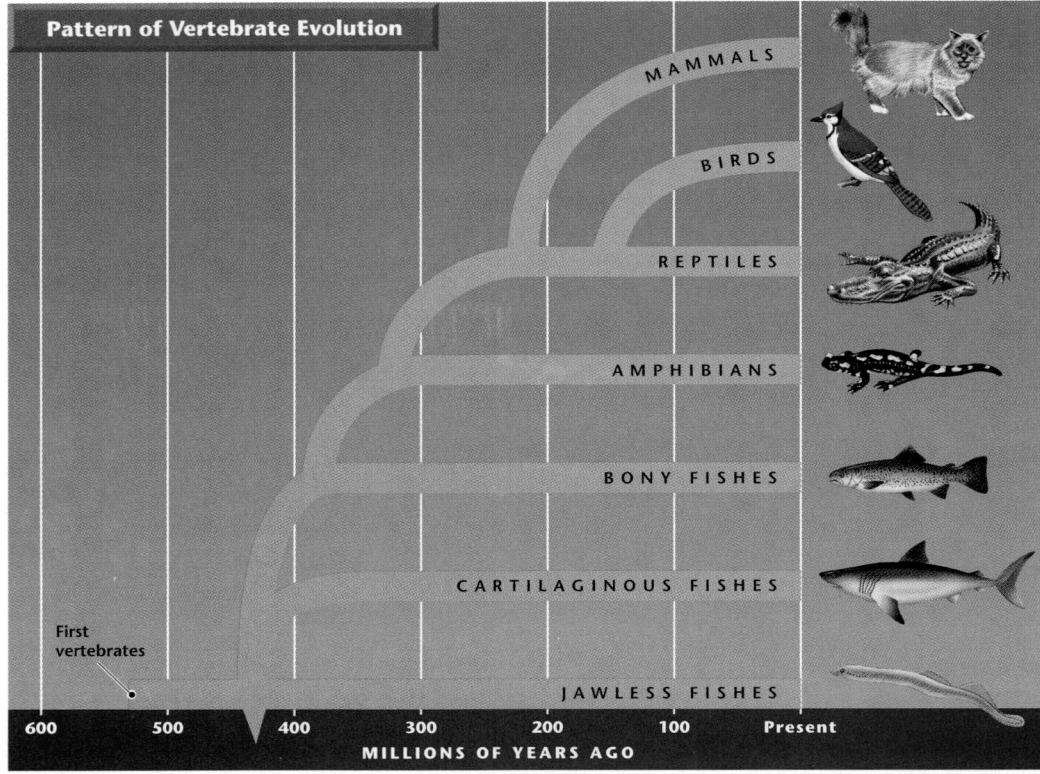

Pattern of Vertebrate Evolution

MAMMALS
BIRDS
REPTILES
AMPHIBIANS
BONY FISHES
CARTILAGINOUS FISHES
JAWLESS FISHES

First vertebrates

| 600 | 500 | 400 | 300 | 200 | 100 | Present |

MILLIONS OF YEARS AGO

Figure 6 The diagram shows the branching pattern of vertebrate evolution. The first vertebrates, the jawless fishes, arose about 530 million years ago. *Interpreting Diagrams About how much time passed between the time when fishes first appeared and the time that birds arose?*

Section 1 Review

1. What are three functions of a backbone?

2. Explain how ectotherms and endotherms differ in the way they control their body temperature. Give two examples of each.

3. What two groups of present-day vertebrates are the descendants of reptiles?

4. Describe how fossils form in sedimentary rock.

5. Thinking Critically Making Generalizations Would you expect ectotherms or endotherms to be more active at night? Explain your answer.

Science at Home

Focus on Backbones Have members of your family feel the tops of the vertebrae running down the center of their backs. Then have them feel the hard skull beneath the skin on their foreheads. If you have fish with bones for dinner, examine the fish skeleton with your family, pointing out the backbone. Show where the spinal cord runs through the vertebrae. Discuss the functions of the backbone and skull.

Performance Assessment

Drawing Have students sketch simple human skeletons and label the skull, ribs, backbone, vertebrae, and spinal cord. Then ask them to title their sketches "An Endotherm" or "An Ectotherm."

 Students can save their sketches in their portfolios.

Background

Facts and Figures One of the oldest known fossil chordates is called *Pikaia* (pee KY uh). It comes from the Burgess Shale of British Columbia and is about 530 million years old. Fossils of primitive chordates are very rare, because these animals had no hard parts. (Hard parts are more easily preserved.) Much of our understanding of early chordates comes from the study of such important fossils as *Pikaia*.

Answers to Self-Assessment

Caption Question

Figure 6 About 380 million years passed between the time when the fishes first appeared and the time that birds arose.

DISCOVER •••••••••••••••••••••••••••••••••••••**ACTIVITY**

How Does Water Flow Over a Fish's Gills?

1. Closely observe a fish in an aquarium for a few minutes. Note how frequently the fish opens its mouth. Water moves through the fish's mouth across its gills.

2. Notice the flaps on each side of the fish's head behind its eyes. Observe how the flaps open and close.

3. Observe the movements of the mouth and the flaps at the same time. Note any relationship between the movements of these two structures.

Think It Over

Observing What do the flaps on the sides of the fish do when the fish opens its mouth? What role do you think these two structures play in a fish's life?

In the warm waters of a coral reef, a fish called a moray eel hovers in the water, barely moving. A smaller fish, a wrasse, swims up to the moray and begins to eat tiny parasites that are attached to the moray's skin. Like a vacuum cleaner on a rug, the wrasse moves slowly over the moray eel, eating dead skin and bacteria as well as parasites. The wrasse even cleans inside the moray's mouth and gills. Both fishes benefit from this cleaning. The moray gets rid of parasites and other unwanted materials, and the wrasse gets a meal.

Both the wrasse and the moray it cleans belong to the vertebrate group known as fishes. A **fish** is a vertebrate that lives in the water and has fins, which are structures used for moving. In addition, most fishes are ectotherms, obtain oxygen through gills, and have scales. Scales are thin, overlapping plates that cover the skin of a fish. They are made of a hard substance similar to that of your fingernails.

Fishes make up the largest group of vertebrates—nearly half of all vertebrate species are fishes. Fishes have been swimming in Earth's waters for more than 500 million years—longer than any other kind of vertebrate has been on Earth.

GUIDE FOR READING

◆ How do fish use their gills?

◆ What are the three groups of fishes?

Reading Tip As you read about the different groups of fishes, make a table that compares and contrasts the characteristics of the groups.

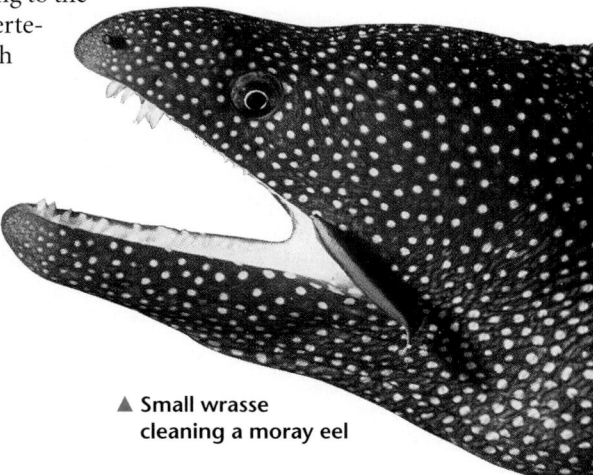

▲ Small wrasse cleaning a moray eel

READING STRATEGIES

Reading Tip Have students preview the headings of the section to identify the three groups of fishes. Ask volunteers to name the three groups and to suggest topics for rows in their tables. Students' tables must include jawless, cartilaginous, and bony fishes. Possible rows for the table include: Type of skeleton; Are jaws present?; Other characteristics; Examples.

Study and Comprehension Help students understand what they read by having them prepare a short lesson to teach other students. Allow students to choose jawless fishes, cartilaginous fishes, or bony fishes as topics for their lessons. Tell them they must use the information from the text.

SECTION
2 Fishes

Objectives

After completing this lesson, students will be able to
◆ explain how fish use their gills, move, feed, and reproduce;
◆ describe the three major groups of fish.

Key Terms fish, swim bladder, buoyant force

1 Engage/Explore

Activating Prior Knowledge

Encourage students to describe characteristics of fish they have observed either directly or indirectly. Ask questions such as: **What did the skin look like? What did the scales feel like? Where are the fins located?**

•••••••• **DISCOVER** ••••••••

Skills Focus observing
Materials *fish in an aquarium or fishbowl*
Time 10 minutes
Tips Use a larger fish, such as a goldfish, with gill movements that can be easily observed. Once the fish is calm, it will breathe with a regular rhythm. After observing the breathing for a while, students should be able to tell that the mouth and flaps open at the same time.
Expected Outcome Students should observe that when the fish opens its mouth, its gill flaps also open.
Extend Ask students to count the number of times the gill flaps open per minute. Direct them to work in pairs and compare their results with those of the other groups.
Think It Over The mouth and the gill flaps open at the same time. The mouth enables water to enter the fish and pass over the gills, which take in oxygen from the water. The flaps open to enable the water to leave.

2 Facilitate

Obtaining Oxygen

Addressing Naive Conceptions

Some students may not realize that gases such as oxygen and carbon dioxide can dissolve in liquids like water. To reinforce this concept, use the example of a carbonated beverage. Ask: **What happens when you pop the top on a soft drink?** (*Bubbles form.*) **learning modality: verbal**

Sharpen your Skills

Skills Focus
communicating
Materials *preserved fish, goggles, dissecting tray, blunt probe, hand lens, disposable gloves*
Time 50 minutes
Tips Provide gloves to all students. Help students see the connection between the mouth and gill slits by letting them pass the end of the probe into the fish's mouth and out through the gill openings. Students should wash their hands after handling the fish.
Extend Have students closely examine the feathery structure of the gills. Ask: **How is the structure of the gills related to their functions?** (*The feathery structure provides more surface area for absorbing oxygen.*) **learning modality: kinesthetic**

Moving and Feeding

Real-Life Learning

Encourage students who have fished before to tell the class about strategies they use to catch various types of fish. Ask: **What do you think people need to know about the feeding and hunting strategies of fish?** (*Sample answer: They must know about the feeding habits and habitats of the fish.*) **learning modality: verbal**

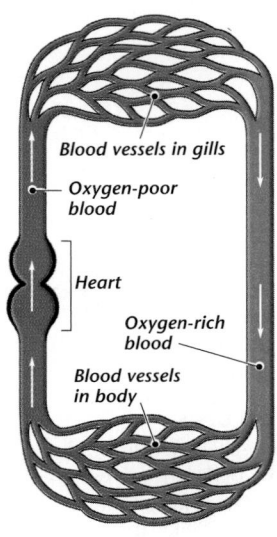

Blood vessels in gills

Oxygen-poor blood

Heart

Oxygen-rich blood

Blood vessels in body

Figure 7 Trace the path of blood through a fish's one-loop circulatory system. *Interpreting Diagrams* *Where does the blood pick up oxygen?*

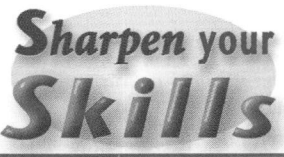

Sharpen your Skills

Communicating

Put on your goggles and disposable gloves. Observe a preserved fish. Note its size, shape, and the number and locations of its fins. Lift the gill cover and observe the gill with a hand lens. Make a diagram of your observations, and include a written description. Wash your hands.

Ask a classmate to check your work to make sure it clearly communicates what you observed. Then make any necessary improvements.

382

Obtaining Oxygen

Fishes get their oxygen from water. As a fish cruises along, it automatically opens its mouth, as you observed in the Discover activity, and takes a gulp of water. The water, which contains oxygen, moves through openings in the fish's throat region that lead to the gills. Gills, which look like tiny feathers, are red because of the many blood vessels within them. **As water flows over the gills, oxygen moves from the water into the fish's blood, while carbon dioxide, a waste product, moves out of the blood and into the water.** After flowing over the gills, water leaves the fish by flowing out through slits beneath the gill covers.

From the gills, the blood travels throughout the fish's body, supplying the body cells with oxygen. Like all vertebrates, fishes have a closed circulatory system, in which blood flows through blood vessels to all regions of the body. The heart of a fish pumps blood in one continuous loop—from the heart to the gills, from the gills to the rest of the body, and back to the heart. Trace this path in Figure 7.

Moving and Feeding

Fins help fish swim. A typical fin, such as those on the angelfish in Figure 8, consists of a thin membrane stretched across bony supports. Like a wide canoe paddle, a fin provides a large surface to push against the water. If you've ever swum wearing a pair of swim fins and noticed how much faster you move through the water, you understand the great advantage of the large surface of a fin.

Because fishes spend most of their time hunting for food or feeding, most of their movements are related to eating. The bodies of most fishes are adapted for efficient feeding. Some carnivores, such as barracuda, have sharp and pointed teeth—good for stabbing smaller fishes. Insect-eating fish, such as trout, have short, blunt teeth with which they grip and crush their prey. Filter feeders, such as basking sharks, use comblike structures on their gills to filter tiny animals and plants from the water.

A fish's highly developed nervous system and sense organs help it find food and avoid predators. Fishes can see much better in water than you can. Keen senses of touch, smell, and taste also help fishes capture food. A shark can smell and taste even a tiny amount of blood—as little as one drop in 115 liters of water! Some fishes have taste organs in unusual places; a catfish, for example, tastes with its whiskers.

☑ *Checkpoint* How does having fins help a fish?

Background

Facts and Figures Many different types of fishes are able to blend into their environment for protection. One example is the coloration of many of the fishes that swim in schools, such as tuna and sardines. Light penetrates only a short distance down in the water in the ocean. Past the point where the light penetrates, the water appears dark. So when predators look down at a school of fish, the dark color of the group of fish helps it blend in with the water's darkness. When predators deep in the ocean look up, they see the light of the sun, and they cannot distinguish the silvery bellies of the fish from the glare of the sun. The two-toned coloration of schooling fishes helps protect them from danger above and below.

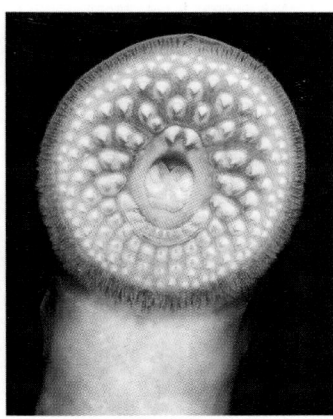

Figure 8 A fish's fins act as paddles to propel it through the water. You can clearly see the bone structure of a fin on the skeleton of an angelfish.

How Fishes Reproduce

Most fishes have external fertilization. Recall from Chapter 11 that in external fertilization, the eggs are fertilized outside of the female's body. The male hovers close to the female and spreads a cloud of sperm over the eggs as she releases them. Sharks and guppies, in contrast, have internal fertilization, in which the eggs are fertilized inside the female's body. The young fish then develop inside her body. When they are mature enough to live on their own, she gives birth to them.

Fishes Without Jaws

Biologists classify fishes into three major groups: jawless fishes, cartilaginous fishes, and bony fishes. They are distinguished from one another by the structure of their mouths and the types of skeletons they have. Jawless fishes were the earliest vertebrates. Today there are only about 60 species. Modern jawless fishes are unlike other fishes in that they have no scales. Their skeletons are made of cartilage, and they do not have pairs of fins. Most remarkably, they cannot bite like other fishes because their mouths do not have jaws! How can a fish without a jaw eat? The mouths of jawless fishes have structures for scraping, stabbing, and sucking.

Hagfishes and lampreys are the only kinds of jawless fishes. Hagfishes look like large, slimy worms. They crawl into the bodies of dead or dying fishes and use their sandpapery tongue to consume their decaying tissues. Many lampreys are parasites of other fishes. They attach their mouths to healthy fishes and then suck in the tissues and blood of their victims. If you look at the lamprey's mouth in Figure 9, you can probably imagine the damage it can do.

Figure 9 Lampreys are fish with eel-shaped bodies. They use their sharp teeth and suction-cup mouth to feed on other fish.
Classifying To what group of fishes do lampreys belong?

Program Resources

◆ **Unit 3 Resources** 12-2 Lesson Plan, p. 73; 12-2 Section Summary, p. 74
◆ **Laboratory Manual** 12, "Adaptations of Fish"

Media and Technology

 Audio CD English-Spanish Summary 12-2

Answers to Self-Assessment

Caption Questions

Figure 7 The blood picks up oxygen in the gills.
Figure 9 Lampreys are jawless fishes.

☑ *Checkpoint*

Fins work like paddles with a large surface. They push against the water and propel the fish.

How Fishes Reproduce

Building Inquiry Skills: Applying Concepts

Challenge students to make inferences about the advantages and disadvantages of external and internal fertilization in fishes. Ask volunteers to list on the board the advantages and disadvantages of each kind of fertilization. *(External fertilization: advantage—more offspring produced; disadvantage—lower survival rate. Internal fertilization: advantage— higher survival rate; disadvantage—fewer offspring produced)* **learning modality: verbal**

Fishes Without Jaws

Using the Visuals: Figure 9

Direct students to locate the mouth of the jawless fish in the figure. Have them describe the mouth. Ask them whether the lamprey's mouth looks like the mouths of fishes they are familiar with. *(Students will probably say no.)* Invite students to infer how the lamprey's specialized mouth helps it feed. Inform students that the lamprey feeds by attaching to a living fish, boring a hole in the fish's side, and eating the fluids that leak out. Its teeth help the lamprey stay attached to its host. **learning modality: verbal**

Ongoing Assessment

Writing Ask students to write several paragraphs that describe an hour in a fish's life. Students' paragraphs should include how the fish hunts for food and eludes predators. Encourage students to focus on how their fish uses its highly developed sense organs. Ask students to think about this question as they write: **How does a fish experience the world through its senses?**

 Students can save their paragraphs in their portfolios.

Cartilaginous Fishes

Building Inquiry Skills: Observing

Materials *partial skeleton from a whole chicken breast (cooked)*

Time 15 minutes

Allow students to work in small groups, to reduce the number of chicken breasts required. Before removing the skeleton from the breast, cut the cartilage away from the meat to ensure the cartilage stays with the bone when removed. Give a skeleton to each group, and direct students to distinguish between the bones and the cartilage. Tell them that the cartilage in the chicken breast is bluish-white; the bone is brown. Urge students to attempt to bend and twist both cartilage and bone. Circulate among groups to verify that students can distinguish between the two. Then have students write brief answers to the following questions.

- **Which is more flexible, bone or cartilage?** *(Cartilage)*
- **Which is more difficult to twist out of shape?** *(Bone)*
- **Which is more likely to break than to bend?** *(Bone)*

Extend Ask students to discuss how having a skeleton made of both bone and cartilage benefits the chicken. *(Bone is stronger than cartilage and so provides stronger support. Cartilage gives flexibility to some parts of the body.)* **cooperative learning**

Cultural Diversity

Cartilaginous is an adjective formed from the noun *cartilage*. English has many words like this. Have students find other examples in the text of an adjective and noun sharing the same root. *(oxygen— oxygenated; nerve—nervous; sense— sensory)* Invite nonnative English speakers to give examples from their own languages. **limited English proficiency**

Cartilaginous Fishes

Sharks, rays, and skates are cartilaginous (cahrt uhl AJ uh nuhs) fishes. As the group's name suggests, the skeletons of these fishes are made of cartilage, just like the skeletons of jawless fishes. However, unlike lampreys and hagfishes, cartilaginous fishes have jaws and pairs of fins. Pointed, toothlike scales cover their bodies, giving them a texture that is rougher than sandpaper. Cartilaginous fishes are all carnivores. Rays and skates live on the ocean floor, where they filter feed or hunt mollusks, crustaceans, and small fishes.

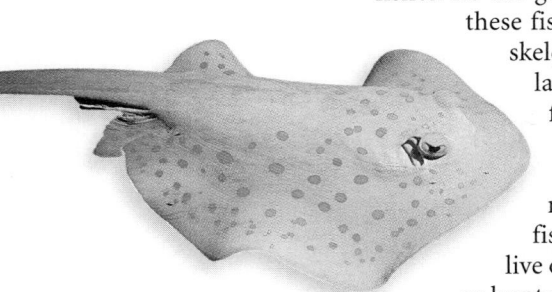

Figure 10 This blue-spotted ray is a cartilaginous fish that lives on the ocean floor. *Comparing and Contrasting How do cartilaginous fishes differ from jawless fishes?*

A Shark's Body Most shark bodies are streamlined so they can move quickly through the water. A shark's mouth is usually on the bottom part of its head. It contains jagged teeth arranged in rows. Most sharks use only the first couple of rows for feeding— the remaining rows are replacements. If a shark loses a front-row tooth, a tooth behind it moves up to replace it.

Always on the Move Most sharks cannot pump water over their gills. Instead they rely on swimming or currents to keep water moving across their gills. When sharks sleep, they position themselves in currents that send water over their gills.

Sharks spend most of their time hunting for food. They will attack and eat nearly anything that smells like food. Because they see poorly, sometimes they swallow strange objects. For example, one shark was found to have a raincoat, three overcoats, and an automobile license plate in its stomach.

☑ *Checkpoint* *Why must sharks always keep water moving over their gills?*

Figure 11 This sand tiger shark exhibits a very familiar shark trait—many sharp teeth. Despite this shark's ferocious appearance, however, sand tiger sharks do not typically attack humans.

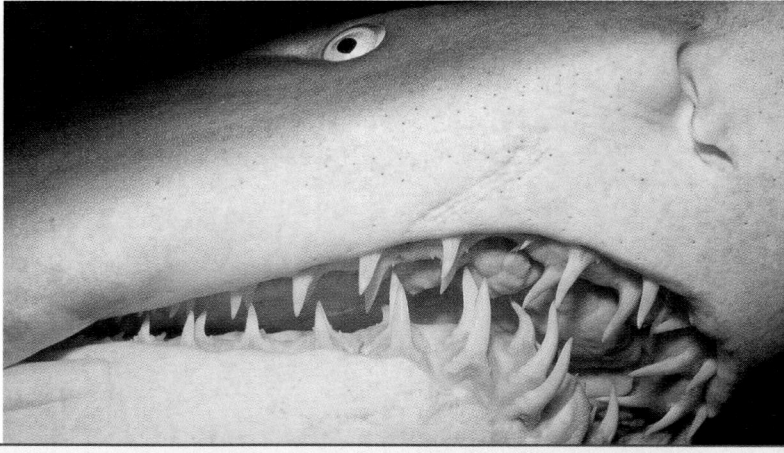

384

Background

Facts and Figures One part of a fish's sensory system consists of a canal called the lateral line that runs along the sides of the fish's body. This important groove can easily be seen in most bony fishes. The lateral line is covered with sensory hairs similar to the sensory hairs found in the inner ears of other vertebrates, including humans.

These hairs respond to the slight pressure changes caused by vibrations in the water. This enables a fish to detect changes in currents or water pressure. Predatory fishes can detect the slightest movement of prey with these sensitive organs. Their lateral lines allow them to hunt for food even if the water is murky.

Bony Fishes

Most familiar kinds of fishes, such as trout, tuna, and goldfish, have skeletons made of hard bone. Their bodies are covered with scales, and a pocket on each side of the head holds the fish's gills. Each gill pocket is covered by a flexible flap that opens to release water. To learn more about the major characteristics of bony fishes, look closely at the perch in *Exploring a Bony Fish*.

Swim Bladders and Buoyancy If you drop a brick into water,

 **INTEGRATING PHYSICS** it sinks to the bottom. A wooden block, in contrast, floats on the surface. Unlike the brick or the block, fishes neither sink nor float on the surface.

EXPLORING *a Bony Fish*

In a quiet, shady area near the bank of a stream or pond, you might find some yellow perch swimming along. These freshwater fish, which like slow-moving water, travel in groups called schools.

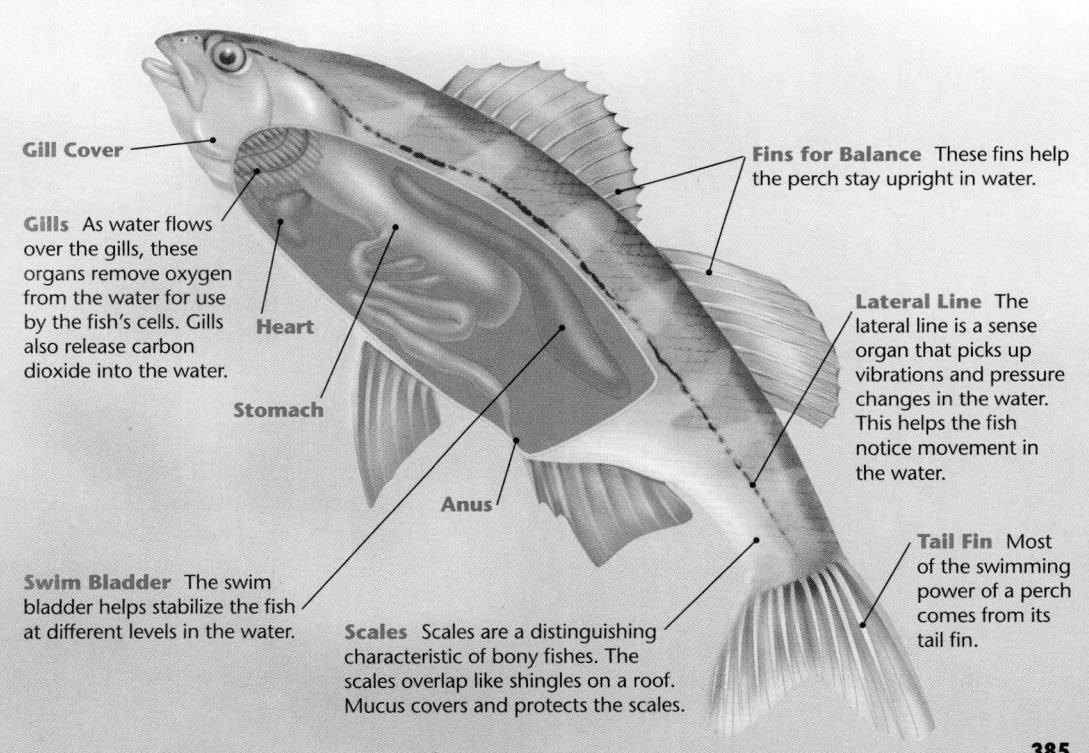

Gill Cover

Gills As water flows over the gills, these organs remove oxygen from the water for use by the fish's cells. Gills also release carbon dioxide into the water.

Heart

Stomach

Anus

Swim Bladder The swim bladder helps stabilize the fish at different levels in the water.

Scales Scales are a distinguishing characteristic of bony fishes. The scales overlap like shingles on a roof. Mucus covers and protects the scales.

Fins for Balance These fins help the perch stay upright in water.

Lateral Line The lateral line is a sense organ that picks up vibrations and pressure changes in the water. This helps the fish notice movement in the water.

Tail Fin Most of the swimming power of a perch comes from its tail fin.

385

Program Resources

◆ **Interdisciplinary Exploration Series** "Where River Meets Sea," pp. 13–14, 22–23

Media and Technology

 Transparencies "Exploring a Bony Fish," Transparency 51

Answers to Self-Assessment

Caption Question

Figure 10 Cartilaginous fishes have jaws and paired fins. Jawless fishes do not.

☑ *Checkpoint*

Because sharks cannot pump water over their gills, they must move through the water or rest in moving water in order to obtain oxygen.

Bony Fishes

EXPLORING

a Bony Fish

Direct students to explain the function of each structure shown in the visual. Then ask them to think of how the structures described in the visual accomplish that function. For example, ask: **How does the tail fin help the perch move through the water?** (*The tail fin provides a large surface to push against the water, propelling the fish.*) Choose pairs of students, and have them describe how they think each structure works.
learning modality: visual

Integrating Physics

ACTIVITY

Materials *small balloon, fishing weight, string, sink or bucket filled with water, ruler, watch or timer*
Time 30 minutes

Explore the concept of neutral buoyancy by challenging students to construct model swim bladders using the given materials. Students should work in pairs. One option is for pairs to partially inflate the balloon, tie it to the weight with a short piece of string, and immerse the model in a sink or aquarium. The goal is to have the balloon/weight combination hang motionless underwater—neither rising nor sinking. While one student immerses the model, the partner can measure the amount of time it takes for the model to either sink to the bottom or float to the top. If it does neither, the model has achieved neutral buoyancy. Even with a fairly heavy weight, students will find that the balloon will have to be inflated only slightly to achieve neutral buoyancy. **learning modality: kinesthetic**

Ongoing Assessment

Skills Check Have students infer what would happen to a shark in still water if the shark could not move. (*The shark would die, because it could not obtain oxygen.*)

Bony Fishes, continued

Building Inquiry Skills: Observing

ACTIVITY

Locate an aquarium or fishpond where students can conduct a scientific study of the behavior of fishes. Students should spend at least 10 minutes (more if possible) observing and recording interesting behavior. Suggest that students choose one species of fish to observe. Give them these questions to direct their observations:

◆ Is this a bony fish, a jawless fish, or a cartilaginous fish?
◆ How does the fish interact with its surroundings?
◆ What does it eat?
◆ How does it find food?
◆ How does it react to stimuli, such as sound?
◆ How does it interact with other fishes?
◆ What habitat does it seem to prefer?

Students will probably not be able to answer all the questions within the allotted time, but they may be able to devise strategies for answering them.

learning modality: visual

Figure 12 The photographs show just a few species of bony fishes. *Making Generalizations What characteristics do all of these fish have in common?*

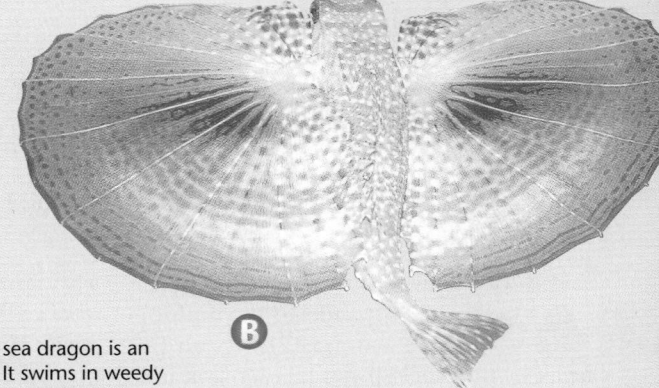

◀ **A.** The leafy sea dragon is an unusual fish. It swims in weedy bays and lagoons with its body in an upright position. And after mating, the male holds several hundred eggs in a pouch on his belly until they are ready to hatch.

▲ **B.** Flying gurnards are Atlantic Ocean fish that have winglike pectoral fins. Though flying gurnards do not really fly, they do use their "wings" for underwater gliding and for attracting mates.

Instead, they swim at different depths in the water. Most bony fishes have an organ called a **swim bladder,** an internal gas-filled sac that helps the fish stabilize its body at different depths.

A swim bladder is filled with oxygen, nitrogen, and carbon dioxide gases. The volume of gases in the swim bladder can become larger or smaller. This change in volume affects the buoyant force on the fish. **Buoyant force** (BOI uhnt force) is the force that water exerts upward on any underwater object. If the buoyant force on an object is greater than the weight of the object, then the object floats. If the buoyant force is less than the weight of the object, the object sinks. A brick sinks because it weighs more than the buoyant force pushing upward against it; a wooden block floats because it weighs less than the buoyant force.

A fish has greater buoyancy when the volume of gases in its swim bladder is large than when the gas volume is small. By adjusting its buoyancy as it moves in the water, a fish can float at different depths without using a large amount of energy.

Diversity of Bony Fishes Bony fishes, which make up about 95 percent of all fish species, live in both salt and fresh water. Some live in the lightless depths of the oceans, and seldom, if ever, come near the surface. Others thrive in light-filled waters, such as those of coral reefs or shallow ponds. Figure 12 shows some of the great variety of bony fishes.

☑ *Checkpoint* **If a pencil floats, how does the buoyant force on the pencil compare to the pencil's weight?**

386

Background

Facts and Figures Some fishes use their swim bladders to communicate. Special muscles located around the bladder tense and vibrate the membrane of the bladder. This membrane acts like the skin of a drum, producing very loud sounds. The sounds produced by the vibrating of the swim bladder can be carried over long distances through water. The sounds can be heard as a kind of drumming or thumping sound. One of the best "drummers" is the croaker, which is named for the sound it makes. It communicates with other croakers and uses its song to find mates. The sounds of many fishes can be heard in the ocean.

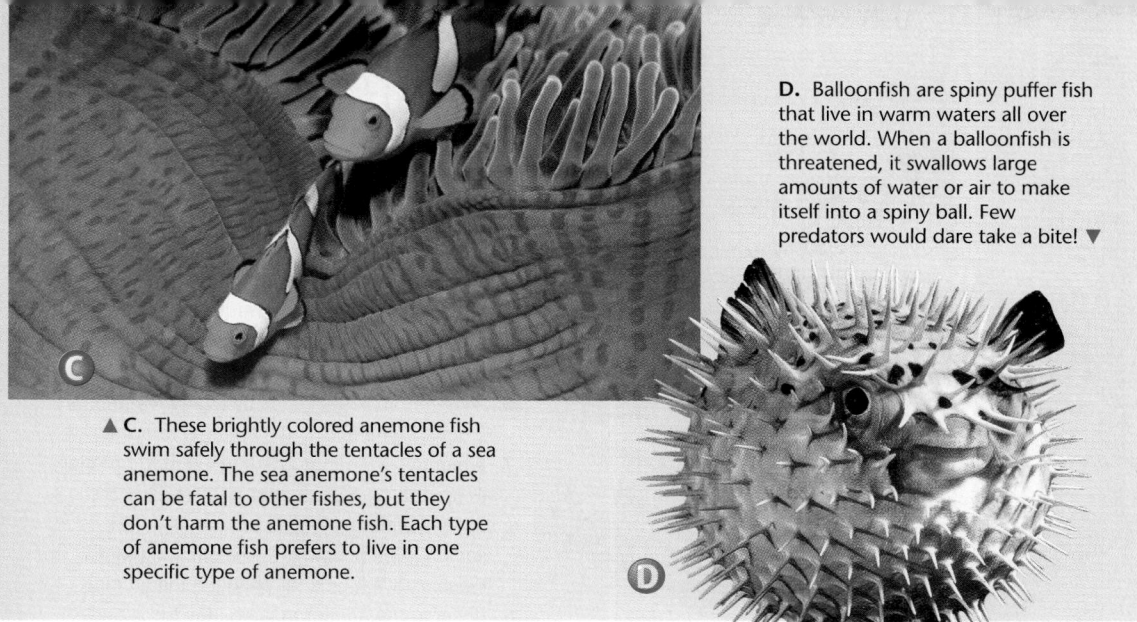

D. Balloonfish are spiny puffer fish that live in warm waters all over the world. When a balloonfish is threatened, it swallows large amounts of water or air to make itself into a spiny ball. Few predators would dare take a bite! ▼

▲ **C.** These brightly colored anemone fish swim safely through the tentacles of a sea anemone. The sea anemone's tentacles can be fatal to other fishes, but they don't harm the anemone fish. Each type of anemone fish prefers to live in one specific type of anemone.

Food for People

INTEGRATING ENVIRONMENTAL SCIENCE People used to think of oceans and rivers as having a limitless supply of fish. Recently, though, overfishing has drastically reduced populations of the Atlantic codfish, Pacific salmon, and many other fish species. Some countries are trying to stop overfishing. The United States, Canada, and other countries have recently set limits on the amounts of certain kinds of fish that can be caught. In addition, some fishes, such as catfish, are being raised in "fish farms." This practice reduces the demand for fish caught in rivers and oceans.

Section 2 Review

1. Could a fish obtain oxygen if it could not open its mouth? In explaining your answer, describe the role of the fish's gills.
2. How is a shark's skeleton different from a perch's?
3. Describe the ways in which two different fishes are adapted to obtain food.
4. **Thinking Critically** **Predicting** How might a shark's hunting be affected if it were unable to smell?

Check Your Progress
CHAPTER PROJECT
By now you should have decided on the adaptation that you want to model. Select a specific fish in which to model this adaptation. Reference books, software, and magazine articles can help you make this choice. Then assemble your materials and build your model. *(Hint: You might want to go to a pet store to observe how fish and other vertebrates move.)*

Program Resources

◆ **Unit 3 Resources** 12-2 Review and Reinforce, p. 75; 12-2 Enrich, p. 76

Answers to Self-Assessment

Caption Question
Figure 12 All the fishes have bony skeletons and swim bladders. Their bodies are covered with scales, and their gills are in flap-covered pockets on each side of the head.

☑ *Checkpoint*
The buoyant force is greater than the weight of the pencil.

Food for People

Integrating Environmental Science

Encourage students to brainstorm other ways to stop overfishing. Ideas could include catch-and-release fishing and fishing bans. **learning modality: verbal**

3 Assess

Section 2 Review Answers
1. No, because water gets to the gills through the mouth. The gills remove oxygen from water.
2. The shark's skeleton is made entirely of cartilage. The perch's is made mostly of bone.
3. Answers will vary. Sample: The barracuda has long, sharp teeth with which it can capture prey. The lamprey has sharp teeth and a suction mouth that allow it to attach itself to a host fish and feed on the host's blood and tissue.
4. A shark that could not smell would be able to hunt only animals that it could see. But because sharks do not have very good vision, the shark would not be able to capture as much prey.

Check Your Progress
CHAPTER PROJECT
Review and approve students' adaptation and fish choices. Make sure that the adaptation they have chosen can be easily modeled for the fish and for an amphibian and a reptile. Help students locate reference sources and materials.

Performance Assessment

Concept Mapping Have each student draw a concept map to show the three main types of fish, their characteristics, and examples.

How It Works

Home Sweet Home

Preparing for Inquiry

Key Concept Organisms need specific habitats in order to survive.

Skills Objective Students will be able to
◆ make a model habitat.

Time 30 minutes to set up, then 10 minutes per day for two weeks

Advance Planning
◆ Provide sufficient clean water for all groups. The chlorine may be removed by letting the water stand for two or three days or by treatment with a special chemical available at pet shops.
◆ Make sure other supplies are thoroughly clean. Do not use soap.

Alternative Methods A large fishbowl can be used in place of an aquarium.

Guiding Inquiry

Troubleshooting the Experiment
◆ Keep plenty of chlorine-free water available to add to the tank.
◆ Remove dead organisms and waste immediately. Do not overfeed fish.

Expected Outcome After a day or two, if the animals have adapted, the snails should be moving about the tank feeding. The fish should be swimming normally and feeding.

Analyze and Conclude
1. **a.** From air entering through the filter and oxygen from plants **b.** From the heater or sunlight **c.** From the plants and students
2. The oxygen is used by the fish. Plants release oxygen, and oxygen in air enters through the filter.
3. In an aquarium, ideal conditions are maintained artificially. In nature, animals have to locate their own food and avoid prey.

Extending Inquiry

More to Explore Questions might include: Will the new fish prey on the guppies? Is there enough space?

Home Sweet Home

For an artificial environment to work, it must meet the needs of the organisms that live in it. In this lab, you will build an aquarium for guppies, whose natural environment is warm, fresh water.

Problem

How does an aquarium enable fish to survive?

Skills Focus

making models, posing questions

Materials

gravel	metric ruler	guppies
snails	guppy food	dip net
tap water	thermometer	water plants
aquarium filter	aquarium heater	

rectangular aquarium tank (15 to 20 liters) with cover

Procedure

1. Wash the aquarium tank with lukewarm water—do not use soap. Then place it on a flat surface in indirect sunlight.
2. Rinse the gravel and spread it over the bottom of the tank to a depth of about 3 cm.
3. Fill the tank about two-thirds full with tap water. Position several water plants in the tank by gently pushing their roots into the gravel. Wash your hands after handling the plants.
4. Add more water until the level is about 5 cm from the top.

5. Place the filter in the water and turn it on. Insert an aquarium heater into the tank, and turn it on. Set the temperature to 25°C. **CAUTION:** *Do not touch electrical equipment with wet hands.*
6. Allow the water to "age" by letting it stand for 2 days. Aging allows the chlorine to evaporate.
7. When the water has aged and is at the proper temperature, add guppies and snails to the tank. Include one guppy and one snail for each 4 liters of water. Cover the aquarium. Wash your hands after handling the animals.
8. Observe the aquarium every day for 2 weeks. Feed the guppies a small amount of food daily. Look for evidence that the fish and snails have adapted to their new environment. Also look for the ways they carry out their life activities, such as feeding and respiration. Record your observations.
9. Use a dip net to keep the gravel layer clean and to remove any dead plants or animals.

Analyze and Conclude

1. How does the aquarium meet the following needs of the organisms living in it: (a) oxygen supply, (b) proper temperature, and (c) food?
2. What happens to the oxygen that the fish take in from the water in this aquarium? How is that oxygen replaced?
3. **Apply** How is an aquarium like a guppy's natural environment? How is it different?

More to Explore

Write a plan for adding a different kind of fish to the aquarium. Include a list of questions that you would need to have answered before you could carry out your plan. Get the approval of your teacher before going ahead with your plan.

Safety

An aquarium with water in it should never be moved. Students should be careful carrying the empty aquariums. They should make sure that the area around the tank is dry and that their hands are dry before they plug in the electrical equipment. Review the safety guidelines in Appendix A.

Program Resources

◆ **Unit 3 Resources** Chapter 12 Real-World Lab, pp. 85–86

DISCOVER ··· ACTIVITY

What's the Advantage of Being Green?

1. Count out 20 dried yellow peas and 20 green ones. Mix them up in a paper cup.

2. Cover your eyes. Have your partner gently scatter the peas onto a large sheet of green paper.

3. Uncover your eyes. Have your partner keep time while you pick up as many peas, one at a time, as you can find in 15 seconds.

4. When 15 seconds are up, count how many peas of each color you picked up.

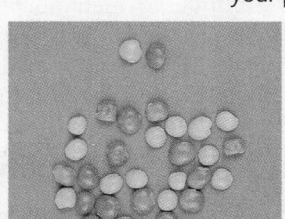

5. Repeat Steps 2 through 4, but this time you scatter the peas and keep time while your partner picks up the peas.

6. Compare your results with those of your partner and your classmates.

Think It Over
Inferring Many frogs are green, and the environment in which they live is mostly green. What advantage does a frog have in being green?

I f you walk through a damp, wooded area in the Northeast, you may be surrounded by them. But chances are good that you'll never see one. During the day, they hide in holes in the ground and cracks in rocks. At night they scramble over the decaying leaves on the forest floor, searching for food. Some climb to the tops of bushes and rocks to find their prey. What are these creatures that roam by night? They are red-backed salamanders.

Most of these slender, long-tailed animals are only as long as your longest finger. They are small, but there are a lot of them. Some northeastern woodlands probably have more red-backed salamanders than all birds and mammals combined.

GUIDE FOR READING

◆ What is the life cycle of an amphibian like?

◆ How are amphibians adapted for movement on land?

Reading Tip Before you begin to read, write two or three things you already know about amphibians. After you have read this section, add three things you have learned.

Figure 13 Red-backed salamanders are the most common amphibians in some damp northeastern woodlands.

Chapter 12 **389**

READING STRATEGIES

Reading Tip Students may not be aware that they know anything about amphibians. If they are not familiar with the term, ask them to write a few things they know about frogs or salamanders. Have them also write one thing they would like to know. (Samples: frogs are comfortable in water as well as on land. I wonder how long frogs can survive on land.)

Program Resources

◆ **Unit 3 Resources** 12-3 Lesson Plan, p. 77; 12-3 Section Summary, p. 78

Media and Technology

 Audio CD English-Spanish Summary 12-3

SECTION
3 Amphibians

Objectives

After completing this lesson, students will be able to
◆ describe the characteristics of amphibians and their life cycles;
◆ explain how amphibians are adapted for land and current threats to their survival;
◆ identify and describe the groups of amphibians.

Key Terms amphibian, atrium, ventricle, habitat

1 Engage/Explore

Activating Prior Knowledge

Ask students: **Do you know of any animals that live part of their life in water and part of their life on land?** (*Students may say frogs, toads, or salamanders.*) **What characteristics allow these animals to do this?** (*Students may mention different life stages or specialized breathing organs.*) Make a list of answers on the board. Re-examine this list after students have completed this section.

········ DISCOVER ········

Skills Focus inferring
Materials *dried yellow and green peas; paper cup; green construction paper, approximately 1 m × 1 m; clock or watch with second hand*
Time 10 minutes
Tips To intensify the camouflage effect, make sure that the green background closely matches the color of the green peas. Tell students to toss the peas gently onto the paper, so the peas do not scatter onto the floor.
Expected Outcome Students should pick up more yellow peas than green peas from the green background.
Think It Over Being a color that blends in with the environment makes it more difficult for frogs to be seen by predators. Thus it is more likely that they will survive and reproduce.

2 Facilitate

Gills to Lungs

Building Inquiry Skills: Inferring

Once students are familiar with amphibian metamorphosis, ask: **Why is water essential for amphibian life?** *(Their eggs are laid and hatch in water. Their larvae live in water. Adult amphibians need to stay moist in order to absorb oxygen through their skin.)* Then ask: **How does acquiring lungs change the life of amphibians?** *(They are able to leave the water, breathe air, and live on land.)* **learning modality: verbal**

Amphibian Circulation

Including All Students

Materials *25 red balloons*
Time 5 minutes

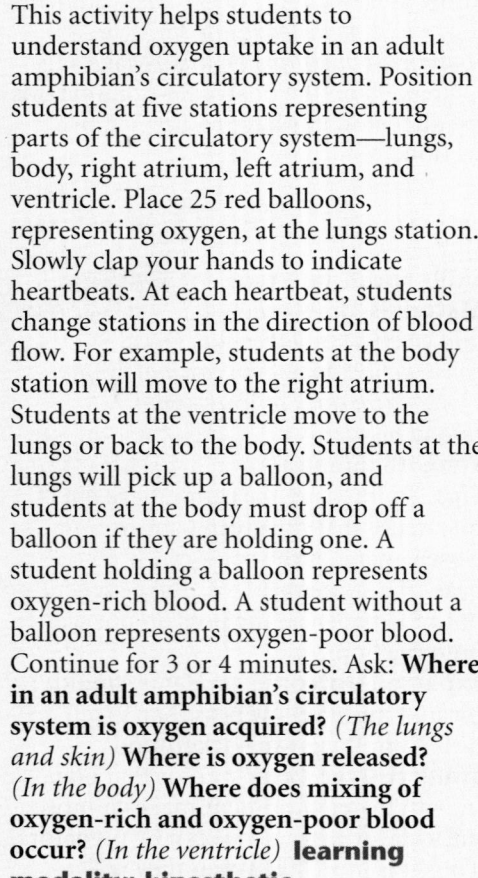

This activity helps students to understand oxygen uptake in an adult amphibian's circulatory system. Position students at five stations representing parts of the circulatory system—lungs, body, right atrium, left atrium, and ventricle. Place 25 red balloons, representing oxygen, at the lungs station. Slowly clap your hands to indicate heartbeats. At each heartbeat, students change stations in the direction of blood flow. For example, students at the body station will move to the right atrium. Students at the ventricle move to the lungs or back to the body. Students at the lungs will pick up a balloon, and students at the body must drop off a balloon if they are holding one. A student holding a balloon represents oxygen-rich blood. A student without a balloon represents oxygen-poor blood. Continue for 3 or 4 minutes. Ask: **Where in an adult amphibian's circulatory system is oxygen acquired?** *(The lungs and skin)* **Where is oxygen released?** *(In the body)* **Where does mixing of oxygen-rich and oxygen-poor blood occur?** *(In the ventricle)* **learning modality: kinesthetic**

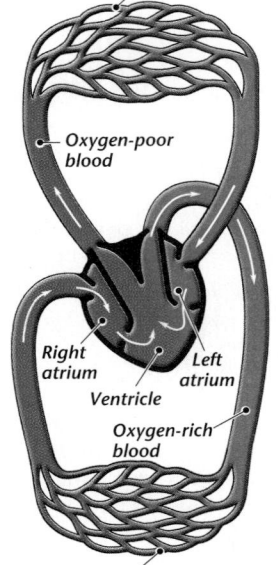

Figure 14 An adult amphibian's circulatory system has two loops. One loop runs from the heart to the lungs and back, and the second runs from the heart to the body and back.

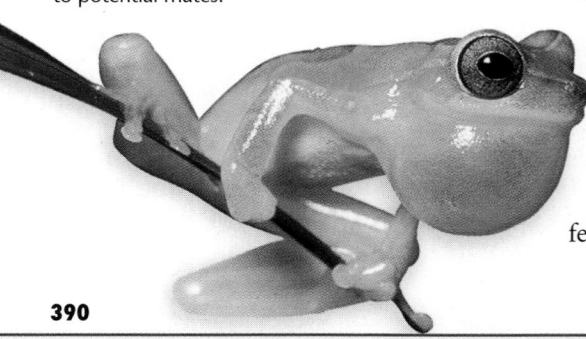

Figure 15 The throat of this "peeper" inflates as he calls out to potential mates.

390

Gills to Lungs

The red-backed salamander is one kind of amphibian; frogs and toads are others. An **amphibian** is an ectothermic vertebrate that spends its early life in water. The word *amphibian* means "double life," and amphibians have exactly that. **After beginning their lives in the water, most amphibians spend their adulthood on land, returning to water to reproduce.**

Most amphibians lay their eggs in water. Amphibian eggs hatch into larvae that swim and have gills for obtaining oxygen. As they undergo metamorphosis and become adults, most amphibians lose their gills and acquire lungs. Adult amphibians also obtain oxygen and get rid of carbon dioxide through their thin, moist skin.

Amphibian Circulation

The circulatory system of a tadpole—the larval form of a frog or toad—has a single loop, like that of a fish. In contrast, the circulatory system of many adult amphibians has two loops. In the first loop, blood flows from the heart to the lungs and skin, and picks up oxygen. This oxygen-rich blood then returns to the heart. In the second loop, the blood flows to the rest of the body, delivering oxygen-rich blood to the cells.

As you read about the heart, trace the path of blood through the amphibian's circulatory system shown in Figure 14. The hearts of most amphibians have three inner spaces, or chambers. The two upper chambers of the heart, called **atria** (singular *atrium*), receive blood. One atrium receives oxygen-rich blood from the lungs, and the other receives oxygen-poor blood from the rest of the body. From the atria, blood moves into the lower chamber, the **ventricle,** which pumps blood out to the lungs and body. Oxygen-rich and oxygen-poor blood mix in the ventricle.

✓ *Checkpoint* Compare the functions of the atria and ventricle.

Reproduction and Development

On spring evenings near a lake or pond, you can usually hear a loud chorus of "peepers," male frogs calling to attract mates. Most frogs and toads have external fertilization—a female frog releases eggs that are then fertilized by the male's sperm. In contrast, most salamanders have internal fertilization—the eggs are fertilized before they are laid.

390

Amphibian eggs are coated with clear jelly that keeps moisture in and helps protect them from infection. Inside each fertilized egg, a tiny embryo develops. In a few days, larvae wriggle out of the jelly and begin a free-swimming, fishlike life.

Most amphibian parents don't take care of their eggs after fertilization, but some do. For example, in one species of South American river toad, the male presses the fertilized eggs into the skin of the female's back. Skin grows over the eggs, and the young go through the tadpole stage beneath their mother's skin, safe from predators. Tiny toads eventually emerge from her skin.

Most amphibians undergo metamorphosis. Trace the process of frog metamorphosis in Figure 16. Hind legs appear first, accompanied by changes in the skeleton, circulatory system, and digestive system. Later the front legs appear. At about the same time, the tadpole loses its gills and starts to breathe with its lungs.

Unlike the tadpoles of frogs and toads, the larvae of salamanders resemble the adults. Most salamander larvae undergo a metamorphosis in which they lose their gills. However, the changes are not as dramatic as those that happen during frog and toad metamorphosis.

Figure 16 During its metamorphosis from tadpole to adult, a frog's body undergoes a series of dramatic changes. *Applying Concepts How do these changes prepare a frog for life on land?*

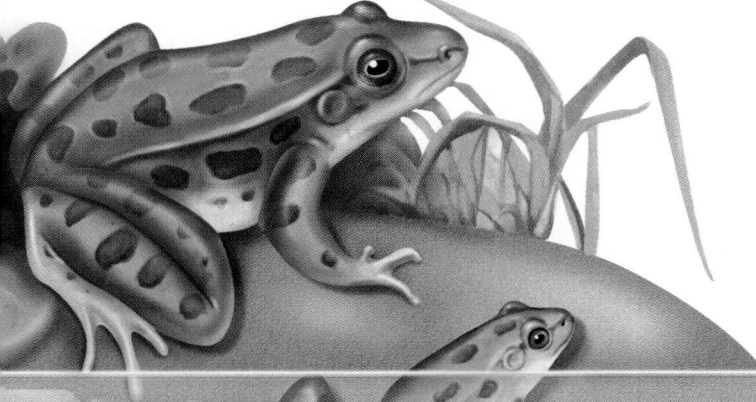
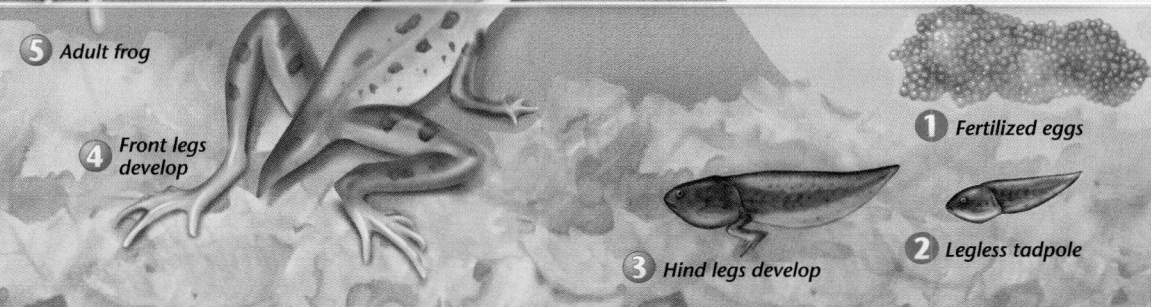

5 Adult frog

4 Front legs develop

3 Hind legs develop

2 Legless tadpole

1 Fertilized eggs

Language Arts
CONNECTION

When a tadpole becomes an adult frog, it moves to an unfamiliar location—a land environment that is very different from the watery one in which it has been living. While real tadpoles need no instructions for how to accomplish this move, you are about to write an imaginary guidebook for tadpoles that prepares them for their move onto land.

In Your Journal

First, brainstorm what types of information might be useful to the tadpole, such as how solid ground is different from water and where a frog might find food. Then choose four or five of your ideas and write a brief suggestion for each. Write in a lively way, using descriptive language.

Reproduction and Development

Using the Visuals: Figure 16
The stages of frog development are shown from right to left. This could possibly be confusing to students who are accustomed to reading from left to right. Have students trace the stages of development from right to left, stating at least one change at each stage. For example, they might trace from stage four to five and say "tail disappears." **learning modality: visual**

Language Arts
CONNECTION

Group students who are learning English with those who are native speakers to discuss issues that their guidebooks should address. You may want to supply students with sample travel guidebooks to show the kinds of information they contain. Review the challenges animals face, such as supporting their weight, breathing air, and retaining moisture. Encourage students to see the humor in writing a guidebook for amphibians; use this activity to promote fun and creativity.

In Your Journal Before students begin to write, discuss a sample journal entry and give them examples of lively writing. **limited English proficiency**

Media and Technology

Transparencies "Frog Metamorphosis," Transparency 52

Answers to Self-Assessment
Caption Question
Figure 16 These changes prepare a frog to breathe air and move about on land.

☑ *Checkpoint*
The atria receive blood from the lungs and body. The ventricle pumps blood to the lungs and body.

Getting Around on Land

Materials *plastic bags, heavy rubber
bands, pail of water or sink*
Time 15 minutes
Tips Make sure that students insert only
their fingers into the water. No part of
their palm should be under water as it
will provide too much resistance.
Encourage students to experiment with
moving their bagged hands through the
water with their fingers spread as wide as
possible and with their hands balled into
a fist. Collect bags and rubber bands
after use. Ask students to explain how
their hand in the plastic bag is like a
frog's webbed foot. (*The plastic acts like
the web between the frog's toes.*)
Extend Ask: **How do some kinds of
birds benefit from webbed feet?** (*These
birds spend some part of their lives in
water, and webbed feet help them move
round there.*) **learning modality:
kinesthetic**

Frogs and Toads

Including All Students

You may wish to have students obtain
additional information about frogs and
toads from the Internet, local zoos, or
pet shops. **learning modality: visual**

Addressing Naive Conceptions

Ask students if they have heard that
someone who touches a toad will get
warts. Explain that this belief is merely a
superstition—touching a toad's skin will
not cause warts. Ask: **Can you think of
any reasons why this superstition came
about?** (*Toads' skin is bumpy and looks
"warty." People assumed that toads'
"warts" were contagious. Though toads
don't cause warts, their secretions can
irritate skin, sometimes severely.*)
**learning modality: logical/
mathematical**

Webbing Through Water

How does
having webbed feet make it
easier to swim?

1. Fill a sink or pail with water.
2. Spread your fingers and put
   your hand into the water
   just far enough so that only
   your fingers are underwater. Drag your fingers
   back and forth through the
   water.
3. Take your hand out of the
   water and dry it. Put a small
   plastic bag over your hand.
   Secure it around your wrist
   with a rubber band.

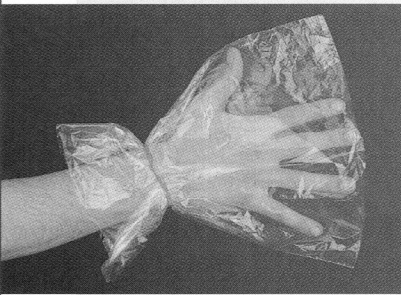

4. Repeat Step 2. Note any
   difference in the way in
   which your fingers push the
   water.

Making Models Use your
model to explain how a frog's
webbed feet help it move
through water.

Getting Around on Land

Because it is not supported by water's buoyancy, a land animal
needs a strong skeleton to support its body against the pull of
gravity. In addition, a land animal needs some way of moving.
Fins work in water, but they don't work on land. **Most adult
amphibians have strong skeletons and muscular limbs
adapted for movement on land.** Amphibians were the first
vertebrates to have legs.

The eyes of amphibians are adapted to life on land. A
transparent membrane helps keep them from drying out.
Amphibians also have eyelids. Unlike fishes and tadpoles, whose
wide-open eyes are always bathed in water, adult amphibians can
close their eyes.

Frogs and Toads

When most people hear the word *amphibian*, they first think of
frogs and toads—amphibians that are adapted for hopping and
leaping. This kind of movement requires powerful hind-leg
muscles and a skeleton that can absorb the shock of landing.
The feet of frogs and toads have other adaptations, too. The
webbed feet and long toes of bullfrogs form swim fins that help
the frogs dart through the water. Tree frogs have toe pads with
adhesive suckers that provide secure holds as the frogs leap from
twig to twig.

It is usually easy to distinguish a frog from a toad. The skin
of a frog is smooth and very moist, while that of a toad is drier
and bumpy. Many toads have large lumps behind their eyes.
These are actually skin glands that ooze a poisonous liquid when
the toad is attacked by a predator such as a raccoon.

Although most tadpoles are herbivores, most adult frogs and
toads are predators that feed on insects or other small animals.
Insects don't usually see the frogs and toads that prey on them,
because many frogs and toads are colored in such a way that they
blend in with their environment. Green frogs, such as the one
shown in *Exploring a Frog*, are brownish-green, making them hard
to see in the ponds and meadows where they live. If you did the
Discover activity, you learned that it is hard to see something green
against a green background. Besides concealing frogs and toads
from prey, their coloring also helps protect them from enemies.

☑ *Checkpoint* How can you tell a frog from a toad?

Salamanders

Salamanders are amphibians that keep their tails as adults. Their
bodies are long and usually slender. Unlike frogs and toads, the

Background

Facts and Figures Some salamanders live
in underground streams that flow through
caves. Over millions of years, these unusual
salamanders acquired adaptations that
enabled them to survive in the dark
conditions of their environment. As with
many cave-dwelling animals, a sense of sight
would be of little value to the salamanders.

Thus their eyesight is weak. Because they are
not exposed to sunlight, their skin has no
need for protection from the sun and has
little pigment. In some species, the skin is
transparent, and the salamander's internal
organs can be seen through the skin. Cave
salamanders have become highly specialized
to survive in their own caves.

EXPLORING a Frog

G reen frogs are common throughout the eastern United States and southeastern Canada.

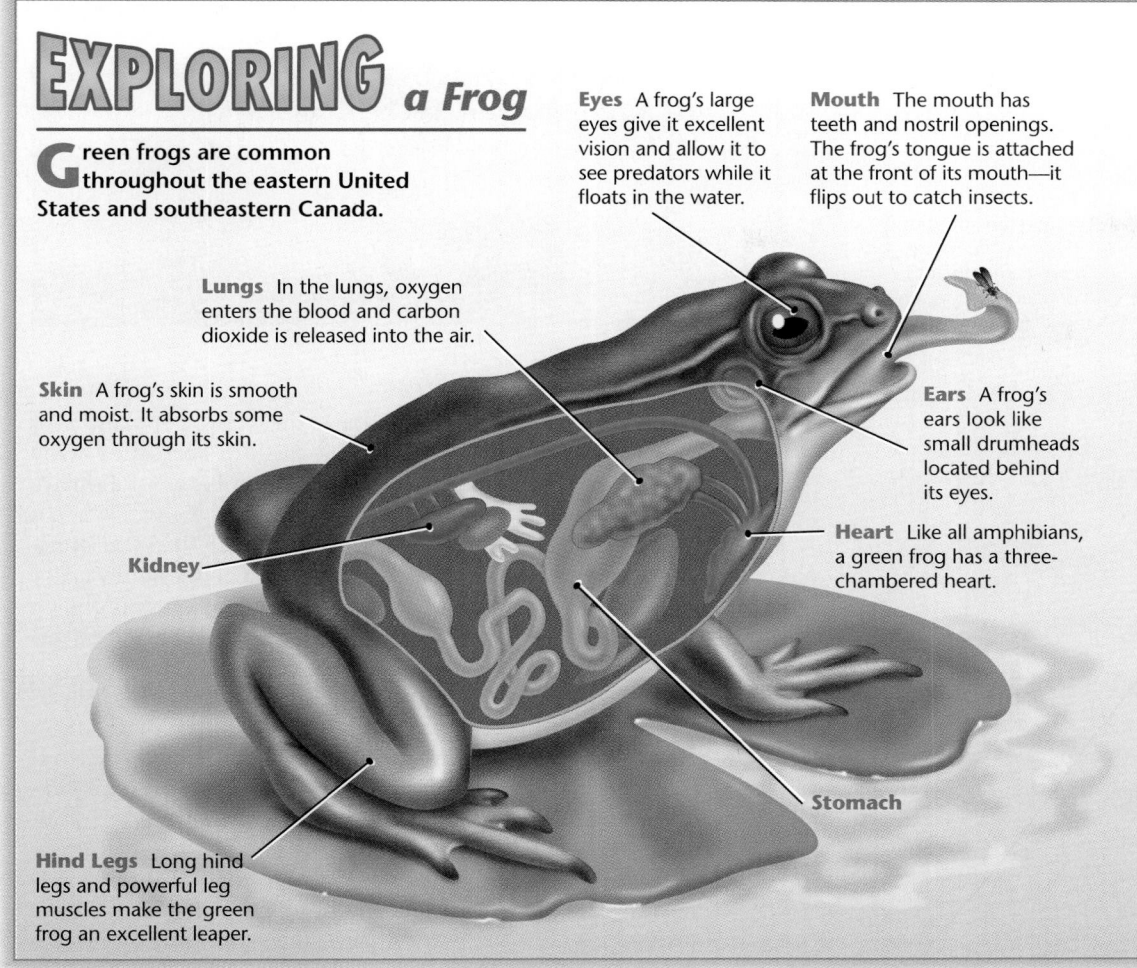

Eyes A frog's large eyes give it excellent vision and allow it to see predators while it floats in the water.

Mouth The mouth has teeth and nostril openings. The frog's tongue is attached at the front of its mouth—it flips out to catch insects.

Lungs In the lungs, oxygen enters the blood and carbon dioxide is released into the air.

Skin A frog's skin is smooth and moist. It absorbs some oxygen through its skin.

Kidney

Ears A frog's ears look like small drumheads located behind its eyes.

Heart Like all amphibians, a green frog has a three-chambered heart.

Stomach

Hind Legs Long hind legs and powerful leg muscles make the green frog an excellent leaper.

legs of salamanders are not adapted for jumping. Rather, salamanders stalk and ambush the small invertebrates that they eat. Most salamanders return to water each year to breed and lay their eggs. The eggs hatch into larvae that swim, feed, and soon grow into adults.

Some kinds of salamanders live in water all of their lives, while many other kinds live almost entirely on land. Some salamanders that live only on land do not have lungs. They rely on their thin, moist skins to obtain oxygen from air and to remove carbon dioxide from their blood. These lungless salamanders do not even return to water to reproduce. They lay their eggs in moist places on land, and they look like miniature adults when they hatch, not like larvae with gills.

Students can compare and contrast this visual with that of Exploring a Bony Fish in Section 2. Make copies of these figures to hand out so that students can examine them side-by-side. Tell students: **Draw circles around the characteristics of each animal that relate to movement.** *(Frog—hind legs; Fish—fins for balance, tail fin, swim bladder)* **Draw squares around the characteristics that help each sense its environment.** *(Frog—eyes, ears; Fish—lateral line)* **Draw triangles around the characteristics that help each obtain oxygen.** *(Frog—lungs, skin; Fish—gills)* **learning modality: visual**

Salamanders

Building Inquiry Skills: Relating Cause and Effect

Lungless salamanders obtain oxygen entirely through their skin. Ask: **What other animals absorb oxygen directly through their skins?** *(Students may mention roundworms, earthworms, and flatworms.)* Then ask: **What do these organisms have in common?** *(They are small.)* Ask: **Do you think animals without gills or lungs can grow very large? Why or why not?** Guide students to understand that only small animals can absorb enough oxygen exclusively through their skin. Earthworms and lungless salamanders are close to the size limit for animals that breathe only through their skin. **learning modality: verbal**

Program Resources

◆ **Interdisciplinary Exploration Series** "Fate of the Rain Forest," p. 11

Media and Technology

 Transparencies "Exploring a Frog," Transparency 53

Answers to Self-Assessment

☑ *Checkpoint*

Most frogs have smooth, moist skin. Toads have drier, bumpier skin. Many toads have large lumps behind their eyes.

Ongoing Assessment

Making Diagrams Ask students to make a Venn diagram to compare and contrast frogs and salamanders.

Amphibians in Danger

Students can research an amphibian that lives in their area and that is being threatened by loss of habitat. Students can find a list of local endangered amphibians by contacting the U.S. Fish and Wildlife Service. **learning modality: verbal**

3 Assess

Section 3 Review Answers

1. Amphibians have a double life because most begin their lives in the water and then spend their adulthood on land.

2. The adult amphibian skeleton has bones for the four limbs that it uses to move on land. The fish skeleton has no bones for limbs. A fish moves by pushing against water with its fins.

3. Forest destruction has caused a decrease in the number of amphibians. This happens because when a forest is destroyed, amphibians' habitats are destroyed as well.

4. A lungless salamander depends on its skin for obtaining oxygen. If the skin dries out, oxygen can no longer dissolve in the moisture and enter the body.

Check Your Progress
CHAPTER PROJECT

Review students' amphibian choices for appropriateness. Before students begin work on their amphibian model, review their fish model. Discuss with students ways in which amphibians differ from fish and how these differences will be reflected in their amphibian model.

Performance Assessment

Organizing Information Have students create a cycle diagram of the life cycle of a frog.

Figure 17 This young red-spotted newt is among the many amphibians in danger from poisons in its environment.

Amphibians in Danger

INTEGRATING ENVIRONMENTAL SCIENCE All over the world, populations of amphibians are decreasing. One reason is the destruction of amphibian habitats. An animal's **habitat** is the specific environment in which it lives. When a swamp is filled in or a forest is cut, an area that was moist becomes drier. Few amphibians can survive in dry, sunny areas. But habitat destruction does not account for the whole problem, because amphibians are declining even in areas where their habitats have not been damaged.

Because their skins are very thin and their eggs lack shells, amphibians are especially sensitive to changes in the environment. Poisons in the environment, such as insecticides and other chemicals, can pollute the waters that are essential to the life of an amphibian. Even small amounts of these chemicals can weaken adult amphibians, kill amphibian eggs, or cause tadpoles to be deformed.

The decline in amphibians may be a warning that other animals are also in danger. The environmental changes that are hurting amphibians may eventually affect other animals, including humans. To try to save amphibians and prevent harm to other animals, scientists are working to understand what is causing amphibian numbers to decline.

Section 3 Review

1. Why is it said that amphibians have a double life?
2. Compare an adult amphibian's skeleton and method of moving to those of a fish.
3. How has forest destruction affected amphibians? Why has it had this effect?
4. **Thinking Critically** **Relating Cause and Effect** A lungless salamander cannot survive if its skin dries out. Explain why.

394

Check Your Progress
CHAPTER PROJECT

At this point, you should have chosen an amphibian to model. Make sure that you are modeling the same type of adaptation that you did for the fish. *(Hint: Before you begin constructing your model, make a sketch of what it will look like.)*

Background

Facts and Figures In 1935, cane toads were introduced to Australia to control the beetles that attack sugar cane crops. The toads did eat the cane beetles, but unfortunately they also ate beneficial insects, frogs, lizards, and even mice. The toads had no natural predators, so their population exploded. Native species have suffered as a result. Cane toads are now a major nuisance for Australians.

Program Resources

◆ **Unit 3 Resources** 12-3 Review and Reinforce, p. 79; 12-3 Enrich, p. 80

Media and Technology

 Interactive Student Tutorial CD-ROM Chapter 12

DISCOVER ••••••••••••••••••••••••••••••••• ACTIVITY

How Do Snakes Feed?

1. To model how a snake feeds, stretch a sock cuff over a grapefruit "prey" by first pulling on one side and then on the other. Work the grapefruit down into the "stomach." A snake's jawbones can spread apart like the sock cuff.

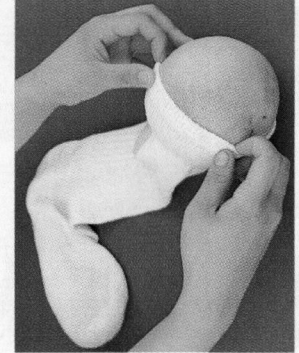

2. Remove the grapefruit and put a rubber band around the sock about 8 cm below the opening. The rubber band represents the firmly joined jawbones of a lizard. Now try to repeat Step 1.

Think It Over
Inferring What is the advantage of having jawbones like a snake's?

The king cobra of Southeast Asia, which can grow to more than 4 meters, is the world's longest venomous snake. When it encounters a predator, a king cobra flattens its neck and rears up. Its ropelike body sways back and forth, and its tongue flicks in and out.

A king cobra's fearsome behavior in response to a predator contrasts with the gentle way it treats its eggs. King cobras are one of the only snakes that build nests. The female builds a nest of grass and leaves on the forest floor. She lays her eggs inside the nest and guards them until they hatch.

Protection from Drying Out

Like other reptiles, king cobras lay their eggs on land rather than in water. A **reptile** is an ectothermic vertebrate that has lungs and scaly skin. In addition to snakes, lizards, turtles, and alligators are also reptiles.

GUIDE FOR READING

◆ What are some adaptations that allow reptiles to live on dry land?

◆ How is a reptile's egg different from an amphibian's egg?

Reading Tip As you read, write brief summaries of the information under each heading.

◀ King cobra

395

READING STRATEGIES

Reading Tip Explain to students that their summaries should focus on a section's main ideas rather than its details. (Sample: The second section explains that reptiles get oxygen from air. Their blood circulation and heart structure resemble those of adult amphibians.) Students can use their summaries to answer some of the Section 4 Review Questions.

Program Resources

◆ **Unit 3 Resources** 12-4 Lesson Plan, p. 81; 12-4 Section Summary, p. 82

Media and Technology

 Audio CD English-Spanish Summary 12-4

SECTION
4 Reptiles

Objectives
After completing this lesson, students will be able to
◆ describe some adaptations that allow reptiles to live on dry land;
◆ state how reptiles' eggs are different from amphibians' eggs;
◆ describe the major groups of reptiles.

Key Terms reptile, urine

1 Engage/Explore

Activating Prior Knowledge

Ask students: **What are some characteristics of snakes?** *(Students may mention snakes' lack of legs, as well as their poisonous venom, or fangs.)* List students' answers on the board. After students have become familiar with the information in the section, revisit this list. Help students to decide which of the characteristics are facts and which are "myths." Make revisions as necessary.

•••••••• DISCOVER ••••••••

Skills Focus inferring
Materials *sock with ribbed cuff, grapefruit, strong rubber band*
Time 10 minutes
Tips Tell students to ease the sock over the grapefruit gently. They might also measure or estimate the diameters of the unstretched sock and the grapefruit to see how they compare. During Step 2 of the activity, use a rubber band that is too small to fit around the grapefruit. Reinforce what students learn by showing them a picture of a snake skull, pointing out that the skull has no large regions of solid bone. Tell students that a snake skull is very delicate but very mobile.
Expected Outcome Students should infer that a snake's spreading jawbones allow it to eat larger prey than is possible with a lizard's firmly joined jawbones.

2 Facilitate

Protection from Drying Out

Addressing Naive Conceptions

Some students may think snakes are slimy. A snake's skin is actually quite dry, especially compared to that of a fish or amphibian. Under supervision, you may allow students to touch the scales of a molted snake skin. They should wash their hands afterwards. **learning modality: kinesthetic**

Building Inquiry Skills: Inferring

Materials *small cut pieces of a sponge, plastic bag, water*

Time 10 minutes over two class periods

To emphasize how eggshells and membranes prevent liquid loss, have students work in small groups to model an egg with a membrane. Provide each group with two pieces of sponge and one resealable plastic bag that will model the shell and membrane. Students should label the bag with their group's name. Have students wet both sponge pieces thoroughly, then put one piece in the plastic bag. They should place the other piece of sponge on top of the sealed bag and leave it overnight. The next day, ask students to describe the condition of their sponges. Lead students to infer that the condition of the sponges left outside the bag is similar to what would happen to a developing embryo if the egg did not have a shell and membranes that retain moisture. **cooperative learning**

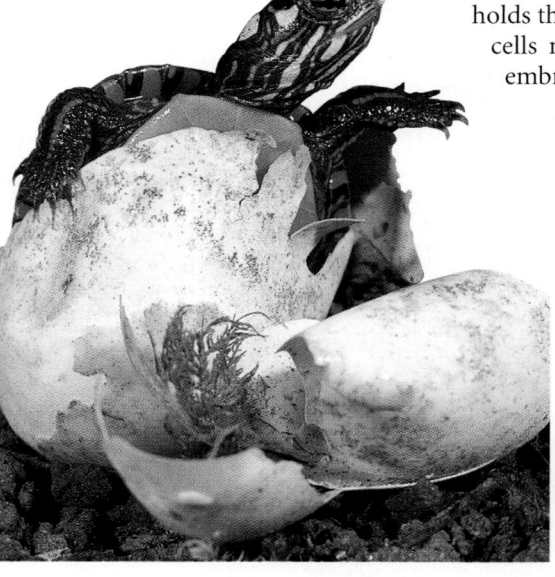

Figure 18 The egg from which this turtle is hatching provided it with food, moisture, and protection when it was an embryo. *Relating Cause and Effect List the parts of the egg that help keep the embryo from drying out.*

396

Unlike amphibians, reptiles can spend their entire lives on dry land. Reptiles were the first vertebrates that were well adapted to live on land, and they were the dominant land animals for about 160 million years. About 7,000 kinds of reptiles are alive today, but they are only a tiny fraction of a group that once dominated the land.

You can think of a land animal as a pocket of water held within a bag of skin. To thrive on land, an animal must have adaptations that keep the water within the "bag" from evaporating in the dry air. **The eggs, skin, and kidneys of reptiles are adapted to conserve water.**

An Egg With a Shell The eggs of reptiles are fertilized internally. While they are still inside the body of the female, fertilized eggs are covered with membranes and a shell. **Unlike an amphibian's egg, a reptile's egg has a shell and membranes that protect the developing embryo and help keep it from drying out.** Reptile eggs look much like bird eggs, except that their shells are soft and leathery, instead of rigid. Tiny holes, or pores, in the shell let oxygen in and carbon dioxide out. Since their eggs conserve water, reptiles—unlike amphibians—can lay their eggs on dry land.

Look carefully at Figure 18 to see how the membranes of a reptile's egg are arranged. One membrane holds the liquid that surrounds the embryo. Like bubble wrap that cushions breakable objects, the liquid keeps the embryo from getting crushed. The liquid also keeps the embryo moist. A second membrane holds the yolk, which provides the embryo with the food its cells must have to grow. A third membrane holds the embryo's wastes.

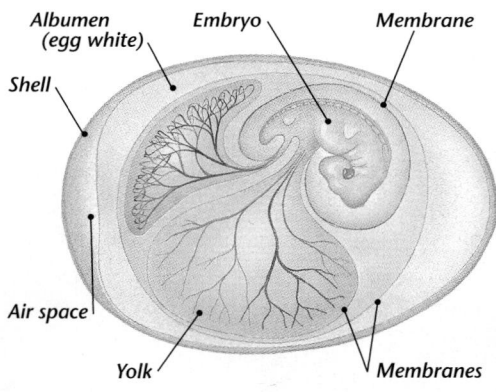

Albumen (egg white) Embryo Membrane
Shell
Air space
Yolk Membranes

Background

History of Science As life evolved on land, there was a general migration and exploitation of drier environments by plants. Plants adapted to habitats that were farther away from a constant water supply. The insects and other animals that fed on these plants soon followed. Amphibians could not take advantage of these dry land plants as a food source because the amphibian life cycle depended on water.

The ancestors of reptiles could move away from water to take advantage of these plants due to the specialized eggs they laid. Once it became possible for animals to live their entire life cycle without depending on constant sources of water, these animals began to adapt to many new environments. Reptiles are one successful group that evolved from these entirely land-dwelling animals. Other such groups are birds and mammals.

Skin and Kidneys Unlike amphibians, which have thin, moist skin, reptiles have dry, tough skins covered with scales. This scaly skin protects reptiles and helps keep water in their bodies. Another adaptation that helps keep water inside a reptile's body is its kidneys, which are organs that filter wastes from the blood. The wastes are then excreted in a watery fluid called **urine**. The kidneys of reptiles concentrate the urine so that they lose very little water.

☑ *Checkpoint* *List two functions of a reptile's skin.*

Obtaining Oxygen from the Air

Reptiles get their oxygen from the air. Like you, most reptiles breathe entirely with lungs. Like adult amphibians, reptiles have two loops in which their blood circulates through their bodies. In the first loop, the blood travels from the heart to the lungs and back to the heart. In the thin, moist surfaces of lung tissue, the oxygen moves into the blood and carbon dioxide moves out. In the second loop, blood travels from the heart to the tissues of the body. In the tissues, oxygen moves out of the blood and carbon dioxide moves into it. Then the blood returns to the heart. Like amphibians, the hearts of most reptiles have three chambers—two atria and one ventricle—and some mixing of oxygen-rich and oxygen-poor blood occurs.

Lizards

Most reptiles alive today are either lizards or snakes. These two groups of reptiles are closely related and share some important characteristics. Both have skin covered with overlapping scales. As lizards and snakes grow, they shed their skins, replacing the worn scales with a new coat. Most lizards and snakes live in warm areas.

Figure 19 The skin color of this chameleon can change in response to factors in its environment, such as changes in temperature.

Using the Visuals: Figure 14

To refresh students' recollection of a two-loop pattern of circulation, have them re-examine Figure 14 on page 390. Explain that the circulation pattern of most reptiles is similar to that of an adult amphibian. **learning modality: visual**

Lizards

Using the Visuals: Figure 19

The chameleon shown in the figure is able to change its skin color to match the environment. Ask: **What advantage would being able to match skin color to the environment give this chameleon?** *(Hide from predators, capture more prey)* **At what other times might the chameleon change color?** *(To defend its territory or attract a potential mate)* Point out to students that anoles are sometimes called American chameleons. They are not true chameleons, but their skin color does change when the animal is excited or when the environmental temperature changes. **learning modality: visual**

Media and Technology

 Transparencies "A Reptile Egg," Transparency 54

 Exploring Life Science Videodisc Unit 3, Side 2, "Travelin' Along"

Chapter 8

Answers to Self-Assessment

Caption Question

Figure 18 The shell, membranes, and liquid that surrounds the embryo.

☑ *Checkpoint*

A reptile's skin protects its body and keeps in water.

Ongoing Assessment

Drawing Direct students to draw a diagram of the reptile circulatory system that indicates the two-loop circulatory system of a reptile, the chambers of a reptile's heart, and the locations of oxygen-rich and oxygen-poor blood in the reptile's circulatory system. *(Students' drawings should be similar to Figure 14, page 390.)*

 Students can save their diagrams in their portfolios.

Lizards, continued

EXPLORING

a Lizard

As students examine the visual essay, remind them that by now they have studied several vertebrate groups. Ask: **What characteristics does the iguana share with the vertebrates you have already studied?** (*Eyes, hearing organs, nostrils for smelling, heart, and kidneys*) Then ask: **What characteristics of the iguana appear to be specialized features of iguanas?** (*Dry, scaly skin, claws, dewlap, crest*) **Extend** Encourage interested students to choose another type of lizard to research. They can make a labeled drawing of this lizard showing its unique characteristics—as well as those shared with other lizards. **learning modality: logical/ mathematical**

Snakes

Real-Life Learning

Skills Focus observing
Time 50 minutes

Arrange a presentation in which students can "meet a snake," either by visiting a zoo or by learning from an invited guest. Have students write a checklist of key features to observe. If possible, arrange for students to observe the movement of snakes across a variety of surfaces. Refer to Section 12-4 Enrich for information on various types of snake movement. Ask students to describe the kinds of movement they observe. Some students may be fearful of snakes. Allow fearful students to observe from a distance. Make sure the snakes are from nonvenomous and nonaggressive species. Garter snakes and grass snakes are common and can be easily and safely handled. **learning modality: visual**

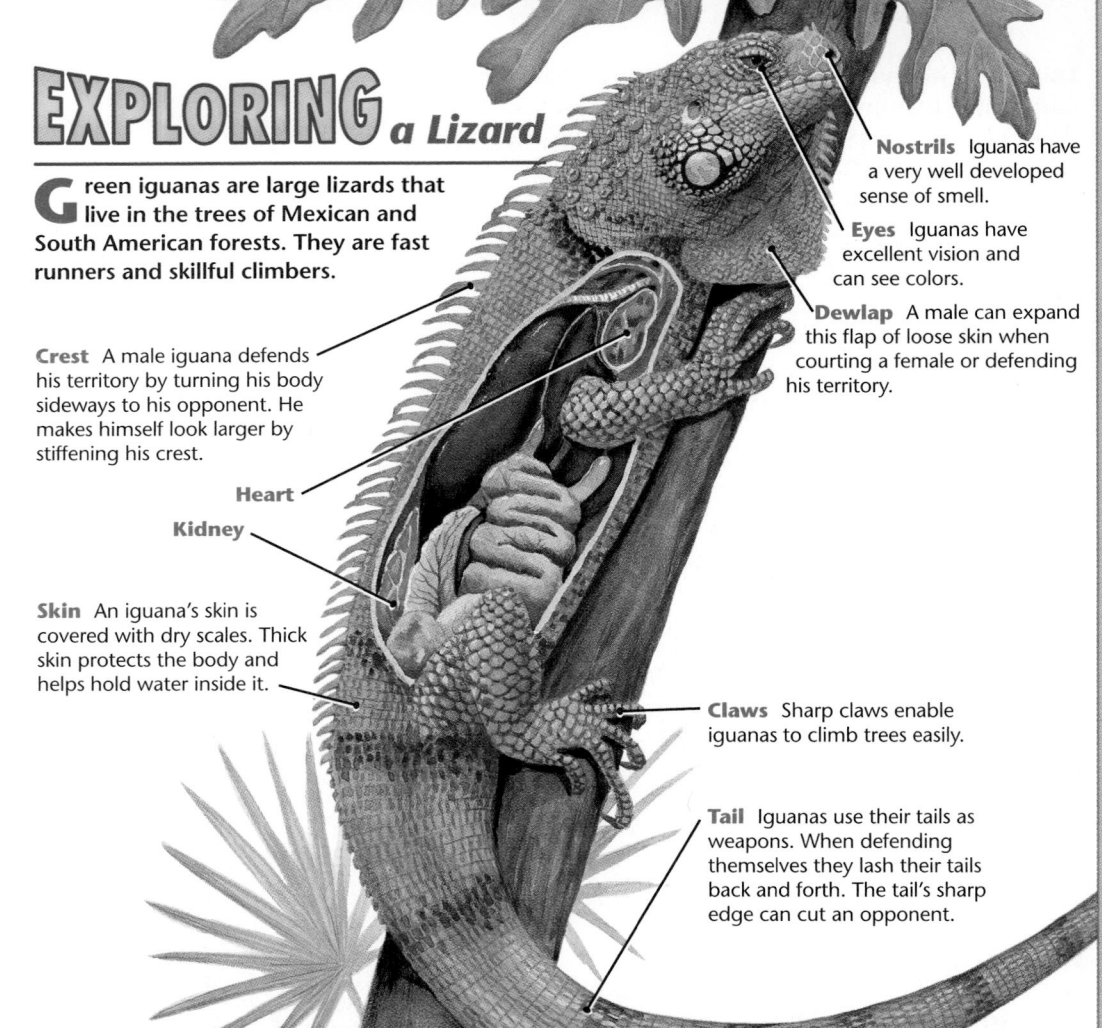

EXPLORING a Lizard

Green iguanas are large lizards that live in the trees of Mexican and South American forests. They are fast runners and skillful climbers.

Nostrils Iguanas have a very well developed sense of smell.

Eyes Iguanas have excellent vision and can see colors.

Dewlap A male can expand this flap of loose skin when courting a female or defending his territory.

Crest A male iguana defends his territory by turning his body sideways to his opponent. He makes himself look larger by stiffening his crest.

Heart

Kidney

Skin An iguana's skin is covered with dry scales. Thick skin protects the body and helps hold water inside it.

Claws Sharp claws enable iguanas to climb trees easily.

Tail Iguanas use their tails as weapons. When defending themselves they lash their tails back and forth. The tail's sharp edge can cut an opponent.

Lizards differ from snakes in one obvious way. Lizards have four legs, usually with claws on the toes. Many lizards have long tails, slender bodies, movable eyelids, and external ears.

A few lizards, including the iguana shown in *Exploring a Lizard*, are herbivores that eat leaves. Most lizards, however, are carnivores that capture food by jumping at it. While large lizards will eat large prey such as frogs and ground-dwelling birds, most small lizards are insect-hunters. Chameleons, which are found in Africa and India, have a sticky tongue adapted for snaring insects. This tongue shoots out rapidly, extending as long as the chameleon's head and body put together!

398

Background

Facts and Figures Venomous snakes have fascinated people throughout history. The structure of the mouth and position of the venom-delivering fangs vary widely among species. Many "rear-fanged" snakes, such as the South African Boomslang, have venom-conducting fangs at the back of their mouths. Cobras and green mambas have short fangs at the front of their mouths. Rattlesnakes are vipers. Their fangs are quite long and fold up against the roof of the mouth when the snakes' mouths are closed. When vipers open their mouths, their fangs rotate downward into the biting position.

Snakes

Snakes are able to live in almost every sort of habitat, from deserts to swamps. They are similar to lizards, but streamlined, both externally and internally. Snakes have no legs, eyelids, or external ears, and most snakes have only one lung.

Snakes on the Move If you've ever seen a snake slither across the ground, you know that when it moves, its long, thin body bends into curves. Snakes move by contracting, or shortening, bands of muscles that are connected to their ribs and backbones. Alternate contractions of muscles on the right and left sides produce a slithering side-to-side motion.

How Snakes Feed All snakes are carnivores, and some eat large prey. If you did the Discover activity, you learned that a snake's jawbones can spread widely apart. In addition, the bones of a snake's skull can move to let the snake swallow an animal much larger in diameter than itself. Most snakes, however, feed on small rodents, such as mice.

Snakes capture their prey in different ways. The sharp-tailed snakes of western North America, which eat only slugs, have long, curved front teeth for hooking their slippery prey. Some West Indian boas are bat hunters that wait in ambush at the entrances to caves where bats live. At twilight, when the bats fly out of the cave to feed, the snakes snatch them out of the air.

Some snakes, such as rattlesnakes and copperheads, have venom glands attached to hollow teeth called fangs. When these snakes bite a prey animal, venom flows down inside the fangs. The venom enters the flesh of the prey and kills it quickly.

☑ *Checkpoint* *How do snakes move?*

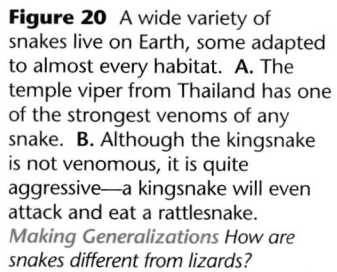

Figure 20 A wide variety of snakes live on Earth, some adapted to almost every habitat. **A.** The temple viper from Thailand has one of the strongest venoms of any snake. **B.** Although the kingsnake is not venomous, it is quite aggressive—a kingsnake will even attack and eat a rattlesnake. *Making Generalizations How are snakes different from lizards?*

Program Resources

◆ **Interdisciplinary Exploration Series** "Sleuth"s Supper," p. 20

Media and Technology

Transparencies "Exploring a Lizard," Transparency 55

Answers to Self-Assessment

Caption Question

Figure 20 Unlike lizards, snakes lack legs, external ears, and eyelids. Most snakes have only one lung.

☑ *Checkpoint*

Snakes move by alternately contracting the muscles on their right and left sides that connect their ribs and vertebrae. This produces a slithering, side-to-side motion.

Addressing Naive Conceptions

Students may mistakenly believe that venomous snakes are vicious and aggressive. Point out that people rightly fear being bitten by venomous snakes. However, students should keep in mind that most venomous snakes are not aggressive toward humans. Normally, they will bite a person only when cornered or startled. Snake venom is primarily an adaptation for capturing prey. **learning modality: verbal**

Using the Visuals: Figure 20

Explain to the class that the kingsnake in the figure mimics the color pattern of the highly venomous coral snake. The color patterns of the two snakes differ mainly in the order of the color bands. Have students observe and describe the color patterns in the kingsnake (red next to black). Explain that the color pattern of the coral snake is red next to yellow. Ask students to infer what benefit the kingsnake receives from looking like a coral snake. (*Potential predators may think the kingsnake is venomous and leave it alone.*) **learning modality: verbal**

Ongoing Assessment

Writing Have students write paragraphs comparing and contrasting the characteristics of lizards and snakes. (*Lizards—four legs, some are herbivores, all have two lungs, many have movable eyelids and external ears; Snakes—no legs, all are carnivores, most have only one lung, no eyelids or external ears; Both—skin covered with overlapping scales, shed their skins as they grow, most live in warm areas*)

 Students can save their paragraphs in their portfolios.

Soaking Up Those Rays

Preparing for Inquiry

Key Concept The temperature of ectotherms changes as the animals approach or avoid heat sources in their environment.

Skills Objective Students will be able to
♦ interpret data associated with an ectotherm.

Time 30 minutes

Guiding Inquiry

Invitation Heat flows from a warmer object to a cooler object. Challenge students to consider whether this rule applies to living organisms. Ask: **What do you notice if you lean against a car parked in the sun?**

Introducing the Procedure

As needed, help individual students understand the significance of each type of information in the illustration.

Troubleshooting the Experiment

Students may have trouble relating to Celsius temperatures. Students can convert a few key temperatures in the diagram into degrees Fahrenheit. This may make it easier for them to understand the lizard's behavior. Students can check each other's work.

Expected Outcome

♦ Through their behavior, lizards can maintain their body temperature within a range that is more limited than the temperature range in the environment.

Analyze and Conclude

1. The lizard's body temperature varied from 25–39.5°C. At 8 P.M. it dropped back down to 25°C.

2. The sun's rays, the surrounding air, and surface rocks. Note: In some periods, the air was cooler than the lizard's body temperature and so served to cool it.

3. Air temperature = 40.3°C, ground temperature = 53.8°C. The lizard

---

Soaking Up Those Rays

In this lab, you will examine and interpret data associated with an ectotherm.

Problem

How do some lizards control their body temperatures in the extreme heat of a desert environment?

Materials

paper   pencil

Procedure

1. The data in the diagram below were collected by scientists studying how lizards control their body temperature. Examine the data.
2. Copy the data table on the next page into your notebook.
3. Organize the data in the diagram by filling in the table, putting the appropriate information in each column. Begin by writing a brief description of each type of lizard behavior.
4. Complete the data table using the information in the diagram.

Analyze and Conclude

1. How did the lizard's body temperature vary from 6 A.M. until 8 P.M.?
2. What are the three sources of heat that caused the lizard's body temperature to rise during the day?
3. During the hottest part of the day, what were the air and ground temperatures? Why do you think the lizard's temperature remained below 40°C?
4. Predict what the lizard's body temperature would have been from 8 P.M. to 6 A.M. Explain your prediction.

6 A.M.–7 A.M.
Emerging from burrow
Air temperature **20ºC**
Ground temperature **28ºC**
Body temperature **25ºC**

7 A.M.–9 A.M.
Basking (lying on ground in sun)
Air temperature **27ºC**
Ground temperature **29ºC**
Body temperature **32.6ºC**

9 A.M.–12 noon
Active (moving about)
Air temperature **27ºC**
Ground temperature **30.8ºC**
Body temperature **36.6ºC**

Program Resources

♦ **Unit 3 Resources** Chapter 12 Skills Lab, pp. 87–89
♦ **Inquiry Skills Activity Book** Provides teaching and review of all inquiry skills

DATA TABLE

Activity	Description of Activity	Time of Day	Air Temperature (°C)	Ground Temperature (°C)	Body Temperature (°C)
1. Emerging					
2. Basking					
3. Active					
4. Retreat					
5. Stilting					
6. Retreat					

5. Based on what you learned from the data, explain why it is misleading to say that an ectotherm is a "coldblooded" animal.

6. Predict what would happen to your own body temperature if you spent a brief period outdoors in the desert at noon. Predict what your temperature would be if you spent time in a burrow at 7 P.M. Explain your predictions.

7. **Think About It** Why is it helpful to organize data in a data table before you try to interpret the data?

More to Explore

Make one or more bar graphs of the temperature data. Explain what the graphs show you. How do these graphs help you interpret the data?

12 noon–2:30 P.M.
Retreat to burrow
Air temperature **40.3°C**
Ground temperature **53.8°C**
Body temperature **39.5°C**

2:30 P.M.–6 P.M.
Stilting (belly off ground)
Air temperature **34.2°C**
Ground temperature **47.4°C**
Body temperature **39.5°C**

6 P.M.–9 P.M.
Retreat to burrow
Air temperature **25°C**
Ground temperature **26°C**
Body temperature **25°C**

remained cooler by staying in its burrow, which was in the shade and cooler than the ground temperature.

4. Accept all reasonable answers. Students may say that the body temperature will probably remain about 25°C, since the burrow tends to have a stable temperature.

5. "Coldblooded" implies that an animal's body temperature is cold. The lizard's temperature gets as high as 39°C, which is hotter than 100°F.

6. Our body temperatures at both times would remain relatively constant, since human body temperature is controlled by its own internal controls.

7. Organizing data in a table allows us to list all the data in the same place and makes data easier to compare. In this lab, the data table lets us quickly see temperature changes that happened over the course of the day. The table also makes comparing the temperatures at different times of the day easier.

Extending Inquiry

More to Explore On the bar graphs, the temperature is plotted on the *y*-axis; the time of the day on the *x*-axis. The graph of ground temperature shows that the rocks are cool in the morning, become hot at noon, and remain hot until evening. A graph of the lizard's body temperature shows that the body temperature changes throughout the day, but not as much as the air or ground temperatures.

Sample Data Table

Activity	Description of Activity	Time	Air Temp °C	Ground Temp °C	Body Temp °C
1. Emerging	leaves burrow	6–7 A.M.	20	28	25
2. Basking	rests on surface	7–9	27	29	32.6
3. Active	moves around	9–12	27	30.8	36.6
4. Retreat	enters burrow	12–12:30 P.M.	40.3	53.8	39.5
5. Stilting	belly away from surface, tail over head	2:30–6	34.2	47.4	39.5
6. Retreat	enters burrow	6	25	26	25

Turtles

Including All Students

Materials *live turtle*
Time 5 minutes

To interest students who need additional challenges, bring a live turtle, such as a box turtle, to class. (Check to make sure your school district permits live animals in the classroom.) Before beginning, ask students: **How does your chest move when you breathe?** *(Students should observe that their chests move in and out.)* Then ask: **If the turtle's chest moves like yours does, do you think its shell gets in the way?** *(Yes)* Allow students to observe the turtle carefully as it breathes. Students should notice that the exposed soft tissue around the turtle's forelimbs and hind limbs moves. Explain that this front-and-back motion of the tissue around the limbs replaces the in-and-out motion of the chests of vertebrates without shells. **learning modality: visual**

Addressing Naive Conceptions

Some students may think that because sea turtles live most of their lives in water, they obtain oxygen through gills, as fish do. Explain that sea turtles obtain oxygen from the air like land-dwelling turtles. They are adapted to holding their breath for long periods of time, but they must still come to the surface for air. This is one reason why fishing nets are so dangerous for sea turtles. If the turtles become tangled in the nets, they can drown. **learning modality: verbal**

Figure 21 Turtles vary greatly in their feeding habits. **A.** The green sea turtle lives entirely at sea and is a carnivore. **B.** The Galapagos tortoise lives on land, where it eats mainly cacti.

Turtles

A turtle is a reptile whose body is covered by a protective shell, which is made from the turtle's ribs and backbone. As you can see in Figure 21, the bony plates of the shell are covered by large scales made from the same material as the skin's scales. Some turtle shells can cover the whole body—a box turtle can draw its head, legs, and tail inside its shell for protection. Turtles like the snapping turtle have much smaller shells. Soft-shelled turtles, as their name suggests, have shells that are as soft as pancakes. Soft-shelled turtles lie in stream beds, concealed from predators, with only their nostrils and eyes above the sand.

The feeding habits of turtles are quite diverse. The largest turtles, the leatherbacks, are carnivores. Leatherbacks, which can weigh over 500 kilograms, are sea turtles that feed mainly on venomous jellyfishes. The stinging cells of the jellyfish can kill other animals, but the leatherback's tough skin seems to be unharmed by them. The giant Galapagos tortoises, on the other hand, are herbivores that feed mainly on cacti. They carefully scrape the prickly spines off before swallowing the cactus. Turtles have sharp-edged beaks instead of teeth. The razor-sharp beaks of soft-shelled turtles can chop fishes in two.

Figure 22 Alligators, left, and crocodiles, right, are the largest reptiles still living on Earth. They are similar in many ways, including appearance.
Comparing and Contrasting How can you tell the difference between an alligator and a crocodile?

402

Background

Facts and Figures Crocodiles roamed on Earth next to dinosaurs. Early crocodiles were strictly land animals, and many were not much larger than iguanas. Modern crocodiles are found in Asia, the Australian region, Africa, Madagascar, and the Americas. The American crocodile is one of only three species of crocodile found outside the tropics. Unlike the American alligator, which has made a successful comeback from the brink of extinction, the American crocodile is still in jeopardy because much of its habitat is disappearing. It makes its home in the saltwater marshes of Florida and the Gulf Coast. In contrast, the American alligator lives in wetlands throughout the southeastern United States. The American alligator population recovered because of regulations regarding the hunting of these animals, which were sought for their skins.

Alligators and Crocodiles

If you walk along a lake in Florida, you just might see an alligator swimming silently in the water. Most of its body lies beneath the surface, but you can see its large, bulging eyes above the surface. Alligators, crocodiles, and their relatives are the largest living reptiles. The American alligator can grow to be more than 5 meters long.

How do you tell an alligator from a crocodile? Look for teeth—but use binoculars and stay far away! Alligators have broad, rounded snouts, with only a few teeth visible when their mouths are shut. In contrast, crocodiles have pointed snouts, and you can see most of their teeth. Both alligators and crocodiles spend much of their days resting in the sun or water.

Alligators and crocodiles are carnivores that hunt mostly at night. They have several adaptations to help them capture prey. They use their strong, muscular tails to swim rapidly through the water. Their jaws are equipped with many large, sharp, and pointed teeth. Their jaw muscles are extremely strong when biting down. Although alligators will eat dogs, raccoons, and deer, they usually do not attack humans.

Unlike most other reptiles, crocodiles and alligators care for their eggs and newly hatched young. After laying eggs in a nest of rotting plants, the female stays near the nest. From time to time she comes out of the water and crawls over the nest to keep it moist. After the tiny alligators or crocodiles hatch, the female scoops them up in her huge mouth. She carries them from the nest to a nursery area in the water where they will be safer. For as long as a year, she will stay near her young, which make gulping quacks when they're alarmed. When their mother hears her young quack, she rushes toward them.

☑ *Checkpoint* *How are alligators and crocodiles adapted for catching prey?*

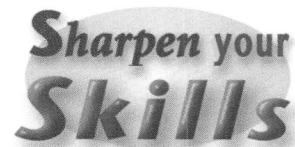

Sharpen your Skills

Drawing Conclusions

ACTIVITY

Scientists incubated, or raised, eggs of one alligator species at four different temperatures. When the alligators hatched, the scientists counted the numbers of males and females. The table below shows the results.

Incubation Temperature	Number of Females	Number of Males
29.4°C	80	0
30.6°C	19	13
31.7°C	13	38
32.8°C	0	106

Use the data to answer these questions.
1. What effect does incubation temperature have on the sex of the alligators?
2. Suppose a scientist incubated 50 eggs at 31°C. About how many of the alligators that hatched would be males? Explain.

Answers to Self-Assessment

Caption Question

Figure 22 Alligators have broad, rounded snouts with only a few teeth visible when their mouths are shut. Crocodiles have pointed snouts with many teeth visible.

☑ *Checkpoint*

Alligators and crocodiles have strong tails for pursuing prey in water, long snouts, sharp teeth, and strong jaws.

Alligators and Crocodiles

Sharpen your Skills

Skills Focus drawing conclusions

Time 15 minutes

Tips So that students can answer Question 1 accurately, make sure they understand that the answer is based on the proportion of males to females in the groups of eggs, not the absolute number. To help students answer Question 2, explain that the incubation temperature is the temperature at which the eggs were kept after they were laid—not the temperature at which the female was kept before she laid them. **learning modality: logical/mathematical**

Answers

1. The warmer the incubation temperature, the greater the proportion of males
2. About half, or 25, would be males, because 31°C is between 30.6°C, at which there were more females than males, and 31.7°C, at which there were more males than females. Accept any answer close to that.

Extend Ask students to think of an experiment that could test whether incubation temperature affects the percentage of eggs that hatch. Do not allow students to perform their experiments. *(Sample experiment: Incubate three groups of 100 eggs at three different temperatures and then count the number of alligators that hatch.)*

Ongoing Assessment

Writing Invite students to write a paragraph comparing and contrasting the beaks of soft-shelled turtles and the teeth of alligators and crocodiles. Have them include an explanation of how each adaptation contributes to the animals' ability to successfully acquire food.

 Students can save their paragraphs in their portfolios.

403

Extinct Reptiles— The Dinosaurs

Addressing Naive Conceptions

Movies have given students a mix of information and misinformation about dinosaurs. Divide students into groups and have them list some of the characteristics they think dinosaurs possessed. Compile the students' lists and assign each characteristic to a category ranging from probably right to probably wrong. Have students do research to determine whether the listed characteristics are accurate. **cooperative learning**

3 Assess

Section 4 Review Answers

1. Dry, watertight skin; an egg with a shell and membranes; kidneys to concentrate urine
2. The shell, membranes, and fluid in a reptile's egg surround and protect the developing embryo.
3. The bones of a snake's skull can move in such a way to make an opening larger in diameter than the snake itself.
4. Endotherms can live in a wider range of climates.

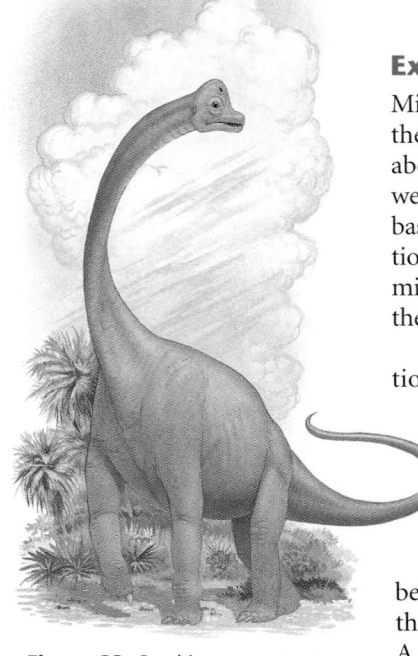

Figure 23 *Brachiosaurus* grew to be over 22.5 meters long—longer than two school buses put together. *Observing What adaptation is demonstrated by the legs of* Brachiosaurus *and many other dinosaurs?*

> **Check Your Progress**   CHAPTER PROJECT
>
> Check to make sure students have chosen appropriate and safe materials for building their reptile models. Be sure that students are modeling the same adaptation in all three models.

Performance Assessment

Organizing Information Have students make a table with column heads "Characteristic," "Amphibians," and "Reptiles." The row labels are "Eggs" and "Skin." In the second column, students should describe how each feature functions in amphibians. In the third column, students should describe how each feature functions differently in reptiles, enabling them to live on dry land.

Extinct Reptiles—The Dinosaurs

Millions of years ago, huge turtles and fish-eating reptiles swam in the oceans. Flying reptiles soared through the skies. And from about 225 million years ago until 65 million years ago, reptiles were the major form of vertebrate life on land. Snakes and lizards basked on warm rocks. And there were dinosaurs of every description. Unlike today's reptiles, dinosaurs may have been endothermic. Some dinosaurs, such as the *Brachiosaurus* in Figure 23, were the largest land animals that have ever lived.

Dinosaurs were the earliest vertebrates that had legs positioned directly beneath their bodies. This adaptation allowed them to move more easily than animals, such as salamanders, whose legs stick out to the sides of their bodies. Most herbivorous dinosaurs, such as *Brachiosaurus*, walked on four legs; most carnivores, such as the huge *Tyrannosaurus rex*, ran on two legs.

Dinosaurs became extinct about 65 million years ago, long before humans appeared on Earth. Several theories try to explain their disappearance, but no one is sure why they became extinct. A change in climate from warm to cool probably played a role. One leading theory suggests that a huge meteorite, a chunk of rock sailing through space, crashed into Earth. The impact sent up thick clouds of dust that blocked out the sun. The decrease in sunlight not only made Earth cooler, it also decreased plant growth, thus limiting food supplies. Dust from massive volcanic eruptions may also have blocked out sunlight. The dinosaurs were unable to survive in these changed conditions and died out.

Today, it's only in movies that dinosaurs shake the ground with their footsteps. But in a way, dinosaurs still exist. Birds may be descended from certain small dinosaurs. Some biologists think that birds are dinosaurs with feathers.

Section 4 Review

1. Describe three adaptations that enabled reptiles to live on land.
2. Explain how the structure of a reptile's egg protects the developing embryo.
3. Explain how snakes are able to eat large prey.
4. **Thinking Critically** **Making Generalizations** If some dinosaurs had been endotherms, what advantage might they have had over other reptiles?

> **Check Your Progress**   CHAPTER PROJECT
>
> Assemble the materials you need in order to build your reptile model. Make sure that your model clearly shows how the animal is adapted for the same function as your fish and amphibian. Begin preparing a written explanation of the adaptations that your three models demonstrate. Your written explanation should include labeled diagrams.

Background

Facts and Figures Some scientists believe that dinosaurs were probably endotherms. This belief gathered support when *Deinonychus* (day NON ik us) was discovered in 1964. This dinosaur was bipedal and could move with speed and agility. These characteristics require a great deal of energy, possibly indicating endothermy.

Answers to Self-Assessment

Caption Question

Figure 23 They have legs positioned directly beneath their bodies.

SECTION 1 Evolution of Vertebrates

INTEGRATING EARTH SCIENCE

Key Ideas

◆ Vertebrates have a backbone that is part of an endoskeleton. The endoskeleton supports, protects, and gives shape to the body.

◆ Most fishes, amphibians, and reptiles are ectotherms. Mammals and birds are endotherms.

◆ Fossils are found primarily in sedimentary rock. Scientists study fossils to learn more about the history of life on Earth.

Key Terms

chordate	vertebra	fossil
notochord	ectotherm	sedimentary rock
cartilage	endotherm	

SECTION 2 Fishes

Key Ideas

◆ A fish is a vertebrate that lives in the water and has fins. Most fishes are ectotherms, obtain oxygen through gills, and have scales.

◆ Major groups of fishes include jawless fishes, cartilaginous fishes, and bony fishes.

Key Terms
fish
swim bladder
buoyant force

SECTION 3 Amphibians

Key Ideas

◆ An amphibian is a moist-skinned, ectothermic vertebrate. Most amphibians spend their early lives in water and their adulthood on land, returning to water to reproduce.

◆ Major groups of amphibians include frogs, toads, and salamanders.

◆ Adult amphibians have strong skeletons and muscular limbs adapted for moving on land.

Key Terms

amphibian	atrium	ventricle	habitat

SECTION 4 Reptiles

Key Ideas

◆ A reptile is an ectothermic vertebrate that has lungs and scaly skin. Reptiles can spend their entire lives on dry land.

◆ The leathery eggs, scaly skin, and kidneys of reptiles are adapted to conserving water.

◆ Major groups of reptiles include lizards, snakes, turtles, and alligators and crocodiles.

Key Terms
reptile
urine

Organizing Information

Compare/Contrast Table Copy the table comparing fish groups onto a separate sheet of paper. Then complete the table and add a title. (For more on compare/contrast tables, see the Skills Handbook.)

Kind of Fish	Kind of Skeleton	Jaws?	Scales	Example
Jawless Fishes	a. ?	no	b. ?	c. ?
d. ?	e. ?	f. ?	toothlike scales	shark
Bony Fishes	bone	g. ?	h. ?	i. ?

Organizing Information

Compare/Contrast Table Sample Title: The Characteristics of Different Fish Groups; **a.** cartilage **b.** none **c.** lamprey or hagfish **d.** cartilaginous fishes **e.** cartilage **f.** yes **g.** yes **h.** yes **i.** Sample: trout, tuna, or goldfish

Program Resources

◆ **Unit 3 Resources** Chapter 12 Project Scoring Rubric, p. 68

◆ **Performance Assessment** Chapter 12, pp. 38–40

◆ **Chapter and Unit Tests** Chapter 12 Test, pp. 56–59

Media and Technology

 Interactive Student Tutorial CD-ROM Chapter 12

 Computer Test Bank Chapter 12 Test

Reviewing Content
Multiple Choice
1. d 2. b 3. b 4. c 5. d

True or False
6. true 7. tooth 8. true 9. in water
10. ventricle

Checking Concepts
11. At some time during their lives, chordates have a notochord, a nerve cord running down their back, and slits in their throat area.

12. Fish reproduce sexually. Most have external fertilization.

13. A frog begins life as an egg, surrounded by jelly, laid in water or a moist environment. The egg hatches into a fishlike tadpole, which gradually develops into an adult frog. Hind legs appear, then front legs. Lungs replace gills as organs for obtaining oxygen. The tadpole loses its tail, and finally develops into an adult that lives on land. The adult frog returns to water to mate and lay eggs, completing the cycle.

14. A fish has a circulatory system with one loop and a simple heart. Amphibians have a circulatory system with two loops and a three-chambered heart.

15. The membranes and shell protect the embryo and hold water inside the egg. One membrane holds cushioning liquid that surrounds the embryo; the yolk holds food for the embryo; and another membrane holds wastes.

16. Both lizards and snakes have skin (covered with overlapping scales) that is shed as the animal grows. Lizards have legs, eyelids, and external ears, but snakes do not. Most snakes have only one lung, whereas lizards have two.

17. A snake moves in a wavelike pattern because of alternating contractions of muscles on opposite sides of its body.

18. A huge meteorite crashing into Earth, or massive volcanic eruptions, may have sent up a thick cloud of dust that blocked out the sun. The dinosaurs could not survive in the changed conditions and died out.

Reviewing Content
 For more review of key concepts, see the Interactive Student Tutorial CD-ROM.

Multiple Choice
Choose the letter of the best answer.

 1. The hardened remains of organisms are called
   a. chordates.
   b. vertebrae.
   c. sedimentary rocks.
   d. fossils.

2. Which fishes do not have jaws, scales, or paired fins?
   a. sharks
   b. lampreys and hagfishes
   c. sturgeons
   d. ocean sunfish

3. A bony fish uses a swim bladder to
   a. propel itself through water.
   b. regulate its buoyancy.
   c. remove wastes.
   d. pump water over its gills.

4. Adult frogs must return to the water to
   a. catch flies.
   b. obtain all their food.
   c. reproduce.
   d. moisten their gills.

5. Which of the following animals breathes with lungs?
   a. shark
   b. lamprey
   c. larval salamander
   d. lizard

True or False
If the statement is true, write true. If it is false, change the underlined word or words to make the statement true.

6. Birds and mammals are <u>endotherms</u>.

7. If a shark loses a <u>fin</u>, another one will move into its place.

8. <u>Buoyant force</u> is the force that pushes upward against an underwater object.

9. Amphibians usually begin their lives <u>on land</u>.

10. The <u>atria</u> pump blood to the lungs and body.

Checking Concepts
11. Describe the main characteristics of chordates.

12. How do fish reproduce?

13. Describe the life cycle of a frog.

14. How is an amphibian's circulatory system different from that of a fish?

15. Explain how the structure of a reptile's egg protects the embryo inside.

16. In what ways are lizards and snakes similar? How do they differ?

17. Why does a snake move in a wavelike pattern rather than in a straight line?

18. What may have caused the dinosaurs to become extinct?

19. **Writing to Learn** Write a description of an hour in the life of a shark. Before you begin to write, list the events you want to include, and arrange those events in the sequence in which you want them to occur. As you write, use words such as *then* and *a moment later* to let your readers know that the shark is progressing from one activity to another.

Thinking Critically
20. **Relating Cause and Effect** Explain why the presence of an endoskeleton allows vertebrates to grow to larger sizes than animals without endoskeletons.

21. **Inferring** A scientist discovers a fossilized fish with a streamlined body, large tail fin, and sharp, pointed teeth. What could the scientist infer about the type of food that this fish ate and how it obtained its food? On what evidence is the inference based?

22. **Comparing and Contrasting** Compare the ways a tadpole and an adult frog obtain oxygen.

23. **Applying Concepts** Imagine that you are in the hot desert sun with a wet paper towel. You must keep the towel from drying out. What strategy can you copy from reptiles to keep the towel wet?

19. Answers will vary. Students' narratives should include realistic details about a shark, such as constant motion, searching for prey, reacting to the smell of blood, and so forth. Check for accurate, realistic events arranged in a logical sequence, with transitions between ideas.

Thinking Critically
20. The endoskeleton grows as the animal grows. Also, its strength supports the animal against the pull of gravity.

21. The fish probably ate other animals in the water because of its sharp pointed teeth. It was most likely a powerful and quick swimmer, based on its tail fin and body shape.

22. A tadpole obtains oxygen through its gills, whereas an adult frog gets oxygen from its lungs and through its skin.

23. Wrap the towel in a material such as foil or plastic wrap that will keep water from escaping.

Applying Skills

A scientist performed an experiment on five goldfish to test the effect of water temperature on "breathing rate"—the rate at which the fish open and close their gill covers. The graph shows the data that the scientist obtained at four different temperatures. Use the graph to answer Questions 24–26.

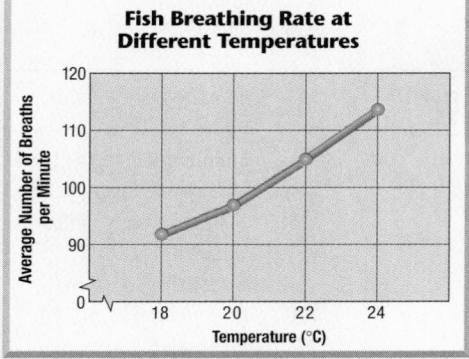

Fish Breathing Rate at Different Temperatures

24. **Controlling Variables** Identify the manipulated variable and the responding variable in this experiment.
25. **Interpreting Data** How does the breathing rate at 18°C compare to the breathing rate at 22°C?
26. **Drawing Conclusions** Based on the data, what is the relationship between water temperature and fish breathing rate?

Performance ▽ Assessment
CHAPTER PROJECT

Present Your Project Display your models in a creative and interesting way—for example, show the models in action and show details of the animals' habitats. Also display your poster.

Reflect and Record In your journal, list all the adaptations you learned about from your classmates' presentations. How did constructing a three-dimensional model help you understand the characteristics of these groups?

Test Preparation
Use these questions to prepare for standardized tests.

Read the passage. Then answer Questions 27–29.

When the snake, *Bothrops jararaca*, attacks, deadly venom enters its victim through its razor-sharp fangs. The bitten animal's blood pressure drops, its lungs burst, and it soon dies.

Why does the snake venom cause the animal's blood pressure to drop? Could the same substance be used to reduce blood pressure in humans? Because hypertension, or high blood pressure, is a leading cause of death in humans, scientists wanted to find answers to these questions.

Scientists collected the venom from many *Bothrops jararaca* snakes and injected it into laboratory animals. The animals' blood vessels widened, causing a large drop in blood pressure. The scientists then set to work to develop an artificial version of the snake venom. The result was captopril, a blood pressure medication that has saved many lives.

27. What is the best title for this passage?
    a. How Poisonous Snakes Kill Their Prey
    b. Hypertension—A Leading Cause of Death
    c. Turning Poison into a Promising New Medication
    d. Is *Bothrops jararaca* a Serious Threat to Humans?
28. Which of the following words is a synonym for *venom*?
    a. medication
    b. poison
    c. chemical
    d. vein
29. What observation led scientists to carry out further investigations of the snake venom?
    a. The bitten animal died.
    b. The venom entered the animal from the snake's razor-sharp fangs.
    c. The bitten animal's lungs burst.
    d. The bitten animal's blood pressure dropped.

Applying Skills

24. The manipulated variable is the water temperature. The responding variable is the breathing rate of the fish.
25. The breathing rate at 18°C is lower than the breathing rate at 22°C.
26. The goldfish breathing rate is directly related to water temperature. The lower the water temperature, the slower the breathing rate, and vice versa.

Performance ▽ Assessment
CHAPTER PROJECT

Present Your Project When students demonstrate their models for the class, some models may not perform the intended function as smoothly as they are designed to do. Locomotion can be a difficult adaptation to demonstrate successfully. Look for realistic and thoughtful ideas. Remind students that the poster can support their ideas. Posters can be flowcharts that convey additional information about the specific adaptation.
Reflect and Record Guide students to record the adaptations that prompted their choices of models. Also, have them record the other adaptations that their classmates modeled. After all students have presented their projects, you may wish to take a census of the class to find out what adaptations were modeled most often.

Test Preparation
27. c 28. b 29. d

Sections	Time	Student Edition Activities	Other Activities	
CHAPTER PROJECT **Bird Watch** p. 409	Ongoing (2–3 weeks)	Check Your Progress, pp. 419, 422, 436 Present Your Project, p. 439		
1 Birds pp. 410–419 ◆ Identify the common characteristics of birds. ◆ Explain how birds are adapted to and affect their environments.	2 periods/ 1 block	**Discover** What Are Feathers Like? p. 410 **Skills Lab: Drawing Conclusions** Looking at an Owl's Leftovers, pp. 414–415 **Try This** Eggs-amination, p. 417	TE TE TE TE TE TE IES LM	Including All Students, pp. 411, 412 Integrating Physics, p. 412 Inquiry Challenge, p. 416 Building Inquiry Skills: Observing, p. 416 Classifying, p. 417 Demonstration, p. 416 Integrating Environmental Science, p. 418 "India Beyond the Golden Age," pp. 36–38 13, "Adaptations of Birds"
2 *INTEGRATING PHYSICS* **The Physics of Bird Flight** pp. 420–422 ◆ Explain how a bird is able to fly.	1 period/ $\frac{1}{2}$ block	**Discover** What Lifts Airplanes and Birds Into the Air? p. 420 **Try This** It's Plane to See, p. 421		
3 What Is a Mammal? pp. 423–430 ◆ Describe the characteristics all mammals share.	2 periods/ 1 block	**Discover** What Are Mammals' Teeth Like? p. 423 **Try This** Insulated Mammals, p. 425 **Sharpen Your Skills** Classifying, p. 427 **Science at Home** p. 428 **Real-World Lab: You, the Consumer** Keeping Warm, p. 429	TE TE	Including All Students, p. 426 Inquiry Challenge, p. 426
4 Diversity of Mammals pp. 431–436 ◆ Identify the characteristic used to classify mammals into three groups. ◆ Describe the characteristics of monotremes, marsupials, and placental mammals.	2 periods/ 1 block	**Discover** How Is a Thumb Useful? p. 431	TE TE	Building Inquiry Skills: Observing, p. 433 Inquiry Challenge, p. 434
Study Guide/Chapter Assessment pp. 437–439	1 period/ $\frac{1}{2}$ block		ISAB	Provides teaching and review of all inquiry skills

For Standard or Block Schedule The Resource Pro® CD-ROM gives you maximum flexibility for planning your instruction for any type of schedule. Resource Pro® contains Planning Express®, an advanced scheduling program, as well as the entire contents of the Teaching Resources and the Computer Test Bank.

CHAPTER PLANNING GUIDE

Program Resources	Assessment Strategies	Media and Technology
UR Chapter 13 Project Teacher Notes, pp. 90–91 **UR** Chapter 13 Project Overview and Worksheets, pp. 92–95	**SE** Performance Assessment: Present Your Project, p. 439 **TE** Check Your Progress, pp. 419, 422, 436 **UR** Chapter 13 Project Scoring Rubric, p. 96	Science Explorer Internet Site at www.phschool.com
UR 13-1 Lesson Plan, p. 97 **UR** 13-1 Section Summary, p. 98 **UR** 13-1 Review and Reinforce, p. 99 **UR** 13-1 Enrich, p. 100 **UR** Chapter 13 Skills Lab, pp. 113–115	**SE** Section 1 Review, p. 419 **TE** Ongoing Assessment, pp. 411, 413, 417 **TE** Performance Assessment, p. 419	Life Science Videotape 3; Videodisc Unit 3 Side 2, "Backbones" Life Science Videotape 3; Videodisc Unit 3 Side 2, "How Does Everything Fit?" Audio CD, English-Spanish Summary 13-1 Transparency 56, "Exploring a Bird" Transparency 57, "Circulation in Fishes, Amphibians, and Birds" Interactive Student Tutorial CD-ROM, Chapter 13
UR 13-2 Lesson Plan, p. 101 **UR** 13-2 Section Summary, p. 102 **UR** 13-2 Review and Reinforce, p. 103 **UR** 13-2 Enrich, p. 104	**SE** Section 2 Review, p. 422 **TE** Ongoing Assessment, p. 421 **TE** Performance Assessment, p. 422	Physical Science Videotape 3; Videodisc Unit 3 Side 2, "How an Airplane Flies" Audio CD, English-Spanish Summary 13-2 Transparency 58, "Bird Flight"
UR 13-3 Lesson Plan, p. 105 **UR** 13-3 Section Summary, p. 106 **UR** 13-3 Review and Reinforce, p. 107 **UR** 13-3 Enrich, p. 108 **UR** Chapter 13 Real-World Lab, pp. 116–117	**SE** Section 3 Review, p. 428 **TE** Ongoing Assessment, pp. 425, 427 **TE** Performance Assessment, p. 428	Life Science Videotape 3; Videodisc Unit 3 Side 2, "Backbones" Life Science Videotape 3; Videodisc Unit 3 Side 2, "How Does Everything Fit?" Audio CD, English-Spanish Summary 13-3
UR 13-4 Lesson Plan, p. 109 **UR** 13-4 Section Summary, p. 110 **UR** 13-4 Review and Reinforce, p. 111 **UR** 13-4 Enrich, p. 112	**SE** Section 4 Review, p. 436 **TE** Ongoing Assessment, pp. 433, 435 **TE** Performance Assessment, p. 436	Audio CD, English-Spanish Summary 13-4
RCA Provides strategies to improve science reading skills **GSW** Provides worksheets to promote student comprehension of content	**SE** Chapter 13 Study Guide/Assessment, pp. 437–439 **PA** Chapter 13 Performance Assessment, pp. 41–43 **CUT** Chapter 13 Test, pp. 60–63 **CTB** Chapter 13 Test	Computer Test Bank, Chapter 13 Test Interactive Student Tutorial CD-ROM, Chapter 13

Key: **SE** Student Edition
CTB Computer Test Bank
ISAB Inquiry Skills Activity Book
GSW Guided Study Worksheets

TE Teacher's Edition
PTA Product Testing Activities by *Consumer Reports*
RCA Reading in the Content Area
PA Performance Assessment

UR Unit Resources
LM Laboratory Manual
IES Interdisciplinary Explorations Series
CUT Chapter and Unit Tests

Meeting the National Science Education Standards and AAAS Benchmarks

National Science Education Standards	Benchmarks for Science Literacy	Unifying Themes
Science as Inquiry (Content Standard A) ◆ **Recognize and analyze alternative explanations and predictions** Students may suggest explanations for observed animal behavior. *(Chapter Project)* ◆ **Design and conduct a scientific investigation** Students implement a plan to investigate the effectiveness of wool as an insulator. Additionally, they will design their own experiment to test the insulation properties of wool to model fur as an adaptation to varying climates. *(Real-World Lab)* **Physical Science** (Content Standard B) ◆ **Motions and forces** The flight of birds depends on lift and can be described using principles from physics. *(Section 2)* **Life Science** (Content Standard C) ◆ **Diversity and adaptations of organisms** Many characteristics of birds and mammals are adaptations that allow the animals to live in different environments. This is reflected in differences in physical and behavioral traits. *(Sections 1–4)* ◆ **Structure and function in living systems** The structural features of both birds and mammals are related to their life-supporting functions. The physical adaptations of different animals correspond to different behaviors. *(Sections 1–4)*	**5A Diversity of Life** Birds and mammals are classified as distinct groups based on morphological structures. Some characteristics of individual species determine further classifications. *(Sections 1–4; Real-World Lab; Skills Lab; Chapter Project)* **5F Evolution of Life** The origins of both birds and mammals can be studied through the fossil record and by comparing the specialized structures of animals with different adaptations. *(Sections 1, 3)* **6C Basic Functions** The major anatomical systems of both birds and mammals correspond to specialized functions. The behavior, diet, and habitat of animals are related to physical adaptations of the species, such as feathers and fur. *(Sections 1–4)* **12D Communication Skills** Students organize and create simple tables and graphs. They may describe, in words, what the tables and graphs show. Students can analyze any variation in results. *(Real-World Lab; Skills Lab)*	◆ **Scale and Structure** Birds and mammals possess many specialized systems, each serving a specific function. *(Sections 1–4)* ◆ **Unity and Diversity** Birds and mammals have some similar characteristics, such as endothermy and a four-chambered heart. Birds share many characteristics that distinguish the group from mammals. Also, within the group there is great diversity. Mammals also share many similar characteristics distinguishing them from birds, and show great diversity within the group. *(Sections 1–4; Skills Lab)* ◆ **Systems and Interactions** The interaction between the respiratory and circulatory systems in both birds and mammals provides these organisms with abundant energy. The interaction of a complex nervous system with keen senses allows fast movement and reaction. *(Sections 1, 3)* ◆ **Modeling** Students create models demonstrating the ability of wool to provide insulation. *(Real-World Lab)*

Take It to the Net

 *Interactive text at www.phschool.com*

Science Explorer comes alive with iText.

- **Complete student text** is accessible from any computer with Internet access or a CD-ROM drive.
- **Animations, simulations, and videos** enhance student understanding and retention of concepts.
- **Self-tests and online study tools** assess student understanding.

STAY CURRENT with **SCIENCE NEWS**®

Find out the latest research and information about animals at:
www.phschool.com

Go to **www.phschool.com** and click on the Science icon. Then click on Science Explorer: Life, Earth, and Physical Science under PH@school.

ACTIVITY	Time (minutes)	Materials Quantities for one work group	Skills
Section 1			
Discover, p. 410	15	**Nonconsumable** feathers, hand lens	Observing
Skills Lab, pp. 414–415	50	**Consumable** owl pellet **Nonconsumable** hand lens, dissecting needle, metric ruler, forceps	Drawing Conclusions
Try This, p. 417	20	**Consumable** uncooked egg, water **Nonconsumable** bowl, hand lens	Observing
Section 2			
Discover, p. 420	10	**Consumable** notebook paper **Nonconsumable** scissors, metric ruler, book	Predicting
Try This, p. 421	30	**Consumable** sheets of different kinds of paper (letter, construction, foil-covered), tape, glue, staples **Nonconsumable** paper clips, string, rubber bands	Making Models
Section 3			
Discover, p. 423	15	**Consumable** cracker **Nonconsumable** hand mirror	Inferring
Try This, p. 425	15	**Consumable** shortening, paper towels, cold water **Nonconsumable** rubber gloves, bucket or sink	Inferring
Sharpen Your Skills, p. 427	15	No special materials are required.	Classifying
Science at Home, p. 428	home	**Consumable** label from milk container	Interpreting Data
Real-World Lab, p. 429	35	**Consumable** hot tap water, graph paper, room temperature tap water **Nonconsumable** scissors, 1-L beaker, 3 thermometers, clock or watch, a pair of wool socks, 3 250-mL containers with lids	Controlling Variables, Interpreting Data
Section 4			
Discover, p. 431	15	**Consumable** masking tape, paper **Nonconsumable** pencil, various objects such as books and shoes	Inferring

A list of all materials required for the Student Edition activities can be found on pages T25–T33. You can obtain information about ordering materials by calling 1-800-848-9500 or by accessing the Science Explorer Internet site at **www.phschool.com**.

Bird Watch

Scientists learn about birds and mammals through careful observation. Watching a bird feeder will exercise students' ability to accurately observe and record observations. By watching a feeder, students can learn about bird communication, territoriality, and food choice.

Purpose In this project, students will model the skills and observations required for the careful study of any group of animals. They will observe the interaction among birds, and record feeding behavior and food preference in different birds.

Skills Focus Students will be able to
◆ observe and identify birds at a feeder;
◆ classify behaviors;
◆ create data tables;
◆ interpret data from their experiment.

Project Time Line During the first week, students select the feeder location and begin to observe and identify the species. During the second week, students make a list of bird species and begin to record common behaviors. In week three, students concentrate on feeding behaviors. Finally, students devise a way to present the information they have collected.

Before beginning the project, see Chapter 13 Project Teacher Notes on pages 90–91 in Unit 3 Resources for more details on carrying out the project. Distribute to students the Chapter 13 Project Overview, Worksheets, and Scoring Rubric on pages 92–96 in Unit 3 Resources.

Possible Materials
◆ a commercial bird feeder or materials to construct a feeder
◆ birdseed
◆ string or wire for hanging bird feeder
◆ field guide for bird identification
◆ guide to bird behaviors

Launching the Project To introduce the project and to stimulate student interest, ask: **What birds have you seen in your neighborhood?**

CHAPTER 13 Birds and Mammals

WEB ACTIVITY www.phschool.com

SECTION 1 Birds

Discover **What Are Feathers Like?**
Skills Lab **Looking at an Owl's Leftovers**
Try This **Eggs-amination**

Integrating Physics
SECTION 2 The Physics of Bird Flight

Discover **What Lifts Airplanes and Birds Into the Air?**
Try This **It's Plane to See**

SECTION 3 What Is a Mammal?

Discover **What Are Mammals' Teeth Like?**
Try This **Insulated Mammals**
Sharpen Your Skills **Classifying**
Science at Home **Mammals' Milk**
Real-World Lab **Keeping Warm**

408

Allow time for students to read the description of the project in their texts and the Chapter Project Overview on pages 92–93 in Unit 3 Resources. Then encourage discussions on bird feeders, bird behavior, and materials that could be used to construct a feeder; then answer initial questions students may have. Pass out copies of the Chapter 13 Project Worksheets on pages 94–95 in Unit 3 Resources for students to review.

Placement of the bird feeders should be discussed with the class. It is important to place the feeders so that they are easily refilled with food and easily observed. They should also be placed in or close to trees or shrubs so that birds have a safe place to go if they are startled.

The feeders should be refilled daily. Harmful molds can grow in wet seeds. If the birdseed gets wet, immediately discard it, wash and dry the feeder, and refill with fresh seed.

Bird Watch

One of the best ways to learn about animals is to watch them in action. In this project, you'll watch birds and other animals that visit a bird feeder. You may be surprised at how much you will discover. How do birds eat? Which ones eat first? How do different birds interact? What happens if a squirrel arrives on the scene? Careful observation and record keeping will reveal answers to these questions. They may also raise new questions for you to answer.

Your Goal To make detailed observations of the birds that appear at a bird feeder.

To complete this project successfully, you must
◆ observe the feeder regularly for at least two weeks, and identify the kinds of birds that visit the feeder
◆ make detailed observations of how the birds at your feeder eat
◆ describe the most common kinds of bird behavior
◆ follow the safety guidelines in Appendix A

Get Started Begin by meeting with some classmates to share your knowledge about the birds in your area. What kinds of birds can you expect to see? What types of foods do birds eat? Brainstorm how you could find out more about the birds that live in your area.

Check Your Progress You'll be working on this project as you study this chapter. To keep your project on track, look for Check Your Progress boxes at the following points.
Section 1 Review, page 419: Identify birds (and mammals) that come to the feeder. Observe how the animals interact.
Section 2 Review, page 422: Observe how birds feed.
Section 4 Review, page 436: Interpret your bird-feeding data, and prepare your graphs.

Present Your Project At the end of this chapter (page 439), you will share what you have learned about birds and their behavior.

This broad-tailed hummingbird enjoys a sip of nectar from a beardtongue flower.

SECTION 4 Diversity of Mammals

Discover **How Is a Thumb Useful?**

Program Resources

◆ **Unit 3 Resources** Chapter 13 Project Teacher Notes, pp. 90–91; Chapter 13 Project Overview and Worksheets, pp. 92–95; Chapter 13 Project Scoring Rubric, p. 96

WEB ACTIVITY www.phschool.com

You will find an Internet activity, chapter self-tests for students, and links to other chapter topics at this site.

Have students observe and record the numbers of a particular species and the interaction of those birds with members of other species. They should collect and interpret bird-feeding data, taking note of what type of seed seems to be preferred by particular species. It is also important to note the birds' interaction with other animals, such as dogs or squirrels.

Performance Assessment

The Chapter 13 Project Scoring Rubric on page 96 of Unit 3 Resources will help you evaluate how well students complete the Chapter 13 Project. You may wish to share the scoring rubric with your students so they are clear about what will be expected of them. Students will be assessed on
◆ how thoroughly they research the birds of the area so that they use appropriate feeders, food, and locations;
◆ the completeness of their observation entries, including what birds appeared, interactions, and foods eaten;
◆ how well they apply chapter concepts to their observations;
◆ the thoroughness and organization of their presentations;
◆ the organization of their written analyses.

SECTION 1 Birds

Objectives

After completing the lesson, students will be able to

◆ identify the common characteristics of birds;

◆ explain how birds are adapted to and affect their environments.

Key Terms birds, contour feather, down feather, insulator, crop, gizzard

1 Engage/Explore

Activating Prior Knowledge

Brainstorm a list of expressions about birds and write them on the board. *(Samples: birds of a feather flock together; bird's-eye view; birdlike appetite)* Ask students whether these are scientifically valid. List students' ideas on the board. Later, after students have read the section, ask them to look at the expressions again. Students should reevaluate the accuracy of each expression on the basis of what they have learned.

•••••• DISCOVER ••••••

Skills Focus observing
Materials *feathers, hand lens*
Time 15 minutes
Tips Try to have a variety of contour feathers. Good sources are wooded areas, beaches, pet stores, bird sanctuaries, or biological supply houses. Fresh feathers should be frozen for 72 hours to kill organisms. Point out the shaft and barbs of a feather.
Expected Outcome Feathers have a central shaft with a vane made up of flexible barbs that link together but can be pulled apart.
Think It Over The barbs rejoin easily; this helps birds smooth their feathers quickly to fly or swim.

SECTION 1 Birds

DISCOVER •••••••••••••••••••••••••••••••••• ACTIVITY

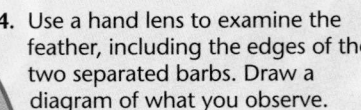

What Are Feathers Like?

1. Examine a feather. Observe its overall shape and structure. Use a hand lens to examine the many hairlike barbs that project out from the feather's central shaft.

2. With your fingertip, gently stroke the feather from bottom to top. Observe whether the barbs stick together or separate.

3. Gently separate two barbs in the middle of the feather. Rub the separated edges with your fingertip.

4. Use a hand lens to examine the feather, including the edges of the two separated barbs. Draw a diagram of what you observe.

5. Now rejoin the two separated barbs by gently pulling outward from the shaft. Then wash your hands.

Think It Over
Observing Once barbs have been separated, is it easy to rejoin them? How might this be an advantage to the bird?

GUIDE FOR READING

◆ What characteristics do birds have in common?

◆ How are birds adapted to their environments?

Reading Tip Before you read, look at *Exploring a Bird* on page 413 and make a list of unfamiliar terms. As you read, write definitions for the terms.

One day in 1861, in a limestone quarry in what is now Germany, Hermann von Meyer was inspecting rocks. Meyer, who was a fossil hunter, spotted something dark in one of the rocks. It was the blackened fossil imprint of a feather! Excited, Meyer began searching for a fossil of an entire bird. Though it took a month, he eventually found what he was looking for—a skeleton surrounded by the clear imprint of many feathers. The fossil was given the scientific name *Archaeopteryx* (ahr kee AHP tur iks), meaning "ancient, winged thing."

Paleontologists estimate that *Archaeopteryx* lived about 145 million years ago. *Archaeopteryx* didn't look much like the birds you know. It looked more like a reptile with wings. While no modern bird has any teeth, *Archaeopteryx* had a mouthful of them. No modern bird has a long, bony tail, either, but *Archaeopteryx* did. However, unlike any reptile, extinct or modern, *Archaeopteryx* had feathers—its wings and tail were covered with them. Paleontologists think that *Archaeopteryx* and today's birds descended from some kind of reptile, possibly from a dinosaur.

Figure 1 The extinct bird *Archaeopteryx* may have looked like this.

READING STRATEGIES

Reading Tip After students write definitions for unfamiliar terms, instruct them to write sentences in which they use each term. (Sample: contour feather— contour feathers give shape to a bird's body. Hummingbirds and turkeys must have very different contour feathers.) Then have students rewrite the sentences on a separate sheet of paper, omitting the key terms and inserting a blank line. Direct partners to exchange papers and fill in the missing terms.

Study and Comprehension Encourage students to set their own purposes for reading this section by rewriting section headings as questions.

Figure 2 John James Audubon painted this little blue heron in 1832. (© Collection of the New York Historical Society)

What Is a Bird?

Modern **birds** all share certain characteristics. **A bird is an endothermic vertebrate that has feathers and a four-chambered heart, and lays eggs.** Birds have scales on their feet and legs, evidence of their descent from reptiles. In addition, most birds can fly.

The flight of birds is an amazing feat that people watch with delight and envy. All modern birds—including ostriches, penguins, and other flightless birds—evolved from ancestors that could fly.

The bodies of birds are adapted for flight. For example, the bones of a bird's forelimbs form wings. In addition, many of a bird's bones are nearly hollow, making the bird's body extremely lightweight. Flying birds have large chest muscles that move the wings. Finally, feathers are a major adaptation that help birds fly.

Checkpoint **List four ways in which birds are adapted for flight.**

Feathers

The rule is this: If it has feathers, it's a bird. Feathers probably evolved from reptiles' scales. Both feathers and reptile scales are made of the same tough material as your fingernails.

Birds have different types of feathers. If you've ever picked up a feather from the ground, chances are good that it was a contour feather. A **contour feather** is one of the large feathers that give shape to a bird's body. The long contour feathers that extend beyond the body on the wings and tail are called flight feathers. When a bird flies, these feathers help it balance and steer.

Visual Arts CONNECTION

John James Audubon (1785–1851) was an American artist who painted pictures of birds and other kinds of animals. Audubon grew up in France. Even as a child he loved to sketch the birds that he observed while roaming through the forest. Later, as an adult in America, he began to study and draw birds seriously, traveling to various parts of the country in search of different varieties of birds.

Audubon's four-volume work, *The Birds of America,* published between 1827 and 1838, contains 435 pictures showing 489 different bird species. Audubon's paintings, such as that of the little blue heron in Figure 2, are known for their accuracy and remarkable detail as well as their beauty.

In Your Journal

List five observations that you can make about the little blue heron in Audubon's painting, such as the shape of its bill and the pattern of color on its body. Then describe the heron's environment.

---

2 Facilitate

What Is a Bird?

Including All Students

To help students understand the characteristics of birds, pair students who are still mastering English with students who are proficient in English. Have each pair list the following terms: *endothermic, vertebrate, feathers, four-chambered heart,* and *egg-laying.* Challenge student pairs to write brief definitions of each term and to list three or four animals that share these characteristics. (*Sample: Vertebrates have backbones and include lizards, giraffes, and fish.*) **limited English proficiency**

Visual Arts CONNECTION

Invite each student to choose a bird in *The Birds of America* and compare its picture with the picture and description of the same bird in a field guide. Ask how each book might be useful in identifying an unknown bird. Also, ask students what the Audubon print shows better than the field guide, and vice versa.

In Your Journal Students should observe that the heron has a long, pointed, mostly blue bill; long, curved neck; black head and tail; blue wings; and long, thin legs. **learning modality: visual**

Answers to Self-Assessment

Checkpoint

Bird adaptations for flight include forelimb bones that form wings, bones that are nearly hollow, large chest muscles, and feathers.

Ongoing Assessment

Oral Presentation Ask students to name at least four characteristics all birds share. (*Accept any four: endothermic, vertebrates, feathers, four-chambered hearts, lay eggs, scales on their feet and legs*)

Feathers

Integrating Physics

Materials *3 plastic containers, 3 ice cubes, clock, insulating materials such as down feathers, shredded paper, cotton balls, shredded plastic foam, aluminum foil, plastic wrap*

ACTIVITY

Time 35 minutes

Have students work in groups to test different insulators. Each group should wrap an ice cube in one of the insulators, place it in a container, and observe it every 5 minutes for 30 minutes. Ask: **What variables must be the same in all your experiments?** *(The size of the ice cube, the temperature, size, and shape of the containers)* Invite students to predict which insulator will be the most effective. Groups can compare data and draw conclusions about which insulator is the most effective. **cooperative learning**

Food and Body Temperature

Including All Students

Materials *saltine cracker, plastic jar, several small pebbles*

ACTIVITY

Time 10 minutes

This activity benefits students who have difficulty seeing, because it conveys concepts through tactile experiences. It also helps other students who need extra help to understand how a gizzard works. Direct students to place a saltine cracker in a plastic jar along with several small pebbles. Have them put the lid on the jar and shake it for 30 seconds. Students who have difficulty seeing may open the jar and feel the cracker. (Caution students not to eat the crackers or crumbs.) Then ask: **What happened to the cracker?** *(It broke into smaller pieces.)* **How is the jar like a gizzard?** *(Both grind food using stones.)* **How are they different?** *(The gizzard is a muscular wall that squeezes as it grinds the food. The jar is a hard container that has to be shaken to grind the food.)* **learning modality: kinesthetic**

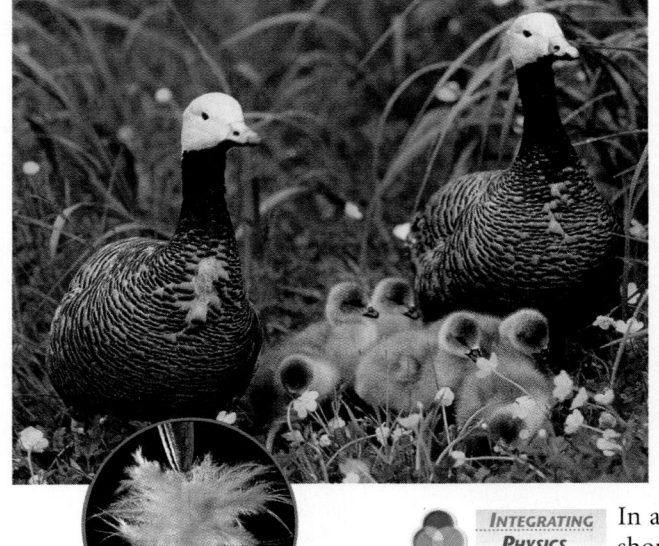

Figure 3 Birds are the only animals that have feathers. **A.** Down feathers act as insulation to trap warmth next to a bird's body. **B.** Contour feathers, like this one from a Steller's jay, give a bird its shape and help it to fly. *Observing Where do you see down feathers and contour feathers on the family of Emperor geese above?*

In Figure 3, you can see that a contour feather consists of a central shaft and many hairlike projections, called barbs, that are arranged parallel to each other. If you examined a contour feather in the Discover activity, you know that you can "unzip" its flat surface by pulling apart the barbs. When birds fly, their feathers sometimes become "unzipped." To keep their flight feathers in good condition, birds often pull the feathers through their bills in an action called preening. Preening "zips" the barbs back together again, smoothing the ruffled feathers.

INTEGRATING PHYSICS In addition to contour feathers, birds have short, fluffy **down feathers** that are specialized to trap heat and keep the bird warm. Down feathers are found right next to a bird's skin, at the base of contour feathers. Down feathers are soft and flexible, unlike contour feathers. Down feathers mingle and overlap, trapping air. Air is a good **insulator**—a material that does not conduct heat well and therefore helps prevent it from escaping. By trapping a blanket of warm air next to the bird's skin, down feathers slow the rate at which the skin loses heat. In effect, down feathers cover a bird in lightweight long underwear.

✓ *Checkpoint* *Why do you think quilts and jackets are often stuffed with down feathers?*

Food and Body Temperature

Birds have no teeth. To capture, grip, and handle food, birds primarily use their bills. Each species of bird has a bill shaped to help it feed quickly and efficiently. For example, the pointy, curved bill of a hawk acts like a meat hook. A hawk holds its prey with its claws and uses its sharp bill to pull off bits of flesh. In contrast, the straight, sharp bill of a woodpecker is a tool for chipping into wood. When a woodpecker chisels a hole in a tree and finds a tasty insect, the woodpecker spears the insect with its long, barbed tongue.

After a bird eats its food, digestion begins. Each organ in a bird's digestive system is adapted to process food. Many birds have an internal storage tank, or **crop,** that allows them to store food inside the body after swallowing it. Find the crop in *Exploring a Bird.* The crop is connected to the stomach.

412

Background

Integrating Science The origin of feathers is not clearly understood. The most common belief is that feathers are modified scales. The scales on the leg of the bird are made of keratin and form the same way a reptile's scales do. In the early stages of development, scales and feathers are very similar to each other. This evidence leads scientists to believe that feathers evolved from early reptilian scales. In fact, many paleontologists believe that today's birds evolved from a certain type of dinosaur. Fossils that were recently discovered in China seem to reveal two different species of feathered dinosaurs. The scientists who studied these fossils think that the feathers probably served as insulation, because they doubt that the dinosaurs could fly.

The first part of the stomach is long and has thin walls. Here food is bathed in chemicals that begin to break it down. Then the partially digested food moves to a thick-walled, muscular part of the stomach called the **gizzard,** which squeezes and grinds the partially digested food. Remember that birds do not have teeth—their gizzard performs the grinding function of teeth. The gizzard may contain small stones that the bird has swallowed. These stones help with the grinding by rubbing against the food and crushing it.

EXPLORING *a Bird*

I f you are strolling through a grassy field or meadow in spring, you might hear the beautiful song of a meadowlark. Notice how a meadowlark's body is adapted for flight and for a high level of activity.

Air Sacs A bird's lungs are connected to a series of air sacs. Air sacs help provide the bird's body with the rich supply of oxygen it needs.

Bill A meadowlark uses its bill to catch insects and pick up seeds.

Contour Feathers Contour feathers give a bird its shape. Without its contour feathers, a bird cannot fly.

Crop

Gizzard The muscular gizzard churns food and grinds it to a paste.

Heart Like all birds, meadowlarks have a four-chambered heart that keeps oxygen-rich blood separate from oxygen-poor blood. Thus the blood arriving at the tissues carries the most oxygen possible.

413

Ask students to find the structures in the visual essay that help the bird fly. Most will select the feathers and wings. Point out other structures. Ask: **How do the air sacs and heart work as a bird flies?** *(The air sacs provide the oxygen. The heart pumps oxygen-rich blood to the body.)* Have students find the structures that are parts of the bird's digestive system. Ask: **How does the crop benefit the bird?** *(It allows the bird to store food.)* Have students trace the path through the digestive system. *(From the bill to the crop, to the stomach, to the gizzard, to the intestines)*

Extend Meadowlarks live in grassy environments and move mostly by flying. Have students examine photos of birds that are adapted for other forms of movement, such as ocean birds that dive and swim. Students can compare the bills, feathers, and body shapes of these birds. **learning modality: visual**

Cultural Diversity

Birds appear in the folklore of many cultures. In the folklore of ancient Egypt, an indestructible bird called a phoenix rises from the ashes of its own funeral pyre. The Yosei are fairies in Japanese folklore that appear as cranes or swans. In Siberian folklore, the Zonget is a goddess who appears as an Arctic bird and decides whether hunted birds and animals will be caught. Ask students: **How are other birds used as symbols?** *(Sample: Doves symbolize peace; peacocks symbolize vanity.)* **learning modality: verbal**

Media and Technology

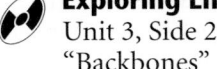 **Exploring Life Science Videodisc**
Unit 3, Side 2, "Backbones"

Chapter 3

Answers to Self-Assessment

Caption Question

Figure 3 Down feathers are found on the young geese. Contour feathers are found on the adults.

☑ *Checkpoint*

Quilts and jackets are often stuffed with down feathers because the feathers are good insulators. This makes the garments very warm.

Ongoing Assessment

Skills Check Have students make a flowchart of the passage of food through a bird's digestive system. Students can save their flowcharts in their portfolios.

Looking at an Owl's Leftovers

Preparing for Inquiry

Key Concept Conclusions about an animal's diet can be drawn by examining the parts that are not digested.

Skills Objective The students will be able to

◆ draw conclusions about the diet of owls by studying the pellets they cough up.

Time 50 minutes

Advance Planning Order owl pellets from a biological supply company. If possible, obtain one for each student and a few extras.

Guiding Inquiry

Invitation Have students think about what they discard when they eat. Ask: **What do you have left over when you eat a chicken wing? What about an apple?** *(Bones, apple core)* Inform students that other animals also leave behind parts of their food, and these leftovers can be studied to determine what the animal ate.

Introducing the Procedure

◆ Before students begin dissecting, allow them to use dissecting needles to examine a cookie with nuts, chocolate chips, or raisins. Warn students not to eat the cookies.

◆ Encourage students to examine the outside of the pellet before making hypotheses.

◆ Owls may eat lizards or snakes. Provide pictures of lizard and snake bones to help students identify them.

Troubleshooting the Experiment

◆ Explain that the pellets have been decontaminated. Have reluctant students work with a partner and perform the roles of data collection and record keeping.

◆ It is helpful to break pellets into pieces and soak them in water to loosen the materials before beginning the dissection.

Like all animals, birds use the food they eat for energy. Because birds are endotherms, they need a lot of energy to maintain their body temperature. It also takes an enormous amount of energy to power the muscles used in flight. Each day an average bird eats food equal to about a quarter of its body weight. When people say, "You're eating like a bird," they usually mean that you're eating very little. But if you were actually eating as a bird does, you would be eating huge meals. You might eat 100 hamburger patties in one day!

Skills Lab

Drawing Conclusions

LOOKING AT AN OWL'S LEFTOVERS

In this lab, you will gather evidence and draw conclusions about an owl's diet.

Problem

What can you learn about owls' diets from studying the pellets that they cough up?

Materials

owl pellet   hand lens   dissecting needle
metric ruler   forceps

Procedure

1. An owl pellet is a collection of undigested materials that an owl coughs up after a meal. Write a hypothesis describing what items you expect an owl pellet to contain. List the reasons for your hypothesis.

2. Use a hand lens to observe the outside of an owl pellet. Record your observations.

3. Use one hand to grasp the owl pellet with forceps. Hold a dissecting needle in your other hand, and use it to gently separate the pellet into pieces. **CAUTION:** *Dissecting needles are sharp. Never cut material toward you; always cut away from your body.*

4. Using the forceps and dissecting needle, carefully separate the bones from the rest of the pellet. Remove any fur that might be attached to bones.

414

Background

Facts and Figures Birds can have unusual ways of obtaining food. Hummingbirds sip nectar while hovering in midair. Woodpecker finches use a broken piece of cactus spine to pry grubs and insects out of tree bark. African secretary birds stamp snakes with their feet before eating them. Owls use a keen sense of hearing to listen for prey. In the dark, an owl can accurately locate a mouse rustling in the leaves and grass. Some vultures can smell a potential meal from a great distance.

Delivering Oxygen to Cells

Cells must receive plenty of oxygen to release the energy contained in food. Flying requires much energy. Therefore, birds need a highly efficient way to get oxygen into their body and to their cells. Birds have a system of air sacs in their body that connects to the lungs. The air sacs enable birds to extract much more oxygen from each breath of air than other animals can.

The circulatory system of a bird is also efficient at getting oxygen to the cells. Unlike amphibians and most reptiles,

Shrew	House mouse	Meadow vole	Mole	Rat
			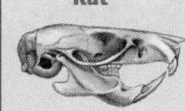	
Upper jaw has at least 18 teeth; tips of the teeth are brown. Skull length is 23 mm or less.	Upper jaw has 2 biting teeth and extends past lower jaw. Skull length is 22 mm or less.	Upper jaw has 2 biting teeth that are smooth, not grooved. Skull length is more than 23 mm.	Upper jaw has at least 18 teeth. Skull length is 23 mm or more.	Upper jaw has 2 biting teeth and extends past lower jaw. Skull length is 22 mm or more.

5. Group similar bones together in separate piles. Observe the skulls, and draw them. Record the number of skulls, their length, and the number, shape, and color of the teeth.

6. Use the chart on this page to determine what kinds of skulls you found. If any skulls do not match the chart exactly, record which animal the skulls resemble most.

7. Try to fit together any of the remaining bones to form complete or partial skeletons. Sketch your results.

8. Wash your hands thoroughly with soap when you are finished.

Analyze and Conclude

1. How many animals' remains were in the pellet? What data led you to that conclusion?

2. Combine your results with those of your classmates. Which three animals were eaten most frequently? How do these results compare to your hypothesis?

3. Owls cough up about two pellets a day. Based on your class's data, what can you conclude about the number of animals an owl might eat in one month?

4. **Think About It** In this lab, you were able to examine only the part of the owl's diet that it did not digest. How might this fact affect your confidence in the conclusions you reached?

Design an Experiment

Design a study that might tell you how an owl's diet varies at different times of the year. Give an example of a conclusion you might expect to draw from such a study.

- Some pellets may not contain identifiable skulls because the skulls were coughed up in a different pellet. Few other animal remains are likely to be present in a pellet containing a skull.

Expected Outcome
Students should find a varying number of identifiable animal remains in their pellets.

Analyze and Conclude
1. Answers will vary. Students should explain that the number of each type of bone can help determine the number of animals eaten. For example, each skull represents one animal. Each pair of femurs represents one animal.
2. Combined data should give an estimate of total number and type of animals in the pellets.
3. The estimated total of animals found in all pellets divided by the number of pellets dissected gives an average number of animals per pellet. Students can multiply this number by 2 to find the average number of animals eaten per day. Then, multiply the average number per day by 30 to find the average number of animals eaten per month.
4. Students may explain that they are less confident in their results because they will probably underestimate the number of animals eaten each month.

Extending Inquiry

Design an Experiment A sample study might be to analyze pellets collected on the last two days of each month for a year. From this study, students would expect to conclude that an owl's diet varies during the year. In winter, hibernating animals will be absent. Animals such as house mice, which are always active, may be common in the diet all year.

Safety

Students should wear safety goggles and handle the sharp dissecting needles carefully. Remind students to wash their hands thoroughly after completing the dissection. Review the safety guidelines in Appendix A.

Program Resources

- **Unit 3 Resources** Chapter 13 Skills Lab, pp. 113–115
- **Inquiry Skills Activity Book** Provides teaching and review of all inquiry skills

Delivering Oxygen to Cells

Inquiry Challenge

Have students find their pulse rates and count how  many times they breathe in 1 minute. Then have able students run in place for 1 minute. (CAUTION: *Students with medical problems that preclude running should be excused from the activity.*) Have students find their new pulse and breathing rates. Ask them to form hypotheses about what happens to a bird's heart and breathing rate when it flies. **learning modality: kinesthetic**

Nervous System and Senses

Building Inquiry Skills: Observing

Materials *binoculars*
Time 30 minutes

Take students outdoors to observe the way birds rely on their nervous systems. Students can use binoculars to observe and record specific activities, such as taking off, pecking, preening, or calling. They should also identify the senses that the bird probably used to perform the behavior. In class, place students in small groups and have them compile a master list of observations. **learning modality: visual**

Reproducing and Caring for Young

Demonstration

Materials *3 uncooked chicken eggs, a heavy book, clay, cotton balls*
Time 10 minutes

Place the eggs in clay supports, small ends up, in a triangular pattern. Pad between the eggs with cotton. Ask students to predict what will happen when you place a book on the eggs. Demonstrate this. Then ask: **How do strong eggs benefit birds?** (*They will not break if they roll or when a bird sits on them.*) **learning modality: visual**

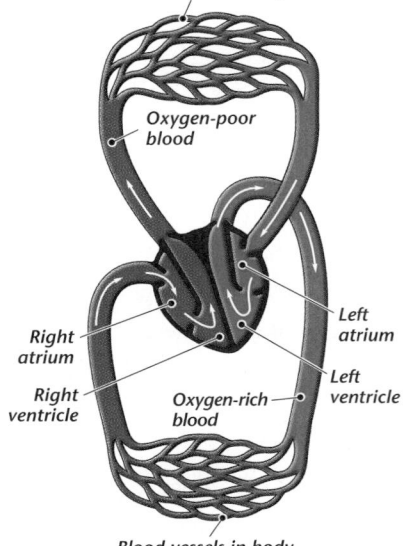

Figure 4 Birds have hearts with four chambers. Notice how the left side of the heart is completely separate from the right side. This separation prevents oxygen-rich blood from mixing with oxygen-poor blood.
Comparing and Contrasting Contrast a bird's circulatory system with that of an amphibian, as shown on page 390, Figure 14. How do the circulatory systems differ?

whose hearts have three chambers, birds have hearts with four chambers—two atria and two ventricles. Trace the path of blood through a bird's two-loop circulatory system in Figure 4. The right side of a bird's heart pumps blood to the lungs, where the blood picks up oxygen. Oxygen-rich blood then returns to the left side of the heart, which pumps it to the rest of the body. The advantage of a four-chambered heart is that there is no mixing of oxygen-rich and oxygen-poor blood. Therefore, blood that arrives in the body's tissues has plenty of oxygen.

Nervous System and Senses

In order to fly, birds must have very quick reactions. To appreciate why, imagine how quickly you would have to react if you were a sparrow trying to land safely on a tree branch. You approach the tree headfirst, diving into a maze of tree branches. As you approach, you only have an instant to find a place where you can land safely and avoid crashing into those branches. If birds had slow reactions, they would not live very long.

A bird can react so quickly because of its well-developed brain and finely tuned senses of sight and hearing. The brain of a bird controls such complex activities as flying, singing, and finding food. Most birds have keener eyesight than humans. A flying vulture, for example, can spot food on the ground from a height of more than one and a half kilometers. Some birds have excellent hearing, too. How could keen hearing help an owl search for prey in a dark forest?

Reproducing and Caring for Young

Like reptiles, birds have internal fertilization and lay eggs. Bird eggs are similar to reptile eggs, except that their shells are harder. In most bird species, the female lays the eggs in a nest that has been prepared by one or both parents.

Bird eggs will only develop at a temperature close to the body temperature of the parent bird. A parent bird usually incubates the eggs by sitting on them to keep them warm. In some species, incubating the eggs is the job of one parent. Female robins, for example, incubate their delicate blue eggs. In other species, such as pigeons, the parents take turns incubating the eggs.

Birds differ in the length of time that it takes for their chicks to develop until hatching. Sparrow eggs take only about 12 days. Chicken eggs take about 21 days, and albatross eggs take about 80 days. In general, the larger the bird species, the longer its incubation time.

Background

Facts and Figures The incubation period for bird eggs depends on the species of bird. Warblers, which are small birds, incubate their eggs for just 10 days. Albatrosses, which are large birds, incubate their eggs for about 10 weeks. The award for the most energy-efficient brooding strategy, however, has to go to the cowbird. Cowbirds do not incubate their eggs at all, but instead lay their eggs in the nests of other birds. Even though the cowbird egg is larger than the other birds' eggs, the unknowing foster parents incubate the egg of the intruder anyway. When the cowbird egg hatches, the cowbird chick is usually much larger than the other chicks. The cowbird chick eventually becomes so large that it pushes the smaller rival chicks out of the nest or takes their food. The foster parents raise the lone cowbird chick, never realizing that it is not their own.

Figure 5 This masked northern weaver bird is literally weaving a nest out of grass. The finished baglike nest will have only a small, weaver bird–sized hole in it. The small entrance helps keep the eggs and young safe from predators.

When it is ready to hatch, a chick pecks its way out of the eggshell. Some newly hatched chicks, such as bluebirds and robins, are featherless, blind, and so weak they can barely lift their heads to beg for food. Other chicks, such as ducks, chickens, and pheasants, are covered with down and can run about soon after they have hatched. Most parent birds feed and protect their young at least until they are able to fly.

☑ *Checkpoint* *How do bird eggs differ from reptile eggs?*

Diversity of Birds

With almost 10,000 species, birds are the most diverse land-dwelling vertebrates. **In addition to adaptations for flight, birds have adaptations—such as the shapes of their legs, claws, and bills—for living in widely diverse environments.** For example, the long legs and toes of wading birds, such as herons and cranes, make wading easy, while the toes of perching birds, such as goldfinches and mockingbirds, can automatically lock onto a branch or other perch. The bills of ducks enable them to filter tiny plants and animals from water. Birds also have adaptations for flying, finding mates, and caring for their young. You can see a variety of bird adaptations in *Exploring Birds* on the next page.

Eggs-amination

Like reptile eggs, bird eggs protect the developing embryo, provide food for it, and keep it from drying out.

1. Look at the surface of a chicken egg with a hand lens. Then gently crack the egg into a bowl. Do not break the yolk.

2. Note the membrane attached to the inside of the shell. Then look at the blunt end of the egg. What do you see?

3. Fill one part of the eggshell with water. What do you observe?

4. Find the egg yolk. What is its function?

5. Look for a small white spot on the yolk. This marks the spot where the embryo would have developed if the egg had been fertilized.

6. Wash your hands with soap.

Observing Draw a labeled diagram of the egg that names each structure and describes its function.

Skills Focus observing
Materials *uncooked egg, bowl, hand lens, water*
Time 20 minutes
Tips Uncooked eggs can carry bacteria. Tell students not to put eggs in their mouths. Suggest using only a little water in Step 3.
Answers There is an air pocket between the shell and the membrane. The water stays in the shell. The yolk provides food.
Observing Diagrams should identify the white spot, shell, yolk, egg white, and membrane. The egg and its shell keep water inside, protect the embryo, and provide nourishment (yolk).
Extend Have students gently roll an uncooked egg on a hard surface, and infer how the shape of an egg protects the embryo. (*The egg rolls in a circle, so it is less likely to roll out of the nest.*)
learning modality: visual

Diversity of Birds

Building Inquiry Skills: Classifying

Materials *pictures of birds, paper, tape, scissors*
Time 20 minutes

Provide pictures showing the legs and feet of various birds. Have students classify the pictures into two or three groups on the basis of the characteristics of the legs and feet—for example, webbed feet, and long, sharp claws. Have students cut out, group, and then tape the pictures to a sheet of paper.

Students can save their pictures in their portfolios. **learning modality: visual**

Media and Technology

 Transparencies "Circulation in Fishes, Amphibians, and Birds," Transparency 57

 **Exploring Life Science Videodisc** Unit 3, Side 2, "How Does Everything Fit?" Chapter 1

Answers to Self-Assessment

Caption Question

Figure 4 The amphibian's heart has three chambers, so oxygen-rich and oxygen-poor blood can mix somewhat. The bird's heart has four chambers that separate oxygen-rich and oxygen-poor blood.

☑ *Checkpoint*

Bird eggs are harder than reptile eggs and are usually laid in a nest.

Ongoing Assessment

Oral Presentation Call on students to briefly describe the functions and locations of a bird's four-chambered heart and air sacs.

Diversity of Birds, continued

EXPLORING
Birds

Invite volunteers to read aloud the description of the birds in the visual essay. When all descriptions have been read, ask:

◆ **What adaptations do the woodpecker and spoonbill have that help them eat the food in their environments?** *(The woodpecker has a sharp beak that chisels into trees. The spoonbill has a long, flat bill that it sweeps underwater to catch small animals.)*

◆ **How do the kestrel's eyes help it find food?** *(The placement of the eyes allows the kestrel to watch the ground while flying.)*

◆ **How are the leg and body proportions of the ostrich adaptations?** *(The ostrich's legs are long compared to its body; it cannot fly to escape predators, but its long legs help it run quickly.)*

Extend Challenge students to consider birds adapted to extreme environments such as penguins in Antarctica or road-runners in the desert. Have students draw conclusions about the adaptations that allow these birds to survive.
learning modality: visual

Why Birds Are Important

Integrating Environmental Science

Emphasize to students the important roles birds **ACTIVITY** play in helping to pollinate plants and eliminate pests. Encourage them to protect and care for birds in their own neighborhood. As trees are cut down, nesting habitats are lost. Building a birdhouse gives some kinds of homeless birds a place to nest. Have students research a particular bird and then design and build a birdhouse for birds that live in their neighborhood.
learning modality: verbal

EXPLORING Birds

Every bird has adaptations that help it live in its environment. Note how the bill and feet of each of these birds are adapted to help the bird survive.

▲ **Bee-eaters**
This rainbow bee-eater feeds on bees and other insects, which it catches as it flies. Bee-eaters, which are found in Africa, Europe, Australia, and Asia, help control insect pests such as locusts.

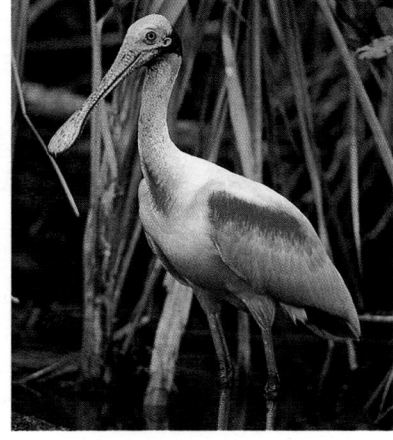

▲ **Long-Legged Waders**
The roseate spoonbill is found in the southern United States and throughout much of South America. The spoonbill catches small animals by sweeping its long, flattened bill back and forth underwater.

▲ **Woodpeckers**
The pileated woodpecker is the largest woodpecker in North America—adults average about 44 centimeters in length. This woodpecker feeds on insects it finds in holes it has chiseled into trees.

Ostriches
The ostrich, found in Africa, is the largest living bird. It cannot fly, but it can run at speeds greater than 60 kilometers per hour. Its speed helps it escape from predators. ▼

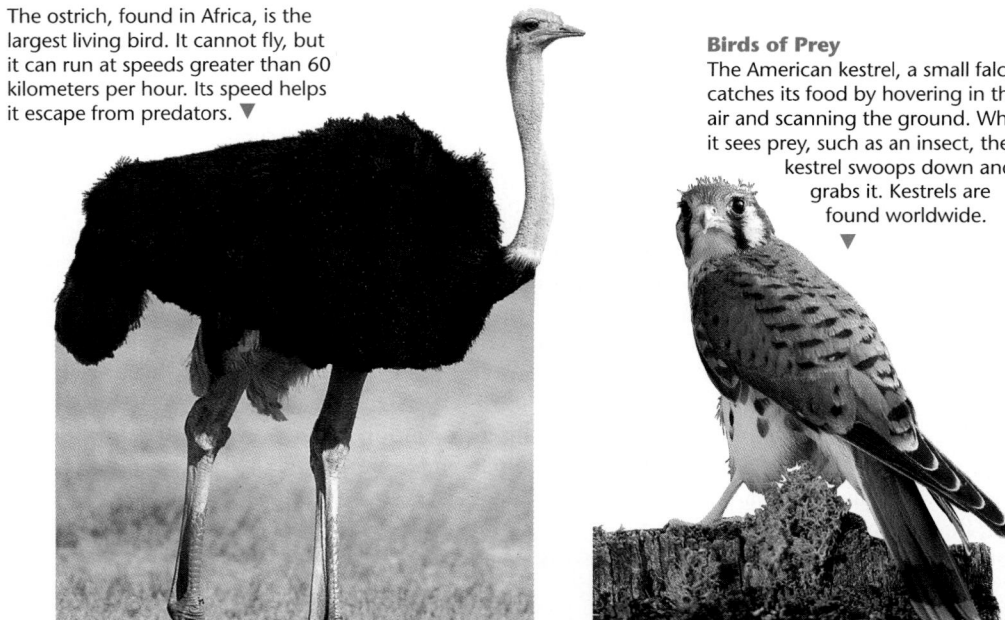

Birds of Prey
The American kestrel, a small falcon, catches its food by hovering in the air and scanning the ground. When it sees prey, such as an insect, the kestrel swoops down and grabs it. Kestrels are found worldwide.
▼

Background

Facts and Figures Animal species are disappearing all over the world. Many people do not realize that there may be threatened species in their backyards and neighborhoods. Some very hardy species of birds, such as sparrows and pigeons, have done very well in urbanized areas. However, recent studies have identified a new threat to these city dwellers—the effective hunting skills of the domestic cat. Cats are wonderful predators.

They can climb trees and remove fledglings from nests. They are excellent ambushers, and lie in wait or sneak up on unwary prey. As a result of the cats' efficient hunting strategies, populations of songbirds are declining all over the United States. The situation will only get worse as cat populations continue to increase. This problem has no immediate solution, but the answer may be as simple as putting bells on cats.

◄ **Owls**
Owls are predators that hunt mostly at night. Sharp vision and keen hearing help owls find prey in the darkness. Razor-sharp claws and great strength allow larger owls, like this eagle owl, to prey on animals as large as deer.

▲ **Perching Birds**
There are over 5,000 species of perching birds. They represent more than half of all the bird species in the world. The painted bunting, a seed-eating bird, lives in the southern United States and northern Mexico.

Why Birds Are Important

A walk through the woods or a park would be dull without birds. You wouldn't hear their musical songs, and you wouldn't see them flitting gracefully from tree to tree. But people benefit from birds in practical ways, too. Birds and their eggs provide food, while feathers are used to stuff pillows and clothing.

INTEGRATING ENVIRONMENTAL SCIENCE Birds also play an important role in the environment. Nectar-eating birds, like hummingbirds, carry pollen from one flower to another, thus enabling some flowers to reproduce. Seed-eating birds, like painted buntings, carry the seeds of plants to new places. This happens when the birds eat the fruits or seeds of a plant, fly to a new location, and then eliminate some of the seeds in digestive wastes. In addition, birds are some of the chief predators of pest animals. Hawks and owls eat many rats and mice, while many perching birds feed on insect pests.

Section 1 Review

1. What characteristics do modern birds share with reptiles? How are birds different from reptiles?
2. Choose two different bird species and describe how they are adapted to obtain food in their environment.
3. Predict how the size of crop harvests might be affected if all birds disappeared from Earth.
4. **Thinking Critically Comparing and Contrasting** Compare contour feathers with down feathers, noting both similarities and differences.

> ### Check Your Progress
> **CHAPTER PROJECT**
> By now you should have set up your bird feeder. As you begin making observations, use a field guide to identify the species of birds. Count and record the number of each species that appears. Also observe the birds' behaviors. How long do birds stay at the feeder? How do birds respond to other birds and mammals? Look for signs that some birds are trying to dominate others.

Program Resources

◆ **Unit 3 Resources** 13-1 Review and Reinforce, p. 99; 13-1 Enrich, p. 100
◆ **Laboratory Manual** 13, "Adaptations of Birds"
◆ **Interdisciplinary Exploration Series** "India Beyond the Golden Age," pp. 36–38

Media and Technology

Interactive Student Tutorial CD-ROM Chapter 13

---

3 Assess

Section 1 Review Answers

1. Shared characteristics: a vertebral column, breathe oxygen, lay eggs, and have scaly legs. Differences: birds—endotherms, feathers, four-chambered hearts; reptiles—ectotherms, lack feathers, and most have three-chambered hearts.
2. Students can use birds in the visual essay *Exploring Birds*. Sample: The woodpecker has a strong, pointy bill that can peck holes into trees. The spoonbill has long legs adapted to wading and a bill shaped to catch prey in the water.
3. Crop harvests would probably decrease, because birds would not be eating insect pests or spreading pollen and seeds.
4. Both are lightweight and made of the same material. Contour feathers are larger and have barbs that lock tightly and smoothly together. Down feathers have soft and fluffy barbs.

Check Your Progress
CHAPTER PROJECT
After students install their bird feeders, provide field guides to help them identify the species they observe. Check to see that students are recording appropriate observations. As students proceed with their observations, meet with them regularly to discuss their progress.

Performance Assessment

Writing Have each student write a paragraph describing at least six adaptations of birds. Students should describe feathers; the four-chambered heart; feeding and digestive-system adaptations; nervous system and senses; and reproductive adaptations.

SECTION 2 The Physics of Bird Flight

Objective

After completing the lesson, students will be able to
◆ explain how a bird is able to fly.

Key Term lift

1 Engage/Explore

Activating Prior Knowledge

Ask students to describe and demonstrate how they have seen birds fly. *(Some students will flap their arms up and down, while others will glide with their arms outstretched.)* Have students notice this difference and speculate how some birds seem to fly without putting forth any effort at all.

DISCOVER

Skills Focus predicting
Materials *notebook*
paper, scissors, metric ruler, book
Time 10 minutes
Tips The paper should be curled so that the free edge of the strip faces away from the student. Make sure students hold the book so that their breath flows across the top of the paper strip. Students should not blow down on the paper. Before students attempt the activity, ask them to predict what will happen. Then have them complete Step 3 and determine if their predictions were accurate.
Expected Outcome When students blow gently across the paper, it lifts slightly. When students blow hard across the paper, it lifts higher and remains in a horizontal position.
Think It Over The air flowing over the bird's wing might lift the bird up into the air.

SECTION 2 The Physics of Bird Flight

DISCOVER ·············· ACTIVITY

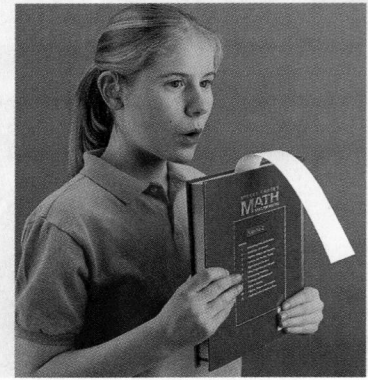

What Lifts Airplanes and Birds Into the Air?

1. Cut a strip of notebook paper 5 centimeters wide and 28 centimeters long. Insert about 5 centimeters of the paper strip into the middle of a book. The rest of the paper strip should hang over the edge.

2. Hold the book up so that the paper is below your mouth.

3. Blow gently across the top of the paper and watch what happens to the paper. Then blow harder.

Think It Over
Predicting If a strong current of air flowed across the top of a bird's outstretched wing, what might happen to the bird?

GUIDE FOR READING

◆ How is a bird able to fly?

Reading Tip Before you read, look at Figure 6 on page 421. Then predict how a bird's wing is similar to that of an airplane.

From ancient times, people have dreamed of soaring into the air like birds. When people first started experimenting with flying machines, they tried to glue feathers to their arms or to strap on feathered wings. Many failures, crash-landings, and broken bones later, these people had learned that feathers by themselves weren't the secret of flight. If an object is to fly, it must be lightweight. Another key to flying—for birds and insects as well as for airplanes—lies in the shape of wings and the way in which air moves across them.

How Air Moves Across a Wing

All objects on land are surrounded by an invisible ocean of air. Air is a mixture of gas molecules that exert pressure on the objects they surround. You see the results of air pressure when

▼ Owl in flight

READING STRATEGIES

Reading Tip Remind students that predicting involves making educated guesses. Show them an illustration of an airplane wing. Lead them to consider the shapes of the two wings, the airflow patterns around the wings, and the functions the wings perform. On the board, make a list of the students' conclusions of similarities of the two types of wings. (Sample: I predict that an airplane's wing and a bird's wing have similar shapes.)

Study and Comprehension Have students use the text to write summaries of how a bird is able to fly. Consider asking volunteers to read their summaries aloud.

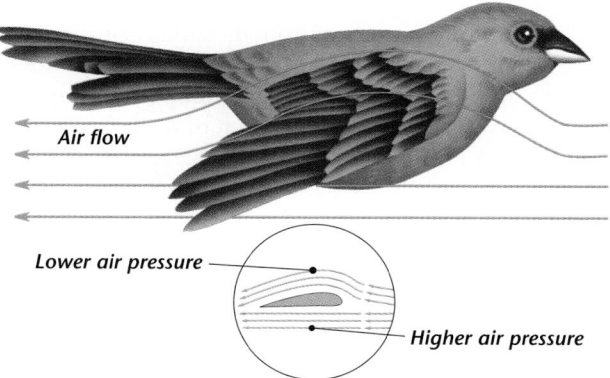

Air flow

Lower air pressure

Higher air pressure

Figure 6 Air moves faster across a wing's upper surface than across its lower surface. The fast-moving air exerts less pressure than the slow-moving air.
Relating Cause and Effect How does this difference in pressure help a bird to fly?

you blow up a balloon. The pressure of the air molecules pushing on the sides of the balloon makes the balloon expand.

Moving air exerts less pressure than air that is not moving. The faster air moves, the less pressure it exerts. In the Discover activity, the air blowing across the top of the paper was in motion. The moving air above the paper exerted less pressure than the air beneath it, so the paper rose.

Like the paper, a wing is surrounded by air molecules that exert pressure on the wing's surfaces. The lower surface of a wing—whether it belongs to a bird, an insect, or an airplane—is flatter than the upper surface. This difference between the shapes of the upper and lower surfaces of a wing helps birds, insects, and airplanes to fly. In Figure 6, you can see that the curved upper surface of a wing is a little longer than the flatter lower surface. When the wing moves forward, air travels the longer distance over the upper wing in the same amount of time as it takes to travel the shorter distance beneath the wing. Therefore, the air moves faster over the upper surface.

Because fast-moving air exerts less pressure than air that is moving slowly, the air above the wing exerts less pressure than the air beneath the wing. **The difference in pressure above and below the bird's wing produces an upward force that causes the wing to rise.** That upward force is called **lift.**

☑️ *Checkpoint How is the air pressure above a moving wing different from the air pressure below the wing?*

Birds in Flight

Wing shape alone does not enable a bird to fly—it must have some way of getting off the ground. To do this, a bird pushes off with its legs. The bird must also move forward, since lift depends

TRY THIS

It's Plane to See

Use this activity to discover how wing shape is important for flight.

ACTIVITY

1. Work with a partner to design a paper airplane with wings shaped like those of a bird. You can use any of these materials: paper, tape, glue, paper clips, string, rubber bands, and staples. Draw a sketch of your design.

2. Construct your "birdplane" and make one or two trial flights. If necessary, modify your design and try again.

3. Compare your design with those of other groups. Which designs were most successful?

Making Models In what ways was the flight of your airplane like the flight of a bird? In what ways was it different?

Program Resources

◆ **Unit 3 Resources** 13-2 Lesson Plan, p. 101; 13-2 Section Summary, p. 102

Media and Technology

 Audio CD English-Spanish Summary 13-2

 Transparencies "Bird Flight," Transparency 58

Answers to Self-Assessment

Caption Question

Figure 6 The difference in pressure produces lift, which makes the wings rise into the air.

☑️ *Checkpoint*

The air pressure above a moving wing is lower than the air pressure below a moving wing.

2 Facilitate

How Air Moves Across a Wing

Using the Visuals: Figure 6

Emphasize that the higher pressure under the wing creates an upward force. Guide students to trace the airflow in the figure with their fingers. **learning modality: visual**

TRY THIS

Skills Focus making models

ACTIVITY

Materials *sheets of different kinds of paper (letter, construction, foil-covered), tape, glue, paper clips, string, rubber bands, staples*

Time 30 minutes

Tips Elicit students' ideas for a design that allows air to flow rapidly over the nose and wing.

Making Models Sample: Both flights were the result of lift. However, a bird flaps its wings, while an airplane glides.

Extend Have students select a factor such as distance or time and compute the average for all their flights. **learning modality: kinesthetic**

Birds in Flight

Addressing Naive Conceptions

Explain that a bird does not simply flap its wings straight up and down; it rotates its wings upward, pulls them in, and opens up the spaces between its flight feathers. On the downward stroke, the bird turns its wings in the other direction with feathers closed so that the wing pushes flat against the air. **learning modality: verbal**

Ongoing Assessment

Writing Have students briefly describe how lift is created. (*The fast-moving air above the bird's wing exerts less pressure than the air below it. This creates an upward force—lift.*)

3 Assess

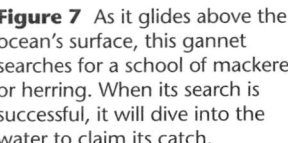

Section 2 Review Answers

1. Lift is an upward force caused by the difference in air pressure above and below a bird's wing.
2. A bird pushes off with its legs and pulls its wings down to move its body forward and upward.
3. Flapping flight requires a lot of wing movement and energy. Gliding and soaring require less energy. Gliding birds coast downward; soaring birds move upward on rising warm air currents.
4. The shape of a wing helps create the air patterns that cause lift. The loss of too many contour feathers will change the shape of the wing, reducing lift and preventing flight.

·· CHAPTER PROJECT

Check Your Progress

At this point, students should have a list of the various species of birds that visit their feeders. While students continue general observations, they should also concentrate on observing specific feeding behaviors. Feeding behavior includes how birds perch while eating, how birds use their beaks, and rituals such as head bobbing. Review students' notebooks and monitor their progress.

Performance Assessment

Drawing Have students draw and label the wing of a flying bird. Tell them to show the direction in which the air moves over the wing using arrows, and clearly label areas of high and low pressure. *(Students' drawings should indicate that air moves over the wing from front to back. The area of low pressure is over the wing, and the area of high pressure is under the wing.)*

Figure 7 As it glides above the ocean's surface, this gannet searches for a school of mackerel or herring. When its search is successful, it will dive into the water to claim its catch.

on air moving over its wings. So, at the same time that the bird pushes off from the ground, it sharply pulls its wings down. This downstroke provides the power that pushes the bird forward and upward.

Once they are in the air, birds fly in a variety of ways. All birds flap their wings at least part of the time. Flapping requires a lot of energy. Most small birds, such as sparrows, depend heavily on flapping flight. Canada geese and many other birds that travel long distances also use flapping flight.

Unlike flapping flight, soaring and gliding flight involve little wing movement. Birds soar and glide with their wings extended, as shown in Figure 7. When soaring, birds rise up into the sky on currents of warm air. In contrast, when gliding, birds coast downward through the air. Because they require less wing movement, soaring and gliding use less energy than flapping.

Sometimes birds fly with a combination of soaring and gliding. They "take the elevator up" by flying into a current of warm, rising air. The birds stretch their wings out and circle round and round within the column of rising air. High in the atmosphere the column of warm air grows cooler and ceases to rise. At this point the soaring bird "gets off the elevator" and begins gliding downward until it reaches the next "up elevator" of rising air. Predatory birds that spot their food from the air, such as hawks, often soar and glide.

The peregrine falcon, a predatory bird, is one of the fastest fliers. It catches its prey—often other birds such as pigeons—in flight. When it is pursuing prey, a peregrine's speed may reach 300 kilometers per hour. But it is not always useful for birds to fly fast. Birds that are migrating, or traveling long distances, take it slow but steady, usually flying 30 to 70 kilometers per hour. You will learn more about bird migrations in Chapter 14.

Section 2 Review

1. How is lift related to air pressure?
2. Explain how a bird takes off from the ground and begins to fly.
3. Compare and contrast flapping flight, soaring, and gliding.
4. **Thinking Critically Relating Cause and Effect** If a bird loses too many contour feathers, it can no longer fly. Relate this to the feathers' role in giving shape to a bird's wing.

422

CHAPTER PROJECT ····

Check Your Progress

As you continue your bird-feeder observations, pay careful attention to the way in which two or three different kinds of birds feed. Note the shapes of their beaks and how they use their beaks to pick up and crack seeds. Note how each bird's head moves during feeding. Also note whether certain birds prefer particular kinds of seeds. Write your detailed observations in your notebook.

Program Resources

◆ **Unit 3 Resources** 13-2 Review and Reinforce, p. 103; 13-2 Enrich, p. 104

Media and Technology

Exploring Physical Science Videodisc Unit 3, Side 2, "How an Airplane Flies"

Chapter 6

DISCOVER ••••••••••••••••••••••••••••••••••••• ACTIVITY

What Are Mammals' Teeth Like?

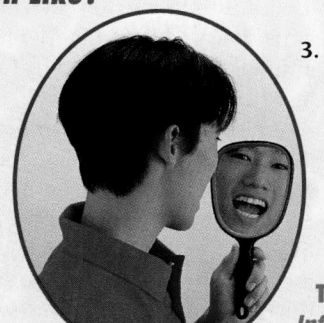

1. Wash your hands before you begin. Then, with a small mirror, examine the shapes of your teeth. Observe the incisors (the front teeth); the pointed canine teeth; the premolars that follow the canine teeth; and the molars, which are the large teeth in the rear of your jaws.

2. Compare and contrast the structures of the different kinds of teeth.

3. Use your tongue to feel the cutting surfaces of the different kinds of teeth in your mouth.

4. Bite off a piece of cracker and chew it. Observe the teeth that you use to bite and chew. Wash your hands when you are finished.

Think It Over
Inferring What is the advantage of having teeth with different shapes?

H igh in the Himalaya Mountains of Tibet, several yaks inch their way, single file, along a narrow cliff path. The cliff plunges thousands of meters to the valley below, so one false step can mean disaster. But the sure-footed yaks, carrying heavy loads of grain, slowly but steadily cross the cliff and make their way through the mountains.

Yaks, which are related to cows, have large lungs and a complex system of chest muscles that enables them to breathe deeply and rapidly. These structures allow yaks to obtain the oxygen necessary to survive at high altitudes. People who live in the mountains of central Asia have depended on yaks for thousands of years. Not only do yaks carry materials for trade, they also pull plows and provide milk. Mountain villagers weave blankets from yak hair and make shoes and ropes from yak hides.

The yak is a member of the group of vertebrates called **mammals,** a diverse group that share many characteristics. **All mammals are endothermic vertebrates with a four-chambered heart, and skin covered with fur or hair. The young of most mammals are born alive, and every young mammal is fed with milk produced in its mother's body.** In addition, mammals have teeth of different shapes that are adapted to their diets.

GUIDE FOR READING

♦ What characteristics do all mammals share?

Reading Tip As you read this section, write one or two sentences summarizing the information under each heading.

▼ Himalayan yak

Chapter 13 **423**

READING STRATEGIES

Reading Tip Remind students to use their own words when summarizing the information under each heading. (Sample: "Mammals First Appear"—Mammals evolved from mammal-like reptiles. The earliest mammals were tiny animals that lived alongside dinosaurs. Mammals are adapted to live on land and in water, or to fly in the air.)

Program Resources

♦ **Unit 3 Resources** 13-3 Lesson Plan, p. 105; 13-3 Section Summary, p. 106

Objective

After completing the lesson, students will be able to
♦ describe the characteristics all mammals share.

Key Terms mammal, incisor, canine, premolar, molar, diaphragm, mammary gland

1 Engage/Explore

Activating Prior Knowledge

Ask students who have mammals as pets to describe their pets' physical characteristics and behavior. Students can use their descriptions as a basis for making generalizations about the characteristics of mammals. If any of their generalizations are incorrect, make sure that students correct them after they have read the chapter.

•••••••••• **DISCOVER** ••••••••

Skills Focus inferring
Materials *hand mirror, cracker*

Time 15 minutes
Tips Tell students that for adult humans, the tooth arrangement from the middle of the row to the back is 2 incisors, 1 canine, 2 premolars, and 3 molars. Suggest that students wash their hands before they feel their teeth with their fingers. Ask: **Which teeth are sharp and good for cutting or tearing food?** *(Incisors and canines)* **For grinding up food?** *(Premolars and molars)* After students eat the cracker, ask: **How did you use your incisors?** *(To bite into the cracker)* **How did you use your molars?** *(To grind or chew up the cracker)* Remind students to wash their hands after this activity.
Think It Over Teeth with different shapes are adapted for different functions. This means that a wider variety of foods can be eaten.

2 Facilitate

Mammals First Appear

Building Inquiry Skills: Inferring

Remind students that small, early mammals lived during the time of the dinosaurs. Ask students to infer what might be some advantages of being small during the time large dinosaurs lived. *(Sample: Small animals could hide in small spaces to avoid the dinosaurs. Small animals would be hard to spot as they ran along the ground.)* **learning modality: verbal**

Cultural Diversity

Nearly all cultures use domesticated mammals. The yak in Tibet, the ox in Western Europe, and the llama in South America transport loads and help farmers plow fields. Ask students: **What domesticated mammals have been used in the United States?** *(Students may mention cows, oxen, or horses.)* Tell students mammals also provide milk and meat, rich sources of protein. In some cultures, such as that of the Masai people in East Africa, the cow is so highly valued that it is used as currency. **learning modality: verbal**

Fur and Hair

Building Inquiry Skills: Comparing and Contrasting

Provide students with pictures of different mammals, including some with a lot of hair and some with very little. Include pictures of the animals' heads and faces. Ask students: **Are there some kinds of hair that all these mammals have?** *(Students may notice that most mammals have whiskers around the eyes, lips, and muzzle.)* **learning modality: visual**

Today there are about 6,000 different species of mammals. There are mammals that you may never have seen, such as kangaroos and wildebeests, as well as familiar mammals such as dogs, cats, bats, and mice.

Mammals First Appear

Two hundred and seventy million years ago, before dinosaurs appeared, and long before birds appeared, there was a group of animals that had a blend of reptilian and mammalian characteristics. They were more like reptiles than mammals, but they resembled mammals in some ways, such as in the shapes of their teeth. These mammal-like reptiles, which became extinct about 160 million years ago, were the ancestors of the true mammals.

The earliest mammals were small, mouse-sized animals that lived in habitats dominated by dinosaurs. These early mammals may have been nocturnal, or active mainly at night, presumably the time when the dinosaurs were inactive or asleep. It was only after the dinosaurs disappeared, about 65 million years ago, that large mammals first evolved.

Most mammals, such as kangaroos and giraffes, became specialized to live on land. Other mammals, such as dolphins, became adapted to life in Earth's waters, while still others, the bats, became adapted to flight.

Fur and Hair

All mammals have fur or hair at some point in their lives. Like a bird's down feathers, thick fur provides lightweight insulation

Figure 8 The amount of fur or hair covering a mammal's body varies greatly. **A.** Hippopotamuses live in hot regions such as Africa year-round and have little hair. **B.** Gray wolves live in the northern half of North America and have thick fur coats during the cold winter months. During the summer, however, their coats are thinner. *Comparing and Contrasting Compare the function of a mammal's fur or hair to that of down feathers.*

424

Background

Integrating Science Scientists have evaluated fossil evidence, including animal jawbones and teeth, to determine that mammals first appeared on Earth about 220 million years ago. Many early mammals resembled shrews. Mammals did not begin to dominate land areas until about 65 million years ago, after the dinosaurs disappeared. At that time, early mammals began to diversify, filling the many niches left empty by the dinosaurs.

that prevents body heat from escaping. Fur and hair help mammals maintain a stable body temperature in cold weather. Each strand of hair or fur is composed of dead cells strengthened with the same tough material that strengthens feathers. Hair grows from living cells located below the surface of the skin.

The amount of hair that covers the skin of a mammal varies a great deal from group to group. Some mammals, such as whales and manatees, have only a few bristles. Others, including dogs and weasels, have thick, short fur. The fur of sea otters is thickest of all—on some areas of its body, a sea otter can have 150,000 hairs per square centimeter! Human bodies are covered with hair, but in places the hairs are spaced widely apart.

In general, animals that live in cold regions have thicker coats of fur than animals in warmer environments, as you can see by contrasting the hippopotamus and wolf in Figure 8. Mammals such as wolves and rabbits that live in places where cold and warm seasons alternate usually grow thicker coats in winter than in summer.

Fur is not the only adaptation that allows mammals to live in cold climates. Mammals also have a layer of fat beneath their skins. Fat, like fur and feathers, is an insulating material that keeps heat in the body. Recall that mammals are endotherms, which means that their bodies produce enough heat to maintain a stable body temperature regardless of the temperature of their environment.

☑ *Checkpoint* *What is the major function of fur or hair?*

Insulated Mammals

In this activity, **ACTIVITY** you will discover whether or not fat is an effective insulator.

1. Put on a pair of rubber gloves.
2. Spread a thick coating of solid white shortening on the outside of one of the gloves. Leave the other glove uncoated.
3. Put both hands in a bucket or sink filled with cold water.

Inferring Which hand got cold faster? Explain how this activity relates to mammalian adaptations.

Chapter 13 **425**

Media and Technology

 Audio CD English-Spanish
Summary 13-3

 Exploring Life Science Videodisc
Unit 3, Side 2,
"Backbones"

Chapter 3

Answers to Self-Assessment

☑ *Checkpoint*

Fur and hair prevent heat from escaping and help maintain a stable body temperature in cold weather.

Caption Question

Figure 8 Fur, hair, and down feathers all provide insulation by trapping air close to the skin.

Using the Visuals: Figure 8

Have students examine the picture of the wolf closely to see if they can recognize more than one type of fur. If the students have a pet dog or cat at home, they can also examine its fur. Ask: **What is the function of the short, woolly hairs?** *(Insulation)* **What is the function of the long, smooth hairs?** *(Protection of the undercoat)*

TRY THIS

Skills Focus inferring **ACTIVITY**
Materials *rubber gloves, shortening, bucket or sink full of cold water, paper towels*
Time 15 minutes
Tips Explain to students that shortening is a form of fat which has been processed for cooking. Have students work in pairs to coat each other's gloves. When students are experimenting with reactions to temperature, be sure they do not use water that is dangerously cold.
Inferring The hand in the glove without the shortening felt cold faster. Shortening is a fat and acts as an insulator. The glove with shortening keeps heat in the hand, just as animal fat keeps heat in the body of an animal.
Extend Have students coat the second glove with twice as much shortening as the first and compare to test whether more fat keeps them warmer. **learning modality: kinesthetic**

Ongoing Assessment

Writing Invite students to speculate about how the fur or hair of a mammal living in the Arctic tundra might differ from the fur or hair of a mammal living in the Amazon rain forest. *(The fur or hair of the mammal living in the tundra will probably be thicker than the fur or hair of the animal living in the rain forest.)*

Teeth

Including All Students

Students who are mastering English may need extra help to remember the names for the types of teeth. Obtain models or preserved jaws of a herbivore and a carnivore, such as a cow and a cat. Label the four types of teeth and have students say the names as they touch the teeth. Have students use the structure of the teeth to determine which animal is a carnivore and which is a herbivore. **limited English proficiency**

Getting Oxygen to Cells

Building Inquiry Skills: Observing

Have students place a hand flat on their abdomens about 6 cm above the navel. Ask students to describe the movement of their rib cages and diaphragms when they take a deep breath and then let it out. *(The diaphragm and ribs expand when they take a deep breath and contract when they let it out.)* **learning modality: kinesthetic**

Nervous System and Senses

Inquiry Challenge

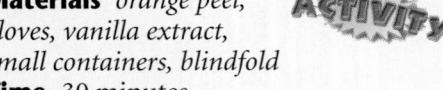

Materials *orange peel, cloves, vanilla extract, small containers, blindfold*
Time 30 minutes

Have groups of students design a simple experiment to answer a question about the senses using these materials. *(Sample: Can humans find their way using only their sense of smell?)* Groups should write plans for your approval before they perform the experiment. Have students predict the outcome, perform the experiment, and draw a conclusion. **cooperative learning**

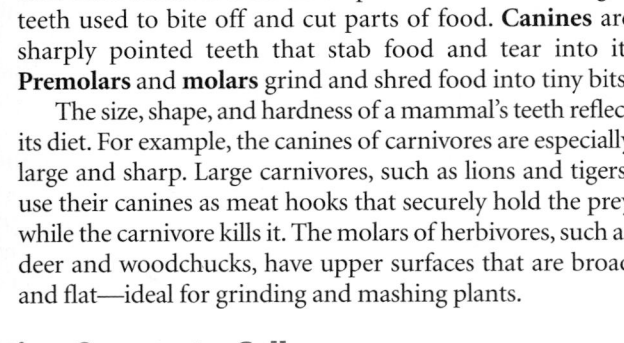

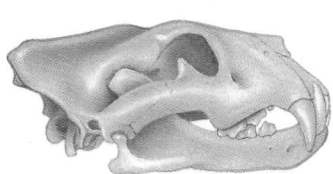

Figure 9 Lions have sharp, pointed teeth. Note the especially long canine teeth.
Inferring What kind of diet do lions eat?

Teeth

Endotherms need a lot of energy to maintain their body temperature, and that energy comes from food. Mammals' teeth are adapted to chew their food, breaking it into small bits that make digestion easier. Unlike reptiles and fishes, whose teeth usually all have the same shape, most mammals have teeth with four different shapes. **Incisors** are flat-edged teeth used to bite off and cut parts of food. **Canines** are sharply pointed teeth that stab food and tear into it. **Premolars** and **molars** grind and shred food into tiny bits.

The size, shape, and hardness of a mammal's teeth reflect its diet. For example, the canines of carnivores are especially large and sharp. Large carnivores, such as lions and tigers, use their canines as meat hooks that securely hold the prey while the carnivore kills it. The molars of herbivores, such as deer and woodchucks, have upper surfaces that are broad and flat—ideal for grinding and mashing plants.

Getting Oxygen to Cells

To release energy, food molecules must combine with oxygen inside cells. Therefore, a mammal needs an efficient way to get oxygen into the body and to the cells that need it.

Like reptiles and birds, all mammals breathe with lungs—even mammals such as whales that live in the ocean. Mammals breathe in and out because of the combined action of rib muscles and a large muscle called the **diaphragm** located at the bottom of the chest. The lungs have a huge, moist surface area where oxygen can dissolve and then move into the bloodstream.

Like birds, mammals have a four-chambered heart and a two-loop circulation. One loop pumps oxygen-poor blood from the heart to the lungs and then back to the heart. The second loop pumps oxygen-rich blood from the heart to the tissues of the mammal's body, and then back to the heart.

☑ *Checkpoint* *How do mammals take air into their bodies?*

Nervous System and Senses

The nervous system and senses of an animal receive information about its environment and coordinate the animal's movements. The brains of mammals enable them to learn, remember, and behave in complex ways. Squirrels, for example, feed on

Background

Facts and Figures The evolution of mammal teeth is fairly easy for paleontologists to trace by studying fossils. The earliest form of a mammal molar was shaped like a triangle. Opossum molars still have this shape. As mammals diversified, they ate different types of food. For example, the anteater is a mammal that has become specialized to eat insects such as ants. The anteater's elongated skull and tongue allow it to remove insects from underground nests. Its lower jaw has become smaller and it has fewer teeth.

nuts. In order to do this, they must crack the nutshell to get to the meat inside. Squirrels learn to use different methods to crack different kinds of nuts, depending on where the weak points in each kind of shell are located.

The senses of mammals are highly developed and adapted for the ways that individual species live. Tarsiers, which are active at night, have huge eyes that enable them to see in the dark. Humans, monkeys, gorillas, and chimpanzees are able to see objects in color. This ability is extremely useful because these mammals are most active during the day when colors are visible.

Most mammals hear well. Bats even use their sense of hearing to navigate. Bats make high-pitched squeaks that bounce off objects. The echoes give bats information about the shapes of objects around them and about how far away the objects are. Bats use their hearing to fly at night and to capture flying insects.

Most mammals have highly developed senses of smell. Many mammals, including dogs and cats, use smell to track their prey. By detecting the scent of an approaching predator, antelopes use their sense of smell to protect themselves.

Movement

One function of a mammal's nervous system is to direct and coordinate complex movement. No other group of vertebrates can move in as many different ways as mammals can. Like most mammals, camels and leopards have four limbs and can walk and run. Other four-limbed mammals have specialized ways of moving. For example, kangaroos hop, gibbons swing by their arms from branch to branch, and flying squirrels glide down from high perches. Moles use their powerful front limbs to burrow through the soil. Bats, in contrast, are adapted to fly through the air—their front limbs are wings. Whales, dolphins, and other sea mammals have no hind limbs—their front limbs are flippers adapted for swimming in water.

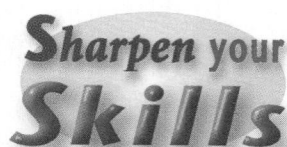

Sharpen your Skills

Classifying

Unlike humans, birds and bats both fly. Does this mean that bats are more closely related to birds than to humans? Use the diagrams below to find out. The diagrams show the front-limb bones of a bird, a bat, and a human. Examine them carefully, noting similarities and differences. Then decide which two animals are more closely related. Give evidence to support your classification.

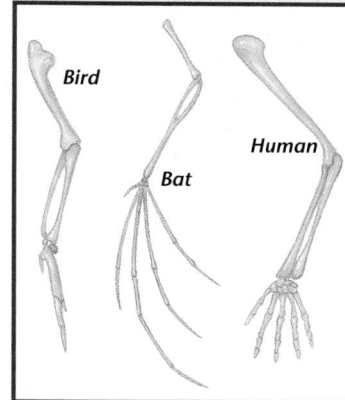

Bird

Bat

Human

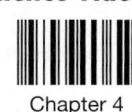

Figure 10 Mammals, like these springboks, have large brains. A springbok's brain processes complex information about its environment and then quickly decides on an appropriate action.

Chapter 13 **427**

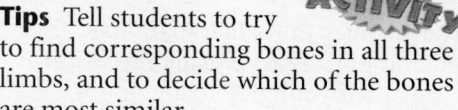

Sharpen your Skills

Classifying
Time 15 minutes
Tips Tell students to try to find corresponding bones in all three limbs, and to decide which of the bones are most similar.
Expected Outcome The bat and human both have bones for five fingers; they are more similar than the bat and the bird.
Extend Challenge students to identify the functions of a human's finger bones and the corresponding bones of a bat.

Movement

Building Inquiry Skills: Comparing and Contrasting

Show students photographs of a porpoise, a rabbit, a bat, a gazelle, and other mammals with interesting styles of movement. After they observe the photographs, ask students to infer what adaptations each animal has that help or affect its movement. *(The porpoise is streamlined for swimming in the sea. The rabbit has strong legs for hopping. The gazelle has long slender legs to run fast. The bat uses its hands covered with skin to fly.)* **learning modality: logical/ mathematical**

Answers to Self-Assessment

Caption Question
Figure 9 Lions eat a diet of meat.

☑ *Checkpoint*
Mammals take air into their bodies through their lungs. They breathe in and out because of the action of rib muscles and the diaphragm.

Reproducing and Caring for Young

Addressing Naive Conceptions

Students may think that mammals, fishes, and amphibians are equally successful at raising their young. Actually, young mammals are more likely to survive, because they receive protection and food from a parent. The survival rate of fish and amphibians is very low, but fish and amphibians produce many offspring, assuring survival of the species.
learning modality: verbal

3 Assess

Section 3 Review Answers

1. All mammals are endothermic vertebrates, have four-chambered hearts, have skin with fur or hair, and produce milk.
2. Mammals and birds are endothermic; they are vertebrates; and they have four-chambered hearts. Unlike birds, mammals have fur or hair, have teeth, and give milk to their young.
3. Sharp, pointy teeth are adapted to biting and tearing flesh. Broad, flat teeth are adapted to grinding and chewing plants.
4. A bat's sense of hearing allows it to navigate at night and to find prey.
5. Mammals are endothermic and have fur or hair and a layer of fat beneath their skin.

Performance Assessment

Drawing Invite students to sketch a mammal or describe it in writing. They should then list those of its characteristics that are unique to mammals. *(Answers will vary depending on the mammal chosen and the detail achieved in students' sketches.)*

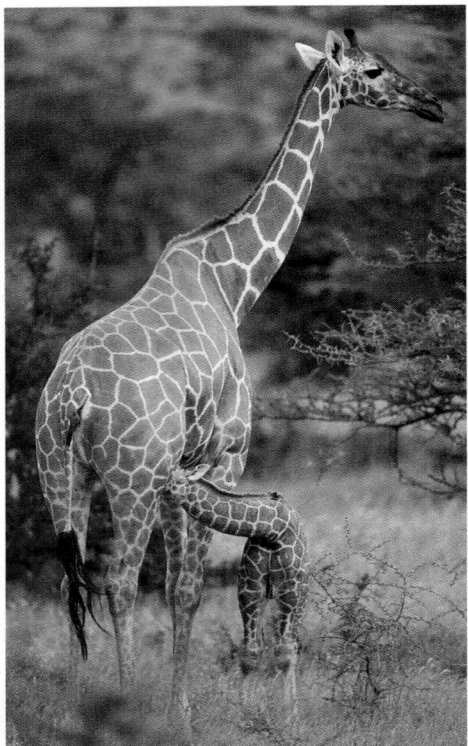

Figure 11 This young giraffe is feeding on milk produced by its mother, as do all young mammals.

Reproducing and Caring for Young

Like reptiles and birds, mammals have internal fertilization. Although a few kinds of mammals lay shelled eggs, the young of most mammals develop within their mothers' bodies and are never enclosed in an eggshell. All mammals, even those that lay eggs, feed their young with milk produced in **mammary glands.** In fact, the word *mammal* comes from the term *mammary*.

Young mammals are usually quite helpless for a long time after being born. Many are born without a coat of insulating fur. Their eyes are often sealed and may not open for weeks. For example, black bear cubs are surprisingly tiny when they are born. The blind, nearly hairless cubs have a mass of only 240 to 330 grams—about as small as a grapefruit. The mass of an adult black bear, in contrast, ranges from about 120 to 150 kilograms—about 500 times as large as a newborn cub!

Young mammals usually stay with their mother or both parents for an extended time. After black bear cubs learn to walk, they follow their mother about for the next year, learning how to be a bear. They learn things that are important to their survival, such as which mushrooms and berries are good to eat and how to rip apart a rotten log and find good-tasting grubs within it. During the winter, when black bears go through a period of inactivity, the young bears stay with their mother. The following spring, she will usually force them to live independently.

Section 3 Review

1. List five characteristics that all mammals share.
2. Name three ways in which mammals are similar to birds. Then list three ways in which they are different.
3. Relate the shape of any mammal's teeth to its diet.
4. Explain how a keen sense of hearing is an advantage to a bat.
5. **Thinking Critically** *Making Generalizations* What characteristics enable mammals to live in colder environments than reptiles can?

Science at Home

Mammals' Milk With a family member, examine the nutrition facts listed on a container of whole milk. What types of nutrients does whole milk contain? Discuss why milk is an ideal source of food for young, growing mammals.

Background

Facts and Figures Milk contains all of the water, nutrients, and calories that a young mammal needs. Milk is made up of water; lactose, a sugar found only in milk; fat, which supplies energy; and protein. Milk also has antibodies that help the young fight infection. The nursing young control the amount of milk produced: the more a young mammal nurses, the more milk its mother's mammary glands makes.

Program Resources

◆ **Unit 3 Resources** 13-3 Review and Reinforce, p. 107; 13-3 Enrich, p. 108
◆ **Unit 3 Resources** Real-World Lab Chapter 13, pp. 116–117

KEEPING WARM

Any time you wear a sweater or socks made of wool, you are using a mammalian adaptation to keep yourself warm. Suppose a manufacturer claims that its wool socks keep your feet as warm when the socks are wet as when they are dry. In this investigation, you will test that claim.

Problem

Do wool products provide insulation from the cold? How well does wool insulate when it is wet?

Skills Focus

controlling variables, interpreting data

Materials

tap water, hot
beaker, 1 L
clock or watch
a pair of wool socks
tap water, room temperature
3 containers, 250 mL, with lids
scissors
3 thermometers
graph paper

Procedure

1. Put one container into a dry woolen sock. Soak a second sock with water at room temperature, wring it out so it's not dripping, and then slide the second container into the wet sock. Both containers should stand upright. Leave the third container uncovered.
2. Create a data table in your notebook, listing the containers in the first column. Provide four more columns in which to record the water temperatures during the experiment.

3. Use scissors to carefully cut a small "X" in the center of each lid. Make the X just large enough for a thermometer to pass through.
4. Fill a beaker with about 800 mL of hot tap water. Then pour hot water nearly to the top of each of the three containers. **CAUTION:** *Avoid spilling hot water on yourself or others.*
5. Place a lid on each of the containers, and insert a thermometer into the water through the hole in each lid. Gather the socks around the thermometers above the first two containers so that the containers are completely covered.
6. Immediately measure the temperature of the water in each container, and record it in your data table. Take temperature readings every 5 minutes for at least 15 minutes.

Analyze and Conclude

1. Graph your results using a different color to represent each container. Graph time in minutes on the horizontal axis and temperature on the vertical axis.
2. Compare the temperature changes in the three containers. Relate your findings to the insulation characteristics of mammal skin coverings.
3. **Apply** Suppose an ad for wool gloves claims that the gloves keep you warm even if they get wet. Do your findings support this claim? Why or why not?

Design an Experiment

Design an experiment to compare how wool's insulating properties compare with those of other natural materials (such as cotton) or manufactured materials (such as acrylic). Obtain your teacher's approval before conducting your experiment.

Sample Data Table

Container	Temp. 0 min (°C)	Temp. 5 min (°C)	Temp. 10 min (°C)	Temp. 15 min (°C)
No Sock	45	36	29	25
Wet Sock	47	44	39	36
Dry Sock	46	44	41	38

Safety

Students should walk slowly when carrying glass containers or hot water to avoid breakage or spills. Students should be cautious when putting holes in lids with scissors. When handling glass thermometers, students should not force thermometers through the holes in lids. They can make a larger hole if the thermometer does not fit. Review the safety guidelines in Appendix A.

Keeping Warm

Preparing for Inquiry

Key Concept Wool is an insulator that helps an animal or object stay warm.
Skills Objective Students will be able to
◆ control variables and determine whether dry and wet wool have different insulating properties.
Time 35 minutes
Advance Planning Make sure groups use identical containers, such as plastic yogurt cups.

Guiding Inquiry

Invitation Discuss different uses of insulation.

Introducing the Procedure
Students will compare temperature changes to find whether wet or dry wool insulates better.

Troubleshooting the Experiment
Supply a large container of hot water so that all "hot water" used will be the same temperature, around 40–45°C.

Expected Outcome
The containers should cool in this order: no sock, wet sock, dry sock.

Analyze and Conclude
1. Students should graph data with time on the *x*-axis, temperature on the *y*-axis.
2. The temperature changed most in the uncovered container, then the wet, then the dry. Wool keeps animals warm even when it is wet.
3. Sample: Yes. Wet gloves will keep you warmer than no gloves.

Extending Inquiry

Design an Experiment Remind students to use materials of the same thickness.

SCIENCE AND SOCIETY

Animals and Medical Research

Purpose

To discuss the issue of using animals in medical research

Role-Play

Time 90 minutes

◆ Stimulate discussion with a role-playing scenario. A family member has a life-threatening illness. Scientists have developed a treatment for the illness, but it must be tested on animals before it can be approved for human use. Should the research be done? Choose volunteers to play the roles of family members, doctors, members of the Food and Drug Administration, and people against using animals in medical research.

◆ Guide students in their understanding of the practical and moral obligations of each character. Remind them that doctors have a responsibility to protect the health and well-being of their patients. The FDA was established to protect the safety of all Americans.

◆ To help students make a decision, they can think about the following issues:

1. What is the potential benefit of the proposed research? How high are the potential benefits to humanity?

2. How many animals will be tested? Research can be categorized as using no animals, a few animals (fewer than 20), or many animals (more than 20).

3. Will the animals be killed? How much pain will they experience? What animals will be involved?

◆ Prior to the role-playing exercise, invite students to interview community members involved in this issue. Students might contact universities or hospitals to speak with medical researchers or local veterinarians and humane society representatives. Suggest they prepare a list of questions before they call. Encourage students to share their findings with classmates and incorporate the results in the role-playing and You Decide writing activity.

Animals and Medical Research

In laboratories around the world, scientists search for cures for cancer, AIDS, and other diseases. Scientists use millions of animals each year in research—mostly to test drugs and surgical procedures. Finding treatments could save millions of human lives. However, these experiments can hurt and even kill animals.

The Issues

Why Is Animal Testing Done? If you have ever used an antibiotic or other medicine, animal testing has helped you. The United States Food and Drug Administration requires that new medicines be tested on research animals before they can be used by humans. Through testing, researchers can learn whether a drug works and what doses are safe. Because of animal research, many serious diseases can now be treated or prevented. New treatments for AIDS, cancer, and Alzheimer's disease are also likely to depend on animal testing.

Which Animals Are Used for Testing? Most often mice, rats, and other small mammals are used. These animals reproduce rapidly, so scientists can study many generations in a year. Since apes and monkeys are similar to humans in many ways, they are often used to test new treatments for serious diseases. In other cases, researchers use animals that naturally get diseases common to humans. Cocker spaniels, for example, often develop glaucoma, an eye disease that can cause blindness. Surgeons may test new surgical treatments for the disease on cocker spaniels.

What Happens to Research Animals? In a typical laboratory experiment, a group of animals will first be infected with a disease. Then they will be given a drug to see if it can fight off the disease. In many cases, the animals suffer, and some die. Some people are concerned that laboratory animals do not receive proper care.

What Are the Alternatives? Other testing methods do exist. For example, in some cases, scientists can use computer models to test drugs or surgical treatments. Another testing method is to mix drugs with animal cells grown in petri dishes. Unfortunately, neither computer models nor cell experiments are as useful as tests on living animals.

You Decide

1. Identify the Problem

In a sentence, describe the controversy over using animals in medical research.

2. Analyze the Options

Review the different positions. Is animal testing acceptable? Is it acceptable for some animals but not for others? Is animal research never acceptable? List the benefits and drawbacks of each option.

3. Find a Solution

Suppose you are a scientist who has found a possible cure for a type of cancer. The drug needs to be tested on research animals first, but you know that testing could harm the animals. What would you do? Support your opinion with sound reasons.

You Decide

◆ Students' responses to Identify the Problem and Analyze the Options should be based on the concepts and issues presented in the text. In response to Find a Solution, students may discuss issues raised in the role-playing.

◆ Make sure students understand that there are no "correct" opinions or solutions. As with many complex social issues, no single solution satisfies everyone. Provide examples of other difficult social issues as models.

Background

Reference Against Animal Research
Peter Singer. *Animal Liberation*. New York. Random House. 1990.

Reference Supporting Animal Research
Julian Groves. *Hearts and Minds: The Controversy over Laboratory Animals*. Philadelphia. Temple University Press. 1997.

SECTION 4 Diversity of Mammals

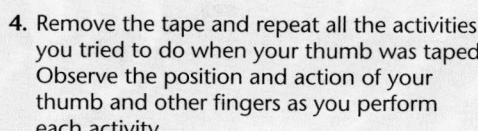

DISCOVER ·············· ACTIVITY

How Is a Thumb Useful?

1. Tape the thumb of your writing hand to your palm so that you cannot move your thumb. The tape should keep your thumb from moving but allow your other fingers to move freely.

2. Pick up a pencil with the taped hand and try to write your name.

3. Keep the tape on for 5 minutes. During that time, try to use your taped hand to do such everyday activities as lifting a book, turning the pages, and untying and retying your shoes.

4. Remove the tape and repeat all the activities you tried to do when your thumb was taped. Observe the position and action of your thumb and other fingers as you perform each activity.

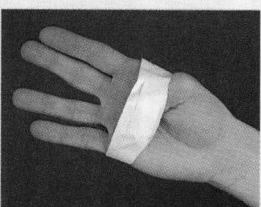

Think It Over
Inferring Humans, chimpanzees, and gorillas all have thumbs that can touch the other four fingers. What advantage does that kind of thumb give to the animal?

How is a koala similar to a panda? Both are furry, cuddly-looking mammals that eat leaves. How is a koala different from a panda? Surprisingly, koalas and pandas belong to very different groups of mammals—koalas are marsupials, and pandas are placental mammals. **Members of the three groups of mammals—monotremes, marsupials, and placental mammals—are classified on the basis of how their young develop.**

GUIDE FOR READING

◆ What characteristic is used to classify mammals into three groups?

Reading Tip As you read this section, write a definition in your own words for each new science term.

Giant panda (left) and koala (right)

Chapter 13 **431**

READING STRATEGIES

Reading Tip After students write their definitions, review the terms and definitions orally. Call out a term and have volunteers read their definitions aloud. (Sample: Monotremes are egg-laying mammals.)

Study and Comprehension Have students organize a chart of the three mammal groups. Have students provide characteristics of each group and examples of animals under each heading.

Program Resources

◆ **Unit 3 Resources** 13-4 Lesson Plan, p. 109; 13-4 Section Summary, p. 110

Media and Technology

 Audio CD English-Spanish Summary 13-4

Objectives

After completing the lesson, students will be able to
◆ identify the characteristic used to classify mammals into three groups;
◆ describe the characteristics of monotremes, marsupials, and placental mammals.

Key Terms monotreme, marsupial, gestation period, placental mammal, placenta

1 Engage/Explore

Activating Prior Knowledge

Show students a photograph of a kangaroo and ask them where they would expect to find the animal's young. *(In the pouch)* Have students list other ways in which the young of animals develop. *(Within eggs, within the mother)* Lead students to conclude that mammals can be classified based on their adaptations for the development of their young.

········· **DISCOVER** ·········

Skills Focus inferring
Materials *masking tape, pencil, paper, various objects such as books and shoes*
Time 15 minutes
Tips Have students work in pairs. Make sure that their taped thumbs will be comfortable for 5 minutes. Ask: **How does your thumb help you write?** *(It allows you to grasp and control the pencil.)* Then ask students what other ways they use their thumbs. *(People use their thumbs to do things such as hold food, climb, or handle tools.)* Develop a list of activities that would be difficult or impossible without an opposable thumb.
Think It Over A thumb that can touch the other fingers allows an animal to grasp food and other objects.

2 Facilitate

Monotremes

Using the Visuals: Figure 12

As students study the two monotremes, ask: **What characteristics that you can see make these two animals different?** *(Spiny anteater—spines, long, pointy nose; duck-billed platypus—webbed feet, a bill, furry body)* Students may infer that these animals are unrelated because they are so different. Then ask: **What do these animals have in common that makes them different from many other mammals?** *(They both lay eggs.)* Ask: **How does this affect their classification?** *(Both animals are monotremes, because monotremes are the only mammals whose young hatch from eggs.)* Guide students to understand that mammals are classified into different groups based on how their young develop, not on how the mammals look. **learning modality: visual**

Marsupials

Building Inquiry Skills: Inferring

Encourage students to infer the functions of a female marsupial's pouch. *(It keeps the newborn warm, protects it from predators, and contains the mother's nipples, which are the newborn's source of food. It helps the mother protect and care for her young while leaving her forepaws, hindpaws, and mouth free to find food, defend against predators, and move from place to place.)* **learning modality: logical/mathematical**

Figure 12 The spiny anteater, left, and the duck-billed platypus, right, could share the "Weirdest Mammal" award. Both are monotremes, the only mammals whose young hatch from eggs.

Monotremes

If you held a "Weirdest Mammal in the World" contest, two main contenders would be spiny anteaters and duck-billed platypuses. There are two species of spiny anteaters and only one species of duck-billed platypus, all living in Australia and New Guinea. These are the only species of monotremes that are alive today. **Monotremes** are mammals that lay eggs.

Spiny Anteaters These monotremes look like pincushions with long noses. They have sharp spines scattered throughout their brown hair. As their name implies, spiny anteaters eat ants, which they dig up with their powerful claws.

A female spiny anteater lays one to three leathery-shelled eggs directly into the pouch on her belly. After the young hatch, still in the pouch, they drink milk that seeps out of pores on the mother's skin. They stay in the pouch until they are six to eight weeks old, when their spines start to irritate the mother anteater, and she scratches them out of her pouch.

Duck-billed Platypuses The duck-billed platypus has webbed feet and a bill, but it also has fur and feeds its young with milk. Platypuses, which live in the water, construct a maze of tunnels in muddy banks. The female lays her eggs in an underground nest. The eggs hatch about two weeks later. After they hatch, the tiny offspring feed by lapping at the milk that oozes onto the fur of their mother's belly.

Marsupials

Koalas, kangaroos, wallabies, and opossums are some of the better-known marsupials. **Marsupials** are mammals whose young are born alive, but at an early stage of development, and they usually continue to develop in a pouch on their mother's body.

432

Marsupials were once widespread, but today they are found mostly in South America, Australia, and New Guinea. Opossums are the only marsupials found in North America.

Marsupials have a very short **gestation period,** the length of time between fertilization and birth. Opossums, for example, have a gestation period of only about 13 days. Newborn marsupials are tiny—the newborns of one opossum species are only about 10 millimeters long! When they are born, marsupials are blind, hairless, and pink. They crawl along the wet fur of their mother's belly until they reach her pouch. Once inside, they find one of her nipples and attach to it. They remain in the pouch at least until they have grown enough to peer out of the pouch opening.

Kangaroos The largest marsupials are kangaroos, which are found in Australia and nearby islands. Some male kangaroos are over 2 meters tall—taller than most humans. Kangaroos have powerful hind legs for jumping and long tails that help them keep their balance. A female kangaroo gives birth to only one baby, called a joey, at a time. Kangaroos are herbivores, so they eat foods such as leaves and grasses.

Opossums The common opossum is an omnivore that comes out of its nest at dusk to search for fruits, plants, insects, or other small animals to eat. Opossums are good climbers. They can grasp branches with their long tails. If a predator attacks it, an opossum will often "play dead"—its body becomes limp, its mouth gapes open, and its tongue lolls out of its mouth. Female opossums may give birth to 21 young at a time, but most female opossums have only 13 nipples. The first 13 young opossums that get into the pouch and attach to nipples are the only ones that survive.

☑ *Checkpoint* *What do the young of marsupials do immediately after they are born?*

Placental Mammals

Unlike a monotreme or a marsupial, a **placental mammal** develops inside its mother's body until its body systems can function independently. In *Exploring Placental Mammals* on the next page, you can see some members of this group.

Figure 13 Gray kangaroos, above, and opossums, below, are marsupials, mammals whose young live for a time in the mother's pouch. *Classifying How do marsupials differ from monotremes?*

Placental Mammals

Building Inquiry Skills: Observing

Materials *pair of breeding mice; 2 wire cages or aquariums with mesh tops; 2 water bottles with metal spouts; large bag of rodent bedding; rodent food; water*

Time 5 minutes daily for 4 to 6 weeks

Obtain a breeding pair of mice. Caution students to wash their hands before and after touching the mice, food, or bedding. Demonstrate that the mice must be handled very gently and should not be taken out except when the cage is being cleaned, so that they cannot bite or run away. Let students place 2 cm of bedding in each cage. Stress the importance of adequate food and water and a clean cage. Assign students turns for cleaning the cage, replacing the bedding, and supplying food and water. Encourage students to predict how the parents will care for their offspring. Keep both mice in the same cage for 2 weeks or until you notice that the female mouse is pregnant. Then move the male to the other cage. (Signs of pregnancy: a large belly, red and swollen teats, and building a nest. The gestation period is about 2 weeks.) Have students record daily observations of the pregnant mouse's behavior, and continue the observations when the young are born. Caution students not to touch the young, or the mother will remove the young from the nest and they will die. The young mice can be taken from the mother when they are 4 weeks old and able to walk around the cage.

cooperative learning

Answers to Self-Assessment

Caption Question

Figure 13 Marsupials give birth to live young. Monotremes lay eggs.

☑ *Checkpoint*

The young of marsupials crawl into their mother's pouch immediately after birth.

Ongoing Assessment

Oral Presentation Ask students to name three characteristics all mammals have in common and the distinguishing characteristic of each group of mammals.

Placental Mammals,
continued

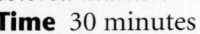

Placental Mammals

To help students focus on the major points presented in this visual essay and make comparisons among the groups of animals shown, organize students into small groups. Ask them to share their observations about the characteristics of the mammals on this page, such as *the young grow inside the mother's body* and *the young receive food and oxygen and eliminate wastes through the placenta.* On index cards, have students write the name of each mammal along with several of its observable characteristics. Students may exchange cards and quiz each other. **learning modality: visual**

Inquiry Challenge

Materials *magazines, scissors, glue, poster board, colored markers*

Time 30 minutes

Tips To help students learn about classifying mammals, ask them to bring from home magazines that contain pictures of mammals. Organize students in small groups. Have groups look through the magazines and cut out as many pictures of mammals as they can find. Challenge students to observe as many traits about each mammal as they can. Students may work in pairs or small groups to list their observations. When their lists are complete, have students evaluate the traits they listed and classify animals based on these criteria. Then encourage them to compare their criteria with those used to classify placental mammals in *Exploring Placental Mammals.* **learning modality: logical/mathematical**

EXPLORING *Placental Mammals*

From tiny moles to huge elephants, placental mammals exhibit a great variety of size and body form. Note how each group is adapted for obtaining food or for living in a particular environment.

▲ Rabbits and Hares
Leaping mammals like this black-tailed jack rabbit have long hind legs specialized for spectacular jumps. Rabbits and hares have long, curved incisors for gnawing.

▲ Insect-eaters
Star-nosed moles and their relatives have sharp cutting surfaces on all of their teeth. Star-nosed moles spend much of their time in water searching for prey with their sensitive, tentacled snouts.

Flying Mammals ▲
Bats fly, but they are mammals, not birds. The wings of bats are made of a thin skin that stretches from their wrists to the tips of their long finger bones.

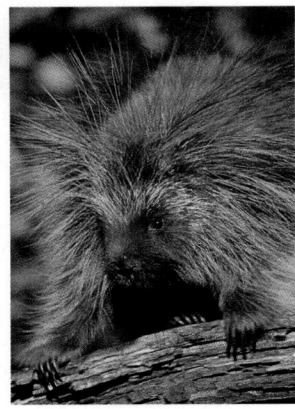

Rodents ▲
Rodents are gnawing mammals such as rats, beavers, squirrels, mice, and the North American porcupine shown here. Their teeth are adapted to grind down their food. The four incisors of most rodents keep growing throughout their lives but are constantly worn down by gnawing.

▲ Primates
This group of mammals with large brains includes humans, monkeys, and apes such as this chimpanzee. Many primates have opposable thumbs—thumbs that can touch the other four fingers. An opposable thumb makes the hand capable of complex movements, such as grasping and throwing.

434

Background

Facts and Figures

◆ The manatee is an endangered mammal. Fewer than 2,000 manatees remain. These large, docile marine mammals are threatened by collisions with boats and the loss of their habitat to human development of the coastline.

◆ Two famous gorillas, Koko and Michael, are part of a project to teach a modified form of American Sign Language to gorillas. These gorillas are able to use hundreds of signs. They also use their hands to grasp a paintbrush and have produced several paintings.

▲ Toothless Mammals
Sloths, such as the one shown here, are toothless mammals, as are armadillos. Although a few members of this group have small teeth, most have none.

▲ Hoofed Mammals
Mammals with hooves are divided into two groups—those with an even number of toes and those with an odd number of toes. Cows, deer, and pigs all have an even number of toes, while horses and zebras belong to the odd-numbered group.

Carnivores ▶
This river otter belongs to the group known as carnivores, or meat eaters. Other mammals in this group include dogs, cats, raccoons, bears, weasels, and seals. Large canine teeth and toes with claws help carnivores catch and eat their prey.

Marine Mammals
Whales, manatees, and these Atlantic spotted dolphins are ocean-dwelling mammals that evolved from cowlike, land-dwelling ancestors. The bodies of marine mammals show no external trace of hind limbs, although hind limbs have been found in their fossilized ancestors. ▼

Mammals With Trunks ▲
Elephants' noses are long trunks that they use for collecting food and water.

Chapter 13 **435**

Addressing Naive Conceptions

Some students may think that bats are birds because they can fly. They may also think that dolphins are fish because they live in the ocean. Stress to students that one of the reasons why bats and dolphins are classified as mammals, not birds or fish, is that they feed their young with milk. Ask: **Can you think of other evidence of the fact that bats are not birds and dolphins are not fishes?** *(Sample answer: Bats do not have feathers, and dolphins have lungs, not gills.)* **learning modality: logical/mathematical**

Including All Students

To help students whose native language is not English, remind students that the English word *mammal* comes from the same Latin root as the word *mammary*. Have students with other native languages provide the words for *mammal* in those languages. *(Examples: mamífero [Spanish], mammifère [French], honyuu [Japanese])* Write these words on the board and try to identify any root word similarities. Ask students to propose other words for mammals based on other mammalian characteristics. **limited English proficiency**

3 Assess

Section 4 Review Answers

1. Monotreme young develop in eggs laid by the mother. Marsupial young are born alive at an early stage of development, then crawl into the mother's pouch, where they continue to grow and develop. Placental mammals develop inside the mother's body, attached to a placenta.

2. Food and oxygen from the mother pass through the placenta to the young. Wastes from the young pass through the placenta to the mother and are eliminated by her body.

3. Sample answer: Carnivores are meat eaters with sharp claws and sharp canine teeth. Insect eaters have sharp cutting surfaces on all teeth. Rodents are gnawing mammals with teeth adapted for grinding. Their incisors grow throughout their lives.

4. Feeding in large herds protects hoofed mammals from predators. It is likely that one animal in a group will see a predator and warn others, and predators who will tackle a lone animal might avoid a large herd.

Check Your Progress
CHAPTER PROJECT

While students continue to observe, they should begin to plan how the observations will be analyzed and presented. Review graphing techniques for the benefit of students who are less familiar with this method of organizing mathematical data. Suggest students group their observations to establish the habits of specific birds of related species.

Performance Assessment

Organizing Information Direct students to create concept maps to help them classify various mammals as marsupials, monotremes, or placental mammals.

Portfolio Students can save their concept maps in their portfolios.

Figure 14 Young mammals usually require much parental care. On a rocky slope in Alaska, this Dall's sheep, a placental mammal, keeps a close watch on her lamb.

The name of this group comes from the **placenta,** an organ in pregnant female mammals that passes materials between the mother and the developing embryo. Food and oxygen pass from the mother to her young through the placenta. Wastes pass from the young through the placenta to the mother, where they are eliminated by her body. The umbilical cord connects the young to the placenta. Most mammals, including humans, are placental mammals.

Placental mammals are classified into groups on the basis of characteristics such as how they eat and how their bodies are adapted for moving. For example, whales, dolphins, and porpoises all form one group of mammals that have adaptations for swimming. The mammals in the carnivore group, which includes cats, dogs, otters, and seals, are all predators that have enlarged canine teeth. Primates, which include monkeys, apes, and humans, all have large brains and eyes that face forward. In addition, the forelimbs of many primates have adaptations for grasping. For example, the human thumb can touch all four other fingers. As you learned if you did the Discover activity, it is difficult to grasp objects if you cannot use your thumb.

Placental mammals vary in the length of their gestation periods. Generally, the larger the placental mammal, the longer its gestation period. For example, African elephants are the largest land-dwelling placental mammals. The gestation period for an elephant averages about 21 months. A house mouse, on the other hand, gives birth after a gestation period of only about 20 days.

Section 4 Review

1. Explain the difference in the development of the young of monotremes, marsupials, and placental mammals.
2. What is the function of the placenta?
3. Describe the feeding adaptations of three groups of placental mammals.
4. **Thinking Critically** **Inferring** Many hoofed mammals feed in large groups, or herds. What advantage could this behavior have?

Check Your Progress
CHAPTER PROJECT

Continue to observe bird behavior at your bird feeder and record your observations in your notebook. Now is the time to plan your presentation. You may want to include the following information in your presentation: drawings of the different birds you observed, detailed descriptions of bird behaviors, and other interesting observations you made. (*Hint:* Prepare bar graphs to present numerical data, such as the number of times that different species visited the feeder.)

Program Resources

◆ **Unit 3 Resources** 13-4 Review and Reinforce, p. 111; 13-4 Enrich, p. 112

SECTION 1 Birds

Key Ideas

- Birds are endothermic vertebrates that have feathers and a four-chambered heart and lay eggs. Most birds can fly.
- Birds care for their young by keeping the eggs warm until hatching and by protecting the young at least until they can fly.
- Birds have adaptations, such as the shapes of their toes and bills, for living and obtaining food in different environments.

Key Terms

bird	down feather	crop
contour feather	insulator	gizzard

SECTION 2 The Physics of Bird Flight

INTEGRATING PHYSICS

Key Ideas

- Air flowing over the curved upper surface of a moving wing exerts less downward pressure than the upward pressure from the air flowing beneath the wing. The difference in pressure produces lift that causes the wing to rise.
- Birds fly by flapping, soaring, and gliding.

Key Term
lift

SECTION 3 What Is a Mammal?

Key Ideas

- Mammals are vertebrates that are endothermic, have skin covered with hair or fur, feed their young with milk from the mother's mammary glands, and have teeth of different shapes adapted to their diets.
- Mammals use a large muscle called the diaphragm to breathe. Mammals have a four-chambered heart and a two-loop circulation.

Key Terms

mammal	premolars	diaphragm
incisors	molars	mammary gland
canines		

SECTION 4 Diversity of Mammals

Key Ideas

- Mammals are classified into three groups on the basis of how their young develop. Monotremes lay eggs. Marsupials give birth to live young who continue to develop in the mother's pouch. The young of placental mammals develop more fully before birth than do the young of marsupials.
- Placental mammals are divided into groups on the basis of adaptations, such as those for feeding and moving.

Key Terms
monotreme
marsupial
gestation period
placental
   mammal
placenta

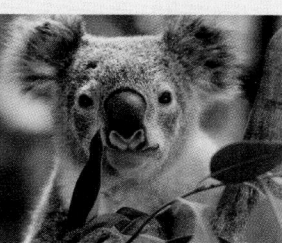

Organizing Information

Compare/Contrast Table Copy the table comparing mammal groups onto a separate sheet of paper. Complete it and add a title. (For more on compare/contrast tables, see the Skills Handbook.)

Characteristic	Monotremes	Marsupials	Placental Mammals
How Young Begin Life	a. _?_	b. _?_	c. _?_
How Young Are Fed	milk from pores or slits on mother's skin	d. _?_	e. _?_
Example	f. _?_	g. _?_	h. _?_

Organizing Information

Compare/Contrast Table Sample Title: The Characteristics of Mammal Groups; **a.** in eggs **b.** in their mother's pouch **c.** at an advanced stage of development **d.** milk from nipples in mother's pouch **e.** milk from nipples **f.** spiny anteater (or another appropriate example) **g.** kangaroo (or another appropriate example) **h.** human (or another appropriate example)

Program Resources

- **Unit 3 Resources** Chapter 13 Project Scoring Rubric, p. 96
- **Performance Assessment** Chapter 13, pp. 41–43
- **Chapter and Unit Tests** Chapter 13 Test, pp. 60–63

Media and Technology

 Interactive Student Tutorial CD-ROM Chapter 13

 Computer Test Bank Chapter 13 Test

Reviewing Content
Multiple Choice
1. c 2. a 3. b 4. b 5. c

True or False
6. true 7. true 8. faster 9. true
10. Monotremes

Checking Concepts
11. The bones are lightweight, and the forelimb bones are modified into wings.
12. The upper surfaces of the wings are more curved than the lower surfaces. Consequently, as air moves over the wing, the air moving over the upper surface travels at a speed greater than the air moving across the lower surface. Because of the difference in speed, the air on the upper surface exerts less pressure, so the wing rises.
13. Warm air rises, and soaring birds are carried upward by the rising air. When the air cools, the birds glide downward until they find another column of rising air.
14. Incisors are thin, with sharp cutting edges, and are used for biting. Molars are thick, with broad surfaces used for grinding.
15. Accept any two: They are endotherms; their fur insulates them; they have a layer of insulating fat.
16. Mammals have complex nervous systems and senses that are capable of directing and coordinating complicated movements.
17. Accept any one: Their bodies show no external trace of hind limbs; they have flippers instead of legs or arms; their bodies are streamlined.
18. The scenes that students describe should contain realistic details about the anteaters, such as their having a spiny coat, eating ants, laying eggs into a pouch, and so forth.

Thinking Critically
19. Endothermic animals have four-chambered hearts. In a four-chambered heart, oxygenated blood does not mix with deoxygenated blood, and therefore the blood that reaches the body tissues is carrying a large amount of oxygen. Oxygen is needed to release the energy that enables endothermy.

Reviewing Content
 For more review of key concepts, see the Interactive Student Tutorial CD-ROM.

Multiple Choice
Choose the letter of the best answer.

1. Which of these characteristics is found only in birds?
   a. scales b. wings
   c. feathers d. four-chambered heart
2. A four-chambered heart is an advantage because
   a. it keeps oxygen-rich and oxygen-poor blood separate.
   b. it allows oxygen-rich and oxygen-poor blood to mix.
   c. blood can move through it quickly.
   d. it slows the flow of blood.
3. What causes the lift that allows a bird's wing to rise?
   a. reduced air pressure beneath the wing
   b. reduced air pressure above the wing
   c. air that is not moving
   d. jet propulsion
4. Which muscle helps mammals move air into and out of their lungs?
   a. air muscle b. diaphragm
   c. placenta d. gestation
5. Kangaroos, koalas, and opossums are all
   a. monotremes.
   b. primates.
   c. marsupials.
   d. placental mammals.

True or False
If the statement is true, write true. If it is false, change the underlined word or words to make the statement true.

6. *Archaeopteryx* shows the link between birds and reptiles.
7. A bird's <u>gizzard</u> grinds food.
8. The <u>slower</u> air moves, the less pressure it exerts.
9. Fur and <u>down</u> feathers have a similar function.
10. <u>Marsupials</u> are mammals that lay eggs.

Checking Concepts
11. Explain how the skeleton of a bird is adapted for flight.
12. How is a bird's ability to fly related to the shape of its wings?
13. Explain how soaring and gliding birds such as vultures and eagles use air currents in their flight.
14. Contrast the structure and function of incisors and molars.
15. Identify and explain two ways in which mammals are adapted to live in cold climates.
16. How is a mammal's ability to move related to the function of its nervous system?
17. What is one way in which the bodies of dolphins are different from those of land mammals?
18. **Writing to Learn** You are a documentary filmmaker preparing to make a short film about spiny anteaters. First, think of a title for the film. Then plan two scenes that you would include in the film and write the narrator's script. Your scenes should show what the animals look like and what they do.

Thinking Critically
19. **Making Generalizations** What is the general relationship between whether an animal is an endotherm and whether it has a four-chambered heart? Relate this to the animal's need for energy.
20. **Comparing and Contrasting** Why do you think some scientists might consider monotremes to be a link between reptiles and mammals?
21. **Predicting** If a rodent were fed a diet consisting only of soft food that it did not need to gnaw, what might its front teeth look like after several months? Explain your prediction.

20. While most mammals do not lay eggs, most reptiles do. Therefore, egg-laying is a characteristic that is more reptilian than mammalian.
21. Since rodents' front teeth grow constantly, they might continue to grow and become very long.

Applying Skills
22. Students' graphs should plot data accurately.
23. Longest—elephants and chimpanzees; Shortest—harp seal
24. In general, the larger the mammal, the more time it spends caring for its young. The harp seal is the exception.

Applying Skills

The data table below shows the approximate gestation period of several mammals and the approximate length of time that those mammals care for their young after birth. Use the information in the table to answer Questions 22–24.

Mammal	Gestation Period	Time Spent Caring for Young After Birth
Deer mouse	0.75 month	1 month
Chimpanzee	8 months	24 months
Harp seal	11 months	0.75 month
Elephant	21 months	24 months
Bobcat	2 months	8 months

22. **Graphing** Decide which kind of graph would be best for showing the data in the table. Then construct two graphs—one for gestation period and the other for time spent caring for young.

23. **Interpreting Data** Which mammals in the table care for their young for the longest time? The shortest time?

24. **Drawing Conclusions** What seems to be the general relationship between the size of the mammal and the length of time for which it cares for its young? Which animal is the exception to this pattern?

Performance CHAPTER PROJECT **Assessment**

Present Your Project When you present your project, display the graphs, charts, and pictures you constructed. Be sure to describe the ways in which birds eat and interesting examples of bird behavior you observed.

Reflect and Record In your journal, analyze how successful the project was. Was the bird feeder located in a good place for attracting and observing birds? Did many birds come to the feeder—if not, why might this have happened? What are the advantages and limitations of using field guides for identifying birds?

Test Preparation

Use these questions to prepare for standardized tests.

Use the information to answer Questions 25–27. Sankong wanted to find out which type of birdseed the birds in his neighborhood preferred—sunflower seeds or thistle. He set up two identical bird feeders on a tree in his backyard. He filled one feeder with sunflower seeds and the other with thistle. He spent one hour each day counting how many birds visited each feeder. The chart below shows the data he collected.

Type of Birdseed	Number of Birds			
	Day 1	Day 2	Day 3	Day 4
Sunflower Seeds	23	6	14	7
Thistle	19	9	16	5

25. What was the manipulated variable in Sankong's experiment?
    a. the day
    b. the number of birds
    c. the type of seed
    d. the type of feeder

26. What was the responding variable?
    a. the day　　　　b. the number of birds
    c. the type of seed　　d. the type of feeder

27. Based on the data, what conclusion could Sankong reach?
    a. The birds in the neighborhood preferred thistle to sunflower seeds.
    b. The birds in the neighborhood preferred sunflower seeds to thistle.
    c. The birds in the neighborhood showed no clear preference.
    d. Sankong's experiment was flawed.

Chapter 13 **439**

Performance CHAPTER PROJECT **Assessment**

Present Your Project Students can present their projects in a number of ways. They can turn in a written report with sketches and graphs, make posters that show the different birds that visited their feeders and their behaviors, or give an oral presentation that focuses on their observations or on the behavior of a single type of bird.

　　Encourage students to be creative in the way they report their data. On their graphs, students could add illustrations of the different types of birds rather than just their names.

Reflect and Record In assessing their work, students should explain why they think the bird feeder was or was not placed in a good location. They should say explicitly which parts of their work were most and least successful and why.

Test Preparation

25. c　26. b　27. c

Program Resources

◆ **Inquiry Skills Activity Book** Provides teaching and review of all inquiry skills.

Sections	Time	Student Edition Activities	Other Activities	
CHAPTER PROJECT **Learning New Tricks** p. 441	Ongoing (2 weeks)	Check Your Progress, pp. 448, 457 Present Your Project, p. 461		
1 **INTEGRATING PSYCHOLOGY** **Why Do Animals Behave as They Do?** pp. 442–449 ◆ Describe the functions of most of an animal's behavior. ◆ Compare instinctive and learned behavior. ◆ Explain the process called imprinting.	2 periods/ 1 block	**Discover** What Can You Observe About a Vertebrate's Behavior? p. 442 **Sharpen Your Skills** Predicting, p. 444 **Try This** Line Them Up, p. 447 **Skills Lab: Designing Experiments** Become a Learning Detective, p. 449	TE TE TE TE IES	Demonstration, p. 443 Inquiry Challenge, p. 445 Including All Students, p. 446 Integrating Technology, p. 446 "Sleuth's Supper," p. 37
2 **Patterns of Behavior** pp. 450–458 ◆ Explain competition and aggression and the role they play in establishing a territory. ◆ Explain the purpose of courtship behavior. ◆ Describe the benefits animals receive from living in groups. ◆ Describe animal behavior cycles and explain how they may affect an animal's survival.	2 periods/ 1 block	**Discover** What Can You Express Without Words? p. 450 **Try This** Worker Bees, p. 453 **Real-World Lab: You and Your Environment** One for All, p. 458	TE TE LM	Demonstration, p. 451 Cultural Diversity, p. 454 14, "Family Life of Bettas"
Study Guide/Chapter Assessment pp. 459–461	1 period/ $\frac{1}{2}$ block		ISAB	Provides teaching and review of all inquiry skills

For Standard or Block Schedule The Resource Pro® CD-ROM gives you maximum flexibility for planning your instruction for any type of schedule. Resource Pro® contains Planning Express®, an advanced scheduling program, as well as the entire contents of the Teaching Resources and the Computer Test Bank.

CHAPTER PLANNING GUIDE

Program Resources	Assessment Strategies	Media and Technology
UR Chapter 14 Project Teacher Notes, pp. 118–119 **UR** Chapter 14 Project Overview and Worksheets, pp. 120–123	**SE** Performance Assessment: Present Your Project, p. 461 **TE** Check Your Progress, pp. 448, 457 **UR** Chapter 14 Project Scoring Rubric, p. 124	Science Explorer Internet Site at www.phschool.com
UR 14-1 Lesson Plan, p. 125 **UR** 14-1 Section Summary, p. 126 **UR** 14-1 Review and Reinforce, p. 127 **UR** 14-1 Enrich, p. 128 **UR** Chapter 14 Skills Lab, pp. 133–134	**SE** Section 1 Review, p. 448 **TE** Ongoing Assessment, pp. 443, 445, 447 **TE** Performance Assessment, p. 448	Audio CD, English-Spanish Summary 14-1 Transparency 59, "Pavlov's Experiment"
UR 14-2 Lesson Plan, p. 129 **UR** 14-2 Section Summary, p. 130 **UR** 14-2 Review and Reinforce, p. 131 **UR** 14-2 Enrich, p. 132 **UR** Chapter 14 Real-World Lab, pp. 135–137	**SE** Section 2 Review, p. 457 **TE** Ongoing Assessment, pp. 451, 453, 455 **TE** Performance Assessment, p. 457	Life Science Videotape 3; Videodisc Unit 3 Side 2, "Travelin' Along" Audio CD, English-Spanish Summary 14-2 Transparency 60, "Exploring a Honeybee Society" Interactive Student Tutorial CD-ROM, Chapter 14
RCA Provides strategies to improve science reading skills **GSW** Provides worksheets to promote student comprehension of content	**SE** Chapter 14 Study Guide/Assessment, pp. 459–461 **PA** Chapter 14 Performance Assessment, pp. 44–46 **CUT** Chapter 14 Test, pp. 64–67 **CTB** Chapter 14 Test	Interactive Student Tutorial CD-ROM, Chapter 14 Computer Test Bank, Chapter 14 Test

Key: **SE** Student Edition
CTB Computer Test Bank
ISAB Inquiry Skills Activity Book
GSW Guided Study Worksheets

TE Teacher's Edition
PTA Product Testing Activities by *Consumer Reports*
RCA Reading in the Content Area
PA Performance Assessment

UR Unit Resources
LM Laboratory Manual
IES Interdisciplinary Explorations Series
CUT Chapter and Unit Tests

Meeting the National Science Education Standards and AAAS Benchmarks

National Science Education Standards	Benchmarks for Science Literacy	Unifying Themes

National Science Education Standards

Science as Inquiry (Content Standard A)

◆ **Ask questions that can be answered by scientific investigations** Students pose questions about teaching an animal and design an procedure to investigate their questions. *(Chapter Project)*

◆ **Think critically and logically to make the relationships between evidence and explanations** Ant social behavior provides a starting point for scientific investigation and discussion. Evidence may be contrary to students' previous opinions and will be the source of scientific inquiry. *(Real-World Lab)*

Life Science (Content Standard C)

◆ **Regulation and Behavior** Behavior is a response to a stimulus. Behavior has an adaptive function, and it enables animals to meet basic needs such as finding food. Animal behaviors, such as migration and hibernation, are regulated by seasonal and other environmental changes. *(Sections 1, 2)*

◆ **Diversity and adaptations of organisms** Different animals behave in different ways, but most behaviors serve adaptive functions, such as reproduction or finding food. Animals may exhibit similar behavior patterns, such as establishing a territory or living in groups. *(Sections 1, 2)*

◆ **Populations and ecosystems** Behavior and environment are related. Interactions with the ecosystem affect animal behaviors, such as hibernation and migration, and animal behaviors can alter the ecosystem. *(Sections 1, 2)*

Benchmarks for Science Literacy

1B Scientific Inquiry Students use both logic and imagination in devising a plan to train an animal. Students base analysis of ant behavior on observations. They also design an experiment to evaluate learning and control the variables in that experiment. *(Chapter Project, Skills Lab, Real-World Lab)*

5F Evolution of Life Like body structures, the behaviors of animals are adaptations that have evolved over long periods of time. *(Section 1)*

Unifying Themes

◆ **Patterns of Change** Behavior is a recognizable pattern of activity that benefits an animal in some way. Behavior patterns change in response to new stimuli, such as changing seasons. Behavior patterns of animals can be altered through a learning process. *(Sections 1, 2; Chapter Project)*

◆ **Modeling** Students perform simple experiments about learning in order to model the concepts incorporated in a behavioral experiment. *(Skills Lab)*

◆ **Systems and Interactions** The environment and the resources within it constitute an ecological system. Interactions in the form of animal behaviors within this system can ensure survival and reproduction. *(Section 2)*

◆ **Unity and Diversity** While different animals behave in different ways, most animal behaviors help an animal survive and reproduce. Different kinds of animals may exhibit similar behavior patterns, such as establishing a territory or living in groups. *(Sections 1, 2)*

Take It to the Net

 *Interactive text at www.phschool.com*

Science Explorer comes alive with iText.

- **Complete student text** is accessible from any computer with Internet access or a CD-ROM drive.
- **Animations, simulations, and videos** enhance student understanding and retention of concepts.
- **Self-tests and online study tools** assess student understanding.

STAY CURRENT with **SCIENCE NEWS** ®

Find out the latest research and information about animals at: **www.phschool.com**

Go to **www.phschool.com** and click on the Science icon. Then click on <u>Science Explorer: Life, Earth, and Physical Science</u> under PH@school.

ACTIVITY	Time (minutes)	Materials Quantities for one work group	Skills
Section 1			
Discover, p. 442	15	**Nonconsumable** one small, active vertebrate such as a gerbil or goldfish in an appropriate cage or aquarium **Consumable** Appropriate food for animal(s)	Predicting
Sharpen Your Skills, p. 444	10	No special materials are required.	Predicting
Try This, p. 447	15	**Consumable** paper and pencil	Inferring
Skills Lab, p. 449	20	**Consumable** paper and pencil	Designing Experiments
Section 2			
Discover, p. 450	15	No special materials are required.	Forming Operational Definitions
Try This, p. 453	15	**Consumable** sheets of paper, 22 × 28 cm **Nonconsumable** scissors; paste, glue, or stapler; timer	Calculating
Real-World Lab, pp. 458	20	**Consumable** water, bread crumbs, sugar, black paper, tape, 20–30 ants **Nonconsumable** large glass jar, sandy soil, shallow pan, wire screen, sponge, wax pencil, forceps, large thick rubber band	Observing, Inferring, Posing Questions

A list of all materials required for the Student Edition activities can be found on pages T25–T33. You can obtain information about ordering materials by calling 1-800-848-9500 or by accessing the Science Explorer Internet site at **www.phschool.com**.

Learning New Tricks

Students learn about animal behavior and types of learning by attempting to teach a specific behavior to a pet or other animal.

Purpose To help students understand the difference between instinctive and learned behavior

Skills Focus Students will be able to
◆ observe natural behavior patterns in animals;
◆ observe the animals' learning over a period of time;
◆ draw conclusions about the animals' ability to learn new behaviors;
◆ communicate to their classmates their findings about the animals' ability to learn.

Project Time Line Before beginning the project, see Chapter 14 Project Teacher Notes on pages 118–119 in Unit 3 Resources for more details on carrying out the project. Also distribute the students' Chapter 14 Project Overview, Worksheets, and Scoring Rubric on pages 120–124 in Unit 3 Resources. During the first week, students should familiarize themselves with their animal's natural behaviors. They should also decide what behavior they plan to teach their animal and what method (trial and error or conditioning) they will use to train the animal. Plan on at least two weeks for training. You will probably need to schedule several different days to allow students to showcase their animals' new behaviors.

Possible Materials Students will need animals. In addition, they may need:
◆ materials to construct a maze
◆ food to use as a reward
◆ glue, tape, stopwatches, timers
◆ posterboard and markers for their presentation
◆ camera, sketchbook, or video camera to record behavior

Launching the Project If your school district permits, bring an animal into the classroom and show the students a behavior it has learned. Talk about who trained the animal, how it was trained,

CHAPTER

14 Animal Behavior

WEB ACTIVITY www.phschool.com

SECTION
1 *Integrating Psychology* 🜨
Why Do Animals Behave as They Do?

Discover **What Can You Observe About a Vertebrate's Behavior?**
Sharpen Your Skills **Predicting**
Try This **Line Them Up**
Skills Lab **Become a Learning Detective**

SECTION
2 **Patterns of Behavior**

Discover **What Can You Express Without Words?**
Try This **Worker Bees**
Real-World Lab **One for All**

440

and any difficulties that were encountered during the training process.

Allow time for students to read the Chapter 14 Project Overview on pages 120–121 in Unit 3 Resources. Then encourage discussions on the types of behaviors that might be taught, materials that could be used, and any initial questions students may have. Pass out copies of the Chapter 14 Project Worksheets on pages 122–123 in Unit 3 Resources for students to review.

Safety

Be sure that students are not allergic to any animals with which they may be working. The animal's owner and, if the owner is a child, an adult should be present during training and handling the animal.

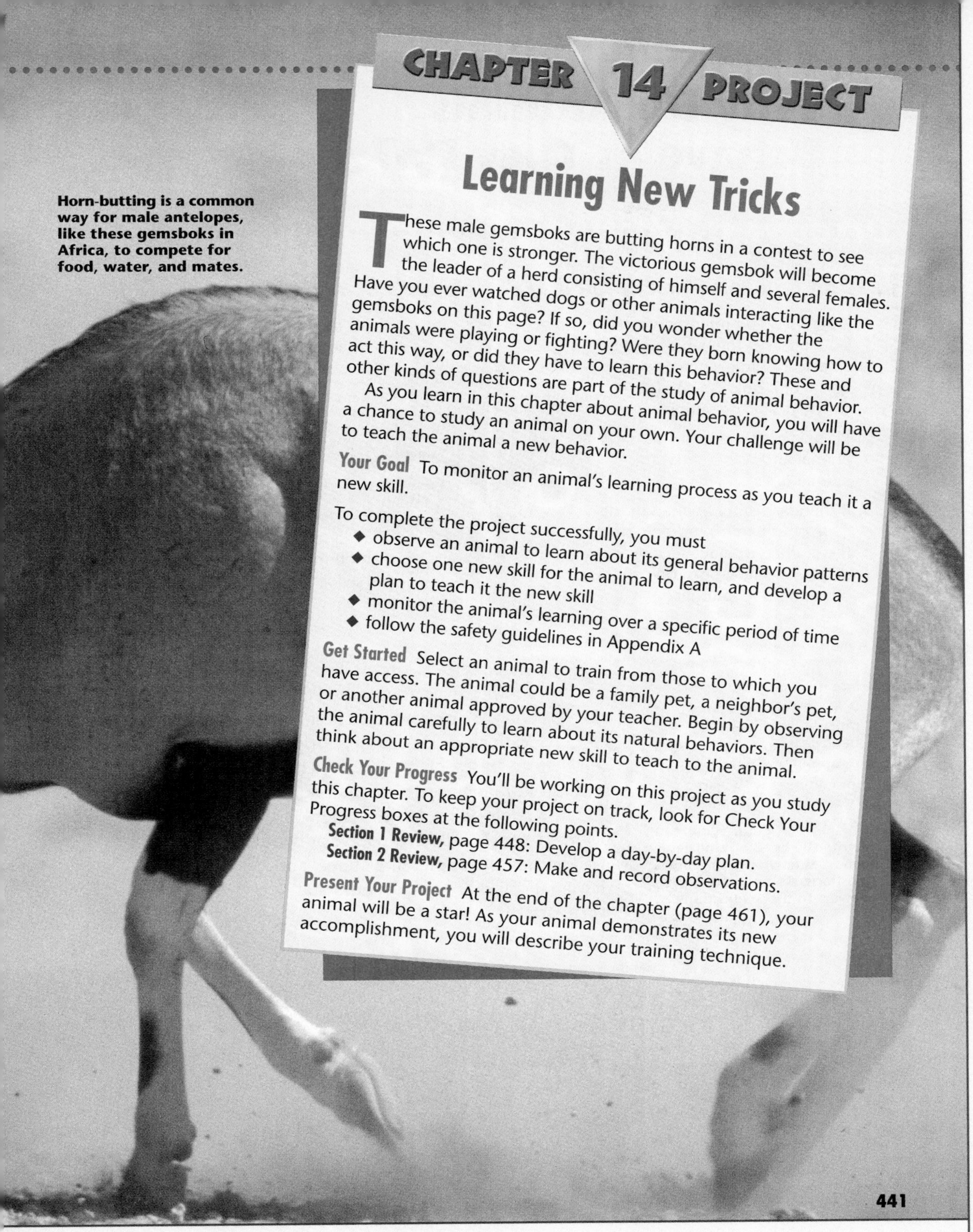

Horn-butting is a common way for male antelopes, like these gemsboks in Africa, to compete for food, water, and mates.

CHAPTER 14 PROJECT

Learning New Tricks

These male gemsboks are butting horns in a contest to see which one is stronger. The victorious gemsbok will become the leader of a herd consisting of himself and several females. Have you ever watched dogs or other animals interacting like the gemsboks on this page? If so, did you wonder whether the animals were playing or fighting? Were they born knowing how to act this way, or did they have to learn this behavior? These and other kinds of questions are part of the study of animal behavior.

As you learn in this chapter about animal behavior, you will have a chance to study an animal on your own. Your challenge will be to teach the animal a new behavior.

Your Goal To monitor an animal's learning process as you teach it a new skill.

To complete the project successfully, you must
- observe an animal to learn about its general behavior patterns
- choose one new skill for the animal to learn, and develop a plan to teach it the new skill
- monitor the animal's learning over a specific period of time
- follow the safety guidelines in Appendix A

Get Started Select an animal to train from those to which you have access. The animal could be a family pet, a neighbor's pet, or another animal approved by your teacher. Begin by observing the animal carefully to learn about its natural behaviors. Then think about an appropriate new skill to teach to the animal.

Check Your Progress You'll be working on this project as you study this chapter. To keep your project on track, look for Check Your Progress boxes at the following points.

Section 1 Review, page 448: Develop a day-by-day plan.
Section 2 Review, page 457: Make and record observations.

Present Your Project At the end of the chapter (page 461), your animal will be a star! As your animal demonstrates its new accomplishment, you will describe your training technique.

441

Students must decide what behaviors they will teach their animals. Worksheet 1 may help them think of ideas. Worksheet 2 will then help students organize their schedules. If students have problems training their animals, they should confer with you. Help them determine whether they need to plan additional trials or develop new strategies for teaching the behaviors. At the conclusion of the project, students should demonstrate their animals' behaviors to the class. If possible, students can bring in the animals to present to the class; check your school's policy regarding live animals in the classroom. If not, students can sketch, photograph, or videotape their trained animals. During their presentations, students should discuss how they trained their animals, including any difficulties they encountered.

Performance Assessment

The Chapter 14 Project Scoring Rubric on page 124 of Unit 3 Resources will help you evaluate how well students complete the Chapter 14 Project. You may wish to share the scoring rubric with your students so they are clear about what will be expected of them. Students will be assessed on
- how well they choose appropriate animal, trick, stimulus, and reward; how thoroughly they plan a workable regimen;
- the completeness of their observation entries, including what their animals do during training and descriptions of external factors that may affect that process;
- the thoroughness and organization of their presentations.

Program Resources

- **Unit 3 Resources** Chapter 14 Project Teacher Notes, pp. 118–119; Chapter 14 Project Student Overview and Worksheets, pp. 120–123; Chapter 14 Project Scoring Rubric, p. 124

WEB ACTIVITY www.phschool.com

You will find an Internet activity, chapter self-tests for students, and links to other chapter topics at this site.

SECTION 1 Why Do Animals Behave as They Do?

Objectives

After completing the lesson, students will be able to
- describe the functions of most of an animal's behavior;
- compare instinctive and learned behavior;
- explain the process called imprinting.

Key Terms behavior, stimulus, response, instinct, learning, conditioning, trial-and-error learning, insight learning, artificial intelligence, imprinting

1 Engage/Explore

Activating Prior Knowledge

Make a two-column table on the board. Labeled "What Happens" and "Way Animal Behaves." List events in the first column that may produce a response in an animal. (*Sample: Dog hears doorbell, kitten sees ball of yarn, fish sees food*) Have students describe how the pet might respond in each case and list the responses in the second column.

DISCOVER

Skills Focus predicting
Materials *small vertebrates, a cage or aquarium, food*
Time 15 minutes
Tips Students should not handle the animals. Advise students to wait patiently for animals to show some kind of behavior. Students must wash their hands afterward.
Expected Outcome Students should observe that food, other animals, or disturbing sounds cause behaviors such as feeding, social interaction, hiding, or escape attempts.
Think It Over Some possible answers include the addition of another animal, a loud noise, or addition of food.
learning modality: visual

442

SECTION 1 Why Do Animals Behave as They Do?

DISCOVER ···································· ACTIVITY

What Can You Observe About a Vertebrate's Behavior?

1. For a few minutes, carefully observe the behavior of a small vertebrate, such as a gerbil or a goldfish. Write down your observations.

2. Place some food near the animal and watch what the animal does.

3. If there are other animals in the cage or aquarium, observe how the animals interact—for example, do they fight, groom one another, or ignore one another?

4. Tap gently on the cage or aquarium and see how the animal reacts. Note any other events that seem to make the animal change its behavior (from resting to moving, for example).

Think It Over
Predicting What are some circumstances under which you might expect an animal's behavior to change suddenly?

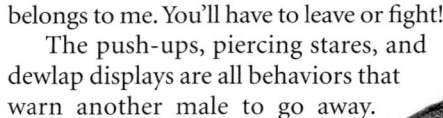

GUIDE FOR READING

- What are the functions of most of an animal's behaviors?
- How does instinctive behavior compare with learned behavior?

Reading Tip Before you read, rewrite the headings in the section as *how, why,* or *what* questions. As you read, write answers to those questions.

Figure 1 These two anoles are displaying their dewlaps in a dispute over space.

A male anole—a kind of lizard—stands in a patch of sun. As another male approaches, the first anole begins to lower and raise its head and chest in a series of quick push-ups. From beneath its neck a dewlap, a bright red flap of skin, flares out and then collapses, over and over. The anoles stare at each other, looking like miniature dinosaurs about to do battle. The first anole seems to be saying, "This area belongs to me. You'll have to leave or fight!"

The push-ups, piercing stares, and dewlap displays are all behaviors that warn another male to go away.

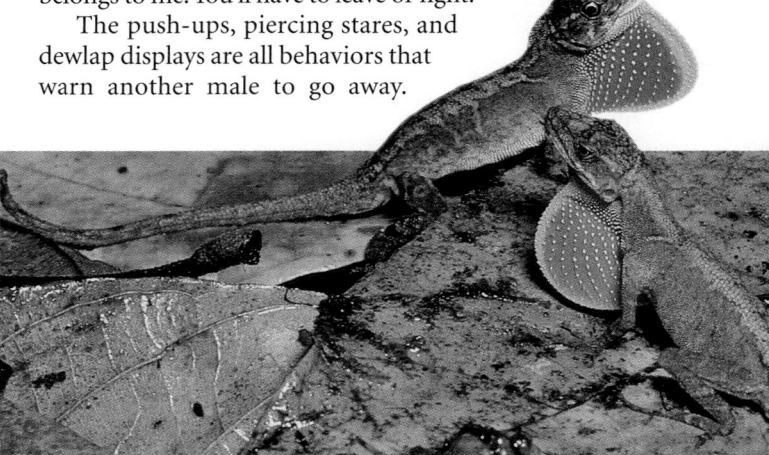

442

READING STRATEGIES

Reading Tip Before students read the section, have partners discuss and jot down possible answers to the *how, why,* and *what* questions they wrote. (Sample questions: Why is behavior important? What is instinctive behavior?) After they have read the section, have students work with the same partners to check the accuracy of their answers.

Vocabulary Have students write the key terms *instinct, insight,* and *imprinting* and underline the related prefixes *in-* and *im-*. Provide student pairs with a dictionary, and have them look up the various meanings of the prefixes.

An animal's **behavior** consists of all the actions it performs—for example, the things that it does to obtain food, avoid predators, and find a mate. To understand animals, it is important to know not only what their body structures are like, but also how and why they behave as they do. Like their body structures, the behaviors of animals are adaptations that have evolved over long periods of time.

Most behavior is a complicated process in which different parts of an animal's body work together. The first anole saw the second anole with his eyes and interpreted the sight with his brain. His brain and nervous system then directed his muscles to perform the push-up movement and to display his bright red dewlap.

Why Behavior Is Important

When an animal looks for food or hides to avoid a predator, it is obviously doing something that helps it stay alive. When animals search for mates and build nests for young, they are behaving in ways that help them reproduce. **Most behaviors help an animal survive or reproduce.**

As an example of a survival behavior, consider what happens when a water current carries a small crustacean to a hydra's tentacles. After stinging cells on the tentacles paralyze the prey, the tentacles bend, pulling the captured crustacean toward the hydra's mouth. At the same time, the hydra's mouth opens to receive the food. If the tentacles didn't pull the food toward the hydra's mouth, or if the mouth didn't open, then the hydra couldn't take the food into its body. If the hydra couldn't feed, it would die.

The small crustacean acted as a stimulus to the hydra. A **stimulus** (plural *stimuli*) is a signal that causes an organism to react in some way. The organism's reaction to the stimulus is called a **response**. The hydra responded to the crustacean by stinging it and then eating it. All animal behavior is caused by stimuli. Some stimuli come from an animal's external environment, while other stimuli, such as hunger, come from inside the animal's body. An animal's response may include external actions, internal changes (such as a faster heartbeat), or both.

☑ *Checkpoint* *Give an example of a stimulus to which a hydra would respond.*

Figure 2 When a hungry sea star finds a clam, the clam acts as a stimulus. The sea star's response is to approach the clam, grab the clam's shell with its tube feet, and open it. The sea star can then force its stomach inside the shell to consume the clam.
Applying Concepts How is this behavior important to the sea star's survival?

Program Resources

◆ **Unit 3 Resources** 14-1 Lesson Plan, p. 125; 14-1 Section Summary, p. 126

Media and Technology

🎧 **Audio CD** English-Spanish Summary 14-1

Answers to Self-Assessment

☑ *Checkpoint*
Having its tentacles touched by a toothpick

Caption Question
Figure 2 The behavior enables the sea star to get food.

2 Facilitate

Why Behavior Is Important

Demonstration

The automatic "blink" response is common among most mammals. Divide students into pairs. Have one member of the pair hold a clear sheet of plastic in front of his or her face, while the other member gently tosses a soft foam ball at the sheet. Most students will involuntarily blink, even though they know the ball can't hit them. Students may exchange places and repeat the activity. Ask: **How does this automatic response aid a mammal's survival?** *(It helps to avoid injury to the eye.).* **learning modality: kinesthetic**

Including All Students

For the benefit of students who lack proficiency in English, point out that *behavior* can have different meanings. It can refer to a person's conduct, as in the sentence, "Proper behavior requires people to cover their mouths when they cough." *Behavior* can also refer to the actions an animal performs. Invite students to name other words with multiple meanings. *(Glass, cry, fork, nail, and so forth)* Ask students to identify words with multiple meanings in languages other than English. **limited English proficiency**

Ongoing Assessment

Writing Have students name one animal behavior and suggest how the behavior is beneficial for the animal.

Instinctive Behavior

Addressing Naive Conceptions

Some students may think that only simple behaviors are instinctive. However, this is not the case. For example, seasonal migration is a complex behavior that is at least partly instinctive. Point out other examples of complex animal behaviors that are wholly or partly instinctive, such as cranes performing elaborate "dances" during courtship.

learning modality: verbal

Learning

Sharpen your Skills

Predicting

Time 10 minutes

Tips Prepare students to predict the chicks' responses by asking them to compare the shadow shapes. Suggest they note similarities and differences that a chick might use as clues for distinguishing among the shadows.

Expected Outcome An older chick would learn not to crouch when it sees a shadow shaped like B, whereas shadows A and C would continue to elicit crouching behavior. This learning is a form of conditioning that modifies instinctive behavior.

Extend Have students propose a design for an experiment that tests whether hawks are more likely to capture chicks that are upright or chicks that are crouching. (*Sample: Set up decoys of upright and crouching chicks. Periodically check for evidence of hawk attacks.*)

learning modality: visual

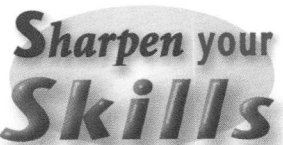

Predicting

Hawks, which have short 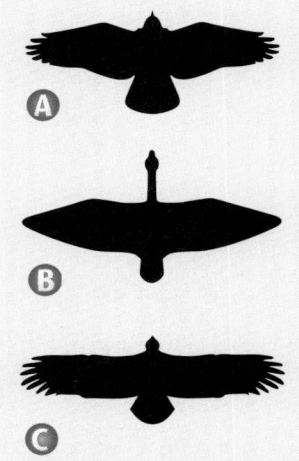 necks, prey on gull chicks. Geese, which have long necks, do not prey on the chicks. When newly hatched gull chicks see any bird's shadow, they instinctively crouch down. As the chicks become older, they continue to crouch when they see the shadow of a hawk, but they learn not to crouch when they see a goose's shadow. Predict how older gull chicks will behave when they see bird shadows shaped like A, B, and C. Which type of learning does this behavior show? Explain.

Instinctive Behavior

Some animal behaviors must be learned, while others are inborn—the animal knows how to do them by **instinct,** without being taught. An instinct is a behavior pattern that is inborn and that an animal performs correctly the first time. For example, a newborn kangaroo instinctively crawls into its mother's pouch and attaches itself to a nipple. A dragonfly nymph will instinctively shoot out its lower jaw and catch any bite-sized animal that comes within range. The dragonfly nymph has not been taught how to capture food. Rather, it knows instinctively how to use its mouthparts to do that. Most behaviors of invertebrates, such as insects, echinoderms, and worms, are instinctive.

Like learned behaviors, instinctive behaviors are responses to stimuli. Earthworms, for example, instinctively crawl away from a bright light. The light is the stimulus, and the earthworms respond by moving away from it.

The behavior of earthworms in response to strong light is fairly simple. However, some instinctive behaviors are complex. Spiders instinctively spin complicated webs without making mistakes in the pattern. Most birds build their nests without ever being taught how.

☑ *Checkpoint* What is instinctive behavior?

Learning

Think back to the first time you rode a bicycle. It probably took a few tries before you could do it well—you had to learn how. **Learning** is the process that leads to changes in behavior based on practice or experience. In general, the larger an animal's brain is, the more the animal can learn.

Unlike instincts, learned behaviors result from an animal's experience and are not usually done perfectly the first time. Lion cubs must practice many times before they can successfully kill prey. Gradually, by participating in hunting and imitating their mother's behavior, cubs learn to creep up on a prey animal, pounce on it, and kill it.

All learned behaviors depend in part on inherited traits that have passed from parents to offspring. Even though lion cubs must learn specific methods of hunting, they are born with claws that help them capture prey. In addition, lion cubs will instinctively pounce on any object that attracts their attention. The cubs have inherited some physical features and skills that are necessary for hunting, in much the same way that a talented basketball player has inherited above-average height and good eye-hand

---

Background

Facts and Figures Most bird songs are vocalizations made by male birds during the mating season. If they do not learn the same songs as other birds of their species, male birds will not be able to defend their territories, warn others of danger, or find and secure a mate.

To learn whether bird songs are inherited or learned, eighteenth-century naturalists studied birds raised without others of their species. They found that some birds could sing their species song from birth, although they did not sing it very well. However, other bird species raised with foster parents of a different species learned the songs of their foster parents.

Recent research has determined that in some bird species, birds must learn their songs during an early critical period, or they will not learn the songs at all.

coordination. But both lions and athletes must practice in order to develop their abilities.

Animals learn new behaviors in different ways. These include conditioning, trial-and-error learning, and insight learning.

Conditioning When a dog sees its owner approaching with a leash, the dog may get excited, eager to go for a walk. The dog has learned to associate the sight of the leash with a walk. Learning to connect some kind of stimulus with a good or bad event is called **conditioning.** In the case of the dog and the leash, the stimulus of the leash is associated with a pleasant event—a brisk walk. Animals can also be conditioned to avoid bad outcomes. Think of what happens when a predator tries to attack a skunk. The skunk sprays the predator with a substance that stings and smells awful. In the future, the predator is likely to avoid skunks, because the predator associates the sight of a skunk with its terrible spray.

During the early 1900s, the Russian scientist Ivan Pavlov performed a series of experiments involving conditioning. In Figure 3, see how Pavlov conditioned a dog to respond to the stimulus of a bell.

Figure 3 Steps 1, 2, and 3 show the procedure that Pavlov used when he conditioned a dog to salivate at the sound of a bell. *Predicting Predict what the dog would do if it heard a bell ringing in another part of the house.*

1 When a hungry dog sees or smells food, it produces saliva. Food is the stimulus, and the dog's response is salivation. Dogs do not usually salivate in response to other stimuli, such as the sound of a ringing bell.

2 For many days, when Pavlov gave food to a dog, he also rang a bell at the same time. The sight and smell of food were associated with the ringing of a bell. Pavlov did this every time he fed the dog. The dog salivated each time the two stimuli were introduced.

3 Finally, Pavlov rang a bell but did not give the dog food. The dog still produced saliva. The stimulus of the bell by itself produced the same response— salivation—that only food would normally produce.

Chapter 14 **445**

Program Resources

◆ **Interdisciplinary Exploration Series** "Sleuth's Supper," p. 37

Media and Technology

Transparencies "Pavlov's Experiment," Transparency 59

Answers to Self-Assessment
Caption Question

Figure 3 The dog would salivate. The dog is conditioned to salivate when it hears a bell, no matter where the bell is located.

☑ *Checkpoint*

Instinctive behavior is an inborn behavior pattern that an animal can perform correctly the first time.

Using the Visuals: Figure 3

Ask students to cover the numbered descriptions in the figure with a sheet of paper. Then have them describe what is happening in the figure, using just the illustrations. Make sure students' descriptions include the dog's behavior and the stimulus for the behavior. Finally, ask students to identify the kind of learning being demonstrated by the sequence of drawings. *(Conditioning)* **learning modality: visual**

Real-Life Learning

Divide the class into small groups. In the groups, have the students describe their response to the school's fire alarm. Have the groups problem-solve to decide whether the described response is an example of instinctive behavior or conditioning. **learning modality: verbal**

Inquiry Challenge

ACTIVITY

Divide the class into cooperative groups. Instruct each group to design an experiment to investigate a particular animal's response to a stimulus, such as a dog's response to the ringing of a doorbell. Groups can assign the tasks of the designing process—posing a question, developing a hypothesis, controlling variables, and forming operational definitions—to specific students. Inform students that if they wish to perform the experiment, they must write a description of the procedure and obtain your approval for their procedure. Advise students to use safe and inexpensive materials, and to treat the animal safely and gently. Allow time for initial brainstorming. At the end of the activity, have groups discuss their experiments and explain why they chose the specific variables they did. **cooperative learning**

Ongoing Assessment

Oral Presentation Ask students to present an example of conditioning they have witnessed in themselves, another person, or in animals. Have them present their example to the class, and explain how the example demonstrates conditioning.

Learning, continued

Including All Students

Students whose hearing is impaired will benefit from this activity because the meanings of trial-and-error learning and insight learning will be communicated visually. Decide beforehand which shape on the charts will be associated with a reward. Divide the class into six groups of three or four students each. Select one student in each group as the test administrator. The administrator will choose another student to select any shape from one chart. The student will continue selecting until the reward is given. Now the administrator will show the second chart to the test subject. The subject will probably choose the shape first associated with the reward. Next, the administrator will ask another student to choose shapes from the charts. The student will probably choose the shape associated with the reward given to the first student. Continue until all students in the group have received a reward. Ask students: **What kind of learning did the first test subject use to find the shape that led to the reward?** *(Trial and error)* **The second subject?** *(Insight)* Instruct students to explain their answers.
learning modality: visual

Integrating Technology

Have students explore the abilities and limits of artificial intelligence by allowing them to play one of the many checkers-playing programs available on the Internet. You can download free trial versions or inexpensive checkers playing programs from **www.shareware.com** or help students find another appropriate site. After students play, ask them to describe how playing checkers with a computer compared to playing with a friend.
learning modality: logical/mathematical

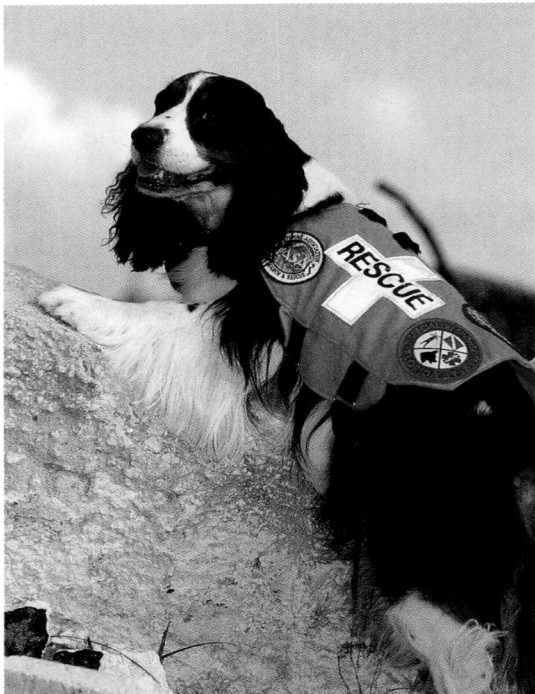

Figure 4 Rescue dogs, like this English springer spaniel, are specially trained to find and rescue people trapped by accidents or natural disasters. Trainers use conditioning to teach rescue dogs these skills.

Conditioning is often used to train animals. Suppose, for example, that you want to train a dog to come to you when you call it. Every time the dog comes when you call, you reward it with a dog biscuit and a friendly pat. Your dog soon will learn to associate the pleasant experience of food and a pat with the behavior of coming when called. So the dog is likely to repeat that behavior.

Trial-and-Error Learning When a young chicken first hatches and begins to look for food, it will peck at almost any spot on the ground. Gradually the chick learns that only some of these spots are seeds or insects that are good to eat. The chicken has learned through trial and error which objects are food. **Trial-and-error learning** occurs when an animal, through repeated practice, learns to perform a behavior more and more skillfully. When you learned to ride a bicycle, you did it by trial and error. You may have wobbled or even fallen at first, especially when turning corners, but after a while you learned to ride smoothly. You got better because you learned that some movements were more likely to keep you upright than others.

Insight Learning The first time you try out a new video game, you may not need someone to explain how to play it. Instead, you may use what you already know about other video games to figure out how the new one works. When you solve a problem or learn how to do something new by applying what you already know, without a period of trial and error, you are using **insight learning.**

Insight learning is most common in primates, such as gorillas, chimpanzees, and humans. Figure 5 shows the results of an experiment done with chimpanzees. The animals used insight to come up with a way to reach a bunch of bananas—they stacked boxes on top of one another. In contrast, if a dog accidentally wraps its leash around a pole, the dog cannot figure out how to unwrap the leash.

INTEGRATING TECHNOLOGY People once thought that machines were incapable of learning. However, some computers can now learn and solve problems. **Artificial intelligence** is the capacity of a computer to perform complex tasks such as learning from experience and solving problems. Computers with artificial intelligence can play chess and beat human opponents. The computer, like a human chess player, can figure out

446

Background

Facts and Figures Recent studies suggest that many birds are capable of insight learning. Both pigeons and canaries can solve the *oddity problem*—picking out the "odd" object in a set of three objects. In addition, canaries can generalize this principle to other sets of odd objects. In other words, they were able to pick out the odd objects in other sets the first time they saw them.

Scientists once believed that birds were capable only of mimicry or simple association. However, Dr. Irene Pepperberg at the University of Arizona has taught African gray parrots to say simple phrases that the birds apparently relate to actual situations. Alex, the most famous of the parrots, can make simple requests for food or at times use language creatively.

Figure 5 In this experiment, a hungry chimpanzee faced a problem—it couldn't reach the bananas. The chimpanzee figured out how to reach the bananas by stacking the boxes and climbing to the top. *Applying Concepts Explain how the chimpanzee's behavior shows insight learning.*

strategies and moves in advance. As scientists working in the field of artificial intelligence try to program computers to learn, they have a growing appreciation for the amazing abilities of the human brain.

☑ *Checkpoint* *In which animals is insight learning most common?*

Imprinting

A female Canada goose swims across a stream. One by one, her goslings paddle after her. The goslings follow their mother wherever she goes because they have undergone a process called imprinting. In **imprinting,** certain newly hatched birds and newborn mammals learn to recognize and follow the first moving object they see, which is usually their mother. Imprinting occurs very shortly after a young animal hatches or is born.

Imprinting involves a combination of instinctive behavior and learning. The young animal has an instinct to follow a moving object, but the youngster is not born knowing what its mother looks like. The young animal must learn from experience what object to follow.

Imprinting is valuable for two reasons. First, it keeps young animals close to their mothers, who know where to find food and how to avoid predators. Second, imprinting allows young

Line Them Up

Try to solve the following problem.
There are five girls: Maureen, Lupita, Jill, PoYee, and Tanya. They are standing in a row. Neither Maureen nor Lupita is next to PoYee. Neither Lupita nor Maureen is next to Tanya. Neither PoYee nor Lupita is next to Jill. Tanya is just to the right of Jill. Name the girls from left to right.
Inferring What kind or kinds of learning did you use to solve the problem? Explain.

TRY THIS

Skills Focus inferring
Materials *paper and pencil*
Time 15 minutes
Tips Have students work in pairs. Suggest they write the names of the girls on slips of paper, then arrange the slips in the correct order.
Expected Outcome The correct order is Lupita, Maureen, Jill, Tanya, and PoYee.
Inferring Students will probably solve the problem by trial-and-error—moving the slips of paper around until they find the correct arrangement.
Extend Ask volunteers to describe and characterize the methods they used.
learning modality: logical/mathematical

Imprinting

Real-Life Learning

Explain that one successful endangered animal-breeding program, the program to reintroduce the California condor, is raising these rare birds in captivity so they can be returned to the wild. Hand puppets that resemble condor parents are used to feed and nurture the babies. Ask students: **If these precautions were not taken, would humans be a danger to these condors when they are released? Why or why not?** *(Yes, because the condors would associate humans with food and be attracted to them. If this happened, the birds might be injured by people who were afraid of them.)* Explain that the only way to be sure that captive animals do not imprint on humans is to keep them away from humans until the animals are mature. **learning modality: verbal**

Answers to Self-Assessment

Caption Question

Figure 5 The chimpanzee solved a problem by applying what it already knew (that stacking the boxes would enable it to get higher).

☑ *Checkpoint*

Insight learning is most common in primates, such as gorillas and humans.

Ongoing Assessment

Skills Check Have students list three of their own learned behaviors and classify them as trial and error or insight learning. *(Sample: learning subtraction based on knowledge of addition—insight; learning to skate on in-line skates—trial and error)*

3 Assess

Section 1 Review Answers

1. Most behaviors help animals survive or reproduce.
2. Instinctive behaviors are inborn. The animal performs them correctly the first time. Learned behaviors result from an animal's experience and are not done perfectly the first time.
3. Trial-and-error learning occurs when an animal, through repetition, learns to perform a behavior more skillfully. In insight learning, an animal performs a behavior by applying previous knowledge, without a period of trial and error.
4. The duckling will probably try to follow the tricycle, because ducklings follow the first moving object they see after hatching. This behavior is called imprinting.

Check Your Progress
CHAPTER PROJECT

Review students' training plans. Check to make sure students have obtained permission from the owners of the animals. Also make sure that the skills students are planning to teach their animals are reasonable. Ensure that students have chosen appropriate rewards for the animals, and that the animals will not be harmed during the training process.

448

Figure 6 These ducks imprinted on scientist Konrad Lorenz when they were ducklings. Even as adults, they followed him when he went for a swim.

animals to learn what other animals of their own species look like. This ability protects the animals while they are young. In addition, it is important later in life when the animals are searching for mates.

Once imprinting takes place, it cannot be changed—even if the animal has imprinted on something other than its mother, such as a moving toy, or even a human. Konrad Lorenz, an Austrian scientist who first described imprinting in 1935, conducted experiments in which he, rather than the mother, was the first moving object that newly hatched birds saw. Figure 6 shows the result of one such experiment. Since the newly hatched birds imprinted on Lorenz, even as adults they followed him around.

Lorenz's experiments sometimes caused surprising results. One bird that had imprinted on Lorenz, a male jackdaw, apparently thought that Lorenz was a possible mate. Because jackdaws feed one another as part of their mating behavior, this bird often tried to feed worms to Lorenz, who politely refused to eat them.

Section 1 Review

1. Explain what roles behavior plays for animals.
2. Contrast instinctive behavior with learned behavior.
3. How is trial-and-error learning different from insight learning?
4. **Thinking Critically Predicting** Right after hatching, before seeing anything else, a duckling sees a child riding a tricycle. What will probably happen the next time the child rides the tricycle in front of the duckling? Explain, and identify the type of behavior that this shows.

448

Check Your Progress
CHAPTER PROJECT

By now, you should have written out a day-by-day plan for teaching your animal a new behavior. You may find ideas in books on training pets. Make sure that your plan will not harm the animal. Obtain your teacher's approval for your plan and begin training your animal. (Hint: Decide how you will monitor learning in your animal. What responses will show that the animal has mastered the skill?)

BECOME A LEARNING DETECTIVE

In this lab, you will design an experiment to investigate how people learn.

Problem

What are some factors that make it easier for people to learn new things?

Suggested Materials

paper and pencil

Design a Plan

1. Look over the two lists of words in the table. Researchers use groups of words like these to investigate how people learn. Notice the way the two groups differ. The words in List A have no meanings in ordinary English. List B contains familiar, but unrelated, words.

2. What do you think will happen if people try to learn the words in each list? Write a hypothesis about which list will be easier to learn. How much easier will it be to learn that list?

3. With a partner, design an experiment to test your hypothesis. Brainstorm a list of the variables you will need to control in order to make your results reliable. Then write out your plan and present it to your teacher.

4. If necessary, revise your plan according to your teacher's instructions. Then perform your experiment using people your teacher has approved as test subjects. Keep careful records of your results.

Analyze and Conclude

1. Find the average (mean) number of words people learned from each list. How did these results compare with your hypothesis?

List A	List B
zop	bug
rud	rag
tig	den
wab	hot
hev	fur
paf	wax
mel	beg
kib	cut
col	sip
nug	job

2. What factors may have made one list easier to learn than the other?

3. Share your results with the rest of the class. How do the results of the different experiments in your class compare? What might explain the similarities or differences?

4. **Think About It** Look back at your experimental plan. Think about how well you were able to carry it out in the actual experiment. What difficulties did you encounter? What improvements could you make, either in your plan or in the way you carried it out?

Design an Experiment

Plan an experiment to investigate how long people remember what they learn. Write a hypothesis, and design an experiment to test your hypothesis. Obtain your teacher's permission before carrying out your experiment.

Analyze and Conclude
1. Most test subjects will learn more from list B than list A.
2. It is easier to remember meaningful words than to recall nonsense words.
3. Experiments with similar designs will probably produce similar results.
4. Sample: Include more people to get a better sample.

Extending Inquiry
Design an Experiment Sample: Students

might hypothesize that familiar words are remembered longer. Have several test subjects learn a list that includes familiar and unfamiliar words. Test the subjects' ability to write down the list after 1, 2 and 4 hours. Test again every day for the next few days.

Program Resources

◆ **Unit 3 Resources** Chapter 14 Skills Lab, pp. 133–134

Designing Experiments

Become a Learning Detective

Preparing for Inquiry
Key Concept Familiarity with a topic makes learning new material easier.
Skills Objective Students will be able to
◆ propose a hypothesis concerning human learning;
◆ design an experiment to test their hypothesis.
Time 40 minutes
Advanced Planning Decide who the test subjects will be. You may wish to use students in other classes.
Alternative Materials If students conduct this experiment on classmates, they must generate new lists that are unfamiliar to the test subjects.

Guiding Inquiry
Invitation To help students think about the various factors that affect how easy it is to learn, ask them if they learn better when they enjoy the subject, when they are motivated by rewards, when they are already familiar with the subject, and when there is much repetition.

Helping Design a Plan
Make sure that students come up with a measure of "easier to learn." For example, students may give a test subject five minutes to look at a list. The subject then has to write down as many words as she or he can remember. The test subject will remember more words from the list that was easier to learn.

Troubleshooting the Experiment
◆ Tell students to have test subjects write down words rather than speaking them so that individuals in other groups will not overhear.

Expected Outcome
◆ List B will be easier to learn than list A.
◆ Familiar words are easier to learn than unfamiliar ones.

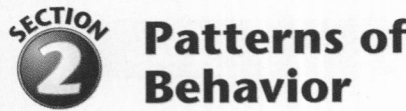
Objectives

After completing the lesson, students will be able to

◆ exlpain competition and aggression and the role they play in establishing a territory;

◆ explain the purpose of courtship behavior;

◆ describe the benefits animals receive from living in groups;

◆ describe animal behavior cycles and explain how they may affect an animal's survival.

Key Terms aggression, territory, courtship behavior, society, circadian rhythm, hibernation, migration

1 Engage/Explore

Activating Prior Knowledge

Instruct students to stop whatever they are doing immediately. Choose students at random and ask them what they were doing when you asked them to stop. Explain that whatever each student was doing was a part of his or her behavior. Elicit students' comments about what they think was the purpose of their behaviors.

••••••• **DISCOVER** •••••••

Skills Focus forming operational definitions
Materials *none*
Time 15 minutes
Tips Have students write down the feeling or situation they are trying to convey. Then, after their partner guesses what is being communicated, students can refer to their notebooks to check. Students should use only natural facial expressions and simple body movements.
Expected Outcome Students should be able to interpret emotional communications. Abstract ideas are difficult to communicate without words.
Think It Over Most students will indicate that gestures and expressions should be included in our definition of communication.

SECTION 2 Patterns of Behavior

DISCOVER ••••••••••••••••••••••••••••••••••••**ACTIVITY**

What Can You Express Without Words?

1. Think of a feeling or situation that you can communicate without words, such as surprise or how to play a sport. Use facial expressions and body movements, but no words, to communicate it to your partner.

2. By observing your behavior, your partner should infer what you are communicating. Your partner should also note the behavior clues that led to this inference.

3. Now your partner should try to communicate a feeling or situation to you without words. Infer what your partner is trying to communicate, and note the behavior clues that led to your inference.

Think It Over
Forming Operational Definitions
Write your own definition of *communication*. How did this activity change your idea of communication?

GUIDE FOR READING

◆ What is the function of courtship behavior?

◆ How do animals benefit from living in groups?

◆ How is migration important for an animal's survival?

Reading Tip As you read, write an outline of this section. Use the headings as the main topics.

At this very moment, somewhere in Earth's oceans, blue whales are calling to one another. Whales communicate with a variety of sounds that scientists call songs. These songs consist of brassy trumpetings, long wails, clicks, and deep grunts. Whales locate one another using these sounds.

Icebergs dot the cold polar waters where these giant mammals spend their summers. After fattening up on small, shrimp-like animals called krill, blue whales migrate to warmer waters near the equator. It is in these tropical seas that the females give birth, usually to one calf.

Blue whales communicate with one another and migrate to breeding and resting places—behavior characteristics that they share with many other animals. In this section you will learn about some common behavior patterns of animals.

Blue whale ▼

READING STRATEGIES

Reading Tip Emphasize the usefulness of outlining as a study tool. Students can use headings as topic names. Remind students to write each main topic next to a Roman numeral. As a class, outline the first main topic, Competition and Aggression. Ask students questions such as: What information supports the main topic? What details support each subtopic?

Sample:
I.   Competition and Aggression
   A.   Reasons for competition
      1.   food and water
      2.   space
      3.   shelter
      4.   mates
   B.   Purpose of aggression
   C.   Results of aggression

Figure 7 These Arctic hares are resolving their conflict by boxing. *Inferring What event might have led to this behavior?*

Competition and Aggression

Animals compete with one another for limited resources, such as food, water, space, shelter, and mates. Competition occurs among different species of animals, as when a pride of lions tries to steal a prey animal from a troop of hyenas that has just killed it. However, competition also occurs between members of the same species, as when a female aphid, a type of insect, kicks and shoves another female aphid while competing for the best leaf on which to lay eggs.

When they compete, animals may display **aggression,** which is a threatening behavior that one animal uses to gain control over another. Before a pride of lions settles down to eat its prey, individual lions show aggression by snapping, clawing, and snarling. First the most aggressive members of the pride eat their fill. Then the less aggressive and younger members of the pride get a chance to feed.

Aggression between members of the same species hardly ever results in the injury or death of any of the competitors. Usually the loser communicates "I give up" with its behavior. For example, to protect themselves from the aggressive attacks of older dogs, puppies roll over on their backs, showing their bellies. This signal calms the older dog, and the puppy can then creep away.

Establishing a Territory

On an early spring day, a male oriole fills the warm air with a flutelike song. You may think he is singing just because it is a beautiful day. But in fact, he is alerting other orioles that he is the "owner" of a particular territory. A **territory** is an area that is occupied and defended by an animal or group of animals.

---

2 Facilitate

Competition and Aggression

Demonstration

To demonstrate competition or aggression in animals, obtain two male bettas (also called Siamese fighting fish). Place each fish in its own glass jar filled with water. Place the jars next to each other on a table with an opaque card between them. Explain to students that the males of this species are very aggressive towards other males. To begin, allow students to observe the behavior of the two fish for a few minutes with the screen in place. Now remove the screen. Be sure each fish can clearly see the other. Have students observe and record behaviors they observe. After the demonstration, ask students to write short paragraphs to explain how they think these behaviors would benefit the bettas. *(The strongest and most aggressive males are those that survive and find mates.)* **learning modality: visual**

Establishing a Territory

Building Inquiry Skills: Predicting

Red-winged blackbirds display their red "epaulets" to defend a territory. Have students predict what would happen to a male blackbird whose red wing patches were dyed black. *(The male would lose its territory.)* **learning modality: logical/mathematical**

Program Resources

- **Unit 3 Resources** 14-2 Lesson Plan, p. 129; 14-2 Section Summary, p. 130

Media and Technology

 Audio CD English-Spanish Summary 14-2

Answers to Self-Assessment

Caption Question

Figure 7 The hares may be fighting over food or over a potential mate.

Ongoing Assessment

Oral Presentation Have students form small groups and list three competitive or aggressive human behaviors they have observed in the school cafeteria. Classify each behavior and describe its purpose. One member of each group can present the group's ideas.

Establishing a Territory, continued

Building Inquiry Skills: Inferring

Many students will have seen squirrels chasing each other in a park. Squirrels mark and aggressively defend their territories. Ask students to recall their observations of a park or other outdoor area in which squirrels live. Instruct students to use their observations to make an inference about whether a squirrel's territorial markings warn *all* animals away, or only other squirrels. *(Only other squirrels)* Ask students what knowledge they used to make this inference. *(Sample: A park may contain grackles and blackbirds as well as squirrels. The squirrels ignore the birds but chase other squirrels.)* Ask students to infer why squirrels do not defend their territory from birds. *(Birds don't compete for the same resources.)* **learning modality: logical/mathematical**

Mating and Raising Young

Addressing Naive Conceptions

What many people describe as "human nature" is not innate behavior at all; it is the result of human culture. Tell students that culture is the way of life of people who share similar beliefs and customs. Ask students to list some behaviors that are aspects of culture. *(Clothes, foods, ideas, sports, jobs, tools, and so on)* **learning modality: verbal**

If another animal of the same species enters the territory, the owner will attack the newcomer and try to drive it away. While birds use songs and aggressive behaviors to maintain their territories, other animals use calls, scratches, droppings, and scents. Cougars rake trees and earth with their claws and leave scent markings that advertise the boundaries of their territories.

By establishing a territory, an animal gains unlimited access to its resources, such as food and possible mates. A territory also provides a safe area in which animals can raise their young without competition from other members of their species. In most songbird species, and in many other animal species, a male cannot attract a mate unless he holds a territory.

☑ *Checkpoint* *How does a territory help an animal survive?*

Mating and Raising Young

A male and female salamander swim gracefully in the water, twining elegantly around each other. They are engaging in **courtship behavior,** which is behavior in which males and females of the same species prepare for mating. Males of some spider species court females by presenting them with prey before mating. Fireflies use light signals to indicate readiness for mating. **Courtship behavior ensures that the males and females of the same species recognize one another, so that mating and reproduction can take place.**

Birds have some of the most dramatic courtship behaviors. Figure 8 shows the elaborate bower that male bowerbirds prepare during courtship. Peregrine falcons have an acrobatic flight display as part of their courtship. As they soar through the air at

Figure 8 In the rain forest of Australia, a male satin bowerbird, left, creates a colorful welcome mat. He is decorating the entrance to the archlike bower he has built to attract a mate. By entering the bower, right, the green female bird lets the male know that she agrees to be his mate.

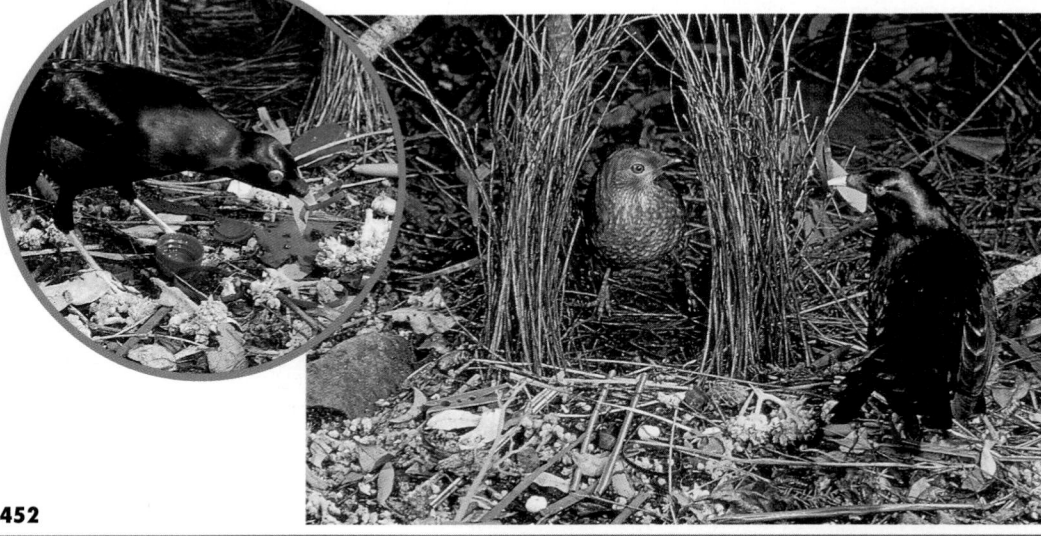

452

top speed, the male and female falcons dive and do figure eights and rolls.

Animal species differ in the amount of care they provide for their young. Most fishes, amphibians, and reptiles provide little or no parental care for their young. In contrast, most parent birds and mammals care for their young after hatching or birth. Not only do they feed and protect their young, but they also teach them survival skills, such as hunting.

Living in Groups

Although many animals are solitary and only rarely meet one of their own kind, other animals live in groups. Some fishes form schools, some insects live in large groups, and hoofed mammals, such as bison, often form herds. **Living in a group usually helps animals survive—group members protect one another and work together to find food.** Group members may help one another. If an elephant gets stuck in a mud hole, for example, other members of its herd will dig it out. When animals such as lions hunt in a group, they usually can kill larger prey than a single hunter can.

Safety in Groups Group living often protects animals against predators. Fishes that swim in schools are often safer than fishes that swim alone, because it is harder for predators to see and select an individual fish. In a herd, some animals may watch for danger while others feed. Furthermore, animals in a group sometimes cooperate in fighting off a predator. For example, North American musk oxen make a defensive circle against a predator, such as a wolf. Their young calves are sheltered in the middle of the circle while the adult musk oxen stand with their horns lowered, ready to charge. The predator often gives up rather than face a whole herd of angry musk oxen.

Worker Bees

In this activity, you will determine whether it is more productive to work alone or in a group, as honeybees do.

1. Make a paper chain by cutting paper strips for loops and gluing or taping the loops together. After 5 minutes, count the loops in the chain.

2. Now work in a small group to make a paper chain. Decide how to divide up the work before beginning. After 5 minutes, count the loops in the chain.

Calculating Find the difference between the number of loops in your individual and group chains. For Step 2, calculate the number of loops made per person by dividing the total number of loops by the number of people in your group. Was it more productive to work alone or as a group?

Figure 9 When a predator threatens, musk oxen form a horn-rimmed circle with their young sheltered in the center. *Predicting Would a potential predator be more or less likely to attack a group arranged in this way?*

TRY THIS

Skills Focus calculating
Materials 22×28 cm *sheets of paper, scissors; paste, glue, or stapler; timer*
Time 15 minutes
Tips Suggest that students plan their work before beginning—both when they work as individuals and when they work in groups. When students work in groups, part of their planning should involve assigning tasks to each group member.
Expected Outcome Students should discover that by working cooperatively, they were able to make more paper-chain links per person.
Calculating The number of loops per individual and group will vary. Students should find it was more productive to work as a group, because group members can divide up the work so that no one person has to perform the whole task.
Extend Have students think about what kinds of tasks may be performed more efficiently by one person than by a group. **cooperative learning**

Building Inquiry Skills: Applying Concepts

Have students name other groups of animals not mentioned in the textbook and describe how living in a group might benefit individuals within the groups. *(Flocks of birds—startle and confuse predators)* Prompt students to think about why humans live in groups. *(Mutual protection, sharing, and division of labor)* **learning modality: visual**

Media and Technology

 Transparencies ""Exploring a Honeybee Society," Transparency 60

 Exploring Life Science Videodisc Unit 3, Side 2, "Travelin' Along"

Chapter 8

Answers to Self-Assessment

☑ *Checkpoint*

A territory helps an animal survive by providing unlimited access to its resources, which may include mates and food, as well as a safe place to raise young.

Caption Question

Figure 9 A predator would be less likely to attack a group arranged this way.

Ongoing Assessment

Writing Have students form groups to make lists of the advantages of aggression, establishing a territory, and living in groups. Be sure all individuals in the groups contribute.

453

Living in Groups, continued

Addressing Naive Conceptions

Students may confuse human societies with animal societies. Human societies usually consist of associations of unrelated humans. On the other hand, all of the ants, termites, honeybees, naked mole rats, and pistol shrimp in a given society are close relatives, usually siblings. In addition, roles in animal societies are usually rigid, whereas roles in human societies can be much more flexible. **learning modality: verbal**

Communication

Cultural Diversity

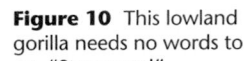

Explain that instinctive physical expressions such as smiling, screaming, and crying mean much the same thing in all human cultures. However, some expressions vary geographically. For example, in North America we shake our heads from side to side when we mean "no." In Greece, people nod their heads, and in Turkey they tilt their heads back and raise their eyebrows to convey the same idea. Cultures also differ in the way individuals greet each other. (Students have probably seen Russian political leaders kissing each other on the cheeks or Japanese political leaders bowing to each other.) Have pairs of students demonstrate examples of nonverbal communication, such as shaking hands, saluting, different forms of waving, and eye rolling, while the class describes the cultural meaning associated with these behaviors. Have students from other cultures explain how any of these gestures convey different meanings in their culture. **learning modality: kinesthetic**

Animal Societies Some animals, including ants, termites, honeybees, naked mole rats, and pistol shrimp, live in groups called societies. A **society** is a group of closely related animals of the same species that work together for the benefit of the whole group. You can see an example in *Exploring a Honeybee Society.* Different members perform specific tasks, such as gathering food or caring for young. The behavior of the animals is instinctive and rigid—an animal in a society is "preprogrammed" to perform a specific job.

Communication

If you've ever seen one cat hissing at another, you've watched two animals communicating. Although animals don't use spoken or written language, they do communicate. In Chapter 11, you read that many insects communicate using chemicals produced in their bodies. Animals also use sounds, body positions, and movements to convey information to one another. Hissing cats, for example, are usually communicating aggression.

Animals communicate various kinds of information. Much communication is involved in courtship. Female crickets, for example, are attracted to the sound of a male's chirping. Other animal communication relates to defense and aggression. While attacking other animals or defending themselves, animals may growl, snarl, hiss, or assume positions that make them look larger—and thus more frightening—than they really are. Animals may also communicate warnings. When it sees a coyote approaching, a prairie dog makes a yipping sound that warns other prairie dogs to take cover in their burrows. This yipping sounds like a dog barking—that's how prairie dogs got their name.

Animals also communicate information about food sources. One of the most complex systems of animal communication is used by honeybees to inform one another about the location of food—flower nectar and pollen. A worker bee that has found a new source of food will return to the hive and begin an excited "dance." The pattern of her movement communicates both the quality of the food and its distance and direction from the hive.

Figure 10 This lowland gorilla needs no words to say "Stay away!"

☑ *Checkpoint* *What are four ways that animals communicate with one another?*

Background

Facts and Figures *Gymnarchus niloticus* is a fish species that lives in streams and rivers in Africa. *Gymnarchus* have poorly developed eyes and feed on other fishes at night and in cloudy water. They cannot easily communicate by sight; however, the species has evolved a system of electronic communication. The main component of this system is an organ in each fish's tail that discharges electricity at a constant frequency.

The discharge sets up an electric field around the fish that is recorded by sensors on the fish's surface.

The field remains constant until solid objects such as predators, prey, or other *Gymnarchus* distort the field. After the fish interprets the distortion, it can react appropriately. As such, the electric fields have a function similar to touch, sound, or sight in other animals.

EXPLORING a Honeybee Society

A honeybee hive usually consists of one queen bee, thousands of female worker bees, and a few hundred male drones.

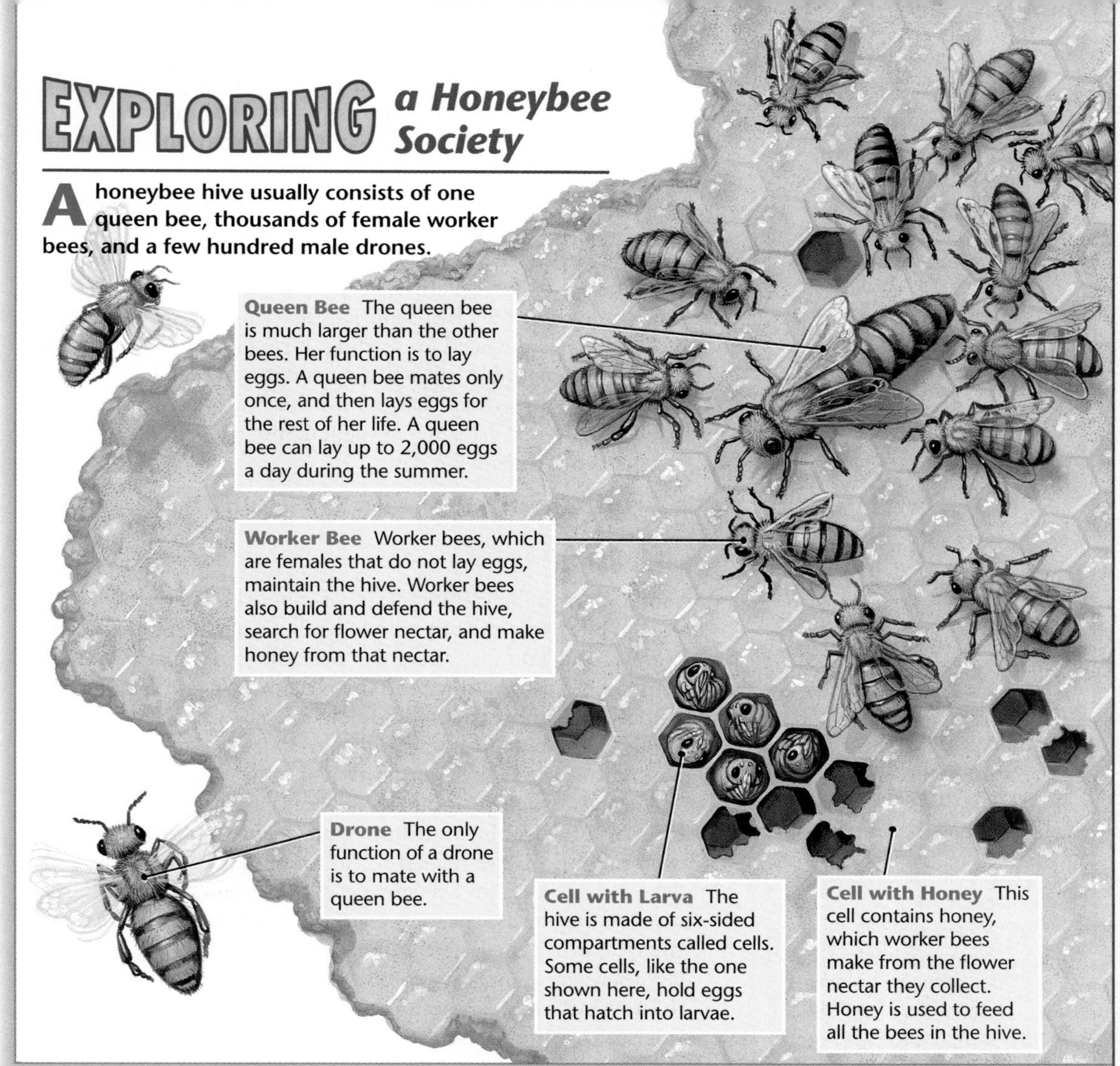

Queen Bee The queen bee is much larger than the other bees. Her function is to lay eggs. A queen bee mates only once, and then lays eggs for the rest of her life. A queen bee can lay up to 2,000 eggs a day during the summer.

Worker Bee Worker bees, which are females that do not lay eggs, maintain the hive. Worker bees also build and defend the hive, search for flower nectar, and make honey from that nectar.

Drone The only function of a drone is to mate with a queen bee.

Cell with Larva The hive is made of six-sided compartments called cells. Some cells, like the one shown here, hold eggs that hatch into larvae.

Cell with Honey This cell contains honey, which worker bees make from the flower nectar they collect. Honey is used to feed all the bees in the hive.

Behavior Cycles

Some animal behavior occurs in regular, predictable patterns. While blowflies, for example, search for food during the day, they are inactive at night. In contrast, field mice are active during the night and quiet by day. These daily behavior cycles of blowflies and mice are examples of **circadian rhythms** (sur KAY dee uhn rhythms), which are behavior cycles that occur over a period of approximately one day.

EXPLORING
a Honeybee Society

After students read the descriptions of the individuals in the honeybee society, ask: **Is any member of the honeybee society unimportant? Why?** (*None is unimportant. All members have their special tasks to perform.*) Invite a volunteer to list the three types of honeybees and their duties on the board. After reviewing the list, ask students why it is advantageous that there are more worker bees than other bees in the hive. (*Because worker bees have many different tasks to perform, such as caring for the hive, the queen, and the larvae, and finding and making food. The queen and the drones each have only one task.*) **learning modality: logical/mathematical**

Behavior Cycles

Real-Life Learning

Explain to students that almost all animals, including humans, display obvious circadian rhythms. Ask students for examples of circadian rhythms in their own lives. (*Samples: Most people get sleepy after dark. Many people get hungry at the same time each day.*) **learning modality: verbal**

Including All Students

To help students remember the definition of *circadian*, break the word into two parts: *circa/dian*. Explain that the prefix *circa-* means "approximately" and that *dian* comes from the Latin word for day, *dies*. **limited English proficiency**

Program Resources

◆ **Laboratory Manual** 14, "Family Life of Bettas"

Answers to Self-Assessment

✓ Checkpoint

Animals communicate using sound, body positions, movements, and scent.

Ongoing Assessment

Drawing Direct students to draw four pictures showing animals—including humans—communicating. (*Samples: A bear standing with its front legs up in the air, a cat with the fur on its back standing straight up*)

 Students can save their drawings in their portfolios.

Behavior Cycles, continued

Including All Students

The shortened daylight hours of winter cause mild behavior problems for some people. Invite the students to discuss if they have trouble waking up when it is still dark outside. Discuss ways of coping with the problem. **learning modality: verbal**

Migration

Social Studies CONNECTION

Time 15 minutes

Students will use map skills to interpret a map. Review the functions of the map key and compass rose.

In Your Journal Students' journals should include the following answers:
1. northern North America, central South America
2. approximately 10,000 km or 6,000 miles
3. southward route primarily over ocean, northward route primarily over land
4. the Mississippi River

Extend Ask students how one route south and another north might benefit the golden plovers. Stimulate discussion by pointing out that these migrations occur at different times of the year. *(Sample: Calmer weather conditions in the fall favor flying over the Atlantic. Spring conditions favor returning over land.)* **learning modality: visual**

Building Inquiry Skills: Comparing and Contrasting

Have students compare and contrast hibernation and migration as survival adaptations. *(Hibernation helps animals get through times of the year when there is insufficient food. Migration allows animals to move to areas with sufficient food.)* **learning modality: logical/ mathematical**

Social Studies CONNECTION

Like geographers, biologists sometimes need to interpret maps. Examine the map below to see the migration pattern of the golden plover, a shorebird. The arrows on the map show the routes of the golden plover's migrations.

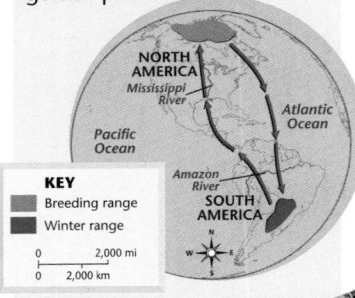

KEY
- Breeding range
- Winter range

0   2,000 mi
0   2,000 km

In Your Journal

Based on information on the map, write answers to the following questions.

1. On what continent does the golden plover spend its breeding season? Where does it spend the other seasons?
2. Use the scale to measure the approximate distance between the golden plover's two homes.
3. Compare the bird's southward route to its northward route. How do the routes differ?
4. What United States river does the golden plover follow when it heads northward?

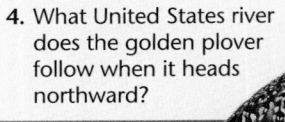

456

Other behavior cycles are related to seasons. Some animals, such as woodchucks and chipmunks, are active during warm seasons, but hibernate during the winter. **Hibernation** is a state of greatly reduced body activity that occurs during the winter. During hibernation, all of an animal's body processes, such as breathing and heartbeat, slow down. Hibernating animals do not eat. Their bodies use stored fat to meet their reduced nutrition needs.

Behavior cycles usually help animals survive in some way. Hibernation not only helps animals live through severe cold, it also eliminates the need for feeding during a season when food is scarce. Animals that are active during the day can take advantage of sunlight, which makes food easy to see. On the other hand, animals that are active at night do not encounter predators that are active during the day.

☑ *Checkpoint* **What happens to an animal during hibernation?**

Migration

Another kind of behavior cycle involves movement from place to place. While many animals spend their lives in a single area, others migrate. **Migration** is the regular, periodic journey of an animal from one place to another and then back again. Some migrating animals travel thousands of kilometers. Arctic terns, for example, fly more than 17,000 kilometers between their summer homes in the Arctic Circle to their winter residence near the South Pole.

Animals usually migrate to an area that provides abundant food, or a favorable environment for reproduction, or both. Most migrations are related to the changing seasons and take place twice a year, in the spring and fall. American redstarts, insect-eating birds, spend the long days of summer in North America, where they mate and raise young. In the fall, however, days there grow shorter and cooler, and insects become scarce. The redstarts then migrate south to Central America, South America, and islands in the Caribbean Sea, where they can again find plentiful food.

Many other animals, such as salmon, migrate to the areas in which they reproduce. Adult salmon live in oceans. However, to mate and lay eggs, an adult salmon must migrate from the ocean to the same stream where it once hatched from an egg—sometimes more than 3,000 kilometers away. In her "home" stream, the female lays her eggs and the male fertilizes them. The young salmon that hatch from those eggs will eventually migrate back to the ocean, and the cycle will begin again.

While there is much yet to learn about how migrating animals find their way, scientists have discovered

---

that animals use sight, taste, and other senses, including some that humans do not have. Some birds and sea turtles, for example, have a magnetic sense that acts something like a compass needle. Migrating birds also seem to navigate by using the positions of the sun, moon, and stars, as human sailors have always done. Salmon use scent and taste to locate the streams where they were born.

 **INTEGRATING ENVIRONMENTAL SCIENCE** Human activities sometimes interfere with animal migration. For example, when fuel and water pipelines are built above ground, migrating animals cannot easily cross over them. Dams across streams and rivers can block the path of fish migration. Bright city lights can confuse birds that migrate at night. Each year, millions of birds strike skyscraper windows and die during migration. But humans are learning how to help migrating animals. During the spring migration of 1998, the lights in more than 80 skyscrapers in Toronto, Ontario, were turned off at night to make a safer path for the birds. The lights of the Empire State Building in New York City also darken at night during migration.

Figure 11 This caribou herd is migrating across Alaska on the same path its ancestors used for thousands of years. Recently, human construction and oil drilling have begun to threaten this migration path. Both native people, who rely on the caribou for food, and corporations are working to find a way to save the path.

Section 2 Review

1. Define courtship behavior and describe an example.
2. Identify two ways in which animals benefit from living in groups.
3. What are the two major advantages that animals gain by migrating?
4. **Thinking Critically** **Applying Concepts** A mockingbird sings from a tree on the left side of the schoolyard. Soon it flies to the pine tree on the right side of the schoolyard and sings again. When another mockingbird flies into the schoolyard, the first mockingbird flies at it and tries to peck it. Explain what is probably happening.

Check Your Progress
CHAPTER PROJECT
At this point, you should be continuing with your training plan and monitoring your animal's progress. Be sure to keep good records of your animal's daily progress. Make modifications to your plan now if they are needed. Also think about how you will present your results to the class. (*Hint:* You may want to make drawings or take photos of your animal in action to use in your presentation.)

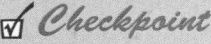

Chapter 14 **457**

Answers to Self-Assessment

☑ *Checkpoint*
During hibernation, all body activities, including breathing and heartbeat, slow down. Animals use stored body fat for nutrition.

 Integrating Environmental Science

Explain that migrating animals depend on different habitats at different times of the year. Protecting animals in only one place may not prevent species' decline. For example, the scarlet tanager and other North American songbirds winter in Central America. Ask the class to brainstorm steps that might help protect these birds. (*International agreements to preserve and restore habitat*) Ask students if they think a migratory animal can be protected if scientists do not know about its full life cycle. (*No*) **learning modality: verbal**

3 Assess

Section 2 Review Answers
1. Courtship behavior is behavior in which males and females of the same species prepare for mating. Example: peacocks displaying tail feathers.
2. Group members protect each other, work together, and divide labor.
3. Migrating animals can move to areas that provide food or favorable environments for reproduction.
4. The first mockingbird is establishing the boundaries of its territory. When it attacks the second mockingbird, it is defending this territory.

Check Your Progress
CHAPTER PROJECT
Ensure that every animal is making some kind of progress. If necessary, help students refocus their plans to allow the animals to learn.

Performance Assessment

Organizing Information Have students list at least five different behaviors they have observed among zoo animals or pets, classify each behavior according to the divisions in this section, and state the survival value of each behavior.

You and Your Environment

One For All

Preparing for Inquiry

Key Concept In ant colonies, individual members perform different tasks.

Skills Objectives Students will be able to:
◆ observe ants perform several different tasks;
◆ infer the division of labor in an ant colony.

Time 45 minutes

Advanced Planning CAUTION: *Avoid fire ants, as they are extremely aggressive. To check if a colony contains fire ants, tap on the mound with a small straw or twig. If the ants immediately swarm in large numbers, they are probably fire ants.*

Have students bring a glass jar to class a few days in advance. Large condiment jars work well. Ants can be collected from a colony in nature. Collect sufficient soil from the area close to the colony for students to use in their jars. Try to collect ants of various sizes from the colony. Dig up only a small part of the colony. Place the container with the ants you have collected in the refrigerator to slow the ants down. Keep ants chilled before adding to students' jars. Place 20-30 ants directly into students' jars so that students do not handle the ants. When finished, return all the ants to the refrigerator and then return them to their original colony.

Alternative Materials Nylon screen can be substituted for the wire screen, as it is easier to cut with scissors. You may prefer to purchase an "ant farm" from a scientific supply house.

Guiding Inquiry

Invitation Have students think about the society in which they live, especially how tasks are divided so that some grow food, some build houses, and so on. Have students predict how these tasks are accomplished in an ant society.

Introducing the Procedure

◆ Tell students that they may not observe some tasks. For example, there may be no eggs, larvae, or pupae for adult ants to care for.

◆ Students should think about how they will describe various behaviors. For example, ants may carry dirt grains (from digging), carry food, or interact with each other. Students should observe the tasks that ants of different sizes perform.

◆ Students should look for tunnels, for food storage locations, and for a refuse pile in the jar.

You and Your Environment

ONE FOR ALL

Have you ever stopped to watch a group of busy ants? In this lab, you will find out what goes on in an ant colony.

Problem

How does an ant society operate?

Skills Focus

observing, inferring, posing questions

Materials

large glass jar	sandy soil	shallow pan
water	wire screen	sponge
20–30 ants	sugar	bread crumbs
wax pencil	black paper	tape
large, thick rubber band		forceps

Procedure

1. Read over the entire lab to preview the kinds of observations you will be making.
2. Mark the outside of a large jar with four evenly spaced vertical lines. Label the sections A, B, C, and D.
3. Fill the jar about three-fourths full with soil. Place the jar in a shallow pan of water to prevent any ants from escaping. Place a wet sponge in the jar as a water source.
4. Observe the condition of the soil, both on the surface and along the sides of the jar. Record your observations for each section.
5. Add the ants to the jar. Immediately cover the jar with the wire screen, using the rubber band to hold the screen firmly in place.
6. Observe the ants for 10 minutes. Look for differences among the adult ants. Look for eggs, larvae, and pupae. Examine both individual behavior and interactions.
7. Remove the screen, and add some bread crumbs and sugar to the jar. Close the cover. Observe for 10 more minutes.
8. Wrap black paper around the jar above the water line. Remove the paper only when making your observations.
9. Observe the ants every day for two weeks. Look at the soil as well, and always examine the food. If any food is moldy, use forceps to remove it. Place the moldy food in a plastic bag, seal the bag, and throw it away. Add more food as necessary, and keep the sponge moist. When you finish your observations, replace the paper.

Analyze and Conclude

1. Describe the various types of ants you saw. What evidence, if any, did you observe that different kinds of ants perform different tasks?
2. How do the different behaviors you observed contribute to the survival of the colony?
3. How did the soil change over the period of your observations? What caused those changes? How do you know?
4. **Apply** Based on this lab, what kinds of environmental conditions do you think ant colonies need to thrive outdoors?

Design an Experiment

Design an experiment to investigate how an ant colony responds to change. Obtain your teacher's approval before carrying out your experiment.

Safety

Do not use fire ants or other ants that aggressively bite or sting. Caution students not to touch ants. Tell them to be very careful when carrying glass jars around the room.

Program Resources

◆ **Unit 3 Resources** Chapter 14 Real-World Lab, pp. 135–137

SECTION 1 — Why Do Animals Behave as They Do?

INTEGRATING PSYCHOLOGY

Key Ideas

◆ Most behaviors help an animal survive and reproduce. Examples include behaviors involved in obtaining food, avoiding predators, and finding a mate.

◆ An instinct is an inborn behavior pattern that the animal performs correctly the first time. Most behaviors of invertebrates are instinctive.

◆ Learning changes an animal's behavior as a result of experience. Some ways in which animals learn include conditioning, trial-and-error learning, and insight learning.

◆ Imprinting, in which very young animals learn to follow the first moving object they see, involves both instinct and learning.

Key Terms

behavior	conditioning
stimulus	trial-and-error learning
response	insight learning
instinct	artificial intelligence
learning	imprinting

SECTION 2 — Patterns of Behavior

Key Ideas

◆ Animals use aggression to compete for limited resources, such as food or shelter.

◆ Many animals establish territories from which they exclude other members of their species.

◆ Courtship behavior ensures that males and females of the same species recognize one another so that they can reproduce.

◆ There is usually some survival advantage to living in a group, such as cooperation in getting food and protection from danger.

◆ Animals use chemicals, sounds, body positions, and movements to communicate.

◆ Some animal behaviors occur in regular patterns. Circadian rhythms are one-day behavior cycles. Hibernation is a period of inactivity during winter.

◆ Some animals migrate to places where they can more easily find food, reproduce, or both.

Key Terms

aggression	circadian rhythm
territory	hibernation
courtship behavior	migration
society	

Organizing Information

Concept Map Copy the concept map below onto a separate sheet of paper. Then complete the map. (For more on concept maps, see the Skills Handbook.)

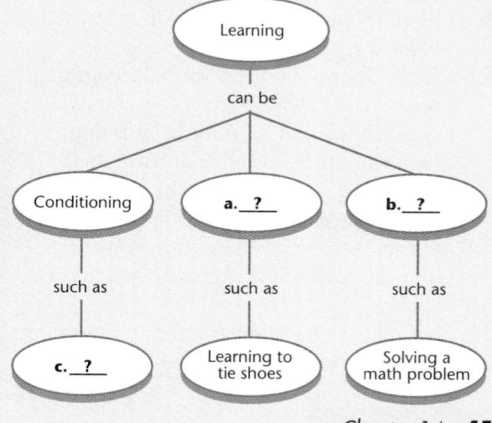

Troubleshooting the Experiment

◆ Students should try not to touch the ants.

Expected Outcome

◆ Ants will excavate tunnels and perform various tasks. Some will carry refuse to a pile (midden). Other ants will place dead ants and dirt on this pile. Ants will retrieve food and place it in a storage tunnel. If eggs, larvae, and pupae are present, they will be stored in an underground location.

◆ The main task for students will be to observe and describe the behaviors. Make sure that students infer how the behavior contributes to the colony's survival.

Analyze and Conclude

1. Sample response: Some ants carried food to the food store, dug tunnels, and took items to the refuse pile.

2. Answers will vary depending on the behavior observed. The behaviors contribute to the building of a home, food storage, waste removal, care of offspring, and the protection of the entire colony.

3. Tunnels were dug through the soil over the course of the experiment. Ants must have caused these changes, since no other organisms were present.

4. Sample response: Ants require soil in which they can dig and a source of food and water.

Extending Inquiry

Design an Experiment Sample: Students could decide to introduce a new kind of food or to present it in a different way.

Organizing Information

Concept Map a. Trial-and-error learning **b.** Insight learning **c.** Sample: Teaching a dog to roll over

Program Resources

◆ **Unit 3 Resources** Chapter 14 Project Scoring Rubric, p. 124

◆ **Performance Assessment** Chapter 14, pp. 44–46

◆ **Chapter and Unit Tests** Chapter 14 Test, pp. 64–67

Media and Technology

 Interactive Student Tutorial CD-ROM Chapter 14

 Computer Test Bank Chapter 14 Test

Reviewing Content

Multiple Choice

1. b 2. a 3. d 4. c 5. c

True or False

6. instinctive 7. conditioning 8. true
9. true 10. migration

Checking Concepts

11. Imprinting involves a combination of instinct and learning because the young animal has an instinct to follow a moving object, but it must learn from experience what object to follow.

12. You are exhibiting aggression; the dog is showing submission.

13. Courtship often occurs within an animal's territory. In some species, a male cannot mate unless he has established a territory.

14. No, this movement is a one-time event, rather than a cyclical, back-and-forth movement.

15. Students' interviews should include details of the structure of the society and roles of the different members. These details should parallel the structure and roles of the honeybee society.

Thinking Critically

16. A racehorse's ability to win races is based on a combination of the traits it inherits—such as strong limbs and lungs—and the training it receives. It may learn through conditioning to associate the event of the race with a stimulus such as a special treat. It may learn the stages of a successful race through trial and error.

17. Sample response: Every time the dog jumps on the sofa, the owner could move it off the sofa and say "No" in a firm voice. That way, the dog would learn by conditioning to associate the stimulus of jumping on the sofa with the negative outcome of its owner's disapproval.

18. Sample response: I learned how to operate a friend's VCR because it was similar to the one my family has.

19. The crickets probably would not be able to reproduce, because they depend on aural cues—chirping—to indicate their readiness and whereabouts for mating.

Reviewing Content

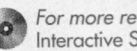 *For more review of key concepts, see the Interactive Student Tutorial CD-ROM.*

Multiple Choice

Choose the letter of the best answer.

1. The scent of a female moth causes a male to fly toward her. The scent is an example of
   a. a response.   **b.** a stimulus.
   c. aggression.   **d.** insight learning.

2. If you could play the saxophone by instinct, you would
   a. play well the first time you tried.
   b. need someone to teach you.
   c. have to practice frequently.
   d. know how to play other instruments.

3. When a male and female falcon share an acrobatic flight display, they exhibit
   a. learning.   **b.** imprinting.
   c. migration.   **d.** courtship behavior.

4. Some squirrels sleep all day and are active all night. This is an example of
   a. migration.   **b.** hibernation.
   c. circadian rhythm.   **d.** aggression.

5. When a bird travels from its winter home in South America to New York, this is called
   a. learning.   **b.** conditioning.
   c. migration.   **d.** hibernation.

True or False

If the statement is true, write true. If it is false, change the underlined word or words to make the statement true.

6. A spider building a web exhibits <u>learned</u> behavior.

7. Every day after school, you take your dog for a walk. Lately, he greets your arrival with his leash in his mouth. Your dog's behavior is an example of <u>instinct</u>.

8. A <u>territory</u> is an area that an animal will fight to defend.

9. Closely related animals of the same species work together for the group's benefit in a <u>society</u>.

10. Salmon return to fresh water to reproduce. This is an example of <u>circadian rhythm</u>.

Checking Concepts

11. Explain how both instinct and learning are involved in imprinting.

12. Your German shepherd puppy has just shredded your favorite pair of sneakers. When you loudly scold him, he rolls over on his back. What kind of behavior are you exhibiting to the dog? What is the meaning of his response?

13. Explain how courtship and territorial behavior are related.

14. Because a highway has been constructed through a forest, many of the animals that once lived there have had to move to a different wooded area. Is their move an example of migration? Explain.

15. Writing to Learn After landing on a distant planet, you discover creatures who look something like humans but whose society is organized like that of honeybees. Write an interview with one creature, who explains the structure of the society and the roles of different members.

Thinking Critically

16. Applying Concepts Explain how a racehorse's ability to win races is a combination of inherited and learned characteristics.

17. Problem Solving A dog keeps jumping onto a sofa. Describe a procedure that the owner might use to train the dog not to do this. The procedure must not involve any pain or harm to the dog.

18. Applying Concepts Give an example of something that you have learned by insight learning. Explain how you made use of your past knowledge and experience in learning it.

19. Predicting Suppose that a disease caused a population of crickets to become deaf. How might the reproduction rate of the cricket population be affected? Explain.

Applying Skills

20. The bee stung the toad, and the toad spat it out in an effort to get rid of it.

21. The toad will probably not try to catch the insect, because the toad will associate the bee with the sting.

22. Conditioning, because the toad has learned to connect a stimulus, the bee, with a bad event, being stung.

Applying Skills

The toad in the pictures below caught a bee and then spit it out. Use the pictures to answer Questions 20–22.

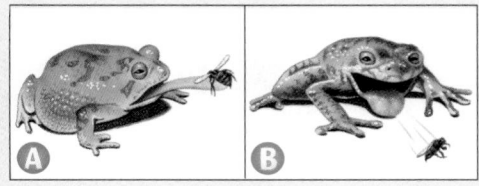

20. **Inferring** Explain why the toad probably behaved as it did in picture B.
21. **Predicting** If another bee flies by, how will the toad probably behave? Why?
22. **Classifying** What type of learning will probably result from the toad's experience? Explain.

Present Your Project Now is your chance to explain—or demonstrate—what your trained animal can do and to describe your training plan. Obtain your teacher's permission before bringing an animal to class. If you cannot bring in the animal, you can show photographs or illustrations of the animal's training. Be sure to discuss any surprises or setbacks you experienced.

Reflect and Record In your journal, describe your success in training your animal. What did you discover about the animal's learning process? How could you have improved your training plan? What questions do you still have about your animal's behavior?

Present Your Project Encourage each student to demonstrate how well his or her animal learned its trick. Students should explain how they trained their animals. Encourage students to use appropriate vocabulary from the text.

Reflect and Record It is likely that some, perhaps many, students will have been unable to train their animals. It is important that every student who made an honest attempt feels successful. Whether the animal was trained or not, students can still write about their experiences and think about ways of improving training.

Test Preparation

Test Preparation

23. a 24. d 25. b

Test Preparation

Use these questions to prepare for standardized tests.

Use the information to answer Questions 23–25.
A scientist conducted an experiment to learn whether mice would learn to run a maze more quickly if they were given rewards. She set up two identical mazes. In one maze, cheese was placed at the end of the correct route through the maze. No cheese was placed in the second maze. The graph below shows the results.

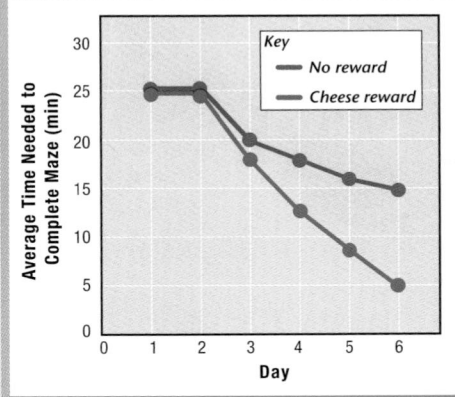

23. Based on the graph, which statement is true?
    a. Learning occurred more quickly when the mice received a reward.
    b. Learning occurred more slowly when the mice received a reward.
    c. The reward had no effect on how quickly the mice learned to run the maze.
    d. None of the mice learned to run the maze.
24. What was the manipulated variable in the experiment?
    a. the length of the maze
    b. the amount of time it took to run the maze
    c. the day
    d. whether or not a reward of cheese was given
25. What type of learning did the mice exhibit in the maze with the cheese reward?
    a. insight learning
    b. conditioning
    c. imprinting
    d. instinctive behavior

Chapter 14 **461**

Program Resources

◆ **Inquiry Skills Activity Book** Provides teaching and review of all inquiry skills

The Secret of Silk

This interdisciplinary feature presents the central theme of silk by connecting four different disciplines: science, social studies, mathematics, and language arts. The four explorations are designed to capture students' interest and help them see how the content they are studying in science relates to other school subjects and to real-world events. The unit is particularly suitable for team teaching.

1 Engage/Explore

Activating Prior Knowledge

Help students recall what they learned in Chapter 11, Section 3, Insects, by asking questions such as: **What is the name of the process by which an insect changes in form during its life cycle?** *(metamorphosis)* and **In which stage of metamorphosis does an insect look most like a worm?** *(larval stage)* Then ask: **What do you know about silkworms?** *(Accept all responses without comment at this time.)*

Introducing the Unit

If possible, bring an item made of silk to show the class. You may not want students to touch the item as silk is easy to damage. If an item is not available, ask students who have seen items made of silk to describe how they look and feel. Point out that insects make silk thread that is woven into silk cloth. Ask: **What is a product we eat that is made by insects?** *(honey)*

Have students name some products that they think are made of silk *(Record students' responses on the board.)*

The Secret of Silk

What animal—

was a secret for thousands of years?

was smuggled across mountains in a hollow cane?

is good to eat, especially stir-fried with garlic and ginger?

is not really what its name says it is?

If you guessed that this amazing animal is the silkworm, you are right. The silk thread that this caterpillar spins is woven into silk cloth. For at least 4,000 years people have treasured silk.

Chinese legends say that in 2640 B.C., a Chinese empress accidentally dropped a silkworm cocoon in warm water and watched the thread unravel. She had discovered silk. But for thousands of years, the Chinese people kept the work of silkworms a secret. Death was the penalty for telling the secret.

Then, it is said, in about A.D. 550, two travelers from Persia visited China and returned to the West carrying silkworm eggs hidden in their hollow canes. Ever since then, the world has enjoyed the beauty of silk—its warmth, strength, softness, and shimmer.

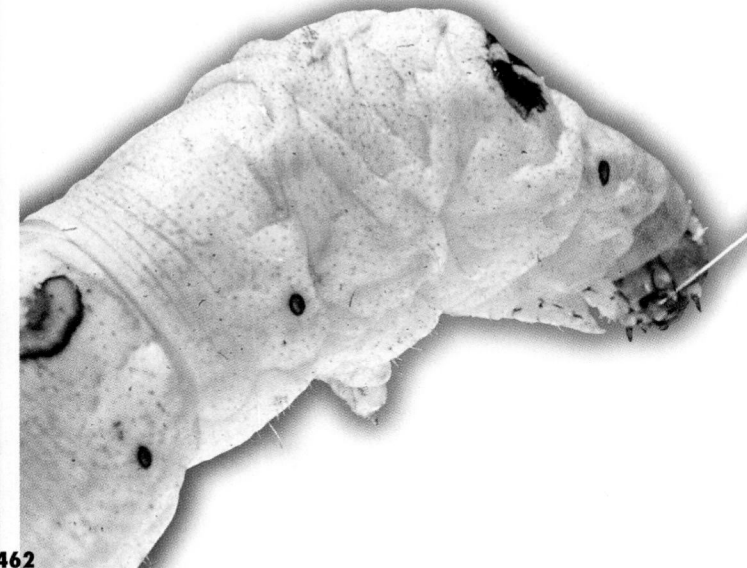

462

Program Resources

◆ **Interdisciplinary Explorations,** Science, pp. 14–15; Social Studies, pp. 16–19; Language Arts, pp. 20–22; Mathematics, pp. 23–25

Metamorphosis of the Silkworm

The silkworm is not really a worm; it's the larva of an insect—a moth named *Bombyx mori*. In its entire feeding period, this larva consumes about 20 times its own weight in mulberry leaves. The silkworm undergoes complete metamorphosis during its life.

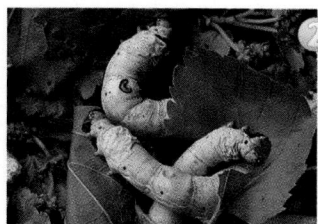

1 The adult female moth lays 300 to 500 eggs, each the size of a pinhead. After about ten days at 27°C, the larvae—which people call silkworms—hatch from the eggs and begin to eat. Mulberry leaves are the insects' source of food.

2 For the next 40 to 45 days, the larvae consume great quantities of mulberry leaves. The silkworms molt each time their exoskeletons become too tight. After the last molting and feeding stage, the silkworms begin to build their cocoons.

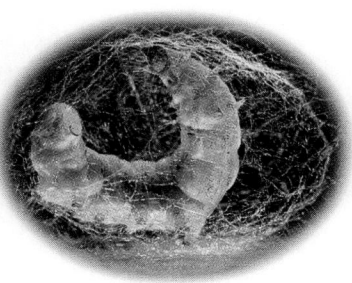

3 To spin its cocoon, each silkworm produces two single strands from its two silk glands. Another pair of glands produces a sticky substance that binds the two strands together. The silkworm pushes this single strand out through a small tube in its head. Once in the air, the strand hardens and the silkworm winds the strand around itself in many layers to make a thick cocoon. The single silk strand may be as long as 900 meters—more than two laps around an Olympic track.

4 After 14 to 18 days, the adult moths emerge from the cocoons. The new moth does not eat or fly. It mates, the female lays eggs, and 2 to 3 days later both the male and female die.

Science Activity

Examine a silkworm cocoon. After softening the cocoon in water, find the end of the strand of silk. Pull this strand, wind it onto an index card, and measure its length.

With a partner, design an experiment to compare the strength of the silk thread you just collected to that of cotton and/or nylon thread of the same weight or thickness.

◆ Develop a hypothesis about the strength of the threads.

◆ Decide on the setup you will use to test the threads.

◆ Check your safety plan with your teacher.

---

2 Facilitate

◆ Silkworm cocoons can be obtained from biological supply companies.

◆ Have students review what they recall about the larval stage of insects. Summarize students' responses on the board.

◆ Ask students: **What is complete metamorphosis?** *(a type of metamorphosis with four stages: egg, larva, pupa, and adult)* **What is the other pattern of metamorphosis? How is it different from complete metamorphosis?** *(Gradual metamorphosis; an egg hatches into a nymph, which can look like an adult insect.)*

◆ Ask a volunteer to review what an exoskeleton is and how larvae molt.

◆ To extend this exploration, invite an entomologist to tell the class more about silkworms. If possible, ask the entomologist to bring some silkworms to show the class.

Science Activity

Ask: **How will you measure the length?** *(Measure the width of the card and multiply by 2. Multiply the answer by the number of times you wind the strand around the card.)*

Interdisciplinary Explorations The following worksheets correlate with this page: Ways the Chinese Use Insects, page 14; and Spider Silk, page 15.

3 Assess

Activity Assessment

Evaluate students' experimental setups. Students should recognize that they will need a very accurate scale to measure the weight of the threads correctly. For students who are choosing to compare threads by width instead of weight, check that they describe a scientific method for measuring the width of the threads. Make sure students start with small weights so they will not immediately break all the threads they test.

2 Facilitate

- Show students a map of the United States and Canada. Challenge students to find two cities that are about 6,400 kilometers apart. Ask: **Start in Miami, Florida, and travel northwest. What city is about 6,400 kilometers from Miami?** *(Answers may vary; sample: Prince Rupert, British Columbia, Canada)* Help students appreciate how formidable a journey this would be traveling with pack animals such as camels, horses, or yaks.

- Have students brainstorm a list of reasons why traveling the Silk Road might be treacherous. Remind students that the travelers were carrying valuable wares. Prompt students by asking: **What dangers would merchants face from other people?**

- Ask: **Why did the Chinese "of course" keep the secret of the silkworm?** *(They were making a lot of money selling silk to Rome.)* Ask: **Do we keep similar secrets today?** *(Answers may vary. Lead students to recognize that patented formulas such as the formulas for soft drinks are similar to the secret of the silkworm.)*

- Invite some students to read the descriptions corresponding to the numbers on the map while other students trace the route with their fingers.

- Students will need help pronouncing many of the place names.

- Under point 6, ask what it means to control part of a route. Explain that this most likely means that the Parthian traders were not allowing other traders to use a stretch of the route or were charging other traders to use it. By doing this, the Parthian traders could make a profit on goods traveling both east and west.

The Silk Road

Long before the rest of the world learned how silk was made, the Chinese were trading this treasured fabric with people west of China. Merchants who bought and sold silk traveled along a system of hazardous routes that came to be known as the Silk Road. The Silk Road stretched 6,400 kilometers from Ch'ang-an in China to the Mediterranean Sea. Silk, furs, and spices traveled west toward Rome along the road. Gold, wool, glass, grapes, garlic, and walnuts moved east toward China.

Travel along the Silk Road was treacherous and difficult. For safety, traders traveled in caravans of many people and animals. Some kinds of pack animals were better equipped to handle certain parts of the journey than others. Camels, for instance, were well suited to the desert; they could go without drinking for several days and withstand most sandstorms. Yaks were often used in the high mountains.

The entire journey along the Silk Road could take years. Many people and animals died along the way. Very few individuals or caravans traveled the whole length of the Silk Road.

Silk fabric became highly prized in Rome. In fact, it was said that the first silk products to reach Rome after 50 B.C. were worth their weight in gold. The Chinese, of course, kept the secret of the silkworm and controlled silk production. They were pleased that the Romans thought that silk grew on trees. It was not until about A.D. 550 that the Romans learned the secret of silk.

In time, silk production spread around the world. The Silk Road, though, opened forever the exchange of goods and ideas between China and the West.

EUROPE

Rome

Black Sea

ASIA MINOR

7 Antioch

The Silk Road
200 B.C. to A.D. 200

1 **Ch'ang-an**
From Ch'ang-an in northern China, the Silk Road headed west along a corridor between the Nan Shan Mountains and the Gobi Desert.

2 **Dunhuang**
At Dunhuang, in an oasis, or fertile green area, of the Gobi Desert, caravans took on rested pack animals. Beyond Dunhuang, the silk route split.

3 **Takla Makan Desert**
The desert is well named— Takla Makan means "Go in and you won't come out!" Most travelers avoided the scorching heat of the desert and journeyed along the edges of this great wasteland of sand.

Social Studies Activity

Suppose you are a merchant traveling from Dunhuang to Kashgar. You will be carrying silk, furs, and cinnamon to Kashgar where you'll trade for gold, garlic, and glass, which you will carry back to Dunhuang. Plan your route and hire a guide.

- Look at the map to find the distances and the physical features you will see on your journey.
- Explain why you chose the route you did.
- List the animals and supplies that you will take.
- Write a help-wanted ad for a guide to lead your caravan.

464

Facts and Figures Yaks are huge animals similar in appearance to American buffalo. They have thick hair and are native to the cold mountains of central Asia. Yaks are valuable as pack animals and because of their milk, meat, hair, and hide.

Camels are native to the deserts of Asia and northern Africa. There are two kinds of camels: Arabian and Bactrian. Both have humps that store fat, enabling them to go without food or water for several days.

The Arabian camel is better adapted to desert conditions. Its feet can tolerate the heat of the sand, and its nostrils and eyes are protected from sandstorms.

The two-humped Bactrian camel is better suited for cooler mountain conditions. It has a furry coat that it sheds every year, allowing it to withstand a wide range of temperatures.

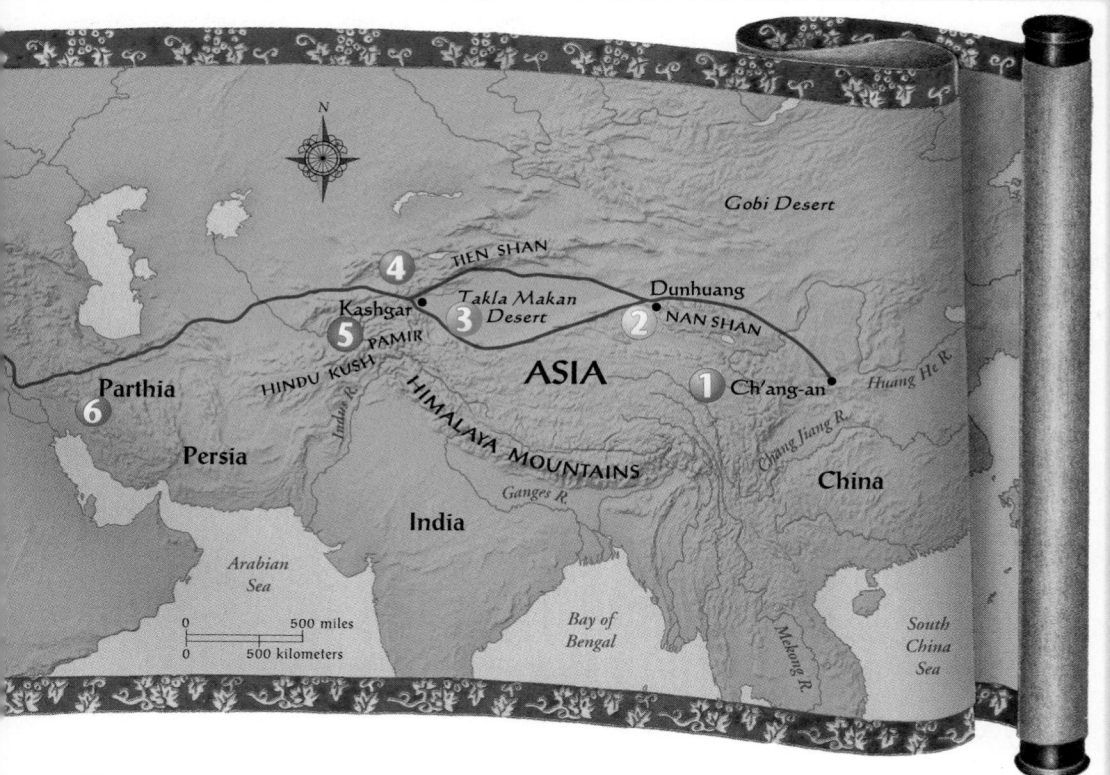

N

Gobi Desert

TIEN SHAN

④ Kashgar ③ Takla Makan Desert ② Dunhuang NAN SHAN

⑤ PAMIR

Parthia

⑥ Persia

HINDU KUSH

Indus R.

HIMALAYA MOUNTAINS

Ganges R.

ASIA

① Ch'ang-an Huang He R.

Chang Jiang R.

China

India

Arabian Sea

0   500 miles
0   500 kilometers

Bay of Bengal

Mekong R.

South China Sea

④ Kashgar

The silk routes along the northern and southern edges of the Takla Makan Desert came together at Kashgar. The perilous part of the Silk Road was still ahead.

⑤ Pamir Mountains

Traveling west from Kashgar, caravans faced some of the highest mountains in the world. The towering Pamir Mountains are more than 6,000 meters high. Once traders crossed the mountains, though, travel on the Silk Road was less difficult. Traders journeyed west through Persia to cities located on the Mediterranean Sea.

⑥ Parthia

For a while, Parthian traders controlled part of the Silk Road. In 53 B.C., Rome was a mighty power around the Mediterranean Sea. That year when the Roman and Parthian armies were at battle, the Parthians suddenly turned to face their enemy and attacked with deadly arrows. Then, in the bright light of noon, the Parthians unrolled huge banners of gold-embroidered silk. The Romans were so dazzled by the brilliance that they surrendered.

⑦ Antioch

Trade flourished in Antioch, where silk was traded for gold. Ships carried silk and spices on the Mediterranean Sea from Antioch to Rome, Egypt, and Greece.

465

♦ Invite interested students to research the typical weather conditions travelers could expect along their routes. Students may wish to sketch a map and add notations about the average maximum and minimum temperatures along the route.

♦ Ask students to define the word *dazzle.* Then ask: **Why do you think the Roman soldiers surrendered when they were dazzled by the gold cloth?** *(They may have been blinded or confused by the display or overwhelmed by the beauty of the cloth.)*

♦ To extend this exploration, challenge interested students to do research on the merchants who traveled the Silk Road. Have students find out the kinds of hardships the travelers encountered. Invite students to share their findings. Alternatively, find students who have experienced mountain hiking trips and primitive camping. Ask the students to share with the class what they learned about the kinds of clothes, equipment, and tools hikers take along. Ask them to describe the kinds of hardships and extreme conditions that hikers might have to deal with.

Social Studies Activity

Make sure students understand how to read and use the scale correctly. **Interdisciplinary Explorations** The following worksheets correlate with this page: World Populations, page 16; Interpreting a Map, page 17; and Finding Cities Along the Silk Road, pages 18–19.

3 Assess

Activity Assessment

Students should have a reasonable estimate of how long the journey will take. Their list of animals and supplies for the journey should take into consideration the length of the trip, the types of terrain, and the types of weather and temperature conditions. Their guide should be experienced.

2 Facilitate

- Before students read the story, draw their attention to the creature on page 180. Ask: **What do you think this is?** *(Answers may vary; samples: a dragon, a silkworm goddess)*
- To extend this exploration, have students describe other myths they have read that explain natural phenomena.
- Make sure students are familiar with the usage of *appears* that means "to come into sight."
- Ask: **Why do you think the girl lied to her father about what she had said to the horse?** *(Accept all reasonable answers.)*
- Ask: **Why do you think the horse was acting strangely and would not eat?** *(Answers may vary; samples: the horse was confused or angry.)*
- Draw students' attention to the second sentence in the paragraph on page 181 that begins "But before she could finish . . ." Point out the semicolon. Explain that you use a semicolon between two sentences that are very closely related. You could use a period instead of a semicolon, but a semicolon is more appropriate in this example. The semicolon tells the reader that the second sentence is closely connected to the first sentence.
- Ask: **What did the other children see happen to the girl?** Challenge students to write a news story for a newspaper or for the evening news on television describing what happened. Students may wish to present a follow-up story covering what the neighbors found some days later.
- Ask a volunteer to explain what the phrase "in vain" means.

The Gift of Silk

A myth is a story handed down from past cultures—often to explain an event or natural phenomenon. Myths may be about gods and goddesses or about heroes.

The Yellow Emperor, Huang Di, who is mentioned in this Chinese myth, was a real person. Some stories say that he was the founder of the Chinese nation. He was thought to be a god who came to rule on Earth. Here the silkworm goddess appears to him at a victory celebration.

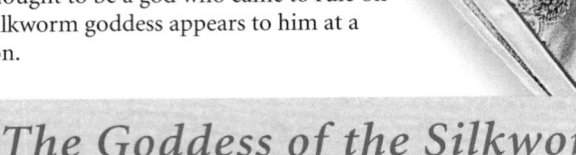

The Goddess of the Silkworm

A GODDESS descended from the heavens with a gift for the Yellow Emperor. Her body was covered with a horse's hide, and she presented two shining rolls of silk to the god. She was the "goddess of the silkworm," sometimes called the "lady with a horse's head." Long, long ago she had been a beautiful girl, but now a horse's skin grew over her body. If she pulled the two sides of the skin close to her body she became a silkworm with a horse's head, spinning a long, glittering thread of silk from her mouth. It is said she lived in a mulberry tree, producing silk day and night in the wild northern plain. This is her story.

Once in ancient times there lived a man, his daughter and their horse. Often the man had to travel, leaving his daughter alone at home to take care of the beast. And often the girl was lonely. One day, because she missed her father she teased the horse: "Dear long-nosed one, if you could bring my father home right how, I'd marry you and be your wife." At that the horse broke out of his harness. He galloped away and came quickly to the place where the master was doing business. The master, surprised to see his beast, grasped his

mane and jumped up on his back. The horse stood mournfully staring in the direction he had come from, so the man decided there must be something amiss at home and hurried back.

When they arrived home, the daughter explained that she had only remarked that she missed her father and the horse had dashed off wildly. The man said nothing but was secretly pleased to own such a remarkable animal and fed him special sweet hay. But the horse would not touch it and whinnied and reared each time he saw the girl.

The man began to worry about the horse's strange behavior, and one day he said to the girl,

Background

History Chinese tradition claims that the wife of the Yellow Emperor discovered silk around the 27th century B.C. The silkworm moth was originally native to China. The Chinese succeeded in guarding the secret of silk for about 3,000 years.

In A.D. 552, a Roman emperor sent two Persian monks to China. They risked their lives stealing mulberry seeds and silkworm eggs. They hid the seeds and eggs inside their walking staffs and smuggled them out of China.

Silk production spread gradually to many countries in Europe. However, the climate in England and the United States was not right for silkworms, and they did not flourish in either country.

Luxurious hand-embroidered silk fabric has been made in China for thousands of years.

"Why is it that our horse behaves so strangely whenever you are about?"

So the young girl confessed the teasing remark she had made.

When he heard this the father was enraged, "For shame to say such a thing to an animal! No one must know of this! You will stay locked in the house!"

Now the man had always liked this horse, but he would not hear of its becoming his son-in-law. That night, to prevent any more trouble, he crept quietly into the stable with his bow and arrow and shot the horse through the heart. Then he skinned it and hung up the hide in the courtyard.

Next day, when the father was away, the girl ran out of the house to join some other children playing in the courtyard near the horse hide. When she saw it she kicked it angrily and said, "Dirty horse hide! What made you think such an ugly long-snouted creature as you could become my . . . ."

But before she could finish, the hide suddenly flew up and wrapped itself around her, swift as the wind, and carried her away out of sight. The other children watched dumbfounded; there was nothing they could do but wait to tell the old man when he arrived home.

Her father set out immediately in search of his daughter, but in vain. Some days later a neighbouring family found the girl wrapped up in the hide in the branches of a mulberry tree. She had turned into a wormlike creature spinning a long thread of shining silk from her horse-shaped head, spinning it round and round her in a soft cocoon.

Such is the story of the goddess of the silkworm. The Yellow Emperor was delighted to receive her exquisite gift of silk. . . . He ordered his official tailor, Bo Yu, to create new ceremonial robes and hats. And Lei Zu, the revered queen mother of gods and people, wife of the Emperor, began then to collect silkworms and grow them. And so it was that the Chinese people learned of silk.

—Yuan Ke, *Dragons and Dynasties*, translated by Kim Echlin and Nie Zhixiong

Language Arts Activity

What two details in the myth tell you that silkworms were important to the Chinese people?

The girl in the myth gets into trouble because she breaks her promise. Write a story of your own using the idea of a broken promise.
◆ Decide on the place, time, and main characters.
◆ Think about the events that will happen and how your story will conclude.

◆ Ask: **How would you describe the personality of the girl?** (*Answers may vary; samples: teasing, selfish*)
◆ Challenge students to create an explanation of how the girl, who was a wormlike creature at the end of the story, ended up becoming a goddess. Interested students may wish to research Chinese mythology to find out how people became gods and goddesses.

Language Arts Activity

Challenge students to write a myth to explain some natural phenomenon. For example, students could write a story that explains where fog or moss or mushrooms came from.

Interdisciplinary Explorations The following worksheets correlate with this page: Silk Vocabulary, page 20; Writing Your Own Myth, page 21; A Broken Promise, page 22.

3 Assess

Activity Assessment

Make sure students' stories include a broken promise. Remind students that, like many myths, their stories do not have to be factual.

2 Facilitate

- Before you work the problem, estimate aloud to demonstrate how to estimate to students. Write on the board "125 trees feed 6,000 silkworms." Write "100 trees" below 125 trees. Point out that 100 trees is about a fifth less than 125 trees. Explain that 1,000 is a bit more than one fifth of 6,000. So you estimate that the answer will be a little less than 5,000 silkworms.

- Review proportions. Make sure students understand that the two ratios must be in the same form each time; for example $\frac{trees}{silkworm}$.

- If students are not familiar with cross multiplication, or cannot recall why it works, show them with a simpler example, such as $\frac{1}{2} = \frac{2}{4}$.

- Once you have calculated the answer, compare it to your original estimate. Stress to students how estimating first can help them avoid mistakes.

- To extend this exploration, have pairs of students write problems for each other that can be solved using a proportion.

Math Activity

Group students in pairs. Remind students to estimate each answer before they calculate. Then they can compare the answers to the estimates to check their work. Remind students to keep the form the same in both ratios.

Interdisciplinary Explorations The following worksheets correlate with this page: Graphing Mountain Heights, page 23; Your Weight in Food, page 24; and A Trip on the Silk Road, page 25.

3 Assess

Activity Assessment

1. 16 sacks
2. 120 trays
3. (a) 1,824 centimeters per hour,
   (b) 109,440 centimeters
4. (a) 9 blouses; (b) 54 ties

Counting on Caterpillars

Lai opened the door to the silkworm room. She was greeted by the loud sound of thousands of silkworms crunching on fresh leaves from mulberry trees. Lai enjoyed raising silkworms, but it was hard work. Over its lifetime, each silkworm eats about twenty times its own weight.

Lai had a chance to care for more silkworms. But first she had to figure out how many more she could raise. She now had 6,000 silkworms that ate the leaves from 125 mulberry trees. Should she have her parents buy another piece of land with another 100 mulberry trees? If she had 100 more trees, how many more silkworms could she feed?

Analyze. 125 trees can feed 6,000 silkworms. You want to know the number of silkworms 100 trees will feed. Write a proportion, using n to represent the number of silkworms.

Write the proportion.

$$\text{trees} \rightarrow \frac{125}{6,000} = \frac{100}{n} \leftarrow \text{trees}$$
$$\text{silkworms} \rightarrow \qquad\qquad \leftarrow \text{silkworms}$$

Cross multiply. $\qquad 125 \times n = 6,000 \times 100$

Simplify. $\qquad 125n = 600,000$

Solve. $\qquad n = \dfrac{600,000}{125} \qquad n = 4,800$

Think about it. "Yes," she decided. She could raise 4,800 more silkworms!

▲ Silkworms are fed fresh mulberry leaves every four hours, around the clock.

Math Activity

Solve the following problems.

1. Lai's friend Cheng also raises silkworms. He buys mulberry leaves. If 20 sacks of leaves feed 12,000 silkworms a day, how many sacks of leaves will 9,600 silkworms eat per day?

2. When Lai's silkworms are ready to spin, she places them in trays. If 3 trays can hold 150 silkworms, how many trays does Lai use for her 6,000 silkworms?

3. A silkworm spins silk at a rate of about 30.4 centimeters per minute. (a) How many centimeters can it spin in an hour? (b) It takes a silkworm 60 hours to spin the entire cocoon. How many centimeters is that?

4. Lai's silk thread contributes to the creation of beautiful silk clothes. It takes the thread of 630 cocoons to make a blouse and the thread of 110 cocoons to make a tie. (a) If each of Lai's 6,000 silkworms produces a cocoon, how many blouses can be made from the thread? (b) How many ties can be made?

Plan a Silk Festival

People use silk in many ways other than just to make fine clothing. Did you know that silk was used for parachutes during World War II? Or that some bicycle racers choose tires containing silk because they provide good traction? Today, silk is used for a variety of purposes, including:

◆ recreation: fishing lines and nets, bicycle tires;

◆ business: electrical insulations, typewriter and computer ribbons, surgical sutures;

◆ decoration: some silkscreen printing, artificial flowers

Work in small groups to learn about one of the ways that people have used silk in the past or are using it today. Devise an interesting way to share your project with the class, such as

◆ a booth to display or advertise a silk product;

◆ a skit in which you wear silk;

◆ a historical presentation on the uses of silk in other countries;

◆ a presentation about a process, such as silkscreen painting or silk flowers.

Ask volunteers to bring pictures or silk products to class. After rehearsing or reviewing your presentation, work with other groups to decide how to organize your Silk Festival.

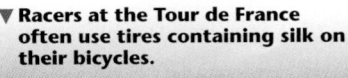

▼ **Racers at the Tour de France often use tires containing silk on their bicycles.**

Time 1 week (2 days for research, 2 days for preparing the displays, 1 day for the Silk Festival)

Tips Have students work in groups of four or five. If possible, group students so that each group contains at least one student who knows how to research on the Internet or in science journals. Have groups each choose one bulleted item from the list on page 469 that they are most interested in. You may need to rearrange groups so that most students are working on the aspect of the project that most interests them.

◆ Most of the students' research should be readily available from encyclopedias. Groups who are researching innovative uses for silk may need to search in science journals or, with supervision, on the Internet.

◆ If students wish to bring a sample of silk to show the class, suggest that they bring it in a clear plastic bag so that it is less likely to be damaged.

◆ Encourage students to bring photocopies of interesting silk products or draw their own illustrations.

Other Resources Some suggested books that students may want to consult include: *The Empress and the Silkworm,* Lily Toy Hong, School & Library Binding, Albert Whitman & Co., 1995; *Between the Dragon and the Eagle,* Mical Schneider, Carolrhoda Books, 1997; *The Silk Route: 7,000 Miles of History,* John S. Major, HarperTrophy, 1996; *Exploration by Land (The Silk and Spice Routes),* Paul Strathern, Library Binding, New Discovery, 1994.

Extend Challenge students to find out how to raise silkworms. (Silkworm eggs and food can be obtained from biological supply companies.) Ask questions such as: **In what kind of container should you keep silkworms? What do silkworms need besides mulberry leaves? Where do you get mulberry leaves? Do silkworms need water? What kind of temperature and humidity do they need? How much do silkworms eat? How do you get the moths to lay eggs? What conditions do the eggs need to hatch?**

469

Bones, Muscles, and Skin

Sections	Time	Student Edition Activities	Other Activities	
CHAPTER PROJECT **On the Move** p. 471	Ongoing (2–3 weeks)	Check Your Progress, pp. 479, 492 Present Your Project, p. 503		
1 INTEGRATING HEALTH **Body Organization and Homeostasis** pp. 472–479 ◆ Identify the levels of organization in the body. ◆ Identify and describe the four basic types of tissues in the human body. ◆ Define homeostasis and describe its importance to the body.	2 periods/ 1 block	**Discover** What Lets You Lift Books?, p. 472 **Try This** How is a Book Organized?, p. 473	TE TE TE IES	Building Inquiry Skills: Making Models, p. 473 Building Inquiry Skills: Observing, p. 474 Integrating Chemistry, p. 477 "Soap From Concept to Consumer," pp. 9–10
2 **The Skeletal System** pp. 480–487 ◆ Identify the functions of the skeleton. ◆ Describe the structure of bones and how they grow and form. ◆ Explain the role of movable joints in the body. ◆ List ways that individuals can keep their bones strong and healthy	2 periods/ 1 block	**Discover** Hard as a Rock?, p. 480 **Try This** Soft Bones?, p. 482 **Sharpen Your Skills** Classifying, p. 484 **Science at Home,** p. 487	TE TE TE TE PTA	Including All Students, p. 482 Using the Visuals: Figure 10, p. 484 Including All Students, p. 485 Integrating Health, p. 486 "Testing Yogurt," pp.1–8
3 **The Muscular System** pp. 488–493 ◆ Identify the three types of muscles found in the body and describe the function of each. ◆ Explain how skeletal muscles work in pairs. ◆ List ways in which people can keep their muscles healthy.	2 periods/ 1 block	**Discover** How Do Muscles Work?, p. 488 **Try This** Get a Grip, p. 490 **Skills Lab: Observing** A Look Beneath the Skin, p. 493	TE TE	Building Inquiry Skills: Observing, p. 490 Inquiry Challenge, p. 491
4 **The Skin** pp. 494–500 ◆ Describe the functions of skin. ◆ Identify and describe the layers of the skin. ◆ List ways that individuals can keep skin healthy.	2 periods/ 1 block	**Discover** What Can You Observe About Skin?, p. 494 **Try This** Sweaty Skin, p. 497 **Real-World Lab: You and Your Environment** Sun Safety, pp. 498–499 **Science at Home,** p. 500	TE PTA PTA LM	Building Inquiry Skills: Observing, p. 495; Observing, p. 497 "Testing Bandages," pp. 1–8 "Testing Lip Balms," pp. 1–8 15, "Examining Bones, Muscles, and Skin"
Study Guide/Chapter Assessment pp. 501–503	1 period/ $\frac{1}{2}$ block		ISAB	Provides teaching and review of all inquiry skills

For Standard or Block Schedule The Resource Pro® CD-ROM gives you maximum flexibility for planning your instruction for any type of schedule. Resource Pro® contains Planning Express®, an advanced scheduling program, as well as the entire contents of the Teaching Resources and the Computer Test Bank.

CHAPTER PLANNING GUIDE

Program Resources	Assessment Strategies	Media and Technology
UR Chapter 15 Project Teacher Notes, pp. 2–3 **UR** Chapter 15 Project Overview and Worksheets, pp. 4–7	**SE** Performance Assessment: Present Your Project, p. 503 **TE** Check Your Progress, pp. 479, 492 **UR** Chapter 15 Project Scoring Rubric, p. 8	Science Explorer Internet Site at www.phschool.com
UR 15-1 Lesson Plan, p. 9 **UR** 15-1 Section Summary, p. 10 **UR** 15-1 Review and Reinforce, p. 11 **UR** 15-1 Enrich, p. 12	**SE** Section 1 Review, p. 479 **TE** Ongoing Assessment, p. 473, 475, 477 **TE** Performance Assessment, p. 479	Life Science Videotape 4; Videodisc Unit 1 Side 2, "Cell Specialization" Audio CD, English-Spanish Summary 15-1
UR 15-2 Lesson Plan, p. 13 **UR** 15-2 Section Summary, p. 14 **UR** 15-2 Review and Reinforce, p. 15 **UR** 15-2 Enrich, p. 16	**SE** Section 2 Review, p. 487 **TE** Ongoing Assessment, pp. 481, 483, 485 **TE** Performance Assessment, p. 487	Audio CD, English-Spanish Summary 15-2 Transparency 61, "The Human Skeleton" Transparency 62, "The Structure of a Bone" Transparency 63, "Exploring Movable Joints" Interactive Student Tutorial CD-ROM, Chapter 15
UR 15-3 Lesson Plan, p. 17 **UR** 15-3 Section Summary, p. 18 **UR** 15-3 Review and Reinforce, p. 19 **UR** 15-3 Enrich, p. 20 **UR** Chapter 15 Skills Lab, pp. 25–26	**SE** Section 3 Review, p. 492 **TE** Ongoing Assessment, pp. 489, 491 **TE** Performance Assessment, p. 492	Life Science Videotape 4; Videodisc Unit 4 Side 1, "Muscles and Bones" Audio CD, English-Spanish Summary 15-3
UR 15-4 Lesson Plan, p. 21 **UR** 15-4 Section Summary, p. 22 **UR** 15-4 Review and Reinforce, p. 23 **UR** 15-4 Enrich, p. 24 **UR** Chapter 15 Real-World Lab, pp. 27–29	**SE** Section 4 Review, p. 500 **TE** Ongoing Assessment, pp. 495, 497 **TE** Performance Assessment, p. 500	Audio CD, English-Spanish Summary 15-4 Transparency 64, "The Skin"
RCA Provides strategies to improve science reading skills **GSW** Provides worksheets to promote student comprehension of content	**SE** Chapter 15 Study Guide/Assessment, pp. 501–503 **PA** Chapter 15 Performance Assessment, pp. 47–49 **CUT** Chapter 15 Test, pp. 72–75 **CTB** Chapter 15 Test	Computer Test Bank, Chapter 15 Test Interactive Student Tutorial CD-ROM, Chapter 15

Key:
SE Student Edition
CTB Computer Test Bank
ISAB Inquiry Skills Activity Book
GSW Guided Study Worksheets

TE Teacher's Edition
PTA Product Testing Activities by *Consumer Reports*
RCA Reading in the Content Area
PA Performance Assessment

UR Unit Resources
LM Laboratory Manual
IES Interdisciplinary Explorations Series
CUT Chapter and Unit Tests

Meeting the National Science Education Standards and AAAS Benchmarks

National Science Education Standards	Benchmarks for Science Literacy	Unifying Themes
Science as Inquiry (Content Standard A) ◆ **Ask questions that can be answered by scientific investigations** What are some characteristics of skeletal muscles? How do skeletal muscles work? *(Skills Lab)* How well do different materials protect the skin from the sun? *(Real-World Lab)* **Life Science** (Content Standard C) ◆ **Structure and function in living systems** Students learn that the bodies of humans are organized into cells, tissues, organs, and organ systems. The cell is the basic unit of structure and function in a living thing. Tissues have specialized jobs and the body has systems that interact with one another. *(Section 1)* The skeleton has five major functions: shape, support, movement, protection, and production of blood cells. Joints allows the body to move in different ways. *(Section 2)* The human body has three types of muscle tissue—skeletal, smooth, and cardiac. Muscles work in pairs to move the bones of the body. *(Section 3)* The skin covers the body, prevents loss of water, protects the body from injury and infection, regulates body temperature, eliminates wastes, and produces Vitamin D. *(Section 4)*	**5C Cells** Characteristics that describe cells, the basic unit of life, are presented in a general format. Characteristics of cells, tissues, organs, and organ systems are described. *(Sections 1, 3, 4)* **6B Human Development** Bones lose mass with age. This may result in a condition called osteoporosis. *(Section 2)* **6C Basic Functions** The functions of organs and organ systems are described in general terms. *(Section 1)* The skin, skeletal, and muscular systems provide essential functions that are integral parts of the overall function of the human body. *(Sections 2, 3, 4)* **6E Physical Health** Regular exercise and a balanced diet are important for maintaining muscle tone and bone strength. *(Sections 2, 3)* **11C Constancy and Change** Homeostasis is the body's ability to maintain an internal balance. An organism's internal environment remains stable in spite of change in the external environment. *(Section 1)*	◆ **Energy** The muscular system obtains, stores, and uses energy to perform its functions. *(Section 2)* ◆ **Patterns of Change** The human body can maintain homeostasis despite changes in its internal and external environments. *(Section 1)* Some bone tissue develops from cartilage tissue. Different types of muscle tissue are specialized to perform specific voluntary and involuntary functions. *(Section 2)* ◆ **Scale and Structure** The human body contains trillions of cells that are organized into tissues, organs, and organ systems. *(Section 1)* The skeletal system is made up of bones, ligaments, tendons, and cartilage. The muscular system is made up of voluntary and involuntary muscles. *(Sections 2, 3)* ◆ **Unity and Diversity** Although human organ systems contain many different organs with different tissues and different functions, the organ systems work together so that humans can survive. *(Section 1)* The structure of bones and muscles differ, but both systems work together to enable the body to move. *(Sections 2, 3)* ◆ **Systems and Interactions** Cells, tissues, organs, and organ systems interact in the human body, enabling it to function and remain stable. *(Section 1)* There are three types of muscles in the human body: cardiac, involuntary muscles found in the heart; smooth, involuntary muscles found in systems such as the digestive system and circulatory system; and skeletal muscles, which permit voluntary movement. *(Sections 2, 3)*

Take It to the Net

 *Interactive text at www.phschool.com*

Science Explorer comes alive with iText.

- **Complete student text** is accessible from any computer with Internet access or a CD-ROM drive.
- **Animations, simulations, and videos** enhance student understanding and retention of concepts.
- **Self-tests and online study tools** assess student understanding.

STAY CURRENT with

Find out the latest research and information about human biology and health at: **www.phschool.com**

Go to **www.phschool.com** and click on the Science icon. Then click on <u>Science Explorer: Life, Earth, and Physical Science</u> under PH@school.

ACTIVITY	Time (minutes)	Materials Quantities for one work group	Skills
Section 1			
Discover, p. 472	10	**Nonconsumable** two medium-sized books, clock or watch with second hand	Inferring
Try This, p. 473	15	**Nonconsumable** student textbook	Making Models
Section 2			
Discover, p. 480	10	**Consumable** leg bone from a cooked chicken or turkey **Nonconsumable** rock of similar size to bone, hand lens	Observing
Try This, p. 482	15 min set up,15 min obser-vation 1 wk later	**Consumable** 2 plastic jars or other containers, vinegar, water, 2 clean chicken bones, gloves	Drawing Conclusions
Sharpen Your Skills, p. 484	15	No special materials are required.	Classifying
Science at Home, p. 487	home	No special materials are required.	Drawing Conclusions
Section 3			
Discover, p. 488	15	**Nonconsumable** spring-type clothespin	Predicting
Try This, p. 490	10	**Nonconsumable** wooden stirrer or other item that is very thin and smooth on its edges, hairpin	Inferring
Skills Lab, p. 493	30	**Consumable** protective gloves; paper towels; water; uncooked chicken wing, treated with bleach **Nonconsumable** scissors, dissecting tray	Observing
Section 4			
Discover, p. 494	15	**Nonconsumable** hand lens, plastic gloves	Inferring
Try This, p. 497	15	**Consumable** wet cotton ball, piece of cardboard **Nonconsumable** 2 thermometers	Measuring
Real-World Lab, pp. 498–499	45 min, plus 2 to 4 hr of sun exposure, and 20 min to analyze the results	**Consumable** 3 different fabrics, plastic knife, photosensitive paper, white construction paper, resealable plastic bag **Nonconsumable** scissors, pencil, metric ruler, stapler, staple remover, 2 sunscreens with SPF ratings of 4 and 30	Predicting, Observing, Drawing Conclusions
Science at Home, p. 500	home	No special materials are required.	Observing, Classifying

A list of all materials required for the Student Edition activities can be found on pages T25–T33. You can obtain information about ordering materials by calling 1-800-848-9500 or by accessing the Science Explorer Internet site at **www.phschool.com**.

On the Move

Bones, movable joints, and skeletal muscles interact in the human body to allow a wide range of movement, from the simple act of holding a spoon to a dramatic gymnastic floor routine.

Purpose In this project, students will apply the chapter's concepts and terms to make working models of a specific simple movement. To demonstrate this movement, students must include the main bones, muscles, and joints involved. Students will then present their models to the class and describe how the movement is produced by the contraction of muscles.

Skills Focus After completing the Chapter 15 Project, students will be able to
◆ identify the main bones, joints, and muscles involved in a simple movement;
◆ create a working model that accurately describes a simple movement;
◆ explain how skeletal muscles contract to produce movement;
◆ describe how skeletal muscles work in pairs.

Project Time Line This project requires at least two weeks for completion. Allow at least three days for students to choose a movement to model. Planning and building the model will require about one week. Students should complete their models at least one day before they will present them. This will give students time to test their models and practice their presentations. Before beginning the project, see Chapter 15 Project Teacher Notes on pages 2–3 in Unit 4 Resources for more details on carrying out the project. Also distribute the Chapter 15 Project Overview and Worksheets and Scoring Rubric on pages 4–8 in Unit 4 Resources.

Suggested Shortcuts You may choose to have students work in small groups as a cooperative learning task. To ensure that every student will have ample opportunity to participate in planning and building the model, each group should consist of no more than four students.

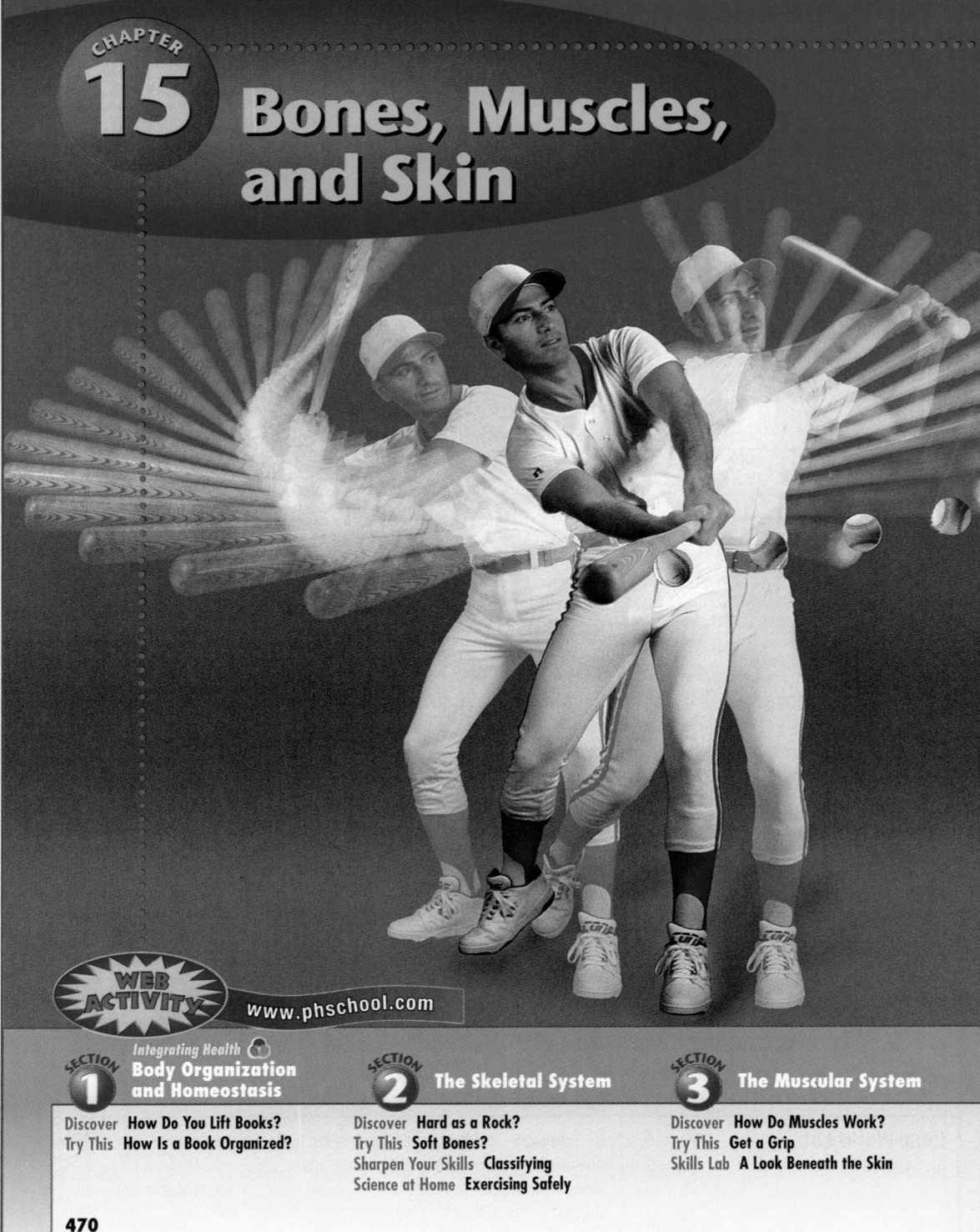

CHAPTER 15 Bones, Muscles, and Skin

WEB ACTIVITY www.phschool.com

SECTION **1** *Integrating Health* **Body Organization and Homeostasis**	SECTION **2** **The Skeletal System**	SECTION **3** **The Muscular System**
Discover **How Do You Lift Books?** Try This **How Is a Book Organized?**	Discover **Hard as a Rock?** Try This **Soft Bones?** Sharpen Your Skills **Classifying** Science at Home **Exercising Safely**	Discover **How Do Muscles Work?** Try This **Get a Grip** Skills Lab **A Look Beneath the Skin**

470

Possible Materials Provide a wide variety of materials from which students can choose. Some possibilities are listed below. Encourage students to suggest and use other materials as well.
◆ *To model bones:* pieces of wood, cardboard, plastic foam, or papier-mâché
◆ *To model muscles:* rubber bands, springs, wire, or string
◆ *To model ligaments and tendons:* paper fasteners, screws, springs, wire, glue, or staples

◆ Another option is to allow students to construct their models using computer animation.

A Look Beneath the Skin

Skills Lab

I n this lab, you will learn about your own skeletal muscles by observing the "arm" muscles of a chicken.

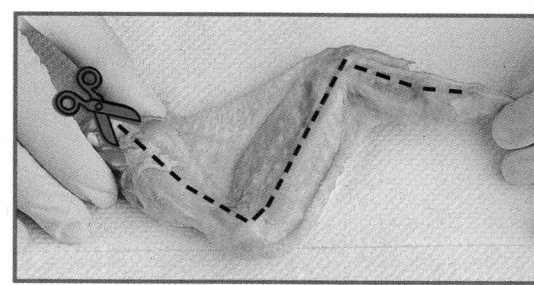

Problem

What are some characteristics of skeletal muscles? How do skeletal muscles work?

Materials

protective gloves	water
paper towels	dissection tray
scissors	uncooked chicken wing, treated with bleach

Procedure

1. Put on protective gloves. **CAUTION:** *Wear gloves whenever you handle the chicken.*
2. Your teacher will give you a chicken wing. Rinse it well with water, dry it with paper towels, and place it in a dissecting tray.
3. Carefully extend the wing to find out how many major parts it has. Draw a diagram of the external structure. Label the upper arm, elbow, lower arm, and hand (wing tip).
4. Use scissors to remove the skin. Cut along the cut line as shown in the photo. Only cut through the skin. **CAUTION:** *Cut away from your body and your classmates.*
5. Examine the muscles, the bundles of pink tissue around the bones. Find the two groups of muscles in the upper arm. Hold the arm down at the shoulder, and alternately pull on each muscle group. Observe what happens.
6. Find the two groups of muscles in the lower arm. Hold down the arm at the elbow, and alternately pull on each muscle group. Then make a diagram of the wing's muscles.

7. Find the tendons—shiny white tissue at the ends of the muscles. Notice what parts the tendons connect. Add the tendons to your diagram.
8. Remove the muscles and tendons. Find the ligaments, the whitish ribbonlike structures between bones. Add them to your diagram.
9. Dispose of the chicken parts according to your teacher's instructions. Wash your hands.

Analyze and Conclude

1. How does a chicken wing move at the elbow? How does the motion compare to how your elbow moves? What type of joint is involved?
2. What happened when you pulled on one of the arm muscles? What muscle action does the pulling represent?
3. Classify the muscles you observed as smooth, cardiac, or skeletal.
4. **Think About It** Why is it valuable to record your observations with accurate diagrams?

More to Explore

Use the procedures from this lab to examine an uncooked chicken thigh and leg. Compare how the chicken leg and a human leg move.

Safety

After students dispose of the wings, have them wash their hands with gloves on, remove the gloves and dispose of them, then wash their hands a second time. Remind students to cut away from themselves and others at all times. Review the safety guidelines in Appendix A.

Extending the Inquiry

More to Explore Students should use chicken leg quarters with the thighs and legs attached, and repeat all safety procedures.

Program Resources

◆ **Unit 4 Resources** Chapter 15 Skills Lab, pp. 25–26
◆ **Inquiry Skills Activity Book** Provides teaching and review of all inquiry skills

---

A Look Beneath the Skin

Preparing for Inquiry

Key Concept Skeletal muscles work in pairs to allow animals to move their limbs.

Skills Objective Students will be able to
◆ observe the structure and function of the muscles in a chicken wing;
◆ classify the muscles based on their observations.

Time 30 minutes

Advance Planning
◆ Use only fresh chicken wings. Wings should be used within 24 hours of purchase and must be stored in a refrigerator.
◆ Soak all wings in a solution of 2 parts household bleach and 8 parts water for 2 hours before the lab. Rinse thoroughly with clear water to remove the bleach.
◆ Use disposable latex or nitrile gloves, or food-handling gloves.
◆ Make sure students wear protective gloves throughout the lab.

Guiding Inquiry

Invitation

Show students a human skeleton or a drawing of the bones in the human arm. Have students compare their arms to the arm of the skeleton and visualize how the muscles move the arm.

Troubleshooting the Experiment

Remind students to work slowly so they do not destroy parts of the wing before they have completely examined it.

Analyze and Conclude

1. Up and down at the elbow, like a human elbow; hinge joint
2. If students pull on the biceps, they bend the arm at the elbow. If they pull on the triceps, the arm straightens. The pulling represents muscle contraction.
3. skeletal
4. Sample: Diagrams allow you to compare structures of the arm even though they are not visible at the same time.

Objectives

After completing the lesson, students will be able to
- ◆ describe the functions of skin;
- ◆ identify and describe the layers of the skin;
- ◆ list ways that individuals can keep skin healthy.

Key Terms epidermis, melanin, dermis, pore, follicle, cancer, acne

1 Engage/Explore

Activating Prior Knowledge

Have students look at the skin on their arms and hands. Ask them to speculate about what they think their skin does. *(Samples: It protects the body tissues, keeps bacteria out of the body, provides feeling through the sense of touch, perspires.)*

DISCOVER

Skills Focus inferring
Materials *hand lens, plastic gloves*
Time 15 minutes
Tips Ask students to predict what they will observe through the hand lens. Ask: **What structures would you expect to see on the surface of your skin?**
Expected Outcome Students should observe perspiration. In addition, they should notice hairs on the back of their hands. Students should be able to observe the ridges of the skin.
Think It Over After students have had the plastic glove on, there will be moisture covering the skin's surface. Students should infer that perspiration is one of the functions of the skin.

494

SECTION 4 — The Skin

DISCOVER •••••••••••••••••••••••••••••• ACTIVITY

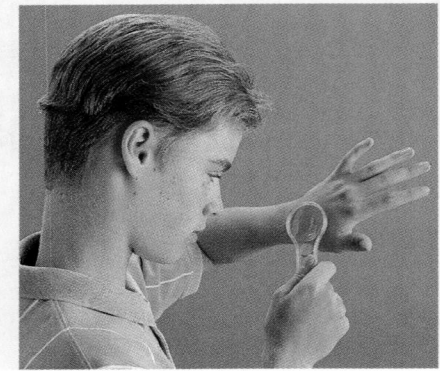

What Can You Observe About Skin?

1. Using a hand lens, examine the skin on your hand. Look for pores and hairs on both the palm and back of your hand.

2. Place a plastic glove on your hand. After five minutes, remove the glove. Then examine the skin on your hand with the hand lens.

Think It Over
Inferring Compare your hand before and after wearing the glove. What happened to the skin when you wore the glove? Why did this happen?

GUIDE FOR READING

- ◆ What are the functions of skin?
- ◆ What habits can help keep your skin healthy?

Reading Tip As you read, create a table that shows the two major layers of skin. Include columns to record the location, structures, and functions of each layer.

Figure 17 The skin forms a barrier that protects the inside of the body from substances such as the chlorine in pool water.

Here's a question for you: What's the largest organ in the human body? If your answer is the skin, you are right! If an adult's skin were stretched out flat, it would cover an area larger than 1.5 square meters—about the size of a mattress on a twin bed. You may think of the skin as nothing more than a covering that separates the inside of the body from the outside environment. You may be surprised to learn about the many important roles that the skin plays.

The Body's Tough Covering

The skin performs several major functions in the body. **The skin covers the body and prevents the loss of water. It protects the body from injury and infection. The skin also helps to regulate body temperature, eliminate wastes, gather information about the environment, and produce vitamin D.**

The skin protects the body by forming a barrier that keeps disease-causing microorganisms and harmful substances outside the body. In addition, the skin helps keep important substances inside the body. Like plastic wrap that keeps food from drying out, the skin prevents the loss of important fluids such as water.

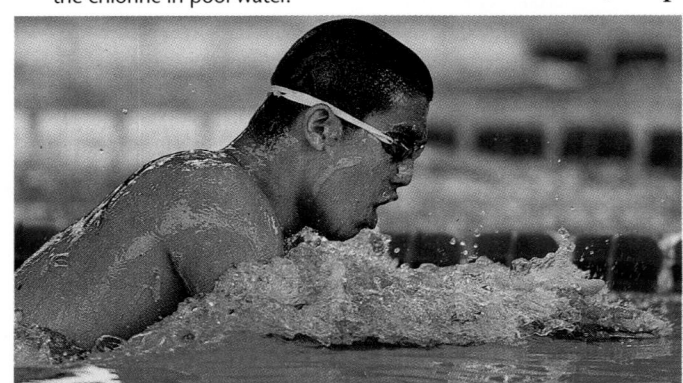

READING STRATEGIES

Reading Tip Help students create a table like the one shown in which to list facts about the two major skin layers.

	Location	Structures	Function
Epidermis	outermost layer		
Dermis	lower layer		

Study and Comprehension Before students read the section, have them work in small groups to discuss whether they agree or disagree with the statements below. After students read the section, have them discuss reasons for their initial opinions and reasons for any changes in their opinions.

1. A well-balanced diet is important in the care of the skin.
2. The dermis is the outer layer of the skin.
3. The skin helps regulate body temperature.
4. Dead cells of the outermost layer of the skin are valuable to the body.

Figure 18 When you exercise, your body becomes warmer. Sweat glands in the skin produce perspiration, which leaves the body through pores like the one you see here. *Relating Cause and Effect How does perspiration help cool your body?*

Another function of the skin is to help the body maintain a steady temperature. Many blood vessels run through skin. When you become too warm, these blood vessels enlarge to increase the amount of blood that flows through them. This allows heat to move from your body into the outside environment. In addition, sweat glands in the skin respond to excess heat by producing perspiration. As perspiration evaporates from your skin, heat moves into the air. Because perspiration contains some dissolved waste materials, your skin also helps to eliminate wastes.

The skin also gathers information about the environment. To understand how the skin does this, place your fingertips on the skin of your arm and press down firmly. Then lightly pinch yourself. You have just tested some of the nerves in your skin. The nerves in skin provide information about such things as pressure, pain, and temperature. Pain messages are important because they warn you that something in your surroundings may have injured you.

Lastly, some skin cells produce vitamin D in the presence of sunlight. Vitamin D is important for healthy bones. This is because Vitamin D helps the cells in your digestive system to absorb the calcium in your food. Your skin cells need only a few minutes of sunlight to produce all the vitamin D you need in a day.

✓ *Checkpoint* How does your skin help eliminate waste materials from your body?

Program Resources

◆ **Unit 4 Resources** 15-4 Lesson Plan, p. 21; 15-4 Section Summary, p. 22

Media and Technology

 Audio CD English-Spanish Summary 15-4

Answers to Self-Assessment

Caption Question

Figure 18 As perspiration evaporates from the skin, heat moves into the air.

✓ *Checkpoint*

Perspiration contains dissolved waste materials.

2 Facilitate

The Body's Tough Covering

Building Inquiry Skills: Applying Concepts

Have pairs of students make lists of the skin's major functions and identify how each function helps the body maintain homeostasis. For each function, ask: **What would happen if the skin could not perform this function?** *(Sample: If the skin could not help regulate temperature, the kinds of environments in which people live would be restricted.)* **learning modality: verbal**

Building Inquiry Skills: Observing

Materials *rubbing alcohol, cotton ball, dishwashing liquid, dropper*
Time 10 minutes

Prepare a dilute solution of dishwashing liquid in advance by mixing one drop of dishwashing liquid and 200 mL of water. Students will work in pairs to investigate the waterproof nature of the skin. Have a member of each pair clean one of their partner's palms with a cotton ball dipped in rubbing alcohol, then use the dropper to put two or three separate drops of the dilute dishwashing liquid on both of their partner's palms. Ask students to describe what they observe. *(The drops on one palm spread out. The drops on the other palm remain rounded.)* Ask: **What caused the drops on one hand to spread out while the drops on the other hand did not?** *(The rubbing alcohol removed the oil from the skin, so that the palm surface was no longer waterproof.)* **learning modality: visual**

Ongoing Assessment

Organizing Information Have students create concept maps that describe the skin and its functions.

The Epidermis

Call students' attention to the epidermis, and ask students to identify the openings found in that layer. *(Pores and openings of hair follicles)* Ask students to infer the function of the pores. *(They allow sweat to reach the surface of the skin.)* Point out that some nerves are located near the hair follicles. Ask students to infer the relationship between the hair and the nerves. *(Sample: When something touches or blows against the hairs, the nerves pick up the sensation.)* **learning modality: visual**

Real-Life Learning

Tell students that researchers have found that household dust—up to 80 percent—is composed of dead human skin cells. However, it is not the dead skin cells that so many people are allergic to. Dust allergies are caused by dust mites, tiny spiderlike creatures that live off dead skin cells and the water vapor that people produce by breathing and perspiring. Ask students: **Where are dust mites most likely to be found in your home? Why?** *(The bedroom; most people spend more time there than in any other room.)* Then ask: **How could you reduce your exposure to dust mites?** *(Samples: Use special covers for mattresses and pillows; wash linens regularly; vacuum frequently; decrease the humidity in your home.)* **learning modality: verbal**

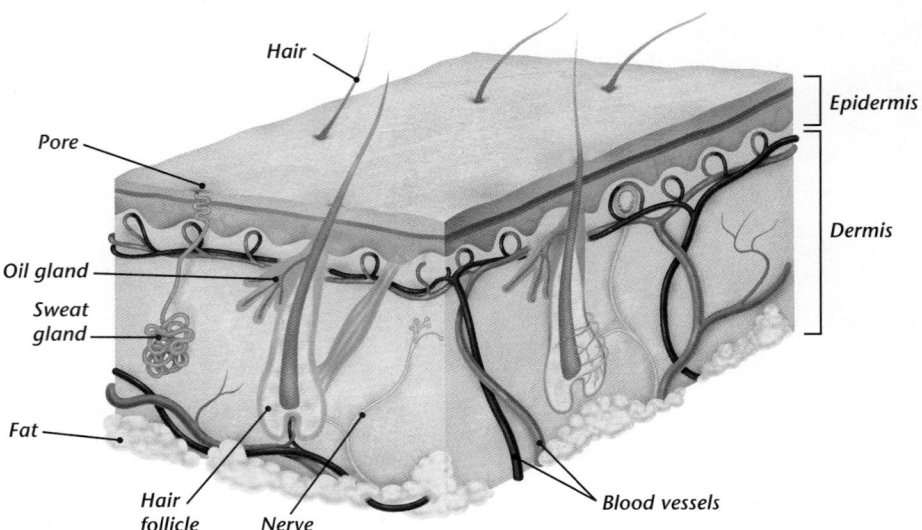

Figure 19 The skin is made of two main layers. The top layer is called the epidermis. The bottom layer is called the dermis. *Interpreting Diagrams In which layer of the skin do you find blood vessels?*

The Epidermis

The skin is organized into two main layers, the epidermis and the dermis. You can see these layers in Figure 19. The **epidermis** is the outermost layer of the skin. In most places, the epidermis is thinner than the dermis. The epidermis does not have nerves or blood vessels. This is why you usually don't feel pain from very shallow scratches and why shallow scratches do not bleed.

Dead or Alive? The cells in the epidermis have a definite life cycle. Each epidermal cell begins life deep in the epidermis, where cells divide to form new cells. The new cells gradually mature and move upward in the epidermis as new cells form beneath them. After about two weeks, the cells die and become part of the surface layer of the epidermis. Under a microscope, this surface layer of dead cells resembles flat bags laid on top of each other. Cells remain in this layer for about two weeks. Then they are shed and replaced by the dead cells below.

Protecting the Body In some ways, the cells of the epidermis are more valuable to the body dead than alive. Most of the protection provided by the skin is due to the layer of dead cells on the surface. The thick layer of dead cells on your fingertips, for example, protects and cushions your fingertips. The shedding of dead cells also helps to protect the body. As the cells fall away, they carry with them bacteria and other substances that settle on the skin. Every time you rub your hands together, you lose hundreds, even thousands, of dead skin cells.

Background

Integrating Science Forensic scientists can use friction ridge patterns, the ridges on the ends of a person's fingers, to identify people. If a suspect is at the scene of a crime, oil or perspiration around the friction ridges will transfer to objects he or she handles. Forensic scientists can expose both recent and old fingerprints by treating them with special chemicals. In addition, prints up to several years old can be recorded by shining lasers at them, then photographing them with time-lapse photography. After the prints are taken, they can be entered into a computer network and compared with prints on file.

Fingerprints can also be taken for medical purposes. Some genetic conditions are associated with certain print patterns.

Some cells in the inner layer of the epidermis help to protect the body, too. On your fingers, for example, some cells produce hard fingernails, which protect the fingertips from injury and help you scratch and pick up objects.

Other cells deep in the epidermis produce **melanin,** a pigment, or colored substance, that gives skin its color. The more melanin in your skin, the darker it is. Exposure to sunlight stimulates the skin to make more melanin. Melanin production helps to protect the skin from burning.

☑ *Checkpoint* How do dead skin cells help to protect the body?

The Dermis

The **dermis** is the lower layer of the skin. Find the dermis in Figure 19. Notice that it is located below the epidermis and above a layer of fat. This fat layer pads the internal organs and helps keep heat in the body.

The dermis contains nerves and blood vessels. The dermis also contains other structures as well—sweat glands, hairs, and oil glands. Sweat glands produce perspiration, which reaches the surface through openings called **pores.** Strands of hair grow within the dermis in structures called **follicles** (FAHL ih kulz). The hair that you see above the skin's surface is made up of dead cells. Oil produced in glands around the hair follicles waterproofs the hair. In addition, oil that reaches the surface helps to keep the skin moist.

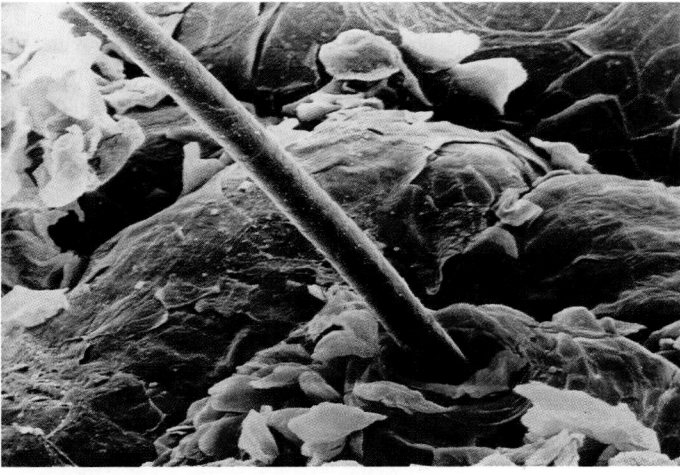

Figure 20 Hairs grow from follicles in the dermis of the skin. Hair is made of dead cells.

Sweaty Skin

This activity illustrates one of the skin's important functions.

1. 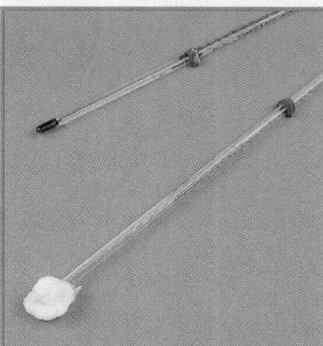 Put on your safety goggles. Wrap a wet cotton ball around the bulb of one thermometer. Place a second thermometer next to the first one.

2. After two minutes, record the temperature reading on each thermometer.

3. Using a piece of cardboard, fan both thermometers for several minutes. The cardboard should be at least 10 cm from the thermometers. Then record the temperatures.

Measuring Which of the two thermometers had a lower temperature after Step 3? How does this activity relate to the role of skin in regulating body temperature?

Answers to Self-Assessment

Caption Question

Figure 19 The dermis

☑ *Checkpoint*

Dead cells protect and cushion the living cells beneath them. They also carry away bacteria and other substances that settle on the skin.

The Dermis

TRY THIS

Skills Focus measuring
Materials *2 thermometers, wet cotton ball, piece of cardboard*
Time 15 minutes
Tips Have students note the temperatures on both thermometers before beginning the activity. Ask students to predict what the temperatures will be at the conclusion of the activity.
Measuring Students should note that the thermometer wrapped in wet cotton has a lower temperature after it is fanned. They should conclude that when skin is moist, sweat evaporates into the air, removing body heat and lowering the temperature of the body.
Extend Ask students why an athlete might put on a jacket after a workout, even though the air is warm. (*The jacket will keep the athlete from getting chilled when sweat evaporates.*) **learning modality: logical/mathematical**

Building Inquiry Skills: Observing

Materials *microscope, prepared slides of hair cells, human hair, hand lens*
Time 15 minutes

Invite students to provide strands of hair that have been carefully removed from their heads. Have students use a hand lens to observe the hair, noting the structure, texture, thickness, and coloration. Have students look at slides of hair cells under the microscope. Have students use their observations and the images in Figure 19 and Figure 20 to make a detailed diagram of how the hair grows out of the dermis. Students should label their diagrams with their observations.
learning modality: visual

Ongoing Assessment

Writing Have students write paragraphs that compare and contrast the structure and function of the dermis and epidermis.

Sun Safety

Preparing for Inquiry

Key Concept Students have probably used commercial lotions, oils, and creams containing sunscreens to protect themselves from sunburn. However, they may not understand the relationship between a product's SPF (sun protection factor) rating and its effectiveness in protecting the skin from burning.

Skills Objective Students will be able to
- predict the outcome of an experiment that compares the sun-blocking ability of different sunscreens;
- make observations during an experiment;
- draw conclusions based on their observations.

Time 45 minutes, plus 2 to 4 hours of sun exposure, and 20 minutes to analyze the results

Advance Planning

- Obtain photosensitive paper from science supply houses or some toy or craft stores.
- Collect fabric or have students bring in scraps of fabric. Try to choose fabrics used in clothing commonly worn by students, such as T-shirt material and denim.

Guiding Inquiry

Invitation

Engage the class in a brief discussion of how sunscreens protect the skin. Point out that sunscreens have an SPF number, and ask: **What does this number mean? Would you be less likely to get a sunburn if you used a sunscreen product with a higher SPF?**

Introducing the Procedure

- Have students work in small groups so each team member can be responsible for a strip of photosensitive paper.
- Demonstrate how to cut the photosensitive and construction paper strips and staple them in place in the plastic bag. Demonstrate the technique for coating the bag with sunscreen.

Caring for Your Skin

Because your skin has so many important functions, it is important to take care of it. **Four simple habits can help you keep your skin healthy. Eat properly. Drink enough water. Limit your exposure to the sun. Keep your skin clean and dry.**

Eating Properly Your skin is always active. The cells in the epidermis are replaced, hair strands and nails grow, and oil is produced. These activities require energy—and a well-balanced diet provides the energy needed for these processes. You will learn more about healthy diets in Chapter 16.

Real-World Lab

You and Your Environment

Sun Safety

In this lab, you'll investigate how sunscreen products and various fabrics protect your skin from the sun.

Problem

How well do different materials protect the skin from the sun?

Skills Focus

predicting, observing, drawing conclusions

Materials

scissors	pencil
3 different fabrics	plastic knife
photosensitive paper	metric ruler
white construction paper	stapler
resealable plastic bag	staple remover
2 sunscreens with SPF ratings of 4 and 30	

Procedure ✂

1. Read over the procedure. Then write a prediction about how well each of the sunscreens and fabrics will protect against the sun.

2. Use scissors to cut five strips of photosensitive paper that measure 5 cm by 15 cm.
3. Divide each strip into thirds by drawing lines across the strips as shown in the photo.
4. Cover one third of each strip with a square of white construction paper. Staple each square down.
5. Use a pencil to write the lower SPF (sun protection factor) rating on the back of the first strip. Write the other SPF rating on the back of a second strip. Set the other three strips aside.
6. Place the two strips side by side in a plastic bag. Seal the bag, then staple through the white squares to hold the strips in place.

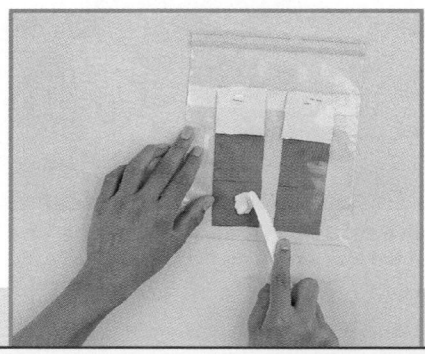

- Make sure students understand that the white construction paper allows them to control the experiment and compare their results. Students should be able to identify other controls, such as using the same amount of sunscreen and making sure the strips are exposed to direct sunlight.
- Place the strips where they will receive direct sunlight, but not in a sunny window, because UV rays cannot penetrate glass. You could use an artificial source of ultraviolet light such as a sun lamp. Make sure no one looks at the light source; it can seriously damage the retina.

Analyze and Conclude

1. Yes. Sections not covered by sunscreen changed color drastically. The covered sections changed color slightly or not at all.
2. The sunscreen with a higher SPF provided more protection. Students' predictions will be correct if they predicted this result.
3. Yes. The sections covered by fabric did not change color as much as the uncovered areas.

Drinking Water To keep your skin healthy, it is also important to drink plenty of water. When you participate in strenuous activities, such as playing soccer, you can perspire up to 10 liters of liquid a day. You need to replace the water lost in perspiration by drinking water or other beverages and by eating foods, such as fruits, that contain water.

Limiting Sun Exposure You can also take actions to protect your skin from cancer and early aging. **Cancer** is a disease in which some body cells divide uncontrollably. Repeated exposure to sunlight can damage skin cells and cause them to become

7. With a plastic knife, spread a thin layer of each sunscreen on the bag over the bottom square of its labeled strip. Make certain each layer has the same depth. Be sure not to spread sunscreen over the middle squares. Place the bag in a drawer or cabinet.

8. Obtain three fabric pieces of different thicknesses. Using the other three photo-sensitive strips, staple a square of each fabric over the bottom square of one of the strips. Write a description of the fabric on the back of the strip.

9. Remove the bag from the drawer or cabinet. Make sure the bag is sunscreen-side up and the fabric strips are fabric-side up. Place the strips in sunlight until the color of the middle squares stops changing.

10. Remove the strips from the bag. Take off the construction paper and fabrics. Rinse the strips for one minute in cold water, then dry them flat.

11. Observe all the squares. Record your observations.

Analyze and Conclude

1. Did the sunscreens protect against sun exposure? How do you know?
2. Which sunscreen provided more protection? Was your prediction correct?

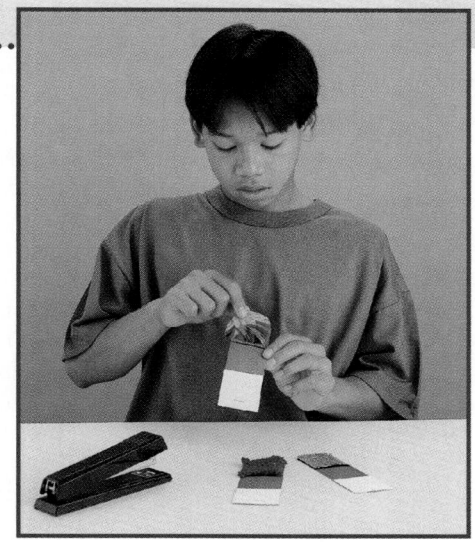

3. Did the fabrics protect against sun exposure? How do you know?
4. Which fabric provided the most protection? The least protection? How did your results compare with your predictions?
5. **Apply** What advice would you give people about protecting their skin from the sun?

Design an Experiment

Design an experiment to find out whether ordinary window glass protects skin against sun exposure. Obtain your teacher's approval before carrying out this experiment.

499

4. The heaviest or most tightly woven fabric, such as denim, provided the most protection. Thin fabrics such as t-shirt material or light gauze provided less protection.
5. Samples: Choose a sunscreen with a high SPF rating, wear clothing that blocks the sun.

Extending the Inquiry

Design an Experiment Students' designs should include placing one strip of photosensitive paper in direct sunlight and one on an inside window sill or under a piece of window glass. Make sure students control variables such as the angle and amount of sunlight received.

Caring for Your Skin

Real-Life Learning

Provide a list of the recommended Daily Values for different vitamins and minerals as well as resources that describe the functions performed by each. Have students identify vitamins and minerals that are important for healthy skin. Encourage students to find food sources that contain these vitamins and minerals. **learning modality: verbal**

Program Resources

◆ **Unit 4 Resources** Chapter 15 Real-World Lab, pp. 27–29

Safety

Remind students to be careful when using scissors. Caution them not to get any sunscreen into their eyes or mouths. They should wash their hands thoroughly after the lab. If sunlamps are used, be sure students observe safety precautions. Review the safety guidelines in Appendix A.

3 Assess

Section 4 Review Answers

1. Skin covers the body and protects it from injury and infection. It also helps regulate body temperature, eliminate wastes, gather information about the environment, and produce Vitamin D.

2. Accept any three: eat properly, drink enough water, limit exposure to the sun, and keep the skin clean and dry.

3. The epidermis contains some dead cells and some living cells, but no blood vessels or nerves. Some of the deepest cells of the epidermis produce melanin. The dermis is located beneath the epidermis and contains blood vessels, nerves, sweat glands, oil glands, and hair follicles.

4. Sample: Washing the skin too much may cause dryness and remove dead skin cells that are necessary to protect the skin.

Science at Home

Before students perform this activity, have them identify ways that people protect themselves from the sun. Encourage students to include items such as hats, parasols, and beach umbrellas. Students may want to ask older family members about items they may have used when they were young to avoid too much exposure to the sun.

Performance Assessment

Oral Presentation Group students into five teams. Assign each team one of the following functions of skin: prevents loss of water, protects body from injury and infection, regulates body temperature, eliminates wastes, and gathers information about the environment. Mention that the skin also produces vitamin D. Encourage each group to integrate material throughout the section to explain the importance of their assigned function and how it is accomplished by the skin.

Figure 21 This person is taking precautions to protect her skin from the sun. *Applying Concepts What other behaviors can provide protection from the sun?*

cancerous. In addition, exposure to the sun can cause the skin to become leathery and wrinkled.

There are many things you can do to protect your skin from damage by the sun. When you are outdoors, wear a hat and sunglasses and use a sunscreen on exposed skin. The clothing you wear can also protect you. Choose clothing made of tightly woven fabrics for the greatest protection. In addition, avoid exposure to the sun between the hours of 10 A.M. and 2 P.M. That is the time when sunlight is the strongest.

Keeping Skin Clean When you wash your skin with mild soap, you get rid of dirt and harmful bacteria. Good washing habits are particularly important during the teenage years when oil glands are more active. When oil glands become clogged with oil, bacterial infections can occur.

One bacterial infection of the skin that can be difficult to control is known as **acne.** If you develop acne, your doctor may prescribe an antibiotic to help control the infection. When you wash, you help to control oiliness and keep your skin from becoming infected with more bacteria.

Other organisms, called fungi, can also live on and infect the skin. Fungi grow best in warm, moist surroundings. Athlete's foot is a very common fungal infection that occurs on the feet, especially between the toes. You can prevent athlete's foot by keeping your feet, especially the spaces between your toes, clean and dry.

 ## Section 4 Review

1. Describe the functions of the skin.
2. List three things you can do to keep your skin healthy.
3. Describe the structure of the two layers of skin.
4. **Thinking Critically** **Making Judgments** Do you think it is possible to wash your skin too much and damage it as a result? Why or why not?

Science at Home

Protection From the Sun With a family member, look for products in your home that provide protection from the sun. You may also want to visit a store that sells these products. Make a list of the products and place them in categories such as sunblocks, clothing, eye protectors, and other products. Explain to your family member why it is important to use such products.

Answers to Self-Assessment

Caption Question

Figure 21 Wearing a hat and sunglasses, using high SPF suntan lotion, wearing protective clothing, and avoiding exposure to the sun between 10 A.M. and 2 P.M.

Program Resources

◆ **Unit 4 Resources** 15-4 Review and Reinforce, p. 23; 15-4 Enrich, p. 24
◆ **Product Testing Activities by** *Consumer Reports,* "Testing Lip Balms," pp. 1–8
◆ **Laboratory Manual,** 15, "Examining Bones, Muscles, and Skin"

SECTION 1 — Body Organization and Homeostasis

INTEGRATING HEALTH

Key Ideas
◆ The levels of organization in the body consist of cells, tissues, organs, and organ systems.
◆ Homeostasis is the process by which an organism's internal environment is kept stable in spite of changes in the external environment.

Key Terms
cell	muscle tissue	organ
cell membrane	nerve tissue	organ system
nucleus	connective tissue	homeostasis
cytoplasm	epithelial tissue	stress
tissue		

SECTION 2 — The Skeletal System

Key Ideas
◆ The skeleton provides shape and support, enables movement, protects internal organs, produces blood cells, and stores materials.
◆ Movable joints allow the body to make a wide range of motions.
◆ A combination of a balanced diet and regular exercise helps keep bones healthy.

Key Terms
vertebra	cartilage	ligament
marrow	joint	osteoporosis

SECTION 3 — The Muscular System

Key Ideas
◆ Skeletal muscles are voluntary muscles that are attached to the bones of the skeleton.
◆ Smooth muscles, which are involuntary muscles, line the walls of many internal organs and blood vessels. Cardiac muscles are involuntary muscles found only in the heart.

Key Terms
involuntary muscle	tendon
voluntary muscle	smooth muscle
skeletal muscle	cardiac muscle

SECTION 4 — The Skin

Key Ideas
◆ Skin covers and protects the body from injury and infection. It also helps to regulate body temperature, get rid of wastes, gather information about the environment, and produce vitamin D.
◆ The epidermis is the top layer of the skin. The dermis is the lower layer of the skin.
◆ For healthy skin, eat a well-balanced diet and drink enough water. Also limit your exposure to the sun and keep your skin clean.

Key Terms
epidermis	follicle
melanin	cancer
dermis	acne
pore	

Organizing Information

Concept Map Copy the concept map about muscles onto a separate sheet of paper. Then complete it and add a title. (For more information on concept maps, see the Skills Handbook.)

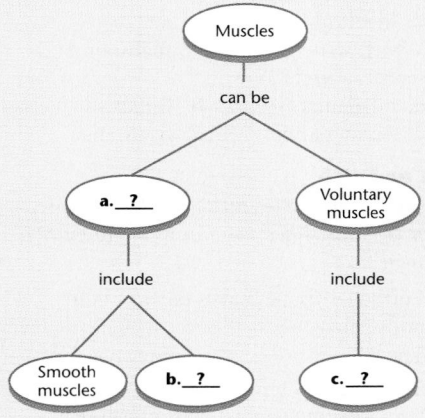

Organizing Information

Concept Map Sample Title: Types of Muscles in the Human Body; **a.** Involuntary muscles **b.** Cardiac muscles **c.** Skeletal muscles

Program Resources
◆ **Unit 4 Resources** Chapter 15 Project Scoring Rubric, p. 8
◆ **Performance Assessment** Chapter 15, pp. 47–49
◆ **Chapter and Unit Tests** Chapter 15 Test, pp. 72–75

Media and Technology

 Interactive Student Tutorial CD-ROM Chapter 15

 Computer Test Bank Chapter 15 Test

Reviewing Content

Multiple Choice

1. c 2. b 3. b 4. c 5. c

True or False

6. muscle 7. true 8. marrow 9. true
10. dermis

Checking Concepts

11. An organ system is a group of organs that perform a major function; an organ is made up of different tissues that together perform a specific function within the organ system; tissues are made up of similar cells that perform a specific function; cells are the basic units of structure and function.

12. Your body needs materials from food in order to function. Hunger prompts you to eat, thus supplying your body with the food it needs and maintaining your body's stability.

13. Sample: You are moving to a new community. Actions you can take to relieve stress: get involved with school activities to make new friends; keep in touch with your friends from the old community; engage in sports or other strenuous activities to relieve stress.

14. Bone is covered by a thin, tough membrane except at its ends. Blood vessels and nerves enter and leave the bone through the membrane. Compact bone, which contains canals that have blood vessels and nerves, is directly under the membrane. Spongy bone is found under compact bone and also at the ends of the bone. Marrow fills the spaces in bone.

15. Ball-and-socket—allows range of motion through a complete circle; pivot—allows one bone to rotate around another; gliding—allows one bone to slide over another; hinge—allows forward and backward motion

16. Smooth muscle is not striated.

17. Because each skeletal muscle can only contract and thereby pull a bone in one direction, there must be another muscle attached to the bone that can pull the bone in the opposite direction.

18. Sunlight can injure skin cells, which may eventually become cancerous.

19. Students' articles should discuss proper exercise techniques such as stretching and wearing safety gear.

Reviewing Content

 For more review of key concepts, see the Interactive Student Tutorial CD-ROM.

Multiple Choice

Choose the letter of the best answer.

1. A group of similar cells that perform a similar function is called a(n)
   a. cell.
   b. organ.
   c. tissue.
   d. organ system.

2. The term most closely associated with homeostasis is
   a. growth.
   b. stability.
   c. temperature.
   d. energy.

3. Blood cells are produced in
   a. compact bone.
   b. red bone marrow.
   c. cartilage.
   d. ligaments.

4. Muscles that help the skeleton move are
   a. cardiac muscles.
   b. smooth muscles.
   c. skeletal muscles.
   d. involuntary muscles.

5. Which structures help to maintain body temperature?
   a. oil glands   b. follicles
   c. sweat glands   d. ligaments

True or False

If the statement is true, write true. If it is false, change the underlined word or words to make the statement true.

6. <u>Epithelial</u> tissue makes parts of your body move.

7. The <u>circulatory</u> system carries needed materials to the body cells.

8. Spongy bone is filled with <u>cartilage.</u>

9. <u>Skeletal</u> muscle is sometimes called striated muscle.

10. The <u>epidermis</u> contains nerve endings and blood vessels.

Checking Concepts

11. Explain the relationship among cells, tissues, organs, and organ systems.

12. How does hunger help your body maintain homeostasis?

13. Think of a situation that might cause long-term stress. Identify some ways in which a person might deal with that stress.

14. Describe the structure of a bone.

15. List the four kinds of movable joints. Describe how each kind of joint functions.

16. How does the appearance of smooth muscle differ from that of skeletal muscle when viewed with a microscope?

17. Explain how skeletal muscles work in pairs to move a body part.

18. Why is it important to limit your exposure to the sun?

19. **Writing to Learn** Write an article for your school newspaper about preventing skeletal and muscular injuries. The article should focus on ways in which athletes can strengthen their muscles and bones and decrease the risk of injuries during sports.

Thinking Critically

20. **Inferring** Why do you think scientists classify blood as a connective tissue?

21. **Making Generalizations** How is homeostasis important to survival?

22. **Applying Concepts** At birth, the joints in an infant's skull are flexible and not yet fixed. As the child develops, the bones become more rigid and grow together. Why is it important that the bones of an infant's skull not grow together too rapidly?

23. **Predicting** If smooth muscle had to be consciously controlled, what problems could you foresee in day-to-day living?

24. **Relating Cause and Effect** A person who is exposed to excessive heat may suffer from a condition known as heat stroke. The first sign of heat stroke is that the person stops sweating. Why is this condition a life-threatening emergency?

Thinking Critically

20. Blood flows through the whole body, connecting all parts of the body.

21. If living things could not maintain a stable internal environment, body functions could not take place. For example, if the body did not have a steady supply of food, the cells would not obtain the materials they need.

22. If the bones grew together too rapidly, there would not be enough space for the brain to grow.

23. Sample: People would have to spend a lot of time consciously controlling processes that normally happen automatically, such as digestion. People would not be able to sleep, since life processes would not happen automatically.

24. Without being able to sweat, a person cannot get rid of excess body heat to maintain homeostasis.

Applying Skills

The graph below shows the effects of the temperature of the environment on a girl's skin temperature and on the temperature inside her body. Use the graph to answer Questions 25–27.

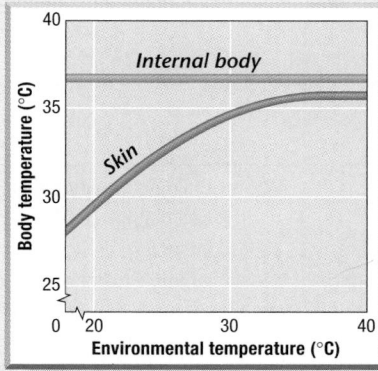

25. Interpreting Data As the temperature of the environment rises, what happens to the girl's internal temperature? How does this demonstrate homeostasis?

26. Inferring What happens to the temperature of the girl's skin? Why is this pattern different from the pattern shown by the girl's internal temperature?

27. Developing Hypotheses Suppose the girl went outdoors on a chilly fall morning. Write a hypothesis that predicts what would happen to her internal body temperature and skin temperature.

Performance ▼ **CHAPTER PROJECT** **Assessment**

Present Your Project Demonstrate your model for the class. Explain how your model shows your chosen motion. Describe how the contraction of muscle is involved.

Reflect and Record Why did you select the motion that you modeled? What new information did you discover about the human body? If you could do the project again, what would you change? Write your thoughts in your journal.

Test Preparation

Use these questions to prepare for standardized tests.

Read the passage. Then answer Questions 28–30.

Magnetic resonance imaging, or MRI, is a method used to take clear images of both the bones and soft tissues of the body. An MRI scanner is a large cylinder that contains electromagnets. The person is placed on a platform that slides into the center of the cylinder. The person is then exposed to short bursts of magnetic energy. This magnetic energy causes atoms within the body to vibrate, or resonate. A computer then analyzes the vibration patterns and produces an image of the area.

   MRI can produce images of body tissues at any angle. The images clearly show muscles and other soft tissues that an X-ray image cannot show. Another advantage of MRI is that it does not damage cells. Because MRI machines are very expensive to buy and use, this technique is not used to examine broken bones.

28. Which of the following is the best title for this passage?
  a. Using X-Rays to Diagnose Bone Injuries
  b. Using MRI to Diagnose Injuries
  c. The Dangers of MRI
  d. Two Methods for Diagnosing Injuries

29. Why is MRI often used to diagnose muscle and other soft tissue injuries?
  a. MRI creates clear images of soft tissues.
  b. MRI can produce images from many angles.
  c. MRI does not damage body cells.
  d. all of the above

30. According to the passage, why are X-rays used instead of MRI to examine broken bones?
  a. X-ray images are less expensive to produce.
  b. MRI involves placing a person inside a cylinder.
  c. Vibration of atoms is uncomfortable.
  d. MRI causes damage to cells.

Applying Skills

25. The girl's internal temperature stays constant as the environmental temperature rises. This demonstrates stability of her internal temperature despite changes in the external temperature.

26. Her skin temperature rises as the external temperature increases. Her skin is in direct contact with the external environment (the air) and thus warms as the external temperature increases.

27. Most students will hypothesize that her internal temperature would remain constant due to homeostasis while her skin temperature would decline.

Performance ▼ **CHAPTER PROJECT** **Assessment**

Present Your Project Encourage students to ask questions after other students make their presentations. Students may want to share their sketches or have another student demonstrate the motion before they show their models. Make sure students' models and explanations include paired muscles.

Reflect and Record For new information, students will probably indicate the names, locations, and functions of the muscles involved in their models. Encourage students to consider other students' projects as they assess their own work. For example, some materials may work better than others to model bones and muscles.

Test Preparation

28. b **29.** d **30.** a

Program Resources

◆ **Inquiry Skills Activity Book** Provides teaching and review of all inquiry skills

16 Food and Digestion

Sections	Time	Student Edition Activities	Other Activities
CHAPTER PROJECT **What's on Your Menu?** p. 505	Ongoing (2–3 weeks)	Check Your Progress, pp. 516, 523, 529 Present Your Project, p. 533	
1 INTEGRATING CHEMISTRY **Food and Energy** pp. 506–517 ◆ List and describe each of the six nutrients needed by the body. ◆ Describe how the Food Guide Pyramid and food labels help people make food choices for nutrient and caloric value.	3 periods/ 1½ blocks	**Discover** Food Claims—Fact or Fiction?, p. 506 **Sharpen Your Skills** Predicting, p. 508 **Real-World Lab: You, the Consumer** Iron for Breakfast, p. 517	TE Building Inquiry Skills: Calculating, p. 507 TE Including All Students, p. 508 TE Inquiry Challenge, p. 512 PTA "Testing Cereals," pp. 1–8 TE Building Inquiry Skills: Classifying, p. 513 TE Real-Life Learning, p. 515
2 **The Digestive Process Begins** pp. 518–525 ◆ Describe the general functions carried out by the digestive system and the specific functions of the mouth, esophagus, and stomach.	2 periods/ 1 block	**Discover** How Can You Speed up Digestion?, p. 518 **Try This** Modeling Peristalsis, p. 521 **Skills Lab: Drawing Conclusions** As the Stomach Churns, pp. 524–525	TE Building Inquiry Skills: Interpreting Diagrams, p. 522 PTA "Testing Antacids," pp. 1–8 LM 16, "Nutrient Identification"
3 **Final Digestion and Absorption** pp. 526–530 ◆ Explain the role of the small intestine in digestion. ◆ Explain the role of the large intestine in digestion.	1 period/ ½ block	**Discover** Which Surface Is Larger?, p. 526 **Try This** Break Up!, p. 527	TE Demonstration, p. 527 TE Including All Students, p. 528 PTA "Testing Yogurt," pp. 1–8 PTA "Testing Sports Drinks," pp. 1–8
Study Guide/Chapter Assessment pp. 531–533	1 period/ ½ block		ISAB Provides teaching and review of all inquiry skills

 For Standard or Block Schedule The Resource Pro® CD-ROM gives you maximum flexibility for planning your instruction for any type of schedule. Resource Pro® contains Planning Express®, an advanced scheduling program, as well as the entire contents of the Teaching Resources and the Computer Test Bank.

504a

CHAPTER PLANNING GUIDE

Program Resources	Assessment Strategies	Media and Technology
UR Chapter 16 Project Teacher Notes, pp. 30–31 **UR** Chapter 16 Project Overview and Worksheets, pp. 32–35	**SE** Performance Assessment: Present Your Project, p. 533 **TE** Check Your Progress, pp. 516, 523, 529 **UR** Chapter 16 Project Scoring Rubric, p. 36	Science Explorer Internet Site at www.phschool.com
UR 16-1 Lesson Plan, p. 37 **UR** 16-1 Section Summary, p. 38 **UR** 16-1 Review and Reinforce, p. 39 **UR** 16-1 Enrich, p. 40 **UR** Chapter 16 Real-World Lab, pp. 49–50	**SE** Section 1 Review, p. 516 **TE** Ongoing Assessment, pp. 507, 509, 511, 513, 515 **TE** Performance Assessment, p. 516	Physical Science Videotape 3; Videodisc Unit 4 Side 1, "Balancing Act" Audio CD, English-Spanish Summary 16-1 Transparency 65, "The Food Guide Pyramid" Life Science Videotape 4; Videodisc Unit 4 Side 1, "You Are What You Eat" Interactive Student Tutorial CD-ROM, Chapter 16
UR 16-2 Lesson Plan, p. 41 **UR** 16-2 Section Summary, p. 42 **UR** 16-2 Review and Reinforce, p. 43 **UR** 16-2 Enrich, p. 44 **UR** Chapter 16 Skills Lab, pp. 51–53	**SE** Section 2 Review, p. 523 **TE** Ongoing Assessment, pp. 519, 521 **TE** Performance Assessment, p. 523	Life Science Videotape 4; Videodisc Unit 4 Side 1, "Digestion and Absorption" Audio CD, English-Spanish Summary 16-2 Transparency 66, "The Digestive System"
UR 16-3 Lesson Plan, p. 45 **UR** 16-3 Section Summary, p. 46 **UR** 16-3 Review and Reinforce, p. 47 **UR** 16-3 Enrich, p. 48	**SE** Section 3 Review, p. 529 **TE** Ongoing Assessment, p. 527 **TE** Performance Assessment, p. 529	Life Science Videotape 4; Videodisc Unit 4 Side 1, "Digestion and Absorption" Audio CD, English-Spanish Summary 16-3
RCA Provides strategies to improve science reading skills **GSW** Provides worksheets to promote student comprehension of content	**SE** Chapter 16 Study Guide/Assessment, pp. 531–533 **PA** Chapter 16 Performance Assessment, pp. 50–52 **CUT** Chapter 16 Test, pp. 76–79 **CTB** Chapter 16 Test	Interactive Student Tutorial CD-ROM, Chapter 16 Computer Test Bank, Chapter 16 Test

Key: **SE** Student Edition
CTB Computer Test Bank
ISAB Inquiry Skills Activity Book
GSW Guided Study Worksheets

TE Teacher's Edition
PTA Product Testing Activities by *Consumer Reports*
RCA Reading in the Content Area
PA Performance Assessment

UR Unit Resources
LM Laboratory Manual
IES Interdisciplinary Explorations Series
CUT Chapter and Unit Tests

Meeting the National Science Education Standards and AAAS Benchmarks

National Science Education Standards	Benchmarks for Science Literacy	Unifying Themes
Science as Inquiry (Content Standard A) ◆ **Ask questions that can be answered by scientific investigations** How can you test whether iron has been added to cereals? *(Real-World Lab)* What conditions are needed for the digestion of proteins in the stomach? *(Skills Lab)* **Life Science** (Content Standard C) ◆ **Structure and function in living systems** The digestive system breaks down food into molecules the body can use. These molecules are absorbed into the blood carried throughout the body. Wastes are eliminated from the body. Most of the chemical digestion takes place in the small intestine. Most of the absorption of water takes place in the large intestine. *(Sections 2, 3)* **Science in Personal and Social Perspectives** (Content Standard F) ◆ **Personal health** Food provides energy and nutrients for growth and development. The six kinds of nutrients are carbohydrates, fats, proteins, vitamins, minerals, and water. Nutrition requirements vary. The Food Guide Pyramid and food nutritional labels can help a person plan a healthy diet. *(Section 1)*	**1A The Scientific World View** Students learn about observations that led to the understanding of how the digestive system works. *(Section 2, Skills Lab)* **5E Flow of Matter and Energy** Food provides molecules that serve as fuel and building material for the human body. *(Section 1)* **6C Basic Functions** The digestive system is composed of organs that enable all cells in the body to be provided with nutrients for energy and building materials. Food is digested into molecules that are absorbed and transported to the cells of the body. *(Sections 2, 3)* **6E Physical Health** The amount of calories a person requires varies with body weight, physical activity, and age. *(Section 1)* **12D Communication Skills** Organize information from experimental data into tables and identify the relationships revealed. *(Skills Lab)*	◆ **Energy** Six kinds of nutrients are necessary for human health. These include carbohydrates, fats, proteins, vitamins, minerals, and water. Carbohydrates, fats, and proteins supply energy. A balanced diet can be obtained by following the guidelines of the Food Guide Pyramid. A balanced diet will help keep the digestive system functioning properly. *(Sections 1, 2)* ◆ **Scale and Structure** As food moves through the digestive system, organs work together to help digest food into molecules that can be absorbed and transported to other areas of the body. This is done by mechanical and chemical digestion. *(Sections 2, 3)* ◆ **Systems and Interactions** Organs in the digestive system secrete various enzymes that enable the digestive process. Each enzyme has a different function, but all work together to help in the breakdown of foods. *(Skills Lab)* The digestive and circulatory systems interact to deliver nutrients to cells. *(Sections 2, 3)*

Take It to the Net

 *Interactive text at www.phschool.com*

Science Explorer comes alive with iText.

- **Complete student text** is accessible from any computer with Internet access or a CD-ROM drive.
- **Animations, simulations, and videos** enhance student understanding and retention of concepts.
- **Self-tests and online study tools** assess student understanding.

STAY CURRENT with **SCIENCE NEWS**®

Find out the latest research and information about human biology and health at: **www.phschool.com**

Go to **www.phschool.com** and click on the Science icon. Then click on <u>Science Explorer: Life, Earth, and Physical Science</u> under PH@school.

Student Edition Activities Planner

ACTIVITY	Time (minutes)	Materials — Quantities for one work group	Skills
Section 1			
Discover, p. 506	15	No special materials are required.	Posing Questions
Sharpen Your Skills, p. 508	20	**Consumable** fruits and vegetables, including potatoes, rice, bread, breakfast cereals; soft drinks (diet and regular); iodine solution **Nonconsumable** plastic dropper, test tubes, notebook	Predicting
Real-World Lab, p. 517	55	**Consumable** white paper towels, plastic spoon, instant oatmeal, warm water, 2 dry breakfast cereals, 3 sealable plastic freezer bags **Nonconsumable** long bar magnet, balance, watch or clock, wooden dowel, plastic jar with sealable cover	Observing, Predicting, Interpreting Data
Section 2			
Discover, p. 518	15	**Consumable** water, sugar cubes **Nonconsumable** 2 jars with lids	Predicting
Try This, p. 521	15	**Consumable** 20-cm clear flexible plastic straw (about 6 mm in diameter) **Nonconsumable** round bead (5–6 mm in diameter)	Making Models
Skills Lab, pp. 524–525	60–80	**Consumable** pepsin, dilute hydrochloric acid, water, plastic stirrers, litmus paper, cubes of boiled egg white **Nonconsumable** test tube rack, marking pencil, 10-mL plastic graduated cylinder, 4 test tubes with stoppers	Drawing Conclusions
Section 3			
Discover, p. 526	10	**Nonconsumable** 1 m string, metric ruler	Predicting
Try This, p. 527	15	**Consumable** oil, baking soda **Nonconsumable** 2 jars, stirring rod or spoon	Observing

A list of all materials required for the Student Edition activities can be found on pages T25–T33. You can obtain information about ordering materials by calling 1-800-848-9500 or by accessing the Science Explorer Internet site at **www.phschool.com**.

504d

What's on Your Menu?

Nutritionists claim that many people who maintain healthy lifestyles do so, in part, by keeping track of their diets. In this project, students will have the opportunity to find out how their eating habits correspond to the diets that are recommended for optimum health.

Purpose In this project, students will keep track of the food they eat for three days. They will learn how to estimate portions and will compare their diets to the Food Guide Pyramid recommendations. Students will be able to use what they learn to improve their eating habits.

Skills Focus After completing the Chapter 16 Project, students will be able to

◆ observe and maintain records of their eating habits;
◆ measure or estimate the size of food servings;
◆ graph data from their data tables;
◆ compare and contrast their data with the recommendations;
◆ interpret their diagrams and make judgments about how to improve their own diets.

Project Time Line The project should take approximately two weeks—three days to record food intake, three or four days to analyze their data, and three more days to implement a diet based on the Food Guide Pyramid. Before beginning the project, see Chapter 16 Project Teacher Notes on pages 30–31 in Unit 4 Resources for more details on carrying out the project. Also distribute to students the Chapter 16 Project Overview, Worksheets, and Scoring Rubric on pages 32–36 in Unit 4 Resources.

Possible Materials Students need graph paper, paper, and pencils. You may want to create a chart for students to record foods or you may allow the layout of the chart to grow out of a class discussion on recordkeeping.

Launching the Project To introduce the project and to stimulate student interest, ask students to write down what they have eaten so far today. Explain to

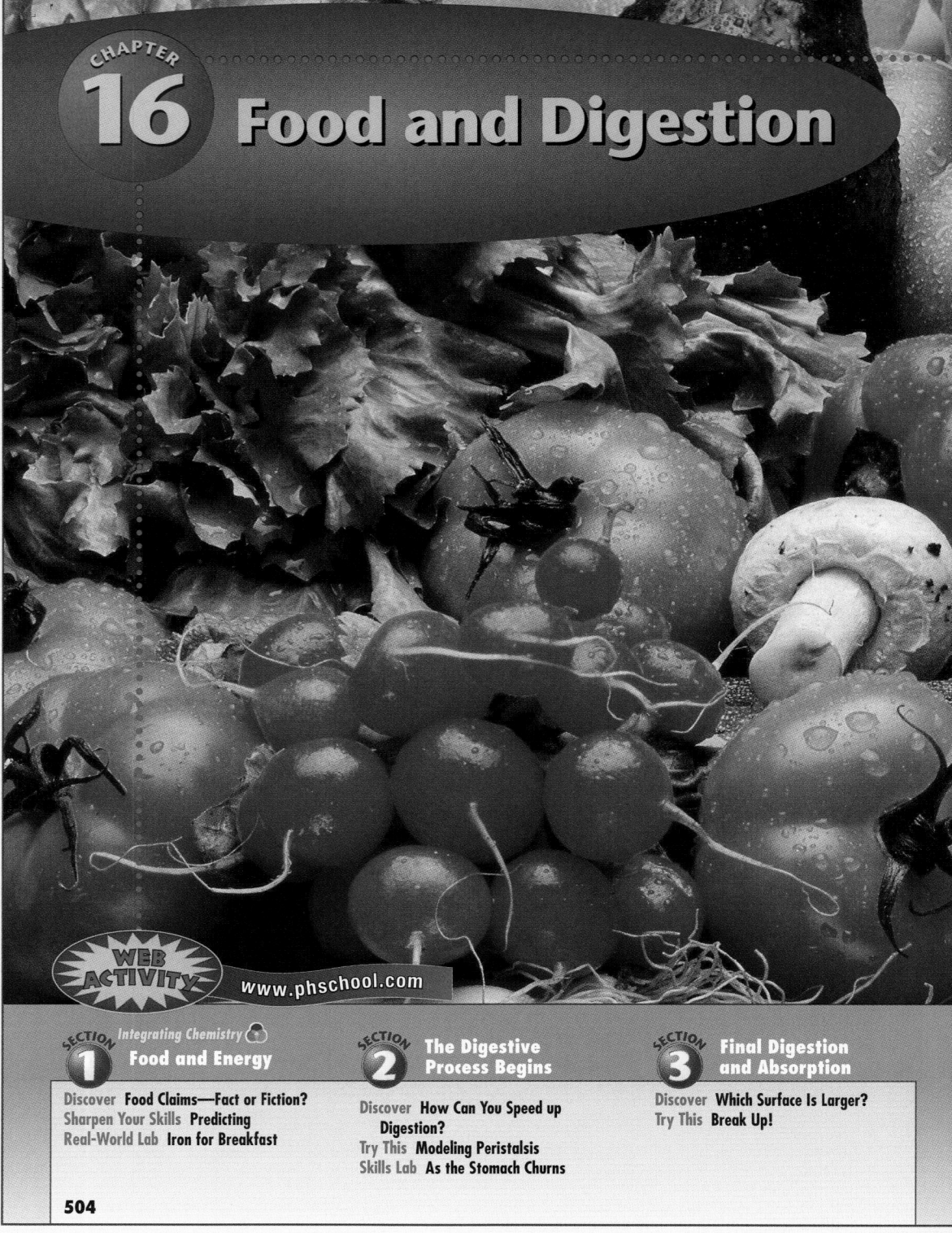

CHAPTER 16 Food and Digestion

WEB ACTIVITY www.phschool.com

SECTION **1** *Integrating Chemistry* **Food and Energy**	SECTION **2** **The Digestive Process Begins**	SECTION **3** **Final Digestion and Absorption**
Discover Food Claims—Fact or Fiction? **Sharpen Your Skills** Predicting **Real-World Lab** Iron for Breakfast	**Discover** How Can You Speed up Digestion? **Try This** Modeling Peristalsis **Skills Lab** As the Stomach Churns	**Discover** Which Surface Is Larger? **Try This** Break Up!

504

students that their notes and lab reports will be kept confidential, so no one else will know what they have eaten. Using the illustration of the Food Guide Pyramid as a guide, ask the students to try to sort their food items into the appropriate groups.

Allow time for students to read the description of the project in their text and the Chapter 16 Project Overview on pages 32–33 in Unit 4 Resources. Then discuss the Food Guide Pyramid and talk about the kind of diet it describes as ideal.

Describe the project by explaining that each student will record all the foods they eat each day for three days. To help students see the importance of daily record keeping, ask them to try to remember what they ate for supper two days ago. Point out that it is difficult to remember things even a few hours later, so they should be sure to write down every meal and snack as soon as possible.

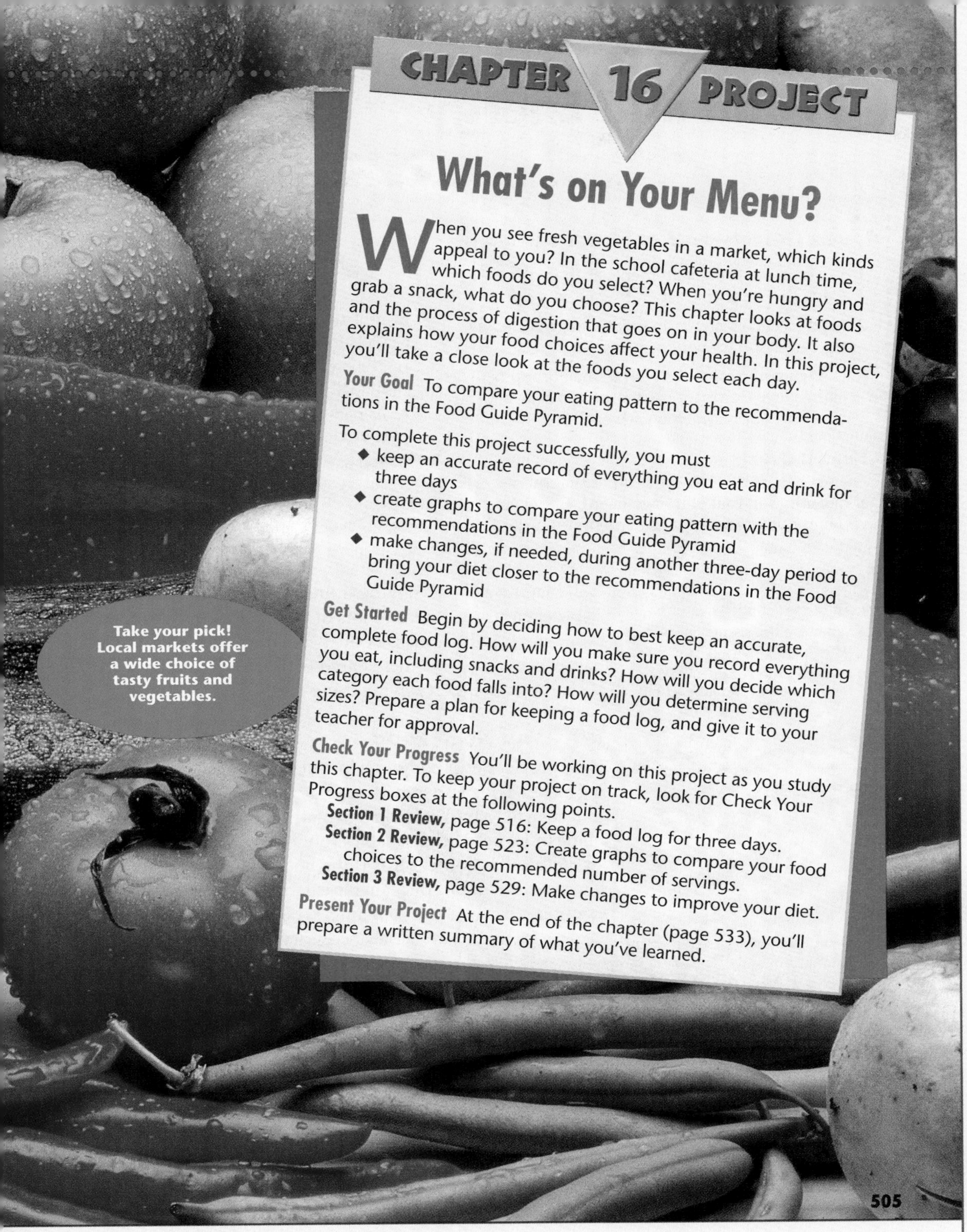

CHAPTER 16 PROJECT

What's on Your Menu?

When you see fresh vegetables in a market, which kinds appeal to you? In the school cafeteria at lunch time, which foods do you select? When you're hungry and grab a snack, what do you choose? This chapter looks at foods and the process of digestion that goes on in your body. It also explains how your food choices affect your health. In this project, you'll take a close look at the foods you select each day.

Your Goal To compare your eating pattern to the recommendations in the Food Guide Pyramid.

To complete this project successfully, you must
- keep an accurate record of everything you eat and drink for three days
- create graphs to compare your eating pattern with the recommendations in the Food Guide Pyramid
- make changes, if needed, during another three-day period to bring your diet closer to the recommendations in the Food Guide Pyramid

Get Started Begin by deciding how to best keep an accurate, complete food log. How will you make sure you record everything you eat, including snacks and drinks? How will you decide which category each food falls into? How will you determine serving sizes? Prepare a plan for keeping a food log, and give it to your teacher for approval.

Check Your Progress You'll be working on this project as you study this chapter. To keep your project on track, look for Check Your Progress boxes at the following points.
Section 1 Review, page 516: Keep a food log for three days.
Section 2 Review, page 523: Create graphs to compare your food choices to the recommended number of servings.
Section 3 Review, page 529: Make changes to improve your diet.

Present Your Project At the end of the chapter (page 533), you'll prepare a written summary of what you've learned.

Take your pick! Local markets offer a wide choice of tasty fruits and vegetables.

505

Review Student Worksheet 1 as an example of a way to record foods. Write a sample of a food record on the board, including spaces to record three meals and snacks. Because students will be using servings to compare their choices with the USDA recommendations, have them brainstorm ways they can record the amounts of food they eat so they can easily convert food listings into servings.

Program Resources

- **Unit 4 Resources** Chapter 16 Project Teacher Notes, pp. 30–31; Chapter 16 Project Overview and Worksheets, pp. 32–35; Chapter 16 Project Scoring Rubric, p. 36

WEB ACTIVITY www.phschool.com

You will find an Internet activity, chapter self-tests for students, and links to other chapter topics at this site.

Performance Assessment

The Chapter 16 Project Scoring Rubric on page 36 of Unit 4 Resources will help you evaluate how well students complete the Chapter 16 Project. Students will be assessed on
- how thoroughly they keep records of the types and amounts of food they eat;
- the completeness of their graphs, including the conversion of servings into totals;
- how well they analyze their diets based on the Food Guide Pyramid;
- the thoroughness and organization of their written presentations and how well they show an understanding of food choices and healthy and unhealthy diets.

By sharing the Chapter 16 Project Scoring Rubric with students at the beginning of the project, you will make it clear to them what they are expected to do.

SECTION 1 Food and Energy

Objectives

After completing the lesson, students will be able to
◆ list and describe each of the six nutrients needed by the body;
◆ describe how the Food Guide Pyramid and food labels help people make food choices for nutrient and caloric value.

Key Terms nutrient, calorie, carbohydrate, glucose, fiber, fat, unsaturated fat, saturated fat, cholesterol, protein, amino acid, vitamin, mineral, Food Guide Pyramid, Percent Daily Value

1 Engage/Explore

Activating Prior Knowledge

Ask students to name foods that they think supply them with energy. Write their responses on the board. Then ask them what they think a calorie is and write these responses on the board. Revisit the responses once students have read the section.

••••••• DISCOVER ••••••••

Skills Focus posing questions
Time 15 minutes
Tips Write the statements on the board or use an overhead projector to project the statements on a screen.
Expected Outcome All the statements are false. At this stage, you may wish to collect students' opinions and look for misconceptions, then address specific issues later as you teach the chapter.
Think It Over Students should volunteer additional statements about nutrition and discuss whether or not the statements are true. Encourage students to identify reliable sources of information about nutrition.

SECTION 1 Food and Energy

DISCOVER ACTIVITY

Food Claims—Fact or Fiction?

1. Examine the list of statements at the right. Copy the list onto a separate sheet of paper.
2. Next to each statement, write *agree* or *disagree.* Give a reason for your response.
3. Discuss your responses with a small group of classmates. Compare the reasons you gave for agreeing or disagreeing with each statement.

Think It Over

Posing Questions List some other statements about nutrition that you have heard. How could you find out whether the statements are true?

Fact or Fiction?
a. Athletes need more protein in their diets than other people do.
b. The only salt that a food contains is the salt that you have added to it.
c. As part of a healthy diet, everyone should take vitamin supplements.
d. You can go without water for longer than you can go without food.

GUIDE FOR READING

◆ What are the six nutrients needed by the body?
◆ How can the Food Guide Pyramid and food labels help you plan a healthy diet?

Reading Tip As you read, create a table that includes the function and sources of each nutrient group.

I magine a Thanksgiving dinner—roast turkey on a platter, delicious stuffing, and lots of vegetables—an abundance of colors and aromas. Food is an important part of many happy occasions, of times shared with friends and family. Food is also essential. Every living thing needs food to stay alive.

Why You Need Food

Food provides your body with materials for growing and for repairing tissues. Food also provides energy for everything you do—running, playing a musical instrument, reading, and even sleeping. By filling those needs, food enables your body to maintain homeostasis. Recall that homeostasis is the body's ability to keep a steady internal state in spite of changing external conditions. Suppose, for example, that you cut your finger. Food provides both the raw materials necessary to grow new skin and the energy that powers this growth.

Your body converts the foods you eat into nutrients. **Nutrients** (NOO tre unts) are the substances in food that provide the raw materials and energy the body needs to carry out all the essential processes. **There are six kinds of nutrients necessary for human health— carbohydrates, fats, proteins, vitamins, minerals, and water.**

READING STRATEGIES

Reading Tip Help students get started by creating the framework for a three-column table on the board. Label the columns *Nutrient, Function,* and *Source.* Then have a volunteer read aloud the boldfaced sentence under *Why You Need Food* that names the six nutrients necessary for human health. List these nutrients in the first column of the table. Students can copy the table and fill in the remaining columns as they read.

Study and Comprehension Before students begin reading, discuss what they already know about the nutrients essential for human health. Then have students preview the section by reading the headings and captions and looking at the pictures. Invite students to dictate questions suggested by this information. Write these on the board. When students finish reading, have them answer the questions.

Carbohydrates, fats, and proteins all provide the body with energy. When nutrients are used by the body for energy, the amount of energy they release can be measured in units called calories. One **calorie** is the amount of energy needed to raise the temperature of one gram of water by one Celsius degree. Most foods contain many thousands of calories of energy. Scientists usually use the term *Calorie,* with a capital *C,* to measure the energy in foods. One Calorie is the same as 1,000 calories. For example, one serving of popcorn may contain 60 Calories, or 60,000 calories, of energy. The more Calories a food has, the more energy it contains.

You need to eat a certain number of Calories each day to meet your body's energy needs. This daily energy requirement depends on a person's level of physical activity. It also changes as a person grows and ages. Infants and small children grow very rapidly, so they generally have the highest energy needs. Your current growth and level of physical activity affect the number of Calories you need. The more active you are, the higher your energy needs are.

Carbohydrates

The nutrients called **carbohydrates** (kar boh HY drayts), which are composed of carbon, oxygen, and hydrogen, are a major source of energy. One gram of carbohydrate provides your body with four Calories of energy. Carbohydrates also provide the raw materials to make parts of cells. Based on their chemical structure, carbohydrates are divided into two groups, simple carbohydrates and complex carbohydrates.

Figure 1 Your body obtains energy from carbohydrates. The sugars in fruits are simple carbohydrates. Starch is a complex carbohydrate found in grains and other plant products.

Program Resources

◆ **Unit 4 Resources** 16-1 Lesson Plan, p. 37; 16-1 Section Summary, p. 38

Media and Technology

 Audio CD English-Spanish Summary 16-1

2 Facilitate

Why You Need Food

 Integrating Physics

Describe how the amount of energy supplied by each food is determined. The food is placed into a strong metal container that is surrounded by a container of water. The whole device is insulated from temperature changes and heat loss. The food is burned inside the metal container, and the heat released raises the temperature of the water. By measuring the change in the temperature of the water, the scientists can determine the calorie content of the food. Ask students: **What measurements would scientists have to take before performing the experiment?** *(The mass of the food and of the water, and the initial temperature of the water)* **learning modality: verbal**

Building Inquiry Skills: Calculating

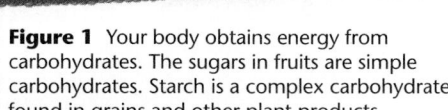

Materials *calorie requirement charts for different age groups, calorie content charts for foods*
Time 20 minutes

Have students use the information to determine their recommended daily calorie intake. Then have them use nutrition textbooks or calorie-counting references to find the calorie content of their favorite foods. They can use the information to calculate the calorie content of a meal that they might have for breakfast, lunch, or dinner. **learning modality: logical/ mathematical**

Ongoing Assessment

Writing Have students explain why they need food and list the six main types of nutrients.

Carbohydrates

Sharpen your Skills

Predicting

Obtain food samples from your teacher. Write a prediction stating whether each food contains starch. Then test your predictions. First, put on your apron. Then use a plastic dropper to add three drops of iodine to each food sample. **CAUTION:** *Iodine can stain skin and clothing. Handle it carefully.* If the iodine turns blue-black, starch is present. Which foods contain starch?

Simple Carbohydrates Simple carbohydrates are also known as sugars. There are many types of sugars. They are found naturally in fruits, milk, and some vegetables. Sugars are also added to foods such as cookies, candies, and soft drinks. One sugar, **glucose** (GLOO kohs), is the major source of energy for your body's cells. However, most foods do not contain large amounts of glucose. The body converts other types of sugars into glucose, the form of sugar the body can use.

Complex Carbohydrates Complex carbohydrates are made up of many sugar molecules linked together in a chain. Starch is a complex carbohydrate found in plant foods such as potatoes, rice, corn, and grain products, such as pasta, cereals, and bread. To use starch as an energy source, your body first breaks it down into smaller, individual sugar molecules. These sugar molecules are then involved in chemical reactions where energy is produced.

Like starch, **fiber** is a complex carbohydrate found in plant foods. However, unlike starch, fiber cannot be broken down into sugar molecules by your body. Instead, the fiber passes through the body and is eliminated. Because your body cannot digest it, fiber is not considered a nutrient. Fiber is an important part of the diet, however, because it helps keep the digestive system functioning properly. Fruits, vegetables, and nuts contain fiber. So do products made with whole grains, such as some breads and cereals.

Nutritionists recommend that 50 to 60 percent of the Calories in a diet come from carbohydrates. When choosing foods containing carbohydrates, it is better to eat more complex carbohydrates than simple carbohydrates. Sugars can give a quick burst of energy, but starches provide a more even, long-term energy source. In addition, foods that are high in starch usually contain a variety of other nutrients. Foods made with a lot of sugar, such as candy, cookies, and soft drinks, usually have few valuable nutrients.

☑ *Checkpoint* *What are the two types of carbohydrates? Give an example of each.*

Figure 2 Fiber is found in fruits, whole-grain foods, and the other foods shown here. *Applying Concepts Why is fiber important in the diet?*

508

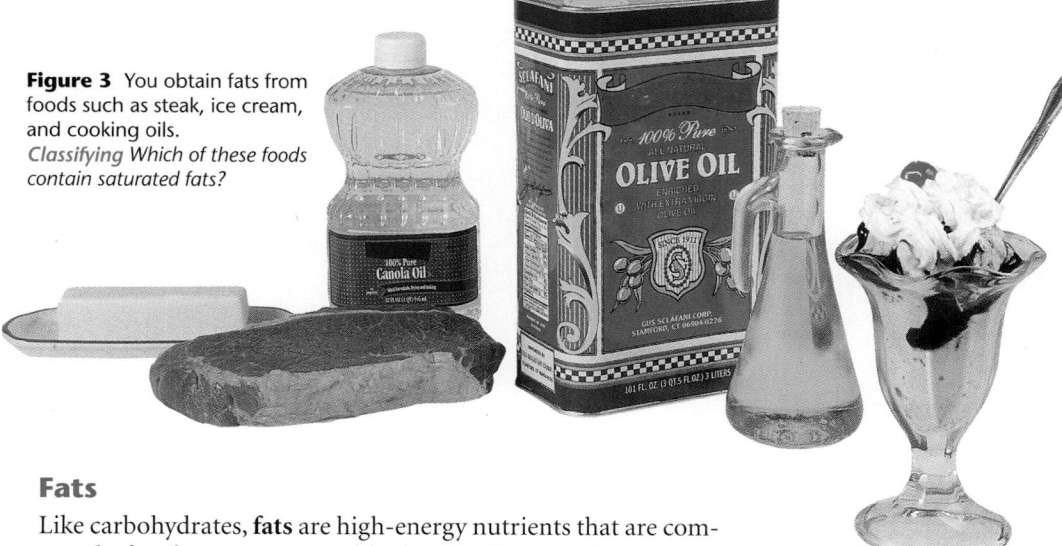

Figure 3 You obtain fats from foods such as steak, ice cream, and cooking oils.
Classifying Which of these foods contain saturated fats?

Fats

Like carbohydrates, **fats** are high-energy nutrients that are composed of carbon, oxygen, and hydrogen. However, fats contain more than twice as much energy as an equal amount of carbohydrates. In addition, fats perform other important functions. For example, they form part of the structure of cells. Fatty tissue also protects and supports your internal organs and acts as insulation to keep heat inside your body.

Fats are classified as either unsaturated fats or saturated fats, based on their chemical structure. **Unsaturated fats** are usually liquid at room temperature. Most oils, such as olive oil and canola oil, are unsaturated fats. Unsaturated fat is also found in some types of seafood, such as salmon. **Saturated fats** are usually solid at room temperature. Animal products, such as meat, dairy products, and egg yolks, contain relatively large amounts of saturated fat. Some oils, such as palm oil and coconut oil, are also high in saturated fat.

Foods that contain saturated fat often contain cholesterol as well. **Cholesterol** (kuh LES tur awl) is a waxy, fatlike substance found only in animal products. Like fats, cholesterol is an important part of your body's cells. But your liver makes all of the cholesterol your body needs. Therefore, cholesterol is not a necessary part of the diet.

Although people need some fats in their diet, they only need a small amount. Nutritionists recommend that no more than 30 percent of the Calories eaten each day come from fats. In particular, people should limit their intake of saturated fats and cholesterol. Extra fats and cholesterol in the diet can lead to a buildup of a fatty material in the blood vessels. This fatty buildup can cause heart disease. You will learn about the connections among fats, cholesterol, and heart disease in Chapter 17.

Math TOOLBOX

Calculating Percent

A percent (%) is a number compared to 100. For example, 30% means 30 out of 100.

Here is how to calculate the percent of Calories from fat in a person's diet. Suppose that a person eats a total of 2,000 Calories in one day. Of those Calories, 500 come from fats.

1. Write the comparison as a fraction:

$$\frac{500}{2,000}$$

2. Multiply the fraction by 100% to express it as a percent:

$$\frac{500}{2,000} \times \frac{100\%}{1} = 25\%$$

Calories from fat made up 25% of the person's diet that day.

Fats

Real-Life Learning

Students may think that eating 30 percent of Calories each day from fat (65 grams from a 2,000 Calorie diet) sounds like too much. Explain that when a person's fat intake is lower, he or she runs the risk of developing a deficiency in chemicals called essential fatty acids, which are building blocks for molecules that help regulate blood pressure, blood clotting, and the immune response. The symptoms of a deficiency are red, irritated skin, infections, and dehydration. Other fats help in the absorption of fat-soluble vitamins, such as A, D, E, and K. In addition, when the fat content of the diet goes below 25 percent, a person feels less satisfied after a meal and may actually eat more. Allow interested students to conduct additional research on diet and nutrition.
learning modality: verbal

Math TOOLBOX

Remind students that when they set up their fractions, they should use the number of Calories in one day as the denominator and the number of Calories from fat as the numerator. To multiply the fraction by 100%, they must multiply the numerators, then divide by the product of the denominators.
Extend Have students find the percent of Calories from carbohydrates in the diet of a person who eats 2,000 Calories per day, of which 1,100 are from carbohydrates. **learning modality: logical/mathematical**

Answers to Self-Assessment

Caption Question

Figure 2 Fiber helps keep the digestive tract functioning properly.
Figure 3 Steak, ice cream, and butter

☑ *Checkpoint*

Simple carbohydrates—sugars; complex carbohydrates—starch

Ongoing Assessment

Skills Check Have students make compare/contrast tables for simple and complex carbohydrates and saturated and unsaturated fats, giving an example of each.

Figure 4 Meats and these other foods are sources of protein.

Proteins

Social Studies CONNECTION

Industry grew rapidly in the 1800s. During that time, many children of factory workers developed rickets, a condition in which the bones become soft. Rickets is caused by a lack of vitamin D. The main source of vitamin D is sunlight, which acts on skin cells to produce the vitamin.

Factory workers in the 1800s often lived in cities with dark, narrow streets. Air pollution from factories also blocked some sunlight. One researcher, Theobald A. Palm, wrote this statement in 1890: "It is in the narrow alleys, the haunts and playgrounds of the children of the poor, that this exclusion of sunlight is at its worst, and it is there that the victims of rickets are to be found in abundance."

In Your Journal

Write several questions that a newspaper reporter might have asked Dr. Palm about rickets among poor city residents. Then write the answers he might have given.

Proteins

Proteins are nutrients that contain nitrogen as well as carbon, hydrogen, and oxygen. Proteins are needed for tissue growth and repair. They also play a part in chemical reactions within cells. Proteins can serve as a source of energy, but they are a less important source of energy than carbohydrates or fats. Foods that contain high amounts of protein include meat, poultry, fish, dairy products, nuts, beans, and lentils. About 12 percent of your daily Calorie intake should come from proteins.

Amino Acids Proteins are made up of small units called **amino acids** (uh MEE noh), which are linked together chemically to form large protein molecules. Thousands of different proteins are built from only about 20 different amino acids. Your body can make about half of the amino acids it needs. The others, called essential amino acids, must come from the foods you eat.

Complete and Incomplete Proteins Proteins from animal sources, such as meat and eggs, are called complete proteins because they contain all the essential amino acids. Proteins from plant sources, such as beans, grains, and nuts, are called incomplete proteins because they are missing one or more essential amino acids. Different plant foods lack different amino acids. Therefore, to obtain all the essential amino acids from plant sources alone, people need to eat a variety of plant foods.

☑ *Checkpoint* What is meant by the term incomplete protein?

Vitamins

The life of a sailor in the 1700s could be difficult indeed. For one thing, sailors on long voyages ate hard, dry biscuits, salted meat, and not much else. In addition, many sailors developed a serious disease called scurvy. People with scurvy suffer from bleeding gums, stiff joints, and sores that do not heal.

510

A Scottish doctor, James Lind, hypothesized that scurvy was the result of the sailors' poor diet. Lind divided sailors with scurvy into groups and fed different foods to each group. The sailors who were fed citrus fruits—oranges and lemons—quickly recovered from the disease. In 1754, Lind recommended that all sailors eat citrus fruits. When Lind's recommendations were finally carried out by the British Navy in 1795, scurvy disappeared from the navy.

Scurvy is caused by the lack of a nutrient called vitamin C. **Vitamins** act as helper molecules in a variety of chemical reactions within the body. The body needs only small amounts of vitamins. Figure 5 lists the vitamins necessary for health. The body can make a few of these vitamins. For example, bacteria that live in your intestines make small amounts of vitamin K.

Figure 5 Both fat-soluble vitamins and water-soluble vitamins are necessary to maintain health. *Interpreting Charts What foods provide a supply of both vitamins A and B$_6$?*

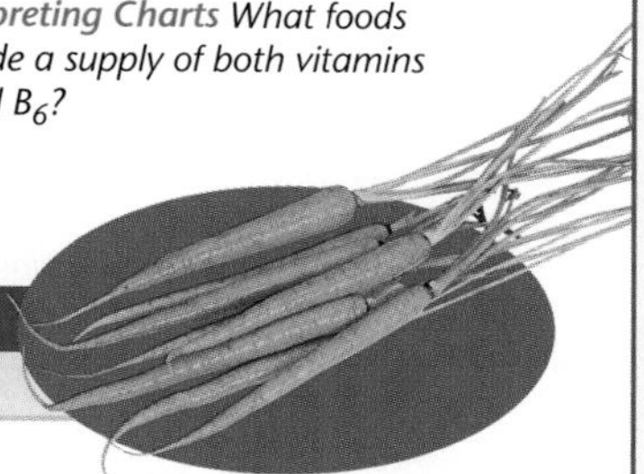

Essential Vitamins

Vitamin	Sources	Function
Fat-soluble		
A	Dairy products; eggs; liver; yellow, orange, and dark green vegetables; fruits	Maintains healthy skin, bones, teeth, and hair; aids vision in dim light
D	Fortified dairy products; fish; eggs; liver; made by skin cells in presence of sunlight	Maintains bones and teeth; helps in the use of calcium and phosphorus
E	Vegetable oils; margarine; green, leafy vegetables; whole-grain foods; seeds; nuts	Aids in maintenance of red blood cells
K	Green, leafy vegetables; milk; liver; made by bacteria in the intestines	Aids in blood clotting
Water-soluble		
B$_1$ (thiamin)	Pork; liver; whole-grain foods; legumes; nuts	Needed for breakdown of carbohydrates
B$_2$ (riboflavin)	Dairy products; eggs; leafy, green vegetables; whole-grain breads and cereals	Needed for normal growth
B$_3$ (niacin)	Many protein-rich foods; milk; eggs; meat; fish; whole-grain foods; nuts; peanut butter	Needed for release of energy
B$_6$ (pyridoxine)	Green and leafy vegetables; meats; fish; legumes; fruits; whole-grain foods	Helps in the breakdown of proteins, fats, and carbohydrates
B$_{12}$	Meats; fish; poultry; dairy products; eggs	Maintains healthy nervous system; needed for red blood cell formation
Biotin	Liver; meat; fish; eggs; legumes; bananas; melons	Aids in the release of energy
Folic acid	Leafy, green vegetables; legumes; seeds; liver	Needed for red blood cell formation
Pantothenic acid	Liver; meats; fish; eggs; whole-grain foods	Needed for the release of energy
C	Citrus fruits; tomatoes; potatoes; dark green vegetables; mangoes	Needed to form connective tissue and fight infection

Social Studies CONNECTION

Explain to students that vitamin D deficiency results in a failure to absorb calcium and phosphorus, causing faulty bone formation. Children with rickets often have deformities of the rib cage and skull, and they also can be bow-legged. Tell students that because milk sold in stores has been fortified with vitamin D, rickets is a rare condition in the United States today. Ask: **Why do you think that vitamin D deficiency used to have a greater incidence in North America or Europe than in tropical countries?** *(Exposure to sunlight is greater in tropical countries, and sunlight is the main source of vitamin D.)*
Extend Allow students to research more about the causes and treatment of rickets.

In Your Journal Sample questions: What can be done to decrease the number of rickets cases? *(Reduce air pollution; build playgrounds where children can be exposed to sunlight.)* What can parents do to keep their children from getting rickets? *(Make sure that their children are exposed to direct sunlight every day.)* **learning modality: verbal**

Using the Visuals: Figure 5

Ask students to identify the water-soluble vitamins. *(B$_1$, B$_2$, B$_3$, B$_6$, B$_{12}$, C, biotin, folic acid, pantothenic acid)* Ask: **Why is it important to include the water-soluble vitamins in your daily diet?** *(These vitamins dissolve in water and are not stored in the body.)* **learning modality: verbal**

Answers to Self-Assessment

Caption Question
Figure 5 Fruits and green vegetables

☑ *Checkpoint*
Proteins from plant sources that are missing one or more of the essential amino acids.

Ongoing Assessment

Writing Have students explain why the proper amounts of proteins and vitamins are important in their daily diets.

Minerals

Using the Visuals: Figure 6
Have students review the minerals in the chart. Ask: **To obtain enough calcium, what foods should people eat if they do not drink milk?** *(Cheese, dark-green leafy vegetables, tofu, legumes)* **What does the body use calcium for?** *(Sample: Building healthy bones and teeth)* **How can vegetarians get enough iron in their diets?** *(By eating green, leafy vegetables; legumes; and dried fruits)* **learning modality: visual**

Inquiry Challenge
Materials *silver nitrate solution from a chemical supply company, test tubes, processed and canned foods and condiments*
Time 20 minutes

Tell students that foods containing salt will react to silver nitrate solution by turning a cloudy white. Ask students to plan experiments to test certain foods for salt. Experiments should include a list of foods to be tested, a control, and a list of materials. Students should predict which foods contain salt, then test each food in a test tube by adding 1 mL of silver nitrate solution. CAUTION: *Silver nitrate solution can cause dark brown stains on skin and clothing. Students should wear aprons, safety goggles, and gloves.* After you review the plans for safety, allow students to carry out their investigations.
cooperative learning

However, people must obtain most vitamins from foods. If people eat a wide variety of foods, they will probably get enough of each vitamin. Most people do not need to take vitamin supplements.

Vitamins are classified as either fat-soluble or water-soluble. Fat-soluble vitamins dissolve in fat, and they are stored in fatty tissues in the body. Vitamins A, D, E, and K are all fat-soluble vitamins. Water-soluble vitamins dissolve in water and are not stored in the body. This fact makes it especially important to include sources of water-soluble vitamins—vitamin C and all the B vitamins—in your diet every day.

Minerals

Like vitamins, minerals are needed by your body in small amounts. **Minerals** are nutrients that are not made by living things. They are present in soil and are absorbed by plants through their roots. You obtain minerals by eating plant foods or animals that have eaten plants. Figure 6 lists some minerals you need. As you know from Chapter 15, calcium is needed for strong bones and teeth. Iron is needed for the proper function of red blood cells.

Figure 6 Eating a variety of foods each day provides your body with the minerals it needs.
Interpreting Charts Which minerals play a role in regulating water levels in the body?

◄ **Source of calcium**

▼ **Source of potassium**

Source of sodium ►

Essential Minerals		
Mineral	**Sources**	**Function**
Calcium	Milk; cheese; dark green, leafy vegetables; tofu; legumes	Helps build bones and teeth; important for blood-clotting, nerve and muscle function
Chlorine	Table salt; soy sauce; processed foods	Helps maintain water balance; aids in digestion
Fluorine	Fluoridated drinking water; fish	Helps form bones and teeth
Iodine	Seafood; iodized salt	Makes up part of hormones that regulate the release of energy
Iron	Red meats; seafood; green, leafy vegetables; legumes; dried fruits	Forms an important part of red blood cells
Magnesium	Green, leafy vegetables; legumes; nuts; whole-grain foods	Needed for normal muscle and nerve function; helps in the release of energy
Phosphorus	Meat; poultry; eggs; fish; dairy products	Needed for healthy bones and teeth; helps in the release of energy
Potassium	Grains; fruits; vegetables; meat; fish	Helps maintain water balance; needed for normal muscle and nerve function
Sodium	Table salt; soy sauce; processed foods	Helps maintain water balance; needed for normal nerve function

512

Background

Facts and Figures Nutritionists, including those at the American Heart Association and the American Dietetic Association, do not recommend that people take vitamin and mineral supplements under normal circumstances. The vitamins and minerals in food are cheaper and absorbed better than supplements. In addition, some vitamins and minerals can be toxic when taken in large amounts over a long period of time. In general, the people who need to take vitamin and mineral supplements include those on weight-loss diets of less than 1,600 calories per day and strict vegetarians who eat no animal products.

Water

Imagine that a boat is sinking. The people are getting into a lifeboat. They have room for one of the following: a bag of fruit, a can of meat, a loaf of bread, or a jug of water. Which item should they choose?

You might be surprised to learn that the lifeboat passengers should choose the water. Although people can probably survive for weeks without food, they will die within days without fresh water. Water is the most abundant substance in the body. It accounts for about 65 percent of the average person's body weight.

Water is the most important nutrient because the body's vital processes—including chemical reactions such as the breakdown of nutrients—take place in water. Water makes up most of the body's fluids, including blood. Nutrients and other important substances are carried throughout the body dissolved in the watery part of the blood. Your body also needs water to produce perspiration.

Under normal conditions, you need to take in about 2 liters of water every day. You can do this by drinking water and other beverages, and by eating foods with lots of water, such as fruits and vegetables. If the weather is hot or you are exercising, you need to drink even more to replace the water that you lose in sweat.

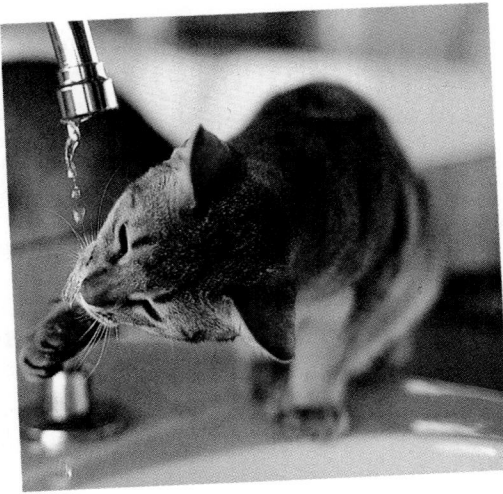

Figure 7 Like all living things, you need water. Without regular water intake, your body cannot carry out the processes that keep you alive.

The Food Guide Pyramid

The **Food Guide Pyramid** was developed by nutritionists to help people plan a healthy diet. **The Food Guide Pyramid classifies foods into six groups. It also indicates how many servings from each group should be eaten every day to maintain a healthy diet.** You can combine the advice within the pyramid with knowledge of your own food preferences. By doing this, you can have a healthy diet containing foods you like.

You can see the six food groups in *Exploring the Food Guide Pyramid* on page 514. Notice that the food group at the base of the pyramid includes foods made from grains, such as bread, cereal, rice, and pasta. This bottom level is the widest part of the pyramid. The large size indicates that these foods should make up the largest part of the diet.

The second level in the pyramid is made of two food groups, the Fruit group and the Vegetable group. Notice that this level is not as wide as the bottom level. This size difference indicates that people need fewer servings of these foods than of foods from the bottom level.

Chapter 16 **513**

Answers to Self-Assessment

Caption Question

Figure 6 Chlorine, potassium, and sodium

Water

Addressing Naive Conceptions

Students may believe they are in no danger of dehydration unless they feel thirsty. Explain that thirst is not an accurate signal of water deficiency. A better indication is a decrease in the production of urine and saliva. By the time the brain signals a feeling of thirst, the water levels in the body may already be too low. **learning modality: verbal**

The Food Guide Pyramid

Building Inquiry Skills: Classifying

Materials *note cards*
Time 15 minutes

Give each student ten note cards and have them list a favorite food on each card. Place students in groups of three or four and have them work together to classify the foods according to the categories in the Food Guide Pyramid. Students can write the classifications on the backs of the cards. Explain that some foods, such as pasta with sauce or pizza, fall into more than one category. Then have groups use their cards to plan nutritious meals. Ask: **Where do most of your favorite foods fall on the Food Guide Pyramid?** *(Answers will vary according to preference.)* Ask students if they need to include more of any food groups in their daily diets. Students can add foods from these food groups to their stack of cards and to their meal plans. **cooperative learning**

Ongoing Assessment

Drawing Have small groups of students prepare posters showing one nutrient needed by the body. Posters should explain why the nutrient is essential and name foods that provide that nutrient.

The Food Guide Pyramid, continued

Building Inquiry Skills: Comparing and Contrasting

Challenge students to identify sources of fat and sugar in the food groups shown in the three bottom levels of the pyramid. Ask: **What foods are naturally high in sugar?** *(Sample: fruits)* **What foods are naturally high in fat?** *(Eggs, nuts, and some meats)* **learning modality: verbal**

EXPLORING
the Food Guide Pyramid

Have students read aloud each of the annotations for the six food groups on the Food Guide Pyramid. Ask: **From which food group should most of your servings come?** *(The bread, cereal, rice, and pasta group)* Have students choose one food that they like from each category. For each food group, ask: **Would you be healthy if you ate only one food from this group, as long as you ate the right number of servings each day? Explain.** *(Probably not. Although the foods in a given category are similar, they do not provide exactly the same nutrients. A variety of each type of food should be eaten from each category.)*

Extend Have students create charts that list the six food groups, then fill in the charts by adding foods that are not listed in the pyramid. **learning modality: visual**

514

EXPLORING *the Food Guide Pyramid*

The Food Guide Pyramid recommends the number of servings that a person should eat each day from six food groups. Note that each number of servings is listed as a range. Active, growing teenagers may need to eat the larger number of servings for each group.

Fats, Oils, and Sweets (Use sparingly.)
Soft drinks, candy, ice cream, mayonnaise, and other foods in this group have few valuable nutrients. In addition, these foods are high in Calories. They should be eaten only in small quantities.

Milk, Yogurt, and Cheese Group (2–3 servings) Milk and other dairy products are rich in proteins, carbohydrates, vitamins, and minerals. Try to select low-fat dairy foods, such as low-fat milk.

Meat, Poultry, Fish, Dry Beans, Eggs, and Nuts Group (2–3 servings)
These foods are high in protein. They also supply vitamins and minerals. Since eggs, nuts, and some meats are high in fat, they should be eaten sparingly.

Vegetable Group (3–5 servings)
Vegetables are low-fat sources of carbohydrates, fiber, vitamins, and minerals.

Fruit Group (2–4 servings)
Fruits are good sources of carbohydrates, fiber, vitamins, and water.

Bread, Cereal, Rice, and Pasta Group (6–11 servings)
The foods at the base of the pyramid are rich in complex carbohydrates and also provide proteins, fiber, vitamins, and some minerals.

● Fat (naturally occurring and added)
▲ Sugars (naturally occurring and added)

514

Background

Facts and Figures In the early 1990s, the traditional four food groups, consisting of meats, dairy products, grains, and fruits and vegetables, were reorganized into the six groups now found in the USDA Food Guide Pyramid. Serving sizes vary according to the foods in the pyramid. For example, in the grain group, one serving may be one slice of bread, 1 oz. of ready-to-eat cereal, or $\frac{1}{2}$ cup of cooked pasta. A serving size in the fruit group may be one medium apple, orange, or banana; in the vegetable group, a serving may be $\frac{1}{2}$ cup cooked vegetables or 1 cup raw leafy vegetables. In the dairy group, 1 cup of milk or $1\frac{1}{2}$ oz. natural cheese counts as a serving. For the meat, dry beans, eggs, and nuts food group, 2 to 3 ounces of cooked meat is a serving; $\frac{1}{2}$ cup of cooked dry beans, 1 egg, or 2 tablespoons of peanut butter count as 1 ounce of meat.

The third level of the pyramid contains the Milk, Yogurt, and Cheese group; and the Meat, Poultry, Fish, Dry Beans, Eggs, and Nuts group. People need still smaller amounts of food from this level.

At the top of the pyramid are foods containing large amounts of fat, sugar, or both. Notice that this is the smallest part of the pyramid. The small size indicates that intake of these foods should be limited. There is a good reason for this advice. Foods in the other groups already contain fats and sugars. Limiting intake of *additional* fats and sugars can help you prevent heart disease and other problems.

☑ *Checkpoint* *What types of foods should make up the largest portion of a person's diet?*

Food Labels

After a long day, you and your friends stop into a store on your way home from school. What snack should you buy? How can you make a wise choice? One thing you can do is to read the information provided on food labels. The United States Food and Drug Administration (FDA) requires that all food items except meat, poultry, fresh vegetables, and fresh fruit must be labeled with specific nutritional information. **Food labels allow you to evaluate a single food as well as to compare the nutritional values of two foods.**

Figure 8 shows a food label that might appear on a box of cereal. Refer to that label as you read about some of the important nutritional information it contains.

Serving Size Notice that the serving size and the number of servings in the container are listed at the top of the label. The FDA has established standard serving sizes for all types of foods. This means that all containers of ice cream, for example, use the same serving size on their labels. The information on the rest of the label, including Calorie counts and nutrient content, is based on the serving size. Therefore, if you eat a portion that's twice as large as the serving size, you'll consume twice the number of Calories and nutrients listed on the label.

Calories from Fat The next item on the food label is the number of Calories in a serving and the number of Calories that come from fat. Notice that a single serving of this cereal supplies the body with 110 Calories of energy.

Figure 8 By law, specific nutritional information must be listed on food labels. *Calculating How many servings of this product would you have to eat to get 90 percent of the Daily Value for iron?*

Nutrition Facts

Serving Size	1 cup (30g)
Servings Per Container	About 10

Amount Per Serving

Calories 110	Calories from Fat 15

	% Daily Value*
Total Fat 2g	3%
Saturated Fat 0g	0%
Cholesterol 0mg	0%
Sodium 280mg	12%
Total Carbohydrate 22g	7%
Dietary Fiber 3g	12%
Sugars 1g	
Protein 3g	

Vitamin A	10%	•	Vitamin C	20%
Calcium	4%	•	Iron	45%

* Percent Daily Values are based on a 2,000 Calorie diet. Your daily values may be higher or lower depending on your caloric needs:

	Calories	2,000	2,500
Total Fat	Less than	65g	80g
Sat. Fat	Less than	20g	25g
Cholesterol	Less than	300mg	300mg
Sodium	Less than	2,400mg	2,400mg
Total Carbohydrate		300g	375g
Fiber		25g	30g

Calories per gram:
Fat 9 • Carbohydrate 4 • Protein 4

Ingredients: Whole grain oats, sugar, salt, milled corn, oat fiber, dried whey, honey, almonds, d...

Program Resources

◆ **Product Testing Activities** by *Consumer Reports,* "Testing Cereals," pp. 1–8

Media and Technology

 Transparencies "The Food Guide Pyramid," Transparency 65

Answers to Self-Assessment

Caption Question

Figure 8 Two

☑ *Checkpoint*

Foods made from grains, such as bread, cereal, rice, and pasta

Food Labels

Building Inquiry Skills: Making Generalizations

Ask students to explain why they think foods such as meat, poultry, and fresh fruits and vegetables are not required to have food labels. *(Because these are unprocessed foods. All apples, for example, have basically the same contents and nutritional value.)* **learning modality: verbal**

Real-Life Learning

Bring—or have students bring—a wide variety of food labels to class. Group students who are less proficient in English with those who are more proficient. Divide the food labels among the groups and have group members work together to read and interpret the labels. Ask students questions such as these: **Which of these cereals is higher in fiber? If you were on a low-sodium diet, which of these foods should you avoid?** **limited English proficiency**

Building Inquiry Skills: Calculating

Give students the following example or have them use labels from snacks to practice finding the percent of Calories that come from fat.
Example: 30 potato chips

Calories	340
Calories from Fat	200

$\frac{200}{340} \times \frac{100\%}{1} = 58.8\%$

Ask: **In order to follow the Food Guide Pyramid, do the Calories from fat in every single food you eat have to be less than 30%?** *(No. Some foods can be higher in fat as long as others are lower. No more than 30% of the entire day's Calories should come from fat.)* **learning modality: logical/mathematical**

Ongoing Assessment

Drawing Have students draw the Food Guide Pyramid, then label the six food groups and the number of servings for each group.

 Students can save their drawings in their portfolios.

3 Assess

Section 1 Review Answers

1. Carbohydrates, fats, proteins, vitamins, minerals, water
2. The Food Guide Pyramid classifies food into six groups. It indicates how many servings from each group should be eaten on a daily basis to maintain a healthy diet.
3. Nutrition fact labels include information about the ingredients and quantities of different nutrients in foods. This information allows a person to evaluate the nutritional contents of a single food and to compare foods.
4. Complex carbohydrates provide more even, long-term energy than do simple carbohydrates. Foods high in complex carbohydrates usually provide more nutrients than simple carbohydrate foods.
5. Proteins in plant foods are incomplete proteins. Therefore, no plant food by itself supplies all the essential amino acids. To obtain all the essential amino acids, vegetarians need to eat a variety of foods.

CHAPTER PROJECT

Check Your Progress

Remind students to record foods soon after they eat, as it can be difficult to remember later. Encourage students not to modify their diets during the project. Recording what they actually eat will help them better understand how their habits affect their health.

Performance Assessment

Writing Provide students with food labels and have them write captions describing the information given on different parts of the labels.

Portfolio Students can save their labels in their portfolios.

Figure 9 If you are very active, you need to eat more servings to provide your body with the Calories and nutrients you need.

Recall that no more than 30 percent of the Calories you consume should come from fats. To calculate whether a specific food falls within this guideline, divide the number of Calories from fat by the total number of Calories, then multiply by 100%. For this cereal,

$$\frac{15}{110} \times \frac{100\%}{1} = 13.6\%.$$

That number shows you that a serving of this cereal is well within the recommended limits for fat intake.

Daily Values Locate the % Daily Value column in Figure 8. The **Percent Daily Value** indicates how the nutritional content of one serving fits into the diet of a person who consumes a total of 2,000 Calories a day. One serving of this cereal contains 280 milligrams of sodium. That's 12 percent of the total amount of sodium a person should consume in one day.

Ingredients Packaged foods, such as crackers and soup mixes, usually contain a mixture of ingredients. The food label lists those ingredients in order by weight, starting with the main ingredient. In a breakfast cereal, for example, that may be corn, oats, rice, or wheat. Often, sugar and salt are added for flavor. The list can alert you to substances that have been added to a food to improve its flavor or color, or to keep it from spoiling. In addition, some people can become sick or break out in a rash if they eat certain substances. By reading ingredient lists, people can find foods that contain nutrients they need and avoid foods that contain substances to which they are allergic.

Section 1 Review

1. List the six nutrients that are needed by the body.
2. What information does the Food Guide Pyramid provide? Into how many groups are foods classified?
3. Explain how food labels can help a person make healthy food choices.
4. Why should you eat more complex carbohydrates than simple carbohydrates?
5. **Thinking Critically Applying Concepts** Why is it especially important that vegetarians eat a varied diet?

516

CHAPTER PROJECT

Check Your Progress

By now, you should have given your teacher your plan for keeping your food log. Adjust the plan as your teacher suggests. Then start your three days of record-keeping. If possible, your record-keeping should span two weekdays and one weekend day. Be sure to keep an accurate record of all the foods and beverages you consume. (*Hint:* Either make your log portable, or plan a method for recording your food intake when you're away from home.)

Media and Technology

Interactive Student Tutorial CD-ROM Chapter 16

Exploring Life Science Videodisc Unit 4, Side 1, "You Are What You Eat"

Chapter 4

Program Resources

◆ **Unit 4 Resources** 16-1 Review and Reinforce, p. 39; 16-1 Enrich, p. 40

Iron for Breakfast

Have you ever looked at the nutrition facts on a cereal box? Some of the listed nutrients occur naturally in the cereal. Others are added as the cereal is processed. In this lab, you will look for evidence that extra iron has been added to some cereals.

Problem

How can you test whether iron has been added to cereals?

Skills Focus

observing, predicting, interpreting data

Materials

long bar magnet	balance
white paper towels	plastic spoon
instant oatmeal	warm water
watch or clock	
wooden dowel	
2 dry breakfast cereals	
3 sealable plastic freezer bags	
plastic jar with sealable cover	

Procedure

1. Read the nutrition facts listed on the packages of the cereals that you'll be testing. Record the percentage of iron listed for each of the cereals.
2. Put a paper towel on the pan of a balance. Use a spoon to measure out 50 grams of instant oatmeal. **CAUTION:** *Do not eat any of the cereals in this lab.*
3. Place the oatmeal in a plastic bag. Push down gently on the bag to remove most of the air, then seal the bag. Roll a dowel over the oatmeal repeatedly to crush it into a fine powder.
4. Pour the powdered oatmeal into a plastic jar. Add water to the jar so that the water line is about five centimeters above the oatmeal.
5. Stir the mixture with a bar magnet for about five minutes.
6. Rinse the bar magnet gently in clear water. Wipe the magnet with a white paper towel. Observe the particles on the paper towel. Record your observations.
7. Repeat Steps 2 through 6 with your other cereal samples.

Analyze and Conclude

1. Describe the material you saw on the paper towel. What evidence do you have that this material is iron?
2. Which sample appeared to have the most added iron? The least? Were those results consistent with the listed amounts?
3. Why is it likely that any iron metal present in the cereal was added during the processing?
4. What roles does iron play in the body?
5. **Apply** Why might adding iron to breakfast cereal be a good way to ensure that children receive an adequate amount of that mineral?

More to Explore

Read the labels on five snack foods. Make a bar graph showing their iron content.

---

4. Sample: Iron becomes part of the hemoglobin, the molecule that makes blood red.
5. Sample: Children can sometimes be picky eaters, but they often eat breakfast cereal.

Extending the Inquiry

More to Explore Make sure students choose a variety of foods and compare similar serving sizes.

Safety

Remind students not to eat any of the cereals. Review the safety guidelines in Appendix A.

Program Resources

◆ **Unit 4 Resources** Chapter 16 Real-World Lab, pp. 49–50

You, the Consumer

Iron for Breakfast

Preparing for Inquiry

Key Concept Students will use the properties of elemental iron to test whether iron has been added to cereals.

Skills Objectives Students will be able to
◆ observe how breakfast cereals react when a magnet is used to test for the presence of iron;
◆ predict the results of the test based on the information contained in the food label for the cereal;
◆ interpret data to determine whether the cereals are fortified with iron.

Time 55 minutes

Advance Planning You can purchase bar magnets from a supply company or hardware store. Make sure at least one cereal is high in iron content.

Guiding Inquiry

Invitation Ask students: **When you see cereals that are fortified with essential vitamins and minerals, what do you think some of the minerals are?** *(Samples: iron, calcium, zinc)* Show students a periodic table and have them find these minerals.

Introducing the Procedure

Ask students how they are going to separate the iron from the cereal in this activity. *(Iron can be mechanically separated because it will be strongly attracted to the magnet.)*

Troubleshooting the Experiment

Make sure students rinse the magnet very gently after stirring the cereal for 5 minutes.

Analyze and Conclude

1. Students should describe small gray filings. It was attracted to the magnet.
2. Answers will vary; fortified cereals usually have the most iron. Students should compare their observations with the labels.
3. The plant products from which cereal is made usually do not contain any metals.

SECTION
2 The Digestive Process Begins

Objective

After completing the lesson, students will be able to

◆ describe the general functions carried out by the digestive system and the specific functions of the mouth, esophagus, and stomach.

Key Terms digestion, absorption, saliva, enzyme, epiglottis, esophagus, mucus, peristalsis, stomach

1 Engage/Explore

Activating Prior Knowledge

Ask students to describe what they think happens after they eat a food. Ask: **How does your body obtain nutrients from the food?** Give students a specific example, such as a baked potato, and have them discuss what they know about the processes that change it from a potato to nutrients and energy.

DISCOVER

Materials *2 plastic jars with lids, water, sugar cubes*
Time 15 minutes
Tips Pair students; each student can shake one jar. Make sure students understand that the jars must receive equal shaking. Have students synchronize their shaking techniques. Have students predict what will happen to the sugar in each jar.
Expected Outcome The crushed sugar cube will dissolve more quickly than the whole cube.
Think It Over Students should predict that a large piece of food would take longer to digest than one that has been cut up into many small pieces.

DISCOVER .... ACTIVITY

How Can You Speed up Digestion?

1. Obtain two plastic jars with lids. Fill the jars with equal amounts of water.

2. At the same time, place a whole sugar cube into one jar. Place a crushed sugar cube into the other jar.

3. Fasten the lids on the jars. Holding one jar in each hand, shake the two jars gently and equally.

4. Place the jars on a flat surface. Observe whether the whole cube or the crushed cube dissolves faster.

Think It Over
Predicting Use the results of this activity to predict which would take longer to digest: a large piece of food or one that has been cut up into many small pieces. Explain your answer.

GUIDE FOR READING

◆ What general functions are carried out in the digestive system?

Reading Tip Before you read, preview the headings in this section. Predict the functions of the mouth, the esophagus, and the stomach.

Dr. William Beaumont ▼

In June of 1822, nineteen-year-old Alexis St. Martin was wounded in the stomach while hunting. William Beaumont, a doctor with the United States Army, saved St. Martin's life. However, the wound left an opening in St. Martin's stomach that never closed completely. Beaumont realized that by looking through the opening, he could observe what was happening inside St. Martin's stomach.

Beaumont observed that milk changed chemically inside the stomach. He hypothesized that chemical reactions inside the stomach broke down foods into smaller particles. To test his hypothesis, Beaumont removed liquid from St. Martin's stomach. He had the liquid analyzed to determine what materials it contained. The stomach liquid contained an acid that could break down foods into simpler substances.

Functions of the Digestive System

Beaumont's observations helped scientists understand the role of the stomach in the digestive system. The digestive system has three main functions. **First, it breaks down food into molecules the body can use. Then, the molecules are absorbed into the blood and carried throughout the body. Finally, wastes are eliminated from the body.**

The process by which your body breaks down food into small nutrient molecules is called **digestion.** There are two kinds of digestion—mechanical and chemical. In mechanical digestion, foods are physically broken down into smaller pieces. Mechanical digestion occurs when you bite into

518

READING STRATEGIES

Reading Tip Students may predict that the mouth breaks up food, the esophagus moves food to the stomach, and the stomach digests food. Have volunteers offer predictions about the functions of the mouth, esophagus, and stomach. Write these on the board. After students have

read the section, work as a class to confirm or revise the predictions.
Vocabulary Have students list boldfaced vocabulary words from the section on a sheet of paper and write a definition for each term using their own words. Students can use their lists as study guides.

a sandwich and chew it into small pieces. In chemical digestion, chemicals produced by the body break foods into their smaller chemical building blocks. For example, the starch in bread is broken down into individual sugar molecules.

After your food is digested, the molecules are ready to be transported throughout your body. **Absorption** (ab SAWRP shun) is the process by which nutrient molecules pass through the wall of your digestive system into your blood. Materials that are not absorbed, such as fiber, are eliminated from the body as wastes.

Figure 10 shows the organs of the digestive system, which is about nine meters long from beginning to end. As food moves through the digestive system, the processes of digestion, absorption, and elimination occur one after the other in an efficient, continuous process.

Figure 10 The work of the digestive system is to break down food into simpler substances that can be used by the body. *Interpreting Diagrams Through which organs does food pass after leaving the mouth?*

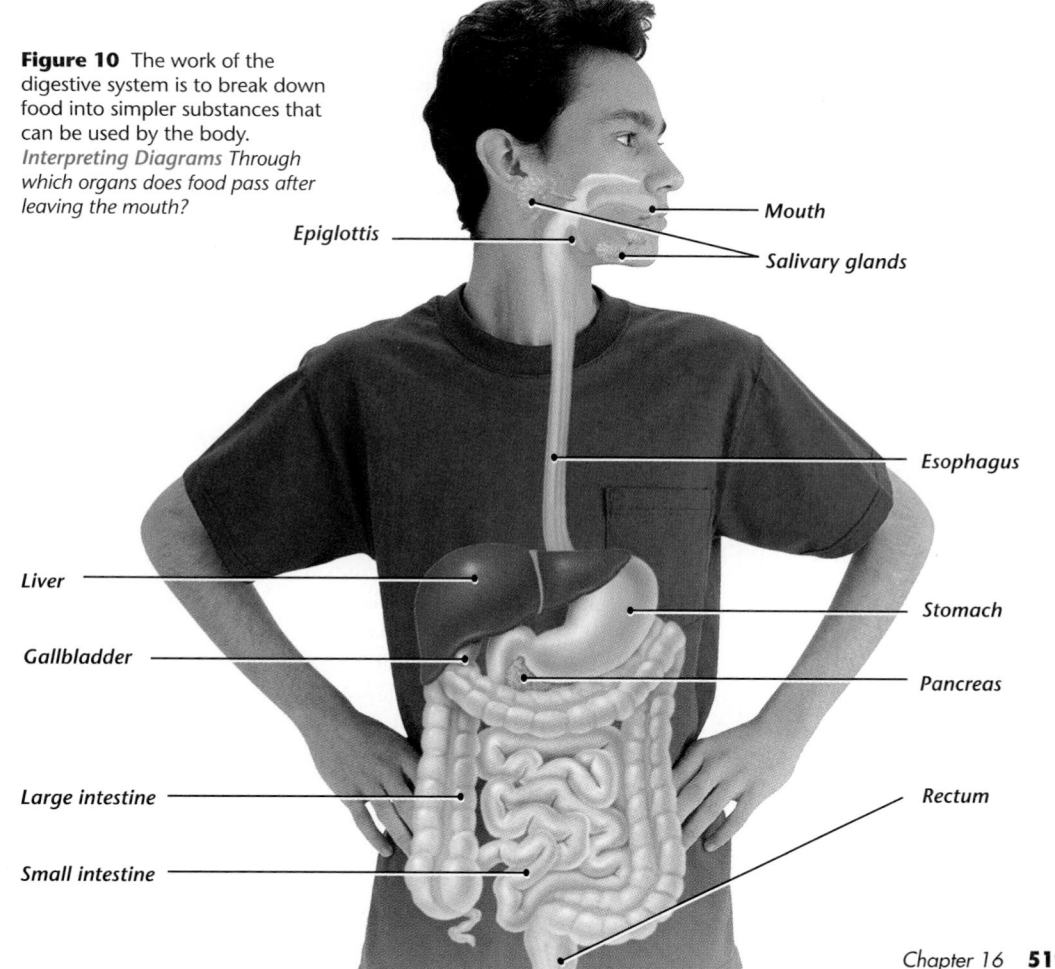

Mouth
Epiglottis
Salivary glands
Esophagus
Liver
Stomach
Gallbladder
Pancreas
Large intestine
Rectum
Small intestine

Functions of the Digestive System

Including All Students

This activity will benefit students who are still mastering English. Have students make a diagram of the human digestive system. Students should label each of the organs in their native languages and in English. Have students practice saying the names of the organs aloud in each language. As they study, students can refer to their diagrams to help them learn the names for each organ. **limited English proficiency**

Using the Visuals: Figure 10

Have students trace the path of food through the digestive system, beginning with the mouth and ending with the rectum. Make certain that students realize that food does not pass through the liver or pancreas. Have students compare the relative lengths and diameters of the small and large intestines. Note that the twists and turns in the small intestine enable it to fit compactly into the abdomen. **learning modality: visual**

Ongoing Assessment

Writing Have students write a short description of the digestive process, explaining what happens to a food when it is digested and absorbed. *(Students should state that mechanical and chemical digestion break the food down first into small pieces and then into individual molecules. These molecules are absorbed into cells in the intestines and are then transported through the body.)*

Portfolio Students can save their descriptions in their portfolios.

Program Resources

◆ **Unit 4 Resources** 16-2 Lesson Plan, p. 41; 16-2 Section Summary, p. 42

Media and Technology

 Audio CD English-Spanish Summary 16-2

 Transparencies "The Digestive System," Transparency 66

Answers to Self-Assessment

Caption Question

Figure 10 The esophagus, the stomach, the small intestine, and the large intestine

The Mouth

Figure 11 Mechanical digestion begins in the mouth, where the teeth cut and tear food into smaller pieces. *Observing Which teeth are specialized for biting into a juicy apple?*

   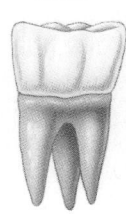

Incisor   *Canine*   *Premolar*   *Molar*

The Mouth

Have you ever walked past a bakery or restaurant and noticed your mouth watering? Smelling or even just thinking about food when you're hungry is enough to start your mouth watering. This response isn't accidental. Your body is responding to hunger and thoughts of food by preparing for the delicious meal it expects. The fluid released when your mouth waters is called **saliva** (suh LY vuh). Saliva plays an important role in both the mechanical and chemical digestive processes that take place in the mouth.

Mechanical Digestion The process of mechanical digestion begins as you take your first bite of food. Your teeth carry out the first stage of mechanical digestion. Your center teeth, or incisors (in SY zurz), cut the food into bite-sized pieces. On either side of the incisors are sharp, pointy teeth called canines (KAY nynz). These teeth tear and slash the food in your mouth into smaller pieces. Behind the canines are the premolars and molars, which crush and grind the food. As the teeth do their work, saliva mixes with the pieces of food, moistening them into one slippery mass.

Chemical Digestion Like mechanical digestion, chemical **INTEGRATING CHEMISTRY** digestion begins in the mouth. If you take a bite of a cracker and roll it around your mouth, the cracker begins to taste sweet. It tastes sweet because a chemical in the saliva has broken down the starch in the cracker into sugar molecules. Chemical digestion—the breakdown of complex molecules into simpler ones—has taken place. Chemical digestion is accomplished by enzymes. An **enzyme** is a protein that speeds up chemical reactions in the body. The chemical in saliva that digests starch is an enzyme. Your body produces many different enzymes. Each enzyme has a specific chemical shape. Its shape enables it to take part in only one kind of chemical reaction. For example, the enzyme that breaks down starch into sugars cannot break down proteins into amino acids.

The Esophagus

If you've ever choked on food, someone may have said that your food "went down the wrong way." That's because there are two openings at the back of your mouth. One opening leads to your windpipe, which carries air into your lungs. Usually, your body keeps food out of your windpipe. As you swallow, muscles in your throat move the food downward. While this happens, a flap of tissue called the **epiglottis** (ep uh GLAHT is) seals off your windpipe, preventing the food from entering. As you swallow, food goes into the **esophagus** (ih SAHF uh gus), a muscular tube that connects the mouth to the stomach. The esophagus is lined with mucus. **Mucus** is a thick, slippery substance produced by the body. In the digestive system, mucus makes food easier to swallow and to be moved along.

Food remains in the esophagus for only about 10 seconds. After food enters the esophagus, contractions of smooth muscles push the food toward the stomach. These involuntary waves of muscle contraction are called **peristalsis** (pehr ih STAWL sis). The action of peristalsis is shown in Figure 12. Peristalsis also occurs in the stomach and farther down the digestive system. These muscular waves keep food moving in one direction.

☑ *Checkpoint* *How is food prevented from entering the windpipe?*

Modeling Peristalsis

1. Obtain a clear, flexible plastic straw.

2. Put on your goggles. Hold the straw vertically and insert a small bead into the top of the straw. The bead should fit snugly into the straw. Do not blow into the straw.

3. Pinch the straw above the bead so that the bead begins to move down the length of the tubing.

4. Repeat Step 3 until the bead exits the straw.

Making Models How does this action compare with peristalsis? What do the bead and the straw represent in this model?

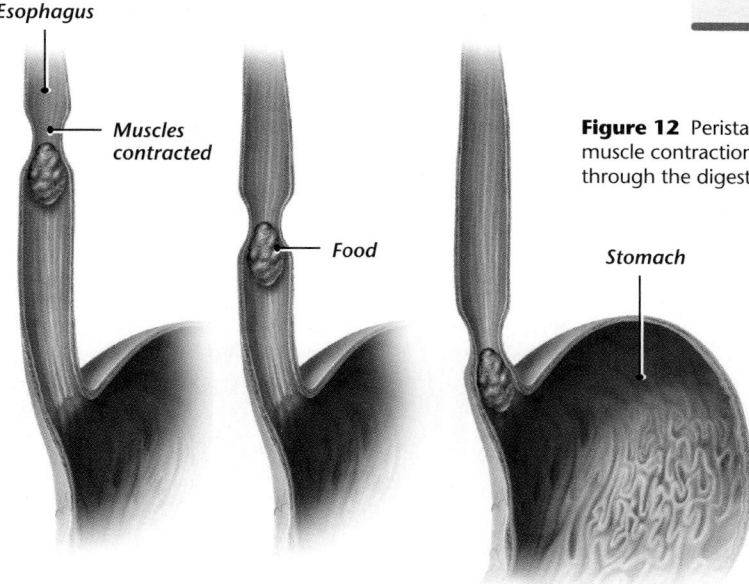

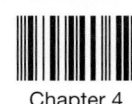

Esophagus

Muscles contracted

Food

Figure 12 Peristalsis—waves of muscle contractions—pushes food through the digestive system.

Stomach

Answers to Self-Assessment

Caption Question

Figure 11 Incisors

☑ *Checkpoint*

The epiglottis seals off the windpipe as you swallow.

The Esophagus

TRY THIS

Skills Focus making models

Materials *20-cm clear flexible plastic straw (about 6 mm in diameter); round bead (5–6 mm in diameter)*

Time 15 minutes

Tips You may substitute a seed, pebble, or other object of similar size for the bead.

Making Models The pinching motion models the muscular contractions of the muscles around the esophagus. The straw models the esophagus. The bead represents food.

Extend Challenge students to modify their models to show how food is prevented from entering the windpipe. *(Students can tape their straw to another straw that represents the windpipe and cut a flap at the top to show the action of the epiglottis.)* **learning modality: kinesthetic**

Ongoing Assessment

Organizing Information Have students make a compare/contrast table to show similarities and differences between mechanical and chemical digestion.

The Stomach

Integrating Chemistry

Ask students: **Why do you think people take antacids?** *(People take antacids when they suffer from indigestion.)* Explain that indigestion can be caused by excess hydrochloric acid in the stomach. Antacids react chemically with hydrochloric acid in such a way that stomach acidity is reduced. One antacid is magnesium hydroxide, or $Mg(OH)_2$. A suspension of magnesium hydroxide in water is called milk of magnesia because of its milky color. **learning modality: verbal**

Building Inquiry Skills: Interpreting Diagrams

Have students work in pairs to draw diagrams of the digestive system as shown in Figure 10. Students should use the information in Figure 13 to label each organ with its name and a description of its role in digestion, including the enzymes and secretions that it produces and what types of nutrients it digests. Then have each student write five questions about the digestive system. Pairs of students can quiz each other, using the diagrams to answer the questions. **learning modality: visual**

Portfolio Students can save their diagrams in their portfolios.

The Stomach

When food leaves the esophagus, it enters the **stomach,** a J-shaped, muscular pouch located in the abdomen. As you eat, your stomach expands to hold all of the food that you swallow. An average adult's stomach holds about 2 liters of food.

Most mechanical digestion occurs in the stomach. Three strong layers of muscle contract to produce a churning motion. This action squeezes the food, mixing it with fluids in somewhat the same way that clothes and soapy water are mixed in a washing machine.

INTEGRATING CHEMISTRY While mechanical digestion is taking place, so too is chemical digestion. The churning of the stomach mixes food with digestive juice, a fluid produced by cells in the lining of the stomach.

Digestive juice contains the enzyme pepsin. Pepsin chemically digests the proteins in your food, breaking them down into amino acids. Digestive juice also contains hydrochloric acid, a very strong acid. This acid would burn a hole in clothes if it were spilled on them. Without this strong acid, however, your stomach could not function properly. First, pepsin works best in an acidic environment. Second, the acid kills many bacteria that you swallow along with your food.

Since the acid is so strong, you may wonder why it doesn't burn a hole in your stomach. The reason is that digestive juice

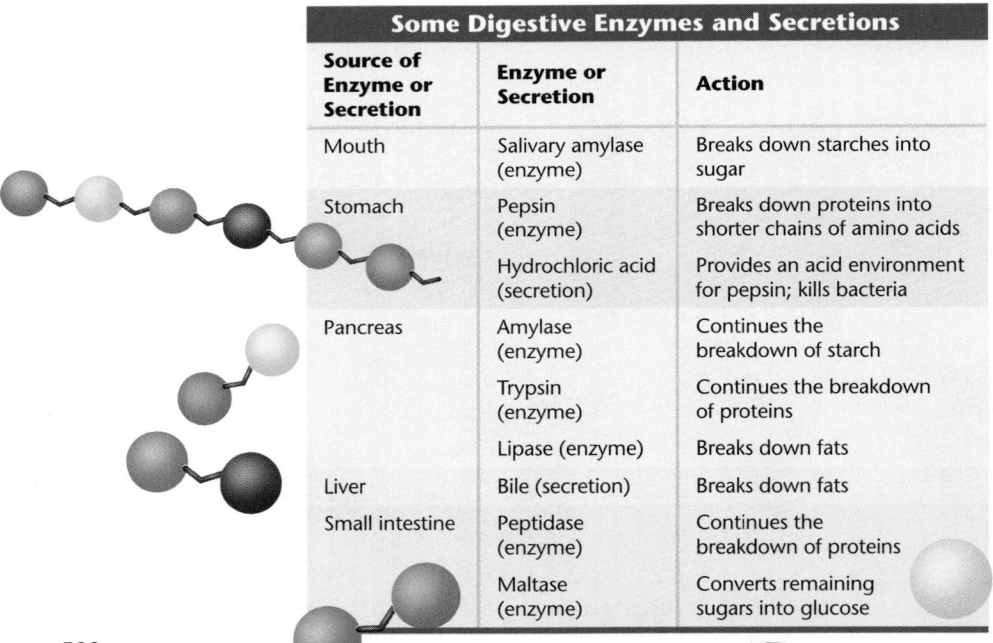

Figure 13 As food passes through the digestive system, the digestive juices gradually break down large food molecules into smaller ones. *Interpreting Charts Which enzymes aid in protein digestion?*

Some Digestive Enzymes and Secretions		
Source of Enzyme or Secretion	Enzyme or Secretion	Action
Mouth	Salivary amylase (enzyme)	Breaks down starches into sugar
Stomach	Pepsin (enzyme)	Breaks down proteins into shorter chains of amino acids
	Hydrochloric acid (secretion)	Provides an acid environment for pepsin; kills bacteria
Pancreas	Amylase (enzyme)	Continues the breakdown of starch
	Trypsin (enzyme)	Continues the breakdown of proteins
	Lipase (enzyme)	Breaks down fats
Liver	Bile (secretion)	Breaks down fats
Small intestine	Peptidase (enzyme)	Continues the breakdown of proteins
	Maltase (enzyme)	Converts remaining sugars into glucose

522

Background

Integrating Science Ulcers are sores in the lining of the stomach. Most ulcers are caused by bacteria called *Heliobacter pylori*—*H. pylori* for short. These bacteria can live in the acid environment of the stomach because they produce an enzyme that neutralizes the acid. *H. pylori* are spiral-shaped. They embed themselves into the lining of the stomach, and produce substances that decrease the amount of mucus, making the stomach lining more vulnerable to stomach acid and pepsin. *H. pylori* can attach to stomach cells, producing inflammation and stimulating the stomach to make more acid.

Ulcers caused by *H. pylori* can be treated with antibiotics. Researchers do not know why some people infected with *H. pylori* get ulcers and some do not. People seem to be infected as children, and the infection lasts for life, even without visible symptoms.

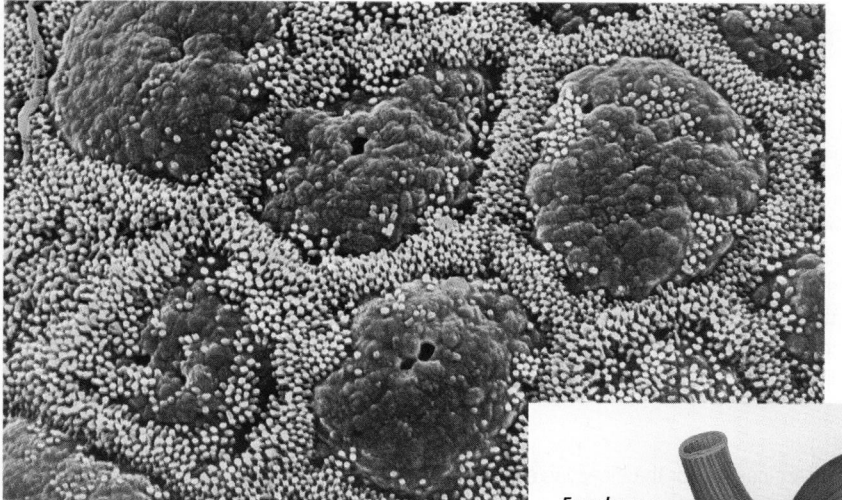

Figure 14 The stomach walls (left) produce mucus, shown here in yellow. Mucus protects the stomach from its own acid and enzymes. The stomach has powerful muscles (below) that help grind up food.

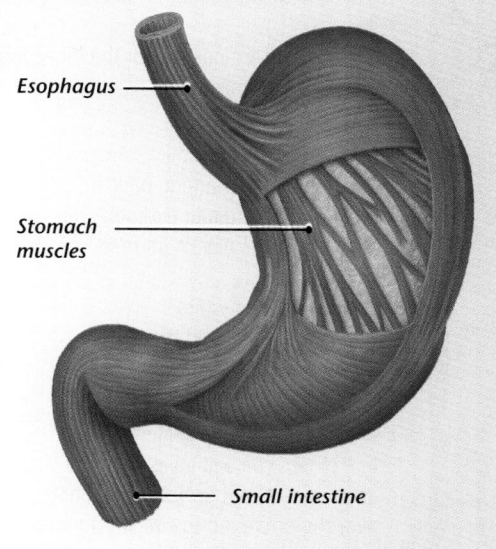

Esophagus

Stomach muscles

Small intestine

also contains mucus, which coats and protects the lining of your stomach. In addition, the cells that line the stomach are quickly replaced when they are damaged or worn out.

Food remains in the stomach until all of the solid material has been broken down into liquid form. A few hours after you finish eating, the stomach completes mechanical digestion of the food. By that time, most of the proteins have been chemically digested into shorter chains of amino acids. The food, now a thick liquid, is released into the next part of the digestive system. That is where final chemical digestion and absorption will take place.

Section 2 Review

1. List the functions of the digestive system.
2. What role does saliva play in digestion?
3. Describe peristalsis and explain its function in the digestive system.
4. What is the function of pepsin?
5. **Thinking Critically Predicting** If your stomach could no longer produce acid, how do you think that would affect digestion?

Check Your Progress CHAPTER PROJECT
By this point, you should have completed three full days of record keeping. Now create bar graphs to compare your food intake to the recommended numbers of servings in the Food Guide Pyramid. Analyze your graphs to identify changes you could make in your diet.

3 Assess

Section 2 Review Answers

1. To break down food into molecules that can be used by the body; to absorb the food molecules into the blood; to eliminate wastes from the body
2. Saliva helps with the mechanical digestion of food by moistening the food so it can be easily swallowed. Enzymes in the saliva begin the breakdown of starches into simple sugars as part of chemical digestion.
3. Peristalsis consists of involuntary waves of muscle contractions that help push food through the digestive system.
4. Pepsin is an enzyme in the digestive juice produced in the stomach; it breaks down proteins into shorter chains of amino acids.
5. Without acid, pepsin cannot function properly, and therefore protein digestion couldn't take place in the stomach.

Check Your Progress CHAPTER PROJECT
Students should identify the categories on the Food Guide Pyramid for each food they list. Provide resources for students to find the established serving sizes for a variety of foods. As students analyze their graphs, remind them that they may need to eat more than 2,000 Calories if they are very active or experiencing growth.

Program Resources

◆ **Product Testing Activities by** *Consumer Reports,* "Testing Antacids," pp. 1–8
◆ **Unit 4 Resources** 16-2 Review and Reinforce, p. 43; 16-2 Enrich, p. 44

Answers to Self-Assessment

Caption Question
Figure 13 Pepsin, trypsin, and peptidase

Performance Assessment

Organizing Information Have students prepare flowcharts that show the process of digestion, from the mouth through mechanical digestion of food in the stomach.

 Students can save their flowcharts in their portfolios.

As The Stomach Churns

Preparing for Inquiry

Key Concept In the stomach, proteins are digested by the chemicals in the digestive juices and by the mechanical processes as the stomach churns.

Skills Objectives Students will be able to
♦ predict the conditions necessary for protein to be digested in the stomach;
♦ conduct controlled experiments to test their predictions;
♦ observe the reactions that occur and identify the relationship between the manipulated variable and the responding variable;
♦ interpret data and draw conclusions.

Time 60–80 minutes

Advance Planning Obtain blue litmus paper and a 0.2% solution of hydrochloric acid. Boil eggs and cut whites into 1-cm cubes. Prepare enough eggs for students to have 3 cubes per test tube.

Guiding Inquiry

Invitation Ask students to name some foods that contain protein. *(Sample: Meat, poultry, fish, dairy, nuts, beans, and lentils)* Ask: **What role does protein play in nutrition?** *(It aids in tissue growth and repair.)* Have students think about the environment in the stomach. Ask: **How does it feel when stomach fluids enter the esophagus, as in heartburn?** *(It burns.)* Ask: **Why might it be important for the stomach to be so acidic?** *(To dissolve needed nutrients like proteins)*

Introducing the Procedure
♦ Discuss safety issues. Hydrochloric acid can cause burns. Make sure all students, teachers, and visitors wear goggles throughout the lab.
♦ Review the litmus test procedure. Discuss ways to prevent cross-contamination of the test tubes by using a clean stirrer for each litmus test, and by using clean graduated cylinders when adding fluids to a new test tube.

AS THE STOMACH CHURNS

The proteins you eat are constructed of large, complex molecules. Your body begins to break down those complex molecules in the stomach. In this lab, you will draw conclusions about the process by which proteins are digested.

Problem

What conditions are needed for the digestion of proteins in the stomach?

Materials

test tube rack	marking pencil
pepsin	dilute hydrochloric acid
water	plastic stirrers
litmus paper	
cubes of boiled egg white	
10-mL plastic graduated cylinder	
4 test tubes with stoppers	

Procedure

1. In this lab, you will investigate how acidic conditions affect protein digestion. Read over the entire lab to see what materials you will be testing. Write a prediction stating which conditions you think will speed up protein digestion. Then copy the data table into your notebook.

2. Label four test tubes *A*, *B*, *C*, and *D* and place them in a test tube rack.

3. In this lab, the protein you will test is boiled egg white, which has been cut into cubes about 1 cm on each side. Add 3 cubes to each test tube. Note and record the size and overall appearance of the cubes in each test tube. **CAUTION:** *Do not put any egg white into your mouth.*

4. Use a graduated cylinder to add 10 mL of the enzyme pepsin to test tube A. Observe the egg white cubes to determine whether an immediate reaction takes place. Record your observations under *Day 1* in your data table. If no changes occur, write "no immediate reaction."

5. Use a clean graduated cylinder to add 5 mL of pepsin to test tube B. Then rinse the graduated cylinder and add 5 mL of water to test tube B. Observe whether or not an immediate reaction takes place.

6. Use a clean graduated cylinder to add 10 mL of hydrochloric acid to test tube C. Observe whether or not an immediate reaction takes place. **CAUTION:** *Hydrochloric acid can burn skin and clothing. Avoid direct contact with it. Wash any splashes or spills with plenty of water, and notify your teacher.*

DATA TABLE

Test Tube	Egg White Appearance		Litmus Color	
	Day 1	Day 2	Day 1	Day 2
A				
B				
C				
D				

Troubleshooting the Experiment
Students' results may be unconvincing if the egg white cubes are too large or if the hydrochloric acid solution is too weak.

Expected Outcome
♦ Students will not observe changes in egg white appearance in test tubes A, B, or C. After one day, the egg white in test tube D will begin to dissolve, then disappear.
♦ The solution of pepsin and hydrochloric acid will digest protein. Pepsin is only effective in an acid environment such as the stomach.

Sample Data Table

Test Tube	Egg White Appearance		Litmus Color	
	Day 1	Day 2	Day 1	Day 2
A	White cubes	Unchanged	Blue	Blue
B	White cubes	Unchanged	Blue	Blue
C	White cubes	Unchanged	Pink	Pink
D	White cubes	Cloudy liquid (digested)	Pink	Pink

7. Use a clean graduated cylinder to add 5 mL of pepsin to test tube D. Then rinse the graduated cylinder and add 5 mL of hydrochloric acid to test tube D. Observe whether or not an immediate reaction takes place. Record your observations.

8. Obtain four strips of blue litmus paper. (Blue litmus paper turns pink in the presence of an acid.) Dip a clean plastic stirrer into the solution in each test tube, and then touch the stirrer to a piece of litmus paper. Observe what happens to the litmus paper. Record your observations.

9. Insert stoppers in the four test tubes and store the test tube rack as directed by your teacher.

10. The next day, examine the contents of each test tube. Note any changes in the size and overall appearance of the egg white cubes. Then test each solution with litmus paper. Record your observations in your data table.

Analyze and Conclude

1. Which material(s) were the best at digesting the egg white? What observations enabled you to determine this?
2. Do you think that the chemical digestion of protein in food is a fast reaction or a slow one? Explain.
3. What did this lab demonstrate about the ability of pepsin to digest protein?
4. Why was it important that the cubes of egg white all be about the same size?
5. **Think About It** How did test tubes A and C help you draw conclusions about protein digestion in this investigation?

Design an Experiment

Design a way to test whether protein digestion is affected by the size of the food pieces. Write down the hypothesis that you will test. Then create a data table for recording your observations. Obtain your teacher's permission before carrying out your plan.

Analyze and Conclude

1. The combination of pepsin and hydrochloric acid digested the egg white best. After one day, the solid egg white in test tube D begins to dissolve. The egg white in the other solutions remained undigested.

2. The reaction did not occur immediately after the materials were put into test tube D, so it was not a quick reaction. However, students should recognize that they cannot be sure exactly how long the reaction took. The time range is from the moment of their last observation on Day 1 to the time just before their observation on Day 2.

3. Pepsin alone (or with water) cannot digest protein. It requires the presence of hydrochloric acid.

4. In a controlled experiment, it is important to keep all variables the same except the one being tested. Egg pieces of different sizes may have reacted at different rates and affected the results.

5. Test tube A had only pepsin. Test tube C had only hydrochloric acid. Neither one of these two substances could digest the egg white by itself. However, when they were combined in test tube D, they could.

Extending the Inquiry

Design an Experiment Students' experiments should involve placing large egg white pieces and small egg white pieces in a pepsin and hydrochloric acid solution to test their hypothesis. If students set up this experiment correctly, they should learn that small pieces of food are digested faster than large pieces.

Safety

Caution students to wear their lab aprons and safety goggles throughout the lab. Hydrochloric acid can burn skin and clothing. Caution students to wash splashes or spills with plenty of water and to contact you immediately. Review the safety guidelines in Appendix A.

Program Resources

◆ **Unit 4 Resources** Chapter 16 Skills Lab, pp. 51–53
◆ **Inquiry Skills Activity Book** Provides teaching and review of all inquiry skills

Objective

After completing the lesson, students will be able to

◆ explain the role of the small intestine in digestion;

◆ explain the role of the large intestine in digestion.

Key Terms small intestine, liver, bile, gallbladder, pancreas, villi, large intestine, rectum, anus

1 Engage/Explore

Activating Prior Knowledge

Challenge students to describe how small they think nutrients from food would have to become to be carried in the blood. Ask: **What are some ways that particles can become that small?** *(Samples: Particles can become small by being dissolved in liquid or broken down chemically.)*

• • • • • • DISCOVER • • • • • •

Skills Focus predicting
Materials *1 m string, metric ruler*
Time 10 minutes
Tips Make sure students clearly mark the end of the string by holding it with their fingers and tying a knot, or by marking it with a marker. Students should realize that they cannot measure the outline directly with a ruler but must measure the length of string.
Think It Over Students' predictions will vary. The length of string needed to outline the hand with outspread fingers should be about twice as long as the length needed to outline the hand when the fingers are held tightly together.

526

SECTION
3 Final Digestion and Absorption

DISCOVER • ACTIVITY

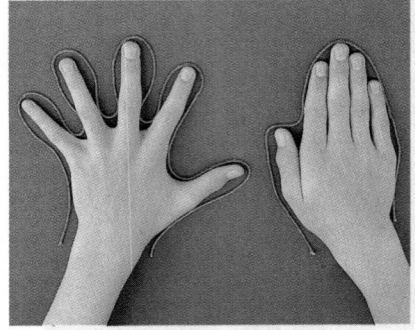

Which Surface Is Larger?

1. Work with a partner to carry out this investigation.

2. Begin by placing your hand palm-side down on a table. Keep your thumb and fingers tightly together. Lay string along the outline of your hand. Have your partner help you determine how long a string you need to outline your hand.

3. Use a metric ruler to measure the length of that string.

Think It Over

Predicting How long would you expect your hand outline to be if you spread out your thumb and fingers? Use string to test your prediction. Compare the two string lengths.

GUIDE FOR READING

◆ What role does the small intestine play in digestion?

◆ What role does the large intestine play in digestion?

Reading Tip As you read, create a table with the headings *Small Intestine, Liver, Pancreas,* and *Large Intestine.* Under each heading, list that organ's digestive function.

Have you ever been part of a huge crowd attending a concert or sports event? Barriers and passageways often guide people in the right direction. Ticket takers make sure that only those with tickets get in, and that they enter in an orderly fashion.

In some ways, the stomach can be thought of as the "ticket taker" of the digestive system. Once the food has been changed into a thick liquid, the stomach releases a little liquid at a time into the next part of the digestive system. This slow, smooth passage of food through the digestive system ensures that digestion and absorption take place smoothly.

The Small Intestine

After the thick liquid leaves the stomach, it enters the small intestine. The **small intestine** is the part of the digestive system where most of the chemical digestion takes place. If you look back at Figure 10, you may wonder how the small intestine got its name. After all, at about 6 meters—longer than many full-sized cars—it makes up two thirds of the digestive system. The small intestine was named for its small diameter. It is about two to three centimeters wide, about half the diameter of the large intestine.

When food reaches the small intestine, it has already been mechanically digested into a thick

READING STRATEGIES

Reading Tip Before students begin reading, have them preview the section by reading the headings and captions and looking at the pictures. Then help them create their tables. Tables should have two columns. One column should list the small intestine, liver, pancreas, and large intestine. The other column should list the digestive function of each organ. After students have read the section, invite volunteers to show their tables to the class and explain each function.

Study and Comprehension After students finish reading, have them review the section and write summaries of the information under each heading. Remind students that summarizing involves writing main points and key details. Suggest students discuss the information with a partner before summarizing it.

liquid. But chemical digestion has just begun. Although starches and proteins have been partially broken down, fats haven't been digested at all. **Almost all chemical digestion and absorption of nutrients takes place in the small intestine.**

The small intestine is bustling with chemical activity. As the liquid moves into the small intestine, it mixes with enzymes and secretions. The enzymes and secretions are produced in three different organs—the small intestine, the liver, and the pancreas. The liver and the pancreas deliver their substances to the small intestine through small tubes.

The Role of the Liver The **liver** is located in the upper portion of the abdomen. It is the largest and heaviest organ inside the body. You can think of the liver as an extremely busy chemical factory that plays a role in many body processes. For example, the liver breaks down medicines and other substances, and it helps eliminate nitrogen from the body. As part of the digestive system, the liver produces **bile,** a substance that breaks up fat particles. Bile flows from the liver into the **gallbladder,** the organ that stores bile. After you eat, bile passes through a tube from the gallbladder into the small intestine.

Bile is not an enzyme. It does not chemically digest foods. It does, however, break up large fat particles into smaller fat droplets. You can compare the action of bile on fats with the action of soap on a greasy frying pan. Soap physically breaks up the grease into small droplets that can mix with the soapy water and be washed away. Bile mixes with the fats in food to form small fat droplets. The droplets can then be chemically broken down by enzymes produced in the pancreas.

Break Up!
In this activity, you will model  the breakup of fat particles in the small intestine.

1. Fill two plastic jars half full of water. Add a few drops of oil to each jar.
2. Add $\frac{1}{4}$ teaspoon baking soda to one of the jars.
3. Stir the contents of both jars. Record your observations.

Observing In which jar did the oil begin to break up? What substance does the baking soda represent?

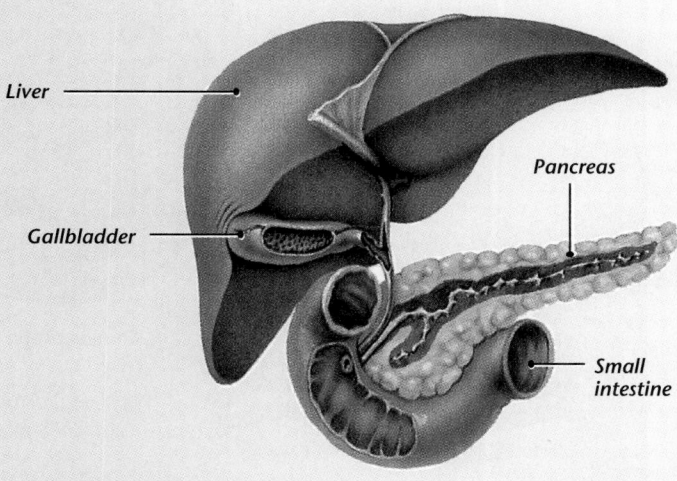

Figure 15 Substances produced by the liver and pancreas aid in the digestion of food.
Applying Concepts Where is bile produced? Where is it stored before it is released into the small intestine?

Liver

Gallbladder

Pancreas

Small intestine

Chapter 16 **527**

Program Resources
◆ **Unit 4 Resources** 16-3 Lesson Plan, p. 45; 16-3 Section Summary, p. 46
◆ **Product Testing Activities by** *Consumer Reports,* "Testing Yogurt," pp. 1–8

Media and Technology
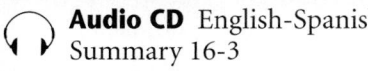
Audio CD English-Spanish Summary 16-3

Answers to Self-Assessment
Caption Question
Figure 15 liver; gallbladder.

Media and Technology
 Exploring Life Science Videodisc Unit 4, Side 1, "Digestion and Absorption"

Chapter 3

2 Facilitate

The Small Intestine

Demonstration
Materials *rope 6 m long*
Time 5 minutes

Show students the length of rope to demonstrate the average length of the small intestine. Ask: **How is it possible for the body to accommodate such a long organ?** *(The small intestine is tightly coiled in the lower abdomen.)* **learning modality: visual**

TRY THIS
Skills Focus observing
Materials *2 jars, oil, baking soda, stirring rod or spoon*
Time 15 minutes
Tips You may want to have students use jars with lids so they can shake the liquid instead of stirring.
Observing The oil begins to break apart in the jar with the baking soda. The baking soda represents bile.
Extend Ask: **What do the jars represent?** *(The small intestine)* **learning modality: visual**

Ongoing Assessment
Writing Ask students to explain the roles of the liver and gallbladder in the digestive process that takes place in the small intestine.

The Small Intestine, continued

Using the Visuals: Figure 16

Make sure students understand that each diagram is a closer view of the part of the small intestine shown in the previous diagram. Ask students: **How do nutrients from the small intestine get to the rest of the body?** *(They pass from the cells on the villi into blood vessels.)* Have students explain how the structure of the villi allows this to happen. *(The villi contain blood vessels covered by a single layer of cells, so nutrients can pass through the cells into the blood.)* **learning modality: visual**

Including All Students

Materials *2 identical pieces of paper, additional paper, tape*

Time 5 minutes

Students who need additional help or students who are mastering English will benefit from this activity. Have students compare the two pieces of paper. Ask: **Do they have the same surface area?** *(yes)* Then have students make folds in one of the pieces of paper. Students should recognize that the two pieces still have the same surface area. Challenge students to fold another piece of paper and tape it to the folded paper to make it cover the same area on the desk as the unfolded piece. Ask: **Now which has the greater surface area?** *(The folded paper)* Ask students to describe how this models the villi in the small intestine. *(The villi allow the organ to have a greater surface area, yet take up the same space in the body.)* **limited English proficiency**

Figure 16 Tiny finger-shaped projections called villi line the inside of the small intestine. In the diagram, you can see that the blood vessels in the villi are covered by a single layer of cells. The photograph shows a closeup view of villi. *Interpreting Diagrams How does the structure of the villi help them carry out their function?*

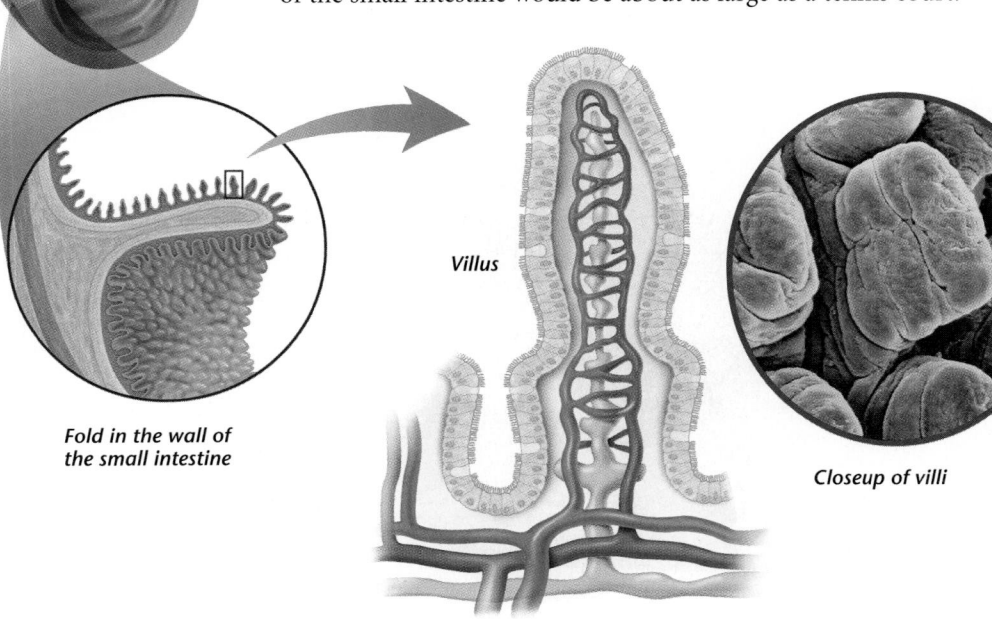

Small intestine

Fold in the wall of the small intestine

Villus

Closeup of villi

Help From the Pancreas The **pancreas** is a triangular organ that lies between the stomach and the first part of the small intestine. Like the liver, the pancreas plays a role in many body processes. As part of the digestive system, the pancreas produces enzymes that flow into the small intestine. These enzymes help break down starches, proteins, and fats.

The digestive enzymes produced by the pancreas and other organs do not break down all food substances, however. Recall that the fiber in food isn't broken down. Instead, fiber thickens the liquid material in the intestine. This makes it easier for peristalsis to push the material forward.

☑ *Checkpoint* How does the pancreas aid in digestion?

Absorption in the Small Intestine After chemical digestion takes place, the small nutrient molecules are ready to be absorbed by the body. The structure of the small intestine makes it well suited for absorption. The inner surface, or lining, of the small intestine looks bumpy. Millions of tiny finger-shaped structures called **villi** (VIL eye) (singular *villus*) cover the surface. The villi absorb nutrient molecules. Notice that tiny blood vessels run through the center of each villus. Nutrient molecules pass from cells on the surface of a villus into blood vessels. The blood carries the nutrients throughout the body for use by body cells.

The presence of villi increases the surface area of the small intestine. If all of the villi were laid out flat, the total surface area of the small intestine would be about as large as a tennis court.

Background

Facts and Figures People who are more than 100 pounds overweight can undergo an operation called a gastric bypass (GB). In a GB, surgeons make a small pouch in the stomach and attach the lower end of the small intestine to an opening in the pouch. People who have had a GB lose weight, because less of the stomach and small intestine is available to absorb nutrients. Because there is less absorption, the side effects include:

◆ Excessive reaction to carbohydrates and sugar. The remainder of the small intestine processes these very quickly, causing an increase in insulin and a drop in blood sugar. This results in dizziness, nausea, and excessive perspiration.

◆ Vitamin B_{12} deficiency, anemia, and protein deficiency

◆ Formation of ulcers at the stomach opening

This greatly increased surface enables digested food to be absorbed faster than if the walls of the small intestine were smooth.

The Large Intestine

By the time material reaches the end of the small intestine, most nutrients have been absorbed. The remaining material moves from the small intestine into the large intestine. The **large intestine** is the last section of the digestive system. It is about one and a half meters long—about as long as the average bathtub. As you can see in Figure 17, the large intestine is shaped somewhat like a horseshoe. It runs up the right-hand side of the abdomen, across the upper abdomen, and then down the left-hand side. The large intestine contains bacteria that feed on the material passing through. These bacteria normally do not cause disease. In fact, they are helpful because they make certain vitamins, including vitamin K.

The material entering the large intestine contains water and undigested food such as fiber. **As the material moves through the large intestine, water is absorbed into the bloodstream. The remaining material is readied for elimination from the body.**

The large intestine ends in a short tube called the **rectum.** Here waste material is compressed into a solid form. This waste material is eliminated from the body through the **anus,** a muscular opening at the end of the rectum.

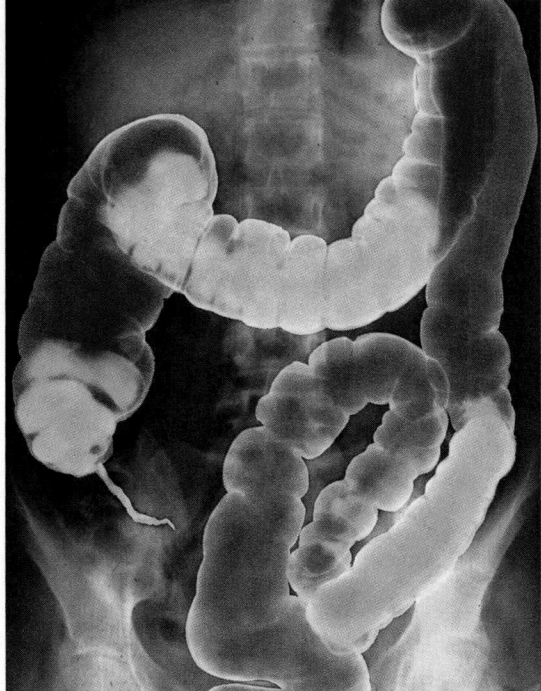

Figure 17 Notice the shape of the large intestine. As material passes through this structure, most of the water is absorbed by the body.

 ## Section 3 Review

1. What two digestive processes occur in the small intestine? Briefly describe each process.
2. Which nutrient is absorbed in the large intestine?
3. How do the liver and pancreas function in the digestive process?
4. **Thinking Critically** **Relating Cause and Effect** Some people are allergic to a protein in wheat. When these people eat foods made with wheat, a reaction destroys the villi in the small intestine. What problems would you expect these people to experience?

> **Check Your Progress** CHAPTER PROJECT
> You should now be trying to eat a more healthful diet. Be sure you keep an accurate log of your food intake during this three-day period. Then graph the results. (*Hint:* You might find it helpful to focus on one food category when trying to improve your eating habits.)

Answers to Self-Assessment

Caption Question

Figure 16 Villi are composed of blood vessels surrounded by single layers of cells, so they can easily absorb nutrients and pass them to the blood vessels; also, villi present a large surface for absorption.

☑ *Checkpoint*

The pancreas produces enzymes that help break down starches, proteins, and fats.

The Large Intestine

Addressing Naive Conceptions

Students may think the waste material leaving a healthy body is made up entirely of undigested fiber. Explain that it also includes mucus, digestive juices, cellular waste materials, and bacterial waste. In fact, up to one-third of the waste material is composed of bacteria and waste products produced by bacteria such as those in the large intestine.
learning modality: verbal

3 Assess

Section 3 Review Answers

1. Chemical digestion—liquefied food mixes with digestive juices and is broken down into the building blocks of starches, proteins, and fats. Absorption—villi absorb nutrients and pass them into blood vessels.
2. water
3. The liver produces bile, a substance that breaks up fat particles. The pancreas produces enzymes that help break down starches, proteins, and fats.
4. Without villi, the body cannot absorb nutrients. A person with this condition may eat large amounts of food and yet not obtain sufficient nutrients.

> **Check Your Progress** CHAPTER PROJECT
> Encourage students to develop plans for improving their diets by identifying specific areas that should be changed. Make sure students do not try to make drastic changes. Remind them they will only be keeping track of their new eating plan for three days, but they should try to implement a plan that they can maintain on a long-term basis.

Performance Assessment

Drawing Have students summarize the digestive process that occurs in the small intestine and the large intestine in a series of drawings and captions.

529

Advertising and Nutrition

Purpose

To provide students with an opportunity to investigate opinions about food advertising aimed at children.

Panel Discussion

Time 40 minutes

◆ Organize the class into small groups. Explain that each group shall argue for a particular point of view on whether unhealthy foods should be advertised on children's television programs. Possible viewpoints could include those of parents, children, advertising firms, nutritionists, snack food manufacturers, television executives, and manufacturers of health foods. Each group can brainstorm the benefits and drawbacks of advertising sugary and high-fat snacks and cereals. Students should consider whether changes in advertising should be made, what these changes might be, and how any changes might affect children and advertisers.

◆ Follow with a panel discussion.

◆ After the panel discussion, discuss whether any students have changed their opinions about foods advertised to children.

Extend

Ask students to compare and contrast the nutrition labels of cereals advertised on television with the information given in advertisements for the cereals.

You Decide

◆ Students can complete the first two steps to raise issues and possible solutions for class discussion. After the panel discussion, students can complete the last step, using what they have learned to design suggestions for improvement or public awareness.

530

Advertising and Nutrition

Millions of children enjoy Saturday morning television programs. As they watch, they see advertisements for high-sugar cereals, candy, soft drinks, and fat-filled foods. Such foods are not healthy choices. For example, in some cereals marketed to children, added sugar makes up almost half the cereal's weight. How greatly are children's eating habits influenced by food ads? Should these ads be allowed on children's television programs?

The Issues

Does Advertising Influence Children?
Advertising products to children between the ages of four and twelve works. Overall, companies spend more than $300 million a year advertising to that age group. In turn, children influence adults to spend more than 500 times that amount—at least $165 billion a year.

Should Food Companies Advertise on Children's Television? Some people want to regulate food ads on children's shows. Evidence indicates that children choose particular foods based on ads. The foods children eat can affect their health not just during childhood but for the rest of their lives.

Other people point out that children don't try to buy every food they see advertised. It is usually parents, not children, who decide what foods to buy. In addition, companies pay for advertisements. Without this money, television producers might not be able to afford to make good programs.

What Responsibilities Do Families and Schools Have? Many people believe that parents and teachers should teach children about nutrition. These people argue that adults should teach children to read food labels and to recognize misleading advertisements. For the rest of children's lives, they will be surrounded by advertising. If they learn to analyze ads critically, children will become wise consumers as adults.

You Decide

1. Describe the Issue
Summarize the debate about food advertisements on children's television.

2. Analyze the Options
List some possible solutions to the problem of food advertisements on children's television. How would each solution affect children and advertisers?

3. Find a Solution
Prepare a leaflet proposing one solution to the problem. Use persuasive arguments to support your proposal.

530

Background

The children's advertising industry regulates itself based on several principles: (**1**) Advertisers have a special responsibility to protect young children from their own susceptibilities. (**2**) Advertisers should be careful not to exploit children's imaginative qualities, creating unrealistic expectations for their products. (**3**) Advertisers should realize that children may try to imitate what they see in ads, which may affect their health and well-being. (**4**) Advertisers should provide examples of positive and beneficial social behavior. (**5**) Advertisers should avoid social stereotyping and appeals to prejudice.

You could have students research the complete guidelines, then review ads to evaluate whether advertisers are following their own guidelines.

SECTION 1 — Food and Energy

INTEGRATING CHEMISTRY

Key Ideas

◆ Nutrients in food provide the body with energy and materials needed for growth, repair, and other life processes. The energy in foods is measured in Calories.

◆ The six nutrients necessary for human health are carbohydrates, fats, proteins, vitamins, minerals, and water.

◆ Water is the most important nutrient because it is necessary for all body processes.

◆ The Food Guide Pyramid classifies foods into six major groups and tells how many servings to eat from each group.

◆ Food labels list the nutrients in foods and shows how the foods fit into your daily diet.

Key Terms

nutrient	cholesterol
calorie	protein
carbohydrate	amino acid
glucose	vitamin
fiber	mineral
fat	Food Guide Pyramid
unsaturated fat	Percent Daily Value
saturated fat	

SECTION 2 — The Digestive Process Begins

Key Ideas

◆ The functions of the digestive system are to break down food, absorb food molecules into the blood, and eliminate wastes.

◆ During mechanical digestion, food is ground into small pieces. During chemical digestion, large food molecules are broken into small molecules by enzymes.

◆ Food first passes from the mouth into the esophagus, and then into the stomach. Waves of muscle contractions, known as peristalsis, keep the food moving in one direction.

Key Terms

digestion	enzyme	mucus
absorption	epiglottis	peristalsis
saliva	esophagus	stomach

SECTION 3 — Final Digestion and Absorption

Key Ideas

◆ Almost all chemical digestion and absorption of nutrients takes place in the small intestine.

◆ Nutrients are absorbed into the bloodstream through the villi of the small intestine.

◆ As material moves through the large intestine, water is absorbed. The remaining material is readied for elimination.

Key Terms

small intestine	gallbladder	large intestine
liver	pancreas	rectum
bile	villus	anus

Organizing Information

Flowchart Copy the incomplete flowchart onto a separate sheet of paper. Complete the flowchart with the names and functions of the missing organs. (For more on flowcharts, see the Skills Handbook.)

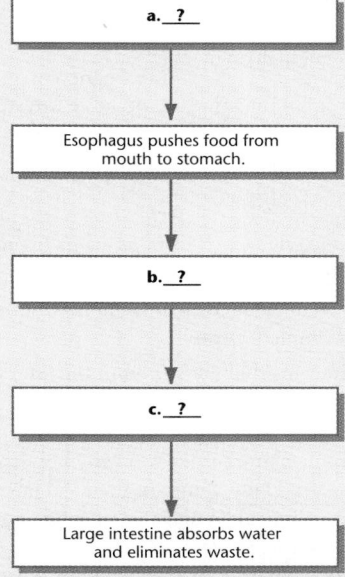

a. ?

↓

Esophagus pushes food from mouth to stomach.

↓

b. ?

↓

c. ?

↓

Large intestine absorbs water and eliminates waste.

Organizing Information

Flowchart **a.** In the mouth, the teeth break food into smaller pieces and saliva begins to break down starches. **b.** In the stomach, food is churned and mixed with digestive juices that break down protein. **c.** In the small intestine, almost all chemical digestion and absorption occurs.

Program Resources

◆ **Unit 4 Resources** Chapter 16 Project Scoring Rubric, p. 36

◆ **Performance Assessment** Chapter 16, pp. 50–52

◆ **Chapter and Unit Tests** Chapter 16 Test, pp. 76–79

Media and Technology

 Interactive Student Tutorial CD-ROM Chapter 16

 Computer Test Bank Chapter 16 Test

Reviewing Content

Multiple Choice
1. c 2. d 3. c 4. d 5. a

True or False
6. complete 7. fat-soluble 8. true 9. true
10. small

Checking Concepts

11. The more physical activity a person does, the higher his or her daily energy needs.
12. Fiber helps keep the digestive system functioning properly.
13. The Food Guide Pyramid gives information about recommended daily servings as a range instead of a single number because different people may need different amounts. For example, an active growing teenager may need to eat more servings than an adult.
14. The epiglottis is located in the back of the throat just above the windpipe, or larynx. It prevents food from going down the windpipe instead of the esophagus.
15. Peristalsis is the wavelike motion of the muscles that pushes food and undigested matter through the digestive system.
16. The villi are finger-shaped structures that line the small intestine. They are specialized for absorbing and transferring nutrients from the small intestine to the bloodstream.
17. Students' descriptions should include mechanical and chemical digestion, beginning in the mouth. They should describe the food's journey down the esophagus, into the stomach, the small intestine, and the large intestine. Students should describe the chemical action of different juices and enzymes, and the absorption of nutrients in the small intestine and water in the large intestine.

Thinking Critically

18. The fat will be stored as an energy source to be used when the animal is hibernating and not taking in food as energy.
19. Similarity: Both an assembly line and the digestive system perform specific jobs in a sequence of steps. Difference: In an assembly line, something is

Reviewing Content

For more review of key concepts, see the Interactive Student Tutorial CD-ROM.

Multiple Choice
Choose the letter of the best answer.

1. Which nutrient makes up about 65 percent of the body's weight?
 a. carbohydrate
 b. protein
 c. water
 d. fat
2. According to the Food Guide Pyramid, from which group should you eat the most servings?
 a. Milk, Yogurt, and Cheese
 b. Meat, Poultry, Fish, Beans, Eggs, and Nuts
 c. Vegetables
 d. Bread, Cereal, Rice, and Pasta
3. Most mechanical digestion takes place in the
 a. mouth.   b. esophagus.
 c. stomach.   d. small intestine.
4. The enzyme in saliva chemically breaks down
 a. fats.   b. proteins.
 c. sugars.   d. starches.
5. Bile is produced by the
 a. liver.   b. pancreas.
 c. small intestine. d. large intestine.

True or False

If the statement is true, write true. If it is false, change the underlined word or words to make the statement true.

6. Proteins that come from animal sources are <u>incomplete</u> proteins.
7. Vitamins that are stored in the fatty tissue of the body are <u>water-soluble</u>.
8. To determine which of two cereals supplies more iron, you can check the <u>Percent Daily Value</u> on the food label.
9. The physical breakdown of food is called <u>mechanical</u> digestion.
10. Most materials are absorbed into the bloodstream in the <u>large</u> intestine.

Checking Concepts

11. How does a person's level of physical activity affect his or her daily energy needs?
12. Why is fiber necessary in a person's diet even though it is not considered a nutrient?
13. Why does the Food Guide Pyramid give the recommended daily servings as a range instead of a single number?
14. Describe the location and function of the epiglottis.
15. Explain the role of peristalsis in the digestive system.
16. What is the function of villi? Where are villi located?
17. **Writing to Learn** Imagine that you are a bacon, lettuce, and tomato sandwich. Describe your journey through a person's digestive system, starting in the mouth and ending with absorption.

Thinking Critically

18. **Applying Concepts** Before winter arrives, animals that hibernate often prepare by eating foods that contain a lot of fat. How is this behavior helpful?
19. **Comparing and Contrasting** The digestive system is sometimes said to be "an assembly line in reverse." Identify some similarities and some differences between your digestive system and an assembly line.
20. **Relating Cause and Effect** "Heartburn" occurs when stomach acid enters the esophagus. Use your knowledge of the digestive system to explain how this condition affects the esophagus and how "heartburn" got its name.
21. **Inferring** Why is it important for people to chew their food thoroughly before swallowing?
22. **Relating Cause and Effect** Suppose a medicine killed all the bacteria in your body. How might this affect vitamin production in your body? Explain.

constructed from many small parts in many steps, but in digestion, the process is reversed—something is broken down into smaller parts step by step.
20. Since acid can burn most of human tissue, when it enters the esophagus it burns tissue, and people feel a burning sensation—heartburn.
21. Chewing thoroughly breaks food into smaller particles and therefore makes it easier for chemical digestion to occur. Chewing food thoroughly also reduces the risk of choking.

22. Bacteria in the large intestine produce vitamin K. If they were killed by the medicine, the production of vitamin K would stop.

Applying Skills

23. Milk, Yogurt, and Cheese Group; 2–3 servings
24. About three cups
25. Low-fat milk; $\frac{20}{110} \times \frac{100\%}{1} = 18\%$. The other foods get 32% (yogurt) and 35% (chocolate milk) of their calories from fat.

Applying Skills

Use the chart below to answer Questions 23–25.

Food (1 cup)	Calcium (% Daily Value)	Calories	Calories from Fat
Chocolate Milk	30	230	80
Low-fat Milk	35	110	20
Plain Yogurt	35	110	35

23. **Classifying** To which group in the Food Guide Pyramid do the foods in the chart belong? What is the recommended range of daily servings for that group?

24. **Interpreting Data** How many cups of low-fat milk provide the daily recommended percentage of calcium?

25. **Calculating** Which of the foods meet the recommendation that no more than 30 percent of a food's calories come from fat? Explain.

Present Your Project Write a summary of what you've learned from keeping a food log. Address these questions in your summary: How close were your eating patterns to those recommended in the Food Guide Pyramid? How did you attempt to change your diet during the second three days? How successful were you at making those changes in your diet?

Reflect and Record Did your eating patterns surprise you? What additional changes could help you improve your diet? How might others help you make those changes? If your eating patterns match those that are recommended in the Food Guide Pyramid, how can you be sure to continue those patterns?

Present Your Project Students' summaries should document the changes they tried to implement in the second phase of the project. Students should describe how their analyses of their eating habits in the first part of the project led them to make specific changes. This project may involve issues that are sensitive for some students. Tell students that their summaries are for their own benefit and for serving as evidence that they completed the project. Make sure students know that their summaries will be held in confidence.

Reflect and Record Encourage students to write reasonable plans for maintaining healthy eating habits. Students' plans should include strategies for dealing with any habits that compromise their nutrition. Make sure students do not try to implement radical plans. Remind students that their diets can be healthful even if some meals or snacks do not meet the guidelines. Encourage them to think of the average effect of each day or even of a whole week instead of focusing on each individual food.

Test Preparation

Use these questions to prepare for standardized tests.

Use the information to answer Questions 26–29.
A scientist performed an experiment to determine the amount of time needed to digest protein. She placed small pieces of hard-boiled egg white (a protein) in a test tube containing hydrochloric acid, water, and the enzyme pepsin. She measured the rate at which the egg white was digested over a 24-hour period. Her data are recorded in the table below.

Time (hours)	Percentage of Egg White Digested
0	0%
4	15%
8	25%
12	40%
16	70%
20	85%
24	90%

26. During which 4-hour period did the most digestion take place?
   a. 0–4 hours   b. 4–8 hours
   c. 8–12 hours   d. 12–16 hours

27. After about how many hours would you estimate that half of the protein was digested?
   a. 8 hours   b. 12 hours
   c. 14 hours   d. 16 hours

28. How much digestion occurred in 16 hours?
   a. 25%   b. 40%
   c. 70%   d. 90%

29. What would have happened if no hydrochloric acid were added to the test tube?
   a. The protein would have been digested faster.
   b. The protein would have been digested slower.
   c. There would have been no change in the rate of protein digestion.
   d. Pepsin alone would have digested the protein.

Chapter 16 **533**

Test Preparation

26. d   27. c   28. c   29. b

Program Resources

◆ **Inquiry Skills Activity Book** Provides teaching and review of all inquiry skills

CHAPTER 17 Circulation

Sections	Time	Student Edition Activities	Other Activities
CHAPTER PROJECT **Travels of a Red Blood Cell** p. 535	Ongoing (2 weeks)	Check Your Progress, pp. 542, 547, 554 Present Your Project, p. 563	
1 The Body's Transportation System pp. 536–542 ◆ Describe the function of the cardiovascular system. ◆ Describe the structure of the heart and explain its function. ◆ Describe the origin of the heartbeat and why the heart rate changes during exercise. ◆ Trace the path taken by blood through the circulatory system.	2 periods/ 1 block	**Discover** How Hard Does Your Heart Work?, p. 536	TE Building Inquiry Skills: Observing, p. 538 TE Including All Students, p. 538 TE Building Inquiry Skills: Interpreting Data, p. 540
2 A Closer Look at Blood Vessels pp. 543–548 ◆ Describe the functions of the arteries, capillaries, and veins. ◆ Identify the cause of blood pressure.	$1\frac{1}{2}$ periods/ 1 block	**Discover** How Does Pressure Affect the Flow of Blood?, p. 543 **Sharpen Your Skills** Creating Data Tables, p. 546 **Skills Lab: Measuring** Heart Beat, Health Beat, p. 548	TE Math Toolbox, p. 544 TE Building Inquiry Skills: Calculating, p. 544 TE Real-Life Learning, p. 547 LM 17, "Direction of Blood Flow"
3 Blood and Lymph pp. 549–555 ◆ Name and describe the four components of blood. ◆ Explain blood type and how it determines what blood a person can receive in a transfusion. ◆ Describe the structure and function of the lymphatic system.	2 periods/ 1 block	**Discover** What Kinds of Cells Are in Blood?, p. 549 **Try This** Caught in the Web, p. 552 **Real-World Lab: You and Your Community** Do You Know Your A-B-O's?, p. 555	TE Demonstration, p. 550 TE Real-Life Learning, p. 553
4 ● **INTEGRATING HEALTH** **Cardiovascular Health** pp. 556–560 ◆ Identify and describe types of cardiovascular disease. ◆ Describe behaviors that maintain cardiovascular health.	1 period/ $\frac{1}{2}$ block	**Discover** Which Foods Are "Heart Healthy"?, p. 556 **Try This** Blocking the Flow, p. 557 **Science at Home,** p. 560	TE Building Inquiry Skills: Predicting, p. 559 TE Building Inquiry Skills: Making Models, p. 559 TE Building Inquiry Skills: Making Judgments, p. 560
Study Guide/Chapter Assessment pp. 561–563	1 period/ $\frac{1}{2}$ block		ISAB Provides teaching and review of all inquiry skills

For Standard or Block Schedule The Resource Pro® CD-ROM gives you maximum flexibility for planning your instruction for any type of schedule. Resource Pro® contains Planning Express®, an advanced scheduling program, as well as the entire contents of the Teaching Resources and the Computer Test Bank.

CHAPTER PLANNING GUIDE

Program Resources	Assessment Strategies	Media and Technology
UR Chapter 17 Project Teacher Notes, pp. 54–55 **UR** Chapter 17 Project Overview and Worksheets, pp. 56–59	**SE** Performance Assessment: Present Your Project, p. 563 **TE** Check Your Progress, pp. 542, 547, 554 **UR** Chapter 17 Project Scoring Rubric, p. 60	Science Explorer Internet Site at www.phschool.com
UR 17-1 Lesson Plan, p. 61 **UR** 17-1 Section Summary, p. 62 **UR** 17-1 Review and Reinforce, p. 63 **UR** 17-1 Enrich, p. 64	**SE** Section 1 Review, p. 542 **TE** Ongoing Assessment, pp. 537, 539, 541 **TE** Performance Assessment, p. 542	Audio CD, English-Spanish Summary 17-1 Transparency 67, "Exploring the Heart"
UR 17-2 Lesson Plan, p. 65 **UR** 17-2 Section Summary, p. 66 **UR** 17-2 Review and Reinforce, p. 67 **UR** 17-2 Enrich, p. 68 **UR** Chapter 17 Skills Lab, pp. 77–78	**SE** Section 2 Review, p. 547 **TE** Ongoing Assessment, p. 545 **TE** Performance Assessment, p. 547	Audio CD, English-Spanish Summary 17-2 Transparency 68, "Artery, Capillary, and Vein"
UR 17-3 Lesson Plan, p. 69 **UR** 17-3 Section Summary, p. 70 **UR** 17-3 Review and Reinforce, p. 71 **UR** 17-3 Enrich, p. 72 **UR** Chapter 17 Real-World Lab, pp. 79–81	**SE** Section 3 Review, p. 554 **TE** Ongoing Assessment, pp. 551, 553 **TE** Performance Assessment, p. 554	Life Science Videotape 4; Videodisc Unit 4 Side 1, "Blood!" Audio CD, English-Spanish Summary 17-3 Interactive Student Tutorial CD-ROM, Chapter 17
UR 17-4 Lesson Plan, p. 73 **UR** 17-4 Section Summary, p. 74 **UR** 17-4 Review and Reinforce, p. 75 **UR** 17-4 Enrich, p. 76	**SE** Section 4 Review, p. 560 **TE** Ongoing Assessment, pp. 557, 559 **TE** Performance Assessment, p. 560	Life Science Videotape 4; Videodisc Unit 4 Side 1, "The Heart of the Matter" Audio CD, English-Spanish Summary 17-4
RCA Provides strategies to improve science reading skills **GSW** Provides worksheets to promote student comprehension of content	**SE** Chapter 17 Study Guide/Assessment, pp. 561–563 **PA** Chapter 17 Performance Assessment, pp. 53–55 **CUT** Chapter 17 Test, pp. 80–83 **CTB** Chapter 17 Test	Computer Test Bank, Chapter 17 Test Interactive Student Tutorial CD-ROM, Chapter 17

Key: **SE** Student Edition   **TE** Teacher's Edition   **UR** Unit Resources
      CTB Computer Test Bank   **PTA** Product Testing Activities by *Consumer Reports*   **LM** Laboratory Manual
      ISAB Inquiry Skills Activity Book   **RCA** Reading in the Content Area   **IES** Interdisciplinary Explorations Series
      GSW Guided Study Worksheets   **PA** Performance Assessment   **CUT** Chapter and Unit Tests

Meeting the National Science Education Standards and AAAS Benchmarks

National Science Education Standards	Benchmarks for Science Literacy	Unifying Themes
Science as Inquiry (Content Standard A) ◆ **Ask questions that can be answered by scientific investigations** How does physical activity affect your pulse rate? *(Skills Lab)* Which blood types can safely receive transfusions of type A blood? Which can receive type O blood? *(Real-World Lab)* ◆ **Develop descriptions, explanations, predictions, and models using evidence** Students design and construct a display showing the path of a red blood cell through the human body. *(Chapter Project)* **Life Science** (Content Standard C) ◆ **Structure and function in living systems** The cardiovascular system consists of the heart, blood vessels, and blood and functions as the transport system of the body. *(Section 1)* Arteries, capillaries, and veins transport blood to organs of the body. *(Section 2)* **Science in Personal and Social Perspectives** (Content Standard F) ◆ **Personal health** Personal behaviors can help maintain cardiovascular health. *(Section 4)* **History and Nature of Science** (Content Standard G) ◆ **History of science** Many people have contributed to cardiovascular advances in the twentieth century. *(Section 4)*	**1B Scientific Inquiry** Students infer which types of blood can be safely received in transfusions. *(Real-World Lab)* **2C Mathematical Inquiry** Students apply mathematics to determine how physical activity affects pulse rate. *(Skills Lab)* **3C Issues in Technology** Technology has been responsible for advances in cardiovascular medicine that have improved treatments and saved human lives. *(Section 4)* **6C Basic Functions** The circulatory system moves needed materials and wastes to or from cells, responding to changing demands. *(Sections 1, 2, 3)* **6E Physical Health** Regular exercise is important to maintain a healthy cardiovascular system. *(Section 4)* White blood cells engulf invaders or produce antibodies that attack them or mark them for killing other white cells. *(Section 3)* **11A Systems** The cardiovascular system is connected to other systems in the human body. *(Section 1)*	◆ **Energy** Red blood cells transport the oxygen that the body needs for energy. The circulatory system delivers the raw materials needed for the production of energy to the cells and carries the waste products of energy production away from the cells. *(Sections 1, 3; Chapter Project)* ◆ **Scale and Structure** The primary components of the cardiovascular system include the heart, blood vessels, and blood. The heart pumps blood; blood carries materials and wastes; and blood vessels transport these materials to other parts of the body. *(Sections 1, 2, 3)* ◆ **Unity and Diversity** Arteries, veins, and capillaries all provide the transport network through which blood travels, although their structures and functions differ. Arteries carry blood away from the heart; capillaries are tiny vessels in which the exchange of materials takes place; and veins carry blood back to the heart. *(Section 2)* ◆ **Systems and Interactions** The components of blood work together as a system, each performing a specific function. The interaction of these components with the rest of the body enables the body to stay healthy and to function normally. *(Section 3)*

Take It to the Net

 *Interactive text at www.phschool.com*

Science Explorer comes alive with iText.

- **Complete student text** is accessible from any computer with Internet access or a CD-ROM drive.
- **Animations, simulations, and videos** enhance student understanding and retention of concepts.
- **Self-tests and online study tools** assess student understanding.

STAY CURRENT with

Find out the latest research and information about human biology and health at: **www.phschool.com**

Go to **www.phschool.com** and click on the Science icon. Then click on <u>Science Explorer: Life, Earth, and Physical Science</u> under PH@school.

ACTIVITY	Time (minutes)	Materials *Quantities for one work group*	Skills
Section 1			
Discover, p. 536	20	**Consumable** water, newspapers, paper towels **Nonconsumable** two large plastic containers, cup with capacity of about 60 mL, watch or clock with a second hand	Inferring
Section 2			
Discover, p. 543	10	**Consumable** water, newspapers, paper towels **Nonconsumable** plastic squeeze bottle, dishpan	Inferring
Sharpen your Skills, p. 546	15	No special materials are required.	Creating Data Tables
Skills Lab, p. 548	40	**Consumable** graph paper **Nonconsumable** watch or clock with second hand	Measuring
Section 3			
Discover, p. 549	15	**Nonconsumable** microscope, prepared slides of human blood	Observing
Try This, p. 552	15	**Consumable** water, newspapers, paper towels **Nonconsumable** two sturdy plastic cups, 20-cm square piece of cheesecloth, rubber band, paper clips, coins	Making Models
Real-World Lab, p. 555	40	**Consumable** 4 paper cups, white paper, four model "blood" types, toothpicks **Nonconsumable** 4 plastic droppers, marking pen, 8 plastic petri dishes	Making Models, Inferring
Section 4			
Discover, p. 556	20	**Nonconsumable** assortment of foods	Forming Operational Definitions
Try This, p. 557	20	**Consumable** water, peanut butter, toothpick, newspaper, paper towels **Nonconsumable** plastic funnel, plastic jar, graduated cylinder, stopwatch or clock with a second hand, plastic knife	Predicting
Science at Home, p. 560	home	**Nonconsumable** cookbooks or magazines with low-fat recipes	Classifying

A list of all materials required for the Student Edition activities can be found on pages T25–T33. You can obtain information about ordering materials by calling 1-800-848-9500 or by accessing the Science Explorer Internet site at **www.phschool.com**.

Travels of a Red Blood Cell

Students may have a hard time visualizing the circulation of blood throughout the body. This project will give them the opportunity to describe the travels of a single blood cell through the circulatory system.

Purpose In this project, students will research what happens as blood moves throughout the body. The students must also design a display to communicate their findings visually.

Skills Focus After completing the Chapter 17 Project, students will be able to

◆ describe the two main circuits in the circulatory system of the human body;
◆ make a model in the form of visual displays showing the two circuits traveled by red blood cells;
◆ communicate information concerning the function of the two circuits.

Project Time Line The entire project will require approximately two to three weeks. On the first day, class time should be allowed for students to exchange ideas on ways to create visual displays. On the second day, have students work on ideas for their own displays and talk with you about their plans. Have students present detailed sketches of their plans to you during the next few days. When you have approved their plans, students should spend eight to ten days building their displays. Allow one or two class periods at the end of the project for students to present their displays. Before beginning the project, see Chapter 17 Project Teacher Notes on pages 54–55 in Unit 4 Resources for more details on carrying out the project. Also distribute the Students' Chapter 17 Project Overview and Worksheets and Scoring Rubric on pages 56–60 in Unit 4 Resources.

Suggested Shortcuts Consider organizing the class in groups to do some or all phases of the project. Students can research the heart and its circulation in groups, or they can brainstorm display ideas in a group. For more ambitious projects, consider allowing students to work in groups for the whole project.

534

17 Circulation

WEB ACTIVITY www.phschool.com

SECTION 1 The Body's Transportation System
Discover How Hard Does Your Heart Work?

SECTION 2 A Closer Look at Blood Vessels
Discover How Does Pressure Affect the Flow of Blood?
Sharpen Your Skills Creating Data Tables
Skills Lab Heart Beat, Health Beat

SECTION 3 Blood and Lymph
Discover What Kinds of Cells Are in Blood?
Try This Caught in the Web
Real-World Lab Do You Know Your A-B-O's?

534

Possible Materials Provide a wide variety of materials from which students can choose. Encourage them to also use videos, computers, and art media.
◆ For posters, provide poster board, colored pens, string, foil, and an assortment of magazines and newspapers.
◆ For displays involving more elaborate construction, provide cardboard, cardboard rolls, straws, scrap wood, assorted plastic bottles, and other materials.

Launching the Project To introduce the project and to stimulate student interest, compare blood circulation to a rural mail route. Each morning a mail carrier goes to the post office and picks up the mail, much as blood picks up oxygen in the lungs. The carrier then drives to where the customers live, delivers the mail, picks up mail from the customer, and returns to the post office. Just as the mail carrier picks up customer mail to be returned to the post office, so is carbon dioxide picked up by the blood and returned to the lungs.

Travels of a Red Blood Cell

Every day, you travel from home to school and then back home again. Your path makes a loop, or circuit, ending where it began. In this chapter, you'll learn how your blood also travels in circuits. You'll find out how your heart pumps your blood throughout your body, bringing that essential fluid to all your living cells. As you learn more about the heart and circulatory system, you'll create a display to show how blood circulates throughout the body.

Your Goal To design and construct a display showing a complete journey of a red blood cell through the human body.

To complete the project successfully, your display must
- ◆ show a red blood cell that leaves from the heart and returns to the same place
- ◆ show where the red blood cell picks up and delivers oxygen and carbon dioxide
- ◆ provide written descriptions of the circuits made by the red blood cell, either with captions or in a continuous story
- ◆ be designed following the safety guidelines in Appendix A

Get Started Look ahead at the diagrams in the chapter. Then discuss the kinds of displays you could use, including a three-dimensional model, posters, a series of drawings, a flip-book, or a video animation. Write down any content questions you'll need to answer.

Check Your Progress You'll be working on this project as you study this chapter. To keep your project on track, look for Check Your Progress boxes at the following points.
Section 1 Review, page 542: Make a sketch of your display.
Section 2 Review, page 547: Begin to construct your display.
Section 3 Review, page 554: Add a written description to your display.

Present Your Project At the end of the chapter (page 563), you will use your display to show how blood travels through the body.

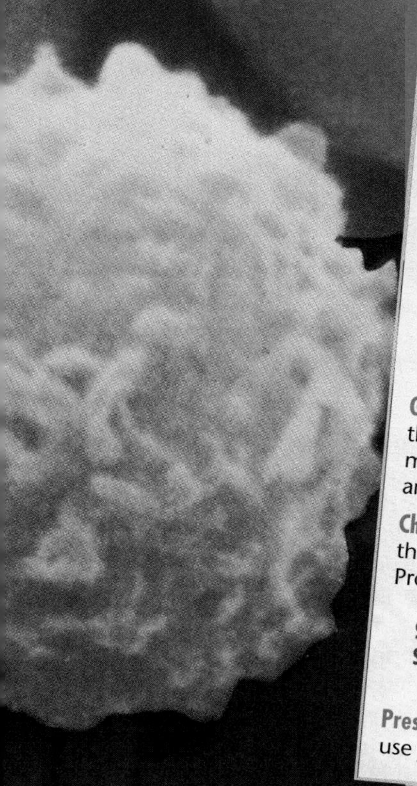

Blood cells travel in blood vessels to all parts of the body.

SECTION
4
Integrating Health
Cardiovascular Health

Discover Which Foods Are "Heart Healthy"?
Try This Blocking the Flow
Science at Home Healthy Hearts

535

Program Resources

◆ **Unit 4 Resources** Chapter 17 Project Teacher Notes, pp. 54–55; Chapter 17 Project Overview and Worksheets, pp. 56–59; Chapter 17 Project Scoring Rubric, p. 60

WEB ACTIVITY www.phschool.com

You will find an Internet activity, chapter self-tests for students, and links to other chapter topics at this site.

Help students brainstorm ideas by reviewing the words that can be used for the way in which blood travels, such as "circuit" or "loop." Help students modify overly ambitious or expensive plans; approve creative ideas that can be completed within the time period and with the resources available.

Allow time for students to read the description of the project in their text and the Chapter Project Overview on pages 56–57 in Unit 4 Resources. Pass out copies of the Chapter 17 Project Worksheets on pages 58–59 in Unit 4 Resources for students to review.

Performance Assessment

The Chapter 17 Project Scoring Rubric on page 60 of Unit 4 Resources will help you evaluate how well students complete the Chapter 17 Project. Students will be assessed on
- ◆ the thoroughness of their research on the circulatory system and the thoroughness of their plans for creating the display;
- ◆ the accuracy and creativity of their display and whether it was completed on time;
- ◆ the thoroughness and organization of their presentation of the display to the rest of the class;
- ◆ how well students work with others and participate in class discussions.

By sharing the Chapter 17 Project Scoring Rubric with students at the beginning of the project, you will make it clear to them what they are expected to do.

Objectives

After completing the lesson, students will be able to
- describe the function of the cardiovascular system;
- describe the structure of the heart and explain its function;
- describe the origin of the heartbeat and why the heart rate changes during exercise;
- trace the path taken by blood through the circulatory system.

Key Terms cardiovascular system, heart, atrium, ventricle, valve, pacemaker, artery, capillary, vein, aorta

1 Engage/Explore

Activating Prior Knowledge

Display a map of a subway, bus, train, or local highway system. Ask students what the function of the transportation system is. Then ask them to compare it with the system for transporting materials through the human body.

DISCOVER

Skills Focus inferring
Materials *newspapers, paper towels, two large plastic containers, cup with capacity of about 60 mL, watch or clock with a second hand*
Time 20 minutes
Tips Because spillage will occur, set up with newspapers, towels, or other materials for quick cleanup. If possible, put the large plastic containers in a larger container to catch spills. Water spilled on floor should be mopped immediately. Students should wear aprons. Consider doing this activity outdoors.
Expected Outcome Students probably cannot make 75 transfers of water.
Think It Over Results will indicate that the heart can work faster than the hand.

DISCOVER · ACTIVITY

How Hard Does Your Heart Work?

1. Every minute, your heart beats about 75 to 85 times. With each beat, it pumps about 60 milliliters of blood. Can you work as hard and fast as your heart does?

2. Cover a table or desk with newspapers. Place two large plastic containers side by side on the newspapers. Fill one with 2.5 liters of water, which is about the volume of blood that your heart pumps in 30 seconds. Leave the other container empty.

3. With a plastic cup that holds about 60 milliliters, transfer water as quickly as possible into the empty container without spilling any. Have a partner time you for 30 seconds. As you work, count how many transfers you make in 30 seconds.

4. Multiply your results by 2 to find the number of transfers for one minute.

Think It Over
Inferring Compare your performance with the number of times your heart beats every minute. What do your results tell you about the strength and speed of a heartbeat?

GUIDE FOR READING

- What is the function of the cardiovascular system?
- What role does the heart play in the cardiovascular system?
- What path does blood take through the circulatory system?

Reading Tip As you read, create a flowchart that shows the path that blood follows as it circulates through the body.

In the middle of the night, a truck rolls rapidly through the darkness. Loaded with fresh fruits and vegetables, the truck is headed for a city supermarket. The driver steers off the interstate and onto a smaller highway. Finally, after driving through narrow city streets, the truck reaches its destination. As dawn begins to break, store workers unload the cargo. They work quickly, because other trucks—carrying meats, canned goods, and freshly baked breads—are waiting to be unloaded. And while workers fill the store with products to be sold, a garbage truck removes yesterday's trash. All these trucks have traveled long distances over roads. Without a huge network of roads, big and small, the supermarket couldn't stay in business.

Movement of Materials

Like the roads that link all parts of the country, your body has a "highway" network, called the cardiovascular system, that links all parts of your body. The **cardiovascular system,** or circulatory system, consists of the heart, blood vessels, and blood. **The cardiovascular system carries needed substances to cells and carries waste products away from cells.** In addition, blood contains cells that fight disease.

READING STRATEGIES

Reading Tip Have students use note cards to write each step that they want to include on their flowcharts. Encourage them to rearrange the cards as they read until they are sure they have the steps in the correct order. Sample Flowchart: body → right atrium → right ventricle → arteries to lungs → lungs → veins from lungs → left atrium → left ventricle → aorta

Study and Comprehension Have students write brief summaries of the information in this section. Remind students to include main ideas and key details in their summaries. Students can then use the summaries as study guides for the section.

Needed Materials Most substances that need to get from one part of the body to another are carried by blood. For example, blood carries oxygen from your lungs to your body cells. Blood also transports the glucose your cells use to produce energy.

Waste Products The cardiovascular system also picks up wastes from cells. For example, when cells use glucose, they produce carbon dioxide as a waste product. The carbon dioxide passes from the cells into the blood. The cardiovascular system then carries carbon dioxide to the lungs, where it is exhaled.

Disease Fighters The cardiovascular system also transports cells that attack disease-causing microorganisms. This process can keep you from becoming sick. If you do get sick, these disease-fighting blood cells will kill the microorganisms to help you get well.

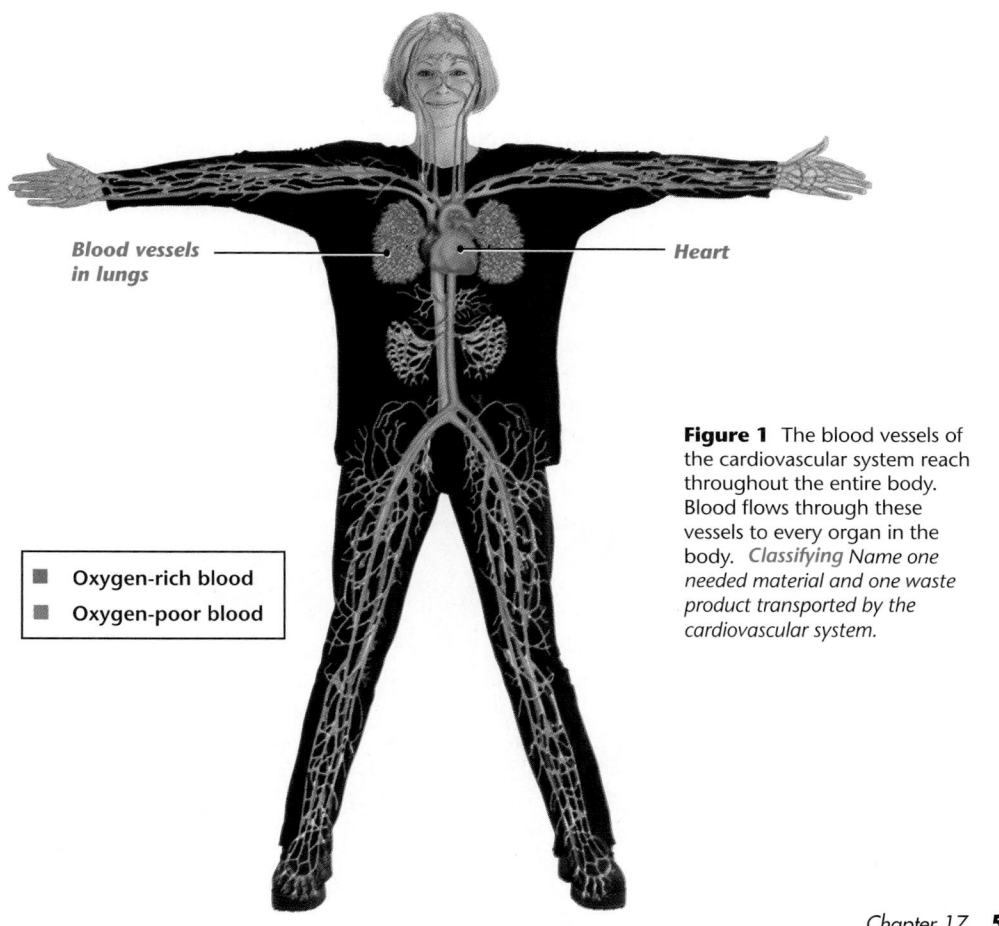

Blood vessels in lungs

Heart

■ Oxygen-rich blood
■ Oxygen-poor blood

Figure 1 The blood vessels of the cardiovascular system reach throughout the entire body. Blood flows through these vessels to every organ in the body. *Classifying Name one needed material and one waste product transported by the cardiovascular system.*

2 Facilitate

Movement of Materials

Including All Students

Some students may have difficulty in understanding how the parts of the cardiovascular system are interrelated. Ask: **What is the relationship between the heart, the blood vessels, and the blood?** *(The heart pumps the blood, enabling the blood to move throughout the body; the blood vessels link all parts of the body so that the blood can circulate; the blood transports glucose and oxygen to body cells and picks up carbon dioxide and other wastes that need to be removed; the blood also transports disease-fighting cells.)* **learning modality: logical/mathematical**

Building Inquiry Skills: Communicating

Tell students they will work in pairs to test each other on their knowledge of the cardiovascular system. Students should first read the section and study Figure 1. Then, each student should write down three questions to ask the other. Instruct students to ask questions that can be answered by reading the section. Provide an example: Which part of the cardiovascular system picks up carbon dioxide from the cells? *(The blood)* After students have tested each other, invite each pair of students to choose one of their questions to present to the class. **limited English proficiency**

Answers to Self-Assessment

Caption Question

Figure 1 Needed materials—oxygen, glucose; waste products—carbon dioxide

Ongoing Assessment

Writing Have students describe the parts of the cardiovascular system and the materials it transports.

The Heart

Building Inquiry Skills: Observing

Materials *stethoscope*
Time 15 minutes

Have students use the stethoscope to listen to their own heartbeats. After each use, use rubbing alcohol to clean the parts of the stethoscope that are inserted into the ears; also clean any parts that are placed on the skin. Then have students describe the sound of the beating heart. (*Students should describe a deeper sound, the "lub," and a higher sound, the "dup."*) **learning modality: kinesthetic**

Using the Visuals: Figure 3

Have students point to the valve in the photograph. Ask: **Which way does the blood move through the valve?** (*Up from the left through the valve.*) Ask students to predict what would happen if the blood began to flow backward. (*The valve would remain closed and would prevent backward flow.*) **learning modality: visual**

Including All Students

Materials *model heart with removable parts*
Time 15 minutes

This activity will benefit students who have difficulty seeing. Invite students to feel each part of the heart as you describe its function. Ask students to describe what they feel, noting differences in the size of the chambers and the thickness of the walls. Have students feel and describe the blood vessels that lead in and out of the chambers. **learning modality: kinesthetic**

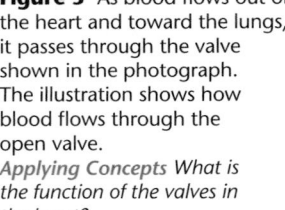

Figure 2 This small stone sculpture, created by ancient Egyptians, represents the heart. Ancient Egyptians believed that feelings, thoughts, and memories were created by the heart.

Figure 3 As blood flows out of the heart and toward the lungs, it passes through the valve shown in the photograph. The illustration shows how blood flows through the open valve. *Applying Concepts What is the function of the valves in the heart?*

The Heart

Without the heart, blood wouldn't go anywhere. The **heart** is a hollow, muscular organ that pumps blood throughout the body. Your heart, which is about the size of your fist, is located in the center of your chest. The heart lies behind the breastbone and inside the ribs. These bones protect the heart from injury.

Each time the heart beats, it pushes blood through the blood vessels of the cardiovascular system. As you learned in Chapter 15, the heart is made of cardiac muscle, which can contract over and over without getting tired. The heart beats continually throughout a person's life, resting only between beats. During your lifetime, your heart may beat over 3 billion times. In a year, it pumps enough blood to fill over 30 competition-size swimming pools.

The Heart's Structure Look closely at *Exploring the Heart* as you read about the structure of the heart. Notice that the heart has two sides—a right side and a left side—completely separated from each other by a wall of tissue. Each side has two compartments, or chambers—an upper and a lower chamber. The two upper chambers, each called an **atrium** (AY tree um) (plural *atria*), receive blood that comes into the heart. The two lower chambers, each called a **ventricle,** pump blood out of the heart. The atria are separated from the ventricles by valves. A **valve** is a flap of tissue that prevents blood from flowing backward. Valves are also located between the ventricles and the large blood vessels that carry blood away from the heart.

How the Heart Works The action of the heart has two main phases. In one phase, the heart muscle relaxes and the atria fill with blood. In the other phase, the atria contract and fill the ventricles, and then the ventricles contract to pump blood forward. The sound of a heartbeat, which sounds something like *lub-dup,* is made during this pumping phase.

Background

Facts and Figures When doctors listen to their patients' hearts and blood vessels, they hope to hear the *lub-dup* sound of a healthy heart, but they listen for other sounds as well. For example, obstruction of or leakage through a heart valve causes turbulence in the flow of blood. This turbulence makes a noise called a heart murmur. Doctors can often tell which valve is obstructed or damaged by listening to the location, duration, intensity, pitch, and quality of the murmur.

When doctors listen to the blood vessels, they may hear bruits, which are sounds made by blood vessels that are partially blocked. When the bruit is heard in the neck area, it may indicate an increased risk for a stroke. A bruit in the abdominal area may be a sign of a partial obstruction of the aorta or other major artery.

When the heart muscle relaxes, blood flows into the chambers. Then the atria contract. This muscle contraction squeezes blood out of the atria, through the valves, and then into the ventricles. Next the ventricles contract. This contraction closes the valves between the atria and ventricles, making the *lub* sound and squeezing blood into large blood vessels. As the valves between the ventricles and the blood vessels snap shut, they make the *dup* sound. All of this happens in less than a second.

☑ *Checkpoint* *Contrast the functions of atria and ventricles.*

EXPLORING *the Heart*

Every second of your life, your heart pumps blood through your body. The right side of the heart pumps blood to the lungs, while the left side pumps blood to the rest of the body.

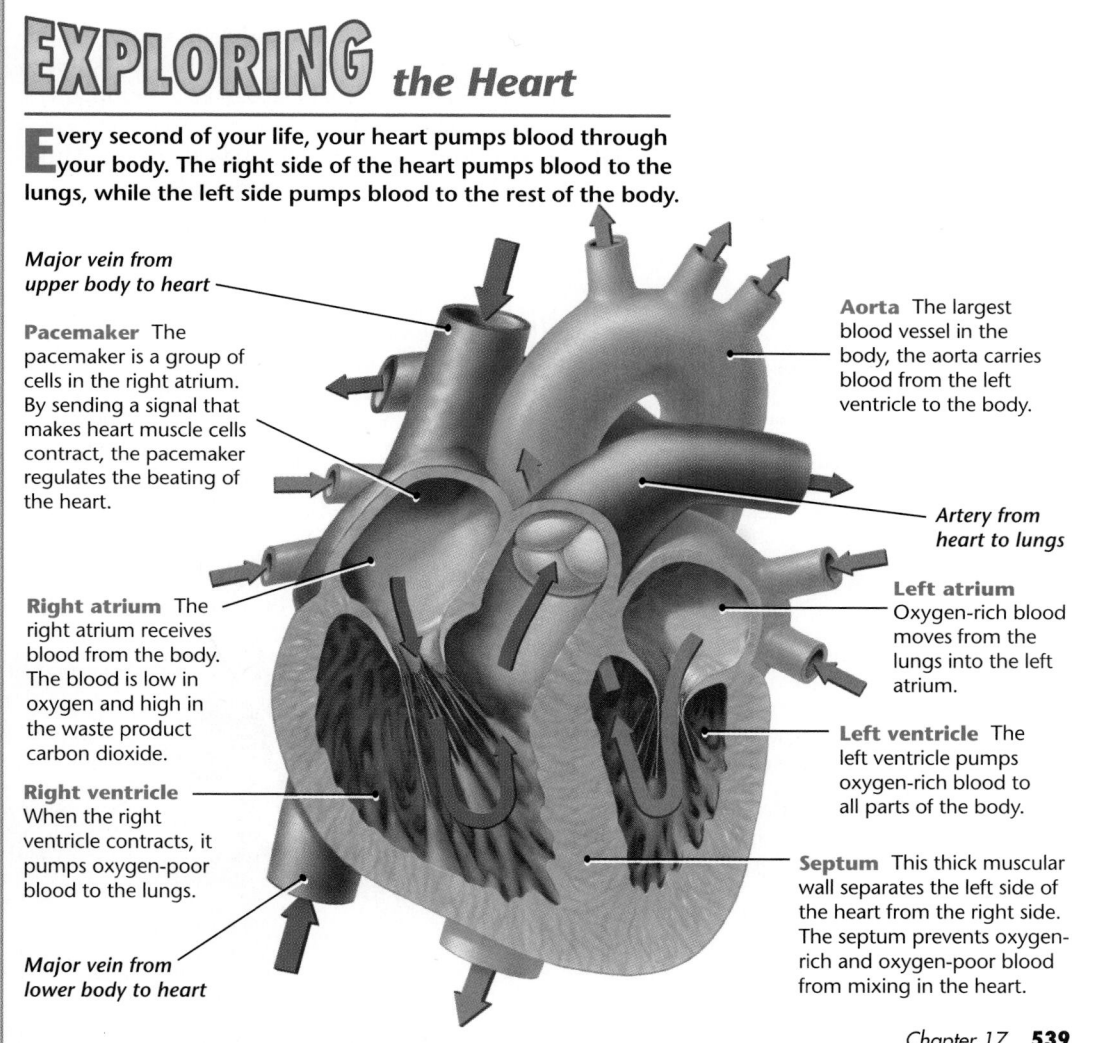

Major vein from upper body to heart

Pacemaker The pacemaker is a group of cells in the right atrium. By sending a signal that makes heart muscle cells contract, the pacemaker regulates the beating of the heart.

Right atrium The right atrium receives blood from the body. The blood is low in oxygen and high in the waste product carbon dioxide.

Right ventricle When the right ventricle contracts, it pumps oxygen-poor blood to the lungs.

Major vein from lower body to heart

Aorta The largest blood vessel in the body, the aorta carries blood from the left ventricle to the body.

Artery from heart to lungs

Left atrium Oxygen-rich blood moves from the lungs into the left atrium.

Left ventricle The left ventricle pumps oxygen-rich blood to all parts of the body.

Septum This thick muscular wall separates the left side of the heart from the right side. The septum prevents oxygen-rich and oxygen-poor blood from mixing in the heart.

Chapter 17 **539**

As students read the descriptions of the parts of the heart, ask: **Which chambers of the heart contain oxygen-rich blood?** *(The left atrium and left ventricle)* Ask students to identify the locations of valves they can see in the illustration. *(Between the left atrium and the left ventricle; between the right atrium and the right ventricle; between the right ventricle and the artery to the lungs)* Point out that the walls of the ventricles are much thicker than the walls of the atria. Then ask: **How could having thick walls benefit the ventricles?** *(Thick walls give ventricles the muscular strength necessary to pump blood out of the heart.)*
Extend Students might look in high school biology textbooks or encyclopedias to learn the names of the valves and other structures in the heart.
learning modality: visual

Media and Technology

 Transparencies "Exploring the Heart," Transparency 67

Answers to Self-Assessment
Caption Question
Figure 3 Valves prevent blood from flowing backward.

☑ *Checkpoint*
The atria receive blood that comes into the heart. The ventricles pump blood out of the heart.

Ongoing Assessment

Drawing Have students draw a heart, label its chambers, and write brief captions describing the function of each chamber.

 Students can save their drawings in their portfolios.

Regulation of Heartbeat

Building Inquiry Skills: Interpreting Data

Materials *watch with second hand*

Time 10 minutes each day over 1 week

Allow students time to practice taking their pulse; have them follow the instructions in the Skills Lab on page 548. Then direct students to take their pulse three times a day for one school week—when they wake up in the morning, after exercising, before going to bed—and record their pulse rates in data tables. Caution students not to exercise if they have a medical condition that rules out vigorous exercise. At the end of the week, students can look for patterns in their data. Ask: **How does your heart rate at a certain time of the day relate to your body's need for oxygen at that time?** *(Students should find a positive correlation between high pulse rate and high demand for oxygen.)* **learning modality: logical/mathematical**

 Integrating Technology

Tell students that scientists have developed artificial pacemakers that are sensitive to changes in body temperature and oxygen needs. Ask: **Why would these be more efficient than pacemakers that do not have these features?** *(They could match the person's heart rate with his or her activity level.)* **learning modality: verbal**

Language Arts CONNECTION

To help students understand what an idiom is, discuss other examples, such as "on my mind," "icy stare," "she was broken up by the news," and "that idea didn't fly."

In Your Journal Change of heart—change of attitude; heart-to-heart talk—serious discussion; making the blood boil—making someone angry. **learning modality: verbal**

Language Arts CONNECTION

When you say that a person has a "heart of gold," you mean that the person is kind and generous—not that the person's heart is actually made of gold metal. "Heart of gold" is an idiom—an expression with a meaning that cannot be understood from the ordinary meanings of the words in it. The words *heart* and *blood* are found in many idioms. For example, a "blood-chilling scream" frightens you, but it doesn't lower the temperature of your blood.

In Your Journal

Learn what each of the following idioms means:
◆ a change of heart
◆ a heart-to-heart talk
◆ make the blood boil
Then write a sentence using each of these idioms.

Regulation of Heartbeat

A group of cells called the **pacemaker,** which is located in the right atrium, sends out signals that make the heart muscle contract. The pacemaker constantly receives messages about the body's oxygen needs. It then adjusts the heart rate to match. Your heart beats much faster when you are exercising than when you are sitting quietly. When you are exercising, the entire process from the beginning of one heartbeat to the beginning of the next can take less than half a second. Your muscles need more oxygen during exercise. Your rapid heartbeat supplies blood that carries the oxygen.

 INTEGRATING TECHNOLOGY In some people, the pacemaker becomes damaged as a result of disease or an accident. This often results in an irregular or slow heartbeat. In the 1950s, doctors and engineers developed an artificial, battery-operated pacemaker. The artificial pacemaker is implanted beneath the skin and connected by wires to the heart. Tiny electric impulses travel from the battery through the wires. These impulses make the heart contract at a normal rate.

✓ *Checkpoint* **What is the function of the pacemaker?**

Two Loops

After leaving the heart, blood travels in blood vessels through the body. Your body has three kinds of blood vessels—arteries, capillaries, and veins. **Arteries** are blood vessels that carry blood away from the heart. From the arteries, blood flows into tiny vessels called **capillaries.** In the capillaries, substances are exchanged between the blood and body cells. From capillaries, blood flows into **veins,** which are the vessels that carry blood back to the heart.

The overall pattern of blood flow through the body is something like a figure eight. The heart is at the center where the two

Figure 4 Activities such as swimming require a lot of energy. A person's heart beats fast in order to supply the muscles with the blood they need. The heart's pacemaker regulates the speed at which the heart beats.

Background

Integrating Science Many people with advanced heart failure could benefit from heart transplants but have to wait a long time for an acceptable donor heart. Potential heart-transplant recipients must often stay in hospitals, connected to cumbersome machinery that supplements the action of their diseased hearts. However, compact implanted heart pumps may soon enable many patients to survive longer—and to experience a better quality of life—while they are waiting for heart transplants. The battery-powered devices, which temporarily pump blood through the body, are surgically implanted into a patient's abdomen and connected to the patient's heart. Eventually, this implanted heart-pump technology may be an alternative to heart transplants.

loops cross. **In the first loop, blood travels from the heart to the lungs and then back to the heart. In the second loop, blood is pumped from the heart throughout the body and then returns again to the heart.** The heart is really two pumps, one on the right and one on the left. The right side pumps blood to the lungs, and the left side pumps blood to the rest of the body.

Blood travels in only one direction. If you were a drop of blood, you could start at any point in the figure eight and eventually return to the same point. The entire trip would take less than a minute. As you read about the path that blood takes through the cardiovascular system, trace the path in Figure 5.

Loop One: to the Lungs and Back When blood from the body flows into the right atrium, it contains little oxygen but a lot of carbon dioxide. This oxygen-poor blood is dark red. The blood then flows from the right atrium into the right ventricle. Then the ventricle pumps the oxygen-poor blood into the arteries that lead to the lungs.

As blood flows through the lungs, large blood vessels branch into smaller ones. Eventually, blood flows through tiny capillaries that are in close contact with the air that comes into the lungs. The air in the lungs has more oxygen than the blood in the capillaries, so oxygen moves from the lungs into the blood. In contrast, carbon dioxide moves in the opposite direction—from the blood into the lungs. As the blood leaves the lungs, it is now rich in oxygen and poor in carbon dioxide. This blood, which is bright red, flows to the left side of the heart to be pumped through the second loop.

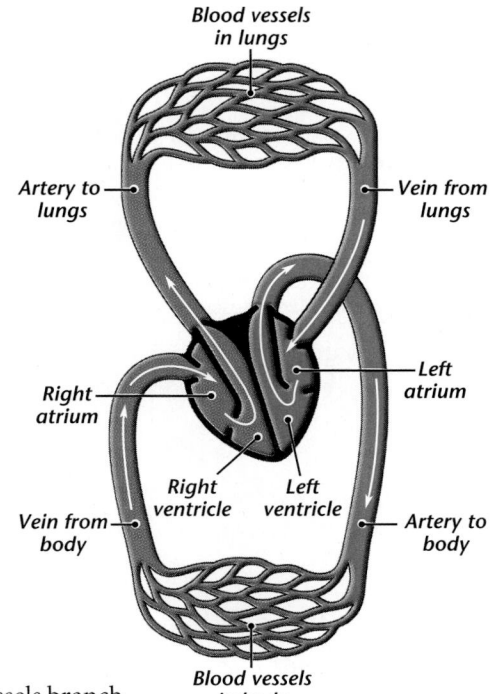

Figure 5 Blood circulates through the body in two loops with the heart at the center. Use the arrows to trace the path of blood, beginning at the right atrium. *Interpreting Diagrams Where does the blood that enters the left atrium come from?*

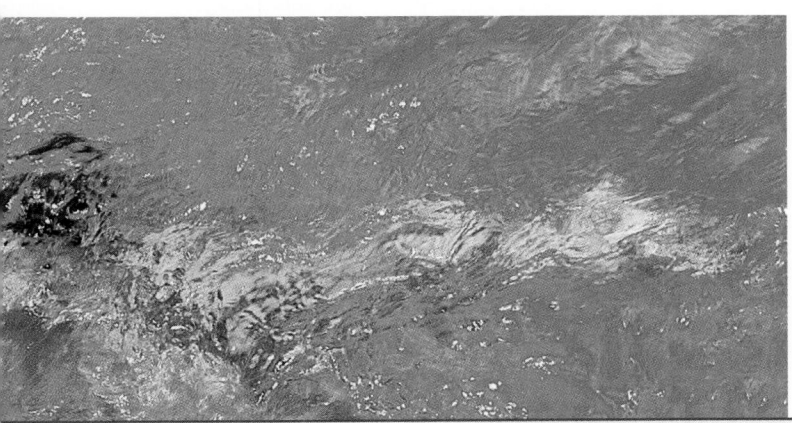

Two Loops

Using the Visuals: Figure 5

Point out that the left atrium is on the right side of the illustration, and the right atrium is on the left side. Explain that the heart and circulatory system are always diagrammed in this way. Also, explain that vessels shown in red carry oxygen-rich blood, while blue vessels carry oxygen-poor blood. Have students place a finger on the right ventricle and follow the arrows to trace the path of the blood as it flows out of the heart and around the body. Students should note that blood goes through both loops before returning to the right ventricle. Ask: **When blood is pumped to the body cells, is it rich in oxygen? How can you tell?** *(Yes; it has just come from the lungs.)* **learning modality: visual**

Addressing Naive Conceptions

Some students may think that some blood is actually blue. Explain that vessels shown in blue in illustrations carry blood that is dark red. Dark red blood contains little oxygen. Red vessels in illustrations carry bright red blood, which contains much more oxygen. **learning modality: verbal**

Answers to Self-Assessment

Caption Question

Figure 5 Blood that enters the left atrium comes from the lungs.

☑ *Checkpoint*

The pacemaker regulates the heartbeat by sending out signals that make the heart muscle contract.

Ongoing Assessment

Organizing Information Have students make flowcharts following the path of blood from one point in its circulation until it reaches the same point again. *(Sample: From the lungs, blood flows to the left atrium, then the left ventricle, and out into the body. From the body, the blood flows into the right atrium, then the right ventricle, then into the lungs.)*

The Force of the Ventricles

Integrating Physics

Ask: Why doesn't the force exerted by the ventricles cause the blood to move back into the atria? *(The valves between the ventricles and atria prevent the blood from flowing backward.)* **learning modality: verbal**

3 Assess

Section 1 Review Answers

1. The cardiovascular system carries needed substances to cells and carries wastes away from them.
2. The heart pumps blood through the vessels of the cardiovascular system.
3. Blood leaves the left ventricle and is pumped throughout the body. It returns to the right atrium and passes to the right ventricle. The right ventricle pumps the blood to the lungs. The blood then returns to the left atrium and the left ventricle.
4. The pacemaker is a group of cells in the right atrium that sends out signals for the heart muscle to contract. It adjusts heartbeat rate to the level of oxygen required by the body.
5. The artery carries blood from the right ventricle to the lungs.

CHAPTER PROJECT

Check Your Progress

Remind students that their displays need to show where the blood acquires and releases oxygen. Also check to make sure that students' plans are realistic.

Performance Assessment

Writing Have students explain the role of the heart in the circulatory system or describe the path the blood takes through the circulatory system.

Figure 6 If the batter hits the ball, the bat will exert a force on the ball. This force will make the ball zoom through the air. Similarly, when the ventricles of the heart contract, they exert a force on the blood inside them. This force pushes blood through the blood vessels.

Loop Two: to the Body and Back The second loop begins as the left atrium fills with oxygen-rich blood coming from the lungs. The blood then moves into the left ventricle. From the left ventricle, the blood is pumped into the **aorta** (ay AWR tuh), the largest artery in the body.

Eventually, after passing through branching arteries, blood flows through tiny capillaries in different parts of your body, such as your brain, liver, and legs. These vessels are in close contact with body cells. Oxygen moves out of the blood and into the body cells. At the same time, carbon dioxide passes from the body cells and into the blood. The blood then flows back to the right atrium of the heart through veins, completing the second loop.

The Force of the Ventricles

 INTEGRATING PHYSICS When the ventricle muscles contract, they exert a force on the blood that is inside them. A **force** is a push or a pull. You see examples of forces all around you. When you lift a book off a table, for example, you exert a force on the book, making it move upward. The force exerted by the ventricles moves blood out of your heart and into arteries.

The contraction of the left ventricle exerts much more force than the contraction of the right ventricle. The right ventricle only pumps blood to the lungs. In contrast, the left ventricle pumps blood throughout the body. As a way of understanding this, think of the force it would take to bunt a baseball. Then think about how hard you would need to hit the ball if you wanted to hit a home run.

Section 1 Review

1. What is the function of the cardiovascular system?
2. What function does the heart perform?
3. Describe the route that blood takes through the cardiovascular system. Begin with blood leaving the left ventricle.
4. What is the heart's pacemaker? What causes the pacemaker to change the rate at which the heart beats?
5. **Thinking Critically Comparing and Contrasting** Most of the arteries in the body carry oxygen-rich blood away from the heart. One artery, however, carries blood that has little oxygen away from the heart. From which ventricle does that artery carry blood? To where does that artery carry blood?

CHAPTER PROJECT

Check Your Progress

At this point, you should have sketched out the two loops your red blood cell will travel. Make sure each pathway forms a complete circuit back to the heart. Begin to plan how you will construct your display. Keep a running list of the materials or equipment you'll need. *(Hint: Think about how you will show the movement of the blood cell in your display.)*

Program Resources

◆ **Unit 4 Resources** 17-1 Review and Reinforce, p. 63; 17-1 Enrich, p. 64

SECTION
2 A Closer Look at Blood Vessels

DISCOVER ••••••••••••••••••••••••••••••• ACTIVITY ••••

How Does Pressure Affect the Flow of Blood?

1. Spread newspapers over a table or desktop. Then fill a plastic squeeze bottle with water.

2. Hold the bottle over a dishpan. Squeeze the bottle with one hand. Observe how far the water travels.

3. Now grasp the bottle with both hands and squeeze again. Observe how far the water travels this time.

Think It Over

Inferring Blood is pushed through arteries with much more force than it is pushed through veins. Which part of the activity models an artery? Which part models a vein? Which organ in the body provides the pushing force?

Like corridors in a large building, blood vessels run through all of the tissues of your body. While some blood vessels are as wide as your thumb, most of them are much finer than a human hair. If all the arteries, capillaries, and veins in your body were hooked together, end to end, they would stretch a distance of almost 100,000 kilometers. That's long enough to wrap around Earth twice—with a lot left over!

Arteries

When blood leaves the heart, it travels through arteries. The right ventricle pumps blood into the arteries that go to the lungs. The left ventricle pumps blood into the aorta, the largest artery in your body. Every organ receives blood from arteries that branch off the aorta. The first branches, called the **coronary arteries,** carry blood to the heart itself. Other branches carry blood to the brain, intestines, and other organs. Each artery branches into smaller and smaller arteries.

Artery Structure The walls of arteries are generally very thick. In fact, artery walls consist of three layers. The innermost layer, which is made up of epithelial

GUIDE FOR READING

◆ What are the functions of arteries, capillaries, and veins?

◆ What causes blood pressure?

Reading Tip As you read, use the text headings to make an outline of the information in this section.

Figure 7 If all the blood vessels in your body were joined end to end, they would wrap around the world almost two and a half times.

Chapter 17 **543**

543

Arteries

Using the Visuals: Figure 8

You can use Figure 8 to help students understand the text differentiation between arteries, veins, and capillaries. Point out that the illustration shows the relative sizes of the three types of blood vessels. Ask which kind has the smallest diameter *(capillaries)*. Then have students note that arteries and veins have the same three layers. Ask students to contrast these three layers in veins and arteries. *(The smooth muscle layer is thicker in arteries.)* **limited English proficiency**

Math TOOLBOX

Explain that rates are often expressed as ratios. **ACTIVITY**
In this example, the pulse rate can be written as 71:1 or as 71 beats per minute. People often calculate their heart rate by counting their pulse for 15 or 30 seconds and then multiplying. Ask: **What are the units of a pulse rate?** *(Beats per minute)* **Extend** Have students find the pulse rate of a person whose heart beats 23 times in 20 seconds. *(69 beats per minute)* **learning modality: logical/mathematical**

Building Inquiry Skills: Calculating

Have students take their pulses and determine **ACTIVITY** how many heartbeats occur in one minute. The Skills Lab, page 548, has instructions for taking pulse. Then challenge students to calculate how many times their heart beats in one hour, one day, one week, one month, and one year. Ask: **What does the blood do on each trip through the body?** *(It delivers oxygen and glucose to the cells and removes wastes such as carbon dioxide.)* **learning modality: logical/ mathematical**

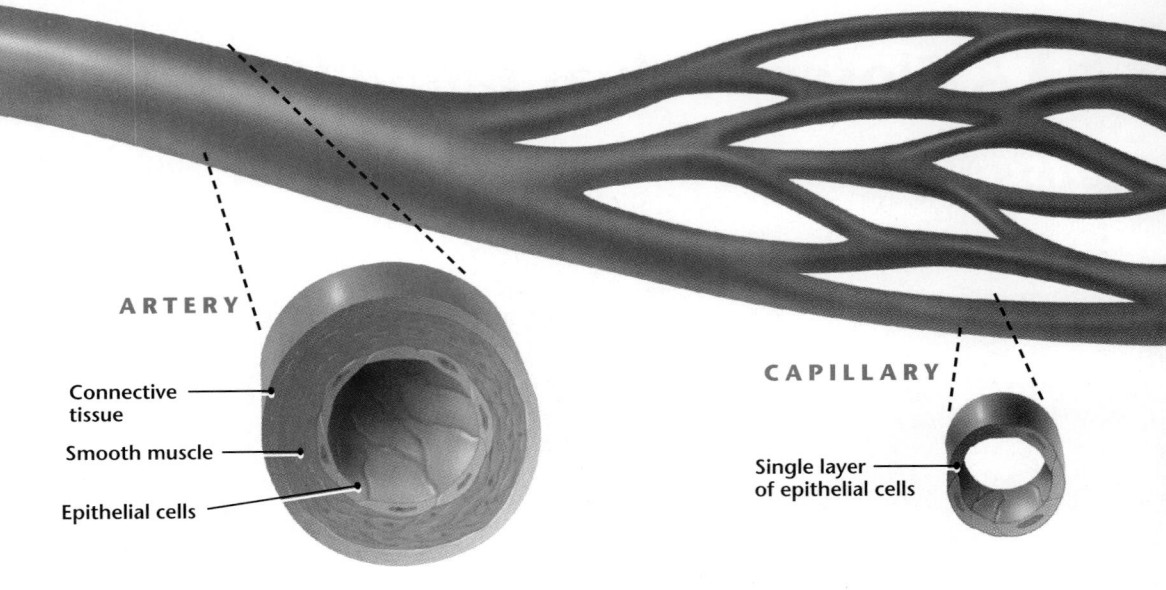

ARTERY

Connective tissue

Smooth muscle

Epithelial cells

CAPILLARY

Single layer of epithelial cells

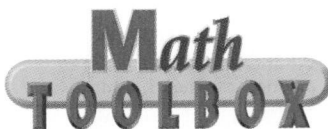

Pulse Rate

A rate is the speed at which something happens. When you calculate a rate, you compare the number of events with the time period in which they occur. Here is how you can calculate the pulse rate of a person whose heart beats 142 times in 2 minutes.

1. Write the comparison as a fraction.

$$\frac{142 \text{ heartbeats}}{2 \text{ minutes}}$$

2. Divide the numerator and the denominator by the denominator.

$$\frac{142 \div 2}{2 \div 2} = \frac{71}{1}$$

The person's pulse rate is 71 heartbeats per minute.

tissue, is smooth. This smooth surface enables blood to flow freely. The middle layer consists mostly of muscle tissue. The outer wall is made up of flexible connective tissue. Because of this layered structure, arteries have both strength and flexibility. Arteries are able to withstand the enormous pressure of blood pumped by the heart, and to expand and relax in response to that pumping.

Pulse If you lightly touch the inside of your wrist, you can feel the artery in your wrist rise and fall repeatedly. The pulse that you feel is caused by the alternating expansion and relaxation of the artery wall. Every time the heart's ventricles contract, they send a spurt of blood out through all the arteries in your body. As this spurt travels through the arteries, it pushes the artery walls and makes them expand. After the spurt passes, the artery walls become narrower again. When you count the number of times an artery pulses beneath your fingers, you are counting heartbeats. By taking your pulse rate, you can determine how fast your heart is beating.

Regulating Blood Flow The muscles in the middle wall of an artery are involuntary muscles, which contract without your thinking about it. When they contract, the opening in the artery becomes smaller. When they relax, the opening becomes larger. These muscles act as control gates, adjusting the amount of blood sent to different organs. For example, after you eat, your stomach

544

Background

History of Science The first person to identify the network of capillaries that connect small arteries to small veins was an Italian named Marcello Malpighi (1628–1694).

Malpighi was pursuing his microscopic research at the University of Bologna in 1661 when he identified the capillaries. In 1662, he moved to another Italian university and continued his research, while also teaching and practicing medicine. He went on to identify the taste buds and describe the structure of the brain and optic nerves. In 1666, Malpighi was the first person to see red blood cells and to relate the red color of blood to the color of the cells.

Malpighi used the microscope to study the organization of living things up close. He is widely considered to be the founder of the study of microscopic anatomy.

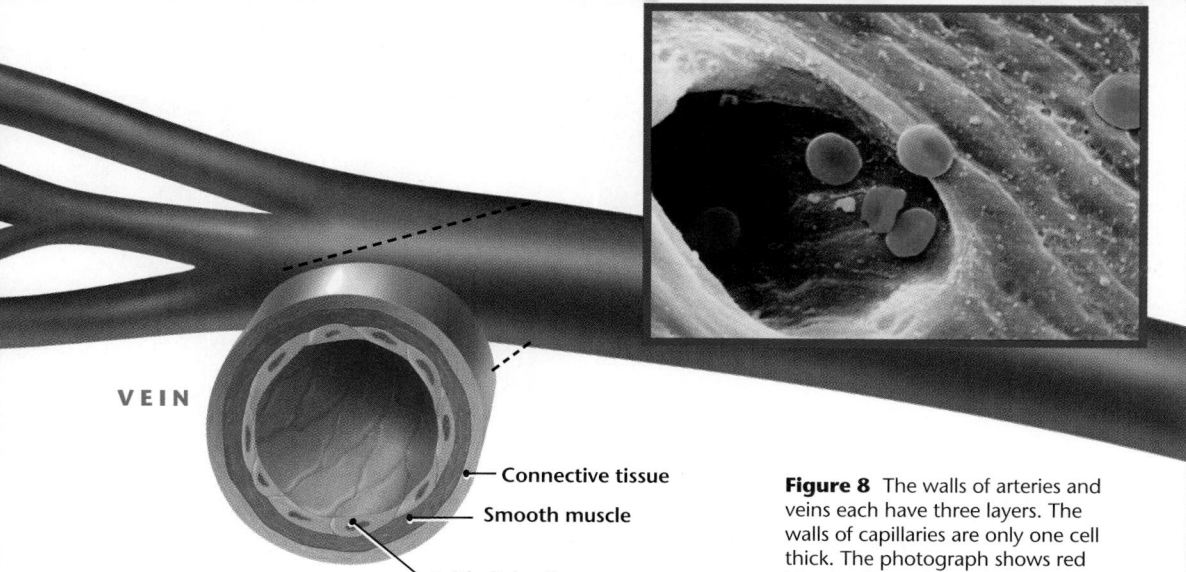

VEIN

Connective tissue

Smooth muscle

Epithelial cells

Figure 8 The walls of arteries and veins each have three layers. The walls of capillaries are only one cell thick. The photograph shows red blood cells moving from an artery into a capillary.

and intestines need a greater blood supply to help power diges-tion. The arteries leading to those organs open wider, so that more blood flows through them. In contrast, when you are running, your stomach and intestines need less blood than the muscles in your legs. The arteries leading to your leg muscles open wider. The arteries leading to the stomach and intestines become narrower, which decreases the blood flow to those organs.

Capillaries

Eventually, blood flows from small arteries into the tiny capil-laries. **In the capillaries, materials are exchanged between the blood and the body's cells.** Capillary walls are only one cell thick. Because capillaries have thin walls, materials can pass easily through them. Materials such as oxygen and glucose pass from blood, through the thin capillary walls, to the cells. Cellular waste products travel in the opposite direction—from cells, through the capillary walls, and into blood.

 INTEGRATING CHEMISTRY Recall from Chapter 2 that materials are exchanged between the blood and the body cells by diffusion. **Diffusion** is the process by which molecules move from an area in which they are highly concentrated to an area in which they are less concentrated. For example, glucose is more highly concentrated in blood than it is in the body cells. Therefore, glucose diffuses from the blood, through the capil-lary wall, and into the body cells.

Language Arts Connection

Tell students that the word *capillaries* comes from the Latin word *capillus,* which means "hair." Ask: **Why do you think capillaries have that name?** *(They are thin, like hair.)* Ask students if they know other words based on the same Latin word. *(Some students may know capellini, the Italian name for angel hair pasta.)* Encourage students to find the origins of other words in this section. (Sample: The word *sphygmomanometer* comes from a Greek word meaning "to beat or throb.") **learning modality: verbal**

 Integrating Chemistry

Tell students that not all substances can diffuse through all membranes. Some membranes are selectively permeable, which means that they allow only certain substances to pass through. For example, a cell membrane may allow glucose molecules to pass through, but block starch molecules. **learning modality: verbal**

Media and Technology

Transparencies "Artery, Capillary, and Vein," Transparency 68

Ongoing Assessment

Oral Presentation Call on students to name and describe the three layers in an artery wall.

545

Veins

Building Inquiry Skills: Inferring

Ask students: **Why would a doctor recommend more exercise for a person with poor circulation in the arms and legs?** *(When you move your skeletal muscles, it helps the blood move through the veins in your arms and legs.)*
learning modality: verbal

Creating Data Tables

Time 15 minutes
Tips Ask students to tell you how many rows and columns the data table should have. *(Three columns; three rows)* Then draw the data table on the board. Ask students for suggestions on column and row heads. *(Column heads—Parts of Body; Volume of Blood During Rest; Volume of Blood During Exercise; Row heads—Organs of the Abdomen; Skeletal Muscles; Kidneys)* Invite volunteers to fill in the appropriate labels and data.
Expected Outcome Students should conclude that the muscles need extra oxygen and glucose during exercise, and the amount of blood flowing to other organs is adjusted.
Extend Have students graph the data.
learning modality: logical/ mathematical

Blood Pressure

Integrating Physics

Ask students to use what they have learned about blood pressure to explain why a cut in an artery is often a more serious injury than a cut in a vein of the same size. *(Since blood pressure is highest in arteries, blood loss from a cut artery can occur rapidly.)* **learning modality: verbal**

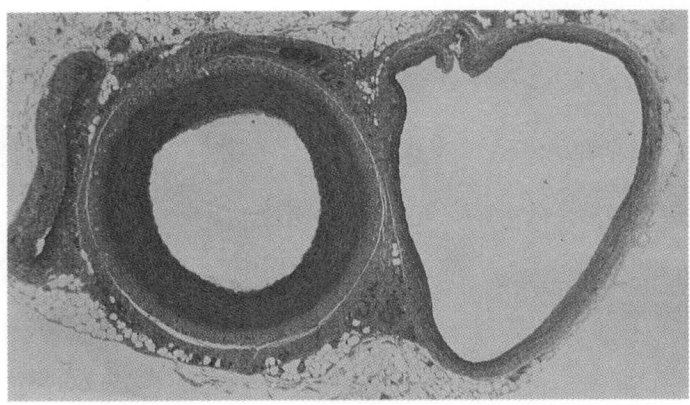

Figure 9 The wall of the artery (left) is much thicker than that of the vein (right).
Making Generalizations Why is it important for artery walls to be both strong and flexible?

Creating Data Tables

Scientists measured the volume of blood that different organs receive, first when a person was resting and then when the person was engaged in vigorous exercise.

- At rest, the organs of the abdomen received approximately 1,400 mL of blood per minute (mL/min). During vigorous exercise, they received 600 mL/min.
- At rest, skeletal muscles received about 1,200 mL/min. During vigorous exercise, the same muscles received about 12,500 mL/min.
- At rest, the kidneys received about 1,100 mL/min. During vigorous exercise, they received 600 mL/min.

Create a table to record these data. Then use the data to explain why some organs receive more blood during exercise, while some receive less.

Veins

After blood moves through capillaries, it enters larger blood vessels called veins, which carry blood back to the heart. The walls of veins, like those of arteries, have three layers, with muscle in the middle layer. However, the walls of veins are generally thinner than those of arteries.

By the time blood flows into veins, the pushing force of the heart has little effect. Several factors help move blood through veins. First, because many veins are located near skeletal muscles, the contraction of the muscles helps push the blood along. For example, as you run or walk, the skeletal muscles in your legs contract and squeeze the veins in your legs. Second, larger veins in your body have valves in them that prevent blood from flowing backward. Third, breathing movements, which exert a squeezing pressure against veins in the chest, also force blood toward the heart.

☑ *Checkpoint* How do skeletal muscles help move blood in veins?

Blood Pressure

 INTEGRATING PHYSICS Suppose that you are washing a car. You attach the hose to the faucet and turn on the faucet. The water flows out in a slow, steady stream. Then, while your back is turned, your little brother turns the faucet on all the way. Suddenly, the water spurts out rapidly, and the hose almost jumps out of your hand.

As water flows through a hose, it pushes against the walls of the hose, creating pressure on the walls. **Pressure** is the force that something exerts over a given area. When your brother turned on the faucet all the way, the additional water flow increased the pressure exerted on the inside of the hose. The extra pressure made the water spurt out of the nozzle faster.

Background

Facts and Figures Varicose veins occur when the valves in the veins of the legs malfunction. Under normal conditions, the blood in the legs returns to the heart through the veins, and the valves prevent the flow of blood from reversing. When the valves don't work, blood collects in the veins, making them swollen and twisted. The swollen veins can lead to varicose ulcers, which are lesions or sores. Varicose veins are often treated with elastic bandages, but doctors in India have found a new treatment—leeches. The leeches seem to prefer the blood in the veins to the oxygen-rich blood in the arteries, and when attached to the area around ulcers, remove blood from the swollen veins.

What Causes Blood Pressure? Blood traveling through blood vessels behaves in a manner similar to that of water moving through a hose. Blood exerts a pressure, called **blood pressure,** against the walls of blood vessels. **Blood pressure is caused by the force with which the ventricles contract.** In general, as blood moves away from the heart, its pressure decreases. This happens because the farther away from the heart the blood moves, the lower the force of the ventricles. Blood flowing through arteries exerts the highest pressure. Blood pressure in capillaries and veins is much lower than in arteries.

Measuring Blood Pressure Blood pressure can be measured with an instrument called a **sphygmomanometer** (sfig moh muh NAHM uh tur). Many sphygmomanometers contain a tube of mercury. Blood pressure is expressed in millimeters of mercury and is recorded as two numbers. The first number, which is the higher of the two numbers, is a measure of the blood pressure while the ventricles contract and pump blood into the arteries. The second number measures the blood pressure while the ventricles relax between heartbeats. The two numbers are written as a fraction. A typical, healthy blood pressure reading for a young adult is 120/80. This is expressed as 120 over 80, or the contraction pressure over the relaxation pressure. You will learn about the effects of high blood pressure in Section 4.

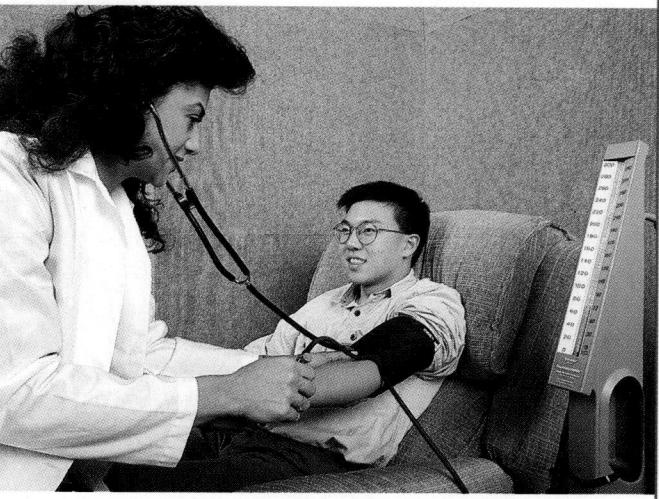

Figure 10 Blood pressure is measured with a sphygmomanometer. The cuff is wrapped around the patient's arm. His blood pressure is recorded by the height of the mercury column in the instrument on the right.

Section 2 Review

1. Contrast the functions of arteries, capillaries, and veins.
2. What causes blood pressure?
3. Explain the factors that enable blood in your leg veins to return to the heart in spite of the downward pull of gravity.
4. **Thinking Critically** **Applying Concepts** Arteries adjust the amount of blood flowing to different parts of the body, depending on where blood is needed. Use this fact to explain why it may not be a good idea to exercise vigorously shortly after you eat.

> **CHAPTER PROJECT**
> *Check Your Progress*
> By now you should have begun constructing your display. Make sure that the blood vessels are depicted accurately. Also check that your display correctly shows the path of a red blood cell and the place where the red blood cell picks up oxygen. (*Hint:* Start to prepare a rough draft of your written description.)

Program Resources

◆ **Unit 4 Resources** 17-2 Review and Reinforce, p. 67; 17-2 Enrich, p. 68

Answers to Self-Assessment
Caption Question
Figure 9 Artery walls need to be strong to withstand the pressure of blood; they must also be flexible in order to respond to changing blood volume.

☑ *Checkpoint*
They squeeze blood in the veins near them. This squeezing helps push the blood through the veins.

Real-Life Learning

Ask a medical professional to read the blood pressures of volunteers. Make sure volunteers have no medical problems that prohibit them from participating. Ask the professional to describe how a sphygmomanometer measures the two numbers in a blood pressure reading. Have volunteers describe what they feel during the reading. **learning modality: kinesthetic**

ACTIVITY

3 Assess

Section 2 Review Answers

1. Arteries carry blood away from the heart. Capillaries carry blood between arteries and veins and are the site of the exchange of materials with cells. Veins return blood to the heart.
2. The force with which the ventricles contract to push blood into arteries
3. Skeletal muscles around the veins squeeze blood upward; valves prevent backward flow.
4. After eating, blood is routed to the digestive system. If someone exercises right after eating, the body might not be able to supply enough blood to both the digestive system and the skeletal muscles.

> **CHAPTER PROJECT**
> *Check Your Progress*
> Encourage students to use their rough drafts of their written descriptions to make sure their displays are accurate. Help students determine the best way to organize the information for their own understanding. Suggest students make flowcharts to help them prepare rough drafts.

Performance Assessment

Drawing Have students diagram the movement of blood through arteries, capillaries, veins, and the heart. Students can save their diagrams in their portfolios.

Heart Beat, Health Beat

Preparing for Inquiry

Key Concept Heart rate increases in response to physical activity.
Skills Objective Students will be able to
◆ measure their own pulse rates;
◆ measure the effects of physical activity.
Time 40 minutes
Advance Planning Students with health problems that restrict physical activity can keep time and record data.

 If using probeware, refer to the *Probeware Lab Manual.*

Guiding Inquiry

Invitation Ask students how they feel after exercising vigorously. (*Samples: breathless, hot*) Tell students that, in this lab, they measure how the heart responds to increased physical activity.

Introducing the Procedure

Have students practice taking their pulses.

Expected Outcome

◆ Resting pulse rate should be around 70–80 beats per minute, increase more in response to running than walking, and return to near the resting rate.
◆ Students may show a great deal of variation in their heart rates.

Analyze and Conclude

1. Graphs should be clearly labeled.
2. Pulse rate increases during exercise.
3. The pulse rate returns to the resting rate; the change may take a few minutes.
4. The heart is beating faster.
5. Answers will vary. Averaging several measurements improves accuracy.

Extending the Inquiry

Design an Experiment Students' plans should include measuring the resting pulse rate of people of different ages.

Safety

Students with health problems should not complete the lab after Step 3.

Skills Lab

Measuring

Heart Beat, Health Beat

Problem

How does physical activity affect your pulse rate?

Materials

watch with second hand
 or heart rate monitor
graph paper

Procedure

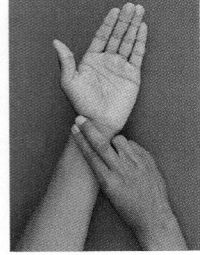

1. Predict how your pulse rate will change as you go from resting to being active, then back to resting again. Then copy the data table into your notebook.

2. Locate your pulse by placing the index and middle finger of one hand on your other wrist at the base of your thumb. Move the two fingers slightly until you feel your pulse. If you are using a heart rate monitor, see your teacher for instructions.

3. Work with a partner for the rest of this lab. Begin by determining your resting pulse rate. Count the number of beats in your pulse for exactly one minute while your partner times you. Record your resting pulse rate in your data table.

CAUTION: *Do not complete the rest of these procedures if there is any medical reason why you should avoid physical activities.*

4. Walk in place for one minute while your partner times you. Stop and immediately take your pulse for one minute. Record the number in your data table.

5. Run in place for one minute. Take your pulse again, and record the result.

6. Sit down right away, and have your partner time you as you rest for one minute. Then take your pulse rate again.

7. Have your partner time you as you rest for 3 more minutes. Then take your pulse rate again and record it.

Analyze and Conclude

1. Use the data you obtained to create a bar graph of your pulse rate under the different conditions you tested.

2. What conclusion can you draw about the relationship between physical activity and a person's pulse rate?

3. What happens to the pulse rate when the physical activity has stopped?

4. What can you infer about the heartbeat when the pulse rate increases?

5. **Think About It** Do you think the pulse measurements you made are completely accurate? Why or why not? How could you improve the accuracy of your measurements?

Design an Experiment

Do the resting pulse rates of adults, teens, and young children differ? Write a plan to answer this question. Obtain your teacher's permission before carrying out your plan.

DATA TABLE

Activity	Pulse Rate
Resting	
Walking	
Running	
Resting after Exercise (1 min)	
Resting after Exercise (3+ min)	

548

Sample Data Table

Activity	Pulse Rate
Resting	75
Walking	88
Running	120
Resting after Exercise (1 min)	97
Resting after Exercise (3+ min)	81

Program Resources

◆ **Unit 4 Resources** Chapter 17 Skills Lab, pp. 77–78
◆ **Probeware Lab Manual** Blackline masters
◆ **Inquiry Skills Activity Book** Provides teaching and review of all inquiry skills.

SECTION 3 Blood and Lymph

DISCOVER • ACTIVITY

What Kinds of Cells Are in Blood?

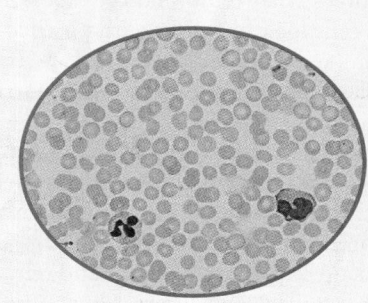

1. Obtain a microscope slide of human blood. Look at the slide under the microscope, first under low power and then under high power.

2. Look carefully at the different kinds of cells that you see.

3. Make several drawings of each kind of cell. Use red pencil for the red blood cells.

Think It Over
Observing How many kinds of cells did you see? How do they differ from one another?

I f someone fills a test tube with blood and lets it sit for a while, the blood separates into layers. The top layer is a clear, yellowish liquid. A dark red material rests on the bottom. The top layer is **plasma,** which is the liquid part of blood. The red material at the bottom is a mixture of blood cells. **Blood is made up of four components: plasma, red blood cells, white blood cells, and platelets.** About 45 percent of the volume of blood is made up of cells. The rest consists of plasma.

Plasma

Blood, as you have learned, transports materials from one part of the body to another. Most of those materials travel in plasma. In fact, 10 percent of plasma is made up of these dissolved materials. The other 90 percent of plasma is water.

Plasma carries molecules that come from the breakdown of digested food, such as glucose and fats. The vitamins and minerals your body needs also travel in plasma. Plasma also carries chemical messengers that direct body activities such as the uptake of glucose by your cells. In addition, many wastes produced by cell processes are carried away by plasma.

Protein molecules give plasma its yellow color. There are three groups of plasma proteins. One group helps to regulate the amount of water in blood. The second group, which is produced by white blood cells, helps fight disease. The third group of proteins interacts with platelets to form blood clots.

> ### GUIDE FOR READING
>
> ◆ What are the four components of blood?
>
> ◆ What determines the type of blood that a person can receive in transfusion?
>
> *Reading Tip* As you read, write definitions for each boldfaced term in your own words.

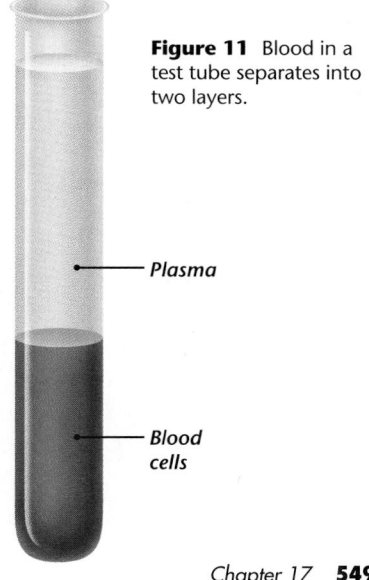

Figure 11 Blood in a test tube separates into two layers.

Plasma

Blood cells

Chapter 17 **549**

READING STRATEGIES

Reading Tip After students write definitions for the boldface terms, have them work in small groups to create vocabulary worksheets. Offer suggestions such as matching activities or fill-in-the-blank activities. Then have each group prepare the worksheet and an answer key. Direct groups to exchange worksheets and complete them. Then have students check their answers against the answer keys.

Program Resources

◆ **Unit 4 Resources** 17-3 Lesson Plan, p. 69; 17-3 Section Summary, p. 70

Media and Technology

 **Audio CD** English-Spanish Summary 17-3

SECTION 3 Blood and Lymph

Objectives

After completing the lesson, students will be able to

◆ name and describe the four components of blood;

◆ explain blood type and how it determines what blood a person can receive in a transfusion;

◆ describe the structure and function of the lymphatic system.

Key Terms plasma, red blood cell, hemoglobin, white blood cell, platelet, fibrin, blood transfusion, lymphatic system, lymph, lymph node

1 Engage/Explore

Activating Prior Knowledge

Fill five clear one-liter bottles with water. Add a few drops of red food coloring. Ask students if they would be surprised to learn that the bottles represent the amount of blood in an average human body. Ask students to name the components of blood with which they are familiar.

• • • • • • • DISCOVER • • • • • • • •

Skills Focus observing
Materials *microscope, prepared slides of human blood*
Time 15 minutes
Tips Remind students to note the shapes and sizes of cells.
Expected Outcome Students should observe three kinds of blood cells. Students will see many more red blood cells than white blood cells or platelets.
Think It Over Students should describe three types of cells: round with a depressed center (red blood cells); irregularly shaped cells (white blood cells); and flat, fragmented bodies (platelets).

549

2 Facilitate

Plasma

Demonstration

Materials *plastic jars with lids, table salt, sugar, sand*

Time 10 minutes setup; 10 minutes observation next day

This demonstration will help students understand that materials dissolve in plasma, as discussed on page 549. Label three jars *Salt, Sugar,* and *Sand,* and fill with water. Add a small amount of each material to the appropriate jar and shake. Have students observe the jars and record their observations. Let the jars stand overnight. Then have students compare the appearance of the materials in the three jars. Ask: **Which jar most closely resembles Figure 11?** *(Sand)* Ask students to infer what parts of blood are modeled in this activity. *(Water—plasma; salt and sugar—materials dissolved in the plasma; sand —blood cells)* **learning modality: visual**

Red Blood Cells

EXPLORING

Blood Cells

This visual can help students who have difficulty comprehending written text. Ask them how many types of cells are found in blood. *(Three)* Have students contrast the relative sizes, structures, and numbers of the three types. Students should note that red blood cells are far more abundant than either white blood cells or platelets. Ask: **When does a red blood cell become bright red?** *(When its hemoglobin combines with oxygen)*
Extend If students performed the Discover activity on page 549, have them compare the appearance of the blood cells they observed to those in the illustration. **limited English proficiency**

Red Blood Cells

Without red blood cells, your body could not use the oxygen that you breathe in. **Red blood cells** take up oxygen in the lungs and deliver it to cells elsewhere in the body. Red blood cells, like most blood cells, are produced in bone marrow.

Exploring Blood Cells shows what red blood cells look like. Under a microscope, these cells look like disks with pinched-in centers. Because they are thin, red blood cells can bend and twist easily. This flexibility enables them to squeeze through narrow capillaries.

A red blood cell is made mostly of **hemoglobin** (HEE muh gloh bin), which is an iron-containing protein that binds chemically to oxygen molecules. When hemoglobin combines with oxygen, the cells become bright red. Without oxygen, they are dark red. Hemoglobin picks up oxygen in the lungs and releases it as blood travels through capillaries in the rest of the body. Hemoglobin also picks up some of the carbon dioxide produced by cells. However, most of the carbon dioxide is carried by plasma. The blood carries the carbon dioxide to the lungs, where it is released from the body.

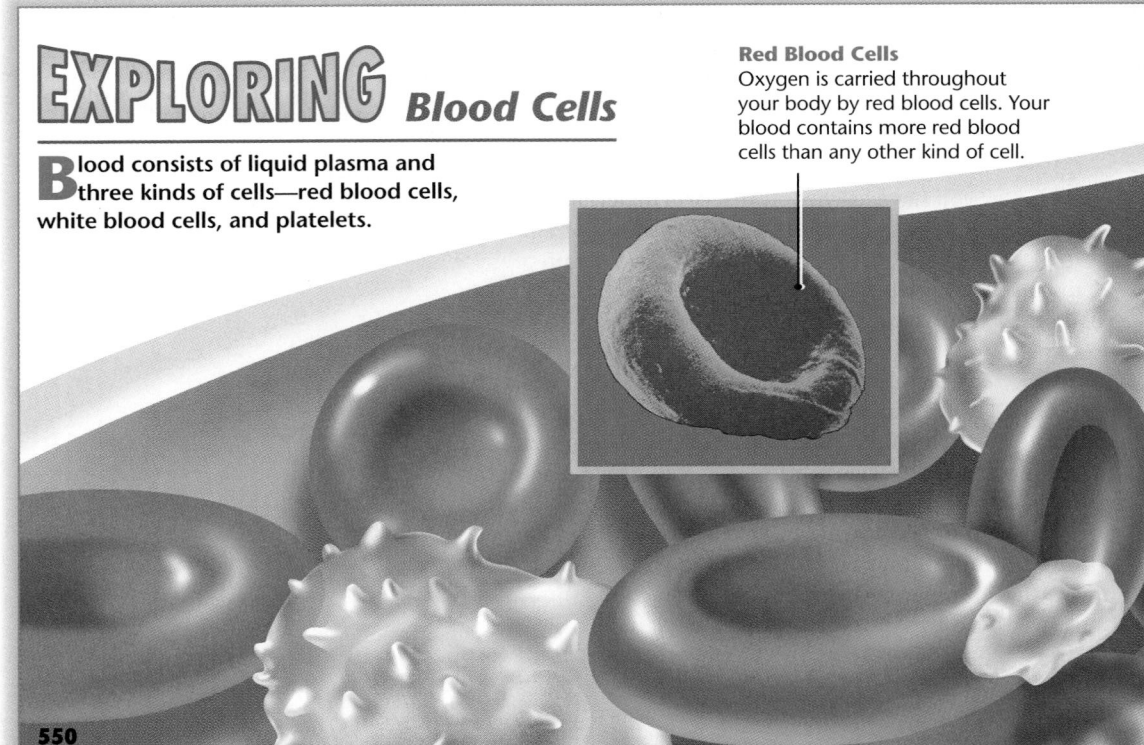

EXPLORING Blood Cells

Blood consists of liquid plasma and three kinds of cells—red blood cells, white blood cells, and platelets.

Red Blood Cells
Oxygen is carried throughout your body by red blood cells. Your blood contains more red blood cells than any other kind of cell.

550

Background

Integrating Science Suppose a forensic scientist is at the scene of a crime. The scientist finds some blood, but no body. How can he or she discover what animal the blood is from? The scientist can examine the hemoglobin in the blood. Hemoglobin carries oxygen in all vertebrates and some invertebrates. Mammalian hemoglobins differ in the amino acids of which they are composed, and the shape of hemoglobin

crystals differs from species to species. For example, rat and horse hemoglobin crystallizes easily, but hemoglobin from humans, cattle, and sheep does not crystallize easily. If the blood is human, the forensic scientist may be able to infer where that human's ancestors came from. People whose ancestors came from Europe are likely to have hemoglobin D; those with ancestors from Southeast Asia, hemoglobin E.

Mature red blood cells have no nuclei. Without a nucleus, a red blood cell cannot reproduce or repair itself. Red blood cells live only about 120 days. Every second, about 2 million red blood cells in your body die. Fortunately, your bone marrow produces new red blood cells at the same rate.

☑ *Checkpoint* **What is the shape of a red blood cell?**

White Blood Cells

Like red blood cells, white blood cells begin their existence in bone marrow. **White blood cells** are the body's disease fighters. Some white blood cells recognize disease-causing organisms such as bacteria and alert the body that it has been invaded. Other white blood cells produce chemicals to fight the invaders. Still others surround and kill the organisms. You will learn more about the functions of white blood cells in Chapter 19.

White blood cells are different from red blood cells in several important ways. There are fewer of them—only about one white blood cell for every 500 to 1,000 red blood cells. White blood cells are also bigger than red blood cells, and they have nuclei. Most white blood cells live for months or even years.

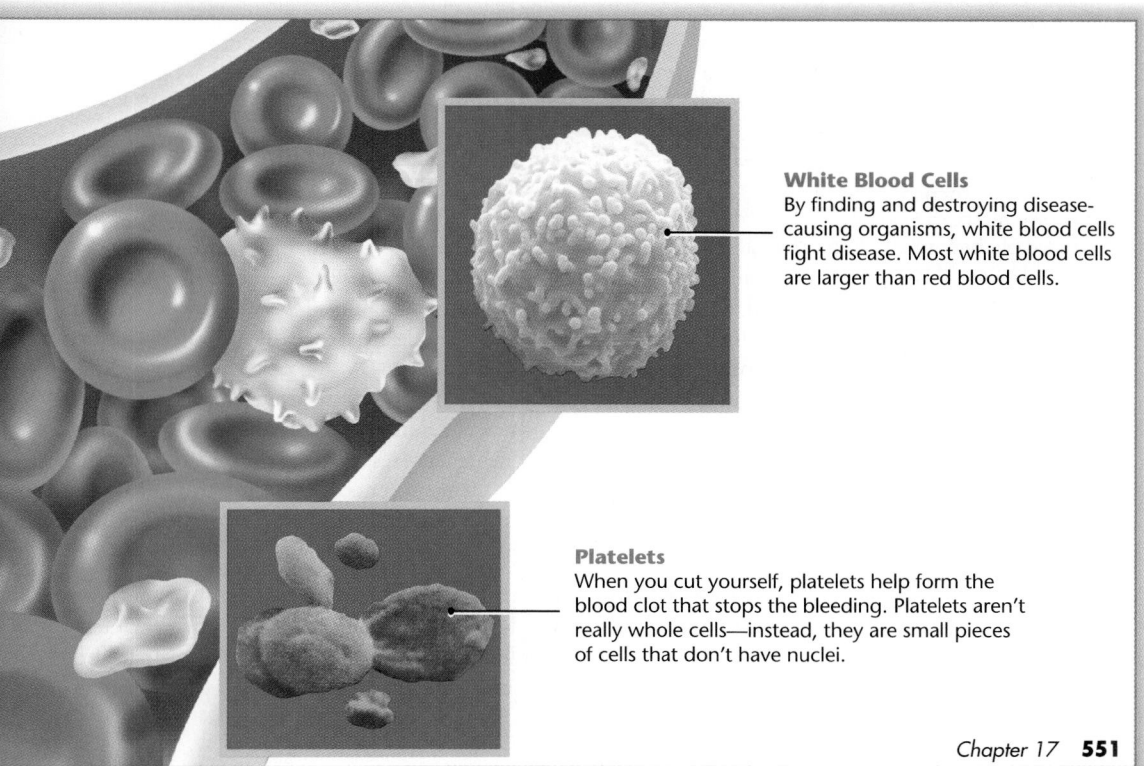

White Blood Cells
By finding and destroying disease-causing organisms, white blood cells fight disease. Most white blood cells are larger than red blood cells.

Platelets
When you cut yourself, platelets help form the blood clot that stops the bleeding. Platelets aren't really whole cells—instead, they are small pieces of cells that don't have nuclei.

Chapter 17 **551**

Media and Technology

 **Exploring Life Science Videodisc**
Unit 4, Side 1,
"Blood!"

Chapter 6

Answers to Self-Assessment

☑ *Checkpoint*
Red blood cells are shaped like disks with pinched-in centers.

Real-Life Learning

Tell students that the hemoglobin in red blood cells is essential for carrying enough oxygen throughout the body. Anemia is an illness caused by a shortage of red blood cells or hemoglobin. There are about 100 varieties of anemia. People with sickle-cell anemia inherit an abnormal type of hemoglobin that distorts their red blood cells into a crescent shape that looks like a sickle. Other anemias may be caused by a lack of iron or folic acid in the diet. Invite interested students to find out more about these diseases. **learning modality: verbal**

White Blood Cells

Health Connection

Inform students that when the body fights infection, the white blood cells go into action to defend the body against attack. Ask students: **What do you think happens to the total number of white blood cells when the body is fighting an infection?** (*The number of white blood cells increases.*) Tell students that the number of white blood cells can increase for reasons other than infection. The number rises temporarily after exercise, during strong emotional reactions, and during painful conditions. Normal blood may have as few as 450,000 white blood cells per milliliter and as many as 1,100,000. Strong physical activity may raise the count to over 2,000,000 cells per mL. On the other hand, when the body is *overwhelmed* with infection, the white blood count can drop below normal. **learning modality: verbal**

Ongoing Assessment

Skills Check Have students create compare/contrast tables that include the structure and functions of red and white blood cells.

 Students can save their tables in their portfolios.

551

Platelets

Blood Types

Figure 12 When you cut your skin, a blood clot forms. The blood clot consists of blood cells trapped in a fiber net. Platelets produce the material of which the fibers are made.

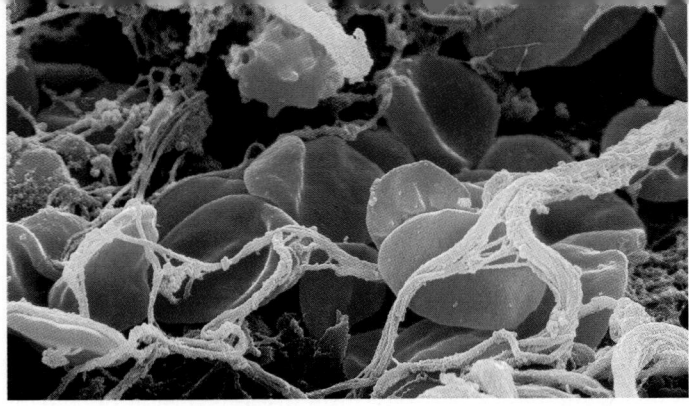

552

Platelets

When you cut your finger, blood flows out of the cut. After a short time, however, a blood clot forms, stopping the blood flow. **Platelets** (PLAYT lits) are cell fragments that play an important part in forming blood clots.

When a blood vessel is cut, platelets collect and stick to the vessel at the site of the wound. The platelets release chemicals that start a chain reaction. This series of reactions eventually produces a protein called **fibrin** (FY brin). Fibrin gets its name from the fact that it weaves a net of tiny fibers across the cut in the blood vessel. The fiber net traps blood cells. As more and more platelets and blood cells become trapped in the net, a blood clot forms. A scab is a dried blood clot on the skin surface.

☑ *Checkpoint* *What role do platelets play in forming blood clots?*

Blood Types

If a person loses a lot of blood—from a wound or during surgery—he or she may be given a **blood transfusion.** A blood transfusion is the transference of blood from one person to another. Most early attempts at blood transfusion failed, but no one knew why until the early 1900s. At that time Karl Landsteiner, an Austrian American physician, tried mixing blood samples from pairs of people. Sometimes the two blood samples blended smoothly. In other cases, however, the red blood cells clumped together. This clumping accounted for the failure of many blood transfusions. If clumping occurs within the body, it clogs the capillaries and may kill the person.

Marker Molecules Landsteiner went on to discover that there are four types of blood—A, B, AB, and O. Blood types are determined by marker molecules on red blood cells. If your blood type is A, you have the A marker. If your blood type is B, you have the B marker. People with type AB blood have both A and B markers. The red blood cells of people with type O blood contain neither A nor B markers.

Your plasma contains clumping proteins that recognize red blood cells with "foreign" markers and make those cells clump together. For example, if you have blood type A, your blood contains clumping proteins that act against cells with B markers. So if you receive a transfusion of type B blood, your clumping proteins will make the "foreign" type B cells clump together.

Safe Transfusions Landsteiner's work led to a better understanding of transfusions. **The marker molecules on your red blood cells determine your blood type and the type of blood that you can safely receive in transfusions.** A person with type A blood can receive transfusions of either type A or type O blood. Neither of these two blood types has B markers. Thus they would not be recognized as foreign by the clumping proteins in type A blood. A person with type AB blood can receive all blood types in transfusion, because type AB blood has no clumping proteins. Figure 13 shows which transfusions are safe for each blood type.

If you ever receive a transfusion, your blood type will be checked. Donated blood that you can safely receive will then be found. This process is called cross matching. You may have heard a doctor on a television show give the order to "type and cross." The doctor wants to find out what blood type the patient has and then cross match it against donated blood.

Blood Types

Blood Type	Marker Molecules on Red Blood Cells	Clumping Proteins	Blood Types That Can Be Safely Received in a Transfusion
A	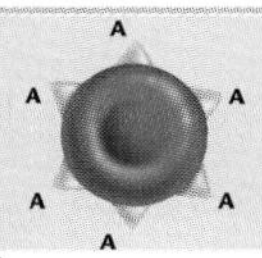	anti-B	A and O
B		anti-A	B and O
AB	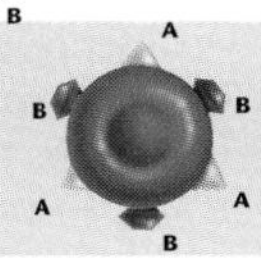	no clumping proteins	A, B, AB, and O
O		anti-A and anti-B	O

Figure 13 The chemical markers on a person's red blood cells determine the types of blood he or she can safely receive in a transfusion. *Interpreting Charts* What types of blood can be given safely to a person with blood type AB? Who can safely receive blood type O?

553

The Lymphatic System

Using the Visuals: Figure 14

Have students trace lymph as it enters the lymph vessels and passes through the nodes. Remind students that lymph passing through the nodes has bacteria and other microorganisms removed from it. Lymph vessels empty into the large veins of the chest, from which lymph re-enters the bloodstream.
learning modality: visual

3 Assess

Section 3 Review Answers

1. Plasma (liquid), red blood cells, white blood cells, platelets (part of a cell)
2. People with type O blood have anti-A and anti-B clumping proteins in their plasma. If they receive type A blood, the clumping proteins will make the type-A red blood cells clump together.
3. Lymph is a fluid that leaks out of blood vessels and bathes the cells. After it travels through the lymphatic system, it enters large veins in the chest and becomes part of blood plasma again.
4. Because hemophiliacs do not have fibrin, their blood does not clot properly.

Check Your Progress

Students should test their displays or practice their presentations as they add the finishing touches. Remind students to check their final written descriptions against their displays to make sure they match and are both correct.

CHAPTER PROJECT

Performance Assessment

Organizing Information Have students work in pairs to create illustrated charts that describe the four components of blood and the roles of each.

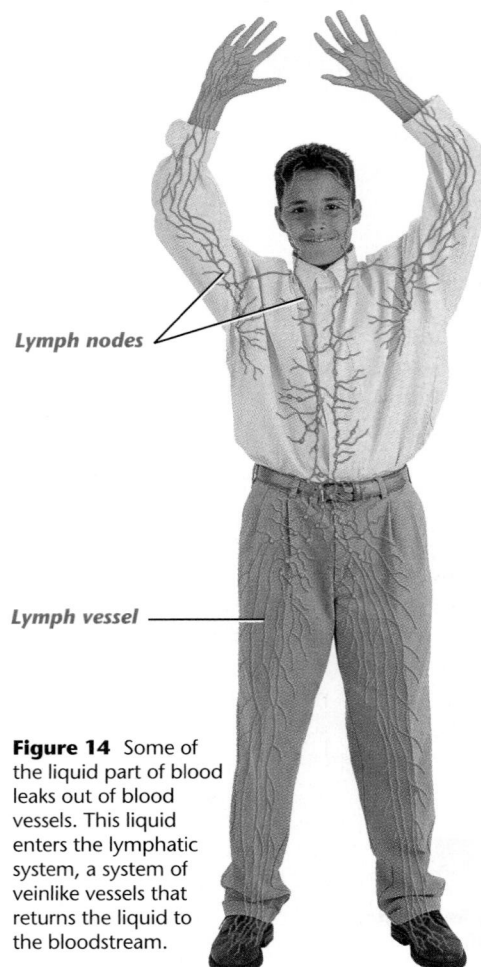

Lymph nodes

Lymph vessel

Figure 14 Some of the liquid part of blood leaks out of blood vessels. This liquid enters the lymphatic system, a system of veinlike vessels that returns the liquid to the bloodstream.

The Lymphatic System

As blood travels through the capillaries in the cardiovascular system, some of the fluid leaks out. It moves through the walls of capillaries and into surrounding tissues. This fluid carries materials that the cells in the tissues need.

After bathing the cells, this fluid moves into the lymphatic system. The **lymphatic system** (lim FAT ik) is a network of veinlike vessels that returns the fluid to the bloodstream. The lymphatic system acts something like rain gutters after a rainstorm, carrying the fluid away.

Lymph Once the fluid is inside the lymphatic system, it is called **lymph.** Lymph consists of water and dissolved materials such as glucose. It also contains some white blood cells that have left the capillaries.

The lymphatic system has no pump, so lymph moves slowly. Lymphatic vessels, which are part of the cardiovascular system, connect to large veins in the chest. Lymph empties into these veins and once again becomes part of blood plasma.

Lymph Nodes As lymph flows through the lymphatic system, it passes through small knobs of tissue called **lymph nodes.** Lymph nodes filter the lymph, trapping bacteria and other microorganisms that cause disease. When the body is fighting an infection, lymph nodes often enlarge. If you've ever had "swollen glands" when you've been sick, you've actually had swollen lymph nodes.

Section 3 Review

1. List the four components of blood. Identify whether each is a cell, a part of a cell, or a liquid.
2. Explain why a person with type O blood cannot receive a transfusion of type A blood.
3. Where does lymph come from? What happens to lymph after it travels through the lymphatic system?
4. Thinking Critically **Relating Cause and Effect** People with the disease hemophilia do not produce the chemical fibrin. Explain why hemophilia is a serious disease.

554

Check Your Progress

By now, you should be completing your display. Write out your description using the correct names of blood vessels and other terms that you've learned in this chapter. (*Hint:* If your display has moving parts, test it to make sure that it works the way you expect it to.)

CHAPTER PROJECT

Program Resources

◆ **Unit 4 Resources** 17-3 Review and Reinforce, p. 71; 17-3 Enrich, p. 72

Media and Technology

Interactive Student Tutorial CD-ROM Chapter 17

You and Your Community

Do You Know Your A-B-O's?

Donated blood is used for blood transfusions. But not every type of blood can be safely donated to every individual. In this lab, you'll investigate why type O blood is especially useful in blood transfusions.

Problem

Which blood types can safely receive transfusions of type A blood? Which can receive type O blood?

Materials

4 paper cups   marking pen
4 plastic droppers   8 plastic petri dishes
white paper   toothpicks
four model "blood" types

Procedure

1. Write down your ideas about why type O blood might be in higher demand than other blood types. Then make two copies of the data table in your notebook.

2. Label 4 paper cups A, B, AB, and O. Fill each cup about one-third full with the model "blood" supplied by your teacher. Insert one clean plastic dropper into each cup. Use each dropper to transfer only that one type of blood.

3. Label the side of each of 4 petri dishes with a blood type: A, B, AB, or O. Place the petri dishes on a sheet of white paper.

4. Use the plastic droppers to place 10 drops of each type of blood in its labeled petri dish. Each sample represents the blood of a potential receiver of a blood transfusion. Record the original color of each sample in your data table as yellow, blue, green, or colorless.

DATA TABLE

Donor: Type _____

Potential Receiver	Original Color	Final Color of Mixture	Safe or Unsafe?
A			
B			
AB			
O			

5. Label your first data table Donor: Type A. To test whether each potential receiver can safely receive type A blood, add 10 drops of type A blood to each sample. Stir each mixture with a separate, clean toothpick.

6. Record the final color of each mixture in the data table. If the color stayed the same, write "safe" in the last column. If the color of the mixture changed, write "unsafe."

7. Label your second data table Donor: Type O. Obtain four clean petri dishes, and repeat Steps 3 through 6 to determine who could safely receive type O blood.

Analyze and Conclude

1. Which blood types can safely receive a transfusion of type A blood? Type O blood?

2. If some blood types are not available, how might type O blood be useful?

3. **Apply** Why should hospitals have an adequate supply of different types of blood?

More to Explore

Repeat this activity to find out which blood types can safely receive donations of type B and type AB blood.

Analyze and Conclude

1. Types A and AB can receive type A blood. Types A, B, AB, and O can receive type O.
2. Type O can safely be given to anyone.
3. To provide blood for people who have lost blood through injury, who are having surgery, or who need regular transfusions

Extending the Inquiry

More to Explore Colors should change when B is added to A or O, and when AB is added to A, B, or O.

Safety

Caution students not to taste any mixtures and to wash their hands thoroughly after the activity. Review the safety guidelines in Appendix A.

Program Resources

◆ **Unit 4 Resources** Chapter 17 Real-World Lab, pp. 79–81

You and Your Community

Do You Know Your A-B-O's?

Preparing for Inquiry

Key Concept Some blood types cannot receive type A transfusions, while all can receive type O.

Skills Objective Students will be able to
◆ model the four blood types using colored water;
◆ infer the compatibilities between blood types by mixing.

Time 40 minutes

Advance Planning To make up the "blood types" for type O, use uncolored water. For A, use 20 drops of yellow dye per liter of water. For B, use 20 drops of blue dye per liter of water. For AB, use 50 drops of yellow plus 50 drops of blue per liter of water. To test the colors, place 10 drops of AB solution in each of four petri dishes, then add 10 drops of a different "blood type" to each. Mix with separate toothpicks; the four mixtures should be about the same green. If some mixtures are too yellowish or bluish, add more dye to darken the AB solution.

Guiding Inquiry

Invitation

Discuss blood transfusions and the need to make sure that the blood types of the donor and the recipient are compatible. Ask students if they know their blood types, and discuss the four types with them (A, B, AB, and O).

Introducing the Procedure

Explain that the four cups of water will model the four blood types.

Troubleshooting the Experiment

Make sure students do not interpret a change in intensity as a change in color.

Expected Outcome

Colors should change only when A is added to B and O.

SECTION 4 Cardiovascular Health

Objectives

After completing the lesson, students will be able to
◆ identify and describe types of cardiovascular disease;
◆ describe behaviors that maintain cardiovascular health.

Key Terms atherosclerosis, heart attack, hypertension

1 Engage/Explore

Activating Prior Knowledge

Ask students: **What factors do you think make a person more likely to have a heart attack?** (*Accept all reasonable answers at this time. Students might mention high-fat diet, high salt intake, little or no exercise.*) Tell students that in this section they will learn about heart disease and the steps they can take to prevent it.

 **DISCOVER**

Skills Focus forming operational definitions
Materials *assortment of foods*
Time 20 minutes
Tips Provide heart-healthy foods such as fresh fruit and vegetables, unbuttered popcorn, low-fat yogurt, and skim milk. Also provide items such as potato chips, crackers, and processed foods high in sodium or fat (especially saturated fat). Information about sodium and fat content is found on food labels.
Think It Over Students' answers will depend on their knowledge of nutrition and the cardiovascular system. Heart-healthy foods include those low in fat and sodium.

SECTION 4 Cardiovascular Health

DISCOVER ·············· **ACTIVITY**

Which Foods Are "Heart Healthy"?

1. Your teacher will give you an assortment of foods. If they have nutrition labels, read the information.
2. Sort the foods into three groups. In one group, put those foods that you think are good for your cardiovascular system. In the second group, put foods that you think might damage your cardiovascular system if eaten often. Place foods you aren't sure about in the third group.

Think It Over
Forming Operational Definitions How did you define a "heart-healthy" food?

GUIDE FOR READING

◆ What behaviors can help maintain cardiovascular health?

Reading Tip Before you read, rewrite the headings in the section as questions that begin with *how, why,* or *what.* Write short answers to these questions as you read.

Shortly after sunrise, when most people are just waking up, the rowers are already out on the river. Rhythmically, with perfectly coordinated movement, the rowers pull on the oars, making the boat glide swiftly through the water. Despite the chilly morning air, sweat glistens on the rowers' faces and arms. And inside their chests, their hearts are pounding, delivering blood to the arm and chest muscles that power the oars.

Rowers cannot perform at their peaks unless their cardiovascular systems are in excellent condition. But cardiovascular health is important to all people, not just athletes. Cardiovascular

556

READING STRATEGIES

Reading Tip As students generate questions based on the section headings, suggest that students predict answers to some or all of the questions. Then direct students to answer the questions based on their reading. Student questions may include, "What is cardiovascular disease?" and "What causes hypertension?"

Study and Comprehension After students read the section, have them write the major headings and subheadings on a sheet of paper, leaving several lines of space after each heading. Then have students review the section and write down the main ideas and important details that apply to each heading. Encourage students to use their own words to paraphrase the information they write.

disease is the leading cause of death in the United States. However, people can practice behaviors that decrease their risks of developing cardiovascular problems.

Cardiovascular Disease

Compare the two arteries shown in Figure 15. The one on the left is a healthy artery. It has a large space in the center through which blood can flow easily. The artery on the right, in contrast, has a thick wall and only a small space in the middle. This artery exhibits **atherosclerosis** (ath uh roh skluh ROH sis), a condition in which an artery wall thickens as a result of the buildup of fatty materials. One of these fatty materials is cholesterol, a waxy, fat-like substance. Atherosclerosis restricts the flow of blood in the arteries.

Atherosclerosis can develop in the coronary arteries that supply the heart. When that happens, the heart muscle receives less blood and therefore less oxygen. This condition may lead to a heart attack. A **heart attack** occurs when blood flow to part of the heart muscle is blocked. Cells die in the part of the heart that does not receive blood. This permanently damages the heart.

Treatment for mild atherosclerosis usually includes a low-fat diet and a moderate exercise program. In addition, medications that lower the levels of cholesterol and fats in the blood may be prescribed. People with severe atherosclerosis may need to undergo surgery or other procedures to unclog blocked arteries.

☑ *Checkpoint* *Why is atherosclerosis especially serious when it affects the coronary arteries?*

Hypertension

High blood pressure, or **hypertension** (hy pur TEN shun), is a disorder in which a person's blood pressure is consistently higher than normal—greater than 140/90. Hypertension makes the heart work harder. It also may damage the walls of the blood

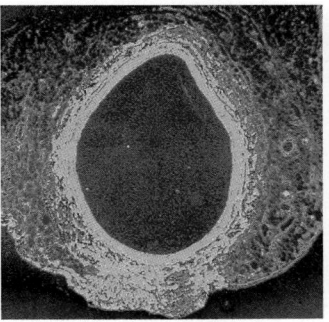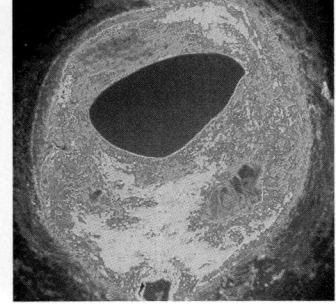

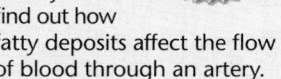

Blocking the Flow

Use this activity to find out how fatty deposits affect the flow of blood through an artery.

1. Put a funnel in the mouth of a plastic jar. The funnel will represent an artery.

2. To model blood flowing through the artery, slowly pour 100 mL of water into the funnel. Have your partner time how many seconds it takes for all the water to flow through the funnel. Then discard the water.

3. Use a plastic knife to spread a small amount of peanut butter along the bottom of the funnel's neck. Then, with a toothpick, carve out a hole in the peanut butter so that the funnel is partly, but not completely, clogged.

4. Repeat Steps 1 and 2.

Predicting If the funnels were arteries, which one—blocked or unblocked—would do a better job of supplying blood to tissues? Explain.

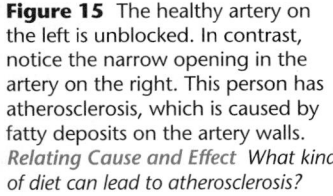

Figure 15 The healthy artery on the left is unblocked. In contrast, notice the narrow opening in the artery on the right. This person has atherosclerosis, which is caused by fatty deposits on the artery walls. *Relating Cause and Effect* What kind of diet can lead to atherosclerosis?

Program Resources

◆ **Unit 4 Resources** 17-4 Lesson Plan, p. 73; 17-4 Section Summary, p. 74

Media and Technology

 Audio CD English-Spanish Summary 17-4

Answers to Self-Assessment

Caption Question

Figure 15 A diet high in fat and cholesterol can lead to atherosclerosis.

☑ *Checkpoint*

When atherosclerosis affects coronary arteries, blood flow to the heart muscle decreases, and this can lead to a heart attack.

2 *Facilitate*

Cardiovascular Disease

TRY THIS

Skills Focus predicting
Materials *plastic funnel, plastic jar, water, graduated cylinder, stopwatch or clock with second hand, peanut butter, plastic knife, toothpick, newspaper, paper towels*
Time 20 minutes
Tips If peanut butter is not available, use modeling clay to block the funnel.
Expected Outcome The unblocked funnel would do a better job of supplying blood, because more liquid can flow through it.
Extend Ask which photo in Figure 15 is represented by the peanut-butter-clogged funnel. (*The one on the right*) **learning modality: kinesthetic**

Hypertension

Language Arts Connection

Ask students to list other words they know that begin with the prefix *hyper*. (*Samples: hyperactivity, hyperspace, hyperventilate*) Write the list on the board, then ask students to infer the meaning of the prefix. (*Very, high, extra*) Explain that *hyper* is a Greek prefix often used in the names of medical conditions. Tell students that the opposite of *hyper* is *hypo*. Ask students to infer what the medical name for dangerously low blood pressure is. (*hypotension*) **learning modality: verbal**

Ongoing Assessment

Writing Have students describe how atherosclerosis causes heart attacks.

557

SCIENCE & History

For each item, have students summarize in their own words how the advancement has helped save lives. Then ask: **Why would some kinds of surgery have been impossible before the discovery of blood types?** *(Some kinds of surgery require blood transfusions.)*
Extend Ask students to speculate why these advances were not made until the twentieth century. *(Sample: Scientists needed technology such as lasers or improved surgical procedures in order to perform this work.)*

In Your Journal You may wish to allow students time to find information about their chosen scientists. When students have written their speeches, they may enjoy role-playing an awards ceremony at which they read their speeches. **learning modality: verbal**

vessels. Over time, both the heart and arteries can be severely harmed by hypertension. Because people with hypertension often have no obvious symptoms to warn them, hypertension is sometimes called the "silent killer."

Hypertension and atherosclerosis are closely related. As the arteries narrow, blood pressure increases. Being overweight and failing to get enough exercise can also increase a person's risk of developing hypertension.

SCIENCE & History

Cardiovascular Advances in the Twentieth Century

Scientists today have an in-depth understanding of how the cardiovascular system works and how to treat cardiovascular problems. This time line describes some advances of the twentieth century.

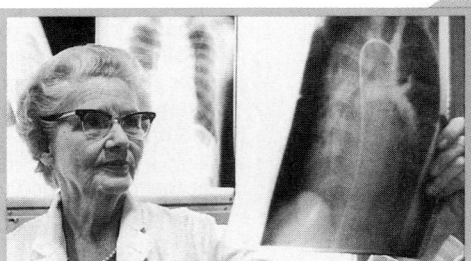

1944
Treatment for "Blue Babies"

Helen Taussig identified the heart defect that causes the skin of some newborn babies to be bluish in color. The blood of these "blue babies" does not receive an adequate amount of oxygen. Taussig and another surgeon, Alfred Blalock, developed an operation to correct the defect and save these babies' lives.

1900	1920	1940

1901
Discovery of Blood Types

Karl Landsteiner demonstrated that people have different blood types, which are determined by marker molecules on their red blood cells. Landsteiner's discovery enabled blood transfusions to be done safely.

1930s–1940s
Blood Banks

Charles Drew demonstrated that emergency transfusions could successfully be done with plasma if whole blood was not available. During World War II, Drew established blood banks for storing donated blood. His work helped save millions of lives on and off the battlefield.

558

Background

Facts and Figures After World War II, America experienced an epidemic of heart disease. The U.S. Public Health Service decided to find out why. In 1948, they went to Framingham, Massachusetts, and signed up 5,209 healthy residents to take part in the Framingham Heart Study. Since that time, participants have had health checkups every two years. Doctors recorded anything that might have an effect on the heart.

Among the findings:
◆ High blood pressure appears to trigger heart attacks.
◆ Cigarette smoking is bad for the heart.
◆ Too much cholesterol in the blood raises the risk of heart attacks.
◆ Physical exercise lowers the risk of heart disease; being overweight increases it.
◆ Diabetes is an important underlying cause of heart disease.

For mild hypertension, regular exercise and careful food choices may be enough to lower blood pressure. People with hypertension need to limit their intake of sodium, which can increase their blood pressure. Sodium is found in salt and in processed foods such as soups and packaged snack foods. For some people who have hypertension, however, medications are needed to reduce their blood pressure.

☑ *Checkpoint* *Why is hypertension called the "silent killer"?*

In Your Journal

Choose one of the scientists whose work is described here. Imagine that you are on a committee that has chosen him or her to receive an award. Write the speech you would give at the award ceremony. The speech should explain the importance of the scientist's contributions.

1967
First Heart Transplant

Christiaan Barnard, a South African surgeon, performed the first transplant of a human heart. Louis Washkansky, the man who received the heart, lived for only 18 days after the transplant. But Barnard's work paved the way for future successes in transplanting hearts and other organs.

1992
Laser Beam Unclogs Arteries

The United States government approved a device that uses a laser beam to burn away the material causing blockage in some arteries. This device can help some people with atherosclerosis.

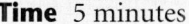

| 1960 | 1980 | 2000 |

1982
Artificial Heart

An artificial heart, developed by Robert Jarvik, was implanted into a patient by surgeon William DeVries at the University of Utah. Barney Clark, the man who received the artificial heart, lived for 112 days. Today artificial hearts are sometimes used temporarily in people waiting for heart transplants.

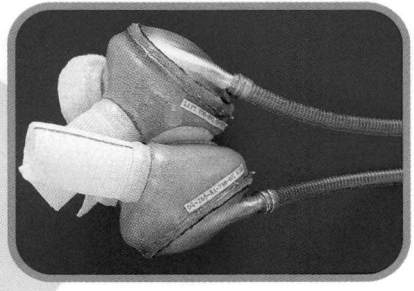

Chapter 17 **559**

Building Inquiry Skills: Predicting

Materials *empty food containers with nutrition labels*
Time 15 minutes

Have students bring in the food containers from home. Group students. Display the containers and ask students to predict which foods are high in sodium. Then have group members work together to examine the labels on all the containers and compare the label information with their predictions. Students may be surprised at the amounts of sodium in foods they might otherwise think of as healthy.
cooperative learning

Building Inquiry Skills: Making Models

Materials *plastic drinking straws, thin plastic coffee stirring straws*
Time 5 minutes

To help students understand the physical reason for the increase in blood pressure when arteries narrow, have them first blow gently through a regular drinking straw. Students can hold one hand a few centimeters below the end of the straw to feel the pressure of the air. Then have students use the same force to blow through the thinner straw. Have them hold their hand the same distance below the end of the straw and compare the pressure they felt through the thin straw. *(When the same force is exerted through a thinner tube, the pressure is higher.)*
limited English proficiency

Answers to Self-Assessment

☑ *Checkpoint*
People with hypertension often have no symptoms to warn them of the disease.

Ongoing Assessment

Writing Ask students to list and describe at least three cardiovascular advances made since 1900.

 Students can save their descriptions in their portfolios.

Keeping Your Cardiovascular System Healthy

Building Inquiry Skills: Making Judgments

Encourage students to use their journals to keep track of their health behaviors for a week. Students should record what they eat, their exercise patterns, and their exposure to smoke. At the end of this period, have students write a short paragraph assessing their risk factors and discussing how they will influence students' lifestyle decisions. Allow students to keep their paragraphs private. **learning modality: verbal**

3 Assess

Section 4 Review Answers

1. Exercise regularly; eat a balanced diet low in fat, cholesterol and sodium; and refrain from smoking.
2. Atherosclerosis is a condition in which an artery wall thickens as a result of the buildup of fatty materials.
3. Hypertension may damage the walls of blood vessels.
4. Diets in other countries may contain less fat and cholesterol, and lifestyles may include more exercise.

Science at Home

Provide students with information about community activities such as walks, bike rides, or "fun runs." Bring cookbooks or magazines with simple low-fat recipes to class. Provide time for students to look at the recipes and choose several they think they would like. Students may make their own cookbooks with low-fat recipe ideas.

Performance Assessment

Writing Have students choose atherosclerosis or hypertension and explain how the condition is caused, how it affects the body, and ways it can be prevented and treated.
 Portfolio Students can save their explanations in their portfolios.

Keeping Your Cardiovascular System Healthy

Few young people have heart attacks, but atherosclerosis can begin to develop in people as young as 20 years old. You can establish habits now that will lessen your risk of developing atherosclerosis and hypertension. **To help maintain cardiovascular health, people should exercise regularly; eat a balanced diet that is low in fat, cholesterol, and sodium; and avoid smoking.**

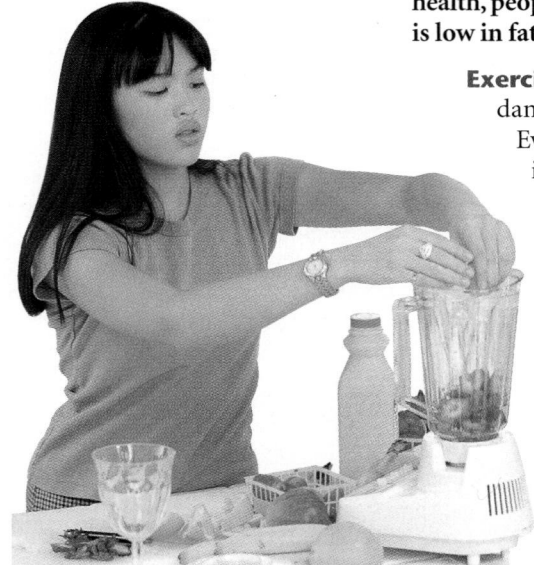

Figure 16 Eating foods that are low in fat can help keep your cardiovascular system healthy.

Exercise Do you participate in sports, ride a bike, swim, dance, or climb stairs instead of taking the elevator? Every time you do one of those activities, you are helping to maintain your cardiovascular health. Exercise strengthens your heart muscle and also helps prevent atherosclerosis.

A Balanced Diet Foods that are high in cholesterol and fats can lead to a buildup of fatty deposits on artery walls. In addition, eating too many high-fat foods can lead to excessive weight gain. Foods such as red meats, eggs, and cheese are high in cholesterol. These foods also contain substances that your body needs. Therefore, a smart approach might be to eat them, but only in small quantities. Some foods that are especially high in fat include butter and margarine, potato chips, doughnuts, and fried foods such as French fries. Eat high-fat foods only occasionally, if at all.

Avoid Smoking Smokers are more than twice as likely to have a heart attack than are nonsmokers. Every year, almost 180,000 people in the United States die from cardiovascular disease caused by smoking. If smokers quit, however, their risk of death from cardiovascular disease decreases.

Section 4 Review

1. List three things you can do to help your cardiovascular system stay healthy.
2. What is atherosclerosis?
3. How does hypertension affect blood vessels?
4. **Thinking Critically Relating Cause and Effect** Coronary heart disease is much less common in some countries than it is in the United States. What factors might account for this difference?

Science at Home

Healthy Hearts With your family, discuss some things that you all can do to maintain healthy cardiovascular systems. Make a list of exercise activities, such as bicycling and swimming, that family members can enjoy together. You might also work with your family to cook and serve a "heart-healthy," low-fat meal.

Program Resources

◆ **Unit 4 Resources** 17-4 Review and Reinforce, p. 75; 17-4 Enrich, p. 76

SECTION 1
The Body's Transportation System

Key Ideas

◆ The heart pumps blood through the blood vessels. The heart has four chambers. The two atria receive blood, and the two ventricles pump blood out of the heart.

◆ Blood travels from the heart to the lungs and back to the heart. It is then pumped to the body and returns again to the heart.

Key Terms

cardiovascular system	valve	vein
heart	pacemaker	aorta
atrium	artery	force
ventricle	capillary	

 SECTION 2
A Closer Look at Blood Vessels

Key Ideas

◆ Arteries carry blood from the heart to capillaries. In the capillaries, materials are exchanged between the blood and the body's cells. From the capillaries, blood flows into veins that carry it back to the heart.

Key Terms

coronary artery	blood pressure
diffusion	sphygmomanometer
pressure	

 SECTION 3
Blood and Lymph

Key Ideas

◆ Red blood cells, which contain hemoglobin, carry oxygen and deliver it to body cells. White blood cells fight disease. Platelets are important in forming blood clots.

Key Terms

plasma	fibrin
red blood cell	blood transfusion
hemoglobin	lymphatic system
white blood cell	lymph
platelet	lymph node

 SECTION 4
Cardiovascular Health

INTEGRATING HEALTH

Key Ideas

◆ Atherosclerosis is a condition in which an artery wall thickens due to the buildup of cholesterol and other fatty materials.

◆ Hypertension is a disorder in which the blood pressure is higher than normal.

◆ To help prevent atherosclerosis and hypertension, people need to exercise regularly; eat a diet low in fat, cholesterol, and salt; and avoid smoking.

Key Terms

atherosclerosis	hypertension
heart attack	

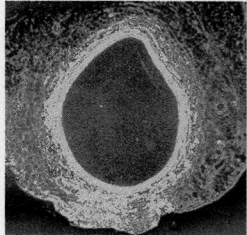 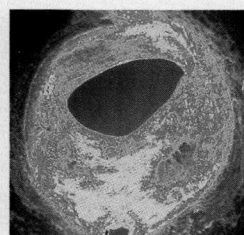

Organizing Information

Compare/Contrast Table Compare the three types of blood vessels by copying and completing the table below. (For more on compare/contrast tables, see the Skills Handbook.)

Blood Vessel	Function	Structure of Wall
Artery	a. _?_	3 layers: inner–epithelial tissue middle–muscle outer–connective tissue
b. _?_	exchange of materials between cells and blood	c. _?_
Vein	d. _?_	e. _?_

Organizing Information

Compare/Contrast Table
a. carries blood away from the heart
b. capillary c. one layer of epithelial cells
d. carries blood from capillaries to heart
e. three layers: inner epithelial, middle muscle, and outer connective tissue

Program Resources

◆ **Unit 4 Resources** Chapter 17 Project Scoring Rubric, p. 60

◆ **Performance Assessment** Chapter 17, pp. 53–55

◆ **Chapter and Unit Tests** Chapter 17 Test, pp. 80–83

Media and Technology

 Interactive Student Tutorial CD-ROM Chapter 17

 Computer Test Bank Chapter 17 Test

Reviewing Content
Multiple Choice
1. b 2. a 3. a 4. a 5. c

True or False
6. true 7. red blood cells 8. true 9. O
10. true

Checking Concepts

11. The cell will pass into a capillary in your leg and into a vein that returns blood to the heart. A vein will then carry the cell to the right atrium.
12. The left ventricle contracts with more force than the right. The left ventricle needs to contract with enough force to pump blood throughout the entire body, while the right pumps blood to the lungs only.
13. Capillaries have thin walls, allowing substances to move in and out of the them easily.
14. Hemoglobin carries oxygen from the lungs and releases it in the body.
15. Accept any two: A high-fat, high-cholesterol diet can lead to atherosclerosis; overeating can lead to excessive weight gain, which puts strain on the heart; dietary sodium can aggravate hypertension.
16. Ads should point out the specific benefits of exercise, show at least two or three ways in which teenagers can obtain exercise, and be appropriate for a teenage audience.

Thinking Critically

17. Oxygen-poor blood from the right ventricle could flow to the left ventricle and be pumped to the rest of the body, impairing the delivery of oxygen.
18. In lung capillaries, oxygen moves from the lungs into the capillaries. In capillaries in other parts of the body, oxygen moves out of the capillaries and into body cells.
19. Iron is an important component of hemoglobin, which is used to transport oxygen. Without enough iron, people could not carry as much oxygen in their blood.

Reviewing Content

 For more review of key concepts, see the Interactive Student Tutorial CD-ROM.

Multiple Choice
Choose the letter of the best answer.

1. The heart's upper chambers are called
   a. ventricles.   b. atria.
   c. valves.   d. hemoglobins.
2. Oxygen-rich blood enters the heart through the
   a. left atrium.
   b. right atrium.
   c. left ventricle.
   d. right ventricle.
3. Which of the following is *not* important in moving blood through veins?
   a. the force with which the atria contract
   b. valves
   c. breathing movements of the chest
   d. the contraction of skeletal muscles
4. Platelets help the body to
   a. control bleeding.
   b. carry oxygen.
   c. fight infection.
   d. regulate the amount of water in plasma.
5. Cholesterol is a fatlike substance associated with
   a. lymph nodes.
   b. fibrin.
   c. atherosclerosis.
   d. salt.

True or False
If the statement is true, write true. If it is false, change the underlined word or words to make the statement true.

6. The two lower heart chambers are called <u>ventricles</u>.
7. <u>White blood cells</u> contain hemoglobin.
8. The <u>capillaries</u> are the narrowest blood vessels in the body.
9. A person with blood type B can receive a transfusion of blood types B and <u>AB</u>.
10. Elevated blood pressure is called <u>hypertension</u>.

Checking Concepts

11. A red blood cell is moving through an artery in your leg. Describe the path that blood cell will follow back to your heart. Identify the chamber of the heart to which it will return.
12. Contrast the forces with which the right and left ventricles contract. How does this relate to each ventricle's function?
13. How is a capillary's structure adapted to its function?
14. What is the function of hemoglobin in the body?
15. Give two reasons why the food choices that people make are important to their cardiovascular health.
16. **Writing to Learn** Write an ad that encourages teenagers to exercise. Your ad will appear in a teen magazine. The ad should point out the health benefits of exercise and identify some ways that teenagers can exercise.

Thinking Critically

17. **Predicting** Some babies are born with an opening between the left and right ventricles of the heart. How would this heart defect affect the ability of the cardiovascular system to deliver oxygen to body cells?
18. **Comparing and Contrasting** Contrast the direction of movement of oxygen in lung capillaries and other capillaries in the body.
19. **Relating Cause and Effect** People who do not have enough iron in their diets sometimes develop a condition in which their blood cannot carry a normal amount of oxygen. Explain why this is so.
20. **Making Generalizations** Why are atherosclerosis and hypertension sometimes called "lifestyle diseases"?

20. Atherosclerosis and hypertension are affected by behavior. The risk of these diseases can be lowered with a diet low in fat, cholesterol, and salt; by regular exercise; and by not smoking.

Applying Skills

21. A man. The line for men is above the line for women for all ages on the graph.
22. Both lines show that, on average, people's blood pressure increases as they age.
23. Yes. The two lines seem to be converging and will probably intersect at some age above 45.

Applying Skills

The graph below shows how average blood pressure, measured when the ventricles contract, changes as men and women grow older. Use the graph to answer Questions 21–23.

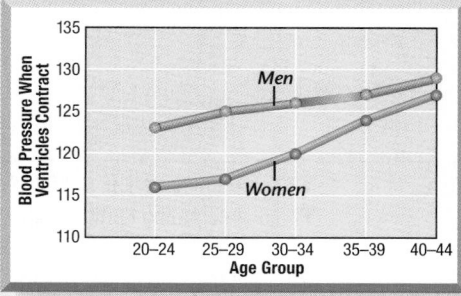

21. Interpreting Data At age 20, who is likely to have the higher blood pressure—a man or a woman?

22. Drawing Conclusions In general, what happens to people's blood pressure as they age?

23. Predicting Do you think that there is some age at which both men and women have about the same blood pressure? Use the graph lines to explain your prediction.

Performance **CHAPTER PROJECT** Assessment

Present Your Project You should now be ready to present your display. First show it to a small group of classmates to make sure it is clear and accurate. When you present your display, be ready to answer questions.

Reflect and Record As you look at all the different projects, decide which display did the best job of teaching you. Use your journal to write about how the display looked and worked. Did you learn more from that display or from working on your own? As you write, try to decide which way of learning works best for you.

Test Preparation

Use these questions to prepare for standardized tests.

Study the table. Then answer Questions 24–27.

Blood Types			
Name	Blood Type	Marker Molecules	Clumping Proteins
Juan	A	A	anti-B
Wanda	B	B	anti-A
Kyoko	AB	A and B	none
Eddie	O	none	anti-A and anti-B

24. What clumping proteins does Kyoko have in her blood?
 a. anti-A
 b. anti-B
 c. anti-A and anti-B
 d. none

25. What marker molecules does Wanda have on her red blood cells?
 a. A   **b.** B
 c. A and B   **d.** none

26. If you have Type B blood, from whom could you receive a blood transfusion?
 a. Wanda and Kyoko
 b. Wanda and Eddie
 c. only Wanda
 d. only Eddie

27. If you have Type AB blood, from whom could you receive a blood transfusion?
 a. only Juan
 b. only Juan and Wanda
 c. only Eddie
 d. Juan, Wanda, Kyoko, and Eddie

Performance **CHAPTER PROJECT** Assessment

Present Your Project If possible, allow one class period for students to work in small groups to present their projects to each other. Encourage students to provide constructive feedback to help each other improve their displays. In order to help students compare all the displays, try to schedule all presentations in two or three consecutive class periods. If possible, allow students to arrange their displays around the room in a large circle so all displays are visible at once.

Students' presentations should include descriptions of the travels of the red blood cell through the body as well as a clear explanation of how the student has chosen to represent the process in his or her display. Encourage other students to ask questions about each model as it is presented.

Reflect and Record Encourage students to identify one aspect of a particular display that helped them understand a concept. Some students may find that they learned more by making their own displays; others may find that they learned more by looking at other displays.

Test Preparation
24. d 25. b 26. b 27. d

Program Resources

◆ **Inquiry Skills Activity Book** Provides teaching and review of all inquiry skills

18 Respiration and Excretion

Sections	Time	Student Edition Activities	Other Activities	
CHAPTER PROJECT **Get the Message Out** p. 565	Ongoing (1½ weeks)	Check Your Progress, pp. 580, 586 Present Your Project, p. 589		
1 The Respiratory System pp. 566–575 ◆ Identify the functions of the respiratory system. ◆ Identify the structures that air passes through as it travels to the lungs. ◆ Describe how oxygen, carbon dioxide, and water move in the lungs. ◆ Explain the process by which people breathe and speak.	2½ periods/ 1½ blocks	**Discover** How Big Can You Blow Up a Balloon?, p. 566 **Try This** Do You Exhale Carbon Dioxide?, p. 571 **Science at Home** p. 574 **Skills Lab: Making Models** A Breath of Fresh Air, p. 575	TE TE TE TE TE LM	Demonstration, p. 567 Integrating Earth Science, p. 567 Inquiry Challenge, p. 568 Integrating Math, p. 570 Integrating Physics, p. 573 18, "Measuring the Volume of Exhaled Air"
2 INTEGRATING HEALTH Smoking and Your Health pp. 576–580 ◆ List the harmful chemicals contained in tobacco smoke. ◆ Explain how tobacco smoke harms the respiratory and circulatory systems. ◆ Define passive smoking and identify its effects on health. ◆ Identify the reasons why some people choose to smoke.	1 period/ ½ block	**Discover** What Are the Dangers of Smoking?, p. 576 **Sharpen Your Skills** Calculating, p. 579	TE	Real-Life Learning, p. 578
3 The Excretory System pp. 581–586 ◆ Identify the function of the excretory system. ◆ State how urine is produced in the kidneys' nephrons. ◆ Explain how the kidneys help maintain water balance in the body. ◆ Name the organs involved in excretion and describe their roles.	1½ periods/ 1 block	**Discover** How Does Filtering a Liquid Change What Is in It?, p. 581 **Real-World Lab: You Solve the Mystery** Clues About Health, pp. 584–585	TE TE	Demonstration, p. 583 Building Inquiry Skills: Inferring, p. 586
Study Guide/Chapter Assessment pp. 587–589	1 period/ ½ block		ISAB	Provides teaching and review of all inquiry skills

For Standard or Block Schedule The Resource Pro® CD-ROM gives you maximum flexibility for planning your instruction for any type of schedule. Resource Pro® contains Planning Express®, an advanced scheduling program, as well as the entire contents of the Teaching Resources and the Computer Test Bank.

CHAPTER PLANNING GUIDE

Program Resources	Assessment Strategies	Media and Technology
UR Chapter 18 Project Teacher Notes, pp. 82–83 **UR** Chapter 18 Project Overview and Worksheets, pp. 84–87	**SE** Performance Assessment: Present Your Project, p. 589 **TE** Check Your Progress, pp. 580, 586 **UR** Chapter 5 Project Scoring Rubric, p. 88	Science Explorer Internet Site at www.phschool.com
UR 18-1 Lesson Plan, p. 89 **UR** 18-1 Section Summary, p. 90 **UR** 18-1 Review and Reinforce, p. 91 **UR** 18-1 Enrich, p. 92 **UR** Chapter 18 Skills Lab, pp. 101–102	**SE** Section 1 Review, p. 574 **TE** Ongoing Assessment, pp. 567, 569, 571, 573 **TE** Performance Assessment, p. 574	Earth Science Videotape 5; Videodisc Unit 2 Side 1, "Air Today, Gone Tomorrow" Audio CD, English-Spanish Summary 18-1 Transparency 69, "Exploring the Respiratory System" Transparency 70, "Gas Exchange in the Alveoli" Interactive Student Tutorial CD-ROM, Chapter 18
UR 18-2 Lesson Plan, p. 93 **UR** 18-2 Section Summary, p. 94 **UR** 18-2 Review and Reinforce, p. 95 **UR** 18-2 Enrich, p. 96	**SE** Section 2 Review, p. 580 **TE** Ongoing Assessment, pp. 577, 579 **TE** Performance Assessment, p. 580	Life Science Videotape 4; Videodisc Unit 4 Side 1, "Caution: Breathing May Be Hazardous to Your Health" Audio CD, English-Spanish Summary 18-2
UR 18-3 Lesson Plan, p. 97 **UR** 18-3 Section Summary, p. 98 **UR** 18-3 Review and Reinforce, p. 99 **UR** 18-3 Enrich, p. 100 **UR** Chapter 18 Real-World Lab, pp. 103–105	**SE** Section 3 Review, p. 586 **TE** Ongoing Assessment, p. 583 **TE** Performance Assessment, p. 586	Life Science Videotape 4; Videodisc Unit 4 Side 1, "Cool Sweat" Transparency 71, "Exploring a Kidney" Audio CD English-Spanish Summary 18-3
RCA Provides strategies to improve science reading skills **GSW** Provides worksheets to promote student comprehension of content	**SE** Chapter 18 Study Guide/Assessment, pp. 587–589 **PA** Chapter 18 Performance Assessment, pp. 56–58 **CUT** Chapter 18 Test, pp. 84–87 **CTB** Chapter 18 Test	Interactive Student Tutorial CD-ROM, Chapter 18 Computer Test Bank, Chapter 18 Test

Key: **SE** Student Edition
CTB Computer Test Bank
ISAB Inquiry Skills Activity Book
GSW Guided Study Worksheets

TE Teacher's Edition
PTA Product Testing Activities by *Consumer Reports*
RCA Reading in the Content Area
PA Performance Assessment

UR Unit Resources
LM Laboratory Manual
IES Interdisciplinary Explorations Series
CUT Chapter and Unit Tests

Meeting the National Science Education Standards and AAAS Benchmarks

National Science Education Standards	Benchmarks for Science Literacy	Unifying Themes

National Science Education Standards

Science as Inquiry (Content Standard A)

◆ **Ask questions that can be answered by scientific investigations** Students conduct an investigation to determine how air gets into the lungs. *(Skills Lab)*

Physical Science (Content Standard B)

◆ **Properties and changes of properties in matter** During metabolism, oxygen combines with carbon to form carbon dioxide. Breathing is accomplished through the action of several groups of muscles that act together to enlarge the chest cavity. Air pressure then forces air into the lungs. *(Section 1)*

Life Science (Content Standard C)

◆ **Structure and function in living systems** The respiratory and excretory systems work together to transport substances to and from the blood. *(Sections 1, 3)*

Science in Personal and Social Perspectives (Content Standard F)

◆ **Personal health** Smoking can damage the respiratory system. Some of the damage can be repaired by the body when the smoker quits. *(Section 2)*

Benchmarks for Science Literacy

4D The Structure of Matter During metabolism, oxygen combines with carbon to form carbon dioxide. *(Section 1)*

5E Flow of Matter and Energy The respiratory system provides body cells with the oxygen they need to combine with nutrients to produce energy. The excretory system removes from the cells the waste products of energy production. *(Sections 1, 3)*

6C Basic Functions The respiratory system permits the exchange of gases between the body cells and the environment. The excretory system removes wastes from the body. *(Sections 1, 3)*

6E Physical Health Smoking causes changes in the structure of the respiratory system that limit its ability to function properly. *(Section 2)*

7A Cultural Effects on Behavior Passive smoke is a recognized problem in society. Friends sometimes influence people to begin to smoke. *(Section 2)*

11C Constancy and Change By delivering oxygen to the blood and removing wastes from the blood, the respiratory and excretory systems help to maintain homeostasis. *(Sections 1, 3)*

Unifying Themes

◆ **Energy** The respiratory system provides body cells with the oxygen they need to combine with nutrients to produce energy. The excretory system removes the waste products of energy production. *(Sections 1, 3)*

◆ **Patterns of Change** The respiratory system brings about the exchange of gases (O_2 and CO_2) with the environment. Smoking damages the respiratory system. The excretory system carries waste products out of the body and returns them to the environment. *(Sections 1, 2, 3)*

◆ **Scale and Structure** The lungs are composed of structures called alveoli, in which the exchange of gases takes place. Smoking causes changes in the structure of the respiratory system that limit its ability to function properly. The kidneys contain structures called nephrons, which remove wastes from the blood. *(Sections 1, 2, 3)*

◆ **Systems and Interactions** The respiratory system permits the exchange of gases between the body cells and the environment. The excretory system removes wastes from the body. *(Sections 1, 3)*

◆ **Unity and Diversity** The structures of the respiratory system and the excretory system are different, yet they work together in transporting materials to and from the blood. *(Sections 1, 3)*

◆ **Stability** The respiratory and excretory systems help to maintain homeostasis. *(Sections 1, 3)*

Take It to the Net

 *Interactive text at www.phschool.com*

Science Explorer comes alive with iText.

- **Complete student text** is accessible from any computer with Internet access or a CD-ROM drive.
- **Animations, simulations, and videos** enhance student understanding and retention of concepts.
- **Self-tests and online study tools** assess student understanding.

STAY CURRENT with

Find out the latest research and information about human biology and health at: **www.phschool.com**

Go to **www.phschool.com** and click on the Science icon. Then click on Science Explorer: Life, Earth, and Physical Science under PH@school.

ACTIVITY	Time (minutes)	Materials Quantities for one work group	Skills
Section 1			
Discover, p. 566	15	**Consumable** round balloon **Nonconsumable** metric measuring tape	Inferring
Try This, p. 569	20	**Consumable** bromthymol blue solution, plastic drinking straw, plastic wrap for covering test tubes **Nonconsumable** 2 test tubes, safety goggles	Predicting
Science at Home, p. 574	home	**Nonconsumable** shoe box, set of wooden blocks	Making Models
Skills Lab, p. 575	30	**Consumable** small balloon, transparent plastic bottle with narrow neck, large balloon **Nonconsumable** scissors	Making Models
Section 2			
Discover, p. 576	20	No special materials are required.	Inferring
Sharpen your Skills, p. 579	5	No special materials are required.	Calculating
Section 3			
Discover, p. 581	15	**Consumable** glucose solution, sand, glucose test strip, filter paper **Nonconsumable** 2 small plastic containers, plastic funnel	Observing
Real-World Lab, pp. 584–585	40	**Consumable** glucose solution, glucose test strips, 3 simulated urine samples, water, protein solution, white paper towels, Biuret solution **Nonconsumable** 6 test tubes, 6 plastic droppers, marking pencil, test tube rack	Observing, Interpreting Data, Drawing Conclusions

A list of all materials required for the Student Edition activities can be found on pages T25–T33. You can obtain information about ordering materials by calling 1-800-848-9500 or by accessing the Science Explorer Internet site at **www.phschool.com**.

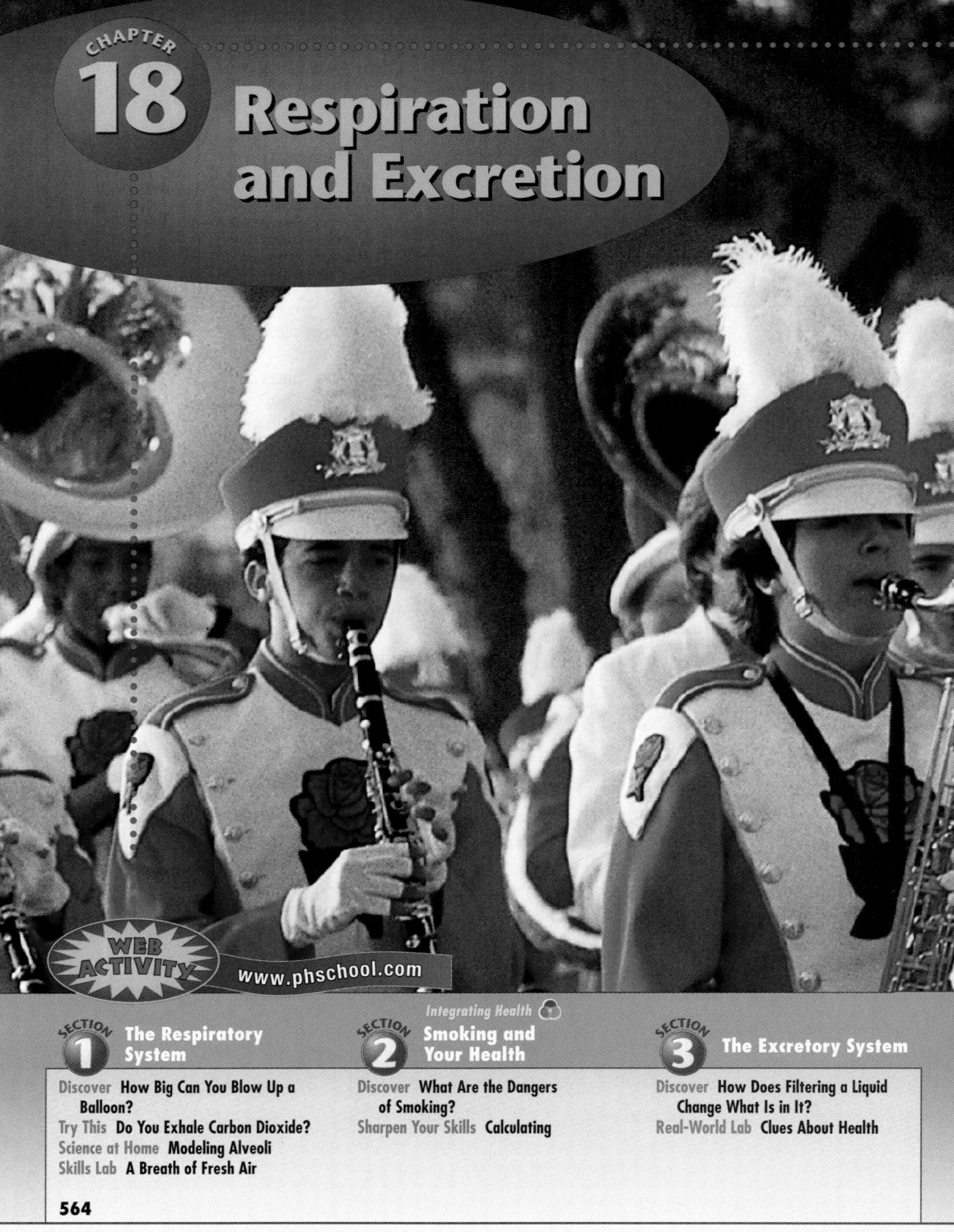

Get the Message Out

Smoking causes damage to the respiratory and circulatory systems and affects smokers' overall health. Anti-smoking campaigns may help convince some adult smokers to quit, and some children and teenagers not to begin.

Purpose In this project, students design ads to discourage minors from smoking, and adults to quit if they do smoke. In the ads, students address the health risks of smoking and the pressures that influence people to smoke. Students use what they learn about respiratory functions and the effects of smoking to formulate compelling arguments against beginning this habit.

Skills Focus Students will be able to
◆ pose questions, make inferences, and draw conclusions about the detrimental effects of smoking;
◆ apply the concepts of healthy behavior to designing ads to discourage people from smoking, and to encourage people to quit if they do smoke;
◆ communicate their findings about smoking to people in three different age groups.

Project Time Line This project will take about three weeks. Spend one day talking about advertising and looking at ads. During the first week, students collect information from the chapter about respiratory functions and the detrimental effects of smoking on the body. In the second week, students address at least two pressures that influence people to start or to continue smoking as they plan, design, and produce their ads. During the third week, students present their work to their classmates and discuss reasons why they chose particular images and messages. Before beginning the project, see Chapter 18 Project Teacher Notes on pages 82–83 in Unit 4 Resources for more details on carrying out the project. Also distribute to students the Chapter 18 Project Overview and Worksheets and Scoring Rubric on pages 84–88 in Unit 4 Resources.

CHAPTER 18 Respiration and Excretion

WEB ACTIVITY www.phschool.com

SECTION 1 The Respiratory System
Discover How Big Can You Blow Up a Balloon?
Try This Do You Exhale Carbon Dioxide?
Science at Home Modeling Alveoli
Skills Lab A Breath of Fresh Air

Integrating Health
SECTION 2 Smoking and Your Health
Discover What Are the Dangers of Smoking?
Sharpen Your Skills Calculating

SECTION 3 The Excretory System
Discover How Does Filtering a Liquid Change What Is in It?
Real-World Lab Clues About Health

564

Possible Materials Fashion, sports, and entertainment magazines will be useful for brainstorming ideas for convincing ads. Students will need poster boards or large sheets of paper along with markers, crayons, or colored pencils for designing their posters. If students elect to do radio or television commercials, they will need to write scripts and bring in props and/or costumes.

Launching the Project Ask: **Why do people start smoking?** (*Samples: Peer pressure, to look "cool"*) Ask: **Why do people who smoke keep smoking?** (*Sample: They might try to stop, but find that they can't.*) Discuss reasons why people might smoke even though they know that smoking is unhealthy. Students should begin thinking about the detrimental effects of smoking and come up with ways to communicate this information to different age groups. To get them thinking about the influences that sway people of different ages, bring in several

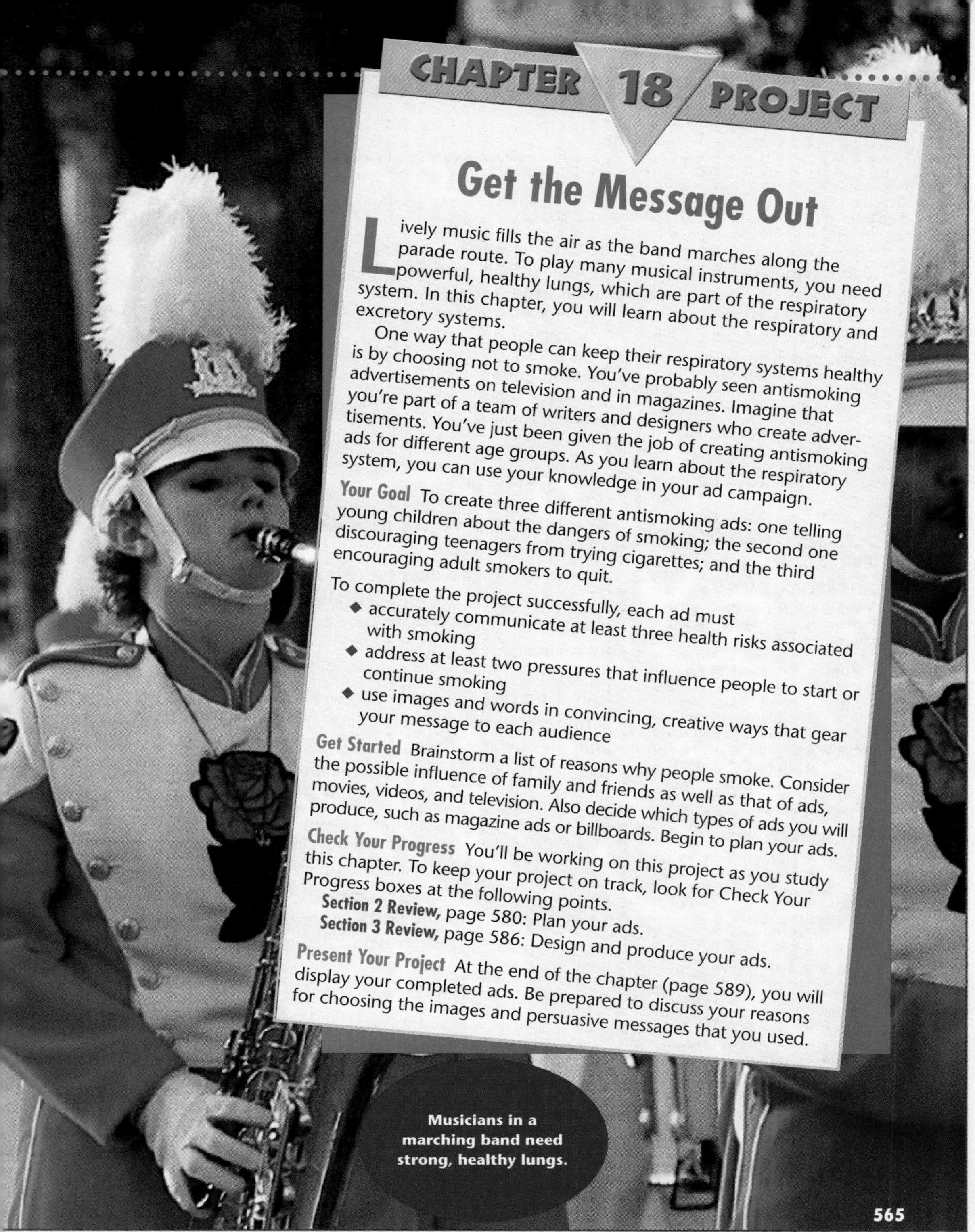

CHAPTER 18 PROJECT

Get the Message Out

Lively music fills the air as the band marches along the parade route. To play many musical instruments, you need powerful, healthy lungs, which are part of the respiratory system. In this chapter, you will learn about the respiratory and excretory systems.

One way that people can keep their respiratory systems healthy is by choosing not to smoke. You've probably seen antismoking advertisements on television and in magazines. Imagine that you're part of a team of writers and designers who create advertisements. You've just been given the job of creating antismoking ads for different age groups. As you learn about the respiratory system, you can use your knowledge in your ad campaign.

Your Goal To create three different antismoking ads: one telling young children about the dangers of smoking; the second one discouraging teenagers from trying cigarettes; and the third encouraging adult smokers to quit.

To complete the project successfully, each ad must
◆ accurately communicate at least three health risks associated with smoking
◆ address at least two pressures that influence people to start or continue smoking
◆ use images and words in convincing, creative ways that gear your message to each audience

Get Started Brainstorm a list of reasons why people smoke. Consider the possible influence of family and friends as well as that of ads, movies, videos, and television. Also decide which types of ads you will produce, such as magazine ads or billboards. Begin to plan your ads.

Check Your Progress You'll be working on this project as you study this chapter. To keep your project on track, look for Check Your Progress boxes at the following points.
Section 2 Review, page 580: Plan your ads.
Section 3 Review, page 586: Design and produce your ads.

Present Your Project At the end of the chapter (page 589), you will display your completed ads. Be prepared to discuss your reasons for choosing the images and persuasive messages that you used.

Musicians in a marching band need strong, healthy lungs.

565

Program Resources

◆ **Unit 4 Resources** Chapter 18 Project Teacher Notes, pp. 82–83; Chapter 18 Project Overview and Worksheets, pp. 84–87; Chapter 18 Project Scoring Rubric, p. 88

WEB ACTIVITY www.phschool.com

You will find an Internet activity, chapter self-tests for students, and links to other chapter topics at this site.

ads for different products. Lead a class discussion about the target audience for each ad and have students explain why the ad would appeal to that audience. Allow time for students to read the description of the project in their text and Chapter 18 Project Overview on pages 84–85 in Unit 4 Resources. Chapter 18 Worksheet 1, on page 86 in Unit 4 Resources, will help students think about how they can use images and words in creative ways to target their messages to audiences of different ages. Chapter 18 Worksheet 2, on page 87 in Unit 4 Resources, will help students identify pressures that encourage people to start smoking.

Performance Assessment

The Chapter 18 Project Scoring Rubric on page 88 of Unit 4 Resources will help you evaluate how well students complete the Chapter 18 Project. Students will be assessed on
◆ how well they support their decisions in terms of what messages will relate to the concerns of the three age groups;
◆ the accuracy of the information contained in their ads;
◆ the thoroughness and organization of their presentations;
◆ how well they work with other students.
By sharing the Chapter 18 Project Scoring Rubric with students at the beginning of the project, you will make it clear to them what they are expected to do.

The Respiratory System

Objectives

After completing the lesson, students will be able to
◆ identify the functions of the respiratory system;
◆ identify the structures that air passes through as it travels to the lungs;
◆ describe how oxygen, carbon dioxide, and water move in the lungs;
◆ explain the process by which people breathe and speak.

Key Terms respiration, cilia, pharynx, trachea, bronchi, lung, alveoli, diaphragm, larynx, vocal cord

1 Engage/Explore

Activating Prior Knowledge

Ask students to explain why astronauts wear space suits and carry oxygen with them when they walk outside a spacecraft. Then ask why deep-sea divers take oxygen with them on a dive. Most students will realize that astronauts and divers need oxygen to survive.

DISCOVER

Skills Focus inferring
Materials *round balloon, metric measuring tape*
Time 15 minutes
Tips Students should blow the balloon up several times and gently stretch it before beginning this activity. Remind students not to share balloons. Students with breathing difficulties may not be able to blow up the balloons. They can act as measurers or calculators.
Expected Outcome Measurements will vary depending upon the amount of air exhaled.
Think It Over Students may infer that factors such as smoking, air pollution, breathing difficulties, and colds may affect the volume of air a person can exhale.

SECTION
1

The Respiratory System

DISCOVER ••• ACTIVITY

How Big Can You Blow Up a Balloon?

1. Take a normal breath, then blow as much air as possible into a balloon. Twist the end and hold it closed. Have your partner measure around the balloon at its widest point.

2. Let the air out of the balloon. Repeat Step 1 and calculate the average of the two measurements.

3. Compare your results with those of your classmates. The bigger the circumference, the greater the volume of air exhaled.

Think It Over
Inferring What factors might affect the volume of air a person can exhale?

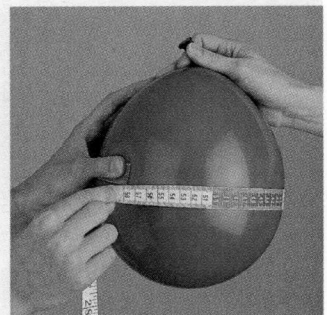

GUIDE FOR READING

◆ What are the functions of the respiratory system?
◆ What structures does air pass through as it travels to the lungs?
◆ How do oxygen, carbon dioxide, and water move in the lungs?

Reading Tip Before you read, preview *Exploring the Respiratory System* on page 569. Write down any unfamiliar terms.

566

Jerry, the main character in Doris Lessing's story "Through the Tunnel," is on vacation at the seaside. Day after day, he watches some older boys dive into deep water on one side of a huge rock. The boys mysteriously reappear on the other side. Jerry figures out that there must be an underwater tunnel in the rock. He finds the tunnel beneath the water and decides to swim through it. Once inside, though, he is terrified. The walls are slimy, and rocks scrape his body. He can barely see where he is going. But worst of all, Jerry has to hold his breath for far longer than ever before. The author describes Jerry this way: "His head was swelling, his lungs were cracking."

Jerry's behavior could have killed him. No one can go for very long without breathing. Your body cells need oxygen, and they get that oxygen from the air you breathe. **The respiratory system moves oxygen from the outside environment into the body. It also removes carbon dioxide and water from the body.**

Why the Body Needs Oxygen

The energy-releasing chemical reactions that take place inside your cells require oxygen. As a result of these reactions, your cells are able to perform all the tasks that keep you alive. Like a fire, which cannot burn without oxygen, your cells cannot "burn" enough substances to keep you alive without oxygen.

READING STRATEGIES

Reading Tip Suggest that students begin previewing *Exploring the Respiratory System* by reading the two boldface sentences at the top. Then students should read the red labels and follow the label lines to the diagram to see where each structure is located. Unfamiliar terms may include *pharynx, epiglottis,* and *larynx.* After students have finished previewing, call on

volunteers to paraphrase the information in the visual.

Study and Comprehension After students read the section, have them outline the information under the headings *Why the Body Needs Oxygen, The Air You Breathe, The Path of Air, Gas Exchange, How You Breathe,* and *How You Speak.* Students can review the information under the headings and write a short summary for each heading.

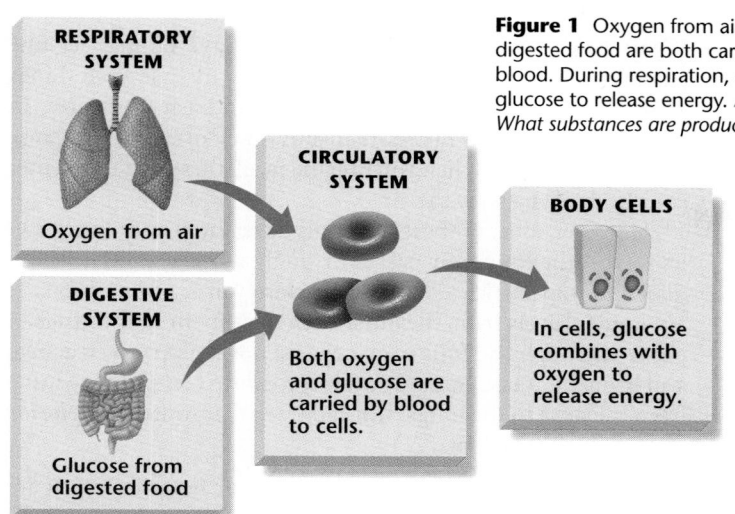

Figure 1 Oxygen from air and glucose from digested food are both carried to cells by the blood. During respiration, oxygen reacts with glucose to release energy. *Applying Concepts What substances are produced during respiration?*

RESPIRATORY SYSTEM
Oxygen from air

DIGESTIVE SYSTEM
Glucose from digested food

CIRCULATORY SYSTEM
Both oxygen and glucose are carried by blood to cells.

BODY CELLS
In cells, glucose combines with oxygen to release energy.

Recall from Chapter 2 that **respiration** is the process in which oxygen and glucose undergo a complex series of chemical reactions inside cells. These chemical reactions release the energy that fuels growth and other cell processes. Besides releasing energy, respiration produces carbon dioxide and water. Your body eliminates the carbon dioxide and some of the water through your lungs. To a scientist, *breathing* and *respiration* mean different things. Respiration, which is also called cellular respiration, refers to the chemical reactions inside cells. Breathing refers to the movement of air into and out of the lungs.

Your respiratory system gets oxygen into your lungs. However, respiration could not take place without your circulatory and digestive systems. The digestive system absorbs glucose from food. The circulatory system carries both oxygen from your lungs and glucose from food to your cells.

Checkpoint Why does your body need oxygen?

The Air You Breathe

INTEGRATING EARTH SCIENCE The oxygen your body needs comes from the atmosphere, which is the blanket of gases that surrounds Earth. The atmosphere is made up of a mixture of gases. Only about 21 percent of air is oxygen. Nitrogen makes up about 78 percent, and the remaining 1 percent includes carbon dioxide, helium, and other gases. Your body doesn't use most of the air that you breathe into your lungs. When you exhale, most of the air goes back into the atmosphere.

Program Resources
◆ **Unit 4 Resources** 18-1 Lesson Plan, p. 89; 18-1 Section Summary, p. 90

Media and Technology
🎧 **Audio CD** English-Spanish Summary 18-1

Answers to Self-Assessment
Caption Question
Figure 1 Carbon dioxide and water
Checkpoint
Without oxygen, cells cannot "burn" substances to release energy.

2 Facilitate

Why the Body Needs Oxygen

Demonstration
Materials *short candle, matches, metal pie plate, glass jar taller than the candle*
Time 15 minutes

 A burning candle can serve as a model for respiration. Secure the candle on the pie plate, and then light the candle. Cover the candle with the jar and direct students to observe what happens. *(The candle flame will burn out within a few seconds.)* Ask students: **Why did the candle go out?** *(After a few seconds, there was not enough air—oxygen—in the jar for the candle to keep burning.)* Explain that just as the candle needs oxygen to burn, body cells need oxygen to break down food and release energy cells need.
learning modality: visual

The Air You Breathe

Integrating Earth Science
Materials *blue, green, white marbles; bag*
Time 10 minutes

Place 21 blue marbles (to represent oxygen), 78 green marbles (to represent nitrogen), and 1 white marble (to represent other gases) in the bag. Ask volunteers to take handfuls of marbles from the bag and count how many blue marbles appear in each handful. Ask students to explain how this models the composition of the air they breathe. *(Air is about 21% oxygen, 78% nitrogen, and 1% other gases, including carbon dioxide and helium.)* **learning modality: kinesthetic**

Ongoing Assessment

Writing Ask students to write brief paragraphs, explaining the difference between breathing and respiration.

The Path of Air

Inquiry Challenge

Materials *cheesecloth, mist sprayer, bits of paper, small plastic bottle with 2 holes in cap, petroleum jelly*
Time 25 minutes

Challenge students to use the materials to make models that show the role the nose plays in respiration. Students can work in groups of four: one to design the model, another to build it, the third to write a description of what the model shows, and the fourth to present the model to the class. *(Sample model: Use the bottle to represent the nose; coat the inside of the bottle with a thin layer of petroleum jelly (mucus), line the bottle with cheesecloth (cilia), and use mist and bits of paper to represent bacteria and pollen that may be breathed in.)* **cooperative learning**

Real-Life Learning

Inform students that pollen makes up a large part of airborne dust and particles. Because many people have allergic reactions to many types of pollen, some government or news agencies publish pollen counts. Encourage students to research pollen counts and allergies at the library or, with supervision, on the Internet. Have students work together to come up with questions they would like to research answers for. Encourage students to focus on the relationship between allergies and respiration. Sample topics: the method for counting pollen, how pollen counts vary with the seasons, and how dust and pollen allergies are diagnosed and treated. Students can prepare presentations to communicate their findings to the class. **learning modality: verbal**

The Path of Air

If you look toward a window on a bright day, you may see tiny particles dancing in the air. These particles include such things as floating grains of dust, plant pollen, and ash from fires. In addition, air contains microorganisms, some of which can cause disease in humans. When you breathe in, all these materials enter your body along with the air.

However, most of these materials never enter your lungs. On its way to the lungs, air passes through a series of organs that filter and trap particles. These organs also warm and moisten the air. **As air travels from the outside environment to the lungs, it passes through the following organs: nose, pharynx, trachea, and bronchi.** It takes air only a few seconds to complete the route from the nose to the lungs. You can trace that route in *Exploring the Respiratory System.*

The Nose Your nose has two openings, or nostrils, which are separated by a thin wall. Air enters the body through the nostrils and then moves into the nose cavities, or nasal cavities. The lining of the nasal cavities contains many blood vessels. Warm blood flowing through these vessels heats the air. Some of the cells lining the cavities produce mucus. This sticky material moistens the air and keeps the delicate tissue from drying out. Mucus also traps particles, such as dust and bacteria. The cells that line the nasal cavities have **cilia** (SIL ee uh), tiny hairlike extensions that can move together like whips. The whiplike motion of these cilia sweeps the mucus into the throat, where you swallow it. In the stomach, the mucus, along with the particles and bacteria trapped in it, is destroyed by stomach acid.

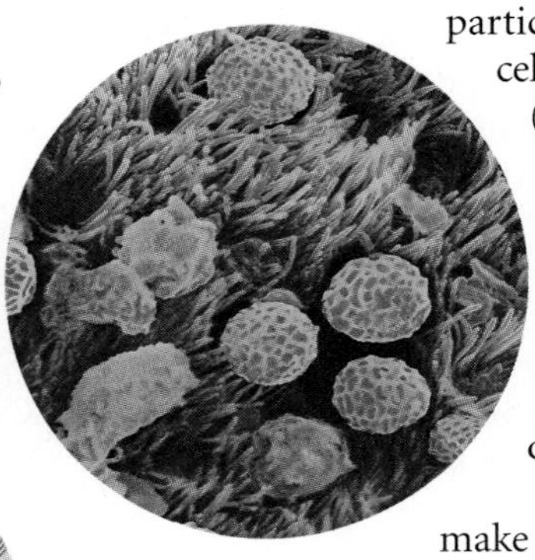

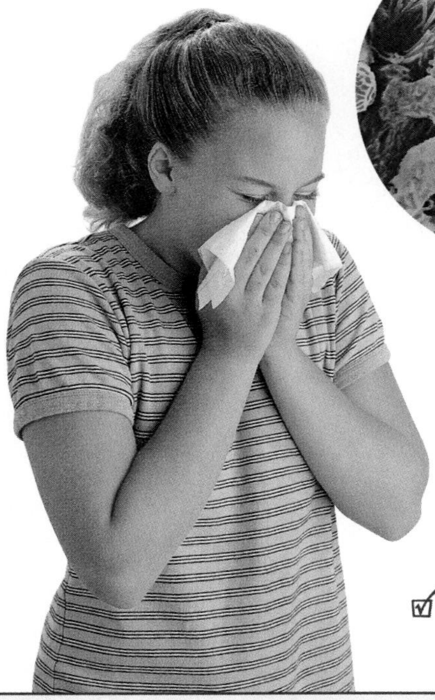

Figure 2 The cilia that line the nasal passages help remove trapped particles. The brown particles in the photograph are dust; the orange particles are pollen grains. When a person sneezes, many of the trapped particles are shot out into the air.

Some particles and bacteria never make it to your stomach. They irritate the lining of your nose or throat, and you sneeze. The powerful force of a sneeze shoots the particles and bacteria out of your nose and into the air.

The Pharynx After flowing through the nasal cavities, air enters the **pharynx** (FAR ingks), or throat. The pharynx is the only part of the respiratory system that is shared with another system—the digestive system. If you look at *Exploring the Respiratory System,* you can see that both the nose and the mouth connect to the pharynx.

☑ *Checkpoint* *To what two body systems does the pharynx belong?*

Background

Facts and Figures Sneezing and coughing are triggered by irritants, such as chemical vapors and dust particles, that stimulate receptors on the epithelial tissue that lines the respiratory passages. During both sneezing and coughing, breathing is first temporarily suspended, and then air is forcefully expelled from the respiratory tract. Air is forced out by sudden contraction of muscles in the abdomen and between the ribs. The expelled air may move as fast as 160 kilometers per hour. Particles and droplets from a sneeze may travel for several meters.

The Trachea From the pharynx, air moves into the **trachea** (TRAY kee uh), or windpipe. You can feel your trachea if you gently run your fingers down the center of your neck. The trachea feels like a tube with a series of ridges. The firm ridges are rings of cartilage that strengthen the trachea and keep it open.

The trachea, like the nose, is lined with cilia and mucus. The cilia in the trachea sweep upward, moving mucus toward the pharynx, where it is swallowed. The trachea's cilia and mucus

EXPLORING *the Respiratory System*

On its path from outside the body into the lungs, air passes through several structures that clean, warm, and moisten it. Once in the lungs, the oxygen in the air can enter your bloodstream.

Pharynx Air moves from the nose downward into the throat, or pharynx. Part of the pharynx is also a passageway for food.

Nose Air enters the body through two nostrils. The lining of the nose is coated with cilia and mucus, which trap particles and warm and moisten the air.

Epiglottis

Larynx

Trachea The trachea leads from the pharynx toward the lungs. The walls of the trachea are made up of rings of cartilage which protect the trachea and keep it from collapsing.

Bronchus Air moves from the trachea into the right and left bronchi. One bronchus leads to each lung. Part of each bronchus is outside the lung and part is inside.

Lung After it reaches the lungs, air moves through smaller and smaller bronchi until it reaches the alveoli. In the alveoli, oxygen passes into the blood and carbon dioxide passes out of the blood.

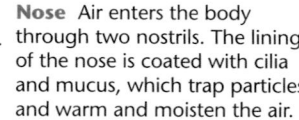

Suggest students finger trace the path of air as it enters the body. Ask students to infer why it is important for the air to be warmed and moistened when it enters the body. *(Because the inside of the body is warm and moist; this helps the body maintain a stable state.)* Instruct students to gently feel their necks for their tracheas. Invite volunteers to describe what their tracheas feel like. Then encourage students to consider the function of the rings of cartilage in the trachea. Ask: **What would happen if the trachea were to close?** *(No air would reach the lungs and the person would suffocate.)*
Extend Suggest students compose three quiz questions based on the information in the visual. Students can then exchange and answer each other's questions.
learning modality: kinesthetic

Media and Technology

 Transparencies "Exploring the Respiratory System," Transparency 69

Answers to Self-Assessment
☑ *Checkpoint*
Respiratory and digestive systems

Ongoing Assessment

Organizing Information Direct students to make flowcharts showing the movement of air through the organs in the respiratory system.

The Path of Air, continued

Including All Students

To help students whose understanding of English is limited, encourage them to write each new or unfamiliar term on the front of a note card and the definition of the term on the back. Students can also include an explanation of what role the organ or process plays in respiration, or draw a small diagram to describe or explain the term. Students can use the cards as flash cards to increase their familiarity with the terms. **limited English proficiency**

Using the Visuals: Figure 3

To help students understand how the processes in Figure 3 relate to the entire process of breathing, ask: **How does the oxygen get into the alveoli?** *(From the trachea to a bronchus, and then through the smaller branches of the bronchial tree.)* Ask students to infer what happens to the carbon dioxide the alveoli receive from the blood cells. *(It is exhaled when the person breathes out.)* **learning modality: visual**

 ## Integrating Mathematics

Materials *meter stick, masking tape*
Time 15 minutes

To help students comprehend just how large an area 70 square meters is, first help them visualize how large 1 square meter is. Provide students with the meter stick and masking tape, and allow them to mark a 1-m by 1-m square on the classroom floor. Invite students to estimate how many of these single square meters they can mark in the classroom. Then have them estimate how many classrooms they would need to be able to mark 70 square meters. **learning modality: visual**

continue the cleaning and moistening of air that began in the nose. If particles irritate the lining of the trachea, you cough. A cough, like a sneeze, sends harmful materials flying out of your body and into the air.

Normally, only air—not food—enters the trachea. If food does enter the trachea, the food can block the opening and prevent air from getting to the lungs. When that happens, a person chokes. Fortunately, food rarely gets into the trachea. Remember from Chapter 16 that the epiglottis is a small flap of tissue that folds over the trachea. The epiglottis seals the trachea off while you swallow.

The Bronchi and Lungs Air moves from the trachea to the **bronchi** (BRAHNG ky)(singular *bronchus*), the passages that direct air into the lungs. The **lungs** are the main organs of the respiratory system. The left bronchus leads into the left lung, and the right bronchus leads into the right lung. Inside the lungs, each bronchus divides into smaller and smaller tubes in a pattern that resembles the branches of a tree.

At the end of the smallest tubes are small structures that look like bunches of grapes. The "grapes" are **alveoli** (al VEE uh ly) (singular *alveolus*), tiny sacs of lung tissue specialized for the movement of gases between air and blood. Notice in Figure 3 that each alveolus is surrounded by a network of capillaries. It is here that the blood picks up its cargo of oxygen from the air.

☑ *Checkpoint* *Describe the structure of the bronchi.*

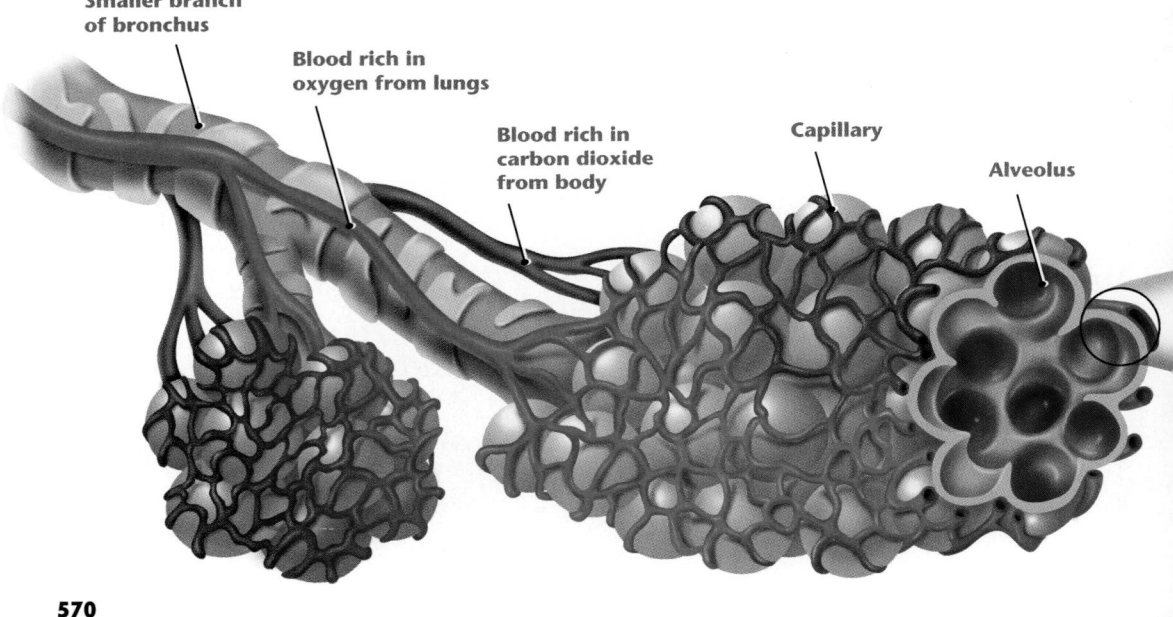

Smaller branch of bronchus

Blood rich in oxygen from lungs

Blood rich in carbon dioxide from body

Capillary

Alveolus

570

Background

Facts and Figures Henry J. Heimlich, an American surgeon, developed a technique used to restore a person's breathing when a foreign object is is lodged in the pharynx or trachea, blocking airflow to the lungs. Heimlich's method, known as the Heimlich maneuver, uses air forced from the lungs to propel the object up and out of the throat of a choking victim, and is much more effective than delivering sharp blows to the back.

The Heimlich maneuver should not be used unless a person is actually choking and is unable to speak or cough vigorously. The person who performs the Heimlich maneuver stands behind the choking victim and uses a fist clasped in a hand to press hard against the victim's upper abdomen with quick, upward thrusts. Students can seek training in the technique from their local Red Cross or community education center.

Gas Exchange

Because the walls of both the alveoli and the capillaries are very thin, materials can pass through them easily. **After air enters an alveolus, oxygen passes through the wall of the alveolus and then through the capillary wall into the blood. Carbon dioxide and water pass from the blood into the alveoli.** This whole process is known as gas exchange.

How Gas Exchange Occurs Imagine that you are a drop of blood beginning your journey through a capillary that wraps around an alveolus. When you begin that journey, you are carrying a lot of carbon dioxide and little oxygen. As you move through the capillary, oxygen gradually attaches to the hemoglobin in your red blood cells. At the same time, you are getting rid of carbon dioxide. At the end of your journey around the alveolus, you are rich in oxygen and poor in carbon dioxide.

A Large Surface Area Your lungs can absorb a large amount of oxygen because of the large surface area of the alveoli. An adult's lungs contain about 300 million alveoli. If you removed the alveoli, opened them, and spread them out on a flat surface, you would have a surface area of about 70 square meters. That's about the area of three lanes in a bowling alley!

INTEGRATING MATHEMATICS

The huge surface area of the alveoli enables the lungs to absorb a large amount of oxygen. The lungs can therefore supply the oxygen that people need—even when they are performing strenuous activities. When you play a musical instrument or a fast-paced game of basketball, you have your alveoli to thank.

Your lungs are not the only organs that provide a large surface area in a relatively small space. Remember that the small intestine contains numerous, tiny villi that increase the surface available to absorb food molecules.

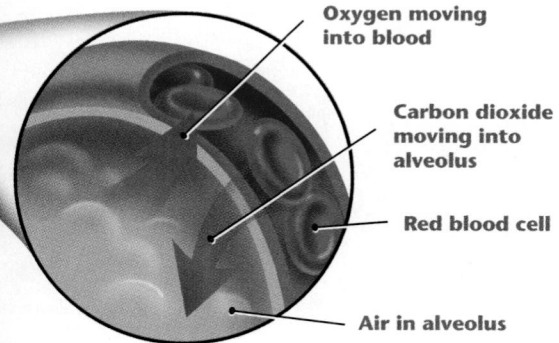

Oxygen moving into blood

Carbon dioxide moving into alveolus

Red blood cell

Air in alveolus

TRY THIS

Do You Exhale Carbon Dioxide? ACTIVITY

Learn whether carbon dioxide is present in exhaled air.

1. 🧪 Put on your goggles. Label two test tubes A and B.

2. Fill each test tube with 10 mL of water and a few drops of bromthymol blue solution. Bromthymol blue solution turns green or yellow in the presence of carbon dioxide.

3. Using a straw, blow air into the liquid in test tube A for a few seconds. Blow gently—if you blow hard, the liquid will bubble out of the test tube. **CAUTION:** *Use the straw to exhale only. Do not suck the solution back through the straw.*

4. Compare the solutions in the test tubes. Wash your hands when you have finished.

Predicting Suppose you had exercised immediately before you blew into the straw. Predict how this would have affected the results.

Figure 3 Alveoli are hollow air sacs surrounded by capillaries. As blood flows through the capillaries, oxygen moves from the alveoli into the blood. At the same time, carbon dioxide moves from the blood into the alveoli. *Interpreting Diagrams How is the structure of the alveoli important for gas exchange?*

Gas Exchange

TRY THIS

Skills Focus predicting ACTIVITY
Materials *bromthymol blue solution, 2 test tubes, plastic drinking straw, plastic wrap for covering test tubes (optional), safety goggles*
Time 20 minutes
Tips Caution students to blow gently, and to not suck the liquid up through the straw. Students can cover the test tube with plastic wrap to prevent liquid from bubbling out of the tube.
Expected Outcome The blue solution in test tube A will turn yellow when students blow into it, indicating the presence of carbon dioxide. Students should predict that, had they exercised before the activity, the color change would have occurred more quickly because their bodies would have been generating more carbon dioxide.
Extend Have students test their predictions by doing several jumping jacks or other exercises and repeating the activity. Before allowing students to exercise, make certain that they do not have a medical condition that precludes exercising. **learning modality: visual**

Answers to Self-Assessment

Caption Question

Figure 3 The thin walls and huge surface area allow high-volume gas exchange.

✓ Checkpoint

The bronchi are tubelike structures that lead into the lungs. Inside the lungs, the bronchi divide into smaller and smaller branches. At the ends of the branches are the alveoli.

Ongoing Assessment

Writing Ask students to write explanations of what happens in the alveoli during gas exchange.

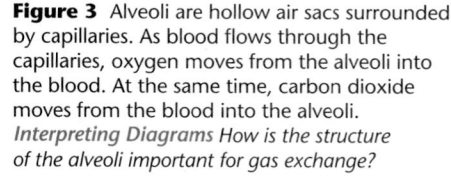

Social Studies
CONNECTION

Display large maps of South America and Asia. Inform students that the Andes are about 8,900 kilometers long. Ask: **In which countries are the Andes located?** *(Venezuela, Colombia, Ecuador, Peru, Bolivia, Chile, and Argentina)* Invite a volunteer to locate Mt. Aconcagua, the highest peak of the Andes at 6,959 meters, on the border between Argentina and Chile. On the map of Asia, show students the Himalayan Range, telling them it is about 2,500 kilometers long. Locate Nepal and tell students that 9 of the 14 highest peaks of the world are found in Nepal. Ask a volunteer to locate Mt. Everest. *(On the border between Nepal and Tibet)*

In Your Journal Students can include descriptions of symptoms associated with mountain sickness in their journals. They should consider how the thin air might affect their judgment and their ability to react quickly.
learning modality: verbal

Integrating Physics

Remind students that gases and liquids generally move from an area of high pressure to an area of low pressure. Point out that the flow of air into and out of the lungs is determined by the difference in pressure between the lungs and the atmosphere. Ask students to use this relationship to explain how relaxed rib and diaphragm muscles cause air to move out of the lungs. *(When the muscles relax, the volume of the lungs decreases. With the same amount of air in a smaller space, the air pressure inside the lungs is greater than the pressure outside, so the air moves outside.)* **learning modality: logical/mathematical**

Social Studies
CONNECTION

Have you ever seen movies or read about climbers scaling mountains in the Andes or Himalayas? Some of the peaks in the Andes rise to almost 7,000 meters. Mount Everest in the Himalayas, which rises about 8,850 meters, is the world's tallest mountain. People who climb these mountains usually experience mountain sickness—dizziness, headaches, and shortness of breath. Their symptoms are due to a shortage of oxygen in their blood. The amount of oxygen in air decreases the farther one goes above sea level.

In contrast to visitors, people who live high in these mountain ranges do not experience these symptoms. Their respiratory and circulatory systems have adjusted to compensate for the low levels of oxygen. For example, they inhale a greater volume of air with each breath than do people at lower levels. In addition, their blood contains a greater number of red blood cells for transporting oxygen.

In Your Journal

Locate the Andes Mountains and Himalaya Mountains on a globe or map. Then imagine that you are climbing a mountain in one of these ranges. Write a diary entry describing your physical reactions and what you might see.

How You Breathe

In an average day, you may breathe more than 20,000 times. The rate at which you breathe depends on your body's need for oxygen. When you exercise, your body needs a lot of oxygen to supply energy. The more oxygen you need, the faster you breathe.

Muscles for Breathing Pay attention to your breathing as you read this paragraph. Can you feel the air flowing in and out through your nose? Do you notice the gentle lift and fall of your chest?

Breathing, like other body movements, is controlled by muscles. Figure 5 shows the structure of the chest, including the muscles that enable you to breathe. Notice that the lungs are surrounded by the ribs, which have muscles attached to them. At the base of the lungs is the **diaphragm** (DY uh fram), a large, dome-shaped muscle that plays an important role in breathing.

The Process of Breathing Here is what happens when you

INTEGRATING PHYSICS inhale, or breathe in. The rib muscles contract, lifting the chest wall upward and outward. At the same time, the diaphragm contracts and moves downward. The combined action of these muscles makes the chest cavity larger, providing extra space for the lungs to expand.

When the chest cavity has expanded, there is more room for air. For a brief moment, however, there is no extra air to fill the space. Because the same amount of air now occupies a larger

Figure 4 These people live high in the Andes Mountains in Ecuador. Despite the low oxygen levels, these people experience no symptoms of mountain sickness. Their respiratory systems have adjusted in order to get enough oxygen into their bodies.

Background

Integrating Technology Sometimes a person who has throat cancer has to have his or her larynx removed. When the larynx must be totally removed, doctors stitch the remaining trachea into a hole above the patient's breastbone, and from then on, the patient breathes through this hole. Without a larynx and the flow of air through it, the person cannot speak.

To give a person without a larynx a voice, therapists often provide him or her with an artificial larynx, or electrolarynx. To speak, the person holds the vibrating head of the electrolarynx against his or her throat. The buzzing sound enters through the skin, producing vibrations that can be articulated into speech. With practice, speech becomes more intelligible, though there remains a mechanical quality to the voice.

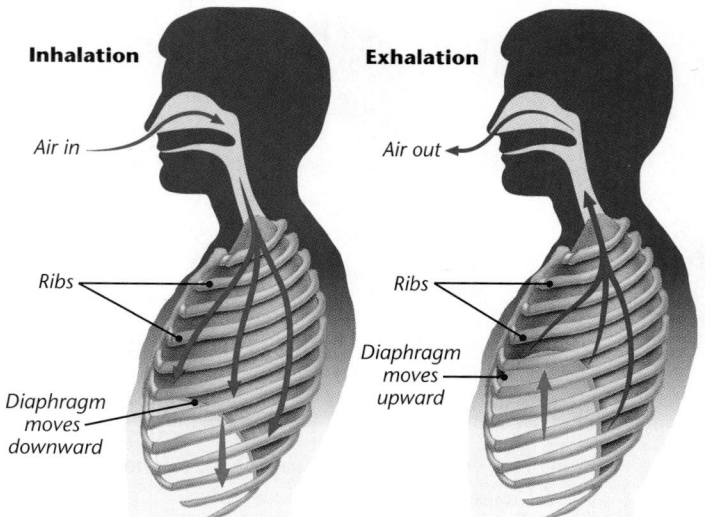

Inhalation

Air in

Ribs

Diaphragm moves downward

Exhalation

Air out

Ribs

Diaphragm moves upward

Figure 5 When you inhale, the diaphragm moves downward, allowing more room in the lungs for air. In contrast, when you exhale, the diaphragm moves upward. This upward movement increases the pressure in the lungs and pushes the air out.
Interpreting Diagrams How does the downward movement of the diaphragm affect the pressure of air inside the chest cavity?

space, the pressure of the air inside your lungs decreases. This means that the pressure of air inside the chest cavity is lower than the pressure of the atmosphere pushing on the body. Because of this difference in air pressure, air rushes into your chest, in the same way that air is sucked into a vacuum cleaner. You have inhaled.

In contrast, when you exhale, or breathe out, the rib muscles and diaphragm relax, and the chest cavity becomes smaller. This decrease in size squeezes air out of the lungs, the way squeezing a container of ketchup pushes ketchup out of the opening.

✔ *Checkpoint* **What muscles cause the chest to expand during breathing?**

How You Speak

The **larynx** (LAR ingks), or voice box, is located in the top part of the trachea, underneath the epiglottis. You can see the larynx if you look back at *Exploring the Respiratory System* on page 569. Place your fingers on your Adam's apple, which sticks out from the front of your neck. You can feel some of the cartilage that makes up the larynx. Two **vocal cords,** which are folds of connective tissue that produce your voice, stretch across the opening of the larynx.

How the Vocal Cords Work If you've ever let air out of a balloon while stretching its neck, you've heard the squeaking sound that the air makes. The neck of the balloon is something like your vocal cords. The vocal

 INTEGRATING PHYSICS

Integrating Physics

Materials *pieces of rubber with a small slit in the center*
Time 10 minutes

Some students may have difficulty visualizing how stretched tissue can be used to produce sounds. To demonstrate this, provide students with the prepared pieces of rubber. Cut small slits in the center of the rubber pieces prior to the activity. You can use a piece of rubber from a balloon. Instruct students to stretch the rubber until it is taut. Next, have the students take deep full breaths and blow across the piece of rubber at different angles. Ask: **What produces the sound?** *(Air flowing through the opening causes the rubber to vibrate. The vibrating rubber causes the air to vibrate and produces sound.)* Have students identify what the rubber represents. *(Vocal cords)*
learning modality: kinesthetic

Program Resources

◆ **Laboratory Manual** 18, "Measuring the Volume of Exhaled Air"

Answers to Self-Assessment

Caption Question

Figure 5 Downward movement of the diaphragm causes a decrease in air pressure inside the chest cavity.

✔ *Checkpoint*
Rib and diaphragm muscles

Ongoing Assessment

Writing Ask students to write short paragraphs describing what happens during the breathing process.

3 Assess

Section 1 Review Answers

1. It moves oxygen from the outside environment into the body and removes carbon dioxide and water from the body.

2. The oxygen molecule moves through the nostrils, pharynx, trachea, bronchus, smaller and smaller branches of the bronchus, and then into the alveolus.

3. Carbon dioxide passes from the blood, through the thin capillary wall, through the wall of the alveolus, and into the alveolus.

4. When you inhale, the chest cavity becomes larger, decreasing the air pressure inside the lungs. This decrease in air pressure causes air to rush into the lungs.

5. Dust irritates breathing passages. Coughs and sneezes are the body's response to the irritation; they act to remove the irritants.

Science at Home

Materials *shoe box, set of wooden blocks*

Encourage students to develop a mathematical expression to describe the surface area of a block. Remind them that the surface area of a single block is the sum of the areas of each of its surfaces. Have students imagine a cube with a side length of 1 cm as an example. Explain that each side has an area of 1 square cm (length × width). Because the cube has six surfaces (four sides, the top, and the bottom), the surface area of the cube is 6 cm².

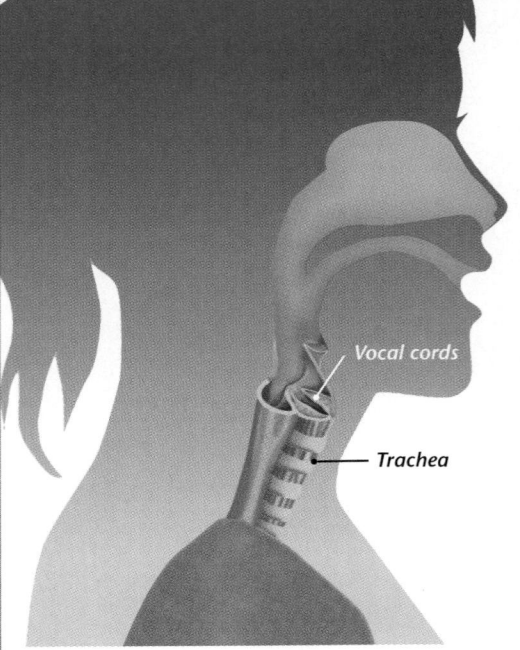

Figure 6 Air moving over this singer's vocal cords causes them to vibrate and produce sound. When her vocal cords contract, or shorten, she sings higher notes. When her vocal cords lengthen, she sings lower notes.

cords have a slitlike opening between them. When you speak, muscles make the vocal cords contract, narrowing the opening. Air from the lungs rushes through this opening. The movement of the vocal cords makes the air molecules vibrate, or move rapidly back and forth. This vibration creates a sound—your voice.

High and Low Tones The length of the vocal cords affects whether you produce low or high tones. When the vocal cords contract and shorten, you speak in a higher voice. When they are longer and in a relaxed position, you speak in a lower voice.

The length of vocal cords changes during a person's lifetime. Small children have high-pitched voices because their larynxes are small and their vocal cords are short. The vocal cords of both boys and girls are about the same length. During the teenage years, however, the vocal cords of boys grow longer than those of girls. This is why men have deeper voices than women.

Section 1 Review

1. List the functions of the respiratory system.
2. Describe the path that a molecule of oxygen takes as it moves from the air into the alveoli.
3. Explain what happens to carbon dioxide in the blood that flows through capillaries in the alveoli.
4. Why does air rush into your body when you inhale?
5. **Thinking Critically** **Relating Cause and Effect** When there is a lot of dust in the air, people often cough and sneeze. Explain why this happens.

Science at Home

Modeling Alveoli Use a shoe box and a set of blocks to show your family how the alveoli increase the surface area of the lungs. The shoe box represents a lung, and each block represents an alveolus. Fill the box with as many blocks as will fit inside. Then have your family imagine how much surface would be covered if all of the blocks were opened up and put together to form a large sheet. How would the surface area of the blocks compare with that of the shoe box?

Performance Assessment

Writing Have students write short stories describing the adventures of an oxygen molecule during respiration. Reports should indicate where the molecule traveled, what sights it saw, and how it was changed by the adventure.

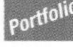 Students can save their short stories in their portfolios.

Program Resources

◆ **Unit 4 Resources** 18-1 Review and Reinforce, p. 91; 18-1 Enrich, p. 92

Media and Technology

Interactive Student Tutorial CD-ROM Chapter 18

Making Models

A Breath of Fresh Air

H ow does air get into your lungs? In this lab, you will make a model of the lungs to demonstrate how breathing takes place.

Problem

What causes your body to inhale and exhale air?

Materials

small balloon   large balloon
scissors
transparent plastic bottle with narrow neck

Procedure

1. In your notebook, explain how you think air gets into the lungs during the breathing process.
2. Cut off and discard the bottom of a small plastic bottle. Trim the cut edge so there are no rough spots.
3. Stretch a small balloon, then blow it up a few times to stretch it farther. Insert the round end of the balloon through the mouth of the bottle. Then, with a partner holding the bottle, stretch the neck of the balloon and pull it over the mouth of the bottle.
4. Stretch a large balloon, then blow it up a few times to stretch it farther. Cut off the balloon's neck, and discard it.
5. Have a partner hold the bottle while you stretch the remaining part of the balloon over the bottom opening of the bottle, as shown in the photo.

6. Use one hand to hold the bottle firmly. With the knuckles of your other hand, push upward on the large balloon, causing it to form a dome. Remove your knuckles from the balloon, letting the balloon flatten. Repeat this procedure a few times. Observe what happens to the small balloon. Record your observations in your notebook.

Analyze and Conclude

1. Make a diagram of the completed model in your notebook. Add labels to show which parts of your model represent the chest cavity, diaphragm, lungs, and trachea.
2. In this model, what is the position of the diaphragm just after you have exhaled? What do the lungs look like just after you have exhaled?
3. In this model, how does the diaphragm move? How do these movements of the diaphragm affect the lungs?
4. **Think About It** How does this model show that pressure changes are responsible for breathing?

More to Explore

How could you improve on this model to more closely show what happens in the chest cavity during the process of breathing? Obtain your teacher's permission before making a new model.

Extending the Inquiry

More to Explore Samples: To improve their models, students could:
◆ use many small balloons and straws to show that the surface area of the lungs is large because of numerous alveoli;
◆ use a flexible plastic bottle to show that the ribs also move during inhalation, increasing the volume of the chest cavity.

Safety

You may want to cut the plastic bottles yourself or make the process easier by making the first cut.

Program Resources

◆ **Unit 4 Resources** Chapter 18 Skills Lab, pp. 101–102
◆ **Inquiry Skills Activity Book** Provides teaching and review of all inquiry skills

A Breath of Fresh Air

Preparing for Inquiry

Key Concept A model of the lungs will demonstrate what happens during inhalation and exhalation.
Skills Objective Students will be able to
◆ make a model of the lungs.
Time 30 minutes
Advance Planning Obtain balloons and small, transparent, plastic bottles.
Alternative Materials You can use different sizes of bottles and balloons, but make sure the small balloon hangs freely. If a balloon does not make an airtight seal with the bottle, tape the seal.

Guiding Inquiry

Invitation

Encourage students to share their responses to Step 1 in the Procedure.

Introducing the Procedure

Have students refer to the photo in the book as they prepare the model.

Troubleshooting the Experiment

Be sure students do not pull the large balloon down to model inhalation. To show the relaxed (exhaled) state, the balloon should be dome-shaped. The balloon flattens during inhalation.

Analyze and Conclude

1. Bottle—chest cavity; large balloon—diaphragm; neck of the bottle —trachea; small balloon—lungs
2. The diaphragm rises into the chest cavity. The lungs are deflated.
3. The diaphragm moves down, becoming flat, then moves upward into its domed shape. When it moves upward, the lungs deflate. When it moves down, the lungs inflate.
4. When the volume inside the plastic bottle increases, it decreases the air pressure inside, and the small balloon inflates. When the volume inside the bottle decreases, it increases the air pressure inside and causes the small balloon to deflate.

SECTION 2 Smoking and Your Health

Objectives

After completing the lesson, students will be able to
◆ list the harmful chemicals contained in tobacco smoke;
◆ explain how tobacco smoke harms the respiratory and circulatory systems;
◆ define passive smoking and identify its effects on health;
◆ identify the reasons why some people choose to smoke.

Key Terms tar, carbon monoxide, nicotine, addiction, bronchitis, emphysema, passive smoking

1 Engage/Explore

Activating Prior Knowledge

Have students discuss their perceptions of smoking and popular culture. Encourage students to talk about how the image of smoking has changed over the years. Students may be aware of laws that restrict the areas where smoking is permitted or of lawsuits that have been brought against cigarette manufacturers.

 **DISCOVER**

Skills Focus inferring
Time 20 minutes
Tips Encourage students to discuss their answers with their partners. After students record their answers, provide the actual answers listed below. Prompt students to discuss any differences between their estimates and the actual numbers.
Answers 1. 400,000 2. 87% 3. 7 years longer 4. About 70% 5. About 25% (Sources: 1 and 3—Centers for Disease Control; 2—American Cancer Society; 4 and 5—Koop-Kessler Report on Tobacco Policy and Public Health)
Think It Over Samples: peer pressure, advertising, family members smoke

SECTION 2 Smoking and Your Health

DISCOVER • ACTIVITY

What Are the Dangers of Smoking?

Pair up with a partner. Read each question below and decide on a reasonable answer based on your current knowledge.

1. In the United States, about how many people die each year from smoking-related illnesses?

2. What percentage of lung cancer deaths are related to smoking?

3. On the average, how much longer do nonsmokers live than smokers?

4. What percentage of smokers say they want to quit smoking?

5. What percentage of smokers actually succeed in quitting?

Think It Over
Inferring Why do you think people start smoking when they know that smoking can cause serious health problems?

GUIDE FOR READING

◆ What harmful chemicals are contained in tobacco smoke?
◆ How does tobacco smoke harm the respiratory and circulatory systems?

Reading Tip Before you read, make a list of smoking-related health problems that you already know about. Add to your list as you read.

Whoosh! Millions of tiny but dangerous aliens are invading the respiratory system. The aliens are pulled into the nose with an inhaled breath. The cilia in the nasal cavities trap some aliens, and others get stuck in mucus. But many aliens get past these defenses. After tumbling in air currents, thousands of the invaders enter the lungs. The aliens implant themselves in the alveoli!

The "aliens" are not tiny creatures from space. They are the substances found in cigarette smoke. In this section you will learn how tobacco smoke damages the respiratory system.

Chemicals in Tobacco Smoke

With each puff, a smoker inhales over 4,000 different chemicals. **Some of the most deadly chemicals in tobacco smoke are tar, carbon monoxide, and nicotine.**

Tar The dark, sticky substance that forms when tobacco burns is called **tar.** When someone inhales tobacco smoke, some tar settles on cilia that line the trachea and other respiratory organs. Tar makes cilia clump together so they can't function to prevent harmful materials from getting into the lungs. Tar also contains chemicals that have been shown to cause cancer.

576

READING STRATEGIES

Reading Tip Students will likely say that smoking has been linked to lung cancer and heart disease. After students make their lists, invite volunteers to read items from their lists to the class. Record the information on the board. After students have read the section, lead a discussion of items on the list and encourage students to add to the list.

Study and Comprehension Students can create concept maps to organize information about smoking and health. Have students choose between these topics: *Harmful Chemicals in Tobacco Smoke* or *Respiratory and Circulatory Problems Caused by Tobacco Smoke.* Refer students to the explanation of concept mapping in the Skills Handbook.

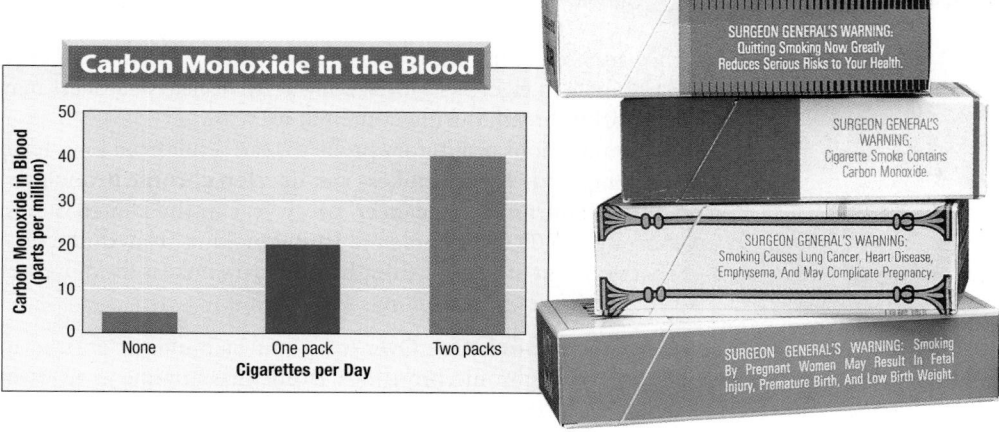

Carbon Monoxide in the Blood

(bar graph)
- y-axis: Carbon Monoxide in Blood (parts per million), values 0, 10, 20, 30, 40, 50
- x-axis: Cigarettes per Day — None, One pack, Two packs

Figure 7 The more cigarettes a person smokes, the more carbon monoxide he or she inhales. *Relating Cause and Effect How does carbon monoxide deprive the body of oxygen?*

Carbon Monoxide When substances—including tobacco—are burned, a colorless, odorless gas called **carbon monoxide** is produced. Carbon monoxide is dangerous to inhale because its molecules bind to hemoglobin in red blood cells. When carbon monoxide binds to hemoglobin, it takes the place of some of the oxygen that the red blood cells normally carry. The carbon monoxide molecules are something like cars that have taken parking spaces reserved for other cars.

When carbon monoxide binds to hemoglobin, red blood cells carry less than their normal load of oxygen throughout the body. To make up for the decrease in oxygen, the breathing rate increases and the heart beats faster. Smokers' blood may contain too little oxygen to meet their bodies' needs.

Nicotine Another dangerous chemical found in tobacco smoke is **nicotine.** Nicotine is a drug that speeds up the activities of the nervous system, heart, and other organs. It makes the heart beat faster and blood pressure rise. Nicotine produces an **addiction,** or physical and psychological dependence. Smokers feel an intense need, or craving, for a cigarette if they go without one. Addiction to nicotine is one reason why smokers have difficulty quitting.

☑ *Checkpoint* **How does the tar in cigarette smoke affect the body?**

Respiratory System Problems

Tobacco smoke harms the respiratory system in several ways. For example, because their cilia can't sweep away mucus, many smokers have a frequent cough. The mucus buildup also limits the space for air flow, and this decreases oxygen intake. Because

Program Resources

◆ **Unit 4 Resources** 18-2 Lesson Plan, p. 93; 18-2 Section Summary, p. 94

Media and Technology

 Audio CD English-Spanish Summary 18-2

Answers to Self-Assessment

Caption Question

Figure 7 Carbon monoxide binds to the hemoglobin in red cells, taking the place of some of the oxygen.

☑ *Checkpoint*

Tar makes cilia clump together so they cannot stop harmful materials from traveling to the lungs. Tar also contains chemicals that cause cancer.

2 *Facilitate*

Chemicals in Tobacco Smoke

Using the Visuals: Figure 7

Ask students what they think the phrase "parts per million" means. Help students understand that the phrase expresses concentration, or the amount of one substance in a certain volume of another substance. If the carbon monoxide in a person's blood has a concentration of two parts per million, that means that there is 500,000 times more blood than carbon dioxide. **limited English proficiency**

Addressing Naive Conceptions

Students may believe smokers can control the amount of dangerous chemicals they receive by smoking "light" or filtered cigarettes. Tell students researchers have found that many people who smoke these cigarettes smoke them in such a way that they actually receive the same amounts of tar and other chemicals as people who smoke "regular" cigarettes. Point out that no cigarettes are safe to smoke. **learning modality: verbal**

Respiratory System Problems

Real-Life Learning

Ask students if they know anyone with chronic bronchitis, emphysema, or lung cancer. Encourage those who do to describe how these illnesses affect quality of life and affect families. **learning modality: verbal**

Ongoing Assessment

Oral Presentation Call on students to name three harmful chemicals in tobacco smoke and to explain the health effects of each of them.

Respiratory System Problems, continued

they are not getting enough oxygen, smokers may not be able to participate in vigorous sports. Long-term or heavy smokers may be short of breath during even light exercise.

Some serious respiratory problems can result from long-term smoking. **Over time, smokers can develop chronic bronchitis, emphysema, and lung cancer.** Every year in the United States, more than 400,000 people die from smoking-related illnesses. That's one out of every five deaths. Tobacco smoke is the most preventable cause of major illness and death.

Chronic Bronchitis Over time, mucus buildup can lead to long-term, or chronic, bronchitis. **Bronchitis** (brahng KY tis) is an irritation of the breathing passages in which the small passages become narrower than normal and may be clogged with mucus. People with bronchitis have a hard time breathing. If bronchitis lasts a long time, it can cause permanent damage to the breathing passages. Chronic bronchitis is often accompanied by infection with disease-causing microorganisms. Chronic bronchitis is five to ten times more common in heavy smokers than in nonsmokers.

Figure 8 These people stay healthy by exercising and by choosing not to smoke.

Emphysema The chemicals in tobacco smoke damage lung tissue as well as breathing passages. **Emphysema** (em fuh SEE muh) is a serious disease that destroys lung tissue and causes difficulty in breathing. People with emphysema do not get enough oxygen and cannot adequately eliminate carbon dioxide. Therefore, they are always short of breath. Some people with emphysema even have trouble blowing out a match. Unfortunately, the damage caused by emphysema is permanent, even if a person stops smoking.

Lung Cancer About 140,000 Americans die each year from lung cancer caused by smoking. Cigarette smoke contains over 40 different chemicals that cause cancer, including chemicals in tar. Cancerous growths, or tumors, take away space in the lungs that should be used for gas exchange. Unfortunately, lung cancer is difficult to detect early, when treatment would be most effective.

☑ *Checkpoint* How does emphysema affect a person's lungs?

578

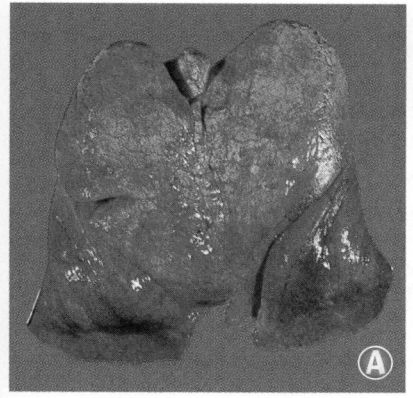

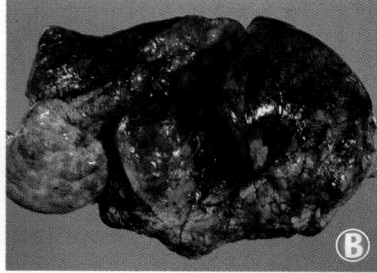

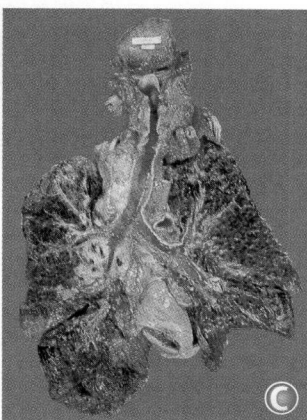

Figure 9 Over time, smoking damages the lungs and leads to serious health problems. Compare the lungs of a nonsmoker (**A**) to those of a person with emphysema (**B**) and a person with lung cancer (**C**).

Circulatory System Problems

The chemicals in tobacco smoke that damage the lungs also harm the circulatory system. Some of the chemicals get into the blood and are absorbed by the blood vessels. The chemicals then irritate the walls of the blood vessels. This irritation contributes to the buildup of the fatty material that causes atherosclerosis. Atherosclerosis can lead to heart attacks. **Compared to nonsmokers, smokers are more than twice as likely to have heart attacks.**

Conditions that harm the lungs, such as bronchitis and emphysema, also strain the circulatory system. The respiratory and circulatory systems work together to get oxygen to the cells and to remove carbon dioxide from the body. If either system is damaged, the other one must work harder.

Passive Smoking

Smokers are not the only people to suffer from the effects of tobacco smoke. In **passive smoking,** people involuntarily inhale the smoke from other people's cigarettes, cigars, or pipes. Since this smoke contains the same harmful chemicals that smokers inhale, it can cause health problems. Each year, passive smoking causes about 300,000 young children in the United States to develop respiratory problems. In addition, long-term exposure to cigarette smoke increases people's risks of heart disease and cancer.

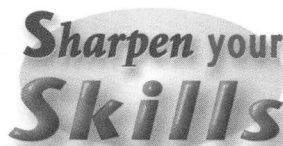

Sharpen your Skills

Calculating

Heavy smokers may smoke two packs of cigarettes every day. Find out what one pack of cigarettes costs. Then use that price to calculate how much a person would spend on cigarettes if he or she smoked two packs a day for 30 years.

Answers to Self-Assessment

☑ *Checkpoint*

Emphysema destroys lung tissue and causes difficulty in breathing.

Circulatory System Problems

Using the Visuals: Figure 9

Ask students to use the photographs to infer how the condition of the lungs shown in each photograph would probably affect a person's circulatory health. Point out how pink and moist the healthy lungs look compared to the lungs in the other two photos. *(Students may speculate that the lungs in B and C would not be able to take in very much air, and that they would not be able to exchange gas efficiently with the circulatory system.)*
learning modality: visual

Sharpen your Skills

Calculating

Provide students with a range of costs for a pack of cigarettes, or give them an average price to work with. Answers will depend on the price of cigarettes.
Extend Have students figure out some things that the person could have bought if he or she had saved the money spent on cigarettes. For example, if an apartment rents for $500 per month, how many months' rent would the saved money pay for?

Passive Smoking

Real-Life Learning

Tell students that smoking is now forbidden in many workplaces, restaurants, public buildings, and aircraft. Ask if students can explain why these restrictions have been imposed and whom they were designed to protect. Interested students can research the laws governing smoking in your community.
learning modality: verbal

Ongoing Assessment

Oral Presentation Ask students to identify and describe three respiratory system problems that result from cigarette smoking.

Choosing Not to Smoke

Real-Life Learning

Inform students that most smokers started smoking as teenagers. Ask: **If most smokers who try to quit are unsuccessful, what is a simple way to avoid becoming part of these statistics?** *(Never start smoking.)* **learning modality: verbal**

3 Assess

Section 2 Review Answers

1. Tar— damages cilia and contains chemicals that cause cancer; carbon monoxide—takes the place of oxygen in hemoglobin and deprives the body of oxygen; nicotine—addictive and speeds up body systems, making the heart beat faster and blood pressure rise

2. Any three: frequent cough, decreased oxygen intake, shortness of breath, chronic bronchitis, emphysema, lung cancer

3. Chemicals in cigarette smoke contribute to a buildup of substances in blood vessels that cause atherosclerosis; problems in the respiratory system put a strain on the cardiovascular system.

4. Sample answer: Peer pressure and advertisements

5. Nonsmokers develop cancer because they are passive smokers—they have inhaled the cigarette smoke produced by other people's cigarettes.

Check Your Progress

Review students' ads to make sure they indicate a relationship between what students are learning about respiratory function and health problems associated with smoking.

Performance Assessment

Writing Have students write paragraphs in which they convince a friend not to smoke.

 Students can save their paragraphs in their portfolios.

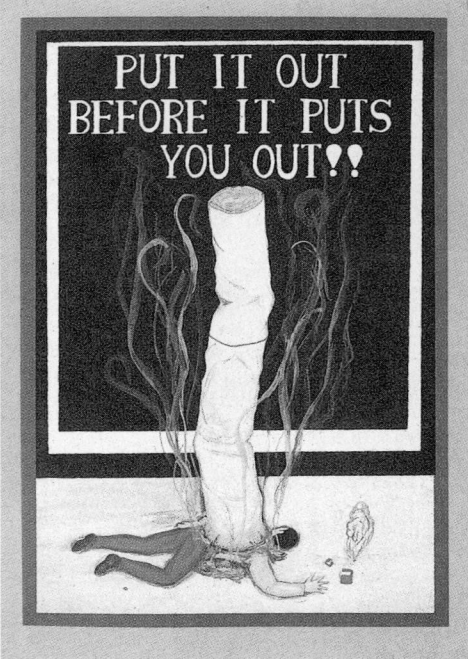

Figure 10 This antismoking advertisement was created by a teenager to encourage smokers to quit.

Choosing Not to Smoke

Today about 50 million Americans are smokers. Of those people, more than 90 percent began smoking when they were teenagers. Studies show that if people do not start smoking when they are teenagers, they probably will not start smoking later in life.

You may be tempted to try smoking. Friends may pressure you, or advertisements may appeal to you. Tobacco advertisements show smokers as young, attractive, popular people. The ads try to make you think that you will be like these people if you use tobacco products.

It is important to remember that it's very hard to quit smoking once you start. Many teenage smokers think that they will quit when they are older—but because nicotine is addictive, they have trouble doing so. And smoking hurts people right away, not just later in life. The lungs of teenagers who smoke develop more slowly than those of nonsmokers and may never reach the same peak level of functioning. In addition, teenage smokers may develop coughs and bronchitis. If someone asks you to try a cigarette, think of your health and politely refuse.

Section 2 Review

1. Name three harmful substances in tobacco smoke. Describe the effects of each substance.

2. Identify three respiratory problems caused by smoking.

3. Describe the effect of smoking on the circulatory system.

4. Identify two factors that may pressure teenagers to try smoking.

5. Thinking Critically Relating Cause and Effect Scientists estimate that about 3,000 nonsmoking Americans die every year from smoking-related lung cancer. Explain why.

Check Your Progress
CHAPTER PROJECT

By now you should have sketched what your ads might look like and written what they might say. In planning your ads, be sure to consider all the effects of smoking, not just those related to health—for example, the expense of smoking. Plan to use ideas and images that are appropriate for each age group. (*Hint:* Look through a variety of magazines to find ads aimed at different age groups. Which techniques seem to work best? How can you use those techniques in your ads?)

Program Resources

♦ **Unit 4 Resources** 18-2 Review and Reinforce, p. 95; 18-2 Enrich, p. 96

DISCOVER •••••••••••••••••••••••••••••••••••ACTIVITY••••

How Does Filtering a Liquid Change What Is in It?

1. Your teacher will give you 50 milliliters of a liquid in a small container. Pour a small amount of sand into the liquid.

2. Use a glucose-test strip to determine whether glucose is present in the liquid.

3. Put filter paper in a funnel. Then put the funnel into the mouth of a second container. Slowly pour the liquid through the funnel into the second container.

4. Look for any solid material on the filter paper. Remove the funnel and carefully examine the liquid that passed through the filter.

5. Test the liquid again to see whether it contains glucose.

Think It Over
Observing Which substances passed through the filter, and which did not? How might a filtering device be useful in the body?

The human body faces a challenge that is a bit like trying to keep a home clean. You learned in Chapter 16 that the body takes in foods through the digestive system and breaks them down into nutrients. As cells use those nutrients in respiration and other processes, wastes are created. **The excretory system is the system in the body that collects wastes produced by cells and removes the wastes from the body.** The removal process is known as **excretion.**

If wastes were not taken away, they would pile up and make you sick. Excretion helps maintain homeostasis by keeping the body's internal environment stable and free of harmful materials.

The Kidneys

As you already know, some wastes that your body must eliminate are carbon dioxide and excess water. Another waste product is urea. **Urea** (yoo REE uh) is a chemical that comes from the breakdown of proteins. Your two **kidneys,** which are the major organs of the excretory system, eliminate urea, excess water, and some other waste materials. These wastes are eliminated in **urine,** a watery fluid produced by your kidneys.

The kidneys act something like filters. As blood flows through the kidneys, they remove wastes from the blood. After the process is complete, urine flows from the kidneys through two narrow tubes called **ureters** (yoo REE turz). The ureters carry the urine

> ### GUIDE FOR READING
>
> ◆ What is the function of the excretory system?
>
> ◆ How is urine produced in the kidneys' nephrons?
>
> ◆ In addition to the kidneys, what other organs play a role in excretion?
>
> *Reading Tip* As you read, write a brief summary of the information under each heading.

Chapter 18 **581**

READING STRATEGIES

Reading Tip Before students read the section, offer these reminders:

◆ The summary should be brief.
◆ Use your own words.
◆ State the main points and key details. Sample summary: The kidneys filter wastes from the blood. The wastes leave the kidneys as urine, which is stored in the urinary bladder until it can be released.

Program Resources

◆ **Unit 4 Resources** 18-3 Lesson Plan, p. 97; 18-3 Section Summary, p. 98

Media and Technology

 Audio CD English-Spanish Summary 18-3

SECTION
③ The Excretory System

Objectives

After completing the lesson, students will be able to
◆ identify the function of the excretory system;
◆ state how urine is produced in the kidneys' nephrons;
◆ explain how the kidneys help maintain water balance in the body;
◆ name the organs involved in excretion and describe their roles.

Key Terms excretion, urea, kidney, urine, ureter, urinary bladder, urethra, nephron

1 Engage/Explore

Activating Prior Knowledge

Have students list some typical items that families discard as trash. Ask students what would happen if no one ever removed this trash from their apartment or house. Then point out that the body produces "trash" substances that need to be eliminated.

•••••••• DISCOVER ••••••••

Skills Focus observing
Materials *glucose solution, sand, two small plastic containers, glucose test strip, plastic funnel, filter paper* ACTIVITY
Time 15 minutes
Tips Prepare the glucose solution using 5 grams of glucose per liter of water. Each plastic container should hold at least 75 mL.
Expected Outcome The glucose solution will pass through the filter, but the sand will not.
Think It Over The glucose and water passed through the filter; the sand did not. A filtering device could remove wastes in the body.

2 Facilitate

The Kidneys

Real-Life Learning

Have students predict what happens when the kidneys fail. *(Students may speculate that urination may cease and the body may fill with waste products.)* Tell students that sometimes, because of disease, people's kidneys stop functioning. Have them develop a list of questions about kidney failure, including symptoms and treatment options. Invite a specialist to talk to the class and answer students' questions, or provide resources for students to perform their own research. Students can present their findings in a poster or pamphlet.
learning modality: verbal

The Filtering Process

EXPLORING
a Kidney

Refer students to the visual essay on the kidney. Ask: **How are the three diagrams related?** *(The first diagram shows the location of the kidneys in the excretory system; the second shows a close-up of a kidney; the third shows details of a nephron inside a kidney.)* Direct students' attention to the illustration of the nephron. After students have examined the illustration, ask them to identify the function of the capillary cluster. *(Filters urea, water, glucose, and other substances out of the blood.)* Students can then make flowcharts that trace the path of filtered material through the tube. Once the flowcharts are completed, ask: **What is the purpose of the nephrons?** *(The nephrons remove wastes from blood and produce urine.)* **learning modality: visual**

 Portfolio Students can save their flowcharts in their portfolios.

to the **urinary bladder,** a sacklike muscular organ that stores urine. When the bladder is full enough that its walls are stretched, you feel a need to urinate. Urine flows from the body through a small tube called the **urethra** (yoo REE thruh), which you can see in *Exploring a Kidney*.

✓ *Checkpoint* What is the role of the ureters?

The Filtering Process

The kidneys are champion filters. Every drop of blood in your body passes through your kidneys and is filtered more than 300 times a day. Contrast this to a typical swimming-pool filter, which only cleans the pool water about 5 times a day.

Each of your kidneys contains about a million tiny filtering factories called **nephrons.** The nephrons are the tiny structures that remove wastes from blood and produce urine. **Urine formation takes place in a number of stages. First, both wastes and needed materials, such as glucose, are removed from the blood. Later, much of the needed material is returned to the blood.**

Filtering Out Wastes After entering the kidneys, blood flows through smaller and smaller arteries. Eventually it reaches a cluster of capillaries in a nephron. These capillaries are surrounded

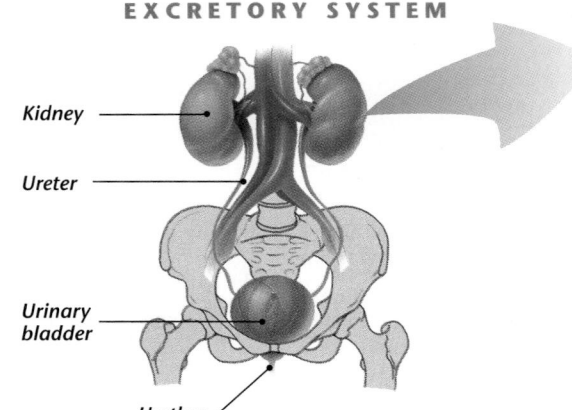

EXPLORING *a Kidney*

Each kidney contains about a million tiny filtering units called nephrons. Urine is produced in the nephrons.

EXCRETORY SYSTEM

Kidney

Ureter

Urinary bladder

Urethra

KIDNEY

582

Background

Facts and Figures People whose kidneys do not function have to undergo dialysis. In hemodialysis, the first dialysis procedure developed, the patients' blood is removed from their bodies, purified by artificial kidneys (called dialyzers), and returned to their bloodstreams. During the procedure, the patient's blood is diverted from an artery into the dialyzer, where it flows along one surface of a membrane. The waste materials pass through the membrane into a sterile solution on the other side. Substances required by the body, such as sugars, amino acids, and salts, are added to the sterile solution where they move through the membrane into the blood. After water is returned across the membrane and the blood is completely filtered, clots and bubbles are removed before the blood flows back into one of the patient's veins.

by a thin-walled, hollow capsule that is connected to a long tube. Find the capillary cluster, the capsule, and the tube in *Exploring a Kidney*. In the capillary cluster, urea, glucose, other chemicals, and some water move out of the blood and into the capsule. In contrast, blood cells and most protein molecules do not move into the capsule. Instead, they remain in the capillaries.

Formation of Urine Urine forms from the filtered material that passes into the capsule. This filtered material flows through the long, twisting tube. Some of the substances that collect in the capsule are needed by the body. As the liquid moves through the tube, many of these substances are reabsorbed, or returned to the blood. Normally all the glucose, most of the water, and small amounts of other materials pass back into the blood in the capillaries that surround the tube. In contrast, urea and other wastes remain in the tube.

The filtering process is something like cleaning your locker by throwing everything in your locker into a wastebasket, and then putting back the things that you want to keep. You can think of the locker as your blood and the wastebasket as the capsule. After the entire process is complete, the fluid that remains in the tube is the urine that will be eliminated.

NEPHRON

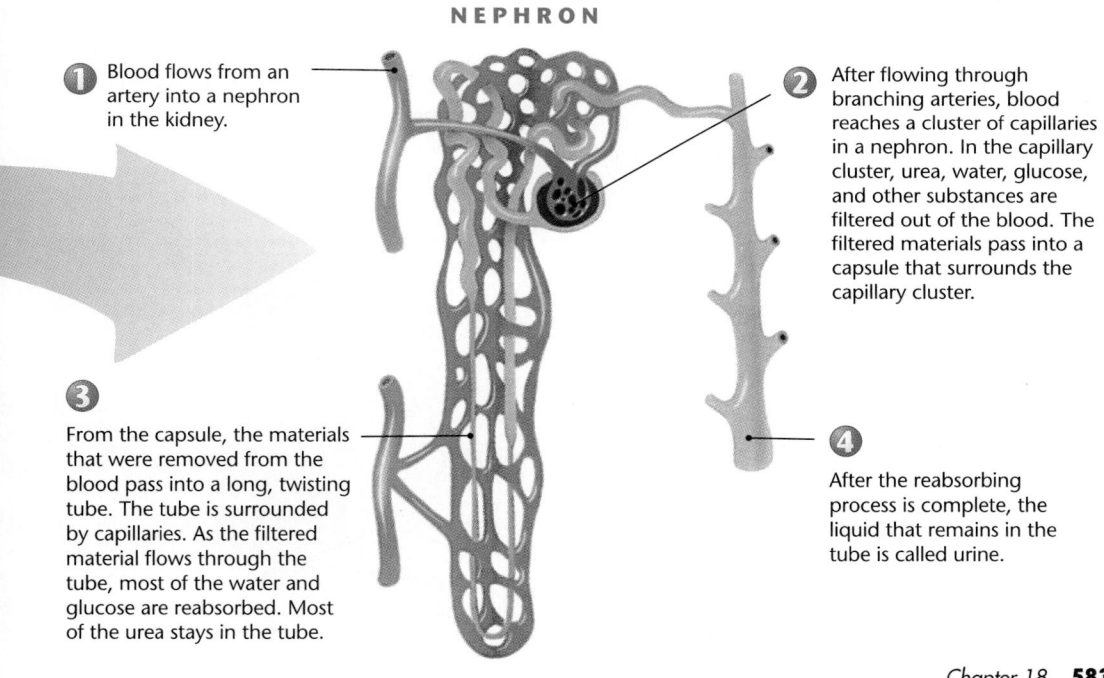

1 Blood flows from an artery into a nephron in the kidney.

2 After flowing through branching arteries, blood reaches a cluster of capillaries in a nephron. In the capillary cluster, urea, water, glucose, and other substances are filtered out of the blood. The filtered materials pass into a capsule that surrounds the capillary cluster.

3 From the capsule, the materials that were removed from the blood pass into a long, twisting tube. The tube is surrounded by capillaries. As the filtered material flows through the tube, most of the water and glucose are reabsorbed. Most of the urea stays in the tube.

4 After the reabsorbing process is complete, the liquid that remains in the tube is called urine.

Chapter 18 **583**

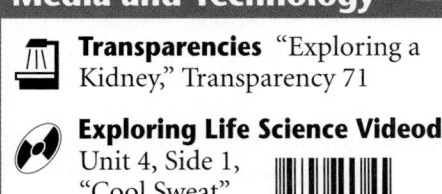
Answers to Self-Assessment

☑ *Checkpoint*
Ureters carry urine to the urinary bladder.

Demonstration ACTIVITY
Materials *30-cm section of cellophane dialysis tubing, 2 large beakers, string, 10 mL of a solution of salt water, distilled water, hand-held conductivity tester*
Time 40 minutes

For the benefit of students who had difficulty comprehending the text description of kidney function, you can use a model to demonstrate how sodium passes back into the blood during the formation of urine. Soak the tubing for several hours in a beaker filled with distilled water. Use string to tie one end of the dialysis tubing tightly closed. After the tubing is tied, store it in the container of distilled water. On the day of the activity, prepare a salt solution by mixing a few teaspoons of table salt in 100 mL of water. Fill the tubing three-quarters full with the salt solution, then tie the open end of the bag tightly closed with string. Suspend the tubing in a beaker of distilled water by tying it to a ruler placed across the rim. Do not allow the beaker to overflow. To begin the demonstration, tell students that the bag contains a salt solution, that salt contains sodium, and that the tester indicates the presence of salt in a solution. After 20 minutes, test the solution in the beaker. The conductivity tester should light. Have students explain how the salt got into the distilled water and how this models the movement of sodium during the formation of urine. *(The salt in the tubing passes into the water the way sodium in the kidney tubes passes back into the blood in the capillaries that surround the tubes.)*
Alternative Materials If you do not have a conductivity tester, pour some of the water from the beaker into a watch glass or other shallow, transparent container. Put the container aside until the water evaporates. Students should be able to see a white residue in the dish, indicating the presence of salt. **limited English proficiency**

Ongoing Assessment

Writing Have students list the functions of the kidneys.

583

You Solve the Mystery

Clues About Health

Preparing for Inquiry

Key Concept Urine tests can provide evidence of disease.

Skills Objectives Students will be able to

◆ observe color changes as solutions react with the test solutions;

◆ interpret data and draw conclusions about the presence or absence of glucose and protein in the solutions.

Time 40 minutes

Advance Planning Make up the patients' samples to match the Sample Data Table on page 585 or according to your own preferences. Prepare a 1% glucose solution by dissolving 10 g of glucose in 990 mL of water. Make a 1% protein solution by dissolving 10 g of albumin or pepsin in 990 mL of water. Add food coloring to make the solutions a pale yellow color (like urine), if desired. Use these solutions to make the simulated urine samples. Glucose, albumin, pepsin, glucose test strips, and Biuret solution can be obtained from biological supply companies.

Guiding Inquiry

Invitation

Ask students to list substances that are filtered from the blood and to identify which of those substances are normally reabsorbed. Students should conclude that some substances should not be found in the urine of a healthy person.

Introducing the Procedure

Ask: **What is the purpose of testing known solutions?** (*They show how the test materials work.*)

Troubleshooting the Experiment

◆ Food coloring may distort color changes and make them less noticeable.

◆ Droppers should be labeled and returned to the proper test tube to avoid contamination.

584

Analyzing Urine for Signs of Disease When people go to a 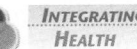 **INTEGRATING HEALTH** doctor for a medical checkup, they usually have their urine analyzed. A chemical analysis of urine can be useful in detecting some medical problems. Normally, urine contains almost no glucose or protein. If glucose is present in urine, it may indicate that a person has diabetes, a condition in which body cells cannot absorb enough glucose from the blood. Protein in urine can be a sign that the kidneys are not functioning properly.

You Solve the Mystery

Real-World Lab

CLUES ABOUT HEALTH

In this lab, you'll become a medical detective as you carry out urine tests to uncover evidence of disease.

Problem

How can you test urine for the presence of glucose and protein?

Skills Focus

observing, interpreting data, drawing conclusions

Materials

test tubes, 6
plastic droppers, 6
glucose solution
marking pencil
glucose test strips
simulated urine samples, 3
test tube rack
water
protein solution
white paper towels
Biuret solution

Procedure

Part 1 Testing for Glucose

1. Label six test tubes as follows: "W" for water, "G" for glucose, "P" for protein, and "A," "B," and "C" for three patients' "urine samples."

2. Place the test tubes in a test tube rack. Label six glucose test strips with the same letters.

3. Copy the data table into your notebook.

4. Fill each test tube about 3/4 full with the solution that corresponds to its label.

5. Place the W glucose test strip on a clean, dry section of a paper towel. Then use a clean plastic dropper to place 2 drops of the water from test tube W on the test strip. Record the resulting color of the test strip in your data table. If no color change occurs, write "no reaction."

584

Expected Outcome

◆ Glucose test strips will turn green if glucose is present.

◆ The solution will turn purple-pink when Biuret solution is added if protein is present.

Analyze and Conclude

1. The normal urine sample (B) is negative in both the glucose and protein tests.

2. The urine sample that tests positive for glucose (C) indicates possible diabetes.

3. A urine sample that tests positive for protein (A) indicates possible kidney disease.

4. Normally proteins are not filtered from blood, and the kidneys reabsorb filtered glucose.

5. No. A single test does not provide enough evidence.

Water Balance in the Body

The kidneys also help maintain homeostasis by regulating the amount of water in your body. Remember that as urine is being formed, water passes from the tube back into the bloodstream. The exact amount of water that is reabsorbed depends on conditions both outside and within the body. Suppose that it's a hot day. You've been sweating a lot, and you haven't had much to drink. In that situation, almost all of the water in the tube will be reabsorbed, and you will excrete only a small amount of urine. If,

DATA TABLE

Test for	W (water)	G (glucose)	P (protein)	A (Patient A)	B (Patient B)	C (Patient C)
Glucose						
Protein						

Test Tube

6. Use the procedure in Step 5 to test each of the other five solutions with the correctly labeled glucose test strip. Record the color of each test strip in the data table.

Part 2 Testing for Protein

7. Obtain a dropper bottle containing Biuret solution. Record the original color of the solution in your notebook.

8. Carefully add 30 drops of Biuret solution to test tube W. **CAUTION:** *Biuret solution can harm skin and damage clothing. Handle it with care.* Gently swirl the test tube to mix the two solutions together. Hold the test tube against a white paper towel to help you detect any color change. Observe the color of the final mixture, and record that color in your data table.

9. Repeat Step 8 for each of the other test tubes.

Analyze and Conclude

1. Which of the three patients' urine samples tested normal? How do you know?
2. Which urine sample(s) indicated that diabetes might be present? How do you know?
3. Which urine sample(s) indicated that kidney disease might be present? How do you know?
4. When a person's health is normal, how are the kidneys involved in keeping glucose and protein out of urine?
5. **Apply** Do you think a doctor should draw conclusions about the presence of a disease based on a single urine sample? Explain.

More to Explore

Propose a way to determine whether a patient with glucose in the urine could reduce the level through changes in diet.

 Integrating Health

Inform students that doctors can find evidence of illness or injury by studying changes in the color, density, and amount of urine. Tell them that urinalysis can also show whether a person has used steroids, marijuana, or other illegal substances. Ask: **What does it indicate when a substance not normally a waste product is found in a urine sample?** (*Sample: The body cannot fully absorb or process the substance.*)
learning modality: verbal

Water Balance in the Body

Building Inquiry Skills: Predicting

Ask students to predict what would happen if they took in significantly more than 2 liters of water each day. (*Sample: The body would produce a volume of urine large enough to maintain homeostasis.*)
learning modality: verbal

Sample Data Table

Test for	W (water)	G (glucose)	P (protein)	A (Patient A)	B (Patient B)	C (Patient C)
Glucose	Yellow	Green	Yellow	Yellow	Yellow	Green
Protein	Lt. Blue	Lt. Blue	Purple	Purple	Lt. Blue	Lt. Blue

Extending the Inquiry

More to Explore Students might suggest the patient eat fewer sugary foods. The amount of glucose in the patient's urine can be monitored to determine if diet affects the glucose level.

Safety

Students should wear aprons and safety goggles and use glassware carefully. Biuret solution can harm skin and damage clothing. Review the safety guidelines in Appendix A.

Program Resources

◆ **Unit 4 Resources** Chapter 5 Real-World Lab, pp. 103–105

Other Organs of Excretion

Building Inquiry Skills: Inferring

Have each student place a plastic sandwich bag over one of his or her hands, then use masking tape to close the bag at the wrist. After a few minutes, students should observe condensation inside the bags. Ask students to infer whether the skin removes wastes from the body all the time, or just when they are aware they are perspiring. (*All the time*)
learning modality: kinesthetic

3 Assess

Section 3 Review Answers

1. To collect and remove wastes from the body.
2. First, both wastes and needed substances are removed from the blood. Then, the substances the body needs are returned to the blood. Once the filtering and reabsorbing processes are complete, the fluid remaining is urine.
3. Lungs remove carbon dioxide and some water; sweat glands in skin excrete water and some chemical wastes; the liver breaks some wastes down into substances that can be excreted.
4. They adjust the amount of water reabsorbed during urine formation.
5. Laura will probably produce less urine, because most of the water she is taking in will be reabsorbed.

> **Check Your Progress** CHAPTER PROJECT
> Groups should have assigned roles for the production of their ads. Arrange a place for students to display their work. If possible, use a common hallway where other students can see the ads. Effective posters may discourage other students from smoking.

Performance Assessment

Writing Have students explain how one organ in the excretory system functions.

Figure 11 Your skin and lungs also function as excretory organs. Water and some chemical wastes are excreted in perspiration. And when you exhale on a cold morning, you can see the water in your breath. *Applying Concepts What other waste product does your exhaled breath contain?*

however, the day is cool and you've drunk a lot of water, less water will be reabsorbed. Your body will produce a larger volume of urine.

Every day, you need to take at least 2 liters of water into your body. You can do this either by drinking or by eating foods such as apples that contain a lot of water. This helps your kidneys maintain the proper water balance in your body.

Other Organs of Excretion

Most of the wastes produced by the body are removed through the kidneys, but not all. **The other organs of excretion are the lungs, skin, and liver.** You've already learned how the lungs and skin remove wastes. When you breathe out, carbon dioxide and some water are removed from the body. Sweat glands also function in excretion, because water and some chemical wastes are excreted in perspiration.

Have you ever torn apart a large pizza box so that it could fit in a wastebasket? If so, then you can understand that some wastes need to be broken down before they can be excreted. The liver performs this function. For example, urea, which comes from the breakdown of proteins, is produced by the liver. The liver also converts part of the hemoglobin molecule from old red blood cells into substances such as bile. Recall from Chapter 16 that bile helps break down fats during digestion. Because the liver produces a usable material from old red blood cells, you can think of the liver as a recycling factory.

Section 3 Review

1. What is the function of the excretory system?
2. Describe the two stages of urine formation.
3. What roles do the lungs, skin, and liver play in excretion?
4. How do the kidneys help regulate the amount of water in the body?
5. **Thinking Critically Predicting** On a long bus trip, Laura does not drink any water for several hours. How will the volume of urine she produces that day compare to the volume on a day when she drinks several glasses of water? Explain.

586

> **Check Your Progress** CHAPTER PROJECT
> By now you should be creating your ads. If you are producing ads for a newspaper or magazine, you need to create original drawings or use images from other sources. If you are preparing television or radio ads, you need to arrange for actors and any necessary props. Write and edit the text or script of your ads. Arrange for a place to display your ads or for a time to present the ads.

Program Resources

◆ **Unit 4 Resources** 18-3 Review and Reinforce, p. 99; 18-3 Enrich, p. 100

Answers to Self-Assessment
Caption Question
Figure 11 Carbon dioxide

SECTION 1 The Respiratory System

Key Ideas

◆ The respiratory system moves oxygen into the body and removes carbon dioxide from the body.
◆ In the process of respiration in cells, glucose is broken down using oxygen to produce energy.
◆ As air travels from the outside environment to the lungs, it passes through the nose, pharynx, trachea, and bronchi.
◆ In the alveoli, oxygen moves from the air into the blood, while carbon dioxide and water pass from the blood into the air.
◆ During inhalation, the diaphragm and rib muscles make the chest cavity expand. The air pressure inside the lungs decreases, and air rushes into the lungs. During exhalation, the chest cavity becomes smaller, pushing air out of the body.
◆ When air passes over the vocal cords, which are folds of tissue in the larynx, they vibrate to produce sound.

Key Terms

respiration	bronchi	diaphragm
cilia	lungs	larynx
pharynx	alveoli	vocal cords
trachea		

SECTION 2 Smoking and Your Health
INTEGRATING HEALTH

Key Ideas

◆ The most harmful substances in tobacco smoke are tar, carbon monoxide, and nicotine.
◆ When people inhale tobacco smoke, they increase their chances of developing respiratory diseases such as chronic bronchitis, emphysema, and lung cancer.
◆ Smokers are more likely to have heart attacks than are nonsmokers.

Key Terms

tar	bronchitis
carbon monoxide	emphysema
nicotine	passive smoking
addiction	

SECTION 3 The Excretory System

Key Ideas

◆ The excretory system removes carbon dioxide, urea, water, and other wastes from the body.
◆ The kidneys are the major organs of excretion. By filtering the blood, the kidneys produce urine.
◆ Urine travels from the kidneys through the ureters to the urinary bladder.
◆ In the kidney's nephrons, wastes and other materials are filtered from the blood. Some useful substances, such as glucose and water, are then reabsorbed into the blood.
◆ The lungs, skin, and liver are also organs of excretion.

Key Terms

excretion	urine	urethra
urea	ureters	nephron
kidney	urinary bladder	

Organizing Information

Flowchart The kidneys eliminate wastes from the body in a series of steps. Copy the flowchart below and complete it by filling in the missing steps.

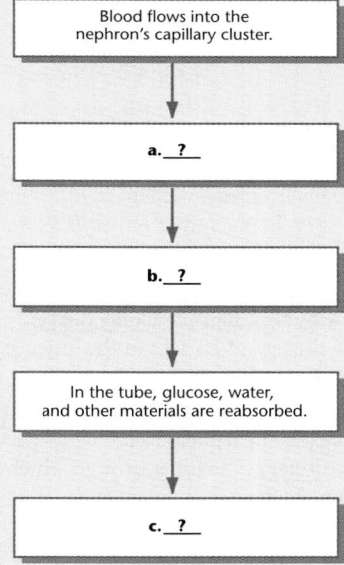

Blood flows into the nephron's capillary cluster.

↓

a. ?

↓

b. ?

↓

In the tube, glucose, water, and other materials are reabsorbed.

↓

c. ?

Chapter 18 **587**

Organizing Information

Flowchart a. Water, urea, glucose, and some chemicals are removed from the blood and flow into the capsule. **b.** From the capsule, the substances flow into a long tube. **c.** Urine flows from the kidneys through ureters to the urinary bladder.

Program Resources

◆ **Unit 4 Resources** Chapter 18 Project Scoring Rubric, p. 88
◆ **Performance Assessment** Chapter 18, pp. 56–58
◆ **Chapter and Unit Tests** Chapter 18 Test, pp. 84–87

Media and Technology

Interactive Student Tutorial CD-ROM Chapter 18

Computer Test Bank Chapter 18 Test

Reviewing Content

Multiple Choice

1. b **2.** a **3.** b **4.** a **5.** d

True or False

6. cilia **7.** true **8.** nicotine **9.** urethra
10. true

Checking Concepts

11. Breathing consists of taking air into the body and removing it from the body. Respiration is the series of chemical reactions in cells in which glucose and oxygen react to release energy.

12. Because there are an enormous number of spherical alveoli, they have an extremely large surface area.

13. During inhalation, the diaphragm moves downward, and the rib muscles lift the chest wall upward and outward. This increases the volume of the chest cavity and decreases the air pressure in the lungs. Therefore, air rushes into the lungs. During exhalation, the diaphragm moves upward and the rib muscles relax. This makes the chest cavity smaller and increases the air pressure in the lungs, which pushes air out of the lungs.

14. Men have longer vocal cords.

15. Carbon monoxide binds to hemoglobin, taking the place of oxygen. This deprives the body of oxygen.

16. Kidneys maintain homeostasis by removing wastes from the body; if wastes were not removed, they would poison body cells. In addition, by adjusting the amount of water reabsorbed, kidneys maintain water balance.

17. Stories should trace the path of the molecule from a nostril, through the pharynx, trachea, and bronchi, and into an alveolus. From there, the oxygen molecule passes into a capillary and enters the blood, which carries it to a body cell. Then it is used in a chemical reaction to release energy.

Thinking Critically

18. Similar—Both are energy-releasing chemical reactions that require oxygen. Different—Respiration takes place within cells. Burning takes place outside cells and may produce light and flames.

19. Water vapor is present in exhaled air, and it condenses on the mirror.

CHAPTER 18 ASSESSMENT

Reviewing Content

 For more review of key concepts, see the Interactive Student Tutorial CD-ROM.

Multiple Choice

1. The process in which glucose and oxygen react in cells to release energy is called
   a. digestion.
   b. respiration.
   c. breathing.
   d. gas exchange.

2. The trachea divides into two tubes called
   a. bronchi.
   b. alveoli.
   c. windpipes.
   d. diaphragms.

3. Your voice is produced by the
   a. pharynx.
   b. larynx.
   c. trachea.
   d. alveoli.

4. The disease in which the respiratory passages become narrower than normal is called
   a. bronchitis.
   b. lung cancer.
   c. diabetes.
   d. emphysema.

5. Normal urine contains both
   a. water and carbon monoxide.
   b. water and large amounts of glucose.
   c. urea and proteins.
   d. urea and water.

True or False

If the statement is true, write true. If it is false, change the underlined word or words to make the statement true.

6. Dust particles trapped in mucus are swept away by tiny, hairlike <u>blood vessels</u>.

7. The clusters of air sacs in the lungs are called <u>alveoli</u>.

8. <u>Tar</u> is a chemical in tobacco smoke that makes the heart beat faster.

9. The <u>ureter</u> is the tube through which urine leaves the body.

10. The <u>lungs</u> are excretory organs.

20. If babies inhale smoke from people's cigarettes, this smoke can damage their respiratory systems.

21. Students' judgments will vary. Check for supported arguments.

22. Blood cells could pass into the nephron and end up in urine.

Checking Concepts

11. Explain the difference between breathing and respiration.

12. Explain how the alveoli provide a large surface area for gas exchange in the lungs.

13. Describe how the diaphragm and rib muscles work together to control inhaling and exhaling.

14. Why do men have deeper voices than women?

15. Describe what happens when carbon monoxide enters the body. How does this affect the body?

16. Explain two ways in which the kidneys help to maintain homeostasis in the body.

17. **Writing to Learn** Imagine that you are a molecule of oxygen. Write an adventure story that describes what happens to you between the time you are inhaled through someone's nose and the time you are used in respiration in a body cell.

Thinking Critically

18. **Comparing and Contrasting** How is respiration similar to the burning of fuel? How is it different?

19. **Inferring** If you exhale onto a mirror, the mirror will become clouded with a thin film of moisture. Explain why this happens.

20. **Applying Concepts** Explain how babies can develop smoking-related respiratory problems.

21. **Making Judgments** Do you think that drugstores, which sell medicines, should also sell cigarettes and other tobacco products? Why or why not?

22. **Predicting** If the walls of the capillary cluster in a nephron were damaged or broken, what substance might you expect to find in urine that is not normally present? Explain.

Applying Skills

23. There is a higher percentage of carbon dioxide in exhaled air. As a waste product of cellular activity, carbon dioxide is released into the air from the lungs.

24. Oxygen; its percentage is lower in exhaled air than in inhaled air. Oxygen is used in respiration within cells.

25. Nitrogen is not used by the body and is not a waste product.

Applying Skills

Use your knowledge of the respiratory system and the information in the graphs to answer Questions 23–25.

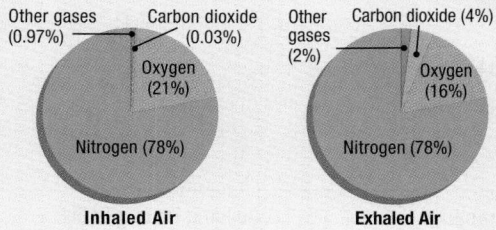

Inhaled Air — Other gases (0.97%), Carbon dioxide (0.03%), Oxygen (21%), Nitrogen (78%)

Exhaled Air — Other gases (2%), Carbon dioxide (4%), Oxygen (16%), Nitrogen (78%)

23. **Interpreting Data** Compare the percentage of carbon dioxide in inhaled air and in exhaled air. How can you account for the difference?

24. **Drawing Conclusions** Based on the data, which gas is used by the body? How is this gas used?

25. **Inferring** Explain why the percentage of nitrogen is the same in both inhaled air and exhaled air.

Performance — CHAPTER PROJECT — Assessment

Present Your Project Your three ads should be ready for display. Be prepared to explain why you chose the message you did for each group of viewers. Why do you think your ads would be effective?

Reflect and Record Of all the ads produced by your classmates, which seemed the most effective? Why? Did any ads change your own ideas about smoking? How can you protect yourself from pressures that might tempt you to smoke? Record your ideas in your journal.

Test Preparation

Use these questions to prepare for standardized tests.

Study the table. Then answer Questions 26–29.

Average Daily Loss of Water in Humans (mL)			
Source	Normal Weather	Hot Weather	Extended Heavy Exercise
Lungs	350	250	650
Urine	1,400	1,200	500
Sweat	450	1,750	5,350
Digestive Waste	200	200	200

26. During normal weather, what is the major source of water loss?
   a. lungs **b.** urine
   c. sweat **d.** digestive waste

27. During hot weather, what is the major source of water loss?
   a. lungs **b.** urine
   c. sweat **d.** digestive waste

28. What is the total amount of water lost on a hot weather day?
   a. 2,400 mL **b.** 3,200 mL
   c. 3,400 mL **d.** 6,700 mL

29. In cool weather, which of the following is most likely to happen?
   a. The body would lose 600 mL of water in digestive wastes.
   b. The body would lose no water.
   c. The body would lose less water in sweat than in urine.
   d. The body would lose more water than on a hot day.

Performance — CHAPTER PROJECT — Assessment

Present Your Project During their presentations, students should discuss messages and images they chose and why they think their ads will be effective in discouraging people in each age group from smoking. After all presentations have been made, lead a discussion on the effectiveness of advertising.

Reflect and Record Encourage students to reflect on advertising tactics that appealed to them personally. Some students may find they respond to colorful graphics or catchy phrases; others may be interested in statistics or personal stories. Encourage students to identify specific images or attitudes that might influence them to start smoking. Have students develop a plan to combat those influences.

Test Preparation

26. b **27.** c **28.** c **29.** c

Program Resources

◆ **Inquiry Skills Activity Book** Provides teaching and review of all inquiry skills

Sections	Time	Student Edition Activities	Other Activities	
CHAPTER PROJECT **Stop the Invasion** p. 591	Ongoing (3 weeks)	Check Your Progress, pp. 595, 604, 616 Present Your Project, p. 619		
1 **Infectious Disease** pp. 592–595 ◆ Explain the cause of infectious disease and identify the kinds of organisms that cause disease. ◆ Describe methods in which pathogens enter the body.	1 period/ $\frac{1}{2}$ block	**Discover** How Does a Disease Spread?, p. 592 **Sharpen Your Skills** Posing Questions, p. 594	TE IES	Building Inquiry Skills: Communicating, p. 594 "Soap From Concept to Consumer," pp. 12–13
2 **The Body's Defenses** pp. 596–604 ◆ Identify the body's barriers against pathogens. ◆ Describe the role of the inflammatory response in fighting disease. ◆ State how the immune system responds to pathogens. ◆ Describe HIV and list the ways it can be spread.	3 periods/ $1\frac{1}{2}$ blocks	**Discover** Which Pieces Fit Together?, p. 596 **Real-World Lab: How It Works** The Skin as a Barrier, pp. 598–599 **Try This** Stuck Together, p. 603	TE TE TE TE TE	Demonstration, p. 597 Including All Students, p. 600 Including All Students, p. 601 Inquiry Challenge, p. 601 Integrating Chemistry, p. 602
3 **INTEGRATING HEALTH** **Preventing Infectious Disease** pp. 605–611 ◆ Define and explain active immunity. ◆ Define and explain passive immunity. ◆ Identify some strategies for staying healthy.	1 period/ $\frac{1}{2}$ block	**Discover** What Substances Can Kill Pathogens?, p. 605 **Science at Home,** p. 609 **Skills Lab: Interpreting Data** Causes of Death, Then and Now, pp. 610–611	TE IES LM	Inquiry Challenge, p. 608 "Fate of the Rain Forest," pp. 35–36 19, "Do Mouthwashes Work?"
4 **Noninfectious Disease** pp. 612–616 ◆ Define an allergy. ◆ Explain how diabetes affects the body. ◆ Explain how cancer affects the body.	2 periods/ 1 block	**Discover** What Happens When Airflow Is Restricted?, p. 612 **Sharpen Your Skills** Drawing Conclusions, p. 613	TE IES	Building Inquiry Skills: Communicating, p. 614 "Fate of the Rain Forest," pp. 12–13
Study Guide/Chapter Assessment pp. 617–619	1 period/ $\frac{1}{2}$ block		ISAB	Provides teaching and review of all inquiry skills

For Standard or Block Schedule The Resource Pro® CD-ROM gives you maximum flexibility for planning your instruction for any type of schedule. Resource Pro® contains Planning Express®, an advanced scheduling program, as well as the entire contents of the Teaching Resources and the Computer Test Bank.

CHAPTER PLANNING GUIDE

Program Resources	Assessment Strategies	Media and Technology
UR Chapter 19 Project Teacher Notes, pp. 106–107 UR Chapter 19 Project Overview and Worksheets, pp. 108–111	SE Performance Assessment: Present Your Project, p. 619 TE Check Your Progress, pp. 595, 604, 616 UR Chapter 19 Project Scoring Rubric, p. 112	Science Explorer Internet Site at www.phschool.com
UR 19-1 Lesson Plan, p. 113 UR 19-1 Section Summary, p. 114 UR 19-1 Review and Reinforce, p. 115 UR 19-1 Enrich, p. 116	SE Section 1 Review, p. 595 TE Ongoing Assessment, pp. 593 TE Performance Assessment, p. 595	Life Science Videotape 4; Videodisc Unit 2 Side 1, "On the Trail of a Disease" Audio CD, English-Spanish Summary 19-1
UR 19-2 Lesson Plan, p. 117 UR 19-2 Section Summary, p. 118 UR 19-2 Review and Reinforce, p. 119 UR 19-2 Enrich, p. 120 UR Chapter 19 Real-World Lab, pp. 129–130	SE Section 2 Review, p. 604 TE Ongoing Assessment, pp. 597, 601, 603 TE Performance Assessment, p. 604	Audio CD, English-Spanish Summary 19-2 Transparency 72, "Exploring the Immune Response" Interactive Student Tutorial CD-ROM, Chapter 19
UR 19-3 Lesson Plan, p. 121 UR 19-3 Section Summary, p. 122 UR 19-3 Review and Reinforce, p. 123 UR 19-3 Enrich, p. 124	SE Section 3 Review, p. 609 TE Ongoing Assessment, p. 607 TE Performance Assessment, p. 609	Life Science Videotape 4; Videodisc Unit 2 Side 1, "Have You Had Your Shots?" Audio CD, English-Spanish Summary 19-3
UR 19-4 Lesson Plan, p. 125 UR 19-4 Section Summary, p. 126 UR 19-4 Review and Reinforce, p. 127 UR 19-4 Enrich, p. 128 UR Chapter 19 Skills Lab, pp. 131–133	SE Section 4 Review, p. 616 TE Ongoing Assessment, p. 613, 615 TE Performance Assessment, p. 616	Life Science Videotape 4; Videodisc Unit 4 Side 1, "Caution: Breathing May Be Hazardous to Your Health" Audio CD English-Spanish Summary 19-4
RCA Provides strategies to improve science reading skills GSW Provides worksheets to promote student comprehension of content	SE Chapter 19 Study Guide/Assessment, pp. 617–619 PA Chapter 19 Performance Assessment: pp. 59–61 CUT Chapter 19 Test, pp. 88–91 CTB Chapter 19 Test	Computer Test Bank, Chapter 19 Test Interactive Student Tutorial CD-ROM, Chapter 19

Key: **SE** Student Edition   **TE** Teacher's Edition   **UR** Unit Resources
      CTB Computer Test Bank   **PTA** Product Testing Activities by *Consumer Reports*   **LM** Laboratory Manual
      ISAB Inquiry Skills Activity Book   **RCA** Reading in the Content Area   **IES** Interdisciplinary Explorations Series
      GSW Guided Study Worksheets   **PA** Performance Assessment   **CUT** Chapter and Unit Tests

Meeting the National Science Education Standards and AAAS Benchmarks

National Science Education Standards	Benchmarks for Science Literacy	Unifying Themes
Science as Inquiry (Content Standard A) ◆ **Develop descriptions, explanations, predictions, and models using evidence** Students develop a model to show how the skin acts as a barrier against infectious diseases. *(Real-World Lab; Chapter Project)* ◆ **Use mathematics in all aspects of scientific inquiry** Students use data and create graphs to compare the leading causes of death today with those in 1900. *(Skills Lab)* **Life Science** (Content Standard C) ◆ **Structure and function in living systems** The human organism has systems for protection from disease that interact with other systems. *(Section 2)* **Science in Personal and Social Perspectives** (Content Standard F) ◆ **Personal health** Environments contain substances that are harmful to human beings. *(Sections 1, 4)*	**1A The Scientific World View** Students learn about how the work of Pasteur contributed to the understanding of infectious disease. *(Section 1)* **1C The Scientific Enterprise** Many people investigated the causes of infectious disease and discovered methods of prevention. *(Section 3)* **6E Physical Health** Pathogens such as bacteria and viruses can infect the human body and interfere with normal human functions. The immune system responds to pathogens by producing antibodies that attack pathogens and by engulfing them with white blood cells. The environment may contain dangerous substances that are harmful to the human body. *(Sections 1, 2, 3; Chapter Project)* **10I Discovering Germs** The work of Louis Pasteur and others in the 19th century led to the modern belief that many diseases are caused by microorganisms, such as bacteria and viruses. *(Sections 1, 3)* **12D Communication Skills** Students use information in data tables to create graphs to compare the leading causes of death today with those in 1900. *(Skills Lab)*	◆ **Energy** Energy is required by the body to fight off disease. *(Section 2)* ◆ **Scale and Structure** The body's three lines of defense are: 1) barriers such as the skin, mucus, and cilia; 2) the inflammatory response; and 3) the immune response. *(Section 2)* ◆ **Systems and Interactions** The body's immune system and the structures that are part of it protect the body by attacking and destroying pathogens. By introducing antigens, vaccination allows the body to fight pathogens as if the antigen had naturally occurred. *(Section 2; Real-World Lab)* ◆ **Stability** The body's immune system helps the body maintain normal functions by attacking and destroying harmful pathogens. *(Sections 2, 3)* ◆ **Modeling** Students model the way a disease spreads by shaking hands with their classmates. Students model how the skin acts as a barrier to disease by infecting apples with material from a rotting apple. They also model the use of a disinfectant. *(Section 1; Real-World Lab)*

Student Edition Activities Planner

ACTIVITY	Time (minutes)	Materials — Quantities for one work group	Skills
Section 1			
Discover, p. 592	10	No special materials are required.	Calculating
Sharpen Your Skills, p. 594	10	No special materials are required.	Posing Questions
Section 2			
Discover, p. 596	10	**Consumable** sheets of paper, each cut into two matching jigsaw pieces	Inferring
Real-World Lab, pp. 598–599	30	**Consumable** 4 sealable plastic bags, 4 fresh apples, rotting apple, cotton swabs, paper towels, toothpick, rubbing alcohol **Nonconsumable** marking pen	Making Models, Controlling Variables, Drawing Conclusions
Try This, p. 603	10	**Consumable** tape **Nonconsumable** large ball, small ball, modeling clay	Making Models
Section 3			
Discover, p. 605	15	**Nonconsumable** disinfectants and antibacterial products such as creams, mouthwashes, hand soaps, household cleaners, and spray disinfectants	Designing Experiments
Science at Home, pp. 609	home	No special materials are required.	Communicating
Skills Lab, pp. 610–611	20–30	**Nonconsumable** colored pencils, calculator (optional), compass, ruler, protractor	Interpreting Data
Section 4			
Discover, p. 612	10	**Consumable** plastic drinking straws	Drawing Conclusions
Sharpen Your Skills, p. 613	10	No special materials are required.	Interpreting Data

A list of all materials required for the Student Edition activities can be found on pages T25–T33. You can obtain information about ordering materials by calling 1-800-848-9500 or by accessing the Science Explorer Internet site at **www.phschool.com**.

Stop the Invasion

Students may think of illness and wellness as opposite states, without really considering the processes the body uses to defend itself against pathogens. This project will allow students to gain an understanding of the ongoing activity of the immune system.

Purpose In this project, students will represent the body's responses to illness as battles in a war. Students will write and present a series of news reports that uses scientific information, visual aids, and creative writing to describe how the body defends itself against pathogens at each stage of infection.

Skills Focus After completing the Chapter 19 Project, students will be able to
◆ pose questions about the progression of a disease;
◆ apply concepts learned in the chapter to their study of a specific disease;
◆ communicate information on how the disease affects the body in the format of a series of news reports.

Project Time Line The entire project should take two to three weeks. Spend one or two days in class discussing how news reports tell stories as they convey information. Allow students to discuss options for presenting their projects, such as using recording equipment or visual aids. By the end of the first week, students should have chosen a disease and begun researching the stages of infection. At this time you may want to distribute the Chapter 19 Project Overview and Worksheets on pages 108–111 in Unit 4 Resources for students to review. Allow students to spend the next week preparing three news reports. Provide class time for all presentations, or allow students to write or record their reports and turn them in.

Suggested Shortcuts You can simplify the project by restricting students to newspaper or radio reports. If there is not enough time for each student to research and present a project, have students work in small groups, pooling their knowledge of disease, as well as their artistic and verbal talents.

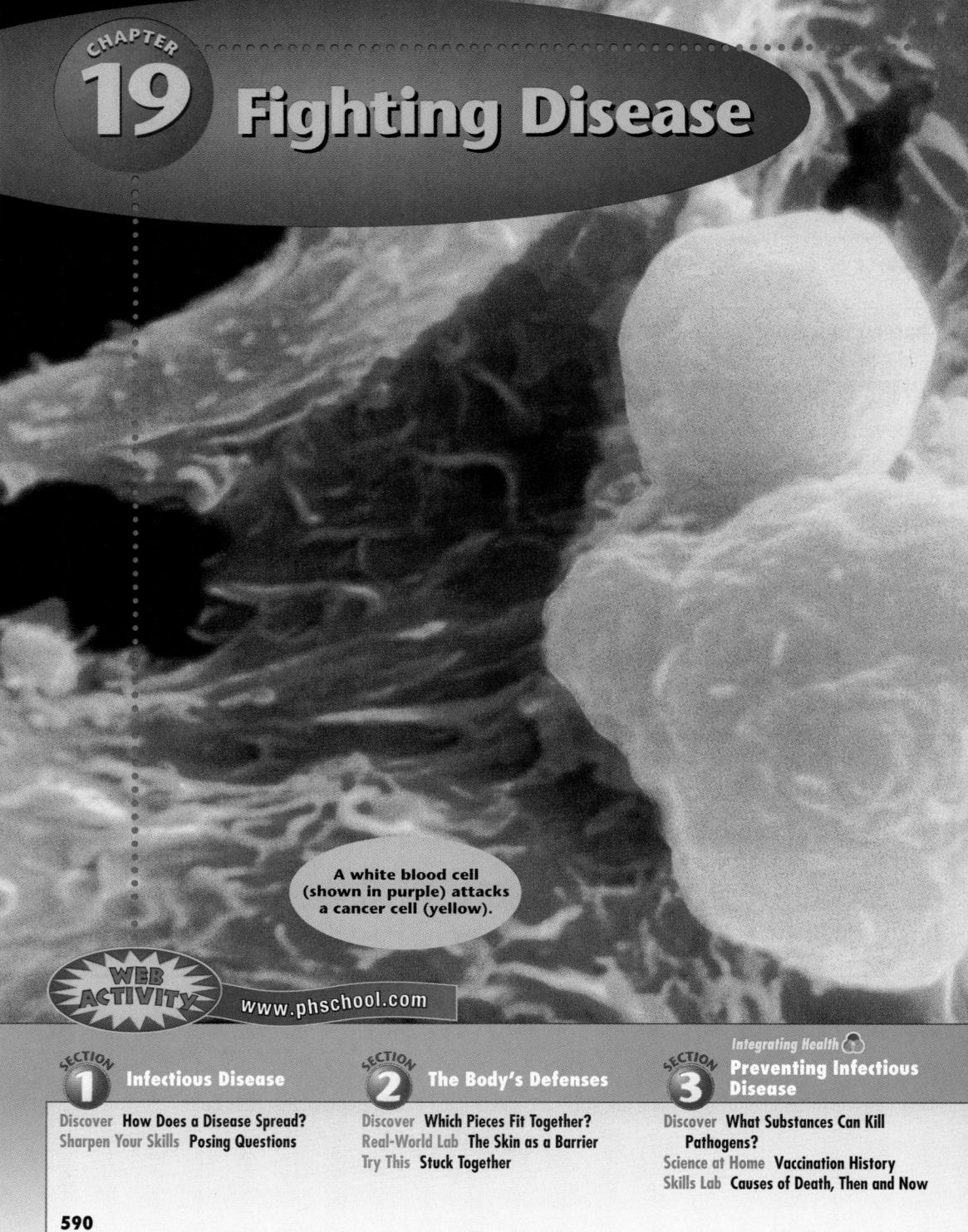

CHAPTER 19 Fighting Disease

A white blood cell (shown in purple) attacks a cancer cell (yellow).

WEB ACTIVITY www.phschool.com

SECTION 1 Infectious Disease
Discover How Does a Disease Spread?
Sharpen Your Skills Posing Questions

SECTION 2 The Body's Defenses
Discover Which Pieces Fit Together?
Real-World Lab The Skin as a Barrier
Try This Stuck Together

SECTION 3 *Integrating Health* Preventing Infectious Disease
Discover What Substances Can Kill Pathogens?
Science at Home Vaccination History
Skills Lab Causes of Death, Then and Now

590

Possible Materials For newspaper or radio reports, students will need only writing materials. If the presentations will include pictures or sound effects, you will need to make art materials available to students. You may want to provide class time for students to prepare their visual aids. Provide
◆ markers;
◆ poster board;
◆ audio or video tape recorders;
◆ newspapers, magazines, and transcripts of radio or television news broadcasts for students to examine.

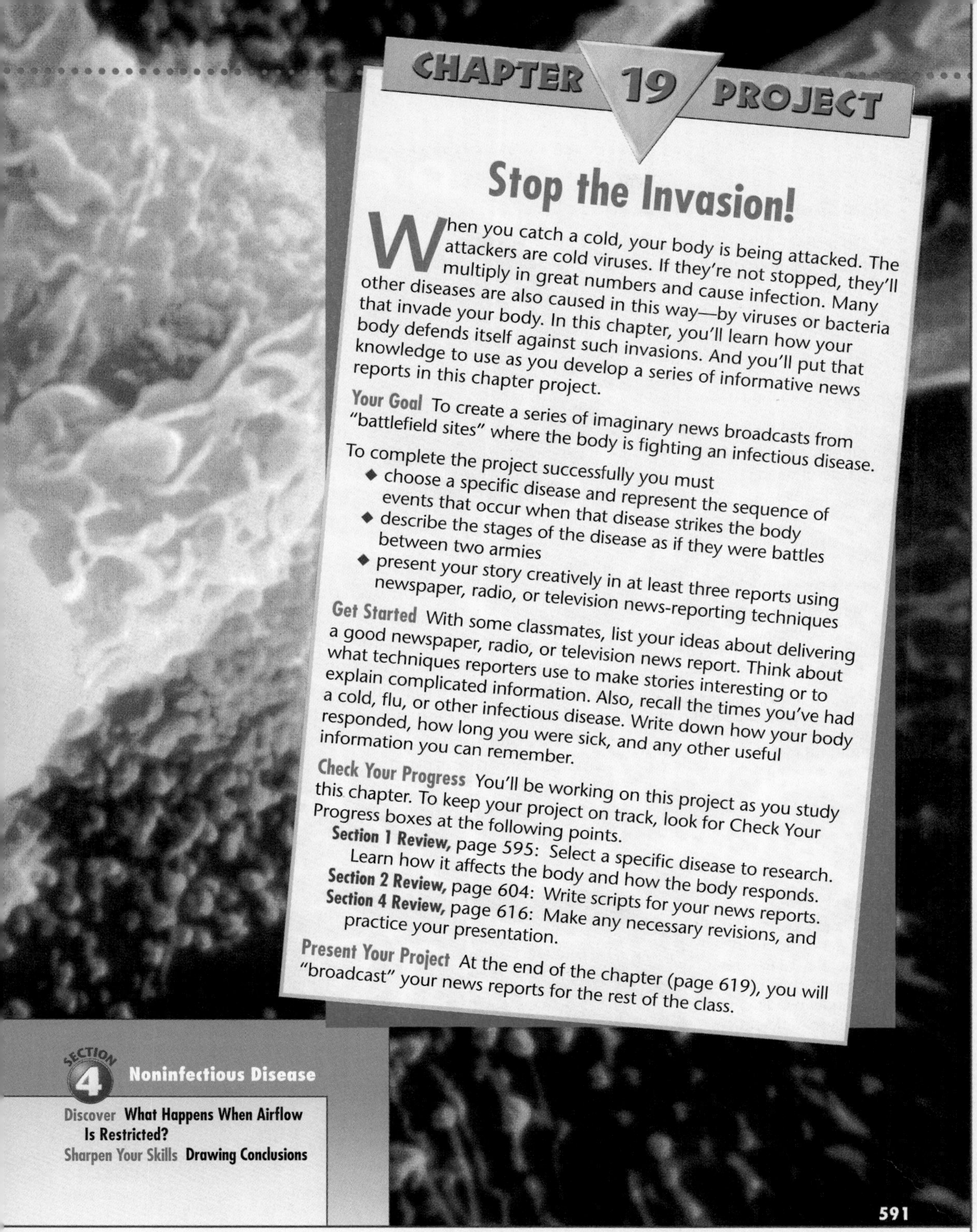

Stop the Invasion!

When you catch a cold, your body is being attacked. The attackers are cold viruses. If they're not stopped, they'll multiply in great numbers and cause infection. Many other diseases are also caused in this way—by viruses or bacteria that invade your body. In this chapter, you'll learn how your body defends itself against such invasions. And you'll put that knowledge to use as you develop a series of informative news reports in this chapter project.

Your Goal To create a series of imaginary news broadcasts from "battlefield sites" where the body is fighting an infectious disease.

To complete the project successfully you must

- ◆ choose a specific disease and represent the sequence of events that occur when that disease strikes the body
- ◆ describe the stages of the disease as if they were battles between two armies
- ◆ present your story creatively in at least three reports using newspaper, radio, or television news-reporting techniques

Get Started With some classmates, list your ideas about delivering a good newspaper, radio, or television news report. Think about what techniques reporters use to make stories interesting or to explain complicated information. Also, recall the times you've had a cold, flu, or other infectious disease. Write down how your body responded, how long you were sick, and any other useful information you can remember.

Check Your Progress You'll be working on this project as you study this chapter. To keep your project on track, look for Check Your Progress boxes at the following points.

Section 1 Review, page 595: Select a specific disease to research. Learn how it affects the body and how the body responds.
Section 2 Review, page 604: Write scripts for your news reports.
Section 4 Review, page 616: Make any necessary revisions, and practice your presentation.

Present Your Project At the end of the chapter (page 619), you will "broadcast" your news reports for the rest of the class.

SECTION 4 Noninfectious Disease

Discover What Happens When Airflow Is Restricted?
Sharpen Your Skills Drawing Conclusions

591

Launching the Project Ask students to speculate on what it means to "fight a cold." Ask: **What weapons do you use in the fight?** (*Samples: Lots of rest, plenty of fluids, vitamins, cold medicine, hot tea, tissues*)

Allow time for students to read the description of the project in their text and the Chapter Project Overview on pages 108–109 in Unit 4 Resources. Then encourage discussions on the stages of specific diseases and on any initial questions students may have.

This is a good opportunity to illustrate how knowledge about the body's active defense systems explains common symptoms such as fever, tiredness, and mucus production. Record any questions that come up about specific effects of illness. You might want to have students read ahead in the text to answer any questions they may have about immune responses.

Performance Assessment

The Chapter 19 Project Scoring Rubric on page 112 of Unit 4 Resources will help you evaluate how well students complete the Chapter 19 Project. Students will be assessed on

- ◆ the thoroughness of their research on their chosen diseases, including pathogens, transmission, symptoms, treatments, and recovery stages;
- ◆ the thoroughness and organization of their presentations, and how well they apply chapter concepts to their research;
- ◆ the organization of their written or oral analyses;
- ◆ their group participation, if they worked in groups.

By sharing the Chapter 19 Project Scoring Rubric with students at the beginning of the project, you will make it clear to them what they are expected to do.

Program Resources

◆ **Unit 4 Resources** Chapter 19 Project Teacher Notes, pp. 106–107; Chapter 19 Project Overview and Worksheets, pp. 108–111; Chapter 19 Project Scoring Rubric, p. 112

WEB ACTIVITY www.phschool.com

You will find an Internet activity, chapter self-tests for students, and links to other chapter topics at this site.

Objectives

After completing the lesson, students will be able to

◆ explain the cause of infectious disease and identify the kinds of organisms that cause disease;

◆ describe methods in which pathogens enter the body.

Key Terms pathogen, infectious disease, pasteurization

1 Engage/Explore

Activating Prior Knowledge

Ask students to brainstorm a list of familiar diseases. Then divide the diseases into two groups: those students think can be spread from one person to another and those they think cannot. Ask students to explain their decisions.

·········· DISCOVER ·········

Skills Focus calculating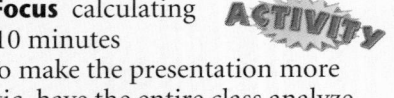
Time 10 minutes
Tips To make the presentation more dramatic, have the entire class analyze their results to determine how one infected person can infect an entire community. Ask a volunteer to represent the first person with the disease. Ask that student to tell whose hands he or she shook in Round 1. Create a flowchart on the board that shows how the infection was spread throughout the class. Help students determine a method for counting how many students became infected.
Think It Over In each round, the student infects 2 students, so the student directly infects 6. The 2 infected in Round 2 infect 2 each in Rounds 2 and 3, for a total of 8. The 6 infected in Round 2 infect 2 each in Round 3, for a total of 12. Therefore, each student infects 26 other students, assuming that no student shakes the hand of a student whose hand had already been shaken.

DISCOVER ···················· ACTIVITY····

How Does a Disease Spread?

1. On a sheet of paper, write three headings: *Round 1, Round 2,* and *Round 3.*

2. Everyone in the class should shake hands with two people. Under *Round 1,* record the names of the people whose hand you shook.

3. Now shake hands with two different people. Record the name of each person whose hand you shook under *Round 2.*

4. Once again, shake hands with two additional people. Under *Round 3,* record the names of the people whose hand you shook.

Think It Over
Calculating Suppose you had a disease that was spread by shaking hands. Everyone whose hand you shook has caught the disease. So has anyone who later shook those people's hands. Calculate how many people you "infected."

GUIDE FOR READING

◆ What kinds of organisms cause disease?

◆ Where do pathogens come from?

Reading Tip As you read, use the headings in the section to make an outline. Write the important concepts under each heading.

Before the twentieth century, surgery was a very risky business. Even if people lived through an operation, they were not out of danger. After the operation, many patients' wounds became infected, and the patients often died. No one knew what caused these infections.

In the 1860s, a British surgeon named Joseph Lister hypothesized that microorganisms caused the infections. To protect his patients, Lister used carbolic acid, a chemical that kills microorganisms. Before performing an operation, Lister washed his hands and surgical instruments with carbolic acid. After the surgery, he covered the patient's wounds with bandages dipped in carbolic acid.

Figure 1 Doctors at Massachusetts General Hospital perform surgery on a patient in 1846. In the 1800s, surgery was performed under conditions that were very different from those used today.

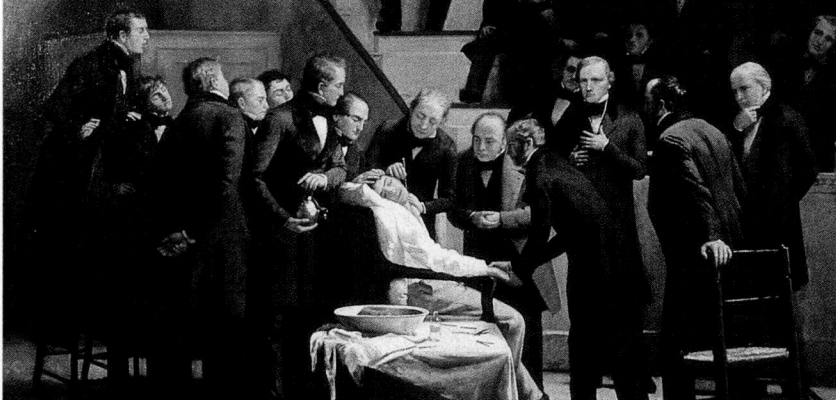

READING STRATEGIES

Reading Tip With the class, outline the information under the first heading.
Sample:
I. Diseases and Pathogens
   A. Organisms that cause disease are called pathogens.
   B. An infectious disease can pass from one organism to another.
   C. Pathogens get inside the body and damage its cells.

Study and Comprehension After students read the section, have them use the outlines they created to generate questions about infectious diseases and pathogens. Instruct students to write five questions and their answers on a sheet of paper. Then have partners use the questions to quiz each other on the information in the section. Suggest students save their questions to use as study guides.

Lister's results were dramatic. Before he used his new method, about 45 percent of his surgical patients died from infection. With Lister's new techniques, only 15 percent died.

Disease and Pathogens

Like the infections that Lister observed after surgery, many illnesses, such as strep throat and food poisoning, are caused by organisms that are too small to see without microscopes. Until Lister's time, few people thought these tiny organisms could cause disease. Most people believed that things like evil spirits and swamp air made people sick.

Organisms that cause disease are called **pathogens.** Diseases caused by pathogens are infectious. An **infectious disease** is a disease that can pass from one organism to another. When you have an infectious disease, pathogens have gotten inside your body and harmed it. Even though you may feel pain in a whole organ or throughout your body, pathogens make you sick by damaging individual cells. For example, when you have an ear infection, pathogens have damaged cells in your ear.

Each infectious disease is caused by a specific pathogen. **The four major groups of human pathogens are bacteria, viruses, fungi, and protists.** Strep throat is caused by a bacterium, a unicellular organism. Colds and influenza are caused by viruses, nonliving things that can reproduce only inside living cells. Athlete's foot is an infectious disease caused by a fungus. Malaria is an example of a tropical disease caused by a protist.

Lister's work with pathogens was influenced by Louis Pasteur, a French scientist. In the 1860s, Pasteur showed that microorganisms cause certain diseases. In addition, Pasteur showed that killing the microorganisms could prevent the spread of those diseases. Pasteur's work led to **pasteurization,** a heating process that is widely used today to kill microorganisms in food products such as milk.

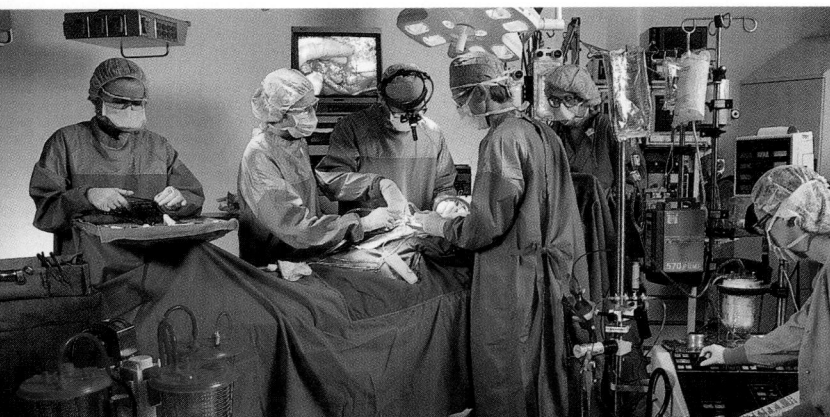

Figure 2 Surgery today is performed in operating rooms that have been cleaned thoroughly to eliminate disease-causing organisms. *Comparing and Contrasting Contrast Figures 1 and 2. How does surgery today differ from surgery in 1846?*

Disease and Pathogens

Language Arts Connection

Point out that the word *pathogen* comes from the Greek *patho*, meaning "disease," and *gennan*, meaning "origin." Tell students that they can think of pathogens as "disease-causers." **limited English proficiency**

Real-Life Learning

Invite a surgeon or a surgical nurse to the class to talk about sterile procedure in modern operating rooms. Have students prepare a list of questions before the visit. Encourage students to ask questions about specific pathogens that once threatened surgical patients and how surgeons prevent infection from those pathogens today. **learning modality: verbal**

Program Resources

◆ **Unit 4 Resources** 19-1 Lesson Plan, p. 113; 19-1 Section Summary, p. 114

Media and Technology

 Audio CD English-Spanish Summary 19-1

Answers to Self-Assessment

Caption Question

Figure 2 The doctors in Figure 1 wear no special clothing. In contrast, the doctors and nurses in Figure 2 wear protective clothing and masks to prevent the transfer of pathogens to the patient.

Ongoing Assessment

Writing Have students explain the contributions of Lister and Pasteur, to the understanding of infectious disease.

593

How Diseases Are Spread

Building Inquiry Skills: Communicating

Time 30 minutes

Divide the class into an even number of small groups. Have each group develop and write a story describing how a group of people contracted a disease. Encourage students to be creative, but make sure their stories are consistent with the sources of pathogens identified in the text. When the stories are finished, have two groups work together. One group should play the part of medical workers and ask questions to determine how the other group became infected. Have groups switch roles. As a class, discuss what kinds of questions were most helpful and write a master list of questions that should be asked when doctors try to determine the cause of an outbreak.
cooperative learning

Sharpen your Skills

Posing Questions

Time 10 minutes

Tips Ask students to point out the location of the pumps and of the cholera victims. Pump 6 was the source of the contaminated water.

Dr. Snow would probably ask where the latest cholera victims lived and from which pumps they obtained water.

Extend Have students write a newspaper story about Dr. Snow's work, including a caption that could accompany the map in Figure 3.
learning modality: visual

Portfolio Students can save their newspaper stories in their portfolios.

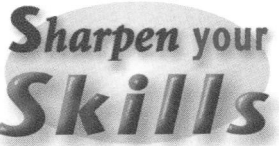

Sharpen your Skills

Posing Questions

Cholera is a deadly disease that is spread through food or water contaminated with cholera bacteria. In 1854, cholera spread through London, England. Dr. John Snow analyzed where most of the cholera victims lived, as well as the locations of the water pumps in the area. The map in Figure 3 shows Dr. Snow's findings. Dr. Snow hypothesized that the disease was spread by water that came from one of the pumps. Which pump was probably the source of the contaminated water?

Suppose that Dr. Snow just learned that two additional people had died of cholera. What questions would Dr. Snow most likely ask about the additional cholera cases?

Figure 3 The map shows the location of cholera cases in the 1854 epidemic in London, England.

How Diseases Are Spread

Pathogens are something like ants at a picnic. They aren't trying to harm you. However, just like the ants, pathogens need food. They also need a place to live and reproduce. Unfortunately, your body may be just the right place for a pathogen to meet those needs.

You can become infected by a pathogen in one of several ways. **Some sources of pathogens include another person, a contaminated object, an animal bite, and the environment.**

Person-to-Person Transfer Many pathogens are transferred from one person to another person. Pathogens often pass from one person to another through direct physical contact, such as kissing, hugging, and shaking hands. For example, if you kiss someone who has a cold sore, cold-sore viruses can then get into your body.

Diseases are also spread through indirect contact with an infected person. For example, if a person with pneumonia sneezes, pathogens shoot into the air. Pathogens from a sneeze can travel most of the way across a small room! Other people may catch pneumonia if they inhale these pathogens. Colds, flu, and tuberculosis can be spread through coughing and sneezing.

✓ *Checkpoint* In what ways can pathogens pass from one person to another?

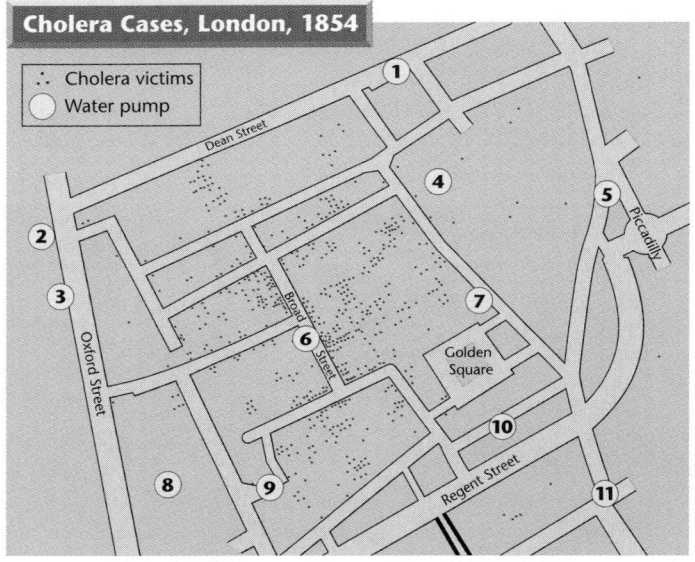

Cholera Cases, London, 1854

∴ Cholera victims
◯ Water pump

Background

History of Science During and shortly after World War I, an estimated 30 million people died from a single cause—the Influenza Epidemic of 1918–1919. Soldiers from the United States apparently spread the virus to Europe. During the following months, the virus spread all over the world, first in ports and then in cities along transportation routes.

Media and Technology

 Exploring Life Science Videodisc
Unit 2, Side 1, "On the Trail of a Disease"

Chapter 2

Contaminated Objects Some pathogens can survive for a time outside a person's body. Water and food can become contaminated. If people then eat the food or drink the water, they may become sick. Some pathogens that cause severe diarrhea are spread through contaminated food and water. People can also pick up pathogens by using objects, such as towels or silverware, that have been handled by an infected person. Colds and flu can be spread in this way. Tetanus bacteria can enter the body if a person steps on a contaminated nail.

Animal Bites If an animal is infected with certain pathogens and then bites a person, it can pass the pathogens to the person. People can get rabies, a serious disease that affects the nervous system, from the bite of an infected animal, such as a dog or a raccoon. Lyme disease and Rocky Mountain spotted fever are both spread by tick bites. The protist that causes malaria is transferred by the bites of mosquitoes that live in tropical regions.

Pathogens from the Environment Some pathogens occur naturally in the environment. The bacterium that causes tetanus lives in soil or water. The bacterium that causes botulism, an especially severe form of food poisoning, also lives in soil. Botulism bacteria can produce a toxin in foods that have been improperly canned. The toxin is extremely powerful.

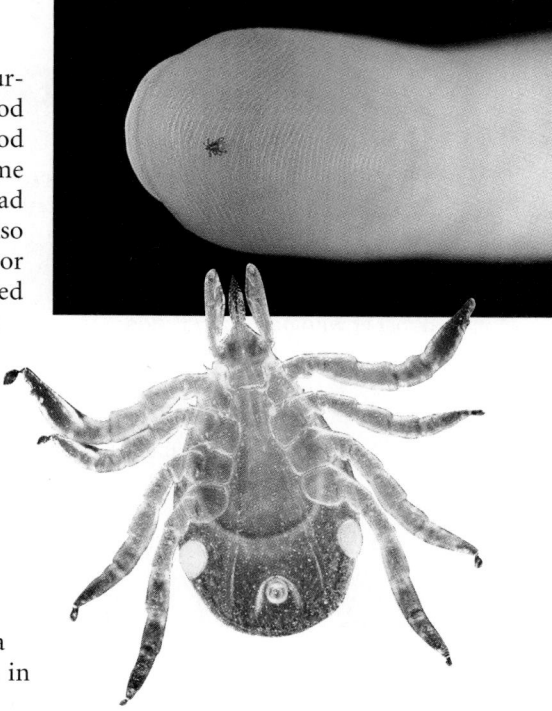

Figure 4 The tiny deer tick may carry the bacterium that causes Lyme disease, a serious condition that can damage the joints. If a deer tick that is carrying Lyme disease bacteria bites a person, the person may get Lyme disease. *Problem Solving How might people reduce their risk of catching Lyme disease?*

Section 1 Review

1. Name four kinds of pathogens that cause disease in humans.
2. Describe four ways that pathogens can infect humans.
3. Explain how Pasteur contributed to the understanding of infectious disease.
4. **Thinking Critically** **Applying Concepts** If you have a cold, what steps can you take to keep from spreading it to other people? Explain.

> **Check Your Progress**
> CHAPTER PROJECT
> At this stage, you should have chosen a specific infectious disease to research. You should also decide whether to do newspaper articles, radio programs, or a television series. Begin to plan how you will explain the way in which the body is invaded by pathogens. Also begin thinking about how you will make your show appropriate for your audience. (*Hint:* To get ideas on how to present news stories, read newspapers or watch or listen to news programs about international conflicts.)

Program Resources

◆ **Interdisciplinary Exploration Series** "Soap from Concept to Consumer," pp. 12–13
◆ **Unit 4 Resources** 19-1 Review and Reinforce, p. 115; 19-1 Enrich, p. 116

Answers to Self-Assessment

Caption Question

Figure 4 A person could avoid walking through areas where ticks may live. People should also cover their legs and arms when hiking and wear tick repellent.

☑ *Checkpoint*

Pathogens are spread through direct physical contact between people or by indirect contact, such as sneezing.

3 Assess

Section 1 Review Answers

1. Bacteria, viruses, fungi, and protists
2. Pathogens may come from other people, contaminated objects, animal bites, and the environment.
3. Pasteur showed that microorganisms cause certain diseases and that killing microorganisms prevents the spread of diseases.
4. Avoid contact with others, wash utensils carefully, do not share food or utensils with others, cover your mouth and nose when sneezing or coughing. These steps help prevent the cold virus from entering the body of another person.

Check Your Progress
CHAPTER PROJECT
Encourage students to make a list of questions that a good news story should answer so they can make sure they answer these questions when they do their research. In addition to providing the essential information, students should be encouraged to highlight interesting facts or stories about the disease. Provide students with newspapers and magazines in a variety of styles to give them ideas for presenting their stories.

Performance Assessment

Writing Have students imagine they are a kind of pathogen. Students should describe themselves and tell how they infected a human.

Objectives

After completing the lesson, students will be able to

◆ identify the body's barriers against pathogens;

◆ describe the role of the inflammatory response in fighting disease;

◆ state how the immune system responds to pathogens;

◆ describe HIV and list the ways it can be spread.

Key Terms inflammatory response, phagocyte, immune response, lymphocyte, T cell, antigen, B cell, antibody, AIDS

1 Engage/Explore

Activating Prior Knowledge

Ask students whether they have ever remained healthy when a parent, brother, or sister came down with a cold. Ask them to suggest reasons why not everyone who is exposed to a pathogen develops the illness. Ask: **What are some factors that allow people to resist illness?** *(Samples: Getting enough rest, eating healthy foods, avoiding using utensils and other objects handled by a sick person.)*

•••••••• **DISCOVER** ••••••••

Skills Focus inferring
Materials *sheets of paper, each cut into two matching jigsaw pieces*
Time 10 minutes
Tips Prepare matching sets of shapes by cutting sheets of paper in half with a zigzag or wavy pattern. Use a different pattern for each piece of paper. All paper should be the same color.
Expected Outcome Each student should find only one matching piece.
Think It Over Each defender cell recognizes only one type of invader.

596

SECTION
2 The Body's Defenses

DISCOVER •••••••••••••••••••••••••••••••••• **ACTIVITY**

Which Pieces Fit Together?

1. Your teacher will give you a piece of paper with one jagged edge.

2. One student in the class has a piece of paper whose edges match your paper edge, like two pieces of a jigsaw puzzle.

3. Find the student whose paper matches yours and fit the two edges together.

Think It Over
Inferring Imagine that one of each pair of matching pieces is a pathogen. The other is a cell in your body that defends your body against the invading pathogen. How many kinds of invaders can each defender cell recognize?

GUIDE FOR READING

◆ What is the body's first line of defense against pathogens?

◆ What happens during the inflammatory response?

◆ How does the immune system respond to pathogens?

Reading Tip Before you read, preview *Exploring the Immune Response* on page 602. List any unfamiliar terms. As you read, write definitions of those terms in your own words.

Your eyes are glued to the screen. The situation in the video game is desperate. Enemy troops have gotten through an opening in the wall. Your soldiers have managed to hold back most of the invaders. However, some enemy soldiers are breaking through the defense lines. You need your backup defenders. They can zap the invaders with their powerful weapons. If your soldiers can fight off the enemy until the backup team arrives, you can save your fortress.

Video games create fantasy wars, but in your body, real battles happen all the time. In your body, the "enemies" are invading pathogens. You are hardly ever aware of these battles. The body's disease-fighting system is so effective that most people get sick only occasionally. By eliminating pathogens that can destroy your cells, your body maintains homeostasis.

Figure 5 The pathogens that invade your body are something like the enemy soldiers in a video game. Your body has to defend itself against the pathogens.

596

READING STRATEGIES

Reading Tip Students will likely list *T cell* and *B cell* and unfamiliar terms. Students probably have heard the term *antibody* but may be unsure of its meaning. As students preview *Exploring the Immune Response*, suggest that they also list questions they have about the information. Have students discuss

their questions with partners. Encourage student pairs to predict answers to the questions. After they have read the section, have the partners meet again to discuss the answers to their questions and the meanings of the terms they listed during their preview.

Barriers That Keep Pathogens Out

Your body has three lines of defense against pathogens. The first line consists of barriers that keep pathogens from getting into the body. You do not wear a sign that says "Pathogens Keep Out," but that doesn't matter. **Barriers such as the skin, breathing passages, mouth, and stomach trap and kill most pathogens with which you come into contact.**

The Skin When pathogens land on the skin, they are exposed to destructive chemicals in oil and sweat. Even if these chemicals don't kill them, the pathogens may fall off with dead skin cells. Washing your skin regularly with soap and warm water can help decrease the number of pathogens on your skin.

If the pathogens manage to stay on the skin, they must get through the tightly packed dead cells that form a barrier on top of living skin cells. Most pathogens get through the skin only when it is cut. Scabs form over cuts so rapidly that the period in which pathogens can enter the body in this way is very short.

The Breathing Passages As you know, you can inhale pathogens when you breathe in. The nose, pharynx, trachea, and bronchi, however, contain mucus and cilia. Together, the mucus and cilia trap and remove most of the pathogens that enter the respiratory system. In addition, irritation by pathogens may make you sneeze or cough. Both actions force the pathogens out of your body.

The Mouth and Stomach Some pathogens are found in foods, even if the foods are washed, cooked, and stored properly. Like the skin on the outside of your body, your mouth and digestive system is an intact passageway that keeps its contents separate from the rest of the body. Unless you have cuts in your mouth or a stomach ulcer, for example, the pathogens you take into your mouth do not mix with blood or other parts of your body. The saliva in your mouth contains destructive chemicals and your stomach produces acid that combats these pathogens. Most pathogens that you swallow are destroyed by saliva or stomach acid.

☑ *Checkpoint* *How do the breathing passages prevent pathogens from entering the body?*

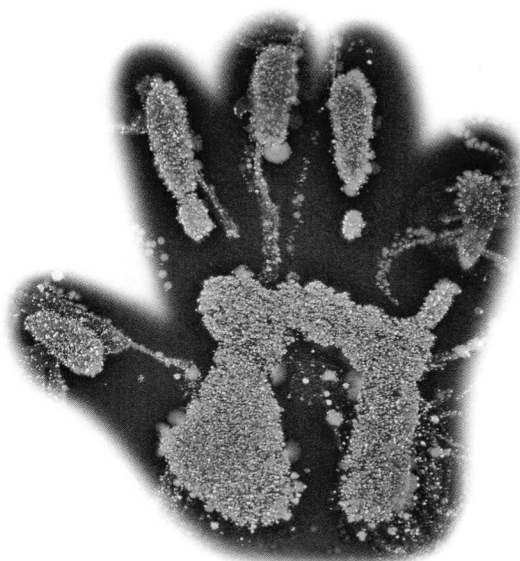

Figure 6 Skin is covered with bacteria. The dots in the photo are colonies of bacteria living on a person's hand.
Relating Cause and Effect How can a cut in the skin lead to an infection?

Program Resources

◆ **Unit 4 Resources** 19-2 Lesson Plan, p. 117; 19-2 Section Summary, p. 118

Media and Technology

🎧 **Audio CD** English-Spanish Summary 19-2

Answers to Self-Assessment

Caption Question

Figure 6 A cut provides an opening for bacteria to enter the body and cause an infection.

☑ *Checkpoint*

Mucus and cilia trap and remove pathogens. If pathogens irritate the breathing passages, coughing or sneezing forces them out.

2 Facilitate

Barriers That Keep Pathogens Out

Demonstration

Materials *disposable petri dish with nutrient agar, sterile cotton ball, tape* **ACTIVITY**

Time 15 minutes for setup; 10 minutes each day over several days

This activity shows the presence of bacteria on a person's hand. Wipe a volunteer's hand with a cotton ball and then gently brush the cotton over the agar of the petri dish. Cover and label the dish. Tape it closed and place it upside down in a warm place. Allow students to observe the petri dish over the next few days. Do not open the dish. Ask students to describe the dish. (*The surface of the agar should be covered with dots or smudges, each consisting of millions of bacteria.*) Ask students to explain the results. (*Bacteria from the student's hand multiplied on the agar.*) Dispose of the petri dishes and all other materials according to the proper procedures. Be sure to check your district's and state's guidelines for the proper disposal of bacterial cultures. **learning modality: visual**

Addressing Naive Conceptions

Students may think that a cut or injury will lead to infection only if the skin is punctured by something that is contaminated with pathogens. Point out that the image in Figure 6 shows the bacteria that live on skin and that some of these bacteria can cause infection. **learning modality: verbal**

Ongoing Assessment

Oral Presentation Ask students to identify the body's barriers that keep pathogens out. (*Skin, mucus and cilia of breathing passages, saliva, stomach acid*)

The Skin as a Barrier

Preparing for Inquiry

Key Concept The skin of most organisms is a barrier to many pathogens.

Skills Objectives Students will be able to
◆ make models using apples to demonstrate how skin acts as a barrier;
◆ control variables by modifying the ability of apple skins to act as effective barriers to bacteria;
◆ draw conclusions about how effective apple skins and alcohol are at preventing bacterial growth.

Time 30 minutes

Advance Planning Provide a rotten apple to use as a source of bacteria, and thick, sturdy toothpicks for piercing apple skins.

Alternative Materials You can substitute disposable plastic knives for the toothpicks. Make sure students touch the rotten apple with the knife tips, then use the tips to make the new cuts.

Guiding Inquiry

Invitation Ask students to recall times they have fallen and perhaps cut and bruised themselves. Then ask: **Did you put an antibiotic cream and a bandage on the cut?** *(yes)* **On the bruise?** *(no)* **Why?** *(Students should explain that the cutting of the skin exposed the body to external pathogens, while the bruise was an internal wound protected by the skin.)*

Introducing the Procedure

You can let students practice the technique before they collect data. Watch students' technique of transferring bacteria to ensure proper results.

Troubleshooting the Experiment

◆ Students should take care not to break the apple skins when washing and drying the apples.
◆ In Step 4, the toothpick should touch but not break the apple skin. In Steps 5 and 6, the toothpick must break the skin.

598

THE SKIN AS A BARRIER

Bacteria are all around you. Many of those bacteria can cause disease, yet you usually remain free of disease. In this lab, you will investigate how the skin protects you from infectious disease.

Problem

How does skin act as a barrier to pathogens?

Skills Focus

making models, controlling variables, drawing conclusions

Materials

sealable plastic bags, 4
fresh apples, 4
rotting apple
cotton swabs
marking pen
paper towels
toothpick
rubbing alcohol

Procedure

1. Read over the entire procedure to see how you will treat each of four fresh apples. Write a prediction in your notebook about the change(s) you expect to see in each apple. Then copy the data table into your notebook.
2. Label four plastic bags *1, 2, 3,* and *4.*
3. Gently wash four fresh apples with water, then dry them carefully with paper towels. Place one apple in plastic bag 1, and seal the bag.
4. Insert a toothpick tip into a rotting apple and withdraw it. Lightly draw the tip of the toothpick down the side of the second apple without breaking the skin. Repeat these actions three more times, touching the toothpick to different parts of the apple without breaking the skin. Insert the apple in plastic bag 2, and seal the bag.

5. Insert the toothpick tip into the rotting apple and withdraw it. Use the tip to make a long, thin scratch down the side of the third apple. Be sure to pierce the apple's skin. Repeat these actions three more times, making additional scratches on different parts of the apple. Insert the apple into plastic bag 3, and seal the bag.
6. Repeat Step 5 to make four scratches in the fourth apple. However, before you place the apple in the bag, dip a cotton swab in rubbing alcohol, and swab the scratches. Then place the apple in plastic bag 4, and seal the bag. **CAUTION:** *Alcohol and its vapors are flammable. Work where there are no sparks, exposed flames, or other heat sources.*
7. Store the four bags in a warm, dark place. Wash your hands thoroughly with soap and water.
8. Every day for one week, remove the apples from their storage place, and observe them without opening the bags. Record your observations, then return the bags to their storage location. At the end of the activity, dispose of the unopened bags as directed by your teacher.

598

◆ Students should dip the toothpick in the rotting apple each time they touch the apple in Step 4, or cut the apple in Steps 5 and 6.

Expected Outcome

When the skin of the apple is cut or removed, two different processes take place. First, in a fairly short time, the white of the apple turns brown because oxidation takes place. This is a chemical reaction, which can be slowed down by adding an acid such as lemon or orange juice to the apple's surface. Second, bacteria begin

Safety

Remind students not to taste anything in the lab and to wash their hands immediately after handling the rotten apple. Review the safety guidelines in Appendix A.

Program Resources

◆ **Unit 4 Resources** Chapter 19 Real-World Lab, pp. 129–130

Analyze and Conclude

1. How did the appearance of the four apples compare? Explain your results.
2. In this activity, what condition in the human body is each of the four fresh apples supposed to model?
3. What is the control in this experiment?
4. What is the role of the rotting apple in this activity?

5. **Apply** How does this investigation show why routine cuts and scrapes should be cleaned and bandaged?

Design an Experiment

Using apples as you did in this activity, design an experiment to model how washing hands can prevent the spread of disease. Obtain your teacher's permission before carrying out your investigation.

DATA TABLE

Date	Apple 1 (no contact with decay)	Apple 2 (contact with decay, unbroken skin)	Apple 3 (contact with decay, scratched, untreated)	Apple 4 (contact with decay, scratched, treated with alcohol)

Sample Data Table

Date	Apple 1 (untouched)	Apple 2 (touched, unbroken skin)	Apple 3 (touched, scratched, untreated)	Apple 4 (touched, scratched, treated with alcohol)
1	no change	no change	scratched areas slightly dark	no change
2	no change	no change	scratched areas dark and soft	scratched areas slightly dark

the process of decay, a biological process resulting in the darkening and softening of the apple. This process takes longer to become visible than browning does. In this lab, decay—caused by bacteria—serves as the model for disease.

Analyze and Conclude

1. Apples 1 and 2 show little or no change because the skin prevented bacteria from entering the apple. Apple 3 shows significant decay; the breaks in the skin allowed bacteria to enter. Apple 4 may show less decay than Apple 3; bacteria were killed by alcohol.
2. The apple represents the human body, the apple skin represents the human skin. The decay-causing bacteria represent bacteria that can infect humans. Apple 1 shows that a person remains healthy when the skin is intact and no bacteria are present. If the skin is unbroken as in Apple 2, the person remains healthy even when bacteria are present. Apple 3 shows that bacteria can enter through a cut and cause infection. The infection may be lessened if a bacteria-killing agent (such as alcohol) is used, as in Apple 4.
3. The control is Apple 1.
4. The rotting apple is the source of decay-causing bacteria.
5. Cleaning cuts and scrapes may remove bacteria present at the time of the injury. Bandages keep bacteria from entering a cut that has not healed.

Extending the Inquiry

Design an Experiment Sample experiment: Use three washed, freshly cut apples to test for the presence and amount of bacteria. The first apple would serve as a control and would not be handled after being washed; the second would be handled by washed hands; and the third would be handled by unwashed hands. All three apples would be sealed in plastic bags for observation.

General Defenses

Including All Students

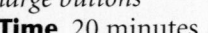

Visually impaired students may have difficulty in conceiving how a phagocyte destroys a pathogen. Have students with normal vision work with visually impaired students. To represent a phagocyte, the student with normal vision spreads a lump of clay on a flat surface in a roughly circular shape. The same student then positions the button, representing the pathogen, next to the phagocyte and has the visually impaired student touch both. The students then work together to peel up the "phagocyte" and wrap the clay around the button, representing the phagocyte engulfing the pathogen. The visually impaired student uses the sense of touch to determine that the "phagocyte" has completely surrounded the "pathogen" and destroyed it. **learning modality: kinesthetic**

Social Studies
CONNECTION

On a globe, have volunteers locate the Panama Canal. Ask students to speculate what route was used for shipping before the canal was built. Point out that the trip from the east coast of the United States through the canal to the west coast is about 15,000 kilometers shorter than sailing around Cape Horn in South America.

In Your Journal Provide time and resources for students to research the building of the Panama Canal. Interested students may want to include illustrations with their articles. **learning modality: verbal**

Social Studies
CONNECTION

Today the Panama Canal is an important shipping route that links the Atlantic and Pacific oceans. But because of two diseases that cause high fever—malaria and yellow fever—the Panama Canal almost didn't get built. Much of the canal passes through the mosquito-filled rain forests of Panama. Mosquitoes carry the pathogens that cause malaria and yellow fever.

In 1889 an attempt at digging a canal was abandoned, partly because so many workers became sick. In 1904, an American physician, Colonel William C. Gorgas, began a project in which swamps in the work area were drained. In addition, brush and grass were cut down. Gorgas's project destroyed the places where mosquitoes lived and reproduced. This action greatly reduced the mosquito population. The Panama Canal was completed in 1914.

Panama Canal

In Your Journal

Write a newspaper article about the construction of the Panama Canal. The article should focus on the problem of disease and the contribution of Colonel Gorgas.

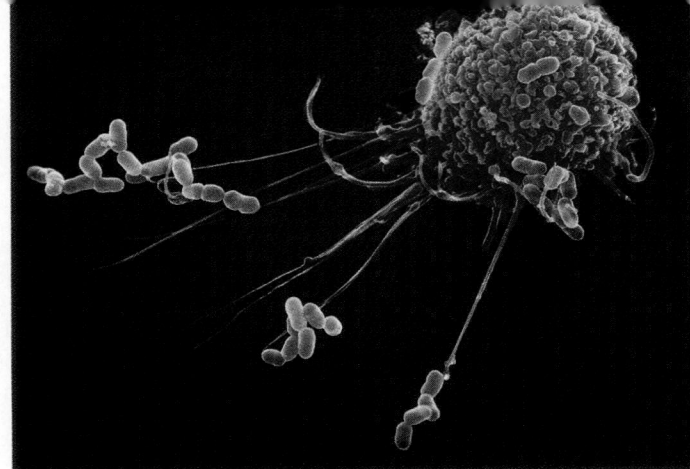

Figure 7 Caught! The bacteria, shown in green, don't stand a chance against the phagocyte, shown in red. Phagocytes are white blood cells that engulf and destroy bacteria.

General Defenses

In spite of barriers, pathogens sometimes get into your body and begin to damage cells. When body cells are damaged, they release chemicals that trigger the **inflammatory response,** which is the second line of defense. **In the inflammatory response, fluid and certain types of white blood cells leak from blood vessels into nearby tissues. The white blood cells then fight the pathogens.** Because the inflammatory response is the same no matter what the pathogen, it is sometimes called the body's general defense.

All white blood cells are disease fighters, but there are different types, each with its own particular function. The kinds involved in the inflammatory response are called phagocytes. A **phagocyte** (FAG uh syt) is a white blood cell that engulfs pathogens and destroys them by breaking them down.

During the inflammatory response, blood vessels widen in the area affected by the pathogens. This enlargement increases blood flow to the area. The enlarged blood vessels—and the fluid that leaks out of them—make the affected area red and swollen. If you touch the swollen area, it will feel slightly warmer than normal. In fact, the term *inflammation* comes from a Latin word meaning "to set on fire."

In some cases, chemicals produced during the inflammatory response cause a fever, raising your body temperature above its normal temperature of 37° Celsius. Although fever makes you feel bad, it actually may help your body fight the infection. Some pathogens may not grow and reproduce well at higher temperatures.

The Immune System

If a pathogen infection is severe enough to cause a fever, it also triggers the third line of defense—the **immune response.** The immune response is controlled by the immune system, your body's disease fighting system. **The cells of the immune system can distinguish between different kinds of pathogens. The immune-system cells react to each kind of pathogen with a defense targeted specifically at that pathogen.** The white blood cells that do this are called **lymphocytes** (LIM fuh syts). There are two major kinds of lymphocytes—T lymphocytes and B lymphocytes, which are also called T cells and B cells. In *Exploring the Immune Response* on the next page, you can see how T cells and B cells work together to destroy flu viruses.

T Cells A major function of **T cells** is to identify pathogens and distinguish one kind of pathogen from another. You have tens of millions of T cells circulating in your blood. Each kind of T cell recognizes a different kind of pathogen. What T cells actually recognize are marker molecules, called antigens, found on each pathogen. **Antigens** are molecules on cells that the immune system recognizes either as part of your body or as coming from outside your body. All cells have antigens, and each person's antigens are different from those of all other people.

You can think of antigens as something like the uniforms that athletes wear. When you watch a track meet, you can look at the runners' uniforms to tell which school each runner comes from. Like athletes from different schools, each different pathogen has its own kind of antigen. Antigens differ from one another because each kind of antigen has a different chemical structure.

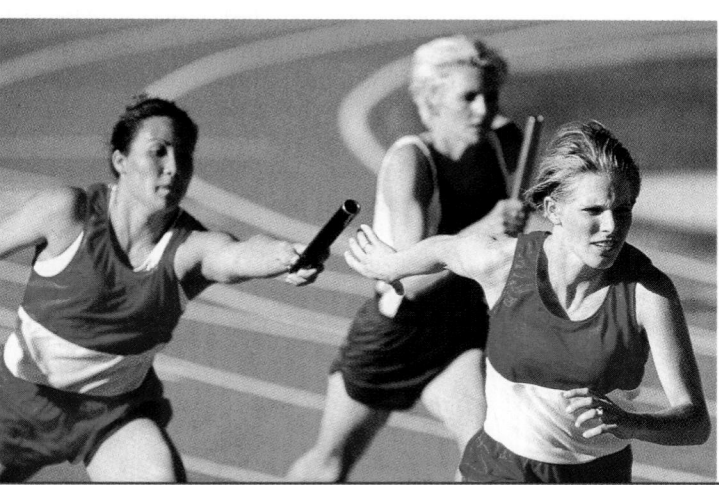

Figure 8 By looking at the runners' uniforms, you can tell that they come from different schools. Similarly, the immune system recognizes a pathogen by its antigens—marker molecules on the pathogen. *Applying Concepts What is the name of the cell that distinguishes one pathogen from another?*

Answers to Self-Assessment

Caption Question
Figure 8 T cell

The Immune System

Including All Students

Time 30 minutes

Some students may have difficulty remembering and distinguishing the terms associated with the immune system. Students can work in groups of three or more to create skits that dramatize the immune response. Group tasks can include research, writing, acting, and narrating, and any one student may take on more than one task. Students should identify components of the immune response in their skits, such as lymphocytes, T cells, B cells, antigens, antibodies, phagocytes, and pathogens. Students can present their skits to the class when finished.
limited English proficiency

 ### Integrating Chemistry

Challenge students to draw two or more pathogens with different antigens. *(Drawings may show a cell with differently patterned surfaces.)* Students should label their drawings and provide a caption that explains how a T cell recognizes a pathogen. **learning modality: visual**  Students can save their drawings in their portfolios.

Inquiry Challenge

Materials *various materials, such as beads, pipe cleaners, paper clips*
Time 10 minutes

Explain to students that when active, antibodies take on a shape something like a Y. Each arm of the Y attaches and binds to an antigen. Challenge students to build models showing how specific antibodies attack specific antigens.
learning modality: kinesthetic

Ongoing Assessment

Writing Ask students to briefly describe two ways in which the body defends itself against pathogens.

601

The Immune System, continued

EXPLORING

the Immune Response

To help students understand how the immune response functions, have volunteers read the captions aloud, as if they were telling a story. Point out that parts 2 and 3 occur at the same time. Also note that when T cells attack damaged cells, they destroy the infected cells as well as the viruses the cells contain. Ask students to identify the functions performed by T cells, B cells and phagocytes. *(T cells identify antigens, then alert B cells; they also attack infected cells. B cells produce antibodies. Phagocytes destroy clumps of viruses.)* **learning modality: verbal**

Building Inquiry Skills: Applying Concepts

Challenge students to create analogies to explain the parts and functions of the immune response system. For example, a T cell might be compared to a computerized missile that moves in on a specific target. Encourage students to share their analogies. **learning modality: logical/mathematical**

Integrating Chemistry
ACTIVITY

Materials *different types and sizes of paper clips such as metal, plastic, coated, colored*

Explain to students that antibodies are complex, three-dimensional proteins. Like all proteins, antibodies are assembled from amino acids. Use the different types and sizes of paper clips to model how amino acids (paper clips) can be assembled into many different combinations. **learning modality: visual**

EXPLORING the Immune Response

The immune system consists of T cells and B cells. The cells of the immune system work together to combat an infection, such as one caused by flu viruses.

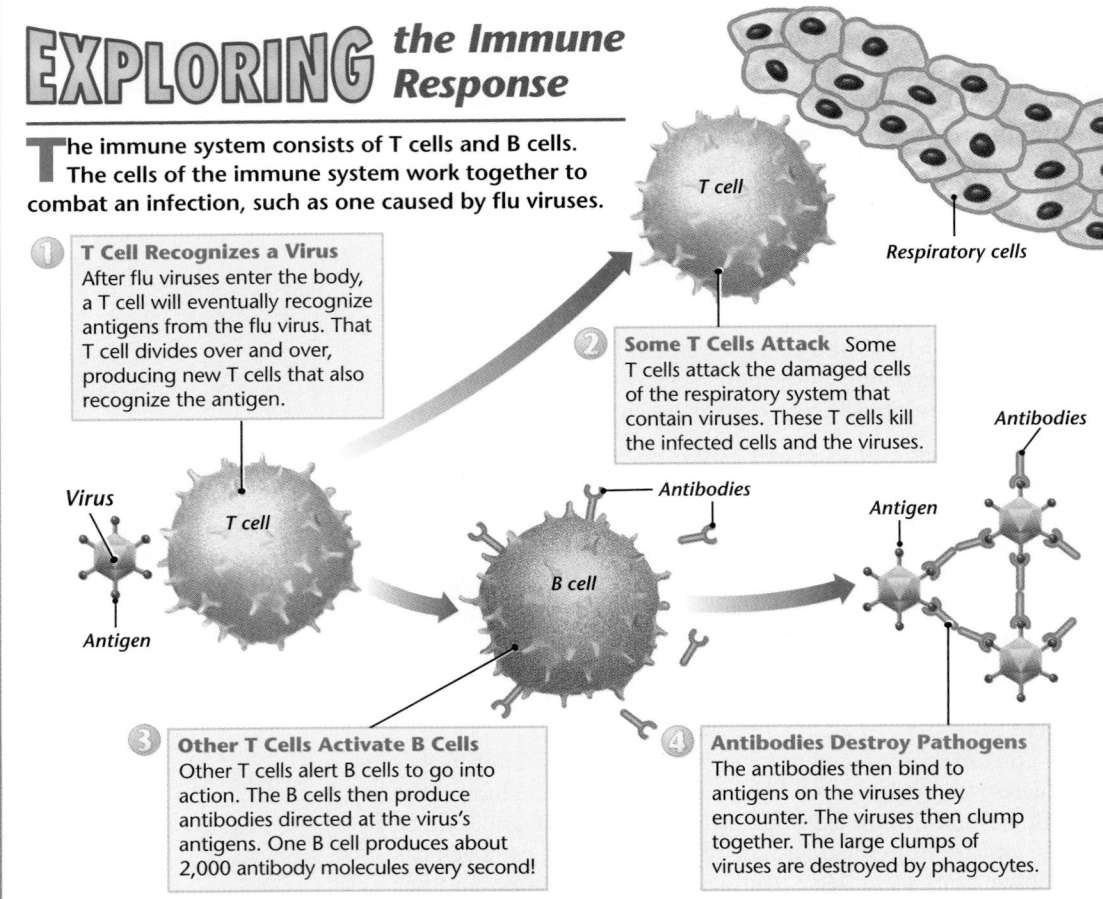

1 T Cell Recognizes a Virus After flu viruses enter the body, a T cell will eventually recognize antigens from the flu virus. That T cell divides over and over, producing new T cells that also recognize the antigen.

2 Some T Cells Attack Some T cells attack the damaged cells of the respiratory system that contain viruses. These T cells kill the infected cells and the viruses.

3 Other T Cells Activate B Cells Other T cells alert B cells to go into action. The B cells then produce antibodies directed at the virus's antigens. One B cell produces about 2,000 antibody molecules every second!

4 Antibodies Destroy Pathogens The antibodies then bind to antigens on the viruses they encounter. The viruses then clump together. The large clumps of viruses are destroyed by phagocytes.

Respiratory cells
T cell
Virus
T cell
Antigen
Antibodies
B cell
Antigen
Antibodies

B Cells The lymphocytes called **B cells** produce chemicals that help destroy each kind of pathogen. These chemicals are called **antibodies.** Antibodies lock onto antigens. Each kind of B cell produces only one kind of antibody. Each kind of antibody has a different structure. Antigen and antibody molecules fit together, like pieces of a puzzle. An antigen on a flu virus will only bind to one kind of antibody—the antibody that acts against that flu virus.

INTEGRATING CHEMISTRY

When antibodies bind to the antigens on a pathogen, they mark the pathogen for destruction. Some antibodies make pathogens clump together. Others keep pathogens from attaching to the body cells that they might damage. Still other antibodies make it easier for phagocytes to destroy the pathogens.

✓ *Checkpoint* What is the function of an antibody?

602

Background

Integrating Science A treatment that may be able to prevent the HIV virus from invading healthy cells was discovered in a study of 128 Italian hemophiliacs who were accidentally given transfusions of HIV-infected blood before a test was developed to screen donated blood. After a test for HIV was developed, only three of the hemophiliacs in the study tested positive. Later, there was an increase in the total number of hemophiliacs in the study who were HIV positive. This suggested that a blood chemical called chemokine temporarily prevented the virus from invading their cells. Their blood samples revealed approximately twice as many chemokines as blood from healthy blood donors.

This finding was very encouraging and AIDS researchers predict that chemokine-based treatments will soon be available.

602

AIDS, a Disease of the Immune System

Acquired immunodeficiency syndrome, or **AIDS**, is a disease caused by a virus that attacks the immune system. In the United States, AIDS is one of the leading causes of death in persons aged 25 to 44. The virus that causes AIDS is called human immunodeficiency virus, or **HIV**.

How HIV Affects the Body HIV is the only kind of virus known to attack the immune system directly. Once it invades the body, HIV enters T cells and reproduces inside them. People can be infected with HIV—that is, have the virus living in their body cells—for years before they become sick. More than 30 million people in the world may be infected with HIV.

Eventually HIV begins to destroy the T cells it has infected. Damage to the immune system is usually slow. But as the viruses destroy T cells, the body loses its ability to fight disease. Most persons infected with HIV eventually develop the disease AIDS.

Because their immune systems no longer function properly, people with AIDS become sick with diseases not normally found in people with healthy immune systems. Many people survive attack after attack of such diseases. But eventually their immune systems fail, ending in death. At this time, there is no cure for AIDS. However, new drug treatments allow people with the disease to survive much longer than in the past.

How HIV Is Spread Like all other viruses, HIV can only reproduce inside cells. In the case of HIV, the virus reproduces inside T cells. However, it can survive for a short time outside the human body in body fluids, such as blood and the fluids produced by the male and female reproductive systems.

HIV can spread from one person to another only if body fluids from an infected person come in contact with those of an uninfected person. Sexual contact is one way in which this can happen. HIV may also pass from an infected woman to her baby

Stuck Together

In this activity, you will model one way in which an antibody prevents a pathogen from infecting a body cell.

1. Use a large ball to represent a body cell, and a smaller ball to represent a pathogen.
2. Press a lump of modeling clay onto the small ball. Then use the clay to stick the two balls together. This models how a pathogen attaches itself to a body cell.
3. Pull the two balls apart, keeping the clay on the small ball (the pathogen).
4. Put strips of tape over the clay, so that the clay is completely covered. The tape represents an antibody.
5. Now try to reattach the small ball to the larger one.

Making Models Use the model to explain how antibodies prevent pathogens from attaching to body cells.

Figure 9 The tiny red particles are HIV viruses emerging from a T cell. The viruses multiply inside the T cell and eventually destroy the T cell.
Relating Cause and Effect Why does the death of T cells interfere with the body's ability to fight disease?

Chapter 19 **603**

AIDS, a Disease of the Immune System

Addressing Naive Conceptions

Students may think that AIDS is one disease with a specific set of symptoms. Explain that because AIDS is a disease of the immune system, people with AIDS are susceptible to a wide range of diseases. Therefore, the illness associated with AIDS is really caused by many different diseases with different symptoms. **learning modality: verbal**

Building Inquiry Skills: Inferring

Point out that just as it may take many years for a person to develop symptoms caused by HIV, it may take up to six months for viruses to show up in a blood test for HIV. Ask: **If someone tests negative for HIV, does this mean that it would be impossible for him or her to spread the virus? Explain.** (*No. It only means that he or she did not have the virus six months ago.*) **learning modality: logical/mathematical**

Answers to Self-Assessment

Caption Question

Figure 9 T cells recognize pathogens' antigens. When T cells are destroyed, the body loses its ability to mount a response aimed at specific pathogens.

✓ *Checkpoint*

An antibody recognizes and binds to a particular antigen. This enables the pathogen to be destroyed.

Ongoing Assessment

Organizing Information Have students make compare/contrast tables showing the similarities and differences between T cells and B cells.

3 Assess

Section 2 Review Answers

1. Skin—chemicals in oil and sweat kill pathogens, tightly packed cells prevent entry of pathogens. Breathing passages—mucus and cilia trap and remove pathogens. Mouth and stomach—saliva and acid destroy pathogens.

2. Blood vessels widen, and the flow of blood increases in the affected area. Fluid and white blood cells leak from blood vessels to nearby tissues. The white blood cells destroy pathogens.

3. The immune system cells react to each kind of pathogen with a defense targeted specifically at that pathogen.

4. HIV directly attacks the immune system, making it easier for other pathogens to infect the body.

5. HIV is not found on the skin, so it cannot be transferred from a hand to a doorknob.

Check Your Progress

CHAPTER PROJECT

By this time, students should have completed their research. Assist students who still have specific questions. Encourage students to write brief, vivid descriptions of each event. Remind students that they should describe battle scenes on each line of defense.

Figure 10 You cannot get HIV, the virus that causes AIDS, by hugging someone infected with the virus.

during pregnancy or childbirth or through breast milk. In addition, when drug users share needles, some infected blood may get into the needle and then infect the next person who uses it. A person can also get HIV through a transfusion of blood that contains the virus. But since 1985, all donated blood in the United States has been tested for signs of HIV, and infected blood is not used in transfusions.

It is important to know the many ways in which HIV is *not* spread. HIV does not live on skin, so you cannot be infected by hugging or shaking hands with an infected person. You can't get infected by using a toilet seat after it has been used by someone with HIV. And HIV is not spread when you bump into someone while playing sports.

Section 2 Review

1. Name four barriers that prevent pathogens from getting into the body. Explain how each barrier prevents infection.
2. Describe the inflammatory response.
3. What is the function of the immune system?
4. How is HIV different from other virus pathogens?
5. **Thinking Critically** **Applying Concepts** Explain why you can't contract HIV by touching a doorknob that someone infected with the virus has touched.

Check Your Progress

CHAPTER PROJECT

At this point you should begin writing the newspaper articles or scripts for each of your broadcasts. Before you begin writing, outline the main ideas that you want to communicate. Work to make your descriptions sound like real news. (*Hint:* Make sure that your articles or scripts include information about each of the body's three lines of defense).

Performance Assessment

Writing Have students work in pairs to create crossword puzzles using the key terms and concepts from the section. Each puzzle should include a list of clues using information from the section.

 Students can save their puzzles in their portfolios.

Performance Assessment

◆ **Unit 4 Resources** 19-2 Review and Reinforce, p. 119; 19-2 Enrich, p. 120

Media and Technology

 Interactive Student Tutorial CD-ROM Chapter 19

SECTION 3 Preventing Infectious Disease

DISCOVER · ACTIVITY · · · ·

What Substances Can Kill Pathogens?

1. Your teacher will give you a variety of products, such as disinfectant soaps and mouthwashes, that claim to kill pathogens. Read the labels to learn the pathogens that each product is supposed to destroy.

2. Also note the ingredients in each product that act against pathogens. These are labeled "active ingredients."

Think It Over
Designing Experiments How could you determine which of two different soaps is more effective at killing bacteria? Design an experiment to find out. Do not perform the experiment without obtaining your teacher's approval.

I tch, itch, itch. That's probably what you remember about chicken pox, if you ever had it. But once you got better, you could be pretty sure that you would never get that disease again. As people recover from some diseases, they develop immunity to the diseases. **Immunity** is the body's ability to destroy pathogens before they can cause disease. There are two basic types of immunity—active and passive.

Active Immunity

If you've been sick with chicken pox, your body was invaded by chicken pox viruses. Your immune system responded to the virus antigens by producing antibodies against them. The next time that chicken pox viruses invade your body, your immune system will probably produce antibodies so quickly that you won't become sick. You now have **active immunity** to chicken pox, because your own body has produced the antibodies that fight the chicken pox pathogens. **Active immunity occurs when a person's own immune system produces antibodies in response to the presence of a pathogen.**

GUIDE FOR READING

◆ What is active immunity?
◆ What is passive immunity?

Reading Tip Before you read, rewrite the headings in the section as questions that begin with *how, why,* or *what.* As you read, write short answers to those questions.

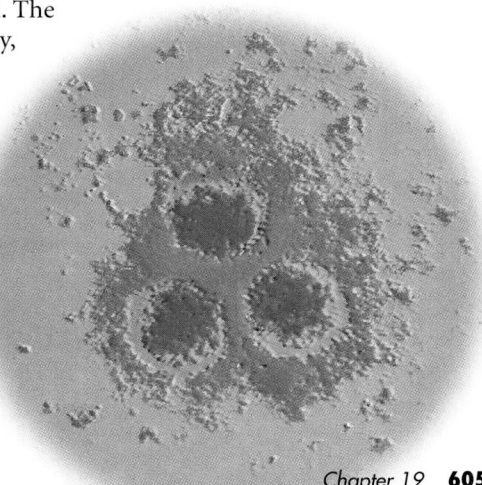

Figure 11 These virus particles cause chicken pox. Once you have had chicken pox, you will probably never get that disease again.

READING STRATEGIES

Reading Tip Student questions may include "What is active immunity?" and "How does a person get a passive immunity?" After students rewrite the section headings as questions, have them preview the photographs and drawings and read the captions. Encourage students to predict answers to their questions based on the pictures and captions.

Program Resources

◆ **Unit 4 Resources** 19-3 Lesson Plan, p. 121; 19-3 Section Summary, p. 122

Media and Technology

 Audio CD English-Spanish Summary 19-3

SECTION 3 Preventing Infectious Disease

Objectives

After completing the lesson, students will be able to
◆ define and explain active immunity;
◆ define and explain passive immunity;
◆ identify some strategies for staying healthy.

Key Terms immunity, active immunity, vaccination, vaccine, passive immunity, antibiotic

1 Engage/Explore

Activating Prior Knowledge

Encourage students to discuss why people get immunizations. Ask students to list diseases for which they think vaccines do and do not exist.

· · · · · · · · · DISCOVER · · · · · · · · ·

Skills Focus designing experiments
Materials *disinfectants and antibacterial products such as creams, mouthwashes, hand soaps, household cleaners, and spray disinfectants*
Time 15 minutes
Tips Use clean, empty containers or seal the tops of containers with tape. Caution students not to taste, smell, or touch any of the products. Have students list the product name, the pathogens it is supposed to kill, and the active ingredients for each. Active ingredients may include bacitracin, neomycin sulfate, benzalkonium chloride, hydrogen peroxide, iodine, isopropyl alcohol, and others.
Think It Over One possible experiment could involve using nutrient agar to grow bacteria from unwashed hands and from hands that have been washed with each soap. Tell students not to perform any experiments without first getting your approval for the procedure.

2 Facilitate

Active Immunity

Real-Life Learning

Tell students that a vaccine for chicken pox became available in the United States in 1995. Some students may have had chicken pox, but others may have received the vaccine. Encourage students to talk to the adults in their families about diseases and vaccinations. Point out that older generations may have been vaccinated against diseases that are no longer threats, such as smallpox. Ask students: **Do you think people will always have to be vaccinated against chicken pox?** *(Some students may think that vaccinations will always be necessary. Others may believe that the disease will disappear when enough people are immune so that it is no longer spread among humans.)* **learning modality: verbal**

Building Inquiry Skills: Inferring

Ask students to describe how people gained immunity to the chicken pox virus before the vaccine was available. *(They had to get the disease to gain immunity.)* Explain that some people intentionally exposed themselves to the virus in order to gain active immunity. Have students brainstorm a list of the benefits and drawbacks of gaining immunity in this way. *(Samples: Benefits—immunity, getting the disease when young and healthy instead of when older or sick; drawbacks—you can spread the disease to others, you may experience complications.)* **learning modality: verbal**

How Active Immunity Is Produced Active immunity is produced by the cells of a person's immune system as part of the immune response. Remember that during the immune response, T cells and B cells help destroy the disease-causing pathogens. After the person recovers, some of the T cells and B cells keep the "memory" of the pathogen's antigen. If that kind of pathogen enters the body again, these memory cells recognize the pathogen's antigen. The memory cells start the immune response so quickly that the person usually doesn't get sick. Active immunity usually lasts for many years, and sometimes it lasts for life.

SCIENCE & History

Fighting Infectious Disease

From ancient times, people have practiced methods for preventing disease and caring for sick people. Ancient peoples, however, did not know what caused disease. About 200 years ago, people began to learn much more about the causes of infectious diseases and how to protect against them.

1854
Florence Nightingale

As an English nurse caring for British soldiers during the Crimean War, Florence Nightingale insisted that army hospitals be kept clean. By doing this, she saved many soldiers' lives. She is considered to be the founder of the modern nursing profession.

1800   **1825**   **1850**

1796
Edward Jenner

Edward Jenner, a country doctor in England, successfully vaccinated a child against smallpox, a deadly viral disease. Jenner used material from a sore of a person with cowpox, a mild but similar disorder. Although Jenner's procedure was successful, he did not understand why it worked.

1860s
Joseph Lister

Joseph Lister, an English surgeon, used carbolic acid to prevent infections in surgical patients. Because of Lister's techniques, far more people recovered from surgery than before.

606

Background

History of Science Smallpox was recorded as far back as the Roman Empire, when in A.D. 189 there were as many as 2,000 deaths per day throughout the empire. Even after the vaccine became available, epidemics continued to occur around the world.

In 1967, the World Health Organization (WHO) launched a worldwide vaccination campaign against smallpox. By 1975, most of the world's nations were free of smallpox.

The world's last known natural case of smallpox occurred in 1977. The only deaths reported thereafter occurred when the virus escaped from a laboratory in England.

In 1979, WHO declared the world to be free of the disease. This marks the first time in history that a naturally occurring disease has been completely eradicated from the human population.

Vaccination One way in which you can gain active immunity is by coming down with the disease. Another way is by being vaccinated against the disease. **Vaccination** (vac suh NAY shun), or immunization, is the process by which harmless antigens are deliberately introduced into a person's body to produce active immunity.

The substance that is used in a vaccination is called a vaccine. A **vaccine** (vak SEEN) usually consists of pathogens that have been weakened or killed but can still trigger the immune system to go into action.

In Your Journal

Learn more about the work of one of these people. Then imagine that a new hospital is going to be dedicated to that person, and that you have been chosen to deliver the dedication speech. Write a speech that praises the person's contributions to fighting disease.

1882

Robert Koch

In Germany, Robert Koch identified one kind of microorganism in many samples of tissue taken from people with tuberculosis. Because he always found the same microorganism, Koch hypothesized that each infectious disease is caused by one specific pathogen.

1875	1900	1925

1868

Louis Pasteur

In France, Louis Pasteur showed that microorganisms were the cause of a disease in silkworms. Pasteur reasoned that he could control the spread of disease by killing microorganisms. He also proposed that infectious diseases in humans are caused by microorganisms.

1928

Alexander Fleming

In Britain, Alexander Fleming observed that bacteria growing on laboratory plates were killed when some kinds of fungi grew on the same plate. He discovered that one fungus produced a substance—penicillin—that killed bacteria. Penicillin became the first antibiotic.

Chapter 19 **607**

Challenge students to identify some of the effects of each discovery. For example, Jenner's discovery led to the effective control of smallpox and saved many lives.

Extend By 2002, the last smallpox viruses, stored in government health offices in Atlanta and Moscow, are scheduled to be destroyed. Challenge students to debate whether viruses that cause diseases that have been eradicated should be destroyed or saved for further scientific research. Students should form teams and debate the issue. *(The advantage of destroying the smallpox virus would be the prevention of another smallpox outbreak. The disadvantage consists of losing the ability to study the virus.)*

In Your Journal Encourage students to use both reference books and the Internet for their research. Remind students to imagine the audience as they write their speeches. **learning modality: verbal**

Program Resources

◆ **Interdisciplinary Exploration Series**
   "Fate of the Rain Forest," pp. 35–36

Media and Technology

 Exploring Life Science Videodisc
Unit 2, Side 1,
"Have You Had
Your Shots?"

Chapter 3

Ongoing Assessment

Writing Have students explain how vaccination can produce active immunity. *(In vaccination, antigens are introduced into the body; usually they do not cause illness, but they make the immune system go into action. The T and B cells will be able to recognize and destroy that type of pathogen if it enters the body again.)*

Passive Immunity

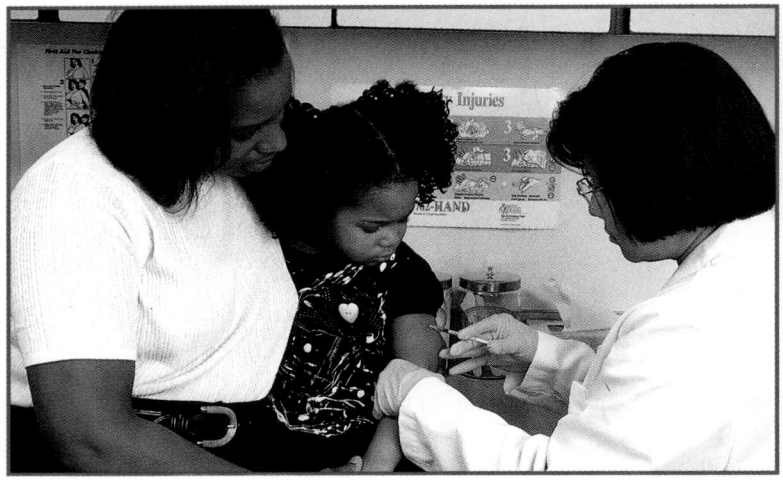

Figure 12 Ouch! The injection may sting a bit, but it is a vaccination that will protect the little girl against disease. Vaccinations consist of dead or weakened pathogens that do not make you sick.
Classifying Why does a vaccination produce active immunity to a disease?

The T cells and B cells still recognize and respond to the antigens of the weakened or dead pathogen. When you receive a vaccination, the weakened pathogens usually do not make you sick. However, your immune system responds by producing memory cells and active immunity to the disease. Vaccinations are given by injection or by mouth. Vaccinations can prevent polio, chicken pox, and other diseases.

☑ *Checkpoint* What are two ways in which a person can gain active immunity?

Passive Immunity

Some diseases, such as rabies, are so uncommon that people rarely receive vaccinations against them. If a person is bitten by an animal that might have rabies, however, the person is usually given injections that contain antibodies to the rabies antigen. The protection that the person acquires this way is an example of passive immunity. This type of immunity is called **passive immunity** because the antibodies are given to the person—the person's own immune system did not make them. **Passive immunity occurs when the antibodies that fight the pathogen come from another source rather than from the person's own body.** Unlike active immunity, which is long-lasting, passive immunity usually lasts no more than a few months.

A baby acquires passive immunity to some diseases before birth. This happens because antibodies from the mother's body pass into the baby's body. After birth, these antibodies protect the baby for a few months. After that time, the baby's own immune system has begun to function.

608

Staying Healthy

You almost certainly have immunity to some diseases, either because you have had the diseases or because you have been vaccinated against them. Nobody, though, is immune to all diseases. But there are several steps you can take to decrease your risk of getting and spreading infectious diseases. Figure 13 summarizes these steps.

Unfortunately, you will probably become sick from time to time. When that happens, there are ways in which you can help yourself recover. One thing you can do is get plenty of rest. In addition, unless your stomach is upset, you should eat well-balanced meals and drink plenty of fluids. These actions are all that you need to recover from most mild illnesses.

Sometimes when you are sick, medications can help you get better. If you have a disease that is caused by bacteria, you may be given an antibiotic. An **antibiotic** (an tih by AHT ik) is a chemical that kills bacteria or slows their growth without harming body cells. Unfortunately, there are no medications that cure viral illnesses, including the common cold. The best way to deal with most viral diseases is to get plenty of rest.

Some medicines don't kill pathogens but may help you feel more comfortable while you get better. Many of these are over-the-counter medications—drugs that can be purchased without a doctor's prescription. Such medications may reduce fever, clear your nose so you can breathe more easily, or stop a cough. Be sure you understand and follow the instructions for all types of medications. And if you don't start to feel better in a short time, you should see a doctor.

Preventing Infectious Diseases

◆ Don't share items that might carry pathogens, such as toothbrushes, drinking straws, or silverware.

◆ Keep clean. Wash your hands before eating and after using the bathroom.

◆ Cover your mouth when sneezing or coughing.

◆ Get eight hours of sleep every night.

◆ Eat a well-balanced diet.

◆ Get regular exercise.

Figure 13 Your actions can help prevent the spread of infectious diseases. *Applying Concepts How does keeping clean prevent the spread of disease?*

Section 3 Review

1. What is active immunity? How is it produced?
2. How is passive immunity produced? How does passive immunity differ from active immunity?
3. Identify four things that you can do that will help you avoid catching an infectious disease.
4. **Thinking Critically** **Applying Concepts** After receiving a vaccination, you may develop mild symptoms of the disease. Explain why.

Science at Home

Vaccination History With a family member, make a list of the vaccinations you have received. For each, note when you received the vaccination. Then, with your family member, learn about one of the diseases for which you were vaccinated. What kind of pathogen causes the disease? What are the symptoms of the disease? Is the disease still common in the United States?

Chapter 19 **609**

Program Resources

◆ **Unit 4 Resources** 19-3 Review and Reinforce, p. 123; 19-3 Enrich, p. 124
◆ **Laboratory Manual,** 19, "Do Mouthwashes Work?"

Answers to Self-Assessment

Caption Question

Figure 13 By keeping clean, a person removes bacteria that might otherwise be able to enter the body and cause infection.

Staying Healthy

Addressing Naive Conceptions

Students may confuse *antibodies* and *antibiotics*. Explain that, although their names sound similar, they are very different. Most antibiotics can kill several types of bacteria, but antibodies can only respond to the antigens of a particular pathogen. In addition, antibiotics cannot be used against viral infections, but antibody serums exist for both viral and bacterial infections, as well as for toxins such as the venom found in snake bites.
limited English proficiency

3 Assess

Section 3 Review Answers

1. Active immunity is produced when a person's immune system produces antibodies in response to the presence of a pathogen.
2. Passive immunity is produced by transferring another organism's antibodies into the body. It usually lasts for a shorter time than active immunity.
3. Do not share items that may carry pathogens, keep clean, get plenty of rest and exercise, eat a balanced diet.
4. Since vaccination introduces antigens of pathogens into the body, the body responds as if the live pathogens themselves were present.

Science at Home

You may wish to provide students with a list of vaccinations required by your school district. Point out that some students may be vaccinated against diseases not required by the school district, such as hepatitis B.

Performance Assessment

Writing Have students prepare lessons for younger students on ways of preventing infectious disease. Students can save their lessons in their portfolios. (Portfolio)

Causes of Death, Then and Now

Preparing for Inquiry

Key Concept The leading causes of death have changed over the past hundred years.

Skills Objectives Students will be able to
- interpret data about the leading causes of death;
- draw conclusions regarding the change in health threats since 1900;
- compare infectious to noninfectious diseases.

Time 20–30 minutes

Guiding Inquiry

Invitation Ask students what they think is the leading cause of death in the United States today. Have them consider news and television reports they have seen. Ask them to think about how household plumbing, safe commercial food handling, and improvements in general cleanliness have improved people's abilities to remain healthy.

Introducing the Procedure
- Refer to the Skills Handbook to teach or review how to make bar graphs and circle graphs.
- Remind students to round decimals to the nearest whole number in their calculations. However, students should make sure the percentages on their circle graphs add up to 100.

Troubleshooting the Experiment
Some students may need extra help with the math. Encourage students who are comfortable with the math to help others.

Expected Outcome
- Students should see that the leading causes of death a hundred years ago were pathogens. They should also observe that heart disease has become a more common problem.
- If students do not make appropriate connections, have them try to identify the sources of their error. Some

students may not be aware of the causes of pneumonia, tuberculosis, or most kinds of lethal diarrhea.

Analyze and Conclude
1. Students' answers should reflect that they could determine top causes of death in each year, as well as compare the total number of deaths to deaths attributed to particular causes.
2. Heart disease showed the greatest increase. Pneumonia/influenza showed the greatest decrease.

Causes of DEATH, Then and Now

In this lab you'll compare data on the leading causes of death in 1900 and today.

Problem
How do the leading causes of death today compare with those of a hundred years ago?

Materials
colored pencils   ruler
calculator (optional)   protractor
compass

Procedure ✂

1. The data table on the next page shows the leading causes of death in the United States during two different years. Examine the data and note that two causes of death—accidents and suicides—are not diseases. The other causes are labeled either "I," indicating an infectious disease, or "NI," indicating a noninfectious disease.

Part 1 Comparing Specific Causes of Death

2. Look at the following causes of death in the data table: (a) pneumonia and influenza, (b) heart disease, (c) accidents, and (d) cancer. Construct a bar graph that compares the numbers of deaths from each of those causes in 1900 and today. Label the horizontal axis "Causes of Death." Label the vertical axis "Deaths per 100,000 People." Draw two bars side by side for each cause of death. Use a key to show which bars refer to 1900 and which refer to today.

Part 2 Comparing Infectious and Noninfectious Causes of Death

3. In this part of the lab, you will make two circle graphs showing three categories: infectious diseases, noninfectious diseases, and "other." You may want to review the information on creating circle graphs on page 798 of the Skills Handbook.

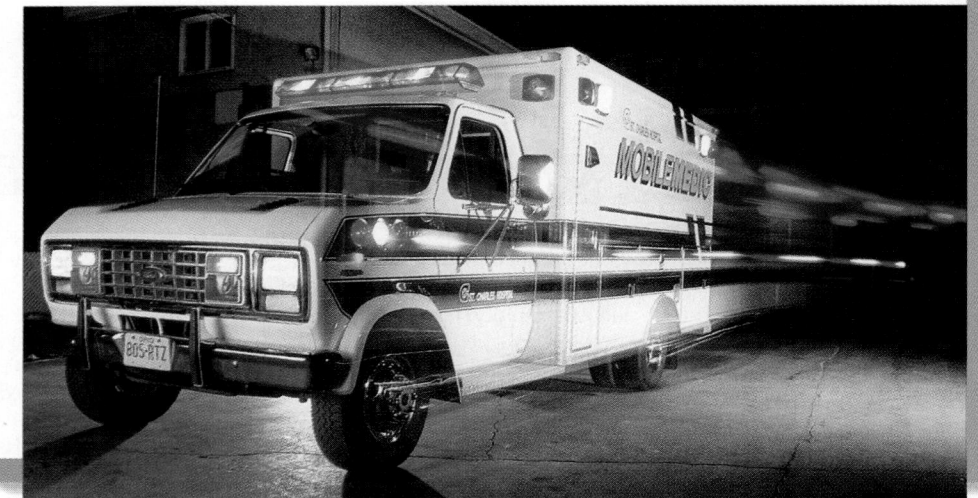

---

3. As a cause of death, infectious disease decreased the most. Noninfectious disease increased the most.

4. Sample: Since 1900, infectious diseases have been prevented by many factors including improvements in water treatment and sanitation, immunization, improved diets, medicines, and other disease treatment procedures.

Ten Leading Causes of Death in the United States, 1900 and Today

1900		Today	
Cause of Death	**Deaths per 100,000**	**Cause of Death**	**Deaths per 100,000**
Pneumonia, influenza (I)*	215	Heart disease (NI)	281
Tuberculosis (I)	185	Cancer (NI)	205
Diarrhea (I)	140	Stroke (NI)	59
Heart disease (NI)	130	Lung disease (NI)	39
Stroke (NI)	110	Accidents	35
Kidney disease (NI)	85	Pneumonia (I)	31
Accidents	75	Diabetes (NI)	22
Cancer (NI)	65	HIV Infection (I)	16
Senility (NI)	55	Suicide	12
Diphtheria (I)	40	Liver disease (NI)	10
Total	**1,100**	**Total**	**710**

*"I" indicates an infectious disease. "NI" indicates a noninfectious disease.

4. Start by grouping the data from 1900 into the three categories—infectious diseases, noninfectious diseases, and other causes. Find the total number of deaths for each category. Then find the size of the "pie slice" (the number of degrees) for each category, and construct your circle graph. To find the size of the infectious disease slice for 1900, for example, use the following formula:

$$\frac{\text{number of deaths from infectious diseases}}{1{,}100 \text{ deaths total}} = \frac{x}{360°}$$

5. Calculate the percentage represented by each category using this formula:

$$\frac{\text{number of degrees in a slice}}{360°} \times 100 = \underline{\ ?\ } \%$$

6. Repeat Steps 4 and 5 using the data from today to make the second circle graph. What part of the formula in Step 4 do you need to change?

Analyze and Conclude

1. What kind of information did you learn just from examining the data table in Step 1?
2. According to your bar graph, which cause of death showed the greatest increase between 1900 and today? The greatest decrease?
3. In your circle graphs, which category decreased the most from 1900 to today? Which increased the most?
4. Suggest an explanation for the change in the number of deaths due to infectious diseases from 1900 to today.
5. **Think About It** How do graphs help you identify patterns and other information in data that you might otherwise overlook?

More to Explore

Write a question related to the data table that you have not yet answered. Then create a graph or work with the data in other ways to answer your question.

5. Sample: When making graphs, data may be rearranged or reclassified in ways that show new information. For example, when the circle graphs were made, combining the data in new categories showed that infectious diseases have decreased dramatically.

Extending the Inquiry

More to Explore Students may find it helpful to work in small groups to list possible questions before they write their question. Sample: Among the ten top causes, how does the percentage of deaths from heart disease today compare with the percentage in 1900? *(Today, about 40% (281÷710) of these deaths are from heart disease; in 1900 about 12% (130 ÷ 1,100) were from heart disease.)* You might want to have students check each other's work before they share their questions and answers with the class.

Program Resources

◆ **Unit 4 Resources** Chapter 19 Skills Lab, pp. 131–133
◆ **Inquiry Skills Activity Book** Provides teaching and review of all inquiry skills

Safety

Make sure students exercise caution when working with sharp objects such as compasses. Review the safety guidelines in Appendix A.

SECTION 4 Noninfectious Disease

Objectives

After completing the lesson, students will be able to

◆ define an allergy;
◆ explain how diabetes affects the body;
◆ explain how cancer affects the body.

Key Terms noninfectious disease, allergy, allergen, histamine, asthma, diabetes, tumor, carcinogen

1 Engage/Explore

Activating Prior Knowledge

Ask groups of students to brainstorm lists of diseases that cannot be spread from one person to another. Record all their responses on the board. Refer to the responses when students finish this section; at that point, help students add to the list and correct any misconceptions that they previously had.

•••••• DISCOVER ••••••

Skills Focus observing
Materials *plastic drinking straws*
Time 10 minutes
Tips Use narrow straws in this activity. Students with respiratory problems should not perform this activity if it will compromise their ability to breathe. Have them keep time and record observations.
Expected Outcome Students should not be able to breathe as deeply through the straws as they can through their noses.
Think It Over Students should be able to take deeper breaths without the straw. Some students may feel short of breath.

612

SECTION 4 Noninfectious Disease

DISCOVER •••••••••••••••••••••••••••••••••ACTIVITY

What Happens When Airflow Is Restricted?

1. Asthma is a disorder in which breathing passages become narrower than normal. This activity will help you understand how this condition affects breathing. Begin by breathing normally, first through your nose and then through your mouth. Observe how deeply you breathe.

2. Put one end of a drinking straw in your mouth. Then gently pinch your nostrils shut so that you cannot breathe through your nose.

3. With your nostrils pinched closed, breathe by inhaling air through the straw.

Continue breathing this way for thirty seconds.

Think It Over
Observing Compare your normal breathing pattern to that when breathing through the straw. Which way were you able to take deeper breaths? Did you ever feel short of breath?

GUIDE FOR READING

◆ What is an allergy?
◆ How does diabetes affect the body?
◆ What is cancer?

Reading Tip As you read, create a table in which you record the characteristics of each noninfectious disease.

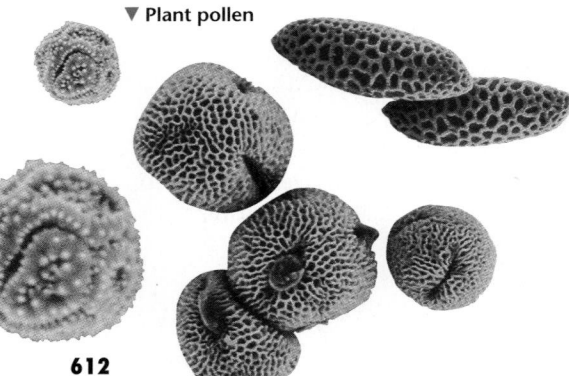
▼ Plant pollen

612

Americans are living longer today than ever before. A person who was born in 1990 can expect to live about 75 years. In contrast, a person born in 1950 could expect to live only about 68 years.

Progress against infectious disease is one reason why life spans have increased. However, as infectious diseases have become less common, noninfectious diseases have grown more prevalent. **Noninfectious diseases** are diseases that are not spread from person to person. Unlike infectious diseases, noninfectious diseases are not caused by microorganisms. A noninfectious disease, cardiovascular disease, is the leading cause of death in America. Allergies, diabetes, and cancer are other noninfectious diseases.

Allergies

Spring has arrived. Flowers are in bloom, and the songs of birds fill the air. Unfortunately for some people, sneezing is another sound that fills the air. People who sneeze and cough in the spring may not have colds. Instead, they may be suffering from an **allergy** to plant pollen in the air. **An allergy is a disorder in which the immune system is overly sensitive to a foreign substance—something not normally found in the body.**

READING STRATEGIES

Reading Tip Have students work individually or in small groups to create their tables. Instruct students to create a framework for their tables before they begin reading. Column heads might be *Disease, Cause,* and *Characteristics.* Students can find the diseases to list in the rows of the table (Allergies, Diabetes, and Cancer) by scanning the section to look for the main headings. As students read, they can complete the tables by writing in the characteristics of each noninfectious disease in their own words.

Allergens An **allergen** is any substance that causes an allergy. In addition to different kinds of pollen, people may be allergic to dust, molds, some foods, and even some medicines. If you are lucky, you have no allergies at all. However, many people are allergic to one or more substances.

Reaction to Allergens Allergens may get into your body when you inhale them, eat them in food, or touch them with your skin. When lymphocytes encounter the allergen, they produce antibodies. These antibodies, unlike the ones made during the immune response, signal cells in the body to release a chemical called histamine. **Histamine** (HIS tuh meen) is a chemical that is responsible for the symptoms of an allergy, such as sneezing and watery eyes. Drugs that interfere with the action of histamine, called antihistamines, may lessen this reaction. However, if you have an allergy, the best strategy is to try to avoid the substance to which you are allergic.

Asthma If some people inhale a substance to which they are allergic, they may develop a condition called asthma. **Asthma** (AZ muh) is a disorder in which the respiratory passages narrow significantly. This narrowing causes the person to wheeze and become short of breath. Asthma attacks may be brought on by factors other than allergies, such as stress and exercise. Severe asthma attacks may require emergency medical care. People who have asthma can prevent asthma attacks with medication, or they can avoid the substances and activities that trigger attacks.

✓ *Checkpoint* *What is the effect of histamine on the body?*

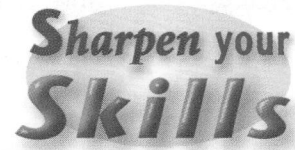

Sharpen your Skills

Drawing Conclusions ACTIVITY

Two weeks ago, after you ate strawberry shortcake with whipped cream, you broke out in an itchy rash. Besides strawberries, the ingredients in the dessert were sugar, flour, butter, eggs, vanilla, baking powder, salt, and cream. Then last night, you ate a strawberry custard tart with whipped cream and again broke out in a rash. The tart's ingredients were strawberries, sugar, cornstarch, milk, eggs, flour, shortening, salt, and vanilla.

You think that you may be allergic to strawberries. Do you have enough evidence to support this conclusion? If so, why? If not, what additional evidence do you need?

Figure 14 Some people have allergic reactions to dust mites, tiny animals found in dust (below), or to cats (right).

2 Facilitate

Allergies

Sharpen your Skills

Drawing Conclusions

Time 10 minutes
Tips Suggest that students list the ingredients side by side in a table to find those the desserts have in common.
Expected Outcome Because many ingredients are in both foods, there is not enough evidence to conclude an allergic reaction to strawberries. A more extensive record of foods eaten and reactions to foods is needed.
Extend Have students do research to learn about common allergies and their symptoms and how allergists determine which substances a person is allergic to.
learning modality: logical/mathematical

Building Inquiry Skills: Making Models

Have students diagram what happens when a pathogen such as a virus invades the body and what happens when an allergen invades the body. Encourage students to label their drawings and write captions describing what happens at each stage. Ask: **What is the same in both drawings?** (*Both drawings show lymphocytes recognizing the foreign substance and producing antibodies in response.*) **What is different?** (*In the immune response, the antibodies attach to the antigens on the pathogen. In the allergic response, the antibodies signal other cells to produce histamine.*)
learning modality: visual

Ongoing Assessment

Oral Presentation Call on students to describe symptoms of allergic reactions.

Answers to Self-Assessment

✓ *Checkpoint*
Histamine causes symptoms of an allergy, including watery eyes and sneezing.

Diabetes

Building Inquiry Skills: Communicating

Materials *paper, colored pencils, markers*
Time 30 minutes

ACTIVITY

Tell students that although diabetes is recognizable by its warning signs, experts believe that about 8 million Americans are unaware that they have it. Have groups of students design information packets describing the warning signs and dangers of diabetes. Students should explain how symptoms, such as thirst and weight loss, are related to the causes of diabetes. You might contact the American Diabetes Association for additional information. Suggest that students use this information in producing their packets. **cooperative learning**

Cancer

Addressing Naive Conceptions

Some students may think that all cancer patients will die of cancer. Emphasize that advances in medical understanding and technology allow many people to survive cancer and go on to lead normal lives. Just as a healthy environment and good health habits can help protect people from developing cancer, factors such as diet and exercise can help people with cancer live longer and even recover from the disease. **learning modality: verbal**

Figure 15 Many people with diabetes must test their blood frequently to determine the level of glucose in their blood. *Relating Cause and Effect What accounts for the high level of glucose in the blood of people with diabetes?*

Diabetes

The pancreas produces a chemical called insulin. **Insulin** (IN suh lin) enables body cells to take in glucose from the blood and use it for energy. In the condition known as **diabetes** (dy uh BEE tis), either the pancreas fails to produce enough insulin or the body's cells can't use it properly. **As a result, a person with diabetes has high levels of glucose in the blood and excretes glucose in the urine. The person's body cells, however, do not have enough glucose.**

Effects of Diabetes People with diabetes may lose weight, feel weak, and be hungry all the time. These symptoms occur because the cells are unable to take in the glucose they need to function efficiently. In addition, these people may urinate frequently and feel thirsty as the kidneys work to eliminate the excess glucose from the body.

Diabetes is a serious condition that, if not treated properly, can result in death. Even with proper treatment, diabetes can have serious long-term effects. These effects can include blindness, kidney failure, and heart disease.

Forms of Diabetes There are two main forms of diabetes. Type I diabetes, the more serious form, usually begins in childhood or early adulthood. In Type I diabetes, the pancreas produces little or no insulin. People with this condition must get insulin injections.

Type II diabetes usually develops during adulthood. In this condition, either the pancreas doesn't make enough insulin or body cells do not respond normally to insulin. People who have Type II diabetes may not need to take insulin. Instead, they may be able to control the symptoms of diabetes through proper diet, weight control, and exercise.

☑ *Checkpoint* **What are some symptoms of diabetes?**

Cancer

Under normal conditions, the body produces new cells at about the same rate that other cells die. In a condition known as cancer, however, the situation is quite different. **Cancer is a disease in which cells multiply uncontrollably, over and over, destroying healthy tissue in the process.** The word *cancer* is the Latin word for crab. Cancerous growths act something like a crab, pinching healthy tissues as they grow.

614

Background

Facts and Figures Cancers are classified by the location in the body where they first develop or by the kind of tissue in which they originate. Carcinomas are tumors that begin in epithelial tissue. About 85 percent of malignant tumors are carcinomas. Sarcomas begin in connective tissue.

The treatment a patient receives is determined by the kind of the cancer and by how far the cancer has spread.

Treatment is considered to be successful only if every trace of the cancer is removed or destroyed. Surgery can only be completely successful if it is performed before the cancer has spread. Radiation can be used to deliver high energy rays to tissues that are deep inside the body, and chemotherapy can be used to destroy cancer cells that are spread throughout the body.

Tumor Formation As cancerous cells divide over and over, they often form abnormal tissue masses called **tumors.** Cancerous tumors invade the healthy tissue around them and destroy the tissue. Cancer cells can break away from a tumor and invade blood or lymph vessels. The blood or lymph then carries the cancer cells to other parts of the body, where they may begin to divide and form new tumors. Unless stopped by treatment, cancer progresses through the body.

Causes of Cancer Different factors may work together to determine what makes cells become cancerous. One such factor is the characteristics that people inherit from their parents. Because of their inherited characteristics, some people are more likely than others to develop certain kinds of cancer. For example, women whose mothers had breast cancer have a higher risk of developing breast cancer than do women with no family history of the disease.

Some substances or factors in the environment, called **carcinogens** (kahr SIN uh junz), can cause cancer. The tar in cigarette smoke is a carcinogen. Ultraviolet light, which is part of sunlight, can also be a carcinogen.

Cancer Treatment Surgery, drugs, and radiation are all used to treat cancer. If cancer is detected before it has spread, doctors remove the cancerous tumors through surgery. Sometimes, however, a surgeon can't remove all of the cancer. In some cases, drugs or radiation may be used to kill the cancer cells or slow their spread.

 INTEGRATING PHYSICS Radiation treatment uses high-energy waves to kill cancer cells. X-rays and gamma rays are two types of radiation used in cancer treatment. These waves are similar to sunlight and the

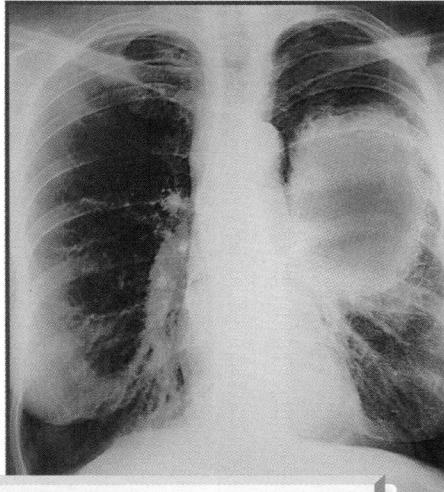

Figure 16 The large orange mass in the X-ray is a cancerous tumor in the lung. The graph shows leading types of cancer that affect men and women in the United States. *Interpreting Graphs Do more women or men develop lung cancer each year?*

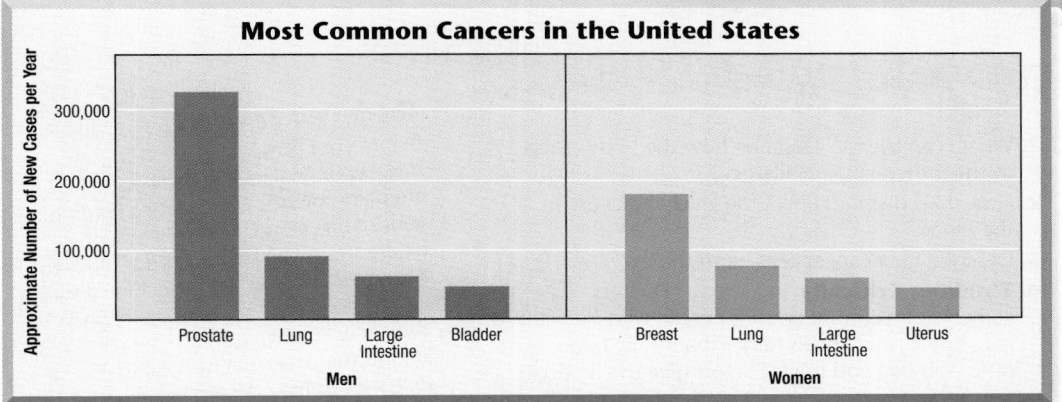

Most Common Cancers in the United States

Approximate Number of New Cases per Year

Men: Prostate, Lung, Large Intestine, Bladder
Women: Breast, Lung, Large Intestine, Uterus

Answers to Self-Assessment

✓ *Checkpoint*

Weight loss, excessive hunger or thirst, frequent urination, high glucose in blood

Caption Questions

Figure 15 The body does not produce enough insulin or the cells cannot use it properly.
Figure 16 More men

Building Inquiry Skills: Inferring

Ask students how tar, ultraviolet light, and other carcinogens damage cells to make them become cancerous. Ask: **What part of a cell does a carcinogen most likely damage to make the cell divide uncontrollably?** *(The nucleus, since it is the cell's control center and contains information that determines the cell's characteristics.)* Help students understand that carcinogens probably damage the complex molecules that determine a cell's characteristics. **learning modality: logical/ mathematical**

Integrating Physics

Tell students that radiation therapy may be applied to the body by implanting radioactive substances into tumors. Ask them to infer why this method would be better in some cases than using a machine like that shown in Figure 17. *(The radioactive substances could affect only the tumor, instead of affecting healthy cells as well.)* **learning modality: verbal**

Ongoing Assessment

Oral Presentation Ask students to choose a noninfectious disease and describe its causes and symptoms. *(Sample: Allergies are caused by an over-sensitive immune response to a foreign substance. Symptoms include burning eyes and sneezing.)*

3 Assess

Section 4 Review Answers

1. An allergy is a disorder in which the immune system is overly sensitive to a foreign substance. When lymphocytes encounter allergens, they produce antibodies that signal the body's cells to release histamine, which causes symptoms such as sneezing.

2. The level of glucose is elevated either because the body does not produce enough insulin or because the cells cannot use it. Therefore, the cells do not take in glucose from the blood.

3. Cancer cells multiply uncontrollably and form tumors that invade and destroy healthy tissue.

4. Eating small meals rather than large ones prevents the glucose level in the blood from changing too rapidly. A diabetic's body can better process a steady level of glucose than a few rapid increases.

Check Your Progress
CHAPTER PROJECT

Ask students to let you know about props or special lighting they need for their presentations. Set aside enough time for all presentations. Students may end their stories with the complete recovery or death of their patient, or they may announce that the disease is spreading to other people.

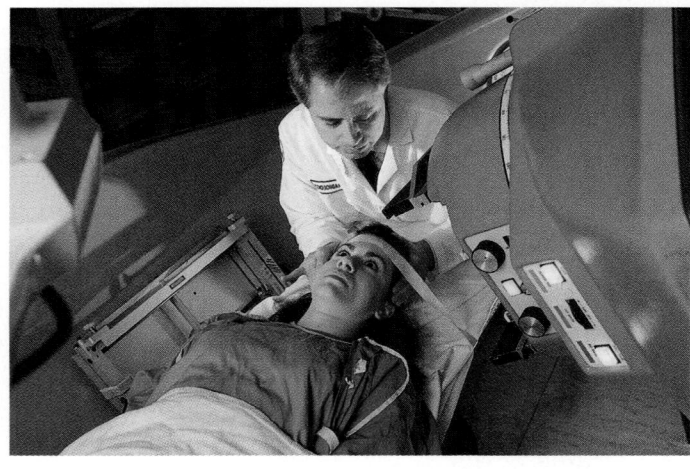

Figure 17 Radiation is one method that is used to treat cancer. The machine beams high-energy radiation at the tumor. This radiation kills cancer cells.

waves that make radios and microwave ovens work. However, X-rays and gamma rays have far more energy than sunlight, radio waves, or microwaves. When X-rays and gamma rays are aimed at tumors, they blast the cancer cells and kill them.

Cancer Prevention People can take steps to reduce their risk of developing cancer. For instance, they can avoid any form of tobacco, since tobacco and tobacco smoke contain carcinogens. Chewing tobacco and snuff contain carcinogens as well—they can cause cancers in the mouth. To prevent skin cancer, people can protect their skin from exposure to too much sunlight. A diet that is low in fat and includes plenty of fruits and vegetables can help people avoid some kinds of cancer, such as certain cancers of the digestive system.

Regular medical checkups are also important. Physicians or nurses may notice signs of cancer during a checkup. The earlier cancer is detected, the more likely it can be treated successfully.

Section 4 Review

1. What is an allergy? Describe how the body reacts to the presence of an allergen.
2. How does diabetes affect the level of glucose in the blood?
3. Describe how cancer cells harm the body.
4. **Thinking Critically** **Inferring** Doctors sometimes recommend that people with diabetes eat several small meals rather than three large ones. Why do you think doctors give this advice?

Check Your Progress
CHAPTER PROJECT

Before your presentation, make your final revisions. If you are doing broadcasts, practice reading your scripts aloud. Experiment with different ways of bringing your series to a dramatic ending. Try to include answers to questions that might occur to your audience. For instance, are people around the patient at risk of invasion? If so, how can they defend themselves?

Performance Assessment

Organizing Information Have students create concept maps titled *Noninfectious Diseases*. Make sure students include symptoms, treatments, and preventive measures for each disease.

 Students can save their concept maps in their portfolios.

Program Resources

◆ **Unit 4 Resources** 19-4 Review and Reinforce, p. 127; 19-4 Enrich, p. 128

SECTION 1 Infectious Disease

Key Ideas
◆ Infectious diseases are caused by pathogens: bacteria, viruses, fungi, and protists.
◆ Pathogens that infect humans can come from another person, a contaminated object, an animal bite, or the environment.

Key Terms
pathogen   infectious disease   pasteurization

SECTION 2 The Body's Defenses

Key Ideas
◆ The body has three lines of defense against pathogens.
◆ The immune system targets specific pathogens. T cells identify pathogens and distinguish one kind from another. B cells produce antibodies that destroy pathogens.
◆ HIV, the virus that causes AIDS, infects and destroys T cells.

Key Terms
inflammatory response   antigen
phagocyte   B cell
immune response   antibody
lymphocyte   AIDS
T cell

SECTION 3 Preventing Infectious Disease
INTEGRATING HEALTH

Key Ideas
◆ In active immunity, a person's own immune system produces antibodies. A person can acquire active immunity by having the disease or by being vaccinated.
◆ In passive immunity, the antibodies come from a source other than the person's body.

Key Terms
immunity   vaccination   passive immunity
active immunity   vaccine   antibiotic

SECTION 4 Noninfectious Disease

Key Ideas
◆ Noninfectious diseases are diseases that are not spread from person to person.
◆ An allergy is a disorder in which the immune system is overly sensitive to a foreign substance, called an allergen.
◆ In diabetes, the body does not produce enough insulin or can't use it properly.
◆ In cancer, cells multiply uncontrollably, destroying healthy tissues.

Key Terms
noninfectious disease   insulin
allergy   diabetes
allergen   tumor
histamine   carcinogen
asthma

Organizing Information

Flowchart Complete the flowchart, which shows what happens after tuberculosis bacteria begin to multiply in the lungs. (For more information on flowcharts, see the Skills Handbook.)

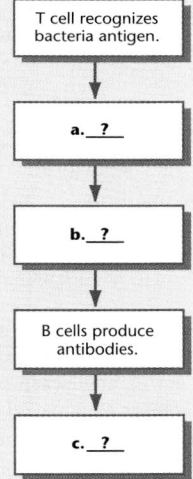

Organizing Information

Flowchart **a.** Some T cells attack pathogens. **b.** Other T cells signal B cells to produce antibodies specific to the antigen. **c.** Antibodies destroy the pathogenic bacteria.

Program Resources
◆ **Unit 4 Resources** Chapter 19 Project Scoring Rubric, p. 112
◆ **Performance Assessment** Chapter 19, pp. 59–61
◆ **Chapter and Unit Tests** Chapter 19 Test, pp. 88–91

Media and Technology
 Interactive Student Tutorial CD-ROM Chapter 19

 Computer Test Bank Chapter 19 Test

Reviewing Content
Multiple Choice
1. b 2. b 3. c 4. b 5. a

True or False
6. pathogens 7. true 8. phagocyte
9. true 10. true

Checking Concepts
11. During pasteurization, foods are heated to kill microorganisms. This process helps keep foods from causing food poisoning in humans.
12. The body has a natural system of barriers to keep pathogens out. The skin, breathing passages, mouth, and stomach trap and kill most pathogens.
13. B cells produce antibodies in response to specific antigens on pathogens; antibodies attach to antigens and prevent the pathogens from attacking cells.
14. Active immunity is a process in which antibodies are produced by a person's own immune system in response to the presence of an external pathogen. In passive immunity, though, antibodies that fight the pathogens come from a source other than the person's body. Vaccinations are an example of passive immunity.
15. Diabetes consists of insufficient insulin or the inability of cells to use insulin. This prevents the cells from properly absorbing and using glucose.
16. Inherited factors; exposure to environmental carcinogens.
17. Students should explain that carbolic acid kills organisms that can get into surgical wounds and cause infection.

Thinking Critically
18. Answers will vary. Answers can include clothing, operating table, surgical instruments, surgical gloves, and bandages.
19. No. Colds are not caused by sitting in chilly drafts, but by viruses.
20. Some T cells recognize antigens and signal B cells to produce antibodies. Other T cells kill pathogens directly. B cells produce antibodies to prevent pathogens from infecting cells.

Reviewing Content

 For more review of key concepts, see the Interactive Student Tutorial CD-ROM.

Multiple Choice
Choose the letter of the best answer.

1. Some pathogenic bacteria produce poisons called
   a. histamines.
   b. toxins.
   c. phagocytes.
   d. pathogens.
2. Antibodies are produced by
   a. phagocytes.
   b. B cells.
   c. T cells.
   d. pathogens.
3. Which disease is caused by HIV?
   a. diabetes
   b. flu
   c. AIDS
   d. tetanus
4. A chemical that kills bacteria or slows their growth without harming body cells is called a(n)
   a. pathogen
   b. antibiotic
   c. allergen
   d. histamine
5. A carcinogen causes
   a. cancer.
   b. colds.
   c. allergies.
   d. food poisoning.

True or False
If a statement is true, write true. If it is false, change the underlined word or words to make the statement true.

6. Bacteria, viruses, fungi, and protists are the major human <u>phagocytes</u>.
7. People can get Lyme disease and rabies from <u>animal bites</u>.
8. A <u>T cell</u> engulfs pathogens and destroys them.
9. Vaccination produces <u>active immunity</u>.
10. A <u>tumor</u> is a mass of cancer cells.

21. The immune system cannot fight HIV because the virus directly attacks T cells and weakens the body's immune response. When T cells are destroyed, the body is unable to produce antibodies or employ other immune defenses.
22. Weight loss, hunger, and weakness are all symptoms of diabetes that can be related to the inability of body cells to obtain enough glucose. Thirst and frequent urination are the results of the extra work the kidneys must perform to eliminate excess glucose from the blood.

Checking Concepts
11. Explain why pasteurization is important in food processing today.
12. Explain why it is difficult for pathogens to get to a part of the body in which they can cause disease.
13. What is the relationship between antigens and antibodies?
14. Explain the differences between active immunity and passive immunity. Then describe one way in which a person can acquire each type of immunity.
15. How does diabetes harm the body?
16. Identify two factors that can make a person likely to develop cancer.
17. **Writing to Learn** A patient of Joseph Lister is angry because Lister has covered her surgery wound with a bandage dipped in carbolic acid. The acid stings and the bandage is uncomfortable. Write a conversation between Lister and the patient in which Lister explains why she shouldn't take the bandage off.

Thinking Critically
18. **Inferring** Given all the sources of pathogens detailed in this chapter, name as many things as you can that must be sterilized in a hospital operating room.
19. **Applying Concepts** Can you catch a cold by sitting in a chilly draft? Explain.
20. **Comparing and Contrasting** Compare the functions of T cells and B cells.
21. **Relating Cause and Effect** Why can the immune system successfully fight most pathogens, but not HIV?
22. **Making Generalizations** If diabetes is not treated, the body cells of the diabetic person do not get enough glucose to function properly. List four symptoms of diabetes. Then explain how the lack of glucose can lead to each of the symptoms you listed.

Applying Skills
23. Students' graphs should show the temperature increasing to a peak in Week 1, remaining high in Week 2, then returning to normal in Weeks 3–5.
24. Week 3
25. Antibody levels rose during Week 2. As the antibody levels rise, the person's temperature returns to normal, and he or she begins to recover. This happens because of the effect the antibodies have on the bacteria that caused the illness.

Applying Skills

A person had an illness caused by bacteria. The table shows how the person's temperature and antibody level changed over the course of the disease. Use the table to answer Questions 23–25.

Week	Body Temperature (°C)	Antibody Level
0	37	low
1	39.8	low
2	39	medium
3	37	high
4	37	medium
5	37	low

23. Graphing Make a line graph of the temperature data. Label the horizontal axis "Week Number" and the vertical axis "Body Temperature."

24. Interpreting Data During what week did the person's temperature return to normal?

25. Drawing Conclusions When do antibody levels start to rise? What effect do antibodies have on the illness? Explain.

Performance CHAPTER PROJECT Assessment

Present Your Project Now you can share your news series with your classmates. Before your presentation, make sure any sound effects and props support the story.

Reflect and Record In your notebook, reflect on what you learned by using your imagination to explore a science topic. Did it help you to better understand how the body fights disease? What new information did you learn from presentations made by other groups? If you had your project to do over, what would you do differently?

Performance CHAPTER PROJECT Assessment

Present Your Project If possible, allow students time to rehearse their presentations before presenting them to the class. You may want to have students perform their news reports for the class, or present written reports or audio or videotapes. Set aside enough time for all students to make their presentations.

Reflect and Record Encourage students to describe what parts of the project helped them to understand the body's defenses against disease. Some students may have had difficulty using the format of a news report, while others may have found that it helped them ask relevant questions and organize information. Have students identify questions they have after completing the project.

Test Preparation

Use these questions to prepare for standardized tests.

Use the information to answer Questions 26–28. A Glucose Tolerance Test is used to determine whether a person may have diabetes. A doctor gives a patient a sugar drink (at time 0) and measures the blood glucose level every 30 minutes for two hours. The graph below reveals that Person A is normal, while Person B has diabetes.

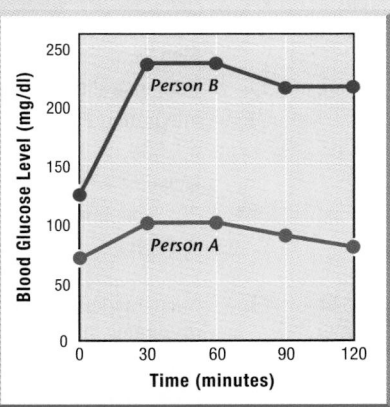

26. What would be the best title for this graph?
  a. How Blood Glucose Levels Rise Over Time
  b. Blood Glucose Levels in a Diabetic and a Non-Diabetic
  c. Normal Blood Glucose Levels
  d. How to Measure Blood Glucose Levels

27. According to the graph, which of the following statements is true?
  a. Person A's starting glucose level is higher than Person B's.
  b. Person A's glucose level rose quickly and then fell to near the starting level.
  c. Person B's glucose level rose quickly and then fell to near the starting level.
  d. Person A's blood glucose level was highest after 90 minutes.

28. What is the name of the hormone that normally controls blood glucose levels?
  a. estrogen   **c.** insulin
  b. testosterone   **d.** collagen

Chapter 19 **619**

Test Preparation
26. b **27.** b **28.** c

Program Resources

◆ **Inquiry Skills Activity Book** Provides teaching and review of all inquiry skills

CHAPTER 20 Nervous System

Sections	Time	Student Edition Activities	Other Activities	
CHAPTER PROJECT **Tricks and Illusions** p. 621	Ongoing (2 weeks)	Check Your Progress, pp. 634, 643, 652 Present Your Project, p. 655		
1 How the Nervous System Works pp. 622–627 ◆ Identify the functions of the nervous system. ◆ Describe the structure of a neuron. ◆ List the three types of neurons and tell how a nerve impulse travels.	$1\frac{1}{2}$ periods/ 1 block	**Discover** How Simple Is a Simple Task?, p. 622 **Science at Home,** p. 626 **Skills Lab: Designing Experiments** Ready or Not, p. 627	TE TE	Building Inquiry Skills: Relating Cause and Effect, p. 623 Inquiry Challenge, p. 624
2 Divisions of the Nervous System pp. 628–635 ◆ Identify the function of the central nervous system, describe its parts, and explain how to keep it safe from injury. ◆ Identify the functions of the peripheral nervous system and its parts. ◆ Describe a reflex. ◆ List activities that can harm the nervous system, and describe how to protect the nervous system.	2 periods/ 1 block	**Discover** How Does Your Knee React?, p. 628 **Sharpen Your Skills** Controlling Variables, p. 630	TE TE	Inquiry Challenge, p. 629 Building Inquiry Skills: Making Models, p. 631
3 The Senses pp. 636–643 ◆ Name the senses and state the overall function performed by the senses. ◆ Describe how eyes enable people to see. ◆ Describe how people hear sounds and maintain balance. ◆ Describe how people experience the senses of touch, taste, and smell.	2 periods/ 1 block	**Discover** What's in the Bag?, p. 636 **Try This** Why Do You Need Two Eyes?, p. 637 **Try This** Tick! Tick! Tick!, p. 640 **Sharpen Your Skills** Designing Experiments, p. 642	TE TE TE TE LM	Building Inquiry Skills: Observing, p. 637; Making Models, p. 641 Demonstration, p. 638 Integrating Physics, pp. 638, 640 Including All Students, p. 639 20, "Locating Touch Receptors"
4 INTEGRATING HEALTH **Alcohol and Other Drugs** pp. 644–652 ◆ Name some commonly abused drugs and state how they affect the body. ◆ Explain how alcohol abuse harms the body.	3 periods/ $1\frac{1}{2}$ blocks	**Discover** How Can You Best Say No?, p. 644 **Sharpen Your Skills** Communicating, p. 646 **Real-World Lab: You, the Consumer** With Caffeine or Without?, pp. 648–649	TE TE TE TE	Building Inquiry Skills: Communicating, p. 645 Demonstration, p. 646 Building Inquiry Skills: Measuring, p. 650 Building Inquiry Skills: Communicating, p. 651
Study Guide/Chapter Assessment pp. 653–655	1 period/ $\frac{1}{2}$ block		ISAB	Provides teaching and review of all inquiry skills

For Standard or Block Schedule The Resource Pro® CD-ROM gives you maximum flexibility for planning your instruction for any type of schedule. Resource Pro® contains Planning Express®, an advanced scheduling program, as well as the entire contents of the Teaching Resources and the Computer Test Bank.

CHAPTER PLANNING GUIDE

Program Resources	Assessment Strategies	Media and Technology
UR Chapter 20 Project Teacher Notes, pp. 134–135 **UR** Chapter 20 Project Overview and Worksheets, pp. 136–139	**SE** Performance Assessment: Present Your Project, p. 655 **TE** Check Your Progress, pp. 634, 643, 652 **UR** Chapter 20 Project Scoring Rubric, p. 140	Science Explorer Internet Site at www.phschool.com
UR 20-1 Lesson Plan, p. 141 **UR** 20-1 Section Summary, p. 142 **UR** 20-1 Review and Reinforce, p. 143 **UR** 20-1 Enrich, p. 144 **UR** Chapter 20 Skills Lab, pp. 157–158	**SE** Section 1 Review, p. 626 **TE** Ongoing Assessment, pp. 623, 625 **TE** Performance Assessment, p. 626	Life Science Videotape 4; Videodisc Unit 4 Side 1, "Quick Reflexes" Audio CD, English-Spanish Summary 20-1 Transparency 73, "Exploring the Path of a Nerve Impulse" Interactive Student Tutorial CD-ROM, Chapter 20
UR 20-2 Lesson Plan, p. 145 **UR** 20-2 Section Summary, p. 146 **UR** 20-2 Review and Reinforce, p. 147 **UR** 20-2 Enrich, p. 148	**SE** Section 2 Review, p. 634 **TE** Ongoing Assessment, pp. 629, 631, 633 **TE** Performance Assessment, p. 634	Life Science Videotape 4; Videodisc Unit 4 Side 1, "Quick Reflexes" Audio CD, English-Spanish Summary 20-2 Transparency 74, "The Brain"
UR 20-3 Lesson Plan, p. 149 **UR** 20-3 Section Summary, p. 150 **UR** 20-3 Review and Reinforce, p. 151 **UR** 20-3 Enrich, p. 152	**SE** Section 3 Review, p. 643 **TE** Ongoing Assessment, pp. 637, 639, 641 **TE** Performance Assessment, p. 643	Audio CD, English-Spanish Summary 20-3 Transparency 75, "The Eye" Transparency 76, "The Ear"
UR 20-4 Lesson Plan, p. 153 **UR** 20-4 Section Summary, p. 154 **UR** 20-4 Review and Reinforce, p. 155 **UR** 20-4 Enrich, p. 156 **UR** Chapter 20 Real-World Lab, pp. 159–161	**SE** Section 4 Review, p. 652 **TE** Ongoing Assessment, p. 645, 647, 651 **TE** Performance Assessment, p. 652	Audio CD, English-Spanish Summary 20-4
RCA Provides strategies to improve science reading skills **GSW** Provides worksheets to promote student comprehension of content	**SE** Chapter 20 Study Guide/Assessment, pp. 653–655 **PA** Chapter 20 Performance Assessment, pp. 62–64 **CUT** Chapter 20 Test, pp. 92–95 **CTB** Chapter 20 Test	Interactive Student Tutorial CD-ROM, Chapter 20 Computer Test Bank, Chapter 20 Test

Key: **SE** Student Edition
CTB Computer Test Bank
ISAB Inquiry Skills Activity Book
GSW Guided Study Worksheets

TE Teacher's Edition
PTA Product Testing Activities by *Consumer Reports*
RCA Reading in the Content Area
PA Performance Assessment

UR Unit Resources
LM Laboratory Manual
IES Interdisciplinary Explorations Series
CUT Chapter and Unit Tests

Meeting the National Science Education Standards and AAAS Benchmarks

National Science Education Standards	Benchmarks for Science Literacy	Unifying Themes
Science as Inquiry (Content Standard A) ◆ **Design and conduct a scientific investigation** Students design a test on people's responses to optical illusions. *(Chapter Project)* Students investigate how time of day affects reaction time. *(Skills Lab)* ◆ **Think critically and logically to make the relationships between evidence and explanations** Students draw conclusions about the effect of stimulants on water fleas. *(Real-World Lab; Chapter Project)* **Life Science** (Content Standard C) ◆ **Structure and function in living systems** The nervous system has specialized cells that allow it to receive information, respond to information, and maintain homeostasis. *(Sections 1, 2)* ◆ **Regulation and behavior** The nervous system maintains stable body conditions. *(Section 1)* The nervous system uses senses to receive information about the environment. The brain processes this information to help humans survive. *(Sections 2, 3; Chapter Project)* **Science in Personal and Social Perspectives** (Content Standard F) ◆ **Personal health** Abusing drugs and alcohol can cause both short-term and long-term damage to a person's health. *(Sections 2, 3, 4; Real-World Lab)* ◆ **Risks and benefits** Students debate whether bicycle helmet laws should be enacted to protect people from injury. *(Science and Society)*	**1C Scientific Inquiry** Students ensure that variables are controlled in experiments examining optical illusions, nervous system reaction time, and the effects of stimulants. *(Chapter Project; Skills Lab; Real-World Lab)* **5C Cells** Nerve cells have dendrites and axons, which are structures that differentiate them from other body cells. *(Section 1)* **6C Basic Functions** The central nervous system processes information that it receives from the peripheral nervous system. All body responses, including learning and thought, result from this function. *(Sections 2, 3; Chapter Project; Skills Lab)* **6D Learning** The brain is divided into three sections; of these, the cerebrum is responsible for the processes that allow humans to learn and remember. *(Section 2)* **6E Physical Health** Injury to the brain or spinal cord can cause severe damage or death; protecting your head with a helmet is one way to minimize the possibility of brain injury. *(Section 2; Science and Society)* Alcohol and other drugs are toxic substances that alter the responses of the nervous system and can cause permanent damage to body systems. *(Section 4; Real-World Lab)*	◆ **Scale and Structure** The nervous system is made up of two parts—the central and peripheral nervous systems. Neurons are the specialized cells of the nervous system. *(Sections 1, 2)* ◆ **Systems and Interactions** Sensory neurons, interneurons, and motor neurons respond to stimuli that affect the senses as well as stimuli within the body. The nervous system controls reaction time; reflexes; the processing of information, such as optical illusions; and the regulation of body systems. Alcohol and other drugs can interfere with the interaction of the nervous system. *(Sections 1, 2, 3, 4; Chapter Project; Skills Lab; Real-World Lab)* ◆ **Stability** The nervous system controls homeostasis of the body. Damage to the nervous system, through drug and alcohol use or injury, upsets the body's stability. *(Sections 1, 4; Real-World Lab; Science and Society)*

Take It to the Net

 *Interactive text at www.phschool.com*

Science Explorer comes alive with iText.

- **Complete student text** is accessible from any computer with Internet access or a CD-ROM drive.
- **Animations, simulations, and videos** enhance student understanding and retention of concepts.
- **Self-tests and online study tools** assess student understanding.

STAY CURRENT with **SCIENCE NEWS®**

Find out the latest research and information about human biology and health at: **www.phschool.com**

Go to **www.phschool.com** and click on the Science icon. Then click on Science Explorer: Life, Earth, and Physical Science under PH@school.

ACTIVITY	Time (minutes)	Materials Quantities for one work group	Skills
Section 1			
Discover, p. 622	15	**Consumable** paper **Nonconsumable** pencil, penny	Inferring
Science at Home, p. 626	home	**Nonconsumable** salt and pepper shakers	Observing
Skills Lab, p. 627	50	**Nonconsumable** meter stick	Designing Experiments
Section 2			
Discover, p. 628	10	No special materials are required.	Inferring
Sharpen Your Skills, p. 630	45	**Nonconsumable** tape player, cassette tape of soft music	Controlling Variables
Section 3			
Discover, p. 636	20	**Nonconsumable** opaque paper bags; small objects, such as erasers, pens, paper clips, sponge, cotton balls, marbles, plastic spoons, bottle caps, coins, buttons	Observing
Try This, p. 637	15	**Nonconsumable** drinking straw, pipe cleaner	Inferring
Try This, p. 640	15	**Nonconsumable** ticking watch, metric ruler	Measuring
Sharpen Your Skills, p. 642	15	**Consumable** peeled pear, apple, and raw potato	Designing Experiments
Section 4			
Discover, p. 644	15	**Nonconsumable** pieces of wrapped candy	Inferring
Sharpen Your Skills, p. 646	45	**Consumable** paper **Nonconsumable** drawing materials	Communicating
Real-World Lab, pp. 648–649	40	**Consumable** noncarbonated spring water, blackworms *(Lumbriculus)*, adrenaline solution (about 0.01%), beverages with and without caffeine **Nonconsumable** plastic dropper, paraffin block, stopwatch or clock with second hand	Developing Hypotheses, Designing Experiments

A list of all materials required for the Student Edition activities can be found on pages T25–T33. You can obtain information about ordering materials by calling 1-800-848-9500 or by accessing the Science Explorer Internet site at **www.phschool.com**.

Tricks and Illusions

Sensory illusions, such as optical illusions, provide an opportunity to study how sensory information is interpreted by the brain. Note: If a person stares at the chapter opener long enough, a scallop shell seems to pop from the page.

Purpose In this project, students will observe their own responses to several illusions and choose at least one to investigate. During a science fair, they will record participants' responses to the illusion. Afterward, they will present their results to the class. This project will give students the opportunity to consider how their senses work and learn that, despite variations, people experience a shared sensory world.

Skills Focus After completing the project, students will be able to
◆ predict typical responses and observe their own responses and those of others to simple illusions;
◆ create a data table to record responses to a particular illusion;
◆ set up an illusion and present it to other students;
◆ create graphs or tables to interpret data and draw conclusions;
◆ communicate the results of their experiment to the class.

Project Time Line The entire project will require about two weeks. The first week will be devoted to trying out and selecting illusions. The second week will involve holding the science fair, gathering data, and presenting results. Class time will be needed for trying out the illusions, for the science fair, and for presentations. Before beginning the project, see Chapter 20 Project Teacher Notes on pages 134–135 in Unit 4 Resources for more details on carrying out the project. Also distribute the Chapter 20 Project Overview, Worksheets, and Scoring Rubric on pages 136–140 in Unit 4 Resources.

Suggested Shortcuts You can simplify the project by choosing a variety of illusions and setting them up in stations around the classroom. To save time, students could test these illusions on

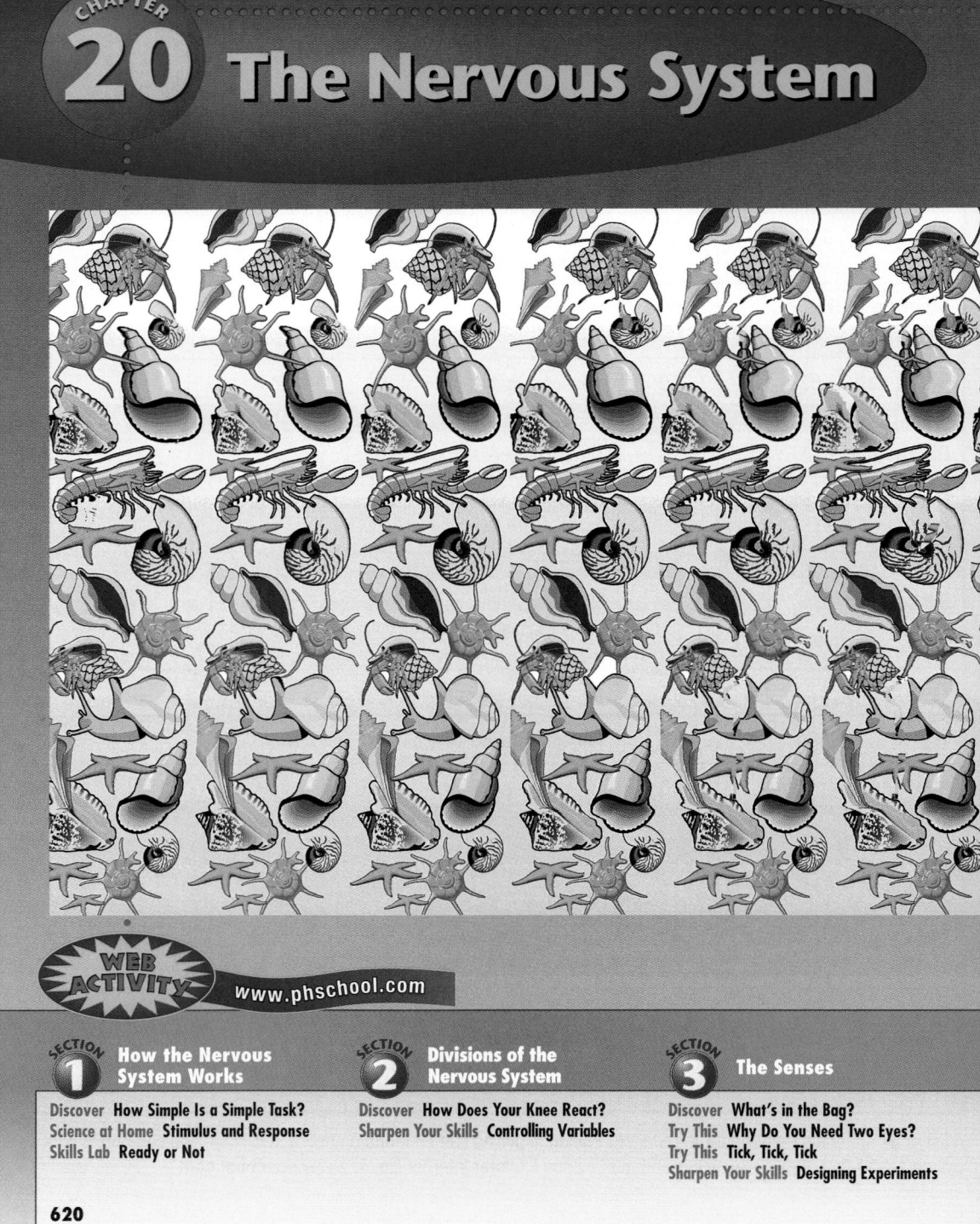

20 The Nervous System

WEB ACTIVITY www.phschool.com

SECTION 1 How the Nervous System Works

Discover **How Simple Is a Simple Task?**
Science at Home **Stimulus and Response**
Skills Lab **Ready or Not**

SECTION 2 Divisions of the Nervous System

Discover **How Does Your Knee React?**
Sharpen Your Skills **Controlling Variables**

SECTION 3 The Senses

Discover **What's in the Bag?**
Try This **Why Do You Need Two Eyes?**
Try This **Tick, Tick, Tick**
Sharpen Your Skills **Designing Experiments**

620

each other during one class period and report on their findings during another.

Possible Materials Materials will vary, depending on the illusions chosen. You can minimize the need for complicated materials by selecting simple illusions for students to use. Alternatively, you may wish to have students obtain materials as a requirement of successfully completing the project.

Some good reference books for this project include *You Won't Believe Your Eyes!* by Catherine O'Neill Grace; *Science, Art and Visual Illusions* by Robert Froman; *How to Really Fool Yourself: Illusions for All Your Senses* by Vicki Cobb; *Illusions: A Journey Into Perception* by Patricia Ann Rainey; and *Optricks* by Melinda Wentzell and D. K. Holland.

Launching the Project To introduce the project and to stimulate student interest, have students play the game of "gossip." Ask one student to start the gossip line by reading in a whisper the following message to a second student: "If a rabbit runs twice around the school, then puts butter on its ears, it will

CHAPTER 20 PROJECT

Tricks and Illusions

Can you be sure of what you see, hear, smell, taste, or touch? In this chapter, you'll learn how you experience your environment through your senses. You'll see how the senses send information to your nervous system and how your brain interprets the messages.

But things aren't always what they seem. For example, an optical illusion is a picture or other visual effect that tricks you into seeing something incorrectly. In this project, you'll investigate how your senses can sometimes be fooled by illusions.

Your Goal To set up a science fair booth to demonstrate how different people respond to one or more illusions.

To complete this project, you must
- try out a variety of illusions, including some that involve the senses of hearing or touch as well as sight
- select one or more illusions, and set up an experiment to monitor people's responses to the illusions
- learn why the illusions fool the senses
- follow the safety guidelines in Appendix A

Get Started In a small group, discuss optical illusions or other illusions that you know about. Look in books to learn about others. Try them out. Which illusions would make an interesting experiment? How could you set up such an experiment at a science fair?

Check Your Progress You'll be working on this project as you study this chapter. To keep your project on track, look for Check Your Progress boxes at the following points.
Section 2 Review, page 634: Plan the experiment you will perform.
Section 3 Review, page 643: Carry out your experiment.
Section 4 Review, page 652: Explain why the illusions trick the senses.

Present Your Project At the end of the chapter (page 655), be prepared to share your findings with your classmates. Then explain how your illusions work.

Now you see it. Now you don't. Sometimes your eyes can play tricks on you. The picture shows rows of seashells and sea animals. Or does it?

Stare at the picture for several seconds, as if it were far away. The picture should look slightly out of focus. After a while, does anything seem to pop out from the picture?

SECTION 4
Integrating Health
Alcohol and Other Drugs

Discover **How Can You Best Say No?**
Sharpen Your Skills **Communicating**
Real-World Lab **With Caffeine or Without?**

621

---

grow green fur." The second student should whisper what was heard to a third, and so on throughout the class. Have every fifth person quietly write down what the message sounded like so students can later see what changes occurred as the message was passed around the room. After the last student says the message aloud and it is compared with the original and with each written version, discuss with students how the mind uses information gathered by the senses and then "makes sense" of it.

Allow time for students to read the description of the project in their text and the Chapter Project Overview on pages 136–137 in Unit 4 Resources. Then discuss with students whether they must research their own illusions or whether you will provide them with a selection of illusions to choose from. Also, answer any initial questions that students may have. Distribute copies of the Chapter 20 Project Worksheets on pages 138–139 in Unit 4 Resources for students to review.

Performance Assessment

The Chapter 20 Project Scoring Rubric on page 140 of Unit 4 Resources will help you evaluate how well students complete the Chapter 20 Project. Students will be assessed on
- their research (if appropriate) and selection of an appropriate illusion;
- their design of data sheets to record responses;
- their participation in and gathering of data during the science fair;
- their class presentation of their results.

By sharing the Chapter 20 Project Scoring Rubric with students at the beginning of the project, you will make it clear to them what they are expected to do.

Program Resources

◆ **Unit 4 Resources** Chapter 20 Project Teacher Notes, pp. 134–135; Chapter 20 Project Overview and Worksheets, pp. 136–139; Chapter 20 Project Scoring Rubric, p. 140

WEB ACTIVITY www.phschool.com

You will find an Internet activity, chapter self-tests for students, and links to other chapter topics at this site.

SECTION
1 How the Nervous System Works

Objectives

After completing the lesson, students will be able to

◆ identify the functions of the nervous system;

◆ describe the structure of a neuron;

◆ list the three types of neurons and tell how a nerve impulse travels.

Key Terms stimulus, response, neuron, nerve impulse, dendrite, axon, nerve, sensory neuron, interneuron, motor neuron, synapse

1 Engage/Explore

Activating Prior Knowledge

Ask students: **What does it mean when someone says that something makes them nervous?** *(Students may say it means that a person is anxious or worried about something.)* Explain that anxiety and worry are different ways in which people react to their environment. Point out that the nervous system allows people to react to their environment.

•••••••• DISCOVER ••••••••

Skills Focus inferring
Materials *paper, pencil, penny*
Time 15 minutes
Tips Remind students to follow directions carefully as they complete the activity.
Think It Over Sample: Sense organs used include eyes and skin. Muscle movements include the muscles of the arms and hands holding the penny down, moving the penny from place to place, picking up the pencil, and tracing the circle. Thought processes involved include reading and understanding the instructions, choosing where to place the penny, and following the sequence of numbers.

DISCOVER

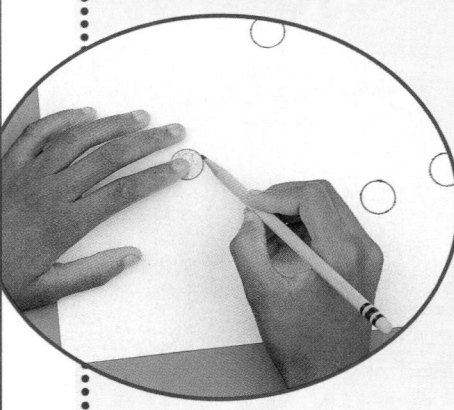

How Simple Is a Simple Task?

1. Trace the outline of a penny in twelve different places on a piece of paper.

2. Number the circles from 1 through 12. Write the numbers randomly, in no particular order.

3. Now pick up the penny again. Put it in each circle, one after another, in numerical order, beginning with 1 and ending with 12.

Think it Over

Inferring Make a list of all the sense organs, muscle movements, and thought processes in this activity. Compare your list with your classmates' lists. What organ system coordinated all the different processes involved in this task?

GUIDE FOR READING

◆ What are the functions of the nervous system?

◆ What are the three types of neurons and how do they interact?

Reading Tip Before you read, preview *Exploring the Path of a Nerve Impulse* on page 625. List any unfamiliar terms. Then, as you read, write a definition for each term.

The drums roll, and the crowd suddenly becomes silent. The people in the audience hold their breaths as the tightrope walker begins his long and dangerous journey across the wire. High above the circus floor, he inches along, slowly but steadily. One wrong movement could mean disaster.

To keep from slipping, tightrope performers need excellent coordination and a keen sense of balance. In addition, they must remember what they have learned from years of practice.

Even though you aren't a tightrope walker, you also need coordination, a sense of balance, memory, and the ability to learn. Your nervous system carries out all those functions. The nervous system consists of the brain, spinal cord, and nerves that run throughout the body. It also includes sense organs such as the eyes and ears.

622

READING STRATEGIES

Reading Tip Students may recognize sensory as being related to the senses, but most other terms will likely be unfamiliar. As students preview *Exploring the Path of a Nerve Impulse* and list unfamiliar terms, encourage them to also list questions they have about receptors, nerve impulses, sensory neurons, interneurons, and motor neurons. As students read the section, have them write answers to their questions.

Suggest students research to find information for any unanswered questions.

Study and Comprehension After students finish reading, have them review the section and jot down the main points and important details. Then have students use these notes to write summaries of the functions of the nervous system and the interactions among neurons.

Jobs of the Nervous System

The Internet lets people gather information from anywhere in the world with the click of a button. Like the Internet, your nervous system is a communications network. Your nervous system is much more efficient, however.

The nervous system receives information about what is happening both inside and outside your body. It also directs the way in which your body responds to this information. In addition, your nervous system helps maintain homeostasis. Without your nervous system, you could not move, think, feel pain, or taste a spicy taco.

Receiving Information Because of your nervous system, you are aware of what is happening in the environment around you. For example, you know that a soccer ball is zooming toward you, that the wind is blowing, or that a friend is telling a funny joke. Your nervous system also checks conditions inside your body, such as the level of glucose in your blood.

Responding to Information Any change or signal in the environment that can make an organism react is a **stimulus** (STIM yoo lus)(plural *stimuli*). A zooming soccer ball is a stimulus. After your nervous system analyzes the stimulus, it causes a response. A **response** is what your body does in reaction to a stimulus—you kick the ball toward the goal.

Some nervous system responses, such as kicking a ball, are voluntary, or under your control. However, many processes necessary for life, such as heartbeat rate, are controlled by involuntary actions of the nervous system.

Maintaining Homeostasis The nervous system helps maintain homeostasis by directing the body to respond appropriately to the information it receives. For example, when you are hungry, your nervous system directs you to eat. This action maintains homeostasis by supplying your body with nutrients and energy it needs.

☑ *Checkpoint* What is a stimulus?

The Neuron—A Message-Carrying Cell

The cells that carry information through your nervous system are called **neurons** (NOO rahnz), or nerve cells. The message that a neuron carries is called a **nerve impulse.** The structure of a neuron enables it to carry nerve impulses.

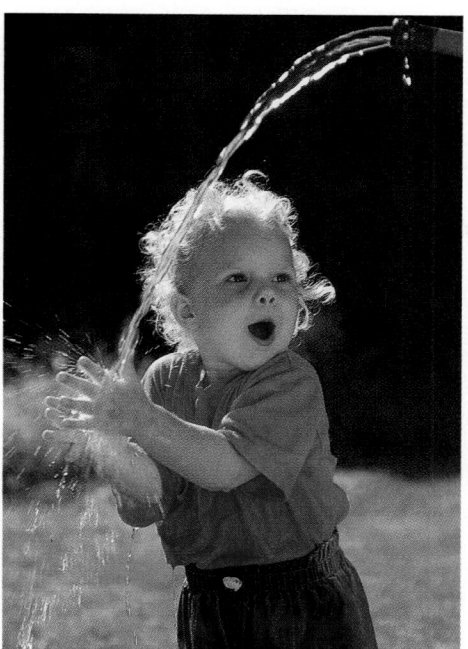

Figure 1 The sparkling water is a stimulus. This toddler responds by thrusting her hands into the water and splashing.

Program Resources

◆ **Unit 4 Resources** 20-1 Lesson Plan, p. 141; 20-1 Section Summary, p. 142

Media and Technology

 Audio CD English-Spanish Summary 20-1

Answers to Self-Assessment

☑ *Checkpoint*

A stimulus is a change or signal in the environment that can make an organism react to it.

2 *Facilitate*

Jobs of the Nervous System

Building Inquiry Skills: Relating Cause and Effect

Materials *lemon wedge, vinegar, rubber ball, assorted materials*
Time 10 minutes

Have students identify the stimuli and responses in several brief activities by recording what information the nervous system receives and how it responds. Make sure students wash their hands before and after tasting any food items. Some activities include:

◆ tasting a lemon wedge *(stimulus—sour taste, wet and cold feeling; response— mouth fills with saliva)*
◆ smelling vinegar *(stimulus—sour smell; response—nose wrinkles)*
◆ bouncing and then catching a ball *(stimulus—speed and direction of ball; response—catching the ball)*
learning modality: kinesthetic

The Neuron—A Message-Carrying Cell

Including All Students

Some students may be confused by the terms *nerve cell, nerve, neuron,* and *nerve fiber.* Emphasize that a nerve cell is the same as a neuron, but not the same as a nerve or a nerve fiber. Explain that a nerve fiber can be either an axon or a dendrite, and that a nerve is composed of many axons, dendrites, or both. **limited English proficiency**

Ongoing Assessment

Oral Presentation Have each student name the three jobs of the nervous system and give one example of each job.

The Neuron—A Message-Carrying Cell, continued

Using the Visuals: Figure 2

Help students understand the neuron. Point out that there are many dendrites, but only one axon, which splits into two branches. Explain that even though the dendrites in this illustration are shorter than the axon, this is not always the case. You might tell students that the sausage-shaped coverings of the axon are a material called myelin; also point out that not all axons are covered with this material. Finally, have students use their fingers to trace the path of a nerve impulse from dendrites to cell body to axon. **learning modality: visual**

Inquiry Challenge

Materials *notecards, markers*

Time 10 minutes

Organize the class into three groups. Assign each group to portray a type of neuron—sensory neurons, interneurons, and motor neurons. Challenge students to write notes to represent nerve impulses and model how nerve impulses are sent through the human body. *(Students in the role of sensory neurons should write notes describing stimuli to students representing interneurons. Interneurons should pass the notes to students playing motor neurons, who should write notes describing responses. Sample: Touching a hot stove. Sensory neurons—the stove is hot; interneurons pass this on; motor neurons—remove hand from stove.)* Make sure students understand the difference between the nerve impulse and the neurons, and can distinguish between different types of neurons. Have a reporter from each group share the group's results with the class. **cooperative learning**

The Structure of a Neuron A neuron has a large cell body that contains the nucleus. The cell body has threadlike extensions. One kind of extension, a **dendrite,** carries impulses toward the cell body. An **axon** carries impulses away from the cell body. Nerve impulses begin in a dendrite, move toward the cell body, and then move down the axon. A neuron can have many dendrites, but it has only one axon. An axon, however, can have more than one tip, so the impulse can go to more than one other cell.

Axons and dendrites are sometimes called nerve fibers. Nerve fibers are often arranged in parallel bundles covered with connective tissue, something like a package of uncooked spaghetti wrapped in cellophane. A bundle of nerve fibers is called a **nerve.**

Kinds of Neurons Different kinds of neurons perform different functions. **Three kinds of neurons are found in the body—sensory neurons, interneurons, and motor neurons. Together they make up a chain of nerve cells that carry an impulse through the nervous system.** *Exploring the Path of a Nerve Impulse* shows how these three kinds of neurons work together.

A **sensory neuron** picks up stimuli from the internal or external environment and converts each stimulus into a nerve impulse. The impulse travels along the sensory neuron until it reaches an interneuron, usually in the brain or spinal cord. An **interneuron** is a neuron that carries nerve impulses from one neuron to another. Some interneurons pass impulses from sensory neurons to motor neurons. A **motor neuron** sends an impulse to a muscle, and the muscle contracts in response.

✓ *Checkpoint* *What is the function of an axon?*

Figure 2 A neuron, or nerve cell, has one axon and many dendrites that extend from the cell body. The dendrites carry a nerve message toward the cell body, and the axon carries the message away from the cell body. *Applying Concepts How many axons can a neuron have?*

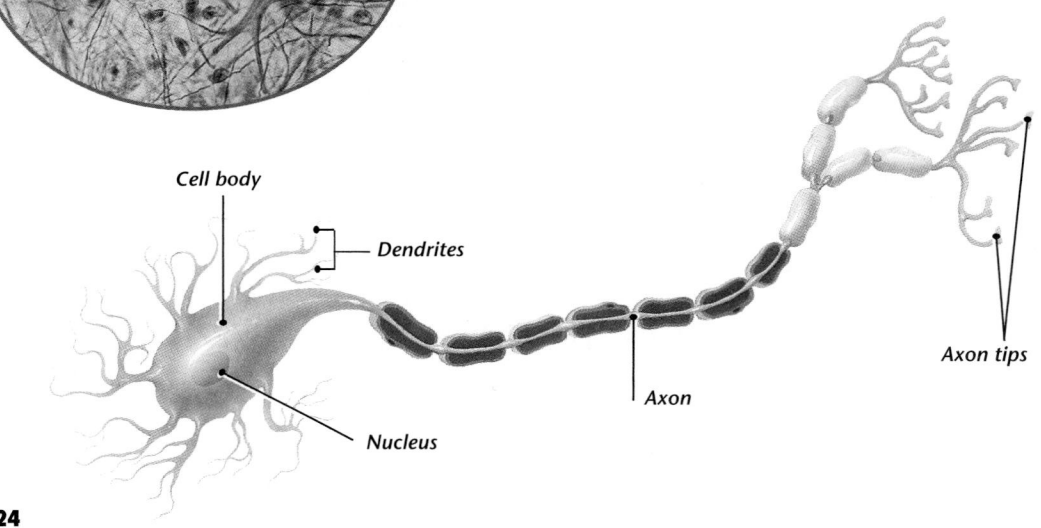

Cell body

Dendrites

Nucleus

Axon

Axon tips

624

EXPLORING the Path of a Nerve Impulse

When you hear the phone ring, you pick it up to answer it. Many sensory neurons, interneurons, and motor neurons are involved in this action.

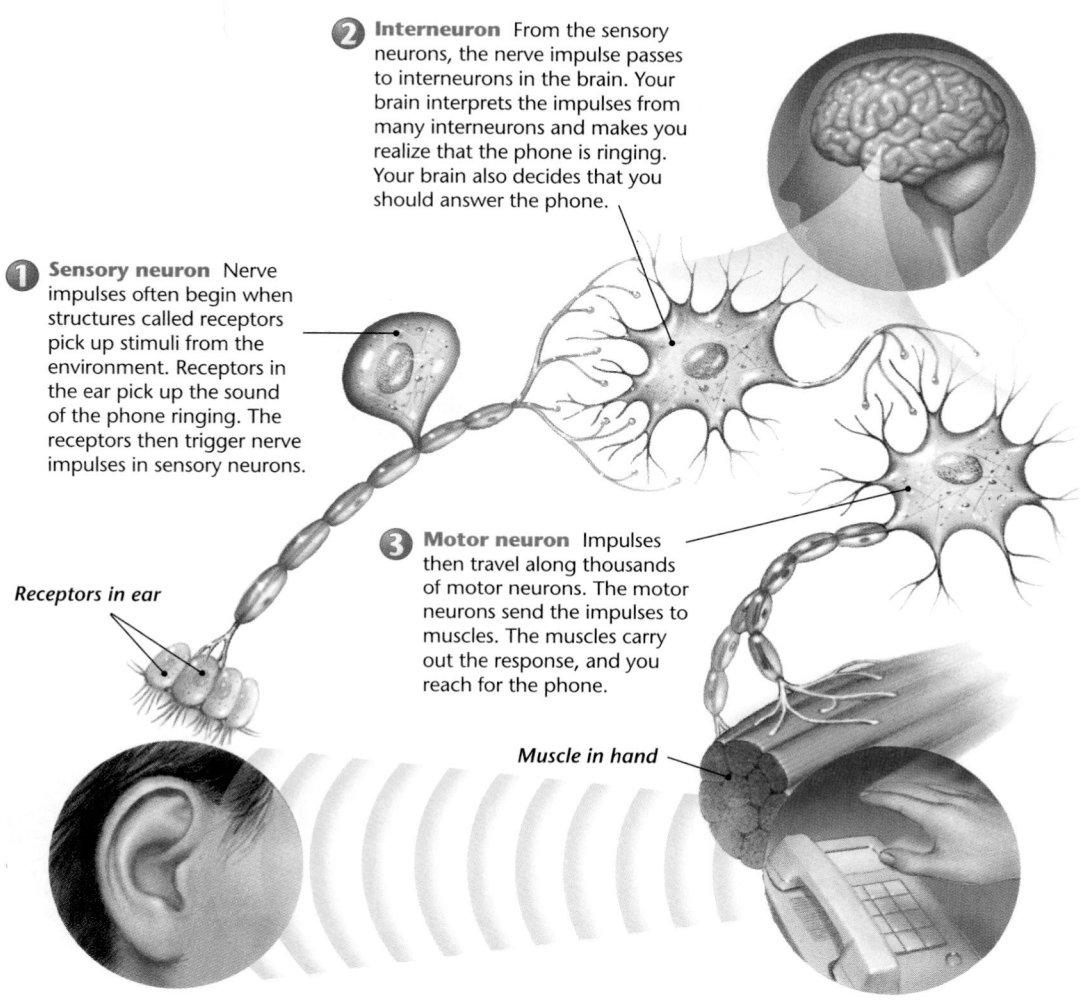

2 **Interneuron** From the sensory neurons, the nerve impulse passes to interneurons in the brain. Your brain interprets the impulses from many interneurons and makes you realize that the phone is ringing. Your brain also decides that you should answer the phone.

1 **Sensory neuron** Nerve impulses often begin when structures called receptors pick up stimuli from the environment. Receptors in the ear pick up the sound of the phone ringing. The receptors then trigger nerve impulses in sensory neurons.

Receptors in ear

3 **Motor neuron** Impulses then travel along thousands of motor neurons. The motor neurons send the impulses to muscles. The muscles carry out the response, and you reach for the phone.

Muscle in hand

EXPLORING the Path of a Nerve Impulse

Have students use the visual essay to study the path of a nerve impulse from a sensory neuron to a motor neuron. Ask: **Which kind of nerve fiber picks up the stimulus from the receptors?** *(dendrites)* Then ask: **Which kind of nerve fiber causes the muscles to contract?** *(axons)* Point out that there would be a tiny space between the motor neuron's axon tips and the muscle fibers. Have students trace the path of the nerve impulse, identifying the stimulus to which each kind of neuron responds. *(Sensory neurons respond to the ringing sound of the phone. Interneurons respond to impulses from sensory neurons. Motor neurons respond to impulses from interneurons.)*
Extend Have students measure on their bodies the distance the nerve impulse travels from the ear, to the brain, and to the hand. **learning modality: visual**

Answers to Self-Assessment
Caption Question
Figure 2 Each neuron has one axon.

 Checkpoint
An axon carries a nerve impulse away from the cell body.

Ongoing Assessment

Writing Have students make flowcharts that explain how a nerve impulse is transmitted through the body. *(Students' flowcharts should include a stimulus that is detected by receptors, which then trigger nerve impulses in sensory neurons. The sensory neuron passes the impulse to an interneuron, usually in the brain or spinal cord, which then sends the impulse to the motor neurons. Motor neurons carry the impulse to muscles, and the muscles carry out the response.)*
Portfolio Students can save their flowcharts in their portfolios.

How a Nerve Impulse Travels

Using the Visuals: Figure 3

Have students trace the path of a nerve impulse down the axon to its tip, across the synapse, and to a dendrite of another cell. Ask: **How can nerve impulses travel from one cell to another if the cells are not touching?** (*Chemicals carry the impulses across the synapse.*) Point out that impulses also travel from axons to muscles or cells in other organs.
learning modality: visual

3 Assess

Section 1 Review Answers

1. Receive information about internal and external events, respond to this information, and maintain homeostasis.
2. Sensory neurons, interneurons, and motor neurons. A sensory neuron detects a stimulus and sends an impulse. The impulse travels to interneurons and then to motor neurons. The motor neuron sends the nerve impulse to a muscle, and a response occurs.
3. Nerve impulses cross a synapse when chemicals are released by the axon.
4. The nerve impulse would not be able to cross the synapse, because the axon tips could not release the necessary chemicals.

Science at Home

Materials *salt and pepper shakers*
Make sure students define stimulus and response for their families. Students may realize that if they say "Thank you" when the salt and pepper are passed, the passing is a stimulus and the thanks is a response.

Performance Assessment

Oral Presentation Ask pairs of students to choose an everyday action and create and present posters that illustrate the path of the nerve impulses the action involves.

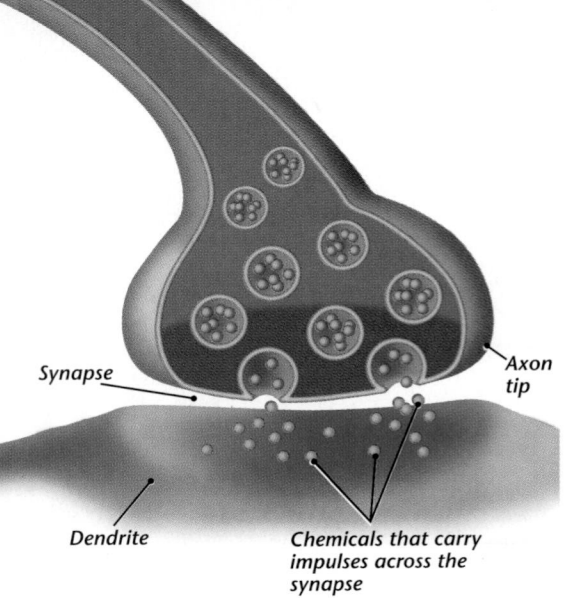

Synapse

Axon tip

Dendrite

Chemicals that carry impulses across the synapse

Figure 3 A synapse is the tiny space between the axon of one neuron and the dendrite of another neuron. When a nerve impulse reaches the end of an axon, chemicals are released into the synapse. These chemicals enable the nerve impulse to cross the synapse.

How a Nerve Impulse Travels

Every day of your life, millions of nerve impulses travel through your nervous system. Each of those nerve impulses begins in the dendrites of a neuron. The impulse moves rapidly toward the neuron's cell body and then down the axon until it reaches the axon tip. A nerve impulse travels along the neuron in the form of electrical and chemical signals. Nerve impulses can travel as fast as 120 meters per second!

There is a tiny space called a **synapse** (SIN aps) between each axon tip and the next structure. Sometimes this next structure is a dendrite of another neuron. Other times the next structure can be a muscle or a cell in another organ, such as a sweat gland. Figure 3 illustrates a synapse between the axon of one neuron and a dendrite of another neuron.

In order for a nerve impulse to be carried along, it must cross the gap between the axon and the next structure. The axon tips release chemicals that enable the impulse to cross the synapse. If that didn't happen, the impulse would stop at the end of the axon. The impulse would not be passed from sensory neuron, to interneuron, to motor neuron. Nerve impulses would never reach your brain or make your muscles contract.

You can think of a synapse as a river, and an axon as a road that leads up to the riverbank. The nerve impulse is like a car traveling on the road. To get to the other side, the car has to cross the river. The car gets on a ferry boat, which carries it across the river. The chemicals that the axon tips release are like a ferry that carries the nerve impulse across the synapse.

 ## Section 1 Review

1. Describe three functions of the nervous system.
2. Identify the three kinds of neurons that are found in the nervous system. Describe how they interact to carry nerve impulses.
3. How does a nerve impulse cross a synapse?
4. **Thinking Critically Predicting** What would happen to a nerve impulse carried by an interneuron if the tips of the interneuron's axon were damaged? Explain.

626

Science at Home

Stimulus and Response During dinner, ask a family member to pass the salt and pepper to you. Observe what your family member then does. Explain that the words you spoke were a stimulus and that the family member's reaction was a response. Discuss other examples of stimuli and responses with your family.

Program Resources

◆ **Unit 4 Resources** 20-1 Review and Reinforce, p. 143; 20-1 Enrich, p. 144

Media and Technology

Interactive Student Tutorial CD-ROM Chapter 20

Ready or Not

D o people carry out tasks better at certain times of day? In this lab, you will design an experiment to answer this question.

Problem

Do people's reaction times vary at different times of day?

Materials

meter stick

Design a Plan

Part 1 Observing a Response to a Stimulus

1. Have your partner hold a meter stick with the zero end about 50 cm above a table.
2. Get ready to catch the meter stick by positioning the top of your thumb and forefinger just at the zero position as shown in the photograph.
3. Your partner should drop the meter stick without any warning. Using your thumb and forefinger only (no other part of your hand), catch the meter stick as soon as you can. Record the distance in centimeters that the meter stick fell. This distance is a measure of your reaction time.

Part 2 Design Your Experiment

4. With your partner, discuss how you can use the activity from Part 1 to find out whether people's reaction times vary at different times of day. Be sure to consider the questions below. Then write up your experimental plan.
   - What hypothesis will you test?
   - What variables do you need to control?
   - How many people will you test? How many times will you test each person?

5. Submit your plan for your teacher's review. Make any changes your teacher recommends. Create a data table to record your results. Then perform your experiment.

Analyze and Conclude

1. In this lab, what is the stimulus? What is the response? Is this response voluntary or involuntary? Explain.
2. Why can you use the distance on the meter stick as a measure of reaction time?
3. Based on your results, do people's reaction times vary at different times of day? Explain.
4. **Think About It** In Part 2, why is it important to control all variables except the time of day?

More to Explore

Do you think people can do arithmetic problems more quickly and accurately at certain times of the day? Design an experiment to investigate this question. Obtain your teacher's permission before trying your experiment.

Program Resources

- **Unit 4 Resources** Chapter 20 Skills Lab, pp. 157–158
- **Inquiry Skills Activity Book** Provides teaching and review of all inquiry skills

Safety

Remind students to use caution while dropping or catching the meter stick. Review the safety guidelines in Appendix A.

Extending the Inquiry

Designing an Experiment Advise students to use simple arithmetic calculations rather than complex exercises, as it is easier to keep the simpler calculations consistent. Also, discuss why students cannot use the same calculations more than once with each person tested.

Ready or Not

Preparing for Inquiry

Key Concept Response time depends on a variety of factors.
Skills Objectives Students will be able to
- form hypotheses regarding whether people perform tasks better at certain times of day;
- design experiments to compare results for different people at different times;
- interpret data and draw conclusions about the effect of time of day on response time.

Time 50 minutes

Guiding Inquiry

Invitation
Ask students to name some situations when a quick reaction time would be advantageous. *(Samples: Applying the brakes to a car to avoid an accident; catching a falling object)*

Introducing the Procedure
Students should test each person at least five times, and then take the average of all trials.

Troubleshooting the Experiment
Students should hold the stick in the same position for every trial.

Analyze and Conclude
1. Stimulus—sight of the dropping stick; response—grabbing the stick. The response is voluntary; the person consciously chooses it.
2. Sample: If people's thumbs and forefingers are at zero at the time of the drop, the number of centimeters the stick drops will be directly proportional to the reaction time, because the stick always falls at the same rate.
3. Answers may vary. Research indicates that the reaction times of an individual do vary during the day.
4. All variables need to be controlled except the time of day so that any differences in reaction time can be directly attributed to the time of day.

SECTION
2 Divisions of
the Nervous
System

Objectives

After completing the lesson, students will be able to

♦ identify the function of the central nervous system, describe its parts, and explain how to keep it safe from injury;

♦ identify the different structures of the brain, and describe the function of each;

♦ identify the functions of the peripheral nervous system and its parts;

♦ describe a reflex;

♦ list activities that can harm the nervous system, and describe ways that individuals can protect the nervous system during these activities.

Key Terms central nervous system, peripheral nervous system, brain, spinal cord, cerebrum, cerebellum, brainstem, somatic nervous system, autonomic nervous system, reflex, concussion

1 Engage/Explore

Activating Prior Knowledge

Ask students: **What happens if you accidentally touch a hot frying pan handle?** (*You quickly move your hand.*) Ask: **Is that response automatic or do you have to think about it?** (*It's automatic.*) Tell the students that they will learn how the body controls this and other automatic responses.

· · · · · · · DISCOVER · · · · · · · ·

Skills Focus inferring
Materials *none*
Time 10 minutes
Tips Caution students not to engage in horseplay or rough-housing while carrying out the activity. Remind students that serious damage can be done if they strike one another too hard on the kneecap.
Expected Outcome Students' legs will swing forward.
Think It Over It might be an advantage in situations that could cause injury, such as touching a hot stove.

628

DISCOVER ·ACTIVITY· · ·

How Does Your Knee React?

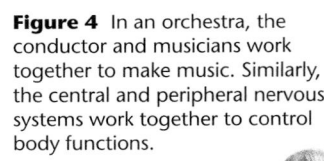

1. Sit on a table or counter so that your legs dangle freely. Your feet should not touch the floor.

2. Have your partner use the side of his or her hand to *gently* tap one of your knees just below the kneecap. Observe what happens to your leg. Note whether you have any control over your reaction.

3. Change places with your partner. Repeat Steps 1 and 2.

Think It Over
Inferring When might it be an advantage for your body to react very quickly and without your conscious control?

GUIDE FOR READING

♦ What is the function of the central nervous system?

♦ What functions does the peripheral nervous system perform?

♦ What is a reflex?

Reading Tip As you read, write four multiple choice questions about the content in this section. Exchange questions with a partner and answer each other's questions.

Figure 4 In an orchestra, the conductor and musicians work together to make music. Similarly, the central and peripheral nervous systems work together to control body functions.

A concert is about to begin. The conductor gives the signal, and the musicians begin to play. The sound of music, beautiful and stirring, fills the air.

To play music in harmony, an orchestra needs both musicians and a conductor. The musicians play the music, and the conductor directs the musicians and coordinates their playing.

Similarly, your nervous system has two divisions that work together—the central nervous system and the peripheral nervous system. The **central nervous system** consists of the brain and spinal cord. The **peripheral nervous system** consists of all the nerves located outside of the central nervous system. The central nervous system is like a conductor. The nerves of the peripheral nervous system are like the musicians.

628

READING STRATEGIES

Reading Tip Suggest that students write statements about the facts of the section as they read. These statements can be turned into multiple choice questions. Point out that the incorrect choices should be carefully chosen so that there is only one correct answer.

Sample question:
The part of the brain that coordinates muscles and maintains balance is the
a. cerebrum   **b.** cerebellum
c. brainstem   **d.** spinal cord
(*The correct answer is b.*)

The Central Nervous System

You can see the central and peripheral nervous systems in Figure 5. **The central nervous system is the control center of the body.** All information about what is happening in the world inside or outside your body is brought to the central nervous system. The **brain,** located in the skull, is the part of the central nervous system that controls most functions in the body. The **spinal cord** is the thick column of nerve tissue that links the brain to most of the nerves in the peripheral nervous system.

Most impulses from the peripheral nervous system travel through the spinal cord to get to the brain. Your brain then directs a response. The response usually travels from the brain, through the spinal cord, and then to the peripheral nervous system.

For example, here is what happens when you reach under the sofa to find a lost quarter. Your fingers move over the floor, searching for the quarter. When your fingers finally touch the quarter, the stimulus of the touch triggers nerve impulses in sensory neurons in your fingers. These impulses travel through nerves of the peripheral nervous system to your spinal cord. Then the impulses race up to your brain. Your brain interprets the impulses, telling you that you've found the quarter. Your brain starts nerve impulses that move down the spinal cord. From the spinal cord, the impulses travel through motor nerves in your arm and hand. The impulses in the motor neurons cause your fingers to grasp the quarter.

✓ *Checkpoint* *What does the spinal cord do?*

The Brain

Your brain contains about 100 billion neurons, all of which are interneurons. Each of those neurons may receive messages from up to 10,000 other neurons and may send messages to about 1,000 more! Three layers of connective tissue cover the brain. The space between the outermost layer and the middle layer is filled with a watery fluid. The skull, layers of connective tissue, and fluid all help protect the brain from injury.

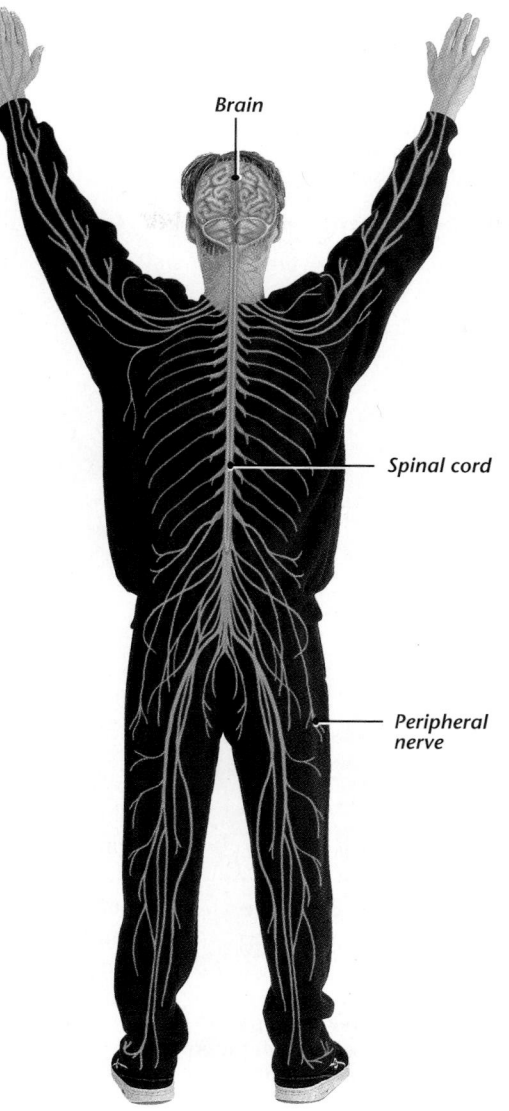

Brain

Spinal cord

Peripheral nerve

Figure 5 The central nervous system consists of the brain and spinal cord. The peripheral nervous system contains all the nerves that branch out from the brain and spinal cord.

629

---

2 Facilitate

The Central Nervous System

Using the Visuals: Figure 5
Have students trace the path of the nerve impulses that originate in the hands of the figure. Ask: **What direction does the nerve impulse move?** *(From the hand to the brain)* **learning modality: visual**

Inquiry Challenge
Materials *coins of different sizes such as nickels, dimes, quarters, pennies*
Time 10 minutes

This activity will allow students to determine how the brain interprets impulses triggered by the senses. Challenge groups of students to design experiments to determine whether they can distinguish between similar objects by touching the objects without looking at them. Have students take on specific tasks, such as writing the hypothesis and experimental plan, testing subjects' ability to distinguish coins, and recording data from the experiment. Check students' plans and allow them to carry out their experiments.
cooperative learning

Program Resources

◆ **Unit 4 Resources** 20-2 Lesson Plan, p. 145; 20-2 Section Summary, p. 146

Media and Technology

 Audio CD English-Spanish Summary 20-2

Answers to Self-Assessment

✓ *Checkpoint*
The spinal cord links the brain to the nerves in the peripheral nervous system.

Ongoing Assessment

Organizing Information Have students make flowcharts to describe the path nerve impulses take from a peripheral nerve to the brain.
 Students can save their flowcharts in their portfolios.

The Brain

Using the Visuals: Figure 6

Direct students to study the relative locations of the cerebrum, the brainstem, and the cerebellum in the illustration. Have students point to their own spinal cord near the base of their skull and then move their fingers up toward their brainstem and cerebellum. Then have students contrast the structure of the cerebrum and cerebellum. (*The cerebrum is larger than the cerebellum, and the cerebrum's surface is creased by deep folds.*) Point out that the folds increase the surface area of the cerebrum in much the same way that villi increase the surface area of the small intestine. **learning modality: visual**

Sharpen your *Skills*

Controlling Variables

Materials *tape player, cassette tape of soft music*

Time 15 minutes, plus 30 minutes to carry out the activity

Tips Caution students to play the tape softly. Remind students to control all variables except the presence or absence of music. Sample hypothesis: Soft music increases the rate of learning. Sample experiment: Make up two lists of words having the same number, length, and familiarity of words. Test three or four people, first in a quiet room, then with music playing softly. Make sure the person looks at a different list each time you test him or her. Play the same music at the same volume each time.

Extend Have students design a similar experiment to test whether the kind of music playing affects people's ability to remember words.

Figure 6 The cerebrum, cerebellum, and brainstem are the three main parts of the human brain. The two halves of the cerebrum have been separated to show the cerebellum and the brainstem.
Applying Concepts What are three functions of the cerebrum?

Cerebrum

Right half of cerebrum

Cerebellum

Spinal cord

Brainstem

Left half of cerebrum

Sharpen your *Skills*

Controlling Variables

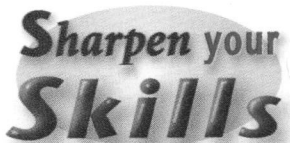

Are people better able to memorize a list of words in a quiet room or in a room where soft music is playing? First write a hypothesis. Then design an experiment to test your hypothesis. Make sure that all variables are controlled except the one you are testing— music versus quiet. Check your procedure with your teacher. Then perform your experiment. Analyze your results to see whether they support your hypothesis.

Cerebrum There are three main regions of the brain. These are the cerebrum, the cerebellum, and the brainstem. Find each in Figure 6. The largest part of the brain is called the cerebrum. The **cerebrum** (suh REE brum) interprets input from the senses, controls the movement of skeletal muscles, and carries out complex mental processes such as learning, remembering, and making judgments. Because of your cerebrum, you can find the comics in a newspaper and locate your favorite comic strip on the page. Your cerebrum also enables you to read the comic strip and laugh at its funny characters.

Notice in Figure 6 that the cerebrum is divided into a right and a left half. The two halves have somewhat different functions. The right half of the cerebrum contains the neurons that send impulses to the skeletal muscles on the left side of the body. In contrast, the left half of the cerebrum controls the right side of the body. When you reach with your right hand for a pencil, the messages that tell you to do so come from the left half of your cerebrum.

In addition, each half of the cerebrum controls slightly different kinds of mental activity. The right half of the cerebrum is usually associated with creativity and artistic ability. The left half, in contrast, is associated with mathematical skills, speech, writing, and logical thinking.

Background

History of Science Almost 2,400 years ago, Hippocrates, an ancient Greek anatomist, determined that the brain was the body's center of intelligence. In the next few centuries, other Greek scientists recognized that the body contained nerves and that nerve impulses traveling to the brain carry sensory information, while nerve impulses traveling away from the brain cause muscles to respond.

In the 1600s, British physician Thomas Willis showed where blood vessels and nerves entered the brain through the brainstem. Willis also distinguished gray and white areas of the cerebrum, as well as the folds in the outer layer of the cerebrum.

Later, scientists used microscopes to conclude that nerve cells and brain cells were similar in structure. This led to the idea that the brain and nerves formed a single system.

Cerebellum and Brainstem The second largest part of your brain is called the cerebellum. The **cerebellum** (sehr uh BEL um) coordinates the actions of your muscles and helps you keep your balance. When you put one foot in front of the other as you walk, the motor neuron impulses that tell your feet to move start in your cerebrum. However, your cerebellum gives you the muscular coordination and sense of balance that keep you from falling down.

The **brainstem,** which lies between the cerebellum and spinal cord, controls your body's involuntary actions—those that occur automatically. For example, the brainstem regulates your breathing and helps control your heartbeat.

☑ *Checkpoint* *What part of your brain coordinates the contractions of your muscles?*

The Spinal Cord

Run your fingers down the center of your back to feel the bones of the vertebral column. The vertebral column surrounds and protects the spinal cord. The spinal cord is the link between your brain and the peripheral nervous system. The layers of connective tissue that surround and protect the brain also cover the spinal cord. In addition, like the brain, the spinal cord is further protected by a watery fluid.

Figure 7 This illustration, by the Dutch artist M. C. Escher, is called "Day and Night." Escher created this picture in 1938.

Chapter 20 **631**

Some artists deliberately create works of art that can be interpreted by the brain in more than one way. The Dutch artist M. C. Escher (1898–1972) delighted in creating illustrations that played visual tricks on his viewers. Glance quickly at Escher's illustration in Figure 7. Then look at it again. Do you see the two different scenes in this single picture?

In Your Journal

Which scene did you see when you first looked at Figure 7? Did your brain interpret the picture differently the second time? Write a description of the visual trick that Escher has played in this illustration.

Building Inquiry Skills: Making Models

Materials *modeling clay of different colors*
Time 20 minutes

Have students create models of a cross-section of the brain. Each part of the brain should be labeled with a description of the processes it controls. Ask: **What part of your brain did you use to determine the size of each section of the model?** *(The cerebrum)* **learning modality: kinesthetic**

Visual Arts
CONNECTION

Provide Escher drawings for students to examine. If they cannot interpret the image in the text, suggest they focus on one side of the scene, then the other.

In Your Journal Students should describe the visual trick by pointing out that there are two sets of birds, identical except for their colors, that are flying in opposite directions over two landscapes that are mirror images in every way except color. Challenge students to create their own drawing using similar techniques. **learning modality: verbal**

The Spinal Cord

Including All Students

Advanced students can do library research on spina bifida, which is a congenital medical condition that occurs when the vertebrae do not seal properly around the spinal cord before birth. The likelihood of this neural tube defect can be decreased if a pregnant woman ingests enough folic acid during the first three months of pregnancy. **learning modality: verbal**

Answers to Self-Assessment

Caption Question

Figure 6 The cerebrum interprets input from the senses, controls the movement of skeletal muscles, and carries out complex mental processes.

☑ *Checkpoint*
The cerebellum

Ongoing Assessment

Writing Have students choose a part of the brain and write a job description for it.

The Peripheral Nervous System

Language Arts Connection

The term *peripheral* may be difficult for some students to spell and pronounce. Write the phonetic spelling *puh RIF er ul* on the board. Allow students to practice saying the word until they are comfortable pronouncing it. Help students remember the meaning of the term by explaining that the *peri-* means "around," and *-phery* comes from the Greek word meaning "to carry." Ask: **How does the peripheral nervous system carry impulses around the body?** *(The peripheral nervous system connects the rest of the body to the central nervous system.)* **limited English proficiency**

Building Inquiry Skills: Comparing and Contrasting

Have students brainstorm lists of actions that are controlled by the somatic nervous system and by the autonomic nervous system. Some students may confuse involuntary actions with voluntary actions, because many voluntary actions seem to happen automatically. Explain that physical activities such as walking or riding a bike are controlled by the somatic nervous system even though we may be unaware that we are doing them. **learning modality: verbal**

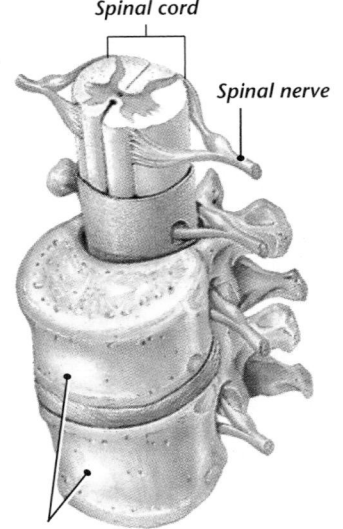

Spinal cord

Spinal nerve

Vertebrae

Figure 8 The spinal nerves, which connect to the spinal cord, emerge from spaces between the vertebrae. Each spinal nerve consists of both sensory and motor neurons.

The Peripheral Nervous System

The second division of the nervous system is the peripheral nervous system. **The peripheral nervous system consists of a network of nerves that branch out from the central nervous system and connect it to the rest of your body.** A total of 43 pairs of nerves make up the peripheral nervous system. Twelve pairs originate in the brain. The other 31 pairs—the spinal nerves—begin in the spinal cord. One nerve in each pair goes to the left side of the body, and the other goes to the right. As you can see in Figure 8, spinal nerves leave the spinal cord through spaces between the vertebrae.

Two-Way Traffic A spinal nerve is a little bit like a two-lane highway. Impulses travel on a spinal nerve in two directions—both to and from the central nervous system. Each spinal nerve contains axons of both sensory and motor neurons. The sensory neurons carry impulses from the body to the central nervous system. The motor neurons carry impulses in the opposite direction—from the central nervous system to the body.

Somatic and Autonomic Systems The nerves of the peripheral nervous system can be divided into two groups, called the somatic (soh MAT ik) and autonomic (awt uh NAHM ik) nervous systems. The nerves of the **somatic nervous system** control voluntary actions such as using a fork or tying your shoelaces. In contrast, nerves of the **autonomic nervous system** control involuntary actions. For example, the autonomic nervous system regulates the contractions of the smooth muscles that adjust the diameter of blood vessels.

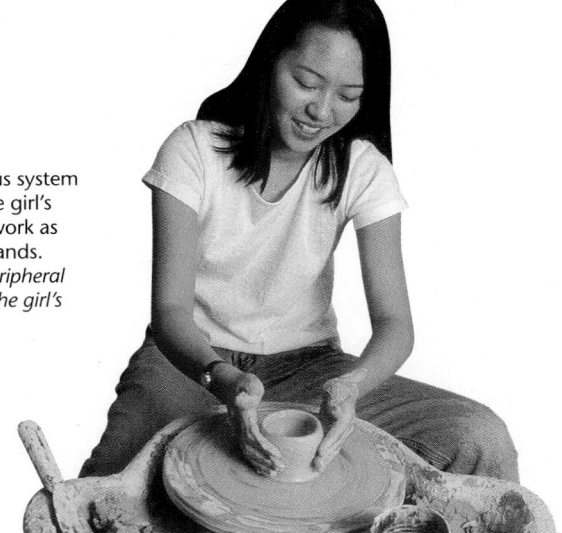

Figure 9 The somatic nervous system controls voluntary actions. The girl's somatic nervous system is at work as she shapes the pot with her hands. *Classifying What part of the peripheral nervous system helps regulate the girl's heartbeat?*

632

Background

Facts and Figures Memory, both short-term and long-term, is one of the functions of the brain. The capacity for short-term memory is limited. For example, while it is relatively easy to remember a seven-digit phone number for a short time after looking it up in a phone book, it is difficult to remember numbers with many digits.

Unlike short-term memory, long-term memory seems to have infinite capacity.

Long-term memories are created when information is somehow stored in the brain. Many scientists think that once information enters long-term memory, it stays there permanently. Long-term memories may include tastes, smells, and physical sensations. At the cellular level, memory probably involves both anatomical and physiological changes in neurons and synapses.

Reflexes

Imagine that you are watching an adventure movie. The movie is so thrilling that you don't notice a fly circling above your head. When the fly zooms right in front of your eyes, however, your eyelids immediately blink shut. You didn't decide to close your eyes. The blink, which is an example of a **reflex,** happened automatically. **A reflex is an automatic response that occurs very rapidly and without conscious control.** If you did the Discover activity, you saw another example of a reflex.

As you have learned, the contraction of skeletal muscles is usually controlled by the brain. However, in some reflex actions, skeletal muscles contract with the involvement of the spinal cord only—not the brain. Figure 10 shows the reflex action that occurs when you touch a sharp object, such as a cactus thorn. When your finger touches the object, sensory neurons send impulses to the spinal cord. The impulses then pass to interneurons in the spinal cord. From there the impulses pass directly to motor neurons in your arm and hand. The muscles then contract, and your hand jerks up and away from the sharp object. By removing your hand quickly, this reflex protects you from getting badly cut.

At the same time that some nerve impulses make your arm muscles contract, other nerve impulses travel up your spinal cord and to your brain. When these impulses reach your brain, your brain interprets them. You then feel a sharp pain in your finger.

Figure 10 If you touch a sharp object, your hand immediately jerks away. This action, which is known as a reflex, happens automatically. Nerve impulses begin in nerve endings (1) and then travel along sensory neurons (2) to interneurons in the spinal cord (3). From there, impulses travel through motor neurons (4) to muscles in your arm (5). The muscles contract to pull your hand away.

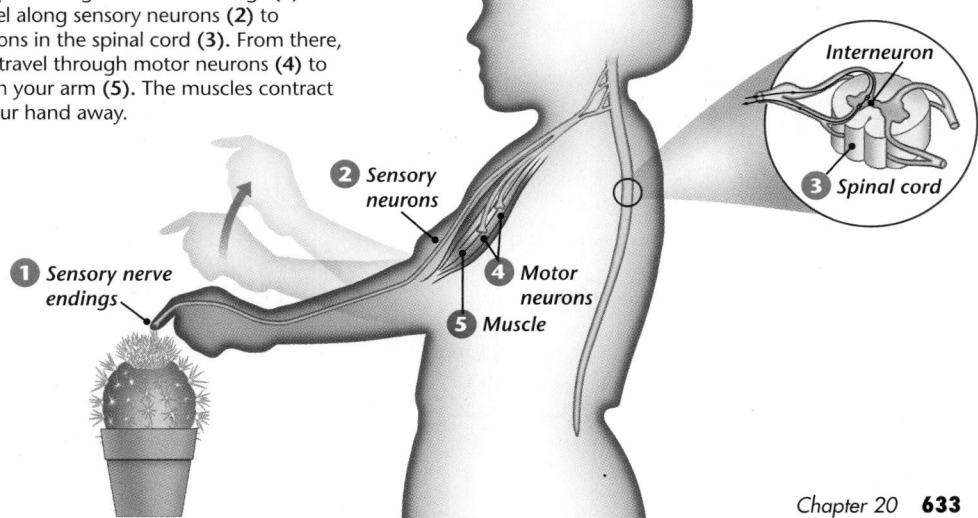

- **1** Sensory nerve endings
- **2** Sensory neurons
- **3** Spinal cord
- **4** Motor neurons
- **5** Muscle
- *Interneuron*

Chapter 20 **633**

Reflexes

Using the Visuals: Figure 10

Direct students to trace the path of the impulse in the figure from the stimulus to its response. Ask: **How does it benefit people that the spinal cord is able to send an impulse to motor neurons in response to a stimulus without involving the brain?** *(It allows people to respond more quickly to danger than if the nerve impulses traveled all the way to and from the brain.)* **learning modality: visual**

Building Inquiry Skills: Applying Concepts

Remind students that a change in the environment that makes an organism react is called a stimulus. Ask: **What is the stimulus in the reflex mentioned in the text?** *(The fly zooming in front of your eyes)* Make sure students understand that although reflexes are automatic, they must involve stimuli, and are not always controlled by the autonomic nervous system. **learning modality: verbal**

Media and Technology

Exploring Life Science Videodisc
Unit 4, Side 1,
"Quick Reflexes"

Chapter 9

Answers to Self-Assessment

Caption Question

Figure 9 The autonomic nervous system

Ongoing Assessment

Oral Presentation Have students give examples of voluntary, involuntary, and reflexive responses and explain how the impulses for each travel through the nervous system.

633

Integrating Health

Ask students to infer how doctors could learn about the functions of the nervous system by studying injuries to the brain. (*Sample: Damage to a particular part of the brain will result in the loss or change to the function controlled by that part.*)
learning modality: verbal

3 Assess

Section 2 Review Answers

1. The central nervous system, which includes the brain and spinal cord, is the control center of the body.
2. A network of nerves that branch out from the central nervous system; carries nerve impulses between the central nervous system and the rest of the body.
3. An automatic response that occurs rapidly and without conscious control. Reflexes allow the body to respond quickly to danger.
4. Loss of balance; poor muscle coordination.

Check Your Progress

CHAPTER PROJECT

Check students' plans for safety. Note that illusions do not necessarily affect all people the same way. Have students try out their illusions on a partner before others write lists of questions.

Performance Assessment

Organizing Information Have students make concept maps that identify parts of the central nervous system and the peripheral nervous system.

 Students can save their concept maps in their portfolios.

Figure 11 By wearing a helmet, this skateboarder is helping to prevent injury to his brain.

It takes longer for the pain impulses to get to the brain and be interpreted than it does for the reflex action to occur. By the time you feel the pain, you have already moved your hand away from the sharp object.

Safety and the Nervous System

INTEGRATING HEALTH Like other parts of the body, the nervous system can suffer injuries that interfere with its functioning. Concussions and spinal cord injuries are two ways in which the nervous system can be damaged.

A **concussion** is a bruiselike injury of the brain. A concussion occurs when soft tissue of the cerebrum bumps against the skull. Concussions can happen during a hard fall, an automobile accident, or contact sports such as football. With most concussions, you may have a headache for a short time, but the injured tissue heals by itself. However, if you black out, experience confusion, or feel drowsy after the injury, you should be checked by a doctor. To decrease your chances of getting a brain injury, wear a helmet when bicycling, skating, or performing other activities in which you risk bumping your head.

Spinal cord injuries occur when the spinal cord is cut or crushed. When the spinal cord is cut, all the nerve axons in that region are split, so impulses cannot pass through them. This type of injury results in paralysis, which is the loss of movement in some part of the body. Car crashes are the most common cause of spinal cord injuries. You can help protect yourself from a spinal cord injury by wearing a seatbelt when you travel in a car. Also, when you swim, make sure the water is deep enough before you dive in.

Section 2 Review

1. What is the function of the central nervous system? Which organs are part of this system?
2. What is the peripheral nervous system and what are its functions?
3. Explain what a reflex is. How do reflexes help protect the body from injury?
4. Thinking Critically Relating Cause and Effect What symptoms might indicate that a person's cerebellum has been injured?

Check Your Progress

CHAPTER PROJECT

At this point, you should have chosen one or more illusions to investigate. Now write up the plan for your experiment. List some questions that you will ask to monitor people's responses to the illusions. (*Hint:* Try out your illusions and your questions on classmates to find out what responses to expect.) With your classmates, make plans for setting up the science fair.

Program Resources

◆ **Unit 4 Resources** 20-2 Review and Reinforce, p. 147; 20-2 Enrich, p. 148

Should People Be Required to Wear Bicycle Helmets?

Bicycle riding is an enjoyable activity. But unfortunately, many bicycle riders become injured while riding. Each year about 150,000 children alone are treated in hospitals for head injuries that occur while bicycling. Head injuries can affect everything your brain does—thinking, remembering, seeing, and being able to move. Experts estimate that as many as 85 percent of bicycle-related head injuries could be prevented if all bicyclists wore helmets. But only about 18 percent of bicyclists wear helmets. What is the best way to get bicycle riders to protect themselves from head injury?

The Issues

Should Laws Require the Use of Bicycle Helmets? About 15 states have passed laws requiring bicycle riders to wear helmets. Nearly all of these laws, however, apply only to children. Some supporters of bicycle laws want to see the laws extended to all bicycle riders. Supporters point out that laws increase helmet use by 47 percent. In contrast, educational programs without laws to back them up increase bicycle helmet use by only 18 percent.

What Are the Drawbacks of Helmet Laws? Opponents of helmet laws believe it is up to the individual, not the government, to decide whether or not to wear a helmet. They say it is not the role of the government to stop people from taking risks. Rather than making people who don't wear helmets pay fines, governments should educate people about the benefits of helmets. Car drivers should also be educated about safe driving procedures near bicycles.

Are There Alternatives to Helmet Laws? Instead of laws requiring people to wear helmets, some communities and organizations have set up educational programs that teach about the advantages of helmets. Effective programs teach about the dangers of head injuries and how helmets protect riders. In addition, they point out that safe helmets can be lightweight and comfortable. Effective education programs, though, can be expensive. They also need to reach a wide audience, including children, teens, and adults.

You Decide

1. Identify the Problem
In your own words, explain the issues concerning laws requiring people to wear bicycle helmets.

2. Analyze the Options
List two different plans for increasing helmet use by bicycle riders. List at least one advantage and one drawback of each plan.

3. Find a Solution
You are a member of the city government hoping to increase helmet use. Write a speech outlining your position for either a helmet law or an alternative plan. Support your position.

Chapter 20 **635**

Background

Facts and Figures Even if people do wear bicycle helmets, they may not be protected from head injury if they do not wear the helmets properly. Therefore, educational programs that teach people about the advantages of helmets often emphasize how to wear a helmet properly. The front edge of the helmet should be positioned 2 to 3 cm above the rider's eyebrows. A simple test is to walk toward a wall; the helmet should touch the wall before the nose does. The helmet and the chin strap should be snug, but not uncomfortable.

Communities can also help to reduce bicycle head injuries by creating safer environments for people to ride their bikes. This might include setting aside special bicycle lanes on roads or making biking trails through parks.

SCIENCE AND SOCIETY

Should People Be Required to Wear Bicycle Helmets?

Purpose
Students will identify and analyze the difficulties involved in getting bicycle riders to protect themselves from head injury.

Role-Play

Time a day to prepare; 30 minutes for role-play

Divide students into four groups: (1) a group to represent state lawmakers, (2) a group to argue for the passage of a bicycle helmet law, (3) a group to argue against a helmet law, but for an education program paid for with taxes, and (4) a group to argue against any government regulation or tax-supported education programs. Tell the first group to work out rules and an agenda for a committee hearing on a proposed helmet law. Students in each of the other groups can work together to prepare a presentation to the committee during the hearing. Then hold the hearing, using the rules and agenda worked out by the committee members. Encourage students to act the way they think citizens would act in a real public hearing of this kind.

Extend Challenge students to find out whether your state or local government has passed a helmet law and, if so, whether it applies only to children or to bicycle riders of all ages. Suggest that students contact a member of a local law enforcement agency to ask what the penalties are for breaking such a law.

You Decide
Have students individually complete the first two steps before the role-play as a way of preparing themselves for their participation. After the role-play is concluded, students can complete the last step, using what they learned in the role-play to find a solution to the problem.

Objectives

After completing the lesson, students will be able to
◆ name the senses and state the overall function performed by the senses;
◆ describe how eyes enable people to see;
◆ describe how people hear sounds and maintain balance;
◆ describe how people experience the senses of touch, taste, and smell.

Key Terms cornea, pupil, iris, lens, retina, nearsightedness, farsightedness, eardrum, cochlea, semicircular canal

1 Engage/Explore

Activating Prior Knowledge

Challenge students to name the senses, then list them on the board. Have the class brainstorm a list of items or activities in the classroom that they perceive through each sense.

DISCOVER

Skills Focus observing
Materials *opaque paper bags; small objects, such as erasers, pens, paper clips, sponges, cotton balls, marbles, plastic spoons, bottle caps, coins, buttons*
Time 20 minutes
Tips Include objects of different sizes, shapes, and textures. Be certain to use objects that are not sharp. Encourage students to take notes about the objects they feel and record what objects they believe are in the bag.
Expected Outcome Students should be able to identify most of the objects using their sense of touch.
Think It Over Students could determine size, shape, texture, and weight. They could not determine color, scent, or taste.

SECTION
3 The Senses

DISCOVER ··················ACTIVITY····

What's in the Bag?

1. Your teacher will give you a paper bag that contains several objects. Your challenge is to use only your sense of touch to identify each object. You will not look inside the bag.

2. Put your hand in the bag and carefully touch each object. Observe the shape of each object. Note whether its surface is rough or smooth. Also note other characteristics, such as its size, what it seems to be made of, and whether it can be bent.

3. After you have finished touching each object, write your observations on a sheet of paper. Then write your inference about what each object is.

Think It Over
Observing What could you determine about each object without looking at it? What could you not determine?

GUIDE FOR READING

◆ What overall function do the senses perform?
◆ How do your eyes enable you to see?
◆ How do you hear?

Reading Tip As you read, write an outline of this section. Use the headings in the section as the main topics in the outline.

You waited in line to get on the ride, and now it's about to begin. You grip the bars as the ride suddenly starts to move. Before you know it, you are lifted high above the ground and you feel the air whipping by. All you see is a dizzy blur.

The thrill you experience from the speed of amusement park rides comes from your senses. **Each of your major senses— vision, hearing, balance, smell, taste, and touch—picks up a specific type of information about your environment. The sense organs change that information into nerve impulses and send the impulses to your brain.** Your brain then interprets the information. Because of the way in which your senses and brain work together, you learn a great deal about your environment.

Figure 12 Riders and bright lights whizzing by—that's what you see when you watch this amusement park ride.

READING STRATEGIES

Reading Tip Have students read the information under the first heading within the section. Work as a class to outline the information under the heading. Then have students work independently to complete the outline. Outline may begin as follows:
I. Vision
   A. How Light Enters the Eye
   B. How Light is Focused
   C. How You See an Image

Study and Comprehension Before students begin reading, have them preview the section by looking at the pictures and read the captions. Discuss with students what they already know about the senses. Encourage students to ask questions about the function of the senses. Write the questions on the board and have students answer them after they have read the section.

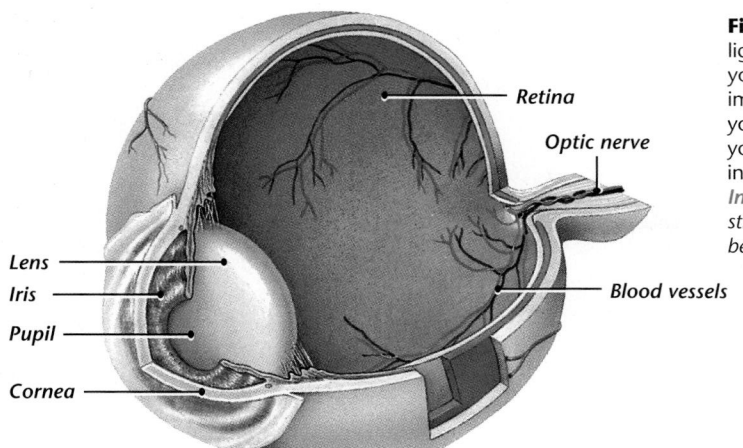

Retina

Optic nerve

Lens

Iris

Pupil

Cornea

Blood vessels

Figure 13 You see an object when light coming from the object enters your eye. The light produces an image on your retina. Receptors in your retina then send impulses to your cerebrum, and your cerebrum interprets these impulses. *Interpreting Diagrams What structures must light pass through before it reaches your retina?*

Vision

Your eyes are the sense organs that enable you to see the objects in your environment. They let you see this book in front of you, the window across the room, and the world outside the window. **Your eyes respond to the stimulus of light. They convert that stimulus into impulses that your brain interprets, enabling you to see.**

How Light Enters Your Eye When rays of light strike the eye, they pass through the structures shown in Figure 13. First, the light strikes the **cornea** (KAWR nee uh), the clear tissue that covers the front of the eye. The light then passes through a fluid-filled chamber behind the cornea and reaches the pupil. The **pupil** is the opening through which light enters the eye.

You may have noticed that people's pupils change size when they go from a dark room into bright sunshine. In bright light, the pupil becomes smaller. In dim light, the pupil becomes larger. The size of the pupil is adjusted by muscles in the iris. The **iris** is a circular structure that surrounds the pupil and regulates the amount of light entering the eye. The iris also gives the eye its color. If you have brown eyes, your irises are brown.

How Light Is Focused Light that passes through the pupil strikes the lens. The **lens** is a flexible structure that focuses light. The lens of your eye functions something like the lens of a camera, which focuses light on photographic film. Because of the way in which the lens of the eye bends the light rays, the image it produces is upside down and reversed. Muscles that attach to the lens adjust its shape. This adjustment produces an image that is clear and in focus.

Why Do You Need Two Eyes?

In this activity, you will investigate how your two eyes work together to allow you to see.

1. With your arms fully extended, hold a plastic drinking straw in one hand and a pipe cleaner in the other.
2. With both eyes open, try to insert the pipe cleaner into the straw.
3. Now close your right eye. Try to insert the pipe cleaner into the straw.
4. Repeat Step 3, but this time close your left eye instead of your right eye.

Inferring How does closing one eye affect your ability to judge distances?

Chapter 20 **637**

Vision

Building Inquiry Skills: Observing

Materials *mounted or hand mirror*
Time 15 minutes

Have students observe their own eyes in the mirror and compare the size of their pupils in bright light, dim light, and extremely dim light. Ask: **What happens to your pupils as the light darkens?** (*Pupils widen.*) Then ask: **What function is served when the pupil gets wider in dim light?** (*It allows more light to enter the eye and thus you see better.*)
learning modality: kinesthetic

Skills Focus inferring
Materials *drinking straw, pipe cleaner*
Time 15 minutes
Tips Students will have more difficulty inserting the pipe cleaner when they have to close one eye than when they have both eyes open.
Inferring Closing one eye impairs a person's ability to judge distances.
Extend Challenge students to design a test that demonstrates how closing one eye reduces their total field of vision. Review all plans, and do not allow students to perform their tests without your approval. (*Students can cover one eye and identify the objects on the edges of their vision, then cover the other eye and repeat. Students should then open both eyes and compare what they can see with both eyes open to what they saw through each eye.*) **learning modality: kinesthetic**

Answers to Self-Assessment

Caption Question

Figure 13 Light must pass through the cornea, pupil, and lens before it reaches the retina.

Ongoing Assessment

Writing Have students list the structures that make up the eye and identify the function of each.
 Students can save their lists in their portfolios.

Vision, continued

Demonstration

Materials *candle in holder, double-convex lens, white paper, optics bench (optional)*
Time 15 minutes

In a dark room, place the candle in the holder on a table and light the candle. CAUTION: *Use safety precautions with open flames. Do not allow students to light the candle or work too close to the flame.* Hold a converging or double-convex lens between the candle and a piece of white paper. Adjust the lens so that it reflects an image of the candle onto the paper. Ask: **What happens to the image of the candle?** *(It appears upside down.)* Extinguish the candle. Then ask: **Where in the eye is the upside-down image focused?** *(On the retina)* **learning modality: visual**

Correcting Vision Problems

Integrating Physics

Materials *candle in holder, double-convex lens, white paper, optics bench (optional)*
Time 15 minutes

In a dark room, place the candle in the holder on a table and light the candle. Use caution with open flames, as noted above. Hold the lens securely between the candle and a piece of white paper. Adjust the lens so that it reflects a clear image of the candle onto the paper. Ask: **What part of the eye does the lens represent?** *(lens)* **The paper?** *(retina)* Ask: **How could you show near-sightedness?** *(Move the paper further away from the lens.)* Then ask: **How could you show farsightedness?** *(Move the lens closer to the paper.)* Point out to students that however the distance between the paper and the lens is changed, the image becomes unfocused. **learning modality: visual**

638

Figure 14 An upside-down image is focused on the retina. *Applying Concepts When you see an object, why does it appear right-side up?*

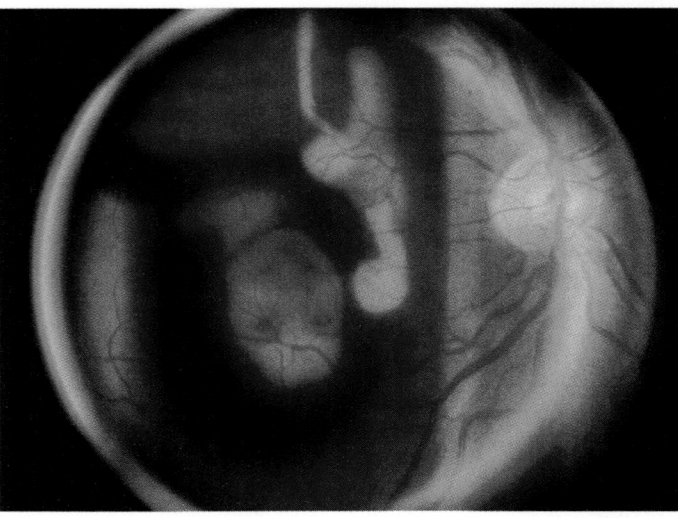

Figure 15 The retina of the eye contains light-sensitive cells. In this photograph, the rods have been colored pink, and the cones have been colored blue.

How You See an Image After passing through the lens, the focused light rays pass through a transparent, jellylike fluid. Then the light rays strike the **retina** (RET 'n uh), the layer of receptor cells that lines the back of the eye. The retina contains about 130 million receptor cells that respond to light. There are two types of receptors, rods and cones. Rod cells work best in dim light and enable you to see black, white, and shades of gray. In contrast, cone cells only work well in bright light and enable you to see colors. This difference between rods and cones explains why you see colors best in bright light, but you see only shadowy gray images in dim light.

When light strikes the rods and cones, nerve impulses begin. These nerve impulses travel to the cerebrum through the optic nerves. One optic nerve comes from the left eye and the other one comes from the right. In the cerebrum, two things happen. The brain turns the reversed image right-side up. In addition, the brain combines the images from each eye to produce a single image.

Correcting Vision Problems

INTEGRATING PHYSICS A lens—whether it is in your eye, in a camera, or in eyeglasses—is a curved, transparent object that bends light rays as they pass through it. If the lens of the eye does not focus light properly on the retina, vision problems result. The glass or plastic lenses in eyeglasses can help correct such vision problems.

638

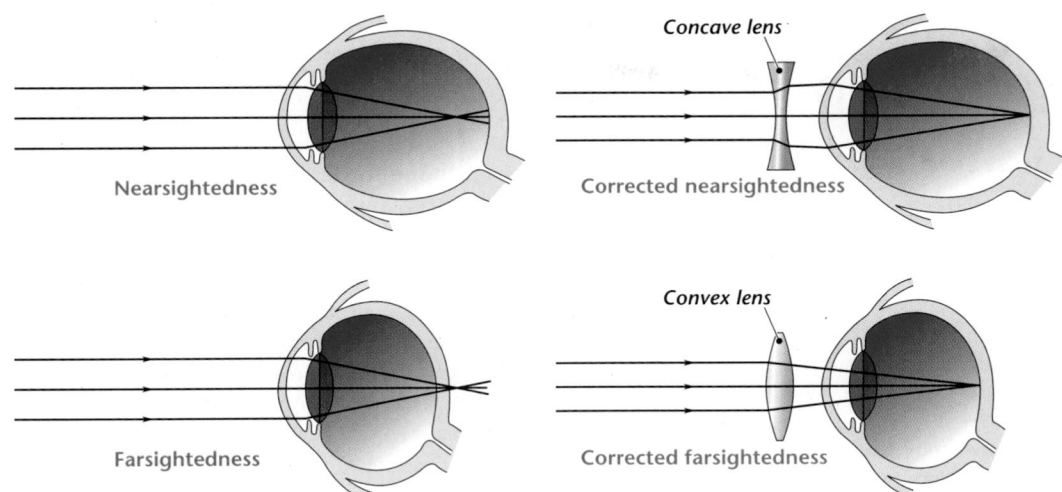

Nearsightedness

Corrected nearsightedness

Concave lens

Farsightedness

Corrected farsightedness

Convex lens

Nearsightedness People with **nearsightedness** can see nearby objects clearly. However, they have trouble seeing objects that are far away. Nearsightedness is caused by an eyeball that is too long. Because of the extra length that light must travel to reach the retina, distant objects do not focus sharply on the retina. Instead, the lens of the eye makes the image come into focus at a point in front of the retina, as shown in Figure 16.

To correct nearsightedness, a person needs to wear eyeglasses with concave lenses. A concave lens is a lens that is thicker at the edges than it is in the center. When light rays pass through a concave lens, they are bent away from the center of the lens. The concave lenses in glasses make light rays spread out before they reach the lens of the eye. Then, when these rays pass through the lens of the eye, they focus on the retina rather than in front of it.

Farsightedness People with **farsightedness** can see distant objects clearly. Nearby objects, however, look blurry. The eyeballs of people with farsightedness are too short. Because of this, the lens of the eye bends light from nearby objects so that the image does not focus properly on the retina. If light could pass through the retina, the image would come into sharp focus at a point behind the retina, as shown in Figure 16.

Convex lenses are used to help correct farsightedness. A convex lens is thicker in the middle than the edges. The convex lens makes the light rays bend toward one another before they reach the eye. Then the lens of the eye bends the rays even more. This bending makes the image focus exactly on the retina.

☑ *Checkpoint* *What type of lens is used to correct nearsightedness?*

Figure 16 Nearsightedness and farsightedness are conditions in which images do not focus properly on the retina. The diagrams on the left show where the images are focused in both of these conditions. The diagrams on the right show how lenses in eyeglasses can help correct these conditions.

Answers to Self-Assessment

Caption Question

Figure 14 The brain reverses the image from the retina so the image appears right-side up.

☑ *Checkpoint*
Concave

Including All Students

Materials *convex and concave lenses*

ACTIVITY

Time 5 minutes

Allow students to feel each type of lens and compare the thickness of the lens at the edges and the center. Ask: **Which lens is thicker in the middle and thinner at the edges?** *(The convex lens)* Then ask students to describe the shape of a concave lens. *(Thinner in the middle; thicker on the edges)* If possible, invite a physical science teacher to demonstrate how convex and concave lenses bend light. **learning modality: kinesthetic**

Using the Visuals: Figure 16

Direct students to trace the path of light rays as they move through the nearsighted eye in Figure 16, then through the nearsighted glasses. Ask: **What do the nearsighted glasses do to the image? How does this correct vision?** *(The glasses bend the light rays outward so they are spread apart when they reach the lens of the eye. Then the lens of the eye can correctly focus the rays.)* Have students repeat the process for the farsighted glasses. *(The glasses bend the light rays inward so they are closer together when they reach the lens of the eye.)* **learning modality: visual**

Real-Life Learning

Many people wear contact lenses to correct their vision. Contact lenses are fitted to cover the cornea and curved to alter the path of light rays passing to the retina. Ask if any students currently wear contact lenses. Allow them to describe the advantages and disadvantages of wearing contact lenses instead of glasses. **learning modality: verbal**

Ongoing Assessment

Skills Check Tell students that people who are farsighted sometimes wear reading glasses to bring nearby objects into focus. Then ask students what kind of lenses are found in reading glasses. *(convex)*

Hearing

Integrating Physics

Materials *spring toy, colored ribbon*
Time 10 minutes

Tell students that sound travels by compression waves. Compression waves consist of areas where particles are compressed alternating with areas where waves are spread out. To demonstrate how a compression wave travels, use a spring toy. Tie a brightly colored ribbon onto one coil of the spring toy. Have two volunteers hold the opposite ends of the spring, and encourage one volunteer to begin a wave by pushing one end of the spring toy toward the other end without letting go. Students can observe a compression wave traveling down the length of the spring toy. **learning modality: visual**

TRY THIS

Skills Focus measuring
Materials *ticking watch, metric ruler*
Time 15 minutes
Tips Make sure students move the watch away from the ear very slowly and at a steady rate.
Measuring Some students may be able to hear the watch at greater distances with one ear; other students will have the same hearing in both ears. This is probably not an accurate way to evaluate a person's hearing because there are too many uncontrolled variables, such as background noise, the speed at which the watch is moved, and the angle at which the watch is held.
Extend Have students find out what happens to the distance at which they can hear the watch ticking if they cup their hearing ear with one hand.
learning modality: kinesthetic

Tick! Tick! Tick!

In this activity, you will determine whether one of a person's ears hears better than the other one.

1. Work in teams of three. Hold a ticking watch next to the right ear of one team member.
2. Slowly move the watch away from the ear. Stop moving it at the point where the student can no longer hear the ticking.
3. At that point, have the third team member measure the distance between the watch and the student's right ear.
4. Repeat Steps 1 through 3 to test the student's left ear.

Measuring How did the two distances compare? Do you think this is an accurate way to evaluate someone's hearing? Why or why not?

Hearing

What wakes you up in the morning? Maybe an alarm clock buzzes, or perhaps your parent calls you. On a summer morning, you might hear birds singing. Whatever wakes you up, there's a good chance that it's a sound of some sort. **Your ears are the sense organs that respond to the stimulus of sound. The ears convert the sound to nerve impulses that your brain interprets.** So when you hear an alarm clock or other morning sound, your brain tells you that it's time to wake up.

How Sound Is Produced Sound is produced by vibrations. The material that is vibrating, or moving rapidly back and forth, may be almost anything—a guitar string, an insect's wings, or splashing water.

INTEGRATING PHYSICS

The vibrations create waves. The waves move outward from the source of the sound, something like ripples moving out from a stone dropped in water. The waves consist of moving particles, such as the molecules that make up air. When you hear a friend's voice, for example, sound waves have traveled from your friend's larynx to your ears. In addition to being able to travel through gases such as air, sound waves can also travel through liquids such as water and solids such as wood.

Sound Vibrations and the Ear The ear is structured to receive sound vibrations. As you can see in Figure 18, the ear consists of three parts— the outer ear, middle ear, and inner ear. The outer ear includes the part of the ear that you see. The visible part of the outer ear is shaped like a funnel.

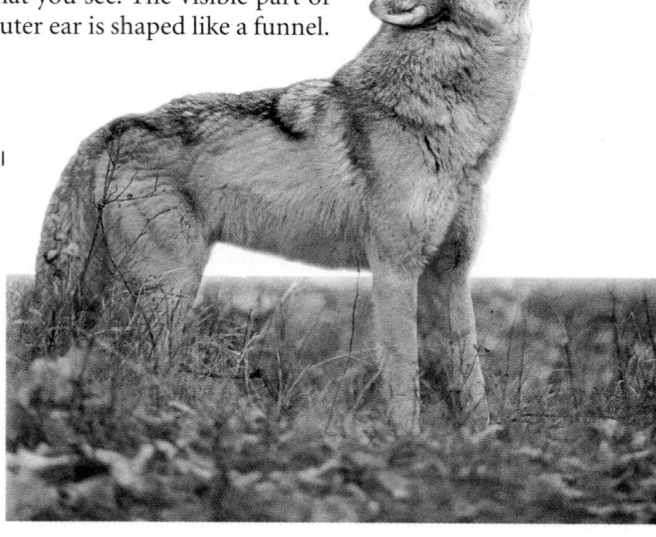

Figure 17 When a wolf howls, its vocal cords vibrate. The vibrating vocal cords produce sound waves. When the sound waves reach a person's ear, the person hears the wolf.

Background

Integrating Science Hearing aids are used to supplement the natural response of the ear to sound. The earliest hearing aids were shaped like long trumpets, with a wide mouth like an open funnel that narrowed to a tube. The narrow end was placed directly in the ear canal. Electrical hearing aids are used today. They increase the loudness of the sounds heard and help the ear respond to sounds of different frequencies. These aids can help people with hearing loss have normal conversations. All hearing aids have a microphone, which produces electrical signals from sound waves, and an amplifier, which amplifies the signals. The receiver converts the amplified electrical signals into amplified sound waves, which are then directed into the ear.

This funnel-like shape enables the outer ear to gather sound waves. The sound waves then travel down the ear canal, which is also part of the outer ear.

At the end of the ear canal, sound waves reach the eardrum. The **eardrum,** which separates the outer ear from the middle ear, is a membrane that vibrates when sound waves strike it. Your eardrum vibrates in much the same way that the surface of a drum vibrates when it is struck. Vibrations from the eardrum pass to the middle ear, which contains the three smallest bones in the body—the hammer, anvil, and stirrup. The names of these bones are based on their shapes. The vibrating eardrum makes the hammer vibrate. The hammer passes the vibrations to the anvil, and the anvil passes them to the stirrup.

How You Hear The stirrup vibrates against a thin membrane that covers the opening of the inner ear. The membrane channels the vibrations into the fluid in the cochlea. The **cochlea** (KAHK le uh) is a snail-shaped tube that is lined with receptors that respond to sound. When the fluid in the cochlea vibrates, it stimulates these receptors. Sensory neurons then send nerve impulses to the cerebrum through the auditory nerve. These impulses are interpreted as sounds that you hear.

 Checkpoint *Where in the ear is the cochlea located?*

Your Sense of Balance

Your ear also controls your sense of balance. Above the cochlea in your inner ear are the **semicircular canals,** which are the structures in the ear that are responsible for your sense of balance.

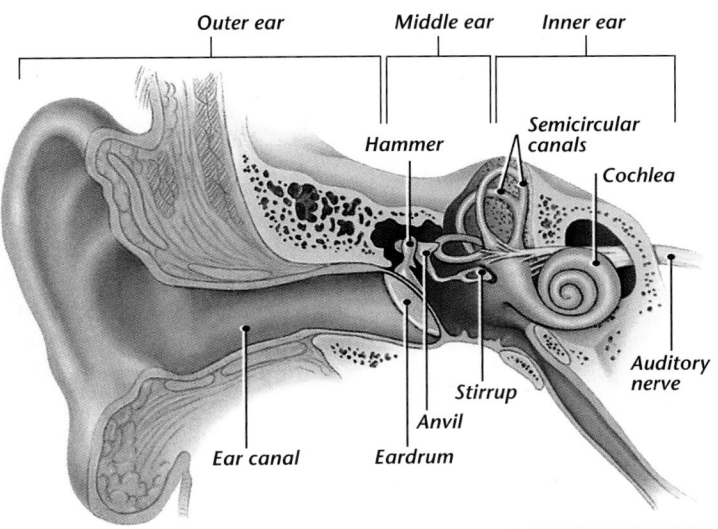

Figure 18 The ear has three regions—the outer ear, the middle ear, and the inner ear. Sound waves enter the outer ear and make structures in the middle ear vibrate. When the vibrations reach the inner ear, nerve impulses travel to the cerebrum through the auditory nerve. *Predicting What would happen if the bones of the middle ear were stuck together and could not move?*

Materials *piece of balloon, rubber band, large funnel, tuning fork*
Time 10 minutes

Have students stretch the piece of balloon tightly over the narrow end of the funnel and fasten it with the rubber band. Ask: **What does the piece of balloon represent?** *(The eardrum)* Have students predict what will happen to the balloon if they place a vibrating tuning fork inside the funnel. Allow students to test their prediction. *(It vibrates.)* Ask: **How does this model what happens in the human ear?** *(Sound waves passing through the outer ear reach an eardrum that vibrates.)* **learning modality: kinesthetic**

Using the Visuals: Figure 18

Direct students to trace the path of a sound wave as it passes from the outer ear to the middle and inner ear. Ask: **What happens when the sound waves reach the eardrum?** *(They make the eardrum vibrate, which in turn passes the vibrations to the bones in the middle ear.)* Finally, ask students to locate where the auditory nerve connects to the ear. Point out the cochlea and ask: **What happens to vibrations in this structure?** *(The vibrations stimulate receptor cells to send impulses to the brain through the auditory nerve.)* **learning modality: visual**

Media and Technology

Transparencies "The Ear," Transparency 76

Answers to Self-Assessment

Caption Question

Figure 18 If the bones of the middle ear could not move, no vibrations would reach the inner ear and a person would be unable to hear.

Checkpoint
The cochlea is in the inner ear.

Ongoing Assessment

Writing Ask students to describe how a sound is created and how it is heard. *(Vibrations create sound waves in air, water, or other matter. If the waves enter the ear, they cause the eardrum to vibrate. These vibrations pass to the middle ear and cause the hammer, anvil, and stirrup to vibrate. In the inner ear, the vibrations pass to fluid in the cochlea, where they stimulate receptors that send nerve impulses to the brain.)*

Your Sense of Balance

Including All Students

Materials *clear plastic jar with lid, water*
Time 5 minutes

Students who need an additional challenge can model how motion affects the semicircular canals. Have pairs of students fill a plastic jar halfway with water and seal it tightly. CAUTION: *Do not use glass containers for this activity. Make sure the outside of the jar is completely dry.* In an open area, have one partner hold the jar and spin quickly for about 10 seconds. The observing student should note the movement of the liquid in the jar. Have students switch roles. Ask: **What happened to the water in the jar?** *(It sloshed around.)* Then ask: **How does this model explain what happens inside the semicircular canals?** *(Like the water, the fluid in the semicircular canals is sloshed around when you move your head.)* **learning modality: kinesthetic**

Smell and Taste

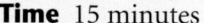
Sharpen your Skills

Designing Experiments

Materials *peeled pear, apple, and raw potato*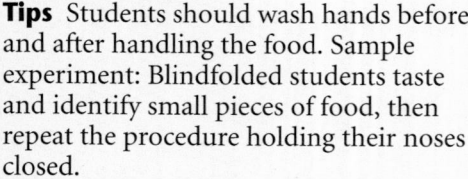
Time 15 minutes
Tips Students should wash hands before and after handling the food. Sample experiment: Blindfolded students taste and identify small pieces of food, then repeat the procedure holding their noses closed.
Extend Have students test whether a person can identify the food based on the food's scent, without tasting it.

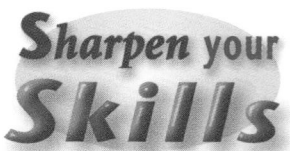
Sharpen your Skills

Designing Experiments

Can people tell one food from another if they can taste the foods but not smell them? Design an experiment to find out. Use these foods: a peeled pear, a peeled apple, and a peeled raw potato. Be sure to control all variables except the one you are testing. Write your hypothesis and a description of your procedure. Show these to your teacher. Do not perform your experiment until your teacher approves your procedure.

Figure 19 The semicircular canals of the inner ear enable people to keep their balance—even in very tricky situations!

You can see how these structures got their name if you look at Figure 19. These canals, as well as two tiny sacs located behind them, are full of fluid. The canals and sacs are also lined with tiny cells that have hairlike extensions.

When your head moves, the fluid in the semicircular canals is set in motion. The moving fluid makes the cells' hairlike extensions bend. This bending produces nerve impulses in sensory neurons. The impulses travel to the cerebellum. The cerebellum then analyzes the impulses to determine the way your head is moving and the position of your body. If the cerebellum senses that you are losing your balance, it sends impulses to muscles that help you restore your balance.

Smell and Taste

You walk into the house and smell the aroma of freshly baked cookies. You bite into one and taste its rich chocolate flavor. When you smelled the cookies, receptors in your nose reacted to chemicals carried by the air from the cookies to your nose. When you took a bite of a cookie, taste buds on your tongue responded to chemicals in the food. These food chemicals were dissolved in saliva, which came in contact with your taste buds.

The senses of smell and taste work closely together, and both depend on chemicals. The chemicals trigger responses in receptors in the nose and mouth. Nerve impulses then travel to the brain, where they are interpreted as smells or tastes.

The nose can distinguish at least 50 basic odors. In contrast, there are only four kinds of taste buds—sweet, sour, salty, and bitter. When you eat, however, you experience a much wider variety of tastes. The flavor of food is determined by both the the senses of smell and taste. When you have a cold, your favorite foods may not taste as good as they usually do. That is because a stuffy nose can decrease your ability to smell food.

Touch

Unlike vision, hearing, balance, smell, and taste, the sense of touch is not found in one specific place. Instead, the sense of touch is found in all areas of your skin. Your skin is your largest sense organ!

Your skin contains different kinds of touch receptors. Some of these receptors respond to light touch and others to heavy pressure. Still other receptors pick up sensations of pain and temperature change.

The receptors that respond to light touch are in the upper part of the dermis. They tell you when something brushes against your skin. These receptors also let you feel the textures of objects, such as smooth glass and rough sandpaper. Receptors deeper in the dermis pick up the feeling of pressure. Press down hard on the top of your desk, for example, and you will feel pressure in your fingers.

The dermis also contains receptors that respond to temperature and pain. Pain is unpleasant, but it can be one of the body's most important feelings, because it alerts the body to possible danger. Have you ever stepped into a bathtub of very hot water and then immediately pulled your foot out? If so, you can appreciate how pain can trigger an important response in your body.

Figure 20 Blind people use their sense of touch to read. To do this, they run their fingers over words written in Braille. Braille uses raised dots to represent letters and numbers. Here a teacher shows a blind child how to read Braille.

 **Section 3 Review**

1. What overall role do the senses perform in the body?
2. Describe the process by which your eyes produce an image of your surroundings. Begin at the point at which light is focused by the lens.
3. How do sound vibrations affect structures in the ear to produce the sensation of hearing?
4. How are the senses of taste and smell similar? How are they different?
5. **Thinking Critically** Relating Cause and Effect Infections of the inner ear sometimes make people more likely to lose their balance and fall. Explain why this is so.

Check Your Progress
CHAPTER PROJECT

By now, you should have submitted your plans for your experiment to your teacher. Make any necessary changes in the plan. Prepare all the materials for the fair, including the illusions and questionnaire. Have a data table ready so you can record all responses. (*Hint:* Be sure the people you test cannot see or hear each other's responses. Also, test a large enough number of individuals.)

Chapter 20 **643**

Touch

Addressing Naive Conceptions

Students may think that the sense of touch refers only to feeling things with their fingers. Point out that there are touch receptors throughout the skin. **learning modality: verbal**

3 Assess

Section 3 Review Answers

1. The senses pick up specific information about the environment and change that information to nerve impulses that travel to the brain.
2. Focused light rays strike the retina. Receptor cells send nerve impulses to the brain, which turns the image right side up and combines the images from each eye into a single image.
3. Sound vibrations make the eardrum vibrate. These vibrations pass to the bones of the middle ear, which vibrate against a thin membrane that channels the vibrations to the cochlear fluid. The vibrating fluid stimulates receptor cells that send nerve impulses to the brain.
4. Taste and smell both respond to chemicals. Taste responds to chemicals in saliva, while smell responds to chemicals in air. There are about 50 basic odors, but only 4 basic tastes.
5. An infection may damage the semicircular canals and upset balance.

Check Your Progress
CHAPTER PROJECT

If possible, set up a testing booth in which students can test each other or students from other classes.

Performance Assessment

Writing Have students write brief explanations of how each of the senses sends information to the brain when students eat a sandwich.

643

SECTION 4 Alcohol and Other Drugs

Objectives

After completing the lesson, students will be able to
◆ name some commonly abused drugs and state how they affect the body;
◆ explain how alcohol abuse harms the body.

Key Terms drug, drug abuse, tolerance, withdrawal, depressant, stimulant, anabolic steroid, alcoholism

1 Engage/Explore

Activating Prior Knowledge

Have a class discussion about drugs and drug abuse. Ask students questions such as these: **If I get sick, is it okay for me to take someone else's prescription medicine?** and **If a medicine makes me feel better, will taking twice as much make me feel better faster?** Encourage students to discuss similar issues. Explain that this section will give them information about the proper way to use medicine and other drugs.

DISCOVER

Skills Focus inferring
Materials *pieces of wrapped candy*
Time 15 minutes
Tips After the activity, have students try to identify different kinds of arguments—for example, suggesting that drug use enhances popularity; insisting that drugs are harmless. Discard all candy after the activity.
Think It Over If peers encourage someone to do something, such as eat candy or use drugs, it may be difficult not to agree with them. Therefore, peer pressure can make it hard for people to say no to drugs.

SECTION 4 Alcohol and Other Drugs

DISCOVER .... ACTIVITY

How Can You Best Say No?

1. In this activity, you will use candy to represent drugs. Your teacher will divide the class into groups of three students. In each group, your teacher will appoint two students to try to persuade the other person to take the "drugs."

2. Depending on your role, you should think of arguments to get the person to accept the candy or arguments against accepting it. After everyone has had a chance to think of arguments, begin the discussion.

3. After a while, students in each group should exchange roles.

Think It Over
Inferring What role does peer pressure play in whether or not a person decides to abuse drugs?

GUIDE FOR READING

◆ How do commonly abused drugs affect the body?
◆ How does alcohol abuse harm the body?

Reading Tip Before you read, preview the table on page 647. List some ways in which drugs affect the central nervous system.

Drugs! You probably hear and see that word in a lot of places. Drugstores sell drugs to relieve headaches, soothe upset stomachs, and stop coughs. Radio and television programs and magazine articles explore drug-related problems. Your school probably has a program to educate students about drugs. When people talk about drugs, what do they mean? To a scientist, a **drug** is any chemical that causes changes in a person's body or behavior. Many drugs affect the functioning of the nervous system.

Medicines

Medicines are legal drugs that help the body fight disease and injury. Aspirin, for example, is a medicine that can relieve pain. To purchase some medicines, you need a doctor's prescription. Other medicines, however, can be bought in drugstores or supermarkets without a prescription. If medicines are used properly, they can help you stay healthy or speed your recovery from sickness. Whenever you take medicines of any kind, it is important to follow the directions for their proper use.

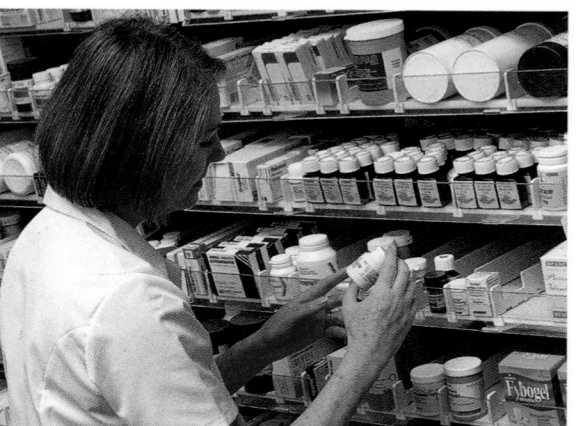

◀ Medicines in a drugstore

READING STRATEGIES

Reading Tip Help students interpret the column headings as they preview the table on effects of abused drugs. Have volunteers explain the difference between immediate effects and long-term effects. Then instruct students to list some of the ways in which drugs affect the central nervous system. Sample answer: Long-term effects include damage to the heart, kidneys, liver and nervous system.

Study and Comprehension While students read the section, have them write a list of their questions about abused drugs. Encourage students to find answers to their questions in the chapter. After students have read the section, hold a question-and-answer session or panel discussion for the students to help each other answer their questions.

Drug Abuse

The deliberate misuse of drugs for purposes other than medical ones is called **drug abuse.** Medicines can be abused drugs if they are used in a way for which they are not intended. Many abused drugs, however, such as cocaine and heroin, are illegal under all circumstances. The use of these drugs is against the law because their effects on the body are very dangerous.

Immediate Effects of Abused Drugs Abused drugs start to affect the body very shortly after they are taken. Different drugs have different effects. Some drugs cause nausea and a fast, irregular heartbeat. Others can cause sleepiness. Drug abusers may also experience headaches, dizziness, and trembling.

Most commonly abused drugs, such as marijuana, alcohol, and cocaine, are especially dangerous because they act on the brain and other parts of the nervous system. For example, alcohol can cause confusion, poor muscle coordination, and blurred vision. These effects are especially dangerous in situations in which an alert mind is essential, such as driving a car.

Most abused drugs can alter, or change, a person's mood and feelings. Because of this effect, these drugs are often called mood-altering drugs. For example, the mood of a person under the influence of marijuana may change from calm to anxious. Alcohol can sometimes make a person angry and even violent. Mood-altering drugs also affect patterns of thinking and the way in which the brain interprets information from the senses.

Tolerance If a person takes a drug regularly, the body may develop a tolerance to the drug. **Tolerance** is a state in which a drug user needs larger and larger amounts of the drug to produce the same effect on the body. Tolerance can cause people to take a very large amount of a drug, or an overdose. People who take an overdose may lose consciousness or even die.

Figure 21 Abused drugs such as these can cause serious physical and emotional problems. *Applying Concepts List three ways in which drugs can affect the body.*

Medicines

Building Inquiry Skills: Communicating

Materials *empty boxes or labels from over-the-counter medications such as aspirin, cold and flu medicines, or skin ointments*
Time 20 minutes

Give each student a box or label. Have students find the symptoms that the medicine treats, the correct dosage, and any possible side effects. Students can summarize their findings from the class in a brief oral report. Ask: **Why is it important to read the label on over-the-counter medications?** *(You need to be sure that the medicine will treat your symptoms, that you take the right amount, and that you are prepared to recognize any dangerous side effects.)* **learning modality: verbal**

Drug Abuse

Addressing Naive Conceptions

Students may not realize that any substance that affects a person's body or behavior is a drug and may be abused. Point out that over-the-counter medications and herbs that are used as medicines can be very dangerous if not taken correctly. **learning modality: verbal**

Program Resources

◆ **Unit 4 Resources** 20-4 Lesson Plan, p. 153 20-4 Section Summary, p. 154

Media and Technology

 Audio CD English-Spanish Summary 20-4

Answers to Self-Assessment

Caption Question

Figure 21 Samples: They can act on the brain and nervous system to cause confusion, poor muscle coordination, altered mood, and blurred vision.

Ongoing Assessment

Writing Have students list some typical effects of abused drugs.

Drug Abuse, continued

Sharpen your Skills

Communicating

Materials *paper, drawing materials*

Time 45 minutes

Tips Allow students to work in teams. After brainstorming ideas, some students can plan the narrative sequence of the commercial; others can create the storyboards; and others can write the script.

Extend Arrange to have students present their commercials to younger students or to another class.
cooperative learning

Other Effects of Drug Abuse

Demonstration

Materials *paper cup, red food coloring, water, plastic droppers*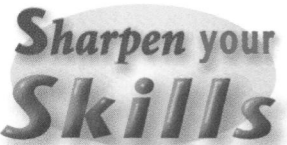

Time 15 minutes

To show students how HIV and other infected blood can be passed through shared needles, give a volunteer a paper cup half full of water to which you have added 20 drops of food coloring. Have the volunteer draw up colored water in a dropper, then expel some of it into an empty cup. Then have the volunteer use the same dropper to draw up some clear water and expel the water in the dropper into another empty cup. The water in the second cup will be tinged with red. Ask: **What does the red liquid represent?** *(Infected blood)* **learning modality: visual**

Sharpen your Skills

Communicating

Plan a 30-second television commercial aimed at teenagers to help them avoid the pressure to try drugs. Your commercial should reveal some harmful effects of drugs and give strategies for avoiding drugs. Create several storyboards to show what the commercial will look like. Then write a script for your commercial.

Addiction For many commonly abused drugs, repeated use can result in addiction. The body becomes physically dependent on the drug. If a drug addict misses a few doses of the drug, the body reacts to the lack of the drug. The person may experience headaches, fever, vomiting, body aches, and muscle cramps. The person is experiencing **withdrawal,** a period of adjustment that occurs when a person stops taking a drug.

Some drugs may also cause a person to become emotionally dependent on them. The person becomes accustomed to the feelings and moods produced by the drug. Therefore, the person has a strong desire to continue using the drug.

☑ *Checkpoint* **What is meant by a tolerance to a drug?**

Other Effects of Drug Abuse

Drugs can also affect a person's health indirectly. Drug users sometimes share needles. When a person uses a needle to inject a drug, some of the person's blood remains in the needle after it is withdrawn. If the person has HIV or another pathogen in the blood, the next person to use the needle may become infected with the pathogen.

The abuse of drugs also has serious legal and social effects. A person who is caught using or selling an illegal drug may have to pay a fine or go to jail. Drug abuse can also make a person unable to get along with others. Drug abusers often have a hard time doing well in school or holding a job.

Kinds of Drugs

Figure 22 lists and describes the characteristics of some commonly abused drugs. Notice in the chart that some drugs are classified as depressants. **Depressants** are drugs that slow down the activity of the central nervous system. When people take depressants, their muscles relax and they may become sleepy. They may take longer than normal to respond to stimuli. For example, depressants may prevent people from reacting quickly to the danger of a car rushing toward them. Alcohol and narcotics, such as heroin, are depressants.

Stimulants, in contrast, speed up body processes. They make the heart beat faster and make the breathing rate increase. Cocaine and nicotine are stimulants, as are amphetamines. Amphetamines (am FET uh meenz) are prescription drugs that are sometimes sold illegally.

Background

Facts and Figures The most common drug tests require samples of blood, urine, or hair. Blood testing is often used after an accident or crime to determine the presence and amount of a drug in the body at the time of the incident. The results of a blood test can be used to estimate the time and amount of drug use that occurred up to twenty-four hours prior to the test. Urine tests can determine whether certain drugs have been used recently. The length of time a drug can be detected in urine varies from several hours to several weeks. Urine tests are often used to test athletes to determine whether there is a consistent pattern of drug use. Hair analysis can reveal chronic drug use that occurred at any point during the growth of the hair.

Some Effects of Commonly Abused Drugs

Drug Type	Short-Term Effects	Long-Term Effects	Physical Addiction?	Emotional Dependence?
marijuana (including hashish)	anxiety, panic, excitement, sleepiness	difficulty with concentration and memory, respiratory disease and lung cancer	probably not	yes
nicotine (in cigarettes, cigars, chewing tobacco)	stimulant; nausea, loss of appetite, headache	heart and lung disease, difficulty breathing, heavy coughing	yes, strongly so	yes
alcohol	depressant; decreased alertness, poor reflexes, nausea, emotional depression	liver and brain damage, inadequate nutrition	yes	yes
inhalants (glue, nail polish remover, paint thinner)	sleepiness, nausea, headaches, emotional depression	damage to liver, kidneys, and brain; hallucinations	no	yes
cocaine (including crack)	stimulant; nervousness, disturbed sleep, loss of appetite	mental illness, damage to lining of nose, irregular heartbeat, heart or breathing failure, liver damage	yes	yes, strongly so
amphetamines	stimulant; restlessness, rapid speech, dizziness	restlessness, irritability, irregular heartbeat, liver damage	possible	yes
hallucinogens (LSD, mescaline, PCP)	hallucinations, anxiety, panic; thoughts and actions not connected to reality	mental illness; fearfulness; behavioral changes, including violence	no	yes
barbiturates (Phenobarbital, Nembutal, Seconal)	depressant; decreased alertness, slowed thought processes, poor muscle coordination	sleepiness, irritability, confusion	yes	yes
tranquilizers (Valium, Xanax)	depressant; blurred vision, sleepiness, unclear speech, headache, skin rash	blood and liver disease	yes	yes
narcotics (opium, codeine, morphine, heroin)	depressant; sleepiness, nausea, hallucinations	convulsion, coma, death	yes, very rapid development	yes, strongly so
anabolic steroids	mood swings	heart, liver, and kidney damage; hypertension; overgrowth of skull and facial bones	no	yes

Figure 22 Abused drugs can have many serious effects on the body. *Interpreting Charts What are the long-term effects of using inhalants?*

Answers to Self-Assessment

Caption Question

Figure 22 The long term effects of using inhalants are damage to the liver, kidneys, and brain, as well as hallucinations.

☑ *Checkpoint*

Tolerance to a drug is the state in which a drug user needs larger and larger amounts of the drug to get the same effect.

Kinds of Drugs

Building Inquiry Skills: Making Generalizations

As students examine the chart in Figure 22, have them make generalizations about the different categories of drugs and their effects. Ask questions such as the following: **What percent of the drugs listed may be physically addictive?** *(64 percent)* **What percent cause emotional dependency?** *(100 percent)* **learning modality: logical/mathematical**

Ongoing Assessment

Skills Check Have students use the table in Figure 22 to compare and contrast the short- and long-term effects of stimulants, depressants, and hallucinogens.

You, the Consumer

With Caffeine or Without?

Preparing for Inquiry

Key Concept Stimulants such as caffeine cause body processes to speed up.

Skills Objectives Students will be able to
- develop hypotheses about the effect of caffeine on an organism;
- design experiments to test their hypotheses.

Time 40 minutes

Advance Planning Purchase blackworms (*Lumbriculus*) and adrenaline (epinephrine) from a biological supply company. To prepare the adrenaline solution (about 0.01%), dissolve 10 mg epinephrine hydrochloride in 100 mL distilled water. Have available all other materials, including beverages with caffeine and "decaffeinated" beverages. Beverages must be diluted to reduce pH levels. Suggested dilution is 1 mL beverage to 99 mL water.

To make the paraffin specimen blocks, use a paper clip to make a shallow trough approximately 4 centimeters long in the center of the block. Use the edge of a microscope slide to push a piece of thread into the bottom of the trough.

Alternative Materials Possible beverage choices include cola or coffee, citrus soda or juice, caffeine-free cola or decaffeinated coffee.

Guiding Inquiry

Invitation

Have students read through the lab. Ask students why adrenaline is used in Part 1 when the experiment is testing the effects of caffeine. (*It illustrates how a known stimulant will affect the blackworms.*) Ask students to describe the advantages and disadvantages of using blackworms as the test subject. (*Samples: The transparent body allows easy observation of changes in pulse rate. Effects of caffeine on blackworms may be different than effects on humans.*)

Some substances, called inhalants, produce mood-altering effects when they are inhaled, or breathed in. Inhalants include paint thinner, nail polish remover, and some kinds of cleaning fluids. Hallucinogens, such as LSD and mescaline, can make people see or hear things that do not really exist.

Some athletes try to improve their performance by taking drugs known as steroids. **Anabolic steroids** (an uh BAH lik steer oydz) are synthetic chemicals that are similar to hormones produced in the body. You will learn more about hormones in Chapter 21.

Anabolic steroids may increase muscle size and strength. However, steroids can cause mood changes that lead to violence.

You, the Consumer

With Caffeine or Without?

Caffeine is a stimulant found in some beverages and foods, such as coffee, cola drinks, and chocolate. In this lab, you'll observe the effect that caffeine has on a nonhuman organism to help understand how caffeine may affect your own body.

Problem

What body changes does caffeine produce in blackworms *(Lumbriculus)*?

Skills Focus

developing hypotheses, designing experiments

Materials

blackworms
plastic dropper
paraffin specimen trough
noncarbonated spring water
adrenaline solution
beverages with and without caffeine
stereomicroscope
stopwatch or clock with second hand

Procedure

Part 1 Observing Effects of a Known Stimulant

1. Use a dropper to remove one worm and a drop or two of water from a blackworm population provided by your teacher.
2. Place the worm and the water in the trough of the paraffin block. Use the dropper or the corner of a paper towel to remove any excess water that does not fit in the trough. Let the blackworm adjust to the block for a few minutes.
3. Place the paraffin block under the stereo-microscope. Select the smallest amount of light and the lowest possible power to view the blackworm.
4. Look through the stereomicroscope and locate a segment near the middle of the worm. Count the number of times blood pulses through this segment for 30 seconds. Multiply this number by two to get the pulse in beats per minute. Record the pulse.

Introducing the Procedure
- Demonstrate the proper procedure for applying a blackworm to the paraffin block.
- Use the illustration of the blackworm to show students where the pulsing blood vessel is located and demonstrate how to determine the pulse rate.

Troubleshooting the Experiment
- Students should use new blackworms for Part 2 and for the Design an Experiment. Exposing a single blackworm to many different substances in quick succession would stress the organism and lead to erroneous data. In addition, residual amounts of the various test substances could remain in the blackworm as it is exposed to new test substances.
- Students should determine the pulse rate as soon as they are able to view the blackworm.

In addition, steroid abuse can cause serious health problems, such as heart damage, liver damage, and increased blood pressure. Steroid use is especially dangerous for teenagers, whose growing bodies can be permanently damaged.

Alcohol

Alcohol is a drug found in many beverages, including beer, wine, cocktails, and hard liquor. Alcohol is a powerful depressant. In the United States, it is illegal for people under the age of 21 to buy or possess alcohol. In spite of this fact, alcohol is the most commonly abused drug in people aged 12 to 17.

5. Remove the block from the stereo-microscope. Use the dropper to add 1 drop of adrenaline solution to the trough. (Adrenaline is a substance that is produced by the human body and that acts in a manner similar to a stimulant.) Let the worm sit in the adrenaline solution for 5 minutes.
6. Place the paraffin block under the stereomicroscope. Again locate a segment near the middle of the worm. Count the number of pulses through this segment for 30 seconds. Multiply this number by two to get the pulse in beats per minute. Record the blackworm's pulse with adrenaline.

Part 2 Testing the Effects of Caffeine

7. Using the procedures you followed in Part 1, design an experiment that tests the effect of caffeine on the blackworm's pulse. You can use beverages with and without caffeine in your investigation. Be sure to write a hypothesis and control all necessary variables.
8. Submit your experimental plan to your teacher for review. After making any necessary changes, carry out your experiment.

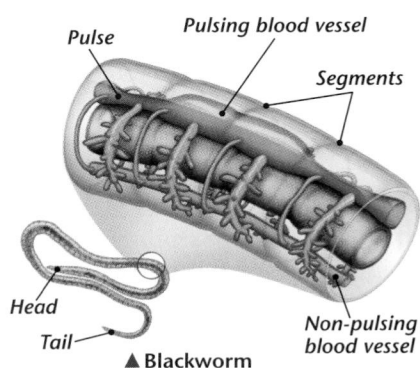

▲ Blackworm

Analyze and Conclude

1. What effect does a stimulant have?
2. In Part 1, how did you know that adrenaline acted as a stimulant?
3. In Part 2, did caffeine act as a stimulant?
4. **Apply** Based on your work in Part 2, how do you think your body would react to drinks with caffeine? To drinks without caffeine?

Design an Experiment

Do you think that "decaffeinated" products will act as a stimulant in blackworms? Design a controlled experiment to find out. Obtain your teacher's approval before performing this experiment.

Safety

Before the lab, remind students to treat the blackworms with as much care as possible. Caution them not to taste any of the beverages. They should wash their hands thoroughly after the lab. Review the safety guidelines in Appendix A.

Program Resources

◆ **Unit 4 Resources** Chapter 20 Real-World Lab, pp. 159–161

Expected Outcome
◆ Normal pulse rate for blackworms, depending on the species, varies from 24 to 32 beats per minute.
◆ Adrenaline and caffeine are stimulants and should cause the pulse rate to increase. Drinks without caffeine should not increase the pulse rate.

Analyze and Conclude
1. A stimulant causes the body of an organism to increase the rate of certain activities, such as heartbeat and breathing.
2. Because adrenaline caused an increase in the blackworm pulse rate
3. Yes, because caffeine caused the pulse rate to increase.
4. Some students may infer that drinks without caffeine will have no effect on humans, whereas drinks with caffeine will cause increased heart rates and related changes. Other students may say that since humans and blackworms are so different, the effect of caffeine on humans cannot be predicted based on this evidence.

Extending the Inquiry

Design an Experiment Students should design an experiment similar to Part 2 of this lab, substituting a "decaffeinated" beverage for the beverage with caffeine. Results may vary depending on how completely the caffeine has been removed from the beverage.

Alcohol

Addressing Naive Conceptions

Many people believe that alcoholism only develops from drinking hard liquor. Explain that all forms of alcohol can be involved in alcohol abuse and alcoholism. A bottle of beer, a wine cooler, a glass of wine, and a shot glass of hard liquor all contain about the same amount of alcohol. Ask: **How can a person who drinks only wine coolers become an alcoholic?** *(If they become physically addicted and emotionally dependent on the alcohol in the wine coolers, they can develop alcoholism.)*
learning modality: verbal

Building Inquiry Skills: Measuring

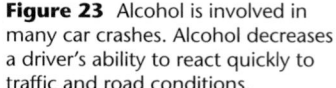

Materials *1 L plastic container, plastic graduated cylinder marked in mL, dropper marked in mL, about 1 L of water, 1 mL of vegetable oil*

Time 15 minutes

Using water and oil to represent blood and alcohol, respectively, let pairs of students demonstrate the relative volumes of blood and alcohol present for a BAC value of 0.1 percent. Have them fill the 1 L container with 999 mL of water, then use the dropper to place 1 mL of oil on top of the water. Use this demonstration to show that even a small amount of alcohol in the bloodstream can have a serious impact on the body. **learning modality: visual**

Including All Students

For students who need an additional challenge, have them calculate how many alcohol-related injuries take place in a 24-hour period. *(24 hours = 1,440 minutes. 1,440 minutes ÷ 2 minutes = 720 accidents)* Then challenge students to determine how many such accidents take place each year. *(365 × 720 = 262,800 accidents per year.)* **learning modality: logical/mathematical**

Social Studies Connection

Tell students that attitudes about drinking alcohol have varied among cultures and through history. Many countries have attempted to control alcohol consumption and alcoholism by prohibiting the sale of alcohol. In 1919, the Eighteenth Amendment to the Constitution of the United States was passed, prohibiting the sale of alcohol. In 1933, the Twenty-First Amendment was passed to repeal the Eighteenth. The years from 1919–1933 are known as Prohibition. Interested students may want to research alcohol-related social issues in the United States during the time leading up to Prohibition and the time following it. **learning modality: verbal**

650

How Alcohol Affects the Body Alcohol is absorbed by the digestive system quickly. If a person drinks alcohol on an empty stomach, the alcohol enters the blood and gets to the brain and other organs almost immediately. If alcohol is drunk with a meal, it takes longer to get into the blood.

To understand what alcohol does to the body, look at *Exploring the Effects of Alcohol.* The more alcohol in the blood, the more serious the effects. The amount of alcohol in the blood is usually expressed as blood alcohol concentration, or BAC. A BAC value of 0.1 percent means that one tenth of one percent of the fluid in the blood is alcohol. In some states, if car drivers have a BAC of 0.08 percent or more, they are legally drunk. In other states, drivers with a BAC of 0.1 are considered drunk.

Alcohol produces serious effects, including loss of normal judgment, at a BAC of less than 0.08 percent. This loss of judgment can have serious consequences. For example, people who have been drinking may not realize that they cannot drive a car safely. In the United States, alcohol is involved in about 40 percent of traffic-related deaths. About every two minutes, a person in the United States is injured in a car crash related to alcohol.

Long-Term Alcohol Abuse Many adults drink occasionally, and in moderation, without serious safety or health problems. However, heavy drinking, especially over a long period, can result in significant health problems. **The abuse of alcohol can cause the destruction of cells in the brain and liver, and it can also lead to addiction and emotional dependence.** Damage to the brain can cause mental disturbances, such as hallucinations and

Figure 23 Alcohol is involved in many car crashes. Alcohol decreases a driver's ability to react quickly to traffic and road conditions.

650

loss of consciousness. The liver, which breaks down alcohol for elimination from the body, can become so scarred that it does not function properly. In addition, long-term alcohol abuse can increase the risk of getting certain kinds of cancer.

Abuse of alcohol can result in **alcoholism,** a disease in which a person is both physically addicted to and emotionally dependent on alcohol. To give up alcohol, alcoholics must go through withdrawal, as with any addictive drug. To give up drinking,

EXPLORING *the Effects of Alcohol*

Alcohol is a drug that affects every system of the body. It also impacts a person's thought processes and judgment.

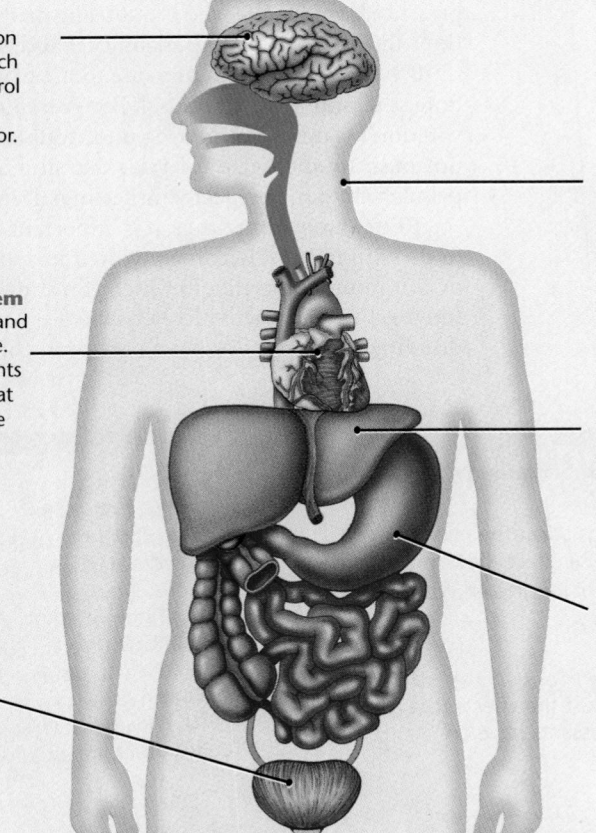

Nervous system Vision becomes blurred. Speech becomes unclear. Control of behavior is reduced. Judgment becomes poor.

Cardiovascular system At first, heartbeat rate and blood pressure increase. Later, with large amounts of alcohol, the heartbeat rate and blood pressure may decrease.

Excretory system Alcohol causes the kidneys to produce more urine. As a result, the drinker loses more water than usual.

Skin Blood flow to the skin increases, causing rapid loss of body heat.

Liver The liver breaks down alcohol. Over many years, liver damage can result.

Digestive system Alcohol is absorbed directly from the stomach and small intestine. The alcohol passes into the bloodstream quickly.

Chapter 20 **651**

EXPLORING

the Effects of Alcohol

As students study the visual essay, ask: **How does alcohol get to different parts of the body?** *(It is carried in the blood.)* Then ask about the short-term effects of alcohol. **Why shouldn't people drink alcohol to keep warm on a cold night?** *(Alcohol causes rapid loss of body heat, so people would get colder if they drank alcohol.)* **Why shouldn't people drink alcohol when they are thirsty?** *(When people are thirsty their bodies need water, and alcohol causes the body to lose water.)* **How does alcohol affect blood pressure and heart rate?** *(First blood pressure and heart rate rise; then they drop.)* **How does alcohol impair a person's ability to drive?** *(It blurs vision, keeps a person from making good judgments, and impairs coordination.)* **What is one long-term effect of alcohol abuse?** *(Liver damage)* **Extend** Invite a guest speaker from an organization such as Mothers Against Drunk Drivers to answer students' questions about alcohol and alcoholism. **learning modality: verbal**

Avoiding Drugs and Alcohol

Building Inquiry Skills: Communicating

Time 20 minutes

ACTIVITY

Have small groups of students role-play scenarios such as confronting a sibling who is using drugs or alcohol, helping a friend decide not to drink a beer at a party, and avoiding a drug pusher's threats. After students have taken turns in different roles, have them present one scenario for the class. **cooperative learning**

Ongoing Assessment

Writing Have students summarize how alcohol affects two different body systems.

3 Assess

Section 4 Review Answers

1. Some abused drugs cause confusion, poor muscle coordination, and blurred vision. These effects can be dangerous in situations where an alert mind, good judgment, and quick reaction time are essential. Other drugs can alter people's mood, which can make them have difficulties in social situations, or can even cause them to be violent.

2. Long-term alcohol abuse can cause destruction of cells in the brain and liver and increase a person's risk of getting certain kinds of cancer. It can also lead to addiction and emotional dependence.

3. Alcoholism is a disease in which a person is both physically addicted to and emotionally dependent on alcohol.

4. Depressants slow down the activity of the central nervous system. They relax the muscles and make people sleepy and slow to respond to stimuli. Stimulants speed up the body processes. They make the heart beat faster and make the breathing rate increase.

Check Your Progress
CHAPTER PROJECT

Encourage groups to work together to plan their presentations, and then divide the work. For example, one student or student pair could analyze the results, another describe the tests, and another explain how illusions trick the senses. Encourage students to prepare visual aids such as pie graphs to support their findings.

Performance Assessment

Drawing Have small groups of students choose one type of drug described in the section and create an informational display poster about its short-term and long-term effects on the body.

652

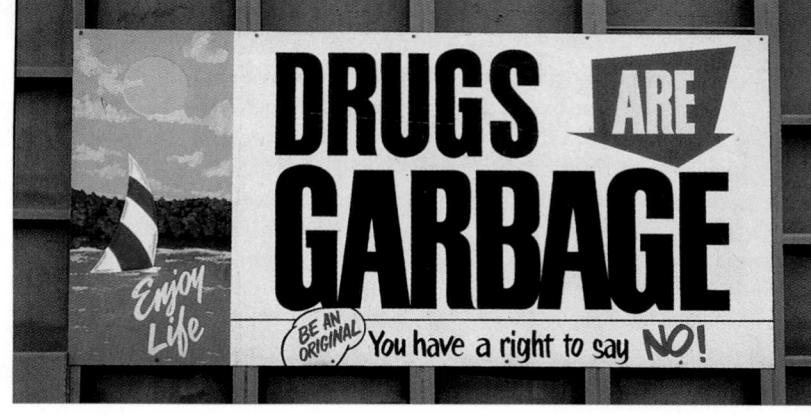

Figure 24 The message is clear: drugs are dangerous, and you have the right to refuse to take them.

alcoholics need both medical and emotional help. Medical professionals and organizations such as Alcoholics Anonymous can help a person stop drinking.

Avoiding Drugs and Alcohol

The best way to avoid depending on drugs and alcohol is not to start using them. Many teenagers who start do so because of peer pressure from people who are abusing drugs. Try to avoid situations in which there is a possibility that drugs may be used.

If you are faced with pressure to use drugs, give a simple but honest reason for your refusal. For example, you might say that you don't want to risk getting into trouble with the law. You do not need to apologize for your decision. And remember that people who don't respect your feelings aren't very good friends.

To stay away from drugs, it is important to find healthy things to do with friends. Become involved in sports and other school or community activities in which you and your friends can have fun together. Such activities help you feel good about yourself. By deciding not to use drugs, you are protecting your health.

Section 4 Review

1. How do abused drugs affect the nervous system? Why can these effects be dangerous?
2. What are the effects of long-term alcohol abuse?
3. What is alcoholism?
4. **Thinking Critically Comparing and Contrasting** Contrast the effects that stimulants and depressants have on the body.

Check Your Progress
CHAPTER PROJECT

By now you should have finished collecting your data and recording your observations. Now begin preparing a report about your findings. Think about the best way to communicate the procedures you followed and the results you obtained. Your report should explain how you think the illusions you chose trick the senses. Decide how to use graphs and other visuals in your report.

652

Program Resources

◆ **Unit 4 Resources** 20-4 Review and Reinforce, p. 155; 20-4 Enrich, p. 156

SECTION 1 How the Nervous System Works

Key Ideas

◆ The nervous system receives information about the external and internal environment and helps maintain homeostasis.

Key Terms

stimulus	dendrite	interneuron
response	axon	motor neuron
neuron	nerve	synapse
nerve impulse	sensory neuron	

SECTION 2 Divisions of the Nervous System

Key Ideas

◆ The central nervous system consists of the brain and spinal cord.
◆ The peripheral nervous system links the central nervous system to the rest of the body.

Key Terms

central nervous system	cerebellum
peripheral nervous system	brainstem
	somatic nervous system
brain	autonomic nervous system
spinal cord	reflex
cerebrum	concussion

SECTION 3 The Senses

Key Ideas

◆ The senses change information about the environment to nerve impulses.
◆ After light enters the eye, it passes through the lens, which focuses it on the retina. Impulses then travel to the brain.
◆ Sound waves start vibrations in structures in the ear. When the vibrations reach the cochlea, impulses are sent to the brain.

Key Terms

cornea	retina	eardrum
pupil	nearsightedness	cochlea
iris	farsightedness	semicircular canal
lens		

SECTION 4 Alcohol and Other Drugs

INTEGRATING HEALTH

Key Ideas

◆ Abused drugs act on the nervous system. Depressants slow down the central nervous system. Stimulants speed up body processes. Marijuana, alcohol, amphetamines, and anabolic steroids are commonly abused drugs.
◆ The long-term abuse of alcohol can damage the liver and brain and lead to alcoholism.

Key Terms

drug	withdrawal	anabolic steroid
drug abuse	depressant	alcoholism
tolerance	stimulant	

Organizing Information

Concept Map Complete the following concept map about nerve cells and their functions. (For more on concept maps, see the Skills Handbook.)

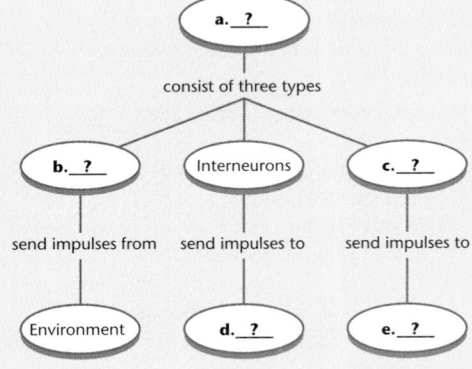

Chapter 20 **653**

Organizing Information

Concept Map a. Nerve cells
b. Sensory neurons c. Motor neurons
d. Other neurons e. Muscles

Program Resources

◆ **Unit 4 Resources** Chapter 20 Project Scoring Rubric, p. 140
◆ **Performance Assessment** Chapter 20, pp. 62–64
◆ **Chapter and Unit Tests** Chapter 20 Test, pp. 92–95

Media and Technology

Interactive Student Tutorial CD-ROM Chapter 20

Computer Test Bank Chapter 20 Test

Reviewing Content
Multiple Choice
1. a **2.** b **3.** d **4.** d **5.** c

True or False
6. true **7.** true **8.** farsightedness
9. stirrup **10.** true

Checking Concepts
11. The axon carries the nerve impulse away from the cell body. The dendrites carry the nerve impulse to the cell body.
12. The autonomic nervous system controls involuntary actions.
13. When you ride a bicycle, the motor neuron impulses that tell your feet to peddle begin in the cerebrum. The cerebellum gives you the muscular coordination and a sense of balance that keep you from falling off the bicycle.
14. To protect your central nervous system, you should wear a helmet when bicycling, skating, or doing other activities where there is a risk of bumping your head. Wear a seatbelt in a motor vehicle. When swimming, make sure that the water is deep enough before diving into it.
15. For nearsightedness, the glasses bend the light rays away from each other so they are spread apart when they reach the lens of the eye. Then the lens of the eye can correctly focus the rays. For farsight-edness, the glasses bend the light rays toward each other so they are closer together when they reach the lens of the eye.
16. Eardrum, hammer, anvil, stirrup, thin membrane, fluid in the cochlea
17. Anabolic steroids may increase strength and muscle size but they also cause mood changes, including violence.
18. Answers will vary. The plan should use the aliens' lack of a sense of touch to reveal who is an alien or to combat the aliens in some way.

Thinking Critically
19. The stroke occurred in the left side of the brain; the left side of the brain has control over the right side of the body.
20. This process is an example of a reflex. It protects the man by making him jerk his foot automatically up, before his foot pushes down further and causes any more damage or pain. The

Reviewing Content
 For more review of key concepts, see the Interactive Student Tutorial CD-ROM.

Multiple Choice
Choose the letter of the best answer.

1. A change or signal in the environment that makes the nervous system react is called a
  a. stimulus.   **b.** response.
  c. receptor.   **d.** synapse.
2. The structures that carry messages toward a neuron's cell body are
  a. axons.
  b. dendrites.
  c. nerves.
  d. impulses.
3. Which structure links the brain and the peripheral nervous system?
  a. the cerebrum
  b. the cerebellum
  c. the cochlea
  d. the spinal cord
4. Which structure adjusts the size of the pupil?
  a. the cornea
  b. the retina
  c. the lens
  d. the iris
5. Physical dependence on a drug is called
  a. withdrawal.
  b. response.
  c. addiction.
  d. tolerance.

True or False
If the statement is true, write true. If it is false, change the underlined word or words to make the statement true.

6. A nerve message is also called a <u>nerve impulse</u>.
7. The <u>brainstem</u> is the part of the brain that controls involuntary actions.
8. In <u>nearsightedness</u>, a person cannot see nearby objects clearly.
9. The hammer, anvil, and <u>wrench</u> are the three bones in the middle ear.
10. Alcohol is a <u>depressant</u>.

reflex action quickly prevents the man from doing any more harm to himself.
21. Answers will vary. Students should give simple but clear reasons such as not wanting to risk addiction, not wanting to get in trouble, and being afraid of the negative side effects of drugs.

Checking Concepts
11. Compare the functions of axons and dendrites.
12. What is the function of the autonomic nervous system?
13. How do the cerebrum and cerebellum work together when you ride a bicycle?
14. What are some steps you can take to protect your central nervous system from injury?
15. Describe how lenses in eyeglasses correct nearsightedness and farsightedness.
16. List all the structures in your ear that must vibrate before you hear a sound. List them in the order in which they vibrate.
17. What are the effects of anabolic steroids on the body?
18. **Writing to Learn** Imagine that Earth has been invaded by space aliens who are exactly like humans except for the fact that they have no sense of touch. These aliens plan to take over Earth. Write a plan for fighting the aliens that makes use of the fact that they lack a sense of touch.

Thinking Critically
19. **Relating Cause and Effect** When a person has a stroke, blood flow to part of the brain is reduced, and severe brain damage can result. Suppose that after a stroke, a woman is unable to move her right arm and right leg. In which side of her brain did the stroke occur? Explain.
20. **Applying Concepts** As a man walks barefoot along a beach, he steps on a sharp shell. His foot automatically jerks upward, even before he feels pain. What process is this an example of? How does it help protect the man?
21. **Making Judgments** If someone tried to persuade you to take drugs, what arguments would you use as a way of refusing? Why do you think these arguments would be effective?

Applying Skills
22. Students' graphs should show a straight line pointing down and to the right.
23. Manipulated variable—the distance from the eye chart; responding variable—the percentage of letters identified correctly
24. A farsighted person would probably not score well when they stood close to the chart.

Applying Skills

A person with normal vision stood at different distances from an eye chart and tried to identify the letters on the chart. The table gives the results. Use the table to answer Questions 22–24.

Distance from Eye Chart	Percent of Letters Identified Correctly
2 meters	100
4 meters	92
6 meters	80
8 meters	71
10 meters	60

22. **Graphing** Make a line graph of the data. Plot the distance from the chart on the horizontal axis. On the vertical axis, plot the percent of letters identified correctly.

23. **Controlling Variables** What was the manipulated variable in this experiment? What was the responding variable?

24. **Predicting** How would you expect the results to differ for a farsighted person? Explain.

Present Your Project Your report should include an explanation of how you did your research, what you were trying to find out, and how your actual results compared with your expected results. Also include information on how the nervous system was involved in your illusions. If you can, try to explain why the illusions work.

Reflect and Record In your journal, summarize what you learned from doing this project. Did the project go as you expected, or were you surprised by some results? If you had a chance to continue your investigations, what would you do next? Why?

Present Your Project In addition to their data and explanations, allow students to demonstrate the illusions they studied. Help each presenter to explain the illusions in terms of the brain's influence on incoming sensory impulses or in terms of a general range of perceptions, depending on the experiment. Conclude the project presentation with a discussion of what students learned about the ways in which their nervous system interprets sensory nerve impulses. Ask the students to discuss how senses can deceive and to think about what kinds of eyewitness accounts they would believe after doing these experiments.

Reflect and Record Ask students to write specifically about what they have learned by doing their experiments. If they would do their experiments differently, have students write descriptions of their revised procedures.

Test Preparation

Answers: Test Preparation

25. c 26. d 27. b 28. a

Test Preparation

Use these questions to prepare for standardized tests.

Study the diagram. Then answer Questions 25–28.

25. Which part of the brain controls muscle coordination and balance?
    a. right half of cerebrum
    b. left half of cerebrum
    c. cerebellum
    d. brainstem

26. Which part of the brain controls involuntary actions such as breathing and the heartbeat?
    a. right half of cerebrum
    b. left half of cerebrum
    c. cerebellum
    d. brainstem

27. Which part of the brain controls your ability to raise your right hand high over your head?
    a. right half of cerebrum
    b. left half of cerebrum
    c. spinal cord
    d. brainstem

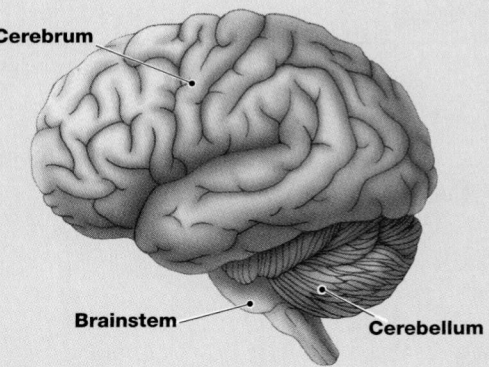

Cerebrum

Brainstem

Cerebellum

28. Which body system consists of the brain and spinal cord?
    a. central nervous system
    b. peripheral nervous system
    c. somatic nervous system
    d. autonomic nervous system

Program Resources

◆ **Inquiry Skills Activity Book** Provides teaching and review of all inquiry skills

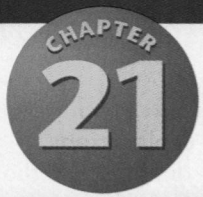

CHAPTER 21 The Endocrine System & Reproduction

Sections	Time	Student Edition Activities	Other Activities
CHAPTER PROJECT **A Precious Bundle** p. 657	Ongoing (2–3 weeks)	Check Your Progress, pp. 662, 668, 677 Present Your Project, p. 681	
1 The Endocrine System pp. 658–662 ◆ Identify the organs of the endocrine system and their functions. ◆ Describe hormones and the effects they have on the body. ◆ Describe how negative feedback controls hormone levels.	1 period/ ½ block	**Discover** What's the Signal?, p. 658	**TE** Integrating Chemistry, p. 659 **TE** Including All Students, p. 661 **LM** 21, "Model of a Negative Feedback System"
2 The Male and Female Reproductive Systems pp. 663–668 ◆ List the organs of the male and female reproductive systems and identify their functions. ◆ Describe the events that occur during the menstrual cycle.	2 periods/ 1 block	**Discover** What's the Big Difference?, p. 663 **Sharpen Your Skills** Graphing, p. 667	
3 *INTEGRATING HEALTH* **The Human Life Cycle** pp. 669–678 ◆ List the stages of human development that occur before birth. ◆ Describe what happens during childbirth. ◆ Describe the physical changes that occur during infancy and childhood. ◆ Describe the changes that occur during adolescence. ◆ Describe the changes that occur during adulthood.	2 periods/ 1 block	**Discover** How Many Ways Does a Child Grow?, p. 669 **Try This** Way to Grow!, p. 671 **Skills Lab: Interpreting Data** Growing Up, p. 678	**TE** Real-Life Learning, p. 675
Study Guide/Chapter Assessment pp. 679–681	1 period/ ½ block		**ISAB** Provides teaching and review of all inquiry skills

For Standard or Block Schedule The Resource Pro® CD-ROM gives you maximum flexibility for planning your instruction for any type of schedule. Resource Pro® contains Planning Express®, an advanced scheduling program, as well as the entire contents of the Teaching Resources and the Computer Test Bank.

CHAPTER PLANNING GUIDE

Program Resources	Assessment Strategies	Media and Technology
UR Chapter 21 Project Teacher Notes, pp. 162–163 **UR** Chapter 21 Project Overview and Worksheets, pp. 164–167	**SE** Performance Assessment: Present Your Project, p. 681 **TE** Check Your Progress, pp. 662, 668, 677 **UR** Chapter 21 Project Scoring Rubric, p. 180	Science Explorer Internet Site at www.phschool.com
UR 21-1 Lesson Plan, p. 169 **UR** 21-1 Section Summary, p. 170 **UR** 21-1 Review and Reinforce, p. 171 **UR** 21-1 Enrich, p. 172	**SE** Section 1 Review, p. 662 **TE** Ongoing Assessment, pp. 659, 661 **TE** Performance Assessment, p. 662	Audio CD, English-Spanish Summary 21-1 Transparency 77, "Exploring the Endocrine System"
UR 21-2 Lesson Plan, p. 173 **UR** 21-2 Section Summary, p. 174 **UR** 21-2 Review and Reinforce, p. 175 **UR** 21-2 Enrich, p. 176	**SE** Section 2 Review, p. 668 **TE** Ongoing Assessment, pp. 665, 667 **TE** Performance Assessment, p. 668	Audio CD, English-Spanish Summary 21-2 Transparency 78, "The Male Reproductive System" Transparency 79, "The Female Reproductive System"
UR 21-3 Lesson Plan, p. 177 **UR** 21-3 Section Summary, p. 178 **UR** 21-3 Review and Reinforce, p. 179 **UR** 21-3 Enrich, p. 180 **UR** Chapter 21 Skills Lab, pp. 181–183	**SE** Section 3 Review, p. 677 **TE** Ongoing Assessment, pp. 671, 673, 675 **TE** Performance Assessment, p. 677	Audio CD, English-Spanish Summary 21-3 Life Science Videotape 4; Videodisc Unit 4 Side 1, "Development is a Lifelong Process" Interactive Student Tutorial CD-ROM, Chapter 21
RCA Provides strategies to improve science reading skills **GSW** Provides worksheets to promote student comprehension of content	**SE** Chapter 21 Study Guide/Assessment, pp. 679–681 **PA** Chapter 21 Performance Assessment, pp. 65–67 **CUT** Chapter 21 Test, pp. 96–99 **CTB** Chapter 21 Test	Interactive Student Tutorial CD-ROM, Chapter 21 Computer Test Bank, Chapter 21 Test

Key: **SE** Student Edition   **TE** Teacher's Edition   **UR** Unit Resources
     CTB Computer Test Bank   **PTA** Product Testing Activities by *Consumer Reports*   **LM** Laboratory Manual
     ISAB Inquiry Skills Activity Book   **RCA** Reading in the Content Area   **IES** Interdisciplinary Explorations Series
     GSW Guided Study Worksheets   **PA** Performance Assessment   **CUT** Chapter and Unit Tests

Meeting the National Science Education Standards and AAAS Benchmarks

National Science Education Standards	Benchmarks for Science Literacy	Unifying Themes
Science as Inquiry (Content Standard A) ◆ **Use mathematics in all aspects of scientific investigation** Students examine data to discover how the proportions of the human body change over time. *(Skills Lab)* **Life Science** (Content Standard C) ◆ **Reproduction and heredity** The female body produces eggs and the male body produces sperm. The egg and sperm unite to form a new individual. *(Sections 2, 3)* ◆ **Regulation and behavior** The endocrine system controls many of the body's daily activities as well as regulating developmental change. *(Section 1)* During the menstrual cycle, the body prepares itself to reproduce by releasing an egg and by thickening the uterine wall. *(Section 2)*	**2C The Nature of Mathematics** Students learn about how the levels of hormones change during the menstrual cycle. *(Section 2)* Students learn about the changing mass of a developing baby during pregnancy. *(Section 3)* **6B Human Development** Fertilization occurs when male and female sex cells are united. Following fertilization, cells divide to produce an embryo. During the first three months of pregnancy, organs begin to form; during the second three months, all organs and body features develop; during the last three months, organs and features mature. The developing embryo is at risk to the mother's use of drugs and alcohol during pregnancy. Various body changes occur as adults age. *(Sections 1, 2, 3)*	◆ **Patterns of Change** The fertilized egg undergoes change and develops into an embryo. All stages of development follow a predictable pattern during the course of nine months. After birth, change occurs during the lifetime of the individual. *(Sections 3)* ◆ **Stability** Hormones produced by the human endocrine system help the body maintain stability. Hormones are produced throughout the lifetime of the male and female and play an important role in the development of sexual characteristics. *(Sections 1, 2, 3)* ◆ **Unity and Diversity** The male and female reproductive systems differ in structure, but the primary function of both is to produce new individuals. *(Sections 1, 2)* ◆ **Systems and Interactions** The male and female reproductive systems produce sex cells needed for reproduction and hormones that regulate body activities. The interaction of the male and female reproductive systems can produce a new human being. *(Sections 1, 2)*

Take It to the Net

 *Interactive text at www.phschool.com*

Science Explorer comes alive with iText.

- **Complete student text** is accessible from any computer with Internet access or a CD-ROM drive.
- **Animations, simulations, and videos** enhance student understanding and retention of concepts.
- **Self-tests and online study tools** assess student understanding.

STAY CURRENT with

Find out the latest research and information about human biology and health at: **www.phschool.com**

Go to **www.phschool.com** and click on the Science icon. Then click on Science Explorer: Life, Earth, and Physical Science under PH@school.

ACTIVITY	Time (minutes)	Materials Quantities for one work group	Skills
Section 1			
Discover, p. 658	15	No special materials are required.	Inferring
Section 2			
Discover, p. 663	20	**Nonconsumable** slides of human egg and sperm cells, microscope	Observing
Sharpen Your Skills, p. 667	20	**Consumable** graph paper **Nonconsumable** ruler	Graphing
Section 3			
Discover, p. 669	15	No special materials are required.	Observing
Try This, p. 671	25	**Nonconsumable** balance, objects of various masses	Making Models
Skills Lab, p. 678	30	No special materials are required.	Interpreting Data

A list of all materials required for the Student Edition activities can be found on pages T25–T33. You can obtain information about ordering materials by calling 1-800-848-9500 or by accessing the Science Explorer Internet site at **www.phschool.com**.

A Precious Bundle

Caring for an infant is a full-time responsibility. Students may not realize how much having a small child would disrupt their everyday lives until they attempt to model the day-to-day activities of a parent.

Purpose In this project, students will model parenting behavior and consider how the presence of a baby could change their lives.

Skills Focus After completing the Chapter 21 project, students will be able to
◆ observe behavior and use their observations to develop a list of tasks involved in caring for an infant;
◆ model behavior and solve problems in terms of the model;
◆ make generalizations based on their feelings and reactions;
◆ communicate their responses.

Project Time Line The project should take at least a week. The first day can be used to explain the project, hand out the materials, and discuss the responsibilities and expectations of the project. The last day could be devoted to a discussion of students' experiences and journal entries. Three days are devoted to the actual modeling phase of the experiment. Provide students with a day or two to reflect on their journal entries and complete the Chapter 21 Project Worksheets. Before beginning the project, see Chapter 21 Project Unit 4 Notes on pages 162–163 in Unit 4 Resources for more details on carrying out the project. Also distribute the Students' Chapter 21 Project Overview and Worksheets and Scoring Rubric on pages 164–168 in Unit 4 Resources.

Possible Materials Provide each student with a bag of flour, and allow him or her to cover the bag with a plastic bag. Students may want to wrap their bags in blankets or provide other accessories. Encourage students to suggest and use other materials as well.
◆ 5-lb bags of flour or suitable substitutes
◆ plastic bags to cover flour bags
◆ twist ties
◆ writing materials

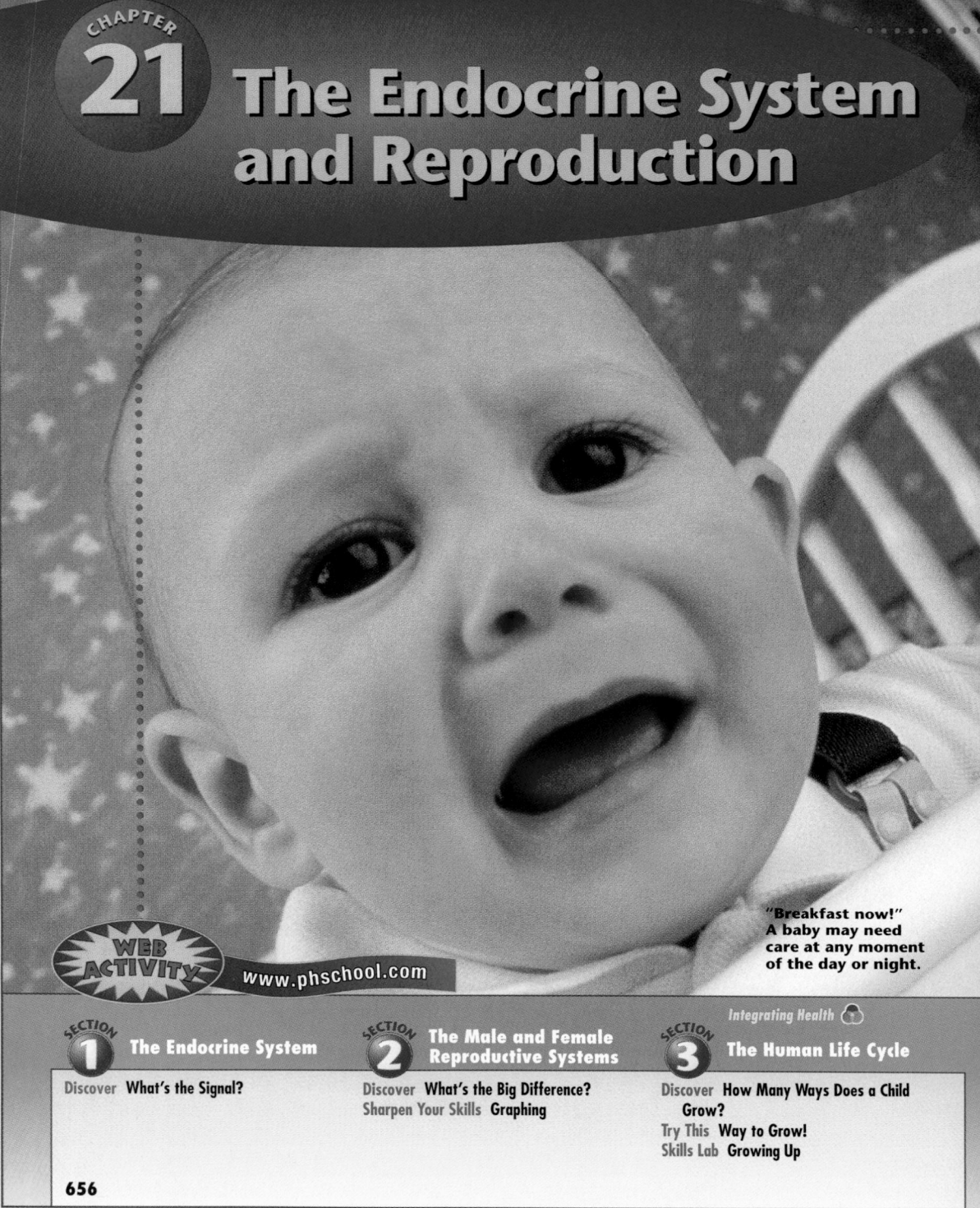

The Endocrine System and Reproduction

WEB ACTIVITY www.phschool.com

"Breakfast now!" A baby may need care at any moment of the day or night.

SECTION **1** The Endocrine System

Discover **What's the Signal?**

SECTION **2** The Male and Female Reproductive Systems

Discover **What's the Big Difference?**
Sharpen Your Skills **Graphing**

Integrating Health
SECTION **3** The Human Life Cycle

Discover **How Many Ways Does a Child Grow?**
Try This **Way to Grow!**
Skills Lab **Growing Up**

656

Launching the Project Babies often communicate by crying. To introduce the project and to stimulate student interest, ask: "Why do babies cry?" *(Samples: Because they're hungry, or when they feel pain.)*

Allow time for students to read the description of the project in their text and the Chapter Project Overview on pages 164–165 in Unit 4 Resources. Then encourage discussions on infant care, materials that could be used, and any initial questions students may have. Pass out copies of the Chapter 21 Project

Worksheets on pages 166–167 in Unit 4 Resources for students to review.

Have students brainstorm a list of daily childcare activities as a class or in small groups. Remind students to include considerations for preparation of baby food, changing diapers, bathing, dressing, and medical check-ups. Students should also include childcare activities that meet infants' need to learn, to feel loved, to observe and interact with their surroundings, and to gain confidence that needs will be met.

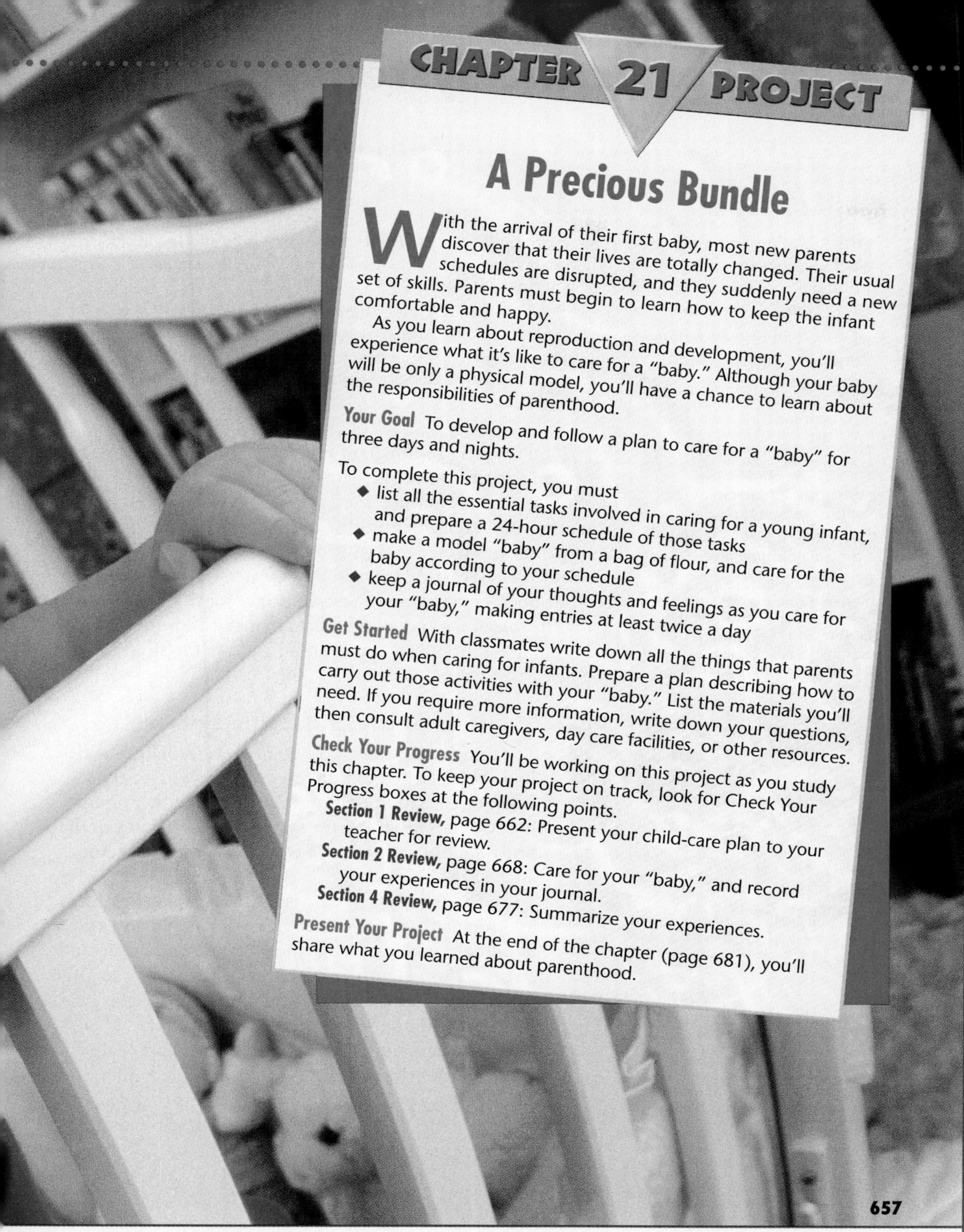

A Precious Bundle

With the arrival of their first baby, most new parents discover that their lives are totally changed. Their usual schedules are disrupted, and they suddenly need a new set of skills. Parents must begin to learn how to keep the infant comfortable and happy.

As you learn about reproduction and development, you'll experience what it's like to care for a "baby." Although your baby will be only a physical model, you'll have a chance to learn about the responsibilities of parenthood.

Your Goal To develop and follow a plan to care for a "baby" for three days and nights.

To complete this project, you must
- ◆ list all the essential tasks involved in caring for a young infant, and prepare a 24-hour schedule of those tasks
- ◆ make a model "baby" from a bag of flour, and care for the baby according to your schedule
- ◆ keep a journal of your thoughts and feelings as you care for your "baby," making entries at least twice a day

Get Started With classmates write down all the things that parents must do when caring for infants. Prepare a plan describing how to carry out those activities with your "baby." List the materials you'll need. If you require more information, write down your questions, then consult adult caregivers, day care facilities, or other resources.

Check Your Progress You'll be working on this project as you study this chapter. To keep your project on track, look for Check Your Progress boxes at the following points.

Section 1 Review, page 662: Present your child-care plan to your teacher for review.

Section 2 Review, page 668: Care for your "baby," and record your experiences in your journal.

Section 4 Review, page 677: Summarize your experiences.

Present Your Project At the end of the chapter (page 681), you'll share what you learned about parenthood.

657

Program Resources

◆ **Unit 4 Resources** Chapter 21 Project Teacher Notes, pp. 162–163; Chapter 21 Project Overview and Worksheets, pp. 164–167; Chapter 21 Project Scoring Rubric, p. 168

WEB ACTIVITY www.phschool.com

You will find an Internet activity, chapter self-tests for students, and links to other chapter topics at this site.

After completing a reasonable list of daily activities, have the students work with each other to translate real child care into facsimiles that use the bag of flour as a surrogate. Tell students that this process of modeling an event is a scientific way of testing a hypothesis or discovering behaviors. Emphasize that the most accurate and valuable information will come from following the routines as accurately as possible.

Performance Assessment

The Chapter 21 Project Scoring Rubric on page 168 of Unit 4 Resources will help you evaluate how well students complete the Chapter 21 Project. Students will be assessed on
- ◆ how well they plan their daily tasks and prepare themselves to take care of the model baby;
- ◆ how thoroughly they complete the task chart;
- ◆ their willingness to take the role seriously, indicated by the completeness of writing and discussion responses that show evidence of child care practices and issues;
- ◆ their communication in class discussions and written work.

By sharing the Chapter 21 Project Scoring Rubric with students at the beginning of the project, you will make it clear to them what they are expected to do.

Objectives

After completing the lesson, students will be able to
◆ identify the organs of the endocrine system and their functions;
◆ describe hormones and the effects they have on the body;
◆ describe how negative feedback controls hormone levels.

Key Terms endocrine gland, hormone, target cell, hypothalamus, pituitary gland, negative feedback

1 Engage/Explore

Activating Prior Knowledge

Tell students you are going to give them a "pop" quiz based on what they learned in a previous chapter. Ask: **What is the name for the reaction when you feel panic or fear?** (*Students should remember the "fight or flight" response from Chapter 15.*) Inform students the same body system that regulates the "fight or flight" response controls their bodies' daily activities and many long-term changes.

••••••• DISCOVER •••••••

Skills Focus inferring
Time 15 minutes
Tips If possible, play this game in a large open area such as in a gym or outdoors.
Expected Outcome Players will be eliminated from the game when they do not immediately respond to the "Freeze!" signal.
Think It Over Winning the game depends on responding quickly to the "Freeze!" signal; one mistake or delayed response will put a player out of the game. The body uses nerve impulses as signals. Tell students they will learn about another type of signal in this chapter.

SECTION 1 The Endocrine System

DISCOVER •••••••••••••••••••••••••••••••• **ACTIVITY**

What's the Signal?

1. Stand up and move around the room until your teacher says "Freeze!" Then stop moving immediately. Stay perfectly still until your teacher says "Start!" Then begin moving again.
2. Anyone who moves between the "Freeze!" command and the "Start!" command has to leave the game.
3. Play until only one person is left in the game. That person is the winner.

Think It Over
Inferring Why is it important for players in this game to respond to signals? What types of signals does the human body use?

GUIDE FOR READING

◆ What is the function of the endocrine system?
◆ How does negative feedback control hormone levels?

Reading Tip Before you read, preview *Exploring the Endocrine System* on pages 660–661. List the terms in the diagram that are new to you. Look for their meanings as you read.

658

You're playing softball on a hot afternoon. Without warning, thick, dark clouds form. Suddenly, there's a flash of lightning. Thunder cracks overhead. Someone screams, you jump, and everyone runs for cover. Your heart is pounding, your palms are sweaty, and your muscles are tight.

Your body's reaction to the sudden storm was caused mainly by your body's endocrine system. In this section, you will learn about the role of the endocrine system in many body processes—from the quick response to a thunder clap, to the slower body changes that turn a child into an adult.

The Role of the Endocrine System

The human body has two systems that regulate its activities. You learned about one, the nervous system, in Chapter 20. The endocrine system is the other regulating system. **The endocrine system controls many of the body's daily activities as well as long-term changes such as development.**

The endocrine system is made up of glands. Glands are organs that produce chemicals. You already know about some glands, such as those that produce saliva and sweat. Those glands release their chemicals into tiny tubes. The tubes deliver the chemicals to a specific location within the body or to the skin's surface.

The endocrine system does not have delivery tubes. **Endocrine glands** (EN duh krin) produce and release their chemical products directly into the bloodstream. The blood then carries those chemicals throughout the body.

READING STRATEGIES

Reading Tip Before students preview *Exploring the Endocrine System*, provide them with note cards on which to write unfamiliar terms, one per card. Have students write definitions on the back of the cards as they read. Then direct student pairs to quiz each other on the terms, using the cards as flashcards. Sample definition: Hypothalamus—the gland that controls the pituitary gland.

Study and Comprehension Have students write brief summaries of the information under each heading. They may choose to construct a diagram or map to organize the information visually. Remind students to include only main ideas and key details in their summaries. Students can then use the summaries as study guides.

Hormones

The chemical product of an endocrine gland is called a **hormone.** Hormones turn on, turn off, speed up, or slow down the activities of different organs and tissues. You can think of a hormone as a chemical messenger. Because hormones are carried by blood, they can regulate activities in tissues and organs far from the glands that produced them.

Hormone Production What causes the release of hormones? In situations such as a sudden storm, nerve impulses from the senses travel to the brain. There, information, such as the sound of thunder, is interpreted. The brain then sends a nerve impulse to a specific endocrine gland. That gland, in turn, releases the hormone adrenaline into the bloodstream. As you read in Chapter 15, adrenaline causes your heart rate to increase, makes you breathe faster and deeper, and releases sugars that power your muscles.

In contrast to the body's response to a nerve impulse, hormones cause a slower, but longer-lasting, response. For example, the brain sends a quick signal to an endocrine gland to release adrenaline into the bloodstream. When the adrenaline reaches the heart, it makes the heart beat more rapidly. The heart continues to race until the amount of adrenaline in the blood drops to a normal level.

Target Cells When a hormone enters the bloodstream, why **INTEGRATING CHEMISTRY** does it affect some organs but not others? The answer lies in its chemical structure. A hormone interacts only with certain **target cells,** cells that recognize the hormone's chemical structure. A hormone and its target cell fit together the way a key fits into a lock. Hormones not meant for a particular organ will travel through the bloodstream until they find the "lock" that they fit.

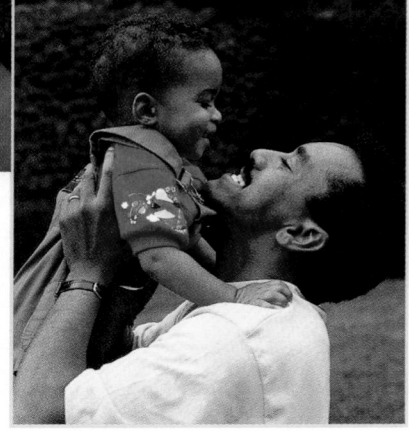

Figure 1 The endocrine system controls the body's response to an exciting situation (left) as well as the changes that occur as a child grows (right). *Applying Concepts* What substances produced by endocrine glands control these body processes?

Chapter 21 **659**

Answers to Self-Assessment

Caption Question
Figure 1 Hormones

Media and Technology

 Audio CD English-Spanish Summary 21-1

The Role of the Endocrine System

Using the Visuals: Figure 1

Point out the images in Figure 1 and ask: **What is the same about these two photos?** (*Both show body processes regulated by the endocrine system.*) **How are the body processes different?** (*Excitement is a short-term response to a situation, while growth and development are long-term processes.*) **learning modality: verbal**

Hormones

Addressing Naive Conceptions

Students may believe that all hormones first become active during puberty. Explain that the human body relies on many different types of hormones throughout life. Some hormones regulate blood levels of substances, such as calcium and sugar. Tell students that insulin, which they learned about in Chapter 19, is a hormone. **learning modality: verbal**

Integrating Chemistry

Materials *construction paper, scissors*

To promote understanding of the "key and lock" concept of hormones and target cells, have student pairs construct a model of a hormone and target cell that fit together. Invite students to exchange the hormone models only and then ask why hormones and target cells no longer fit. (*The hormone "key" no longer fits into the target cell "lock" because each hormone/target unit has a unique design.*) **limited English proficiency**

Ongoing Assessment

Writing Ask students to describe the relationship between the endocrine system and hormones.

The Hypothalamus

Building Inquiry Skills: Inferring

Ask students: **How does the hypothalamus link the nervous system and the endocrine system?** (*The hypothalamus releases hormones and also sends nerve impulses.*) Explain that the hypothalamus uses both nerve impulses and hormones to control endocrine glands such as the pituitary. Ask: **Do the endocrine glands only respond to hormones? Explain.** (*No, the endocrine glands also respond to nerve impulses.*)
learning modality: verbal

EXPLORING
the Endocrine System

As students read the captions, ask: **Are all the same glands found in both males and females?** (*No*) Then ask: **Which endocrine glands are found only in females?** (*ovaries*) **Which are only found in males?** (*testes*) Finally, have students make a table with three columns. In the first, list the names of all of the endocrine glands. In the second column, state the function of that gland in females, and in the third column, state the function of that gland in males. (*All will be the same except for the ovaries and testes.*)

Extend Have students predict the symptoms of a malfunction in various endocrine glands. For example, ask: **What do you think would happen to a person whose pancreas was not functioning properly?** (*The control of the amount of glucose in the blood would be impaired.*) Encourage interested students to use reference books or an electronic resource in the school library to find out whether their predictions are correct.
learning modality: logical/mathematical

Each endocrine gland releases different hormones and thus controls different processes. *Exploring the Endocrine System* shows the locations of the endocrine glands and describes some activities they control.

The Hypothalamus

The nervous system and the endocrine system work together. The **hypothalamus** (hy poh THAL uh mus), a tiny part of the brain near the middle of your head, is the link between the two systems. Nerve messages controlling sleep, hunger, and other conditions come from the hypothalamus. The hypothalamus also produces hormones that control other endocrine glands and organs. Through its nerve impulses and hormones, the hypothalamus plays a major role in maintaining homeostasis.

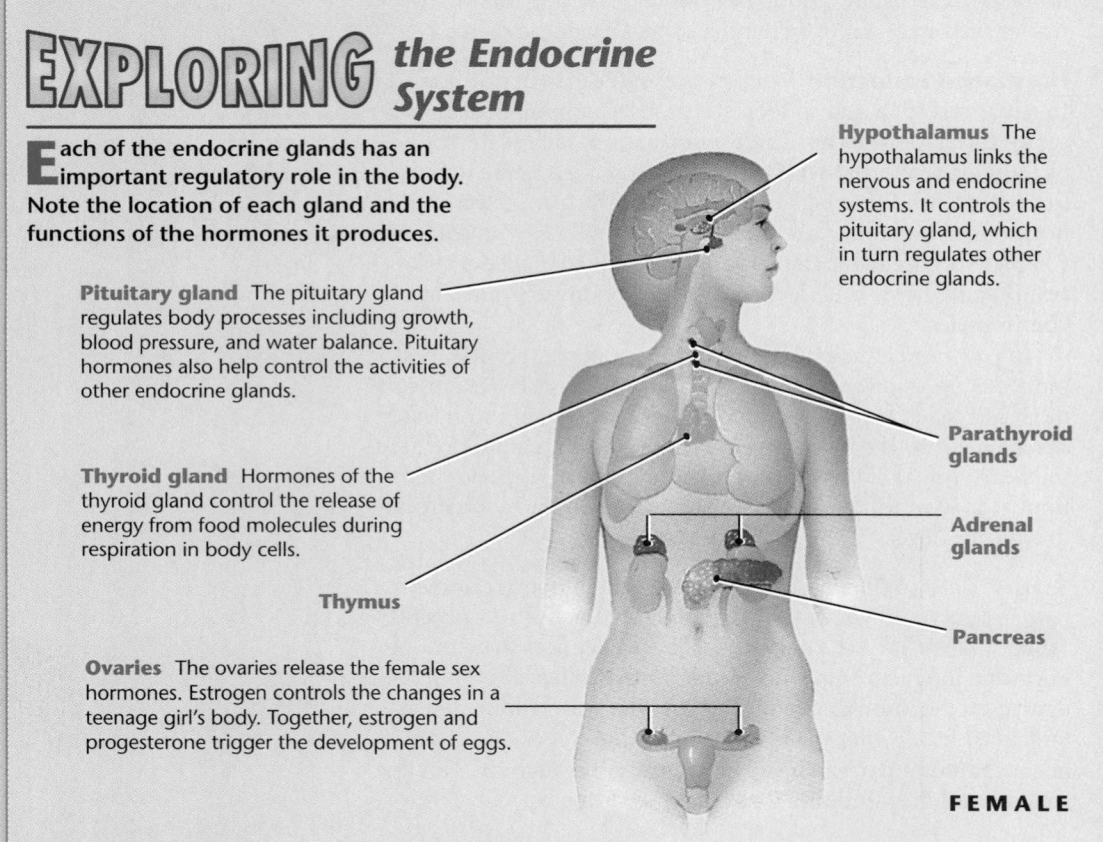

EXPLORING the Endocrine System

Each of the endocrine glands has an important regulatory role in the body. Note the location of each gland and the functions of the hormones it produces.

Pituitary gland The pituitary gland regulates body processes including growth, blood pressure, and water balance. Pituitary hormones also help control the activities of other endocrine glands.

Thyroid gland Hormones of the thyroid gland control the release of energy from food molecules during respiration in body cells.

Thymus

Ovaries The ovaries release the female sex hormones. Estrogen controls the changes in a teenage girl's body. Together, estrogen and progesterone trigger the development of eggs.

Hypothalamus The hypothalamus links the nervous and endocrine systems. It controls the pituitary gland, which in turn regulates other endocrine glands.

Parathyroid glands

Adrenal glands

Pancreas

FEMALE

660

The Pituitary Gland

Just below the hypothalamus is an endocrine gland about the size of a pea. The **pituitary gland** (pih TOO ih tehr ee) communicates with the hypothalamus to control many body activities. In response to nerve impulses or hormone signals from the hypothalamus, the pituitary gland releases its hormones. Some of those hormones act as an "on" switch for other endocrine glands. For example, one pituitary hormone signals the thyroid gland to produce hormones. Other pituitary hormones control body activities directly. Growth hormone regulates growth from infancy to adulthood. Another pituitary hormone directs the kidneys to regulate the amount of water in the blood.

✓ *Checkpoint* What causes the pituitary gland to release hormones?

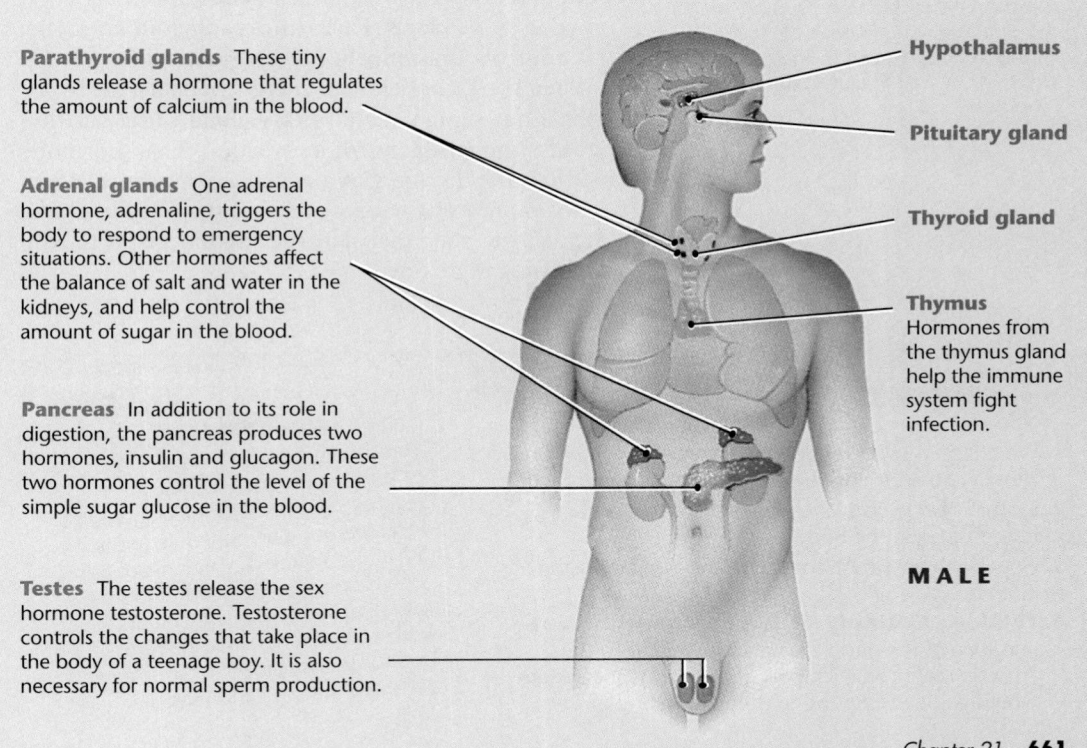

Parathyroid glands These tiny glands release a hormone that regulates the amount of calcium in the blood.

Adrenal glands One adrenal hormone, adrenaline, triggers the body to respond to emergency situations. Other hormones affect the balance of salt and water in the kidneys, and help control the amount of sugar in the blood.

Pancreas In addition to its role in digestion, the pancreas produces two hormones, insulin and glucagon. These two hormones control the level of the simple sugar glucose in the blood.

Testes The testes release the sex hormone testosterone. Testosterone controls the changes that take place in the body of a teenage boy. It is also necessary for normal sperm production.

Hypothalamus

Pituitary gland

Thyroid gland

Thymus Hormones from the thymus gland help the immune system fight infection.

MALE

Chapter 21 **661**

Media and Technology

 Transparencies "Exploring the Endocrine System," Transparency 77

Answers to Self-Assessment

✓ *Checkpoint*
The pituitary gland responds to nerve impulses or hormone signals from the hypothalamus.

The Pituitary Gland

Including All Students

To help students pronounce the scientific **ACTIVITY** terms in this section and to identify the endocrine glands and their functions, have students work in small groups. Each group can make note cards with the name of an endocrine gland on one side and its function on the other. Prepare several large outlines of the human body. Have each group use their note cards to label an outline with the name of each gland. Students can pronounce the name of the gland aloud as they locate it on the outline. Then have groups write captions for the glands using the function side of their note cards. **cooperative learning**

Building Inquiry Skills: Organizing Information

Have students locate the pituitary glands in the figures shown in the Exploring. On the board, write *Hypothalamus*. Beneath that, write *Pituitary*, and *Thyroid* and *Adrenal* below. Ask students: **How can this list help you remember both the locations and the functions of these glands?** *(The glands are placed in the body in the same order as the list, from top to bottom. Also, the hypothalamus controls the pituitary, and the pituitary controls the thyroid and adrenal glands.)* **learning modality: visual**

Ongoing Assessment

Writing Have students list the glands in the endocrine system and describe one function of each gland.
 Students can save their lists in their portfolios.

661

Negative Feedback

Using the Visuals: Figure 2

Ask students: **What sequence of events makes the thyroid stop producing thyroxine?** *(The hypothalamus signals the pituitary to stop producing TSH, and the thyroid stops producing thyroxine.)* Ask students to explain why this is called "negative" feedback. *(Because it results in a reduction in the activity of the thyroid and pituitary.)* Make sure students understand that "negative feedback" in this context does not refer to criticism.
learning modality: verbal

3 Assess

Section 1 Review Answers

1. Controls many of the body's daily activities as well as long-term changes; endocrine glands
2. When the amount of a hormone in the blood reaches the right level, the endocrine system signals the gland to stop producing that hormone.
3. The pituitary gland produces hormones in response to nerve impulses or hormones sent out by the hypothalamus.
4. Sample: The hypothalamus. It controls the function of the pituitary gland, which regulates many other glands of the endocrine system.

Check Your Progress
CHAPTER PROJECT

As you review students' schedules, make sure each student has included all essential child care tasks. Encourage students to be realistic. Remind them that babies need to eat several times a day, and that real babies will often disrupt scheduled events by crying or being ill. Make sure students arrange for alternative childcare when they need to meet other obligations.

Performance Assessment

Writing Have students write short paragraphs describing how the endocrine system helps the body maintain homeostasis.

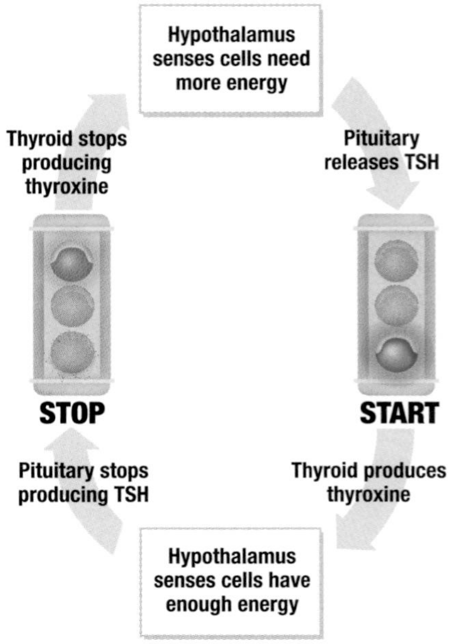

662

Hypothalamus senses cells need more energy

Thyroid stops producing thyroxine

Pituitary releases TSH

STOP

START

Pituitary stops producing TSH

Thyroid produces thyroxine

Hypothalamus senses cells have enough energy

Figure 2 The release of the hormone thyroxine is controlled through negative feedback. When enough thyroxine is present, the system signals the thyroid gland to stop releasing the hormone. *Inferring Why is this process called negative feedback?*

Section 1 Review

1. What role does the endocrine system play in the body? What are the organs of the endocrine system called?
2. Explain how negative feedback helps to maintain homeostasis in the body.
3. How do the hypothalamus and the pituitary gland interact?
4. **Thinking Critically Making Judgments** Years ago, one of the endocrine glands was called the "master gland." Which part of the endocrine system would you consider the master gland? Explain.

662

Program Resources

◆ **Unit 4 Resources** 21-1 Review and Reinforce, p. 171; 21-1 Enrich, p. 172

Negative Feedback

One way that the endocrine system maintains homeostasis may remind you of the way a heating system works. Suppose you set a thermostat at 20°C. If the temperature falls below 20°, the thermostat signals the furnace to turn on. When the furnace heats the area to the proper temperature, information about the warm conditions "feeds back" to the thermostat. The thermostat then gives the furnace a negative signal that means "no more heat." That signal turns the furnace off.

The type of signal used in a heating system is called **negative feedback** because the system is turned off by the condition it produces. The endocrine system often works in this way. Through negative feedback, when the amount of a particular hormone in the blood reaches a certain level, the endocrine system sends signals that stop the release of that hormone. **Negative feedback is an important way that the body maintains homeostasis.**

You can see an example of negative feedback in Figure 2. Like a thermostat in a cool room, the endocrine system senses when there's not enough thyroxine in the blood. Thyroxine is a thyroid hormone. It controls how much energy is available to cells. When there's not enough energy available, the hypothalamus signals the pituitary gland to release thyroid-stimulating hormone (TSH). That hormone signals the thyroid gland to release thyroxine. When the amount of thyroxine reaches the right level, the endocrine system signals the thyroid gland to stop releasing thyroxine.

Check Your Progress
CHAPTER PROJECT

You should now be ready to turn in your plan for your teacher's review. Your plan should include your daily schedule and a list of the materials you'll need. Be sure to describe the kind of journal you plan to keep. (*Hint:* Discuss with your teacher any problems you foresee in caring for the "baby" for three full days and nights.)

Answers to Self-Assessment

Caption Question

Figure 2 It is called negative feedback because the system is turned off by the condition it produces—the production of thyroxine by the thyroid is turned off by the increasing levels of thyroxine.

SECTION 2 The Male and Female Reproductive Systems

DISCOVER ••••••••••••••••••••••••••••••••••••••• ACTIVITY

What's the Big Difference?

1. 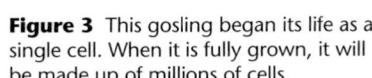 Your teacher will provide prepared slides of eggs and sperm.

2. Examine each slide under the microscope, first under low power, then under high power. Be sure you view at least one sample of egg and sperm from the same species.

3. Sketch and label each sample.

Think It Over

Observing What differences did you observe between sperm cells and egg cells? What general statement can you make about eggs and sperm?

Many differences between an adult animal and its young are controlled by the endocrine system. In humans, two endocrine glands—the ovaries in girls and the testes in boys—control many of the changes that occur as a child matures. These glands release hormones that cause the body to develop as a person grows older.

Sex Cells

You may find it hard to believe that you began life as a single cell. That single cell was produced by the joining of two other cells, an egg and a sperm. An **egg** is the female sex cell. A **sperm** is the male sex cell.

The joining of a sperm and an egg is called **fertilization.** Fertilization is an important part of **reproduction,** the process by which living things produce new individuals of the same type. When fertilization occurs, a fertilized egg, or **zygote,** is produced. Every one of the trillions of cells in your body is descended from the single cell that formed during fertilization.

> **GUIDE FOR READING**
>
> ◆ What are the functions of the male and female reproductive systems?
>
> ◆ What events occur during the menstrual cycle?
>
> *Reading Tip* As you read, create a table comparing the male and female reproductive systems. Include the type of sex cells and primary reproductive organs of each.

Figure 3 This gosling began its life as a single cell. When it is fully grown, it will be made up of millions of cells.

Chapter 21 **663**

READING STRATEGIES

Reading Tip As students read, have them list differences between the male and female reproductive systems in a table such as the one shown.

Characteristic	Male	Female
Sex cell	sperm	egg
Organs	testes	ovaries
Hormones	testosterone	estrogen

Program Resources

◆ **Unit 4 Resources** 21-2 Lesson Plan, p. 173; 21-2 Section Summary, p. 174

Media and Technology

 Audio CD English-Spanish Summary 21-2

SECTION 2 The Male and Female Reproductive Systems

Objectives

After completing the lesson, students will be able to

◆ list the organs of the male and female reproductive systems and identify their functions;

◆ describe the events that occur during the menstrual cycle.

Key Terms egg, sperm, fertilization, reproduction, zygote, chromosome, testis, testosterone, scrotum, semen, penis, ovary, estrogen, oviduct, uterus, vagina, menstrual cycle, ovulation, menstruation

1 Engage/Explore

Activating Prior Knowledge

Organize students in small discussion groups and have them brainstorm lists of things they think they already know about the male and female reproductive systems. Use these lists to address any naive conceptions students may have.

•••••••• DISCOVER ••••••••

Skills Focus observing
Materials *slides of human egg and sperm cells,* microscope
Time 20 minutes
Tips Students may need help focusing the microscope and finding the egg and sperm cells. Encourage them to begin at low power before switching to high power.
Expected Outcome Students should be able to view both types of cells.
Think It Over Sperm cells are much smaller than egg cells, and have long tail-like parts. Eggs are round, usually much larger than sperm from the same species, and do not have tails.

Sex Cells

Building Inquiry Skills: Inferring

Point out that both a sperm and an egg are single-celled. Ask: **How many cells does a zygote have?** *(one)* Then ask students to infer how the two sex cells can join to form only one zygote. *(Students should infer that each sex cell contributes only part of a complete zygote cell.)* **learning modality: logical/ mathematical**

The Male Reproductive System

Real-Life Learning

Tell students that high fevers, or even hot summer weather, can cause temporary infertility in men by raising the temperature of the testes. Although it is important for the testes to be protected against heat, point out that they are also protected against cold by the muscle that lines the skin of the scrotum. In cold temperatures and under other conditions, this muscle contracts so that the testes are held closer to the body. **learning modality: verbal**

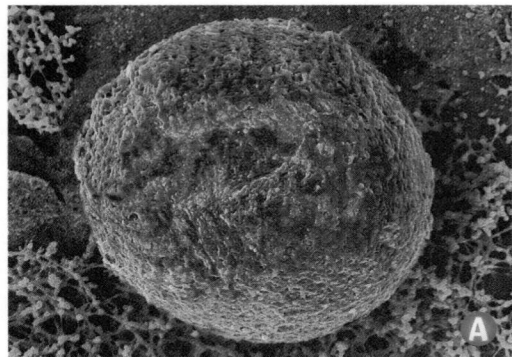
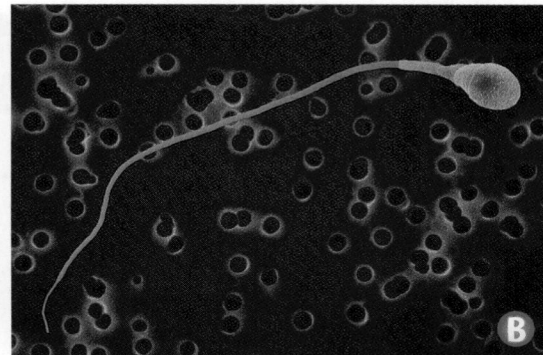

Figure 4 The human reproductive system produces either eggs or sperm. **A.** An egg is one of the largest cells in the body. **B.** A sperm, which is much smaller than an egg, has a tail that allows it to move.

Like other cells in the body, sex cells contain rod-shaped structures called chromosomes. **Chromosomes** (KROH muh sohmz) carry the information that controls inherited characteristics, such as eye color and blood type. Every cell in the human body, except the sex cells, contains 46 chromosomes. Each sex cell contains half that number, or 23 chromosomes. During fertilization, the 23 chromosomes in a sperm join the 23 chromosomes in an egg. The result is a zygote with 46 chromosomes. The zygote contains all of the information needed to produce a new human being.

☑ *Checkpoint* *What happens to the number of chromosomes when a male sex cell and a female sex cell join?*

The Male Reproductive System

The male reproductive system is shown in Figure 5. **The male reproductive system is specialized to produce sperm and the hormone testosterone.**

The Testes The oval-shaped **testes** (tes teez) (singular *testis*), are the organs of the male reproductive system in which sperm are produced. The testes are actually clusters of hundreds of tiny coiled tubes. Sperm are formed inside the tubes.

The testes also produce the hormone **testosterone** (tes TAHS tuh rohn). Testosterone controls the development of physical characteristics in men. Some of those characteristics include facial hair, a deep voice, broad shoulders, and the ability to produce sperm.

Notice in Figure 5 that the testes are located in an external pouch of skin called the **scrotum** (SKROH tum). That external location keeps the testes about 2° to 3°C below the usual body temperature of 37°C. That temperature difference is important. Sperm need the slightly cooler conditions to develop normally.

664

Sperm Production The production of sperm cells begins in males at some point during the teenage years. Each sperm is composed of a head that contains chromosomes and a long, whiplike tail. Basically, a sperm cell is a tiny package of chromosomes that can swim.

The Path of Sperm Cells Once sperm cells form in the testes, they travel through other structures in the male reproductive system. During this passage, sperm mix with fluids produced by nearby glands. This mix of sperm cells and fluids is called **semen** (SEE mun). Semen contains a huge number of sperm—about 5 to 10 million per drop! The fluids in semen provide an environment in which sperm can swim. Semen also contains nutrients that the moving sperm use as a source of energy.

Semen leaves the body through an organ called the **penis.** The male urethra runs through the penis. The urethra is the tube through which the semen travels as it leaves the body.

Urine also leaves the body through the urethra, as you learned in Chapter 18. When semen passes through the urethra, however, muscles near the bladder contract. Those muscles prevent urine and semen from mixing.

☑ *Checkpoint* *What is a sperm composed of?*

Figure 5 In the male reproductive system, the testes produce sperm and the hormone testosterone. *Interpreting Diagrams What pathway do sperm follow to reach the urethra?*

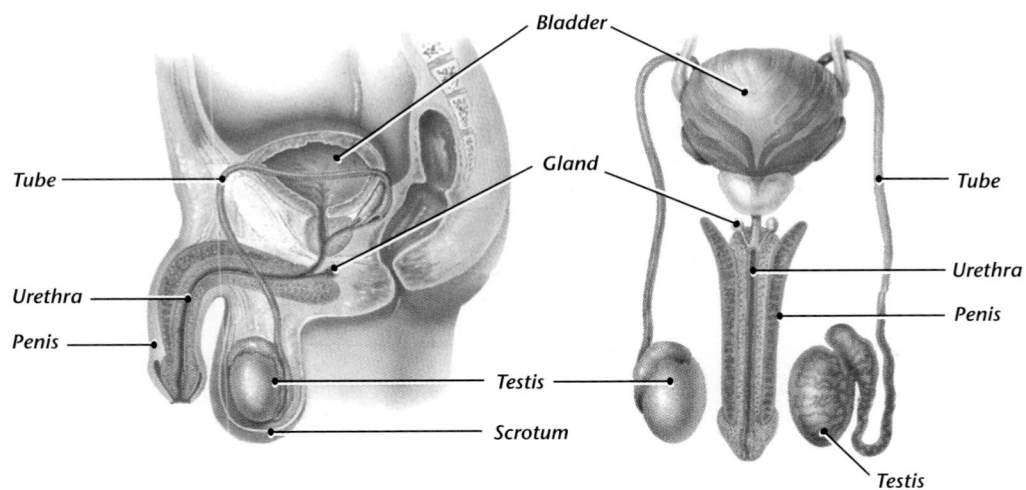

Bladder

Tube

Gland

Tube

Urethra

Urethra

Penis

Penis

Testis

Scrotum

Testis

Some students may have difficulty remembering the terms associated with the male reproductive system. Encourage students to use the text and Figure 5 to create a list of terms and definitions they may have trouble recalling. Pair students after they complete their lists to quiz each other. Students can then revise their lists by adding any terms they missed or by correcting erroneous definitions. **limited English proficiency**

 Students can save their definitions in their portfolios.

Language Arts Connection

Tell students that the word *semen* is a Latin word meaning *seed.* Some other words that come from the same root are *seminar* and *seminal.* Have students look these words up in the dictionary and discuss how the idea of seeds is relevant to the meaning of each word. **learning modality: verbal**

Addressing Naive Conceptions

Students may think that testosterone is not produced until puberty. In fact, testosterone production begins in the fetal stage. If it is not produced at exactly the right time during the fetus's development in the womb, male reproductive organs will not develop. Small amounts of testosterone are produced until puberty, when production increases dramatically. **learning modality: verbal**

Media and Technology

 Transparencies "The Male Reproductive System," Transparency 78

Answers to Self-Assessment

Caption Question

Figure 5 The sperm travel from the testes, through the tubes, and into the urethra.

☑ *Checkpoint*

The number of chromosomes doubles.

☑ *Checkpoint*

Each sperm cell is composed of a head that contains chromosomes and a long tail.

Ongoing Assessment

Organizing Information Have students draw concept maps describing the production and path of sperm.

 Students can save their concept maps in their portfolios.

665

The Female Reproductive System

Using the Visuals: Figure 6

Have students trace the path of the egg as they study the structures in the figure. Ask students to describe the path of the egg after it matures. *(The mature egg is released by an ovary and passes through an oviduct into the uterus.)* **Where does fertilization take place?** *(The oviduct)* **limited English proficiency**

Building Inquiry Skills: Comparing and Contrasting

Explain that the ovaries perform functions similar to those performed by the testes. One difference between them is that, while the testes do not begin producing sperm until puberty, the ovaries produce undeveloped egg cells, called *oocytes*, before the female is born. In fact, by the time a female child is born, her ovaries already contain, in the form of oocytes, all the eggs that she will ever produce. Challenge students to use both the text and additional research to gather information on the similarities and differences between the ovaries and testes. Students can then use the information to develop compare and contrast tables. Invite students to share their tables or diagrams with the class.
learning modality: visual

 Students can save their tables or diagrams in their portfolios.

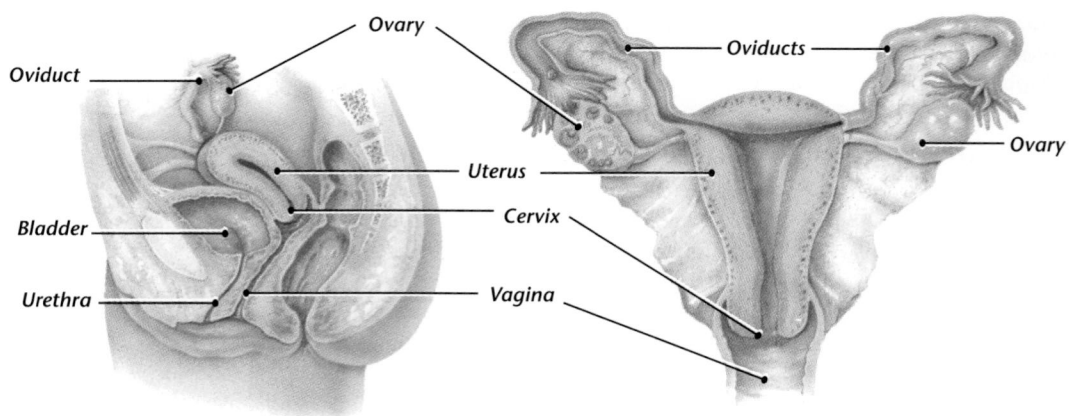

Figure 6 In the female reproductive system, the two ovaries produce eggs and hormones such as estrogen. From an ovary, an egg travels through an oviduct to the uterus. *Interpreting Diagrams Through what opening does an unfertilized egg pass when leaving the uterus?*

The Female Reproductive System

Unlike the male reproductive system, almost all of the female reproductive system is inside the body. **The role of the female reproductive system is to produce eggs and, if an egg is fertilized, to nourish a developing baby until birth.** The organs of the female reproductive system are shown in Figure 6.

The Ovaries Find the two ovaries in Figure 6. The **ovaries** (OH vuh reez) are located slightly below the waist, one on each side of the body. The name for these organs comes from the word *ova*, meaning "eggs." One major role of the ovaries is to produce egg cells.

Like the testes in males, the ovaries also are endocrine glands that produce hormones. One hormone, **estrogen** (ES truh jun), triggers the development of some adult female characteristics. For example, estrogen causes the hips to widen and the breasts to develop. Estrogen also plays a role in the process by which egg cells develop.

The Path of the Egg Cell As you can see in Figure 6, each ovary is located near an **oviduct** (OH vih duct). The two oviducts are passageways for eggs. They are also the places where fertilization usually occurs. Each month, one of the ovaries releases a mature egg, which enters the nearest oviduct. The egg moves through the oviduct, which leads to the uterus, or womb. The **uterus** (YOO tur us) is a hollow muscular organ about the size of a pear. If the egg has been fertilized, it remains in the uterus and begins to develop.

Background

Integrating Science Biologists have identified many pheromones, which are chemicals released by animals that trigger behavior in animals of the same species. Insects use pheromones to attract mates and to warn of danger. In 1998, researchers at the University of Chicago identified one human pheromone by proving that chemicals released by women could cause changes in the menstrual cycles of other women. Dr. Martha McClintock, the lead investigator on the new study, has been studying this effect since 1971. In the 1998 study, researchers used cotton pads to collect the underarm secretions of women at different times of their cycles. When these pads were treated with alcohol and rubbed under the noses of other women for 4 months, 68 percent of these women found their menstrual cycles changed.

An egg that has not been fertilized starts to break down as it enters the uterus. It leaves the uterus through an opening at its base called the cervix. The egg then enters the vagina. The **vagina** (vuh JY nuh) is a muscular passageway leading to the outside of the body. The vagina is also called the birth canal. It is the passageway through which a baby leaves the mother's body during the birth process.

✓ *Checkpoint* *What is one of the roles of the ovaries?*

The Menstrual Cycle

When the female reproductive system becomes mature during the teenage years, there are about 400,000 undeveloped eggs in a woman's ovaries. However, only about 500 of those eggs will actually leave the ovaries and reach the uterus. An egg is released about once a month in a mature female's body. The monthly cycle of changes that occurs in the female reproductive system is called the **menstrual cycle** (MEN stroo ul).

During the menstrual cycle, an egg develops in an ovary. At the same time, the uterus prepares for the arrival of a fertilized egg. In this way, the menstrual cycle prepares the female's body for pregnancy, the condition that begins after fertilization has taken place.

Stages of the Cycle The menstrual cycle begins when an egg starts to mature in one of the ovaries. At the same time, the lining of the uterus begins to thicken. About halfway through a typical cycle, the mature egg is released from the ovary into an oviduct. This process is called **ovulation** (OH vyuh lay shun).

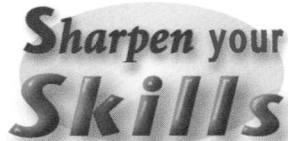

Sharpen your Skills

Graphing

A woman's hormone levels change throughout the menstrual cycle. The table below shows the levels of one female hormone, known as LH, during the menstrual cycle.

Day	Level of LH
1	12
5	14
9	14
13	70
17	12
21	12
25	8

Construct a line graph using the information in the table. Label the horizontal axis *Day*. Label the vertical axis *Hormone Level*. What event takes place about the same time that LH reaches its highest level?

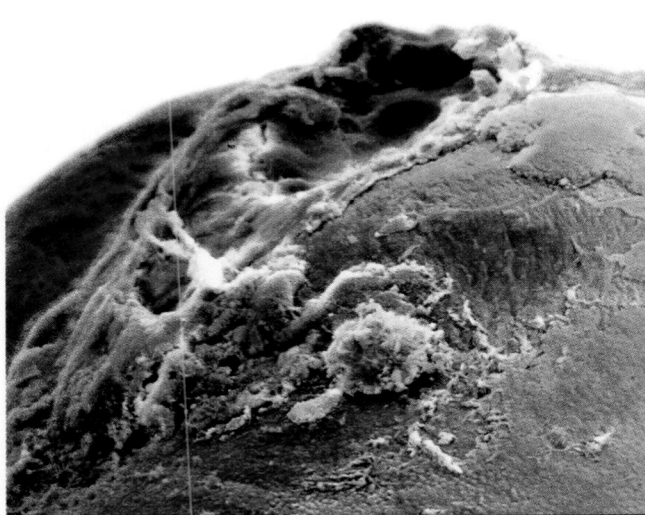

Figure 7 During ovulation an egg bursts from the side of an ovary. In this photograph, the egg is the round red structure on the right.

Sharpen your Skills

Graphing

Materials *graph paper, ruler*
Time 20 minutes
Tips Students should be able to infer from their graphs that ovulation takes place at about the time LH reaches its highest levels.
Extend Tell students that another hormone called estrogen is responsible for the buildup of the uterine lining. Ask students to draw a line that might show the level of estrogen in the body during a 25-day cycle. (*The graph line would look very similar to the one for LH.*) **learning modality: logical/mathematical**

Addressing Naive Conceptions

Students may confuse the menstrual cycle with menstruation. The menstrual cycle includes the maturation of the egg, the thickening of the uterine lining, the release of the egg, and the breakdown of the uterine lining, as well as menstruation. Menstruation describes the process by which the blood and tissue of the lining exit the body. **learning modality: verbal**

Media and Technology

 Transparencies "The Female Reproductive System," Transparency 79

Answers to Self-Assessment

Caption Question

Figure 6 The cervix

✓ *Checkpoint*

Either one: produce eggs, produce hormones

Ongoing Assessment

Writing Have students explain the processes that take place during the menstrual cycle.

 Students can save their explanations in their portfolios.

Using the Visuals: Figure 8

Draw the outline of a cycle diagram on the board, with space for five captions. Tell students they will use information in Figure 8 to fill in the cycle diagram on the board. Have student volunteers read each caption aloud, while another volunteer fills in the caption on the board. After students finish the diagram, ask students to infer what would prevent the cycle from beginning again. *(If the egg is fertilized, the cycle will be interrupted.)* **limited English proficiency**

3 Assess

Section 2 Review Answers

1. Male—sperm cells; female—egg cells

2. The lining of the uterus thickens during the beginning of the cycle. If the egg is not fertilized after its release, the lining of the uterus breaks down and menstruation begins.

3. The head of the sperm cell is a package of chromosomes. The tail helps the sperm swim toward the egg.

4. Ovulation consists of the release of a mature egg from an ovary. It occurs about once a month.

5. Similar—both produce sex cells and hormones. Different—testes produce sperm and testosterone, while ovaries produce eggs and estrogen.

Check Your Progress · CHAPTER PROJECT

Some students may be more thoughtful and responsive if they are allowed to complete the project alone. Others may benefit from role-playing discussions in which they compare child-care experiences and give each other pointers. Assess the mood of the class to determine the best way to approach the project.

Performance Assessment

Organizing Information Have students create flowcharts of the path traveled by the sperm or the path of the egg through the appropriate reproductive system.

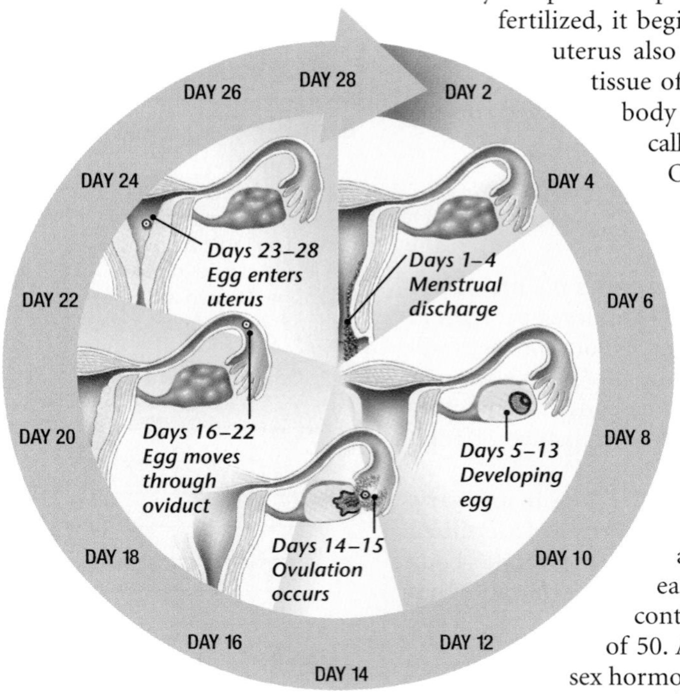

Once the egg is released, it can be fertilized for the next few days if sperm are present in the oviduct. If the egg is not fertilized, it begins to break down. The lining of the uterus also breaks down. The extra blood and tissue of the thickened lining pass out of the body through the vagina. This process is called **menstruation** (men stroo AY shun). On average, menstruation lasts about 4 to 6 days. At the same time that menstruation occurs, a new egg begins to mature in the ovary, and the cycle continues. You can follow the main steps in the cycle in Figure 8.

Endocrine Control The menstrual cycle is controlled by hormones of the endocrine system. Hormones also trigger a girl's first menstruation. Many girls begin menstruation sometime between the ages of 10 and 14 years. Some girls start earlier, while others start later. Women continue to menstruate until about the age of 50. At around that age, the production of sex hormones drops. As a result, the ovaries stop releasing mature egg cells.

Figure 8 During the menstrual cycle, the lining of the uterus builds up with extra blood and tissue. About halfway through a typical cycle, ovulation takes place. If the egg is not fertilized, menstruation occurs.

Section 2 Review

1. What specialized cells are produced in the male and female reproductive systems?

2. How does the uterus change during the menstrual cycle?

3. How does a sperm's structure help it function?

4. What is ovulation? How often does it occur?

5. Thinking Critically Comparing and Contrasting In what ways are the functions of the ovaries and the testes similar? How do their functions differ?

Check Your Progress · CHAPTER PROJECT

You should now be caring for your "baby," taking it with you everywhere or arranging for a responsible person to care for it. You or your substitute must continue to perform all the child-care tasks, such as feeding the baby, changing diapers, and playing with the baby. Whenever you travel, you must have a safe method for transporting the baby. Don't forget to make at least two journal entries each day.

Background

Facts and Figures Premenstrual syndrome (PMS) can occur during the last 7 to 10 days of the menstrual cycle. PMS produces physical symptoms such as cramping, headaches, breast tenderness, and fluid retention. It also leads to behavioral symptoms such as anxiety, crying spells, and appetite changes. Although the exact cause of PMS is unknown, it is thought to be due to changing hormonal levels.

Program Resources

◆ **Unit 4 Resources** 21-2 Review and Reinforce, p. 175; 21-2 Enrich, p. 176

SECTION 3 The Human Life Cycle

DISCOVER

How Many Ways Does a Child Grow?

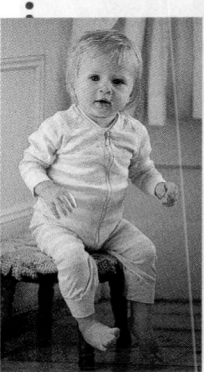

1. Compare the two photographs at the left. One shows a baby girl. The other shows the same girl at the age of five.

2. Make two lists—one of the similarities and the other of the differences you see.

3. Compare your lists with those of your classmates.

Think It Over
Observing Based on your observations, list three physical changes that occur in early childhood.

An egg can be fertilized during the first few days after ovulation. When sperm are deposited into the vagina, the sperm move through the uterus into the oviducts. If a sperm fertilizes an egg, pregnancy can occur. Then the amazing process of human development begins.

A fertilized egg, or zygote, is no larger than the period at the end of this sentence. Yet after fertilization, the zygote undergoes changes that result in the formation of a new human. **The zygote develops first into an embryo and then into a fetus.** About nine months after fertilization, a baby is born.

The Zygote

After an egg cell and sperm cell join, the zygote moves down the oviduct toward the uterus. During this trip, which takes about four days, the zygote begins to divide. The original cell divides to make two cells, these two cells divide to make four, and so on. Eventually, the growing mass of hundreds of cells forms a hollow ball. The ball attaches to the lining of the uterus. For the next eight weeks or so, the developing human is called an **embryo** (EM bree oh).

> ### GUIDE FOR READING
> ◆ What are the stages of human development that occur before birth?
> ◆ What happens during childbirth?
> ◆ What changes occur during adolescence?
>
> *Reading Tip* As you read, use the headings to outline the events that occur during pregnancy, birth, adolescence, and adulthood.

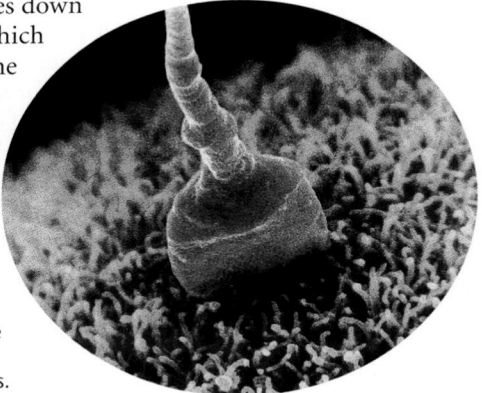

Figure 9 Only one sperm can fertilize an egg. Once fertilization occurs, the process of human development begins.

INTEGRATING HEALTH

SECTION 3 The Human Life Cycle

Objectives
After completing the lesson, students will be able to
◆ list the stages of human development that occur before birth;
◆ describe what happens during childbirth;
◆ describe the physical changes that occur during infancy and childhood;
◆ describe the changes that occur during adolescence;
◆ describe the changes that occur during adulthood.

Key Terms embryo, amniotic sac, placenta, umbilical cord, fetus

1 Engage/Explore

Activating Prior Knowledge
Show students several pictures of a variety of baby mammals, including human beings. Encourage students to brainstorm a list of characteristics that they all have in common. *(Sample: Feed on mother's milk, depend on parents for food, are smaller than parents but have similar characteristics.)*

DISCOVER

Skills Focus observing
Time 15 minutes
Tips Bring in additional photographs showing individuals as babies and as children.
Think It Over Students should note several major differences between the two photos. Overall, the child has grown to be taller and heavier than the baby. The proportions of her body have also changed—the child's head is smaller in proportion to the rest of her body, and the child's limbs are longer in proportion to the rest of her body. The child's features have become less rounded.

READING STRATEGIES

Reading Tip As a class, outline the information under the first section heading. Then have students complete the rest of the outline independently.
I. Zygote
  A. The zygote (fertilized egg) moves down the oviduct.
    1. It begins to divide.
    2. It forms a hollow ball.
  B. The ball attaches to the uterus.

Program Resources

◆ **Unit 4 Resources** 21-3 Lesson Plan, p. 177; 21-3 Section Summary, p. 178

Media and Technology

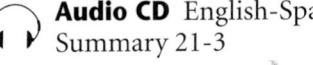 **Audio CD** English-Spanish Summary 21-3

669

2 Facilitate

The Zygote

Building Inquiry Skills: Calculating

Remind students that every zygote starts out as a single cell. Tell students that when cells divide, the number continually doubles. Ask them to predict how many divisions of the single-celled zygote will be necessary to produce more than 1,000 cells. *(10 cell divisions equals 1,024 cells)* Ask: **If cell division occurs every 26 hours, how long would it take for the embryo to have over 1,000 cells?** *(260 hours or about 11 days)* **learning modality: logical/mathematical**

The Development of the Embryo

Using the Visuals: Figure 10

Refer students to Figure 10. Draw their attention to the uterus. Tell students to examine the uterus and the uterine wall. Point out the enlargement. Explain to students that the enlargement shows details of the placenta shown in the main diagram. Ask: **Is the embryo connected directly to a part of the mother's reproductive system? Explain.** *(No. It is connected to the placenta.)* **learning modality: visual**

 Integrating Health

Inform students that women who drink during pregnancy have an increased risk of giving birth to children with fetal alcohol syndrome (FAS). FAS consists of a variety of birth defects, including low birth weight, an abnormally small head, facial deformities, and mild to moderate mental retardation. As FAS children develop, they often exhibit behavioral and cognitive problems. **learning modality: verbal**

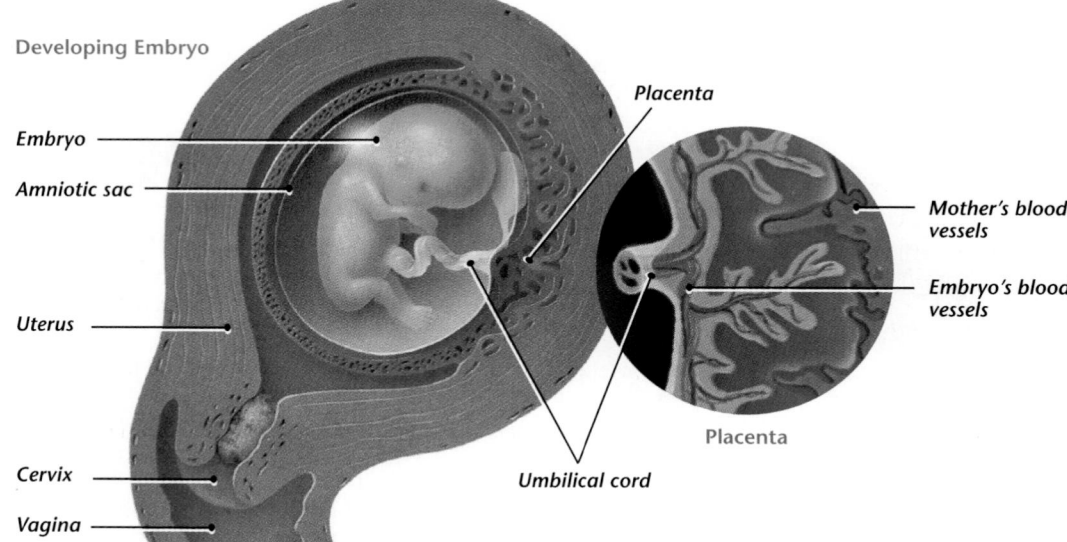
Developing Embryo

Embryo
Amniotic sac
Uterus
Cervix
Vagina
Placenta
Mother's blood vessels
Embryo's blood vessels
Placenta
Umbilical cord

Figure 10 The placenta connects the mother and the developing embryo. But the mother's and the embryo's blood vessels remain separate, as you can see in the closeup of the placenta. *Interpreting Diagrams What structure carries nutrients and oxygen from the placenta to the embryo?*

The Development of the Embryo

Soon after the embryo attaches to the uterus, many changes take place. The hollow ball of cells grows inward. New membranes form. One membrane surrounds the embryo and develops into a fluid-filled sac called the **amniotic sac** (am nee AHT ik). Locate the amniotic sac in Figure 10. The fluid in the amniotic sac cushions and protects the developing baby.

Another membrane that forms is the **placenta** (pluh SEN tuh). The placenta becomes the link between the developing embryo and the mother. In the placenta, the embryo's blood vessels are located next to the mother's blood vessels. Blood from the two systems does not mix, but many substances are exchanged. The embryo receives nutrients, oxygen, and other substances from the mother. It gives off carbon dioxide and other wastes.

The embryo soon moves a short distance from the placenta. A ropelike structure called the **umbilical cord** forms between the embryo and the placenta. It contains blood vessels that link the embryo to the mother, but the two circulatory systems remain separated by a thin barrier.

INTEGRATING HEALTH The barrier that separates the embryo's and mother's blood prevents some diseases from spreading from the mother to the embryo. However, substances such as chemicals in tobacco smoke, alcohol, and some other drugs can pass through the barrier to the embryo. For this reason, pregnant women should not smoke tobacco, drink alcohol, or take any drug without a doctor's approval.

✓ *Checkpoint* *How does an embryo obtain oxygen?*

670

Background

Facts and Figures In-vitro fertilization (IVF) involves the fertilization of mature egg cells by sperm cells in a petri dish or test tube. The term *in vitro* comes from the Latin words meaning "in glass." After the eggs are fertilized, the potential embryos are transferred into a petri dish containing a suitable growth medium and allowed to divide until they form hollow balls of cells (blastocysts). During this time, hormone treatments are being used to prepare the mother's uterus to accept the embryos. When the embryos are ready, they are introduced through the cervix into the mother's uterus. The first successful birth of a child by means of IVF occurred in England in 1978. The IVF procedure was carried out by Patrick Steptoe and R. G. Edwards.

The Development of the Fetus

From the ninth week of development until birth, the embryo is called a **fetus** (FEE tus). Although the fetus starts out about as small as a walnut shell, it now looks more like a baby. Many internal organs have developed. The head is about half the body's total size. The fetus's brain is developing rapidly. It also has dark eye patches, fingers, and toes. By the end of the third month, the fetus is about 9 centimeters long and has a mass of about 26 grams.

Between the fourth and sixth months, the tissues of the fetus continue to develop into more recognizable shapes. Bones become distinct. A heartbeat can be heard with a stethoscope. A layer of soft hair grows over the skin. The arms and legs develop more completely. The fetus begins to move and kick, a sign that its muscles are growing. At the end of the sixth month, the mass of the fetus is approaching 700 grams. Its body is about 20 centimeters long.

The final 3 months prepare the fetus to survive outside the mother's body. The brain surface develops grooves and ridges. The lungs become developed enough to carry out the exchange of oxygen and carbon dioxide. The eyelids can open. The fetus doubles in length. Its mass may reach 3 kilograms or more.

Birth

After about 9 months of development inside the uterus, the baby is ready to be born. **The birth of a baby takes place in three stages—labor, delivery, and afterbirth.**

Labor During the first stage of birth, strong muscular contractions of the uterus begin. These contractions are called labor. The contractions cause the cervix to enlarge, eventually allowing the baby to fit through the opening. Labor may last from about 2 hours to more than 20 hours.

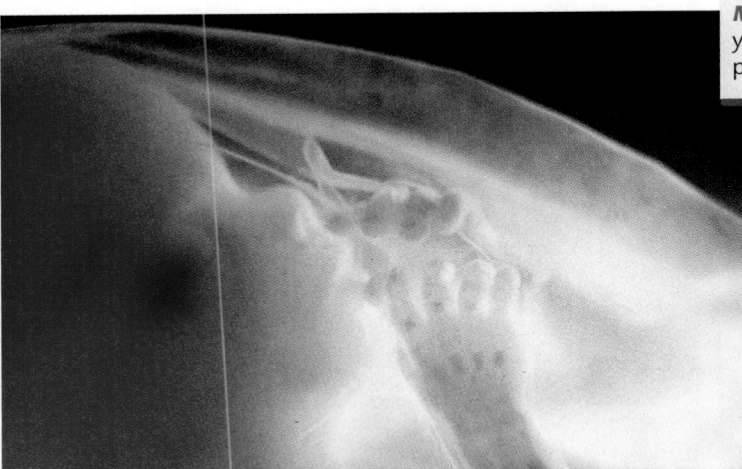

Way to Grow!

The table lists the average mass of a developing baby at different months of pregnancy.

ACTIVITY

Month of Pregnancy	Mass (grams)
1	0.02
2	2.0
3	26
4	150
5	460
6	640
7	1,500
8	2,300
9	3,200

1. Use a balance to identify an everyday object with a mass equal to each mass listed in the table. You may need to use different balances to cover the range of masses listed.
2. Arrange the objects in order by month.

Making Models What did you learn by gathering these physical models?

Figure 11 At the beginning of the fourth month of development, a fetus has developed internal organs, dark eye patches, fingers, and toes. Later, its eyes will open, and fingernails and toenails will form.

Answers to Self-Assessment

Caption Question

Figure 10 The umbilical cord

☑ *Checkpoint*

The embryo obtains oxygen from the mother. Substances such as nutrients, oxygen, carbon dioxide, and other wastes are exchanged in the placenta.

The Development of the Fetus

TRY THIS

ACTIVITY

Skills Focus making models
Materials *balance, objects of various masses*
Time 25 minutes
Provide balances that can handle the listed range of masses. If necessary, shorten the list. Students can combine objects to reach the higher masses.
Extend Challenge students to create graphs showing the relative gain in mass of the developing fetus. **learning modality: kinesthetic**

Social Studies Connection

Ask students if they have ever heard of the drug thalidomide. Explain that in the late 1950s, this drug was given to pregnant women in Europe to treat nausea and vomiting. In 1961, the drug was found to be associated with a number of birth defects, including severely shortened arms and legs. Women who took this drug during the first three months of their pregnancies sometimes had babies with these birth defects, though those who took the drug during the last three months had normal babies. Thalidomide was never approved for use in the United States. The head of the Food and Drug Administration, Dr. Frances Kelsey, delayed approval of the drug because of concerns with numbness in some of the users. It was during this interim that the dangers of using thalidomide during pregnancy became known. **learning modality: verbal**

Ongoing Assessment

Writing Ask students to choose a stage in the development of the embryo or fetus and describe what happens at that stage. *(Sample: From the first through the third month, the fetus develops internal organs, the head is half the size of the body, the brain develops rapidly. The fetus has dark eye patches, fingers, and toes.)*

Portfolio Students can save their descriptions in their portfolios.

Birth

Real-Life Learning

Students have probably heard descriptions of childbirth from their family members, on television, or in movies. Encourage students to think about some of the terms they have heard used in these descriptions. Use the text to help explain what the terms mean. For example, a television doctor may use the term *dilating*. Explain that this refers to the cervix enlarging to allow the baby to pass through, and that this is the main activity during the labor stage. Students may have other questions, or may use words other than those in the text to describe births they have heard or read about. Help them relate each stage to the stages described in the text. **limited English proficiency**

Delivery The second stage of birth is called delivery. During delivery, the baby is pushed completely out of the uterus, through the vagina, and out of the mother's body. The head usually comes out first. At this time, the baby is still connected to the placenta by the umbilical cord. Delivery usually takes less time than labor does—from several minutes to a few hours.

Shortly after delivery, the umbilical cord is clamped, then cut about five centimeters from the baby's abdomen. Within 7 to 10 days, the remainder of the umbilical cord dries up and falls off, leaving a scar called the navel, or belly button.

Afterbirth About 15 minutes after delivery, the third stage of the birth process begins. Contractions push the placenta and other membranes out of the uterus through the vagina. This stage, called afterbirth, is usually completed in less than an hour.

Birth and the Baby The birth process is stressful for both the baby and the mother. The baby is pushed and squeezed as it travels out of the mother's body. Contractions put pressure on the placenta and umbilical cord, briefly cutting off the baby's supply of oxygen.

In response to the changes, the baby's endocrine system releases adrenaline. The baby's heart rate increases. Within a few seconds of delivery, the baby will begin breathing with a cry or a cough. This action helps rid the lungs of fluid and fills them with air. The newborn's heart rate then slows to a steady pace. Blood travels to the lungs and picks up oxygen from the air that the baby breathes in. The newborn's cry helps it adjust to the changes in its surroundings.

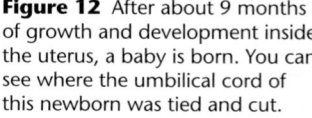 *Checkpoint* **What events occur during labor?**

Figure 12 After about 9 months of growth and development inside the uterus, a baby is born. You can see where the umbilical cord of this newborn was tied and cut.

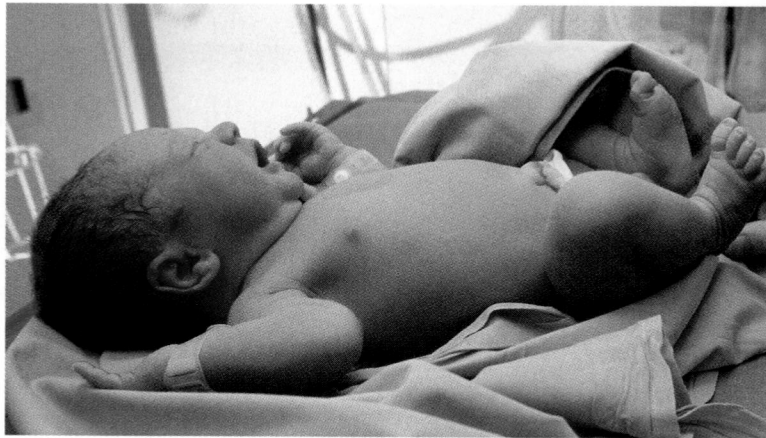

672

Background

History of Science Until the middle of the nineteenth century, women who had to go to maternity hospitals faced a mortality rate as high as 30 percent. Most deaths resulted from an infection called puerperal fever. In 1844, a Hungarian doctor named Ignaz Semmelweis worked at an obstetric clinic in Vienna. Semmelweis observed that in one part of the clinic, where medical students were taught, mortality rates were two to three times higher than in another part, where midwives were taught. Semmelweis concluded that the medical students, who often dissected cadavers right before examining women in labor, were carrying infection. When he directed the students to disinfect their hands before examining women, the mortality rate in that part of the clinic dropped to around 1 percent.

Figure 13 Fraternal twins (right) develop from two different fertilized eggs. Identical twins (below) develop from the same fertilized egg. They share identical characteristics.
Applying Concepts Why can fraternal twins be different sexes while identical twins cannot?

Multiple Births

The delivery of more than one baby from a single pregnancy is called a multiple birth. In the United States, a set of twins is born in about one out of every 90 births.

There are two types of twins: identical twins and fraternal twins. Identical twins develop from a single fertilized egg, or zygote. Early in development, the embryo splits into two identical embryos. The two embryos have identical inherited traits and are the same sex. Fraternal twins develop when two eggs are released from the ovary and are fertilized by two different sperm. Fraternal twins are no more alike than any other brothers or sisters. Fraternal twins may or may not be the same sex.

Infancy

What can a newborn baby do? You might say "Not much!" A newborn can perform only simple actions, such as crying, sucking, yawning, and blinking. But during infancy—the first two years of life—babies undergo many changes and learn to do many things.

Physical Changes A baby's shape and size change greatly during infancy. When a baby is born, its head makes up about one fourth of its body length. As the infant develops, its head grows more slowly, and its body, legs, and arms begin to catch up. Its nervous and muscular systems become better coordinated. The baby then starts to develop new physical skills.

The exact ages at which physical skills develop vary from baby to baby. A newborn cannot lift its head. But after about 3 months, it can hold its head up and reach for objects. At about 7 months, most infants can move around by crawling. Somewhere between 10 and 16 months, most infants begin to walk by themselves.

Chapter 21 **673**

Multiple Births

Addressing Naive Conceptions

Students may have heard that the tendency to have twins runs in families. Explain that this is only true for fraternal twins. The tendency for a woman's ovaries to release more than one mature egg cell during a cycle seems to be inherited. On the other hand, identical twins are not produced by an inherited trait, so they do not run in families. An increasing number of multiple births are the results of treatments for infertility, including in-vitro fertilization and drugs that cause the ovaries to release several mature eggs at once. The birth of fraternal twins under these circum-stances does not indicate that the family has the tendency to produce twins. **learning modality: verbal**

Infancy

Real-Life Learning

Students who have siblings in the infant stage may wish to share their experiences with the rest of the class. Ask students to tell the age of their siblings and describe for the class their physical characteristics such as weight and length. Students may also describe motor skills the infants demonstrate, as well as other infant behavior such as crying, feeding, and sleeping habits. Ask students whether their family's infant recognizes family members and whether they note any facial expressions indicating emotions. **learning modality: verbal**

Answers to Self-Assessment

✓ *Checkpoint*

During labor, strong muscular contractions of the uterus cause the cervix to enlarge. As labor progresses, the contractions become stronger and more frequent.

Answers to Self-Assessment

Caption Question

Figure 13 Fraternal twins develop from two different fertilized eggs, so the chances that they are the same sex is the same as for any other brothers or sisters. Identical twins develop from the same fertilized egg, so they must be the same sex.

Ongoing Assessment

Writing Have students create flowcharts for the events in the three stages of childbirth.

 Students can save their flowcharts in their portfolios.

Childhood

Language Arts Connection

Students may be interested to learn that the beginning of childhood is defined as the time when children acquire language. Many infants can say one or two words by the time they are a little over one year old. By the time children are three years old, they learn more than two new words a day, and their working vocabulary contains about 1,000 words. Although there is slight variation from child to child, most humans develop language at about the same rate. This is even true for deaf children whose families communicate using sign language. Ask students: **Why is language acquisition a good determination of the stages of life for children?** (*Because it happens at the same ages for almost all children.*)
learning modality: verbal

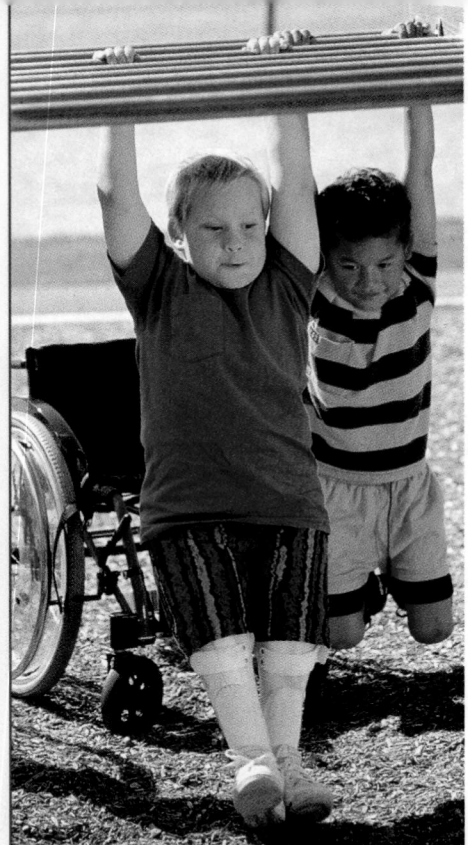

Figure 14 During childhood, children learn to get along with others. Their physical activities and games help them become stronger and more coordinated.

Other Changes How does an infant communicate? You may think that babies display feelings mostly by crying. But young infants can show pleasure by smiling and laughing. They can turn their heads or spit out food they don't like. Babies also begin to make babbling sounds. Sometime between the ages of one and three years, many children speak their first word. By the end of infancy, children can do many things for themselves, such as understand simple directions, feed themselves, and play with toys. However, infants are too young to know when something can hurt them. They must be watched carefully at all times.

Childhood

Infancy ends and childhood begins at about two years of age. Childhood continues until about the age of 13 years. Children gradually become more active and independent, and experience many physical and mental changes.

Physical Changes Throughout childhood, children continue to grow. They become taller and heavier as their bones and muscles increase in size. They become more coordinated as they practice skills such as walking, holding a fork, using a pencil, and playing games. Over a period of several years, baby teeth fall out and are replaced by permanent teeth. Toward the end of childhood, the bones, especially the legs, begin to grow faster. An increased appetite signals that the body needs more nutrients for its next stage of growth and development.

Other Changes As they develop, children show a growing curiosity and increasing mental abilities. Their curiosity helps them learn about their surroundings. With the help of family members and teachers, children learn to read and to solve problems. Language skills improve rapidly. For example, most four-year-olds can express themselves clearly and can carry on conversations.

Over time, children learn to make friends, care about others, and behave responsibly. Between the ages of 3 and 6, they learn to share and play with others. As children think about and care more for others, friends become more important. About the age of 10, children develop a strong wish to fit in with others of their age group. As their independence increases, children take on more responsibilities at home and school.

Background

Facts and Figures The word *infant* comes from the Latin for "nonspeaker." A child usually begins to speak words between the ages of one and two, although children understand words before they speak.

Some components of language acquisition appear to be inherited. When learning grammatical rules, all children follow a characteristic sequence, regardless of what language they are learning. The American linguist Noam Chomsky based his theory of transformational-generative grammar on this remarkable fact. In this theory, children are born with an understanding of the logical rules that determine the grammatical structure of all languages.

Adolescence

If you compared a current photo of yourself with one taken three years ago, you would notice many changes. Starting at about the age of 12, you gradually begin to change from a child to an adult. Although many changes happen during infancy and childhood, some of the most significant changes occur during adolescence. **Adolescence** (ad ul es uns) is the stage of development when children become adults physically and mentally.

Physical Changes Sometime between the ages of about 9 and 14 years, a child enters puberty. **Puberty** (PYOO bur tee) is the period of sexual development in which the body becomes able to reproduce. The physical changes of puberty are controlled by the hormones of the endocrine system.

In girls, hormones produced by the pituitary gland and the ovaries control the physical changes of puberty. The sex organs develop. Ovulation and menstruation begin. The breasts begin to enlarge, and the hips start to widen. The skin begins to produce more oils, and body odor increases.

In boys, hormones from the testes and the pituitary gland govern the changes. The sex organs develop, and sperm production begins. The voice deepens. Hair appears on the face and chest. As with girls, more skin oils are produced, and body odor increases.

Just as infants and children experience growth spurts, or periods of rapid growth, so do adolescents. Girls tend to experience their growth spurt slightly younger than boys do. Thus, during early adolescence girls tend to be taller than boys. Later in adolescence boys display rapid growth. Overall, boys tend to reach taller adult heights than girls.

Figure 15 During adolescence, teens mature both physically and mentally. It's a time when many teens try new experiences and take on more responsibilities. Working in the community is one way that teens can explore their interests while helping others.

Addressing Naive Conceptions

Some students may think that, once they begin puberty, the physical changes associated with that stage of development should occur at a steady pace over a relatively brief period of time. Some may be worried that they have begun to change but have not progressed further. Reassure students that on average, puberty lasts about four years and can proceed at varying rates.
learning modality: verbal

Real-Life Learning

Stress the fact that teens  need to eat well-balanced and nutritious diets because their bodies are growing and changing so rapidly. Point out that the recommended amounts of nutrients and calories listed on food labels are calculated for adults, not growing adolescents. Adolescents often need more calories and larger amounts of certain nutrients than adults. Provide reference materials and have students work in groups to create tables that summarize the various nutritional requirements for growing teens. Encourage students to plan a healthful diet for adolescence based on their tables.
cooperative learning

Media and Technology

 Exploring Life Science Videodisc
Unit 4, Side 1, "Development is a Lifelong Process"
Chapter 10

Ongoing Assessment

Writing Ask students to list the physical changes that take place during puberty in males and females.

Adolescence, continued

Building Inquiry Skills: Communicating

Encourage students to talk to an older relative of the same sex about the relative's personal development and how it affected him or her. However, make sure students know that everyone develops at his or her own pace. **limited English proficiency**

Social Studies CONNECTION

In the traditional Apache culture, the Changing Woman ceremony also serves the community in many ways. The celebration and its elaborate preparations bring the entire community together and remind them of four cultural values: physical strength, good disposition, prosperity, and a long life of good health.

In Your Journal Students can research to find more information on the Changing Woman ceremony and identify events in their own experience that have similar meanings.

Life as an Adult

Building Inquiry Skills: Communicating

Ask students to write about what they expect their lives to be like when they are adults. Have them describe how they think their lives will change from the period of adolescence to adulthood. Ask them to think about at what age they expect themselves to be adults and to give explanations for their thinking. Encourage them to think about how decisions they make today might affect their adult life. **learning modality: verbal**

Social Studies CONNECTION

In many cultures, adolescence is seen as a passage from childhood to adulthood. In the Apache culture, girls who have entered puberty and begun their menstrual cycles undergo the Changing Woman ceremony. Often the whole community enjoys the feasting, dancing, and performances that are part of the ceremony. The girl dresses in a decorated buckskin dress and is sprinkled with cattail pollen. Other parts of the ceremony include fasting followed by special meals and prayer. After the ceremony, the girl is considered a woman by tribal members.

In Your Journal

Imagine you have just witnessed the Changing Woman ceremony. Write a short letter to a friend describing the event. Include information about the significance of the ceremony. Relate the experience to events with which you are familiar.

Figure 16 In the ceremony being celebrated here, tribal members help this 14-year-old Apache girl mark her passage to adulthood.

Mental and Social Changes Adolescence includes more than just the physical changes of puberty. Many important mental and social changes take place as well. Adolescents may notice changes in the way they think, feel, and get along with others. Many teenagers have mixed feelings about the changes they are experiencing. They may feel excited and happy about them one day, and shy and confused the next day.

Between about the ages of 13 and 15, a teenager gradually becomes able to think and reason like an adult. Teens can think in ways that they could not as children. For example, young children think of hunger only when their stomachs are empty, or of pain only when they are hurt. Teenagers' thoughts are no longer limited to their immediate experiences. They begin to consider the consequences of their actions and make thoughtful judgments. Memory and problem-solving skills also improve. These and other mental abilities are often developed at school or through interests such as music or theater.

Because friends' opinions become very important during adolescence, peer pressure may influence the decisions and actions of teenagers. **Peer pressure** consists of pressure from your friends and classmates to behave in certain ways. Peer pressure can produce both negative and positive results. Negative peer pressure can lead teens to do things that go against their values. The support of friends, on the other hand, can encourage teens to work toward their goals or develop new interests and skills.

Background

Facts and Figures The mental and social changes that occur during adolescence can be traced to hormones and other biological factors. In boys, the production of larger quantities of testosterone has been associated with strong emotions and moodiness, especially aggressiveness. Estrogen has been associated with moodiness and strong emotions in girls, who are more prone to depression.

Studies have shown that adolescents report feeling happier and less prone to moodiness in highly structured activities including adults, as opposed to spending time alone or with friends. Taking classes, having a job, or being involved in church or civic activities may help students deal more effectively with the stresses and changes of adolescence.

Life as an Adult

At what point does adolescence end and adulthood begin? On a certain birthday? If you look up the word *adult* in the dictionary, it is defined as being grown up, or mature. Legally, Americans are considered to be adults at the age of 16 or 18 for some activities and at the age of 21 for others. From a physical and mental standpoint, however, it is difficult to say when adulthood begins.

Physical changes continue to occur throughout adulthood. After about the age of 30, the process of aging begins. Aging becomes more noticeable between the ages of 40 and 65. The skin starts to become wrinkled, the eyes lose their ability to focus on close objects, the hair may lose its coloring, and muscle strength decreases.

After age 65, aging intensifies, often leading to less efficient heart and lung action. But the effects of aging can be slowed if people follow sensible diets and good exercise plans. With the help of such healthy behaviors, more and more adults remain active throughout their lives.

Responsibilities—as well as opportunities, rights, and privileges—arrive with adulthood. As an adult, you may need to make decisions that affect not just yourself, but your spouse and your children as well. You will need know what values are important to you, and make decisions that match those values.

Figure 17 Adulthood is a time when opportunities and choices expand. Adults can also share their knowledge and experience with younger people.

Section 3 Review

1. What three steps of development does a fertilized egg go through before birth?
2. Briefly describe what happens during each of the three stages of birth.
3. Describe three physical changes that occur in boys and girls during puberty. Name two mental changes and one social change that adolescents experience.
4. What behaviors can adults practice to slow down the effects of aging?
5. **Thinking Critically Relating Cause and Effect** Why is it dangerous for a pregnant woman to drink alcohol or to smoke?

Check Your Progress CHAPTER PROJECT

By now, you should be preparing a summary of what you learned about being a parent. What skills do parents need? What are some of the rewards of parenthood? What are some of the challenges? How would you feel if you had to continue caring for the "baby" past the project deadline? Write answers to these questions as your final journal entry.

Chapter 21 **677**

---

3 Assess

Section 3 Review Answers

1. Zygote, embryo, and fetus
2. During labor, uterine contractions cause the opening of the cervix to enlarge. During delivery, the baby is pushed out of the uterus through the vagina and out of the mother's body. In afterbirth, contractions push the placenta out of the uterus through the vagina.
3. Physical changes (accept any three): In both boys and girls, the sex organs develop rapidly, body odor increases, and the skin produces more oils. In girls, the breasts enlarge, the hips widen, and ovulation and menstruation begin. In boys, the voice deepens, hair appears on the face and chest, and sperm production begins. Mental changes (accept any two): Adolescents are able to think and reason as adults; they can question the opinions and actions of others, consider consequences, and make judgments. Social changes (accept any): They begin to spend more time with friends, respond to peer pressure, and may become interested in the opposite sex.
4. Sensible diet and exercise plans.
5. Because alcohol and substances in tobacco smoke can pass from the mother to the developing embryo through the placenta.

Check Your Progress CHAPTER PROJECT

Students can use their daily journal entries to help them prepare summaries of their experiences. Challenge students to imagine how they would feel after three days of caring for a real baby, and to express how they feel about no longer having to care for their flour "baby."

Performance Assessment

Writing Have students create time lines of events that begin with a zygote and end at childhood. Students should write at least one characteristic to describe each stage of development. Students can save their time lines in their portfolios.

Growing Up

Preparing for Inquiry

Key Concept As the human body develops and grows, it not only increases in size, but its proportions change in a regular way from conception to adulthood.

Skills Objectives Students will be able to
- organize information about the proportions of the human body during development;
- calculate percentages;
- interpret data to make inferences about the rates at which different body parts grow;
- design experiments to test their predictions about the relationship between the circumference of the head compared to body height.

Time 30 minutes

Guiding Inquiry

Invitation

Obtain illustrations from magazines showing people of various ages. If possible, use pictures taken from different distances or perspectives so that the total image height is similar, even though the pictures show people of different heights. Invite students to compare the images and describe general differences between people of different ages.

Introducing the Procedure

Have students find the lines on the diagram that represent 50% and 100%. Ask them what height measurements would correspond to those figures for their own height, and for familiar animals such as horses, birds, dogs, and cats. Make sure students understand that the diagram compares the whole height at each stage without comparing the heights directly.

Troubleshooting the Experiment

Students may have trouble estimating between the lines. Copy the diagram onto the board or photocopy the diagram so students can add and label additional marks.

Growing Up

Problem

How do the proportions of the human body change during development?

Procedure

1. Examine the diagram below. Notice that the figures are drawn against a graph showing percents. You can use this diagram to determine how the lengths of major body parts compare to each figure's height. Make a data table in which to record information about each figure's head size and leg length.
2. Look at Figure D. You can use the graph to estimate that the head is about 15% of the figure's full height. Record that number in your data table.
3. Examine Figures A through C. Determine the percent of the total height that the head makes up. Record your results. (*Hint:* Figure A shows the legs folded. You will need to estimate the data for that figure.)
4. Now compare the length of the legs to the total body height for Figures A through D. Record your results.

Analyze and Conclude

1. How do the percents for head size and leg length change from infancy to adulthood?
2. What can you infer about the rate at which different parts of the body grow? Explain.
3. **Think About It** If you made a line graph using the data in the diagram, what would be on the horizontal axis? On the vertical axis? What additional information could you gain from this line graph?

Design an Experiment

Make a prediction about the relationship between the circumference of the head compared to body height. Then design an experiment to test your prediction, using people for test subjects. Obtain your teacher's permission before carrying out the experiment.

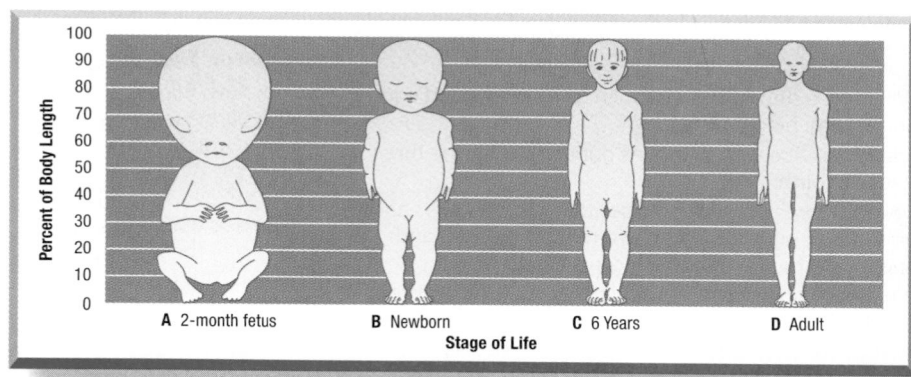

A 2-month fetus   B Newborn   C 6 Years   D Adult

Stage of Life

Percent of Body Length

Program Resources

- **Unit 4 Resources** Chapter 21 Skills Lab, pp. 181–183
- **Inquiry Skills Activity Book** Provides teaching and review of all inquiry skills

---

Sample Data Table

Comparison of Selected Body Parts to Height

Figure	Head Size	Leg Length
A	about 45%	about 35%
B	about 25%	about 35%
C	about 20%	about 40%
D	about 15%	about 50%

CHAPTER 21 STUDY GUIDE

SECTION 1 — The Endocrine System

Key Ideas
◆ The endocrine system controls many of the body's daily activities, as well as the body's overall development.
◆ The endocrine system releases chemical messages called hormones. Hormones travel through the bloodstream to their target organs.
◆ Homeostasis in the body is maintained partly through negative feedback: the right amount of a particular hormone signals the body to stop producing that hormone.

Key Terms
endocrine gland
hormone
target cell
hypothalamus
pituitary gland
negative feedback

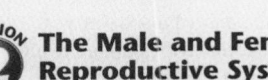

SECTION 2 — The Male and Female Reproductive Systems

Key Ideas
◆ The male reproductive system is specialized to produce sperm and the hormone testosterone.
◆ The role of the female reproductive system is to produce eggs and to nourish a developing baby until birth.
◆ Eggs are produced in the ovaries of the female. During the menstrual cycle, an egg develops, and the uterus prepares for the arrival of a fertilized egg.

Key Terms
egg
sperm
fertilization
reproduction
zygote
chromosome
testis
testosterone
scrotum
semen
penis
ovary
estrogen
oviduct
uterus
vagina
menstrual cycle
ovulation
menstruation

SECTION 3 — The Human Life Cycle
INTEGRATING HEALTH

Key Ideas
◆ If an egg is fertilized, pregnancy begins. The zygote develops into an embryo and then a fetus.
◆ A fetus develops inside the mother's uterus for about 9 months before it is born. Birth takes place in three stages—labor, delivery, and afterbirth.
◆ Infancy is a time of rapid physical growth and mastery of basic skills. During childhood, children become more independent.
◆ Adolescence includes the physical changes of puberty as well as mental and social changes.
◆ Puberty is the period of sexual development in which the body becomes able to reproduce.

Key Terms
embryo
amniotic sac
placenta
umbilical cord
fetus
adolescence
puberty
peer pressure

Organizing Information

Flowchart Copy this flowchart and fill in the main stages that occur between fertilization and birth. (For more on flowcharts, see the Skills Handbook.)

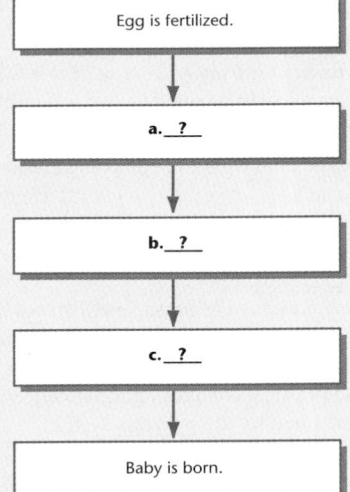

Egg is fertilized.
↓
a. ?
↓
b. ?
↓
c. ?
↓
Baby is born.

Chapter 21 **679**

Analyze and Conclude
1. In the newborn, the head makes up about 45% of body length; by adulthood, it makes up about 15%. For infants, leg length is only about 35–40% of the total body height; it increases throughout life to about 50% of total height.
2. Different parts of the body grow at different rates. For example, the legs grow much more throughout life than the head.
3. Horizontal axis—age in years; vertical axis—body length. Graphing the data would enable you to find new information by estimating values between the ages given in the diagram.

Extending the Inquiry
Design an Experiment Students' predictions will vary. Make sure that plans are safe, that students explain the predictions they want to test, and that they obtain permission from possible subjects before conducting their investigations.

Organizing Information
Flowchart a. Zygote is formed.
b. Embryo develops. **c.** Fetus develops.

Program Resources
◆ **Unit 4 Resources** Chapter 21 Project Scoring Rubric, p. 168
◆ **Performance Assessment** Chapter 21, pp. 65–67
◆ **Chapter and Unit Tests** Chapter 21 Test, pp. 69–99

Media and Technology
 Interactive Student Tutorial CD-ROM Chapter 21
 Computer Test Bank Chapter 21 Test

Reviewing Content
Multiple Choice
1. d 2. b 3. a 4. c 5. c

True or False
6. adrenal 7. true 8. true 9. true
10. endocrine

Checking Concepts
11. The hypothalamus is the link between the nervous system and the endocrine system. It sends nerve messages controlling sleep, hunger, and other conditions. It also controls the pituitary gland, which in turn regulates other endocrine glands.
12. The signal to stop secreting thyroxine. It is sent through negative feedback. After the hypothalamus senses that cells have enough energy, it signals the pituitary to stop producing TSH, which then makes the thyroid stop producing thyroxine.
13. At the beginning of the cycle, the uterine lining builds up in preparation for a fertilized egg. If the egg is unfertilized, the uterus sheds its lining.
14. A zygote is a fertilized egg. A zygote forms when a sperm fertilizes an egg. During the first four days, the zygote rapidly divides to become a hollow ball of cells. After about four days, it reaches the uterus and attaches to the uterine lining.
15. A fetus receives food and oxygen and gets rid of wastes through the placenta, which provides a connection between the developing fetus and the mother. The umbilical cord connects the fetus to the placenta. The umbilical cord contains blood vessels that carry oxygen and nutrients from the placenta to the embryo. It also contains blood vessels that carry waste products from the embryo to the placenta.
16. An infant grows rapidly. Its nervous and muscular systems become better coordinated. The baby gradually masters basic physical skills such as sitting up, crawling, and walking.
17. Sample: Physical—sex organs develop, bones grow rapidly; mental—begin to question the consequences of his actions, try out new experiences; social—become more independent, become influenced by peer pressure.

Reviewing Content
 For more review of key concepts, see the Interactive Student Tutorial CD-ROM.

Multiple Choice
Choose the letter of the best answer.

1. Which structure links the nervous system and the endocrine system?
   a. pituitary gland
   b. adrenal gland
   c. parathyroid gland
   d. hypothalamus
2. What is the male sex cell called?
   a. testis   b. sperm
   c. egg   d. ovary
3. The release of an egg from an ovary is known as
   a. ovulation.
   b. fertilization
   c. menstruation.
   d. afterbirth.
4. Two individuals that develop from the same zygote are called
   a. embryos.
   b. fraternal twins.
   c. identical twins.
   d. triplets.
5. Sex organs develop rapidly during
   a. infancy.   b. childhood.
   c. puberty.   d. adulthood.

True or False
If the statement is true, write true. If it is false, change the underlined word or words to make the statement true.

6. The <u>pituitary</u> gland produces adrenaline.
7. The female reproductive glands are the <u>ovaries</u>.
8. The joining of a sperm and an egg is called <u>fertilization</u>.
9. An <u>oviduct</u> is the passageway through which an egg travels from the ovary to the uterus.
10. The physical changes of adolescence are controlled by the <u>nervous</u> system.

Checking Concepts
11. What is the function of the hypothalamus in the body?
12. When enough thyroxine has been released into the blood, what signal is sent to the thyroid gland? How is that signal sent?
13. What changes occur in the uterus during the menstrual cycle?
14. What is a zygote and how does it form? What happens to the zygote about four days after it forms?
15. Describe how a fetus receives food and oxygen and gets rid of wastes.
16. Summarize the physical changes that take place during infancy.
17. List six changes a ten-year-old boy should expect to occur in the next five years. Include physical, mental, and social changes.
18. **Writing to Learn** Imagine you're a skeleton in the body of a sixteen-year-old person. Write about the changes you've experienced since infancy.

Thinking Critically
19. **Inferring** The pancreas produces insulin, a hormone that lowers the level of sugar in the blood. Glucagon, another hormone of the pancreas, increases the level of sugar in the blood. Suggest how these two hormones might work together to maintain homeostasis in the body.
20. **Applying Concepts** In what ways is the functioning of the endocrine system similar to the way in which a heating system works? What part of the endocrine system functions like the heating system's thermostat? Explain.
21. **Relating Cause and Effect** How can playing games help children develop important skills?
22. **Comparing and Contrasting** In what way is development during adolescence similar to development before birth? How are the two stages different?

18. Students may refer to bone growth in childhood, changes in bone proportions from infancy to childhood, and the spurts of growth that usually occur during adolescence.

Thinking Critically
19. These two hormones work together to maintain homeostasis in the body by regulating the amount of sugar in the blood. When the sugar levels are high, the pancreas produces insulin to lower the blood sugar levels. When the sugar in the blood is low, the pancreas produces glucagon to increase the blood sugar levels.
20. Both a heating system and the endocrine system turn on and off based on signals from the external environment. When the temperature or hormone levels are low, both systems work to increase the temperature or hormone levels. Once the termperature or hormone levels reach a certain level, the systems turn off. The endocrine system's negative feedback system functions like the heating system's thermostat.

Applying Skills

The data table below shows how the length of a developing baby changes during pregnancy. Use the table to answer Questions 23–25.

Week of Pregnancy	Average Length (mm)	Week of Pregnancy	Average Length (mm)
4	7	24	300
8	30	28	350
12	75	32	410
16	180	36	450
20	250	38	500

23. **Measuring** Use a metric ruler to mark each length on a piece of paper. During which four-week period did the greatest increase in length occur?
24. **Graphing** Graph the data by plotting time on the horizontal axis and length on the vertical axis.

25. **Interpreting Data** At the twelfth week, a developing baby measures about 75 mm. By which week has the fetus grown to four times that length? Six times that length?

Performance CHAPTER PROJECT Assessment

Present Your Project You now have the chance to discuss what you learned as you cared for your "baby." What do you now know about parenting that you didn't know before? Consider reading passages from your journal to the class, including the summary you wrote.

Reflect and Record In your journal, describe how well you carried out this project. Did you care for the baby for three complete days? Did you do each task as carefully as you would have for a real infant? How do you think this project was similar to caring for a real baby? How was it different?

Test Preparation *Use these questions to prepare for standardized tests.*

Study the graph. Then answer Questions 26–29.

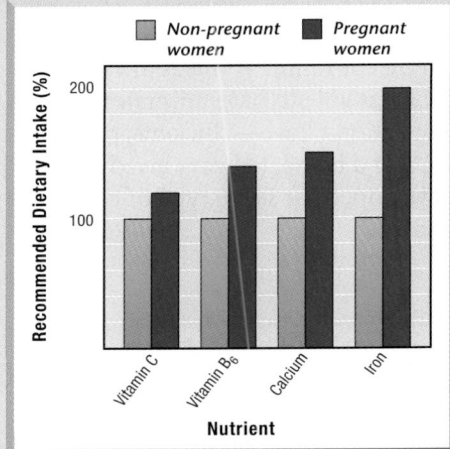

26. What would be the best title for this graph?
    a. Nutrient Needs of Pregnant Women
    b. Recommended Dietary Intake
    c. Vitamin Needs of Pregnant Women
    d. Mineral Needs of Non-pregnant Women
27. How much more iron does a pregnant woman need than a non-pregnant woman?
    a. 20%   b. 100%
    c. 120%   d. 150%
28. If non-pregnant adult women normally need 800 mg of calcium a day, how much calcium do pregnant women need?
    a. 800 mg   b. 1,000 mg
    c. 1,200 mg   d. 1,600 mg
29. Which nutrient do pregnant women need in the greatest amount?
    a. vitamin C
    b. vitamin B$_6$
    c. iron
    d. can't tell from the information in this graph

Chapter 21 **681**

Program Resources

◆ **Inquiry Skills Activity Book** Provides teaching and review of all inquiry skills.

---

21. Playing games can help children learn to get along with others and become stronger and more coordinated. Some games also help them develop important mental and social skills.
22. Development during adolescence is similar to development before birth because during both of these stages, development occurs very rapidly. They are different in that adolescence includes mental and social changes as well as physical changes.

Applying Skills

23. During weeks 12 through 16
24. Graphs should show length increasing as time increases. The slope of the line should change until it becomes a fairly straight diagonal line after 20 weeks.
25. The fetus has grown to four times that length by week 24, and six times that length by week 36.

Performance CHAPTER PROJECT Assessment

Present Your Project Have a class discussion in which volunteers can read selections from their journals. To start the discussion, refer to the list of tasks the class developed at the beginning of the project. Ask students to describe how they addressed these tasks in their projects and to explain how they feel after the project. Encourage students to talk about their experiences and how their attitudes have changed.

Reflect and Record Encourage students to write honest reflections of their experiences doing this project. Make sure students know that, although they are being evaluated on how well they carried out the procedures, a greater value can be obtained by reflecting honestly on their experiences and using their assessments as a basis for future behaviors.

Test Preparation

26. a 27. b 28. c 29. d

Protecting Desert Wildlife

Focus on Ecology

This four-page feature focuses on the process of scientific inquiry by involving students in a high-interest, magazine-like article about a working scientist, wildlife management biologist Elroy Masters. Using Masters's efforts to protect desert wildlife and habitats as an example, the feature shows how observing, collecting data, and problem solving are key elements of scientific inquiry.

The concept of habitat and scientific methods used to study populations are presented in Chapter 22. However, students do not need to have any previous knowledge of the chapter's content to understand and appreciate this feature.

Scientific Inquiry

Before students read the feature, invite them to preview the pages and the photographs and maps. Then ask: **What kinds of animals does Elroy Masters study?** (*Fish, bighorn sheep, birds, tortoises, bats*) **Where does he work?** (*In the area around Lake Havasu in western Arizona*) **How were you able to determine these things?** (*By looking at the pictures and map and reading the captions*) Confirm this response by emphasizing that students learned these things by observing. Then point out to students that just as they were able to learn about Masters's work by observing the illustrations, scientists learn by observing the world around them.

PROTECTING DESERT WILDLIFE

E lroy Masters likes working outdoors. One day he hikes a mountain trail, looking for desert tortoises. The next morning he may be in a boat on the Colorado River, counting birds along the riverbank. Another day he may be in the Arizona hills, building a water container for thirsty bighorn sheep. Elroy is a biologist working for the federal government's Bureau of Land Management (BLM). His job is to protect wildlife habitat in the desert along the Colorado River between California and Arizona.

"People may come in wanting to run a pipeline across public land or needing to build a road," he explains. "Part of my job is to check out the biological effect of that action on different species of animals and plants. If people are going to build a road where there are a lot of tortoises, we might try to have them work from November to March. Since tortoises hibernate during those months, we reduce the chance of a tortoise getting run over."

Growing up in Arizona, Elroy lived in a farming community. "I was always outdoors. I was able to have animals that a lot of people don't have—chickens, pigeons, ducks, and a horse. I always loved animals. I always hoped for some type of career with them."

Elroy Masters studied biology at Phoenix College and Northern Arizona University. He started working for the Bureau of Land Management when he was still a college student. He now works as a Wildlife Management Biologist. In this photograph, Elroy is about to release a razorback sucker, an endangered species of fish, into the Colorado River.

682

Background

Ecology is the study of how living things interact with each other and with the nonliving things in their environment. Environmental science is the study of how humans affect these interactions.

Environmental science is an applied science in which problem solving is a key element. Because environmental problems are so complex, environmental scientists must be knowledgeable in many disciplines: biology, chemistry, geology, physics, meteorology, geography, economics, mathematics, sociology, natural resource management, law, and politics. Environmental science is thus a truly interdisciplinary study.

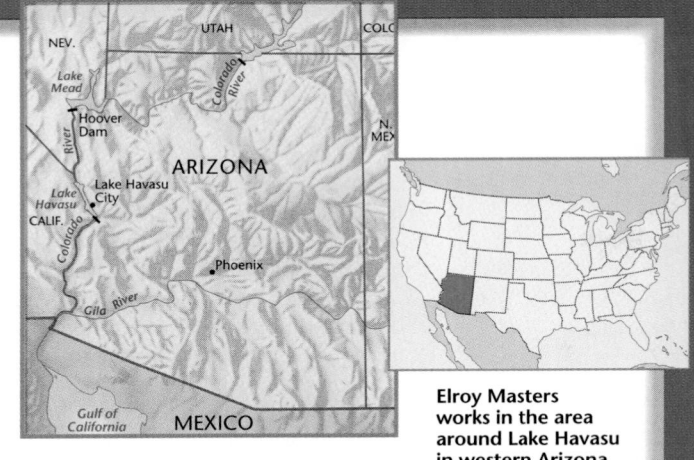

Elroy Masters works in the area around Lake Havasu in western Arizona.

Today, Elroy and his co-workers make surveys of desert animals. They count the animals in different areas and make maps of their habitats. They locate where the animals live, what they eat, and where they build their nests and raise their young. Elroy uses that information to protect the animals when natural events or human activities threaten them.

TALKING WITH ELROY MASTERS

Q *What wildlife do you protect?*

A One of the neatest animals we deal with is the desert bighorn sheep. In an average summer, it can get as hot as 120 degrees here. Sometimes the heat lasts for weeks. But with the number of people living around the river, the animals are no longer able to travel to water. So we go up into the mountains to construct catchments (containers) to collect water and store it. That way the sheep can stay in the mountains without trying to cross freeways to get to water.

We fly in big storage tanks that hold about 10,000 gallons of water. We bury them in the ground or put them on a platform. We use paint to mask them into the color of the scenery. We sometimes build a dam or put out a metal sheet to catch drizzle rain.

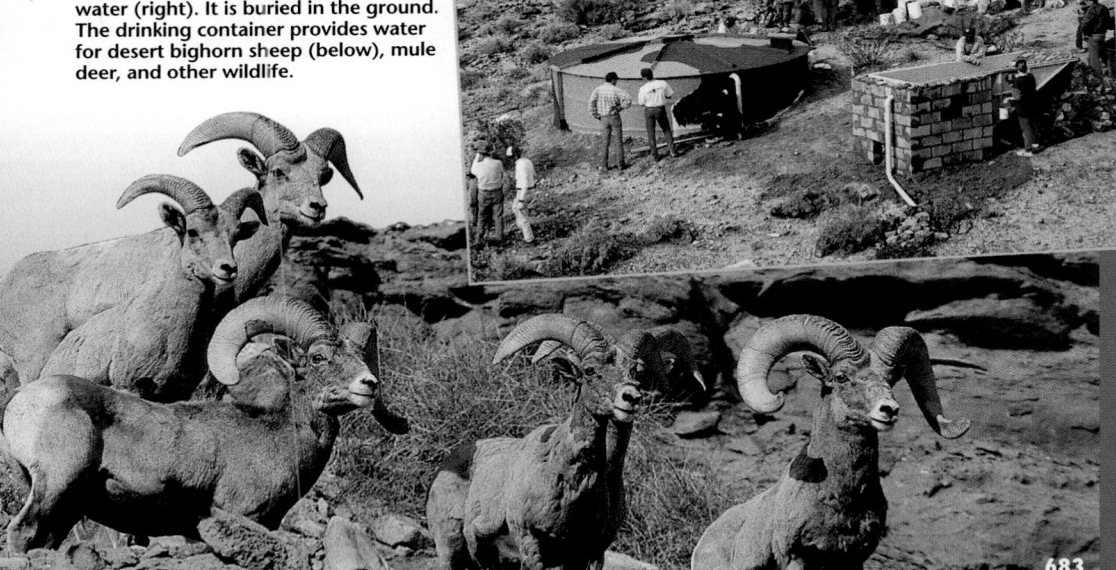

A catchment can hold 10,000 gallons of water (right). It is buried in the ground. The drinking container provides water for desert bighorn sheep (below), mule deer, and other wildlife.

683

♦ Ask students: **What is a wildlife biologist?** *(A scientist who studies living things in their environment)* You may want to share the information in Background on the previous page.

♦ After students read the introductory text on pages 682–683, ask: **What is a habitat?** *(A specific place where an organism lives and that provides the things the organism needs; if students are not familiar with the term, explain it for them.)* **Is the entire desert a single habitat?** *(no)* **Why not?** *(A desert has many different kinds of "specific places" where organisms live, such as sandy flatlands, rocky hills, and riverbanks. Different types of organisms live in different specific places, or habitats.)*

♦ Ask: **What is the major purpose of the surveys that Elroy conducts?** *(To collect information about the desert animals' habitats and behaviors)* **Why is that information important to him?** *(Knowing where the animals live and what they need in order to survive helps him know what can threaten the animals.)* **Once Elroy knows the animals' needs and how they are being threatened, what does he have to do next?** *(Figure out a way to protect the animals from these threats)* Confirm this response by emphasizing that Elroy has to solve problems. Point out that collecting data and problem solving are two important aspects of a scientist's work.

♦ Have students read the first section of the interview on this page. Then ask: **What is the bighorn sheep's habitat?** *(The desert mountains)* **What threat to the sheep did Elroy identify?** *(The sheep were unable to get to the river for water because human settlements and highways blocked their route.)* **How did the scientists solve this problem?** *(They supplied water for the sheep by building catchments in the mountains where the sheep live.)* **Why do you think the catchments are camouflaged to match the scenery?** *(To make the sheep and other wild animals less afraid of the artificial structures; to make the tanks look like a natural and attractive part of the desert landscape)*

683

◆ After students read the first question and answer on this page, ask: **What does Elroy mean when he says that a group of sheep in his area "aren't doing as well as expected"?** (*Students should be able to infer that many of the sheep are being killed by mountain lions.*) **How would Elroy know that?** (*From counting how many sheep there are in the group from one season or year to the next, from finding carcasses of sheep killed by lions, from seeing a lion track the sheep, and other observations*)

◆ After students read the second question and answer, ask: **What is a population?** (*Confirm all answers that include the idea of a group of organisms of the same kind, or species, that live in the same area. If necessary, define the term for students.*) **Why does Elroy talk about "two different populations" of desert tortoises?** (*The two groups of desert tortoises live on opposite sides of the river, so they are considered different populations.*)

◆ After students read the third question and answer, pose the following question: **Imagine you're conducting a survey to find out how many desert tortoises live in one particular habitat, but you don't see any tortoises above ground. What could you do to estimate the size of the tortoise population?** (*Based on the text alone, students should be able to infer that they could count the number of tortoise burrows they find. Some students may also suggest counting the separate sets of tortoise tracks they see on the ground.*) Explain that these are the methods actually used by biologists who study animals in the wild.

Q *What else are you doing to protect the bighorn sheep?*

A We're going to work with the Fish and Wildlife Department to capture and transplant bighorn sheep to a mountain range in my area. There are already sheep and some mountain lions here. But the sheep aren't doing as well as we expected. We want to bring in some bighorn sheep that are used to lions. We hope these lion-savvy sheep will teach the sheep in our area how to avoid lions. To catch the sheep, we'll use a helicopter. We'll shoot a net over the sheep and a couple of guys will jump out to secure the animals and then bring them to our herd.

Q *What other animals are you responsible for protecting?*

A I work a lot with desert tortoises. I'm responsible for two different populations, one on either side of the river. The tortoises live in the drier, hilly areas away from the river. Any time we go out into the field, we try to collect data. We keep track of where they've been and where they feed.

Q *How do you find the tortoises?*

A We have maps that indicate their habitat. Based on the habitat, we'll go out, walk around, and look under rocks and boulders to see if we can find a burrow. The tortoises are good diggers. They find a good boulder and go underground 10 or 12 feet. That's where they'll spend the winter.

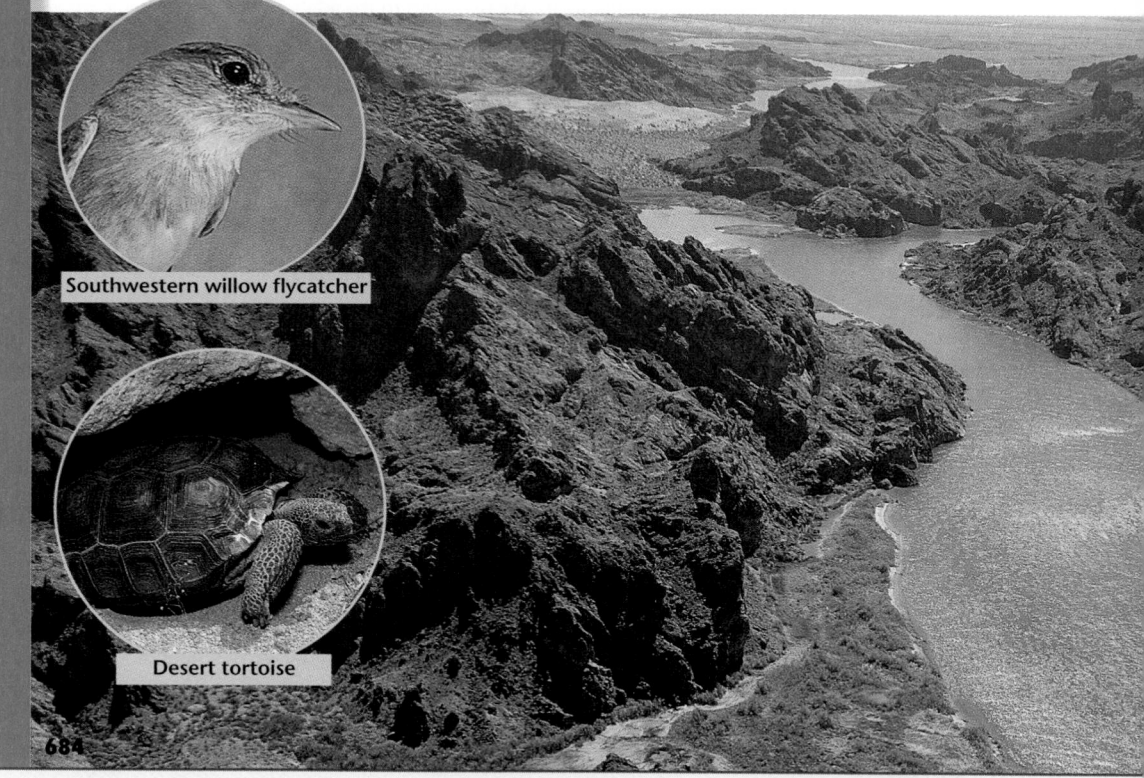

The Colorado River valley is home to the Southwestern willow flycatcher and the desert tortoise.

Southwestern willow flycatcher

Desert tortoise

684

Q *Do you also work with birds?*

A Right now we're working with the Southwestern willow flycatcher. It's a small bird that depends on thick riparian (riverbank) vegetation to build nests and breed. The flycatcher is a migratory bird. Each spring, the birds fly to Arizona from Central America and Mexico. In the early summer months, we go out to find how many are breeding. We're trying to learn what's needed to prevent flycatchers from becoming extinct. We need to survey and protect the remaining stands of habitat. The flycatchers like to nest in thick stands of willow. But they will also build nests in another tree, salt cedar. The birds don't prefer it, but sometimes salt cedar is the only vegetation remaining, so they use it.

Q *What's threatening the riverbank plants?*

A The low water level in the river—due to human use—is a big threat. So is fire. During summer months, there are large numbers of recreational boats. Careless boaters can cause fires. Some fires get pretty big along the river and destroy a lot of the habitat where the birds nest and raise their young.

Q *Can you see the benefits of your work?*

A Yes, I see it especially in riverbank zones where areas are protected so that vegetation and trees can grow back. This year we did a new bird count in one area. Species that hadn't been seen in a while, like tanagers, showed up. Some of the migratory birds are already stopping in young cottonwood trees. That's the best gauge I've had—seeing birds returning to these new trees.

There are also quick results with the water catchments in the hills. We put the water in a year ago. They're aimed at bighorn sheep and mule deer. But now we've also got a lot of different birds—doves and quails—that come into the area.

Elroy Masters also works with populations of the California leaf-nosed bat. This bat has large ears and a leaf-shaped, turned-up nose. The bats are threatened by the loss of their habitat.

In Your Journal

Elroy Masters and his co-workers "survey" the wildlife in their area in order to learn how to protect them. Think of a wild animal that lives in a park or open area near you—squirrels, frogs, birds, even insects. Work out a step-by-step plan to draw a simple map marking the places where the animal is found.

685

◆ After students read about the birds and riverbank plants, draw their attention to the bat photograph and its caption. Ask: **What common problem threatens the survival of willow flycatchers, riverbank plants, and leaf-nosed bats in Elroy's area?** *(Loss of habitat)* **Why do you think the flycatchers' habitat is being lost?** *(Willows are being destroyed as people build along the river; accept other reasonable answers.)* **What causes habitat loss along riverbanks?** *(Lower water levels and fires—both caused by human activities)* **What do you think could destroy the bats' habitat?** *(Accept all responses without comment, then share the information in Background below.)*

◆ After students read the last question and answer, ask: **How do you think Elroy and his co-workers feel when their work is successful?** *(Satisfied, glad, relieved)* **Why do they feel that way?** *(They were able to use their knowledge and problem-solving skills to help wild animals survive.)*

In Your Journal

This activity is suitable for students to do either individually or in cooperative learning groups of three or four students each. Have students share their plans with the rest of the class. Also encourage students to carry out their plans, if feasible, and share their maps and other findings with the class. (CAUTION: *Students should visit their areas with an adult. Remind students not to try to touch wild animals.*)

Background

The California leaf-nosed bat (*Macrotus californicus*) does not hibernate or migrate and cannot reduce its body temperature. To remain active year-round, the bats must have warm daytime roosts, which they find in caves, mine tunnels, and buildings.

Roosting areas are destroyed when large numbers of people visit caves, old mines, and "ghost town" buildings and when old mine entrances are sealed to prevent injury to people. New land development also reduces the bats' habitat. Bats that roost in occupied buildings are usually exterminated or kept from re-entering by blocking the entrances.

CHAPTER 22 Populations and Communities

Sections	Time	Student Edition Activities	Other Activities	
CHAPTER PROJECT **What's a Crowd?** p. 687	Ongoing (2–3 weeks)	Check Your Progress, pp. 693, 710 Present Your Project, p. 713		
1 **Living Things and the Environment** pp. 688–694 ◆ Identify the needs that are met by an organism's habitat. ◆ Identify biotic and abiotic parts of an ecosystem. ◆ Describe the levels of organization within an ecosystem. ◆ Define ecology and state what ecologists do.	2 periods/ 1 block	**Discover** What's in the Scene?, p. 688 **Try This** With or Without Salt?, p. 690 **Skills Lab: Making Models** A World in a Bottle, p. 694	TE TE IES	Building Inquiry Skills: Observing, p. 691 Using the Visuals: Figure 4, p. 692 "Where River Meets Sea," pp. 18–21
2 ⬤ *INTEGRATING MATHEMATICS* **Studying Populations** pp. 695–702 ◆ Describe how ecologists determine the size of a population. ◆ Explain what causes populations to change in size. ◆ Identify factors that limit population growth.	2 periods/ 1 block	**Discover** What's the Bean Population?, p. 695 **Sharpen Your Skills** Calculating, p. 696 **Try This** Elbow Room, p. 699 **Science at Home,** p. 700 **Real-World Lab: Careers in Science** Counting Turtles, p. 701	TE TE LM	Inquiry Challenge, p. 696 Building Inquiry Skills: Calculating, p. 698 22, "Weather and Whooping Cranes"
3 **Interactions Among Living Things** pp. 703–710 ◆ Explain how an organism's adaptations help it to survive. ◆ Describe the major types of interactions among organisms. ◆ Identify the three forms of symbiotic relationships.	2–3 periods/ 1–1½ blocks	**Discover** How Well Can You Hide a Butterfly?, p. 703 **Sharpen Your Skills** Classifying, p. 709	TE TE TE	Inquiry Challenge, p. 704 Building Inquiry Skills: Observing, p. 705 Building Inquiry Skills: Observing, p. 706
Study Guide/Chapter Assessment pp. 711–713	1 period/ ½ block		ISAB	Provides teaching and review of all inquiry skills

For Standard or Block Schedule The Resource Pro® CD-ROM gives you maximum flexibility for planning your instruction for any type of schedule. Resource Pro® contains Planning Express®, an advanced scheduling program, as well as the entire contents of the Teaching Resources and the Computer Test Bank.

CHAPTER PLANNING GUIDE

Program Resources	Assessment Strategies	Media and Technology
UR Chapter 22 Project Teacher Notes, pp. 2–3 **UR** Chapter 22 Project Overview and Worksheets, pp. 4–7	**SE** Performance Assessment: Chapter 22 Present Your Project, p. 713 **TE** Check Your Progress, pp. 693, 710 **UR** Chapter 22 Project Scoring Rubric, p. 8	Science Explorer Internet Site at www.phschool.com
UR 22-1 Lesson Plan, p. 9 **UR** 22-1 Section Summary, p. 10 **UR** 22-1 Review and Reinforce, p. 11 **UR** 22-1 Enrich, p. 12 **UR** Chapter 22 Skills Lab, pp. 21–22	**SE** Section 1 Review, p. 693 **TE** Ongoing Assessment, pp. 689–691 **TE** Performance Assessment, p. 693	Earth Science Videotape 6; Videodisc Unit 6 Side 2, "Touch the Earth Gently" Audio CD, English-Spanish Summary 22-1 Transparency 80, "Levels of Organization in an Ecosystem" Interactive Student Tutorial CD-ROM, Chapter 22
UR 22-2 Lesson Plan, p. 13 **UR** 22-2 Section Summary, p. 14 **UR** 22-2 Review and Reinforce, p. 15 **UR** 22-2 Enrich, p. 16 **UR** Chapter 22 Real-World Lab, pp. 23–25	**SE** Section 2 Review, p. 700 **TE** Ongoing Assessment, pp. 697, 699 **TE** Performance Assessment, p. 700	Audio CD, English-Spanish Summary 22-2
UR 22-3 Lesson Plan, p. 17 **UR** 22-3 Section Summary, p. 18 **UR** 22-3 Review and Reinforce, p. 19 **UR** 22-3 Enrich, p. 20	**SE** Section 3 Review, p. 710 **TE** Ongoing Assessment, pp. 705, 707, 709 **TE** Performance Assessment, p. 710	Life Science Videotape 5; Videodisc Unit 3 Side 2, "How Does Everything Fit?" Audio CD, English-Spanish Summary 22-3
RCA Provides strategies to improve science reading skills **GSW** Provides worksheets to improve student comprehension of content	**SE** Chapter 22 Review, pp. 711–713 **PA** Chapter 22 Performance Assessment, pp. 68–70 **CUT** Chapter 22 Test, pp. 104–107 **CTB** Chapter 22 Test	Interactive Student Tutorial CD-ROM, Chapter 22 Computer Test Bank, Chapter 22 Test

Key: **SE** Student Edition
    CTB Computer Test Bank
    ISAB Inquiry Skills Activity Book
    GSW Guided Study Worksheets

TE Teacher's Edition
PTA Product Testing Activities by *Consumer Reports*
RCA Reading in the Content Area
PA Performance Assessment

UR Unit Resources
LM Laboratory Manual
IES Interdisciplinary Explorations Series
CUT Chapter and Unit Tests

Meeting the National Science Education Standards and AAAS Benchmarks

National Science Education Standards	Benchmarks for Science Literacy	Unifying Themes
Science As Inquiry (Content Standard A) ◆ **Design and conduct a scientific investigation** Students design an experiment to determine the effect of crowding on plant growth. (*Chapter Project*) ◆ **Use appropriate tools and techniques to gather, analyze, and interpret data** Students model using the mark-and-recapture method to estimate the size of a population. (*Real-World Lab*) ◆ **Develop descriptions, explanations, predictions, and models using evidence** Students study the interactions between biotic and abiotic factors in a model ecosystem. (*Skills Lab*) ◆ **Communicate scientific procedures and explanations** Students present a report and graph of their project results. (*Chapter Project*) **Life Science** (Content Standard C) ◆ **Populations and ecosystems** The levels of organization in the environment include organism, population, community, and ecosystem. Populations can change in size when new members enter the population or when members leave the population. The three major types of interactions among organisms are competition, predation, and symbiosis. (*Sections 1, 2, 3*) **Science in Personal and Social Perspectives** (Content Standard F) ◆ **Science and technology in society** Students analyze the issue of animal overpopulation. (*Science and Society*)	**1B Scientific Inquiry** Students design and conduct an experiment to determine the effect of crowding on plant growth. Students study the interactions between biotic and abiotic factors in a model ecosystem. (*Chapter Project; Skills Lab*) **2B Mathematics, Science, and Technology** Students model using the mark-and-recapture method to estimate the size of a population. (*Real-World Lab*) **5D Interdependence of Life** An organism obtains food, water, shelter, and other things it needs to live, grow, and reproduce from its surroundings. Some limiting factors for populations are food, space, and weather conditions. The three major types of interactions among organisms are competition, predation, and symbiosis. (*Sections 1, 2, 3*) **7D Social Trade-Offs** Students analyze the issue of animal overpopulation. (*Science and Society*)	◆ **Energy** Sunlight is necessary for photosynthesis, a process plants and algae use to make food that supplies energy to most living things. (*Section 1; Skills Lab*) ◆ **Evolution** Changes that make organisms better suited to their environment develop through natural selection. (*Section 3*) ◆ **Modeling** Students use a model ecosystem to study biotic and abiotic factors. Students model using the mark-and-recapture method to estimate the size of a population. (*Skills Lab; Real-World Lab*) ◆ **Patterns of Change** Populations can change in size when new members enter the population or when members leave the population. Over time, species develop adaptations through natural selection. (*Sections 2, 3*) ◆ **Stability** Organisms can live in a closed ecosystem. A limiting factor is an environmental factor that prevents a population from increasing. (*Skills Lab; Section 2*) ◆ **Systems and Interactions** Students observe the effect of crowding on plant growth. An organism obtains food, water, shelter, and other things it needs to live, grow, and reproduce from its surroundings. Some limiting factors for populations are food, space, and weather conditions. Overpopulation of white-tailed deer affects the environment, humans, and the deer themselves. The three major types of interactions among organisms are competition, predation, and symbiosis. (*Chapter Project; Sections 1, 2, 3; Science and Society*)

Take It to the Net

 *Interactive text at www.phschool.com*

Science Explorer comes alive with iText.

- **Complete student text** is accessible from any computer with Internet access or a CD-ROM drive.
- **Animations, simulations, and videos** enhance student understanding and retention of concepts.
- **Self-tests and online study tools** assess student understanding.

STAY CURRENT with

Find out the latest research and information about ecology at:
www.phschool.com

WEB ACTIVITY www.phschool.com

Go to **www.phschool.com** and click on the Science icon. Then click on Science Explorer: Life, Earth, and Physical Science under PH@school.

Student Edition Activities Planner

ACTIVITY	Time (minutes)	Materials — Quantities for one work group	Skills
Section 1			
Discover, p. 688	10–15	**Consumable** old magazines, paste or glue, sheet of white paper **Nonconsumable** scissors, three pencils of different colors	Inferring
Try This, p. 690	10–15; 5 × 3 days	**Consumable** masking tape, 2 L spring water, 25 g noniodized salt, 4 paper squares, brine shrimp eggs **Nonconsumable** 4 600-mL beakers, pen, stirrers, hand lens (optional)	Drawing Conclusions
Skills Lab, p. 694	40; 5 × 10 days	**Consumable** 2-day-old tap water, 2 guppies, 4 aquatic plants, 4 small pond snails **Nonconsumable** aquarium gravel, plastic stirring rod, large jar with cover (about 2 L), lamp with 60-watt bulb, metric ruler, dip net	Making Models, Predicting, Inferring
Section 2			
Discover, p. 695	5–10	**Nonconsumable** 2 large plastic jars, ruler, small beaker, timer, dried beans	Forming Operational Definitions
Sharpen Your Skills, p. 696	5	No special materials are required.	Calculating
Try This, p. 699	10–15	**Consumable** masking tape **Nonconsumable** meter stick, small jigsaw puzzle, watch or clock	Making Models
Science at Home, p. 700	home	**Nonconsumable** dictionary or other book	Calculating
Real-World Lab, p. 701	40	**Consumable** model paper turtle population, graph paper **Nonconsumable** calculator	Calculating, Graphing, Predicting
Section 3			
Discover, p. 703	10–15	**Consumable** sheet of white paper, tape **Nonconsumable** colored pencils or markers	Predicting
Sharpen Your Skills, p. 709	5–10	No special materials are required.	Classifying

A list of all materials required for the Student Edition activities can be found on pages T25–T33. You can obtain information about ordering materials by calling 1-800-848-9500 or by accessing the Science Explorer Internet site at **www.phschool.com**.

What's a Crowd?

Limiting factors affect the distribution, health, and size of populations. In this project, students will design their own experiments to test the effect of one limiting factor—crowding—on sample populations of plants.

Purpose In addition to giving students an opportunity to observe the effect of crowding on plant growth, this project will enhance understanding of the procedures involved in scientific experimentation. To complete the project successfully, students must develop a testable hypothesis about crowding and plant growth; design an experiment that involves identifying and controlling variables, measuring plant growth, and recording data; infer the effects of the limiting factor; and communicate results to the rest of the class. Use the Skills Handbook in the back of this text to support students who need help with these skills.

Skills Focus After completing the Chapter 22 Project, students will be able to
◆ design an experiment to test the effect of crowding on plant growth;
◆ identify and control variables;
◆ measure plant growth, record data, and analyze results;
◆ communicate experimental procedures and results in a written report and graph.

Project Time Line The project requires two to three weeks to complete, depending on the type of plants students use. During the first phase, each group should plan an experiment and submit the plan for your review, culminating with planting the seeds before the conclusion of Section 1. While students study sections 2 and 3, each group should conduct its experiment and record data. At the conclusion of Section 3, groups should prepare their written reports and their presentations to the class.

Possible Materials
◆ Wisconsin Fast Plants™ (*Brassica rapa*), a strain of radishlike plants specifically developed for their short life cycle, are the preferred choice for this project. They germinate within

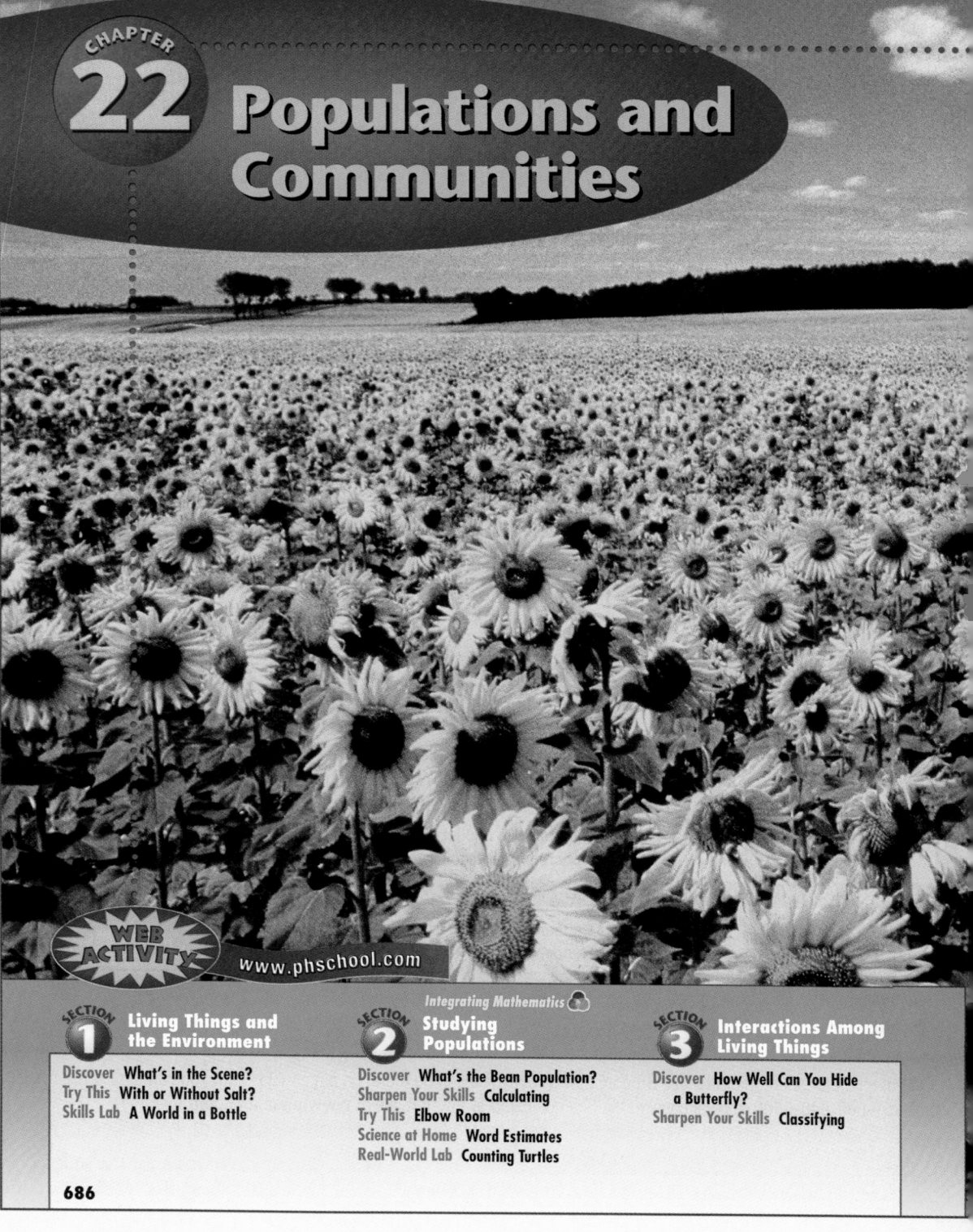

WEB ACTIVITY
www.phschool.com

Integrating Mathematics

SECTION 1 **Living Things and the Environment**	SECTION 2 **Studying Populations**	SECTION 3 **Interactions Among Living Things**
Discover **What's in the Scene?** Try This **With or Without Salt?** Skills Lab **A World in a Bottle**	Discover **What's the Bean Population?** Sharpen Your Skills **Calculating** Try This **Elbow Room** Science at Home **Word Estimates** Real-World Lab **Counting Turtles**	Discover **How Well Can You Hide a Butterfly?** Sharpen Your Skills **Classifying**

686

24 hours, develop leaves within one week and flowers in about two weeks, and can be grown easily in a small space. Fast Plant seeds are available from biological supply houses. Alternatively, students could use radish seeds.
◆ Each group will need several identical planting containers. Possibilities include large margarine tubs, or half-gallon milk cartons with one of the larger sides removed.
◆ Provide potting soil, trowels or large spoons, watering cans or spray bottles, and rulers.

◆ Set aside a location in the classroom where the plant containers will receive direct sunlight or strong indirect light for several hours each day. If sunlight is limited, set up lamps on tables.

Launching the Project To introduce the project, have students examine the photograph and read the first paragraph on page 687. Then ask: **What do sunflowers need to grow well?** (*Students may mention sunlight, water, and soil or the nutrients in soil.*) **Do you think every sunflower seed in this field grew into a mature**

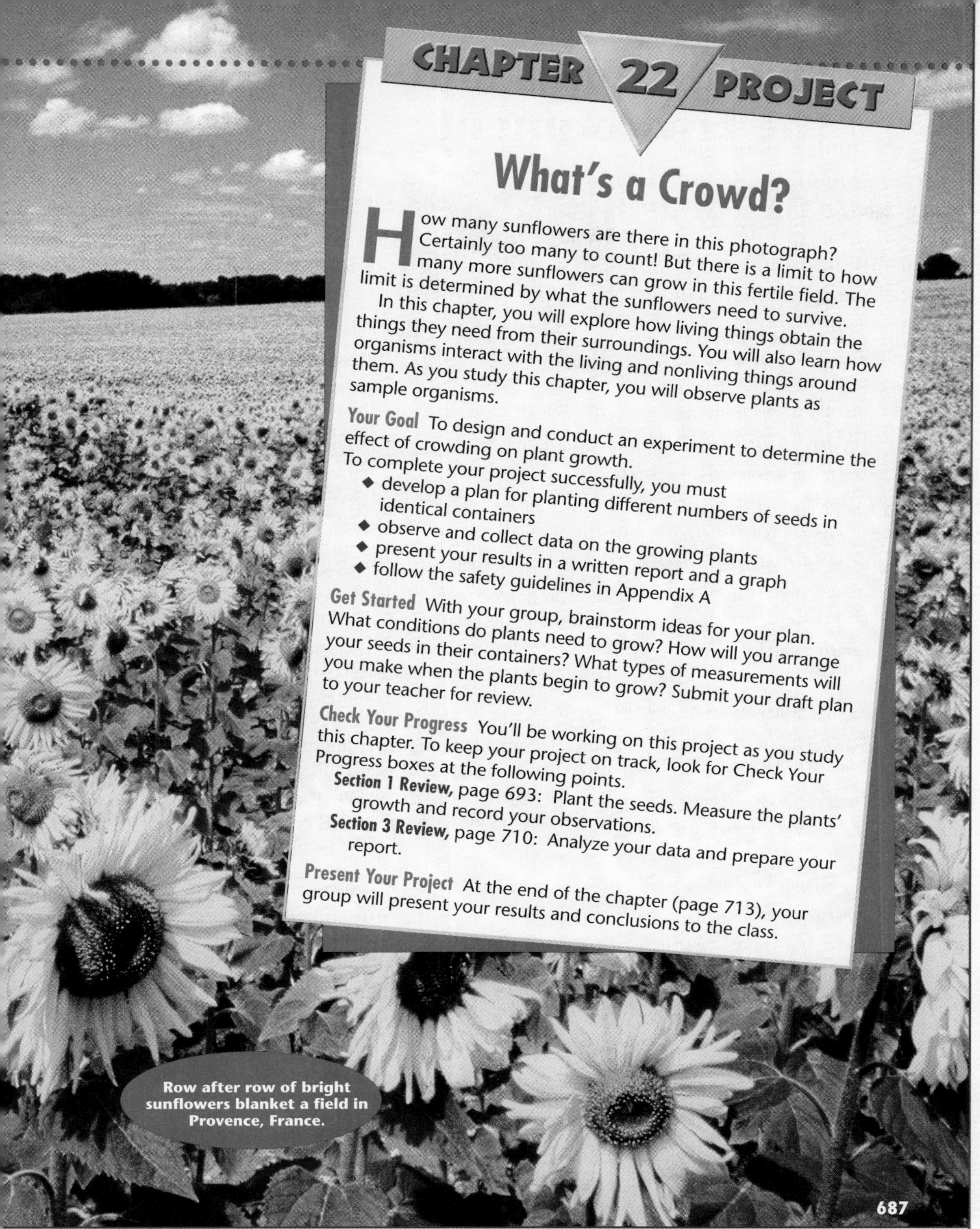

What's a Crowd?

How many sunflowers are there in this photograph? Certainly too many to count! But there is a limit to how many more sunflowers can grow in this fertile field. The limit is determined by what the sunflowers need to survive.

In this chapter, you will explore how living things obtain the things they need from their surroundings. You will also learn how organisms interact with the living and nonliving things around them. As you study this chapter, you will observe plants as sample organisms.

Your Goal To design and conduct an experiment to determine the effect of crowding on plant growth.

To complete your project successfully, you must
- ◆ develop a plan for planting different numbers of seeds in identical containers
- ◆ observe and collect data on the growing plants
- ◆ present your results in a written report and a graph
- ◆ follow the safety guidelines in Appendix A

Get Started With your group, brainstorm ideas for your plan. What conditions do plants need to grow? How will you arrange your seeds in their containers? What types of measurements will you make when the plants begin to grow? Submit your draft plan to your teacher for review.

Check Your Progress You'll be working on this project as you study this chapter. To keep your project on track, look for Check Your Progress boxes at the following points.

Section 1 Review, page 693: Plant the seeds. Measure the plants' growth and record your observations.

Section 3 Review, page 710: Analyze your data and prepare your report.

Present Your Project At the end of the chapter (page 713), your group will present your results and conclusions to the class.

Row after row of bright sunflowers blanket a field in Provence, France.

687

Program Resources

◆ **Unit 5 Resources** Chapter 22 Project Teacher Notes, pp. 2–3; Chapter 22 Project Overview and Worksheets, pp. 4–7; Chapter 22 Project Scoring Rubric, p. 8

WEB ACTIVITY www.phschool.com

You will find an Internet activity, chapter self-tests for students, and links to other chapter topics at this site.

---

plant? Why or why not? *(Students should realize that due to overcrowding, some sprouting plants probably died.)*

Have students read the project description on page 687. Distribute Chapter 22 Project Overview on pages 4–5 in Unit 5 Resources, and let students review the project's procedures. Encourage questions and comments.

Divide the class into groups of two to four students each. Give each student a copy of Chapter 22 Project Worksheet 1 on page 6 in Unit 5 Resources. Allow time for the groups to meet and begin brainstorming ideas. Tell students to use the worksheet to take notes as they brainstorm. Also explain that when their group decides on a final experiment, they should prepare a written plan based on the worksheet steps. Emphasize that you will review the plans before groups begin their experiments.

Tell students that each group's members may divide the project responsibilities among themselves in any way they wish. However, emphasize that *every* group member should be involved in all stages and be prepared to answer questions about the experiment.

In Check Your Progress at the conclusion of Section 3, distribute Chapter 22 Project Worksheet 2 on page 7 in Unit 5 Resources. This worksheet is designed to help students prepare their written reports and graphs.

Performance Assessment

The Chapter 22 Project Scoring Rubric on page 8 in Unit 5 Resources will help you evaluate how well students complete the Chapter 22 Project. Students will be assessed on
- ◆ their ability to design an experiment to test the effect of crowding on plant growth;
- ◆ how carefully they have identified and controlled variables in the experiment, made observations and recorded data;
- ◆ how well they have communicated their procedures, results, and conclusion to the rest of the class;
- ◆ their participation in their groups.

You may want to share the scoring rubric with students so they are clear about what will be expected of them.

Living Things and the Environment

Objectives

After completing the lesson, students will be able to

- identify the needs that are met by an organism's habitat;
- identify biotic and abiotic parts of an ecosystem;
- describe the levels of organization within an ecosystem;
- define ecology and state what ecologists do.

Key Terms ecosystem, habitat, biotic factor, abiotic factor, photosynthesis, species, population, community, ecology

1 Engage/Explore

Activating Prior Knowledge

Ask: **What is an ecosystem?** *(Students may say it is a particular type of place with different kinds of plants, animals, and other living things living in it. Accept all responses without comment at this time.)*
What kinds of ecosystems do you know of? *(Students may mention a swamp, desert, seashore, forest, and so forth.)*

DISCOVER

Skills Focus inferring
Materials *old magazines, scissors, paste or glue, sheet of white paper, three pencils of different colors*
Time 10–15 minutes
Tips Encourage students to look for pictures with close-enough views to allow them to distinguish various living and nonliving things. Also emphasize that the scenes do not have to be "beautiful" so long as each shows a variety of living and nonliving things.
Expected Outcome The specific living things shown will vary. Students should identify water, soil, sunlight, and air among the nonliving things.
Think It Over Students should indicate that living things need water, air, and sunlight and that plants also need soil.

Living Things and the Environment

DISCOVER

What's in the Scene?

1. Choose a magazine picture of a nature scene. Paste the picture onto a sheet of paper, leaving space all around the picture.

2. Identify all the things in the picture that are alive. Use a colored pencil to draw a line from each living thing, or organism. Label the organism if you know its name.

3. Use a different colored pencil to draw a line from each nonliving thing and label it.

Think It Over

Inferring How do the organisms in the picture depend on the nonliving things? Using a third color, draw lines connecting organisms to the nonliving things they need.

GUIDE FOR READING

- What needs are met by an organism's surroundings?
- What are the levels of organization within an ecosystem?

Reading Tip Write the section headings in your notebook. As you read, make a list of main ideas and supporting details under each heading.

Black-tailed prairie dogs ▼

A s the sun rises on a warm summer morning, the Nebraska town is already bustling with activity. Some residents are hard at work building homes for their families. They are building underground, where it is dark and cool. Other inhabitants are collecting seeds for breakfast. Some of the town's younger residents are at play, chasing each other through the grass.

Suddenly, an adult spots a threatening shadow approaching—an enemy has appeared in the sky! The adult cries out several times, warning the others. Within moments, the town's residents disappear into their underground homes. The town is silent and still, except for a single hawk circling overhead.

Have you guessed what kind of town this is? It is a prairie dog town on the Nebraska plains. As these prairie dogs dug their burrows, searched for food, and hid from the hawk, they interacted with their environment, or surroundings. The prairie dogs interacted with living things, such as the grass and the hawk, and with nonliving things, such as the soil. All the living and nonliving things that interact in a particular area make up an **ecosystem.**

READING STRATEGIES

Outlining Students should list the main headings *Habitats, Biotic Factors, Abiotic Factors, Populations, Communities,* and *What Is Ecology?* The subheadings *Water, Sunlight, Oxygen, Temperature,* and *Soil* on pages 690–691 can be listed below the main heading *Abiotic Factors.* Students should also place the boldface terms (with their definitions) and the boldface sentences under the appropriate headings. If any students had difficulty identifying main ideas and supporting details or differentiating between them, work with those students individually or in small groups to provide guidance.

A prairie is just one of the many different ecosystems found on Earth. Other ecosystems in which living things make their homes include mountain streams, deep oceans, and dense forests.

Habitats

A prairie dog is one type of organism, or living thing. Organisms live in a specific place within an ecosystem. **An organism obtains food, water, shelter, and other things it needs to live, grow, and reproduce from its surroundings.** The place where an organism lives and that provides the things the organism needs is called its **habitat.**

A single ecosystem may contain many habitats. For example, in a forest ecosystem, mushrooms grow in the damp soil, bears live on the forest floor, termites live in fallen tree trunks, and flickers build nests in the trunks.

Organisms live in different habitats because they have different requirements for survival. A prairie dog obtains the food and shelter it needs from its habitat. It could not survive in a tropical rain forest or on the rocky ocean shore. Likewise, the prairie would not meet the needs of a gorilla, a penguin, or a hermit crab.

Biotic Factors

An organism interacts with both the living and nonliving things in its environment. The living parts of an ecosystem are called **biotic factors** (by AHT ik factors). Biotic factors in the prairie dogs' ecosystem include the grass and plants that provide seeds and berries. The hawks, ferrets, badgers, and eagles that hunt the prairie dogs are also biotic factors. In addition, worms, fungi, and bacteria are biotic factors that live in the soil underneath the prairie grass. These organisms keep the soil rich in nutrients as they break down the remains of other living things.

✓ *Checkpoint* *Name a biotic factor in your environment.*

Figure 1 A stream tumbles over mossy rocks in a lush Tennessee forest. This ecosystem contains many different habitats. *Comparing and Contrasting How is the mushrooms' habitat in the forest different from the flicker's habitat?*

Program Resources

◆ **Unit 5 Resources** 22-1 Lesson Plan, p. 9; 22-1 Section Summary, p. 10

Media and Technology

🎧 **Audio CD** English-Spanish Summary 22-1

Answers to Self-Assessment

Caption Question

Figure 1 Mushrooms grow in damp soil on the forest floor, whereas the flicker builds nests in tree trunks.

✓ *Checkpoint*

Students may name living organisms such as other people, trees, dogs, or birds.

Habitats

Addressing Naive Conceptions

Students may not have a clear understanding of the difference between the terms *ecosystem* and *habitat*, since both refer to places where organisms live. Emphasize that the *type* of place where an organism lives—a prairie or a forest, for example—is an ecosystem. The specific *part* of the ecosystem that meets the organism's needs and in which it lives is its habitat. To clarify this difference, first have students name the four specific habitats identified in the text as being part of a forest ecosystem. Create a concept map on the board with *Forest* in one circle and the four habitats in circles below it. Invite students to identify another ecosystem and several habitats within it, and let them come to the board to create another concept map. Continue with other ecosystems and habitats. **learning modality: visual**

Biotic Factors

Including All Students

Invite students who need extra help to identify examples of biotic factors found in other ecosystems, such as the forest ecosystem described on this page and the ecosystems that the class has discussed. (*In the forest ecosystem, biotic factors include mushrooms, rabbits, termites, trees, and flickers.*) **learning modality: verbal**

Ongoing Assessment

Concept Mapping Have each student choose one ecosystem and create a concept map about it. The ecosystem should be identified in the top circle and at least three specific habitats in circles below it.

 Students can save their concept maps in their portfolios.

Abiotic Factors

Including All Students

Write *abiotic* on the board and underline the prefix *a-*. Ask: **What does *a-* at the beginning of the word mean?** *("Not" or "opposite of"; if students do not know, have them compare the terms* biotic *and* abiotic *and infer the meaning of* a-.) Emphasize that the English language uses several different prefixes to change the meanings of words. Ask: **What are some other prefixes in English that mean "not"?** *(ab-, un-, non-, dis-)* List the prefixes on the board as students identify them, and ask them to give examples of words with those prefixes, such as *unhappy, nontoxic,* and *disagree.* **limited English proficiency**

Skills Focus drawing conclusions
Materials *4 600-mL beakers, masking tape, pen, 2 L spring water, 25 g noniodized salt, stirrers, brine shrimp eggs, 4 paper squares large enough to cover cups, hand lens (optional)*
Time 10–15 minutes for initial setup, 5 minutes per day for follow-up observations
Tips Let the spring water sit overnight to reach room temperature. Put a small sample of brine shrimp eggs in a paper cup for each group. You may add $\frac{1}{2}$ teaspoon of dry yeast to each beaker to feed the shrimp when they hatch. NOTE: Newly hatched brine shrimp are very tiny and orange in color.
Expected Outcome Eggs will not hatch in beaker A. Eggs will likely hatch best in beaker B, less well in beaker C, and not well or not at all in beaker D. The brine shrimp's habitat must contain salt, but cannot be too salty.
Extend Have each group prepare a larger jar with the saltwater solution that they think is best for brine shrimp, add $\frac{1}{4}$ teaspoon of eggs, and set the covered jar aside. Encourage students to examine the jar every day or two to observe changes in the population's size.
learning modality: kinesthetic

Figure 2 This eastern banjo frog is burrowing in the sand to stay cool in the hot Australian desert. *Interpreting Photographs With which abiotic factors is the frog interacting in this scene?*

With or Without Salt?

In this activity you will explore salt as an abiotic factor.

1. Label four 600-mL beakers A, B, C, and D. Fill each with 500 mL of room-temperature spring water.
2. Set beaker A aside. It will contain fresh water. To beaker B, add 2.5 grams of noniodized salt. Add 7.5 grams of salt to beaker C and 15 grams of salt to beaker D. Stir beakers B, C, and D.
3. Add about $\frac{1}{4}$ of a spoonful of brine shrimp eggs to each beaker.
4. Cover each beaker with a square of paper. Keep them away from direct light or heat. Wash your hands.
5. Observe the beakers daily for three days.

Drawing Conclusions In which beakers did the eggs hatch? What can you conclude about the amount of salt in the shrimps' natural habitat?

Abiotic Factors

The nonliving parts of an ecosystem are called **abiotic factors** (ay by ᴀʜᴛ ik factors). Abiotic factors that affect living things in the prairie are similar to those found in most ecosystems. They include water, sunlight, oxygen, temperature, and soil.

Water All living things require water to carry out their life processes. Water also makes up a large part of the bodies of most organisms. Your body, for example, is about 65 percent water. A watermelon consists of more than 95 percent water! Water is particularly important to plants and algae. As you have learned, these organisms use water, along with sunlight and carbon dioxide, to make food in a process called photosynthesis. Other living things eat the plants and algae to obtain energy.

Sunlight Because sunlight is necessary for photosynthesis, it is an important abiotic factor for plants, algae, and other living things. In places that do not receive sunlight, such as dark caves, plants cannot grow. Without plants or algae to provide a source of food, few other organisms can live.

Oxygen Most living things require oxygen to carry out their life processes. Oxygen is so important to the functioning of the human body that you can live only a few minutes without it. Organisms that live on land obtain oxygen from the air, which is about 20 percent oxygen. Fish and other water organisms obtain dissolved oxygen from the water around them.

Temperature The temperatures that are typical of an area determine the types of organisms that can live there. For example, if you took a trip to a warm tropical island, you would see palm trees, bright hibiscus flowers, and tiny lizards. These organisms could not survive on the frozen plains of Siberia. But the thick, warm fur of wolves and short, strong branches of dwarf willows are suited to the blustery winters there.

Background

Integrating Science Students may already know that plants and algae require carbon dioxide to carry on photosynthesis. Chlorophyll, the green pigment in plants and some algae, absorbs energy in sunlight. The organism uses this energy to combine carbon dioxide (CO_2) and water (H_2O) in a reaction that produces sugars, including glucose ($C_6H_{12}O_2$), with water and oxygen (O_2) as byproducts. The sugars provide energy for sustaining the organism's life processes. Other organisms can obtain and use this energy by eating plants or algae. Cellular respiration breaks down glucose into carbon dioxide and water, releasing energy.

Some animals alter their environments to overcome very hot or very cold temperatures. For example, prairie dogs dig underground dens to find shelter from the blazing summer sun. They line the dens with grass. The grass keeps the prairie dogs warm during the cold and windy winters.

Soil Soil is a mixture of rock fragments, nutrients, air, water, and the decaying remains of living things. Soil in different areas consists of varying amounts of these materials. The type of soil in an area influences the kinds of plants that can grow there. Many animals, such as the prairie dogs, use the soil itself as a home. Billions of microscopic organisms such as bacteria also live in the soil. These tiny organisms play an important role in the ecosystem by breaking down the remains of other living things.

☑ *Checkpoint* *How do biotic factors differ from abiotic factors?*

Populations

In 1900, travelers saw a prairie dog town in Texas covering an area twice the size of the city of Dallas. The sprawling town contained more than 400 million prairie dogs! These prairie dogs were all members of one species. Recall from Chapter 6 that a species is a group of organisms that are physically similar and can reproduce with one another to produce fertile offspring.

All the members of one species in a particular area are referred to as a **population.** The 400 million prairie dogs in the Texas town are one example of a population. All the pigeons in New York City make up a population, as do all the daisies in a field. In contrast, all the trees in a forest do not make up a population, because they do not all belong to the same species. There may be pines, maples, birches, and many other tree species in the forest.

The area in which a population lives can be as small as a single blade of grass or as large as the whole planet. Scientists studying a type of organism usually limit their study to a population in a defined area. For example, they might study the population of bluegill fish in a pond, or the population of alligators in the Florida Everglades.

Some populations, however, do not stay in a contained area. For example, to study the population of finback whales, a scientist might need to use the entire ocean.

Figure 3 This milkweed plant is home to a small population of ladybug beetles.

691

Answers to Self-Assessment

Caption Question

Figure 2 Soil (sand), oxygen (air), sunlight, temperature

☑ *Checkpoint*

Biotic factors are living; abiotic factors are nonliving.

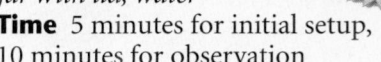

Building Inquiry Skills: Observing

Materials *soil sample, jar with lid, water*
Time 5 minutes for initial setup, 10 minutes for observation

Invite students to bring in a soil sample (about 200 mL) collected outdoors. Each student can put the soil in a jar, add water to about 3 cm from the top, screw the lid on tightly, and then shake the jar to thoroughly mix the water and soil. When the soil particles have settled, students will be able to see the materials contained in the sample separated into layers. Challenge students to identify the materials that make up the soil. Students should wash their hands after this activity. **learning modality: kinesthetic**

Including All Students

For students who need extra challenges, ask: **What are some abiotic factors in your own environment?** *(Students may name any nonliving things. If necessary, prompt them to consider manufactured objects and materials such as automobiles and plastics.)* **How are these nonliving things different from the nonliving things in "wild" ecosystems?** *(They do not occur in nature; people create them.)* **learning modality: logical/ mathematical**

Populations

Using the Visuals: Figure 3

After students have examined the photo and read the caption, ask: **Why is this group of ladybug beetles considered a population?** *(They are all of the same species, and they live in the same area.)* **Is the plant a population? Why or why not?** *(No; to have a population, there would have to be other plants of the same species living in the same area.)* **learning modality: verbal**

Ongoing Assessment

Writing Have each student identify at least three abiotic factors found in most ecosystems and explain why each is necessary for life.

691

Communities

Using the Visuals: Figure 4

Materials *pencil and paper*

Time 10–15 minutes

Challenge students to think of a way to show an ecosystem's levels of organization in a diagram. Have each student create a diagram for an ecosystem of his or her own choice. Let students share their diagrams in a class discussion. *(Possible diagram: Concentric circles with the individual organism in the center circle, a population in the second circle, a community with that population and other species in the third circle, and the entire ecosystem with abiotic factors in the outer circle.)* **learning modality: visual**

What Is Ecology?

Language Arts
CONNECTION

Challenge students to think of other words that end in *-ology. (biology, geology)* Then have them use a dictionary to learn what the first root word in each means. *(Bio-* means life, geo- *means earth.)*

In Your Journal Students' answers may vary slightly depending on the dictionaries they used.

Habitat: from Latin *habitare,* "to inhabit, live in"; *inhabit, habitation, habitual*

Biotic: from Greek *bios,* "life"; *biology, biography, biome*

Community: from Latin *communis,* "common"; *communicate, communication, communal*

Population: from Latin *populus,* "people"; *popular, popularity, populous*

learning modality: verbal

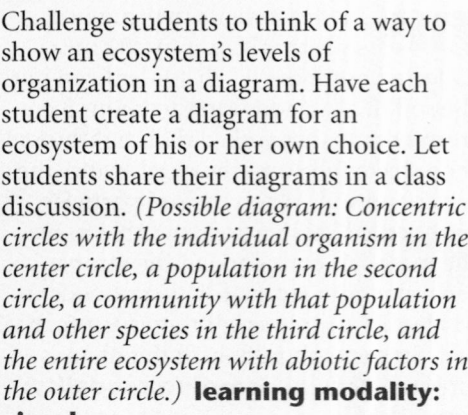

Organism　　　　　　**Population**

Language Arts
CONNECTION

The word *ecology* comes from two Greek root words: *oikos,* which means house or place to live, and *logos,* which means *study.* Put together, these root words create a term for studying organisms in the place where they live. Many science terms are derived from Greek and Latin root words.

In Your Journal

Use a dictionary to find root words for the following terms from this section: *habitat, biotic, community,* and *population.* For each root word, list its meaning, original language, and other English words containing the root.

692

Communities

Of course, most ecosystems contain more than one type of organism. The prairie, for instance, includes prairie dogs, hawks, grasses, badgers, and snakes, along with many other organisms. All the different populations that live together in an area make up a **community.**

Figure 4 shows the levels of organization in the prairie ecosystem. **The smallest unit of organization is a single organism, which belongs to a population of other members of its species. The population belongs to a community of different species. The community and abiotic factors together form an ecosystem.**

To be considered a community, the different populations must live close enough together to interact. One way the populations in a community may interact is by using the same resources, such as food and shelter. For example, the tunnels dug by the prairie dogs also serve as homes for burrowing owls and black-footed ferrets. The prairie dogs share the grass with other animals. Meanwhile, prairie dogs themselves serve as food for many species.

What Is Ecology?

Because the populations in the prairie ecosystem interact with one another, any changes in a community affect all the different populations that live there. The study of how living things interact with one another and with their environment is called **ecology.** Ecologists, scientists who study ecology, look at how all the biotic and abiotic factors in an ecosystem are related.

Background

Integrating Science All of Earth's communities are part of a higher level of organization, the *biosphere.* The organisms that make up the biosphere interact with each other. But they also interact in various ways with Earth's other "spheres": the atmosphere (the gases that envelop Earth); the hydrosphere (Earth's water); and the lithosphere (Earth's rocky outer covering and soils). While ecologists study the relationships among the organisms of the biosphere, they also consider the biosphere in relation to the other spheres of the physical environment.

Community

Ecosystem

Figure 4 The smallest level of ecological organization is an individual organism. The largest is the entire ecosystem.

As part of their work, ecologists study how organisms react to changes in their environment. Living things constantly interact with their surroundings, responding to changes in the conditions around them. Some responses are very quick. When a prairie dog sees a hawk overhead, it gives a warning bark. The other prairie dogs hear the bark and respond by returning to their burrows to hide. Other responses to change in the environment occur more slowly. For example, after a fire on the prairie, it takes some time for the grass to reach its former height and for all the animals to return to the area.

 Section 1 Review

1. What basic needs are provided by an organism's habitat?
2. List these terms in order from the smallest unit to the largest: population, organism, ecosystem, community.
3. Explain how water and sunlight are two abiotic factors that are important to all organisms.
4. Why do ecologists study both biotic and abiotic factors in an ecosystem?
5. **Thinking Critically Applying Concepts** Would all the insects in a forest be considered a population? Why or why not?

Check Your Progress CHAPTER PROJECT
After your teacher has reviewed your plan, prepare the containers and plant the seeds. Design a data table to record the information you will use to compare the growth in the different containers. When the plants begin to grow, examine them daily and record your observations. Be sure to continue caring for your plants according to your plan. *(Hint:* Use a metric ruler to measure your growing plants. Besides size, look for differences in leaf color and the number of buds among the plants.)

Chapter 22 **693**

3 *Assess*

Section 1 Review Answers

1. Food, water, shelter, air, and other things it needs to grow and reproduce
2. Organism, population, community, ecosystem
3. All organisms need water to survive and carry out their life processes. Plants and algae need water and sunlight to make their own food in photosynthesis. All other organisms depend, directly or indirectly, on plants and algae for food.
4. Accept all reasonable answers. *Sample answer:* The biotic and abiotic factors in an ecosystem are all related to one another.
5. No; the insects would be of many different species. Only organisms of the same species form a population.

Check Your Progress CHAPTER PROJECT
Evaluate each group's plan to make sure students have identified and will control the major variables that will affect plant growth in the containers. These include the size of the containers, the amount of soil in each, how densely and how deep the seeds will be planted, the amount and frequency of watering, and the location in which the containers will be placed. Also review students' data tables to make sure they will be recording all relevant data, including plant heights and other observations such as the number and color of leaves and the number of buds on the developing plants.

Media and Technology

 Transparencies "Levels of Organization in an Ecosystem," Transparency 80

 Interactive Student Tutorial CD-ROM Chapter 22

Program Resources

◆ **Unit 5 Resources** 22-1 Review and Reinforce, p. 11; 22-1 Enrich, p. 12

Performance Assessment

Concept Mapping Have each student choose any organism and draw a concept map to identify several biotic and abiotic factors in the organism's habitat.

 Students can save their concept maps in their portfolios.

A World in a Bottle

Preparing for Inquiry

Key Concept Organisms can survive in a closed ecosystem so long as their biotic and abiotic needs are met.

Skills Objectives Students will be able to
- build a model of a terrestrial ecosystem;
- predict whether the habitat will meet the organisms' needs;
- make inferences about how the model ecosystem operates.

Time 30 minutes for set-up; 10 minutes per day for observation and notetaking

Advance Planning Collect materials. Cut off the tops of clear plastic 2-liter soda bottles to make 18-cm-tall containers. Obtain small, short vascular plants and mosses from moist, shaded areas.

Guiding Inquiry

Troubleshooting the Experiment

- Use vascular plants that require similar amounts of light and moisture.
- If the plants are taller than the bottles' sides, have students place three unsharpened pencils in the soil and make a tent with the plastic wrap.
- If fogging is a problem, students can remove the cover until the sides clear. This opens the system, but students will learn that reproducing a miniature ecosystem is difficult.

Expected Outcome

The plants should thrive and grow.

Analyze and Conclude

1. *Biotic:* guppies, snails, plants, algae; *abiotic:* gravel, water, light, jar
2. Yes, light (an abiotic factor)
3. Students' diagrams should show the plants using light, water, and carbon dioxide to make food and oxygen, and using oxygen and producing carbon dioxide to respire. They should also show transpiration.
4. The plant-eating insect would probably survive for a while. At first the ecosystem would meet the insect's needs. Eventually, the insect may run out of

food if it eats the plants faster than the plants can reproduce.

5. The model shows that organisms interact with nonliving things in their environment. It differs in that it is closed, not as complex, and contains fewer organisms and no animals.

Extending the Inquiry

More to Explore Review students' plans for feasibility in the classroom and for proper handling of living organisms.

Skills Lab

A World in a Bottle

In this lab, you will study the interactions between biotic and abiotic factors in a model ecosystem.

Problem

How do organisms survive in a closed ecosystem?

Materials

pre-cut, clear plastic bottle
gravel
soil
moss plants
plastic spoon
charcoal
spray bottle
2 vascular plants
plastic wrap

Procedure

1. In this lab, you will place plants in moist soil in a bottle that is then sealed. This setup is called a terrarium. Predict whether the plants can survive in this habitat.

2. Spread about 2.5 cm of gravel on the bottom of a pre-cut bottle. Then sprinkle a spoonful or two of charcoal over the gravel.

3. Use the spoon to layer about 8 cm of soil over the gravel and charcoal. As you add the soil, tap it down to pack it.

4. Scoop out two holes in the soil. Remove the vascular plants from their pots. Gently place their roots in the holes. Then pack the loose soil firmly around the plants' stems.

5. Fill the spray bottle with water. Spray the soil until you see water collecting in the gravel.

6. Cover the soil with the moss plants, including the areas around the stems of the vascular plants. Lightly spray the mosses with water.

7. Tightly cover your terrarium with plastic wrap. Secure the cover with a rubber band. Place the terrarium in bright, indirect light.

8. Observe the terrarium daily for two weeks. Record your observations in your notebook. If its sides fog, move the terrarium to an area with a different amount of light. You may have to move it a few times before the fog disappears. Write down any changes you make in your terrarium's location.

Analyze and Conclude

1. What biotic and abiotic factors are part of the ecosystem in the bottle?
2. Were any biotic or abiotic factors able to enter the terrarium? If so, which ones?
3. Draw a diagram of the interactions between the terrarium's biotic and abiotic factors.
4. Suppose a plant-eating insect were added to the terrarium. Predict whether it would be able to survive. Explain your prediction.
5. **Think About It** Explain how your terrarium models an ecosystem. How does your model differ from an ecosystem on Earth?

More to Explore

Make a plan to model a freshwater ecosystem. How would this model be different from the land ecosystem? Obtain your teacher's approval before carrying out your plan.

Safety

Make sure students handle the jars, electrical plug, and living organisms carefully. Review the safety guidelines in Appendix A. After the lab, use the organisms in a classroom aquarium.

Program Resources

- **Unit 5 Resources** Chapter 22 Skills Lab, pp. 21–22

SECTION 2 Studying Populations

DISCOVER ······································· ACTIVITY

What's the Bean Population?

1. Fill a plastic jar with dried beans. This is your model population.

2. Your goal is to determine the number of beans in the jar, but you will not have time to count every bean. You may use any of the following to help you determine the size of the bean population: a ruler, a small beaker, another large jar. Set a timer for two minutes when you are ready to begin.

3. After two minutes, record your answer. Then count the actual number of beans. How close was your answer?

Think It Over

Forming Operational Definitions
In this activity, you came up with an estimate of the size of the bean population. Write a definition of the term *estimate* based on what you did.

How would you like to change jobs for the day? Instead of being a student, today you are an ecologist. You are working on a project to study the bald eagle population in your area. One question you might ask is how the population has changed over time. Is the number of bald eagles more, less, or the same as it was 50 years ago? To answer these questions, you must first determine the present size of the bald eagle population.

Population Density

One way to state the size of a population is in terms of **population density** — the number of individuals in a specific area. Population density can be written as an equation:

$$\text{Population density} = \frac{\text{Number of individuals}}{\text{Unit area}}$$

For instance, suppose you counted 50 monarch butterflies in a garden measuring 10 square meters. The population density would be 50 butterflies per 10 square meters, or 5 butterflies per square meter.

GUIDE FOR READING

◆ How do ecologists determine the size of a population?

◆ What causes populations to change in size?

◆ What factors limit population growth?

Reading Tip Before you read, predict some factors that might cause a population to increase or decrease.

Bald eagles in Alaska ▶
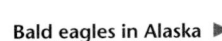

695

INTEGRATING MATHEMATICS

SECTION 2 Studying Populations

Objectives

After completing the lesson, students will be able to
◆ describe how ecologists determine the size of a population;
◆ explain what causes populations to change in size;
◆ identify factors that limit population growth.

Key Terms population density, estimate, birth rate, death rate, immigration, emigration, limiting factor, carrying capacity

1 Engage/Explore

Activating Prior Knowledge

Ask: **What does *density* mean?** (*Answers will vary but should include the idea of "how tightly packed something is."*) **What are some examples of dense populations of organisms?** (*Grass in a lawn, bees in a hive, a school of fish*)

········· DISCOVER ·········

Skills Focus forming operational definitions
Materials *2 large plastic jars, dried beans, ruler, small beaker, timer*
Time 5–10 minutes
Tips If you do not have enough timers, set one timer yourself for the entire class.
Expected Outcome Students could use various ways of estimating, including the following: (1) Fill the small beaker with beans, count those beans, estimate how many small beakers would fit in the large jar, and multiply the first bean count by that number. (2) Put a 1-cm-deep layer of beans in the second large jar, count those beans, measure the height of the jar, and multiply the height by the number of beans in one layer.
Think It Over Students' definitions may vary but should focus on the idea of making a "rough guess" or "close guess."

READING STRATEGIES

Reading Tip Suggest that students begin with factors they have just studied, such as biotic and abiotic factors including food and water. Then guide them to think about other factors, such as births and deaths, that they know affect population size.

Program Resources

◆ **Unit 5 Resources** 22-2 Lesson Plan, p. 13; 22-2 Section Summary, p. 14

Media and Technology

Audio CD English-Spanish Summary 22-2

2 Facilitate

Population Density

Including All Students

For students who need extra help, provide additional examples so they can practice the calculations—for example, 144 dandelion plants in a lawn 12 m long by 6 m wide (2 plants per square meter). You may want to let students use calculators to solve the problems. Also invite students to make up problems for the class to solve. **learning modality: logical/mathematical**

Determining Population Size

Sharpen your Skills

Calculating

Time 5 minutes
Expected Outcome The total population is 100,000 oysters (100 m × 50 m = 5000 square meters × 20 oysters per square meter).
Extend Ask: **Why is your answer only an estimate of the total population?** *(Maybe not every square meter has exactly 20 oysters.)* **learning modality: logical/mathematical**

Inquiry Challenge

Materials *500 wooden toothpicks*
Time 10–15 minutes

Scatter 500 toothpicks over a rectangular area large enough to provide a 1-square-meter section for each student, or use a floor with 1-square-foot tiles, allowing one tile per student. Tell students the total area, but not how many toothpicks you used. Let each student count the number of toothpicks in his or her section (the sample) and then calculate the total "population" of toothpicks. In a follow-up discussion, ask: **Why did different students get different estimates?** *(Different sections—samples—contained different numbers of toothpicks.)* **learning modality: logical/mathematical**

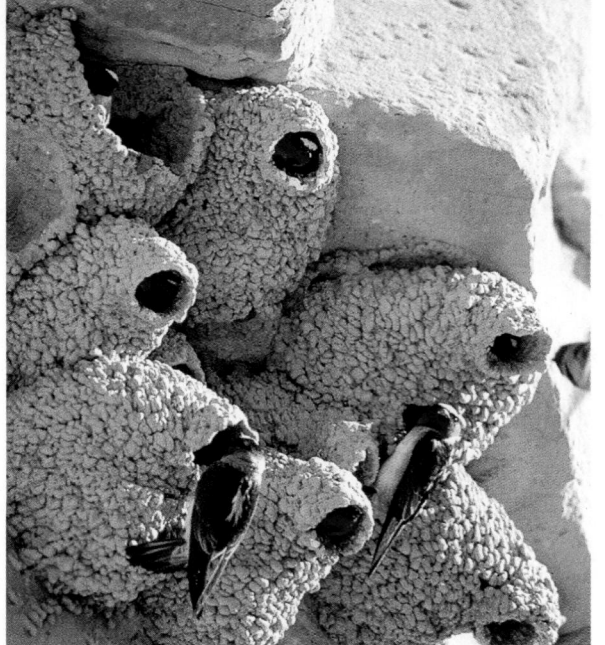

Figure 5 These cone-shaped structures are nests built by cliff swallows in Dinosaur National Monument, Utah. Counting the nests is one way to estimate the cliff swallow population.

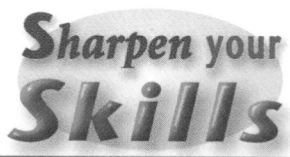

Calculating

A bed of oysters measures 100 meters long and 50 meters wide. In a one-square-meter area you count 20 oysters. Estimate the population of oysters in the bed. *(Hint: Drawing a diagram may help you set up your calculation.)*

Determining Population Size

In your work as an ecologist, how can you determine the size of the population you are studying? **Some methods of determining the size of a population are direct and indirect observations, sampling, and mark-and-recapture studies.**

Direct Observation The most obvious way to determine the size of a population is to count, one by one, all of its members. You could count all the bald eagles that live along a river, all the red maple trees in a forest, or all the elephants in a valley in Kenya.

Indirect Observation The members of a population may be small or hard to find. It may then be easier to observe their tracks or other signs rather than the organisms themselves. Look at the mud nests built by cliff swallows in Figure 5. Each nest has one entrance hole. By counting the entrance holes, you can determine the number of swallow families nesting in this area. Suppose that the average number of swallows per nest is four: two parents and two offspring. If there are 120 nests in an area, you can find the number of swallows by multiplying 120 by 4, or 480 swallows.

Sampling In most cases, it is not possible to count every member of a population. The population may be very large, or it may be spread over a wide area. It may be hard to find every individual or to remember which ones have already been counted. Instead, ecologists usually make an estimate. An **estimate** is an approximation of a number, based on reasonable assumptions.

One type of estimating involves counting the number of organisms in a small area (a sample), and then multiplying to find the number in a larger area. To get an accurate estimate, the sample should have the same population density as the larger area. For example, suppose you count 8 red maples in a 10 meter-by-10 meter area of the forest. If the entire forest were 100 times that size, you would multiply your count by 100 to estimate the total population, or 800 red maples.

Mark-and-Recapture Studies Another estimating method is a technique called "mark and recapture." This technique gets its name because some animals are first captured, marked, and released into the environment. Then another group of animals is captured. The

---

Facts and Figures For a species to survive, there must be enough males and females present in a range to mate and reproduce successfully. If the population density and size fall below a critical minimum level, the population declines and may become extinct. This very nearly occurred with the California condor, a scavenger that requires a large range in which to feed.

Development has greatly reduced the California condor's wilderness habitat. In the late 1980s, there were no condors living in the wild. A program to reintroduce zoo-bred condors into the wild began in 1992. Two colonies, one in California and one in Arizona, appear to be succeeding.

number of marked animals in this second group indicates the population size. For example, if half the animals in the second group are marked, it means that the first sample represented about half the total population.

Here's an example showing how mark and recapture works. First, deer mice in a field are caught in a trap that does not harm the mice. Ecologists count the mice and mark each mouse with a dot of hair dye before releasing it again. Two weeks later, the researchers return and capture mice again. They count how many mice have marks, showing that they were captured the first time, and how many are unmarked. Using a mathematical formula, the scientists can estimate the total population of mice in the field. You can try this technique for yourself in the Real-World Lab at the end of this section.

✓ *Checkpoint* When is sampling used to estimate a population?

Changes in Population Size

By returning to a location often and using one of the methods described here, ecologists can monitor the size of a population over time. **Populations can change in size when new members enter the population or when members leave the population.**

Births and Deaths The major way in which new individuals are added to a population is through the birth of offspring. The **birth rate** of a population is the number of births in a population in a certain amount of time. For example, suppose a population of 1,000 snow geese produces 1,400 goslings in a year. The birth rate in this population would be 1,400 goslings per year.

Similarly, the major way that individuals leave a population is by dying. The **death rate** is the number of deaths in a population in a certain amount of time. Suppose that in the same population, 500 geese die in a year. The death rate would be 500 geese per year.

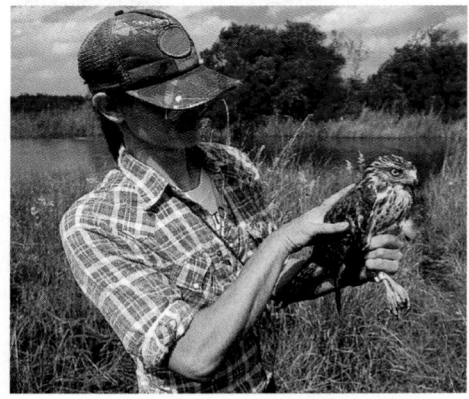

Figure 6 This young hawk is part of a mark-and-recapture study in a Virginia marsh. *Inferring What is the purpose of the silver band on the hawk's leg?*

Figure 7 The birth of new individuals can increase the size of a population. This cheetah mother added five offspring to the population in her area.

Chapter 22 **697**

Real-Life Learning

Ask students: **Have you ever seen scientists using the mark-and-recapture method in a television documentary? What was done?** (*Answers will vary depending on students' experience. Documentaries have shown wolves, grizzly bears, birds, and other animals being tranquilized with a dart gun or caught in a net or safe trap, tagged with an identification number, and then released.*) Ask: **What is the purpose of studies like these?** (*Accept all reasonable responses, such as to find out whether a population of endangered animals is increasing, decreasing, or staying the same.*) **learning modality: verbal**

Changes in Population Size

Building Inquiry Skills: Calculating

Tell students that ecologists use the birth and death rates to calculate a population's *growth rate*, the rate at which the population is changing. The birth rate (*b*) minus the death rate (*d*) equals the growth rate (*g*): $b - d = g$. Have students use this formula to calculate the growth rate of the population of snow geese discussed in the text. (1,400 births − 500 deaths = a growth rate of 900 geese per year) **learning modality: logical/mathematical**

Ongoing Assessment

Oral Presentation Call on various students to name a method of determining population size and to briefly explain what the method involves.

Changes in Population Size, continued

Building Inquiry Skills: Calculating

Continuing with the example on the previous page, ask: **Suppose 1,600 snow geese died in the same year that 1,400 were born. What would the growth rate be for that year?** *(1,400 − 1,600 = a growth rate of −200 geese per year)* **What does a negative growth rate mean?** *(The population is declining.)* **What might account for a death rate that is higher than the birth rate?** *(Disease; not enough food; eggs, young geese, or adults being eaten by other animals; poisons in the environment; and so on)* **learning modality: logical/mathematical**

Using the Visuals: Figure 8

Review the population changes described in the caption and shown on the graph. Then ask: **Why is it helpful to show population changes in a graph?** *(The lines make the changes easier to see and understand than reading a list of numbers.)* **learning modality: visual**

Math TOOLBOX

If students have difficulty comparing a fraction and a decimal, suggest that they convert the fraction to a decimal.
1. $5 > -6$
2. $0.4 < \frac{3}{5}$
   $0.4 < 0.6$
3. $-2 -(-8) > 7-1.5$
   $6 > 5.5$
learning modality: logical/ mathematical

Math TOOLBOX

Inequalities

The population statement is an example of an inequality. An inequality is a mathematical statement that compares two expressions. Two signs that represent inequalities are:

  $<$ (is less than)
  $>$ (is greater than)

For example, an inequality comparing the fraction $\frac{1}{2}$ to the decimal 0.75 would be written:

$$\frac{1}{2} < 0.75$$

Write an inequality comparing each pair of expressions below.

1. 5 **?** −6
2. 0.4 **?** $\frac{3}{5}$
3. −2 − (−8) **?** 7 − 1.5

Figure 8 From Year 0 to Year 4, more rabbits joined the population than left it, so the population increased. From Year 4 to Year 8, more rabbits left the population than joined it, so the population decreased. From Year 8 to Year 10, the rates of rabbits leaving and joining the population were about equal, so the population remained steady. *Interpreting Graphs In what year did the rabbit population reach its highest point? What was the size of the population in that year?*

698

The Population Statement When the birth rate in a population is greater than the death rate, the population will generally increase in size. This statement can be written as a mathematical statement using the "is greater than" sign:

If birth rate > death rate, population size increases.

For example, in the snow goose population, the birth rate of 1,400 goslings per year was greater than the death rate of 500 geese per year, and the population would increase in size.

However, if the death rate in a population is greater than the birth rate, the population size will generally decrease. This can also be written as a mathematical statement:

If death rate > birth rate, population size decreases.

Immigration and Emigration The size of a population also can change when individuals move into or out of the population, just as the population of your town changes when families move into town or move away. **Immigration** (im ih GRAY shun) means moving into a population. **Emigration** (em ih GRAY shun) means leaving a population. Emigration can occur when part of a population gets cut off from the rest of the population. For instance, if food is scarce, some members of an antelope herd may wander off in search of better grassland. If they become permanently separated from the original herd, they will no longer be part of that population.

Graphing Changes in Population You can see an example of changes in a population of rabbits in Figure 8. The vertical axis shows the numbers of rabbits in the population, while the horizontal axis shows time. The graph shows the size of the population over a 10-year period.

☑ *Checkpoint Name two ways individuals can join a population.*

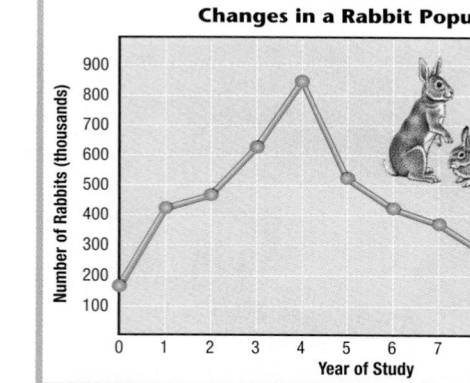

Changes in a Rabbit Population

Background

Facts and Figures When the size of a population grows beyond the carrying capacity of its habitat, a *population crash* may occur. Food shortages, insufficient space for successful reproduction, disease, and other limiting factors result in a death rate much higher than the birth rate, and the population declines sharply.

One example of such a crash occurred with the moose population on Isle Royale (see page 708) before wolves arrived in 1949. Moose came to Isle Royale around 1900 by walking across the frozen lake in winter. Over the next 35 years, the moose population increased to about 3,000. This exhausted their food supply, leading to starvation for 90 percent of the moose. The population increased again until 1948, then declined sharply once more because of lack of food.

Figure 9 These gannets seem to have heard the saying "Birds of a feather flock together." When there are more birds than the space can support, the population will have exceeded the carrying capacity of the shore.

Limiting Factors

When conditions are good, a population will generally increase. But a population does not keep growing forever. Eventually, some factor in its environment causes the population to stop growing. A **limiting factor** is an environmental factor that prevents a population from increasing. **Some limiting factors for populations are food, space, and weather conditions.**

Food Organisms require food to survive. In an area where food is scarce, this becomes a limiting factor. Suppose a giraffe needs to eat 10 kilograms of leaves each day to survive. The trees in an area can provide 100 kilograms of leaves a day while remaining healthy. Five giraffes could live easily in this area, since they would only require a total of 50 kilograms of food. But 15 giraffes could not all survive—there would not be enough food for all of them. No matter how much shelter, water, and other resources there might be, the population will not grow much higher than 10 giraffes. The largest population that an environment can support is called its **carrying capacity.** The carrying capacity of this environment is 10 giraffes.

Space The birds in Figure 9 are rarely seen on land. These birds, called gannets, spend most of their lives flying over the ocean. They only land on this rocky shore to nest. But as you can see, the shore is very crowded. If a pair of gannets does not have room to build a nest, that pair will not be able to produce any offspring.

Elbow Room

Using masking tape, mark off several one-meter squares on the floor of your classroom. Your teacher will form groups of 2, 4, and 6 students. Each group's task is to put together a small jigsaw puzzle in one of the squares. All the group members must keep their feet within the square. Time how long it takes your group to finish the puzzle.

Making Models How long did it take each group to complete the task? How does this activity show that space can be a limiting factor? What is the carrying capacity of puzzle-solvers in a square meter?

Limiting Factors

Building Inquiry Skills: Inferring

Ask students: **Is food a limiting factor for plants?** *(no)* **Why not?** *(Plants make their own food.)* **What factors do limit the size of plant populations?** *(The amount of available sunlight, carbon dioxide in the air, water, and nutrients in the soil)* **Why do these factors limit plant populations?** *(Plants need them for their other life processes.)* **learning modality: logical/mathematical**

Including All Students

To assess students' understanding of carrying capacity, direct their attention back to the graph in Figure 8 and ask: **What part of the graph shows the carrying capacity of the rabbits' environment? Why?** *(The vertical axis— Number of Rabbits—shows the carrying capacity of the rabbits' environment because it indicates how many rabbits can live in this area.)* **limited English proficiency**

TRY THIS

Skills Focus making models
Materials *masking tape, meter stick, small jigsaw puzzle, watch or clock*
Time 10–15 minutes
Tips Use very simple jigsaw puzzles so that puzzle difficulty is not a factor in how long it takes each group to complete the task.
Expected Outcome Specific times will vary, but the smaller groups will probably complete their puzzles first, with the largest groups taking longest. Crowding made the task more difficult.
Extend Invite students to suggest other simple models of space as a limiting factor. If time allows, let them carry out their ideas. **learning modality: kinesthetic**

Answers to Self-Assessment

Caption Question

Figure 8 Year 4; about 850,000 rabbits

☑ *Checkpoint*

Individuals can join a population by being born into it or by immigrating into it.

Ongoing Assessment

Writing Have each student write a brief paragraph explaining how birth rate and death rate affect the size of a population.

3 Assess

Science at Home

Tips Let students try the activity in class before they present it to their family members. Possible methods include: (1) Count the number of words in one line, then multiply by the number of lines on the page. (2) Count the number of words in each of three or four lines, calculate the average number of words per line, and multiply by the number of lines on the page. The second method should produce a more accurate estimate.

Performance Assessment

Oral Presentation Call on various students to identify a factor that affects the size of a population (birth/death rates and immigration/emigration numbers as well as limiting factors).

Figure 10 A snowstorm can limit the size of the orange crop.

Those gannets will not contribute to an increase in the gannet population. This means that space for nesting is a limiting factor for these gannets. If the shore were bigger, more gannets would be able to nest there, and the population would increase.

Space is often a limiting factor for plants. The amount of space in which a plant grows can determine how much sunlight, water, and other necessities the plant can obtain. For example, many pine seedlings sprout each year in a forest. But as the trees get bigger, those that are too close together do not have room to spread their roots underground. Other tree branches block out the sunlight they need to live. Some of the seedlings die, limiting the size of the pine population.

Weather Weather conditions such as temperature and amount of rainfall can also limit population growth. Many insect species breed in the warm spring weather. As winter begins, the first frost kills many of the insects. This sudden rise in the death rate causes the insect population to decrease.

A single severe weather event can dramatically change the size of a population by killing many organisms. For instance, a flood or hurricane can wash away nests and burrows just as it damages the homes of humans. If you live in a northern state, you may have seen an early frost limit the population of tomato plants in a vegetable garden.

Section 2 Review

1. List four ways of determining population size.
2. How is birth rate related to population size?
3. List three limiting factors for populations. Choose one and explain how this factor can limit population growth.
4. Explain why it is often necessary for ecologists to estimate the size of a population.
5. **Thinking Critically Problem Solving** A field measures 50 meters by 90 meters. In one square meter, you count 3 grasshoppers. Estimate the total population of grasshoppers in the field. What method did you use to make your estimate?

Science at Home

Word Estimates Choose a page of a dictionary or other book that has a lot of type on it. Challenge your family members to estimate the number of words on the page. After everyone has come up with an estimate, have each person explain the method he or she used. Now count the actual number of words on the page. Whose estimate was closest?

700

Program Resources

◆ **Unit 5 Resources** 22-2 Review and Reinforce, p. 15; 22-2 Enrich, p. 16
◆ **Laboratory Manual** 22, "Weather and Whooping Cranes"

Counting Turtles

For three years, ecologists have been using the mark-and-recapture method to monitor the population of turtles in a pond. In this lab, you will model recapturing the turtles to complete the study. Then you will analyze the results.

Problem

How can the mark-and-recapture method help ecologists monitor the size of a population?

Skills Focus

calculating, graphing, predicting

Materials

model paper turtle population
calculator   graph paper

Procedure

1. The data table shows the results from the first three years of the study. Copy it into your notebook, leaving spaces for your data as shown.
2. Your teacher will give you a box representing the pond. Fifteen of the turtles have been marked, as shown in the data table for Year 4.
3. Capture a member of the population by randomly selecting one turtle. Set it aside.
4. Repeat Step 3 nine times. Record the total number of turtles you captured.
5. Examine each turtle to see whether it has a mark. Count the number of recaptured (marked) turtles. Record this number in your data table.

Analyze and Conclude

1. Use the equation below to estimate the turtle population for each year. The first year is done for you as a sample. If your answer is a decimal, round it to the nearest whole number so that your estimate is in "whole turtles." Record the population for each year in the last column of the data table.

$$\text{Total population} = \frac{\text{Number marked} \times \text{Total number captured}}{\text{Number recaptured (with marks)}}$$

Sample (Year 1):
$$\frac{32 \times 28}{15} = 59.7 \text{ or } 60 \text{ turtles}$$

2. Graph the estimated total populations for the four years. Mark years on the horizontal axis. Mark population size on the vertical axis.
3. Describe how the turtle population has changed over the four years of the study. Suggest three possible causes for the changes.
4. **Apply** Use your graph to predict the turtle population in Year 5. Explain your prediction.

Getting Involved

Find out whether any wildlife populations in your area are being monitored by national, state, or local agencies. Make a poster or write an article for the school paper about the population and the method being used to study it.

DATA TABLE

Year	Number Marked	Total Number Captured	Number Recaptured (with Marks)	Estimated Total Population
1	32	28	15	
2	25	21	11	
3	23	19	11	
4	15			

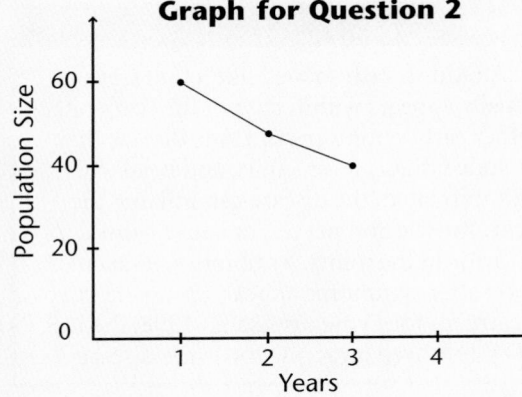

Graph for Question 2

(vertical axis: Population Size, 0, 20, 40, 60; horizontal axis: Years, 1, 2, 3, 4)

Extending the Inquiry

Getting Involved

To find information, students can contact their state department of natural resources and wildlife.

Program Resources

◆ **Unit 5 Resources** Chapter 22 Real-World Lab, pp. 23–25

Careers in Science

Counting Turtles

Preparing for Inquiry

Key Concept The mark-and-recapture method can be used to estimate the size of a population over time.

Skills Objectives Students will be able to
◆ calculate to estimate a population using the mark-and-recapture method;
◆ graph population estimates;
◆ predict the future population.

Time 40 minutes

Advance Planning Prepare a model turtle population for each group. Use 30 small squares cut from paper or index cards to represent turtles. Mark a dot on one side of 15 turtles. Spread all 30 turtles in a box, marked sides down.

Guiding Inquiry

Troubleshooting the Experiment

◆ In Step 2, clarify that the 15 marked turtles refers to the bottom box in the second column of the table, the number marked in Year 4.
◆ Work through the sample calculation in Question 1 with the class.

Expected Outcome

The number of marked turtles recaptured will vary. Thus, students' estimates of the total population for Year 4 will also vary.

Analyze and Conclude

1. The estimated total populations for Years 1–3 are 60, 48, and 40. The total number captured for Year 4 is 10. The number recaptured and the total population for Year 4 will vary. If 0 recaptured, total population = 0; if 1, 150; if 2, 75; if 3, 50; if 4, 38; if 5, 30; if 6, 25; if 7, 21; if 8, 19; if 9, 17; and if 10, 15.
2. See sample graph. Year 4 will vary.
3. The turtle population has declined steadily. Possible causes include limited food, overcrowding, disease, predation, and use of insecticides or herbicides in the pond.
4. Most students will probably predict a continuing decline in the population. Accept other responses so long as students defend their predictions.

SCIENCE AND SOCIETY

Animal Overpopulation: How Can People Help?

Purpose

Identify problems caused by deer overpopulation, evaluate possible solutions, and recommend one way for a community to deal with the problem.

Panel Discussion

Time 40 minutes

◆ Allow time for students to read the introductory text and the three sections under The Issues. Then ask: **What solution would you support if our area had a deer overpopulation problem? Why would you choose that solution?** As students identify possible solutions, list them on the board. Let students discuss the issues freely until different viewpoints are clear.

◆ Divide the class into as many groups as there are solutions listed. Provide time for each group to discuss the pros and cons of each possibility.

◆ Ask each group to select one student to take part in a panel discussion of people who are trying to solve the deer problem in the community.

Extend If your community has had an actual problem with animal overpopulation—with deer, starlings, gypsy moths, or pigeons, for example—suggest that students discuss the issue with family members and, if possible, consult with community and state agencies to find out how people have dealt with the problem.

You Decide

Students' responses to Identify the Problem and Analyze the Options should be based on the concepts and issues presented in the text. In response to Find a Solution, however, students may suggest their own ideas or solutions based on their small-group discussions.

Animal Overpopulation: How Can People Help?

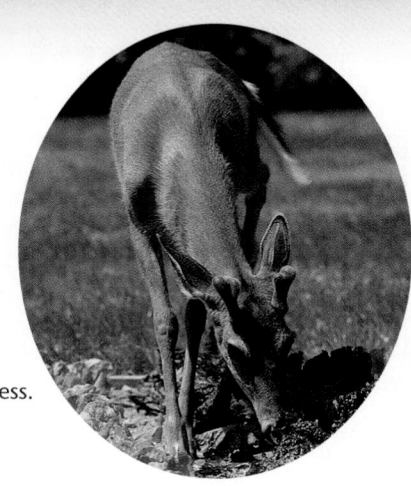

Populations of white-tailed deer are growing rapidly in many parts of the United States. As populations soar, food becomes a limiting factor. Many deer die of starvation. Others grow up small and unhealthy. In search of food, hungry deer move closer to where humans live. There they eat farm crops, garden vegetables, shrubs, and even trees. This affects birds and small animals that depend on the plants for shelter or food. In addition, increased numbers of deer near roads can cause more automobile accidents.

People admire the grace, beauty, and swiftness of deer. Most people don't want these animals to suffer from starvation or illness. Should people take action to limit growing deer populations?

The Issues

Should People Take Direct Action?
Many people argue that hunting is the simplest way to reduce animal populations. Wildlife managers look at the supply of resources in an area and determine its carrying capacity. Then hunters are issued licenses to help reduce the number of deer to the level that can be supported.

Other people favor nonhunting approaches to control deer populations. One plan is to trap the deer and relocate them. But this method is expensive and requires finding another location that can accept the deer without unbalancing its own system. Few such locations are available.

Scientists are also working to develop chemicals to reduce the birth rate in deer populations. This plan will help control overpopulation, but it is effective for only one year at a time.

Should People Take Indirect Action?
Some suggest bringing in natural enemies of deer, such as wolves, mountain lions, and bears, to areas with too many deer. But these animals could also attack cattle, dogs, cats, and even humans. Other communities have built tall fences around areas they don't want deer to invade. Although this solution can work for people with small yards, it is impractical for farmers or ranchers.

Should People Do Nothing? Some people oppose any kind of action. They support leaving the deer alone and allowing nature to take its course. Animal populations in an area naturally cycle up and down over time. Doing nothing means that some deer will die of starvation or disease. But eventually, the population will be reduced to a size within the carrying capacity of the environment.

You Decide

1. Identify the Problem
In your own words, explain the problem created by the over-population of white-tailed deer.

2. Analyze the Options
List the ways that people can deal with overpopulation of white-tailed deer. State the negative and positive points of each method.

3. Find a Solution
Suppose you are an ecologist in an area that has twice as many deer as it can support. Propose a way for the community to deal with the problem.

Background

Facts and Figures Deer overpopulation can also be hazardous to human health, as shown by the increasing occurrence of Lyme disease in the United States. White-tailed deer may carry tiny ticks that are smaller than the head of a pin. The ticks in turn carry a bacterium, *Borrelia burgdorferi,* which causes Lyme disease. The ticks attach themselves to people walking through infested areas. The tick's bite transfers the bacteria to humans.

A reddish rash shaped like a bull's-eye usually appears within days of the tick's bite. Other early symptoms of Lyme disease may include fatigue, fever, chills, and headache. Left untreated, the disease can inflame the heart muscle and nerves, or cause painful arthritis in the joints. Antibiotics, if taken soon after symptoms appear, are an effective treatment for Lyme disease. In 1998, the U.S. FDA approved a vaccine for Lyme disease.

SECTION
3 Interactions Among Living Things

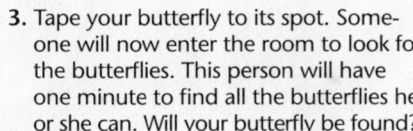

DISCOVER ··· ACTIVITY····

How Well Can You Hide a Butterfly?

1. Using the outline at the right, trace a butterfly onto a piece of paper.

2. Look around the classroom and pick a spot where you will place your butterfly. The butterfly must be placed completely in the open. Color your butterfly so it will blend in with the spot you choose.

3. Tape your butterfly to its spot. Someone will now enter the room to look for the butterflies. This person will have one minute to find all the butterflies he or she can. Will your butterfly be found?

Think It Over

Predicting Over time, how do you think the population size would change for butterflies that blend in with their surroundings?

I magine giving a big hug to the plant in the photo. Ouch! The sharp spines on its trunk would make you think twice before hugging—or even touching—the saguaro (suh GWAHR oh) cactus. But if you could spend a day hidden inside a saguaro, you would see that many species do interact with this spiky plant.

As the day breaks, you hear a twittering noise coming from a nest tucked in one of the saguaro's arms. Two young red-tailed hawks are preparing to fly for the first time. Farther down the trunk, a tiny elf owl peeks out of its nest in a small hole. The elf owl is so small it could fit in your palm! A rattlesnake slithers around the base of the saguaro, looking for lunch. Spying a nearby shrew, the snake moves in for the kill. With a sudden movement, it strikes the shrew with its sharp fangs.

The activity around the saguaro doesn't stop after the sun goes down. At night, long-nosed bats feed on the nectar from the saguaro's blossoms. They stick their faces into the flowers to feed, covering their long snouts with a dusting of white pollen in the process. As the bats move from plant to plant, they carry the pollen along. This enables the cactuses to reproduce.

GUIDE FOR READING

◆ How do an organism's adaptations help it to survive?

◆ What are the major types of interactions among organisms?

◆ What are the three forms of symbiotic relationships?

Reading Tip As you read, use the section headings to make an outline. Fill in details under each heading.

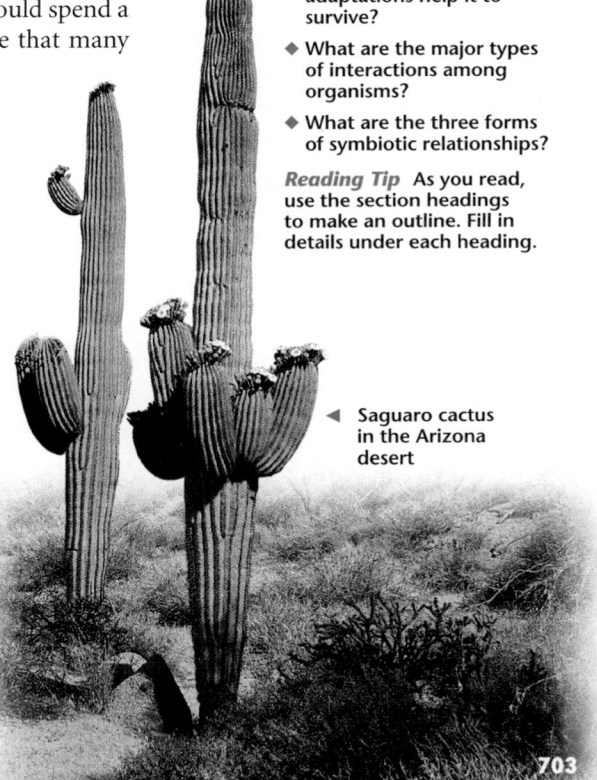

◀ Saguaro cactus in the Arizona desert

READING STRATEGIES

Reading Tip Students should use the headings *Adapting to the Environment, Competition, Predation,* and *Symbiosis* as the main headings in their outlines. They can use the purple subheads in the text as their secondary headings. They should use boldface terms and sentences from the text to complete their outlines. Students can use their outlines as study aids.

Program Resources

◆ **Unit 5 Resources** 22-3 Lesson Plan, p. 17; 22-3 Section Summary, p. 18

Media and Technology

Audio CD English-Spanish Summary 22-3

Objectives

After completing the lesson, students will be able to

◆ explain how an organism's adaptations help it to survive;

◆ describe the major types of interactions among organisms;

◆ identify the three forms of symbiotic relationships.

Key Terms natural selection, niche, competition, predation, predator, prey, symbiosis, mutualism, commensalism, parasitism, parasite, host

1 Engage/Explore

Activating Prior Knowledge

Ask students: **What features enable fish to survive in an underwater habitat?** *(Fins and a tail for moving through the water, gills for breathing oxygen dissolved in the water)* Encourage students to think of other examples of how organisms are adapted to their environments.

········ DISCOVER ········

Skills Focus predicting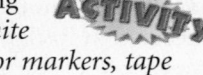
Materials *sheet of white paper, colored pencils or markers, tape*
Time 10–15 minutes
Tips Tell students that the butterflies do not have to be colored realistically. Arrange to have another staff member or a student from another class look for the butterflies.
Expected Outcome Butterflies whose colors and patterns closely match their background will be most difficult to see.
Think It Over Butterflies that blend well with their surroundings will escape predators and survive to reproduce, thus increasing the population.

2 Facilitate

Adapting to the Environment

Addressing Naive Conceptions

When students have read about species changing over time, emphasize that the changes are not deliberate or conscious on the organisms' part. That is, organisms do not "decide" to develop characteristics that will enable them to survive more successfully. Also explain that individual organisms do not develop new physical adaptations within their own lifespans. Rather, the species changes over time as organisms are born with new, favorable adaptations (caused by mutations) that are then passed on to their offspring. To illustrate this point, share the example described in Background below, then present the following Inquiry Challenge. **learning modality: verbal**

Inquiry Challenge

Materials *construction paper in shades of gray; black and gray markers*

Time 10–15 minutes

Challenge small groups of students to make a model illustrating the changes in the peppered moth populations described in Background below. Let each group present its model to the rest of the class and describe the changes. **cooperative learning**

Red-tailed hawk

Flycatcher

Hawk nest

Woodpecker

Elf owl

Purple martin

Wasps

Saguaro cactus

Rattlesnake

Gila monster

Scorpion

Roadrunner

Adapting to the Environment

Each organism in this desert ecosystem has some unique characteristics. In response to their environments, species evolve, or change over time. The changes that make organisms better suited to their environments develop through the process of natural selection.

Recall from Chapter 5 how natural selection works: Individuals in a population have different characteristics. Those individuals whose characteristics are best suited for their environment tend to survive and produce offspring. Offspring that inherit the characteristics that made their parents successful also live to reproduce. Over many generations individuals with those characteristics continue to reproduce. Individuals that are poorly suited to the environment are less likely to survive and reproduce. Over time, these poorly suited characteristics may disappear from the population. The behaviors and physical characteristics of species that allow them to live successfully in their environment are called adaptations.

Every organism has a variety of adaptations that are suited to its specific living conditions. The adaptations of the organisms in the desert ecosystem create unique roles for each organism. An organism's particular role, or how it makes its living, is called its **niche.** A niche includes the type of food the organism eats, how it obtains this food, and which other species use the organism as food. The niche also includes when and how the organism reproduces and the physical conditions it requires to survive.

An organism's niche may include how it interacts with other organisms. During your day in the saguaro community, you observed a range of such interactions. **There are three major types of interactions among organisms: competition, predation, and symbiosis.**

Figure 11 The organisms in the saguaro community are well adapted to their desert environment. *Observing Identify two interactions between organisms that are taking place in this scene.*

Background

History of Science Although we tend to think of natural selection as occurring over vast periods of time, species can and do change relatively quickly when subjected to environmental pressures. The case of the English peppered moth is a famous example. The peppered moth occurs in both a speckled light-gray form and a dark-gray form.

During the day, the moths rest on tree trunks covered with light-colored lichens.

Before the Industrial Revolution, the dark form was more obvious to predators and thus very rare. Then soot and other pollutants from factories killed the lichens and darkened the tree trunks. Within a 50-year period, the dark moths became more abundant. Environmental conditions changed again in the early 1950s when anti-pollution laws were enacted. Lichens grew again on soot-free tree trunks, and the frequency of dark moths declined.

The bay-breasted warbler *feeds in the middle part of the tree.*

The Cape May warbler *feeds at the tips of branches near the top of the tree.*

The yellow-rumped warbler *feeds in the lower part of the tree and at the bases of the middle branches.*

Competition

Different species can share the same habitat, such as the many animals that live in and around the saguaro. Different species can also share similar food requirements. For example, the red-tailed hawk and the elf owl both live on the saguaro and eat similar food. However, these two species do not occupy exactly the same niche. The hawk is active during the day, while the owl is active mostly at night. If two species occupy the same niche, one of the species will eventually die off. The reason for this is **competition,** the struggle between organisms to survive in a habitat with limited resources.

An ecosystem cannot satisfy the needs of all the living things in a particular habitat. There is a limited amount of food, water, and shelter. Organisms that survive have adaptations that enable them to reduce competition. For example, the three species of warblers in Figure 12 live in the same spruce forest habitat. They all eat insects that live in the spruce trees. How do these birds avoid competing for the limited insect supply? Each warbler "specializes" in feeding in a certain part of a spruce tree. By finding their own places to feed, the three species can coexist.

 INTEGRATING CHEMISTRY Many plants use chemicals to ward off their competition. Plants often compete with one another for growing space and water. Some shrubs release toxic, or poisonous, chemicals into the ground around them. These chemicals keep grass and weeds from growing around the shrubs, sometimes forming a ring of bare ground a meter or two wide.

☑ *Checkpoint* Why can't two species occupy the same niche?

Figure 12 Each of these warblers occupies a different niche in its spruce tree habitat. By feeding in different areas of the tree, the birds avoid competing with one another for food.

Answers to Self-Assessment

Caption Question

Figure 11 *Sample answers:* The owl is nesting in a hole in the cactus. The woodpecker is eating insects on the cactus.

☑ *Checkpoint*

If two species try to occupy the same niche, they will compete directly against each other, and one species eventually will die off.

Competition

Building Inquiry Skills: Observing

Materials *several male crickets, terrarium, soil, materials to provide hiding places, paint of different colors*

ACTIVITY

Time 15 minutes for initial setup

Obtain several male crickets from a pet shop. Tell students that male crickets in the wild compete for territory. Let volunteers set up a cricket habitat in a terrarium, with soil on the bottom and several items under which the crickets can hide, such as rocks, dead leaves, pieces of tree bark, or small branches. Before students put the crickets in the terrarium, have them mark each one's back with a different color dot of paint so they can tell the crickets apart. (Remind students to handle the crickets gently and to wash their hands afterward.) When the crickets are first introduced into the habitat, they will fight each other. In time, however, each cricket will establish its own territory, remain in it most of the time, and defend it against the other males. (After the activity, you can release the crickets or return them to the pet store.) **learning modality: visual**

Integrating Chemistry

Point out that some plants produce bad-tasting or toxic chemicals that discourage animals from eating them. The leaves of the milkweed plant, for example, contain chemicals that are toxic to most animals except monarch butterfly caterpillars. Poison ivy, poison oak, and poison sumac produce chemicals that are extremely irritating to humans' skin. Animals also have chemical defenses, as shown by the frog pictured and described on page 707. **learning modality: verbal**

Ongoing Assessment

Writing Have students explain how natural selection causes changes in a species over time.

Predation

Building Inquiry Skills: Inferring

Ask students: **Suppose you set up a cricket habitat in a terrarium. What do you think would happen if you added a toad to the habitat?** *(It would eat the crickets.)* **What would happen if you then added a snake to the habitat?** *(It would eat the toad.)* **Which of these animals would be the prey?** *(The crickets and the toad, when it is eaten by the snake.)* **Which would be a predator?** *(The toad, when it eats crickets, and the snake.)* Challenge students to identify other feeding relationships in which one organism is a predator at some times and the prey at other times. **learning modality: logical/mathematical**

Building Inquiry Skills: Observing

Materials *sundew or Venus flytrap, cooked hamburger, tweezers*
Time periodic observation

Students are often intrigued by insect-eating plants. Obtain a sundew or Venus flytrap from a plant shop, the plant section of a large supermarket, or a biological supply house. Let students take turns feeding the plant small pieces of cooked hamburger from time to time. (Remind students to wash their hands afterward.) Encourage interested students to find out why the plant catches and digests insects. *(Carnivorous plants are capable of making their own food through photosynthesis, but the boggy, acidic soil in which they grow does not provide sufficient nitrogen for the plants' needs. The plants obtain nitrogen from the insects they catch.)* **learning modality: kinesthetic**

Predation

A tiger shark lurks beneath the surface of the clear blue water, looking for shadows of young albatrosses floating above it. The shark sees a chick and silently swims closer. Suddenly, the shark bursts through the water and seizes the albatross with one snap of its powerful jaw. This interaction between two organisms has an unfortunate ending for the albatross.

An interaction in which one organism hunts and kills another for food is called **predation.** Recall from Chapter 10 that the organism that does the killing, in this case the tiger shark, is the **predator.** The organism that is caught, the albatross, is the **prey.**

Predator Adaptations Predators have adaptations that help them catch and kill their prey. For example, a cheetah can run very fast for a short time, enabling it to catch its prey. A jellyfish's tentacles contain a poisonous substance that paralyzes tiny water

EXPLORING *Defense Strategies*

Organisms display a wide array of adaptations that help them avoid becoming prey.

Camouflage ▲
These delicate spiny bugs are a perfect match for their branch habitat. The more an organism resembles its surroundings, the less likely it is that a predator will notice it. Some animals, such as flounder, can even change their colors to match a variety of settings.

Protective Coverings
This sea urchin sends a clear message to predators: "Don't touch!" Porcupines, hedgehogs, and cactuses all use the same spiny strategy. After a few painful encounters, a predator will look for less prickly prey. ▼

Background

History of Science In nature, predator species rarely kill and eat all their prey species, which would reduce community diversity. In fact, studies have shown that predation can actually help *maintain* diversity.

One example of this process involves the gray wolf, a top predator in its ecosystem. Where wolves were hunted to extinction, such as in many parts of North America,

populations of deer and other herbivores increased dramatically. As these populations overgrazed the vegetation, many plant species that could not tolerate such grazing pressure disappeared from the ecosystem. In turn, many insects and other small animals that depended on the plants for food also disappeared. The elimination of wolves thus produced an ecosystem with considerably less species diversity.

animals. You can probably think of many predators that have claws, sharp teeth, or stingers. Some plants, too, have adaptations for catching prey. The sundew is covered with sticky bulbs on stalks—when a fly lands on the plant, it remains snared in the sticky goo while the plant digests it.

Some predators have adaptations that enable them to hunt at night. For example, the big eyes of an owl let in as much light as possible to help it see in the dark. Bats can hunt without seeing at all. Instead, they locate their prey by producing pulses of sound and listening for the echoes. This precise method enables a bat to catch a flying moth in complete darkness.

Prey Adaptations How do prey organisms manage to avoid being caught by such effective predators? In *Exploring Defense Strategies,* below, you can see some examples of how an organism's physical characteristics can help protect it.

Warning Coloring ▲
A frog this bright certainly can't hide. How could such a color be an advantage? The bright red and blue of this poison arrow frog warn predators not to eat it— glands on the frog's back that release toxic chemicals make it a bad choice for a meal.

Mimicry
If you've ever been stung by a bee, you'd probably keep your distance from this insect. But actually this "bee" is a harmless fly. The fly's resemblance to a stinging bee protects it from birds and other predators, who are fooled into staying away. ▼

◄ False Coloring
Which way is this butterfly fish swimming? The black dot on its tail is a false eye. A predator may bite this end of the fish, allowing it to escape with only part of its tail missing.

Chapter 22 **707**

Review each of the defense strategies with the class, then list the five strategies on the board. Ask: **What kind of defense strategy does a poison ivy plant have?** (*Chemical defense; add this defense to the list on the board.*) Ask: **Can you think of an example of an animal using a chemical defense?** (*Students might mention a skunk spraying.*) **How does this defense help a skunk survive?** (*The foul odor repels predators that try to attack it; any predator who has been sprayed by a skunk will avoid skunks in the future.*) Tell students that some animals use another defense strategy called a threat display. When attacked by a predator, the prey animal does something to startle or intimidate the predator. For example, a baboon being chased by a leopard may suddenly turn to face the leopard, bare its teeth, and scream loudly, startling the leopard long enough for the baboon to escape. Add *threat display* to the list. Then divide the class into seven groups, and secretly assign one of the listed defenses to each group. Have each group act out its defense strategy and challenge the rest of the students to guess what it is. **cooperative learning**

Ongoing Assessment

Oral Presentation Call on various students to each identify and describe a defense strategy used by prey organisms.

Predation, continued

Using the Visuals: Figure 13

To help students focus on specific phases of the cycles, ask questions such as the following: **What happened to the wolf population from 1965 to 1969?** *(It declined—from 29 wolves in 1965 to 19 wolves in 1969.)* **What happened to the moose population during that same period?** *(It increased—from about 700 moose in 1965 to about 1,200 moose in 1969.)* **Why do you think the moose population increased so much during those years?** *(The wolf population was declining, so fewer moose were killed by wolves.)* **After 1969, in what year did the moose population first reach a peak? What was the size of the population?** *(1974; about 1,400 moose)* **What was the size of the wolf population that year?** *(22 or 23 wolves)* **When did the wolf population reach its peak? How many wolves were there?** *(In 1980; 50 wolves)* **How many wolves were there two years later?** *(About 25)* **Why did the wolf population decline so much during that period?** *(The moose population continued to decline and reached one of its lowest points, so there was less food for the wolves.)* **What do you think accounts for the two dramatic increases in the moose population between 1986 and 1995?** *(The wolf population was small during those years.)* **What might have accounted for the sharp dip in the moose population between 1990 and 1991?** *(Since the number of wolves did not increase significantly in that year, students should suggest other limiting factors, possibly disease or insufficient food.)* **What do you think caused the sharp dip in the moose population between 1995 and 1996?** *(The wolf population increased again during that period.)* **learning modality: logical/mathematical**

Figure 13 The populations of wolves and moose on Isle Royale are related. The predator wolf population depends on the size of the prey moose population, and vice versa.
Predicting How might a disease in the wolf population one year affect the moose population the next year?

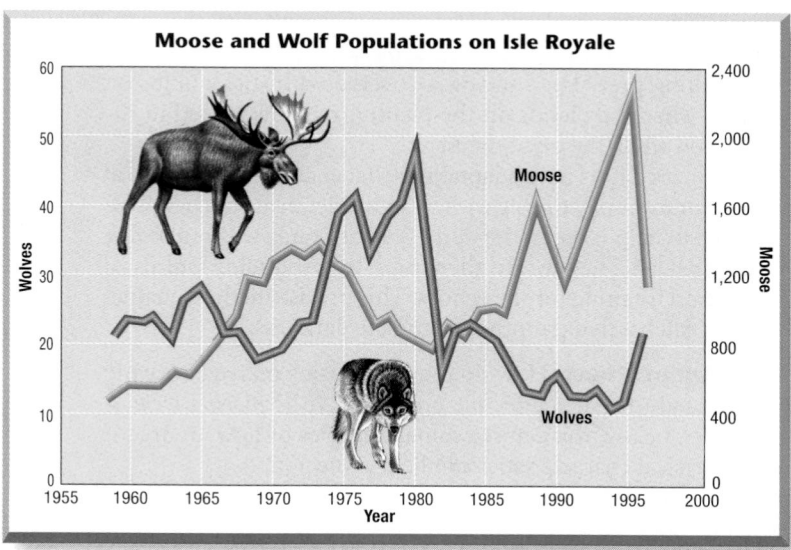

The Effect of Predation on Population Size Predation can have a major effect on the size of a population. As you learned in Section 2, when the death rate exceeds the birth rate in a population, the size of the population usually decreases. If predators are very effective at hunting their prey, the result is often a decrease in the size of the prey population. But a decrease in the prey population in turn affects the predator population.

To see how predator and prey populations can affect each other, look at the graph above. The graph shows the number of moose and wolves living on Isle Royale, an island in Lake Superior. From 1965 to 1975, the number of prey moose increased. The wolves now had enough to eat, so more of them survived. Within a few years, the wolf population began to increase. The growing number of wolves killed more and more moose. The moose population decreased. By 1980, the lack of moose had greatly affected the wolves. Some wolves starved, and others could not raise as many young. Soon the moose population began to climb again. This cycle for the two species has continued.

Of course, other factors also affect the populations on Isle Royale. For instance, cold winters and disease can also reduce the size of one or both of the populations.

☑ *Checkpoint* *If predation removes more members of a population than are born, how will the population change?*

Background

Facts and Figures Although the moose and wolf populations on Isle Royale have cycled up and down for decades, a new phase may have begun in the early 1980s when the wolf population declined sharply. Biologists hypothesize that the extreme genetic uniformity of the wolf population is one of the reasons for this decline. Populations that lack genetic variability often have low reproductive success. For example, in 1994 only two wolf pups were born on the island. Genetic uniformity also makes a population more susceptible to disease. Analysis of the wolves' blood has revealed antibodies to canine parvovirus, indicating that the wolves had been exposed to this lethal disease. The population may continue to have such poor reproductive success that it will disappear completely from Isle Royale.

Symbiosis

Many of the interactions in the saguaro community you read about earlier are examples of symbiosis. **Symbiosis** (sim bee OH sis) is a close relationship between two species that benefits at least one of the species. **The three types of symbiotic relationships are mutualism, commensalism, and parasitism.**

Mutualism A relationship in which both species benefit is called **mutualism** (MYOO choo uh liz um). The relationship between the saguaro and the long-eared bats is an example of mutualism. The bat benefits because the cactus flowers provide it with food. The saguaro benefits as its pollen is carried on the bat's nose to another plant.

 INTEGRATING HEALTH At this very moment, you are participating in a mutualistic relationship with a population of bacteria in your large intestine. These bacteria, called *Escherichia coli*, live in the intestines of most mammals. These bacteria break down some foods that the mammal cannot digest. The bacteria benefit by receiving food and a place to live. You also benefit from the relationship because the bacteria provide you with vitamin K, a nutrient that is needed to make your blood clot.

Commensalism A relationship in which one species benefits and the other species is neither helped nor harmed is called **commensalism** (kuh MEN suh liz um). The red-tailed hawks' interaction with the saguaro is an example of commensalism. The hawks are helped by having a place to build their nest, while the cactus is not affected by the birds.

Commensalism is not very common in nature because two species are usually either helped or harmed a little by any interaction. For example, by creating a small hole for its nest in the cactus trunk, the elf owl slightly damages the cactus.

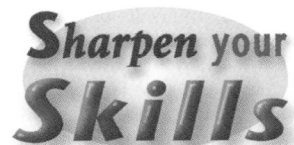

Classifying

Classify each interaction as an example of mutualism, commensalism, or parasitism. Explain your answers.

- A remora fish attaches itself to the underside of a shark without harming the shark, and eats leftover bits of food from the shark's meals.
- A vampire bat drinks the blood of horses.
- Bacteria living in cows' stomachs help them break down the cellulose in grass.

Figure 14 Three yellow-billed oxpeckers get a cruise and a snack aboard an obliging hippopotamus. The oxpeckers eat ticks living on the hippo's skin. Since both the birds and the hippo benefit from this interaction, it is an example of mutualism.

Answers to Self-Assessment

Caption Question

Figure 13 The moose population would probably increase, since there would be fewer predators.

☑ *Checkpoint*

The size of the population will decrease.

Symbiosis

Including All Students

Give students dictionaries and have them find the word derivations for *symbiosis, mutualism, commensalism,* and *parasitism.* Then students can use index cards to make vocabulary review cards that have the term on the front and the term's derivation, definition, and an example on the back. **limited English proficiency**

Integrating Health

Students are probably unaware that their bodies are normally inhabited by other types of living things. For example, microscopic mites *(Demodex folliculorum)* live at the base of eyelashes, feeding on tiny bits of dead skin and other detritus. The mites benefit, and humans are neither harmed nor helped—an example of commensalism. Obtain a video about the human body's invisible inhabitants so students can observe them. **learning modality: visual**

Sharpen your *Skills*

Classifying

Time 5–10 minutes
Tips Have students do this activity after they have read about parasitism on the next page.
Expected Outcome *Remora/shark:* Commensalism; the remora benefits, and the shark is neither helped nor harmed. *Vampire bat/horses:* Parasitism; the bat benefits, and the horses are harmed. *Bacteria/cows:* Mutualism; the bacteria receive food and a place to live, and the cows benefit because the bacteria help them digest their food.
Extend Challenge students to find and classify symbiotic relationships shown in Figure 11 on page 704. **learning modality: logical/mathematical**

Ongoing Assessment

Writing Have each student name and briefly describe the three types of symbiotic relationships and give an example of each.

709

3 Assess

Section 3 Review Answers

1. An organism's adaptations enable it to fill a unique role in its ecosystem—eating particular types of food, obtaining its food in unique ways, and using other abiotic and biotic factors to meet its needs.
2. *Competition*: the struggle between organisms to survive in a habitat with limited resources; *predation*: an interaction between organisms in which one kills and eats the other; *symbiosis*: a close relationship between two species that benefits at least one of the species
3. *Mutualism*: a relationship in which both species benefit: *commensalism*: a relationship in which one species benefits and the other species is neither helped nor harmed; *parasitism*: a relationship in which one organism lives on or inside another organism and harms it
4. By staying motionless among a plant's branches, the walking stick is camouflaged and cannot easily be seen by predators.
5. *Similarity:* One organism (the parasite or the predator) benefits, while the other organism (the host or the prey) is harmed. *Difference:* In parasitism, the parasite usually does not kill the host, whereas in predation, the predator kills the prey.

....
Check Your Progress

CHAPTER PROJECT

Distribute Chapter 1 Project Worksheet 2, which is designed to help students prepare their written reports and graphs. All groups should graph the data they collected on plant height; some groups may want to create additional graphs for the numbers of leaves and buds. (See Chapter 22 Project Teacher Notes, Unit 5 Resources page 3, for information on graphing possibilities.)

Performance Assessment

Writing Have each student explain how each of the types of interactions among species described in this section affects organisms' survival.

Figure 15 The white objects on this sphinx moth larva are wasp cocoons. When the wasps emerge, they will feed on the larva. *Applying Concepts Which organism in this interaction is the parasite? Which organism is the host?*

Parasitism The third type of symbiosis is called parasitism. **Parasitism** (PA ruh sit iz um) involves one organism living on or inside another organism and harming it. Recall from Chapter 6 that the organism that benefits is called a **parasite.** The organism the parasite lives on or in is called a **host.** The parasite is usually smaller than the host. In a parasitic relationship, the parasite benefits from the interaction while the host is harmed.

Some common parasites you may be familiar with are fleas, ticks, and leeches. These parasites have adaptations that enable them to attach to their host and feed on its blood. Other parasites live inside the host's body, such as tapeworms that live inside the digestive systems of many mammals, such as dogs and wolves.

Unlike a predator, a parasite does not usually kill the organism it feeds on. If the host dies, the parasite loses its source of food. An interesting example of this rule is shown by a species of mite that lives in the ears of moths. The mites almost always live in just one of the moth's ears. If they live in both ears, the moth's hearing is so badly affected that it is likely to be quickly caught and eaten by its predator, a bat.

Section 3 Review

1. How do an organism's adaptations help it to survive?
2. Name and define the three major types of interactions among organisms.
3. List the three types of symbiosis. For each one, explain how the two organisms are affected.
4. A walking stick is an insect that resembles a small twig. How do you think this insect avoids predators?
5. **Thinking Critically Comparing and Contrasting** How are parasitism and predation similar? How are they different?

Program Resources

◆ **Unit 5 Resources** 22-3 Review and Reinforce, p. 19; 22-3 Enrich, p. 20

Check Your Progress

CHAPTER PROJECT

By now you should be making your final observations of your plants and planning your report. How can you present your data in a graph? Think about what you should put on each axis of your graph. (*Hint:* Draft the written portion of your report early enough to look it over and make any necessary changes.)

Answers to Self-Assessment

Caption Question

Figure 15 The wasp is the parasite, and the sphinx moth larva is the host.

SECTION 1 — Living Things and the Environment

Key Ideas

◆ An organism's habitat provides food, water, shelter, and other things the organism needs to live, grow, and reproduce.

◆ An ecosystem includes both biotic and abiotic factors. Abiotic factors found in many environments include water, sunlight, oxygen, temperature, and soil.

◆ A population consists of a single species. The different populations living together in one area make up a community. The community plus abiotic factors form an ecosystem.

◆ Ecologists study how the biotic and abiotic factors interact within an ecosystem.

Key Terms

ecosystem	population
habitat	community
biotic factor	ecology
abiotic factor	

SECTION 2 — Studying Populations

INTEGRATING **MATHEMATICS**

Key Ideas

◆ Ecologists can estimate population size by direct and indirect observations, sampling, and mark-and-recapture studies.

◆ A population changes in size as a result of changes in the birth rate or death rate, or when organisms move into or out of the population.

◆ Population size is controlled by limiting factors such as food, space, and weather conditions.

Key Terms

population density	immigration
estimate	emigration
birth rate	limiting factor
death rate	carrying capacity

SECTION 3 — Interactions Among Living Things

Key Ideas

◆ Over time, species of organisms develop specialized adaptations and behaviors that help them succeed in their environments.

◆ The major types of interactions among organisms are competition, predation, and symbiosis.

◆ Symbiosis is a close relationship between two species. The three types of symbiotic relationships are mutualism, commensalism, and parasitism.

Key Terms

niche	prey	parasitism
competition	symbiosis	parasite
predation	mutualism	host
predator	commensalism	

Organizing Information

Concept Map Copy the concept map about interactions among organisms onto a sheet of paper. Complete it and add a title. (For more on concept maps, see the Skills Handbook.)

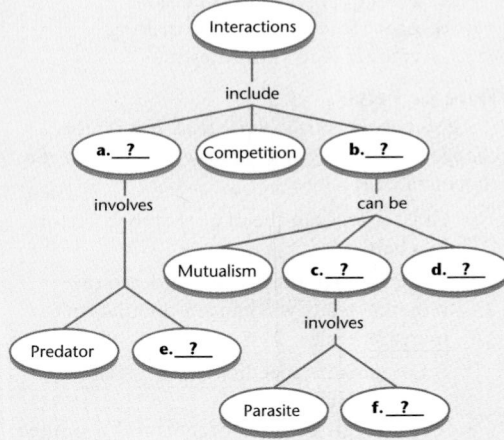

Organizing Information

Concept Map a. Predation b. Symbiosis c. Parasitism d. Commensalism e. Prey f. Host. Sample title: Types of Interactions Among Organisms

Program Resources

◆ **Unit 5 Resources** Chapter 22 Project Scoring Rubric, p. 8
◆ **Performance Assessment** Chapter 22, pp. 68–70
◆ **Chapter and Unit Tests** Chapter 22 Test, pp. 104–107

Media and Technology

Interactive Student Tutorial CD-ROM Chapter 22

Computer Test Bank Chapter 22 Test

711

Reviewing Content
Multiple Choice
1. a **2.** b **3.** c **4.** b **5.** c

True or False
6. biotic **7.** true **8.** true **9.** competition
10. host

Checking Concepts
11. Sample answer: *Biotic:* trees, birds *Abiotic:* sunlight, soil
12. Plants and algae use the energy of sunlight to combine water and carbon dioxide to make their own food in photosynthesis. All living things feed directly or indirectly on plants and algae.
13. Ecologists count the number of organisms in a small area, then multiply by the number of units in the entire area to estimate the total population.
14. Limited space may make it impossible for all members of the population to find places to breed or make nests.
15. Any two: *Camouflage:* The organism blends in with its surroundings, making it difficult for predators to see. *Protective covering:* The organism's spines, shell, or other outer covering makes it painful or difficult for predators to eat it. *Warning coloring:* An organism that is poisonous has bright colors to warn predators not to eat it. *Mimicry:* A harmless organism looks like another organism that predators have learned not to eat. *False coloring:* False "eyes" or other structures fool predators into attacking the wrong part of an organism.
16. Students' descriptions will vary. Make sure they describe several biotic and abiotic factors on which they depend for survival—plants and animals they use for food, for example—and interactions with other species, such as pets, insects carrying diseases that can infect humans, and the like.

Thinking Critically
17. It is usually not possible to study the entire population of the species because it is too spread out. In addition, because the organism's interaction with other organisms and the environment is specific to that environment, studying a population produces more accurate results than studying an entire species.

Reviewing Content

 For more review of key concepts, see the Interactive Student Tutorial CD-ROM.

Multiple Choice
Choose the letter of the best answer.

1. Which of the following is *not* an example of a population?
  a. the pets in your neighborhood
  b. the people in a city
  c. the rainbow trout in a stream
  d. the ants in an anthill
2. A prairie dog, a hawk, and a badger all are members of the same
  a. habitat. **b.** community.
  c. species. **d.** population.
3. All of the following are examples of limiting factors for populations *except*
  a. space **b.** food
  c. time **d.** weather
4. In which type of interaction do both species benefit?
  a. predation **b.** mutualism
  c. commensalism **d.** parasitism
5. Which of these relationships is an example of parasitism?
  a. a bird building a nest on a tree branch
  b. a bat pollinating a saguaro cactus
  c. a flea living on a cat's blood
  d. *Escherichia coli* bacteria making vitamin K in your intestine

True or False
If the statement is true, write true. If it is false, change the underlined word or words to make the statement true.

6. Grass is an example of a(n) <u>abiotic</u> factor in a habitat.
7. A rise in birth rate while the death rate remains steady will cause a population to <u>increase</u> in size.
8. An organism's specific role in its habitat is called its <u>niche</u>.
9. The struggle between organisms for limited resources is called <u>mutualism</u>.
10. A parasite lives on or inside its <u>predator</u>.

Checking Concepts
11. Name two biotic and two abiotic factors you might find in a forest ecosystem.
12. Explain how sunlight is used by plants and algae. How is this process important to other living things in an ecosystem?
13. Describe how ecologists use the technique of sampling to estimate population size.
14. Give an example showing how space can be a limiting factor for a population.
15. What are two adaptations that prey organisms have developed to protect themselves? Describe how each adaptation protects the organism.
16. Writing to Learn Write a description of your niche in the environment. Include details about your habitat, including both biotic and abiotic factors around you. Be sure to describe your feeding habits as well as any interactions you have with members of other species.

Thinking Critically
17. Making Generalizations Explain why ecologists usually study a specific population of organisms rather than studying the entire species.
18. Problem Solving In a summer job working for an ecologist, you have been assigned to estimate the population of grasshoppers in a field. Propose a method to get an estimate and explain how you would carry it out.
19. Relating Cause and Effect Competition for resources in an area is usually more intense within a single species than between two different species. Can you suggest an explanation for this observation? (*Hint:* Consider how niches help organisms avoid competition.)
20. Comparing and Contrasting Explain how parasitism and mutualism are similar and how they are different.

---

18. Answers may include indirect observation (counting egg clusters), sampling (counting the number in a small area, then multiplying by the number of units in the entire area), or mark and recapture.
19. Within a single species, there is a smaller range of adaptation than between species. Organisms within a species share the same niche. Because individuals within a species are more similar, they will share many of the same advantages and disadvantages in surviving in a certain environment, which intensifies competition for the limited resources.
20. In both parasitism and mutualism, one of the organisms benefits from the interaction. However, in mutualism the other organism also benefits, whereas in parasitism the other organism is harmed.

Applying Skills

Ecologists monitoring a deer population collected data during a 30-year study. Use the data to answer Questions 21–24.

Year	0	5	10	15	20	25	30
Population (thousands)	15	30	65	100	40	25	10

21. Graphing Make a line graph using the data in the table. Plot years on the horizontal axis and population on the vertical axis.

22. Interpreting Data In which year did the deer population reach its highest point? Its lowest point?

23. Communicating Write a few sentences describing how the deer population changed during the study.

24. Developing Hypotheses In Year 16 of the study, this region experienced a very severe winter. How might this have affected the deer population?

Performance CHAPTER PROJECT **Assessment**

Present Your Project Review your report and graph to be sure that they clearly state your conclusion about the effects of crowding on plant growth. With your group, decide how you will present your results. Do a practice run-through to make sure all group members feel comfortable with their part.

Reflect and Record Compare your group's results with those of your classmates. Suggest possible explanations for any differences. How could you have improved your plan for your experiment?

Test Preparation
Use these questions to prepare for standardized tests.

Study the graph. Then answer Questions 25–28.

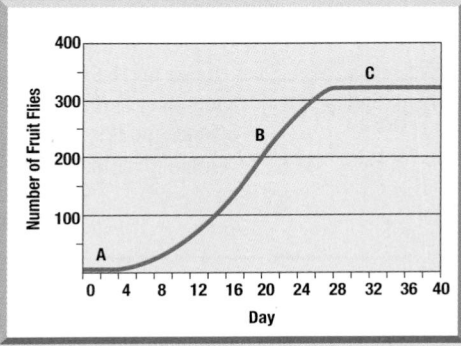

25. What is the best title for this graph?
a. Fruit Fly Population Density
b. Abiotic Factors and Fruit Flies
c. Fruit Fly Population Growth
d. Fruit Fly Death Rate

26. At what point on the graph is the population of fruit flies increasing?
a. Point A   b. Point B
c. Point C   d. none of the above

27. Which of the following statements may be true of the fruit fly population at Point C?
a. The death rate is approximately equal to the birth rate.
b. A limiting factor in the environment is preventing the population from increasing.
c. There may not be enough food or space to support a larger population.
d. All of the above statements may be true.

28. Based on the graph, what is the carrying capacity of the environment in which the fruit flies live?
a. approximately 320 fruit flies
b. approximately 220 fruit flies
c. approximately 410 fruit flies
d. approximately 160 fruit flies

Chapter 22 **713**

Program Resources

◆ **Inquiry Skills Activity Book** Provides teaching and review of all inquiry skills

---

Applying Skills

21.

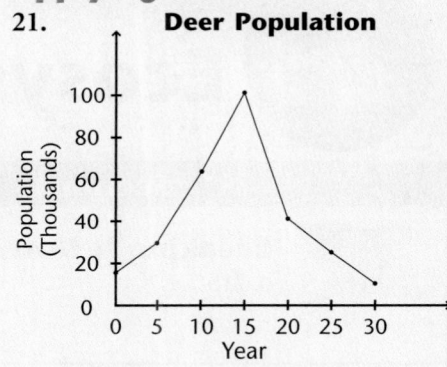

22. *Highest:* Year 15; *lowest:* Year 30

23. *Example:* Beginning with 15,000 deer at the beginning of the study, the population increased steadily through Year 15. From Year 15 through the end of the study, the deer population declined steadily, reaching the population's lowest point, 10,000 deer, in Year 30.

24. The severe winter may have killed weak or injured deer. Food shortages during this winter also may have weakened deer or caused them to starve.

Performance CHAPTER PROJECT **Assessment**

Present Your Project Review each group's written report, and let groups present their results to the rest of the class in a poster, display, or oral report. As indicated in the Scoring Rubric, base your evaluation of each group's report on both the written report and the class presentation.

Reflect and Record After all groups have made their class presentations, allow time for students to compare their results and discuss the factors that may have accounted for any differences.

Test Preparation

25. c **26.** b **27.** d **28.** a

Ecosystems and Biomes

Sections	Time	Student Edition Activities	Other Activities	
CHAPTER PROJECT ▼ **Breaking It Down** p. 715	Ongoing (4 weeks minimum)	Check Your Progress, pp. 722, 727, 745 Present Your Project, p. 753		
1 Energy Flow in Ecosystems pp. 716–722 ◆ Describe the energy roles of organisms in an ecosystem. ◆ Explain food chains and food webs. ◆ Describe how much energy is available at each level of an energy pyramid.	2–3 periods/ 1–1½ blocks	**Discover** Where Did Your Dinner Come From?, p. 716 **Sharpen Your Skills** Observing, p. 718 **Try This** Weaving a Food Web, p. 721	TE	Building Inquiry Skills: Predicting, p. 717; Observing, p. 719
			TE	Real-Life Learning, p. 718
			TE	Using the Visuals: Figure 5, p. 719
			TE	Including All Students, p. 720
			LM	23, "Ecosystem Food Chains"
2 ⬤ *INTEGRATING CHEMISTRY* **Cycles of Matter** pp. 723–727 ◆ Describe the three processes that make up the water cycle. ◆ Describe the carbon-oxygen cycle and the nitrogen cycle.	1–2 periods/ ½–1 block	**Discover** Are You Part of a Cycle?, p. 723 **Sharpen Your Skills** Developing Hypotheses, p. 724	TE	Inquiry Challenge, p. 725
			TE	Using the Visuals: Figure 10, p. 726
			IES	"Where River Meets Sea," pp. 15–16
3 Biogeography pp. 728–731 ◆ Describe some different means that disperse organisms. ◆ Identify the factors that limit the distribution of a species.	1–2 periods/ ½–1 block	**Discover** How Can You Move a Seed?, p. 728 **Science at Home,** p. 731	TE	Integrating Earth Science, p. 729 ⬤
			IES	"Where River Meets Sea," pp. 28–29
4 Earth's Biomes pp. 732–745 ◆ List and describe Earth's major land biomes. ◆ List and describe Earth's major freshwater and ocean biomes.	3 periods/ 1½ blocks	**Real-World Lab: How It Works** Biomes in Miniature, pp. 732–733 **Discover** How Much Rain Is That?, p. 734 **Try This** Desert Survival, p. 737 **Sharpen Your Skills** Inferring, p. 739 **Sharpen Your Skills** Interpreting Data, p. 741	TE	Building Inquiry Skills: Communicating, p. 735; Making Models, pp. 736, 738; Inferring, pp. 739, 744
			TE	Inquiry Challenge, p. 741
			TE	Real-Life Learning, p. 742
5 Succession pp. 746–750 ◆ Describe the differences between primary and secondary succession.	1–2 periods/ ½–1 block	**Skills Lab: Observing** Change in a Tiny Community, pp. 746–747 **Discover** What Happened Here?, p. 748 **Science at Home,** p. 750	TE	Building Inquiry Skills: Observing, p. 749
Study Guide/Chapter Assessment pp. 751–753	1 period/ ½ block		ISAB	Provides teaching and review of all inquiry skills

For Standard or Block Schedule The Resource Pro® CD-ROM gives you maximum flexibility for planning your instruction for any type of schedule. Resource Pro® contains Planning Express®, an advanced scheduling program, as well as the entire contents of the Teaching Resources and the Computer Test Bank.

CHAPTER PLANNING GUIDE

Program Resources	Assessment Strategies	Media and Technology
UR Chapter 23 Project Teacher Notes, pp. 26–27 **UR** Chapter 23 Project Overview and Worksheets, pp. 28–31	**SE** Performance Assessment: Present Your Project, p. 753 **TE** Check Your Progress, pp. 722, 727, 745 **UR** Chapter 23 Project Scoring Rubric, p. 32	Science Explorer Internet Site at www.phschool.com
UR 23-1 Lesson Plan, p. 33 **UR** 23-1 Section Summary, p. 34 **UR** 23-1 Review and Reinforce, p. 35 **UR** 23-1 Enrich, p. 36	**SE** Section 1 Review, p. 722 **TE** Ongoing Assessment, pp. 717, 719, 721 **TE** Performance Assessment, p. 722	Life Science Videotape 5; Videodisc Unit 6 Side 2, "The Wonder of Ngorongoro" Audio CD, English-Spanish Summary 23-1 Transparencies 81, "Exploring a Food Web"; 82, "An Energy Pyramid" Interactive Student Tutorial CD-ROM, Chapter 23
UR 23-2 Lesson Plan, p. 37 **UR** 23-2 Section Summary, p. 38 **UR** 23-2 Review and Reinforce, p. 39 **UR** 23-2 Enrich, p. 40	**SE** Section 2 Review, p. 727 **TE** Ongoing Assessment, p. 725 **TE** Performance Assessment, p. 727	Life Science Videotape 5; Videodisc Unit 6 Side 2, "Cycles in Nature" Audio CD, English-Spanish Summary 23-2 Transparencies 83, "The Water Cycle"; 84, "The Carbon and Oxygen Cycles"; 85, "The Nitrogen Cycle"
UR 23-3 Lesson Plan, p. 41 **UR** 23-3 Section Summary, p. 42 **UR** 23-3 Review and Reinforce, p. 43 **UR** 23-3 Enrich, p. 44	**SE** Section 3 Review, p. 731 **TE** Ongoing Assessment, p. 729 **TE** Performance Assessment, p. 731	Life Science Videotape 5; Videodisc Unit 5 Side 2, "Extinction" Audio CD, English-Spanish Summary 23-3
UR 23-4 Lesson Plan, p. 45 **UR** 23-4 Section Summary, p. 46 **UR** 23-4 Review and Reinforce, p. 47 **UR** 23-4 Enrich, p. 48 **UR** Chapter 23 Real-World Lab, pp. 53–55	**SE** Section 4 Review, p. 745 **TE** Ongoing Assessment, pp. 735, 737, 739, 741, 743 **TE** Performance Assessment, p. 745	Life Science Videotape 5; Videodisc Unit 6 Side 2, "Earth's Many Biomes" Audio CD, English-Spanish Summary 23-4
UR 23-5 Lesson Plan, p. 49 **UR** 23-5 Section Summary, p. 50 **UR** 23-5 Review and Reinforce, p. 51 **UR** 23-5 Enrich, p. 52 **UR** Chapter 23 Skills Lab, pp. 56–57	**SE** Section 5 Review, p. 750 **TE** Ongoing Assessment, p. 749 **TE** Performance Assessment, p. 750	Audio CD, English-Spanish Summary 23-5 Transparency 86, "Primary and Secondary Succession"
RCA Provides strategies to improve science reading skills **GSW** Provides worksheets to improve student comprehension of content	**SE** Chapter 23 Study Guide/Assessment, pp. 751–753 **PA** Chapter 23 Performance Assessment, pp. 71–73 **CUT** Chapter 23 Test, pp. 108–111 **CTB** Chapter 23 Test	Interactive Student Tutorial CD-ROM, Chapter 23 Computer Test Bank, Chapter 23 Test

Key: **SE** Student Edition
CTB Computer Test Bank
ISAB Inquiry Skills Activity Book
GSW Guided Study Worksheets

TE Teacher's Edition
PTA Product Testing Activities by *Consumer Reports*
RCA Reading in the Content Area
PA Performance Assessment

UR Unit Resources
LM Laboratory Manual
IES Interdisciplinary Explorations Series
CUT Chapter and Unit Tests

Meeting the National Science Education Standards and AAAS Benchmarks

National Science Education Standards	Benchmarks for Science Literacy	Unifying Themes
Science As Inquiry (Content Standard A) ◆ **Design and conduct a scientific experiment** Students investigate the effects of variables on decomposition. *(Chapter Project)* ◆ **Develop descriptions, explanations, predictions, and models using evidence** Students investigate how abiotic factors create different biomes. Students observe how a community changes over time. *(Real-World Lab; Skills Lab)* **Life Science** (Content Standard C) ◆ **Populations and ecosystems** Students observe the role of soil organisms on decomposition. An organism's energy role in an ecosystem may be that of producer, consumer, or decomposer. Producers use carbon from carbon dioxide to produce other carbon-containing molecules. Biogeography is the study of where organisms live. Students observe how climate affects biomes. A biome is a group of ecosystems with similar climates and organisms. Students observe succession in a pond community. Succession is the series of predictable changes that occur in a community over time. *(Chapter Project; Sections 1, 2, 3, 4, 5; Real-World Lab; Skills Lab)* **Earth and Space Science** (Content Standard D) ◆ **Structure of the Earth system** The water cycle is the continuous process by which water moves from Earth's surface to the atmosphere and back. Primary succession is the series of changes that occur in an area where no ecosystem previously existed. *(Sections 2, 5)*	**1B** **Scientific Inquiry** Students investigate the effects of different variables on decomposition. Students investigate how abiotic factors create different biomes. Students observe how a community changes over time. *(Chapter Project; Real-World Lab; Skills Lab)* **4B** **The Earth** The water cycle is the continuous process by which water moves from Earth's surface to the atmosphere and back. *(Section 2)* **4C** **Processes That Shape the Earth** Primary succession is the series of changes that occur in an area where no ecosystem previously existed. *(Section 5)* **5A** **Diversity of Life** A food web consists of many overlapping food chains in an ecosystem. *(Section 1)* **5D** **Interdependence of Life** Students observe the role of soil organisms on decomposition. An organism's energy role in an ecosystem may be that of producer, consumer, or decomposer. Biogeography is the study of where organisms live. Students observe how climate affects biomes. A biome is a group of ecosystems with similar climates and organisms. Succession is the series of predictable changes that occur in a community over time. *(Chapter Project; Sections 1, 3, 4, 5; Real-World Lab)* **5E** **Flow of Matter and Energy** The most energy is available at the producer level. Producers use carbon from carbon dioxide to produce other carbon-containing molecules. Students observe succession in a pond community. *(Sections 1, 2; Skills Lab)*	◆ **Energy** Energy first enters most ecosystems as sunlight. Unlike matter, energy is not recycled in an ecosystem. *(Sections 1, 2)* ◆ **Evolution** The movement of the continents has had a great impact on the distribution and development of species. *(Section 3)* ◆ **Modeling** Students build model compost chambers to investigate decomposition. Students model abiotic factors to study different biomes. Students use a model pond community to observe succession. *(Chapter Project; Real-World Lab; Skills Lab)* ◆ **Patterns of Change** Water, oxygen, carbon, and nitrogen cycle continuously through an ecosystem. Succession is the series of predictable changes that occur in a community over time. *(Sections 2, 5; Skills Lab)* ◆ **Stability** Matter is recycled in ecosystems. Biomes are areas with similar climates and organisms. *(Sections 2, 4)* ◆ **Systems and Interactions** Students investigate decomposition. Each organism has a role in the movement of energy. One factor that can limit dispersal of a species is competition. The types of plants determine the kinds of animals that live in an area. *(Chapter Project; Sections 1, 3, 4)* ◆ **Unity and Diversity** An organism's energy role may be that of a producer, consumer, or decomposer. Ecologists classify ecosystems into land and water biomes. The two kinds of succession are primary succession and secondary succession. *(Sections 1, 4, 5)*

Take It to the Net

 *Interactive text* at www.phschool.com

Science Explorer comes alive with iText.

■ **Complete student text** is accessible from any computer with Internet access or a CD-ROM drive.

■ **Animations, simulations, and videos** enhance student understanding and retention of concepts.

■ **Self-tests and online study tools** assess student understanding.

STAY CURRENT with

Find out the latest research and information about ecology at:
www.phschool.com

Go to **www.phschool.com** and click on the Science icon. Then click on Science Explorer: Life, Earth, and Physical Science under PH@school.

ACTIVITY	Time (minutes)	Materials — Quantities for one work group	Skills
Section 1			
Discover, p. 716	10	No special materials are required.	Classifying
Sharpen Your Skills, p. 718	5	**Consumable** slice of bread, water, sealable plastic bag, tape	Observing
Try This, p. 721	10–15	**Consumable** long pieces of yarn	Making Models
Section 2			
Discover, p. 723	5	**Nonconsumable** small mirror	Inferring
Sharpen Your Skills, p. 724	5	No special materials are required.	Developing Hypotheses
Section 3			
Discover, p. 728	10–15	**Consumable** corn kernels, water, straw, tape **Nonconsumable** shallow pan	Predicting
Science at Home, p. 731	home	**Consumable** potting soil, water **Nonconsumable** thick white sock, pan	Classifying
Section 4			
Real-World Lab, pp. 732–733	30; 5–10 × 5 days	**Consumable** tape; index card; 10 impatiens seeds; 5 lima bean seeds; 30 rye grass seeds; empty, clean cardboard milk carton; sandy soil or potting soil; clear plastic wrap **Nonconsumable** scissors, lamp, stapler	Making Models, Observing, Drawing Conclusions
Discover, p. 734	20	**Consumable** adding-machine paper, masking tape **Nonconsumable** meter stick, scissors	Developing Hypotheses
Try This, p. 737	10	**Nonconsumable** small potted cactus, hand lens, scissors	Observing
Sharpen Your Skills, p. 739	5	No special materials are required.	Inferring
Sharpen Your Skills, p. 741	10	No special materials are required.	Interpreting Data
Section 5			
Skills Lab, pp. 746–747	15; 20 × 3 days	**Consumable** hay solution, pond water **Nonconsumable** small baby-food jar, wax pencil, plastic dropper, microscope slide, coverslip, microscope	Observing, Comparing and Contrasting, Drawing Conclusions
Discover, p. 748	10	No special materials are required.	Posing Questions
Science at Home, p. 750	home	**Nonconsumable** tape recorder (optional)	Communicating

A list of all materials required for the Student Edition activities can be found on pages T25–T33. You can obtain information about ordering materials by calling 1-800-848-9500 or by accessing the Science Explorer Internet site at **www.phschool.com**.

Breaking It Down

In Chapter 23, students study organisms' energy roles in ecosystems. The Chapter 23 Project focuses on decomposition, the process in which organic matter is broken down into simpler molecules, returning raw materials to the environment.

Purpose Each student or student group will construct two compost chambers and investigate how one variable affects decomposition. This project gives students an opportunity to apply the procedures involved in scientific experimentation. This project is challenging in that students must choose which variable to investigate and then design an experiment on their own. To complete the project successfully, students will identify and control variables, monitor changes in the compost chambers, record observations, analyze data, draw conclusions, and communicate their results to the class.

Skills Focus After completing the Chapter 23 Project, students will be able to
◆ make a model compost chamber;
◆ design an experiment to test the effect of one variable on decomposition;
◆ observe, measure, and record changes in the composted material;
◆ communicate experimental procedures and results in a report, poster, or other product.

Project Time Line This project requires at least four weeks to complete. During the first phase, each student or group will choose one variable to investigate (moisture, oxygen, temperature, or activity of soil organisms), design the experiment, and construct the compost chambers. At the end of Section 2, students will add organic material to the chambers and begin the experiment. While students study Sections 3 and 4, they will observe the decomposition process occurring in the two chambers and record data daily. At the end of Section 4, students will analyze the data collected and prepare their reports.

CHAPTER
23 Ecosystems and Biomes

WEB ACTIVITY www.phschool.com

Integrating Chemistry

SECTION 1	SECTION 2	SECTION 3
Energy Flow in Ecosystems	Cycles of Matter	Biogeography
Discover Where Did Your Dinner Come From?	Discover Are You Part of a Cycle?	Discover How Can You Move a Seed?
Sharpen Your Skills Observing	Sharpen Your Skills Developing Hypotheses	Science at Home Sock Walk
Try This Weaving a Food Web		

714

Possible Materials

◆ Each student or group will need to build two compost chambers—one as the control and the other as the test chamber in which the chosen variable is changed. Instructions for building the chambers are provided on the Chapter 23 Project Student Worksheet, pages 30–31 in Unit 5 Resources.
◆ Provide chopped leaves as the base material to be composted. You may wish to add other types of organic waste, such as eggshells, paper, grass clippings, and orange peels, or nonorganic waste such as bottle caps or plastic foam pieces. This will allow students to make predictions about decomposition.
◆ Provide garden soil (not commercial potting soil) and earthworms for groups that choose to investigate the effect of soil organisms.
◆ Set aside suitable locations in the classroom where students can leave their compost chambers during the experiments.

Breaking It Down

Nothing in this toad's ecosystem is wasted. Even when the living things die, they will be recycled by other organisms like the mushrooms. This natural breakdown process is called decomposition. In this chapter, you will study decomposition and other processes in ecosystems.

When fallen leaves and other waste products decompose, a fluffy, brown mixture called compost is formed. You can observe decomposition firsthand by building a compost chamber.

Your Goal To design an experiment to learn more about the process of decomposition.

To complete your project successfully, you must
◆ build two compost chambers
◆ investigate the effect of one of the following variables on decomposition: moisture, oxygen, temperature, or activity of soil organisms
◆ analyze your data and present your results
◆ follow the safety guidelines in Appendix A

Get Started Your teacher will provide you with a sample of compost material. Observe the wastes in the mixture with a hand lens. Write a hypothesis about which kinds of waste will decay and which will not. Begin thinking about which variable you will test.

Check Your Progress You'll be working on this project as you study this chapter. To keep your project on track, look for Check Your Progress boxes at the following points.

Section 1 Review, page 722: Build your compost chambers and design your experimental plan.
Section 2 Review, page 727: Observe your compost chambers and collect data.
Section 4 Review, page 745: Analyze your data.

Present Your Project At the end of the chapter (page 753), you will compare the compost produced in each of your compost chambers. Will your results support your hypothesis?

> This toad is right at home in its habitat. It is surrounded by living leaves, grass, and mushrooms, as well as nonliving rocks, soil, and air.

SECTION 4 **Earth's Biomes**

Real-World Lab **Biomes in Miniature**
Discover **How Much Rain Is That?**
Try This **Desert Survival**
Sharpen Your Skills **Inferring**
Sharpen Your Skills **Interpreting Data**

SECTION 5 **Succession**

Skills Lab **Change in a Tiny Community**
Discover **What Happened Here?**
Science at Home **Succession Interview**

715

Program Resources

◆ **Unit 5 Resources** Chapter 23 Project Teacher Notes, pp. 26–27; Chapter 23 Project Overview and Worksheets, pp. 28–31; Chapter 23 Project Scoring Rubric, p. 32

WEB ACTIVITY www.phschool.com

You will find an Internet activity, chapter self-tests for students, and links to other chapter topics at this site.

Advance Preparation Before introducing the project, construct a compost chamber yourself as a prototype, following the instructions on the Chapter 23 Project Worksheet. Fill the chamber with the compost material, but do not add water. Set your chamber aside until the end of the project so students can compare their composted material with the original material.

Launching the Project Have students read the project description on page 715. Then show and describe the compost chamber you made. Explain that each student or group will need to make two such chambers—a control chamber and a test chamber.

Distribute to students the Chapter 23 Project Overview and Worksheet on pages 28–31 in Unit 5 Resources, and let students review the procedures.

If you divide the class into groups, tell students that every group member should help plan the experiment, make observations, analyze results, and develop the report.

Additional information on guiding the project is provided in Chapter 23 Project Teacher Notes on pages 26–27 in Unit 5 Resources.

Performance Assessment

The Chapter 23 Project Scoring Rubric on page 32 in Unit 5 Resources will help you evaluate how well students complete the Chapter 23 Project. You may want to share the scoring rubric with students so they are clear about what will be expected of them. Students will be assessed on
◆ their ability to design an experiment to test the effect of one variable— moisture, oxygen, temperature, or the presence of soil organisms—on decomposition;
◆ their completeness and accuracy in doing the experiment, making observations, and recording data;
◆ their ability to draw reasonable conclusions based on experimental results and communicate their procedures, results, and conclusions;
◆ their group participation, if they worked in groups.

SECTION
1 Energy Flow in Ecosystems

Objectives

After completing the lesson, students will be able to
- describe the energy roles of organisms in an ecosystem;
- explain food chains and food webs;
- describe how much energy is available at each level of an energy pyramid.

Key Terms producer, consumer, herbivore, carnivore, omnivore, scavenger, decomposer, food chain, food web, energy pyramid

1 Engage/Explore

Activating Prior Knowledge

Help students recall what they learned in the previous chapter by asking: **What is an ecosystem?** *(All the living and nonliving things that interact in a particular area)* **What are some things you learned about ecosystems in the last chapter?** *(Major concepts include habitat, biotic and abiotic factors, levels of organization, methods of determining population size, the causes of changes in population size, limiting factors, adaptations, and types of interactions among organisms.)*

•••••••• DISCOVER ••••••••

Skills Focus classifying
Time 10 minutes
Tips Circulate among students as they work to answer questions about the sources or ingredients of some foods.
Expected Outcome As a class, students will undoubtedly cite a wide variety of foods and sources.
Think It Over Answers will vary depending on the foods eaten. Except for students whose families are strict vegetarians and eat no animal products of any kind, most students will probably cite both plant and animal sources and possibly fungi, protists, or monerans.

716

SECTION
1 Energy Flow in Ecosystems

DISCOVER •••••••••••••••••••••••••••• **ACTIVITY**

Where Did Your Dinner Come From?

1. Across the top of a page, list the different types of foods you ate for dinner last night.
2. Under each item, write the name of the plant, animal, or other organism that is the source of that food. Some foods have more than one source. For example, bread is made from flour (which is made from a plant such as wheat) and yeast (which is a fungus).

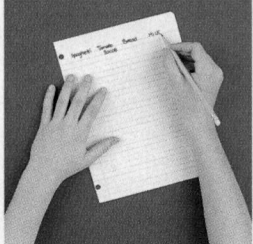

Think It Over
Classifying Count all the different organisms that contributed to your dinner. How many of your food sources were plants? How many were animals?

GUIDE FOR READING

- What energy roles do organisms play in an ecosystem?
- How much energy is available at each level of an energy pyramid?

Reading Tip As you read, create a flowchart showing one possible path of energy through an ecosystem.

P ushing off from its perch on an oak tree limb, the kestrel glides over a field dotted with yellow flowers. In the middle of the field, the bird pauses. It hovers above the ground like a giant hummingbird. Despite strong gusts of wind, the bird's head remains steady as it looks for prey. It takes a lot of energy for the kestrel to hover in this way, but from this position it can search the field below for food.

Soon the kestrel spots a mouse munching the ripening seedhead of a blade of grass. Seconds later the kestrel swoops down and grasps the mouse in its talons. The bird carries the mouse back to the tree to feed.

Meanwhile, a lynx spider hides among the petals of a nearby flower. An unsuspecting bee lands on the flower for a sip of nectar. The spider grabs the bee and injects its venom into the bee's body. The venom kills the bee before it can respond with its own deadly sting.

This sunny field is an ecosystem, made up of living and nonliving things that interact with one another. You can see that many interactions in this ecosystem involve eating. The spider eats a bee that eats nectar, while the kestrel eats a mouse that eats grass. Ecologists study such feeding patterns to learn how energy flows within an ecosystem.

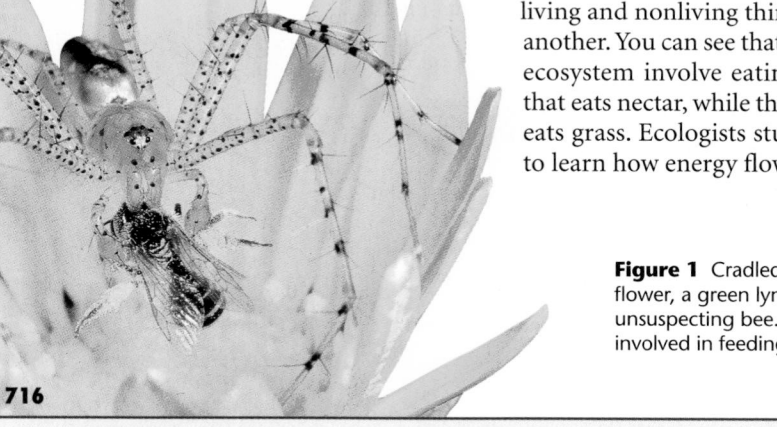

Figure 1 Cradled in a gumweed flower, a green lynx spider attacks an unsuspecting bee. These organisms are involved in feeding interactions.

716

READING STRATEGIES

Reading Tip Point out that energy flow in an ecosystem is usually indicated by drawing an arrow *from* the organism being eaten *to* the organism doing the eating, as shown in Figure 5 on page 719. Let students complete their flowcharts without any further assistance. One possible flowchart would be leaf→caterpillar→bird→cat

Study and Comprehension After students have read about food chains and food webs, have each student write a paragraph describing the food chain shown in Figure 5. They should incorporate the terms *producer, herbivore, carnivore, first-level consumer,* and *second-level consumer.* In a follow-up discussion, ask students to share their paragraphs.

Energy Roles

Do you play an instrument in your school band? If so, you know that each instrument has a role in a piece of music. For instance, the flute may provide the melody, while the drum provides the beat. Although the two instruments are quite different, they both play important roles in creating the band's music. In the same way, each organism has a role in the movement of energy through its ecosystem. This role is part of the organism's niche in the ecosystem. The kestrel's role is different from that of the giant oak tree where it was perched. But all parts of the ecosystem, like all parts of the band, are necessary for the ecosystem to work.

An organism's energy role is determined by how it obtains energy and how it interacts with the other living things in its ecosystem. **An organism's energy role in an ecosystem may be that of a producer, consumer, or decomposer.**

Producers Energy first enters most ecosystems as sunlight. Some organisms, such as plants, algae, and some bacteria, are able to capture the energy of sunlight and store it as food energy. These organisms use the sun's energy to turn water and carbon dioxide into molecules such as sugars and starches through photosynthesis.

As you have learned, organisms that carry out photosynthesis are called autotrophs. Another word for an organism that can make its own food is a **producer.** Producers are the source of all the food in an ecosystem. For example, the grass and oak tree are the producers for the field ecosystem.

In a few ecosystems the producers obtain energy from a source other than sunlight. One such ecosystem is found in rocks deep beneath the ground. Since the rocks are never exposed to sunlight, how is energy brought into this ecosystem? Certain bacteria in this ecosystem produce their own food using the energy in a gas, hydrogen sulfide, which is found in their environment.

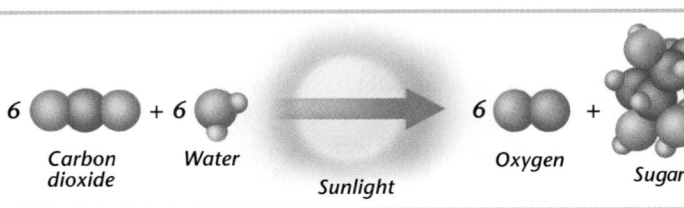

Carbon dioxide **Water** **Sunlight** **Oxygen** **Sugar**

Figure 2 The sunlight streaming through this redwood forest is the source of energy for the ecosystem. Plants convert the sun's energy to stored food energy through the process of photosynthesis.
Interpreting Diagrams What substances are needed for photosynthesis? What substances are produced?

717

Program Resources

◆ **Unit 5 Resources** 23-1 Lesson Plan, p. 33; 23-1 Section Summary, p. 34

Media and Technology

 Audio CD English-Spanish Summary 23-1

Answers to Self-Assessment

Caption Question

Figure 2 The substances needed for photosynthesis are water and carbon dioxide. The substances produced are sugar and oxygen.

2 Facilitate

Energy Roles

Using the Visuals: Figure 2

Focus students' attention on the chemical formula and ask: **What happens during photosynthesis?** (*The plant uses the energy in sunlight to combine carbon dioxide and water to make its own food. Oxygen is also produced.*) **What happens when photosynthetic organisms do not get sunlight?** (*They die because they cannot make food.*) **learning modality: verbal**

Building Inquiry Skills: Predicting

Materials *sheet of cardboard about 30 cm by 40 cm, rock or other heavy object*
Time 10–15 minutes for set-up; 5 minutes for later observation

Give each small group a sheet of cardboard, and take the class outdoors to a grassy area. Have each group select a spot to put the cardboard on the ground, weighting it down with a rock or other heavy object. Ask: **What do you predict will happen to the plants under the cardboard?** (*Accept all responses without comment.*) Let students check under the cardboard each day for a week. Ask: **What happened to the plants?** (*They turned yellow as photosynthesis stopped.*) **What do you predict will happen if you remove the cardboard and allow the plants to receive light again?** (*Accept all responses, then let students test their ideas. The grass will turn green again after a few days.*) **learning modality: visual**

Ongoing Assessment

Drawing Have each student draw a simple diagram to show what happens during photosynthesis and write a brief caption summarizing the process. Students can save their diagrams in their portfolios.

717

Energy Roles, continued

Addressing Naive Conceptions

Many students might think that all ecosystems are dependent on photosynthesis. Ask: **Do you know of any ecosystems in which producers do not depend on sunlight?** Students may be aware of the ecosystem that exists around deep-ocean hydrothermal vents known as "black smokers." If so, ask them to describe this ecosystem. *(Bacteria use chemicals spewed out of the vents to make their own food; the bacteria in turn are food for other organisms such as shrimp and giant clams.)* **learning modality: verbal**

Sharpen your Skills

Observing

Materials *slice of bread, water, sealable plastic bag, tape*
Time 5 minutes for setup
Tips Students will be able to observe changes most easily if they use white sandwich bread.
Expected Outcome After a few days, students should observe mold growing on the bread. Gradually, the mold will cover the bread and cause it to break down.
Extend Have students classify what energy role the mold plays. *(decomposer)* **learning modality: visual**

Real-Life Learning

Ask students: **What examples of herbivores, carnivores, and scavengers have you seen in your own environment?** *(Answers will depend on where students live.)* Suggest that students visit an outdoor area near their homes and sit quietly for a time to observe interactions among organisms. The area can be as simple as a vacant lot or small patch of weeds. Have students list the types of organisms they see, note any feeding behaviors they observe, and classify each organism as an herbivore, carnivore, omnivore, or scavenger. Let students share their lists and classifications in a class discussion. **learning modality: visual**

Figure 3 Consumers are classified by what they eat. **A.** An agile gerenuk stands on its hind legs to reach these leaves. Consumers that eat plants are called herbivores. **B.** Carnivores like this collared lizard eat only animals. **C.** A black vulture is a scavenger, a carnivore that feeds on the remains of dead organisms.

Sharpen your Skills

Observing ACTIVITY

Sprinkle a few drops of water on a slice of bread. Enclose the bread in a sealable plastic bag. Seal the bag tightly with tape and put it in a warm, dark place. Observe the bread daily for about two weeks. **CAUTION:** *Do not open the bag.* Write a few sentences describing the changes you observe. What is responsible for the change?

718

Consumers Recall that other members of an ecosystem, called heterotrophs, cannot make their own food. These organisms depend on the producers for food and energy. Another word for an organism that obtains energy by feeding on other organisms is a **consumer.**

Consumers are classified by what they eat. Consumers that eat only plants are called **herbivores.** This term comes from the Latin words *herba,* which means grass or herb, and *vorare,* which means to eat. Some familiar herbivores are caterpillars, cattle, and deer. Consumers that eat only animals are called **carnivores.** This term comes from the same root word *vorare,* plus the Latin word for flesh, *carnis.* Lions, spiders, and snakes are some examples of carnivores. A consumer that eats both plants and animals is called an **omnivore.** The Latin word *omni* means all. Crows, goats, and most humans are examples of omnivores.

Some carnivores are scavengers. A **scavenger** is a carnivore that feeds on the bodies of dead organisms. Scavengers include catfish and vultures.

Decomposers What would happen if there were only producers and consumers in an ecosystem? As the organisms in the ecosystem continued to take water, minerals, and other raw materials from their surroundings, these materials would begin to run low. If these materials were not replaced, new organisms would not be able to grow.

All the organisms in an ecosystem produce waste and eventually die. If these wastes and dead organisms were not somehow removed from the ecosystem, they would pile up until they

Background

Facts and Figures Other important consumers in ecosystems are detritus feeders, or *detritivores.* These organisms, which are sometimes classified as decomposers, are similar to scavengers in that they feed on the remains of dead animals. Like decomposers, they also consume dead plants, leaf litter, animal wastes, and other organic matter.

Detritus feeders such as snails, crabs, and clams are plentiful in aquatic ecosystems. Detritus feeders on land include land snails, beetles, millipedes, and earthworms. Along with microbial decomposers (fungi and bacteria), detritus feeders break down dead organisms and animal wastes.

overwhelmed the living things. Organisms that break down wastes and dead organisms and return the raw materials to the environment are called **decomposers.** Two major groups of decomposers are bacteria and fungi, such as molds and mushrooms. While obtaining energy for their own needs, decomposers return simple molecules to the environment. These molecules can be used again by other organisms.

☑ *Checkpoint* *How are herbivores and carnivores similar?*

Food Chains and Food Webs

As you have read, energy enters most ecosystems as sunlight, and is converted into sugar and starch molecules by producers. This energy is transferred to each organism that eats a producer, and then to other organisms that feed on these consumers. The movement of energy through an ecosystem can be shown in diagrams called food chains and food webs.

A **food chain** is a series of events in which one organism eats another and obtains energy. You can follow one food chain from the field ecosystem below. The first organism in a food chain is always a producer, such as the grass in the field. The second organism is a consumer that eats the producer, and is called a first-level consumer. The mouse is a first-level consumer. Next, a second-level consumer eats the first-level consumer. The second-level consumer in this example is the kestrel.

A food chain shows one possible path along which energy can move through an ecosystem. But just as you do not eat the same thing every day, neither do most other organisms. Most producers and consumers are part of many food chains. A more realistic way to show the flow of energy through an ecosystem is a food web. A **food web** consists of the many overlapping food chains in an ecosystem.

Figure 4 A cluster of honey mushrooms grows among dead leaves. Mushrooms are familiar decomposers.

Figure 5 These organisms make up one food chain in a field ecosystem. *Classifying Which organism shown is acting as an herbivore? Which is a carnivore?*

Grass **(Producer)**

Mouse **(First-level consumer)**

Kestrel **(Second-level consumer)**

Chapter 23 **719**

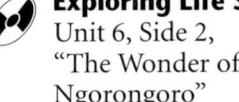

Answers to Self-Assessment

Caption Question

Figure 5 The mouse is acting as an herbivore, and the kestrel is a carnivore.

☑ *Checkpoint*

Herbivores and carnivores are similar in that both are consumers; they cannot make their own food but must obtain food by eating other organisms.

Building Inquiry Skills: Observing

Materials *earthworms, terrarium, potting soil, shredded leaves or grass clippings, water*
Time 15 minutes for set-up

ACTIVITY

Explain to students that earthworms, snails, mites, sowbugs, and many other small animals that live in soil help decompose dead material by breaking it down into smaller pieces. Give students an opportunity to closely observe earthworms by having them set up and maintain a class earthworm farm. Fill a terrarium about two thirds full of potting soil, mix in some shredded leaves or grass clippings, moisten the soil, and add the worms. Students can bury food scraps in the soil periodically and observe how they are broken down by the worms. (Earthworms will not eat meat scraps or bones, but will eat most types of fruits and vegetables cut into small pieces.) At the end of the chapter, students can add the worms and composted soil to an outdoor garden.
learning modality: visual

Food Chains and Food Webs

Using the Visuals: Figure 5

Time 5–10 minutes

ACTIVITY

Ask students: **Why do the arrows in a food-chain diagram point** *from* **the organism being eaten** *to* **the organism doing the eating?** (*To show the flow of energy up through the chain*) Challenge students to use the lists they compiled if they did the Real-Life Learning strategy on page 718 to draw their own food-chain diagrams. If they did not observe enough feeding relationships to diagram a complete chain, suggest that they add other organisms based on their previous knowledge or on research in field guides.
learning modality: visual

Ongoing Assessment

Oral Presentation Randomly ask students to name a type of consumer and explain how it is classified. Ask other students to give examples.

Food Chains and Food Webs, continued

EXPLORING
a Food Web

Call on different students in turn to name the organisms in each food chain shown in the food web, starting with a producer and ending with the top consumer, the fox. As students identify each chain, make a tally mark on the board. When students have identified all the chains, ask: **With just this one top consumer, the fox, how many food chains are in the web?** *(at least 6)* **What are the producers in this food web?** *(grasses, trees, and other plants)* **What are the first- level consumers?** *(rabbit, mouse, grasshopper, and termite)* **What are the second-level consumers?** *(mouse, garter snake, shrew, fox, and woodpecker)* **What are the third-level consumers?** *(garter snake and fox)* **How can the mouse be both a first- and second-level consumer?** *(It's an omnivore that eats both plants and insects.)* **How do the decomposers fit into this food web?** *(Their energy needs are met by consuming the wastes and remains of the other organisms in this food web, and, in turn, they supply raw materials needed by the producers.)* **learning modality: visual**

Including All Students

To help students who are having difficulty understanding the concept of a food web, challenge them to make two or three food-chain diagrams for any ecosystem. Then have students combine their food chains to create a food web. Encourage students to use the same color coding as in *Exploring a Food Web* to indicate the various levels of consumers. Have students identify where the individual food chains overlap in the food web. **learning modality: visual**

720

EXPLORING *a Food Web*

A food web consists of many inter-connected food chains. Trace the path of energy through the producers, consumers, and decomposers.

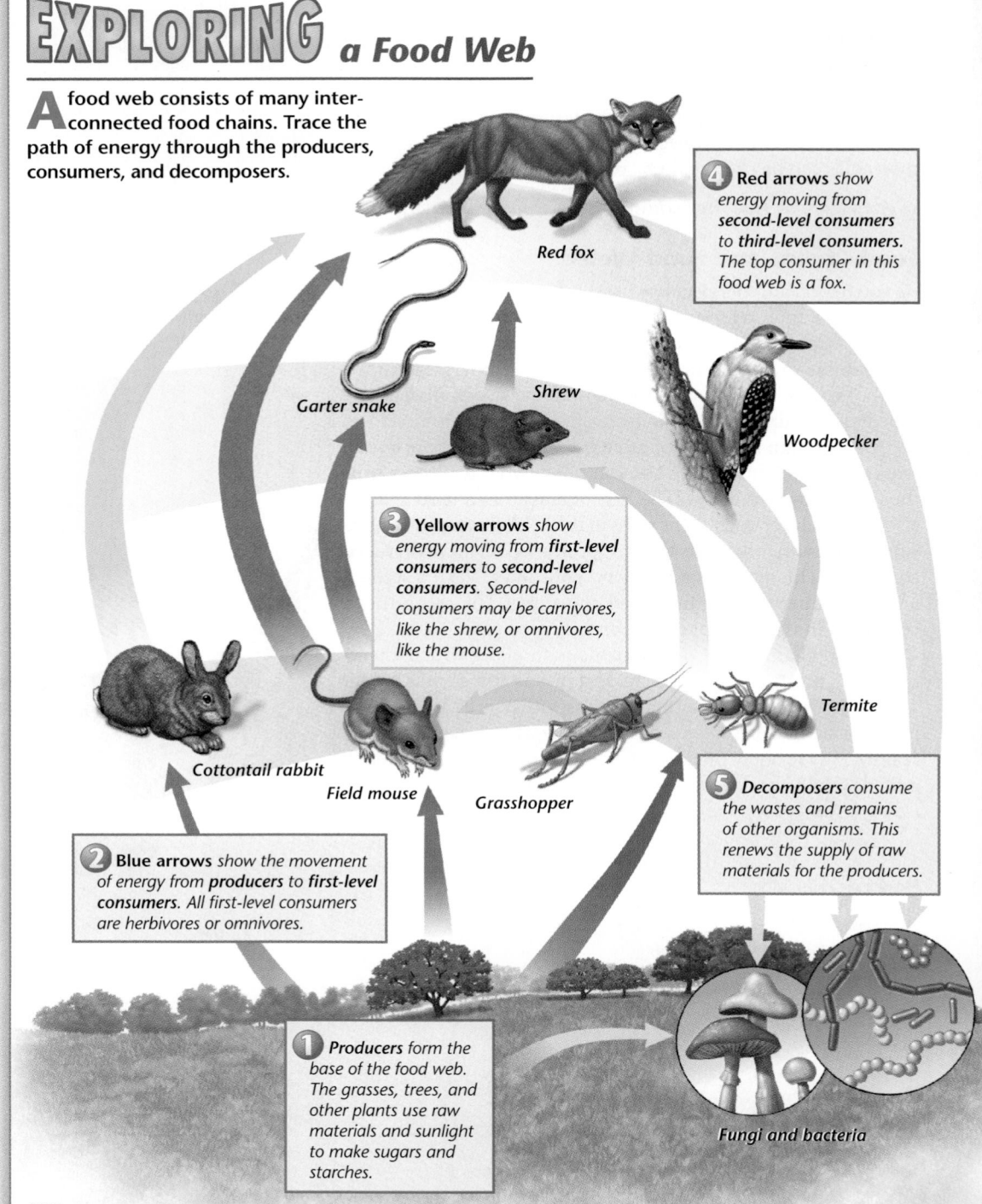

Red fox

4 **Red arrows** *show energy moving from* **second-level consumers** *to* **third-level consumers.** *The top consumer in this food web is a fox.*

Garter snake

Shrew

Woodpecker

3 **Yellow arrows** *show energy moving from* **first-level consumers** *to* **second-level consumers.** *Second-level consumers may be carnivores, like the shrew, or omnivores, like the mouse.*

Cottontail rabbit

Field mouse

Grasshopper

Termite

5 **Decomposers** *consume the wastes and remains of other organisms. This renews the supply of raw materials for the producers.*

2 **Blue arrows** *show the movement of energy from* **producers** *to* **first-level consumers.** *All first-level consumers are herbivores or omnivores.*

1 **Producers** *form the base of the food web. The grasses, trees, and other plants use raw materials and sunlight to make sugars and starches.*

Fungi and bacteria

720

History of Science Unlike energy, toxic substances become more concentrated as they move through a food web. This process, called *biological magnification,* can have dire results. A famous example occurred in Borneo when the World Health Organization sprayed DDT to control malaria-carrying mosquitoes. The DDT also killed wasps that preyed on caterpillars. The caterpillars increased rapidly and devoured the thatched roofs of homes, causing them to collapse.

When more DDT was sprayed indoors to kill house flies, gecko lizards that ate flies were poisoned. The dying lizards in turn were eaten by house cats, who also died. The rat population then increased dramatically, attacking human food supplies and threatening an outbreak of bubonic plague. The government had to parachute healthy cats into villages to control the rats.

In *Exploring a Food Web* on the facing page, you can trace the many food chains in a woodland ecosystem. Note that an organism may play more than one role in an ecosystem. For example, an omnivore such as the mouse is a first-level consumer when it eats grass. But when the mouse eats a grasshopper, it is a second-level consumer.

✓ *Checkpoint* What are the organisms in one food chain shown in the food web on the facing page?

Energy Pyramids

When an organism in an ecosystem eats, it obtains energy. The organism uses some of this energy to move, grow, reproduce, and carry out other life activities. This means that only some of the energy will be available to the next organism in the food web.

A diagram called an **energy pyramid** shows the amount of energy that moves from one feeding level to another in a food web. The organisms at each level use some of the energy to carry out their life processes. **The most energy is available at the producer level. At each level in the pyramid, there is less available energy than at the level below.** An energy pyramid gets its name from the shape of the diagram—wider at the base and narrower at the top, resembling a pyramid.

In general, only about 10 percent of the energy at one level of a food web is transferred to the next, higher, level. The other

Weaving a Food Web

This activity shows how the organisms in a food web are interconnected.

ACTIVITY

1. Your teacher will assign you a role in the food web.
2. Hold one end of each of several pieces of yarn in your hand. Give the other ends of your yarn to the other organisms to which your organism is linked.
3. Your teacher will now eliminate one of the organisms. Everyone who is connected to that organism should drop the yarn connecting them to it.

Making Models How many organisms were affected by the removal of one organism? What does this activity show about the importance of each organism in a food web?

Figure 6 Organisms use energy to carry out their life activities. A lioness uses energy to chase her zebra prey. The zebras use energy to flee.

Answers to Self-Assessment

✓ *Checkpoint*
Students should identify a food chain of three or four organisms shown in the food web.
Sample answer: grass, rabbit, fox

TRY THIS

Skills Focus making models

ACTIVITY

Materials *long pieces of yarn*
Time 10–15 minutes
Tips You can use the food web shown in *Exploring a Food Web*. If you use another food web, be prepared to help students decide which organisms eat and are eaten by other organisms. In Step 3, eliminate either a first- or second-level consumer.
Expected Outcome The number of other organisms affected will depend on the food web you use and the organism you eliminate. In all cases, however, students should recognize that all or most of the food web is affected.
Extend Let students repeat the activity using a different food web.
learning modality: kinesthetic

Energy Pyramids

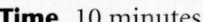

Including All Students

Materials *graph paper, scissors*

ACTIVITY

Time 10 minutes

Use the following activity for students who need more help in visualizing the energy transfers represented by an energy pyramid. Divide the class into groups of three. The first student, the "producer," should cut a 10-by-10 block of squares from graph paper. The block represents the total amount of food energy stored in the producer. The "producer" should then cut a row of 10 squares from the block and pass it to the second student, the "first-level consumer." That student should cut one square from the row and pass it to the third student, the "second-level consumer." Students will see that only a small portion of the original energy stored in the producer reaches the second-level consumer. **learning modality: kinesthetic**

Ongoing Assessment

Writing Have students explain in their own words what happens to energy as it moves from one level to the next in a food web.

3 Assess

Section 1 Review Answers

1. *Producers* use energy, usually in the form of sunlight, to make their own food. *Consumers* obtain energy by eating other living organisms. *Decomposers* obtain energy by breaking down wastes and the remains of dead organisms.

2. Each organism uses 90 percent of the energy for its own life processes. Only 10 percent is available to the next-level consumer.

3. *Herbivores* eat only plants. *Carnivores* eat only animals. *Omnivores* eat both plants and animals. *Scavengers* eat the remains of dead organisms.

4. Sunlight is the energy source for most ecosystems. It is used by organisms to carry out photosynthesis.

5. Most producers and consumers are part of many overlapping food chains.

Check Your Progress   CHAPTER PROJECT

When students prepare their written plans, instruct them to use this format: a statement of the hypothesis, a list of materials, a step-by-step procedure, and a data table for recording results. Review students' plans to make sure they will keep all variables the same for both chambers except for the variable being tested with the second chamber. Also review students' planned data tables.

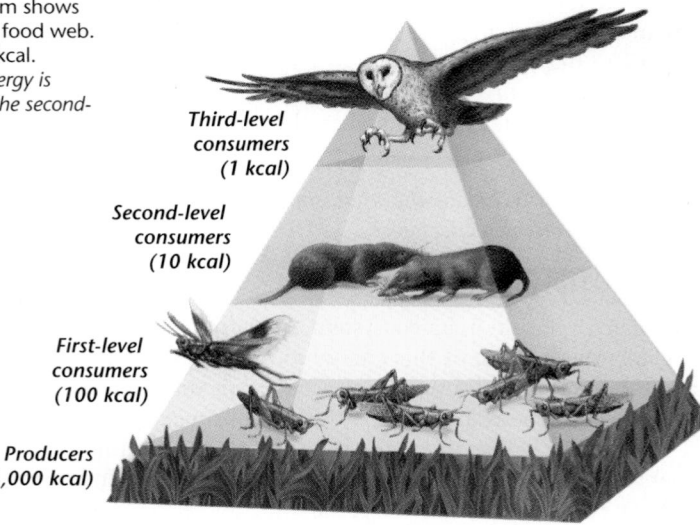

Figure 7 This energy pyramid diagram shows the energy available at each level of a food web. Energy is measured in kilocalories, or kcal. *Calculating How many times more energy is available at the producer level than at the second-level consumer level?*

Third-level consumers (1 kcal)

Second-level consumers (10 kcal)

First-level consumers (100 kcal)

Producers (1,000 kcal)

90 percent of the energy is used for the organism's life processes or is lost as heat to the environment. Because of this, most food webs only have three or four feeding levels. Since 90 percent of the energy is lost at each step, there is not enough energy to support many feeding levels.

But the organisms at higher feeding levels of an energy pyramid do not necessarily require less energy to live than organisms at lower levels. Since so much energy is lost at each level, the amount of energy in the producer level limits the number of consumers the ecosystem can support. As a result, there usually are few organisms at the highest level in a food web.

Section 1 Review

1. Name the three energy roles of organisms in an ecosystem. How does each type of organism obtain energy?

2. How does the amount of available energy change from one level of an energy pyramid to the next level up?

3. Name and define the four types of consumers.

4. What is the source of energy for most ecosystems?

5. **Thinking Critically Making Generalizations** Why are food webs a more realistic way of portraying ecosystems than food chains?

Check Your Progress   CHAPTER PROJECT

By now you should have constructed your compost chambers and chosen a variable to investigate. Design your plan for observing the effect of this variable on the decomposition process. Submit your plan to your teacher for approval. (*Hint:* As part of your plan, include how you will collect data to measure decomposition in your compost chambers.)

Performance Assessment

Drawing Have each student draw a food chain of his or her own choice and label each organism to show *(1)* its energy role, *(2)* whether each consumer is an herbivore, carnivore, omnivore, or scavenger, and *(3)* the percentage of energy available at each level in the food chain.

Program Resources

♦ **Unit 5 Resources** 23-1 Review and Reinforce, p. 35; 23-1 Enrich, p. 36
♦ **Laboratory Manual** 23 "Ecosystem Food Chains"

Media and Technology

Interactive Student Tutorial CD-ROM Chapter 23

Answers to Self-Assessment

Caption Question

Figure 7 There is 100 times as much energy available at the producer level as at the second-level consumer level.

SECTION 2 Cycles of Matter

DISCOVER ··········  ·········· ACTIVITY

Are You Part of a Cycle?

1. Hold a small mirror a few centimeters from your mouth.
2. Exhale onto the mirror.
3. Observe the surface of the mirror.

Think It Over
Inferring What is the substance that forms on the mirror? Where did this substance come from?

A pile of crumpled cars is ready for loading into a giant compactor. Junkyard workers have already removed many of the cars' parts. The aluminum and copper pieces were removed so that they could be recycled, or used again. Now a recycling plant will reclaim the steel in the bodies of the cars. Earth has a limited supply of aluminum, copper, and the iron needed to make steel. Recycling old cars is one way to provide a new supply of these materials.

Recycling Matter

The way matter is recycled in ecosystems is similar to the way the metal in old cars is recycled. Like the supply of metal for building cars, the supply of matter in an ecosystem is limited. If matter could not be recycled, ecosystems would quickly run out of the raw materials necessary for life.

Energy, on the other hand, is not recycled. You must constantly supply a car with energy in the form of gasoline. Ecosystems must also be constantly supplied with energy, usually in the form of sunlight. Gasoline and the sun's energy cannot be recycled—they must be constantly supplied.

As you read in Section 1, energy enters an ecosystem and moves from the producers to the consumers to the decomposers. In contrast, matter cycles through an ecosystem over and over. Matter in an ecosystem includes water, oxygen, carbon, nitrogen, and many other substances. To understand how these substances cycle through an ecosystem, you need to know a few basic terms that describe the structure of matter. Matter is made

GUIDE FOR READING

◆ What three major processes make up the water cycle?
◆ How is carbon dioxide used by producers?

Reading Tip As you read, use the section headings to make an outline of the section.

Cars awaiting recycling at a Utah plant ▼
723

INTEGRATING CHEMISTRY

SECTION 2 Cycles of Matter

Objectives

After completing the lesson, students will be able to
◆ describe the three major processes that make up the water cycle;
◆ describe the carbon-oxygen cycle and the nitrogen cycle .

Key Terms water cycle, evaporation, condensation, precipitation, nitrogen fixation, nodules

1 Engage/Explore

Activating Prior Knowledge

Ask students: **What is a cycle?** *(A series of things that repeat over and over again)* **What are some examples of cycles?** *(Seasons of the year, days of the week, life cycles of plants and animals, and so forth)*

········ DISCOVER ········

Skills Focus inferring
Materials *small mirror*
Time 5 minutes
Tips If the weather is very warm and humid when students do this activity, moisture may not condense on the mirror. In this case, you can cool the mirrors in a refrigerator for a short time beforehand.
Expected Outcome As water vapor from the students' breath cools, tiny droplets of liquid water will condense on the mirrors.
Think It Over Water; it came from water vapor in the students' exhaled breath.

READING STRATEGIES

Reading Tip Students' outlines should include the heads *Recycling Matter, The Water Cycle, The Carbon and Oxygen Cycles,* and *The Nitrogen Cycle.* They may use the purple subheadings as subheads in their outlines. All boldface terms and sentences should appear in the outlines under the appropriate headings.

Program Resources

◆ **Unit 5 Resources** 23-2 Lesson Plan, p. 37; 23-2 Section Summary, p. 38
◆ **Interdisciplinary Exploration Series** "Where River Meets Sea," pp. 15–16

Media and Technology

Audio CD English-Spanish Summary 23-2

2 Facilitate

Recycling Matter

Including All Students

To reinforce the role of decomposers for students who need more help, ask: **What role do decomposers play in recycling matter?** *(They break down living organisms' wastes and dead organisms' remains into simple molecules and return the molecules to the environment so they can be used again.)* **learning modality: verbal**

The Water Cycle

Sharpen your Skills

Developing Hypotheses

Time 5 minutes

Tips Have students do this activity after they have read the section about the water cycle.

Expected Outcome The water droplets on the cold window condensed from the water vapor that evaporated from the boiling water.

Extend Have students draw and label a simple diagram, similar to Figure 8, showing the water cycle operating in this example. For precipitation, students could show tiny water droplets joining to form larger drops that trickle down the window. **learning modality: logical/mathematical**

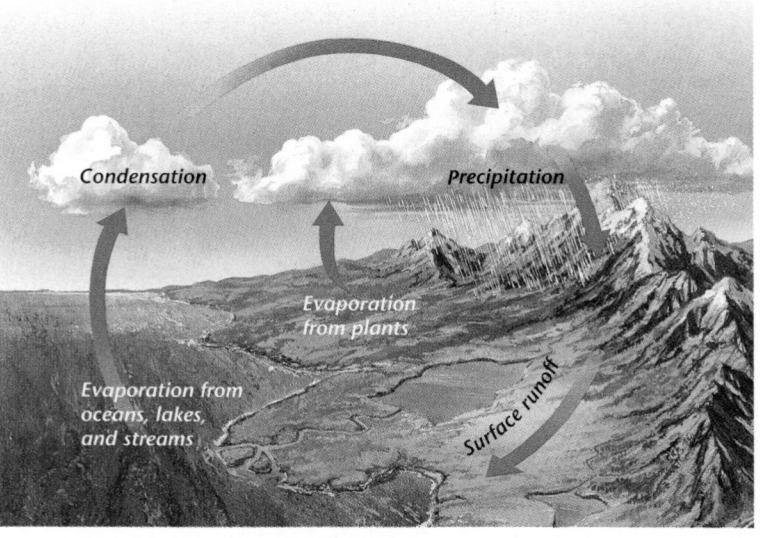

Figure 8 In the water cycle, water moves continuously from Earth's surface to the atmosphere and back. *Interpreting Diagrams In which step of the water cycle does water return to Earth's surface?*

Condensation Precipitation
Evaporation from plants
Evaporation from oceans, lakes, and streams
Surface runoff

Sharpen your Skills

Developing Hypotheses

You're having cocoa at a friend's house on a cold, rainy day. As your friend boils some water, you notice that a window next to the stove is covered with water droplets. Your friend thinks the window is leaking. Using what you know about the water cycle, can you propose another explanation for the water droplets on the window?

up of tiny particles called atoms. Combinations of two or more atoms chemically bonded together are called molecules. For example, a molecule of water consists of two hydrogen atoms bonded to one oxygen atom. In this section, you will learn about some of the most important cycles of matter: the water cycle, the carbon and oxygen cycles, and the nitrogen cycle.

The Water Cycle

How could you determine whether life has ever existed on another planet in the solar system? One piece of evidence scientists look for is the presence of water. This is because water is the most common compound in all living cells on Earth. Water is necessary for life as we know it.

Water is recycled through the water cycle. The **water cycle** is the continuous process by which water moves from Earth's surface to the atmosphere and back. **The processes of evaporation, condensation, and precipitation make up the water cycle**. As you read about these processes, follow the cycle in Figure 8.

Evaporation The process by which molecules of liquid water absorb energy and change to the gas state is called **evaporation.** In the water cycle liquid water evaporates from Earth's surface and forms water vapor, a gas, in the atmosphere. Most water evaporates from the surfaces of oceans and lakes. The energy for evaporation comes from the sun.

Background

Integrating Science In 1998, new photographs of Jupiter's moon Europa revealed shapes and contours that many scientists believe could only be created by liquid water. Pictures taken by the *Voyager* and *Galileo* spacecraft have suggested that a giant ocean lies beneath Europa's permanent layer of ice. Further evidence of water on Europa may come from a NASA mission scheduled for launch in 2003.

Also in 1998, space scientists studying photographs taken by the *Mars Global Surveyor* reported finding a possible ice-covered lake on Mars. Scientists hypothesize that the lake may be similar to lakes in Antarctica where algae and other organisms thrive under a thick layer of ice.

Some water is also given off by living things. For example, plants take in water through their roots and release water vapor from their leaves. You take in water when you drink and eat. You release liquid water in your wastes and water vapor when you exhale.

Condensation What happens next to the water vapor in the atmosphere? As the water vapor rises higher in the atmosphere, it cools down. When it cools to a certain temperature the vapor turns back into tiny drops of liquid water. The process by which a gas changes to a liquid is called **condensation.** The water droplets collect around particles of dust in the air, eventually forming clouds like those in Figure 8.

Precipitation As more water vapor condenses, the drops of water in the cloud grow larger and heavier. Eventually the heavy drops fall back to Earth as a form of **precipitation**—rain, snow, sleet, or hail. Most precipitation falls back into oceans or lakes. The precipitation that falls on land may soak into the soil and become groundwater. Or the precipitation may run off the land, ultimately flowing into a river or ocean once again.

☑ *Checkpoint* *What change of state occurs when water from the surface of the ocean enters the atmosphere as water vapor?*

The Carbon and Oxygen Cycles

Two other chemicals necessary for life are carbon and oxygen. The processes by which they are recycled are linked together, as shown in Figure 9. Carbon is the building block for the matter that makes up the bodies of living things. It is present in the atmosphere in the gas carbon dioxide. Producers take in carbon

Figure 9 This scene shows how the carbon and oxygen cycles are linked together. Producers use carbon dioxide to carry out photosynthesis. In this process, carbon is used to create sugar molecules such as those found in apples. The producers release oxygen, which is then used by other organisms. These organisms take in carbon in food and release it in the form of carbon dioxide again.

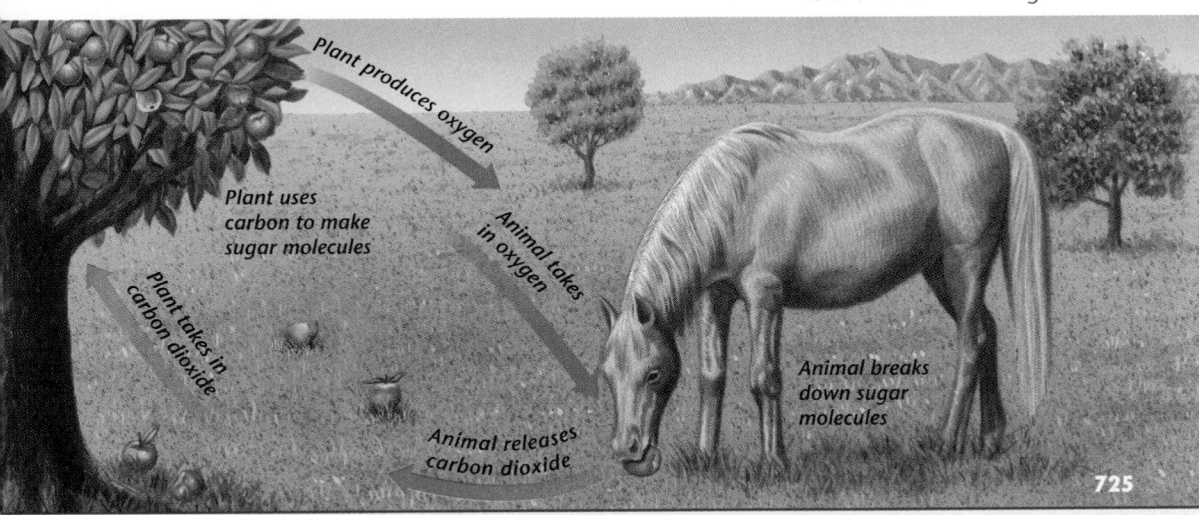

Plant produces oxygen

Plant uses carbon to make sugar molecules

Plant takes in carbon dioxide

Animal takes in oxygen

Animal releases carbon dioxide

Animal breaks down sugar molecules

725

Answers to Self-Assessment
Caption Question
Figure 8 Precipitation
☑ *Checkpoint*
Evaporation (a liquid changes into a gas)

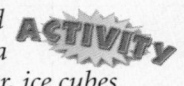

Give each small group a glass jar. Provide the cutoff bottom of a soda bottle, hot water, and ice cubes in a central location. (CAUTION: *Make sure the water is not too hot for students to safely handle.*) Challenge students to use the materials to devise a simple model of the water cycle that shows all three processes—evaporation, condensation, and precipitation. (*Possible model: Fill the jar about half full with hot water, put the soda bottle bottom on top of the jar, and place several ice cubes in the soda bottle bottom. Water vapor will evaporate from the hot water, condense on the underside of the cold soda bottle bottom, and collect into drops large enough to drip back into the jar.*) **learning modality: kinesthetic**

The Carbon and Oxygen Cycles

Building Inquiry Skills: Predicting

Describe for students a sealed jar containing guppies, plants, algae, and snails. Ask: **Which organisms in the jar are producers?** *(The plants and algae)* **What do the producers release when they conduct photosynthesis?** *(oxygen)* **What happens to the oxygen?** *(It is "breathed in" by the guppies and snails.)* **Where do the producers get the carbon dioxide they need?** *(It is released by the guppies and snails.)* **Would you predict that this cycle could go on indefinitely? Why, or why not?** *(Yes; so long as the producers receive sunlight and the guppies and snails receive food, the carbon and oxygen will continue to cycle between the producers and the consumers.)* **learning modality: logical/mathematical**

Ongoing Assessment

Drawing Have each student draw and label a simple diagram of the water cycle without referring to Figure 8.

 Students can save their drawings in their portfolios.

The Nitrogen Cycle

Including All Students

Since students normally think of the word *fixed* as meaning "repaired," they may be confused by the word's other usage in the text. Suggest that they consult dictionaries to find other definitions of *fix* and *fixed*. Then have students suggest a sample sentence illustrating each other meaning—for example, "He looked at me with a fixed stare," "I'll fix lunch now," "I think the game was fixed," and "I'm in a fix!"
limited English proficiency

Using the Visuals: Figure 10

Materials *white and blue index cards, tape*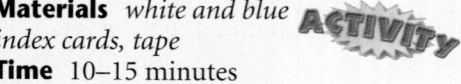
Time 10–15 minutes

To help students understand the nitrogen cycle, let them role-play the materials and organisms shown in the figure. Assign the following roles: air, clover plants, rabbits, nitrogen-fixing bacteria in nodules on the clover's roots, decomposers in the soil, and bacteria in the soil. Give the "air" students white index cards representing free nitrogen. Give the "nodule bacteria" students blue index cards and tape. Begin the cycle with the air students handing white cards to the nodule bacteria students, who attach, or "fix," each white card to one of their blue cards and then hand the cards to the "clover plants." To show that some plants are eaten by consumers, some clover plants should hand their cards to "rabbits." To show that some plants and animals die and decompose, other clover plants and some rabbits should hand their cards to "decomposers," who in turn hand the cards to "soil bacteria." The soil bacteria detach the blue cards from the white cards and hand the white cards back to the air students, completing the cycle.
learning modality: kinesthetic

dioxide from the atmosphere during photosynthesis. **In this process, the producers use carbon from the carbon dioxide to produce other carbon-containing molecules.** These molecules include sugars and starches. To obtain energy from these molecules, consumers break them down into simpler molecules. Consumers release water and carbon dioxide as waste products.

At the same time, oxygen is also cycling through the ecosystem. Producers release oxygen as a result of photosynthesis. Other organisms take in oxygen from the atmosphere and use it in their life processes.

☑ *Checkpoint* How is oxygen returned to the environment?

The Nitrogen Cycle

Like carbon, nitrogen is a necessary building block in the matter that makes up living things. Since the air around you is about 78 percent nitrogen gas, you might think that it would be easy for living things to obtain nitrogen. However, most organisms cannot use the nitrogen gas in the air. Nitrogen gas is called "free" nitrogen, meaning it is not combined with other kinds of atoms. Most organisms can use nitrogen only once it has been "fixed," or combined with other elements to form nitrogen-containing compounds. You can follow this process in Figure 10 below.

Figure 10 In the nitrogen cycle, nitrogen moves from the air to the soil, into living things, and back into the air.
Interpreting Diagrams How do consumers obtain nitrogen?

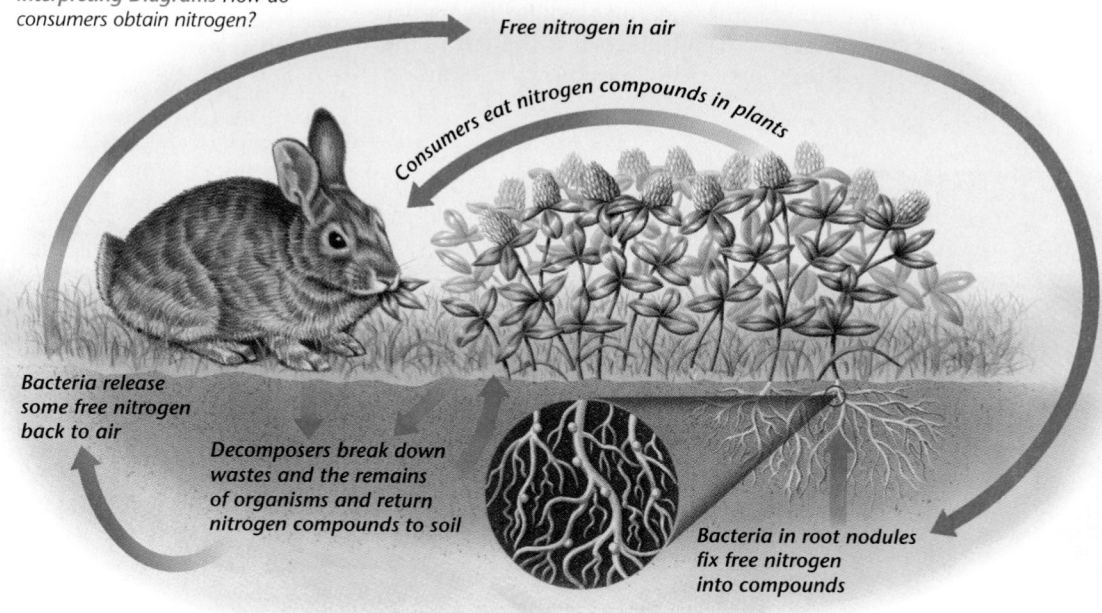

Free nitrogen in air

Consumers eat nitrogen compounds in plants

Bacteria release some free nitrogen back to air

Decomposers break down wastes and the remains of organisms and return nitrogen compounds to soil

Bacteria in root nodules fix free nitrogen into compounds

726

Nitrogen Fixation The process of changing free nitrogen gas into a usable form of nitrogen is called **nitrogen fixation.** Most nitrogen fixation is performed by certain kinds of bacteria. Some of these bacteria live in bumps called **nodules** (NAHJ oolz) on the roots of certain plants. These plants, known as legumes, include clover, beans, peas, alfalfa, and peanuts.

The relationship between the bacteria and the legumes is an example of mutualism. As you recall from Chapter 22, a symbiotic relationship in which both species benefit is called mutualism. Both the bacteria and the plant benefit from this relationship: The bacteria feed on the plant's sugars, and the plant is supplied with nitrogen in a usable form.

 **INTEGRATING TECHNOLOGY** Many farmers make use of the nitrogen-fixing bacteria in legumes to enrich their fields. Every few years, a farmer may plant a legume such as alfalfa in a field. The bacteria in the alfalfa roots build up a new supply of nitrogen compounds in the soil. The following year, the new crops planted in the field benefit from the improved soil.

Return of Nitrogen to the Environment Once the nitrogen has been fixed into chemical compounds, it can be used by organisms to build proteins and other complex substances. Decomposers break down these complex compounds in animal wastes and in the bodies of dead organisms. This returns simple nitrogen compounds to the soil. Nitrogen can cycle from the soil to producers and consumers many times. At some point, however, bacteria break down the nitrogen compounds completely. These bacteria release free nitrogen back into the air. Then the cycle starts again.

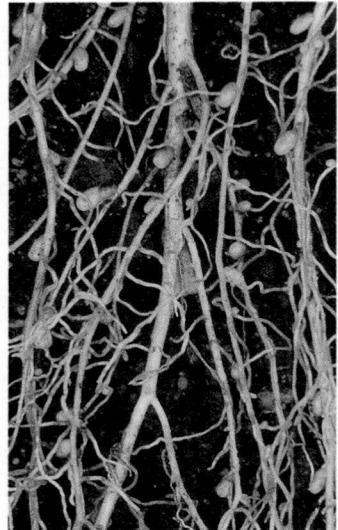

Figure 11 Lumpy nodules are clearly visible on the roots of this clover plant. Bacteria inside the nodules carry out nitrogen fixation.

Section 2 Review

1. Name and define the three major processes that occur during the water cycle.
2. Explain the role of plants in the carbon cycle.
3. How is nitrogen fixation a necessary part of the nitrogen cycle?
4. Where do nitrogen-fixing bacteria live?
5. **Thinking Critically** **Comparing and Contrasting** Explain how the movement of matter through an ecosystem is different from the movement of energy through an ecosystem.

Check Your Progress CHAPTER PROJECT

Once your teacher has approved your plan, place the waste into your compost chambers. Record your hypothesis about the effect of the variable you are investigating. Observe the two containers daily. (*Hint:* If there are no signs of decomposition after several days, you may wish to stir the contents of each chamber. Stirring allows more oxygen to enter the mixture.)

Chapter 23 **727**

Program Resources

◆ **Unit 5 Resources** 23-2 Review and Reinforce, p. 39; 23-2 Enrich, p. 40

Media and Technology

 Transparencies "The Nitrogen Cycle," Transparency 85

Answers to Self-Assessment

☑ *Checkpoint*
Plants and other producers release oxygen as a byproduct of photosynthesis.

Caption Question
Figure 10 They eat nitrogen compounds in plants.

 Integrating Technology

Ask students: **What happens to nitrogen that is fixed in plant roots?** (*The plants take it in and use it for their life processes.*) **How do consumers get the nitrogen?** (*By eating the plants*) **If the plants aren't eaten, what happens to the nitrogen?** (*It enters the soil when the plants die and decompose.*) **learning modality: logical/mathematical**

3 Assess

Section 2 Review Answers

1. *Evaporation:* Liquid water changes into water vapor. *Condensation:* Water vapor cools and changes into liquid water. *Precipitation:* Drops of water fall as rain, snow, sleet, or hail.
2. Plants take in carbon dioxide and produce carbon-containing molecules through photosynthesis.
3. Most organisms cannot use free nitrogen in the atmosphere. Nitrogen fixation combines free nitrogen with other elements to form compounds that organisms can use.
4. They live in the nodules on the roots of legumes.
5. Matter can be recycled over and over again. In contrast, once energy has moved from the producers to the consumers and then to the decomposers, it cannot be recycled. A new supply must be "captured" by the producers.

Check Your Progress CHAPTER PROJECT

Provide compost materials. Remind students to put the same amount of waste in both chambers. CAUTION: *As students do their daily observations, make sure those who are allergic to molds do not sniff or handle the chambers' contents. Remind students to wash their hands after each observation.*

Performance Assessment

Skills Check Have students explain various phrases that you point out in each cycle diagram in this section.

Objectives

After completing the lesson, students will be able to

♦ describe some different means that disperse organisms;

♦ identify the factors that limit the distribution of a species.

Key Terms biogeography, continental drift, dispersal, native species, exotic species, climate

1 Engage/Explore

Activating Prior Knowledge

Ask students: **What are some reasons that animals move from one place to another?** (*Seasonal migration, overpopulation or too much competition in the original area, need for food or water, and so forth*)

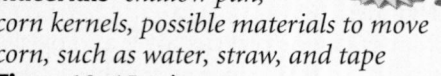 DISCOVER

Skills Focus predicting
Materials *shallow pan, corn kernels, possible materials to move corn, such as water, straw, and tape*
Time 10–15 minutes
Tips Students may have their own ideas about materials to use besides those you have provided.
Expected Outcome Students will find various ways to move the kernels—by pouring water next to them, blowing at them through a straw, picking them up with a piece of tape, and so forth.
Think It Over Based on the results of this activity, students might suggest that seeds are moved by wind, by moving water, and by being caught on an animal's fur or a person's clothing.

728

SECTION 3 Biogeography

DISCOVER •••••••••••••••••••••••••••••••••••••• ACTIVITY

How Can You Move a Seed?

1. Place a few corn kernels at one end of a shallow pan.

2. Make a list of ways you could move the kernels to the other side of the pan. You may use any of the simple materials your teacher has provided.

3. Now try each method. Record whether or not each was successful in moving the kernels across the pan.

Think It Over
Predicting How might seeds be moved from place to place on Earth?

GUIDE FOR READING

♦ How does dispersal of organisms occur?

♦ What factors can limit the distribution of a species?

Reading Tip As you read, look for reasons why organisms live in certain places in the world. Make a list of these reasons.

◄ Australian wallaby

728

Imagine how European explorers must have felt when they saw the continent of Australia for the first time. Instead of familiar grazing animals such as horses and deer, they saw what looked like giant rabbits with long tails. Peering into the branches of eucalyptus trees, these explorers saw bearlike koalas. And who could have dreamed up an egg-laying animal with a beaver's tail, a duck's bill, and a thick coat of fur? You can see why people who heard the first descriptions of the platypus accused the explorers of lying!

Ecologists had many questions about the plants and animals of Australia. Why had no one ever seen a kangaroo, a eucalyptus tree, or a koala in Europe? Why were there no reindeer, camels, or gorillas in Australia?

Different species live in different parts of the world. The study of where organisms live is called **biogeography.** The word *biogeography* is made up of three Greek word roots: *bio*, meaning "life"; *geo*, meaning "Earth"; and *graph*, meaning "description." Together, these root words tell what biogeographers do—they describe where living things are found on Earth.

Continental Drift

INTEGRATING EARTH SCIENCE In addition to studying where species live today, biogeographers also study how these species spread into different parts of the world. One factor that has affected how species are distributed is the motion of Earth's continents. The continents are huge blocks of solid rock floating on a layer of hot, dense liquid. The very slow motion of the continents is called **continental drift.**

READING STRATEGIES

Reading Tip Suggest that students preview the section by scanning the blue-green and purple headings. This should give students an idea of possible reasons why organisms live in certain places. After students have previewed the section, invite volunteers to predict some reasons. Students may offer such reasons as being carried to a place by wind or being carried by water. After students have read the section, lead a discussion of the predictions and ask students to revise and add to the list of reasons why organisms live where they do.

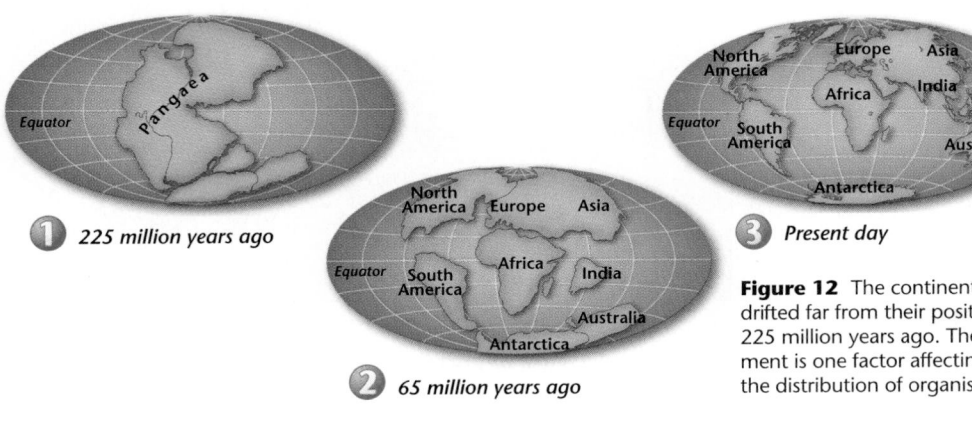

① 225 million years ago

② 65 million years ago

③ *Present day*

Figure 12 The continents have drifted far from their positions 225 million years ago. Their movement is one factor affecting the distribution of organisms.

Figure 12 shows how much the continents have moved. About 225 million years ago, all of today's continents were part of one large land mass called Pangaea. But after millions of years of slow drifting, they have moved to their present locations. Looking at the globe today, it is hard to believe that at one time India was next to Antarctica, or that Europe and North America were once connected.

The movement of the continents has had a great impact on the distribution of species. Consider Australia, for example. Millions of years ago Australia drifted apart from the other land masses. Organisms from other parts of the world could not reach the isolated continent. Kangaroos, koalas, and other unique species developed in this isolation.

Means of Dispersal

The movement of organisms from one place to another is called **dispersal.** Organisms may be dispersed in several different ways. **Dispersal can be caused by wind, water, or living things, including humans.**

Wind and Water Many animals move into new areas by simply walking, swimming, or flying. But plants and small organisms need assistance to move from place to place. Wind provides a means of dispersal for seeds, the spores of fungi, tiny spiders, and many other small, light organisms. Similarly, water transports objects that float, such as coconuts and leaves. Insects and other small animals may get a free ride to a new home on top of these floating rafts.

Other Living Things Organisms may also be dispersed by other living things. For example, a goldfinch may eat seeds in one area and deposit them elsewhere in its wastes. A duck may carry algae or fish eggs on its feet from pond to pond. And if your dog or cat has ever come home covered with sticky plant burs, you know another way seeds can get around.

Figure 13 The stiff brown pods of the milkweed plant contain seeds fringed with silky threads.
Inferring By what means of dispersal are milkweed seeds spread?

Media and Technology

🎧 **Audio CD** English-Spanish Summary 23-3

💿 **Exploring Life Science Videodisc** Unit 5, Side 2, "Extinction"

Chapter 7

Answers to Self-Assessment

Caption Question
Figure 13 By wind

Program Resources

◆ **Unit 5 Resources** 23-3 Lesson Plan, p. 41; 23-3 Section Summary, p. 42

2 Facilitate

Continental Drift

Integrating Earth Science

Materials *world outline map, scissors*
Time 15 minutes

Give each student a copy of a world outline map. Invite students to cut out the continents and arrange them in the positions shown in the first map in Figure 12. Then have students move the continents apart until they are in the locations shown in the second map. Ask: **Where would organisms still be able to move freely from one continent to another?** *(Between North America and Europe/Asia and between Antarctica and Australia)* **Which continents became separated from the others?** *(South America, Africa, India, and Australia/ Antarctica)* Have students move the continents to their present locations in the third map. **What happened to India as continental drift continued?** *(It joined Europe/Asia.)* **What do you think happened to organisms on the continents that remained separated?** *(They evolved into unique species found nowhere else in the world.)* **learning modality: kinesthetic**

Means of Dispersal

Including All Students

If students did the Discover activity at the beginning of this section, connect the activity to the section's content for students who need extra help by asking: **Which of these dispersal methods did you model when you moved the corn kernels?** *(Answers will vary, though most will have modeled all of the methods of dispersal mentioned in the text.)* **learning modality: logical/ mathematical**

Ongoing Assessment

Oral Presentation Call on students at random to describe how wind, water, and living things help disperse organisms.

Social Studies
CONNECTION

Have students brainstorm a list of other crops to investigate, so a wide variety of crops are reported on. Provide almanacs and other sources for students' research.

In Your Journal Encourage students to share their findings with the class in brief oral reports or posters.
learning modality: verbal

Limits to Dispersal

Building Inquiry Skills: Comparing and Contrasting

Ask students: **Do any of the factors that limit dispersal also limit a population's size? Which ones?** *(Students can compare these factors with those described in Chapter 22, on pages 699–700. Competition limits both dispersal and population size. Physical barriers are also a common factor, since barriers can limit the amount of space available to a population. Seasonal changes, an aspect of climate, also limit some populations' sizes, but students should not equate weather conditions and climate.)* **learning modality: logical/mathematical**

Integrating Earth Science

For students who are having difficulty with the difference between weather and climate, give examples of climate and weather conditions, and ask students to identify each as an example of climate or weather. For example: **It's very cold out today.** *(weather)* **Our part of the country usually has cold winters.** *(climate)* **We don't get much rain in the summer.** *(climate)* **The meteorologist predicts rain tonight.** *(weather)* **learning modality: verbal**

Figure 14 Clumps of purple loosestrife line the banks of a Massachusetts river. Loosestrife is an exotic species that has thrived in its new home, often crowding out native species.

Social Studies
CONNECTION

Many important crops are actually exotic species. When settlers in new lands brought crops with them from their old homes, they caused the dispersal of these species. Some examples of crops dispersed by people are peanuts, potatoes, cotton, corn, and rice.

In Your Journal

Choose a crop to investigate. Research your crop to learn where it is a native species and how it spread to different parts of the world. In what conditions does it grow well? *(Hint: Almanacs and encyclopedias are good sources of this information.)*

Humans are important to the dispersal of other species. As people move around the globe, they take plants, animals, and other organisms with them. Sometimes this is intentional, such as when people bring horses to a new settlement. Sometimes it is unintentional, such as when someone carries a parasite into a country.

Species that have naturally evolved in an area are referred to as **native species.** When an organism is carried into a new location by people, it is referred to as an **exotic species.** Some exotic species are so common in their new environment that people think of them as native. For example, you probably know the dandelion, one of the most common flowering plants in North America. But the dandelion is not a native species. It was brought by colonists who valued its leaves for eating and for tea for the sick.

☑ *Checkpoint* How can humans disperse a species?

Limits to Dispersal

With all these means of dispersal, you might expect to find the same organisms everywhere in the world. Of course, that's not so. Why not? What determines the limits of a species' distribution? **Three factors that limit dispersal of a species are physical barriers, competition, and climate.**

Physical Barriers Barriers such as water, mountains, and deserts are hard to cross. These features can limit the movement of organisms. For example, once Australia became separated from the other continents, the ocean acted as a barrier to dispersal. Organisms could not easily move to or from Australia.

Competition When an organism enters a new area, it must compete for resources with the species already there. To survive, the organism must find a unique niche. If the existing species are thriving, they may outcompete the new species. In this case competition is a barrier to dispersal. Sometimes, however, the new species is more successful than the existing species. The native species may be displaced.

Background

Facts and Figures Ecologists estimate that there are 6,000 exotic species in the United States. While most are harmless, some of these exotic species pose a significant threat to native species. Ecologists search for ways to control harmful invaders without causing other environmental problems. As one example, Eurasian watermilfoil, a freshwater weed, entered the United States as an aquarium decoration, then escaped and spread through waterways nationwide. Lakes in Michigan and Massachusetts that were being overgrown with watermilfoil were stocked with thousands of water weevils, one of the few organisms that attack the plant. Within months the weevils caused noticeable damage to the watermilfoil.

Climate The typical weather pattern in an

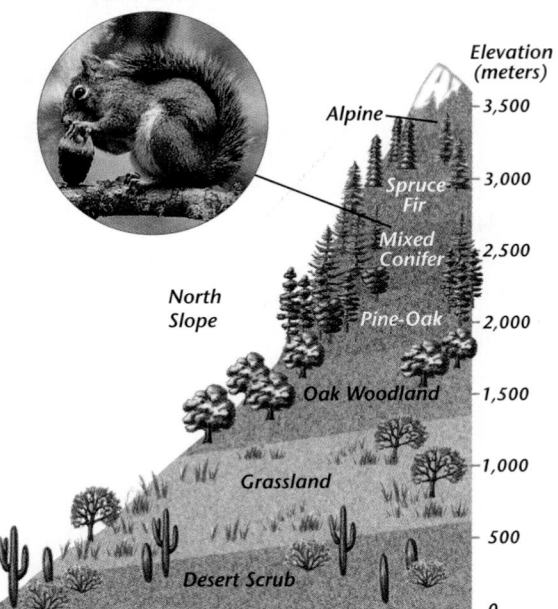

INTEGRATING EARTH SCIENCE

area over a long period of time is the area's **climate.** Climate is different from weather, which is the day-to-day conditions in an area. Climate is largely determined by temperature and precipitation.

Differences in climate can be a barrier to dispersal. For example, conditions at the top of the mountain shown in Figure 15 are very different from those at the base. The base is warm and dry. Low shrubs and cactuses grow there. Just up the mountain, mostly grasses grow. Higher up the mountain, the climate becomes cooler and wetter. Larger trees such as pines, oaks, and firs can grow. The squirrel in the closeup lives in this region. Climate differences act as a barrier that keeps the squirrel species from dispersing down or up the mountain. Near the top of the mountain, it is very cold and windy. Small alpine wildflowers and mosses grow best in this region.

Places with similar climates tend to have species that occupy similar niches. For example, most continents have a large area of flat, grassy plains. The organisms that occupy the niche of "large, grazing mammal" on each continent have some similarities. In North America, the large, grazing mammals of the grasslands are bison; in Africa, they are wildebeests and antelopes; in Australia, they are kangaroos.

Elevation (meters)
— 3,500
— 3,000
— 2,500
— 2,000
— 1,500
— 1,000
— 500
— 0

Alpine
Spruce-Fir
Mixed Conifer
North Slope
Pine-Oak
Oak Woodland
Grassland
Desert Scrub

Figure 15 Climate conditions change at different elevations on this mountainside. These conditions determine the distribution of species on the mountain. Each zone begins at a lower elevation on the north slope of the mountain, which is cooler than the south slope.

Section 3 Review

1. List three ways that species can disperse.
2. Explain how mountain ranges and climate can each limit a species' distribution.
3. What is biogeography?
4. Give an example of a physical barrier. How might it affect where species are found?
5. **Thinking Critically** **Predicting** If an exotic insect species were introduced to your area, do you think it would be easy or difficult to eliminate the species? Give reasons to support your answer.

Science at Home

Sock Walk Take an adult family member on a "sock walk" to learn about seed dispersal. Each person should wear a thick white sock over one shoe. Take a short walk through woods, a field, or a park. Back at home, remove the socks and observe how many seeds you collected. Plant the socks in pans of soil. Place the pans in a sunny spot and water them regularly. How many species did you successfully disperse?

Chapter 23 **731**

Program Resources

◆ **Unit 5 Resources** 23-3 Review and Reinforce, p. 43; 23-3 Enrich, p. 44
◆ **Interdisciplinary Exploration Series** "Where River Meets Sea," pp. 28–29

Answers to Self-Assessment

☑ *Checkpoint*

They take plants, animals, and other organisms with them as they move, sometimes intentionally and sometimes unintentionally.

3 Assess

Section 3 Review Answers

1. Wind, water, other organisms
2. Mountain ranges may be impossible or difficult for a species to cross. A species that is adapted for life in one climate could not survive in a climate with different temperatures and precipitation amounts.
3. The study of where organisms live
4. Physical barriers include water, mountains, deserts, and canyons. *Sample answer:* A species that requires a constant supply of water would not be able to disperse by crossing a large desert.
5. Accept divergent responses so long as students support their answers with well-reasoned explanations. Some students may say that the exotic species might be difficult to eliminate if there are few or no natural competitors, predators, or parasites in the new environment. Others may say exotic species that are not well adapted to the new environment might be eliminated easily.

Science at Home

Materials *thick white sock, potting soil, pan, water*

Tips Before students do the activity at home, discuss seed characteristics that would allow them to identify each seed's method of dispersal—fluffy structures for dispersal by wind, for example, and sharp stickers for dispersal by other organisms. Encourage students to make sketches of any plants that grow. Students can display their sketches and compare their results.

Performance Assessment

Writing Have each student define climate in his or her own words, then explain how climate conditions limit a species' habitat.

How It Works

Biomes in Miniature

NOTE: *Biomes are presented in detail in the next section, Section 4. However, this lab has been placed immediately before that section because it is appropriate as an introduction to the section's concepts and also to allow sufficient time for plant growth while students study biomes.*

Preparing for Inquiry

Key Concept Differences in soil, light, and precipitation create different biomes.
Skills Objectives Students will be able to
◆ make models of given biomes by varying abiotic factors;
◆ observe and compare the growth of different plants in the model biomes;
◆ conclude that each plant is adapted to conditions in a specific biome.
Time 30 minutes for set-up; 5–10 minutes each day for at least one week for follow-up observations and recording data

Advance Planning
◆ Ask students to bring in large milk or juice cartons that have been thoroughly washed.
◆ Obtain sufficient quantities of potting soil and sandy (cactus) soil from a nursery or gardening store.
◆ Allocate enough table space and lamps for students to expose each model biome to the amount of light required.

Guiding Inquiry

Invitation Ask students: **Why don't we see** *[name a non-native plant]* **growing in our area?** (*Students should describe climate conditions needed by the plant that would not be met in your area.*)

Introducing the Procedure
◆ Invite students to read the entire lab procedure. Then ask: **What is the purpose of this lab?** (*To determine how well three kinds of plants grow in different biomes*)
◆ Direct students' attention to the Growing Conditions chart and ask: **What variables will you change to create models of four different**

BIOMES IN MINIATURE

Climate is one factor that affects where organisms live. A group of ecosystems with similar climates and organisms is called a biome. In this lab, you will investigate some key factors that make biomes different from one another.

Problem

What biotic and abiotic factors create different biomes around the world?

Skills Focus

making models, observing, drawing conclusions

Materials

scissors
index card
10 impatiens seeds
5 lima bean seeds
about 30 rye grass seeds
empty, clean cardboard milk carton
sandy soil or potting soil

clear plastic wrap
lamp
tape
stapler

Procedure

1. Your teacher will assign your group a biome. You will also observe the other groups' biomes. Based on the chart below, predict how well you think each of the three kinds of seeds will grow in each set of conditions. Record these predictions in your notebook. Then copy the data table on the facing page four times, once for each biome.
2. Staple the spout of the milk carton closed. Completely cut away one of the four sides of the carton. Poke a few holes in the opposite side for drainage, then place that side down.
3. Fill the carton to 3 centimeters from the top with the type of soil given in the table. Divide the surface of the soil into three sections by making two lines in it with a pencil.
4. In the section near the spout, plant the impatiens seeds. In the middle section, plant the lima bean seeds. In the third section, scatter the rye grass seeds on the surface.

GROWING CONDITIONS			
Biome	**Soil Type**	**Hours of Light Per Day**	**Watering Instructions**
Forest	Potting soil	1–2 hours direct light	Let the surface dry, then add water.
Desert	Sandy soil	5–6 hours direct light	Let the soil dry to a depth of 2.5 cm below the surface.
Grassland	Potting soil	5–6 hours direct light	Let the surface dry, then add water.
Rain forest	Potting soil	No direct light; indirect light for 5–6 hours	Keep the surface of the soil moist.

biomes? (*Soil type, amount of light, and amount of water*)

Troubleshooting the Experiment
◆ In Step 1, do not comment on the accuracy of students' predictions. Rather, have them review their predictions at the end of the investigation and write a conclusion based on their actual results.
◆ Step 8 does not specify the kinds of observations to be made and recorded. You may want to discuss possibilities with

students beforehand and agree on one or more criteria for all groups to use. Criteria could include the number of seeds that germinate successfully, plant height, the number and color of leaves, and yellowing (a sign of too much water) or wilting (a sign of not enough water). Alternatively, you could allow each group to choose the criteria it will use.

DATA TABLE

Name of biome: _____			
Day	Impatiens	Lima Beans	Rye Grass
1			
2			
3			

5. Water all the seeds well. Then cover the open part of the carton with plastic wrap.
6. On an index card, write the name of your biome, the names of the three types of seeds in the order you planted them, and the names of your group members. Tape the card to the carton. Put it in a warm place where it will not be disturbed.
7. Once the seeds sprout, provide your biome with light and water as specified in the chart. Keep the carton covered with plastic wrap except when you add water.
8. Observe all the biomes daily for at least one week. Record your observations.

Analyze and Conclude

1. In which biome did each type of seed grow best? In which biome did each type of seed grow least well?
2. How was each type of seed affected by the soil type, amount of light, and availability of water? How do your results relate to biomes in nature?
3. Ecologists studying land biomes often begin a description of the biome by describing key abiotic factors and the typical plants. Why do you think they do this?
4. **Apply** Describe the rainfall pattern and other abiotic factors that make up the climate where you live. How do those factors affect the kinds of plants and animals that live there?

Design an Experiment

After reading Section 4, write a plan for setting up a model rain forest or desert terrarium. Include typical plants found in that biome. Obtain your teacher's approval before trying this activity.

Analyze and Conclude

1. In general, the rye and beans will grow best in the grassland biome, and the impatiens will grow best in the deciduous forest biome. The seeds will all likely grow most poorly in the dry conditions of the desert biome.
2. In general, the seeds will sprout most rapidly when water is plentiful. Every type of plant is adapted to survive in a specific set of soil, light, and water conditions, so each of the three plant types in this lab thrived in only one or two biomes. In nature, the same abiotic factors limit the types of plants that can survive in a specific biome.
3. The abiotic factors limit the types of plants that can grow in a particular biome, and the types of plants in turn determine the types of animals and other consumers that can survive in that biome.
4. Answers will depend on the climate conditions in your region.

Extending the Inquiry

Design an Experiment Provide field guides and other resources for students to use in selecting typical plants. Discourage students from trying to start plants from seed; provide small but mature plants that will do well in a model rain forest or desert. To simulate the damp conditions found in a rain forest, students will need to put a cover on the rain forest container to prevent evaporation.

Data Table
Students' data tables will vary depending on the criteria they used for assessing the health of the plants. For general guidelines, see Analyze and Conclude Question 1 answer.

Program Resources

◆ **Unit 5 Resources** Chapter 23 Real-World Lab, pp. 53–55

Safety

Make sure students wash their hands after they handle the soil and seeds. Review the safety guidelines in Appendix A.

Objectives

After completing the lesson, students will be able to
- list and describe Earth's major land biomes;
- list and describe Earth's major freshwater and ocean biomes.

Key Terms biome, canopy, understory, desert, grassland, savanna, deciduous trees, hibernation, coniferous trees, tundra, permafrost, estuary, intertidal zone, neritic zone

1 Engage/Explore

Activating Prior Knowledge

Ask: **What is the climate like in our area?** *(Students should describe conditions of temperature, precipitation, amount of sunlight during the seasons, and so forth.)* **How do you think our climate affects which organisms live here?** *(Answers will vary depending on the climate of the area. For example, students may say that a warm, humid climate allows a great variety of organisms to live in the area.)*

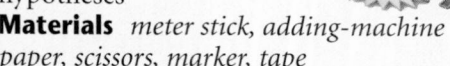

DISCOVER

Skills Focus developing hypotheses
Materials *meter stick, adding-machine paper, scissors, marker, tape*
Time 20 minutes

CAUTION: *Hanging the Costa Rican rain forest strip will require the use of a ladder. Choose three reliable students for this task, one to climb the ladder and two to hold the ladder securely. If you are not certain that students can do this task safely, have them hang the strips horizontally.*
Expected Outcome Students should sequence the strips from least to most rainfall, as indicated in the table.
Think It Over The Costa Rican rain forest receives the most precipitation, and the Mojave Desert the least. The amount of rainfall affects what plant species can survive in a particular biome, and the plants in turn determine the consumer species found there.

SECTION 4 Earth's Biomes

DISCOVER · ACTIVITY

How Much Rain Is That?

The table shows the average amount of precipitation that falls each year in four different regions. With your classmates, you will create a full-size bar graph on a wall to help you visualize these amounts of rain.

Biome	Rainfall (cm)
Mojave Desert	15
Illinois prairie	70
Smoky Mountains	180
Costa Rican rain forest	350

1. Using a meter stick, measure a strip of adding-machine paper 15 centimeters long. Label this piece of paper "Mojave Desert."

2. Repeat Step 1 for the other three locations. If necessary, tape strips of paper together to make the correct length. Label each strip.

3. Now find a place where you can display the four strips vertically. If the wall of your classroom is not tall enough, you may need to use another wall in your school building. Follow your teacher's instructions to hang your precipitation strips.

Think It Over
Developing Hypotheses Which ecosystem receives the most precipitation? Which receives the least? What effect do you think the amount of rainfall might have on the types of species that live in these ecosystems?

GUIDE FOR READING

- What determines the type of biome found in an area?
- Where can photosynthesis occur in water biomes?

Reading Tip As you read, make a list of the biomes described in this section. Under each biome name, take notes on the characteristics of that biome.

Congratulations! You and your classmates have been selected as the student members of an around-the-world scientific expedition. Your mission is to study the major types of ecosystems on Earth. You will be collecting data on the climate conditions and typical organisms found in each of these ecosystems. The result of this expedition will be a database of information on the biomes you visit. A **biome** is a group of ecosystems with similar climates and organisms.

Classifying ecosystems into biomes helps ecologists describe the world. As you might expect, not all ecologists agree on the exact number and kinds of biomes. The scientists guiding your expedition have chosen to focus on six major land biomes and two major water biomes.

Be sure to pack a variety of clothing for your journey. During your trip, you will visit places ranging from frozen, windy Arctic plains to steamy tropical jungles. **In fact, it is mostly the climate conditions—temperature and rainfall—in an area that determine its biome.** This is because climate limits the distribution of plants in the area. In turn, the types of plants determine the kinds of animals that live there.

734

READING STRATEGIES

Reading Tip Invite students to preview the headings in this section and name the eight major biomes described (rain forest, desert, grassland, deciduous forest, boreal forest, tundra, freshwater, and marine) and the "sub-biomes" or ecosystems within those biomes (tropical rain forests, temperate rain forests, freshwater ponds and lakes, freshwater streams and rivers, estuaries, and the ocean's intertidal, neritic, surface, and deep zones). To organize their notes, students can construct a table with the names of the biomes listed in the first column and the characteristics that differentiate biomes labeled across the top of the table—*Temperature, Rainfall, Variety of Species,* and *Typical Organisms,* for example. Students can use their completed biome summaries as a study guide.

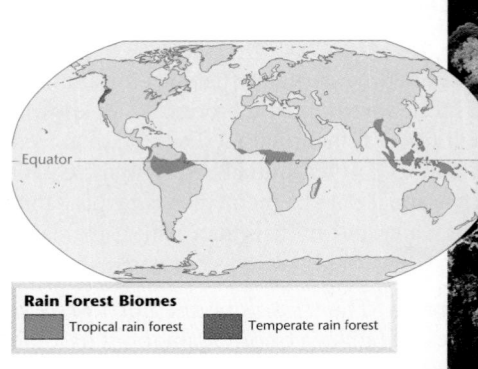

Rain Forest Biomes
- Tropical rain forest
- Temperate rain forest

Rain Forest Biomes

The first stop on your expedition is a tropical rain forest close to the equator. The rain forest is warm and humid—in fact, it's pouring rain! Fortunately, you remembered to pack a poncho. After just a short rain shower, the sun reappears. But even though the sun is shining, very little light penetrates the thick vegetation.

Plants are everywhere in the rain forest. Some, such as the ferns, orchids, and vines you observe hanging from tree limbs, even grow on other plants. Among the plants are many species of birds as bright as the numerous flowers all around you.

Tropical Rain Forests Tropical rain forests are found in warm regions close to the equator. Tropical rain forests typically receive a lot of rain. The warm temperatures do not vary much throughout the year, and the sunlight is fairly constant all year.

Tropical rain forests contain an astounding variety of species. For example, scientists studying a 100-square-meter area of one rain forest identified 300 different kinds of trees! These trees form several distinct layers. The tall trees form a leafy roof called the **canopy.** A few giant trees poke out above the canopy. Below the canopy, a second layer of shorter trees and vines form an **understory.** Understory plants grow well in the shade formed by the canopy. Finally, some plants thrive in the near-darkness of the forest floor.

Figure 16 Tropical rain forests contain an amazing variety of plants and other organisms. In the large photo, a river winds through the lush Indonesian rain forest. The top closeup shows a young orangutan swinging from tree limbs. In the bottom closeup, a tarantula climbs over a brightly colored bracket fungus on the forest floor.

2 Facilitate

Rain Forest Biomes

Building Inquiry Skills: Communicating

As an ongoing activity throughout this section, **ACTIVITY** encourage students to research additional information about the biomes described in the text. Divide the class into eight groups, and assign one biome to each group. (You may want to use 12 groups and divide the 5 marine habitats among different groups.) Explain that each group should look for additional photographs of the biome and of organisms typically found in it. Students can photocopy (or print out) the pictures and incorporate them into a large poster labeled with the name of the biome. As students read about each biome in the text, call on the group who researched that biome to present its poster to the class. Display the posters in the classroom. **cooperative learning**

Using the Visuals: Figure 16

Display a world map or globe, and have students locate Indonesia. Then have them locate Indonesia on the biome map. Ask: **What do you notice about the locations of the world's tropical rain forests?** *(All are located at or close to the equator.)* **learning modality: visual**

Program Resources

◆ **Unit 5 Resources** 23-4 Lesson Plan, p. 45; 23-4 Section Summary, p. 46

Media and Technology

🎧 **Audio CD** English-Spanish Summary 23-4

💿 **Exploring Life Science Videodisc** Unit 6, Side 2, "Earth's Many Biomes"

Chapter 5

Ongoing Assessment

Writing Have each student explain how temperature and rainfall determine the types of organisms that live in a particular biome.

Rain Forest Biomes, continued

Cultural Diversity

Have students examine a map of the northwestern United States and locate temperate rain forests. They will undoubtedly notice the unusual names of several forests—for example, Tillamook State Forest, Siuslaw National Forest, Siskiyou National Forest (all in Oregon), and Klamath National Forest (California). Ask: **Where do you think those names came from?** (*They are the names of Native American tribes living in those areas.*) Encourage interested students to find out about the history and cultures of indigenous peoples of the American northwest. **learning modality: verbal**

Desert Biomes

Building Inquiry Skills: Making Models

Materials *terrarium with cover; sandy soil; water; desert organisms such as cactus plants, insects, small lizard*

ACTIVITY

Time 20 minutes

Ask students: **If you wanted to build a model of a desert biome in a terrarium, what abiotic materials would you need?** (*Sandy soil; perhaps some gravel and rocks; a source of strong, direct sunlight or artificial light; some water for infrequent watering*) **What organisms would you place in the model biome?** (*Cactus plants, desert insects, a small lizard or other organism*) Encourage a group of volunteers to gather the materials and construct a model desert biome. **learning modality: kinesthetic**

Figure 17 Desert organisms have adaptations that enable them to live in the harsh conditions of their biome. For example, this shovel-snouted lizard "dances" to avoid burning its feet on the hot sand dunes of the Namib Desert in Africa. *Making Generalizations Describe the climate conditions of a typical desert.*

Equator

Desert and Grassland Biomes
Desert   Grassland

The abundant plant life provides many habitats for animals. The number of insect species in tropical rain forests is not known, but has been estimated to be in the millions. These in turn feed many bird species, which feed other animals. Although tropical rain forests cover only a small part of the planet, they probably contain more species of plants and animals than all the other land biomes combined.

Temperate Rain Forests The land along the northwestern coast of the United States resembles a tropical rain forest in some ways. This region receives more than 300 centimeters of rain a year. Huge trees grow there, including cedars, redwoods, and Douglas firs. However, it is difficult to classify this region. It is too far north and too cool to be a tropical rain forest. Instead many ecologists refer to this ecosystem as a temperate rain forest. The term *temperate* means having moderate temperatures.

Desert Biomes

The next stop on your expedition is a desert. It couldn't be more different from the tropical rain forest you just left. You step off the bus into the searing summer heat. At midday, you cannot even walk into the desert—the sand feels as hot as the hot water that comes from your bathroom faucet at home.

A **desert** is an area that receives less than 25 centimeters of rain per year. The amount of evaporation in a desert is greater than the amount of precipitation. Some of the driest deserts may not receive any rain at all in a year! Deserts often also undergo large shifts in temperature during the course of a day. A scorching hot desert like the

Background

Facts and Figures The continuing destruction of tropical rain forests around the world may be a factor in climate change. Each year, thousands of square kilometers of rain forest are cut and burned to clear land and access mineral resources. Burning the forests not only kills the unique organisms of the rain forest ecosystem but also releases large quantities of carbon dioxide, contributing to global warming.

Between 1978 and 1996, more than 12.5 percent of the Amazon rain forest was destroyed. In 1998, after analysis of satellite photographs, the Brazilian government reported that rain forest destruction reached a record level of 30,000 square kilometers in 1995. Brazil planned to increase its monitoring and control of the area and implement new measures to protect the rain forest.

Namib Desert cools rapidly each night when the sun goes down. Other deserts, such as the Gobi in central Asia, are cooler, even experiencing freezing temperatures in the winter.

The organisms that live in the desert are adapted to the lack of rain and to the extreme temperatures. For example, the trunk of a saguaro cactus has folds that work like the pleats in an accordion. The trunk of the cactus expands to hold more water when it is raining. Many desert animals are most active at night when the temperatures are cooler. A gila monster, for instance, spends much of its time in a cool underground burrow. It may go for weeks without coming up to the surface of the desert.

Checkpoint What are some adaptations that help an organism to live in the desert?

Grassland Biomes

The next stop on the expedition is a grassland called a prairie. The temperature here is much more comfortable than that in the desert. The breeze carries the scent of soil warmed by the sun. This rich soil supports grass as tall as you and your classmates. Sparrows flit among the grass stems, looking for their next meal. Startled by your approach, a rabbit quickly bounds away.

Like other grasslands located in the middle latitudes, this prairie receives more rain than deserts, but not enough for many trees to grow. A **grassland** receives between 25 and 75 centimeters of rain each year, and is typically populated by grasses and other non-woody plants. Grasslands that are located closer to the equator than prairies, called **savannas,** receive as much as 120 centimeters of

Desert Survival

Use a hand lens to carefully observe a small potted cactus. Be careful of the spines! With a pair of scissors, carefully snip a small piece from the tip of the cactus. Observe the inside of the plant. Note any characteristics that seem different from those of other plants.

Observing How is the inside of the cactus different from the outside? Suggest how the features you observe might be related to its desert habitat.

Figure 18 Migrating wildebeest make their way across a vast Kenyan savanna.

Chapter 23 **737**

Deciduous Forest Biomes

Building Inquiry Skills: Making Models

ACTIVITY

Ask students: **Could you build a model of a deciduous forest in a terrarium?** *(No, not of the entire forest, but specific habitats could be modeled in a terrarium.)* **Suppose you want to model a rotting-log habitat on the forest floor. What abiotic materials would you need?** *(Soil, a source of filtered light, water, a rotting log, dead leaves or other plant material)* **What organisms would you place in the model habitat?** *(Mosses, ferns, fungi, earthworms, sowbugs, crickets, toad or salamander)* Encourage volunteers to gather materials and construct a model rotting-log habitat. **learning modality: kinesthetic**

Addressing Naive Conceptions

After students have read about hibernation on the next page, ask: **What animals hibernate during the winter?** *(Students will probably mention bears, among other animals. List responses on the board without commenting on their accuracy.)* Encourage students to find out whether the animals they named do indeed hibernate and what other animals should be added to the list. *(Animals that undergo true hibernation include bats, ground squirrels, chipmunks, groundhogs, frogs, toads, lizards, snakes, and turtles. Students will also discover that some of the animals they named—bears, for example—do not undergo true hibernation, which involves extreme metabolic changes. These animals go through prolonged periods of deep sleep over the winter months but wake up from time to time.)* **learning modality: verbal**

Forest Biomes
- Deciduous forest
- Boreal forest

Figure 19 This Michigan forest in autumn is a beautiful example of a deciduous forest. The closeup shows a red fox, a common resident of North American deciduous forests. *Comparing and Contrasting How do deciduous forests differ from rain forests?*

rain each year. Scattered shrubs and small trees grow on savannas along with the grass.

Grasslands are home to many of the largest animals on Earth—herbivores such as bison, antelopes, zebras, rhinoceros, giraffes, and kangaroos. Grazing by these large herbivores helps to maintain the grasslands. They keep young trees and bushes from sprouting and competing with the grass for water and sunlight.

Deciduous Forest Biomes

Your trip to the next biome takes you to another forest. It is now late summer. Cool mornings here give way to warm days. Several members of the expedition are busy recording the numerous plant species. Others are looking through their binoculars, trying to identify the songbirds in the trees. You step carefully to avoid a small salamander on the forest floor. Chipmunks chatter at all the disturbance.

You are now visiting the deciduous forest biome. The trees found in this forest, called **deciduous trees** (dee SIJ oo us), shed their leaves and grow new ones each year. Oaks and maples are examples of deciduous trees. Deciduous forests receive enough rain to support the growth of trees and other plants, at least 50 centimeters per year. Temperatures vary during the year. The growing season usually lasts five to six months. As in the rain forest, different plants grow to different heights, ranging from a canopy of tall trees to small ferns and mosses on the forest floor.

Background

Facts and Figures In North America, autumn's shorter days and cooler temperatures cause deciduous trees to drop their leaves. Leaf drop protects trees, which would otherwise dry out during the winter. When the ground is frozen, roots cannot absorb water to replace what is lost by evaporation from leaf surfaces. A leafless tree does not lose as much water in winter as would a tree with leaves.

Conifers' needlelike leaves are also an adaptation to conserve water. For example, a pine needle has a much smaller surface area from which water can evaporate than does a maple leaf. Needles also have a thick, waxy covering that holds in water.

The variety of plants in the forest creates many different habitats. You and your classmates note that different species of birds live at each level, eating the insects and fruits that live and grow there. You observe opossums, mice, and a skunk looking for food in the thick layer of damp leaves on the ground. Other common North American deciduous forest species include wood thrushes, white-tailed deer, and black bears.

If you were to return to this biome in the winter, you would not see much of the wildlife you are now observing. One reason is that many of the bird species migrate to warmer areas. Some of the mammals enter a low-energy state similar to sleep called hibernation. During hibernation an animal relies on fat it has stored in its body.

☑ *Checkpoint* **What are deciduous trees?**

Boreal Forest Biomes

Now the expedition heads north into a colder climate. The expedition leaders claim they can identify the next biome, a boreal forest, by its smell. When you arrive, you catch a whiff of the spruce and fir trees that blanket the hillsides. Feeling the chilly early fall air, you pull a jacket and hat out of your bag.

This forest contains **coniferous trees** (koh NIF ur us), that produce their seeds in cones and have leaves shaped like needles. The boreal forest is sometimes referred to by its Russian name, the *taiga* (TY guh). Winters in these forests are very cold. The yearly

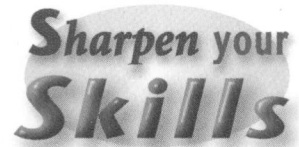

Figure 20 Common organisms of the boreal forest include moose like this one in Alaska's Denali National Park, and porcupines.

Tundra Biomes

Using the Visuals: Figure 21

Direct students' attention to the photograph and ask: **What does the land look like in this photograph of the tundra?** *(It is generally flat with low hills.)* Tell students that the term tundra comes from a Lapp word meaning "marshy plain." Ask: **Do you think "marshy plain" is a good description of the tundra?** *(Students may be unsure about the "marshy" part of the description.)* Explain that because the permafrost does not allow water to drain from the soil and because the low temperatures slow evaporation, the tundra's soil is constantly saturated with water, even though the area receives little precipitation. **learning modality: visual**

Cultural Diversity

Ask students: **Do you think any people live in the tundra? If not, why not?** *(Many students may think that people don't live in the tundra because the climate is so harsh.)* Explain that the Lapp people do live in the tundra and that in fact the word "tundra" originally came from a word in their language. Encourage students who need additional challenges to find out more about the Lapp culture and report their findings to the class in posters, displays, or brief oral reports. **learning modality: verbal**

snowfall can reach heights well over your head—or even two or three times your height! Even so, the summers are rainy and warm enough to melt all the snow.

A limited number of trees have adapted to the cold climate of boreal forests. Fir, spruce, and hemlock are the most common species because their thick, waxy needles keep water from evaporating. Since water is frozen for much of the year in these areas, prevention of water loss is a necessary adaptation for trees in the boreal forest.

Many of the animals of the boreal forest eat the seeds produced by the conifers. These animals include red squirrels, insects, and birds such as finches and chickadees. Some of the larger herbivores, such as porcupines, deer, elk, moose, and beavers, eat tree bark and new shoots. This variety of herbivores in the boreal forest supports a variety of large predators, including wolves, bears, wolverines, and lynxes.

Tundra Biomes

The driving wind brings tears to the eyes of the members of the expedition as you arrive at your next stop. It is now fall. The slicing wind gives everyone an immediate feel for this biome, the tundra. The **tundra** is an extremely cold, dry, land biome. Expecting deep snow, many are surprised that the tundra may receive no more precipitation than a desert. Most of the soil in the tundra is frozen all year. This frozen soil is called **permafrost.**

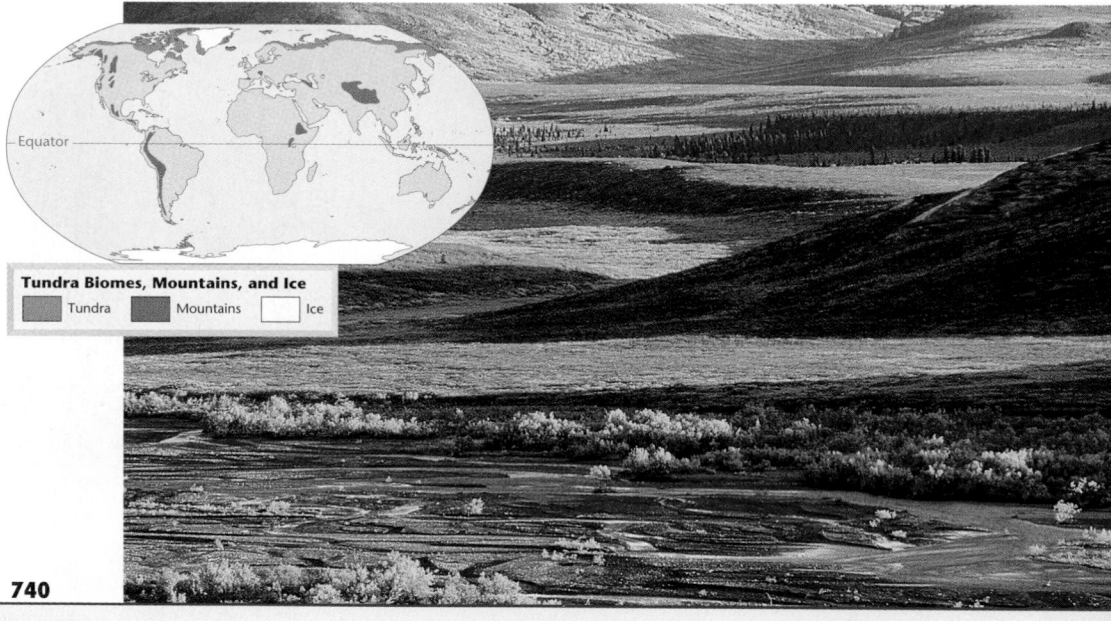

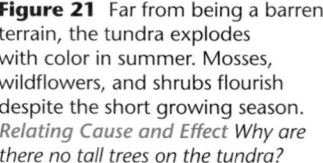
Figure 21 Far from being a barren terrain, the tundra explodes with color in summer. Mosses, wildflowers, and shrubs flourish despite the short growing season. *Relating Cause and Effect Why are there no tall trees on the tundra?*

Tundra Biomes, Mountains, and Ice
Tundra   Mountains   Ice

Equator

Background

Facts and Figures Tundra generally occurs in the far north, in regions near or above the Arctic Circle, where the snow melts in the summer. In the Southern Hemisphere, tundra occurs on the Antarctic Peninsula, which is the only sizable land area at those latitudes.

Mosses, lichens, grasses and small shrubs carpet the tundra. But life is not easy for tundra plants. Tundra soils are thin, poor in nutrients and humus, and poorly drained. A short distance beneath the surface lies a layer of frozen subsoil called permafrost. Permafrost blocks the downward growth of plant roots. In addition, plants must grow, flower, and produce seeds very quickly during the tundra's short growing season.

During the short summer the top layer of soil on the tundra thaws, but the underlying soil remains frozen.

Plants on the tundra include mosses, grasses, shrubs, and dwarf forms of a few trees, such as willows. Looking across the tundra, you observe that the landscape is already brown and gold. The short growing season is over. Most of the plant growth takes place during the long summer days when many hours of sunshine combine with the warmest temperatures of the year. North of the Arctic Circle the sun does not set during midsummer.

If you had visited the tundra during the summer, the animals you might remember most are insects. Swarms of black flies and mosquitos provide food for many birds. The birds take advantage of the plentiful food and long days by eating as much as they can. Then, when winter approaches again, many birds migrate south to warmer climates.

Mammals of the tundra include caribou, foxes, wolves, and hares. The animals that remain in the tundra during the winter grow thick fur coats. What can these animals find to eat on the tundra in winter? The caribou scrape snow away to find lichens, which are fungi and algae that grow together on rocks. Wolves follow the caribou and look for weak members of the herd to prey upon.

☑ *Checkpoint* What is the climate of the tundra?

Mountains and Ice

Some areas of land on Earth do not fall into one of the major land biomes. These areas include mountain ranges and land that is covered with thick sheets of ice.

You read in Section 3 that the climate conditions of a mountain change from its base to its summit. As a result, different species of plants and other organisms inhabit different parts of the mountain. If you hiked to the top of a tall mountain, you would pass through a series of biomes. At the base of the mountain, you might find a grassland. As you climbed, you might pass through a deciduous forest, and then a boreal forest. Finally, as you neared the top, the trees would disappear. Your surroundings would resemble the rugged tundra.

Some land on Earth is covered year-round with thick ice sheets. Most of the island of Greenland and the continent of Antarctica fall into this category. Some organisms are adapted to life on the ice, including penguins, polar bears, and seals.

Figure 22 Many waterfowl spend summers on the tundra. This black brant is tending her nest.

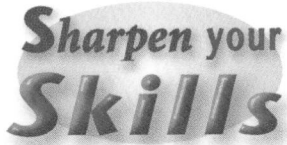

Sharpen your Skills

Interpreting Data

An ecologist has collected climate data from two locations. The total yearly precipitation is 250 cm in Location A and 14 cm in Location B. The graph below shows the average monthly temperature in the two locations. Based on this information, of which biome is each location a part? Explain.

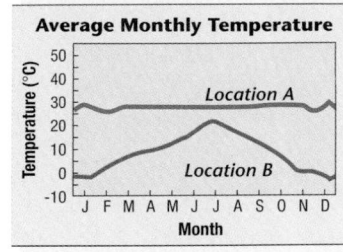

Chapter 23 **741**

Sharpen your Skills

Interpreting Data

Time 10 minutes

ACTIVITY

Tips If students have difficulty determining whether Location B is a desert or tundra, focus their attention on the biome's average monthly temperatures, which are too high for the tundra.

Expected Outcome Location A is a rain forest; it receives a lot of rain, and its warm temperatures are steady throughout the year. Location B is a desert; it receives little rainfall, and its temperatures are cold—but not extremely so—in winter and warm in summer.

Extend Invite students to describe the shape of the line that would be shown on the graph if they plotted the average monthly temperatures for the biome in which they live. **learning modality: logical/mathematical**

Mountains and Ice

Inquiry Challenge

Time 10 minutes

ACTIVITY

Have each small group draw a side-view diagram of a mountain and label it with the biome names given in the text: grassland at the base, deciduous forest next, then boreal forest, and finally tundra at the top. Challenge students to use the diagram, with any additions they choose, to answer the following question: **Why do the biomes vary at different locations on a mountain?** (*By adding information on temperature to the labels, students will be able to see that the climate becomes colder at higher elevations on a mountain. They should then be able to conclude that the altitude of a location on a mountain determines its climate conditions and thus its biome.*) **cooperative learning**

Ongoing Assessment

Skills Check Have students add the tundra biome to the compare/contrast table they created in Ongoing Assessment on page 737.

Freshwater Biomes

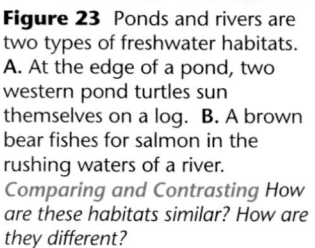

Figure 23 Ponds and rivers are two types of freshwater habitats. **A.** At the edge of a pond, two western pond turtles sun themselves on a log. **B.** A brown bear fishes for salmon in the rushing waters of a river. *Comparing and Contrasting How are these habitats similar? How are they different?*

Freshwater Biomes

The next stops for the expedition are located in water biomes. Since almost three quarters of Earth's surface is covered with water, it is not surprising that many living things make their homes in the water. Water biomes include both freshwater and saltwater (also called marine) biomes. All of these are affected by the same abiotic factors: temperature, sunlight, oxygen, and salt content.

An especially important factor in water biomes is sunlight. Sunlight is necessary for photosynthesis in the water just as it is on land. **However, because water absorbs sunlight, there is only enough light for photosynthesis near the surface or in shallow water.** The most common producers in most water biomes are algae rather than plants.

Ponds and Lakes First stop among the freshwater biomes is a calm pond. Ponds and lakes are bodies of standing, or still, fresh water. Lakes are generally larger and deeper than ponds. Ponds are often shallow enough that sunlight can reach the bottom even in the center of the pond, allowing plants to grow there. Plants that grow along the shore have their roots in the soil, while their leaves stretch to the sunlit water at the surface. In the center of a lake, algae floating at the surface are the major producers.

Many animals are adapted for life in the still water. Along the shore of the pond you observe insects, snails, frogs, and salamanders. Sunfish live in the open water, feeding on insects and algae from the surface. Scavengers such as catfish live near the pond bottom. Bacteria and other decomposers also feed on the remains of other organisms.

742

Streams and Rivers When you arrive at a mountain stream, you immediately notice how different it is from the still waters of a lake. Where the stream begins, called the headwaters, the cold, clear water flows rapidly. Animals that live in this part must be adapted to the strong current. Trout, for instance, have stream-lined bodies that allow them to swim despite the pull of the rushing water. Insects and other small animals may have hooks or suckers to help them cling to rocks. Few plants or algae can grow in this fast-moving water. Instead, first-level consumers rely on leaves and seeds that fall into the stream.

As the river flows along, it is joined by other streams. The current slows. The water becomes cloudy with soil. With fewer rapids, the slower-moving, warmer water contains less oxygen. Different organisms are adapted to live in this lower part of the river. More plants take root among the pebbles on the river bottom, providing homes for insects and frogs. As is true in every biome, organisms are adapted to live in this specific habitat.

☑ *Checkpoint* *What are two abiotic factors that affect organisms in a river?*

Marine Biomes

Next the members of the expedition head down the coast to explore some marine biomes. The oceans contain many different habitats. These habitats differ in sunlight amount, water temperature, wave action, and water pressure. Different organisms are adapted to life in each type of habitat. The first habitat, called an **estuary** (ES choo ehr ee), is found where the fresh water of a river meets the salt water of the ocean.

Estuaries The shallow, sunlit water, plus a large supply of nutrients carried in by the river, makes an estuary a very rich habitat for living things. The major producers in estuaries are plants, such as marsh grasses, as well as algae.

Figure 24 Fresh river water and salty ocean water meet in an estuary. Estuaries such as this Georgia salt marsh provide a rich habitat for many organisms, including a wading tricolored heron.

Answers to Self-Assessment

Caption Question

Figure 23 *Similarities:* Both have fresh water. *Differences:* The pond has warm, calm water, whereas the river has cold, fast-moving water.

☑ *Checkpoint*

Any two: temperature, speed of current, rocks and pebbles, soil in water, oxygen level

---

Marine Biomes

Using the Visuals: Figure 24

After students have examined the photos and read the caption, ask: **What abiotic factor makes an estuary so different from the river flowing into it and the ocean beyond it?** *(Fresh water and salt water mix together in the estuary.)* **How do you think this affects the types of organisms that can live there?** *(They must be able to tolerate changes in the water's salt content throughout the day.)* **learning modality: verbal**

Building Inquiry Skills: Comparing and Contrasting

After students have read about the intertidal zone on the next page, ask: **How are an estuary and the intertidal zone different?** *(Different organisms live there; the water in the intertidal zone is saltier than the water in an estuary; the estuary is calmer because it is not subjected to heavy waves.)* **How are an estuary and the intertidal zone alike?** *(In both, the land is sometimes covered with water and at other times exposed to the air and sunlight.)* To identify this similarity, students must infer that estuaries are affected by the ocean's tides so mudflats are exposed during low tide and completely covered with water during high tide. If students have difficulty making this inference, guide them by asking: **Do you think estuaries are affected by ocean tides? learning modality: logical/mathematical**

Ongoing Assessment

Oral Presentation Call on various students to each choose one freshwater biome, identify one specific habitat in that biome, and name at least three organisms found in that habitat.

Marine Biomes, continued

Real-Life Learning

If students live in or have visited a coastal area, encourage them to describe what an estuary and an ocean beach (the intertidal zone) look like and to name some of the organisms they have seen there. **learning modality: verbal**

Building Inquiry Skills: Inferring

Materials *coral*
Time 10 minutes

Provide samples of different types of coral for students to examine. Visually impaired students can closely examine the coral by feeling it. Emphasize that these pieces of coral are not the coral animals, which are soft, but the hard structures they produced and left behind when they died. Ask: **Where do you think the coral animals lived?** *(Inside the tiny holes)* **How do you think this hard structure helps coral animals survive?** *(It provides protection for the animals' soft bodies and also anchors them to the ocean floor.)* **learning modality: visual**

Including All Students

Encourage students who need extra challenges to consult field guides, encyclopedias, nonfiction library books, nature magazines, and other sources to find additional photographs of organisms that live in the intertidal, neritic, surface, and deep zones. Suggest that students photocopy or hand copy the pictures they find and arrange the pictures in a bulletin-board display of the four ocean zones with each organism placed in its correct zone. **learning modality: visual**

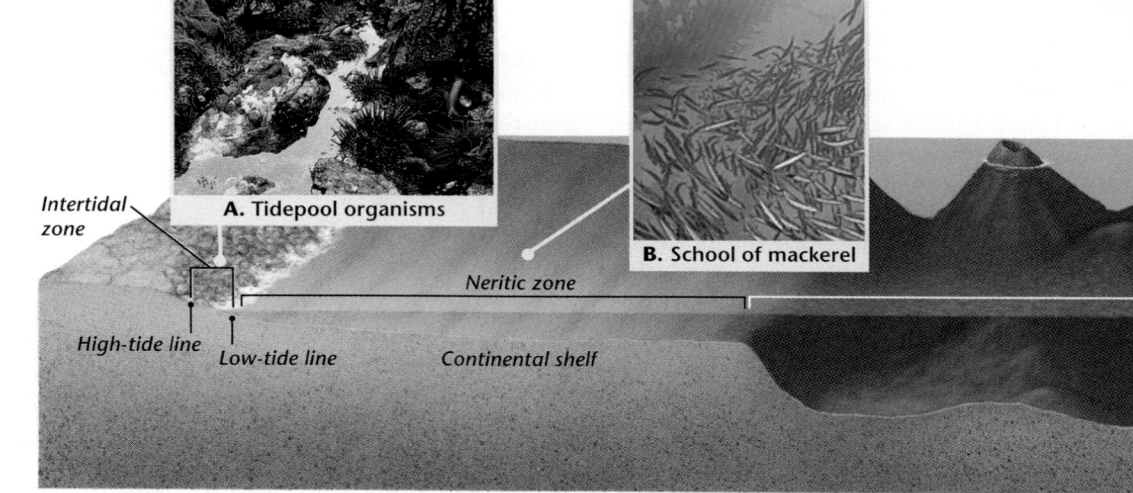

A. Tidepool organisms
B. School of mackerel
Intertidal zone
Neritic zone
High-tide line
Low-tide line
Continental shelf

Figure 25 The marine biome is divided into several zones. **A.** Tidepools are common in the intertidal zone. This zone lies between the highest high-tide line and lowest low-tide line. **B.** Many fish, such as these silvery mackerel, inhabit the shallow waters over the continental shelf, called the neritic zone. **C.** A humpback whale feeds on algae at the surface of the open-ocean zone. **D.** This eerie deep-sea gulper is a predator in the deepest part of the ocean.

These organisms provide food and shelter for a variety of animals, including crabs, worms, clams, oysters, and fish. Many of these organisms use the calm waters of estuaries for breeding grounds.

Intertidal Zone Next, you take a walk along the rocky shoreline. The part of the shore between the highest high-tide line and the lowest low-tide line is called the **intertidal zone.** Organisms here must be able to withstand the pounding action of waves, sudden changes in temperature, and being both covered with water and then exposed to the air. It is a difficult place to live! You observe many animals, such as barnacles and sea stars, clinging to the rocks. Others, such as clams and crabs, burrow in the sand.

Neritic Zone Now it's time to set out to sea to explore the waters near shore. From your research vessel, your group will explore the next type of marine habitat. The edge of a continent extends into the ocean for a short distance, like a shelf. Below the low-tide line is a region of shallow water, called the **neritic zone** (nuh RIT ik), that extends over the continental shelf. Just as in freshwater biomes, the shallow water in this zone allows photosynthesis to occur. As a result, this zone is particularly rich in living things. Many large schools of fish such as sardines and anchovies feed on the algae in the neritic zone. In the warm ocean waters of the tropics, coral reefs may form in the neritic zone. Though a coral reef may look like stone, it is actually a living home to a wide variety of other organisms.

Surface Zone Out in the open ocean, light penetrates through the water only to a depth of a few hundred meters. Algae floating in these surface waters carry out photosynthesis. These algae

---

Background

Facts and Figures The deep zone includes over 90 percent of the ocean. Because food is extremely scarce in the deep ocean, predators there have developed some unusual adaptations. The bodies of many fish consist almost entirely of their mouths—for example, the viper fish has huge curved teeth and gaping jaws that enable it to catch and swallow prey even larger than itself. Other fish, such as the gulper eel, have baglike stomachs that expand to hold prey of any size they are fortunate enough to catch.

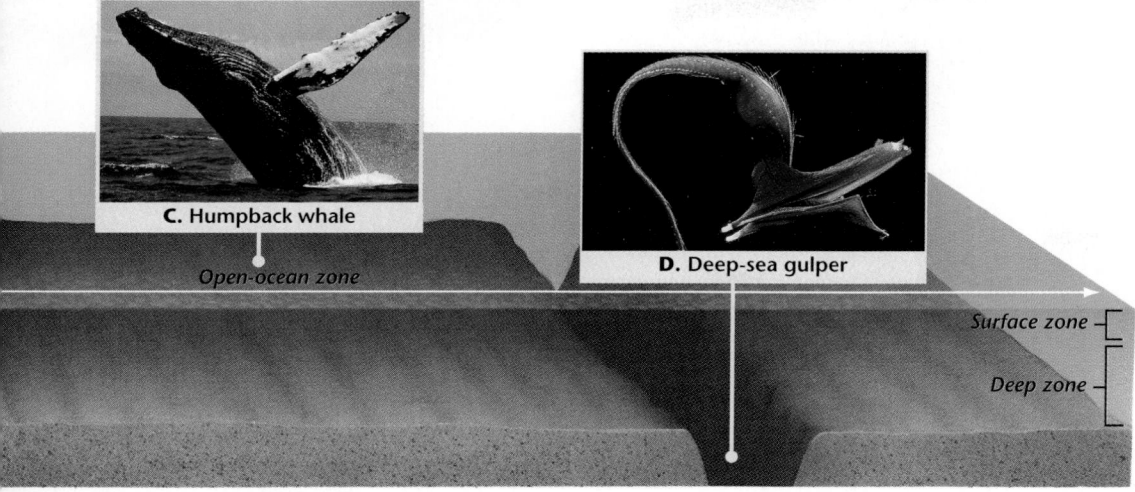

C. Humpback whale

D. Deep-sea gulper

Open-ocean zone

Surface zone
Deep zone

are the producers that form the base of almost all open-ocean food webs. Other marine animals, such as tuna, swordfish, and whales, depend directly or indirectly on the algae for food.

Deep Zone The deep zone is located in the open ocean below the surface zone. Throughout most of the deep ocean, the water is completely dark. Your expedition will need to use a submarine with bright headlights to explore this region. How can anything live in a place with no sunlight? Most animals in this zone feed on remains of organisms that sink down from the surface zone. The deepest parts of the deep zone are home to bizarre-looking animals, such as giant squid that glow in the dark and fish with rows and rows of sharp teeth.

After you have recorded your deep-zone observations, your long expedition is over at last. You can finally return home.

 Section 4 Review

1. How does climate determine a biome's characteristics?
2. Where in water biomes can photosynthesis occur?
3. Which land biome receives the most precipitation? Which two receive the least?
4. In which biome would you find large herbivores such as antelope and elephants? Explain your answer.
5. **Thinking Critically Comparing and Contrasting** How are the three forest biomes (rain forests, deciduous forests, and boreal forests) alike? How are they different?

Check Your Progress CHAPTER PROJECT

By now you should be ready to start analyzing the data you have collected about your compost chambers. Do your observations of the two chambers support your hypothesis? Begin to prepare your report.

Chapter 23 **745**

Program Resources

◆ **Unit 5 Resources** 23-4 Review and Reinforce, p. 47; 23-4 Enrich, p. 48

Change in a Tiny Community

NOTE: This lab has been placed immediately before its related section to allow sufficient time for succession to occur as students study Section 5.

Preparing for Inquiry

Key Concept The types of organisms that predominate in a community change over time.

Skills Objectives Students will be able to
◆ make and observe a model of a microscopic pond community;
◆ compare and contrast the types of organisms and the sizes of the populations present in the community at intervals;
◆ conclude that the predominance of various populations changed during the observation period.

Time *Day 1, set up community: 15 minutes; Days 3, 6, and 9, examine community: 20 minutes each day*

Advance Planning

◆ The day before students will begin the lab, prepare a hay solution by adding a small amount of hay (preferably timothy hay) for each liter of hot water. Let the hay soak overnight, then use a strainer to remove the hay from the solution.
◆ Collect a sample of pond water.
◆ Ask students to help you collect enough clean baby-food jars to provide one for each student or group.
◆ Collect field guides and other sources showing the types of microscopic organisms found in ponds.

Alternative Materials Instead of pond water, use water from a freshwater aquarium or add a commercially prepared culture of microorganisms.

Guiding Inquiry

Invitation Focus students' attention on the illustrations of microorganisms and ask: **Have you ever seen organisms like these before? Where? What were they like?** (*Answers will depend on students'*

Skills Lab

Observing

CHANGE IN A TINY COMMUNITY

The types of organisms in an ecosystem may change gradually over time. You will learn more about this process, called succession, in the next section. In this lab you will observe succession in a pond community.

Problem

How does a pond community change over time?

Materials

hay solution	pond water
small baby-food jar	wax pencil
plastic dropper	microscope slide
coverslip	microscope

Procedure

1. Use a wax pencil to label a small jar with your name.
2. Fill the jar about three-fourths full with hay solution. Add pond water until the jar is nearly full. Examine the mixture, and record your observations in your notebook.
3. Place the jar in a safe location out of direct sunlight where it will remain undisturbed. Always wash your hands thoroughly with soap after handling the jar or its contents.
4. After two days, examine the contents of the jar, and record your observations.
5. Use a plastic dropper to collect a few drops from the surface of the solution in the jar. Make a slide following the procedures in the box at the right. **CAUTION:** *Slides and coverslips are fragile, and their edges are sharp. Handle them carefully.*
6. Examine the slide under a microscope using both low and high power following the procedures in the box at the right. Draw each type of organism you observe. Estimate the number of each type in your sample. The illustration below shows some of the organisms you might see.
7. Repeat Steps 5 and 6 with a drop of solution taken from the side of the jar beneath the surface.
8. Repeat Steps 5 and 6 with a drop of solution taken from the bottom of the jar. When you are finished, follow your teacher's directions about cleaning up.
9. After 3 days, repeat Steps 5 through 8.
10. After 3 more days, repeat Steps 5 through 8 again. Then follow your teacher's directions for returning the solution.

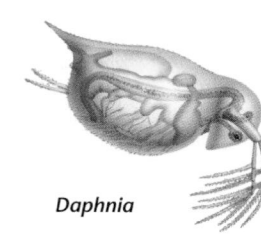

Daphnia

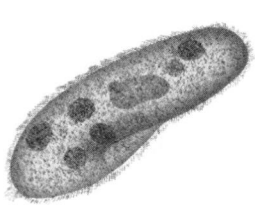

Paramecium

Spirogyra

---

prior experience. If they have not observed living microorganisms, they may have at least seen photographs or drawings.)

Introducing the Procedure

◆ Review the safe handling of slides, coverslips, and microscopes. If students have not prepared slides or used a microscope before, demonstrate these processes.
◆ Introduce or review guidelines for making scientific drawings: the drawings should be as realistic and accurate as possible, labeled

appropriately, and drawn to scale in proportion to each other.

Troubleshooting the Experiment

◆ Make sure students store their jars where they will not be exposed to bright sunlight.
◆ Caution students not to tip or shake the jars.
◆ In Steps 5–10, circulate among students to assist them in preparing the slides and using the microscope. You may need to show students how to regulate the light, adjust the mirror, or make other adjustments.

Making and Viewing a Slide

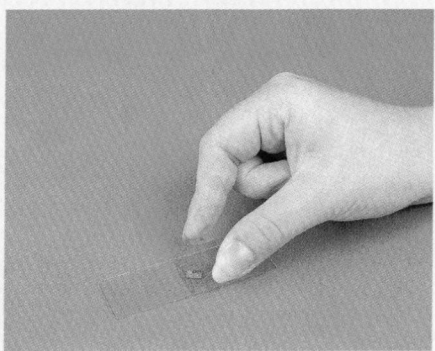

A. Place one drop of the solution to be examined in the middle of a microscope slide. Place one edge of a coverslip at the edge of the drop, as shown above. Gently lower the coverslip over the drop. Try not to trap any air bubbles.

B. Place the slide on the stage of a microscope so the drop is over the opening in the stage. Adjust the stage clips to hold the slide.

C. Look from the side of the microscope, and use the coarse adjustment knob to move the low-power objective close to, but not touching, the coverslip.

D. Look through the eyepiece, and use the coarse adjustment knob to raise the body tube and bring the slide into view. Use the fine adjustment knob to bring the slide into focus.

E. To view the slide under high power, look from the side of the microscope, and revolve the nosepiece until the high-power objective clicks into place just over, but not touching, the slide.

F. While you are looking through the eyepiece, use the fine adjustment knob to bring the slide into focus.

Analyze and Conclude

1. Identify as many of the organisms you observed as possible. Use the diagrams on the facing page and any other resources your teacher provides.

2. How did the community change over the time that you made your observations?

3. What factors may have influenced the changes in this community?

4. Where did the organisms you observed in the jar come from?

5. **Think About It** Do you think your observations gave you a complete picture of the changes in this community? Explain your answer.

Design an Experiment

Write a hypothesis about what would happen if you changed one biotic or abiotic factor in this activity. Design a plan to test your hypothesis. Obtain your teacher's permission before carrying out your experiment.

♦ Emphasize to students that they should always view each slide under low power first, then switch to high power. Remind them to take care in switching lenses so they do not break the slide.

Program Resources

♦ **Unit 5 Resources** Chapter 23 Skills Lab, pp. 56–57

Safety

Make sure students handle the slide and coverslip carefully and wash their hands each time they handle the jar and solution. Review the safety guidelines in Appendix A. Follow the guidelines in Appendix A Teacher's Edition for the recommended safe disposal of bacteria cultures.

Expected Outcome

In general, large populations of smaller organisms such as bacteria and tiny protists will be present early in the succession, whereas populations of larger protists and tiny animals will increase toward the end of the succession.

Analyze and Conclude

1. Answers will vary. Students can usually expect to see a variety of microorganisms, including the three pictured.

2. After one or two days, the solution may become cloudy as bacteria and other microorganisms multiply. Small protists may appear early, followed by larger protists such as green algae, paramecia, and amoebas. Tiny animals such as water fleas and rotifers may be visible toward the end of the sequence.

3. Abiotic factors include the amount of light received, the temperature of the water, and the space available for the populations. Biotic factors include predation of some organisms by other organisms. As smaller organisms multiplied, they provided a growing food supply for larger organisms, which could in turn increase in numbers as well.

4. The organisms were already in the hay solution or pond water, are offspring of those original organisms, or developed from fertilized eggs in the hay solution or pond water.

5. Answers may vary. Some students may say the picture of the model community was complete because they used a valid method of taking samples and made logical inferences and generalizations. Other students may say the picture was incomplete because only three small samples were taken on just three occasions, revealing only a small percentage of the organisms living in the community.

Extending the Inquiry

Design an Experiment Possible changes in abiotic factors include keeping the jar in a slightly warmer or cooler place or exposing it to more or less light. Changes in biotic factors include varying the amounts of hay solution and pond water (the sources of organisms) or adding a specific population of producers or consumers to the community.

Objective

After completing the lesson, students will be able to
◆ describe the differences between primary and secondary succession.

Key Terms succession, primary succession, pioneer species, secondary succession

1 Engage/Explore

Activating Prior Knowledge

Ask students: **Have you ever observed a vacant lot or an untended garden over time? What changes did you see?** *(Answers will depend on students' experience. They will probably say that first small, grassy weeds grew, then larger weeds and some shrubs, and finally small trees.)*

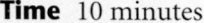

DISCOVER

Skills Focus posing questions
Time 10 minutes
Expected Outcome *A:* Soil is bare and scorched; trees in background have been damaged. *B:* Soil is covered with small plants; damaged trees are leafy.
Think It Over Small plants began to grow again; the existing trees recovered. Students' questions will vary. *Sample questions:* What kinds of plants come back first? Will the area ever look like it did before the fire? How long will that take?

748

 SECTION 5 Succession

DISCOVER ·········· ACTIVITY

What Happened Here?

1. The two photographs at the right show the same area in Yellowstone National Park in Wyoming. Photograph A was taken soon after a major fire. Photograph B was taken a few years later. Observe the photographs carefully.

2. Make a list of all the differences you notice between the two scenes.

Think It Over

Posing Questions How would you describe what happened during the time between the two photographs? What questions do you have about this process?

GUIDE FOR READING

◆ How are primary and secondary succession different?

Reading Tip Before you read, write a definition of what you think the term *succession* might mean. As you read, revise your definition.

In 1988, a huge fire raged through Yellowstone National Park. The fire was so hot that it jumped from tree to tree without burning along the ground between them. In an instant, huge trees burst into flame from the intense heat. It took weeks for the fires to burn themselves out. All that remained of that part of the forest were thousands of blackened tree trunks sticking out of the ground like charred toothpicks.

You might think it unlikely that Yellowstone could recover from such a disastrous fire. But within just a few months, signs of life had returned. First tiny green shoots of new grass appeared in the black ground. Then small tree seedlings began to grow again. The forest was coming back!

Fires, floods, volcanoes, hurricanes, and other natural disasters can change communities in a very short period of time. But even without a disaster, communities change. The series of predictable changes that occur in a community over time is called **succession.** This section describes two types of succession: primary succession and secondary succession.

748

READING STRATEGIES

Reading Tip Students' definitions of *succession* will most likely focus on the idea of succeeding at some activity. Invite students to look in dictionaries to find definitions of *succeed* and read them aloud. (1. to come next in time; 2. to accomplish something desired or intended) Then ask which meaning fits the word *succession.* (To come next in time)

Primary Succession

Primary succession is the series of changes that occur in an area where no ecosystem previously existed. Such an area might be a new island formed by the eruption of an undersea volcano, or an area of rock uncovered by a melting sheet of ice.

You can follow the series of changes an area might undergo in Figure 26 below. These scenes show an area after a violent volcanic eruption. At first there is no soil, just ash and rock. The first species to populate the area are called **pioneer species.** Pioneer species are often lichens and mosses carried to the area by wind or water. These species can grow on bare rocks with little or no soil. As these organisms grow, they help break up the rocks. When they die, they provide nutrients that enrich the thin layer of soil that is forming on the rocks.

Over time, plant seeds land in the new soil and begin to grow. The specific plants that grow depend on the biome of the area. For example, in a cool, northern area, early seedlings might include alder and cottonwood trees. As the soil grows older and richer, these trees might be replaced by spruce and hemlock. Eventually, succession may lead to a community of organisms that does not change unless the ecosystem is disturbed. Reaching this stable community can take several centuries.

Checkpoint *What are some pioneer species?*

Figure 26 Primary succession occurs in an area where no ecosystem previously existed. **A.** After a volcanic eruption, the ground surface consists of ash and rock. **B.** The first organisms to appear are lichens and moss. **C.** Weeds and grasses take root in the thin layer of soil. **D.** Eventually, tree seedlings and shrubs sprout. *Applying Concepts What determines the particular species that appear during succession?*

Program Resources

◆ **Unit 5 Resources** 23-5 Lesson Plan, p. 49; 23-5 Section Summary, p. 50

Media and Technology

 Audio CD English-Spanish Summary 23-5

Answers to Self-Assessment

Caption Question

Figure 26 The particular species depend on the biome of the area.

Checkpoint

Lichens and mosses

Primary Succession

Building Inquiry Skills: Inferring

Read aloud the definition of *succession* on the previous page, stressing the word "predictable." Then ask: **Why are the changes predictable? How can ecologists tell what will happen in a particular community after a natural disaster?** (*Students should infer that the types of plants that will grow in the area and the types of animals that will live there are determined by climate conditions, which are usually not changed over the long term by a disaster. Certain organisms appear first because they can survive in those conditions. Other organisms appear later when conditions become suitable for them.*) **learning modality: logical/ mathematical**

Building Inquiry Skills: Observing

Materials *lichens, mosses, hand lens*
Time 10–15 minutes

Encourage students to bring in lichens and mosses they have found growing on small rocks and loose tree bark. Let them examine the samples and draw what they see, first without and then with a hand lens. Ask: **What are lichens?** (*Fungi and algae that grow together; if students cannot recall this information, let them look back at page 741.*) **How are mosses different from other plants you've seen?** (*They are smaller and do not have true leaves or roots. Students may know of other differences from previous science classes.*) Have students return the lichens and mosses to the area where they were collected. **learning modality: visual**

Ongoing Assessment

Drawing Have each student draw a flowchart showing the stages of primary succession.

 Students could save their flow charts in their portfolios.

749

Secondary Succession

Real-Life Learning

Provide students with a variety of resources that show examples of secondary succession after human disturbances to natural ecosystems—for example, the regrowth of a forest after logging or the natural renewal of a prairie ecosystem when cattle or sheep are no longer grazed there (nature magazines often feature such articles). After reviewing several resources, encourage discussion about each disturbance's benefits to people and the environmental costs. **learning modality: visual**

3 Assess

Section 5 Review Answers

1. Primary succession occurs in an area where no ecosystem existed before, whereas secondary succession occurs after a disturbance in an existing ecosystem. Secondary succession generally occurs more rapidly than primary succession.
2. The first species to populate an area
3. *Natural disturbances:* fires, hurricanes, volcanoes, tornadoes; *human disturbances:* farming, logging, mining
4. Secondary succession; before the sidewalk was built, an ecosystem existed there.

Science at Home

Tips Suggest to students that they use a tape recorder during the interview. If not, they should take notes so they do not forget what the person said. Let students present their summaries in a class discussion, focusing on any examples of succession they identified.

Performance Assessment

Writing Have students explain the difference between primary and secondary succession and give an example of each.

Figure 27 Secondary succession occurs following a disturbance to an ecosystem, such as clearing a forest for farmland. When the farm is abandoned, the forest gradually returns. **A.** After two years, weeds and wildflowers fill the field. **B.** After five years, pine seedlings and other plants populate the field. **C.** After 30 years, a pine forest has grown up. **D.** After 100 years, a mixed forest of pine, oak, and hickory is developing in the field.

Secondary Succession

The changes following the Yellowstone fire were an example of secondary succession. **Secondary succession** is the series of changes that occur after a disturbance in an existing ecosystem. Natural disturbances that have this effect include fires, hurricanes, and tornadoes. Human activities, such as farming, logging, or mining, may also disturb an ecosystem. **Unlike primary succession, secondary succession occurs in a place where an ecosystem has previously existed.**

Secondary succession occurs somewhat more rapidly than primary succession. Consider, for example, an abandoned field in the southeastern United States. Follow the process of succession in such a field in Figure 27. After a century, a hardwood forest is developing. This forest is very stable and will remain for a long time. Of course, the particular species that come and go in the process of succession depend on the biome.

Section 5 Review

1. How are primary and secondary succession different?
2. What is a pioneer species?
3. Give two examples of natural disturbances and two examples of human disturbances that can result in secondary succession.
4. Thinking Critically Classifying Grass poking through the cracks in a sidewalk is an example of succession. Is this primary or secondary succession? Explain.

Science at Home

Succession Interview Interview an older family member or neighbor who has lived in your neighborhood for a long time. Ask the person to describe how the neighborhood has changed over time. Have areas that were formerly grassy been paved or developed? Have any farms or lots returned to a wild state? Write a summary of your interview. Are any of the changes examples of succession?

Program Resources

◆ **Unit 5 Resources** 23-5 Review and Reinforce, p. 51; 23-5 Enrich, p. 52

Media and Technology

Transparencies "Primary and Secondary Succession," Transparency 86

1 Energy Flow in Ecosystems

Key Ideas
- The energy role of an organism is that of a producer, consumer, or decomposer.
- Producers are the source of all the food in an ecosystem.
- Consumers include herbivores, carnivores, omnivores, and scavengers.
- Decomposers return nutrients to the environment where they can be used again.
- A food web shows feeding relationships.
- At each level in an energy pyramid, there is less available energy than at the level below.

Key Terms
producer   omnivore   food chain
consumer   scavenger   food web
herbivore   decomposer   energy pyramid
carnivore

2 Cycles of Matter
INTEGRATING CHEMISTRY

Key Ideas
- Matter cycles through an ecosystem. Energy must be supplied constantly.
- The processes of evaporation, condensation, and precipitation form the water cycle.

Key Terms
water cycle   condensation   nitrogen fixation
evaporation   precipitation   nodule

3 Biogeography

Key Ideas
- Means of dispersal of organisms include continental drift, wind, water, and living things.
- Three factors that limit dispersal are physical barriers, competition, and climate.

Key Terms
biogeography   native species
continental drift   exotic species
dispersal   climate

4 Earth's Biomes

Key Ideas
- Temperature and rainfall mostly determine the biome in an area. Land biomes include rain forests, deserts, grasslands, deciduous forests, boreal forests, and tundras.
- Photosynthesis occurs only near the surface or in shallow areas of water biomes.

Key Terms
biome   savanna   permafrost
canopy   deciduous tree   estuary
understory   coniferous tree   intertidal zone
desert   tundra   neritic zone
grassland

5 Succession

Key Idea
- Primary succession occurs where no previous ecosystem exists. Secondary succession occurs after a disturbance.

Key Terms
succession   pioneer species
primary succession   secondary succession

Organizing Information

Cycle Diagram Complete the cycle diagram to show how carbon cycles through an ecosystem.

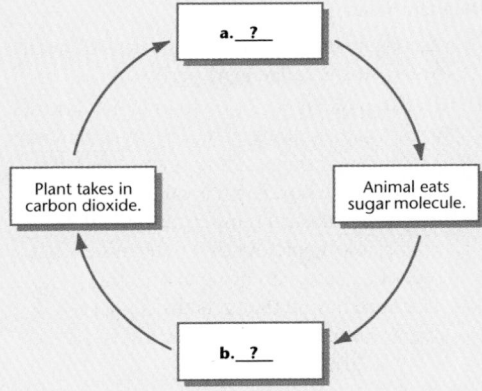

Organizing Information

Cycle Diagram a. Plant uses carbon to make sugar molecules. **b.** Animal releases carbon dioxide into the air.

Program Resources
- **Unit 5 Resources** Chapter 23 Project Scoring Rubric, p. 32;
- **Performance Assessment** Chapter 23, pp. 71–73;
- **Chapter and Unit Tests** Chapter 23 Test, pp. 108–111

Media and Technology

 Interactive Student Tutorial CD-ROM Chapter 23

 Computer Test Bank Chapter 23 Test

Reviewing Content
Multiple Choice
1. b **2.** d **3.** d **4.** c **5.** b

True or False
6. scavenger **7.** true **8.** biogeography
9. true **10.** rain forest

Checking Concepts
11. *Producers* capture the energy of sunlight to make their own food. *Consumers* obtain energy by feeding on other organisms. *Decomposers* obtain energy by breaking down wastes and dead organisms.
12. A food chain is a single path of events in which one organism eats another. A food web is a combination of interconnected and overlapping food chains.
13. The sun or sunlight
14. Nitrogen-fixing bacteria convert free nitrogen gas in the atmosphere into nitrogen-containing molecules that other organisms can use.
15. When the continents were touching one another in one land mass, organisms could move freely between them. When the continents moved apart, organisms were separated and evolved independently.
16. A native species is one that naturally evolved in an area. An exotic species is one that was introduced to the area.
17. Algae
18. Students should describe the temperature and precipitation conditions, the plants, and the other organisms typically found in the chosen biome.

Thinking Critically
19. Clover plants are legumes that have nitrogen-fixing bacteria in nodules on their roots. Planting clover enriches the field by returning nitrogen-containing molecules to the soil.
20. Climate; polar bears' thick, insulating fur would make it difficult for them to live in a warmer environment; the white fur would make them stand out against land that was not covered with ice and snow.
21. Both the desert and the tundra are very dry and have extreme living conditions. The desert may be very hot during the day in summer, with large

---

Reviewing Content
 For more review of key concepts, see the Interactive Student Tutorial CD-ROM.

Multiple Choice
Choose the letter of the best answer.

1. Which of the following organisms are typical decomposers?
  a. grasses and ferns
  b. bacteria and mushrooms
  c. mice and deer
  d. lions and snakes
2. A diagram that shows how much energy is available at each feeding level in an ecosystem is a(n)
  a. food chain.   **b.** food web.
  c. succession.   **d.** energy pyramid.
3. Which of the following is *not* recycled in an ecosystem?
  a. carbon   **b.** nitrogen
  c. water   **d.** energy
4. Organisms may be dispersed in all the following ways *except* by
  a. wind.   **b.** water.
  c. temperature.   **d.** other organisms.
5. Much of Canada is covered in pine and spruce forests. The winter is cold and long. What is this biome?
  a. tundra   **b.** boreal forest
  c. deciduous forest   **d.** grassland

True or False
If the statement is true, write true. If it is false, change the underlined word or words to make the statement true.

6. An organism that eats the remains of dead organisms is called a(n) <u>herbivore</u>.
7. The step of the water cycle in which liquid water changes to water vapor is <u>evaporation</u>.
8. The study of the past and present distribution of species on Earth is called <u>succession</u>.
9. <u>Precipitation</u> and temperature are the two major abiotic factors that determine what types of plants can grow in an area.
10. The land biome that gets the highest average amount of precipitation is the tropical <u>grassland</u> biome.

Checking Concepts
11. Name and briefly define each of the three energy roles organisms can play in an ecosystem.
12. How are food chains and food webs different?
13. What is the source of energy for most ecosystems?
14. Describe the role of nitrogen-fixing bacteria in the nitrogen cycle.
15. How has continental drift affected the distribution of species on Earth?
16. Explain the difference between a native species and an exotic species.
17. What organisms are the producers in most marine ecosystems?
18. Writing to Learn Choose any of the biomes described in this chapter. Imagine that you are a typical animal found in that biome. Write a paragraph describing the conditions and other organisms in your animal's biome.

Thinking Critically
19. Relating Cause and Effect Every few years, a farmer plants clover in a wheat field. Explain how this practice might benefit the farmer.
20. Inferring Polar bears are very well adapted to life around the Arctic Ocean. Their white fur camouflages them in the snow. They can withstand freezing temperatures for a long time. They swim and hunt in very cold water. Is the distribution of polar bears limited by physical barriers, competition, or climate? Explain your answer.
21. Comparing and Contrasting How are the desert biome and the tundra biome similar? How are they different?
22. Predicting A volcano has just erupted in the ocean near Hawaii, forming a new island. How might succession change this island over time?

---

shifts in temperature between day and night; the tundra is cool in summer and bitterly cold in winter. Desert soil is sandy; most of the soil in the tundra is frozen all year long.
22. First, lichens and mosses would grow on the bare volcanic rock and begin to break it up to form soil. Next, seeds would float or be blown onto the island or be carried and deposited there by birds; the seeds would grow in the thin layer of soil created by the lichens and mosses. As more plants grew and died, more soil would

form, supporting larger plants and trees. In time, a mature biome would develop.

Applying Skills
23. Grass: producer; mouse, rabbit, and deer: first-level consumers; snake and mountain lion: second-level consumers
24. The producers (grass)

Applying Skills

Use the diagram of a food web below to answer Questions 23–25.

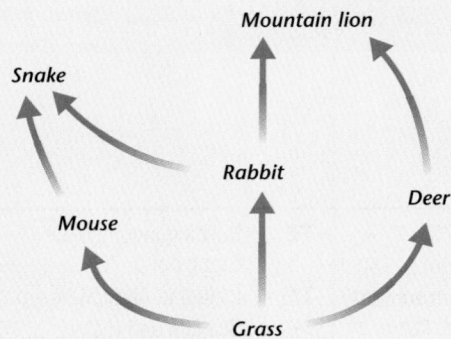

Mountain lion

Snake

Rabbit

Deer

Mouse

Grass

23. **Classifying** Identify the energy role of each organism in this food web. For consumers, specify whether they are first-level, second-level, or third-level.

24. **Inferring** Which level of the food web contains the greatest amount of available energy?

25. **Predicting** If a disease were to kill most of the rabbits in this area, predict how the snakes, deer, and mountain lions would be affected.

Performance CHAPTER PROJECT **Assessment**

Present Your Project Check over your report, poster, or other product. It should clearly present your data and conclusions about the effect of your variable on the decomposition process.

Reflect and Record In your notebook, compare your results to your predictions about the different waste materials in the compost mixture. Were you surprised by any of your results? Based on what you have learned from your project and those of your classmates, make a list of the ideal conditions for decomposition.

Test Preparation

Use these questions to prepare for standardized tests.

Study the diagram. Then answer Questions 26–29.

26. Which of the following is a producer in the jar ecosystem?
    a. fresh water
    b. fish
    c. snails
    d. water plants

27. Which of the following is a consumer in the jar ecosystem?
    a. gravel
    b. snails
    c. water plants
    d. fresh water

28. Which gas do the snails and fish release into the water?
    a. hydrogen
    b. oxygen
    c. carbon dioxide
    d. nitrogen

29. A gas released by the water plants as a result of photosynthesis is
    a. hydrogen.   b. oxygen.
    c. carbon dioxide.   d. nitrogen.

---

25. The snake and mountain lion populations would decrease because there would be fewer prey organisms for them to eat. The deer population would probably decrease at first as hungry lions preyed on deer. Later as the lion population decreased, the deer population would increase. Also, the deer would have less competition for grass.

Performance CHAPTER PROJECT **Assessment**

Present Your Project Review students' written reports, posters, and other products. You may wish to have each student or group present their report to the rest of the class. Alternatively, you could have half the class present a "poster session" to the other half, then reverse roles.

Reflect and Record Allow time for all students to compare their results so they can compile a list of "ideal" conditions. In general, compost will form most quickly when the compost is kept moist (molds grow better), well-aerated (many decomposers are aerobic), and warm (metabolic activity is higher) and when soil organisms are added.

Test Preparation

26. d 27. b 28. c 29. b

Program Resources

◆ **Inquiry Skills Activity Book** Provides teaching and review of all inquiry skills

24 Living Resources

Sections	Time	Student Edition Activities		Other Activities
CHAPTER PROJECT **Variety Show** p. 754	Ongoing (2–3 weeks)	Check Your Progress, pp. 760, 776 Present Your Project, p. 779		
1 *INTEGRATING ENVIRONMENTAL SCIENCE* **Environmental Issues** pp. 756–761 ◆ Identify the main types of environmental issues. ◆ Define environmental science.	1 period/ $\frac{1}{2}$ block	**Discover** How Do You Decide?, p. 756 **Sharpen Your Skills** Communicating, p. 760 **Real-World Lab: You and Your Environment** Is Paper a Renewable Resource?, p. 761		**TE** Building Inquiry Skills: Graphing, p. 757 **TE** Including All Students, p. 758 **TE** Science and History, p. 759 **IES** "Fate of the Rain Forest," pp. 32–35; "Where River Meets Sea," pp. 39–40
2 **Forests and Fisheries** pp. 762–767 ◆ Describe different ways that forests and fisheries can be managed to provide resources.	1–2 periods/ $\frac{1}{2}$–1 block	**Discover** What Happened to the Tuna?, p. 762 **Sharpen Your Skills** Calculating, p. 765 **Science at Home,** p. 766 **Skills Lab: Interpreting Data** Tree Cookie Tales, p. 767		**TE** Inquiry Challenge, p. 764 **TE** Real-Life Learning, p. 765 **LM** 24, "Managing Fisheries"
3 **Biodiversity** pp. 768–776 ◆ Identify the factors that affect biodiversity. ◆ Explain the value of biodiversity. ◆ Name some human activities that threaten biodiversity. ◆ List some ways that biodiversity can be protected.	1–2 periods/ $\frac{1}{2}$–1 block	**Discover** How Much Variety Is There?, p. 768 **Sharpen Your Skills** Communicating, p. 774		**TE** Building Inquiry Skills: Observing, p. 769, Communicating, pp. 770, 775; Predicting, p. 771; Making Models p. 774 **TE** Demonstration, pp. 770, 775 **TE** Addressing Naive Conceptions, p. 771 **TE** Inquiry Challenge, p. 773 **IES** "Fate of the Rain Forest," pp. 10–11, 22–23
Study Guide/Chapter Assessment pp. 777–779	1 period/ $\frac{1}{2}$ block			**ISAB** Provides teaching and review of all inquiry skills

ACTIVITY

For Standard or Block Schedule The Resource Pro® CD-ROM gives you maximum flexibility for planning your instruction for any type of schedule. Resource Pro® contains Planning Express®, an advanced scheduling program, as well as the entire contents of the Teaching Resources and the Computer Test Bank.

CHAPTER PLANNING GUIDE

Program Resources	Assessment Strategies	Media and Technology
UR Chapter 24 Project Teacher Notes, pp. 58–59 **UR** Chapter 24 Project Overview and Worksheets, pp. 60–63	**SE** Performance Assessment: Present Your Project, p. 779 **TE** Check Your Progress, pp. 760, 776 **UR** Chapter 24 Project Scoring Rubric, p. 64	Science Explorer Internet Site at www.phschool.com
UR 24-1 Lesson Plan, p. 65 **UR** 24-1 Section Summary, p. 66 **UR** 24-1 Review and Reinforce, p. 67 **UR** 24-1 Enrich, p. 68 **UR** Chapter 24 Real-World Lab, pp. 77–79	**SE** Section 1 Review, p. 760 **TE** Ongoing Assessment, pp. 757, 759 **TE** Performance Assessment, p. 760	Life Science Videotape 5; Videodisc Unit 1 Side 2, "Can We Still Get What We Need?" Audio CD, English-Spanish Summary 24-1 Interactive Student Tutorial CD-ROM, Chapter 24
UR 24-2 Lesson Plan, p. 69 **UR** 24-2 Section Summary, p. 70 **UR** 24-2 Review and Reinforce, p. 71 **UR** 24-2 Enrich, p. 72 **UR** Chapter 24 Skills Lab, pp. 80–81	**SE** Section 2 Review, p. 766 **TE** Ongoing Assessment, p. 764 **TE** Performance Assessment, p. 766	Audio CD, English-Spanish Summary 24-2 Transparency 87, "Logging Methods"
UR 24-3 Lesson Plan, p. 73 **UR** 24-3 Section Summary, p. 74 **UR** 24-3 Review and Reinforce, p. 75 **UR** 24-3 Enrich, p. 76	**SE** Section 3 Review, p. 776 **TE** Ongoing Assessment, pp. 769, 771, 773 **TE** Performance Assessment, p. 776	Life Science Videotape 5; Videodisc Unit 6, Side 2, "Can We Save the Tigers?"; "It's All Happening at the Zoo" Audio CD, English-Spanish Summary 24-3
RCA Provides strategies to improve science reading skills **GSW** Provides worksheets to promote student comprehension of content	**SE** Chapter 24 Study Guide/Assessment, pp. 777–779 **PA** Chapter 24 Performance Assessment, pp. 74–76 **CUT** Chapter 24 Test, pp. 112–115 **CTB** Chapter 24 Test	Interactive Student Tutorial CD-ROM, Chapter 24 Computer Test Bank, Chapter 24 Test

Key: **SE** Student Edition
CTB Computer Test Bank
ISAB Inquiry Skills Activity Book
GSW Guided Study Worksheets

TE Teacher's Edition
PTA Product Testing Activities by *Consumer Reports*
RCA Reading in the Content Area
PA Performance Assessment

UR Unit Resources
LM Laboratory Manual
IES Interdisciplinary Explorations Series
CUT Chapter and Unit Tests

Meeting the National Science Education Standards and AAAS Benchmarks

National Science Education Standards	Benchmarks for Science Literacy	Unifying Themes
Science As Inquiry (Content Standard A) ◆ **Design and conduct an investigation** Students observe diversity of organisms. *(Chapter Project)* ◆ **Develop descriptions, explanations, predictions, and models using evidence** Students model paper recycling. Students observe a tree cross section to draw conclusions about how the tree grew. *(Real-World Lab; Skills Lab)* **Life Science** (Content Standard C) ◆ **Diversity and adaptions of organisms** The number of different species in an area is called biodiversity. *(Chapter Project; Section 3)* **Science in Personal and Social Perspectives** (Content Standard F) ◆ **Populations, resources, and environments** Environmental science is the study of natural processes and how humans affect them. Forests and fisheries are renewable resources. Human activities can threaten biodiversity. *(Sections 1, 2, 3)* ◆ **Science and technology in society** Environmental issues include resource management, population growth, and pollution. *(Sections 1, 2)* **History and Nature of Science** (Content Standard G) ◆ **History of science** Certain individuals have influenced the viewpoints of others toward the environment. *(Science & History)*	**1B Scientific Inquiry** Students survey a plot of land to observe the diversity of organisms, model paper recycling, and observe a tree cross section to draw conclusions about the conditions in which the tree grew. *(Chapter Project; Real-World Lab; Skills Lab)* **1C The Scientific Enterprise** Certain individuals have influenced the viewpoints of many others toward environmental issues. *(Science & History)* **3A Technology and Society** Students model the process of recycling paper. *(Real-World Lab)* **3C Issues in Technology** The three main types of environmental issues are resource management, population growth, and pollution. Some methods of logging and fishing are harmful to the environment. Human activities can threaten biodiversity. *(Sections 1, 2, 3)* **4B The Earth** Forests and fisheries are renewable resources if managed properly. *(Section 2)* **5A Diversity of Life** The number of different species in an area is called biodiversity. *(Chapter Project; Section 3)*	◆ **Evolution** Extinction is the disappearance of all members of a species from Earth. *(Section 3)* ◆ **Modeling** Students model paper recycling. *(Real-World Lab)* ◆ **Patterns of Change** Any change to the environment that has a negative effect on the environment is called pollution. If fish are caught at a faster rate than they can breed, the population of a fishery decreases. Human activities have reduced biodiversity. *(Sections 1, 2, 3)* ◆ **Scale and Structure** Each pair of light and dark rings in a tree cross section represents one year's growth. *(Skills Lab)* ◆ **Stability** Managing forests and fisheries helps conserve these living resources for the future. Many people are working to preserve the world's biodiversity. *(Sections 2, 3)* ◆ **Systems and Interactions** Environmental science is the study of the natural processes that occur in the environment and how humans can affect them. Factors that affect biodiversity in an ecosystem include area, climate, and diversity of niches. Some plants produce chemicals that protect them from predators, parasites, and diseases. *(Sections 1, 3)* ◆ **Unity and Diversity** The three main types of environmental issues are resource management, population growth, and pollution. The number of different species in an area is called biodiversity. *(Sections 1, 3; Chapter Project)*

Take It to the Net

 *Interactive text at www.phschool.com*

Science Explorer comes alive with iText.

- **Complete student text** is accessible from any computer with Internet access or a CD-ROM drive.
- **Animations, simulations, and videos** enhance student understanding and retention of concepts.
- **Self-tests and online study tools** assess student understanding.

STAY CURRENT with **SCIENCE NEWS**®

Find out the latest research and information about ecology at:
www.phschool.com

Go to **www.phschool.com** and click on the Science icon. Then click on <u>Science Explorer: Life, Earth, and Physical Science</u> under PH@school.

ACTIVITY	Time (minutes)	Materials Quantities for one work group	Skills
Section 1			
Discover, p. 756	15	No special materials are required.	Forming Operational Definitions
Real-World Lab, p. 761	15; 40; 10	**Consumable** newspaper, water, plastic wrap **Nonconsumable** microscope, microscope slide, eggbeater, square pan, screen, heavy book, mixing bowl	Observing, Designing Experiments
Section 2			
Discover, p. 762	15	**Consumable** graph paper **Nonconsumable** ruler, pencil	Inferring
Sharpen Your Skills, p. 765	15	**Nonconsumable** calculator	Calculating
Science at Home, p. 766	home	No special materials are required.	Classifying
Skills Lab, p. 767	40	**Nonconsumable** tree cookie (tree cross section), metric ruler, hand lens, colored pencils, calculator (optional)	Observing, Measuring, Drawing Conclusions
Section 3			
Discover, p. 768	20	**Nonconsumable** two different birdseed or dried bean mixtures, two cups, paper plate	Inferring
Sharpen Your Skills, p. 774	20	No special materials are required.	Communicating

A list of all materials required for the Student Edition activities can be found on pages T25–T33. You can obtain information about ordering materials by calling 1-800-848-9500 or by accessing the Science Explorer Internet site at **www.phschool.com**.

Variety Show

The Chapter 24 Project is designed to develop students' appreciation for the rich diversity of living things that can be found in even a very small plot of land. The project also provides an opportunity for students to apply methods and skills that are used by field biologists.

Purpose After marking study plots of land, students will observe their plots regularly and record observations and data in a notebook. To conclude the project, students will communicate their findings in a class presentation.

Skills Focus After completing the Chapter 24 Project, students will be able to
- observe, compare and contrast, and classify organisms;
- infer relationships among organisms and between organisms and the abiotic factors in their environment;
- create a data table for recording observations;
- communicate observations and conclusions to others.

Project Time Line The Chapter 24 Project requires two to three weeks to complete. Each small group of students will begin by staking out a 1.5-by-1.5 meter plot of land and preparing a notebook for recording observations, including notes and drawings of the organisms observed, and the date, time, air temperature, and weather conditions during each observation. The major portion of the project involves making regular observations and recording data. During this time, students can use field guides to identify organisms. At the conclusion of the observation period, each group will prepare a class presentation that may include support materials such as photographs, drawings, videos, or computer displays.

Possible Materials
- To mark the plot, each group will need a meter stick or metric tape measure, four small stakes, a hammer, surveyor's tape or sturdy string, and a directional compass.
- When students observe their plots, each group will need a thermometer, hand lenses, rulers, and trowels.

CHAPTER 24 Living Resources

WEB ACTIVITY www.phschool.com

SECTION 1 Integrating Environmental Science
Environmental Issues

Discover **How Do You Decide?**
Sharpen Your Skills **Communicating**
Real-World Lab **Is Paper a Renewable Resource?**

SECTION 2 **Forests and Fisheries**

Discover **What Happened to the Tuna?**
Sharpen Your Skills **Calculating**
Science at Home **Renewable Survey**
Skills Lab **Tree Cookie Tales**

SECTION 3 **Biodiversity**

Discover **How Much Variety Is There?**
Sharpen Your Skills **Communicating**

754

- Provide a variety of field guides so students can research the names and classification of any unfamiliar organisms they observe. A field guide to animal tracks will also be helpful for students who find trace evidence of organisms that have visited the plot.
- When students are ready to prepare their class presentations, provide art supplies and audiovisual equipment such as cameras and videocassette recorders, if available.

Advance Preparation Before introducing the Chapter 24 Project, survey the grounds around your school so that you can guide students to areas where they are likely to find a good variety of organisms. If the school grounds are not appropriate, locate a nearby field, park, vacant lot, or other natural area to which you can take the class during school hours. Obtain permission to use the land, if necessary.

Launching the Project Invite students to read the project description on page 755. Then guide a class brainstorming session about nearby areas that might be good for setting up the study plots. Share what you know about

CHAPTER 24 PROJECT

Variety Show

The colors in this meadow show that many different types of organisms live here. In other places, life's variety is less obvious. In this chapter's project, you will become an ecologist as you study the diversity of life in a small plot of land. Keep in mind that the area you will study has just a small sample of the huge variety of organisms that live on Earth.

Your Goal To observe the diversity of organisms in a plot of land.

To complete this project you must
- ◆ stake out a 1.5 meter-by-1.5 meter plot of ground
- ◆ keep a record of your observations of the abiotic conditions
- ◆ identify the species of organisms you observe
- ◆ follow the safety guidelines in Appendix A

Get Started Read over the project and prepare a notebook in which to record your observations. Include places to record the date, time, air temperature, and other weather conditions during each observation. Leave space for drawings or photographs of the organisms in your plot.

Check Your Progress You'll be working on this project as you study this chapter. To keep your project on track, look for Check Your Progress boxes at the following points.

Section 1 Review, page 760: Stake out your plot, and begin to observe it.

Section 3 Review, page 776: Identify the organisms in your plot. Begin to prepare your presentation.

Present Your Project At the end of the chapter (page 779), you will present your findings to the class. You will describe your observations and share the diversity of life in your plot.

A woodchuck feasts on wildflowers in a meadow exploding with color. Black-eyed Susans, Queen Anne's lace, and butterflyweed are part of the meadow's diversity.

755

possible areas. Help students agree on appropriate areas. Suggest that students may select an area near their homes where they can carry out observations.

Distribute Chapter 24 Project Overview on pages 60–61 in Unit 5 Resources. Have students review the project rules and procedures. Encourage students' questions. Clarify whether students will be given class time for observing the plots or they must carry out the observations on their own time.

Divide the class into groups of four to six students. Explain that each group's members may decide how to divide the project responsibilities among themselves. However, every member should help plan the notebook, stake out the plot, make and record observations, and develop the group's presentation. Every member should also be prepared to answer questions about the project. You may consider allowing students to work alone surveying plots near their homes if space in the schoolyard is an issue.

To get students started, allow time for groups to meet and begin planning the project notebook. Distribute Worksheet 1, which provides instructions and a grid for making a scale drawing of the study plot. At the end of Section 1, distribute Worksheet 2, which provides guidance for recording information about the organisms that students observe.

Additional information on guiding the project is provided in Chapter 24 Project Teacher Notes on pages 58–59 in Unit 5 Resources.

Performance Assessment

The Chapter 24 Project Scoring Rubric on page 64 in Unit 5 Resources will help you evaluate how well students complete the Chapter 24 Project. You may want to share the scoring rubric with students so they are clear about what will be expected of them. Students will be assessed on
- ◆ their completeness and accuracy in making observations and recording data;
- ◆ their ability to use previous knowledge and reference sources to identify and classify organisms;
- ◆ how well they have communicated their findings to the rest of the class;
- ◆ participation in their groups.

Program Resources

- ◆ **Unit 5 Resources** Chapter 24 Project Teacher Notes, pp. 58–59; Chapter 24 Project Overview and Worksheets, pp. 60–63; Chapter 24 Project Scoring Rubric, p. 64

WEB ACTIVITY www.phschool.com

You will find an Internet activity, chapter self-tests for students, and links to other chapter topics at this site.

SECTION 1 Environmental Issues

SECTION 1 Environmental Issues

Objectives

After completing the lesson, students will be able to

◆ identify the main types of environmental issues;

◆ define environmental science.

Key Terms renewable resources, nonrenewable resources, pollution

1 Engage/Explore

Activating Prior Knowledge

Ask students: **What is an "issue"?** *(Students' responses should include the idea of a problem or question on which people have different viewpoints.)* **What are some examples of issues that you've heard about?** *(Sample answers: Should a run-down historic building in town be restored or demolished? Should owners of beachfront property be allowed to restrict public access to beaches? Should the federal government fund daycare facilities?)*

ACTIVITY

········ DISCOVER ········

Skills Focus forming operational definitions
Time 15 minutes
Tips As students identify general issues such as "air pollution," encourage them to think of specific, *debatable* questions such as "Should car manufacturers be forced to build more efficient engines so our air is cleaner?"
Expected Outcome Decisions regarding the most important issue will vary.
Think It Over Students' definitions will vary but should include the idea of environment-related questions or problems on which people have different viewpoints.

DISCOVER ··· ACTIVITY

How Do You Decide?

1. On a sheet of paper, list the three environmental issues you think are most important.

2. Form a group with three other classmates. Share your lists. As a group decide which one of the issues is the most important.

Think It Over
Forming Operational Definitions
Based on your group's discussion, how would you define the term *environmental issue*?

GUIDE FOR READING

◆ What are the main types of environmental issues?

◆ What is environmental science?

Reading Tip Before you read, make a list of ways that humans depend on the environment. As you read, add examples from the text.

Figure 1 This leopard seal's habitat could be affected if oil drilling is allowed in Antarctica. This tradeoff is an example of an environmental issue.

756

Here's a puzzle for you: What is bigger than the United States and Mexico combined; is covered with two kilometers of ice; is a source of oil, coal, and iron; and is a unique habitat for many animals? The answer is Antarctica. People once thought of Antarctica as a useless, icy wasteland. But when explorers told of its huge populations of seals and whales, hunters began going to Antarctica. Then scientists set up research stations to study the unique conditions there. They soon discovered valuable minerals beneath the thick ice.

Now the puzzle is what to do with Antarctica. Many people want its rich deposits of minerals and oil. Others worry that mining will harm the delicate ecosystems there. Some people propose building hotels, parks, and ski resorts. But others feel that Antarctica should remain undisturbed. It is not even obvious who should decide Antarctica's fate.

In 1998, 26 nations agreed to ban mining and oil exploration in Antarctica for at least 50 years. As resources become more scarce elsewhere in the world, the debate will surely continue. What is the best use of Antarctica?

Types of Environmental Issues

People have always used Earth's resources. But as the human population has grown, so has its effect on the environment. People compete with each other and with other living things for Earth's limited resources. Disposing of wastes created by people can change ecosystems. And while people are continuing to take resources from the environment, many of them cannot be replaced. These resources could eventually run out.

READING STRATEGIES

Reading Tip Prompt students' thinking by guiding them to recall what they learned about biotic and abiotic factors in Chapter 22 and about cycles of matter and relationships among organisms in Chapter 23. Students should list air, water, and food as factors that humans depend on. Some students may specify *clean* air and *clean* water. Students should add examples as they read the section.

Paraphrasing This section includes many abstract concepts that some students may find difficult to comprehend or to relate directly to their own experience. To ensure understanding as students read the section, have different volunteers summarize the text under each heading and subheading in their own words.

Figure 2 Cherries are a renewable resource. After they are harvested, new cherries will grow in their place. In contrast, the aluminum and iron used to make these kitchen tools are nonrenewable resources.

The three main types of environmental issues are resource use, population growth, and pollution. These issues are all connected, making them very difficult to solve.

Resource Use Any living or nonliving thing in the environment that is used by people is a natural resource. Some natural resources, called **renewable resources,** are naturally replaced in a relatively short time. Renewable resources include sunlight, wind, and trees. But it is possible to use up some renewable resources. For example, if people cut down trees faster than they can grow back, the supply of this resource will decrease.

Natural resources that are not replaced as they are used are called **nonrenewable resources.** Most nonrenewable resources, such as coal and oil, exist in a limited supply. As nonrenewable resources are used, the supply may eventually be depleted.

Population Growth Figure 3 shows how the human population has changed in the last 3,000 years. You can see that the population grew very slowly until about A.D. 1650. Around that time, improvements in medicine, agriculture, and sanitation enabled people to live longer. The death rate decreased. But as the population has continued to grow, the demand for resources has also grown.

Pollution Any change to the environment that has a negative effect on living things is called **pollution.** Pollution is an issue because it is often the result of an activity that benefits humans. For example, generating electricity by burning coal can result in air pollution. Some pesticides used to kill insects that eat crops are harmful to other animals.

☑ *Checkpoint* *What is a natural resource?*

Figure 3 If two's company, six billion is certainly a crowd! The human population has grown rapidly in the last few centuries. *Calculating How much has the population grown since 1650?*

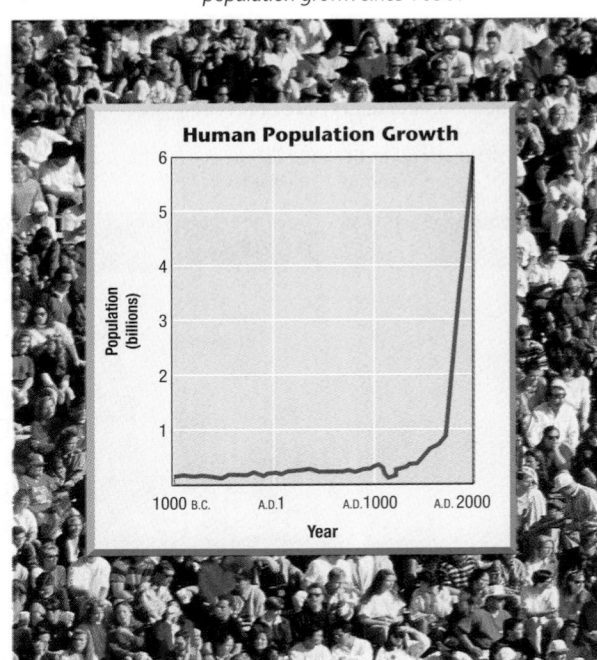

Human Population Growth

(Graph: Population (billions) on y-axis from 0 to 6; Year on x-axis: 1000 B.C., A.D.1, A.D.1000, A.D.2000)

Program Resources

◆ **Unit 5 Resources** 24-1 Lesson Plan, p. 65; 24-1 Section Summary, p. 66
◆ **Interdisciplinary Exploration Series** "Fate of the Rain Forest," pp. 32–35; "Where River Meets Sea," pp. 39–40

Media and Technology

🎧 **Audio CD** English-Spanish Summary 24-1

Answers to Self-Assessment

Caption Question

Figure 3 By more than 5 million people (from about 750 thousand to about 6 million)

☑ *Checkpoint*

A natural resource is anything in the environment that is used by people.

2 *Facilitate*

Types of Environmental Issues

Building Inquiry Skills: Graphing

Materials *graph paper, ruler, pencil, world map*
Time 15 minutes

Point out that Figure 3 shows the entire world population and that growth rates and population sizes vary among different regions and countries of the world. Give students the current populations of several countries listed below, and have each student make a bar graph to compare the population sizes. Then have students use their graphs to answer the following questions: **Which country has the largest population?** *(China)* **The next largest?** *(India)* **How many times larger than Japan's population is the U.S. population?** *(About twice as large)* Have students compare the United States' and Japan's land areas on a world map, and ask: **Which country has a higher population density?** *(Japan; if needed, help students recall the term* population density *from Chapter 22.)* **learning modality: logical/mathematical**

1998 Population of Selected Countries	
Brazil	165,200,000
China	1,255,100,000
Great Britain	58,200,000
India	975,800,000
Indonesia	207,400,000
Japan	125,900,000
Mexico	95,800,000
Nigeria	121,800,000
Russia	147,200,000
United States	270,000,000

Ongoing Assessment

Writing Have each student explain why the world's human population has grown so dramatically in the past 350 years.

Approaches to Environmental Issues

Real-Life Learning

Ask students: **What things that you do now or could start doing would help protect the environment if a lot of other people did them, too?** *(Accept all reasonable responses, such as recycling soft-drink cans instead of throwing them in the trash or putting on a sweater instead of turning up the heat at home.)* As students suggest actions, list each one on the board and ask: **How does this help solve environmental problems?** *(Sample answers: Recycling cans reduces our need to mine more aluminum, which is a nonrenewable resource. Putting on a sweater instead of turning up the heat reduces our use of heating fuel, another nonrenewable resource, and the air pollution that is released when fuels are burned.)* **learning modality: logical/mathematical**

Including All Students

Materials *current newspapers and magazines, scissors, large sheet of construction paper, tape or glue, markers*
Time *20–40 minutes*

For students who need additional challenges, provide a variety of magazines and local and national newspapers. Let students work in groups of two or three to look through the sources and find articles about environmental issues in their community, state, or region. Suggest that each group choose one issue to use as the subject of a poster that summarizes the problem in the students' own words, briefly describes different viewpoints on or proposed solutions to the problem, and includes a photograph, graph, or other visual related to the issue. Display the completed posters in the classroom. Allow time for students to review one another's posters and discuss their ideas and views about the issues. **learning modality: verbal**

758

Approaches to Environmental Issues

Dealing with environmental issues means making choices. These choices can be made at personal, local, national, or global levels. Whether to ride in a car, take a bus, or ride your bicycle to the mall is an example of a personal choice. Whether to build a landfill or an incinerator for disposing of a town's wastes is a local choice. Whether the United States should allow oil drilling in a wildlife refuge is a national choice. How to protect Earth's atmosphere is a global choice.

Choices that seem personal are often part of much larger issues. Choices of what you eat, what you wear, and how you travel all affect the environment in a small way. When the choices made by millions of people are added together, each person's actions can make a difference.

SCIENCE & History

Making a Difference

Can one individual change the way people think? The leaders featured in this time line have influenced the way that many people think about environmental issues.

1892
California writer John Muir founds the Sierra Club. The group promotes the setting aside of wild areas as national parks. Muir's actions lead to the establishment of Yosemite National Park.

1905
Forestry scientist Gifford Pinchot is appointed the first director of the United States Forest Service. His goal is to manage forests scientifically to meet current and future lumber needs.

1875   **1900**   **1925**

1903
President Theodore Roosevelt establishes the first National Wildlife Refuge on Pelican Island, Florida, to protect the brown pelican.

Theodore Roosevelt (left) and John Muir (right)

758

Background

History of Science Students could also research these people for *In Your Journal.*

◆ **Jacques Cousteau** Through his many TV films, marine explorer Cousteau educated millions about ocean life and environmental damage caused by humans.

◆ **Dian Fossey** A zoologist known for her field studies of the rare mountain gorilla in east-central Africa, Fossey urged the preservation of this endangered species.

◆ **Jane Goodall** This animal behaviorist's multigenerational studies discovered meat eating and tool use among wild chimpanzees and increased our knowledge of the ecology of nonhuman primates.

◆ **Chico Mendes** Brazilian rubber tapper Mendes fought to prevent the destruction of rain forests and to establish extractive reserves where products could be harvested without causing ecological damage.

The first step in making environmental decisions is to understand how humans interact with the environment. **Environmental science is the study of the natural processes that occur in the environment and how humans can affect them.**

When people make decisions about environmental issues, the information provided by environmental scientists is a starting point. The next step is to decide what to do with the information. But environmental decisions also involve discussions of values, not just facts and figures. The lawmakers and government agencies that make environmental decisions must consider the needs and concerns of people with many different viewpoints.

☑ *Checkpoint* *What is an example of a local choice about an environmental issue?*

In Your Journal

Find out more about one of the people featured in this time line. Write a short biography of the person's life explaining how he or she became involved in environmental issues. What obstacles did the person overcome to accomplish his or her goal?

1949
Naturalist Aldo Leopold publishes *A Sand County Almanac.* This classic book links wildlife management to the science of ecology.

1969
At the age of 79, journalist Marjory Stoneman Douglas founds Friends of the Everglades. This grassroots organization is dedicated to preserving the unique Florida ecosystem. She continues to work for the Everglades until her death in 1998.

1950   **1975**   **2000**

1962
Biologist Rachel Carson writes *Silent Spring,* which describes the harmful effects of pesticides on the environment. The book raises awareness of how human activities can affect the environment.

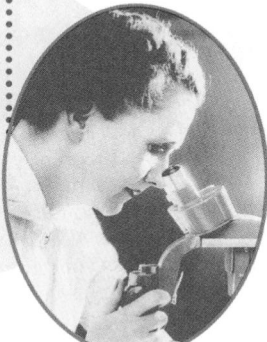

1977
Biologist Wangari Maathai founds the Green Belt Movement. This organization encourages restoring forests in Kenya and other African nations.

Chapter 24   **759**

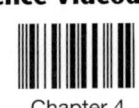
Answers to Self-Assessment

☑ *Checkpoint*
Answers will vary. *Sample answer:* Whether to build a landfill or an incinerator for disposing of a town's wastes

Building Inquiry Skills: Inferring

Point out the text statement that making decisions about environmental issues involves values, and ask: **What is a value?** *(An idea or standard that people think is important or worthwhile)* **What are some examples of values?** *(People should be honest, fair, reliable, and so forth.)* Draw students' attention to an environmental issue discussed in the text, and ask: **How would people's values affect their opinions and decisions about this issue?** *(Sample answer: Government decision makers might decide that wildlife refuges are too important to the survival of certain species to risk damaging them by oil drilling.)* **learning modality: verbal**

SCIENCE & History

ACTIVITY

Call on volunteers to read the entries on the time line. Provide a U.S. and world map and ask other volunteers to locate the places mentioned in the entries. Ask students to share any experiences or information that they have about the featured people or places. Ask students to consider which of these people they would like to learn more about.

In Your Journal Provide a variety of source materials for students' research. After students have written their biographical sketches, encourage them to work in small groups to create short skits based on their research, with one member of each group playing the role of the historical person. Encourage students to make their skits fun and interesting by using costumes and props in their portrayal of the person. Also suggest that they incorporate quotations taken from the person's writings, speeches, or interviews. **learning modality: verbal**

Ongoing Assessment

Writing Have each student explain how the actions of individuals can have a large effect on environmental issues.
 Students can save their explanations in their portfolios.

Communicating

Time 30 minutes

Tips Tell students to assume they are writing a letter to be published in their local newspaper.

Expected Outcome Students should propose a solution to an environmental issue facing their community. The potential benefits of their solution should outweigh the risks.

Extend Hold a class debate on one of the environmental issues that students have written about.

3 Assess

Section 1 Review Answers

1. Resource management, population growth, pollution

2. The study of natural processes that occur in the environment and how humans can affect those processes

3. *Costs:* Setting up drilling operations and transporting the oil would be difficult and expensive. Oil spills could damage ecosystems. *Benefits:* New oil supplies would provide fuel. Drilling for and transporting the oil would provide new jobs. Setting up oil operations in Antarctica would allow people to study its ecosystems.

4. Renewable resources are replaced naturally within a fairly short time as they are used, such as trees, sunlight, and wind. Nonrenewable resources are not replaced within a short time as they are used, such as coal and oil.

Check Your Progress ▼ CHAPTER PROJECT

Make sure students leave enough space between the plots so they can move around without walking on another group's plot. Encourage students to note any animal behaviors they see, such as feeding, fighting, or cooperating.

Performance Assessment

Skills Check Have students choose one action related to an environmental issue and create a table listing the costs and benefits.

Figure 4 The environment is valued for many different reasons.
Applying Concepts In what other ways might this area be valuable?

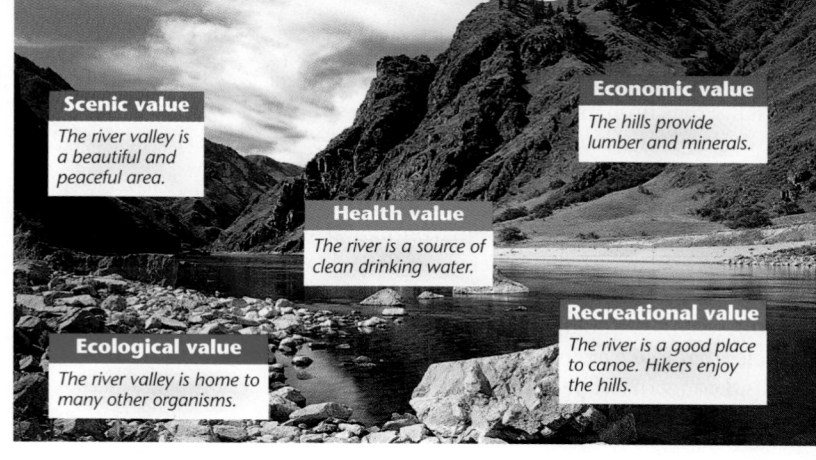

Scenic value
The river valley is a beautiful and peaceful area.

Economic value
The hills provide lumber and minerals.

Health value
The river is a source of clean drinking water.

Recreational value
The river is a good place to canoe. Hikers enjoy the hills.

Ecological value
The river valley is home to many other organisms.

Sharpen your **Skills**

Communicating

Research an environmental issue that is currently being debated in your community. List the possible costs and benefits associated with the issue. Then write a letter proposing a possible solution for the problem.   **ACTIVITY**

Weighing Costs and Benefits

To help balance different opinions, decision makers weigh the costs and benefits of a proposal. Costs and benefits are often economic. Will a proposal provide jobs? Will it cost too much money? But costs and benefits are not only measured in terms of money. For example, building an incinerator might reduce the beauty of a natural landscape (a scenic cost). But the incinerator might be safer than an existing open dump (a health benefit). It is also important to consider short-term and long-term effects. A proposal's short-term costs might be outweighed by its long-term benefits.

Consider the costs of drilling for oil in Antarctica. It would be very expensive to set up a drilling operation in such a cold and distant place. Transporting the oil would be difficult and costly. An oil spill in the seas around Antarctica could harm the fish, penguins, and seals there.

On the other hand, there would be many benefits to the drilling. A new supply of oil would provide fuel for heat, electricity, and transportation. The plan would create many new jobs. There would be more opportunity to study Antarctica. Do the benefits of drilling outweigh the costs? This is the kind of question people ask when they make environmental decisions.

 Section 1 Review

1. List the three main types of environmental issues.
2. Define environmental science.
3. List three costs and three benefits of drilling for oil in Antarctica.
4. **Thinking Critically Comparing and Contrasting** Compare renewable and non-renewable resources. Give an example of each.

Check Your Progress CHAPTER PROJECT

Stake out a square plot measuring 1.5 meters on each side. Record the date, time, temperature, and weather. Observe and record the organisms in your plot. (*Hint:* Also note evidence such as feathers or footprints that shows that other organisms have visited the plot.)

Program Resources

◆ **Unit 5 Resources** 24-1 Review and Reinforce, p. 67; 24-1 Enrich, p. 68

Media and Technology

Interactive Student Tutorial CD-ROM Chapter 24

Answers to Self-Assessment

Caption Question

Figure 4 Accept all reasonable responses. *Sample answer:* The valley might be the source of fish or other animals used for food.

You and Your Community

Is Paper a Renewable Resource?

Recycling is a common local environmental issue. In this lab, you will explore how well paper can be recycled.

Problem

What happens when paper is recycled?

Skills Focus

observing, designing experiments

Materials

newspaper   microscope   water
eggbeater   square pan   screen
plastic wrap   mixing bowl   heavy book
microscope slide

Procedure

1. Tear off a small piece of newspaper. Place the paper on a microscope slide and examine it under a microscope. Record your observations.
2. Tear a sheet of newspaper into pieces about the size of postage stamps. Place the pieces in the mixing bowl. Add enough water to cover the newspaper. Cover the bowl and let the mixture stand overnight.
3. The next day, add more water to cover the paper if necessary. Use the eggbeater to mix the wet paper until it is smooth. This thick liquid is called paper pulp.
4. Place the screen in the bottom of the pan. Pour the pulp onto the screen, spreading it out evenly. Then lift the screen above the pan, allowing most of the water to drip into the pan.
5. Place the screen and pulp on several layers of newspaper to absorb the rest of the water. Lay a sheet of plastic wrap over the pulp. Place a heavy book on top of the plastic wrap to press more water out of the pulp.
6. After 30 minutes, remove the book. Carefully turn over the screen, plastic wrap, and pulp. Remove the screen and plastic wrap. Let the pulp sit on the newspaper for one or two more days to dry. Replace the newspaper layers if necessary.
7. When the pulp is dry, observe it closely. Record your observations.

Analyze and Conclude

1. What kind of structures did you observe when you examined torn newspaper under a microscope? What are these structures made of? Where do they come from?
2. What do you think happens to the structures you observed when paper is recycled?
3. Based on your results, predict how many times a sheet of newspaper can be recycled.
4. **Apply** Should paper be classified as a renewable or nonrenewable resource? Explain.

Design an Experiment

Using procedures like those in this lab, design an experiment to recycle three different types of paper, such as shiny magazine paper, paper towels, and cardboard. Find out how the resulting papers differ. Obtain your teacher's approval for your plans before you try your experiment.

Program Resources

◆ **Unit 5 Resources** Chapter 24 Real-World Lab, pp. 77–79

Safety

Students should handle the microscope slide carefully to avoid breakage. Review the safety guidelines in Appendix A.

3. Eventually (after two or three recyclings), the fibers would become too short or too fragile to intertwine again.
4. Renewable; paper can be recycled, and new trees can be planted. However, students should note that paper cannot be recycled endlessly.

Extending the Inquiry

Design an Experiment Students' plans should be similar to the lab procedure.

You and Your Community

Is Paper a Renewable Resource?

Preparing for Inquiry

Key Concept Paper is a renewable resource because it can be recycled.
Skills Objectives Students will be able to
◆ observe and compare dry newspaper and recycled paper made from newspaper pulp;
◆ design an experiment to recycle other types of paper.
Time *Day 1:* 15 minutes; *Day 2:* 40 minutes; *Day 3:* 10 minutes
Advance Planning Gather an ample supply of old newspapers.

Guiding Inquiry

Introducing the Procedure

◆ Have students read the entire procedure. Clarify that they will do the lab on three different days: Steps 1–2 on Day 1, Steps 3–6 on Day 2, and Step 7 on Day 3.

Troubleshooting the Experiment

◆ *Day 1:* Draw students' attention to the fibers in Step 1 by asking: What do you see in the paper?
◆ *Day 2:* Have students reread Steps 3–6. Remind them to replace the newspaper under the screen each day if it is wet.
◆ *Day 3:* Tell students to make sure the pulp is completely dry before handling it.

Expected Outcome

The dried pulp will be rough, stiff, and grayish—like cardboard egg cartons. Cellulose fibers will be visible.

Analyze and Conclude

1. Fibers; they are made of plant material and come from the plants used to make the paper.
2. When the paper is soaked in water and mashed into a pulp, the fibers are broken up and separated. When the pulp is flattened and dried, the fibers intertwine again.

SECTION 2 Forests and Fisheries

Objective

After completing the lesson, students will be able to

◆ describe different ways that forests and fisheries can be managed to provide resources.

Key Terms clear-cutting, selective cutting, sustainable yield, fishery, aquaculture

1 Engage/Explore

Activating Prior Knowledge

Invite students to look around the classroom and identify as many products as they can that are derived from trees. (*Examples include writing paper, cardboard, posterboard, paper towels, wood furniture, pencils, rulers, and plywood.*)

DISCOVER

Skills Focus inferring
Materials *graph paper, ruler, pencil*
Time 15 minutes
Expected Outcome Increments used for the vertical axis may vary.
Sample Graph

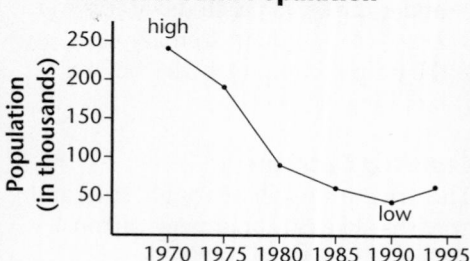

Changes in Western Atlantic Bluefin Tuna Population

Think It Over The tuna population declined steadily from 1970 to 1990, then increased from 1990 to 1994. The decline was probably due to overfishing of tuna; the rebound may have resulted from limits on tuna fishing.

DISCOVER

What Happened to the Tuna?

1. Use the data in the table to make a line graph. Label the axes of the graph and add a title. (To review graphing, see the Skills Handbook.)

2. Mark the high and low points on the graph.

Think It Over

Inferring How did the tuna population change during this period? Can you suggest a possible reason for this change?

Year	Western Atlantic Bluefin Tuna Population
1970	240,000
1975	190,000
1980	90,000
1985	60,000
1990	45,000
1994	60,000

GUIDE FOR READING

◆ How can forests and fisheries be managed?

Reading Tip As you read, make a list of ways to conserve forests and fisheries.

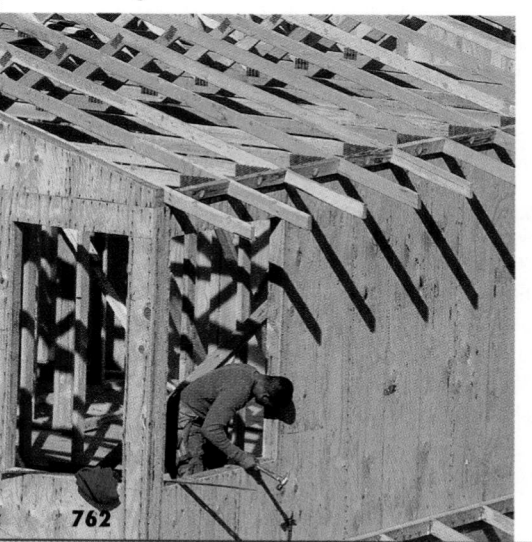

Figure 5 One important use of forest resources is for building housing.

762

At first glance, a bluefin tuna and a pine tree may not seem to have much in common. One is an animal and the other is a plant. One lives in the ocean and the other lives on land. However, tuna and pine trees are both living resources. Tuna are a source of food for people. People don't eat pine trees, but they do use them to make lumber, paper, and turpentine. People also use pine needles as mulch in gardens.

Every day you use many different products that are made from living organisms. In this section, you will read about two major types of living resources: forests and fisheries. As you read, think about how they are similar and how they are different.

Forest Resources

Forests are a resource because they contain valuable materials. Many products are made from the flowers, fruits, seeds, and other parts of forest plants. Some of these products, such as maple syrup, rubber, and nuts, come from living trees. Other products, such as lumber and pulp for paper, require cutting trees down. Conifers, including pine and spruce, are used for construction and for making paper. Hardwoods, such as oak, cherry, and maple, are used for furniture because of their strength and beauty.

Trees and other plants produce oxygen that other organisms need to survive. They also absorb carbon dioxide and many pollutants from the air. Trees also help prevent flooding and control soil erosion. Their roots absorb rainwater and hold the soil together.

Figure 6 Clear-cutting has left large portions of these hillsides bare. *Interpreting Photographs What problems might clear-cutting cause?*

Managing Forests

There are about 300 million hectares of forests in the United States. That's nearly a third of the nation's area! Many forests are located on publicly owned land. Others are owned by private timber and paper companies or by individuals. Forest industries provide jobs for 1.5 million people.

Because new trees can be planted to replace trees that are cut down, forests can be renewable resources. The United States Forest Service and environmental organizations work with forestry companies to conserve forest resources. They try to develop logging methods that maintain forests as renewable resources.

Logging Methods There are two major methods of logging: clear-cutting and selective cutting. **Clear-cutting** is the process of cutting down all the trees in an area at once. Cutting down only some trees in a forest and leaving a mix of tree sizes and species behind is called **selective cutting.**

Each logging method has advantages and disadvantages. Clear-cutting is usually quicker and cheaper than selective cutting. It may also be safer for the loggers. In selective cutting, the loggers must move the heavy equipment and logs around the remaining trees in the forest. But selective cutting is usually less damaging to the forest environment than clear-cutting. When an area of forest is clear-cut, the habitat changes. Clear-cutting exposes the soil to wind and rain. Without the protection of the tree roots, the soil is more easily blown or washed away. Soil washed into streams may harm the fish and other organisms that live there.

Sustainable Forestry Forests can be managed to provide a sustained yield. A **sustainable yield** is a regular amount of a renewable resource such as trees that can be harvested without

Social Studies CONNECTION

Many of the world's living resources are owned by no one—they are shared by everyone. A word that is sometimes used to describe such a shared resource is a "commons." This word comes from a time when villages were built around common areas of open land. All the town's residents grazed their cattle on the commons. This worked well as long as there weren't too many people. But as more and more people brought their cattle to the commons, the area would become overgrazed. There would not be enough pasture to feed even one cow—the "tragedy of the commons."

In Your Journal

Suppose you live in a farming community with a central commons. Propose a solution that will allow residents to use the commons while protecting it from overuse.

Forest Resources

Including All Students

Review for students who need more help the amount of land area on Earth suitable for forests. Have students look back at the following biome maps in Chapter 23: page 735, tropical and temperate rain forests; page 738, deciduous and boreal forests; and page 740, mountains. Trace each map onto an overhead transparency. Overlay the maps while projecting them so students can see the total land area where forests can grow. **learning modality: visual**

Managing Forests

Social Studies CONNECTION

Provide a picture of a small village with a commons, such as ones found in England or New England. To help students understand how this problem could arise, ask them to put themselves in the place of the local people. Would they stop bringing their cattle to the commons for the greater good, or would they expect others to stop?

In Your Journal Volunteers can share their ideas in a class discussion. Encourage students to comment on each idea's feasibility. **learning modality: verbal**

Media and Technology

 Transparencies "Logging Methods," Transparency 87

 Audio CD English-Spanish Summary 24-2

Answers to Self-Assessment

Caption Question

Figure 6 The soil on the hill may erode, and it may then clog streams. Areas may flood. Many organisms would lose their habitat.

Ongoing Assessment

Skills Check Have each student construct a compare/contrast table comparing the advantages and disadvantages of clear-cutting and selective cutting.

 Students could save their tables in their portfolios.

Managing Forests, continued

Inquiry Challenge

Materials *colored plastic chips, construction paper squares, or similar objects*

Time 15 minutes

Tell students that another sustainable forestry practice is to harvest all the mature trees in an area at intervals—a practice known as shelterwood cutting. In the first harvest, all the unwanted tree species and dead or diseased trees are cut down. The forest is then left alone so the remaining trees can continue to grow and new seedlings can become established. After a period of time, many of the mature trees are removed in a second harvest, and the forest is again left alone to grow. In a third harvest, the remaining mature trees are cut down. By this time, though, the seedlings have grown into young trees, and more new seedlings are growing. Challenge small groups of students to devise a simple model of shelterwood cutting. Team students who have difficulty seeing or whose movements are limited with students who do not have these disabilities. *(Sample model: Use green paper squares to represent mature trees and brown squares to represent unwanted trees. For the "first harvest," remove all brown squares. Add red squares to represent seedlings. In the "second harvest," remove some of the green squares. Replace the red squares with yellow squares to represent the growth of the seedlings into young trees, and add more red squares. In the "third harvest," remove the remaining green squares, replace the yellow squares with green squares and the red squares with yellow squares, and add more red squares.)* Have each group describe their model in writing. Ask: **How does shelterwood cutting provide a sustainable yield?** *(The forest constantly replenishes itself.)* **learning modality: kinesthetic**

reducing the future supply. This works sort of like a book swap: as long as you donate a book each time you borrow one, the total supply of books will not be affected. Planting a tree to replace one being cut down is like donating a book to replace a borrowed one.

Part of forest management is planning how frequently the trees must be replanted to keep a constant supply. Different species grow at different rates. Trees with softer woods, such as pines, usually mature faster than trees with harder woods, such as hickory, oak, and cherry. Forests containing faster-growing trees can be harvested and replanted more often. For example, pine forests may be harvested every 20 to 30 years. On the other hand, some hardwood forests may be harvested only every 40 to 100 years. One sustainable approach is to log small patches of forest. This way, different sections of forest can be harvested every year.

Certified Wood Forests that are managed in a sustainable way can be certified by the Forest Stewardship Council. Once a forest is certified, all wood logged from that forest may carry a "well-managed" label. This label allows businesses and individuals to select wood from forests that are managed for sustainable yields.

☑ *Checkpoint* **What is a sustainable yield?**

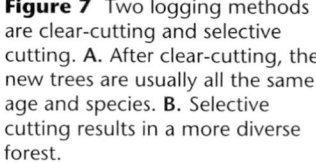

Figure 7 Two logging methods are clear-cutting and selective cutting. **A.** After clear-cutting, the new trees are usually all the same age and species. **B.** Selective cutting results in a more diverse forest.

Original forest   *Clear-cutting*   *Replanted growth*

Original forest   *Selective cutting*   *Diverse regrowth*

Background

Integrating Science Forests can have a profound effect on climate. Scientists think that deforestation contributes to changes in climate at regional and global scales. Through transpiration, trees add huge amounts of water vapor to the atmosphere. In fact, a tree returns to the air about 97 percent of the water that the tree's roots absorb from the ground. This water eventually falls back to Earth through the water cycle. Removal of a forest may cause the rainfall in a region to decline and increase the frequency of droughts.

The deforestation of tropical rain forests, so prevalent in recent years, may contribute to an increase in global temperatures. Burning the felled trees adds carbon dioxide to the atmosphere. The higher the concentration of CO_2 in the atmosphere, the more heat the atmosphere holds in and does not radiate back into space.

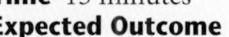

Calculating

Materials *calculator*
Time 15 minutes
Expected Outcome
China–21.6%, Japan–6.0%, United States–5.0%, Peru–7.9%
Extend Have students devise a way of visually comparing these amounts (such as a circle graph or bar graph).
learning modality: logical/ mathematical

Real-Life Learning

Suggest that students visit a fish market or the seafood and canned-fish sections of a supermarket and list the names of all the fish and seafoods they see on display. Encourage students to interview store personnel and examine labels to determine each food's country of origin. Which foods are obtained locally? Which are shipped in from other parts of the country? Which are imported from other countries? Have students report and compare their findings in class. (As an alternative, you could bring supermarket flyers and cookbooks to class and have students make a list of all the fish and seafood they find.) **learning modality: visual**

Fisheries

Until recently, the oceans seemed like an unlimited resource. The waters held huge schools of fish, and fish reproduce in incredible numbers. A single codfish can lay as many as nine million eggs in a single year! It seemed impossible that fish populations could ever disappear. But people have discovered that this resource has limits. After many years of big catches, the number of sardines off the California coast suddenly declined. The same thing happened to the huge schools of cod off the New England coast. What caused these changes?

An area with a large population of valuable ocean organisms is called a **fishery.** Some major fisheries include the Grand Banks off Newfoundland, Georges Bank off New England, and Monterey Canyon off California. Fisheries like these are valuable renewable resources. But if fish are caught at a faster rate than they can breed, the population decreases. This situation is known as overfishing.

Scientists estimate that 70 percent of the world's major fisheries have been overfished. But if those fish populations are allowed to recover, a sustainable yield of fish can once again be harvested. **Managing fisheries for a sustainable yield includes setting fishing limits, changing fishing methods, developing aquaculture techniques, and finding new resources.**

Fishing Limits Laws can help protect individual fish species. Laws may also limit the amount that can be caught or require that fish be at least a certain size. This ensures that young fish

Figure 8 A fishing boat returns to harbor at the end of a long day. Overfishing has forced the crews of many boats to find other work until the fisheries recover.

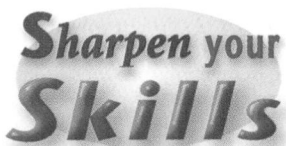

Sharpen your Skills

Calculating

In a recent year, the total catch of fish in the world was 112.9 million metric tons. Based on the data below, calculate the percent of this total each country caught.

Country	Catch (millions of metric tons)
China	24.4
Japan	6.8
United States	5.6
Peru	8.9

Answers to Self-Assessment

Checkpoint
A regular amount of a renewable resource that can be harvested without reducing the future supply

Ongoing Assessment

Writing Have each student write a paragraph comparing forests and fisheries as resources.

3 Assess

Section 2 Review Answers

1. *Any one:* replant trees, plan frequency of cutting, log small patches of forest in stages
2. *Any three:* Fishing limits can be imposed; nets with a larger mesh size can be used; dynamiting, poisoning, and other fishing methods that kill all the fish in an area can be outlawed; aquaculture can replace fishing in natural areas.
3. New trees can be planted to replace trees that are cut down.
4. Clear-cutting is quicker, cheaper, and may be safer for loggers, but selective cutting is less damaging to the environment.

Science at Home

ACTIVITY

Encourage students to look beyond the most obvious products, such as wood and paper from forests, and salt and seafood from oceans, and check labels closely to see if they can find the names of other items. Examples include nuts, spices, tree bark and salt hay for mulch, seaweeds (used both as food and in shampoos and other products), and cuttlebone for pet birds.

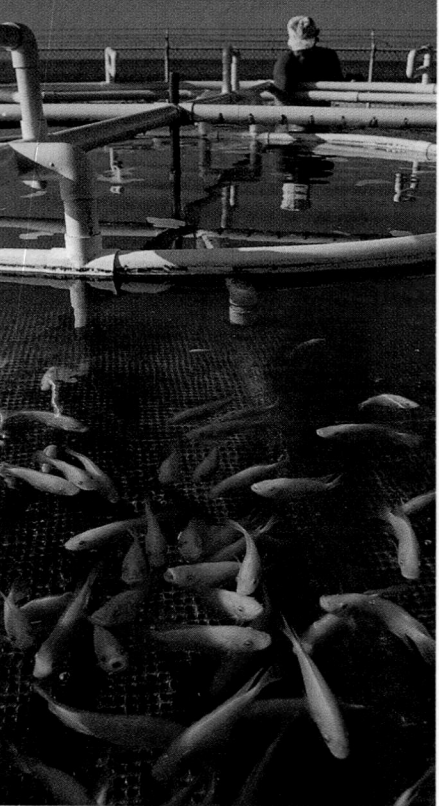

Figure 9 As fishing limits become stricter, aquaculture is playing a larger role in meeting the worldwide demand for fish. This fish farm in Hawaii raises tilapia.

survive long enough to reproduce. Also, setting an upper limit on the size of fish caught ensures that breeding fish remain in the population. But if a fishery has been severely overfished, the government may need to completely ban fishing until the populations can recover.

Fishing Methods Today fishing practices are regulated by laws. Some fishing crews now use nets with a larger mesh size to allow small, young fish to escape. Some methods have been outlawed. These methods include poisoning fish with cyanide and stunning them by exploding dynamite underwater. These techniques kill all the fish in an area rather than selecting certain fish.

Aquaculture The practice of raising fish and other water-dwelling organisms for food is called **aquaculture.** The fish may be raised in artificial ponds or bays. Salmon, catfish, and shrimp are farmed in this way in the United States.

However, aquaculture is not a perfect solution. The artificial ponds and bays often replace natural habitats such as salt marshes. Maintaining the farms can cause pollution and spread diseases into wild fish populations.

New Resources Today about 9,000 different fish species are harvested for food. More than half the animal protein eaten by people throughout the world comes from fish. One way to help feed a growing human population is to fish for new species. Scientists and chefs are working together to introduce people to deep-water species such as monkfish and tile fish, as well as easy-to-farm freshwater fish such as tilapia.

Section 2 Review

1. Describe one example of a sustainable forestry practice.
2. What are three ways fisheries can be managed so that they will continue to provide fish for the future?
3. Why are forests considered renewable resources?
4. **Thinking Critically** **Comparing and Contrasting** Describe the advantages and disadvantages of clear-cutting and selective cutting.

Science at Home

Renewable Survey With a family member, conduct a "Forest and Fishery" survey of your home. Make a list of all the things that are made from either forest or fishery products. Then ask other family members to predict how many items are on the list. Are they surprised by the answer?

Program Resources

◆ **Unit 5 Resources** 24-2 Review and Reinforce, p. 71; 24-2 Enrich, p. 72
◆ **Laboratory Manual** 24, "Managing Fisheries"

Tree Cookie Tales

Tree cookies aren't snacks! They're slices of a tree trunk that contain clues about the tree's age, past weather conditions, and fires that occurred during its life. In this lab, you'll interpret the data hidden in a tree cookie.

Problem

What can tree cookies reveal about the past?

Materials

tree cookie	metric ruler	hand lens
colored pencils	calculator (optional)	

Procedure

1. Use a hand lens to examine your tree cookie. Draw a simple diagram of your tree cookie. Label the bark, tree rings, and center, or pith.

2. Notice the light-colored and dark-colored rings. The light ring results from fast springtime growth. The dark ring, where the cells are smaller, results from slower summertime growth. Each pair of rings represents one year's growth, so the pair is called an annual ring. Observe and count the annual rings.

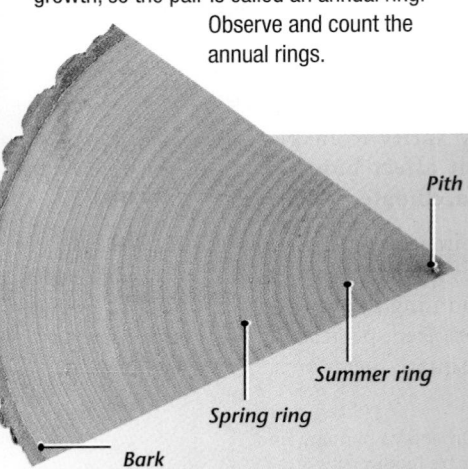

Pith

Summer ring

Spring ring

Bark

3. Compare the spring and summer portions of the annual rings. Identify the thinnest and thickest rings.

4. Measure the distance from the center to the outermost edge of the last summer growth ring. This is the radius of your tree cookie. Record your measurement.

5. Measure the distance from the center to the outermost edge of the 10th summer growth ring. Record your measurement.

6. Examine your tree cookie for any other evidence of its history, such as damaged bark or burn marks. Record your observations.

Analyze and Conclude

1. How old was your tree? How do you know?
2. What percent of the tree's growth took place during the first 10 years of its life? (*Hint:* Divide the distance from the center to the 10th growth ring by the radius. Then multiply by 100. This gives you the percent of growth that occurred during the tree's first 10 years.)
3. How did the spring rings compare to the summer rings for the same year? Suggest a reason.
4. Why might the annual rings be narrower for some years than for others?
5. Using evidence from your tree cookie, summarize the history of the tree.
6. **Think About It** Suppose you had cookies from two other trees of the same species that grew near your tree. How could you verify the interpretations you made in this lab?

More to Explore

Examine and compare several tree cookies. Do you think any of the tree cookies came from trees growing in the same area? Support your answer with specific evidence.

---

patterns, students may note holes made by insects or birds, blackening due to fire or lightning, a hollow pith due to disease, or cracks or gashes from tools.

6. You could look for annual growth patterns indicating the weather conditions and additional evidence of fire, disease, or other environmental conditions.

Extending the Inquiry

More to Explore Answers will depend on the specific tree cookies used.

Tree Cookie Tales

Preparing for Inquiry

Key Concept Growth rings provide information about a tree's age and the growing conditions during its life.

Skills Objectives Students will be able to
◆ observe growth rings in a tree cookie to determine a tree's age;
◆ draw conclusions from their observations about conditions that affected the tree's growth.

Time 40 minutes

Advance Planning Purchase or prepare a tree cookie for each group. Inexpensive classroom sets of tree cookies are available from biological supply houses. The tree cookies should come from trees that were more than 10 years old. You can also make tree cookies by sawing a tree trunk into cross sections 1.5–2.5 cm thick. To preserve homemade tree cookies, spray or paint all surfaces with clear polyurethane or other clear sealant.

Guiding Inquiry

Troubleshooting the Experiment

◆ Clarify that each year's growth is shown by a pair of rings—a light ring for spring and a dark ring for summer.

Expected Outcome

Results will vary depending on the particular tree cookies used.

Analyze and Conclude

1. Ages will vary. The tree's age is equal to the number of annual rings.
2. Answers will vary. The largest proportion of tree growth usually occurs during a tree's early years.
3. Observations may vary. Spring rings are usually wider, as trees undergo a burst of new growth in the spring when it is usually wetter followed by slower growth in the summer when it is usually drier.
4. Growth rings reflect weather conditions. Generally, rings are wider during years when temperatures are warmer and rainfall is plentiful.
5. Answers will vary. In addition to the tree's age and weather-related growth

Objectives

After completing the lesson, students will be able to
- identify the factors that affect biodiversity;
- explain the value of biodiversity;
- name some human activities that threaten biodiversity;
- list some ways that biodiversity can be protected.

Key Terms biodiversity, keystone species, extinction, endangered species, threatened species, habitat destruction, habitat fragmentation, poaching, captive breeding

1 Engage/Explore

Activating Prior Knowledge

Ask students: **What organisms are native to our area?** (*Answers will vary. Encourage students to consider a wide variety of organism types, including insects, worms, mosses, algae, and bacteria, as well as mammals, birds, fish, reptiles, and amphibians.*) Write the name of each organism on the chalkboard, and after students have finished naming organisms, ask: **Would you say there is very much diversity of species living here?** (*Answers may vary, but in most cases students will say there is.*)

DISCOVER

Skills Focus inferring
Materials *two labeled cups containing different seed mixtures, paper plate*
Time 20 minutes
Advance Preparation Use a mixture of at least ten types of seeds for Cup A and four or five types for Cup B.
Expected Outcome The average number of different kinds of seeds should be greater for the tropical rain forest.
Think It Over The tropical rain forest has a greater variety of trees than the deciduous forest. The wider variety of tree species supports a wider variety of other organisms that depend on the trees for habitat and food.

768

SECTION

3 Biodiversity

DISCOVER

.... ACTIVITY

How Much Variety Is There?

1. You will be given two cups of seeds and a paper plate. The seeds in Cup A represent the trees in a section of tropical rain forest. The seeds in Cup B represent the trees in a section of deciduous forest.

2. Pour the seeds from Cup A onto the plate. Sort the seeds by type. Count the different types of seeds. This number represents the number of different kinds of trees in that type of forest.

3. Pour the seeds back into Cup A.

4. Repeat Steps 2 and 3 with the seeds in Cup B.

5. Share your results with your class. Use the class results to calculate the average number of different kinds of seeds in each type of forest.

Think It Over
Inferring How does the variety of trees in the tropical rain forest compare with the variety of trees in a deciduous forest? Can you suggest any advantages of having a wide variety of species?

GUIDE FOR READING

- What factors affect an area's biodiversity?
- Which human activities threaten biodiversity?
- How can biodiversity be protected?

Reading Tip Before you read, use the headings to make an outline on biodiversity.

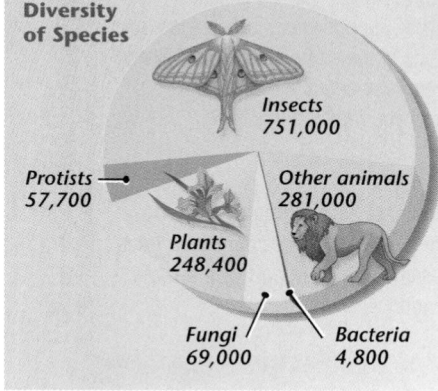

Diversity of Species

Protists → 57,700

Plants 248,400

Fungi 69,000

Insects 751,000

Other animals 281,000

Bacteria 4,800

No one knows exactly how many species live on Earth. So far, more than 1.7 million species have been identified. The number of different species in an area is called its **biodiversity.** It is difficult to estimate the total biodiversity on Earth because many areas of the planet have not been thoroughly studied. Some experts think that the deep oceans alone could contain 10 million new species! Protecting this diversity is a major environmental issue today.

Factors Affecting Biodiversity

Biodiversity varies from place to place on Earth. **Factors that affect biodiversity in an ecosystem include area, climate, and diversity of niches.**

Area Within an ecosystem, a large area will contain more species than a small area. For example, suppose you were counting tree species in a forest. You would find far more tree species in a 10-square-meter area than in a 1-square-meter area.

Figure 10 Organisms of many kinds are part of Earth's biodiversity.
Interpreting Graphs Which group of organisms has the greatest number of species?

768

READING STRATEGIES

Reading Tip As students preview the headings, suggest that they leave space between headings to add details as they read. Sample Outline:

I.   Factors Affecting Biodiversity
   A.   Area
   B.   Climate
   C.   Niche Diversity

II. The Value of Biodiversity
   A.   Economic Value
   B.   Value to the Ecosystem
III. Gene Pool Diversity
IV. Extinction of Species

In Costa Rica, which is half the size of Tennessee, there are 850 species of birds—200 more than in all the rest of North America.

A 10-hectare area of forest in Borneo contains 700 species of trees, as many as all of North America.

A single river in Brazil contains more species than all of the rivers in the United States combined.

Climate In general, the number of species increases from the poles toward the equator. The tropical rain forests of Latin America, southeast Asia, and central Africa are the most diverse ecosystems in the world. These forests cover about 6 percent of Earth's land surface and contain over half of the world's species.

The reason for the great biodiversity in the tropics is not fully understood. Many scientists hypothesize that it has to do with climate. For example, tropical rain forests have fairly constant temperatures and large amounts of rainfall throughout the year. Many plants in these regions have year-round growing seasons. This means that food is available for other organisms year-round.

Niche Diversity Coral reefs make up less than 1 percent of the oceans' area. But reefs are home to 20 percent of the world's saltwater fish species. Coral reefs are the second most diverse ecosystems in the world. Found only in shallow, warm waters, coral reefs are often called the rain forests of the sea. A reef supports many different niches for organisms that live under, on, and among the coral. This enables more species to live in the reef than in a more uniform habitat such as a flat sandbar.

☑ *Checkpoint* *What is one possible reason that tropical regions have the greatest biodiversity?*

The Value of Biodiversity

Perhaps you are wondering how biodiversity is important. Does it matter whether there are 50 or 5,000 species of ferns in some faraway rain forest? Is it necessary to protect every one of these species?

Figure 11 Tropical ecosystems tend to be more diverse than those farther from the equator.

Figure 12 Coral reefs are the second most diverse ecosystems. *Applying Concepts What is one reason why coral reefs are so diverse?*

Chapter 24 **769**

Program Resources

◆ **Unit 5 Resources** 24-3 Lesson Plan, p. 73; 24-3 Section Summary, p. 74
◆ **Interdisciplinary Exploration Series** "Fate of the Rain Forest," pp. 10–11, 22–23

Media and Technology

 Audio CD English-Spanish Summary 24-3

Answers to Self-Assessment

Caption Questions

Figure 10 insects
Figure 12 A coral reef provides many different niches, which enables a wide variety of species to live there.

☑ *Checkpoint*

Because of its unique climate, the tropical rain forest provides food year-round.

2 *Facilitate*

Factors Affecting Biodiversity

Including All Students

For students who need more help, review the meanings of the terms *area* (length times width), *climate* (the typical weather pattern in an area over a long period of time—Chapter 2, page 59), and *niche* (an organism's unique role in an ecosystem—Chapter 1, page 32). If students have difficulty defining *climate* and *niche* correctly, let them look back at the text definitions in the earlier chapters. **learning modality: verbal**

Building Inquiry Skills: Observing

Materials *books and magazines with photographs of coral reefs*
Time 15 minutes

To illustrate the rich diversity of life on coral reefs, encourage small groups of students to examine other photographs similar to Figure 12, choose a "favorite" photo, and list all the organisms shown in the photo and named in its caption or accompanying text. In a follow-up class discussion, list the number of species on the board for each group. **learning modality: visual**

Ongoing Assessment

Writing Have each student identify and briefly explain the three major factors that affect an ecosystem's biodiversity.

 Students can save their work in their portfolios.

The Value of Biodiversity

Building Inquiry Skills: Communicating

Time 20 minutes

ACTIVITY

Divide the class into small groups, and pose the following hypothetical environmental issue for each group to debate: **A chemical for making a new drug has been discovered in a plant species growing in the Amazon rain forest. Several rare species of butterflies depend on the plant for food. To harvest the chemical for human use, the plants have to be cut down and removed from the forest. Should people make use of this new resource, and if so, how?** Encourage each group to try to reach consensus on the issue. After students have debated for a time, let each group report its decision and the reasoning behind it to the rest of the class. **learning modality: verbal**

Demonstration

Materials *model architectural building blocks or photo of arch with keystone*

ACTIVITY

Time 5–10 minutes

Use model architectural building blocks to construct an arch with a keystone. (If such blocks are not available, use a photo of an arch with a keystone.) Point to the keystone, and ask: **What do you predict will happen if I remove this block?** (*Some may predict the arch will fall.*) Remove the keystone to confirm students' predictions. Explain that the block you removed is called a keystone. Ask: **Why is a keystone a good analogy for a keystone species?** (*Because when a keystone species is removed, the entire ecosystem may collapse*) **learning modality: visual**

Figure 13 Ecosystem tours such as safaris can provide income for local people. These tourists are observing giraffes in Botswana.

Figure 14 These sea stars on the Washington coast are an example of a keystone species. By preying on mussels, the sea stars keep the mussels from taking over the ecosystem.

There are many reasons why preserving biodiversity is important. The simplest reason is that wild organisms and ecosystems are a source of beauty and recreation.

Economic Value Many plants, animals, and other organisms are essential for human survival. In addition to providing food and oxygen, these organisms supply raw materials for clothing, medicine, and other products. No one knows how many other useful species have not yet been identified.

Ecosystems are economically valuable, too. For example, many companies now run wildlife tours in rain forests, savannas, mountain ranges, and other locations. This ecosystem tourism, or "ecotourism," is an important source of jobs and money for nations such as Brazil, Costa Rica, and Kenya.

Value to the Ecosystem All the species in an ecosystem are connected to one another. Species may depend on one another for food and shelter. A change that affects one species will surely affect all the others.

Some species play a particularly important role. A species that influences the survival of many other species in an ecosystem is called a **keystone species.** If a keystone species disappears, the entire ecosystem may change. For example, the sea stars in Figure 14 are a keystone species in their ecosystem. The sea stars prey mostly on the mussels that live in tide pools. When researchers removed the sea stars from an area, the mussels began to outcompete many of the other species in the tide pool. The sea star predators had kept the population of mussels in check, allowing other species to live. When the keystone species disappeared, the balance in the ecosystem was destroyed.

770

Background

Facts and Figures Scientists have not yet studied most species of plants, animals, fungi, and microorganisms to determine whether they might be useful to humans. Of approximately 250,000 known plant species, only about 25,000 have been investigated.

Insects are an often overlooked biological resource. They play a major role in pollinating crops, controlling weeds, and in controlling other insects that are pests. Some insects produce unusual chemical compounds for which humans may find some use. For example, scientists discovered a compound made by fireflies that has potential as an antiviral agent in humans. A fungicide produced by centipedes to protect their eggs might also protect crops from fungus attack.

Gene Pool Diversity

The organisms in a healthy population have a diversity of traits. As you learned in Chapter 3, these traits are determined by genes. Every organism receives a combination of genes from its parents. Genes determine the organism's characteristics, from its size and appearance to its ability to fight disease. The organisms in one species share many genes. But each organism also has some genes that differ from those of other individuals. These individual differences make up the total gene "pool" of that species.

Species that lack a diverse gene pool are less able to adapt to disease or parasites. For example, most crops, such as wheat and corn, have very little diversity. These species are bred to be very uniform. If a disease or parasite attacks, the whole population could be affected. A fungus once wiped out much of the corn crop in the United States in this way. Fortunately, there are many wild varieties of corn that have slightly different genes. At least some of these plants contain genes that make them more resistant to the fungus. Scientists were able to breed corn that was not affected by the fungus. Keeping a diverse gene pool helps ensure that crops can survive such problems.

☑ *Checkpoint* **What do an organism's genes determine?**

Extinction of Species

The disappearance of all members of a species from Earth is called **extinction.** Extinction is a natural process. Many species that once lived on Earth, from dinosaurs to dodos, are now extinct. But in the last few centuries, the number of species becoming extinct has increased dramatically.

Figure 15 Just as diversity of species is important to an ecosystem, diversity of genes is important within a species. Diverse genes give these potatoes their rainbow of colors.

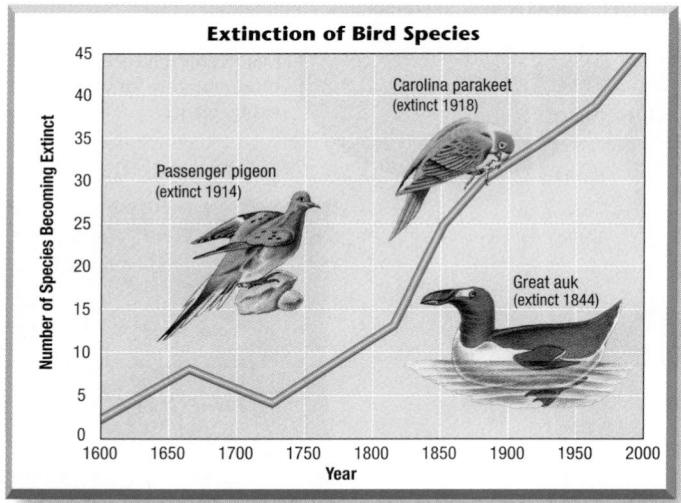

Figure 16 This graph shows the rate of extinction of bird species in the last 400 years.
Interpreting Graphs How many bird species became extinct in 1750? In 1850? In 1950?

Answers to Self-Assessment

☑ *Checkpoint*
Genes determine an organism's traits.

Caption Question
Figure 16 1750–6; 1850–24; 1950–37

Gene Pool Diversity

Building Inquiry Skills: Predicting

Ask students: **What is cloning?** (*Making an exact duplicate of an organism—more precisely, using genes taken from an organism's cells to create a new individual that is genetically identical to the original organism*) Pose the following question: **Suppose scientists found an easy and inexpensive way to create large herds of sheep, cattle, and other domestic animals through cloning. Do you think this would be a good idea? Why or why not?** (*Some students may say that cloned herds could have traits that increase our supply of meat, milk, wool, leather, and other products. However, students should realize that entire herds of genetically identical animals could increase susceptibility to disease.*) **learning modality: logical/mathematical**

Extinction of Species

Addressing Naive Conceptions

Materials *large sheet of construction paper, colored markers, source books*

When students consider extinction, they usually think of species that became extinct in the distant past. Explain that many species have become extinct in relatively recent times. Let each pair of students research one species that became extinct in the past 300 years. Examples include the quagga, dodo, moa, Tasmanian wolf (thylacine), dusky seaside sparrow, Santa Barbara song sparrow, Greek auk, Hawaii oo, passenger pigeon, and Sampson's pearly mussel. Suggest that one student in each pair draw a picture of the organism and the other student write a brief, first-person description of it—for example, *I'm a quagga, a variety of zebra. I used to live in huge, wild herds in South Africa, but I was hunted for my hide. I became extinct in 1883.* **learning modality: verbal**

Ongoing Assessment

Writing Have students explain why gene pool diversity is so important to a species' survival.

EXPLORING
Endangered Species

Make sure students realize that all of the species shown in this feature are native to the United States. Locate and label the area where each species is found on a large wall map. (Grizzly bear–northern and western U.S.; piping plover–east coastal areas; Eureka Valley primrose–Oregon; whooping crane–central and southwestern U.S.) Encourage interested students to research the names and locations of other endangered species in the United States and add them to the map. Then challenge students to create a large table on the chalkboard listing all the endangered species and the reason why each is endangered. **learning modality: visual**

Real-Life Learning

Point out to students that the tropical fish and parrots sold in reputable pet shops in this country are specifically bred for the pet trade, not imported illegally. Invite a local pet store owner or manager to speak to students about obtaining fish, parrots and other birds, exotic reptiles, and other nonnative species. **learning modality: verbal**

Once a population drops below a certain level, the species may not be able to recover. For example, millions of passenger pigeons once darkened the skies in the United States. People hunted the birds for sport and food, killing many hundreds of thousands. This was only part of the total population of passenger pigeons. But at some point, there were not enough birds to reproduce and increase the population. Only after the birds disappeared did people realize that the species could not survive without its enormous numbers.

Species in danger of becoming extinct in the near future are considered **endangered species.** Species that could become endangered in the near future are considered **threatened species.**

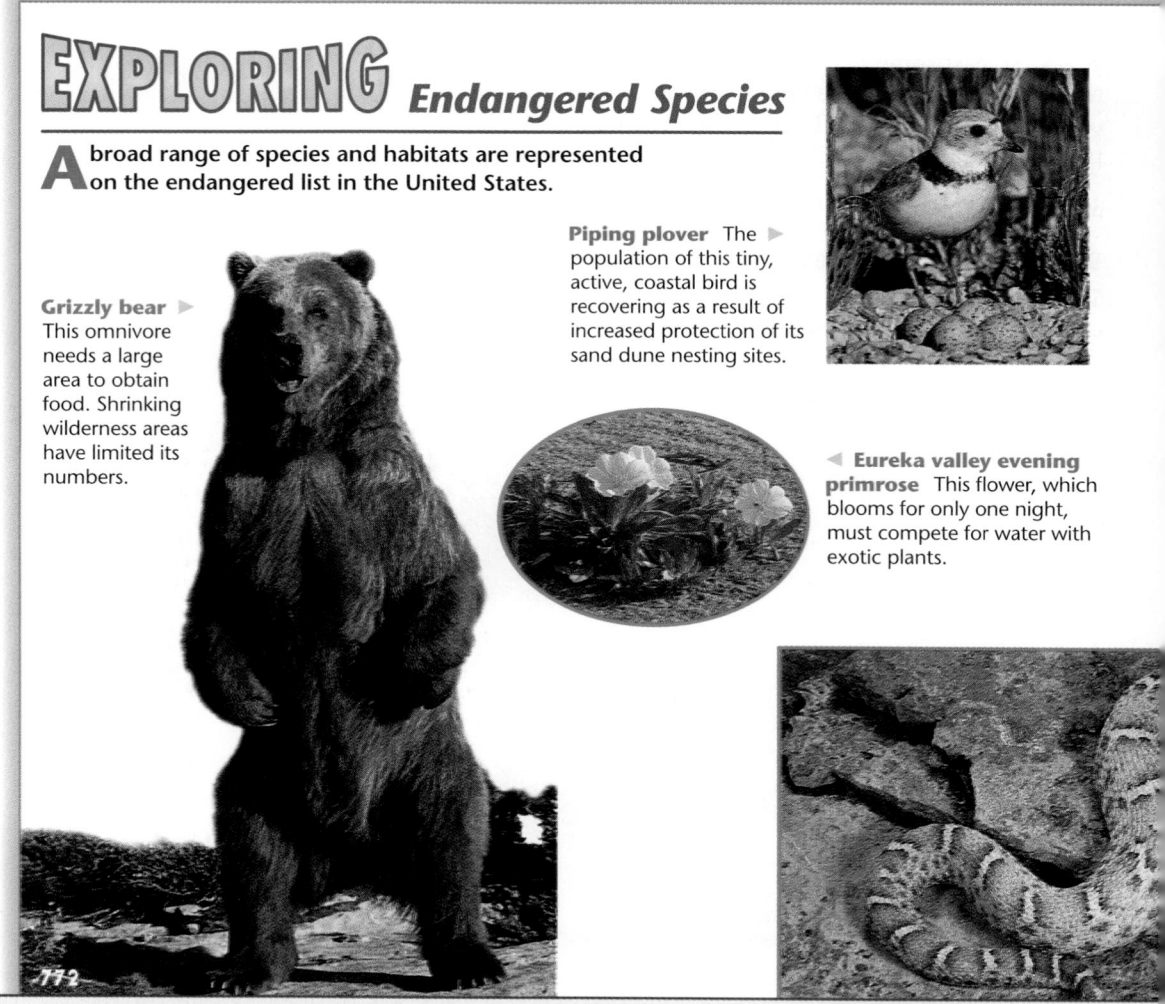

EXPLORING *Endangered Species*

Abroad range of species and habitats are represented on the endangered list in the United States.

Grizzly bear ▶ This omnivore needs a large area to obtain food. Shrinking wilderness areas have limited its numbers.

Piping plover The ▶ population of this tiny, active, coastal bird is recovering as a result of increased protection of its sand dune nesting sites.

◀ **Eureka valley evening primrose** This flower, which blooms for only one night, must compete for water with exotic plants.

772

Background

Facts and Figures According to Worldwatch, a research institute that monitors environmental issues, primates are one of the most threatened groups of species on Earth today. Almost half of the world's more than 200 primate species are in danger of extinction.

The declines are due largely to human activity, as forests are lost through logging and clearing for building homes and agriculture. In Malaysia and Indonesia, nearly 80 percent of the forests used by orangutans have been cut down. Japan's macaques are losing living space to cities. Primates are also hunted in various places. Orangutans, gorillas, gibbons, and chimps are trapped for the pet trade.

Exploring Endangered Species shows some organisms that are endangered in the United States. Threatened and endangered species are found on every continent and in every ocean. Ensuring that these species survive is one way to protect Earth's biodiversity.

Causes of Extinction

A natural event, such as an earthquake or volcano, can damage an ecosystem, wiping out populations or even some species. **Human activities can also threaten biodiversity. These activities include habitat destruction, poaching, pollution, and the introduction of exotic species.**

◀ **Steller's sea lion** This mammal competes with fishermen for its prey along the Pacific coast.

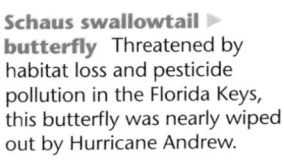

Schaus swallowtail ▶ butterfly Threatened by habitat loss and pesticide pollution in the Florida Keys, this butterfly was nearly wiped out by Hurricane Andrew.

▲ **Whooping crane** Threatened by habitat destruction and disease, half of the remaining population of this wading bird is in captivity. The species seems to be recovering well since its lowest point in the 1940s.

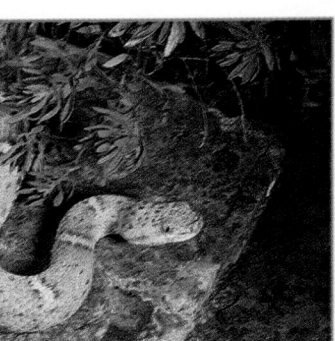

◀ **New Mexico ridgenose rattlesnake** Illegal collectors have reduced the population of this rare snake, the largest known group of which lives in a single canyon.

Chapter 24 **773**

Causes of Extinction

Inquiry Challenge

Materials *plastic chips or paper squares*
Time 10 minutes

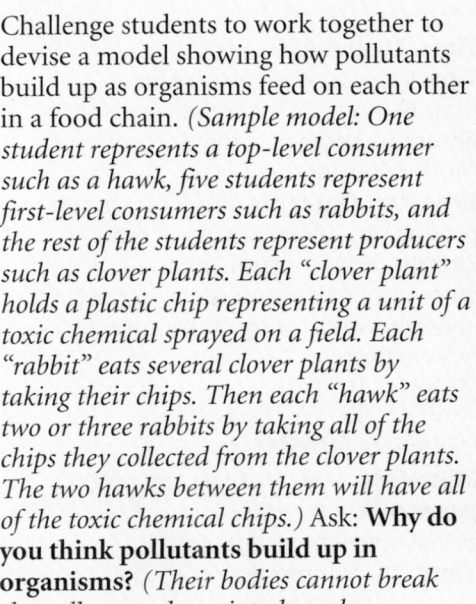

Challenge students to work together to devise a model showing how pollutants build up as organisms feed on each other in a food chain. *(Sample model: One student represents a top-level consumer such as a hawk, five students represent first-level consumers such as rabbits, and the rest of the students represent producers such as clover plants. Each "clover plant" holds a plastic chip representing a unit of a toxic chemical sprayed on a field. Each "rabbit" eats several clover plants by taking their chips. Then each "hawk" eats two or three rabbits by taking all of the chips they collected from the clover plants. The two hawks between them will have all of the toxic chemical chips.)* Ask: **Why do you think pollutants build up in organisms?** *(Their bodies cannot break the pollutants down into harmless materials or get rid of them as waste products.)* **cooperative learning**

Including All Students

Encourage students who need additional challenges to research other examples of exotic species that have been introduced to the United States that compete with native species, and what has happened to the native species as a result. Examples include the blue water hyacinth, purple loosestrife, kudzu, leafy spurge, Eurasian milfoil, tamarisk tree, flathead catfish, sea lamprey, green crab, zebra mussel, gypsy moth, brown tree snake, and starling. Let students share their findings in a class discussion. **learning modality: verbal**

Ongoing Assessment

Oral Presentation Call on volunteers to give a one-minute speech about the importance of saving endangered species. Suggest that each student choose one reason and make that the subject of the speech.

Causes of Extinction, continued

Sharpen your Skills

Communicating

Time 20 minutes
Tips Caution students to obtain permission from store managers or librarians before leaving the brochures for distribution.
Expected Outcome Students should produce an informative brochure.
Extend Have a member of a local environmental group speak to the class about how the group distributes its information.

Building Inquiry Skills: Making Models

Materials *sheet of graph paper ruled in centimeters, pencil, calculator (optional)*
Time 10–15 minutes

Use the following activity to demonstrate habitat fragmentation. Have each student draw a rounded rectangle, roughly 20 by 25 cm, on a sheet of graph paper. Explain that the rectangle represents a rain forest in Indonesia and that each centimeter on the graph paper represents 10 m on the actual land. Ask: **How much land does each square centimeter represent?** *(100 m²)* Have students calculate the forest's approximate area. *(50,000 m²)* Next, have students draw a 9-cm by 8-cm rectangle in the middle of one side of the forest, to represent land that was cleared for farming, and a 1-cm-wide "road" through the middle of the forest along the cleared area, dividing the forest into three smaller pieces. Let students calculate the area of each smaller piece and the total area remaining. *(6,300 m² + 4,500 m² + 30,000 m² = 40,800 m²)* Pose the following question: **Suppose orangutans live in this rain forest. Each one needs 10,000 m² of land area to survive. How many orangutans could have lived in the original forest?** *(5)* **How many can live in the remaining forest?** *(3)* **Why not four?** *(The two smaller pieces of forest are too small to support any orangutans at all.)* **learning modality: logical/mathematical**

Figure 17 Building this subdivision caused the habitats in the area to change. Open land was replaced by houses, streets, and yards. *Inferring How would these changes affect species in this area?*

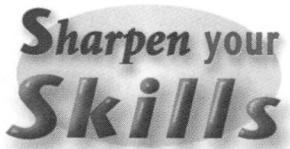

Sharpen your Skills

Communicating

Use references from environmental organizations or your library to discover what threatened and endangered species live in your state. With your classmates, develop a brochure featuring pictures and facts about these species. With your teacher's permission, distribute your brochure at stores or libraries in your area.

Habitat Destruction The major cause of extinction is **habitat destruction,** the loss of a natural habitat. This can occur when forests are cleared to build towns or create grazing land. Plowing grasslands or filling in wetlands greatly changes those ecosystems. Some species may not be able to survive such changes to their habitats.

Breaking larger habitats into smaller, isolated pieces, or fragments, is called **habitat fragmentation.** For example, building a road through a forest disrupts habitats. This makes trees more vulnerable to wind damage. Plants may be less likely to successfully disperse their seeds. Habitat fragmentation is also very harmful to large mammals. These animals usually need large areas of land to find enough food to survive. They may not be able to obtain enough resources in a small area. They may also be injured trying to cross to another area.

Poaching The illegal killing or removal of wildlife species is called **poaching.** Many endangered animals are hunted for their skin, fur, teeth, horns, or claws. These things are used for making medicines, jewelry, coats, belts, and shoes.

People illegally remove organisms from their habitats to sell them as exotic pets. Tropical fish, tortoises, and parrots are very popular pets, making them valuable to poachers. Endangered plants may be illegally dug up and sold as houseplants. Others are poached to be used as medicines.

Pollution Some species are endangered because of pollution. Substances that cause pollution, called pollutants, may reach animals through the water they drink or air they breathe. Pollutants may also settle in the soil. From there they are absorbed by plants, and build up in other organisms through the food chain. Pollutants may kill or weaken organisms or cause birth defects.

Exotic Species Introducing exotic species into an ecosystem can threaten biodiversity. When European sailors began visiting Hawaii a couple of hundred years ago, rats from their ships escaped onto the islands. Without any predators in Hawaii, the rats multiplied quickly. They ate the eggs of the nene goose. To protect the geese, people brought the rat-eating mongoose from India to help control the rat population. Unfortunately, the mongooses preferred eating eggs to eating rats. With both the rats and the mongoose eating its eggs, the nene goose is now endangered.

Background

Facts and Figures While people are most aware of endangered birds and mammals, many other kinds of living things are listed as endangered species. At the beginning of 2000, 482 kinds of animals and 719 kinds of plants were listed as endangered or threatened in the United States. Most of the plants listed were flowering plants, but there were also 26 ferns and 3 conifers. In addition, 2 lichens were included on the roster. Many invertebrates also were listed, including 69 clams, 4 crayfish, and 2 spiders.

Protecting Biodiversity

Many people are working to preserve the world's biodiversity. Some focus on protecting individual endangered species, such as the giant panda or the Florida panther. Others try to protect entire ecosystems, such as the Great Barrier Reef in Australia. **Many programs to protect biodiversity combine scientific and legal approaches.**

Captive Breeding   One scientific approach to protecting severely endangered species is captive breeding. **Captive breeding** is the mating of animals in zoos or wildlife preserves. Scientists care for the young to increase their chance of survival. These offspring are then released back into the wild.

A captive breeding program was the only hope for the California condor. California condors are the largest birds in North America. They became endangered as a result of habitat destruction, poaching, and pollution. By the mid-1980s there were fewer than ten California condors in the wild. Fewer than 30 were in zoos. Scientists captured all the wild condors and brought them to the zoos. Soon afterward, the first California condor chick was successfully bred in captivity. Today, there are more than 100 California condors in zoos. Some condors have even been returned to the wild. Though successful, this program has cost more than $20 million. It is not possible to save many species in this costly way.

Laws and Treaties   Laws can help protect individual species. Some nations have made it illegal to sell endangered species or products made from them. In the United States, the Endangered Species Act of 1973 prohibits importing or trading products made from threatened or endangered species. This law also requires the development of plans to save endangered species.

Figure 18 Captive breeding programs use a scientific approach to protect endangered species.
A. California condor chicks raised in captivity need to learn what adult condors look like. Here, a scientist uses a condor puppet to feed and groom a chick.
B. These young green turtles were hatched in the laboratory. Now a researcher is releasing the turtles into their natural ocean habitat.

Building Inquiry Skills: Communicating

Time 15 minutes

ACTIVITY

After students read about the California condor, share the following information: In 1973, the federal government listed the gray wolf (timber wolf) as endangered after its population dropped to a few hundred in Minnesota and to almost zero in the other lower-48 states. This protected gray wolves from hunting and trapping. In addition, captive breeding programs released more gray wolves into the wild. Biologists estimate that there are now 2,380 wolves in Minnesota and Wisconsin. In 1998 the government recommended removing the gray wolf from the endangered species list. Divide the class into groups to debate the issue of hunting and trapping bans from two viewpoints—that of farmers and ranchers who are losing animals to gray wolf predation, and that of people who support continued protection of the species. **learning modality: verbal**

Demonstration

Materials *aquarium, sand, water, 2 crayfish, several cans and/or boards*

ACTIVITY

Time 15 minutes for initial set-up

Explain that people can help preserve biodiversity by constructing artificial habitats to replace ones that were destroyed or damaged. Let students help you create an "artificial" habitat: set up an aquarium with only sand in the bottom, and add two crayfish. Have students observe the crayfish for a day or two. Then add several cans and/or boards to the aquarium to provide hiding places. Let students continue to observe the crayfish. **learning modality: visual**

Answers to Self-Assessment

Caption Question

Figure 17 Organisms could no longer meet their food and shelter needs from their surroundings. The number of species probably decreased.

Ongoing Assessment

Skills Check Have each student draw a concept map identifying and explaining the four human causes of extinction described in the text.
 Students can save their concept maps in their portfolios.

3 Assess

Section 3 Review Answers

1. Area, climate, and diversity of niches
2. Habitat destruction, poaching, pollution, and exotic species
3. *Legal approach:* Laws such as the Endangered Species Act and the Convention on International Trade in Endangered Species; *Scientific approach:* captive breeding in zoos or wildlife preserves, habitat preservation
4. Tropical rain forests and coral reefs
5. Biodiversity is important for beauty and recreation, economic reasons, the health of ecosystems, and genetic diversity.
6. A keystone species is one that influences the survival of many other species in an ecosystem. If something happens to the keystone species, all other species in the ecosystem are affected.

Check Your Progress

CHAPTER PROJECT

As students observe their plots, encourage them to draw the organisms in detail so they can identify them later using field guides. Remind students to make notes about abiotic factors as well. Check each group's notebook occasionally to make sure students are recording data.

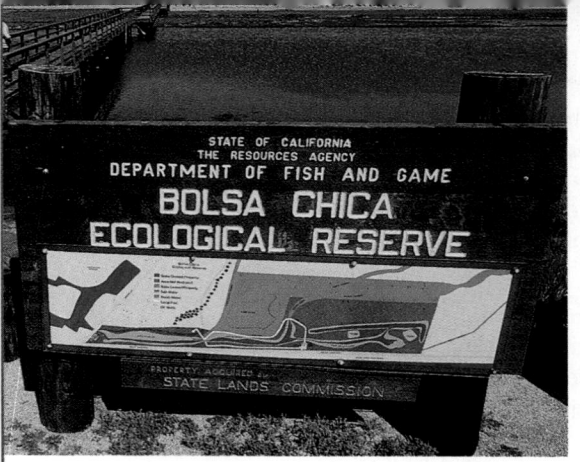

Figure 19 Preserving whole habitats is probably the most effective way to protect biodiversity.

American alligators, Pacific gray whales, and green sea turtles are just a few of the species that have begun to recover as a result of legal protection.

The most important international treaty protecting wildlife is the Convention on International Trade in Endangered Species. Eighty nations signed this treaty in 1973. This treaty lists nearly 700 threatened and endangered species that cannot be traded for profit. Laws like these are difficult to enforce. Even so, they have helped to reduce the poaching of many endangered species, including African elephants, snow leopards, sperm whales, and mountain gorillas.

Habitat Preservation The most effective way to preserve biodiversity is to protect whole ecosystems. Preserving whole habitats saves not only endangered species, but also other species that depend on them.

Beginning in 1872 with Yellowstone National Park, the world's first national park, many countries have set aside wildlife habitats as parks and refuges. In addition, private organizations have purchased millions of hectares of endangered habitats throughout the world. Today, there are about 7,000 nature parks, preserves, and refuges in the world.

To be most effective, reserves must have the characteristics of diverse ecosystems. For example, they must be large enough to support the populations that live there. The reserves must contain a variety of niches. And of course, it is still necessary to keep the air, land, and water clean, remove exotic species, and control poaching.

Section 3 Review

1. What are three factors that affect biodiversity?
2. List four possible causes of extinction.
3. Give an example of a legal approach and a scientific approach to preventing extinction.
4. Which are the most diverse ecosystems on Earth?
5. Identify three ways in which biodiversity is important.
6. **Thinking Critically Making Generalizations** Explain how the statement "In the web of life, all things are connected" relates to keystone species.

Check Your Progress

CHAPTER PROJECT

Visit your plot regularly. Use field guides to identify the organisms you observe. Record their locations within your plot along with their common and scientific names. You should also be planning how to present your findings. Consider using a series of drawings, a flip chart, a computer presentation, or a video of your plot with closeups of the species you have identified. (*Hint:* Be sure to include the data you collected on abiotic factors.)

Program Resources

◆ **Unit 5 Resources** 24-3 Review and Reinforce, p. 75; 24-3 Enrich, p. 76

Media and Technology

 Exploring Life Science Videodisc
Unit 6, Side 2,
"It's All Happening at the Zoo"

Chapter 6

Performance Assessment

Writing Have each student identify and briefly describe the four causes of extinction presented in the text.

Portfolio Students can save their work in their portfolios.

CHAPTER 24 STUDY GUIDE

SECTION 1 — Environmental Issues

INTEGRATING ENVIRONMENTAL SCIENCE

Key Ideas
- Three types of environmental issues are resource use, population growth, and pollution.
- Environmental science is the study of the natural processes that occur in the environment and how humans can affect them.
- Making environmental decisions requires balancing different viewpoints and weighing the costs and benefits of proposals.

Key Terms
renewable resources
nonrenewable resources
pollution

SECTION 2 — Forests and Fisheries

Key Ideas
- Because new trees can be planted to replace those that are cut down, forests can be renewable resources.
- Managing fisheries involves setting fishing limits, changing fishing methods, developing aquaculture techniques, and finding new resources.

Key Terms
clear-cutting
selective cutting
sustainable yield
fishery
aquaculture

SECTION 3 — Biodiversity

Key Ideas
- Factors that affect biodiversity include area, climate, and diversity of niches.
- Tropical rain forests and coral reefs are the two most diverse ecosystems.
- Human activities that threaten biodiversity include habitat destruction, poaching, pollution, and the introduction of exotic species.
- Three techniques for protecting biodiversity are regulating capture and trade, captive breeding, and habitat preservation.

Key Terms
biodiversity	habitat destruction
keystone species	habitat fragmentation
extinction	poaching
endangered species	captive breeding
threatened species	

Organizing Information

Concept Map Copy the biodiversity concept map below onto a sheet of paper. Complete it and add a title. (For more on concept maps, see the Skills Handbook.)

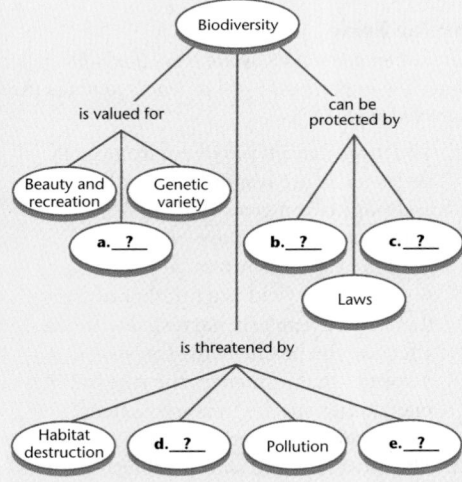

Chapter 24 **777**

Organizing Information

Concept Map **a.** Economic value; **b., c.** Captive breeding, Habitat preservation; **d., e.** Poaching, Exotic species. Sample title: Facts About Biodiversity

Program Resources

- **Unit 5 Resources** Chapter 24 Project Scoring Rubric, p. 64
- **Performance Assessment** Chapter 24, pp. 74–76
- **Chapter and Unit Tests** Chapter 24 Test, pp. 112–115

Media and Technology

 Interactive Student Tutorial CD-ROM Chapter 24

 Computer Test Bank Chapter 24 Test

Reviewing Content

Multiple Choice

1. b 2. a 3. d 4. a 5. b

True or False

6. true 7. renewable 8. true 9. keystone
10. preservation

Checking Concepts

11. *Sample answers: personal/local issue*—deciding whether to recycle materials; *national/global issue*—setting aside land for wildlife refuges
12. By considering the viewpoints of many different people and weighing the costs and benefits of different solutions
13. Clear-cutting exposes soil to erosion by wind and water, damages streams with eroded silt, and destroys forest habitats. Selective cutting is less damaging to the forest environment and maintains diversity.
14. *Any one:* Set limits on the amount and/or size of fish that can be caught; use nets with a larger mesh size; outlaw fishing methods that kill all the fish in an area rather than selected species; raise fish on farms (aquaculture)
15. Species lose the places where they feed, breed, and nest. If they cannot find a substitute niche, they must move to a new location to survive. If they cannot relocate, they will not survive.
16. Building houses carries scenic, ecological, and recreational costs but an economic benefit. A factory may carry health costs and would be economically beneficial. The health and scenic value of community gardens would balance the ecological and recreational costs. A wildlife refuge would be economically costly but a scenic, ecological and recreational benefit. Each student's editorial should demonstrate an understanding of both the costs and benefits of the student's chosen proposal.

Thinking Critically

17. As the number of humans increases, they compete with other species for space, food, water, and other resources. More humans also create more pollution and develop more land, which in turn destroys natural habitats. Pollution and habitat destruction can threaten the survival of some species.

Reviewing Content

For more review of key concepts, see the Interactive Student Tutorial CD-ROM.

Multiple Choice

Choose the letter of the best answer.

1. Which of the following is a benefit of drilling for oil in Antarctica?
   a. It would be expensive to drill there.
   b. It would create new jobs.
   c. It could harm the area wildlife.
   d. It would be difficult to transport the oil.
2. The practice of raising fish for food is called
   a. aquaculture.   b. overfishing.
   c. poaching.   d. captive breeding.
3. The most diverse ecosystems in the world are
   a. coral reefs.   b. deserts.
   c. grasslands.   d. tropical rain forests.
4. If all members of a species disappear from Earth, that species is
   a. extinct.   b. endangered.
   c. nonrenewable.   d. threatened.
5. The illegal removal from the wild or killing of an endangered species is called
   a. habitat destruction.
   b. poaching.
   c. pollution.
   d. captive breeding.

True or False

If the statement is true, write true. If it is false, change the underlined word or words to make the statement true.

6. The three main types of environmental issues today are resource use, pollution, and population growth.
7. Forests and fisheries are examples of nonrenewable resources.
8. A sustainable yield is a number of trees that can be regularly harvested without affecting the health of the forest.
9. A species that influences the survival of many other species in an ecosystem is called a(n) endangered species.
10. The most effective way to protect biodiversity is through habitat fragmentation.

Checking Concepts

11. Give an example of a personal or local environmental issue and an example of a national or global environmental issue.
12. Explain how environmental decisions are made.
13. Compare the effects of clear-cutting and selective cutting on forest ecosystems.
14. Describe one way that people can prevent overfishing.
15. Explain how habitat destruction affects species.
16. **Writing to Learn** You are a member of the county land use commission. Hundreds of people are moving to your county every day. You must make a decision regarding how to manage a 5,000-hectare woodland area in your county. The proposals include using the land for housing, for a new factory, for community gardens, or for a wildlife refuge. List the costs and benefits of each option. Then choose one and write an editorial for a newspaper explaining your position.

Thinking Critically

17. **Relating Cause and Effect** Explain how human population growth affects other species on Earth.
18. **Making Generalizations** Describe how an exotic species can threaten other species in an ecosystem.
19. **Predicting** How could the extinction of a species today affect your life 20 years from now?
20. **Making Judgments** Suppose you were given $1 million toward saving an endangered turtle species. You could use the money to start a captive breeding program for the turtles. Or you could use the money to purchase and protect part of the turtle's habitat. How would you spend the money? Explain your answer.

---

18. An exotic species may compete with native species for limited resources. If the exotic species has no natural predators in its new habitat, it may outcompete the native species.
19. *Sample answers:* The species might have been the source of a medicine or had another use that is unknown today. The species might have been the source of genes for rare traits that could help other species survive.

20. Accept all reasonable responses so long as students support their choices with well-reasoned arguments that include why the method has a greater chance of success or can achieve more for the money invested.

Applying Skills

One study identifies the reasons that mammal and bird species are endangered or threatened. Use the table to answer Questions 21–23.

Reason	Mammals	Birds
Poaching	31%	20%
Habitat loss	32%	60%
Exotic species	17%	12%
Other causes	20%	8%

21. Graphing Make a bar graph comparing the reasons that mammals and birds are endangered and threatened. Show percents for each animal group on the vertical axis and reasons on the horizontal axis.

22. Interpreting Data What is the major reason that mammals become endangered or threatened? What mainly endangers or threatens birds?

23. Developing Hypotheses Suggest explanations for the differences between the data for mammals and birds.

CHAPTER PROJECT

Performance ▼ Assessment

Present Your Project In your presentation, describe the biodiversity in your plot. Suggest an explanation for any patterns you observed. Make sure each person in your group has a role in the presentation. Before the presentation day, brainstorm questions your classmates might ask. Then prepare answers for them.

Reflect and Record In your journal, write what you learned from observing a single location. Which of your findings were surprising? What was the hardest part of this project? What would you do differently if you did this project again?

Test Preparation
Use these questions to prepare for standardized tests.

Read the passage. Then answer Questions 24–26.
The Pacific yew tree is very resistant to disease and insects. Scientists began studying the bark of the Pacific yew to find out why it was so hardy. They discovered a chemical in the tree's bark, named taxol, that protects the tree from damage.

When scientists experimented with taxol in the laboratory, they found that the chemical affects cancer cells in an unusual way. Typically, cancer cells grow and divide rapidly, forming a mass of cells called a tumor. Taxol prevents cancer cells from dividing and shrinks certain types of tumors. Today, taxol is used to treat thousands of cancer patients each year.

Many scientists are concerned that the supply of Pacific yew trees has dwindled. Unfortunately, much of the yew tree's natural habitat has been lost. Only recently have people realized the importance of protecting the remaining Pacific yew trees for future generations.

24. What is the main idea of this passage?
   a. Taxol is used to treat cancer patients.
   b. Pacific yew trees produce a cancer-fighting substance.
   c. The Pacific yew tree is resistant to diseases.
   d. Cancer cells grow and divide rapidly.

25. According to this passage, what effect does taxol have on cancer cells?
   a. Taxol causes cancerous tumors to form.
   b. Taxol causes cancer cells to divide rapidly.
   c. Taxol prevents cancer cells from dividing.
   d. Taxol has no effect on cancer cells.

26. Why did scientists first become interested in studying the Pacific yew tree?
   a. The tree's habitat was being destroyed.
   b. They wanted to understand how taxol shrunk tumors.
   c. They wanted to learn about taxol's chemical structure.
   d. They wanted to find out why the Pacific yew tree was so hardy.

Chapter 24 **779**

---

22. Habitat loss is the major cause for both birds and mammals. Poaching is almost as significant for mammals.

23. *Sample answer:* Areas where birds tend to nest and breed, such as wetlands, are particularly threatened by habitat destruction.

CHAPTER PROJECT

Performance ▼ Assessment

Present Your Project Before groups give their presentations to the entire class, meet with each group briefly to review students' plans. Suggest any questions that may not have occurred to them.
Reflect and Record Let each group reconvene to discuss their answers to these questions, then encourage all groups to share their ideas in a class discussion.

Test Preparation
24. b **25.** c **26.** d

Applying Skills

21.

Program Resources

◆ **Inquiry Skills Activity Book** Provides teaching and review of all inquiry skills

INTERDISCIPLINARY EXPLORATION

African Rain Forests

This Interdisciplinary Exploration presents the central theme of rain forest diversity from four different curriculum perspectives: science, mathematics, social studies, and language arts. The four explorations are designed to capture students' interest and help them see how the content they are studying in science relates both to other school subjects and to interesting real-world events. The unit is particularly suitable for team teaching.

1 Engage/Explore

Activating Prior Knowledge

Help students recall what they learned about rain forests in Chapter 23, Ecosystems and Biomes, by asking: **Where are Earth's tropical rain forests located?** (*South and Central America, southeast Asia, Indonesia, and Africa*) **What other kind of rain forest is there? Where is it located?** (*Temperate rain forest; along the northwestern coast of the United States*) Let students look back at the rain forest biome map on page 735 in Chapter 23 to verify their responses.

Introducing the Exploration

Draw students' attention to the map on this page. Ask: **Where are the African rain forests located?** (*At or close to the equator*) **What is the climate like in a tropical rain forest?** (*Warm, humid, and rainy*) **Why do you think the nations in east Africa have no tropical rain forests?** (*East Africa's climate must not be humid and rainy enough for rain forests.*) Invite students to read the text on this page to see whether their response is correct. (*The text describes east Africa as both drier and more heavily populated than central Africa.*) Then ask: **How great is the biodiversity in tropical rain forests compared with the biodiversity in other biomes?** (*Tropical rain forests are the most diverse biomes on Earth.*)

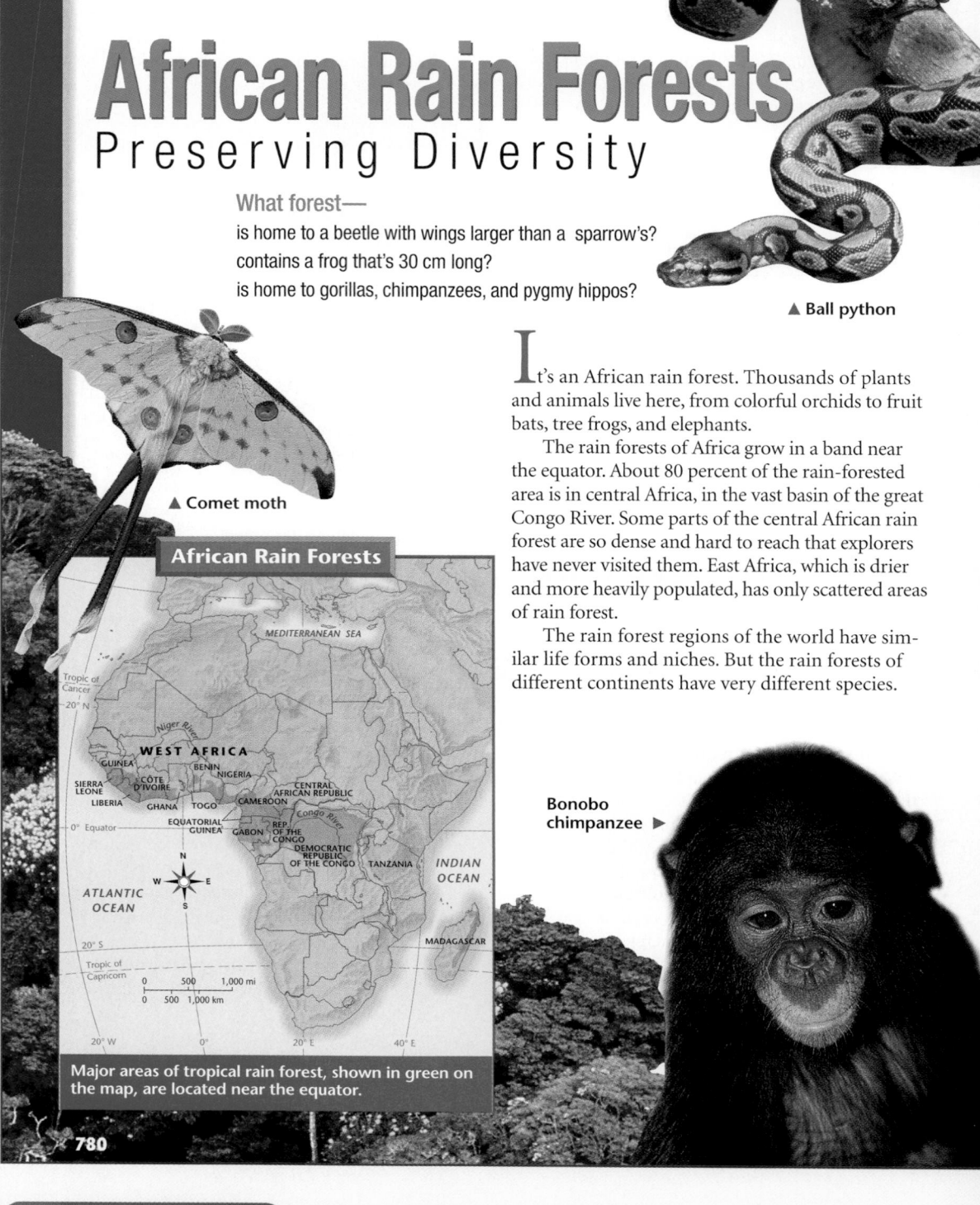

African Rain Forests
Preserving Diversity

What forest—

is home to a beetle with wings larger than a sparrow's?

contains a frog that's 30 cm long?

is home to gorillas, chimpanzees, and pygmy hippos?

▲ Ball python

▲ Comet moth

It's an African rain forest. Thousands of plants and animals live here, from colorful orchids to fruit bats, tree frogs, and elephants.

The rain forests of Africa grow in a band near the equator. About 80 percent of the rain-forested area is in central Africa, in the vast basin of the great Congo River. Some parts of the central African rain forest are so dense and hard to reach that explorers have never visited them. East Africa, which is drier and more heavily populated, has only scattered areas of rain forest.

The rain forest regions of the world have similar life forms and niches. But the rain forests of different continents have very different species.

Bonobo chimpanzee ▶

African Rain Forests

Major areas of tropical rain forest, shown in green on the map, are located near the equator.

780

Program Resources

◆ **Interdisciplinary Explorations** Science, pp. 26–29; Mathematics, pp. 30–32; Social Studies, pp. 33–34; Language Arts, pp. 35–37

Layers of the Rain Forest

From above, the rain forest may look like a mass of broccoli. But it's really many forests in one—like different levels in an apartment building.

Each layer from the forest floor to the emergent, or top, layer varies in climate and is home to different plants and animals. The emergent layer captures the most rain, sunlight, heat, and wind. Colobus monkeys swing from vines and branches. Vast numbers of birds live in the trees.

Over time, African rain forest plants and animals have developed unusual adaptations to life at different layers of the forest. Some monkeys living in the canopy have long, muscular legs. They can run and leap through the branches. Guenons and baboons have strong teeth and jaws that allow them to crunch fruits, nuts, and seeds. Other monkeys have shorter tails but longer front legs. They live mainly on the forest floor.

In the understory, small animals such as frogs and squirrels "fly." They have tough membranes that stretch between their front and hind legs and allow them to glide from branch to branch.

The forest floor is dark, humid, and still. Termites feed on dead leaves and brush. Many plants have large leaves that allow them to catch the dim light. Some animals, such as frogs and insects, grow to gigantic sizes. Others are little, like the pygmy hippo that runs through the forest.

Science Activity

Design a rain forest animal that is adapted to life at a certain level of the rain forest. Consider how your animal lives, how it travels, and what food it eats. Outline its characteristics and explain how each adaptation helps the animal survive. Draw a sketch.

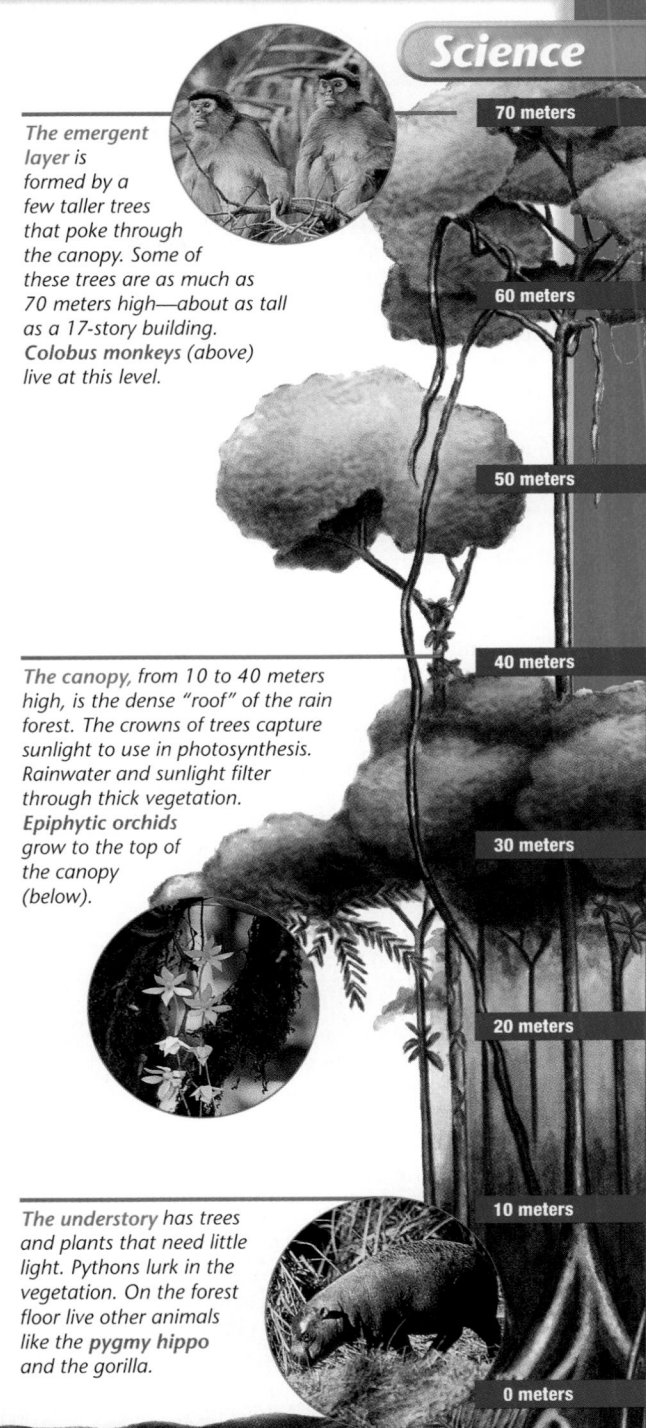

The emergent layer is formed by a few taller trees that poke through the canopy. Some of these trees are as much as 70 meters high—about as tall as a 17-story building. Colobus monkeys (above) live at this level.

70 meters

60 meters

50 meters

The canopy, from 10 to 40 meters high, is the dense "roof" of the rain forest. The crowns of trees capture sunlight to use in photosynthesis. Rainwater and sunlight filter through thick vegetation. Epiphytic orchids grow to the top of the canopy (below).

40 meters

30 meters

20 meters

10 meters

The understory has trees and plants that need little light. Pythons lurk in the vegetation. On the forest floor live other animals like the pygmy hippo and the gorilla.

0 meters

781

2 Facilitate

◆ Suggest that students make a table to compare the three layers' features, with the names of the layers in the left column and the headings *Height, Rainfall, Light,* and *Sample Organisms* across the top. This can be done as a cooperative learning activity, with the class divided into groups of three and each student in the group filling in the row for one layer.

◆ Challenge students to identify specific phrases in the text and captions that describe adaptations of rain forest animals and plants. As students identify adaptations, list each on the board and ask: **How does this adaptation help the organism survive?** *(Some answers are explicitly stated in the text; others must be inferred.)*

Science Activity

Let students work individually or in pairs. Encourage them to refer to the list on the board and to think of other characteristics that would help animals survive in a specific layer of the rain forest. Students could create a bulletin board display, with an enlarged version of the text's illustration in the center and each student's sketch posted next to the appropriate layer.

Interdisciplinary Explorations The following worksheets correlate with this page: Dwarf Rain Forest Animals, p. 26; Classifying the Great Apes, pp. 27–28; Bat Adaptations, p. 29.

3 Assess

Activity Assessment

Students' designs will vary. Give each student or pair an opportunity to describe the animal to the rest of the class. During these presentations, assess students' understanding of the conditions in each rain forest layer and the adaptations needed for survival there.

Background

History In less space than the area of Texas, Madagascar contains some 200,000 species of plants and animals, making it one of the most biologically diverse countries in the world. Separated from the African continent by plate tectonics, the island has been an isolated area of speciation for more than 100 million years. Most of the species that evolved on the island are found nowhere else on Earth.

People have lived on Madagascar for only about 2,000 years, but during that time the island has lost 80 percent of its rain forests and about 50 percent of its native species. Except for a few patches, the forests that once covered the island's eastern half have been cleared to create farms and housing for Madagascar's 15 million people.

2 Facilitate

♦ Ask students: **What do you think evergreens are?** *(Trees that keep their leaves all year long)* **What are trees that shed their leaves in autumn called?** *(Deciduous trees; if students cannot recall the term, let them turn back to page 738 in Chapter 23.)* **What are conifers?** *(Trees that produce seeds in cones and have leaves shaped like needles; see page 739.)*

♦ Have students compare the tree heights listed in the table with the figure of forest layers on the previous page. Ask: **Which trees' tops are found in each forest layer?** *(Emergent layer: kapok and teak; canopy: African oil palm, African yellowwood, ebony, and raffia palm; understory: Cape fig)*

Math Activity

Have each student make his or her own graph. Some students may want to sequence the trees from shortest to tallest (or vice versa) on the horizontal axis. **Interdisciplinary Explorations** The following worksheets correlate with this page: Modeling Rain Forest Layers, p. 30; Giant Rain Forest Animals, p. 31; Comparing Tree Heights, p. 32.

3 Assess

Activity Assessment

Students' graphs should look like the one shown here.
♦ *Greatest:* kapok; *least:* Cape fig
♦ 63 m
♦ 29 m

Reaching for Sunlight

Most rain forest trees are evergreens with broad leathery leaves. Some, like the African yellowwood, are conifers. Because the forest is so dense, trees must grow tall and straight to reach sunlight at the top of the canopy.

Along rivers, the floor and understory of the rain forest are a tangle of plants. Early explorers traveling the rivers assumed that the entire rain forest had similar thick vegetation, or jungle. In fact, the rain forest floor is surprisingly bare.

The canopy trees block the sunlight from plants below. Shaded by the dense canopy, the understory and forest floor are humid and dark. Water drips from the leaves of the canopy high overhead. Young trees have the best chance to grow when trees fall, opening up sunny clearings.

West Africa's tropical forests contain many valuable trees. African mahogany and teak are used to make furniture, tools, and boats. Oil from the oil palm is used in soaps, candles, and some foods. Trees such as ebony that can tolerate shade, grow slowly and develop dark, hard, long-lasting wood.

Math Activity

The table on this page gives the height of some of the trees in the rain forest. Use the information in the table to make a bar graph. On the horizontal axis, label the trees. Use the vertical axis to show the height of the trees.

♦ Which tree has the greatest maximum height? The least maximum height?
♦ What is the height difference between the tallest and the shortest trees?
♦ What is the average height of all the trees shown in the graph?

782

Trees of the Rain Forest	
Tree	**Maximum Height**
African oil palm	18 m
African yellowwood	20 m
Cape fig	7 m
Ebony	30 m
Kapok	70 m
Raffia palm	12 m
Teak	46 m

African oil palms ▲ grow in Nigeria.

◄ **This African sculpture is made of wood from the African rain forest.**

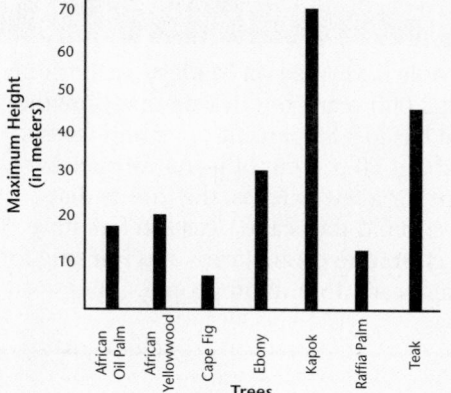

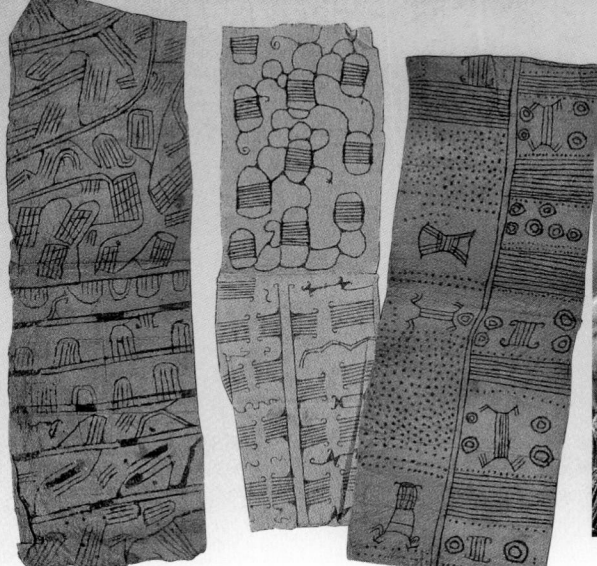

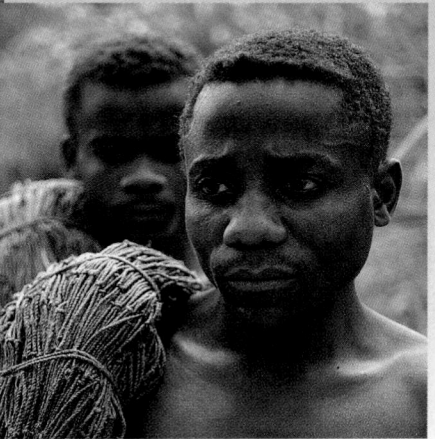

The Mbuti (above) hunt and fish along the Congo River. Their clothing is made of bark cloth (left).

Ituri Forest People

The native peoples of the African rain forest live as they have for thousands of years—by hunting and gathering. The forest supplies them with everything they need—food, water, firewood, building materials, and medicines.

One group of rain forest dwellers is the Mbuti people. The Mbuti live in the Ituri forest of the Democratic Republic of the Congo. Many of the Mbuti are quite small. The men hunt game, such as gazelle and antelope. The women gather wild fruits, nuts, and greens. Their traditional Mbuti clothing is made of tree bark and is wrapped around the waist. The bark is beaten to make it soft. It is then decorated with geometric designs.

Most Mbuti live as nomads, with no single settled home. Every few months they set up new hunting grounds. They build temporary dome-shaped huts of branches and leaves. Hunting groups of about 10 to 25 families live together. They divide the hunting area among the family groups. On occasion, larger groups gather for ceremonies with dances and ritual music.

Modern Africa has brought changes to the forest people, especially for those who live near the edges of the rain forest. For a few months of the year, some Mbuti work as laborers for farmers who live in villages at the edge of the forest. When their work is finished, the Mbuti return to the Ituri forest. Most forest people prefer not to cultivate their own land. Since the farmers don't hunt, they trade their goods for meat. In exchange for meat, the Mbuti receive goods such as iron tools, cooking pots, clothes, bananas, and other farm produce.

Social Studies Activity

List the goods that forest people and farmers might have to trade. Assume that no modern conveniences, such as tractors and stoves, are available. Write a paragraph or two explaining how goods might be exchanged. Assign a value to the farmers' goods and the Mbuti goods, depending upon each group's needs. For example, decide how much meat a farmer should pay for medicines from the rain forest. How would the trading process change if money were exchanged?

783

Background

History Anthropologists use the term Pygmies to refer to human groups in which the average stature of adult males is less than 150 cm. The Mbuti, averaging less than 137 cm, are the shortest Pygmies in Africa.

The Mbuti have traded goods with their farming neighbors, the Bantu, for over 2,000 years. Although they have adopted a few Bantu customs, Mbuti culture has remained essentially unchanged. Groups are not governed by chiefs or tribal councils; group discussion is the usual means of settling any disputes. Mbuti technology meets the needs of hunter-gatherers. For example, some groups hunt with net and spear, while others use bow and arrow. Special songs honoring the forest are important in Mbuti rites of passage associated with puberty, marriage, and death. Values are reinforced in music, dance, and mime. Family bonds are strong and lasting.

2 Facilitate

◆ Have students find the Democratic Republic of the Congo (formerly Zaire) on the map on page 780. Point out that the Democratic Republic of the Congo and the Republic of the Congo are separate nations.

◆ Ask: **What does the first sentence mean by "gathering"?** *(Collecting items from the forest)* Encourage students to imagine what their lives would be like if everything they needed for survival had to be obtained from hunting and gathering. Ask: **What things that you have now would you not have as hunter-gatherers? How would you prepare and cook food? Where would you sleep? What would you do if you became ill? How would you spend most of your time?** To extend this activity, suggest that students write brief, first-person stories describing a typical Mbuti day for someone their own age.

Social Studies Activity

Students can work in pairs, with one student acting as a Mbuti and the other a neighboring farmer. Give volunteers an opportunity to role-play a trading session for the rest of the class.
Interdisciplinary Explorations The following worksheets correlate with this page: Reading a Map of Madagascar, p. 33; Peoples of the Rain Forest, page 34.

3 Assess

Activity Assessment

Students' paragraphs or role-plays will vary. Accept a variety of reasonable responses to the question about money. Students should realize that money would have no immediate value to either the Mbuti or the farmers; its value lies only in its potential use in another exchange.

783

2 Facilitate

- You can enhance comprehension by reading this selection aloud yourself or by asking your most proficient readers to take turns reading paragraphs aloud for the class. The "drama" of an oral presentation—with its vocal inflections, pauses, word emphasis, gestures, and facial expressions—should enable less capable readers to understand the selection more easily and help them appreciate its touches of humor and richly descriptive narrative.

- After the passage has been read, ask students: **Why did Durrell use the word *magical* to describe his experience?** (*He had never seen the rain forest and its wildlife from that viewpoint before.*) Ask students if they have ever ridden in an airplane or been on a mountain or in a tall building where they could look down on things they usually see only from ground level. If they have, encourage them to describe the experience.

Language Arts Activity

To make the task more manageable, set a four- or six-page limit for the pamphlet. (Six pages can be created by folding a standard sheet of paper into thirds.) Although students do not need to do any research to complete the activity successfully, you may want to provide a variety of source materials to prompt their ideas. Use materials that are generously illustrated with colored photographs of the rain forest and its wildlife. Allow students to photocopy or print photographs and incorporate them into their pamphlets. Have students share their pamphlets by posting them on the bulletin board. Save the source materials for students' use in Tie It Together on the next page.

Interdisciplinary Explorations The following worksheets correlate with pages 784–785: Word Meanings, p. 35; The Aye-Aye, pp. 36–37.

Climbing the Canopy

Much of the rain forest is still a mystery because it's so difficult for scientists to study the canopy. Native forest people sometimes climb these tall trees using strong, thick vines called lianas as support. But rain forest scientists have had to find different methods. Naturalist Gerald Durrell, working in the African rain forest, was lucky enough to find another way to observe the canopy. He describes it here:

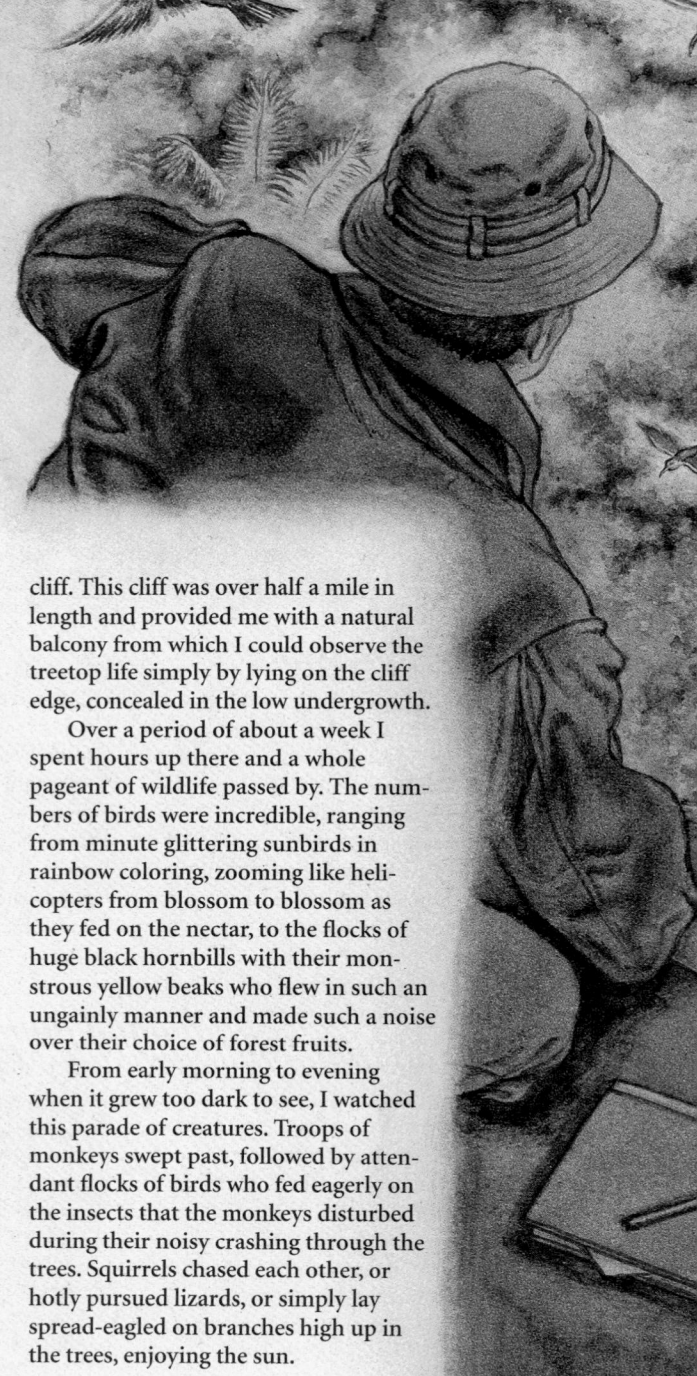

*W*hile the canopy is one of the most richly inhabited regions of the forest it is also the one that causes the naturalist the greatest frustration. There he is, down in the gloom among the giant tree trunks, hearing the noises of animal life high above him and having half-eaten fruit, flowers, or seeds rained on him by legions of animals high in their sunlit domain—all of which he cannot see. Under these circumstances the naturalist develops a very bad temper and a permanent crick in the neck.

However, there was one occasion when I managed to transport myself into the forest canopy, and it was a magical experience. It happened in West Africa when I was camped on the thickly forested lower slopes of a mountain called N'da Ali. Walking through the forest one day I found I was walking along the edge of a great step cut out of the mountain. The cliff face, covered with creepers, dropped away for about 50 yards, so that although I was walking through forest, just next to me and slightly below was the canopy of the forest growing up from the base of the

cliff. This cliff was over half a mile in length and provided me with a natural balcony from which I could observe the treetop life simply by lying on the cliff edge, concealed in the low undergrowth.

Over a period of about a week I spent hours up there and a whole pageant of wildlife passed by. The numbers of birds were incredible, ranging from minute glittering sunbirds in rainbow coloring, zooming like helicopters from blossom to blossom as they fed on the nectar, to the flocks of huge black hornbills with their monstrous yellow beaks who flew in such an ungainly manner and made such a noise over their choice of forest fruits.

From early morning to evening when it grew too dark to see, I watched this parade of creatures. Troops of monkeys swept past, followed by attendant flocks of birds who fed eagerly on the insects that the monkeys disturbed during their noisy crashing through the trees. Squirrels chased each other, or hotly pursued lizards, or simply lay spread-eagled on branches high up in the trees, enjoying the sun.

784

Background

History Gerald Durrell (1925–1995) first developed his love of animals and ambition to be a naturalist during his childhood on the island of Corfu, off the west coast of Greece. Long hours spent observing wildlife led Durrell to collect many local animals as pets—to the consternation of his family.

Durrell's first job was as a student keeper at England's Whipsnade Zoo. After joining several collecting expeditions abroad, he began organizing them himself. After trips to remote parts of Africa and other continents, it struck Durrell that zoos should encourage the breeding of threatened species. In the 1950s, he founded the Jersey Wildlife Preservation Trust and Zoological Garden to raise, study, and breed rare species. Durrell wrote the first of his many books, *The Overloaded Ark,* when he was only 22.

British conservationist Gerald Durrell wrote about his adventures with wildlife around the world. He established a zoo on the British island of Jersey and worked to preserve threatened species. In the photo, Durrell holds an anteater.

785

3 Assess

Activity Assessment

Students' pamphlets will vary widely. Evaluate students' work on the basis of their ability to evoke sensory images of the rain forest and to make a visit seem appealing to the pamphlet's readers.

Tie It Together

Time 4 class periods (2 for research, 2 for designing and creating the display)

Tips Have students work in groups of three or four. Monitor each group's choices of plant and animal species to make sure the group's research will be well-focused and not too wide-ranging. Arrange with your school office for a suitable display area, such as the school entryway, a heavily trafficked hallway, the library, or the cafeteria.

Extend After students have displayed their work in their own school, encourage them to post the displays in areas accessible to the general public—the town library, for example.

Developing scientific thinking in students is important for a solid science education. To learn how to think scientifically, students need frequent opportunities to practice science process skills, critical thinking skills, as well as other skills that support scientific inquiry. The *Science Explorer* Skills Handbook introduces the following key science skills:

◆ Science Process Skills
◆ SI Measuring Skills
◆ Skills for Conducting a Scientific Investigation
◆ Critical Thinking Skills
◆ Information Organizing Skills
◆ Data Table and Graphing Skills

The Skills Handbook is designed as a reference for students to use whenever they need to review a science skill. You can use the activities provided in the Skills Handbook to teach or reinforce the skills.

Think Like a Scientist

Observing

Before students look at the photograph, remind them that an observation is only what they can see, hear, smell, taste, or feel. Ask: **Which senses will you use to make observations from this photograph?** *(Sight is the only sense that can be used to make observations from the photograph.)* **What are some observations you can make from the photograph?** *(Any three: the boy is wearing protective elbow pads and a helmet; the boy's arms are spread to his sides and straight; the skateboard is off the ground.)* List the observations on the chalkboard. If students make any inferences or predictions about the boy at this point, ask: **Can you be sure your statement is factual and accurate from just observing the photograph?** Help students understand how observations differ from inferences and predictions.

Inferring

Review students' observations from the photograph. Then ask: **What inferences can you make from your observations?** *(Students will probably say that the boy has ridden the skateboard up the ramp and is in the*

Think Like a Scientist

Although you may not know it, you think like a scientist every day. Whenever you ask a question and explore possible answers, you use many of the same skills that scientists do. Some of these skills are described on this page.

Observing

When you use one or more of your five senses to gather information about the world, you are **observing.** Hearing a dog bark, counting twelve green seeds, and smelling smoke are all observations. To increase the power of their senses, scientists sometimes use microscopes, telescopes, or other instruments that help them make more detailed observations.

An observation must be an accurate report of what your senses detect. It is important to keep careful records of your observations in science class by writing or drawing in a notebook. The information collected through observations is called evidence, or data.

Inferring

When you interpret an observation, you are **inferring,** or making an inference. For example, if you hear your dog barking, you may infer that someone is at your front door. To make this inference, you combine the evidence—the barking dog—and your experience or knowledge—you know that your dog barks when strangers approach—to reach a logical conclusion.

Notice that an inference is not a fact; it is only one of many possible interpretations for an observation. For example, your dog may be barking because it wants to go for a walk. An inference may turn out to be incorrect even if it is based on accurate observations and logical reasoning. The only way to find out if an inference is correct is to investigate further.

Predicting

When you listen to the weather forecast, you hear many predictions about the next day's weather—what the temperature will be, whether it will rain, and how windy it will be. Weather forecasters use observations and knowledge of weather patterns to predict the weather. The skill of **predicting** involves making an inference about a future event based on current evidence or past experience.

Because a prediction is an inference, it may prove to be false. In science class, you can test some of your predictions by doing experiments. For example, suppose you predict that larger paper airplanes can fly farther than smaller airplanes. How could you test your prediction?

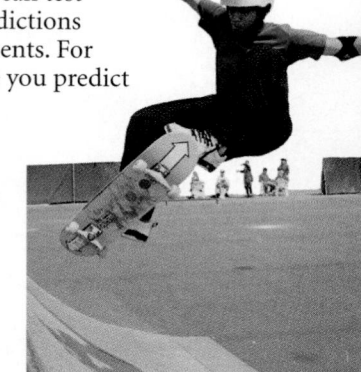

ACTIVITY Use the photograph to answer the questions below.

Observing Look closely at the photograph. List at least three observations.

Inferring Use your observations to make an inference about what is happening. What experience or knowledge did you use to make the inference?

Predicting Predict what will happen next. On what evidence or experience do you base your prediction?

middle of a jump.) **What experience or knowledge helped you make this inference?** *(Students should say that they have either skateboarded themselves or seen others riding skateboards.)* **How can you find out whether an inference is correct?** *(by further investigation)*

Predicting

After reaching consensus about the inference that the boy is in the middle of a jump, encourage students to predict what will happen next. *(Answers will*

ACTIVITY

vary. Some might say that the boy is in control and will land and ride smoothly down the ramp. Others might say that the boy will fall to the ground.)
On what did you base your prediction? *(Student predictions will be based on their experiences with skateboarding.)* Point out that in science, predictions can often be tested with experiments.

Classifying

Could you imagine searching for a book in the library if the books were shelved in no particular order? Your trip to the library would be an all-day event! Luckily, librarians group books on similar topics or by the same author. Grouping items that are alike in some way is called **classifying.** You can classify items in many ways: by size, by shape, by use, and by other important characteristics.

Like librarians, scientists use the skill of classifying to organize information and objects. When things are sorted into groups, the relationships among them become easier to understand.

Classify the objects in the photograph into two groups **ACTIVITY** based on any characteristic you choose. Then use another characteristic to classify the objects into three groups.

Making Models

Have you ever drawn a picture to help someone understand what you were saying? Such a drawing is one type of model. A model is a picture, diagram, computer image, or other representation of a complex object or process. **Making models** helps people understand things that they cannot observe directly.

Scientists often use models to represent things that are either very large or very small, such as the planets in the solar system, or the parts of a cell. Such models are physical models—drawings or three-dimensional structures that look like the real thing. Other models are mental models—mathematical equations or words that describe how something works.

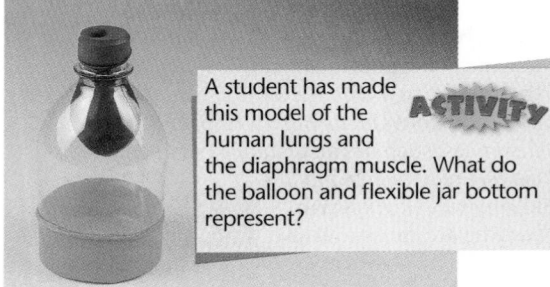

A student has made this model of the **ACTIVITY** human lungs and the diaphragm muscle. What do the balloon and flexible jar bottom represent?

Communicating

Whenever you talk on the phone, write a letter, or listen to your teacher at school, you are communicating. **Communicating** is the process of sharing ideas and information with others. Communicating effectively requires many skills, including writing, reading, speaking, listening, and making models.

Scientists communicate to share results, information, and opinions. Scientists often communicate about their work in journals, over the telephone, in letters, and on the Internet. They also attend scientific meetings where they share their ideas with one another in person.

On a sheet of paper, write out **ACTIVITY** clear, detailed directions for making a peanut butter and jelly sandwich. Then exchange directions with a partner. Take your partner's directions home and follow the directions exactly. How successful were you at making the sandwich? How could your partner have communicated more clearly?

787

Classifying **ACTIVITY**

Encourage students to think of other common things that are classified. Then ask: **What things at home are classified?** (*Clothing might be classified by placing it in different dresser drawers; glasses, plates, and silverware are grouped in different parts of the kitchen; screws, nuts, bolts, washers, and nails might be separated into small containers.*) **What are some things that scientists classify?** (*Scientists classify many things they study, including organisms, geological features and processes, and kinds of machines.*) After students have classified the different fruits in the photograph, have them share their criteria for classifying them. (*Some characteristics students might use include shape, color, size, and where they are grown.*)

Making Models **ACTIVITY**

Ask students: **What are some models you have used to study science?** (*Students may have used human anatomical models, solar system models, maps, stream tables.*) **How did these models help you?** (*Models can help you learn about things that are difficult to study, either because they are too big, too small, or complex.*) Be sure students understand that a model does not have to be three-dimensional. For example, a map in a textbook is a model. Ask: **What do the balloon and flexible jar bottom represent?** (*The balloon represents the lungs, and the flexible jar bottom represents the diaphragm muscle.*)

Communicating **ACTIVITY**

Challenge students to identify the methods of communication they've used today. Then ask: **How is the way you communicate with a friend similar to and different from the way scientists communicate about their work to other scientists?** (*Both may communicate using various methods, but scientists must be very detailed and precise, whereas communication between friends may be less detailed and precise.*) Encourage students to communicate like a scientist as they carry out the activity. (*Students should write clear directions that someone who has never made a peanut butter and jelly sandwich can follow. If students have trouble, suggest that they try the exercise again by speaking the directions and writing down exactly what they say.*)

Making Measurements

Measuring in SI

Review SI units in class with students. Begin by providing metric rulers, graduated cylinders, balances, and Celsius thermometers. Use these tools to reinforce that the meter is the unit of length, the liter is the unit of volume, the gram is the unit of mass, and the degree Celsius is the unit for temperature. Ask: **If you want to measure the length and width of the floor in this classroom, which SI unit would you use?** *(meter)* **Which unit would you use to measure the amount of matter in your textbook?** *(gram)* **Which would you use to measure how much water a drinking glass holds?** *(liter)* **When would you use the Celsius scale?** *(To measure the temperature of something)* Then use the measuring equipment to review SI prefixes. For example, ask: **What are the smallest units on the metric ruler?** *(millimeters)* **How many millimeters are there in 1 cm?** *(10 mm)* **How many in 10 cm?** *(100 mm)* **How many centimeters are there in 1 m?** *(100 cm)* **What does 1,000 m equal?** *(1 km)*

Length *(Students should state that the leaf is 6.4 centimeters, or 64 millimeters, long.)* If students need more practice measuring length, have them use meter sticks and metric rulers to measure various objects in the classroom.

Liquid Volume *(Students should state that the volume of water in the graduated cylinder is 46 milliliters.)* If students need more practice measuring liquid volume, have them use a graduated cylinder to measure different volumes of water.

Making Measurements

When scientists make observations, it is not sufficient to say that something is "big" or "heavy." Instead, scientists use instruments to measure just how big or heavy an object is. By measuring, scientists can express their observations more precisely and communicate more information about what they observe.

Measuring in SI

The standard system of measurement used by scientists around the world is known as the International System of Units, which is abbreviated as SI (in French, *Système International d'Unités*). SI units are easy to use because they are based on multiples of 10. Each unit is ten times larger than the next smallest unit and one tenth the size of the next largest unit. The table lists the prefixes used to name the most common SI units.

Common SI Prefixes

Prefix	Symbol	Meaning
kilo-	k	1,000
hecto-	h	100
deka-	da	10
deci-	d	0.1 (one tenth)
centi-	c	0.01 (one hundredth)
milli-	m	0.001 (one thousandth)

Length To measure length, or the distance between two points, the unit of measure is the **meter (m).** One meter is the approximate distance from the floor to a doorknob. Long distances, such as the distance between two cities, are measured in kilometers (km). Small lengths are measured in centimeters (cm) or millimeters (mm). Scientists use metric rulers and meter sticks to measure length.

Common Conversions

1 km = 1,000 m
1 m = 100 cm
1 m = 1,000 mm
1 cm = 10 mm

The larger lines on the metric ruler in the picture show centimeter divisions, while the smaller, unnumbered lines show millimeter divisions. How many centimeters long is the leaf? How many millimeters long is it?

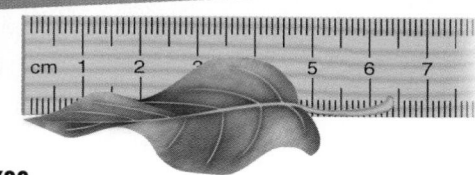

Liquid Volume To measure the volume of a liquid, or the amount of space it takes up, you will use a unit of measure known as the **liter (L).** One liter is the approximate volume of a medium-sized carton of milk. Smaller volumes are measured in milliliters (mL). Scientists use graduated cylinders to measure liquid volume.

Common Conversion

1 L = 1,000 mL

The graduated cylinder in the picture is marked in milliliter divisions. Notice that the water in the cylinder has a curved surface. This curved surface is called the *meniscus.* To measure the volume, you must read the level at the lowest point of the meniscus. What is the volume of water in this graduated cylinder?

Mass To measure mass, or the amount of matter in an object, you will use a unit of measure known as the **gram (g).** One gram is approximately the mass of a paper clip. Larger masses are measured in kilograms (kg). Scientists use a balance to find the mass of an object.

Common Conversion

1 kg = 1,000 g

The mass of the egg in the picture is measured in kilograms. What is the mass of the egg? Suppose a recipe for egg salad called for one kilogram of eggs. About how many eggs would you need?

Temperature
To measure the temperature of a substance, you will use the **Celsius scale.** Temperature is measured in degrees Celsius (°C) using a Celsius thermometer. Water freezes at 0°C and boils at 100°C.

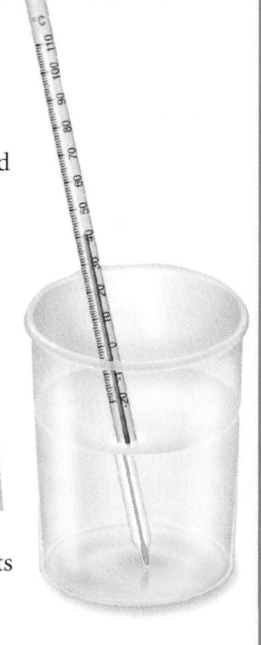

ACTIVITY
What is the temperature of the liquid in degrees Celsius?

Time The unit scientists use to measure time is the **second (s).**

Mass *(Students should state that the mass of the egg is 0.05 kilograms. They would need 20 eggs to make 1 kilogram.)* If students need practice determining mass, have them use a balance to determine the masses of various common objects, such as coins, paper clips, and books.

Temperature *(Students should state that the temperature of the liquid is 40°C.)* If students need practice measuring temperature, have them use a Celsius thermometer to measure the temperature of various water samples.

Time Make sure students know how to convert from seconds to minutes or hours. *(Students should state that 60 seconds = 1 minute; 3,600 seconds = 1 hour.)*

Converting SI Units

To use the SI system, you must know how to convert between units. Converting from one unit to another involves the skill of **calculating,** or using mathematical operations. Converting between SI units is similar to converting between dollars and dimes because both systems are based on multiples of ten.

Suppose you want to convert a length of 80 centimeters to meters. Follow these steps to convert between units.

1. Begin by writing down the measurement you want to convert—in this example, 80 centimeters.

2. Write a conversion factor that represents the relationship between the two units you are converting. In this example, the relationship is *1 meter = 100 centimeters.* Write this conversion factor as a fraction, making sure to place the units you are converting from (centimeters, in this example) in the denominator.

3. Multiply the measurement you want to convert by the fraction. When you do this, the units in the first measurement will cancel out with the units in the denominator. Your answer will be in the units you are converting to (meters, in this example).

Example

80 centimeters = ___?___ meters

$$80 \text{ centimeters} \times \frac{1 \text{ meter}}{100 \text{ centimeters}} = \frac{80 \text{ meters}}{100}$$

$$= 0.8 \text{ meters}$$

Convert between the following units. **ACTIVITY**
1. 400 millimeters = _?_ meters
2. 0.25 liters = _?_ milliliters
3. 1,350 grams = _?_ kilograms

Converting SI Units

Review the steps for converting SI units and work through the example with students. Then ask: **How many millimeters are in 80 centimeters?** *(Students should follow the steps to calculate that 80 centimeters is equal to 800 millimeters.)*

Have students do the conversion problems in the activity. *(**1.** 400 millimeters = 0.4 meters; **2.** 0.25 liters = 250 milliliters; **3.** 1,350 grams = 1.35 kilograms)* If students need more practice converting SI units, have students make up conversion problems and trade with a partner.

789

Conducting a Scientific Investigation

Posing Questions

Before students do the activity on the next page, walk them through the steps of a typical scientific investigation. Begin by asking: **Why is a scientific question important to a scientific investigation?** *(It is the reason for conducting a scientific investigation and how every investigation begins.)* **What is the scientific question in the activity at the bottom of the next page?** *(Do the birds in your neighborhood prefer to eat sunflower seeds or worms?)*

Developing a Hypothesis

Emphasize that a hypothesis is a possible explanation or suggested answer to a question, but it is *not* a guess. Ask: **On what information do scientists base their hypotheses?** *(Their observations and previous knowledge or experience)* Point out that a hypothesis does not always turn out to be correct. Ask: **In that case, do you think the scientist wasted his or her time? Explain your answer.** *(No, because the scientist probably learned from the investigation and maybe could develop another hypothesis that could be supported.)*

Designing an Experiment

Have a volunteer read the Experimental Procedure in the box. Then call on students to identify the manipulated variable *(amount of salt added to water)*, the variables that are kept constant *(amount and starting temperature of water, placing containers in freezer)*, the responding variable *(time it takes water to freeze)*, and the control *(Container 3)*.

Ask: **How might the experiment be affected if Container 1 had only 100 mL of water?** *(It wouldn't be a fair comparison with the containers that have more water.)* **What if Container 3 were not included in the experiment?** *(You wouldn't have anything to compare with the other two containers to know if their freezing times were faster or slower than normal.)* Help students understand the importance of

Conducting a Scientific Investigation

In some ways, scientists are like detectives, piecing together clues to learn about a process or event. One way that scientists gather clues is by carrying out experiments. An experiment tests an idea in a careful, orderly manner. Although not all experiments follow the same steps in the same order, many follow a pattern similar to the one described here.

Posing Questions

Experiments begin by asking a scientific question. A scientific question is one that can be answered by gathering evidence. For example, the question "Which freezes faster—fresh water or salt water?" is a scientific question because you can carry out an investigation and gather information to answer the question.

Developing a Hypothesis

The next step is to form a hypothesis. A **hypothesis** is a possible explanation for a set of observations or answer to a scientific question. In science, a hypothesis must be something that can be tested. A hypothesis can be worded as an *If…then…* statement. For example, a hypothesis might be *"If I add salt to fresh water, then the water will take longer to freeze."* A hypothesis worded this way serves as a rough outline of the experiment you should perform.

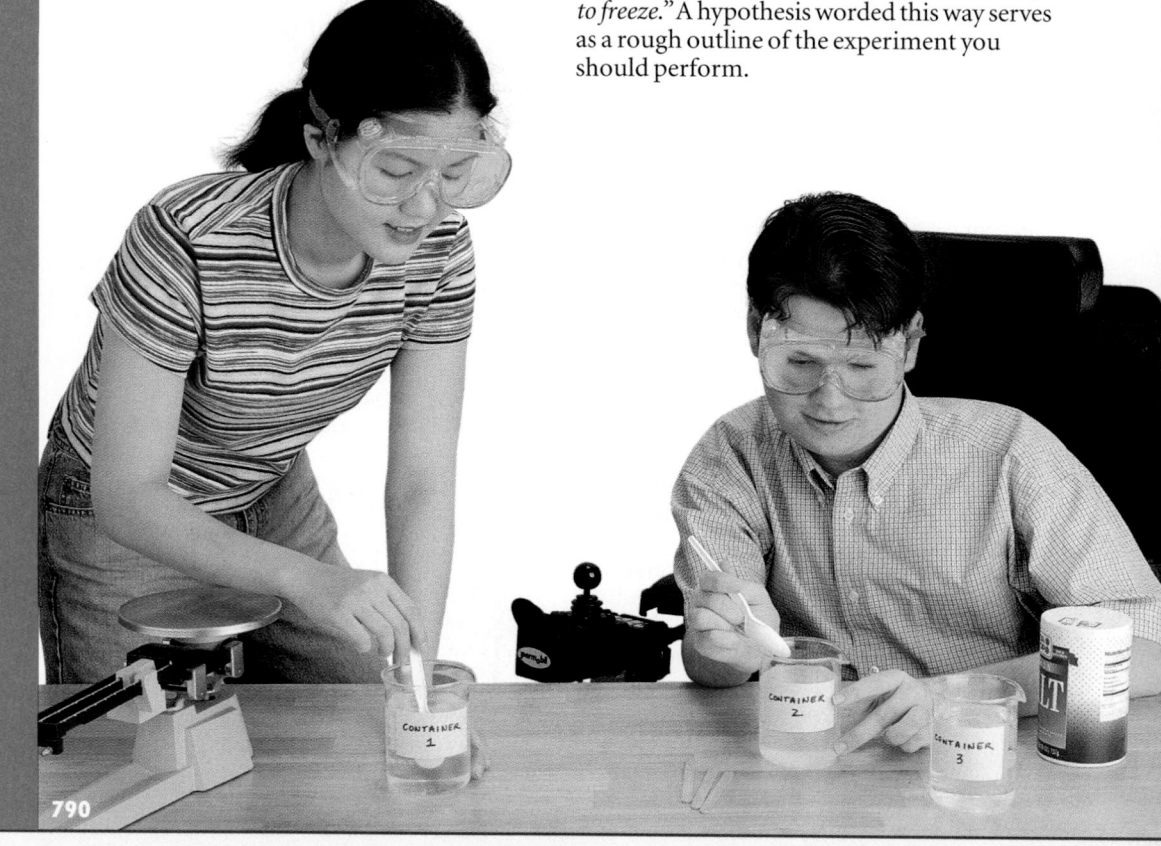

keeping all variables constant except the manipulated variable. Also be sure they understand the role of the control. Then ask: **What operational definition is used in this experiment?** *("Frozen" means the time at which a wooden stick can no longer move in a container.)*

Designing an Experiment

Next you need to plan a way to test your hypothesis. Your plan should be written out as a step-by-step procedure and should describe the observations or measurements you will make.

Two important steps involved in designing an experiment are controlling variables and forming operational definitions.

Controlling Variables In a well-designed experiment, you need to keep all variables the same except for one. A **variable** is any factor that can change in an experiment. The factor that you change is called the **manipulated variable.** In this experiment, the manipulated variable is the amount of salt added to the water. Other factors, such as the amount of water or the starting temperature, are kept constant.

The factor that changes as a result of the manipulated variable is called the responding variable. The **responding variable** is what you measure or observe to obtain your results. In this experiment, the responding variable is how long the water takes to freeze.

An experiment in which all factors except one are kept constant is a **controlled experiment.** Most controlled experiments include a test called the control. In this experiment, Container 3 is the control. Because no salt is added to Container 3, you can compare the results from the other containers to it. Any difference in results must be due to the addition of salt alone.

Forming Operational Definitions

Another important aspect of a well-designed experiment is having clear operational definitions. An **operational definition** is a statement that describes how a particular variable is to be measured or how a term is to be defined. For example, in this experiment, how will you determine if the water has frozen? You might decide to insert a stick in each container at the start of the experiment. Your operational definition of "frozen" would be the time at which the stick can no longer move.

EXPERIMENTAL PROCEDURE

1. Fill 3 containers with 300 milliliters of cold tap water.

2. Add 10 grams of salt to Container 1; stir. Add 20 grams of salt to Container 2; stir. Add no salt to Container 3.

3. Place the 3 containers in a freezer.

4. Check the containers every 15 minutes. Record your observations.

Interpreting Data

The observations and measurements you make in an experiment are called data. At the end of an experiment, you need to analyze the data to look for any patterns or trends. Patterns often become clear if you organize your data in a data table or graph. Then think through what the data reveal. Do they support your hypothesis? Do they point out a flaw in your experiment? Do you need to collect more data?

Drawing Conclusions

A conclusion is a statement that sums up what you have learned from an experiment. When you draw a conclusion, you need to decide whether the data you collected support your hypothesis or not. You may need to repeat an experiment several times before you can draw any conclusions from it. Conclusions often lead you to pose new questions and plan new experiments to answer them.

Do birds in your neighborhood prefer to eat sunflower seeds or worms? Using the steps just described, plan a controlled experiment to investigate this problem. **ACTIVITY**

791

Interpreting Data

Emphasize the importance of collecting accurate and detailed data in a scientific investigation. Ask: **What if the students forgot to record the times that they made their observations in the experiment?** (*They wouldn't be able to completely analyze their data to draw valid conclusions.*) Then ask: **Why are data tables and graphs a good way to organize data?** (*They often make it easier to compare and analyze data.*) You may wish to have students review the Skills Handbook pages on Creating Data Tables and Graphs at this point.

Drawing Conclusions

Help students understand that a conclusion is not necessarily the end of a scientific investigation. A conclusion about one experiment may lead right into another experiment. Point out that in scientific investigations, a conclusion is a summary and explanation of the results of an experiment.

Tell students to suppose that for the Experimental Procedure described on this page, they obtained the following results: Container 1 froze in 45 minutes, Container 2 in 80 minutes, and Container 3 in 25 minutes. Ask: **What conclusions can you draw about this experiment?** (*Students might conclude that the more salt that is added to fresh water, the longer it takes the water to freeze. The hypothesis is supported, and the question of which freezes faster is answered—fresh water.*)

You might wish to have students work in pairs to plan the controlled experiment. **ACTIVITY** (*Students should develop a hypothesis, such as "If I set out both seeds and worms, then the birds will eat the worms first." They can test the hypothesis by setting up two platform-type bird feeders and placing worms on one and seeds on the other. Feeders should be the same size and distance above the ground. Students can observe the feeders to see which food is chosen first.*)

Thinking Critically

Comparing and Contrasting

Emphasize that the skill of comparing and contrasting often relies on good observation skills, as in this activity. *(Students' answers may vary. Sample answer: Similarities—both are dogs and have four legs, two eyes, two ears, brown and white fur, black noses, pink tongues; Differences—smooth coat vs. rough coat, more white fur vs. more brown fur, shorter vs. taller, long ears vs. short ears.)*

Applying Concepts

Point out to students that they apply concepts that they learn in school in their daily lives. For example, they learn to add, subtract, multiply, and divide in school. If they get a paper route or some other part-time job, they can apply those concepts. Challenge students to practice applying concepts by doing the activity. *(If calcium and phosphorus are needed to make bones strong, a diet that does not include enough of these minerals will cause bones to be more likely to break.)*

Interpreting Illustrations

Again, point out the need for good observation skills. Ask: **What is the difference between "interpreting illustrations" and "looking at the pictures"?** *("Interpreting illustrations" requires thorough examination of the illustration, caption, and labels, while "looking at the pictures" implies less thorough examination.)* Encourage students to thoroughly examine the diagram as they do the activity. *(Students' paragraphs may vary, but should describe the internal anatomy of an earthworm, including some of the organs in the earthworm.)*

Thinking Critically

Has a friend ever asked for your advice about a problem? If so, you may have helped your friend think through the problem in a logical way. Without knowing it, you used critical-thinking skills to help your friend. Critical thinking involves the use of reasoning and logic to solve problems or make decisions. Some critical-thinking skills are described below.

Comparing and Contrasting

When you examine two objects for similarities and differences, you are using the skill of **comparing and contrasting.** Comparing involves identifying similarities, or common characteristics. Contrasting involves identifying differences. Analyzing objects in this way can help you discover details that you might otherwise overlook.

ACTIVITY Compare and contrast the two animals in the photo. First list all the similarities that you see. Then list all the differences.

Applying Concepts

When you use your knowledge about one situation to make sense of a similar situation, you are using the skill of **applying concepts.** Being able to transfer your knowledge from one situation to another shows that you truly understand a concept. You may use this skill in answering test questions that present different problems from the ones you've reviewed in class.

ACTIVITY The minerals calcium and phosphorus are important for bone growth and strength. Use this knowledge to explain why diets low in these minerals put people at risk for developing osteoporosis, also known as "brittle bone disease."

Interpreting Illustrations

Diagrams, photographs, and maps are included in textbooks to help clarify what you read. These illustrations show processes, places, and ideas in a visual manner. The skill called **interpreting illustrations** can help you learn from these visual elements. To understand an illustration, take the time to study the illustration along with all the written information that accompanies it. Captions identify the key concepts shown in the illustration. Labels point out the important parts of a diagram or map, while keys identify the symbols used in a map.

Upper blood vessel
Reproductive organs
Arches
Brain
Mouth
Bristles
Waste-removal organs
Intestine
Digestive tract
Lower blood vessel
Nerve cord

▲ Internal anatomy of an earthworm

ACTIVITY Study the diagram above. Then write a short paragraph explaining what you have learned.

Relating Cause and Effect

If one event causes another event to occur, the two events are said to have a cause-and-effect relationship. When you determine that such a relationship exists between two events, you use a skill called **relating cause and effect.** For example, if you notice an itchy, red bump on your skin, you might infer that a mosquito bit you. The mosquito bite is the cause, and the bump is the effect.

It is important to note that two events do not necessarily have a cause-and-effect relationship just because they occur together. Scientists carry out experiments or use past experience to determine whether a cause-and-effect relationship exists.

You walk into your kitchen one morning and notice a long line of ants marching toward a cupboard. List some possible causes for the appearance of the ants. How could you determine which cause and effect relationship is responsible for the ants in the kitchen?

ACTIVITY

Making Generalizations

When you draw a conclusion about an entire group based on information about only some of the group's members, you are using a skill called **making generalizations.** For a generalization to be valid, the sample you choose must be large enough and representative of the entire group. You might, for example, put this skill to work at a farm stand if you see a sign that says, "Sample some grapes before you buy." If you sample a few sweet grapes, you may conclude that all the grapes are sweet—and purchase a large bunch.

A team of scientists needs to determine whether fish in a large lake were harmed by smoke and debris from a nearby forest fire. How could they use the skill of making generalizations to help them? What should they do?

ACTIVITY

Making Judgments

When you evaluate something to decide whether it is good or bad, or right or wrong, you are using a skill called **making judgments.** For example, you make judgments when you decide to eat healthful foods or to pick up litter in a park. Before you make a judgment, you need to think through the pros and cons of a situation, and identify the values or standards that you hold.

Should children and teens be required to wear helmets when bicycling? Explain why you feel the way you do.

ACTIVITY

Problem Solving

When you use critical-thinking skills to resolve an issue or decide on a course of action, you are using a skill called **problem solving.** Some problems, such as how to convert a fraction into a decimal, are straightforward. Other problems, such as figuring out why your computer has stopped working, are complex. Some complex problems can be solved using the trial and error method—try out one solution first, and if that doesn't work, try another. Other useful problem-solving strategies include making models and brainstorming possible solutions with a partner.

793

Relating Cause and Effect

Emphasize that not all events that occur together have a cause-and-effect relationship. For example, tell students that you went to the grocery and your car stalled. Ask: **Is there a cause-and-effect relationship in this situation? Explain your answer.** (*No, because going to the grocery could not cause a car to stall. There must be another cause to make the car stall.*) Have students do the activity to practice relating cause and effect. (*Students should identify that the presence of ants is the effect. Some possible causes are that spilled food attracted the ants or a plant or other object brought into the house had ants on it.*)

Making Generalizations

Point out the importance of having a large, representative sample before making a generalization. Ask: **If you went fishing at a lake and caught three catfish, could you make the generalization that all fish in the lake are catfish? Why or why not?** (*No, because there might be other kinds of fish you didn't catch because they didn't like the bait or they may be in other parts of the lake.*) **How could you make a generalization about the kinds of fish in the lake?** (*By having a larger sample*) Have students do the activity to practice making generalizations. (*The scientists should collect samples of fish from a number of different parts of the reservoir and examine the fish to see if they are healthy.*)

Making Judgments

Remind students that they make a judgment almost every time they make a decision. Ask: **What steps should you follow to make a judgment?** (*Gather information, list pros and cons, analyze values, make judgment*) Invite students to do the activity, and then to share and discuss the judgments they made. (*Students' judgments will vary, but should be supported by valid reasoning. Sample answer: Children and teens should be required to wear helmets when bicycling because helmets have been proven to save lives and reduce head injuries.*)

Problem Solving

ACTIVITY

Challenge student pairs to solve a problem about a soapbox derby. Explain that their younger brother is building a car to enter in the race. The brother wants to know how to make his soapbox car go faster. After student pairs have considered the problem, have them share their ideas about solutions with the class. (*Most will probably suggest using trial and error by making small changes to the car and testing the car after each change. Some students may suggest making and manipulating a model.*)

Organizing Information

Concept Maps

Challenge students to make a concept map with at least three levels of concepts to organize information about types of transportation. All students should start with the phrase *types of transportation* at the top of the concept map. After that point, their concept maps may vary. *(For example, some students might place* private transportation *and* public transportation *at the next level, while other students might have* human-powered *and* gas-powered. *Make sure students connect the concepts with linking words. Challenge students to include cross-linkages as well.)*

Compare/ Contrast Tables

Have students make their own compare/contrast tables using two or more different sports or other activities, such as playing musical instruments. Emphasize that students should select characteristics that highlight the similarities and differences between the activities. *(Students' compare/contrast tables should include several appropriate characteristics and list information about each activity for every characteristic.)*

Organizing Information

As you read this textbook, how can you make sense of all the information it contains? Some useful tools to help you organize information are shown on this page. These tools are called *graphic organizers* because they give you a visual picture of a topic, showing at a glance how key concepts are related.

Concept Maps

Concept maps are useful tools for organizing information on broad topics. A concept map begins with a general concept and shows how it can be broken down into more specific concepts. In that way, relationships between concepts become easier to understand.

A concept map is constructed by placing concept words (usually nouns) in ovals and connecting them with linking words. Often, the most general concept word is placed at the top, and the words become more specific as you move downward. Often the linking words, which are written on a line extending between two ovals, describe the relationship between the two concepts they connect. If you follow any string of concepts and linking words down the map, it should read like a sentence.

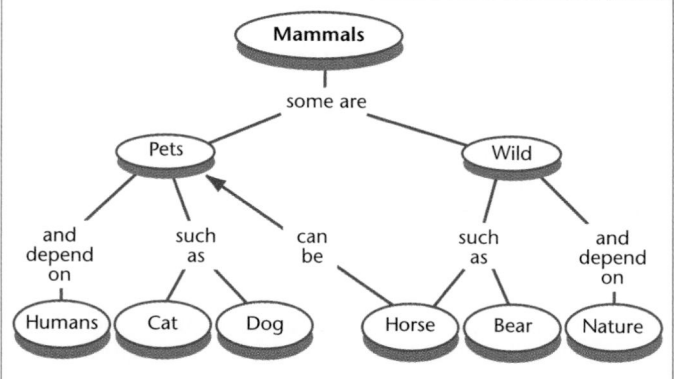

Some concept maps include linking words that connect a concept on one branch of the map to a concept on another branch. These linking words, called cross-linkages, show more complex interrelationships among concepts.

Compare/Contrast Tables

Compare/contrast tables are useful tools for sorting out the similarities and differences between two or more items. A table provides an organized framework in which to compare items based on specific characteristics that you identify.

To create a compare/contrast table, list the items to be compared across the top of a table. Then list the characteristics that will form the basis of your comparison in the left-hand column. Complete the table by filling in information about each characteristic, first for one item and then for the other.

Characteristic	Baseball	Basketball
Number of Players	9	5
Playing Field	Baseball diamond	Basketball court
Equipment	Bat, baseball, mitts	Basket, basketball

Venn Diagrams

Another way to show similarities and differences between items is with a Venn diagram. A Venn diagram consists of two or more circles that partially overlap. Each circle represents a particular concept or idea. Common characteristics, or similarities, are written within the area of overlap between the two circles. Unique characteristics, or differences, are written in the parts of the circles outside the area of overlap.

To create a Venn diagram, draw two overlapping circles. Label the circles with the names of the items being compared. Write the

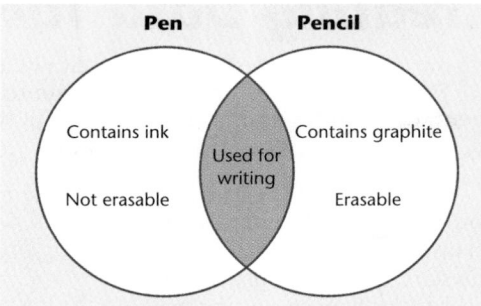

unique characteristics in each circle outside the area of overlap. Then write the shared characteristics within the area of overlap.

Flowcharts

A flowchart can help you understand the order in which certain events have occurred or should occur. Flowcharts are useful for outlining the stages in a process or the steps in a procedure.

To make a flowchart, write a brief description of each event in a box. Place the first event at the top of the page, followed by the second event, the third event, and so on. Then draw an arrow to connect each event to the one that occurs next.

Preparing Pasta

Boil water
↓
Cook pasta
↓
Drain water
↓
Add sauce

Cycle Diagrams

A cycle diagram can be used to show a sequence of events that is continuous, or cyclical. A continuous sequence does not have an end because, when the final event is over, the first event begins again. Like a flowchart, a cycle diagram can help you understand the order of events.

To create a cycle diagram, write a brief description of each event in a box. Place one event at the top of the page in the center. Then, moving in a clockwise direction around an imaginary circle, write each event in its proper sequence. Draw arrows that connect each event to the one that occurs next, forming a continuous circle.

Steps in a Science Experiment

Pose a question → Develop a hypothesis → Design an experiment → Interpret data → Draw conclusions → (back to Pose a question)

Venn Diagrams ACTIVITY

Students can use the same information from their compare/contrast tables to create a Venn diagram. Make sure students understand that the overlapping area of the circles is used to list similarities and the parts of the circles outside the overlap area are used to show differences. If students want to list similarities and differences among three activities, show them how to add a third circle that overlaps each of the other two circles and has an area of overlap for all three circles. *(Students' Venn diagrams will vary. Make sure they have accurately listed similarities in the overlap area and differences in the parts of the circles that do not overlap.)*

Flowcharts ACTIVITY

Encourage students to create a flowchart to show the things they did this morning as they got ready for school. Remind students that a flowchart should show the correct order in which events occurred or should occur. *(Students' flowcharts will vary somewhat. A typical flowchart might include: got up → ate breakfast → took a shower → brushed teeth → got dressed → gathered books and homework → put on jacket.)*

Cycle Diagrams ACTIVITY

Review that a cycle diagram shows a sequence of events that is continuous. Then challenge students to create a cycle diagram that shows how the weather changes with the seasons where they live. *(Students' cycle diagrams may vary, though most will include four steps, one for each season.)*

Creating Data Tables and Graphs

Data Tables

Have students create a data table to show how much time they spend on different activities during one week. Suggest that students first list the main activities they do every week. Then they should determine the amount of time they spend on each activity each day. Remind students to give this data table a title. *(Students' data tables will vary. A sample data table is shown below.)*

Bar Graphs

Students can use the data from their data table above to make a bar graph showing how much time they spend on different activities during a week. The vertical axis should be divided into units of time, such as hours. Remind students to label both axes and give their graph a title. *(Students' bar graphs will vary. A sample bar graph is shown below.)*

Creating Data Tables and Graphs

How can you make sense of the data in a science experiment? The first step is to organize the data to help you understand them. Data tables and graphs are helpful tools for organizing data.

Data Tables

You have gathered your materials and set up your experiment. But before you start, you need to plan a way to record what happens during the experiment. By creating a data table, you can record your observations and measurements in an orderly way.

Suppose, for example, that a scientist conducted an experiment to find out how many Calories people of different body masses burn while doing various activities. The data table shows the results.

Notice in this data table that the manipulated variable (body mass) is the heading of one column. The responding variable (for Experiment 1, the number of Calories burned while bicycling) is the heading of the next column. Additional columns were added for related experiments.

CALORIES BURNED IN 30 MINUTES OF ACTIVITY			
Body Mass	Experiment 1 Bicycling	Experiment 2 Playing Basketball	Experiment 3 Watching Television
30 kg	60 Calories	120 Calories	21 Calories
40 kg	77 Calories	164 Calories	27 Calories
50 kg	95 Calories	206 Calories	33 Calories
60 kg	114 Calories	248 Calories	38 Calories

Bar Graphs

To compare how many Calories a person burns doing various activities, you could create a bar graph. A bar graph is used to display data in a number of separate, or distinct, categories. In this example, bicycling, playing basketball, and watching television are three separate categories.

To create a bar graph, follow these steps.

1. On graph paper, draw a horizontal, or *x-*, axis and a vertical, or *y-*, axis.
2. Write the names of the categories to be graphed along the horizontal axis. Include an overall label for the axis as well.
3. Label the vertical axis with the name of the responding variable. Include units of measurement. Then create a scale along the axis by marking off equally spaced numbers that cover the range of the data collected.
4. For each category, draw a solid bar using the scale on the vertical axis to determine the

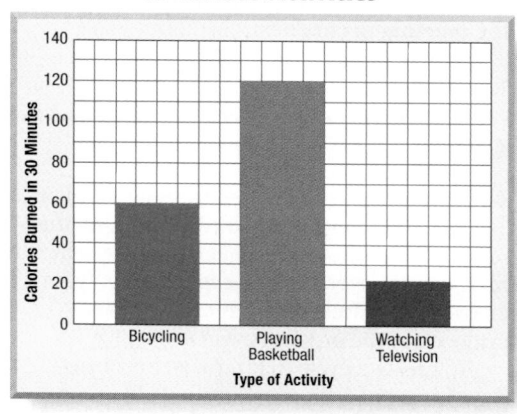

Calories Burned by a 30-kilogram Person in Various Activities

appropriate height. For example, for bicycling, draw the bar as high as the 60 mark on the vertical axis. Make all the bars the same width and leave equal spaces between them.
5. Add a title that describes the graph.

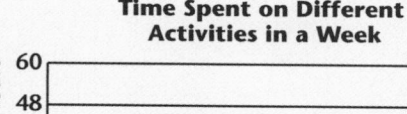

Time Spent on Different Activities in a Week (in hours)

	Going to Classes	Eating Meals	Playing Soccer	Watching Television
Monday	6	2	2	0.5
Tuesday	6	1.5	1.5	1.5
Wednesday	6	2	1	2
Thursday	6	2	2	1.5
Friday	6	2	2	0.5
Saturday	0	2.5	2.5	1
Sunday	0	3	1	2

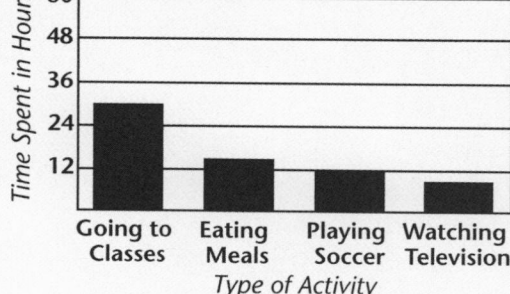

Time Spent on Different Activities in a Week

Line Graphs

To see whether a relationship exists between body mass and the number of Calories burned while bicycling, you could create a line graph. A line graph is used to display data that show how one variable (the responding variable) changes in response to another variable (the manipulated variable). You can use a line graph when your manipulated variable is *continuous*, that is, when there are other points between the ones that you tested. In this example, body mass is a continuous variable because there are other body masses between 30 and 40 kilograms (for example, 31 kilograms). Time is another example of a continuous variable.

Line graphs are powerful tools because they allow you to estimate values for conditions that you did not test in the experiment. For example, you can use the line graph to estimate that a 35-kilogram person would burn 68 Calories while bicycling.

To create a line graph, follow these steps.
1. On graph paper, draw a horizontal, or *x*-, axis and a vertical, or *y*-, axis.
2. Label the horizontal axis with the name of the manipulated variable. Label the vertical axis with the name of the responding variable. Include units of measurement.
3. Create a scale on each axis by marking off equally spaced numbers that cover the range of the data collected.
4. Plot a point on the graph for each piece of data. In the line graph above, the dotted lines show how to plot the first data point (30 kilograms and 60 Calories). Draw an imaginary vertical line extending up from the horizontal axis at the 30-kilogram mark. Then draw an imaginary horizontal line extending across from the vertical axis at the 60-Calorie mark. Plot the point where the two lines intersect.

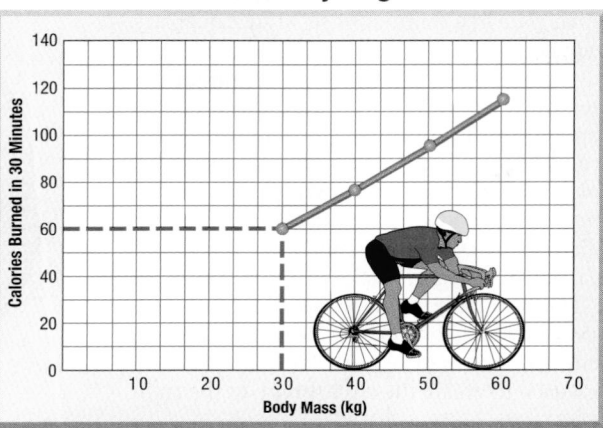

Effect of Body Mass on Calories Burned While Bicycling

5. Connect the plotted points with a solid line. (In some cases, it may be more appropriate to draw a line that shows the general trend of the plotted points. In those cases, some of the points may fall above or below the line. Also, not all graphs are linear and it may be more appropriate to draw a curve to connect the points.)
6. Add a title that identifies the variables or relationship in the graph.

> **ACTIVITY**
> Create line graphs to display the data from Experiment 2 and Experiment 3 in the data table.

> **ACTIVITY**
> In one middle school there are 190 sixth graders, 245 seventh graders, and 175 eighth graders. What type of graph would you use to display these data? Use graph paper to create the graph.

Line Graphs

Walk students through the steps involved in creating a line graph using the example illustrated on the page. For example, ask: **What is the label on the horizontal axis? On the vertical axis?** *(Body Mass (kg); Calories Burned in 30 Minutes)* **What scales are used on each axis?** *(3 squares per 10 kg on the x-axis and 2 squares per 20 Calories on the y-axis)* **What does the second data point represent?** *(77 Calories burned for a body mass of 40 kg)* **What trend or pattern does the graph show?** *(The number of Calories burned in 30 minutes of cycling increases with body mass.)*

Have students follow the steps to carry out the first activity. *(Students should make a different graph for each experiment with different y-axis scales to practice making scales appropriate for data. See sample graphs below.)* **ACTIVITY**

Have students carry out the second activity. *(Students should conclude that a bar graph would be best to display the data. A sample bar graph for these data is shown below.)* **ACTIVITY**

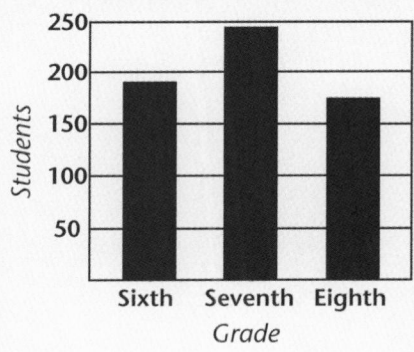

Students in Middle School

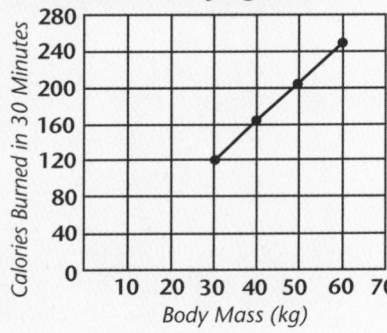

Effect of Body Mass on Calories Burned While Playing Basketball

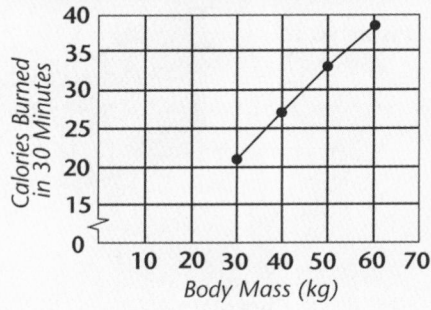

Effect of Body Mass on Calories Burned While Watching Television

Circle Graphs

Emphasize that a circle graph has to include 100 percent of the categories for the topic being graphed. For example, ask: **Could the data in the bar graph titled "Calories Burned by a 30-kilogram Person in Various Activities" (on page 796) be shown in a circle graph? Why or why not?** (*No, because it does not include all the possible ways a 30-kilogram person can burn Calories.*) Then walk students through the steps for making a circle graph. Help students to use a compass and a protractor. Use the protractor to illustrate that a circle has 360 degrees. Make sure students understand the mathematical calculations involved in making a circle graph.

You might wish to have students work in pairs to complete the activity.

ACTIVITY

(*Students' circle graphs should look like the graph below.*)

Circle Graphs

Like bar graphs, circle graphs can be used to display data in a number of separate categories. Unlike bar graphs, however, circle graphs can only be used when you have data for *all* the categories that make up a given topic. A circle graph is sometimes called a pie chart because it resembles a pie cut into slices. The pie represents the entire topic, while the slices represent the individual categories. The size of a slice indicates what percentage of the whole a particular category makes up.

The data table below shows the results of a survey in which 24 teenagers were asked to identify their favorite sport. The data were then used to create the circle graph at the right.

Sports That Teens Prefer

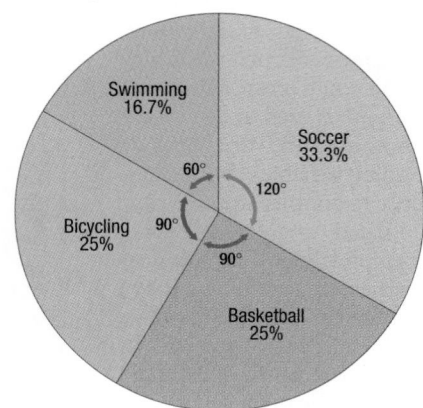

FAVORITE SPORTS	
Sport	Number of Students
Soccer	8
Basketball	6
Bicycling	6
Swimming	4

To create a circle graph, follow these steps.

1. Use a compass to draw a circle. Mark the center of the circle with a point. Then draw a line from the center point to the top of the circle.

2. Determine the size of each "slice" by setting up a proportion where *x* equals the number of degrees in a slice. (NOTE: A circle contains 360 degrees.) For example, to find the number of degrees in the "soccer" slice, set up the following proportion:

$$\frac{\text{students who prefer soccer}}{\text{total number of students}} = \frac{x}{\text{total number of degrees in a circle}}$$

$$\frac{8}{24} = \frac{x}{360}$$

Cross-multiply and solve for *x*.

$$24x = 8 \times 360$$
$$x = 120$$

The "soccer" slice should contain 120 degrees.

3. Use a protractor to measure the angle of the first slice, using the line you drew to the top of the circle as the 0° line. Draw a line from the center of the circle to the edge for the angle you measured.

4. Continue around the circle by measuring the size of each slice with the protractor. Start measuring from the edge of the previous slice so the wedges do not overlap. When you are done, the entire circle should be filled in.

5. Determine the percentage of the whole circle that each slice represents. To do this, divide the number of degrees in a slice by the total number of degrees in a circle (360), and multiply by 100%. For the "soccer" slice, you can find the percentage as follows:

$$\frac{120}{360} \times 100\% = 33.3\%$$

6. Use a different color to shade in each slice. Label each slice with the name of the category and with the percentage of the whole it represents.

7. Add a title to the circle graph.

ACTIVITY

An ice cream shop sold 80 ice cream cones today—24 vanilla cones, 36 chocolate cones, and 20 pistachio cones. Create a circle graph to display these data.

Ice Cream Cones Sold

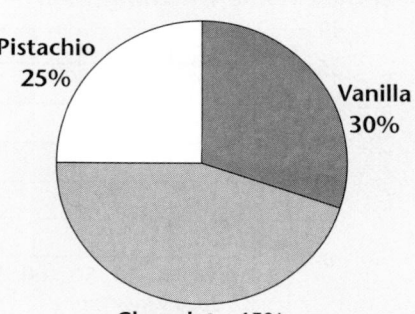

Laboratory Safety

Safety Symbols

These symbols alert you to possible dangers in the laboratory and remind you to work carefully.

Safety Goggles Always wear safety goggles to protect your eyes in any activity involving chemicals, flames or heating, or the possibility of broken glassware.

Lab Apron Wear a laboratory apron to protect your skin and clothing from damage.

Breakage You are working with materials that may be breakable, such as glass containers, glass tubing, thermometers, or funnels. Handle breakable materials with care. Do not touch broken glassware.

Heat-resistant Gloves Use an oven mitt or other hand protection when handling hot materials. Hot plates, hot glassware, or hot water can cause burns. Do not touch hot objects with your bare hands.

Heating Use a clamp or tongs to pick up hot glassware. Do not touch hot objects with your bare hands.

Sharp Object Pointed-tip scissors, scalpels, knives, needles, pins, or tacks are sharp. They can cut or puncture your skin. Always direct a sharp edge or point away from yourself and others. Use sharp instruments only as instructed.

Electric Shock Avoid the possibility of electric shock. Never use electrical equipment around water, or when the equipment is wet or your hands are wet. Be sure cords are untangled and cannot trip anyone. Disconnect the equipment when it is not in use.

Corrosive Chemical You are working with an acid or another corrosive chemical. Avoid getting it on your skin or clothing, or in your eyes. Do not inhale the vapors. Wash your hands when you are finished with the activity.

Poison Do not let any poisonous chemical come in contact with your skin, and do not inhale its vapors. Wash your hands when you are finished with the activity.

Physical Safety When an experiment involves physical activity, take precautions to avoid injuring yourself or others. Follow instructions from your teacher. Alert your teacher if there is any reason you should not participate in the activity.

Animal Safety Treat live animals with care to avoid harming the animals or yourself. Working with animal parts or preserved animals also requires caution. Wash your hands when you are finished with the activity.

Plant Safety Handle plants in the laboratory or during field work only as directed by your teacher. If you are allergic to certain plants, tell your teacher before doing an activity in which those plants are used. Avoid touching harmful plants such as poison ivy, poison oak, or poison sumac, or plants with thorns. Wash your hands when you are finished with the activity.

Flames You may be working with flames from a lab burner, candle, or matches. Tie back loose hair and clothing. Follow instructions from your teacher about lighting and extinguishing flames.

No Flames Flammable materials may be present. Make sure there are no flames, sparks, or other exposed heat sources present.

Fumes When poisonous or unpleasant vapors may be involved, work in a ventilated area. Avoid inhaling vapors directly. Only test an odor when directed to do so by your teacher, and use a wafting motion to direct the vapor toward your nose.

Disposal Chemicals and other laboratory materials used in the activity must be disposed of safely. Follow the instructions from your teacher.

Hand Washing Wash your hands thoroughly when finished with the activity. Use antibacterial soap and warm water. Lather both sides of your hands and between your fingers. Rinse well.

General Safety Awareness You may see this symbol when none of the symbols described earlier appears. In this case, follow the specific instructions provided. You may also see this symbol when you are asked to develop your own procedure in a lab. Have your teacher approve your plan before you go further.

Laboratory Safety

Laboratory safety is an essential element of a successful science class. It is important for you to emphasize laboratory safety to students. Students need to understand exactly what is safe and unsafe behavior, and what the rationale is behind each safety rule.

Review with students the Safety Symbols and Science Safety Rules listed on this and the next two pages. Then follow the safety guidelines below to ensure that your classroom will be a safe place for students to learn science.

◆ Post safety rules in the classroom and review them regularly with students.
◆ Familiarize yourself with the safety procedures for each activity before introducing it to your students.
◆ Review specific safety precautions with students before beginning every science activity.
◆ Always act as an exemplary role model by displaying safe behavior.
◆ Know how to use safety equipment, such as fire extinguishers and fire blankets, and always have it accessible.
◆ Have students practice leaving the classroom quickly and orderly to prepare them for emergencies.
◆ Explain to students how to use the intercom or other available means of communication to get help during an emergency.
◆ Never leave students unattended while they are engaged in science activities.
◆ Provide enough space for students to safely carry out science activities.
◆ Keep your classroom and all science materials in proper condition. Replace worn or broken items.
◆ Instruct students to report all accidents and injuries to you immediately.

Laboratory Safety

Additional tips are listed below for the Science Safety Rules discussed on these two pages. Please keep these tips in mind when you carry out science activities in your classroom.

General Precautions

♦ For open-ended activities like Chapter Projects, go over general safety guidelines with students. Have students submit their procedures or design plans in writing and check them for safety considerations.

♦ In an activity where students are directed to taste something, be sure to store the material in clean, *nonscience* containers. Distribute the material to students in *new* plastic or paper dispensables, which should be discarded after the tasting. Tasting or eating should never be done in a lab classroom.

♦ During physical activity, make sure students do not overexert themselves.

♦ Remind students to handle microscopes and telescopes with care to avoid breakage.

Heating and Fire Safety

♦ No flammable substances should be in use around hot plates, light bulbs, or open flames.

♦ Test tubes should be heated only in water baths.

♦ Students should be permitted to strike matches to light candles or burners *only* with strict supervision. When possible, you should light the flames, especially when working with sixth graders.

♦ Be sure to have proper ventilation when fumes are produced during a procedure.

♦ All electrical equipment used in the lab should have GFI switches.

Using Chemicals Safely

♦ When students use both chemicals and microscopes in one activity, microscopes should be in a separate part of the room from the chemicals so that when students remove their goggles to use the microscopes, their eyes are not at risk.

Science Safety Rules

To prepare yourself to work safely in the laboratory, read over the following safety rules. Then read them a second time. Make sure you understand and follow each rule. Ask your teacher to explain any rules you do not understand.

Dress Code

1. To protect yourself from injuring your eyes, wear safety goggles whenever you work with chemicals, burners, glassware, or any substance that might get into your eyes. If you wear contact lenses, notify your teacher.
2. Wear a lab apron or coat whenever you work with corrosive chemicals or substances that can stain.
3. Tie back long hair to keep it away from any chemicals, flames, or equipment.
4. Remove or tie back any article of clothing or jewelry that can hang down and touch chemicals, flames, or equipment. Roll up or secure long sleeves.
5. Never wear open shoes or sandals.

General Precautions

6. Read all directions for an experiment several times before beginning the activity. Carefully follow all written and oral instructions. If you are in doubt about any part of the experiment, ask your teacher for assistance.
7. Never perform activities that are not assigned or authorized by your teacher. Obtain permission before "experimenting" on your own. Never handle any equipment unless you have specific permission.
8. Never perform lab activities without direct supervision.
9. Never eat or drink in the laboratory.
10. Keep work areas clean and tidy at all times. Bring only notebooks and lab manuals or written lab procedures to the work area. All other items, such as purses and backpacks, should be left in a designated area.
11. Do not engage in horseplay.

First Aid

12. Always report all accidents or injuries to your teacher, no matter how minor. Notify your teacher immediately about any fires.
13. Learn what to do in case of specific accidents, such as getting acid in your eyes or on your skin. (Rinse acids from your body with lots of water.)
14. Be aware of the location of the first-aid kit, but do not use it unless instructed by your teacher. In case of injury, your teacher should administer first aid. Your teacher may also send you to the school nurse or call a physician.
15. Know the location of emergency equipment, such as the fire extinguisher and fire blanket, and know how to use it.
16. Know the location of the nearest telephone and whom to contact in an emergency.

Heating and Fire Safety

17. Never use a heat source, such as a candle, burner, or hot plate, without wearing safety goggles.
18. Never heat anything unless instructed to do so. A chemical that is harmless when cool may be dangerous when heated.
19. Keep all combustible materials away from flames. Never use a flame or spark near a combustible chemical.
20. Never reach across a flame.
21. Before using a laboratory burner, make sure you know proper procedures for lighting and adjusting the burner, as demonstrated by your teacher. Do not touch the burner. It may be hot. Never leave a lighted burner unattended. Turn off the burner when not in use.
22. Chemicals can splash or boil out of a heated test tube. When heating a substance in a test tube, make sure that the mouth of the tube is not pointed at you or anyone else.
23. Never heat a liquid in a closed container. The expanding gases produced may blow the container apart.
24. Before picking up a container that has been heated, hold the back of your hand near it. If you can feel heat on the back of your hand, the container is too hot to handle. Use an oven mitt to pick up a container that has been heated.

Using Glassware Safely

♦ Use plastic containers, graduated cylinders, and beakers whenever possible. If using glass, students should wear safety goggles.

♦ Use only nonmercury thermometers with anti-roll protectors.

♦ Check all glassware periodically for chips and scratches, which can cause cuts and breakage.

Using Chemicals Safely

25. Never mix chemicals "for the fun of it." You might produce a dangerous, possibly explosive substance.
26. Never put your face near the mouth of a container that holds chemicals. Many chemicals are poisonous. Never touch, taste, or smell a chemical unless you are instructed by your teacher to do so.
27. Use only those chemicals needed in the activity. Read and double-check labels on supply bottles before removing any chemicals. Take only as much as you need. Keep all containers closed when chemicals are not being used.
28. Dispose of all chemicals as instructed by your teacher. To avoid contamination, never return chemicals to their original containers. Never simply pour chemicals or other substances into the sink or trash containers.
29. Be extra careful when working with acids or bases. Pour all chemicals over the sink or a container, not over your work surface.
30. If you are instructed to test for odors, use a wafting motion to direct the odors to your nose. Do not inhale the fumes directly from the container.
31. When mixing an acid and water, always pour the water into the container first and then add the acid to the water. Never pour water into an acid.
32. Take extreme care not to spill any material in the laboratory. Wash chemical spills and splashes immediately with plenty of water. Immediately begin rinsing with water any acids that get on your skin or clothing, and notify your teacher of any acid spill at the same time.

Using Glassware Safely

33. Never force glass tubing or thermometers into a rubber stopper or rubber tubing. Have your teacher insert the glass tubing or thermometer if required for an activity.
34. If you are using a laboratory burner, use a wire screen to protect glassware from any flame. Never heat glassware that is not thoroughly dry on the outside.
35. Keep in mind that hot glassware looks cool. Never pick up glassware without first checking to see if it is hot. Use an oven mitt. See rule 24.
36. Never use broken or chipped glassware. If glassware breaks, notify your teacher and dispose of the glassware in the proper broken-glassware container. Never handle broken glass with your bare hands.
37. Never eat or drink from lab glassware.
38. Thoroughly clean glassware before putting it away.

Using Sharp Instruments

39. Handle scalpels or other sharp instruments with extreme care. Never cut material toward you; cut away from you.
40. Immediately notify your teacher if you cut your skin when working in the laboratory.

Animal and Plant Safety

41. Never perform experiments that cause pain, discomfort, or harm to animals. This rule applies at home as well as in the classroom.
42. Animals should be handled only if absolutely necessary. Your teacher will instruct you as to how to handle each animal species brought into the classroom.
43. If you know that you are allergic to certain plants, molds, or animals, tell your teacher before doing an activity in which these are used.
44. During field work, protect your skin by wearing long pants, long sleeves, socks, and closed shoes. Know how to recognize the poisonous plants and fungi in your area, as well as plants with thorns, and avoid contact with them. Never eat any part of a plant or fungus.
45. Wash your hands thoroughly after handling animals or the cage containing animals. Wash your hands when you are finished with any activity involving animal parts, plants, or soil.

End-of-Experiment Rules

46. After an experiment has been completed, turn off all burners or hot plates. If you used a gas burner, check that the gas-line valve to the burner is off. Unplug hot plates.
47. Turn off and unplug any other electrical equipment that you used.
48. Clean up your work area and return all equipment to its proper place.
49. Dispose of waste materials as instructed by your teacher.
50. Wash your hands after every experiment.

Using Sharp Instruments

◆ Always use blunt-tip safety scissors, except when pointed-tip scissors are required.

Animal and Plant Safety

◆ When working with live animals or plants, check ahead of time for students who may have allergies to the specimens.
◆ When growing bacteria cultures, use only disposable petri dishes. After streaking, the dishes should be sealed and not opened again by students. After the lab, students should return the unopened dishes to you. Students should wash their hands with antibacterial soap.
◆ Two methods are recommended for the safe disposal of bacteria cultures. *First method:* Autoclave the petri dishes and discard without opening. *Second method*: If no autoclave is available, carefully open the dishes (never have a student do this) and pour full-strength bleach into the dishes and let stand for a day. Then pour the bleach from the petri dishes down a drain and flush the drain with lots of water. Tape the petri dishes back together and place in a sealed plastic bag. Wrap the plastic bag with a brown paper bag or newspaper and tape securely. Throw the sealed package in the trash. Thoroughly disinfect the work area with bleach.
◆ To grow mold, use a new, sealable plastic bag that is two to three times larger than the material to be placed inside. Seal the bag and tape it shut. After the bag is sealed, students should not open it. To dispose of the bag and mold culture, make a small cut near an edge of the bag and cook in a microwave oven on high setting for at least 1 minute. Discard the bag according to local ordinance, usually in the trash.
◆ Students should wear disposable nitrile, latex, or food-handling gloves when handling live animals or nonliving specimens.

End-of-Experiment Rules

◆ Always have students use antibacterial soap for washing their hands.

Using the Microscope

The microscope is an essential tool in the study of life science. It allows you to see things that are too small to be seen with the unaided eye.

You will probably use a compound microscope like the one you see here. The compound microscope has more than one lens that magnifies the object you view.

Typically, a compound microscope has one lens in the eyepiece, the part you look through. The eyepiece lens usually magnifies 10 ×. Any object you view through this lens would appear 10 times larger than it is.

The compound microscope may contain one or two other lenses called objective lenses. If there are two objective lenses, they are called the low-power and high-power objective lenses. The low-power objective lens usually magnifies 10 ×. The high-power objective lens usually magnifies 40 ×.

To calculate the total magnification with which you are viewing an object, multiply the magnification of the eyepiece lens by the magnification of the objective lens you are using. For example, the eyepiece's magnification of 10 × multiplied by the low-power objective's magnification of 10 × equals a total magnification of 100 ×.

Use the photo of the compound microscope to become familiar with the parts of the microscope and their functions.

The Parts of the Compound Microscope

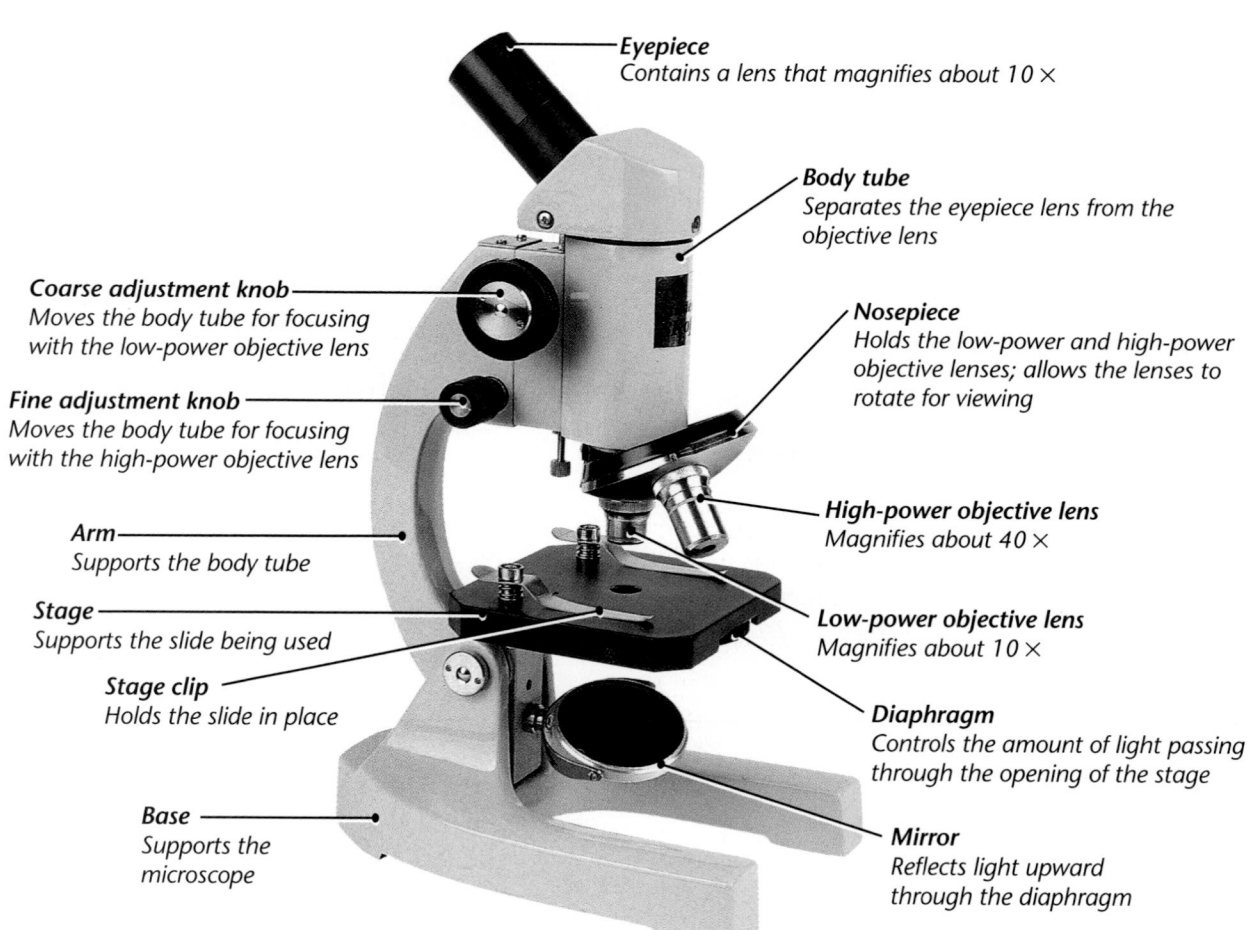

Eyepiece
Contains a lens that magnifies about 10 ×

Body tube
Separates the eyepiece lens from the objective lens

Coarse adjustment knob
Moves the body tube for focusing with the low-power objective lens

Fine adjustment knob
Moves the body tube for focusing with the high-power objective lens

Nosepiece
Holds the low-power and high-power objective lenses; allows the lenses to rotate for viewing

High-power objective lens
Magnifies about 40 ×

Arm
Supports the body tube

Stage
Supports the slide being used

Low-power objective lens
Magnifies about 10 ×

Stage clip
Holds the slide in place

Diaphragm
Controls the amount of light passing through the opening of the stage

Base
Supports the microscope

Mirror
Reflects light upward through the diaphragm

Using the Microscope

Use the following procedures when you are working with a microscope.

1. To carry the microscope grasp the microscope's arm with one hand. Place your other hand under the base.

2. Place the microscope on a table with the arm toward you.

3. Turn the coarse adjustment knob to raise the body tube.

4. Revolve the nosepiece until the low-power objective lens clicks into place.

5. Adjust the diaphragm. While looking through the eyepiece, also adjust the mirror until you see a bright white circle of light. **CAUTION:** *Never use direct sunlight as a light source.*

6. Place a slide on the stage. Center the specimen over the opening on the stage. Use the stage clips to hold the slide in place. **CAUTION:** *Glass slides are fragile.*

7. Look at the stage from the side. Carefully turn the coarse adjustment knob to lower the body tube until the low-power objective almost touches the slide.

8. Looking through the eyepiece, very slowly turn the coarse adjustment knob until the specimen comes into focus.

9. To switch to the high-power objective lens, look at the microscope from the side. Carefully revolve the nosepiece until the high-power objective lens clicks into place. Make sure the lens does not hit the slide.

10. Looking through the eyepiece, turn the fine adjustment knob until the specimen comes into focus.

Making a Wet-Mount Slide

Use the following procedures to make a wet-mount slide of a specimen.

1. Obtain a clean microscope slide and a coverslip. **CAUTION:** *Glass slides and coverslips are fragile.*

2. Place the specimen on the slide. The specimen must be thin enough for light to pass through it.

3. Using a plastic dropper, place a drop of water on the specimen.

4. Gently place one edge of the coverslip against the slide so that it touches the edge of the water drop at a 45° angle. Slowly lower the coverslip over the specimen. If air bubbles are trapped beneath the coverslip, tap the coverslip gently with the eraser end of a pencil.

5. Remove any excess water at the edge of the coverslip with a paper towel.

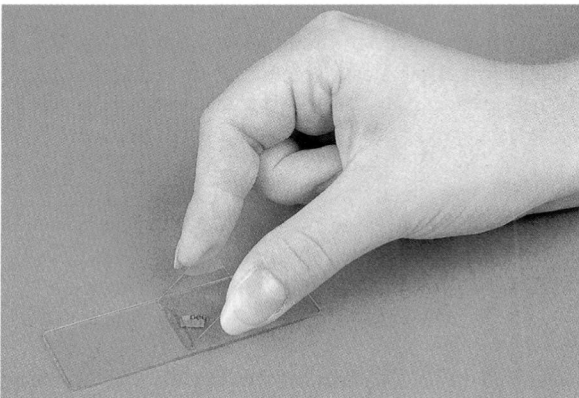

803

Glossary

·········· **A** ··········

abdomen The hind section of an arachnid's body that contains its reproductive organs and part of its digestive tract; the hind section of an insect's body. (p. 350)

abiotic factor A nonliving part of an ecosystem. (p. 690)

absolute dating A technique used to determine the actual age of a fossil. (p. 160)

absorption The process by which nutrient molecules pass through the wall of the digestive system into the blood. (p. 519)

acne A bacterial infection of the skin in which the oil glands become blocked and swollen. (p. 500)

active immunity Immunity that occurs when a person's own immune system produces antibodies in response to the presence of a pathogen. (p. 605)

active transport The movement of materials through a cell membrane using energy. (p. 59)

adaptation A characteristic that helps an organism survive in its environment or reproduce. (pp. 149, 312)

addiction A physical dependence on a substance; an intense need by the body for a substance. (p. 577)

adolescence The stage of development between childhood and adulthood when children become adults physically and mentally. (p. 675)

aggression A threatening behavior that one animal uses to gain control over another. (p. 451)

AIDS (acquired immunodeficiency syndrome) A disease caused by a virus that attacks the immune system. (p. 603)

alcoholism A disease in which a person is both physically addicted to and emotionally dependent on alcohol. (p. 651)

alga A plantlike protist. (p. 224)

algal bloom The rapid growth of a population of algae. (p. 228)

alleles The different forms of a gene. (p. 89)

allergen A substance that causes an allergy. (p. 613)

allergy A disorder in which the immune system is overly sensitive to a foreign substance. (p. 612)

alveoli Tiny sacs of lung tissue specialized for the movement of gases between the air and the blood. (p. 570)

amino acids Small units that are linked together chemically to form large protein molecules. (pp. 53, 510)

amniocentesis A technique by which a small amount of the fluid that surrounds a developing baby is removed; the fluid is analyzed to determine whether the baby will have a genetic disorder. (p. 128)

amniotic sac A fluid-filled sac that cushions and protects a developing fetus in the uterus. (p. 670)

amphibian An ectothermic vertebrate that spends its early life in water and its adulthood on land, returning to water to reproduce. (p. 390)

anabolic steroids Synthetic chemicals that are similar to hormones produced in the body and that may increase muscle size and cause mood swings. (p. 648)

angiosperm A plant that produces seeds that are enclosed in a protective structure. (p. 289)

antenna An appendage on the head of some animals that contains sense organs. (p. 349)

antibiotic A chemical that kills bacteria or slows their growth without harming the body cells of humans. (pp. 201, 609)

antibody A chemical produced by a B cell of the immune system that destroys a specific kind of pathogen. (p. 602)

antigen A molecule on a cell that the immune system can recognize either as part of the body or as coming from outside the body. (p. 601)

anus The opening at the end of an organism's digestive system through which wastes exit. (pp. 331, 529)

aorta The largest artery in the body. (p. 542)

aquaculture The practice of raising fish and other water organisms for food. (p. 766)

arachnid An arthropod with only two body sections. (p. 350)

artery A blood vessel that carries blood away from the heart. (p. 540)

arthropod An invertebrate that has an external skeleton, a segmented body, and jointed attachments called appendages. (p. 347)

artificial intelligence The capacity of a computer to perform complex tasks such as learning from experience and solving problems. (p. 446)

asexual reproduction The reproductive process that involves only one parent and produces offspring that are identical to the parent. (p. 195)

asthma A disorder in which the respiratory passages narrow significantly. (p. 613)

atherosclerosis A condition in which an artery wall thickens as a result of the buildup of fatty materials. (p. 557)

atom The smallest unit of an element. (p. 52)

atrium Each of the two upper chambers of the heart that receives blood that comes into the heart. (pp. 390, 538)

autonomic nervous system The group of nerves that controls involuntary actions. (p. 632)

autotroph An organism that makes its own food. (p. 23)

auxin The plant hormone that speeds up the rate of growth of plant cells. (p. 298)

axon A threadlike extension of a neuron that carries nerve impulses away from the cell body. (p. 624)

B cell A lymphocyte that produces chemicals that help destroy a specific kind of pathogen. (p. 602)

bacteriophage A virus that infects bacteria. (p. 206)

bacterium A single-celled organism that is a prokaryote; belongs to one of two kingdoms—Archaebacteria or Eubacteria. (p. 193)

behavior All the actions an animal performs. (p. 443)

bilateral symmetry Line symmetry; the quality of being divisible into two halves that are mirror images. (p. 316)

bile A substance produced by the liver that breaks up fat particles. (p. 527)

binary fission A form of asexual reproduction in which one cell divides to form two identical cells. (p. 195)

binomial nomenclature The naming system for organisms in which each organism is given a two-part name—a genus name and a species name. (p. 183)

biodiversity The number of different species in an area. (p. 768)

biogeography The study of where organisms live. (p. 728)

bioluminescence The production of light by a living organism. (p. 364)

biome A group of ecosystems with similar climates and organisms. (p. 734)

biotic factor A living part of an ecosystem. (p. 689)

bird An endothermic vertebrate that has feathers and a four-chambered heart, and lays eggs. (p. 411)

birth rate The number of births in a population in a certain amount of time. (p. 697)

bivalve A mollusk that has two shells held together by hinges and strong muscles. (p. 342)

blood pressure The pressure that is exerted by the blood against the walls of blood vessels. (p. 547)

blood transfusion The transference of blood from one person to another. (p. 552)

bog A wetland where sphagnum moss grows on top of acidic water. (p. 258)

brain The part of the central nervous system that is located in the skull and controls most functions in the body. (p. 629)

brainstem The part of the brain that controls many body functions that occur automatically. (p. 631)

branching tree A diagram that shows how scientists think different groups of organisms are related. (p. 168)

bronchi The passages that branch from the trachea and direct air into the lungs. (p. 570)

bronchitis An irritation of the breathing passages in which the small passages become narrower than normal and often clogged with mucus. (p. 578)

budding A form of asexual reproduction in which a new organism grows out of the body of a parent. (p. 236)

buoyant force The force that water exerts upward on any underwater object. (p. 386)

calorie The amount of energy needed to raise the temperature of one gram of water by one Celsius degree. (p. 507)

cambium The layer of cells in a plant that produces new phloem and xylem cells. (p. 281)

camouflage Protective coloration; a common animal defense. (p. 358)

cancer A disease in which some body cells grow and divide uncontrollably, damaging the parts of the body around them. (p. 499)

canines Sharply pointed teeth that stab food and tear into it. (p. 426)

canopy A leafy roof formed by tall trees. (p. 735)

capillary A tiny blood vessel where substances are exchanged between the blood and the body cells. (p. 540)

captive breeding The mating of endangered animals in zoos or preserves. (p. 775)

carbohydrates Energy-rich organic compounds, such as sugars and starches, that are made of the elements carbon, hydrogen, and oxygen. They provide the raw materials to make parts of cells. (pp. 54, 507)

carbon monoxide A colorless, odorless gas produced when substances—including tobacco—are burned. (p. 577)

carcinogen A substance or a factor in the environment that can cause cancer. (p. 615)

cardiac muscle Muscle tissue found only in the heart. (p. 489)

cardiovascular system The body system that consists of the heart, blood vessels, and blood, and that carries needed substances to cells and carries waste products away from cells. (p. 536)

carnivore An animal that eats only other animals. (pp. 313, 718)

carrier A person who has one recessive allele for a trait and one dominant allele, but does not have the trait. (p. 122)

carrying capacity The largest population that an area can support. (p. 699)

cartilage A connective tissue that is more flexible than bone and that gives support to some parts of the body. (pp. 375, 484)

cast A fossil that is a copy of an organism's shape, formed when minerals seep into a mold. (p. 158)

cell The basic unit of structure and function in living things. (pp. 19, 473)

cell cycle The regular sequence of growth and division that cells undergo. (p. 73)

cell membrane The outside boundary of a cell; controls which substances can enter or leave the cell. (pp. 35, 473)

cell theory A widely accepted explanation of the relationship between cells and living things. (p. 30)

cell wall A rigid layer of nonliving material that surrounds the cells of plants and some other organisms. (p. 35)

central nervous system The brain and spinal cord; the control center of the body. (p. 628)

cephalopod A mollusk with feet adapted to form tentacles around its mouth. (p. 344)

cerebellum The part of the brain that coordinates the actions of the muscles and helps maintain balance. (p. 631)

cerebrum The part of the brain that interprets input from the senses, controls the movement of skeletal muscles, and carries out complex mental processes. (p. 630)

chitin The tough, flexible material from which arthropod exoskeletons are made. (p. 347)

chlorophyll A green pigment found in the chloroplasts of plants, algae, and some bacteria. (p. 63)

chloroplast A structure in the cells of plants and some other organisms that captures energy from sunlight and uses it to produce food. (p. 40)

cholesterol A waxy, fatlike substance, found only in animal products, that is an important part of the body's cells; can build up on artery walls. (p. 509)

chordate The phylum whose members have a notochord, a nerve cord, and slits in their throat area at some point in their lives. (p. 374)

chromatid One of the identical rods of a chromosome. (p. 74)

chromatin Material in cells that contains DNA and carries genetic information. (p. 37)

chromosome A rod-shaped cellular structure made of condensed chromatin; contains DNA, which carries the genetic information that controls inherited characteristics such as eye color and blood type. (pp. 74, 664)

cilia The hairlike projections on the outside of cells that move in a wavelike manner. (pp. 221, 568)

circadian rhythm Behavior cycles that occur over a period of approximately one day. (p. 455)

classification The process of grouping things based on their similarities. (p. 182)

clear-cutting The process of cutting down all the trees in an area at once. (p. 763)

climate The typical weather pattern in an area over a long period of time. (p. 731)

clone An organism that is genetically identical to the organism from which it was produced. (p. 134)

cnidarians Animals whose stinging cells are used to capture their prey and defend themselves, and who take their food into a hollow central cavity. (p. 323)

cochlea A snail-shaped tube in the inner ear lined with sound receptors; nerve impulses are sent from the cochlea to the brain. (p. 641)

codominance A condition in which neither of two alleles of a gene is dominant or recessive. (p. 98)

commensalism A relationship between two species in which one species benefits and the other is neither helped nor harmed. (p. 709)

community All the different populations that live together in an area. (p. 692)

competition The struggle between organisms for the limited resources in a habitat. (p. 705)

complete metamorphosis A type of metamorphosis characterized by four dramatically different stages: egg, larva, pupa, and adult. (p. 356)

compound Two or more elements that are chemically combined. (p. 52)

compound microscope A light microscope that has more than one lens. (p. 28)

concussion A bruiselike injury of the brain that occurs when the soft tissue of the cerebrum bumps against the skull. (p. 634)

conditioning The process of learning to connect a stimulus with a good or bad event. (p.445)

cone The reproductive structure of a gymnosperm. (p. 286)

condensation The process by which a gas changes to a liquid (p. 725)

coniferous trees Trees that produce their seeds in cones and have needle-shaped leaves. (p. 739)

conjugation The process in which a unicellular organism transfers some of its genetic material to another unicellular organism. (p. 196)

connective tissue A body tissue that provides support for the body and connects all of its parts. (p. 474)

consumer An organism that obtains energy by feeding on other organisms. (p. 718)

continental drift The very slow motion of the continents. (p. 728)

contour feather A large feather that helps give shape to a bird's body. (p. 411)

contractile vacuole The cell structure that collects extra water from the cytoplasm and then expels it from the cell. (p. 220)

controlled experiment An experiment in which all of the variables except for one remain the same. (pp. 7, 21)

convex lens A curved lens in which the center is thicker than the edges. (p. 32)

cornea The clear tissue that covers the front of the eye. (p. 637)

coronary artery An artery that supplies blood to the heart itself. (p. 543)

cotyledon A seed leaf that stores food. (p. 276)

courtship behavior The behavior that animals of the same species engage in to prepare for mating. (p. 452)

crop A bird's internal storage tank that allows it to store food inside its body after swallowing it. (p. 412)

crustacean An arthropod that has two or three body sections, five or more pairs of legs, two pairs of antennae, and usually three pairs of appendages for chewing. (p. 349)

cuticle The waxy, waterproof layer that covers the leaves and stems of some plants. (p. 249)

cytokinesis The final stage of the cell cycle, in which the cell's cytoplasm divides, distributing the organelles into each of the two new cells. (p. 75)

cytoplasm The region of a cell located inside the cell membrane (in prokaryotes) or between the cell membrane and nucleus (in eukaryotes); contains a gel-like material and cell organelles. (pp. 37, 473)

data The facts, figures, and other evidence gathered through observation. (p. 5)

death rate The number of deaths in a certain amount of time. (p. 697)

deciduous trees Trees that shed their leaves and grow new ones each year. (p. 738)

decomposer An organism that breaks down large chemicals from dead organisms into small chemicals and returns important materials to the soil and water. (pp. 199, 719)

dendrite A threadlike extension of a neuron that carries nerve impulses toward the cell body. (p. 624)

depressant A drug that slows down the activity of the central nervous system. (p. 646)

dermis The lower layer of the skin. (p. 497)

desert An area in which the yearly amount of evaporation is greater than the amount of precipitation. (p. 736)

development The process of change that occurs during an organism's life to produce a more complex organism. (p. 20)

diabetes A condition in which either the pancreas fails to produce enough insulin, or the body's cells can't use it properly. (p. 614)

diaphragm A large, dome-shaped muscle that plays an important role in breathing. (pp. 426, 572)

dicot An angiosperm that has two seed leaves. (p. 293)

diffusion The process by which molecules move from an area in which they are highly concentrated to an area in which they are less concentrated. (pp. 57, 545)

digestion The process by which the body breaks down food into small nutrient molecules. (p. 578)

dispersal The movement of organisms from one place to another. (p. 729)

DNA Deoxyribonucleic acid; the genetic material that carries information about an organism and is passed from parent to offspring. (p. 55)

dominant allele An allele whose trait always shows up in the organism when the allele is present. (p. 89)

down feathers Short, fluffy feathers that trap heat and keep a bird warm. (p. 412)

drug Any chemical that causes changes in a person's body or behavior. (p. 644)

drug abuse The deliberate misuse of drugs for purposes other than appropriate medical ones. (p. 645)

eardrum The membrane that separates the outer ear from the middle ear, and that vibrates when sound waves strike it. (p. 641)

echinoderm A radially symmetrical invertebrate that lives on the ocean floor and has a spiny internal skeleton. (p. 365)

ecology The study of how living things interact with each other and their environment. (p. 692)

ecosystem All the living and nonliving things that interact in an area. (p. 688)

ectotherm An animal whose body does not produce much internal heat. (p. 376)

egg A female sex cell. (pp. 102, 663)

element A type of matter in which all the atoms are the same; cannot be broken down into simpler substances. (p. 52)

embryo The young plant that develops from a zygote. (p. 276) Also, a developing human during the first eight weeks after fertilization has occurred. (p. 669)

emigration Leaving a population. (p. 698)

emphysema A serious disease that destroys lung tissue and causes difficulty in breathing. (p. 578)

endangered species A species in danger of becoming extinct in the near future. (p. 772)

endocrine gland An organ of the endocrine system that produces and releases its chemical products directly into the bloodstream. (p. 658)

endoplasmic reticulum A cell structure that forms a maze of passageways in which proteins and other materials are carried from one part of the cell to another. (p. 40)

endoskeleton An internal skeleton. (p. 365)

endospore A small, rounded, thick-walled, resting cell that forms inside a bacterial cell. (p. 197)

endotherm An animal whose body controls and regulates its temperature by controlling the internal heat it produces. (p. 377)

energy pyramid A diagram that shows the amount of energy that moves from one feeding level to another in a food web. (p. 721)

enzyme A protein that speeds up chemical reactions in the bodies of living things. (pp. 54, 520)

epidermis The outermost layer of the skin. (p. 496)

epiglottis A flap of tissue that seals off the windpipe and prevents food from entering. (p. 521)

epithelial tissue A body tissue that covers the surfaces of the body, inside and out. (p. 474)

esophagus A muscular tube that connects the mouth to the stomach. (p. 521)

estimate An approximation of a number based on reasonable assumptions. (p. 696)

estrogen A hormone produced by the ovaries that controls the development of adult female characteristics. (p. 666)

estuary A habitat in which the fresh water of a river meets the salt water of the ocean. (p. 743)

eukaryote An organism with cells that contain nuclei and other cell structures. (p. 41)

eutrophication The buildup over time of nutrients in freshwater lakes and ponds that leads to an increase in the growth of algae. (p. 230)

evaporation The process by which molecules of a liquid absorb energy and change to the gas state. (p. 724)

evolution The gradual change in a species over time. (p. 149)

excretion The process by which wastes are removed from the body. (p. 581)

exoskeleton An outer skeleton. (p. 347)

exotic species Species that are carried to a new location by people. (p. 730)

extinct A species that does not have any living members. (p. 160)

extinction The disappearance of all members of a species from Earth. (p. 771)

farsightedness The condition in which distant objects can be seen clearly but nearby objects look blurry. (p. 639)

fats High-energy nutrients that are composed of carbon, oxygen, and hydrogen and contain more than twice as much energy as an equal amount of carbohydrates. (p. 509)

fermentation The process by which cells break down molecules to release energy without using oxygen. (p. 69)

fertilization The joining of a sperm cell and an egg cell. (pp. 252, 663)

fetus A developing human from the ninth week of development until birth. (p. 671)

fiber A complex carbohydrate, found in plant foods, that cannot be broken down into sugar molecules by the body. (p. 508)

fibrin A chemical that is important in blood clotting because it forms a net of tiny fibers that traps red blood cells. (p. 552)

fish A vertebrate that lives in the water and has fins. (p. 381)

fishery An area with a large population of valuable ocean organisms. (p. 765)

flagellum A long, whiplike structure that helps a unicellular organism move. (p. 194)

flower The reproductive structure of an angiosperm. (p. 290)

follicle A structure in the dermis of the skin from which a strand of hair grows. (p. 497)

food chain A series of events in which one organism eats another. (p. 719)

food web The pattern of overlapping food chains in an ecosystem. (p. 719)

Food Guide Pyramid A chart that classifies foods into six groups to help people plan a healthy diet. (p. 513)

force A push or a pull exerted on an object. (p. 542)

fossil The preserved remains or traces of an organism that lived in the past. (pp. 46, 157, 377)

fossil record The millions of fossils that scientists have collected. (p. 160)

frond The leaf of a fern plant. (p. 264)

fruit The ripened ovary and other structures that enclose one or more seeds of an angiosperm. (p. 291)

fruiting body The reproductive hypha of a fungus. (p. 236)

G

gallbladder The organ that stores bile after it is produced by the liver. (p. 527)

gamete A sperm cell or an egg cell. (p. 253)

gametophyte The stage in the life cycle of a plant in which the plant produces gametes, or sex cells. (p. 253)

gastropod A mollusk with a single shell or no shell. (p. 342)

gene A segment of DNA on a chromosome that codes for a specific trait. (p. 89)

gene therapy The insertion of working copies of a gene into the cells of a person with a genetic disorder in an attempt to correct the disorder. (p. 136)

genetic disorder An abnormal condition that a person inherits through genes or chromosomes. (p. 125)

genetic engineering The transfer of a gene from the DNA of one organism into another organism, in order to produce an organism with desired traits. (p. 134)

genetics The scientific study of heredity. (p. 86)

genome All of the DNA in one cell of an organism. (p. 138)

genotype An organism's genetic makeup, or allele combinations. (p. 98)

genus A classification grouping that consists of a number of similar, closely related species. (p. 184)

germination The early growth stage of the embryo plant in a seed. (p. 278)

gestation period The length of time between fertilization and the birth of a mammal. (p. 433)

gill An organism's breathing organ that removes oxygen from water. (p. 341)

gizzard A thick-walled, muscular part of a bird's stomach that squeezes and grinds partially digested food. (p. 413)

glucose A sugar that is the major source of energy for the body's cells. (p. 508)

Golgi body A structure in a cell that receives proteins and other newly formed materials from the endoplasmic reticulum, packages them, and distributes them to other parts of the cell. (p. 40)

gradual metamorphosis A type of metamorphosis in which an egg hatches into a nymph that resembles an adult, and which has no distinctly different larval stage. (p. 356)

gradualism The theory that evolution occurs slowly but steadily. (p. 164)

grassland An area populated by grasses that gets 25 to 75 centimeters of rain each year. (p. 737)

gymnosperm A plant that produces seeds that are not enclosed by a protective covering. (p. 284)

H

habitat The place where an organism lives and that provides the things the organism needs. (p. 394, 689)

habitat destruction The loss of a natural habitat. (p. 774)

habitat fragmentation The breaking of a habitat into smaller, isolated pieces. (p. 774)

half-life The time it takes for half of the atoms of a radioactive element to decay. (p. 160)

heart A hollow, muscular organ that pumps blood throughout the body. (p. 538)

heart attack A condition in which blood flow to a part of the heart muscle is blocked, which causes heart cells to die. (p. 557)

hemoglobin An iron-containing protein that binds chemically to oxygen molecules and makes up most of a red blood cell. (p. 550)

herbivore An animal that eats only plants. (pp. 312, 718)

heredity The passing of traits from parents to offspring. (p. 86)

heterotroph An organism that cannot make its own food. (p. 24)

heterozygous Having two different alleles for a trait. (p. 98)

hibernation A state of greatly reduced body activity that occurs during the winter. (p. 456)

histamine A chemical that is responsible for the symptoms of an allergy. (p. 613)

homeostasis The process by which an organism's internal environment is kept stable in spite of changes in the external environment. (pp. 25, 476)

homologous structures Body parts that are structurally similar in related species; provide evidence that the structures were inherited from a common ancestor. (p. 166)

homozygous Having two identical alleles for a trait. (p. 98)

hormone A chemical that affects a plant's growth and development. (p. 298) Also, the chemical product of an endocrine gland that speeds up or slows down the activities of an organ or tissue. (p. 659)

host An organism that provides a source of energy or a suitable environment for a virus or for another organism to live. (pp. 205, 710)

hybrid An organism that has two different alleles for a trait; an organism that is heterozygous for a particular trait. (p. 90)

hybridization A selective breeding method in which two genetically different individuals are crossed. (p. 133)

hydroponics The method of growing plants in a solution of nutrients instead of in soil. (p. 268)

hypertension A disorder in which a person's blood pressure is consistently higher than normal. (p. 557)

hypha One of many branching, threadlike tubes that make up the body of a fungus. (p. 234)

hypothalamus A tiny part of the brain that links the nervous system and the endocrine system. (p. 660)

hypothesis A possible explanation for a set of observations or answer to a scientific question; must be testable. (p. 6)

immigration Moving into a population. (p. 698)

immune response Part of the body's defense against pathogens in which cells of the immune system react to each kind of pathogen with a defense targeted specifically at that pathogen. (p. 601)

immunity The ability of the immune system to destroy pathogens before they can cause disease. (p. 605)

imprinting A process in which newly hatched birds or newborn mammals learn to follow the first object they see. (p. 447)

inbreeding A selective breeding method in which two individuals with identical or similar sets of alleles are crossed. (p. 133)

incisors Flat-edged teeth used to bite off and cut parts of food. (p. 426)

infectious disease A disease that can pass from one organism to another. (pp. 200, 593)

inference An interpretation of an observation that is based on evidence or prior knowledge. (p. 5)

inflammatory response Part of the body's defense against pathogens, in which fluid and white blood cells leak from blood vessels into tissues; the white blood cells destroy pathogens by breaking them down. (p. 600)

inorganic compound A compound that does not contain carbon. (p. 53)

insect An arthropod with three body sections, six legs, one pair of antennae, and usually one or two pairs of wings. (p. 355)

insight learning The process of learning how to solve a problem or do something new by applying what is already known. (p. 446)

instinct An inborn behavior pattern that an animal performs correctly the first time. (p. 444)

insulator A material that does not conduct heat well and thus helps to prevent heat from escaping. (p. 412)

insulin A chemical produced in the pancreas that enables the body's cells to take in glucose from the blood and use it for energy. (p. 614)

interneuron A neuron that carries nerve impulses from one neuron to another. (p. 624)

interphase The stage of the cell cycle that takes place before cell division occurs; during this stage, the cell grows, copies its DNA, and prepares to divide. (p. 73)

intertidal zone The area between the highest high-tide line and the lowest low-tide line. (p. 744)

invertebrate An animal that does not have a backbone. (p. 313)

involuntary muscle A muscle that is not under conscious control. (p. 488)

iris The circular structure that surrounds the pupil and regulates the amount of light entering the eye. (p. 637)

joint A place where two bones come together. (p. 484)

karyotype A picture of all the chromosomes in a cell arranged in pairs. (p. 129)

keystone species A species that influences the survival of many other species in an ecosystem. (p. 770)

kidney A major organ of the excretory system; eliminates urea, excess water, and other waste materials from the body. (pp. 341, 581)

large intestine The last section of the digestive system, where water is absorbed from food and the remaining material is eliminated from the body. (p. 529)

larva The immature form of an animal that looks very different from the adult. (p. 322)

larynx The voice box, located in the top part of the trachea, underneath the epiglottis. (p. 573)

learning The process that leads to change in behavior based on practice or experience. (p. 444)

810

lens The flexible structure that focuses light that has entered the eye. (p. 637)

lichen The combination of a fungus and either an alga or an autotrophic bacterium that live together in a mutualistic relationship. (p. 242)

lift An upward force on an object that results from the difference in pressure between the upper and lower surfaces of the object. (p. 421)

ligament Strong connective tissue that holds together the bones in a movable joint. (p. 486)

limiting factor An environmental factor that prevents a population from increasing. (p. 699)

lipids Energy-rich organic compounds, such as fats, oils, and waxes, that are made of carbon, hydrogen, and oxygen. (p. 54)

liver The largest and heaviest organ inside the body; it breaks down substances and eliminates nitrogen from the body. (p. 527)

lungs The main organs of the respiratory system, where gas exchange takes place. (p. 570)

lymph The fluid that the lymphatic system collects and returns to the bloodstream. (p. 554)

lymph node A small knob of tissue in the lymphatic system that filters lymph. (p. 554)

lymphatic system A network of veinlike vessels that returns the fluid that leaks out of blood vessels to the bloodstream. (p. 554)

lymphocyte White blood cell that reacts to each kind of pathogen with a defense targeted specifically at that pathogen. (p. 601)

lysosome A small round cell structure that contains chemicals that break down large food particles into smaller ones. (p. 41)

············ Ⓜ ············

magnification The ability to make things look larger than they are. (p. 32)

mammal An endothermic vertebrate with a four-chambered heart, skin covered with fur or hair, and has young fed with milk from the mother's body. (p. 423)

mammary glands The organs that produce the milk with which mammals feed their young. (p. 428)

manipulated variable The one factor that a scientist changes to test a hypothesis during an experiment; also called the independent variable. (pp. 7, 21)

marrow The soft tissue that fills the internal spaces in bone. (p. 484)

marsupial A mammal whose young are born alive at an early stage of development, and which usually continue to develop in a pouch on their mother's body. (p. 432)

medusa The cnidarian body plan characterized by a bowl shape and which is adapted for a free-swimming life. (p. 324)

meiosis The process that occurs in sex cells (sperm and egg) by which the number of chromosomes is reduced by half. (p. 104)

melanin A pigment that gives the skin its color. (p. 497)

menstrual cycle The monthly cycle of changes that occurs in the female reproductive system, during which an egg develops and the uterus prepares for the arrival of a fertilized egg. (p. 667)

menstruation The process that occurs if fertilization does not take place, in which the thickened lining of the uterus breaks down and blood and tissue then pass out of the female body through the vagina. (p. 668)

messenger RNA RNA that copies the coded message from DNA in the nucleus and carries the message into the cytoplasm. (p. 109)

metamorphosis A process in which an animal's body undergoes dramatic changes in form during its life cycle. (p. 350)

microscope An instrument that makes small objects look larger. (p. 28)

migration The regular, periodic journey of an animal from one place to another and back again for the purpose of feeding or reproducing. (p. 456)

minerals Nutrients that are needed by the body in small amounts and are not made by living things. (p. 512)

mitochondria Rod-shaped cell structures that produce most of the energy needed to carry out the cell's functions. (p. 37)

mitosis The stage of the cell cycle during which the cell's nucleus divides into two new nuclei and one copy of the DNA is distributed into each daughter cell. (p. 74)

molars Teeth that, along with premolars, grind and shred food into tiny bits. (p. 426)

mold A fossil formed when an organism buried in sediment dissolves, leaving a hollow area. (p. 158)

molecule The smallest unit of most compounds. (p. 52)

mollusk An invertebrate with a soft, unsegmented body; most are protected by hard outer shells. (p. 340)

molting The process of shedding an outgrown exoskeleton. (p. 348)

monocot An angiosperm that has only one seed leaf. (p. 293)

monotreme A mammal that lays eggs. (p. 432)

motor neuron A neuron that sends an impulse to a muscle, causing the muscle to contract. (p. 624)

mucus A thick, slippery substance produced by the body. (p. 521)

multicellular A type of organism that is made up of many cells. (p. 19)

multiple alleles Three or more forms of a gene that code for a single trait. (p. 119)

muscle tissue A body tissue that contracts or shortens, making body parts move. (p. 474)

mutation A change in a gene or chromosome. (p. 110)

mutualism A type of symbiosis in which both partners benefit from living together. (pp. 222, 709)

native species Species that have naturally evolved in an area. (p. 730)

natural selection The process by which individuals that are better adapted to their environment are more likely to survive and reproduce than other members of the same species. (p. 150)

nearsightedness The condition in which nearby objects can be seen clearly but distant objects look blurry. (p. 639)

negative feedback A process in which a system is turned off by the condition it produces; examples of negative feedback systems include regulation of temperature by a thermostat and the regulation of the levels of many hormones in the blood. (p. 662)

nephron One of a million tiny, filtering structures found in the kidneys that removes wastes from blood and produces urine. (p. 582)

neritic zone The region of shallow ocean water over the continental shelf. (p. 744)

nerve A bundle of nerve fibers. (p. 624)

nerve impulse The message carried by a neuron. (p. 623)

nerve tissue A body tissue that carries messages back and forth between the brain and every other part of the body. (p. 474)

neuron A cell that carries messages through the nervous system. (p. 623)

niche An organism's particular role in an ecosystem, or how it makes its living. (p. 704)

nicotine A drug in tobacco that speeds up the activities of the nervous system, heart, and other organs of the body. (p. 577)

nitrogen fixation The process of changing free nitrogen gas into a usable form. (p. 727)

nodules Bumps on the roots of certain plants that house nitrogen-fixing bacteria. (p. 727)

noninfectious disease A disease that is not spread from person to person. (p. 612)

nonrenewable resource A natural resource that is not replaced as it is used. (p. 85)

nonvascular plant A low-growing plant that lacks vascular tissue. (p. 256)

notochord A flexible rod that supports a chordate's back. (p. 374)

nucleic acid A very large organic molecule made of carbon, oxygen, hydrogen, nitrogen, and phosphorus, that contains instructions that cells need to carry out all the functions of life. (p. 55)

nucleus The control center of a cell that directs the cell's activities; contains the chemical instructions that direct all the cell's activities and determine the cell's characteristics. (pp. 36, 473)

nutrients Substances in food that provide the raw materials and energy the body needs to carry out all the essential life processes. (p. 506)

nymph A stage of gradual metamorphosis that usually resembles the adult insect. (p. 356)

observation A skill that involves the use of one or more of the senses—sight, hearing, touch, smell, and sometimes taste—to gather information and collect data. (p. 5)

omnivore An animal that eats both plants and animals. (pp. 313, 718)

operational definition A statement that describes how a particular variable is to be measured or how a term is to be defined. (p. 791)

organ A structure in the body that is composed of different kinds of tissue. (pp. 311, 475)

organ system A group of organs that work together to perform a major function in the body. (p. 475)

organelle A tiny cell structure that carries out a specific function within the cell. (p. 35)

organic compound A compound that contains carbon. (p. 53)

organism A living thing. (p. 18)

osmosis The diffusion of water molecules through a selectively permeable membrane. (p. 58)

osteoporosis A condition in which the body's bones become weak and break easily. (p. 487)

ovary A protective structure in plants that encloses the developing seeds. (p. 290) Also, an organ of the female reproductive system in which eggs and estrogen are produced. (p. 666)

oviduct A passageway for eggs from an ovary to the uterus; the place where fertilization usually occurs. (p. 666)

ovulation The process in which a mature egg is released from the ovary into an oviduct; occurs about halfway through a typical menstrual cycle. (p. 667)

ovule A plant structure in seed plants that contains an egg cell. (p. 286)

pacemaker A group of cells located in the right atrium that sends out signals that make the heart muscle contract and that regulates heartbeat rate. (p. 540)

pancreas A triangular organ that produces enzymes that flow into the small intestine. (p. 528)

parasite An organism that lives on or in a host and causes harm to the host. (pp. 205, 710)

parasitism A relationship in which one organism lives on or inside another and harms it. (p. 710)

passive immunity Immunity in which the antibodies that fight a pathogen come from another organism rather than from the person's own body. (p. 608)

passive smoking The involuntary inhalation of smoke from other people's cigarettes, cigars, or pipes. (p. 579)

passive transport The movement of materials through a cell membrane without using energy. (p. 59)

pasteurization A heating process that is widely used to kill microorganisms in food products such as milk. (p. 593)

pathogen An organism that causes disease. (p. 593)

peat The blackish-brown material consisting of compressed layers of dead sphagnum mosses that grow in bogs. (p. 258)

pedigree A chart or "family tree" that tracks which members of a family have a particular trait. (p. 123)

peer pressure The pressure from friends and classmates to behave in certain ways. (p. 676)

penis The organ through which both semen and urine leave the male body. (p. 665)

Percent Daily Value An indication on a food label of how the nutritional content of a food fits into the diet of a person who consumes a total of 2,000 Calories a day. (p. 516)

peripheral nervous system All the nerves located outside the central nervous system; connects the central nervous system to all parts of the body. (p. 628)

peristalsis Involuntary waves of muscle contraction that keep food moving along in one direction through the digestive system. (p. 521)

permafrost Soil that is frozen all year. (p. 740)

petal One of the colorful, leaflike structures of a flower. (p. 290)

petrified fossil A fossil in which minerals replace all or part of an organism. (p. 158)

phagocyte A white blood cell that destroys pathogens by engulfing them and breaking them down. (p. 600)

pharynx The throat; part of both the respiratory and digestive systems. (p. 568)

phenotype An organism's physical appearance, or visible traits. (p. 98)

pheromone A chemical released by one animal that affects the behavior of another animal of the same species. (p. 362)

phloem The vascular tissue through which food moves in some plants. (p. 275)

photosynthesis The process by which plants and some other organisms capture light energy and use it to make food from carbon dioxide and water. (p. 62)

pigment A colored chemical compound that absorbs light, producing color. (pp. 63, 225)

pioneer species The first species to populate an area. (p. 749)

pistil The female reproductive parts of a flower. (p. 291)

pituitary gland An endocrine gland just below the hypothalamus that communicates with the hypothalamus to control many body activities. (p. 661)

placenta A membrane that becomes the link between the developing embryo or fetus and the mother. (pp. 436, 670)

placental mammal A mammal that develops inside its mother's body until its body systems can function independently. (p. 433)

plasma The liquid part of blood. (p. 549)

platelet A cell fragment that plays an important part in forming blood clots. (p. 552)

poaching The illegal killing or removal of wildlife species. (p. 774)

pollen Tiny particles produced by plants that contain the microscopic cells that later become sperm cells. (p. 286)

pollination The transfer of pollen from male reproductive structures to female reproductive structures in plants. (p. 288)

pollution A change to the environment that has a negative effect on living things. (p. 757)

polyp The cnidarian body plan characterized by a vaselike shape and which is usually adapted for life attached to an underwater surface. (p. 323)

population All the members of one species in a particular area. (p. 691)

population density The number of individuals in a specific area. (p. 695)

pore An opening through which sweat reaches the surface of the skin. (p. 497)

precipitation Rain, snow, sleet, or hail. (p. 725)

predation An interaction in which one organism hunts and kills another animal for food. (p. 706)

predator A carnivore that hunts and kills other animals for food and has adaptations that help it capture the animals it preys upon. (pp. 313, 706)

premolars Teeth that, along with molars, grind and shred food into tiny bits. (p. 426)

pressure The force that something exerts over a given area. (p. 546)

prey An animal that a predator feeds upon. (pp. 313, 706)

primary succession The changes that occur in an area where no ecosystem had existed. (p. 749)

probability The likelihood that a particular event will occur. (p. 94)

producer An organism that can make its own food. (p. 717)

prokaryote An organism whose cells lack a nucleus and some other cell structures. (p. 41)

proteins Large organic molecules made of carbon, hydrogen, oxygen, nitrogen, and sometimes sulfur; they are needed for tissue growth and repair and play a part in chemical reactions within cells. (pp. 53, 510)

protozoan An animal-like protist. (p. 219)

pseudopod A "false foot" or temporary bulge of the cell membrane used for feeding and movement in some protozoans. (p. 219)

puberty The period of sexual development during the teenage years in which the body becomes able to reproduce. (p. 675)

punctuated equilibria The theory that species evolve during short periods of rapid change. (p. 164)

Punnett square A chart that shows all the possible combinations of alleles that can result from a genetic cross. (p. 96)

pupa The second stage of complete metamorphosis, in which an insect is enclosed in a protective covering and gradually changes from a larva to an adult. (p. 356)

pupil The opening through which light enters the eye. (p. 637)

purebred An organism that always produces offspring with the same form of a trait as the parent. (p. 87)

radial symmetry The quality of having many lines of symmetry that all pass through a central point. (p. 316)

radioactive element An unstable particle that breaks down into a different element. (p. 160)

radula A flexible ribbon of tiny teeth in mollusks. (p. 341)

recessive allele An allele that is masked when a dominant allele is present. (p. 89)

rectum A short tube at the end of the large intestine where waste material is compressed into a solid form before being eliminated. (p. 529)

red blood cell A cell in the blood that takes up oxygen in the lungs and delivers it to cells elsewhere in the body. (p. 550)

red tide An algal bloom that occurs in salt water. (p. 229)

reflex An automatic response that occurs very rapidly and without conscious control. (p. 633)

regeneration The ability of an organism to regrow body parts. (p. 328)

relative dating A technique used to determine which of two fossils is older. (p. 159)

renewable resource A resource that is naturally replaced in a relatively short time. (p. 757)

replication The process by which a cell makes a copy of the DNA in its nucleus. (p. 73)

reproduce The production of offspring that are similar to the parents. (p. 21)

reproduction The process by which living things produce new individuals of the same type. (p. 663)

reptile An ectothermic vertebrate with lungs and scaly skin; lays eggs with tough, leathery shells. (p. 395)

resolution The ability to clearly distinguish the individual parts of an object. (p. 33)

respiration The process by which cells break down simple food molecules to release the energy they contain. (pp. 67, 567)

responding variable The factor that changes as a result of changes to the manipulated variable in an experiment; also called the dependent variable. (p. 7)

response An action or change in behavior that occurs as a result of a stimulus. (pp. 21, 443, 623)

retina The layer of receptor cells at the back of the eye on which an image is focused; nerve impulses are sent from the retina to the brain. (p. 638)

rhizoid The thin, rootlike structure that anchors a moss and absorbs water and nutrients for the plant. (p. 257)

ribosome A tiny structure in the cytoplasm of a cell where proteins are made. (p. 40)

RNA Ribonucleic acid; a nucleic acid that plays an important role in the production of proteins. (p. 55)

root cap A structure that covers the tip of a root, protecting the root from injury. (p. 283)

saliva The fluid released when the mouth waters that plays an important role in both mechanical and chemical digestion. (p. 520)

saturated fats Fats, such as butter, that are usually solid at room temperature. (p. 509)

savanna A grassland close to the equator. (p. 737)

scavenger A carnivore that feeds on the bodies of dead organisms. (p. 718)

science A way of learning about the natural world and the knowledge gained through that process. (p. 4)

scientific inquiry The diverse ways in which scientists study the natural world. (p. 4)

scientific theory A well-tested concept that explains a wide range of observations. (pp. 9, 149)

scrotum An external pouch of skin in which the testes are located. (p. 664)

secondary succession The changes that occur after a disturbance in an ecosystem. (p. 750)

sedimentary rock A type of rock that forms when particles from other rocks or the remains of plants and animals are pressed and cemented together. (pp. 158, 378)

seed The plant structure that contains a young plant inside a protective covering. (p. 276)

selective breeding The process of selecting a few organisms with desired traits to serve as parents of the next generation. (p. 132)

selective cutting The process of cutting down only some trees in an area. (p. 763)

selectively permeable A property of cell membranes that allows some substances to pass through, while others cannot. (p. 56)

semen A mixture of sperm cells and fluids. (p. 665)

semicircular canals Structures in the inner ear that are responsible for the sense of balance. (p. 641)

sensory neuron A neuron that picks up stimuli from the internal or external environment and converts each stimulus into a nerve impulse. (p. 624)

sepal A leaflike structure that encloses the bud of a flower. (p. 290)

sex-linked gene A gene that is carried on the X or Y chromosome. (p. 122)

sexual reproduction The reproductive process that involves two parents who combine their genetic material to produce a new organism, which differs from both parents. (p. 196)

skeletal muscle A muscle that is attached to the bones of the skeleton. (p. 489)

small intestine The part of the digestive system in which most chemical digestion takes place. (p. 526)

smooth muscle Involuntary muscle found inside many internal organs of the body. (p. 489)

society A group of closely related animals that work together for the benefit of the whole group. (p. 454)

somatic nervous system The group of nerves that controls voluntary actions. (p. 632)

species A group of similar organisms whose members can mate with one another and produce fertile offspring. (pp. 147, 184)

sperm A male sex cell. (pp. 102, 663)

sphygmomanometer An instrument that measures blood pressure. (p. 547)

spinal cord The thick column of nerve tissue that is enclosed by the vertebrae and that links the brain to most of the nerves in the peripheral nervous system. (p. 629)

spontaneous generation The mistaken idea that living things arise from nonliving sources. (p. 21)

spore A tiny cell that is able to grow into a new organism. (p. 223)

sporophyte The stage in the life cycle of a plant in which the plant produces spores for reproduction. (p. 253)

stamen The male reproductive parts of a flower. (p. 290)

stimulant A drug that speeds up body processes. (p. 646)

stimulus A change in an organism's surroundings that causes the organism to react. (pp. 20, 443, 623)

stomach A J-shaped, muscular pouch located in the abdomen that expands to hold all of the food that is swallowed. (p. 522)

stomata The small openings on the undersides of most leaves through which oxygen and carbon dioxide can move. (pp. 63, 278)

stress The reaction of a person's body and mind to threatening, challenging, or disturbing events. (p. 477)

succession The series of predictable changes that occur in a community over time. (p. 748)

sustainable yield A regular amount of a renewable resource that can be harvested without reducing the future supply. (p. 763)

swim bladder An internal gas-filled organ that helps a bony fish stabilize its body at different water depths. (p. 386)

symbiosis A close relationship between two organisms in which at least one of the organisms benefits. (pp. 222, 709)

synapse The tiny space between the tip of an axon and the next structure. (p. 626)

T cell A lymphocyte that identifies pathogens and distinguishes one pathogen from another. (p. 601)

tar A dark, sticky substance produced when tobacco burns. (p. 576)

target cell A cell in the body that recognizes a hormone's chemical structure; a cell to which a hormone binds chemically. (p. 659)

taxonomic key A series of paired statements that describe the physical characteristics of different organisms. (p. 186)

taxonomy The scientific study of how living things are classified. (p. 183)

tendon Strong connective tissue that attaches a muscle to a bone. (p. 490)

territory An area that is occupied and defended by an animal or group of animals. (p. 451)

testis Organ of the male reproductive system in which sperm and testosterone are produced. (p. 664)

testosterone A hormone produced by the testes that controls the development of physical characteristics in men. (p. 664)

thorax An insect's mid-section, to which its wings and legs are attached. (p. 355)

threatened species A species that could become endangered in the near future. (p. 772)

tissue A group of similar cells that perform a specific function in an organism. (pp. 252, 474)

tolerance A state in which a drug user, after repeatedly taking a drug, needs larger and larger doses of the drug to produce the same effect. (p. 645)

toxin A poison that can harm an organism. (p. 200)

trachea The windpipe; a passage through which air moves in the respiratory system. (p. 569)

trait A characteristic that an organism can pass on to its offspring through its genes. (p. 86)

transfer RNA RNA in the cytoplasm that carries an amino acid to the ribosome and adds it to the growing protein chain. (p. 109)

transpiration The process by which water is lost through a plant's leaves. (p. 280)

trial-and-error-learning The learning that occurs when an animal learns to perform a behavior more and more skillfully through repeated practice. (p. 446)

tropism The growth response of a plant toward or away from a stimulus. (p. 297)

tumor A mass of abnormal cells that develops when cancerous cells divide and grow uncontrollably. (p. 615)

tundra An extremely cold, dry biome. (p. 740)

umbilical cord A ropelike structure that forms in the uterus between the embryo and the placenta. (p. 670)

understory A layer of shorter plants that grow in the shade of a forest canopy. (p. 735)

unicellular A type of organism that is made up of a single cell. (p. 19)

unsaturated fats Fats, such as olive oil and canola oil, that are usually liquid at room temperature. (p. 509)

urea A chemical that comes from the breakdown of proteins and is removed from the body by the kidneys. (p. 581)

ureter A narrow tube that carries urine from one of the kidneys to the urinary bladder. (p. 581)

urethra A small tube through which urine flows from the body. (p. 582)

urinary bladder A sacklike muscular organ that stores urine until it is eliminated from the body. (p. 582)

urine A watery fluid produced by the kidneys that contains urea and other waste materials. (pp. 397, 581)

uterus The hollow muscular organ of the female reproductive system in which a baby develops. (p. 666)

vaccination The process by which harmless antigens are deliberately introduced into a person's body to produce active immunity. (p. 607)

vaccine A substance used in a vaccination that consists of pathogens that have been weakened or killed but can still trigger the immune system into action. (pp. 211, 607)

vacuole A water-filled sac inside a cell that acts as a storage area. (p. 41)

vagina A muscular passageway through which a baby leaves the mother's body. (p. 667)

valve A flap of tissue in the heart or a vein that prevents blood from flowing backward. (p. 538)

variable Any factor that can change in an experiment. (p. 6)

variation Any difference between individuals of the same species. (p. 151)

vascular plant A plant that has vascular tissue. (p. 262)

vascular tissue The internal transporting tissue in some plants that is made up of tubelike structures. (p. 252)

vein A blood vessel that carries blood back to the heart. (p. 540)

ventricle A lower chamber of the heart that pumps blood out to the lungs and body. (pp. 390, 538)

vertebrae The bones that make up the backbone of an animal. (pp. 375, 481)

vertebrate An animal with a backbone. (p. 313)

villi Tiny finger-shaped structures that cover the inner surface of the small intestine and provide a large surface area through which digested food is absorbed. (p. 528)

virus A small, nonliving particle that invades and then reproduces inside a living cell. (p. 204)

vitamins Molecules that act as helpers in a variety of chemical reactions within the body. (p. 511)

vocal cords Folds of connective tissue that stretch across the opening of the larynx and produce a person's voice. (p. 573)

voluntary muscle A muscle that is under conscious control. (p. 488)

water cycle The continuous process by which water moves from Earth's surface to the atmosphere and back. (p. 724)

water vascular system A system of fluid-filled tubes in an echinoderm's body. (p. 366)

white blood cell A blood cell that fights disease. (p. 551)

withdrawal A period of adjustment that occurs when a drug-dependent person stops taking the drug. (p. 646)

xylem The vascular tissue through which water and nutrients move in some plants. (p. 275)

zygote A fertilized egg, produced by the joining of a sperm and an egg. (pp. 252, 663)

Index

Abbé, Ernst 31
abdomen
   of arachnid 350
   of crayfish 351
   of insect 355
Abert's squirrel 155
abiotic factors 690
absolute dating 160
absorption 519, 528–529
acne 500
acquired immunodeficiency syndrome
   (AIDS) 210, 603–604
active immunity 605–608
active transport 59–60
active viruses 207–208
adaptations 149, 312, 373
   of animals 312–313
   of birds 417–418
   to environment 704, 706
   of plants 250–251
   predator 313, 706–707
   prey 313, 706–707
   of primates for grasping 436
   in reptiles to conserve water 395–396
addiction, drug 646
   alcoholism 651
   nicotine 577
adenine 78, 108
adolescence 675–676
adrenal glands 660, 661
adrenaline 477–478, 659
adulthood 677
advertising, nutrition and 530
African rain forests 780–785
afterbirth 672
aggression 451, 454
aging 677
agrochemicals 305, 306
AIDS 210, 603–604
air pressure, bird wings and 420–421
air sacs in bird lungs 412, 413, 415
Akita 177
alcohol 645, 647, 649–652
   effects of 650–652
alcoholic fermentation 70
alcoholism 651
algae 224–230, 249
   brown 227
   colors of 225
   diatoms 218, 226, 229
   dinoflagellates 226, 229
   euglenoids 225
   green 226
   red 227
algal blooms 228–230
alleles 89–90
   dominant 122
   multiple 119–120
   recessive 122
   sickle-cell 127
allergens 613
allergies 612–613
alligators 403
alveoli 570, 571
ameba 220

amino acids 53, 510, 522–523
amniocentesis 128
amniotic sac 670
amphetamines 646, 647
amphibians 389–394
   circulation in 390
   frogs 391, 392, 393
   mobility of 392
   reproduction in 390–391
   respiration in 390
   salamanders 389, 391, 392–393
   threats to 394
   toads 392
anabolic steroids 647, 648
anal pore 221
anaphase 74, 77
Andes Mountains 572
anemone fish 387
angiosperms 289–296
   flowers 290–95
   life cycle of 292
   reproduction in 291
   types of 293
   uses of 296
animal(s) 191, 309, 310–439. *See also*
   invertebrates; vertebrates
   adaptations of 312–313
   amphibians 389–394
   arthropods 346–353
   of boreal forest 740
   characteristics of 310–312
   classification of 313–314
   cloning of 134
   cnidarians 323–325
   of deciduous forests 739
   of desert 737
   echinoderms 365–368
   fishes 381–387
   in freshwater biomes 742, 743
   of grassland 738
   insects 346, 348, 354–364
   in marine biomes 744, 745
   mollusks 340–344
   of mountains and ice biome 741
   movement by 311–312
   needs of 312
   of rain forest 736
   reptiles 395–404
   sponges 320–322
   symmetry in 316–317, 341, 365
   of tundra 741
   worms 327–334
animal behavior 441–458
   aggression 451, 454
   behavior cycles 455–456
   communication 450, 454
   competition 451
   conditioning 445–446
   group living 453–454, 455, 458
   imprinting 447–448
   instinctive 444
   learning 444–447, 449
   mating 452–453
   migration 456–457
   parenting 453

   pheromones and 363
   territory, establishing 451–452
animal bites, disease spread by 595
animal cells 19, 39, 43, 75, 311
animalcules 29
animal-like protists 219–223
Annelida (phylum) 327
Anning, Mary 378
annual plants 298
annual rings 281–282
anole 442
Antarctica 756, 760
antennae of crayfish 348–349, 351
anther 290, 292
antibiotics 201, 609
antibodies 602, 605
antigens 601
ants 362
anus 331, 529
anvil 641
aorta 539, 542
appendages, arthropod 347, 348–349
appendix 165
aquaculture 766
arachnids 348, 350–352
Archaebacteria 189–190, 194
Archaeopteryx 379, 410
Aristotle 183
arteries 540, 543–545
Arthropoda (phylum) 347
arthropods 346–353. *See also* **insects**
   arachnids 348, 350–352
   centipedes 353
   characteristics of 347–349, 360–361
   crustaceans 348, 349–350, 351
   millipedes 353
   origin of 349
artificial heart 559
artificial intelligence 446–447
asexual reproduction 195, 236, 311
   in bacteria 195
   budding 236
   in cnidarians 324
   in corals 325
   in fungi 236
   in paramecium 221
   in sponges 322
   in worms 328
asthma 613
atherosclerosis 557, 579
atmosphere 567
   of early Earth 44–45
atom 52, 724
atrium, atria of heart 390, 538, 539
Audubon, John James 411
Australia 156
autonomic nervous system 632
autotrophs 23, 65, 249, 717
auxin 298
axons 624, 626, 632

baby
   birth of 671–672
   in infancy 673–674
   sex of 121

backbone 374, 375–376, 481. *See also* **vertebrates**
bacteria 29, 181, 192–203, 593, 719
  cell of 41, 192–194
  environmental recycling by 199–200
  fermentation and 305
  in food 198–199
  fuel produced by 197
  genetic engineering in 135–136
  health-promoting 201
  infectious diseases caused by 200–201
  kingdoms of 189–190, 194–195
  nitrogen-fixing 727
  reproduction in 192, 195–196
  survival needs of 196–197
bacteriophage 205, 206
ball-and-socket joint 485
balloonfish 387
barbiturates 647
bases, nitrogen 78, 108, 109
basset hound 176
bats 434
B cells 601, 602, 606
Beaumont, William 518
bee-eaters 418
behavior 443. *See also* **animal behavior**
biceps 491
biennials 299
bighorn sheep, desert 683, 684
bilateral symmetry 316, 317, 341
bile 527, 586
bill of bird 412, 413
binary fission 195
binomial nomenclature 183
biodiversity 768–776, 780–785
  factors affecting 768–769
  of gene pool 771
  protection of 775–776
  species extinction and 771–774
  value of 769–770
biogeography 728–731
  continental drift 156, 728–729
  dispersal, means and limits of 729–731
biological controls 359
bioluminescence 364
biomes 732–751
  boreal forest 739–740
  deciduous forest 738–739
  desert 736–737
  freshwater 742–743
  grassland 737–738
  marine 743–745
  mountains and ice 741
  rain forest 735–736, 780–785
  succession 746–750
  tundra 740–741
biotic factors 689
birds 409, 410–422
  body temperature of 414
  diversity of 417–419
  feathers of 411–412
  flight of 411, 420–422
  food of 412–415
  getting oxygen 415–416
  importance of 419

  nervous system of 416
  of prey 418
  reproduction and caring for young in 416–417
birth 671–673
birth canal 667
birth rate 697
bivalves 342–344
bladderwort 297
Blalock, Alfred 558
blood
  blood types and 552–553, 555
  components of 549–553
  plasma 549
  platelets 549, 551, 552
  red blood cells 42, 58, 126, 531, 549, 550–551
  water content of 24
  white blood cells 531, 549, 551, 600
blood alcohol concentration (BAC) 650
blood banks 558
blood cells 42, 58, 126, 531, 535, 549, 550–552, 600
blood flow, regulating 544–545, 546
blood pressure 546–547
blood transfusion 552–553, 555
blood types 119, 552–553, 555, 558
blood vessels 540–546
  arteries 540, 543–545
  capillaries 540, 544, 545, 570, 582–583
  veins 540, 545, 546
body defenses against infectious disease 596–600
body organization 472–479
  cells 473
  homeostasis in 25, 476–479
  levels of 472–475
  organs 311, 475
  tissues 474–475
body temperature 477
  of birds 414
  skin and maintenance of 495
  in vertebrates 376–377
bog 258
bones 480–487. *See also* **skeletal system**
  growth 483
  strength 482–483
bony fish 383, 385–386
Border collie 176
Border terrier 178
boreal forest biome 739–740
Borrelia burgdorferi 193
botanists 12
botulism 595
box jellyfish 310
Brachiosaurus 404
brain
  of bird 416
  concussion of 634
  of human 629–630
  of worm 328
brainstem 630, 631
branching tree diagram 168–169, 314, 380
breathing 567, 572–573, 575
  path of air in 568–570

  processing of 572–573
breeding 132–133, 150
bristlecone pine 250
brittle stars 367
bronchi 568, 569, 570
bronchitis 578
Brown, Barnum 379
brown algae 227
bubonic plague (Black Death) 358
budding 236, 322, 324
buoyancy 386
  swim bladders in fish and 385–386
butterflies 315, 354, 773

caffeine 648–649
calcium 482, 483, 486, 512
California condors, captive breeding of 775
California leaf-nosed bat 685
calipers 7
calorie 507
Calorie (1000 calories) 507
  from fat 515–516
cambium 281, 283
Cambrian period 162
camouflage 358, 706
cancer 112, 499–500, 578, 579, 614–616
  causes of 615
  prevention of 616
  treatment of 615–616
canines 426, 520
canopy 735, 781, 782, 784–785
capillaries 540, 544, 545, 570, 582–583
captive breeding 775
carbohydrates 19, 46, 53, 54, 506, 507–508
  converting to agrochemicals 305
carbolic acid 592
carbon 53
carbon cycle 725–726
carbon dioxide 44, 53
  in alcoholic fermentation 70
  in gas exchange 571
  photosynthesis and 63, 64
  in red blood cells 550
Carboniferous period 162
carbon monoxide 577
carcinogens 615, 616
cardiac muscle 489, 491, 538
cardiovascular diseases 557–559, 612
  atherosclerosis 557, 558, 559
  heart attack 557, 559
  hypertension 557–559
cardiovascular health 556–560
  advances in 558–559
  maintaining 560
cardiovascular system 536–537. *See also* **circulation**
  alcohol's effect on 651
carnivores 313, 718
  mammal 435, 436
carrageenan 227
carrier 122, 123
  of hemophelia 127
carrying capacity 699
Carson, Rachel 759
cartilage 375, 484

cartilaginous fish 383, 384
casts 158
cell(s) 16–49, 473
  active transport in 59–60
  animal 19, 39, 43, 75, 311
  bacterial 41, 192–194
  chemical composition of 19, 52–55
  diffusion in 57, 58–59
  energy use by 20, 67
  first (early) 46
  first sightings of 28–29
  fungal 234
  nucleus of 36–37, 38, 39
  osmosis in 58–59
  plant 19, 35, 38, 43, 54, 75
  sex 102–106, 663–664
  specialized 19, 42
cell cycle 73–77
  cytokinesis 75, 76
  interphase 73–74, 76
  length of 75, 80
  mitosis 74, 76–77
cell division
  cytokinesis 75, 76
  DNA replication 78–79
  mitosis 74, 76–77
  preparation for 74
cell membrane 35–36, 38, 39, 53, 54, 220, 473
  engulfment by 60
  selective permeability of 56
cell theory 30–31
cellular organization 19
cellular respiration 67
cellulose 35, 54
cell wall 35, 38
Celsius scale 789
Cenozoic era 163
centipedes 353
central nervous system 628, 629–631
  brain 629–630
  spinal cord 629, 631
centromere 74, 77
cephalopods 342, 344
cerebellum 630, 631
cerebrum 630
certified wood 764
cervix 666, 667
chameleon 373, 397, 398
chelipeds 351
chemical digestion 519, 520, 522, 523, 526–528
chemicals
  compund cells in 53–55
  plant-based 304–307
  in tobacco smoke 576–577
chicken pox 210
chitin 347–348
Chlamydomonas 190
chlorine 512
chlorophyll 63, 64, 278
chloroplast 38, 40, 62–63, 278, 279
cholera 594
cholesterol 509
Chordata (phylum) 374
chordates 374–375

chow chow 177
chromatids 74, 77
chromatin 36, 37, 74
chromosomes 74, 106, 664
  DNA and 108
  inheritance and 102–103
  sex 121, 122
chrysalis 357
cilia 221, 341, 568, 569, 597
ciliates 221
circadian rhythms 455
circle graphs 798
circulation 535–560
  blood, components of 549–553
  blood pressure 546–547
  blood vessels and 540–546
  cardiovascular health and 556–560
  functions of 536–537
  heart and 538–540
  lymphatic system and 554
circulatory system 475, 536–537, 567
  closed 332, 382
  of amphibians 390
  of arthropods 347
  of bird 415–416
  of fish 382
  of mammals 426
  of segmented worms 332
  open 332, 347
  smoking and 579
clams 343
classification 182–188, 787
  early systems of 183
  of fungi 237
  levels of 185–186, 187
  Linnean system of 183–185
  reasons for 182–183
  using 186
clear-cutting 763
climate
  biodiversity and 769
  biome and 734
  as limit to dispersal 731
cloning 134
Closterium 226
Clostridium tetani 200–201
club fungi 237
club mosses 265
cnidarians 323–325
  body plans of 323–324
  characteristics of 323
  in coral reef 325–326
  feeding by 324
  reproduction in 324
coal, formation of 262
cocaine 645, 647
cochlea 641
cocoon 357
codominance 98–99
coelenterates. See cnidarians
cold sores 209
Colorado River valley 684
colorblindness, red-green 122–123
commensalism 709
commons 763

communication
  animal 450, 454
  insect 362–364
  in science 9, 787
communities
  in ecosystem 692
  succession in 746–750
compact bone 483
compare/contrast tables 794
competition 151, 451, 704, 705, 730
complete metamorphosis 356, 357
complete proteins 510
complex carbohydrates 508
compound eyes 351, 355
compound microscope 28, 30, 31, 802
compounds 52
  in cells 53–55
  inorganic 53
  organic 53
concave lenses 639
concept maps 794
conclusions, drawing 8, 791
concussion 634
condensation 725
conditioning 445–446
cones 286, 287, 288, 638
coniferous trees (conifers) 286, 288, 739–740
conjugation 196
connective tissue 474, 475, 484, 490
consumers 718, 719, 720
contaminated objects, spread of disease by 595
continental drift 156, 728–729
contour feathers 411, 413
contractile vacuole 220, 221
controlled experiment 7, 21, 22, 791
Convention on International Trade in Endangered Species (1973) 776
convex lens 32, 639
coral reef 323, 325–326, 769
corn, products made from 306
cornea 637
coronary arteries 543, 557
cortisone 296
cotton plants 296
cotyledons 276
cough 570
courtship behavior 452–453, 454
crayfish 348–349, 351
Cretaceous period 163
Crick, Francis 78
critical thinking skills 792–793
crocodiles 403
crop 412, 413
cross matching of blood types 553
crustaceans 348, 349–350, 351
Culex nigripalpus 211
cuticle 249, 264, 279
cuttlefish 344
cycads 285
cycle diagrams 795
cycles of matter 723–727
  carbon and oxygen cycle 725–726
  nitrogen cycle 726–727
  water cycle 724–725

cystic fibrosis 126
cytokinesis 75, 76
cytoplasm 37–41, 68, 75, 220, 473
cytosine 78, 108

dachshund 176
Dall's sheep 436
dandelions 274
Darwin, Charles 146–151
data 5
  collecting 7
  interpreting 8, 791
data tables 8, 796
date palm 251
dating techniques 159–160
Datta, Rathin 304–307
death, leading causes of 610–611
death rate 697
deciduous forest biome 738–739
decomposers 199–200, 718–719, 720, 727
deep zone 745
defenses against infectious disease 596–600
defense strategies 706–707
defensive communication 454
Deinonychus 379
dendrite 624, 626
deoxyribonucleic acid. *See* DNA
deoxyribose 78
dependent (responding) variable 7, 791
depressants 646
  alcohol 649–652
dermis 496, 497, 643
desert biome 736–737
desert wildlife, protecting 682–685
development. *See also* human life cycle
  evolutionary similarities in early 166–167
  of living things 20
Devonian period 162
DeVries, William 559
dewlap 398
diabetes 584, 614
diaphragm 426, 572, 573
diatomaceous earth 226
diatoms 218, 226, 229
dicots 293
diffusion 57, 59, 322, 545
  of water molecules 58–59
digestion 518–530
  chemical 519, 520, 522, 523, 526–528
  esophagus and 519, 521
  large intestine 519, 529
  liver function in 519, 527
  mechanical 518–519, 520, 522, 523
  mouth and 519, 520
  pancreas function in 519, 528
  small intestine and 519, 526–528
  stomach and 519, 522–525
digestive system 475, 567
  alcohol's effect on 651
  of birds 412–413
  functions of 518–519
  organs of 519, 520–529
  of planarian 330
  of roundworms 331
digitalis 296

dinoflagellates 226, 229
dinosaur eggs 379
dinosaurs 378–379, 404
direct observation 696
disease(s). *See also* infectious disease;
    noninfectious disease
  analyzing urine for signs of 584
  cardiovascular 557, 612
  cardiovascular system and fight against
    537
  fungal 240–241
  insects carrying 358
dispersal 729
  limits of 730–731
  means of 729–730
DNA 55, 107–112
  chromosomes and 108
  evolutionary similarities in 167–168
  extracted from fossils 168
  genetic code 107–108
  mutations and 110–112
  replication of 73, 78–79
  structure of 78–79
DNA fingerprinting 137
dogs 174–179
dog tapeworms 329
Dolly (cloned sheep) 116, 134
dolphins 435
dominant alleles 89–90, 122
double helix 78
Douglas, Marjory Stoneman 759
down feathers 412
Down syndrome 128
downy mildews 223
Drew, Charles 558
drinking and driving 650
drone (bee) 455
drugs 644–652
  alcohol 645, 647, 649–652
  drug abuse 645–646, 647
  kinds of 646–649
  medicines 644
duck-billed platypuses 432
Durrell, Gerald 784–785

ear, hearing and 640–641
eardrum 641
Earth, early atmosphere of 44–45
earthworms 331, 332–333, 334, 444
Ebola virus 205
Echinodermata (phylum) 365
echinoderms 365–368
  brittle stars 367
  characteristics of 365–366
  sand dollars 367
  sea cucumbers 368
  sea stars 366–367
  sea urchins 365, 368
ecological interactions 703–710
  competition 151, 451, 704, 705, 730
  environmental adaptations 704, 706
  predation 704, 706–708
  symbiosis 222, 704, 709–710
ecology 692–693
economic value of biodiversity 770

ecosystems 688–694, 715–731. *See also*
    biomes
  abiotic factors in 690
  biogeography 728–731
  biotic factors in 689
  communities in 692
  cycles of matter in 723–727
  ecology and 692–693
  energy flow in 716–722
  habitats 394, 689
  populations in 691
ecotourism 770
ectotherm 376. *See also* amphibians; fishes;
    reptiles
egg cells 102
  human 663, 666–667
eggs
  bird 416–417
  dinosaur 379
  insect 356, 357
  reptile 396
Eldridge, Niles 164
electron microscopes 33
elements 52, 160
elephants 435
elephant shrew 167–168
elimination of wastes 529
embryo 669
  development of 669–670
  of seed 276
emergency medical technician (EMT) 13
emergent layer of rain forest 781
emigration 698
emphysema 578, 579
endangered species 772–773
Endangered Species Act of 1973 775
endocrine glands 658
endocrine system 475, 658–662
  in adolescence 675
  hormones 659, 666, 668, 675
  hypothalamus 660, 661
  menstrual cycle and 668
  negative feedback and 662
  pituitary gland 660, 661
  role of 658, 660–661
endoplasmic reticulum 38, 39, 40
  rough 40
  smooth 40
endoskeleton 365
  backbone 375–376
endospores 197
endotherm 377, 379. *See also* birds;
    mammals
energy
  as product of respiration 68
  in carbohydrates 54
  cellular use of 20, 67
  in lipids 54
  mitochondrial production of 37
  organisms' need for 23–24
  photosynthesis and 62–63, 64
energy flow in ecosystems 716–722
  energy pyramids 721–722
  energy roles 717–719
  food chains and food webs 719–721

energy pyramids 721–722
English peppered moth 154
engulfment by cell membrane 60
environment. *See also* **ecosystems**
  adaptations to 704, 706
  of crustaceans 350
  genetics and 120
  pathogens from 595
environmental issues 755–776
  approaches to 758–760
  biodiversity 768–776, 780–785
  fisheries 765–766
  forest resources 762–764, 767
  history of 758–759
  types of 756–757
environmental recycling
  by bacteria 199–200
  by fungi 240
environmental science 759
enzymes 54, 520, 522
epidermis 496–497
epiglottis 519, 521, 569, 570
epithelial tissue 474, 475
Epstein-Barr virus 205
Escher, M.C. 631
Escherichia coli 193, 195, 709
esophagus 519, 521
estrogen 666
estuary 743–744
Eubacteria 190, 194–195, 200
euglena 225
euglenoids 225
eukaryotes 41, 249.
Eureka valley evening primrose 772
eutrophication 230, 231–232
evaporation 724–725
evolution 146–173
  in action 154
  adaptations and 149
  body structure similarities and 165–166
  combining evidence of 168–169
  continental drift and 156
  Darwin's work and 146–151
  defined 149
  DNA similarities and 167–168
  early development similarities and
    166–167
  fossil record of 157–164
  genes and 154
  natural selection 146, 150–153, 154, 704
  protein structure and 170
  rate of 164
  species formation 155–156
  of vertebrates 374–380
excretion 581
excretory system 475, 581–586
  kidneys 581–586
  other organs of 586
  water balance and 585–586
exercise
  cardiovascular health and 560
  healthy bones and 487
  healthy muscles and 492
exoskeleton 347–348
exotic species 730, 774

experiment 790–791
  controlled 21, 22
  designing 6–7, 10, 26, 791
  laboratory safety 11, 799–801
extinction 771–774
  causes of 773–774
  of dinosaurs 404
extinct species 160
eye
  amphibian 392
  vision and 637–639
eye dominance 120
eyespots 330, 367

"fairy rings" 241
farms, efficiency of 267–268
farsightedness 639
fats 54, 506, 509
  Calories from 515–516
fat-soluble vitamins 511, 512
feathers 411–412
Felis **genus** 184
female reproductive system 666–668
  egg cells 663, 666–667
  menstrual cycle 667–668
  ovaries 660, 666
fermentation 69–70, 305
ferns 261, 263–264
fertilization. *See also* **reproduction**
  in amphibians 390
  in angiosperms 291, 292
  in arthropods 347
  in birds 416
  in fishes 383
  in gymnosperms 287, 288
  in humans 663
  in mammals 428
  in plants 252, 253
fertilizer 5, 268
fetus, development of 671
fiber 508, 528
fibrin 552
fibrous roots 282–283
fiddleheads 264
fight-or-flight response 478
filament 290
filter feeders 342
finches 149, 154
fins 381, 382, 385
fireflies 357, 364
fisheries 765–766
fishes 381–387
  bony 383, 385–386
  cartilaginous 383, 384
  classification of 383–386
  feeding by 382
  as food 387
  getting oxygen 382, 388
  jawless 374, 383
  mobility of 382
  reproduction in 383
fishing limits 765–766
flagellum, flagella 194, 222
flapping flight 422
flatworms 328–329

Fleming, Alexander 241, 607
flight of birds 411, 420–422
flowcharts 795
flowers 292
  of monocots vs. dicots 293
  structure of 290–291, 294–295
fluorine 512
flying gurnards 386
follicles 497
food 196, 504–516. *See also* **digestion**
  animal adaptations for getting 312–313
  bacteria in 198–199
  carbohydrates 19, 46, 53, 54, 305, 506,
    507–508
  contaminated, disease spread by 595
  efficiency of farms 267–268
  fats 54, 506, 509, 515–516
  Food Guide Pyramid 513–515
  functions of 506–507
  fungi and 240
  hydroponics 268
  as limiting factor 699
  minerals 506, 512, 517
  photosynthesis and 63
  plants as 266–268
  proteins 19, 53–54, 506, 510
  vitamins 506, 510–512
food, methods of obtaining 311
  in alligators and crocodiles 403
  in birds 412–415
  of cnidarians 324
  in crustaceans 350
  by fishes 382
  in fungi 235
  in insects 356
  in lizards 398
  in snakes 399
  of sponges 322
  in turtles 402
food chains 719–721
food groups 513, 514
Food Guide Pyramid 513–515
food labels 515–516
food vacuole 220, 221
food web 719–721
foot
  mollusk 342
  of snail 343
force, ventricular 542
forest(s)
  boreal 739–740
  deciduous 738–739
  rain 248, 735–736, 780–785
forest resources 762–764, 767
Forest Stewardship Council 764
fossil record 160
fossils 46, 157–164, 377, 410
  determining age of 159–160
  DNA extracted from 168
  formation of 157–159
  Geologic Time Scale and 161–164
  information yielded by 160–161
  of mollusks 341
  petrified 158
  vertebrate history in 377–379

fraternal twins 673
free nitrogen 726
freshwater biome 742–743
freshwater blooms 230
Friedman, Cindy xxii, 1–3
Friends of the Everglades 759
frogs 391, 392, 393
fronds 264
fruiting bodies 236
fruits 291, 292
fuel
  bacteria and production of 197
  coal deposits 262
  peat 258
fungi 191, 233–245, 593, 719
  cell structure of 234
  classification of 237
  food acquisition by 235
  living world and 240–242
  reproduction in 235–236
  skin infection with 500
funguslike protists 223–224
fur 424–425, 429

Galapagos Islands 147–148
gallbladder 519, 527
gametes 253
gametophytes 253, 257, 264, 275
gannets 699–700
gas exchange 571
gasohol 304
gastropods 342
gemsboks 441
gene(s) 89, 102, 106
  on chromosomes 106
  evolution and 154
  main function of 107
  sex-linked 122–123
  traits controlled by many 120
  traits controlled by single 118–119
gene pool diversity 771
generalizations, making 793
gene therapy 136–137
genetic code 107–108
genetic counseling 129
genetic crosses 100–101
  monohybrid and Punnett squares
    96–97, 118–119
genetic disorders 125–131
  cystic fibrosis 126
  diagnosing 128–129
  Down syndrome 128
  genetic counseling and 129
  hemophilia 127
  Huntington's disease 128
  from inbreeding 175
  sickle-cell disease 126–127
genetic engineering 134–137, 267
genetics 84–143. See also DNA; traits
  alleles 89–90, 119–120, 122, 127
  cloning 134
  codominance 98–99
  environment and 120
  genetic engineering 134–137, 267
  Human Genome Project 138–139
  Mendel's work on 86–91

mutations 110–112, 125
pedigrees in 117, 123–124
phenotypes and genotypes 98, 112
probability and 94–101
Punnett squares and 96–97, 104
selective breeding 132–133, 150
sex of baby and 121
symbols in 90–91
genetic testing 139
genotypes 98
genus 184, 186
geographic isolation 155–156
Geologic Time Scale 161–164
germination 278
gestation period 433, 436
giant sequoia trees 284
Giardia lamblia 222
gills 341, 381, 382, 385
ginkgo 285
gizzard 413
glands 658. See also endocrine system
gliding flight 422
gliding joint 485
glucose 67, 508
  diabetes and blood level of 614
  from photosynthesis 63, 64
gnetophytes 285
Golden retriever 176
Golgi body 38, 39, 40
Gonyaulax 226
Gorgas, William C. 600
Gould, Stephen Jay 164
gradualism 164
gradual metamorphosis 356, 357
gram (g) 789
graphic organizers 794–795
grasshopper 357
grassland biome 737–738
gravitropism 298, 300
gray wolf 174
great horned owl 186, 187
green algae 226
Green Belt Movement 759
87–88, 90, 96–97, 98–99
Greyhound 176
grizzly bear 772
group living 453–454, 455, 458
growth of living things 20
growth spurt 675
guanine 78, 108
gymnosperms 284–288
  life cycle of 287
  reproduction in 286–288
  types of 285–286

habitat 394, 689
habitat destruction 774
habitat fragmentation 774
habitat preservation 776
hagfishes 383
hair 424–425, 429
hair follicles 497
half-life 160
hallucinogens 647, 648
hammer 641

hares 434
hearing 636, 640–641
heart 538–540
  action of 538–539, 548
  amphibian 390
  artificial 559
  of bird 416
  mammal 426
  regulation of beat of 540
  of snail 343
  structure of human 538
heart attack 557, 579
heartbeat 538
heart transplants 559
heartwood 281
helmets, wearing 634, 635
hemoglobin 550, 577
hemophilia 127
Henry, Mike 305
herbaceous stems 280–281
herbivores 312, 718
heredity 86. See also genetics
Herriot, James 178
heterotrophs 24, 65, 311, 718
heterozygous trait 98
hibernation 456, 739
hidden viruses 208–209
hinge joint 485
histamine 613
HIV 207, 603, 646
Hoh rain forest (Washington State) 248
homeostasis 25, 476–479
  hypothalamus and 660
  negative feedback and 662
  nervous system and maintaining 623
  stress and 477–479
  water balance in body 585–586
homologous structures 166
homozygous trait 98
honeybees 454–455
hoofed mammals 435
Hooke, Robert 28, 30
hormones 659–662
  in adolescence 675
  estrogen 666
  menstruation triggered by 668
  plant 298
  testosterone 664
hornworts 259
horsetails 265
host 205, 710
Human Genome Project 138–139
human immunodeficiency virus (HIV)
  207, 603, 646
human life cycle 669–678
  adolescence 675–676
  adulthood 677
  birth 671–673
  childhood 674
  embryo, development of 669–670
  fetus, development of 671
  infancy 657, 673–674
Huntington's disease 128
hybridization 133
hybrids 90

hydra 29
hydrochloric acid 522
hydroponics 268
hypertension 557–559
hyphae 234, 235, 241
hypothalamus 660, 661
hypothesis 6, 8, 790

ice sheets 741
Ichthyosaurus 378
identical twins 673
iguanas, green 398
Iguanodon 378
immigration 698
immovable joints 484
immune response 601, 602, 606
immune system 475, 601–602
    AIDS and 603–604
imperfect fungi 237
imprinting 447–448
inbreeding 133, 175
incisors 426, 520
incomplete proteins 510
independent (manipulated) variable 7
indirect observation 696
Industrial Revolution 154
infancy 657, 673–674
infectious disease 592–611
    active immunity to 605–608
    AIDS 210, 603–604
    from bacteria 200–201
    body defenses against 596–600
    immune system and 601–602
    medications and 609
    passive immunity to 608
    pathogens and 593
    prevention of 605–608, 609
    spread of 594–595
    from viruses 200, 210–211
inference 5, 786
inflammatory response 600
influenza 210
inhalants 647
inheritance, chromosomes and 102–103.
    See also **genetics**
inherited traits 89, 444–445
inner ear 640, 641
inorganic compounds 53
insect-eating mammals 434
insects 346, 348, 354–364
    body of 355
    communication by 362–364
    control of 359
    defenses of 358
    development of 355–356, 357
    humans and 358–359
insight learning 446
instinctive behavior 444
insulator 412
    fat as 425
    fur and hair as 424–425
insulin 135, 614
interneurons 624, 625, 629
interphase 73–74, 76
intertidal zone 744

invertebrates 313. *See also* **arthropods**
involuntary muscles 488
iodine 512
iris 637
iron 512, 517
isolation, geographic 155–156
Ituri forest 783

Janssen, Hans and Zacharias 30
Jarvik, Robert 559
jawless fish 374, 383
jellyfish 310, 323
Jenner, Edward 606
jet propulsion, swimming by 344
Jurassic period 163

Kaibab squirrel 155
kangaroos 433
karyotype 129
kelps 227
kestrels 418, 716
keystone species 770
kidneys 581–586
    as filters 582–583
    of mollusks 341
    reptile 397
    water balance in body and 585–586
king cobra 395
kingdoms 186, 189–191
    bacterial 189–190, 194–195
    Plant Kingdom 248–255
Koch, Robert 607
krill 350, 450
kudzu 289

laboratory safety 11, 799–801
labor during birth 671
Labrador retrievers 175
lactic-acid fermentation 69, 70
lakes 742
lampreys 383
Landsteiner, Karl 552, 558
large intestine 519, 529
large nucleus 221
larva 322
    amphibian 390, 391
    insect 357
larynx 573, 574
laser surgery 559
lateral line 385
laws to protect biodiversity 775–776
leafy sea dragon 386
learning 444–447, 449
    conditioning 445–446
    insight 446
    trial and error 446
leaves
    controlling water loss in 280
    of monocots vs. dicots 293
    photosynthesis and 278–279
    of seed plants 278–280
    structure of 278, 279
Leeuwenhoek, Anton van 29, 30, 192
legumes 727
length, measuring 788

lens 637, 638–639
    in microscopes 32
Leonardo da Vinci 486
Leopold, Aldo 759
Lessing, Doris 566
Lhasa apso 177
lice 33
lichens 242
life. *See* **living things**
life cycle
    of angiosperms 292
    of crustaceans 350
    of gymnosperms 287
    human 669–678
    of plants 253
life science
    branches of 11–13
    careers in 12–13
life span of seed plants 298–299
lift 421
ligaments 486
light
    insect communication with 364
    plant responses to 298
light microscope 31, 32–33
limestone 341
limiting factors 699–700
Lind, James 511
line graphs 797
Linnaeus, Carolus 183–185
lipids 19, 53, 54
liquid volume 788
Lister, Joseph 592–593, 606
liter (L) 788
liver
    alcohol's effect on 651
    digestion and 519, 527
    excretion and 586
liverworts 259
living space, organisms' need for 25
living things 18–49
    cell theory and 30–31
    characteristics of 18–21
    chemical composition of 19, 45–46
    as means of dispersal 729–730
    needs of 22–28
    origin of 44–46
    photosynthesis and 65
    water and 55
lizards 397–398, 400–401
lodgepole pines 275
logging methods 763
Lorenz, Konrad 448
Lovejoy, Asa L. 94
lung cancer 578, 579
lungs
    circulation to and from 541
    excretion and 586
    mammal 426
    breathing and 569, 570, 571
Lyme disease 352, 595
lymph 554
lymphatic system 554
lymph nodes 554
lymphocytes 601, 602

lynx spider 716
lysosomes 39, 41

Maathai, Wangari 759
magnesium 512
magnification of microscope 32
malaria 223, 595, 600
male reproductive system 664–665
mammals 423–436
    diversity of 431–436
    early 424
    fur and hair of 424–425, 429
    getting oxygen 426
    marsupials 156, 431, 432–433
    monotremes 431, 432
    movement of 428
    nervous system and senses of 426–427
    placental 431, 433–436
    reproduction and parenting in 428
    teeth of 426
    of tundra 741
mammary glands 428
mangrove trees 251
manipulated variable 7, 21, 791
Mantell, Mary Ann and Gideon 378
mantle of mollusk 340, 343
marijuana 645, 647
marine biologists 12
marine biome 743–745
marine mammals 435
mark-and-recapture studies 696–697, 701
marker molecules 552–553
marrow 485
marsupials 156, 431, 432–433
mass, measuring 789
Masters, Elroy 682–685
mating 452–453. See also reproduction
matter 723–724
    cycles of 723–727
    recycling 723–724
Mbuti people 783
measles 210
measurements, making 7, 788–789
mechanical digestion 518–519, 520, 522, 523
medications, infectious disease and 609
medicine 296, 644
medusa 324
meiosis 104–106
melanin 497
Mendel, Gregor 86–91, 96
meniscus 788
menstrual cycle 667–668
menstruation 668
mental changes
    in adolescence 676
    in childhood 674
Mesozoic era 163
messenger RNA 109, 110–111
metamorphosis 350, 463
    amphibian 390, 391
    insect 355–356
metaphase 74, 77
meter (m) 788
methane 44, 197
Meyer, Hermann von 410

microscope 29, 192–193
    improvements over time 3–31
    invention of 28
    magnification of 32
    resolution of 33
    types of 28, 30, 31, 32–33, 802
    use of 802–803
middle ear 640, 641
migration 456–457
Miller, Stanley 45
millipedes 353
mimicry as defense strategy 707
minerals 506, 512, 517
mites 352
mitochondria 37, 38, 39, 68
mitosis 74, 76–77
models, making 787
molars 426, 520
molds 18, 223–224
molds (fossil) 158
molecules 52, 724
    diffusion of 57
Mollusca (phylum) 340
mollusks 340–344
    evidence of early 341
    snails 342, 343, 345
    with tentacles 343, 344
    two-shelled 342–344
molting 348
monarch butterflies 354
Monerans 189, 194
monocots 293
monohybrid crosses 96–97, 118–119
monotremes 431, 432
mood-altering drugs 645
moray eel 381
mosses 257–258, 260
motor neuron 624, 625, 632
mountains and ice biome 741
mouth
    as barrier against pathogens 597
    digestion and 519, 520
movable joints 484, 485
movement of animals 311–312
    of amphibians 392
    of fishes 382
    of mammals 428
    skeleton and 482
mucus 521, 523, 568, 569, 597
Muir, John 758
multicellular organisms 19
multiple alleles 119–120
multiple births 673
muscles and muscular system 488–493
    action of 488, 491
    for breathing 572
    care of 492
    types of muscles 489–491, 492, 493
muscle tissue 474
muscular system 475
mushrooms 217
musk oxen 453
mussels 343
mutations 110–112, 125
mutualism 222, 709, 727

nanometers (nm) 206
narcotics 647
native species 730
natural selection 146, 150–153, 154, 704
nautiluses 344
nearsightedness 639
negative feedback 662
Nematoda (phylum) 327
nephrons 582, 583
neritic zone 744
nerve cells 19, 42
nerve cord 375
nerve impulse 623, 624, 625–626
    how it travels 626
    path of 625
nerve tissue 474
nervous system 475, 621–652
    alcohol's effect on 651
    of birds 416
    divisions of 628–632
    drugs and 644–652
    functions of 523, 527
    of mammals 426–427
    nerve impulse 623, 624, 625–626
    nerves in skin 495
    neurons in 623–624, 625, 629, 632
    reflexes and 633–634
    safety and 634, 635
    senses 636–642
neurons 623–624, 625, 632
    in brains 629
New Mexico ridgenose rattlesnake 773
niche diversity 769
niches 704, 731
nicotine 577, 647
Nightingale, Florence 606
nitrogen 44
nitrogen bases 78, 108, 109
nitrogen cycle 726–727
nitrogen fixation 726, 727
nodules 727
noninfectious disease 612
    allergies 612–613
    cancer 112, 499–500, 578, 579, 614–616
    diabetes 584, 614
nonrenewable resources 756
nonvascular plants 256–260
    characteristics of 256–257
    hornworts 259
    liverworts 259
    mosses 257–258, 260
nose 568, 569
notochord 374
nuclear membrane 36
nucleic acids 19, 46, 53, 55
nucleolus 36, 37
nucleus 220, 221, 473
    cell 36–37, 38, 39
nutrients 506. See also food
nutrition 506–507
nymph 356, 357

observation 5, 6, 696, 786
octopuses 344
oil glands 497

O'Keeffe, Georgia 291
omnivore 313, 718
open-ocean zone 745
operational definition 791
opossums 433
optical illusions 620–621
optic nerve 638
oral groove 221
Orchrobactrum anthropi 200
orders 186
Ordovician period 162
organelles 35, 37–41, 53
organic compounds 53
organisms 18. *See also* **living things**
    classifying 182–188
    multicellular 19
    unicellular (single-celled) 19
organizing information 794–795
organpipe cacti 275
organs 311, 475
organ systems 475. *See also* **circulatory system; digestive system; endocrine system; excretory system; muscles and muscular system; nervous system; skeletal system; skin**
Origin of Species, The (Darwin) 150
osculum 321
osmosis 58–59
osteoporosis 487
ostriches 418
Ostrom, John 379
outer ear 640, 641
ovaries 660, 666
    of angiosperm 290, 291, 292
overfishing 387
overpopulation 702
overproduction 150
oviduct 666
ovulation 667
ovules 286, 287, 291, 292
owls 186, 187, 419
oxygen 67
    as abiotic factor 690
    body's need for 566–567
    in gas exchange 571
    methods of obtaining. *See* **breathing**
    from photosynthesis 63, 64
    in red blood cells 550
oxygen cycle 725–726
oyster drill 342
oysters 343, 344

pacemaker 539, 540
Paleozoic era 162–163
Palm, Theobald A. 510
Panama Canal, disease and construction of 600
pancreas 527, 660, 661
    digestion and 519, 528
pandas 168–169
Pangaea 156
papilloma viruses 205
paralysis 634
paramecium 221
parasites 205, 710

flatworms 328–329
    roundworms 331
    tapeworms 329
parasitism 710
parathyroid glands 660, 661
parenting, animal 428, 453
park rangers 13
pasque flower 250
passive immunity 608
passive smoking 579
passive transport 59
Pasteur, Louis 22, 23, 45, 593, 607
pasteurization 593
pathogens 593
    barriers keeping out 597
    transfer of 594–595
Pavlov, Ivan 445
peas, Mendel's experiments on 86–91
peat 258
peat moss 256, 258
pedigree (family tree) 117, 123–124
peer pressure 676
Pekingese 177
penicillin 201, 241, 607
Penicillium 235, 237, 241
Penicillium roqueforti 240
penis 665
pepsin 522
Percent Daily Value 516
perching birds 419
peregrine falcon 422
perennials 299
peripheral nervous system 632
peristalsis 521, 528
permafrost 740
permeability, selective 56
Permian period 163
person-to-person transfer of pathogens 594
perspiration 495
pest control, pheromones and 364
pesticides 359
petals 87, 290
petrified fossils 158
petrochemicals 305, 306
Pettygrove, Francis W. 94
phagocytes 600
pharyngeal slits 375
pharynx 568, 569
phenotypes 98, 112
pheromones 362–364
phloem 275, 279, 281, 283
phosphate 78
phosphorus 482, 483, 486, 512
photosynthesis 61–65, 249, 254–255
    in chloroplast 62–63
    energy capture process 62–63, 64
    equation for 64
    food production process 63
    leaves and 278–279
    living things and 65
    by producers 717
    respiration and 69
    in water biomes 742, 744
phototropism 298
physical changes

in adolescence 675
    in adulthood 677
    in childhood 675
    in infancy 673
physical therapists 13
physicians 12
pie charts 798
pigments 63, 225
pill bugs 350
Pinchot, Gifford 758
pioneer plants 258
pioneer species 749
piping plover 772
pistil 87, 290, 291
pith 281
pituitary gland 660, 661
pivot joint 485
placenta 436, 670
placental mammals 431, 433–436
planarians 330
plant(s) 191, 247–268. *See also* **forest(s); seed plants**
    adaptations of 250–251
    chemicals from 304–307
    cloning of 134
    competition among 705
    desert 737
    as food 266–268
    fungi and 241
    life cycles of 253
    limiting factors for 700
    living on land 249–252
    nonvascular plants 256–260
    obtaining and retaining water in 249
    photosynthesis. *See* **photosynthesis**
    reproduction in 252, 253
    seedless vascular plants 261–265
    support in 252
    transporting materials in 252
    vascular plants 252, 272–299
plant cells 19, 35, 38, 43, 54, 75
plantlike protists 224–230
plasma 549
Plasmodium 222–223
platelets 549, 551, 552
Platyhelminthes (phylum) 327
Plot, Robert 378
poliomyelitis 210
pollen 286
pollination 287, 288
    of angiosperms 291, 292
pollution 757, 774
polymers 347–348
polyp 323–324
ponds 742, 746–747
population growth 757
populations 695–702
    in ecosystem 691
    limiting factors in 699–700
    overpopulation in 702
    population density 695
    size of 696–698, 701, 708
population statement 698
pores 36, 497
    in sponge 321

Porifera (phylum) 321
potassium 512
prairie 737
prairie dogs 688, 689, 692–693
Precambrian 161, 162
precipitation 725
precision farming 267–268
predation 704, 706–708
predator 313, 706–707
preening 412
pregnancy 669
premolars 426, 520
preserved remains 158–159
pressure 546
prey 313, 706–707
primary succession 749
primates 434, 436
probability 94–101
  calculating 95
problem solving 793
producers 717, 719, 720
prokaryotes 41, 190
prophase 74, 77
protective coverings 706
protein(s) 19, 53–54, 506, 510
  blood clotting 136
  digestion of 524–525
  evolutionary similarities in 170
  genes and 107
  plasma, groups of 549
  ribosomal production of 40
  RNA's role in 109, 110
  structure of 53
  transport 59
  in viral coat 207
protein synthesis 108–111
protists 190, 218–232, 593
  animal-like 219–223
  funguslike 223–224
  plantlike 224–230
protozoans 219–223
  with cilia 221
  with flagella 222
  with pseudopods 219–220
  sporozoans 222–223
pseudopods 219–220
puberty 675
punctuated equilibria 164
Punnett squares 96–97, 104, 118–119
pupa 357
pupil (eye) 637
purebred 87

Quaternary period 163
queen bee 455

rabbits 434
rabies 205, 210, 595, 608
radial symmetry 316, 365
radiation treatment 615–616
radioactive elements 160
radula 341, 343
rafflesia 251
rain forest biome 248, 735–736
  African 780–785

  trees of 782
rays 384
recessive alleles 89–90, 122
rectum 529
recycling 199–200, 240, 723–724, 761
red algae 227
red blood cell 42, 58, 126, 531, 549, 550–551
Redi, Francesco 21, 22, 45
red tides (saltwater blooms) 229
reefs, coral 323, 325–326, 769
reflexes 633–634
regeneration 328, 366
relative dating 159
renewable resources 757, 761
  forests as 763
replication, DNA 73, 78–79
reproduction 21
  in amphibians 390–391
  in angiosperms 291
  asexual 195, 236, 311, 322, 324, 325, 328
  in bacteria 192, 195–196
  in birds 416–417
  in cnidarians 324
  in ferns 264
  in fishes 383
  in fungi 235–236
  in gymnosperms 286–288
  in humans 663
  in mammals 428
  in plants 252, 253
  sexual 196, 236, 311, 324, 328, 347
  in sponges 322
  spores for 263
  in worms 328
reproductive systems 475, 663–668
  in females 666–668
  in males 664–665
  sex cells 102–106, 663–664
reptiles 395–404
  adaptations to conserve water in 395–396
  alligators 403
  crocodiles 403
  dinosaurs 378–379, 404
  eggs with shells in 396
  lizards 397–398, 400–401
  obtaining oxygen from air 397
  skin and kidneys in 397, 398
  snakes 395, 399
  turtles 402
resolution of microscope 33
resource use 756
  forest resources 762–764
respiration 66–71, 567
  bacterial 196
  equation for 68
  fermentation 69–70
  photosynthesis and 69
respiratory system 475, 566–580
  barriers keeping pathogens out of 597
  breathing 567, 572–573, 575
  gas exchange 571
  lungs 569, 570, 571
  need for oxygen and 566–567
  path of air through 568–570
  smoking and 577–578

  speaking 573–574
responding variable 7, 791
response 443, 444, 623
  to surroundings 20–21
retina 638
rhizoids 257
ribonucleic acid (RNA) 55, 109, 110–111
ribosomes 37, 38, 39, 40, 110
ribs 376
rickets 510
ringworm 240–241
RNA 55
  protein synthesis and 109, 110
  types of 109–111
rocks, vertebrate history in 377–379
rockweed 227
Rocky Mountain spotted fever 595
rodents 434
rods 638
Roosevelt, Theodore 758
root cap 283
roots 282–283
roseate spoonbill 418
roundworms 330–331
Ruska, Ernst 31

sac fungi 237
safety
  in groups 453
  laboratory 11, 799–801
  nervous system and 634, 635
saguaro cactus 703
salamanders 389, 391, 392–393
saliva 520, 597
salivary glands 519
salmonella xxii
saltwater blooms (red tides) 229
sampling 696
sand dollars 367
sarcodines 219–220
saturated fats 509
savannas 737–738
scales on fish 381, 385
scallops 343
scanning electron microscope (SEM) 31
scanning tunneling microscope (STM) 31
scavenger 330, 333, 718
Schaus swallowtail butterfly 773
science 4
  communicating in 9, 787
scientific inquiry 4
scientific investigation, conducting 4–9, 790–791
scientific theory 9, 149
scorpions 352
scrotum 664
scuba divers, coral reefs and 326
scurvy 510–511
sea anemones 323
sea cucumbers 368
sea stars 366–367
sea urchins 365, 368
seaweeds 227
secondary succession 750

sedimentary rock 158, 378
seed(s) 276–278
  germination of 278
  of monocot vs. dicots 293
seed coat 276
seed dispersal 277
  of angiosperms 291, 292
  for gymnosperms 288
seedless vascular plants 261–265
  characteristics of 262–263
  club mosses 265
  ferns 261, 263–264
  horsetails 265
seed plants 272–300
  angiosperms 289–296
  characteristics of 274–283
  growth of 298–299, 300
  gymnosperms 284–288
  responses of 297–299
segmented bodies of arthropods 348
segmented worms 331–333, 334
selective breeding 132–133, 150
selective cutting 763
selective permeability 56
self-pollination 87
semen 665
semicircular canals 641–642
senses 636–642
  balance 636, 641–642
  hearing 636, 640–641
  of mammals 427
  smell 636, 642–643
  taste 636, 642–643
  touch 636, 643
  vision 636, 637–639
sensory neuron 624, 625, 632
sepals 290
septum 539
serving size 515
sex cell 102–106, 663–664
sex chromosomes 121, 122
sex-linked genes 122–123
sexual reproduction 196, 236, 311
  of arthropods 347
  in cnidarians 324
  in worms 328
sharks 384
Siberian husky 177
sickle-cell disease 126–127
Sierra Club 758
SI Système International d'Unités 7,
  788–789
silk 462–469
  feeding silkworms 468
  goddess of 466–467
  metamorphosis of silkworm and 463
  Silk Road and 464–465
Silk Road 464–465
silkworm moth 363
Silurian period 162
simple carbohydrates 508
skates 384
skeletal muscles 489–490, 492, 493
skeletal system 311, 475, 480–487
  bone growth 483

bone strength 482–483
  formation of 484
  functions of 480–482
  joints 484–486
  structure of 483–484
skeleton. *See* **endoskeleton; exoskeleton**
skin 475, 494–500
  as barrier against pathogens 597, 598–599
  care of 498–500
  dermis 496, 497, 643
  epidermis 496–497
  excretion and 586
  functions of 494–495
  as sense organ 643
skin cancer 112
skull 376
slime molds 18, 224
sloths 435
slugs 342
small intestine 519, 526–528
smallpox 606
smoking 576–580
  cardiovascular health and 560
  chemicals in tobacco smoke 576–577
  choosing not to smoke 580
  circulatory system problems from 579
  passive 579
  respiratory system problems from
    577–578
smooth muscle 489, 490–491
snails 342, 343, 345
snakes 395, 399
Snow, John 594
soaring flight 422
society, animal 454, 455
sodium 512
  hypertension and intake of 559
soil
  as abiotic factor 691
  arthropods living in 360–361
  earthworms and 333
solvents, agrochemical 306–307
somatic nervous system 632
sound vibrations 640–641
southwestern willow flycatcher 685
speaking 573–574
species 147, 184
  extinct 160, 771–774
  formation of new 155–156
sperm 102, 663, 665
sphagnum moss 258
sphygmomanometer 547
spiders 346, 350–352
spikes in sponges 321, 322
spinal cord 629, 631
spinal cord injuries 634
spinal nerves 632
spindle fibers 77
spiny anteaters 432
sponges 320–322
  characteristics of 320–321
  food and oxygen, obtaining 322, 323
  reproduction in 322
  spikes in 321, 322
  structure of 321

spongy bone 483
spontaneous generation 21–22
spore cases 264
spores 223, 235, 236
  for reproduction 263
sporophyte 253, 257, 264, 275
sporozoans 222–223
squids 344
squirrels 155
staghorn fern 250
stamens 87, 290
Staphylococcus aureus 193
starch 54, 508. *See also* **carbohydrates**
starfishes. *See* **sea stars**
star-nosed moles 434
Steller's sea lion 773
stems 280–282
  of monocots vs. dicots 293
  structure of 280–281
stigma 290, 291
stimulants 646
stimulus/stimuli 20–21, 443, 444, 623
stirrup 641
stomach
  as barrier against pathogens 597
  digestion and 519, 522–525
stomach acid 597
stomata 63, 278, 279
Streptococci 190
stress 477–479
  dealing with 479
  fight-or-flight response 478
  long-term 479
  physical responses to 477–478
striated muscle 489–490. *See also* **skeletal
  muscle**
succession 746–750
  primary 749
  secondary 750
sugars 54, 508. *See also* **carbohydrates**
sunlight 690
  limiting exposure to 499–500
sunscreens 498–499
surface zone 744–745
survival behavior 443
sustainable yield 763–764
Sutton, Walter 102–103
sweat glands 497
swim bladders 385–386
swimmerets 351
symbiosis 222, 704, 709–710
symmetry 315–317
  in animals 316–317, 341, 365
synapse 626

tadpoles 390, 391
tail fin 385
tail of iguana 398
taproot system 282
tar 576
target cells 659–660
taste buds 642–643
Taussig, Helen 558
taxonomic key 186–188
taxonomy 183, 186. *See also* **classification**

T cells 601, 602, 603, 606
teeth 426, 520
telophase 74, 76
temperate rain forest 736
temperature. *See also* **body temperature**
    as abiotic factor 690–691
    measuring 789
temperature regulation 25
tendons 490
tentacles, mollusks with 343, 344
territory, establishing 451–452
Tertiary period 163
testes 661, 664
testosterone 664
tetanus 595
theory, scientific 9, 149
thigmotropism 297
thorax 355
threadlike fungi 237
threatened species 772
thumb 436
thymine 78, 108
thymus 660, 661
thyroid gland 660, 661, 662
thyroid-stimulating hormone (TSH) 662
thyroxine 662
ticks 352, 595
time, measuring 789
tissues 474–475
    animal 311
    plant 252
toads 392
tobacco mosaic viruses 205
tolerance, drug 645
toothless mammals 435
tortoises, desert 684
toxin 200–201
trachea 568, 569–570
traits 98, 175. *See also* **genetics**
    controlled by many genes 120
    controlled by single gene 118–119
    inheritance of 89, 444–445
tranquilizers 647
transfer RNA 109, 110–111
transmission electron microscope (TEM) 31
transpiration 280
transport proteins 59
tree cookies, data hidden in 767
trees, annual rings of 281–282. *See also* **forest(s)**
trial and error learning 446
Triassic period 163
triceps 491
tropical ecosystems, diversity in 769
tropical rain forests 735–736
tropisms 297–298
Tsai, Shih-Perng 305
tumors, formation of 615
tundra biome 740–741
tunicates 374
turtles 402
twins 673

Tyrannosaurus rex 379, 404

ulva 226
umbilical cord 670
understory 735, 781, 782
unicellular organisms 19
United States Food and Drug
    Administration (FDA) 430, 515
unsaturated fats 509
uracil 109
urea 581
ureters 581
urethra 582, 665
Urey, Harold 45
urinary bladder 582
urine 397, 581, 583–584, 665
Ursus horribilis 184
uterus 666

vaccination 607–608
vaccine 211, 607
vacuoles 38, 39, 41
vagina 666, 667
valve 538
variables 6–7, 21, 791
vascular plants 252
    seedless 261–265
vascular tissue 252, 257, 262–263, 275, 283
veins 540, 545, 546
Venette, Jean de 358
Venn diagrams 795
ventricle of heart 538, 539
    amphibian 390
    blood pressure and contraction of 547
    force of 542
Venus fly trap 251
vertebra, vertebrae 375, 481
vertebrates 313
    backbone and endoskeleton of 374,
        375–376, 481
    body temperature in 376–377
    chordates 374–375
    evolution of 374–380
    history of 377–380
veterinarians 13
vibrations, sound 640–641
villi 528, 571
Virchow, Rudolf 29
viruses 181, 204–212, 593
    active 207–208
    hidden 208–209
    infectious diseases caused by 200, 210–211
    multiplication of 205, 207–209
    shapes and sizes of 206, 212
    structure of 206–207
vision 636, 637–639
vision problems, correcting 638–639
vitamin(s) 506, 510–512
    C 511
    D 495, 510
    K 511
vocal cords 573–574
voluntary muscles 488

walking legs of crayfish 351
Wallace, Alfred Russel 150
wampum 340
waste products. *See also* **excretory system**
    cellular 36
    movement by cardiovascular system 537
water
    as abiotic factor 690
    in cells 19
    diffusion of water molecules 58–59
    importance to plants of 249
    living things and 55
    molecular structure of 52
    as nutrient 506, 513
    organisms' need for 24
water balance, excretory system and
        585–586
water biomes 742–745
water cycle 724–725
water lily 250
water molds 223
water-soluble vitamins 511, 512
water vapor 44
water vascular system 366, 367
Watson, James 78
waxes 54
weather as limiting factor 700
Weiss Lake 232
wet-mount slide 803
whales, communication among 450
wheat 275
white blood cells 531, 549, 551, 600
whooping crane 773
windpipe. *See* **trachea**
wing of bird 420–421
withdrawal 646
woodpeckers 418
woody stems 281
worker bee 455
worms 327–334
    classification of 327
    flatworms 328–329
    reproduction in 328
    responses of 328, 334
    roundworms 330–331
    segmented 331–333, 334
    tapeworms 329–330
wrasse 381

X chromosome 121, 122
xylem 275, 279, 281, 283

yaks 423
Y chromosome 121, 122
yeast 70, 75, 238–239, 240
yellow fever 600
Yellowstone National Park 748, 776

Zeiss, Carl 31
zooflagellates 222
zygote 252, 253, 663–664, 669

Acknowledgments

Staff Credits

The people who made up the **Life, Earth, and Physical Science** team—representing design services, editorial, editorial services, electronic publishing technology, manufacturing & inventory planning, marketing, marketing services, market research, online services & multimedia development, production services, product planning, project office, and publishing processes are listed below.

Carolyn Belanger, Barbara Bertell, Peggy Bliss, Kristen Braghi, Roger Calado, Jonathan Cheney, Lisa Clark, Ed Cordero, Christine Cuccio, Patricia Cully, Patricia Dambry, Kathleen Dempsey, Judy Elgin, Jim Fellows, Barbara Foster, Barnard Gage, Julie Gecha, Joel Gendler, Adam Goldberg, Jessica Gould, Robert Graham, Dennis Higbee, Joanne Hudson, Anne Jones, Dorothy Kavanaugh, Toby Klang, Don Manning, Jeanne Maurand, Carolyn McGuire, Brent McKenzie, Natania Mlawer, Cindy Noftle, Julia Osborne, Caroline M. Power, Shelley Ryan, Robin Santel, Diane Walsh, Beth A. Winickoff, Helen Young

Illustrations

Alexander and Turner: 253, 287, 292, 293
Sally Bensusen: 343, 357
Suzanne Biron: 26, 43, 80, 92, 100, 152, 170, 212, 238, 260, 300
Phil & Jim Bliss: 1b, 1m
Annette Cable: 306–307
Carmella Clifford: 637, 641
Warren Cutler: 413
Bruce Day: 478,
David Fuller: 146–147
Andrea Golden: 179, 319, 682t
Biruta Hansen: 362, 398, 692–693
Floud E. Hosmer: 624
JB Woolsey Associates: xvii, 5, 7, 8, 8tl, 8tr, 20, 64t, 87, 92b, 93br, 96, 97, 99, 104, 119, 121, 123, 124, 135, 143, 162, 163, 166, 169, 174, 183, 187, 188, 207b, 227, 235t, 271t, 283, 290, 295, 300, 314, 317, 332, 348, 374, 380, 382, 390, 400, 416, 421, 444, 461, 520, 541, 567, 573, 619, 633, 639, 651, 655, 668, 678, 681, 694, 698, 708, 719, 725b, 746, 753b, 792, 401
John Edwards & Associates: 45, 483, 625, 630, 649, 722, 731, 744
Keith Kasnot: 37br, 40tr, 521, 523
MapQuest.com,Inc.: 155, 683tm, 683tr, 735, 736, 738
Martucci Studio: 75, 215, 245t, 303, 407, 503, 515, 563, 577, 594, 615, 705, 741, 753t, 796b, 797, 798
Matt Mayerchak: 47, 81, 14, 171, 213, 243, 335, 369, 459, 501, 531, 587, 617, 653, 679, 751, 794, 795b, 795m
Fran Milner: xii, xxi, 311, 351, 355, 385, 391b, 393, 528, 544, 550–51, 570
Karen Minot: 465, 466
Paul Mirocha: 447
Morgan Cain & Associates: 19b, 19t, 22, 23, 32, 49, 52, 57, 59, 68, 76–77, 78, 79, 105, 108, 109, 110, 160, 206b, 206t, 207t, 236, 245b, 271b, 279, 350, 371, 388, 429, 473, 496, 522, 539, 543, 549, 553, 589, 596, 600, 609, 626, 632, 662, 711, 713, 717, 749, 750, 788l, 788r, 789tl, 789tr
Ortelius Design: 189br, 198bl, 198t, 199b, 199t, 232, 456, 464–65, 602, 729
Stephanie Pershing: ix, 261
Judith Pinkham: 334, 345, 400, 414, 449, 493, 498, 524, 548, 575, 610, 627, 678, 694, 767
Matthew Pippin: 377, 724b
Pat Rossi: 208–209, 220b, 221b, 329, 375, 375r, 396, 426, 427, 445, 485bl, 485br, 485tl, 485tr
Richard Salzman-Walter Stuart: xviii, 404, 455
Sandra Sevigny: 475, 481
Walter Stuart: 538, 158tl, 234bl, 321, 367, 720, 257, 263
Cynthia Turner: 276b, 291

Photography

Photo Research Sharon Donahue, Sue McDermott, Paula Wehde

Cover Image Steve Bloom/Masterfile

Front Matter: Page i, ii, Steve Bloom/Masterfile; **iiil,** Courtesy of Michael J. Padilla, Ph.D.; **iiir,** Courtesy of Martha Cyr, Ph.D. and Ioannis Miaoulis, Ph.D ; **viiit,** Fran Lanting/Minden Pictures; **viiib,** Dr. David Scott/CNRI/Phototake; **ixt,** Frans Lanting/Minden Pictures; **ixbm,** Ray Coleman/Photo Researchers; **ixbr,** Biozentrum, University of Basel/Science Photo Library/Photo Researchers; **xl,** Frans Lanting/Minden Pictures; **xm,** Belinda Wright/DRK Photo; **xr,** Fred Whitehead/Animals Animals; **xitl,** Renee Lynn/Tony Stone Images; **xibl,** Stuart Westmorland/Natural Selection**; xitr,** Robert Calentine/Visuals Unlimited; **xibr,** Joe McDonald/Tom Stack & Associates; **xiit,** Andrew Syred/Science Photo Library/ Photo Researchers; **xiib,** Bill Longcore/Science Source/Photo Researchers; **xiiit,** Pete Saloutos/The Stock Market; **xiiibl, bm,** Superstock; **xiiibr,** Salisbury District Hospital/Science Photo Library/Photo Researchers; **xivt,** David Lassman/The Image Works; **xivm,** David Liebman; **xivb,** Daryl Balfour/Tony Stone Images; **xv,** Richard Haynes; **xvi,** James L. Amos/Photo Researchers; **xvii, xviii,** Richard Haynes; **xviii inset,** Runk/Schoenberger/Grant Heilman Photography; **xixt,** Images International/Erwin C. Bud Nielsen/Visuals Unlimited; **xixb,** Richard Haynes; **xxt,** James Watt/Animals Animals; **xxb,** The Granger Collection, NY; **xxi,** Art Wolfe/Tony Stone Images; **xxii,** Courtesy of Cindy Friedman; **2,** Michael Dick/Animals Animals; **3l,** Courtesy of Cindy Friedman; **3r,** USDA/S.S./Photo Researchers.

Introduction to Life Science
Page 4, David Young-Wolff/PhotoEdit; **5,** Daniel J. Cox/Tony Stone Images; **6,** John Warden/Tony Stone Images; **7,** Bill Banaszewski/Visuals Unlimited; **9,** Roger Tully/Tony Stone Images; **10,** Photo Spin/Artville/PNI; **11,** Richard Haynes; **12t,** Charles Gupton/Tony Stone Images; **12m,** Nieto/Jerrican/Photo Researchers; **12b,** Douglas Faulkner/The Stock Market; **13tl,** Andrea Sacks/Tony Stone Images; **13bl,** Jeff Dunn/ IndexStock Imagery; **13tr,** Paula Lerner/IndexStock Imagery; **13br,** Tim Thompson/Tony Stone Images; **14,** David Young-Wolff/PhotoEdit.

Chapter 1
Pages 16–17, Joe McDonald/DRK Photo; **18t,** Russ Lappa; **18b,** Beatty/Visuals Unlimited; **19,** John Pontier/Animals Animals; **21,** Michael Quinton/Minden Pictures; **22, 23,** The Granger Collection, NY; **24l,** James Dell/Science Source/Photo Researchers; **24r,** Zig Leszcynski/Animals Animals; **25,** Jim Brandenburg/Minden Pictures; **27t,** Richard Haynes; **27b,** Joseph Nettis/Photo Researchers; **27 inset,** John Coletti/Stock Boston; **28, 29l,** The Granger Collection, NY; **29r,** Caroline Biological Supply Company/Phototake; **30 both,** The Granger Collection, NY., **31t,** H.R. Bramaz/Peter Arnold; **31bl,** Corbis-Bettmann; **31br,** Lawrence Migdale/Stock Boston; **33,** CNRI/Science Photo Library/Photo Researchers; **34t,** Runk/Schoenberger/Grant Heilman Photography; **34b,** Doug Wilson/Westlight; **35l,** M. Abbey/Visuals Unlimited; **35r,** Runk/Schoenberger/ Grant Heilman Photography; **36,** Dr. Dennis Kunkel/Phototake; **37,** Bill Longcore/Photo Researchers; **40,** K.G. Murtis/Visuals Unlimited; **41,** John Cardamone/Tony Stone Images; **42l,** Dr. David Scott/CNRI/Phototake; **42r,** Dr. Dennis Kunkel/Phototake; **43,** Runk/ Schoenberger/Grant Heilman Photography; **44,** Russ Lappa; **46,** Biological Photo Service.

Chapter 2
Pages 50–51, Julie Habel/Westlight; **52,** Russ Lappa; **53,** Gary Bell/Masterfile; **54,** Okapia-Frankfurt/Photo Researchers; **54 inset,** Andrew Syred/Science Photo Library/Photo Researchers; **55,** Hans Blohm/Masterfile; **56,** NASA; **58l,** Stanley Flegler/Visuals Unlimited; **58m, 58r,** David M. Phillips/Visuals Unlimited; **60,** M. Abbey/Visuals Unlimited; **61t,** Russ Lappa; **61b,** Paul Barton/The Stock Market; **62,** Cosmo Condina/Tony Stone Images; **62 inset,** Biophoto Associates/Photo Researchers; **63t,** Russ Lappa; **63bl&br,** Dr. Jeremy Burgess/Science Photo Library/Photo Researchers; **65t,** Frans Lanting/Minden Pictures; **65b,** Tom J. Ulrich/Visuals Unlimited; **66,** William Johnson/Stock Boston; **67l,** Phil Dotson/Photo Researchers; **67r,** Stephen Dalton/Photo Researchers; **69,** Mark Newman/Visuals Unlimited; **70,** Terje Rakke/The Image Bank; **72t,** David Scharf/Peter Arnold; **72b,** Larry Lefever/Grant Heilman Photography; **73,** Art Wolfe/Tony Stone Images; **74,** Biophoto Associates/Science Source/Photo Researchers; **75b,** Roy Morso/The Stock Market; **76 all, 77 all,** M. Abbey/Photo Researchers; **80,** Robert Knauft/Biology Media.

Chapter 3

Pages 84–85, Ron Kimball; **86t,** Mike Rothwell/Tony Stone Images; **86b,** Corbis-Bettmann; **87,** Barry Runk/Grant Heilman Photography; **90 both,** Meinrad Faltner/The Stock Market; **91,** Inga Spence/Index Stock Imagery; **94–95,** Image Stop/Phototake; **98,** Hans Reinhard/Bruce Coleman; **101,** Richard Haynes; **102l,** David M. Phillips/Photo Researchers; **102r,** University "La Sapienza," Rome/Science Photo Library/Photo Researchers; **103l,** Jonathan D. Speer/Visuals Unlimited; **103r,** M. Abbey/Photo Researchers; **107,** AP/Wide World Photos; **112,** William E. Ferguson; **113,** Mike Rothwell/Tony Stone Images.

Chapter 4

Pages 116–117, Herb Snitzer/Stock Boston; **118,** Richard Haynes; **120,** Camille Tokerud/Tony Stone Images; **121 both,** Biophoto Associates/Science Source/Photo Researchers; **122,** Andrew McClenaghan/Science Photo Library/Photo Researchers; **124,** Superstock; **125t,** CNRI/Science Photo Library/Photo Researchers; **125b,** Lawrence Migdale/Tony Stone Images; **126t,** Simon Fraser/RVI, Newcastle-upon-TYNE/Science Photo Library/Photo Researchers; **126b,** Stanley Flegler/Visuals Unlimited; **127,** Corbis-Bettmann; **128,** Mugshots/The Stock Market, **128 inset,** CNRI/Science Photo Library/Photo Researchers; **129,** Will and Deni McIntyre/Photo Researchers Inc.; **130,** Richard Haynes; **132,** AP/Wide World Photos; **133,** Tim Barnwell/Stock Boston; **134,** Patricia J. Bruno/Positive Images; **135,** LeLand Bobbe/Tony Stone Images; **136,** Gary Wagner/Stock Boston; **137,** AP/Wide World Photos; **138,** U.S. Department of Energy/Human Genome Management Information System, Oak Ridge National Laboratory; **139,** Michael Newman/PhotoEdit; **140,** David Parker/Science Photo Library/Photo Researchers.

Chapter 5

Pages 144–145, Bill Varie/Westlight; **146t,** Portrait by George Richmond/Down House, Downe/The Bridgeman Art Library; **146b,** Corbis-Bettmann; **147t,** Tui De Roy/Minden Pictures; **147m,** Frans Lanting/Minden Pictures; **147b,** Tui De Roy/Minden Pictures; **148l,** Zig Leszczynski/Animals Animals; **148r,** Tui De Roy/Minden Pictures; **149,** Dr. Jeremy Burgess/Science Photo Library/Photo Researchers; **150,** Mitsuaki Iwago/Minden Pictures; **151,** Jeff Gnass Photography/The Stock Market; **153,** Richard Haynes; **154 both,** Breck P. Kent; **155 both,** Pat & Tom Leeson/Photo Researchers; **156t,** John Cancalosi/Tom Stack & Associates; **156b,** Tom McHugh/Photo Researchers; **157t,** James L. Amos/Photo Researchers; **157b,** Sinclair Stammers/Science Photo Library/Photo Researchers; **161,** Robert Landau/Westlight; **165,** Richard Haynes; **167l,** Keith Gillett/Animals Animals; **167m,** George Whiteley/Photo Researchers; **167r,** David Spears Ltd./Science Photo Library/Photo Researchers; **168l,** Gary Milburn/Tom Stack & Associates; **168r,** Daryl Balfour/Tony Stone Images; **174t,** Peter Cade/Tony Stone Images; **174m,** Tim Fitzharris/Minden Pictures; **174b,** Bridgeman Art Library; **175,** Ron Kimball; **176tr,** Charles Philip/Westlight; **176br,** Jack Daniels/Tony Stone Images; **176 the rest,** Corel Corp.; **177b,** C. Jeanne White/Photo Researchers; **177 the rest,** Corel Corp.; **178t,** Peter Cade/Tony Stone Images; **178–179b,** Nick Meers/Panoramic Images; **178 inset,** AP/ Wide World Photos.

Chapter 6

Pages 180–181, Institut Pasteur/CNRI/Phototake; **182t,** Russ Lappa; **182b,** Inga Spence/IndexStock Imagery; **184l,** Gerard Lacz/Animals Animals; **184m,** Tom Brakefield/DRK Photo; **184r,** Ron Kimball; **185,** J. Serrao/Visuals Unlimited; **186–187,** Thomas Kitchin/Tom Stack & Associates; **189,** Alan L. Detrick/Photo Researchers; **190t,** David M. Phillips/Photo Researchers; **190b,** Microfield Scientific Ltd/Science Photo Library/Photo Researchers; **191,** Ray Coleman/Photo Researchers; **192t,** Richard Haynes; **192b,** Science Photo Library/Photo Researchers; **193t,** Oliver Meckes/Photo Researchers; **193m,** David M. Phillips/Visuals Unlimited; **193b,** Scott Camazine/Photo Researchers; **194,** Dr. Rony Brain/Science Photo Library/Photo Researchers; **195,** Dr. K. S. Kim/Peter Arnold; **196,** Dr. Ennis Kunkel/Phototake; **197,** Alfred Pasieka/Peter Arnold; **198t,** PhotoDisc, Inc.; **198b,** Sally Ann Ullmann/FoodPix; **199t,** John Marshall/Tony Stone Images; **199b,** FoodPix; **200t,** E. Webben/Visuals Unlimited; **200b,** Ben Osborne/Tony Stone Images; **200 inset,** Michael Abbey/Photo Researchers; **203,** Richard Haynes; **204t,** Russ Lappa; **204bl,** Dr. Linda Stannard, UCT/Science Photo Library/Photo Researchers; **204bm,** Lee D. Simon/Science Source/Photo Researchers; **204br,** Dr. Brad Fute/Peter Arnold; **205m,** Tektoff-RM/CNRI/Science Photo Library/Photo Researchers; **205r,** CDC/Science Source/Photo Researchers; **208,** Biozentrum, University of Basel/Science Photo Library/Photo Researchers; **209,** Lee D. Simon/Science Source/Photo Researchers; **210,** James Darell/Tony Stone Images; **211,** David M. Dennis/Tom Stack & Associates; **212,** Custom Medical Stock; **213,** Biozentrum, University of Basel/Science Photo Library/Photo Researchers.

Chapter 7

Pages 216–217, David M. Dennis/Tom Stack & Associates; **218t,** Science VU/Visuals Unlimited; **218b,** Jan Hinsch/Science Photo Library/Photo Researchers; **219tl,** O.S.F./Animals Animals; **219tr,** A. Le Toquin/Photo Researchers; **219b,** Gregory G. Dimijian/Photo Researchers; **220,** Astrid & Hanns-Frieder Michler/Science Photo Library/Photo Researchers; **221,** Eric Grave/Science Source/Photo Researchers; **222,** Michael P. Gadomski/Photo Researchers; **222 inset,** Jerome Paulin/Visuals Unlimited; **223t,** Oliver Meckes/Photo Researchers; **223b,** Dwight R. Kuhn; **224 both,** David M. Dennis/Tom Stack & Associates; **225t,** Russ Lappa; **225b,** Sinclair Stammers Oxford Scientific Films; **226t,** David M. Phillips/Visuals Unlimited; **226bl,** D.P.Wilson/Eric & Daid Hosking/Photo Researchers; **226br,** Andrew Syred/Science Photo Library/Photo Researchers; **228t,** Richard Haynes; **228b,** Doug Perrine/Hawaii Whale Research Foundation - NMFS permit#882/Innerspace Visions; **229,** Sanford Berry/Visuals Unlimited; **230,** Kenneth H. Thomas/Photo Researchers; **232,** Robert P. Falls; **233t,** Russ Lappa; **233b,** Michael Fogden/Animals Animals; **234,** Fred Unverhau/Animals Animals/Earth Scenes; **235,** Nobel Proctor/Science Source/Photo Researchers; **236,** David Scharf/Peter Arnold; **237tl,** E.R. Degginger/Photo Researchers; **237bl,** Michael Fogden/Animals Animals/Earth Scenes; **237tr,** Rod Planck/Tom Stack & Associates; **237br,** Andrew McClenagham/Science Photo Library/Photo Researchers; **239,** Richard Haynes; **240,** David M. Dennis/Tom Stack & Associates; **241,** Rob Simpson/ Visuals Unlimited; **242l,** Rod Planck/Tom Stack & Associates; **242r,** Frans Lanting/Minden Pictures; **243,** Gregory G. Dimijian/Photo Researchers.

Chapter 8

Pages 246–247, J. Lotter Gurling/Tom Stack & Associates; **248,** Joanne Lotter/Tom Stack & Associates; **249,** Kjell B. Sandved/Photo Researchers; **250tl,** Richard J. Green/Photo Researchers; **250tr,** Brenda Tharp/Photo Researchers; **250m,** R. Van Nostrand/Photo Researchers; **250b,** Joe McDonald/Visuals Unlimited; **251tl,** Prenzel/Animals Animals/Earth Scenes; **251tr,** Frans Lanting/Minden Pictures; **251m,** Andrew J. Martinez/Photo Researchers; **251b,** Runk/Schoenberger/Grant Heilman Photography; **252,** Doug Wechsler/ Animals Animals/Earth Scenes; **254,** Richard Haynes; **255,** Images International/ Erwin C. Bud Nielsen/Visuals Unlimited; **256t,** Russ Lappa; **256b,** Christi Carter from Grant Heilman Photography; **257,** Runk/Schoenberger/Grant Heilman Photography; **258t,** Silkeborg Museum; **258b,** Farrell Grehan/Photo Researchers; **259l,** Runk/Schoenberger/Grant Heilman Photography; **259r,** William E. Ferguson; **260, 261,** Richard Haynes; **262,** Runk/Schoenberger/Grant Heilman Photography; **263,** Rod Planck/Tom Stack & Associates; **264t,** Milton Rand/Tom Stack & Associates; **264b,** Joanne Lotter/Tom Stack & Associates; **265l,** Frans Lanting/Minden Pictures; **265r,** Runk/Schoenberger/Grant Heilman Photography; **266,** Herve Donnezan/Photo Researchers; **267,** William James Warren/Westlight; **268,** Arthur C. Smith III/Grant Heilman Photography; **269,** Frans Lanting/Minden Pictures.

Chapter 9

Pages 272–273, E.R. Degginger; **274t,** Russ Lappa; **274b,** E. R. Degginger/Animals Animals/Earth Scenes; **275l,** Thomas Kitchin/Tom Stack & Associates; **275m,r,** Carr Clifton/Minden Pictures; **277tl,** D. Cavagnaro/Visuals Unlimited; **277bl,** E. R. Degginger; **277tr,** Frans Lanting/Minden Pictures; **277br,** William Harlow/Photo Researchers; **278 both,** Runk/Schoenberger/Grant Heilman Photography; **280,** Dani/Jeske/Animals Animals/Earth Scenes; **282t,** Runk/Schoenberger/Grant Heilman Photography; **282 the rest,** Robert Calentine/Visuals Unlimited; **284t,** Richard Haynes; **284b,** Bruce M. Herman/Photo Researchers; **285tl,** Ken Brate/Photo Researchers; **285tr,** Jim Strawser/Grant Heilman Photography; **285b,** Michael Fogden/Animals Animals/Earth Scenes; **286l,** Breck P. Kent/Animals Animals/Earth Scenes; **286r,** Breck P. Kent; **288,** C.J. Allen/Stock Boston; **289t,** Russ Lappa; **289b,** Jim Strawser/Grant Heilman Photography; **290,** E. R. Degginger; **291,** Private Collections/Art Resource; **294,** Richard Haynes; **296,** Alan Pitcairn/Grant Heilman Photography; **297,** William J. Weber/Visuals Unlimited; **298,** Porterfield-Chickering/Photo Researchers; **299tl,** E. R. Degginger; **299tr,** Mark E. Gibson/The Stock Market; **299b,** Larry Lefever/Grant Heilman Photography; **301,** Larry Lefever/Grant Heilman Photography; **304t,** Holt Studios International/Photo Researchers; **304b,** Andy Goodwin/Discover Magazine; **305t,** Courtesy of Rathin Datta; **305b,** Martin Bond/SDL/Photo Researchers; **306,** Paul Conklin/PhotoEdit.

Chapter 10

Pages 308–309, Hal Beral/Visuals Unlimited; **310t,** Richard Haynes; **310b,** Gary Bell/Masterfile; **312l,** Frans Lanting/Minden Pictures; **312r,** Oliver Strewe/Tony Stone Images; **313,** David & Tess Young/Tom Stack & Associates; **315,** Corel Corp.; **316,** William C. Jorgensen/Visuals Unlimited; **317l,** Daniel W. Gotshall/Visuals Unlimited; **317r,** Tim Davis/Tony Stone Images; **318,** Ted Kerasote/Photo Researchers; **320t,** Russ Lappa; **320b,** Gregory Ochocki/Photo Researchers;

323t, Biophoto Associates/Photo Researchers; **323bl,** Stuart Westmorland/ Natural Selection; **323br,** David B. Fleetham/Tom Stack & Associates; **325t,** Nancy Sefton/Photo Researchers; **325b,** Linda Pitkin/Masterfile; **326,** James Watt/Animals Animals; **327t,** Richard Haynes; **327bl,** Ed Robinson/ Tom Stack & Associates; **327br,** Mary Beth Angelo/Photo Researchers; **328,** Kjell B. Sandved/ Visuals Unlimited; **330t,** David M. Dennis/Tom Stack & Associates; **330b,** Sinclair Stammers/Science Photo Library/Photo Researchers; **331l,** Kjell B. Sandved/ Visuals Unlimited; **331r,** Kjell B. Sandved/Visuals Unlimited.

Chapter 11
Pages 338–339, Michael Fogden/DRK Photo.; **340t,** Corel Corp.; **340b,** Richard Nowitz; **341l,** Douglas Faulkner/Photo Researchers; **341r,** Bruce Watkins/Animals Animals; **344,** Kevin & Cat Sweeney/Tony Stone Images; **346t,** Richard Haynes; **346b,** Ron Broda/Masterfile; **347l,** John Gerlach/Tom Stack & Associates; **347r,** Donald Specker/Animals Animals; **348,** Robert A. Lubeck/Animals Animals; **349,** Andrew Syred/Science Photo Library/Photo Researchers; **352t,** Robert Calentine/ Visuals Unlimited; **352m,** Tim Flach/Tony Stone Images, **352b,** Tom McHugh/ Photo Researchers, **353l,** Marty Cordano/DRK Photo; **353r,** Simon D. Pollard/ Photo Researchers; **354t,** R Calentine/Visuals Unlimited; **354b,** Patti Murray/ Animals Animals, **355,** CNRI/Science Photo Library/Photo Researchers; **356,** Belinda Wright/DRK Photo; **358l,** Valorie Hodgson/Visuals Unlimited; **358r,** Art Wolfe/Tony Stone Images; **359,** John Trager/Visuals Unlimited; **360,** Robert A. Lubeck/Animals Animals; **361,** Richard Haynes; **363,** Michael Fogden/Animals Animals; **364,** PNI; **365t,** Richard Haynes; **365b,** Kjell B. Sandved/Visuals Unlimited; **366,** Ed Robinson/Tom Stack & Associates; **368tl,** Brian Parker/Tom Stack & Associates, **368tr,** Tammy Peluso/Tom Stack & Associates, **368b,** Fred Whitehead/Animals Animals.

Chapter 12
Pages 372–373, Norbert Wu/DRK Photo; **374,** Russ Lappa; **375,** G.J. Bernard/ Animals Animals; **376,** Michael Fodgen/DRK Photo; **377,** Corel Corp.; **378t,** Ernst Mayr Library of the Museum of Comparative Zoology, Harvard University. ©President and Fellows of Harvard; **378b,** By permission of the Houghton Library, Harvard University; **379t,** Louis Psihoyos Matrix; **379b,** James L. Amos/Photo Researchers; **381t,** Gerard Lacz/Animals Animals; **381b,** Flip Micklin/Minden Pictures; **383tl,** Larry Lipsky/DRK Photo; **383tr,** John D. Cummingham/Visuals Unlimited; **383b,** Herve Berthoule Jacana/Photo Researchers; **384t,** Frank Burek/Animals Animals; **384b,** Jeff Rotman; **386l,** Norbert Wu; **386r,** Stuart Westmorland/Photo Researchers; **387l,** Norbert Wu/Tony Stone Images; **387r,** Stuart Westmorland/Tony Stone Images; **389t,** Russ Lappa; **389b,** John M. Burnley/Photo Researchers; **390,** Michael Fogden/Photo Researchers; **392,** Richard Haynes; **394,** Justin W. Verforker/ Visuals Unlimited; **395t,** Richard Haynes; **395b,** Joe McDonald/Tom Stack & Associates; **396,** Zig Leszczynski/Animals Animals; **397,** Brian Kenney/Natural Selection; **399l,** Joe McDonald/Tom Stack & Associates; **399r,** A.B. Sheldon/ Animals Animals; **402t,** Dave B. Fleetham/Visuals Unlimited; **402m,** T.A. Wiewandt/ DRK Photo; **402b,** M.C. Chamberlain/DRK Photo; **403,** Gerald & Buff Corsi/Tom Stack & Associates; **405l,** Stuart Westmorland/Tony Stone Images; **405r,** Joe McDonald/Tom Stack & Associates.

Chapter 13
Pages 408–409, Robert A. Tyrrell; **410,** Richard Haynes; **411,** Collection of The New York Historical Society; **412t,** Art Wolfe/TSI; **412m,** Jerome Wexler/Photo Researchers; **412b,** Darrell Gulin/DRK Photo; **414,** Richard Haynes; **417,** David Hosking/TSI; **418tl,** Dave Watts/Tom Stack & Associates; **418tm,** Stephen Krasemann/DRK Photo; **418tr,** S. Nielsen/DRK Photo; **418br,** Joe McDonald/ Visuals Unlimited; **419l,** Manfred Danegger/Tony Stone Images; **419r,** Wayne Lankinen/DRK Photo; **420t,** Richard Haynes; **420b,** Stephen Dalton/Photo Researchers; **422,** David Tipling/Tony Stone Images; **423t,** Richard Haynes; **423b,** Eric Valli/Minden Pictures; **424,** Daryl Balfour/Tony Stone Images; **425,** Art Wolfe/ Tony Stone Images; **426t,** Hilary Pooley/Animals Animals; **426–427b,** Michael Fogden/DRK Photo; **428,** Joe McDonald/Visuals Unlimited; **430,** Colin Milkins/ Animals Animals; **431t,** Richard Haynes; **431bl,** Keren Su/Tony Stone Images; **431br,** Penny Tweedie/Tony Stone Images; **432 both,** Tom McHugh/Photo Researchers; **433t,** Dave Watts/Tom Stack & Associates; **433b,** Jack Dermid; **434tl,** Michael Habicht/Animals Animals; **434tm,** Art Wolfe/Tony Stone Images; **434tr,** Roger Aitkenhead/Animals Animals; **434mr,** Jeanne Drake/Tony Stone Images; **434bl,** Renee Lynn/Tony Stone Images; **434–435b,** Chuck Davis/Tony Stone Images; **435tl,** Corel Corp.; **435tr,** M.P. Kahl/DRK Photo; **435m,** Stephen Krasemann/Tony Stone Images; **435br,** Johnny Johnson/DRK Photo.

Chapter 14
Pages 440–441, Tim Davis/ Tony Stone Images; **442t,** Jerome Wexler/Photo Researchers; **442b,** Michael Fogden/DRK Photo; **443,** Fred Winner/Jacana/Photo

Researchers; **446,** Robert & Eunice Pearcy/Animals Animals; **448,** Nina Leen/ Time-Warner, *Life Magazine*; **450t,** Richard Haynes; **450b,** Mark Jones/Minden Pictures; **451,** Art Wolfe/TSI; **452 both,** Michael Fogden/DRK Photo; **453,** Jeff Lepore/Natural Selection; **454,** John Cancalosi/DRK Photo; **456,** M.A. Chappell/ Animals Animals; **457,** Michio Hoshino/Minden Pictures; **459,** John Cancalosi/ DRK Photo; **462,** Cary Wolinsky/Stock Boston; **463t ,** E.R. Degginger/Animals Animals; **463ml,mr,** Cary Wolinsky/Stock Boston; **463b,** Harry Rogers/Photo Researchers; **466–467,** Russ Lappa; **468,** Xinhua/Liaison Agency; **469t,** Russ Lappa; **469b,** Jean Marc Barey/Angence Vandystadt/Photo Researchers.

Chapter 15
Pages 470–471, Globus, Holway & Lobel/The Stock Market; **472t,** Richard Haynes; **472b,** Russ Lappa; **474tl,** Robert Becker/Custom Medical Stock; **474bl,** Fred Hossler/Visuals Unlimited; **474m,** Clive Brunckill/Allsport; **474tr,** Biophoto Associates/Science Source/Photo Researchers; **474br,** John D. Cunningham/ Visuals Unlimited; **476,** Lori Adamski Peek/Tony Stone Images; **477,** Paul J. Sutton/Duomo; **479,** Michael P. Manheim/MidwestStock; **480t,** Russ Lappa; **480b,** Cathy Cheney/Stock Boston; **481,** Richard Haynes; **483,** Andrew Syred/ Science Photo Library/Photo Researchers; **484,** Salisbury District Hospital/Science Photo Library/Photo Researchers; **485,** William R. Sallaz/Duomo; **486,** The Granger Collection, NY; **487 both,** Superstock; **488t,** Richard Haynes; **488b,** Superstock, **489tl,** Astrid & Hanns-Frieder Michler/Science Photo Library/Photo Researchers; **489bl,** Eric Grave/Photo Researchers; **489m,** Richard Haynes; **489r,** Ed Reschke/Peter Arnold; **490l,** Richard Haynes; **490r,** Jim Cummins/FPG International; **492,** Superstock; **493, 494t,** Richard Haynes; **494b,** Jed Jacobson/ Allsport; **495l,** David Young Wolff/Tony Stone Images; **495r,** Lennart Nilsson/ Behold Man; **497l,** Prof. P. Motta/Dept. of Anatomy/University "La Sapienza," Rome/Science Photo Library/Photo Researchers; **497r,** Russ Lappa; **498, 499,** Richard Haynes; **500,** Bob Daemmrich/Stock Boston.

Chapter 16
Pages 504–505, Superstock; **506,** Bob Daemmrich/Stock Boston; **507l,** Richard Haynes; **507r, 508, 509, 510, 511 both, 512 all,** Russ Lappa; **513,** Joan Baron/ The Stock Market; **516,** David Young Wolff/Tony Stone Image; **517,** Russ Lappa; **518,** The Granger Collection, NY; **519, 520,** Richard Haynes; **523,** CNRI/Science Photo Library/Photo Researchers; **525, 526t,** Richard Haynes; **526b,** Llewellyn/Uniphoto; **528,** Prof. P. Motta/Dept. of Anatomy/University "La Sapienza," Rome/Science Photo Library/Photo Researchers; **529,** CNRI/Science Photo Library/Photo Researchers; **530,** Donna Day/Tony Stone Images.

Chapter 17
Pages 534–535, National Cancer Institute/Science Photo Library/Photo Researchers; **536, 537,** Richard Haynes; **538t,** Erich Lessing/Art Resource; **538b,** Science Photo Library/Photo Researchers; **540,** Pete Saloutos/The Stock Market; **542,** Scott Weersing/AllSport; **543,** Richard Haynes; **545,** Prof. P. Motta/ Dept. of Anatomy/University "La Sapienza," Rome/Science Photo Library/Photo Researchers; **546,** Cabisco/Visuals Unlimited; **547,** Matt Meadows/Peter Arnold; **548,** Richard Haynes; **549,** Andrew Syred/Science Photo Library/Photo Researchers; **550,** Bill Longcore/Science Source/Photo Researchers; **551t,** Andrew Syred/Science Photo Library/Photo Researchers; **551b,** National Cancer Institute/Science Photo Library/Photo Researchers; **552,** Oliver Meckes/Photo Researchers; **554,** Richard Haynes; **556t,** Daemmrich/Stock Boston; **556b,** Thom Duncan/Adventure Photo; **557 both,** Custom Medical Stock; **558t,** AP/Wide World Photos; **558b,** The Granger Collection, NY; **559t,** Liaison Agency; **559b,** Brad Nelson/Custom Medical Stock; **560,** Nicole Katodo/Tony Stone Images; **561 both,** Custom Medical Stock.

Chapter 18
Pages 564–565, Lawrence Migdale/Photo Researchers; **566t,** Richard Haynes; **566b,** Dick Dickinson/Photo Network; **568l,** Richard Haynes; **568r,** Eddy Gray/Science Photo Library/Photo Researchers; **569,** Richard Haynes; **572,** Paul Harris/Tony Stone Images; **574,** J. Sohm/The Image Works; **575,** Russ Lappa; **576,** Spencer Jones/FPG International; **577,** Ken Karp; **578,** Al Bello/Tony Stone Images; **579l,** Clark Overton/Phototake; **579m,** SIV/Photo Researchers; **579r,** Martin Rotker/ Phototake; **580,** Smoke Free Educational Services; **581, 584,** Richard Haynes; **586,** Ken Karp.

Chapter 19
Pages 590–591, Microworks/Phototake; **592t,** Richard Haynes; **592b,** The Granger Collection, NY; **593,** Pete Saloutos/The Stock Market; **595t,** Scott Camazine/Photo Researchers; **595b,** Mike Peres/Custom Medical Stock Photo; **596,** Russ Lappa; **597,** Science Pictures Ltd./Science Photo Library/Photo Researchers; **598, 599,** Richard Haynes; **600,** Lennart Nilsson/Boehringer

Ingelheim International GmbH; **601,** Lori Adamski Peek/Tony Stone Images; **603,** NIBSC/Science Photo Library/Photo Researchers; **604,** Jon Riley/Tony Stone Images; **605t,** Russ Lappa; **605b,** CNRI/Science Photo Library/Photo Researchers; **606t,** Historical Picture Service/Custom Medical Stock; **606b, 607t,** The Granger Collection, NY; **607b,** Giraudon/Art Resource; **608,** Aaron Haupt/Photo Researchers; **610,** Stevie Grand/Science Photo Library/Photo Researchers; **612t,** Richard Haynes; **612b,** Dr. Dennis Kunkel/Phototake; **613l,** Andrew Syred/Science Photo Library/Photo Researchers; **613r,** Ron Kimball; **614,** Therisa Stack/Tom Stack & Associates; **615,** Dept. of Clinical Radiology, Salisbury District Hospital/Science Photo Library/Photo Researchers; **616,** Yoav levy/Phototake.

Chapter 20
Page 620, 1998 Magic Eye Inc.; **622t,** Richard Haynes; **622b,** Lee Snider/The Image Works; **623,** Gordon R. Gainer/The Stock Market; **624,** Biophoto Associates/Photo Researchers; **627, 628t,** Richard Haynes; **628b,** Milton Feinberg/Index Stock Imagery; **629,** Richard Haynes; **631,** Art Resouce; **632,** Tom Stewart/The Stock Market; **634,** William Sallaz/Duomo; **635,** Robert E. Daemmrich/Tony Stone Images; **636,** Superstock; **638t,** Lennart Nilsson; **638b,** Prof. P. Motta/Dept. of Anatomy/U. "La Sapienza," Rome/Science Photo Library/Photo Researchers; **640,** Renee Lynn/Tony Stone Images; **642l,** Spencer Grant/Index Stock Imagery; **642r,** Lennart Nilsson; **643,** Mugshots/The Stock Market; **644t,** Russ Lappa; **644b,** Uniphoto; **645,** Tom Croke/Liaison Agency; **646,** David Young-Wolff/PhotoEdit; **650,** Index Stock Imagery; **652,** Bob Daemmrich/Stock Boston; **653,** Lee Snider/The Image Works.

Chapter 21
Pages 656–657, Uniphoto; **658,** Keith Kent/Photo Researchers; **659l,** Chad Slattery/Tony Stone Images; **659r,** Nancy Sheehan/Index Stock Imagery; **663,** Mitsuaki Iwago/Minden Pictures; **664 both,** Dr. Dennis Kunkel/Phototake; **667,** Prof. P.M. Motta & J. Van Blerkom/Science Photo Library/ Photo Researchers; **669tl,tr,** Stephen R. Swinburne/Stock Boston; **669b,** David Phillips/Science Photo Library/Photo Researchers; **671,** Lennart Nilsson; **672,** Index Stock Imagery; **673t,** Frauke/Mauritius/H. Armstrong Roberts; **673b,** Roy Morsch/The Stock Market; **674,** Don Semtzer/Tony Stone Images; **675,** Roy Morso/The Stock Market; **676,** Bruce Dale/National Geographic Society; **677,** David Young Wolff/Tony Stone Images; **682t,** Jeff Foott/Tom Stack & Assoc.; **682b,** Courtesy of Elroy Masters; **683t,** Courtesy of Elroy Masters; **683b,** Pat O'Hara/DRK Photo; **684–685,** M. Collier/DRK Photo; **684t inset,** VIREO; **684b inset,** Jeff Foott/Tom Stack & Assoc.; **685t,** Gilbert Grant/Photo Researchers.

Chapter 22
Pages 686–687, Tony Craddock/Tony Stone Images; **688t,** Richard Haynes; **688–689,** Shin Yoshino/Minden Pictures; **689t,** Carr Clifton/Minden Pictures; **689t inset,** Corel Corp.; **689b inset,** S. Nielsen/DRK Photo; **690,** John Cancalosi/Tom Stack & Associates; **691,** Patti Murray/Animals Animals; **695t,** Richard Haynes; **695b,** Michlo Hoshino/Minden Pictures; **696,** C. Allan Morgan/DRK Photo; **697t,** Rob Simpson/Visuals Unlimited; **697b,** Bas van Beek/Leo de Wys; **699,** Mitsuaki Iwago/Minden Pictures; **700t,** Dan Budnick/Woodfin Camp & Associates; **700b,** Russ Lappa; **702,** Gary Griffen/Animals Animals; **703,** J. Alcock/Visuals Unlimited; **705l,** Patti Murray/Animals Animals; **705tr,** Wayne Lankinen/DRK Photo; **705br,** Ron Willocks/Animals Animals; **706l,** Michael Fogden/DRK Photo; **706r,** D. Holden Bailey/Tom Stack & Associates; **707tl,** Stephen J. Krasemann/DRK Photo; **707tr,** Donald Specker/Animals Animals; **707b,** Jeanne White/Photo Researchers; **709,** Daryl Balfour/Tony Stone Images; **710,** John Gerlach/DRK Photo.

Chapter 23
Pages 714–715, Tom McHugh/Steinhart Aquarium/Photo Researchers; **716t,** Richard Haynes; **716b,** Byron Jorjorian/Tony Stone Images; **717,** Breck P. Kent/Animals Animals/Earth Scenes; **718l,** Stephen J. Krasemann/DRK Photo; **718tr,** John Cancalosi/DRK Photo; **718br,** John Netherton/Animals Animals; **719,** S. Nielsen/DRK Photo; **721,** Stephen J. Krasemann/DRK Photo; **723t,** Richard Haynes; **723b,** R.J. Erwin/DRK Photo; **727,** Dr. Jeremy Burgess/Science Photo library/Photo Researchers; **728t,** Richard Haynes; **728b,** J. Cancalosi/DRK Photo; **729,** D. Cavagnaro/DRK Photo; **730,** Stephen G. Maka/DRK Photo; **731,** John Canalosi/DRK Photo; **733,** Richard Haynes; **734,** Russ Lappa; **735,** Frans Lanting/Minden Pictures; **735t inset,** Renee Lynn/Tony Stone Images; **735b inset,** Mark Hones/Minden Pictures; **736,** Joe McDonald/DRK Photo; **736 inset,** Michael Fogden/DRK Photo; **737,** Art Wolfe/Tony Stone Images; **738,** Carr Clifton/Minden Pictures; **738 inset,** Stephen J. Krasemann/DRK Photo; **739,** Stephen J. Krasemann/ DRK Photo; **739 inset,** Michael Quinton/Minden Pictures; **740, 741,** Michio Hoshino/ Minden Pictures; **742l,** David Boyle/Animals Animals; **742r,** Kim Heacox/DRK Photo; **743l,** Stephen G. Maka/DRK Photo; **743r,** Steven David Miller/Animals Animals; **744l,** Anne Wertheim/Animals Animals; **744r,** Gregory Ochocki/Photo Researchers; **745l,** Michael Nolan/Tom Stack & Associates; **745r,** Norbert Wu; **747,** Russ Láppa; **748 both,** Tom & Pat Leeson/Photo Researchers.

Chapter 24
Pages 754–755, Gay Bumgarner/Tony Stone Images; **756,** Frans Lanting/Minden Pictures; **757tl,** Inga Spence/Tom Stack & Associates; **757tr,** Charles D. Winters/Photo Researchers; **757b,** Key Sanders/Tony Stone Images; **758t,** UPI/Corbis-Bettmann; **758b,** Corbis-Bettmann; **759t,** UPI/Corbis-Bettmann; **759bl,** Underwood & Underwood/Corbis-Bettmann; **759br,** William Campbell /Peter Arnold; **760,** Jeff Gnass/The Stock Market; **761,** Russ Lappa; **762,** Martin Rogers/Stock Boston; **763,** Gary Braasch/Tony Stone Images; **765,** Tom Stewart/The Stock Market; **766,** Greg Vaughn/Tom Stack & Associates; **767,** Russ Lappa; **768,** Richard Haynes; **769tl,** Dave Watts/Tom Stack & Associates; **769tm,** Lanting/Minden Pictures; **769tr,** George G. Dimijian/Photo Researchers; **769b,** Fred Bavendam/Minden Pictures; **770t,** Frans Lanting/Minden Pictures; **770b,** Jim Zipp/Photo Researchers; **771,** D. Cavagnaro/DRK Photo; **772t,** Stephen J. Krasemann/DRK Photo; **772m,** Dan Suzio/Photo Researchers; **772b,** John Shaw/Tom Stack & Associates; **772–773b,** Phil A. Dotson/Photo Researchers; **773l,** Frans Lanting/Minden Pictures; **773m,** David Liebman; **773r,** Lynn M. Stone/DRK Photo; **774,** Randy Wells/Tony Stone Images; **775l,** Roy Toft/Tom Stack & Associates; **775r,** Frans Lanting/Minden Pictures; **776,** Tom McHugh/Photo Researchers; **777,** Gary Braasch/Tony Stone Images; **780t,** Alan Carey/Photo Researchers; **780m,** Frans Lanting/Minden Pictures; **780bl,** Frans Lanting/Minden Pictures; **780br,** Roy Toft/Tom Stack & Associates; **781t,** Starin/Ardea London Ltd.; **781m,** Peter Steyn/Ardea London Ltd.; **781b,** Tom Brakefield/DRK Photo; **782t,** Dr. Migel Smith/ Earth Scenes; **782b,** Werner Forman Archive/Art Resource; **783l,** Christie's Images; **783r,** Jose Anzel/Aurora; **785,** Corbis-Bettmann.

Skills Handbook
Page 786, Tony Freeman/PhotoEdit; **787t,** FoodPix; **787m, b,** Russ Lappa; **790,** Richard Haynes; **792,** Ron Kimball; **793,** Renee Lynn/Photo Researchers.

Appendix
Page 802, 803 both, Russ Lappa.